Glencoe Life Science

Contents in Brief

Teacher Wraparound Edition

Correlations and Standards

Program Resources

Support for All Learners

Classroom Activities and Materials

Student Edition

SAFETY SYMBOLS	HAZARD	EXAMPLES	PRECAUTION	REMEDY
DISPOSAL	Special disposal procedures need to be followed.	certain chemicals, living organisms	Do not dispose of these materials in the sink or trash can.	Dispose of wastes as directed by your teacher.
BIOLOGICAL	Organisms or other biological materials that might be harmful to humans	bacteria, fungi, blood, unpreserved tissues, plant materials	Avoid skin contact with these materials. Wear mask or gloves.	Notify your teacher if you suspect contact with material. Wash hands thoroughly.
EXTREME TEMPERATURE	Objects that can burn skin by being too cold or too hot	boiling liquids, hot plates, dry ice, liquid nitrogen	Use proper protection when handling.	Go to your teacher for first aid.
SHARP OBJECT	Use of tools or glassware that can easily puncture or slice skin	razor blades, pins, scalpels, pointed tools, dissecting probes, broken glass	Practice common-sense behavior and follow guidelines for use of the tool.	Go to your teacher for first aid.
FUME	Possible danger to respiratory tract from fumes	ammonia, acetone, nail polish remover, heated sulfur, moth balls	Make sure there is good ventilation. Never smell fumes directly. Wear a mask.	Leave foul area and notify your teacher immediately.
ELECTRICAL	Possible danger from electrical shock or burn	improper grounding, liquid spills, short circuits, exposed wires	Double-check setup with teacher. Check condition of wires and apparatus.	Do not attempt to fix electrical problems. Notify your teacher immediately.
IRRITANT	Substances that can irritate the skin or mucous membranes of the respiratory tract	pollen, moth balls, steel wool, fiberglass, potassium permanganate	Wear dust mask and gloves. Practice extra care when handling these materials.	Go to your teacher for first aid.
CHEMICAL	Chemicals that can react with and destroy tissue and other materials	bleaches such as hydrogen peroxide; acids such as sulfuric acid, hydrochloric acid; bases such as ammonia, sodium hydroxide	Wear goggles, gloves, and an apron.	Immediately flush the affected area with water and notify your teacher.
TOXIC	Substance may be poisonous if touched, inhaled, or swallowed	mercury, many metal compounds, iodine, poinsettia plant parts	Follow your teacher's instructions.	Always wash hands thoroughly after use. Go to your teacher for first aid.
OPEN FLAME	Open flame may ignite flammable chemicals, loose clothing, or hair	alcohol, kerosene, potassium permanganate, hair, clothing	Tie back hair. Avoid wearing loose clothing. Avoid open flames when using flammable chemicals. Be aware of locations of fire safety equipment.	Notify your teacher immediately. Use fire safety equipment if applicable.

Eye Safety
Proper eye protection should be worn at all times by anyone performing or observing science activities.

Clothing Protection
This symbol appears when substances could stain or burn clothing.

Animal Safety
This symbol appears when safety of animals and students must be ensured.

Radioactivity
This symbol appears when radioactive materials are used.

Teacher Wraparound Edition

Glencoe Science

Life Science

NATIONAL GEOGRAPHIC SOCIETY

science.glencoe.com

New York, New York Columbus, Ohio Woodland Hills, California Peoria, Illinois

GLENCOE LIFE SCIENCE

Student Edition
Teacher Wraparound Edition
Interactive Teacher Edition CD-ROM
Interactive Lesson Planner CD-ROM
Lesson Plans
Content Outline for Teaching
Directed Reading for Content Mastery
Foldables: Improving Reading and Study Skills
Assessment
- *Chapter Review*
- *Chapter Tests*
- *ExamView® Pro Test Bank Software*
- *Assessment Transparencies*
- *Performance Assessment in the Science Classroom*
- *The Princeton Review Test Practice Booklet*

Directed Reading for Content Mastery in Spanish
Spanish Resources
English/Spanish Guided Reading Audio Program
Reinforcement
Enrichment
Activity Worksheets
Section Focus Transparencies
Teaching Transparencies
Laboratory Activities
Science Inquiry Labs
Critical Thinking/Problem Solving
Reading and Writing Skill Activities
Mathematics Skill Activities
Cultural Diversity
Laboratory Management and Safety in the Science Classroom
MindJogger Videoquizzes and Teacher Guide
Interactive CD-ROM with Presentation Builder
Vocabulary PuzzleMaker Software
Cooperative Learning in the Science Classroom
Environmental Issues in the Science Classroom
Home and Community Involvement
Using the Internet in the Science Classroom
Dinah Zike's Teaching Science with Foldables

"Test-Taking Tip," "Study Tip," and "Test Practice" features in this book were written by The Princeton Review, the nation's leader in test preparation. Through its association with McGraw-Hill, The Princeton Review offers the best way to help students excel on standardized assessments.

The Princeton Review is not affiliated with Princeton University or Educational Testing Service.

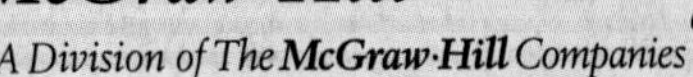

A Division of The McGraw-Hill Companies

Send all inquiries to:

Glencoe/McGraw-Hill
8787 Orion Place
Columbus, OH 43240

ISBN 0-07-823695-9

Printed in the United States of America

4 5 6 7 8 9 10 027/043 10 09 08 07 06 05 04 03

Authors, Reviewers, and Consultants

for the *Teacher Wraparound Edition*

Authors

National Geographic Society
Education Division
Washington, D.C.

Alton Biggs
Biology Teacher
Allen High School
Allen, Texas

Lucy Daniel, EdD
Teacher/Consultant
Rutherford County Schools
Rutherfordton, North Carolina

Norman G. Lederman, PhD
Professor of Science and Math Education
Oregon State University
Corvallis, Oregon

Edward Ortleb
Science Consultant
St. Louis Public Schools
St. Louis, Missouri

Peter Rillero, PhD
Professor of Science Education
Arizona State University West
Phoenix, Arizona

Dinah Zike
Educational Consultant
Dinah-Might Activities, Inc.
San Antonio, Texas

Reviewers

Sandra K. Enger, PhD
Coordinator
UAH Institute for Science Education
Huntsville, Alabama

Gilbert Naizer, PhD
Assistant Professor of Elementary Education
Texas A&M University
Commerce, Texas

Cultural Diversity Consultants

Nedaro Bellamy
Associate Director,
Rice Model Science Laboratory
Lanier Middle School, Houston ISD
Houston, Texas

Joyce Hilliard-Clark, PhD
Director, Imhotep Academy
North Carolina State University
Raleigh, North Carolina

Inclusion Strategies Consultant

Barry Barto
Special Education Teacher
John F. Kennedy Elementary School
Manistee, Michigan

National Science Education Standards

"The **National Science Education Standards** *are premised on a conviction that all students deserve and must have the opportunity to become scientifically literate. The* **Standards** *look toward a future in which all Americans, familiar with basic scientific ideas and processes, can have fuller and more productive lives."*

—National Science Education Standards

About the Standards

This book, published by the National Research Council, represents the contributions of thousands of educators and scientists, and offers a comprehensive vision of a scientifically literate society. The standards describe what all students should know at the end of grades 4, 8, and 12, and offer guidelines for science teaching and assessment.

How *Glencoe Life Science* Aligns with *The National Science Education Standards*

Content Standards

The correlations that follow show the close alignment between ***Glencoe Life Science*** and the grade-appropriate standards. ***Glencoe Life Science*** allows students to discover concepts within each of the content standards and gives students opportunities to make connections among the science disciplines. Hands-on activities and inquiry-based lessons reinforce the science processes emphasized in the standards.

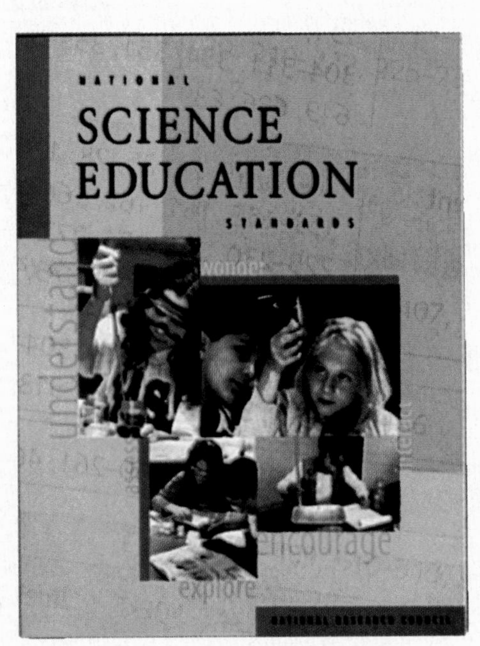

Teaching Standards

Glencoe Life Science provides activities and discussions that allow students to discover science concepts through inquiry and to apply the knowledge they've constructed to their own lives. The ***Teacher Wraparound Edition*** supports this endeavor with an abundance of effective strategies for guiding students of different ability levels and interests as they explore science.

Assessment Standards

Glencoe Life Science provides many opportunities in many different formats to assess students' understanding of important concepts. Ideas for portfolios, performance activities, and written assessments accompany every section. Glencoe's Professional Series booklet *Performance Assessment in the Science Classroom* contains rubrics and Performance Task Assessment Lists. This booklet also contains information about evaluating cooperative work. Learning outcomes improve for students of all ability levels in a cooperative learning environment.

Correlation to National Science Education Standards

The following chart illustrates how *Glencoe Life Science* addresses the National Science Education Standards.

Content Standard	Chapter and Section
(UCP) Unifying Concepts and Processes	
1. Systems, order, and organization	1-4, 2-1, 2-2, 3-3, 8-1, 8-2, 9-1, 11-1, 11-2, 17-1, 17-2, 17-3, 18-2, 19-1, 20-1, 20-2, 21-1, 21-2, 22-1, 22-2, 23-1, 24-1, 24-2, 24-3, 25-1, 25-2, 25-3, 26-1, 26-2, 26-3
2. Evidence, models, and explanation	1-1, 1-2, 1-3, 3-1, 5-1, 5-2, 5-3, 7-2, 23-2, 27-1, 27-2, 27-3
3. Change, constancy, and measurement	4-1, 4-2, 4-3, 10-1, 13-1, 13-2, 13-3, 13-4, 14-1, 14-2, 14-3, 14-4, 15-1, 15-2, 16-1, 16-2, 18-1, 22-2, 26-1
4. Evolution and equilibrium	3-2, 4-2, 4-3, 6-1, 6-2, 6-3, 23-3
5. Form and function	2-1, 2-3, 7-1, 8-1, 8-2, 9-2, 9-3, 10-2, 10-3, 12-1, 12-2, 12-3, 19-2, 19-3, 22-1, 22-3
(A) Science as Inquiry	
1. Abilities necessary to do scientific inquiry	1-1, 1-4, 2-1, 2-2, 2-3, 3-1, 3-2, 3-3, 4-1, 4-3, 5-1, 5-2, 5-3, 6-1, 6-3, 7-1, 7-2, 8-1, 8-2, 9-2, 9-3, 10-1, 10-2, 10-3, 11-1, 11-2, 12-1, 12-2, 12-3, 13-3, 13-4, 14-1, 14-2, 14-3, 14-4, 15-1, 15-2, 16-1, 16-2, 17-1, 17-2, 17-3, 18-1, 18-2, 19-1, 19-2, 19-3, 20-1, 20-2, 21-1, 21-2, 22-2, 22-3, 23-1, 23-2, 23-3, 24-1, 24-2, 24-3, 25-1, 25-2, 25-3, 26-2, 26-3, 27-1, 27-2, 27-3
2. Understandings about scientific inquiry	1-1, 1-3, 1-4, 2-2, 5-1, 6-1, 6-2, 16-2, 23-2, 23-3
(B) Physical Science	
1. Properties and changes of properties in matter	3-1, 25-1, 25-2, 25-3
2. Motion and forces	13-1, 17-1, 17-2, 19-1
3. Transfer of energy	3-3, 11-1, 24-2, 24-3, 25-3, 27-1
(C) Life Science	
1. Structure and function in living systems	1-2, 1-3, 1-4, 2-1, 2-2, 2-3, 3-1, 3-2, 3-3, 4-1, 4-3, 6-1, 6-2, 6-3, 7-1, 8-1, 8-2, 9-1, 9-2, 9-3, 10-1, 10-2, 10-3, 11-1, 11-2, 12-1, 12-2, 12-3, 13-1, 13-2, 13-3, 13-4, 14-1, 14-2, 14-3, 14-4, 15-1, 15-2, 17-1, 17-2, 17-3, 18-1, 18-2, 19-1, 19-2, 19-3, 20-1, 20-2, 21-1, 21-2, 22-1, 22-2, 22-3, 23-1, 23-2, 23-3, 24-1, 24-2, 24-3, 25-1, 25-2, 25-3
2. Reproduction and heredity	2-3, 4-2, 4-3, 5-1, 5-2, 5-3, 6-1, 6-2, 6-3, 7-1, 8-2, 10-1, 10-2, 10-3, 13-2, 13-3, 14-2, 14-3, 14-4, 15-1, 15-2, 16-2, 22-2, 22-3
3. Regulation and behavior	3-2, 11-1, 11-2, 12-1, 12-2, 12-3, 13-4, 14-1, 14-2, 14-3, 14-4, 15-1, 15-2, 16-1, 16-2, 17-3, 18-2, 20-1, 21-1, 21-2, 22-1, 22-2, 22-3
4. Populations and ecosystems	1-2, 3-3, 7-2, 12-2, 14-2, 14-3, 14-4, 15-2, 24-1, 24-2, 24-3, 25-1, 25-2, 25-3, 26-1, 26-2, 26-3
5. Diversity and adaptations of organisms	6-1, 6-2, 6-3, 7-1, 8-1, 8-2, 9-1, 9-2, 9-3, 10-2, 10-3, 12-1, 12-2, 12-3, 13-1, 13-2, 13-3, 13-4, 14-1, 14-2, 14-3, 14-4, 15-1, 15-2, 16-1, 16-2, 26-2, 26-3
(D) Earth and Space Science	
1. Structure of the Earth system	24-1, 24-2, 24-3, 25-1, 25-2, 25-3, 26-2, 26-3
2. Earth's history	1-3, 6-1, 6-2
3. Earth in the solar system	24-1, 24-3
(E) Science and Technology	
1. Abilities of technological design	2-2, 5-3, 6-2, 7-2, 23-2, 23-3, 27-1, 27-2, 27-3
2. Understandings about science and technology	2-3, 4-3, 5-3, 9-3, 23-3, 27-2, 27-3
(F) Science in Personal and Social Perspectives	
1. Personal Health	2-3, 5-2, 5-3, 7-2, 12-3, 17-2, 17-3, 18-1, 18-2, 19-2, 19-3, 20-1, 20-2, 22-2, 22-3, 23-1, 23-2, 23-3, 27-2
2. Populations, resources, and environments	12-2, 13-1, 13-2, 13-4, 15-2, 25-1, 25-2, 25-3, 26-1, 26–2, 26-3, 27-1, 27-2, 27-3
3. Natural hazards	7-2, 24-1, 26-1
4. Risks and benefits	7-2, 23-2, 23-3, 27-1, 27-2, 27-3
5. Science and technology in society	1-4, 4-3, 5-3, 7-2, 8-2, 9-3, 10-3, 14-4, 18-2, 24-3, 26-3, 27-1, 27-2, 27-3
(G) History and Nature of Science	
1. Science as a human endeavor	1-1, 2-2, 4-3, 5-3, 6-1, 6-2, 6-3, 11-2, 15-2, 16-2, 17-3, 21-2, 23-3, 24-3, 26-3, 27-3
2. Nature of science	1-1, 1-4, 6-2, 6-3, 7-2, 9-3
3. History of science	1-3, 1-4, 2-2, 2-3, 5-1, 6-1, 6-2, 6-3, 12-3, 15-2, 16-1, 19-3, 20-2, 23-2, 24-3

National Council of Teachers of Mathematics
Principles and Standards for School Mathematics

Students often make personal, educational, and career choices on their own that can influence the rest of their lives. Throughout their school years, they acquire skills that help them make these decisions. The development of keen mathematical skills can ensure that students have a wide variety of life options.

Principles and Standards for School Mathematics of the National Council of Teachers of Mathematics describes the foundation of mathematical concepts and applications that can provide students with the necessary mathematical skills to help achieve their life goals.

The ten categories of mathematical concepts and applications, as shown in the table below, include a broad range of topics that build on previous knowledge. They also allow students to increase their abilities to visualize, describe, and analyze situations in mathematical terms.

In ***Glencoe Life Science***, each Math Skill Activity and Problem-Solving Activity provides students with the opportunity to practice and apply some of the mathematical concepts and applications described in the Standards. These activities serve to reinforce mathematical skills in real-life situations, thus preparing students to meet their needs in an ever-changing world.

Correlation of *Glencoe Life Science* to NCTM Standards Grades 6–8

Standard	Page
1. Number and Operations	11, 13, 21, 63, 72, 85, 107, 131, 145, 147, 169, 193, 201, 205, 253, 281, 292, 315, 351, 378, 408, 421, 453, 474, 493, 547, 560, 586, 588, 615, 629, 642, 649, 667, 699, 703, 739, 741, 764, 798
2. Algebra	44, 51, 72, 85, 102, 147, 193, 281, 292, 311, 315, 346, 378, 408, 453, 474, 493, 588, 615, 637, 703, 751, 764, 784, 794, 854
3. Geometry	44, 333, 493
4. Measurement	12, 27, 37, 44, 201, 408, 493, 522, 578, 615, 699, 724, 764, 839
5. Data Analysis and Probability	9, 11, 27, 29, 35, 57, 128, 131, 132, 136, 145, 175, 295, 423, 443, 473, 560, 596, 625, 667, 699, 711, 843, 844, 856
6. Problem Solving	3, 11, 21, 44, 63, 72, 85, 102, 131, 147, 157, 169, 193, 205, 253, 281, 292, 315, 346, 351, 378, 408, 421, 453, 474, 493, 522, 560, 578, 588, 615, 629, 667, 681, 699, 703, 737, 764, 784, 794, 798
7. Reasoning and Proof	193, 221, 373, 522
8. Communication	3, 11, 27, 44, 80, 133, 194, 312, 378, 408, 453, 473, 493, 507, 555, 609, 615, 629, 649, 681, 699, 724, 739, 741, 764, 845
9. Connections	11, 44, 72, 107, 131, 157, 200, 221, 250, 292, 315, 351, 378, 408, 443, 473, 493, 522, 560, 586, 615, 629, 667, 699, 724, 764, 798
10. Representation	44, 131, 132, 134, 139, 149–151, 189, 250, 560, 724, 798

Benchmarks for Science Literacy

Benchmarks for Science Literacy is a publication by the American Association for the Advancement of Science that describes how students should progress toward science literacy. People who are science literate are "equipped with knowledge and skills they need to make sense of how the world works, to think critically and independently, and to lead interesting, responsible, and productive lives in a culture increasingly shaped by science and technology." *Benchmarks* was the culmination of Project 2061, the work of scientists, mathematicians, engineers, and educators to develop benchmarks, or statements, of what *all* students should know or be able to do in science, mathematics, and technology by the end of grades 2, 5, 8, and 12.

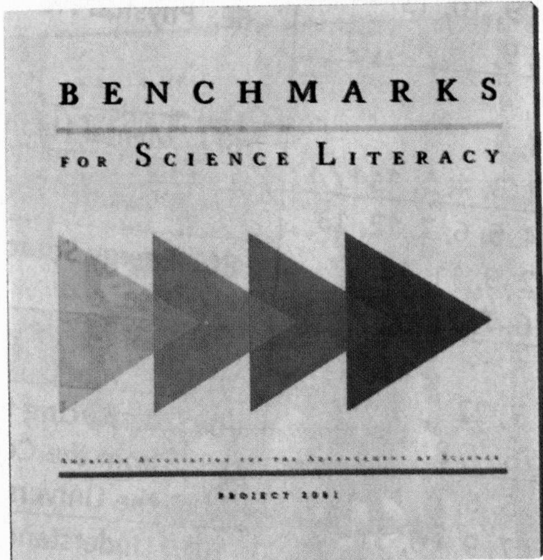

Glencoe Life Science is aligned with *Benchmarks* in the following ways:

- Concepts are presented in ways that help students understand the how and why of science, not just requiring them to learn facts that they commit to short-term memory.
- Science concepts are related to students' daily experiences.
- Teachers are provided strategies for encouraging students in independent work and for addressing the needs of students of varied abilities.
- Specific strategies are provided for identifying and addressing student misconceptions.

IDENTIFYING Misconceptions

Educators are becoming increasingly aware of the importance of identifying and addressing misconceptions—prescientific or naïve ideas—that students may hold about science. Students often develop these from their experiences as a way to make sense of the world.

A one-page feature, Identifying Misconceptions, is found on the F interleaf pages preceding selected chapters in the ***Teacher Wraparound Edition.*** This feature provides specific teaching strategies to find out what students think about a particular concept, to help them understand the concept, and to assess the accuracy of their understanding after learning the concept. These strategies were developed by Norman G. Lederman, Ph.D., Professor of Science and Math Education at Oregon State University.

Correlation to Benchmarks

Glencoe Life Science **addresses many of the Benchmarks for Science Literacy.**

Benchmark	Chapter(s)
4 The Physical Setting	
4B. The Earth	6, 24, 25, 27
4C. Processes That Shape the Earth	6, 25, 26, 27
4D. Structure of Matter	3, 25
4E. Energy Transformation	3, 11, 18, 24, 25, 26, 27
5 The Living Environment	
5A. Diversity of Life	1, 7, 8, 9, 10, 12, 13, 14, 15
5B. Heredity	4, 5, 6, 10
5C. Cells	2, 3, 4, 11, 18
5D. Interdependence of Life	6, 7, 8, 11, 24, 25, 26, 27
5E. Flow of Matter and Energy	3, 11, 18, 24, 25, 26
5F. Evolution of Life	4, 5, 6, 7, 8, 9, 10, 12, 13, 14, 15
6 The Human Organism	
6A. Human Identity	6, 15, 17, 18, 19, 20, 21, 22, 23
6B. Human Development	6, 22
6C. Basic Functions	3, 17, 18, 19, 20, 21, 22, 23
6D. Learning	6, 16, 21
6E. Physical Health	2, 7, 8, 17, 18, 19, 20, 21, 22, 23
6F. Mental Health	16
8 The Designed World	
8A. Agriculture	5, 7, 9, 10, 27
8F. Health Technology	2, 7, 8, 17, 18, 19, 20, 21, 22, 23, 24, 27
9 The Mathematical World	
9A. Numbers	All Math Skills and Problem-Solving Activities
9B. Symbolic Relationships	All Math Skills and Problem-Solving Activities
9C. Reasoning	All Math Skills and Problem-Solving Activities
10 Historical Perspectives	
10H. Explaining the Diversity of Life	1, 5, 6
10I. Discovering Germs	1, 2, 7, 23
12 Habits of Mind	
12A. Values and Attitudes	1, All "Oops! Accidents in Science," and "Science and History" features.
12B. Computation and Estimation	All Chapters 1–27
12D. Communication Skills	All Activities and Skill Builders

Planning Your Course

Glencoe Life Science is a flexible program that allows you to decide the pace at which you cover the content and which topics to present, based on the needs of your students and on district requirements. The _Glencoe Interactive Lesson Planner_ integrates the _Teacher Classroom Resources_ with an electronic lesson planner to make your job easier.

Pacing Options

Two approaches to covering all content are provided in the Planning Guide.

- A **traditional, full-year** course comprises 180 periods of approximately 45 minutes each.
- A **block scheduling** approach involves covering the same information in fewer days but in longer class periods.

Chapter Organizers

A two-page organizer (A–B pages) precedes every chapter in the teacher edition. These organizers include:

- pacing information and objectives.
- correlations to standards.
- lists of activities and the materials needed.
- lists of reproducible resources, assessments, and technologies with page or booklet references.

Interactive Lesson Planner

This easy-to-use CD-ROM allows you to:

- plan daily, weekly, monthly, or yearlong lessons in a versatile calendar format.
- select or customize a built-in plan, or make a new plan.
- print lesson plans.
- access all print components of the *Teacher Classroom Resources* through a convenient pop-up menu.
- print student pages and answer keys from the resource list or from the lesson plan.

Unit	Chapter	Single-Class (180 days*)	Block (90 days*)
1	Life's Structure and Function		
	1 Exploring and Classifying Life	8	4.0
	2 Cells	7	3.5
	3 Cell Processes	7	3.5
	4 Cell Reproduction	7	3.5
	5 Heredity	7	3.5
	6 Adaptations Over Time	7	3.5
2	From Bacteria to Plants		
	7 Bacteria	5	2.5
	8 Protists and Fungi	7	3.5
	9 Plants	7	3.5
	10 Plant Reproduction	7	3.5
	11 Plant Processes	5	2.5
3	Animal Diversity		
	12 Introduction to Animals	7	3.5
	13 Mollusks, Worms, Arthropods, Echinoderms	9	4.5
	14 Fish, Amphibians, and Reptiles	9	4.5
	15 Birds and Mammals	5	2.5
	16 Animal Behavior	5	2.5
4	Human Body Systems		
	17 Structure and Movement	7	3.5
	18 Nutrients and Digestion	5	2.5
	19 Circulation	7	3.5
	20 Respiration and Excretion	5	2.5
	21 Control and Coordination	5	2.5
	22 Regulation and Reproduction	7	3.5
	23 Immunity and Disease	7	3.5
5	Ecology		
	24 Interactions of Life	7	3.5
	25 The Nonliving Environment	7	3.5
	26 Ecosystems	7	3.5
	27 Conserving Resources	7	3.5

**The suggested number of days is the recommended maximum number of days needed to thoroughly cover a chapter. Individual planning will vary.*

Program Resources

Student Edition Features

This table will help you choose from many options that will help you teach the chapter.

Program Resources

Feature	Location and Suggestions For Use
Design Your Own Experiment	• Find near end of chapter where concept is taught. • Promote inquiry learning through open-ended activities. • Reinforce understanding of scientific methods.
Use the Internet	• Find near end of chapter where concept is taught. • Strengthen skills in collecting, organizing, and sharing data. • Integrate the Internet into your class easily.
Model and Invent	• Find near end of chapter where concept is taught. • Reinforce the use of models to represent relationships or abstract ideas, and to predict outcomes. • Strengthen investigative skills.
Other Full-Length Activities	• Find near end of chapter where concept is taught. • Strengthen lab skills. • Reinforce understanding of science process.
Mini LAB TRY AT HOME Mini LAB	• Find in every chapter. • Do as a demonstration. • Involve parents in the student's learning. • Reinforce that science is not restricted to the classroom.
EXPLORE ACTIVITY	• Find at beginning of each chapter. • Stimulate curiosity for the topic and focus students' attention.
Problem-Solving Skills Math Skills Activity	• Find one in every chapter at the point where the concept is taught. • Use after reading or other work to strengthen critical thinking and math skills.
SCIENCE Online	• Find in every chapter. • Focus students' Internet time with predetermined links.

Feature	Location and Suggestions For Use
Skill Builders	• Find at the end of every Section Assessment. • Assign as homework or class work.
FOLDABLES Reading & Study Skills	• Find on every Chapter Opener and Chapter Study Guide. • Provide a purpose for reading with these fun, simple, hands-on activities. • Encourage students to use as a study tool for review of chapter content.
Interdisciplinary Connections	• Find one of these five features in every chapter.
Oops! Accidents in Science	• Stimulate students' interest by studying science-related events that are out of the ordinary.
Science and Language Arts	• Advance reading and writing skills through literature connected to science.
Science Stats	• Show students the fun side of mathematics and how it is an integral part of science.
TIME Science & History	• Illustrate how scientific phenomena, discoveries, and inventions shape history.
TIME Science & Society	• Connect science to people's everyday lives.
NATIONAL GEOGRAPHIC Visualizing	• Find in every chapter. • Use the discussion and activities to teach science content.
Career Connection	• Find in every Science & Language Arts feature. • Point out that people of all ages, ethnicities, and training work in science.
Field GUIDE	• Find in the back of the student text. • Promote interest and independent study. • Teach students how to use a classification key.
Science, Technology, and Math Skill Handbooks	• Find at the back of the student and teacher editions. • Use to teach students scientific processes. • Use to teach students how to organize information. • Refer students to handbooks for assistance.

Teacher Wraparound Edition Features

This table will help you locate features of the *Teacher Wraparound Edition* that will help you develop your lesson plans.

Component	Where and How Many	What It Provides
Teacher to Teacher	Every Unit Opener	Teaching tip that relates to teaching unit content or activities.
Chapter Organizer	A and B pages preceding every chapter	• Objectives • Occurrence of activities and other features within each section • List of materials needed for each activity • List of materials from the *Teachers Classroom Resources* box • List of technology resources
Science Content Background	In every chapter on E page and F page where an Identifying Misconceptions feature does not appear	• Helps you prepare for the lesson by giving you more information about each section • Assists you with questions the students might ask
IDENTIFYING Misconceptions	F page of some chapters	Strategies to • determine misconceptions students may hold • promote understanding of concept • assess understanding
Key to Teaching Strategies	B page preceding every chapter	Coding to assist in planning for individual needs
Three-Step Teaching Cycle 1 Motivate 2 Teach 3 Assess	Every chapter	• Help for a first-year teacher • Help for experienced teacher in the first year in a new program
Resource Manager	C and D pages of every chapter Every two pages throughout each chapter	**C and D pages:** • List of transparencies • List of chapter teacher resources **Throughout chapter:** • List of reproducible resources • List of technology resources
Activity	Throughout all chapters in side wrap	Reinforces science concepts

Program Resources

Component	Where and How Many	What It Provides
Quick Demo	Throughout all chapters in side wrap	Idea to illustrate a concept; performed in a short amount of time, using available materials
LAB DEMONSTRATION	Throughout all chapters in bottom wrap	Teacher-performed activity, more complex than Quick Demo, often involving students
Extension	Throughout all chapters in side wrap	An activity idea for: • more advanced students • students who finish their work early • students who want to learn more about the topic
Teacher FYI	Throughout all chapters in side wrap	Additional information about a concept
Visual Learning	Throughout all chapters in side and bottom wrap	Idea for discussion or activity related to a graphic
Fun Fact	Throughout all chapters in side and bottom wrap	Interesting science content to share with students
Make a Model	Throughout all chapters in side wrap	Idea for model that students can make to clarify or illustrate abstract concepts
Use an Analogy	Throughout all chapters in side wrap	Way to make abstract concepts more concrete
Curriculum Connection	Throughout all chapters in bottom wrap	Way that science ties in with other curricular areas
Cultural Diversity	Throughout all chapters in bottom wrap	Current or historical background on a custom or belief associated with a science concept
Use Science Words	Throughout all chapters in side wrap	Strategies for students to learn word origins, meanings, and uses
Active Reading Strategies	Throughout all chapters in bottom wrap	Strategies to help students read and understand content
Science Journal	Throughout all chapters in bottom wrap	Writing exercises that promote writing and critical thinking skills
Assessment **Section Assessment** **Chapter Assessment** **Assessment Resources**	 First page of every section Chapter Assessment page Chapter Assessment page	 • Location of Portfolio, Performance, and Content Assessments in the section • Ideas for Portfolio and Performance Assessments • List of Reproducible Masters, CD-ROMs, and other technologies for assessment

Program Resources

Glencoe Science is also online at mhln.com

The Interactive E-Textbook that will change the way you teach!

The McGraw-Hill Learning network is an online learning space connecting parents, teachers, and students.

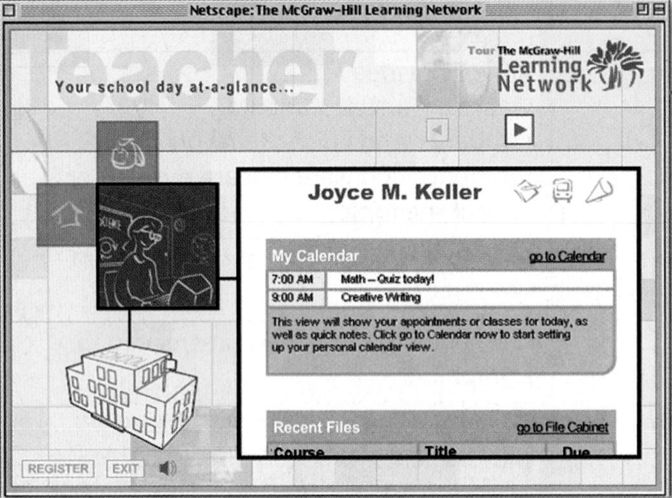

For Teachers

- Online Lesson Planner
- Calendar/Class Organizer
- Assignment Creator (Teachers can create, grade, and send assignments to students.)
- Grade Book/Class Roster
- And much more . . .

There's a ton of helpful tools, such as a Web site builder and thousands of educational Web links.

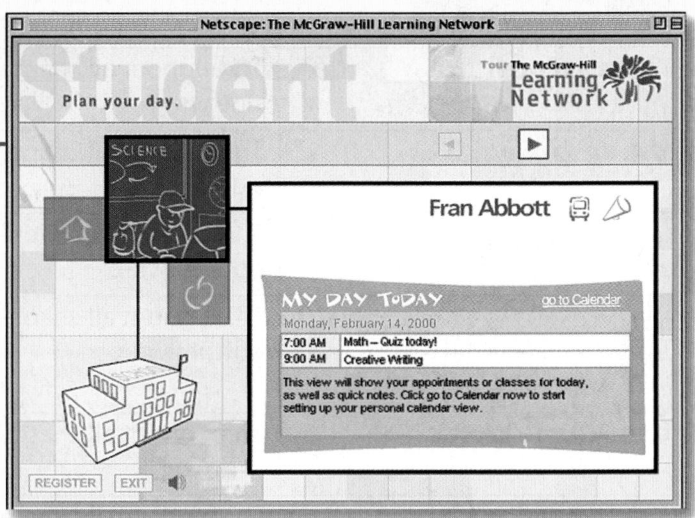

For Students

- Interactive games
- 24–hour homework help
- Online planner
- Instant feedback with diagnostic assessments
- Unlimited practice
- And much more . . . including movies, animations, sound, Web links, and an online encyclopedia

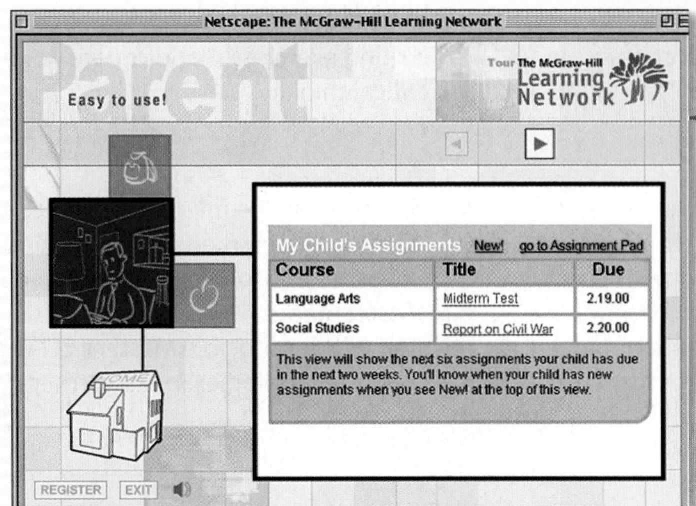

For Parents

- Tips to help their child succeed in school
- Instant access to textbooks, homework assignments, and progress reports

Online Science

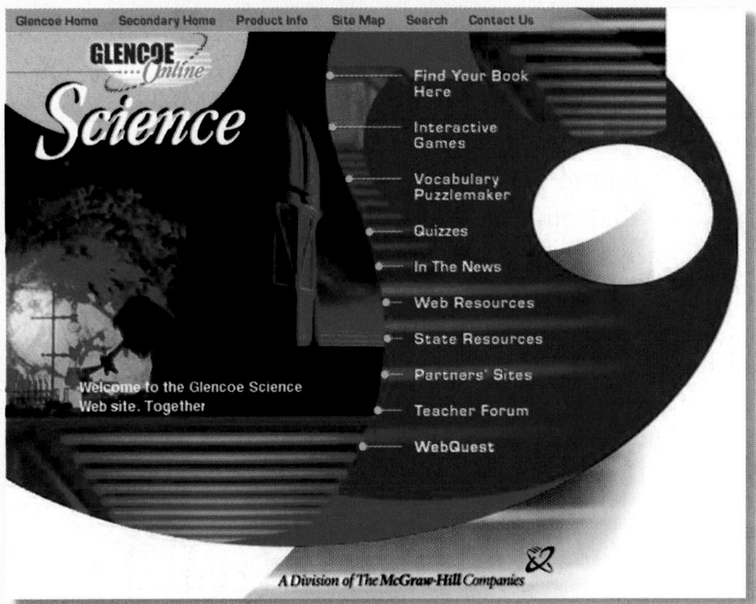

The Glencoe Science Web site **science.glencoe.com** is an invaluable resource for all teachers and students.

Teachers can:

- share ideas on Teacher Bulletin Board.
- access current scientific information on textbook updates.

Students can:

- access the ***Student Edition*** online.
- access previewed Web links.
- record information on printable Internet log worksheets.
- review chapter content with the Interactive Tutor.
- prepare for tests using Interactive Quizzes.
- share data with students worldwide using our exclusive Internet Activities.

TeachingTODAY

Access *Teaching Today* at **teachingtoday.glencoe.com** for teaching tips, annotated Web resources, educational news, and more. New material is added each week to meet the diverse needs of secondary classroom teachers.

Interactive CD-ROM with Presentation Builder

Provides students the opportunity to:

- develop hypotheses.
- manipulate variables.
- build presentations.
- review content.
- think critically.

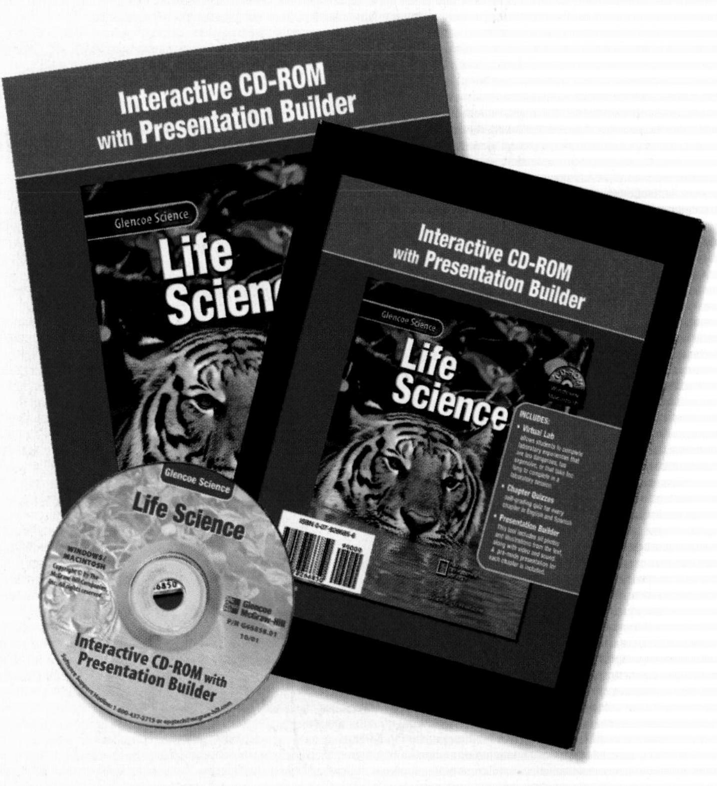

ExamView® Pro TestMaker Software

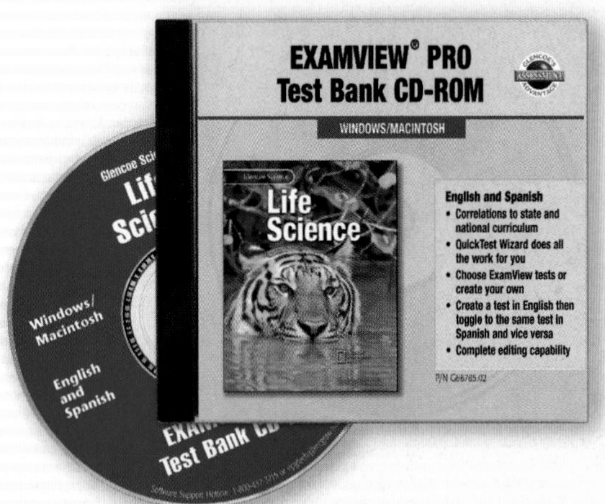

You can design and create your own test instruments in minutes, using Glencoe Life Science ExamView Pro TestMaker software. This versatile program allows you to create paper tests as well as tests that can be used on your school LAN system, or posted on your class Web site. Choose and edit questions from a question bank, or write your own.

Interactive Lesson Planner

Need help planning your lessons and organizing your resources? Glencoe's Interactive Lesson Planner is the perfect solution. All you need to do is to identify your length of course and number of class days and the program automatically places all the materials available for each day for each chapter into the calendar. Every page of your Teacher Classroom Resources is available to you at the click of a mouse.

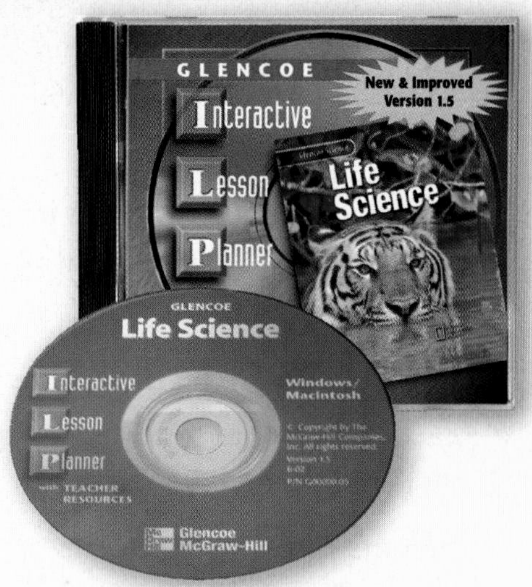

Interactive Teacher Edition

Imagine having your entire Teacher Edition and all your Teacher Classroom Resources available to you on one CD-ROM. That is what the Interactive Teacher Edition provides for you. The program allows you to view all teacher material and the student text on your computer screen. You can export all worksheet masters to your own word processor for editing.

MindJogger Videoquizzes

The interactive quiz-show format of the Glencoe Life Science MindJogger Videoquizzes provides fun for your students while reviewing key concepts for every chapter. The three levels of increasing difficulty add to the drama and excitement of the game, and help you assess your students' understanding of the concepts.

Guided Reading Audio Program

English/Spanish

Complete chapter text read in English provides another way for students who are auditory learners, or for ELL students, to access chapter content. Students can listen individually in class or at home. They can also choose to read along with their texts to improve reading skills. Tie to the Directed Reading for Content Mastery in the *Chapter Resources* booklets to give students a way to check their understanding of the material. The Guided Reading program is provided in CD format.

Vocabulary PuzzleMaker Software

This software program allows you to create crossword puzzles, jumble puzzles, or word searches in minutes to review chapter vocabulary. The puzzles can be printed or played on the computer screen.

Teacher Classroom Resources

Program Resources

Chapter Resources

We've organized all of the materials you need for each chapter into chapter-based booklets. The cover of each booklet becomes a file folder to help you stay organized.

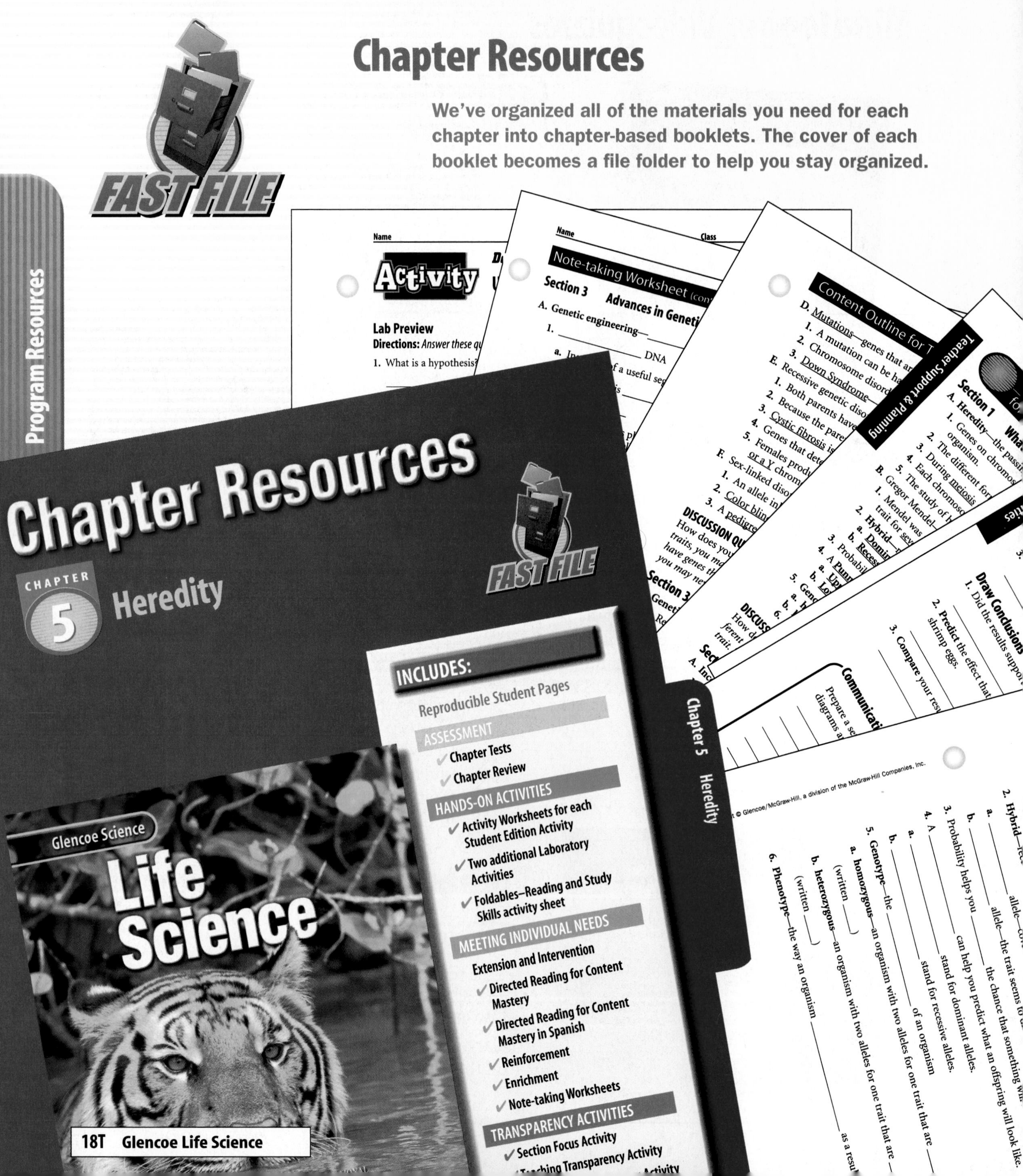

Each **Chapter Resources** booklet contains:

Reproducible Student Pages

Assessment
- Chapter Review
- Chapter Test

Hands-On Activities
- Activity Worksheets for each activity in the ***Student Edition***
- Two additional laboratory activities
- Foldables: Reading and Study Skills

Meeting Individual Needs
(Extension and Intervention)
- Directed Reading for Content Mastery
- Directed Reading for Content Mastery *in Spanish*
- Reinforcement
- Enrichment
- Note-taking Worksheets

Transparency Activities
- Section Focus Activity
- Teaching Transparency Activity
- Assessment Transparency Activity

Teacher Support and Planning
- Content Outline for Teaching
- Spanish Resources
- Teacher Guide and Answers

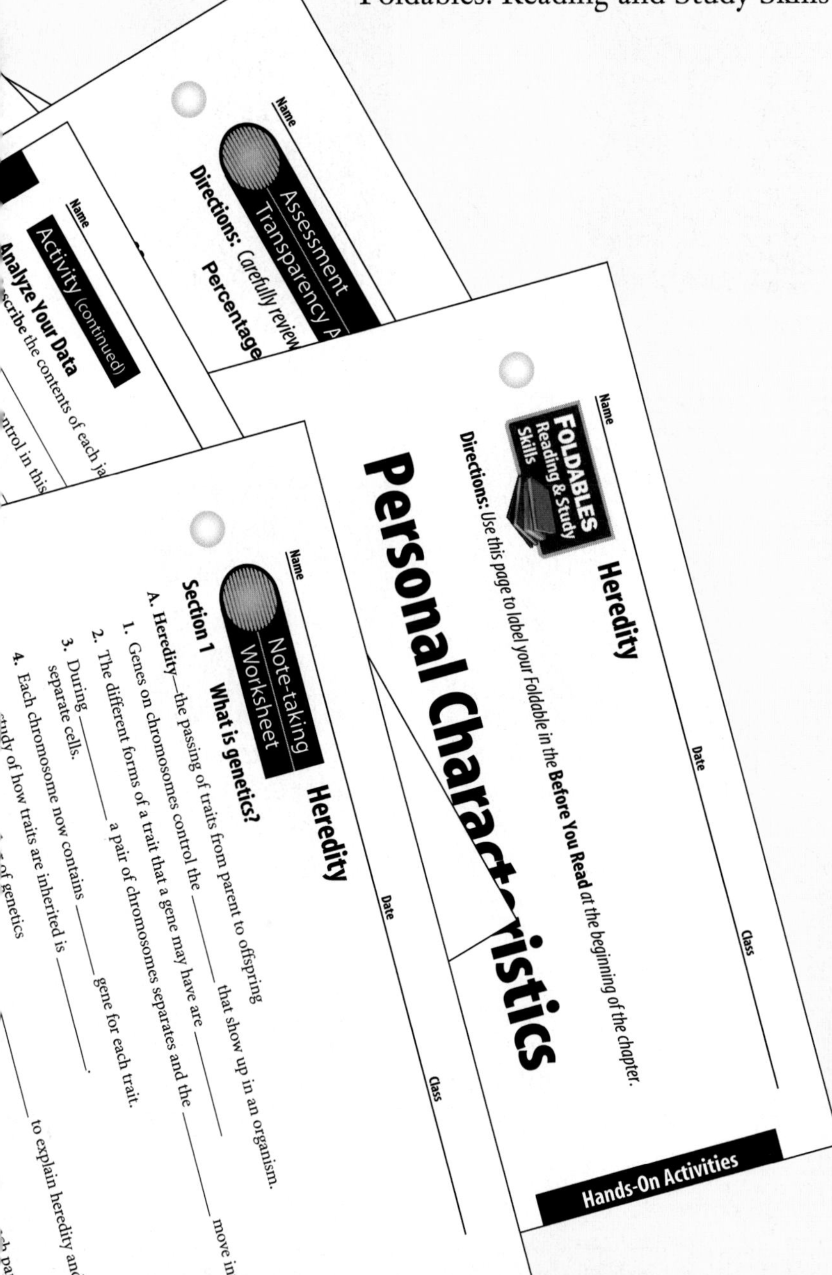

Program Resources

Additional Resources

These resources are available as stand-alone booklets to give you the flexibility to decide when to use them.

Transparencies

Section Focus Transparencies
Teaching Transparencies
Assessment Transparencies

Content Outline for Teaching

Lesson Plans

Laboratory Activities *SE*

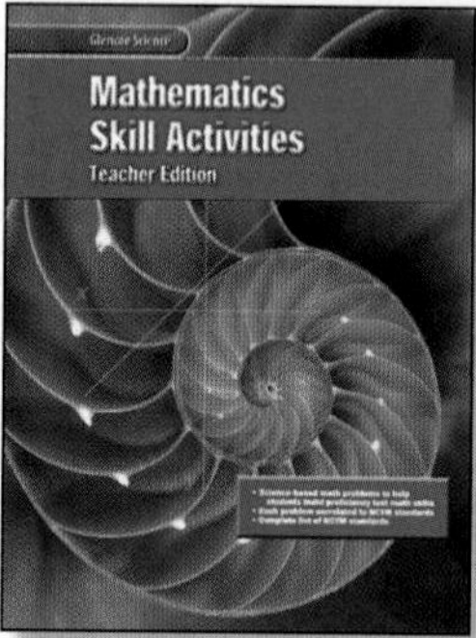

Math Skill Activities *(SE and TE)*

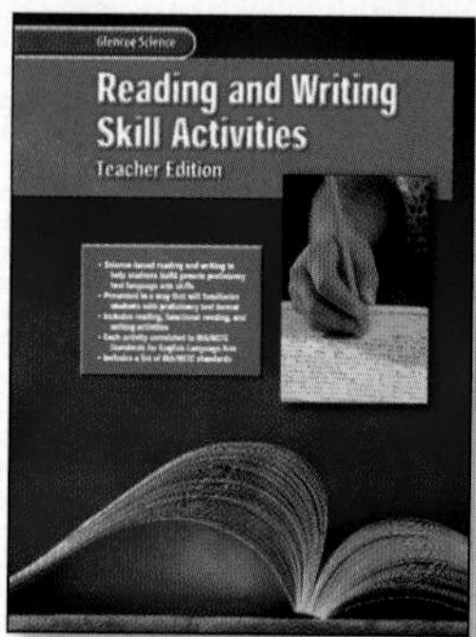

Reading and Writing Skill Activities *(SE and TE)*

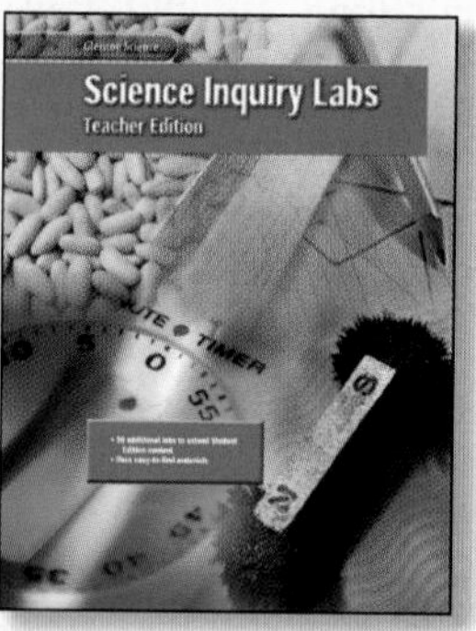

Science Inquiry Labs *(SE and TE)*

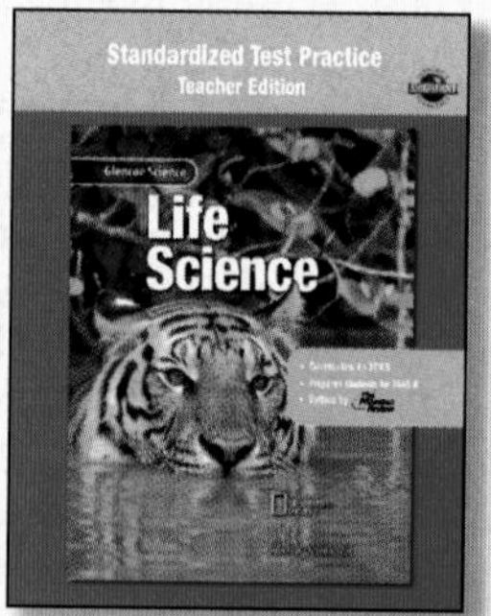

Standardized Test Practice *(SE and TE)*

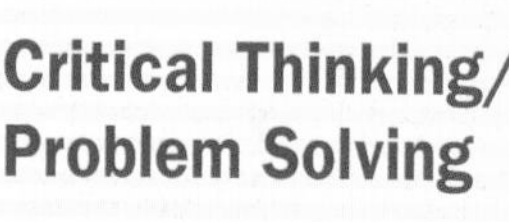

Critical Thinking/ Problem Solving

Life Science

Home and Community Involvement

Laboratory Management and Safety

Program Resources

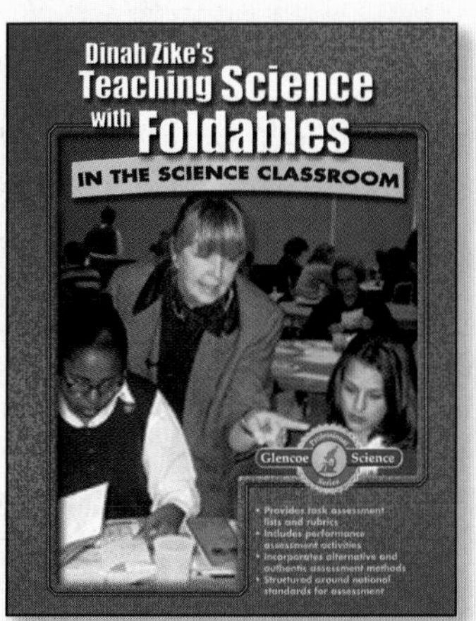

Dinah Zike's Teaching Science with Foldables

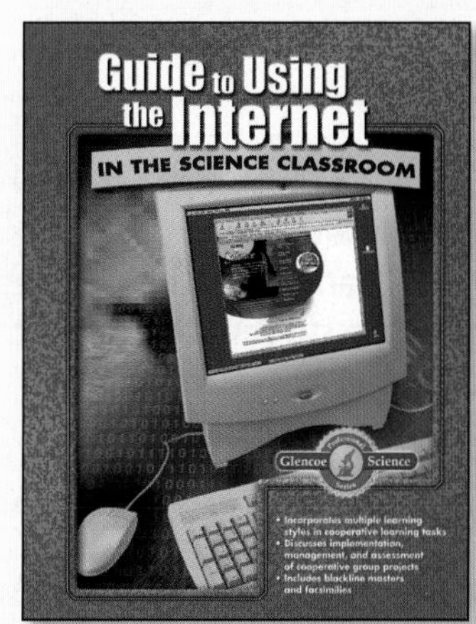

Guide to Using the Internet in the Science Classroom

Cooperative Learning

Cultural Diversity

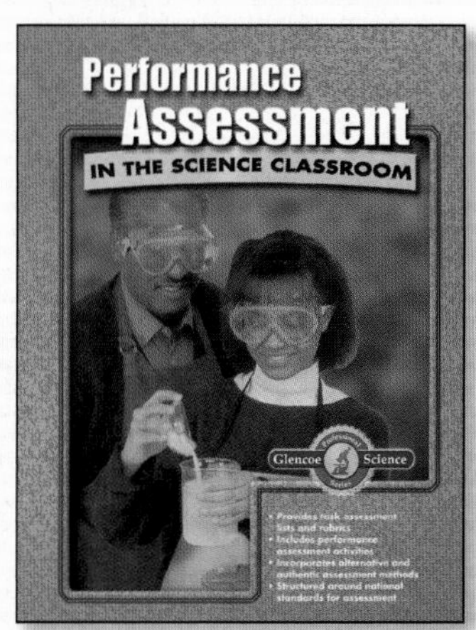

Performance Assessment in the Science Classroom

Meeting Individual Needs

Each student brings his or her unique set of abilities, perceptions, and needs into the classroom. *Glencoe Life Science Teacher Wraparound Edition* offers you a variety of strategies so that your students can learn science concepts through many different methods.

Strategy	Designation
Ability Levels Activities are provided that accommodate students of all ability levels.	L1 Basic activities that reinforce the concepts for lower-ability students L2 Application activities that give all students an opportunity for practical application of concepts L3 Challenging activities that allow students to expand their perspectives on the basic concepts
English-Language Learners These strategies focus on overcoming a language barrier. It is important not to confuse ability in speaking/reading English with academic ability or "intelligence."	ELL These activities reinforce content and aid in the development of science vocabulary.
Learning Styles A variety of instructional strategies help students to learn science concepts through their preferred learning styles. Students generally display more than one of these styles. You may want to assign activities to students that accommodate their strongest learning styles, but assign other activities that help to develop their weaker styles.	LS Look for these bold-faced designations wherever you see this logo: • **Kinesthetic** learners learn through touch, movement, and manipulating objects. • **Visual-Spatial** learners think in terms of images, illustrations, and models. • **Logical-Mathematical** learners understand numbers easily and have highly-developed reasoning skills. • **Linguistic** learners write clearly and easily understand the written word. • **Auditory-Musical** learners remember spoken words and can create rhythms and melodies. • **Interpersonal** learners understand and work well with other people. • **Intrapersonal** learners can analyze their own strengths and weaknesses and may prefer to work on their own.

Strategy	Designation
Inclusion Strategies Inclusion strategies provide you with additional support for helping students with special needs.	Look for these bold-faced designations and strategies wherever you see the **Inclusion Strategies** • **Learning Disabled**—ideas for additional concept review • **Behaviorally Disordered**—activities for helping to keep students on task • **Physically Challenged**—tips for adjusting activities to accommodate students who have less mobility or dexterity than others • **Visually Impaired** or **Hearing Impaired**—ideas for aiding these students in grasping concepts • **Gifted**—challenging activities and research projects that extend chapter concepts
Cooperative Learning In cooperative learning, students work together in small groups to learn content and interpersonal skills. Group members learn that each is responsible for accomplishing an assigned group task as well as for learning the material. Cooperative learning fosters academic, personal, and social success for all students.	COOP LEARN Strategies with this designation are suitable for group work that will help students to: • develop positive attitudes toward science and school; • build respect for others, regardless of race, ethnic origin, or gender; and • increase their sensitivity to and tolerance of diverse perspectives.
Cultural Diversity Classrooms in the United States reflect the rich and diverse cultural heritage of the American people. Students come from different ethnic backgrounds and different cultural experiences into a common classroom that must assist all of them in learning.	**Cultural Diversity** The Cultural Diversity features provide insights into unique ways in which different people have approached science or adapted to their environments. The intent of these features is to build awareness and appreciation for the global community in which we live.
Misconceptions Students have had many experiences outside the science classroom that have shaped their understandings of the natural world. Unfortunately, interpretations based on casual observation are not always accurate. For example, based on their observations, some students might think that the Sun moves around Earth. As a science teacher, you need strategies to help replace these naive conceptions with scientific facts.	IDENTIFYING Misconceptions This one-page feature provides ideas about the types of misconceptions your students may have. It provides you with teaching strategies to uncover misconceptions and to help students understand concepts. You can find these preceding many chapters on the F interleaf pages of the Teacher Wraparound Edition. In addition, you will find several misconceptions stated, followed by the correct information, in the teacher wrap throughout each chapter.

Reading and Writing in the Content Area

***Glencoe Life Science* is designed to increase science literacy through improving reading comprehension and deepening students' understanding of ideas and concepts. The reading strategies are active, constructive, and engaging.**

In the Student Edition

Reading Checks throughout each chapter stimulate quick recall to keep students focused on main ideas and important details.

Reading Check

How does fertilization occur in plants?

Caption Questions throughout each chapter help students to comprehend what they have read through interpreting the visual. This is especially useful for less proficient readers.

Figure 17
This energy pyramid shows that each feeding level contains less energy than the level below it. *What would happen if the hawks and snakes outnumbered the rabbits and mice in this ecosystem?*

Skill Builder Activities in each Section Assessment often include questions that directly address reading and writing skills. Students are referred to the *Science Skill Handbook* for help.

Communicating In your Science Journal write your own analogy about the diploid and haploid stages of a plant life cycle. **For more help, refer to the Science Skill Handbook.**

The Before You Read and After You Read Activities in every chapter set a purpose for reading and help students to construct a graphic organizer to use for learning content and as a study aide.

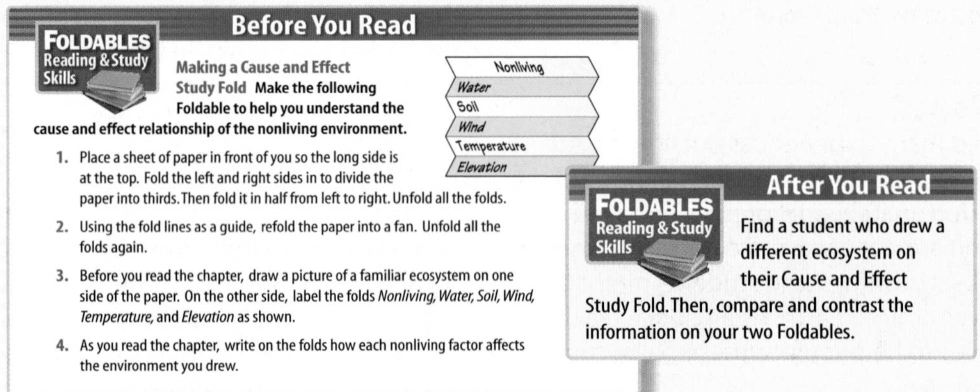
Before You Read
FOLDABLES Reading & Study Skills
Making a Cause and Effect Study Fold Make the following Foldable to help you understand the cause and effect relationship of the nonliving environment.
1. Place a sheet of paper in front of you so the long side is at the top. Fold the left and right sides in to divide the paper into thirds. Then fold it in half from left to right. Unfold all the folds.
2. Using the fold lines as a guide, refold the paper into a fan. Unfold all the folds again.
3. Before you read the chapter, draw a picture of a familiar ecosystem on one side of the paper. On the other side, label the folds Nonliving, Water, Soil, Wind, Temperature, and Elevation as shown.
4. As you read the chapter, write on the folds how each nonliving factor affects the environment you drew.
Nonliving
Water
Soil
Wind
Temperature
Elevation
After You Read
FOLDABLES Reading & Study Skills
Find a student who drew a different ecosystem on their Cause and Effect Study Fold. Then, compare and contrast the information on your two Foldables.

Print and **Technology Resources** to Promote **Reading** and **Writing** in the Content Area

Ancillaries

Chapter Resources

- Directed Reading for Content Mastery pages *(in English and Spanish)*
- Foldables: Reading and Study Skills Worksheets
- Note-taking Worksheets

Dinah Zike's Teaching Science with Foldables

Reading and Writing Skill Activities

Technology

Guided Reading Audio Program *(English and Spanish)*

MindJogger VideoQuizzes

Interactive CD-ROM

Vocabulary PuzzleMaker

Glencoe Science Online

Support for All Learners

Glencoe Exclusive

Foldables: Improving Reading and Study Skills

Students love Foldables because they're fun. Teachers love them because they're effective.

What is a Foldable?

FOLDABLES Reading & Study Skills

Foldables are three-dimensional, interactive graphic organizers. As students fold paper, cut tabs, write, and manipulate what they have made, they are kinesthetically involved in learning. These unique, hands-on tools for studying and reviewing were created exclusively for Glencoe Science by teaching specialist Dinah Zike.

Foldables are Useful!

Reading in the Content Area Foldables help students develop ways of organizing information that are fun and creative. These useful activities help students practice basic writing skills, find and report main ideas, organize information, review key vocabulary terms, and much more!

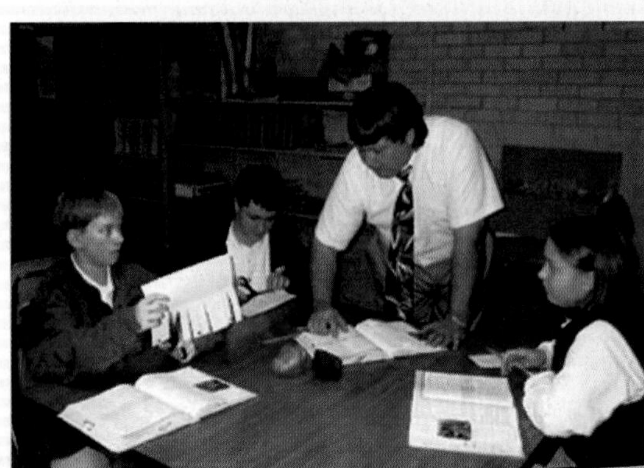

Every chapter begins with a Foldable activity. Students make the physical structure of a Foldable that incorporates one of many prereading strategies. Then, as students read through the chapter and do the activities, students record information as they learn it in the appropriate part of the foldable. In the Chapter Study Guide, the After You Read feature gives students a strategy for using the fold they made to help them review the chapter concepts.

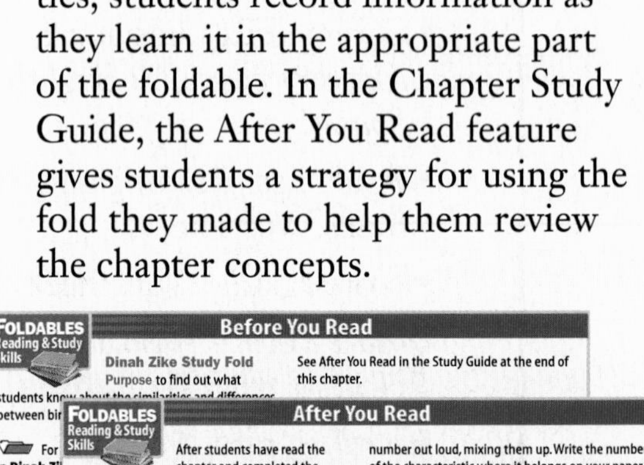
FOLDABLES Reading & Study Skills

Before You Read

Dinah Zike Study Fold
Purpose to find out what students kn... between bi...

For ... in **Dinah Zi**... Science Web...

See After You Read in the Study Guide at the end of this chapter.

FOLDABLES Reading & Study Skills

After You Read

After students have read the chapter and completed the Foldable described in Before You Read, have them do the following activity.

Number the characteristics you have written under the flap. Give your fold to a partner. On another sheet of paper, draw a Venn diagram and label it. Have your partner read each characteristic and its number out loud, mixing them up. Write the number of the characteristic where it belongs on your paper. Then repeat the process with your partner's fold, while you read the characteristics and have him or her write the numbers. Check your answers to make sure they are correct.

Dinah Zike

Review One advantage of Foldables is that they result in an organized study guide. The Foldables then can be used not only while preparing for the chapter test, but they can also be used for reviewing for unit tests, end of course exams, and even standardized tests.

Assessment Foldables present an ideal opportunity for you to probe the depth of your students' knowledge. You'll get detailed feedback on exactly what they know and what misconceptions they may have.

Foldables are Easy!

Anyone who has paper, scissors, and maybe a stapler or some glue can implement Foldables in the classroom. Glencoe's Foldables have been tested with teachers and middle school students to make sure the directions are easy for both students and teachers. After doing a couple of them, your class will quickly become seasoned experts. Don't be surprised if you find them inventing their own for use in projects and reports in all of their classes!

A message from **the creator of Foldables,** Dinah Zike

You might not know my name or me, but I bet you have seen at least one of my graphic organizers or folds used in supplemental programs or teacher workshops. Today, my graphic organizers and manipulatives are used internationally. I present workshops and keynote presentations to over 50,000 teachers a year, sharing the manipulatives I began inventing, designing, and adapting over thirty years ago. Around the world, students of all ages are using them as daily work, note-taking activities, student-directed projects, forms of alternative assessment, science lab journals, quantitative and qualitative observation books, graphs, tables, and more. But through all my years of teaching, designing, and publishing, my materials had never been featured in a middle school textbook. When Glencoe/McGraw-Hill approached me to share some of my three-dimensional, manipulative graphic organizers with you in this new and innovative science series, I was thrilled.

Working with Glencoe, we all had the vision that Foldables should be an integral part of the curriculum, not simply tacked on. What we ended up with was a strategy that will help students read and learn science concepts. One of the advantages of using the same manipulative repeatedly is that students are immersed in what they are learning. It is not out of sight and out of mind. How long is your average student actively involved with a duplicated activity sheet? Ten minutes? Fifteen? Students will use the Foldable at the beginning of each chapter, before reading the chapter, during reading, and after reading. That's a lot of immersion!

Dinah Zike

Reading and Writing in the Content Area

In the Teacher Edition

Science & Language Arts

Pre-Reading Activity helps students draw upon their personal experience and sets a purpose for reading.

Respond to the Reading provides active reading strategies that provide a variety of ways for students to respond to the feature through listening, speaking, and writing activities. It also provides students with an opportunity to make connections to the theme.

Linking Science and Writing provides options that all students can use to respond in writing to the feature.

Support for All Learners

Use Science Words

Word Meaning Have students compare the meaning of the word cuticle in relation to plants (protective layer on plant surface) and in relation to the human body (hardened skin at the base of nails). Both are derived from the Latin *cutis* meaning "skin." L2

LS **Linguistic**

Use Science Words appears throughout each chapter and provides three types of reading strategies. Students structurally analyze root words (Word Origin), develop vocabulary (Word Meaning), or apply their knowledge of science terms (Word Usage).

Science Journal

Nerve Analogy Have students write a paragraph in their Science Journals that explains how a nerve is similar to a wire going from a controlling switch (stimulus) to a light bulb (response). Possible response: The switch receives a stimulus, which travels along the wire. The bulb responds to the stimulus by lighting up. L2 LS **Linguistic** P

Science Journals throughout each chapter provide opportunities for students to write responses to questions that require critical thinking; to conduct research and write about it; or to practice creative writing skills.

Active Reading Strategies

A variety of active reading strategies are provided throughout the *Teacher Wraparound Edition.* These strategies utilize a variety of learning styles, and encourage cooperative learning and intrapersonal reflection on chapter content.

Active Reading

Think-Pair Share This strategy encourages students to think first before discussing their ideas or thoughts about a topic. Ask students to respond to a question by writing a response. After thinking for a few minutes, partners share responses to the question. Finally, ask the students to share responses with the class. Have students become involved in a Think-Pair Share about cathode rays.

Making Concept Maps and Charts

Bubble Map Students brainstorm and organize words in clusters to describe concepts.

Double-Bubble Map Students compare concepts using two bubble maps.

Flow Chart Students logically analyze and draw a sequence of events.

Cause and Effect Chart Students visually represent the causes and effects of an event or process.

Supporting Idea Chart Students make a concept map to analyze the relationship between a whole and its parts.

Using the Science Journal

Double Entry Journal Students read and record ideas, then reflect on the text and respond to the ideas.

Metacognition Students analyze what and how they have learned.

Learning Journal Students write and reflect on notes about content.

Problem-Solution Journal Students analyze problems and suggest workable solutions.

Speculation About Effects/ Prediction Journal Students examine events and speculate about their possible long-term effects.

Synthesis Journal Students reflect on a project, a paper, or a performance task and plan how to apply what they have learned to their own lives.

Reflective Journal Students identify what they learned in an activity and record responses.

Quickwrites Students use spontaneous writing to discover what they already know.

Collaborative Learning Strategies

Pair of Pairs Partners respond to a question and compare their response to that of other pairs and to the class.

Write-Draw-Discuss Students write about and draw a picture of a concept, then share it with the class.

Four-Corner Discussion The class works in four groups to debate a complex issue.

Jigsaw Students work in groups to become experts on a portion of text and share their expertise with their "home" group.

Buddy Interviews Students interview one another to find out what helps them to understand what they are reading.

Reciprocal Teaching Students take turns reading the text and retelling it in their own words, then asking one another questions.

News Summary Students are given several minutes to summarize, retell, or analyze an activity for a "TV" audience.

ReQuest The teacher reads aloud an article or story. Student pairs then construct discussion questions and review the content.

Concept Maps

Helping students understand concepts through visuals

Concept maps are visual representations or graphic organizers of relationships among particular concepts. Concept maps can be generated by individual students, small groups, or an entire class. Four types of concept maps that are most applicable to studying science are developed and reinforced in this program. Students can learn how to construct each of these types of concept maps by referring to the Skill Handbook in the ***Student Edition.***

Concept maps can be used to increase understanding of science concepts, to strengthen reading skills, to promote cooperative learning, and to assess learning. When evaluating concept maps, look for the conceptual strength of student responses, not absolute accuracy.

- **Science Concepts** Concept mapping helps students to understand science concepts through analyzing relationships among ideas and reinforcing those relationships by visualizing them.
- **Reading Skills** Concept maps can help students preview a chapter's content by visually relating the concepts to be learned and aiding students to read with purpose. Students learn key science terms by choosing the terms to use, supplying connecting words, or by placing terms and connecting words when provided by the teacher. To further develop concept mapping skills, the *Chapter Resources* booklet for each chapter contains concept maps in the reproducible student pages Directed Reading for Content Mastery.
- **Cooperative Learning** Construction of concept maps using cooperative learning strategies allows students to practice interpersonal skills as they work together to build the map.
- **Review and Assessment** As a review, constructing concept maps reinforces main ideas and clarifies their relationships. As an assessment tool, concept maps can be constructed by students or students can fill in the terms. Look for concept mapping assessment in the Chapter Assessment section of every chapter.

Support for All Learners

Network Tree

- Order information from general to specific.
- Show a hierarchy.
- Use branching procedures.
- Explain relationships with connecting terms.

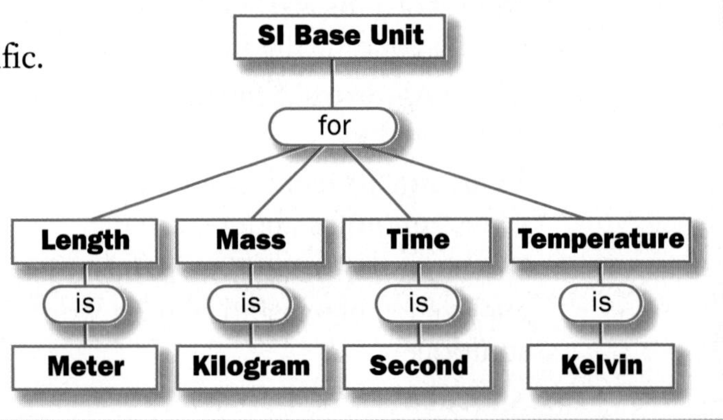

Events Chain

- Describe the stages of a process.
- Order the steps in a linear procedure.
- Show a sequence of events.

Initiating Event

Determine the problem.

Make a hypothesis.

Test your hypothesis.

Analyze the results.

Draw conclusions.

Cycle Concept Map

- Show how a series of events interact.
- Depict how the last event relates to the initiating event.

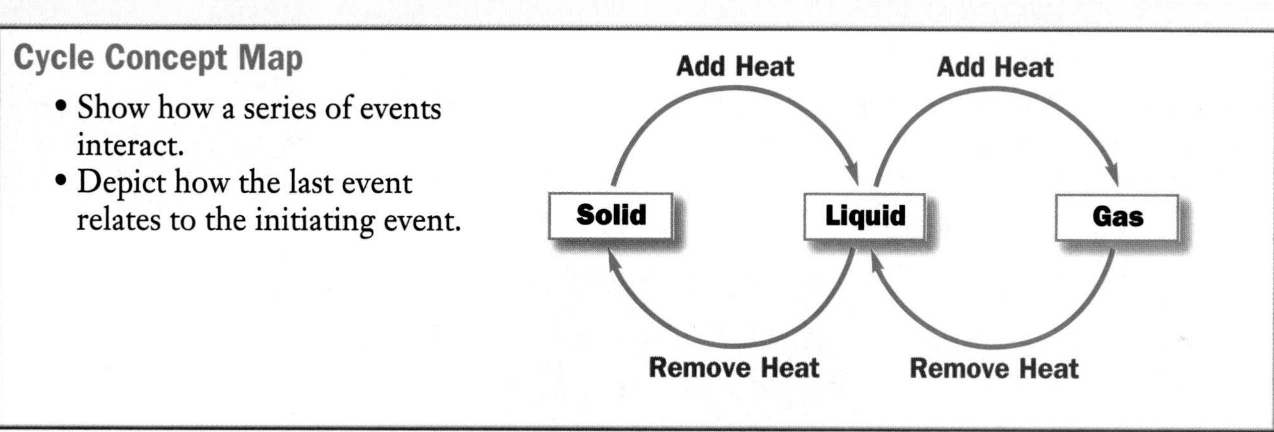

Spider Concept Map

- Use for brainstorming.
- Separate and group unrelated terms.
- Show relationship of nonrelated terms to a central idea.

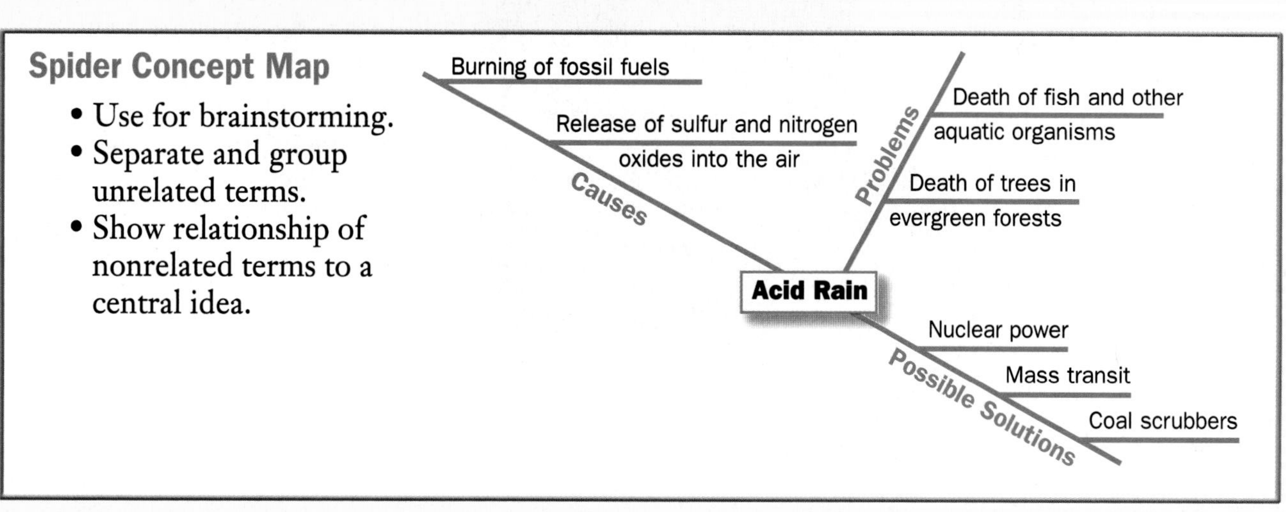

Assessment Support

Glencoe Life Science offers the Glencoe Assessment Advantage, a system of assessment options designed to give you the flexibility and tools to conduct standardized test preparation, and content and performance assessment.

Glencoe has partnered with *The Princeton Review*, a nationally renowned company that helps students prepare for state and national tests. This partnership has resulted in the Study Tips and Test Practice questions at the end of each Chapter Assessment in the ***Student Edition.*** Test practice booklets help prepare students for success on standardized tests.

Content Assessment

- **Section Assessment** questions and **Skill Builder Activities** appear in every chapter of the ***Student Edition.***
- A **Study Guide** at the end of each chapter in the ***Student Edition*** allows you to determine whether reteaching is needed.
- The **Chapter Assessment** questions in the ***Student Edition*** help you evaluate students' knowledge and ability to apply science concepts.

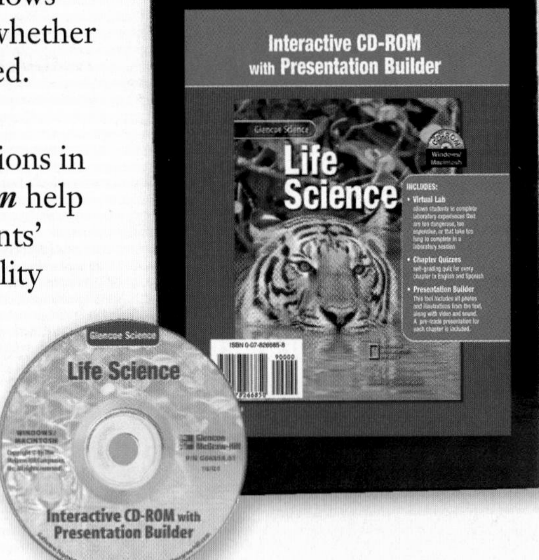

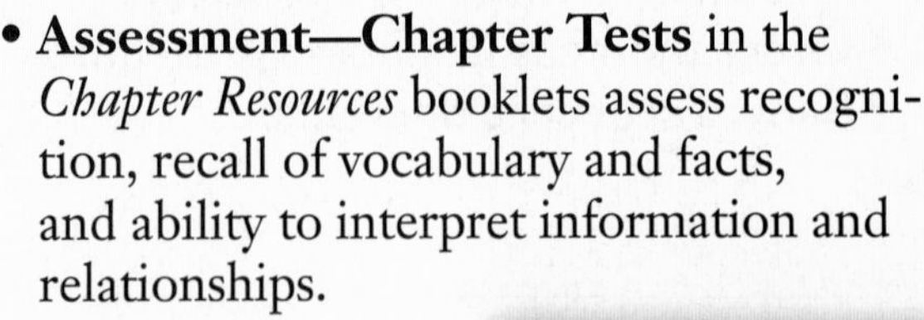

- **Assessment—Chapter Tests** in the *Chapter Resources* booklets assess recognition, recall of vocabulary and facts, and ability to interpret information and relationships.
- **MindJogger Videoquizzes** offer interactive videos that provide a fun way for your students to review chapter concepts.
- The **Interactive CD-ROM** provides quizzes that can be used as a whole-class presentation or as a review for individual students. These materials also are available on the Glencoe Science Web site.

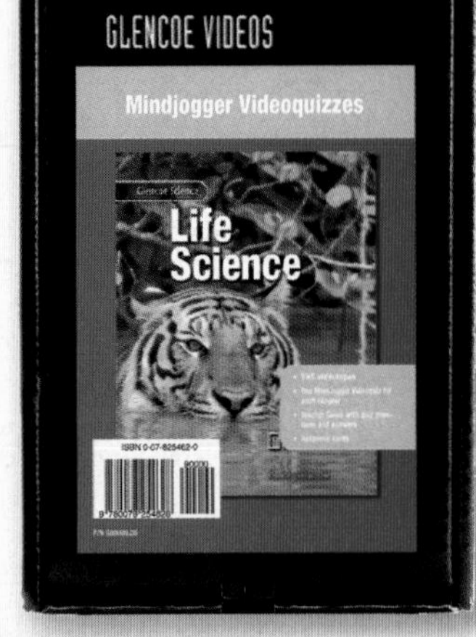

- **ExamView® Pro Test Bank CD-ROM (English/Spanish)** Software for Macintosh and Windows provides an easy way to make, edit, and print tests. You can add your own questions and graphics.

Performance Assessment

Performance Assessment refers to the strategies used to assess students' level of science literacy. Performance Assessment is based on judging the quality of a student's response to a performance task. A performance task is constructed to require the use of important concepts with supporting information, work habits important to science, and one or more of the elements of scientific literacy.

Performance Task Assessment Lists

Performance Assessments accompany **Activities** and **Chapter Assessments** in the ***Glencoe Life Science Student Edition***. Task Assessment Lists are provided in Glencoe's *Performance Assessment in the Science Classroom*. Both the teacher and the student assess the work and assign points based on the well-defined categories and possible points for each category. These task lists were developed for the summative performance tasks included in the booklet.

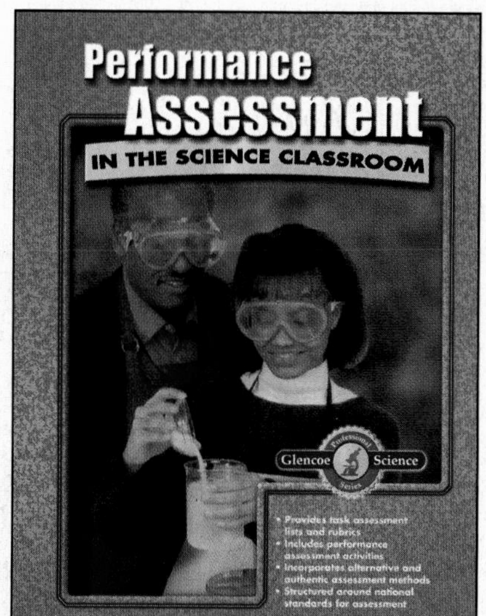

Assessing Student Work with Rubrics

A rubric is a set of descriptions of the quality of a process and a product. The set of descriptions includes a continuum of quality from excellent to poor. Rubrics for various types of assessment products are provided in the Glencoe Professional Development Series booklet *Performance Assessment in the Science Classroom*. In addition to sample rubrics, blank rubric forms allow teachers to customize assessment methods. The booklet also provides a step-by step model showing teachers how to use the materials most effectively.

Portfolios

Portfolio suggestions are featured throughout each chapter in the ***Glencoe Life Science Teacher Wraparound Edition***. The Portfolio should help the student see the big picture of how he or she is performing in gaining knowledge and skills and how effective his or her work habits are. The performance portfolio is not a complete collection of all worksheets and other assignments but rather a collection that reflects the student's growth in concept attainment and skill development. Writings and drawings from the student's **Science Journal**, featured in the ***Student Edition*** and the ***Teacher Wraparound Edition***, often are suggested to include in portfolios.

Group Assessment

All students benefit from a cooperative learning environment. Research has shown that student-learning outcomes improve for students of all ability levels. An example, along with information about evaluating cooperative work, is provided in the booklet *Performance Assessment in the Science Classroom*.

Lab Safety

The activities in *Glencoe Life Science* have been tested in the laboratory and have been reviewed by safety consultants. Even so, there are no guarantees against accidents. For additional help, refer to the *Laboratory Management and Safety* booklet, which contains safety guidelines and masters to test students' lab and safety skills.

General Guidelines

- Post safety guidelines, fire escape routes, and a list of emergency procedures in the classroom. Make sure students understand these procedures. Remind them at the beginning of *every* lab session.

- Understand and make note of the Safety Symbols used in each activity.
- Have students fill out a safety contract. Students should pledge to follow the rules, to wear safety attire, and to conduct themselves in a responsible manner.
- Know where emergency equipment is stored and how to use it.
- Supervise students at all times. Check assembly of all setups.
- Perform all activities before you allow students to do so.
- Instruct students to follow directions carefully.
- Make sure that all students are wearing proper safety attire. They should wear goggles at all times. They should secure long hair and loose clothing. Do not permit wearing contact lenses, even with safety glasses; splashing chemicals could infuse under a lens and cause eye damage.

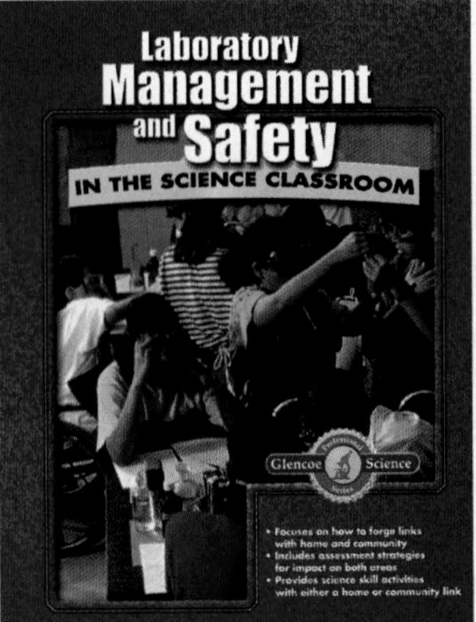

Handling Chemicals

- Handle chemicals carefully at all times. Always wear safety goggles, gloves, and an apron when handling chemicals. Treat all chemicals as potentially dangerous.
- Never ingest chemicals. Use proper techniques to smell solutions.
- Use a fume hood when handling chemicals that are poisonous or corrosive or that give off a vapor.
- *Always add acids to water, never the reverse.*
- Prepare solutions by adding the solid to a small amount of distilled water and then diluting with water to the volume listed. If you use a hydrate that is different from the one specified in a particular preparation, you will need to adjust the amount of hydrate to obtain the correct concentration.

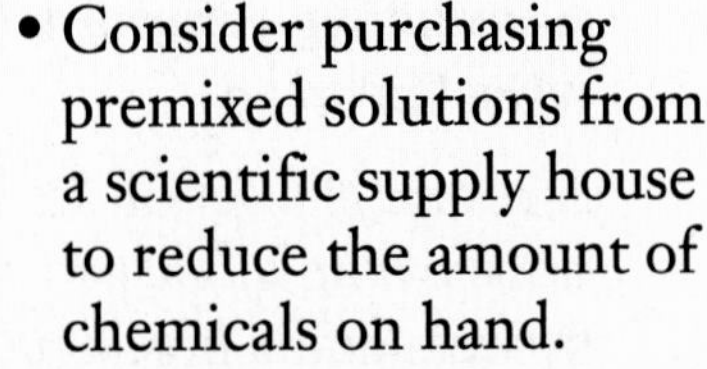

- Consider purchasing premixed solutions from a scientific supply house to reduce the amount of chemicals on hand.
- Maintain appropriate MSDS (Materials Safety Data Sheets) in the laboratory.

Chemical Storage and Disposal

The following are some commonly used guidelines for chemical storage and disposal, but your school or local government may have additional requirements for handling chemicals. It is your responsibility to be informed of the rules governing chemical storage and disposal in your area.

- Use wood shelving rather than metal. All shelving should be firmly attached to the wall and have antiroll edges.
- Store only those chemicals you intend to use. Do not store chemicals above eye level.
- Store chemicals in labeled containers that indicate the contents, concentration, source, date purchased (or prepared), safety precautions for handling, and expiration date.
- Separate chemicals by reaction type. Store acids in one place and bases in another. Oxidants should be stored away from easily oxidized materials, for example.
- Dispose of outdated or waste chemicals properly.
- Follow regulations for storing hazardous chemicals.

Disposal of Chemicals

Local, state, and federal laws regulate the disposal of chemicals. Consult these laws before attempting to dispose of any chemicals. The following resource provides some general guidelines for handling and disposing of chemicals: *Prudent Practices in the Laboratory: Handling and Disposal of Chemicals.* Washington, DC: National Academy Press, 1995. Current laws in your area supersede the information in this book.

Disclaimer

Glencoe/McGraw-Hill makes no claims to the completeness of this discussion of laboratory safety and chemical storage. The material presented is not all-inclusive, nor does it address all of the hazards associated with handling, storage, and disposal of chemicals, or with laboratory management.

Activity Materials

Glencoe Life Science **makes it easy for you to plan and facilitate activities in your classroom.**

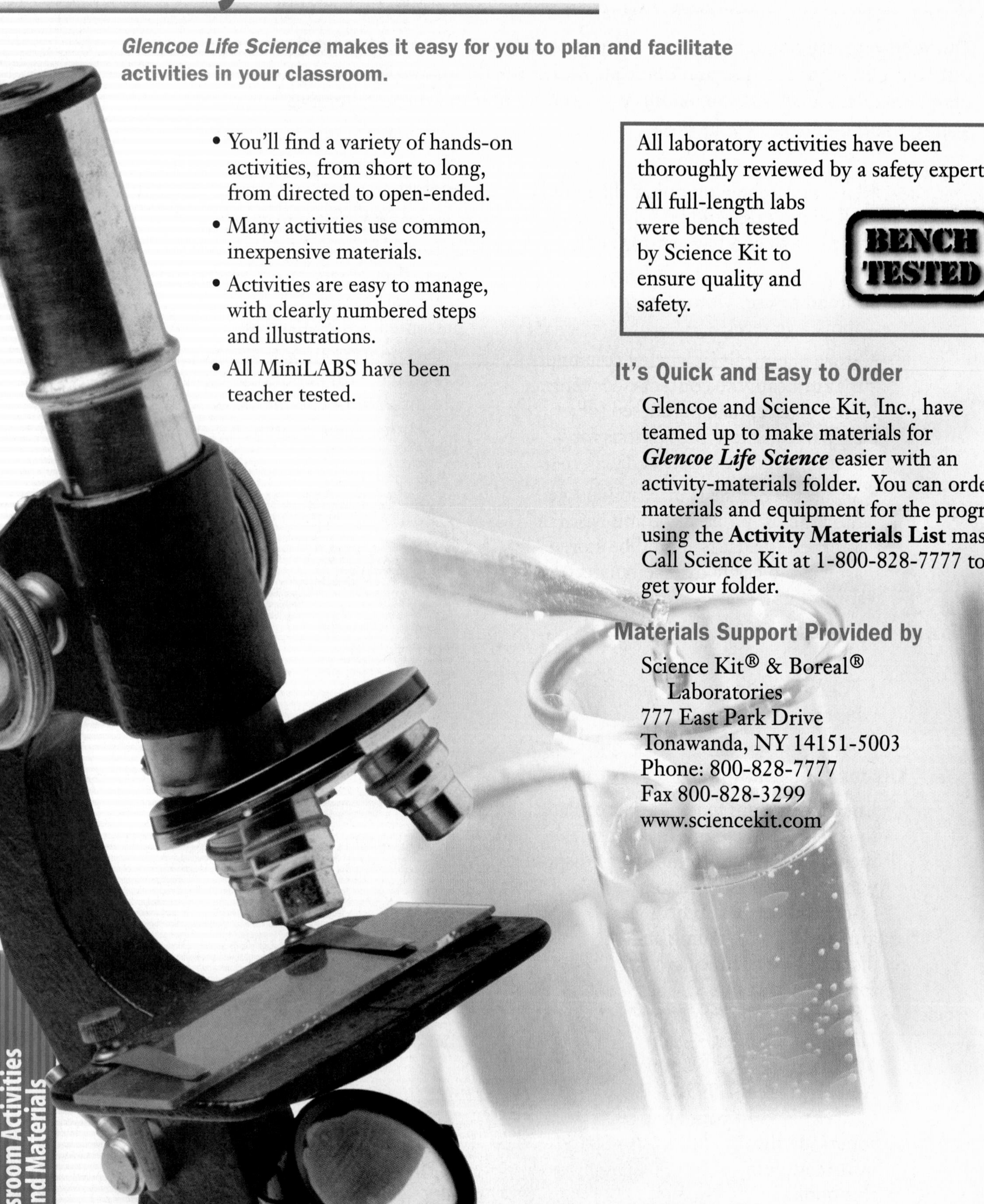

- You'll find a variety of hands-on activities, from short to long, from directed to open-ended.
- Many activities use common, inexpensive materials.
- Activities are easy to manage, with clearly numbered steps and illustrations.
- All MiniLABS have been teacher tested.

All laboratory activities have been thoroughly reviewed by a safety expert.

All full-length labs were bench tested by Science Kit to ensure quality and safety.

It's Quick and Easy to Order

Glencoe and Science Kit, Inc., have teamed up to make materials for ***Glencoe Life Science*** easier with an activity-materials folder. You can order materials and equipment for the program using the **Activity Materials List** master. Call Science Kit at 1-800-828-7777 to get your folder.

Materials Support Provided by

Science Kit® & Boreal® Laboratories
777 East Park Drive
Tonawanda, NY 14151-5003
Phone: 800-828-7777
Fax 800-828-3299
www.sciencekit.com

List of Activity Materials

It is assumed that laboratory aprons, goggles, tap water, meter sticks, metric rulers, textbooks, scissors, calculators, paper, pencils, and pens are available.

Non-Consumables

Item	Explore Activity Page	MiniLAB Page	Activity Chapter/Section
Aquarium			13-1, 14-4
Balance	65	9	3-2, 18-1, 18-2, 25-3
Basin	777	697	
Beaker(s)	65, 777	40, 196, 249	10-3, 14-4, 18-2
Bellows			20-2
Bicycle pump			20-2
Binoculars			26-2
Blindfold		616	
Bowl	65	50, 407, 442, 534, 547, 578	24-3
Clam shell	363		
Clock or watch	65	75, 547, 722	
Clock or watch with second hand	153, 573	385	19-1, 27-2
Cloth, cotton		434, 534	
Cloth, terry		534	
Coat hangers, wire			27-3
Collection jars			8-2
Compass			26-2
Container		40, 249, 255, 275, 534, 722, 762	1-4, 3-2, 14-4
Cooking pot			23-2
Cookware, black			27-3
Cup(s)		71, 275, 585, 787	
Dish			11-1, 12-2, 12-3
Dissecting needle			10-2
Dropper bottle			3-3, 18-1
Dropper(s)	627	75, 350, 558, 666	2-1, 2-3, 8-1, 10-2, 12-2, 12-3, 18-1, 19-3
Fertilizer, houseplant		731	
Fishnet, small		762	14-4
Flashlight		40	16-2
Forceps			2-1, 10-2, 11-1

Classroom Activities and Materials

Activity Materials

Non-Consumables *continued*

Item	Explore Activity Page	MiniLAB Page	Activity Chapter/Section
Funnel		585	
Glass(es), drinking		50, 75	23-3
Gloves, disposable			20-2, 23-2
Graduated cylinder		249	10-3, 18-1, 19-3, 25-1
Hand lens	37, 95, 211, 363, 691	50, 220, 255, 376, 414, 504, 762	1-4, 6-3, 8-2, 10-2, 20-2, 24-3, 26-2
Hole punch	153		
Humidity meter	747		
Insect collection	5		
Jar(s)		376, 414, 722	7-2, 11-1, 11-2, 13-4, 18-2, 25-1
Lamp			12-3, 27-2
Marble(s)		578	
Measuring cup		534	
Microscope			2-1, 2-3, 4-1, 7-1, 8-1, 8-2, 10-2, 11-1, 12-3
Microscope slide(s)			2-1, 2-3, 8-1, 8-2, 10-2, 11-1
Model of a kidney			20-2
Mortar and pestle			18-2
Paintbrush, small			12-3
Pennies		661	
Petri dish(es)			2-3, 12-3
Photo of furniture		25	
Photos of camouflaged animals			6-1
Photos of foods		464	
Photos of frogs			6-1
Photos of landscapes		464	
Plant trays			10-3
Plate	187, 627	666, 780	
Prepared slide or micrograph photo of *Anabaena*			7-1
Prepared slide of human cheek cells			2-1
Prepared slide or micrograph photo of *Gloeocapsa*			7-1

Non-Consumables *continued*

Item	Explore Activity Page	Mini LAB Page	Activity Chapter/Section
Prepared slide or micrograph photo of *Nostoc*			7-1
Prepared slide of onion root tip			4-1
Prepared slide or micrograph photo of *Oscillatoria*			7-1
Prepared slide of slime mold			8-1
Prepared slide of tapeworm			12-3
Rain gauge		787	
Reference-city, county, or state map	545		
Reference-classified ads	153		
Reference-field guide to fungi or club fungi			8-2
Reference-field guides			26-2
Reference-globe or world map	719		
Reference-source on birds			15-2
Reference-source on weather	719		
Rubber bands		376	13-4, 27-3
Scale		249	25-3
Scalpel			20-2
Socks	431		
Spoons		722	3-2, 23-3
Sports bottle			20-2
Spray bottle	777	756	
Stereomicroscope		350	2-3, 12-2, 12-3
Stirring rod or other stirrer	65	40	3-3, 14-4, 18-2
Stopwatch	153, 573	547	18-2, 27-3
Tape measure			22-3
Temperature probe			27-2
Test tube(s)			3-3, 18-1
Test-tube rack			3-3, 18-1
Test-tube stoppers			3-3
Thermometer(s)	747		10-3, 14-1, 14-4, 18-2, 26-2, 27-2, 27-3

Activity Materials

Non-Consumables *continued*

Item	Explore Activity Page	MiniLAB Page	Activity Chapter/Section
Timer			16-2, 27-3
Tuning fork	397		
Watch glass		350	
Watering can		697	7-2
Wire screen		585	

Consumables

Item	Explore Activity Page	MiniLAB Page	Activity Chapter/Section
Aluminum foil	303	558	7-2, 11-2, 27-3
Art supplies			8-2
Balloons		407	
Beads			6-1
Bottle, plastic beverage, 1-L			27-2
Branches			9-1
Buttons		290, 336	
Candy wrapper, plastic			7-2
Cardboard			6-1
Cardboard boxes			27-3
Cardboard tube		578	20-2
Cheesecloth		249, 376	
Cloth			14-1, 24-3
Coffee filter			23-3
Cologne/Perfume		469, 616	
Construction paper, black		307	13-4
Cotton balls	657	616	23-2
Coverslips			2-1, 2-3, 8-1, 8-2, 10-2, 11-1
Crayons			6-1
Culture containers			24-3
Cup(s)		585	19-3, 25-3
Dishwashing liquid		722	
Elodea sprig			3-3

Consumables *continued*

Item	Explore Activity Page	MiniLAB Page	Activity Chapter/Section
Fabric scraps		336	
Fiberfill			14-1
Filter paper	627	585	
Flavoring oil		469	
Food coloring		75, 255	19-3
Food-apple			7-2, 13-4, 23-2
Food-banana		316, 376	7-2, 13-4, 24-3
Food-beans, dried		196	5-1
Food-brownie with nuts		780	
Food-carrot sticks	65		
Food-cheese		521	
Food-cookies		780	
Food-corn starch			18-1
Food-corn syrup, light			3-2
Food-cracked corn	431		
Food-egg, raw			3-2
Food-fruit (various kinds)		521, 701	6-3, 24-3
Food-gelatin		40, 71	
Food-grapes	273		
Food-green onion		255	
Food-ground beef, raw			13-3
Food-kiwi			13-4
Food-lemon juice			19-3, 23-3
Food-lettuce			11-1, 24-3
Food-liver, raw			12-3, 24-3
Food-meat		521	24-3
Food-milk, low-fat			19-3
Food-mushrooms (from grocery)	211	227	
Food-nuts	431		
Food-orange juice			18-1, 23-3
Food-oranges			13-4, 24-3
Food-peanuts		521	
Food-peppermint flavoring	657		

Activity Materials

Consumables *continued*

Item	Explore Activity Page	Mini LAB Page	Activity Chapter/Section
Food-pineapple		71	
Food-potato chips		521	
Food-pretzels		521	
Food-red cabbage			23-3
Food-salt	65, 627		1-4, 10-3, 11-1
Food-samples of different ones		616	
Food-sugar			18-2
Food-sunflower seeds	431		
Food-vegetable shortening		442	
Food-vegetables		521	
Food-yeast, dried		666	1-4
Fruit fly culture kit			24-3
Gauze		558	
Glitter		336	
Glue		101, 290, 336	6-1, 21-2, 26-2, 27-3
Graph paper		636, 642	6-3, 22-3
Grass clippings			25-1
Grass clumps	777		
Gravel	431	585	
Hairstyling gel	187		
Household products-samples		616	
Humus			13-4
Ice		442	14-4
Index cards	517		21-2
Kidney, large animal			20-2
Labels	65, 517	75, 731	1-4, 23-3
Leaves			7-2, 25-1
Liquid bandage solution		558	
Magazine	241		
Markers/marking pens	517	75, 101	5-3, 6-1, 11-2, 12-4, 16-2, 19-3, 25-1
Modeling clay			6-1, 20-2
Newspaper	153	50	7-2, 17-3, 23-3

Consumables *continued*

Item	EXPLORE ACTIVITY Page	Mini LAB Page	Activity Chapter/Section
Paper bags		316, 521	5-1
Paper plates		780	
Paper towels	95, 273	701	11-2, 16-2, 23-2, 25-3
Pencil, glass-marking		75	18-1
Pencils, colored			6-1, 16-2
Petroleum jelly		434	
Plastic bags, clear			27-3
Plastic bags, sandwich		504	
Plastic bags, self-sealing	95, 303	442	23-2
Plastic cup			10-2
Plastic knife	273	701	
Plastic lids			24-3
Plastic spoon			1-4
Plastic wrap			27-2
Pond debris or sediment		762	
Poster board		101, 756	5-3, 16-2, 27-3
Potting soil	777		
Sand	777		
Sandpaper			23-3
Seeds	95, 431	697	1-4, 6-2, 10-3, 11-2, 25-3
Sequins			6-1
Shoe box with lid			16-2
Soap			23-2
Sod	691		
Soil		275, 585, 697, 722	7-2, 10-3, 13-4, 25-1, 25-3, 27-2
Sphagnum moss		249	
Sponge	187	9	
Stirring rod, wooden			18-1
String		189, 290	27-3
Tape	517	171, 307, 504, 614	13-4, 16-2, 17-3, 18-1, 21-2, 27-2, 27-3
Thread		101	

Consumables *continued*

Item	Explore Activity Page	Mini LAB Page	Activity Chapter/Section
Toothpicks		101, 780	12-2, 21-2
Water, carbonated			3-3
Water, distilled		196, 787	1-4, 2-3, 3-2
Water, pond		762	24-3
Water, rain		787	
Water, stream			24-3
Weighing paper			18-1, 18-2
Yarn		101, 189	

Chemical Supplies

Item	Explore Activity Page	Mini LAB Page	Activity Chapter/Section
Ammonia, clear			23-3
Bicarbonate of soda	627		23-3
Bromothymol blue solution			3-3
Hydrogen peroxide		666	
Iodine, 2% tincture			18-1
Isopropyl (rubbing) acohol			23-2
pH indicator paper		787	
Vinegar	627		23-3

Live Organisms

Item	Explore Activity Page	MiniLAB Page	Activity Chapter/Section
Brine shrimp			12-1
Brine shrimp eggs			1-4
Coleus		275	
Crayfish			13-3
Culture of *Amoeba*			8-1
Culture of *Euglena*			8-1
Culture of hydra			12-2
Culture of *Paramecium*			8-1
Culture of planarians		350	12-3, 24-3
Culture of *Spirogyra*			8-1
Daphnia			12-2
Earthworms			13-4, 16-2
Elodea plant			2-1, 3-3
Ferns with gametophytes and sporophytes			10-2
Frog		414	
Fruit flies			24-3
Goldfish			14-4
Guppies			24-3
Houseplant with leaves	747	303, 307, 275	
Liverworts			10-2
Moss	777		10-2
Organisms from pond water		762	
Physarum polycephalum		220	
Pond plants		762	

Suppliers

Scientific Suppliers

Carolina Biological Supply Company
2700 York Road
Burlington, NC 27215
800-334-5551
www.carolina.com

Fisher Scientific Company
4500 Turnberry Drive
Hanover Park, IL 60103
800-766-7000
www.fishersci.com

Fisher Scientific Educational
485 South Frontage Road
Burr Ridge, IL 60521
800-955-1177
www.fisheredu.com

Flinn Scientific
P.O. Box 219
770 N. Raddant Road
Batavia, IL 60510
800-452-1261
www.flinnsci.com

Frey Scientific
100 Paragon Road
Mansfield, OH 44903
800-225-3739
www.freyscientific.com

Sargent-Welch/Cenco
P.O. Box 5229
911 Commerce Court
Buffalo Grove, IL 60089
800-727-4368
www.sargentwelch.com

Science Kit & Boreal Laboratories
777 East Park Drive
Tonawanda, NY 14150
800-828-7777
www.sciencekit.com

Ward's Natural Science Establishment, Inc.
P.O. Box 92912
5100 Henrietta Road
Rochester, NY 14692
800-962-2660
www.wardsci.com

Software Distributors

(AIT) Agency for Instructional Technology
Box A
Bloomington, IN 47402-0120
800-457-4509
www.ait.net

Educational Activities, Inc.
1937 Grand Avenue
Baldwin, NY 11510
800-645-3739
www.edact.com

IBM Educational Systems
Department PC
4111 Northside Parkway
Atlanta, GA 30327
800-426-4968
www.IBM.com

Microphys
12 Bridal Way
Sparta, NJ 07871
800-832-6591
www.microphys.com

Queue, Inc.
338 Commerce Drive
Fairfield, CT 06432
800-335-0906
www.queueinc.com

School Division of The Learning Company
6160 Summit Drive
Minneapolis, MN 55430
www.learningcompanyschool.com

Ventura Educational Systems
P.O. Box 425
Grover Beach, CA 93483
2782 Sevada
Arroyo, CA 93420
800-336-1022
www.venturaES.com

Audiovisual Distributors

Aims Multimedia
9710 Desoto Avenue
Chatsworth, CA 91311-4409
800-367-2467
www.aimsmultimedia.com

BFA Educational Media
2349 Chaffee Drive
St. Louis, MO 63146
800-221-1274
www.phoenixcoronet.com

CRM Films
2215 Faraday Avenue
Carlsbad, CA 92008
800-421-0833
www.crmfilms.com

Encyclopedia Britannica Educational Corp. (EBEC)
310 S. Michigan Avenue
Chicago, IL 60604
800-554-9862 ext. 7007
www.ebec.com

Hawkill Associates, Inc.
125 E. Gilman Street
Madison, WI 53703
800-422-4295
www.hawkill.com

Lumivision
877 Federal Boulevard
Denver, CO 80204
303-446-0400
www.lumivision.com

National Geographic School Publishing
P.O. Box 10579
Des Moines, IA 50340
17th and "M" Streets, NW
Washington, DC 20009
800-368-2728
www.nationalgeographic.com\education

Time-Life Education
P.O. Box 8502
Richmond, VA 23285
800-449-2010
www.timelifeedu.com

Video Discovery
Suite 600
1700 Westlake Avenue, N
Seattle, WA 98109
800-548-3472
www.videodiscovery.com

Glencoe Science

Life Science

NATIONAL GEOGRAPHIC SOCIETY

science.glencoe.com

New York, New York Columbus, Ohio Woodland Hills, California Peoria, Illinois

Glencoe Science

Glencoe Life Science

Student Edition
Teacher Wraparound Edition
Interactive Teacher Edition CD-ROM
Interactive Lesson Planner CD-ROM
Lesson Plans
Content Outline for Teaching
Dinah Zike's Teaching Science with Foldables
Directed Reading for Content Mastery
Foldables: Reading and Study Skills
Assessment
- *Chapter Review*
- *Chapter Tests*
- *ExamView Pro Test Bank Software*
- *Assessment Transparencies*
- *Performance Assessment in the Science Classroom*
- *The Princeton Review Standardized Test Practice Booklet*

Directed Reading for Content Mastery in Spanish
Spanish Resources
English/Spanish Guided Reading Audio Program
Reinforcement
Enrichment
Activity Worksheets
Section Focus Transparencies
Teaching Transparencies
Laboratory Activities
Science Inquiry Labs
Critical Thinking/Problem Solving
Reading and Writing Skill Activities
Mathematics Skill Activities
Cultural Diversity
Laboratory Management and Safety in the Science Classroom
MindJogger Videoquizzes and Teacher Guide
Interactive CD-ROM with Presentation Builder
Vocabulary PuzzleMaker Software
Cooperative Learning in the Science Classroom
Environmental Issues in the Science Classroom
Home and Community Involvement
Using the Internet in the Science Classroom

"Study Tip," "Test-Taking Tip," and "Test Practice" features in this book were written by The Princeton Review, the nation's leader in test preparation. Through its association with McGraw-Hill, The Princeton Review offers the best way to help students excel on standardized assessments.

The Princeton Review is not affiliated with Princeton University or Educational Testing Service.

Glencoe/McGraw-Hill
A Division of The **McGraw·Hill** *Companies*

Cover Images: A partially submerged Indo-Chinese tiger somewhere in Thailand.

Send all inquiries to:
Glencoe/McGraw-Hill
8787 Orion Place
Columbus, OH 43240

ISBN 0-07-823694-0
Printed in the United States of America.
5 6 7 8 9 10 027/043 06 05 04 03

Authors

National Geographic Society
Education Division
Washington, D.C.

Edward Ortleb
Science Consultant
St. Louis Public Schools
St. Louis, Missouri

Alton Biggs
Biology Teacher
Allen High School
Allen, Texas

Peter Rillero, PhD
Professor of Science Education
Arizona State University West
Phoenix, Arizona

Lucy Daniel, PhD
Life and Physical Science Teacher/Consultant
Rutherford County Schools
Rutherfordton, North Carolina

Dinah Zike
Educational Consultant
Dinah-Might Activities, Inc.
San Antonio, Texas

Series Reading Consultants

Elizabeth Babich
Special Education Teacher
Mashpee Public Schools
Mashpee, Massachusetts

Rachel Swaters
Science Teacher
Rolla Middle Schools
Rolla, Missouri

Barry Barto
Special Education Teacher
John F. Kennedy Elementary
Manistee, Michigan

Carol A. Senf, PhD
Associate Professor of English
Georgia Institute of Technology
Atlanta, Georgia

Nancy Woodson, PhD
Professor of English
Otterbein College
Westerville, Ohio

Series Math Consultants

Michael Hopper, D.Eng
Manager of Aircraft Certification
Raytheon Company
Greenville, Texas

Teri Willard, EdD
Department of Mathematics
Montana State University
Belgrade, Montana

Series Safety Consultants

Malcolm Cheney, PhD
OSHA Chemical Safety Officer
Hall High School
West Hartford, Connecticut

Sandra West, PhD
Associate Professor of Biology
Southwest Texas State University
San Marcos, Texas

Aileen Duc, PhD
Science II Teacher
Hendrick Middle School
Plano, Texas

Content Consultants

Sandra K. Enger, PhD
Coordinator UAH
Institute for Science Education
Huntsville, Alabama

Leanne Field, PhD
Lecturer of Molecular Genetics and Microbiology
University of Texas
Austin, Texas

Michael A. Hoggarth, PhD
Department of Life and Earth Sciences
Otterbein College
Westerville, Ohio

Jerry Jackson, PhD
Program Director Center for Science, Mathematics, and Technology Education
Florida Gulf Coast University
Fort Meyers, Florida

Homer Montgomery, PhD
Department of Geosciences
University of Texas at Dallas
Richardson, Texas

Connie Rizzo, MD
Professor of Biology
Pace University
New York, New York

Dominic Salinas, PhD
Middle School Science Supervisor
Caddo Parish Schools
Shreveport, Louisiana

Betsy Wrobel-Boerner
Department of Microbiology
Ohio State University
Columbus, Ohio

Series Activity Testers

José Luis Alvarez, PhD
Math and Science Mentor Teacher
El Paso, Texas

Nerma Coats Henderson
Teacher
Pickerington Jr. High School
Pickerington, Ohio

Mary Helen Mariscal-Cholka
Science Teacher
William D. Slider Middle School
El Paso, Texas

José Alberto Marquez
TEKS for Leaders Trainer
El Paso, Texas

Science Kit and Boreal Laboratories
Tonawanda, New York

Reviewers

Michelle Bailey
Northwood Middle School
Houston, Texas

Maureen Barrett
Thomas E. Harrington Middle School
Mt. Laurel, New Jersey

Desiree Bishop
Baker High School
Mobile, Alabama

Janice Bowman
Coke R. Stevenson Middle School
San Antonio, Texas

Cory Fish
Burkholder Middle School
Henderson, Nevada

Linda V. Forsyth
Merrill Middle School
Denver, Colorado

Tammy Ingraham
Westover Park Intermediate School
Canyon, Texas

Amy Morgan
Berry Middle School
Hoover, Alabama

Michelle Punch
Northwood Middle School
Houston, Texas

Billye Robbins
Lomax Junior High School
LaPorte, Texas

Delores Stout
Bellefonte Middle School
Bellefonte, Pennsylvania

Darcy Vetro-Ravndal
Middleton Middle School of Technology
Tampa, Florida

Contents in Brief

UNIT 1 Life's Structure and Function—2

CONTENTS

Contents

Cell Processes—64

Cell Reproduction—94

Heredity—124

Adaptations Over Time—152

UNIT 2 From Bacteria to Plants—184

CHAPTER 7 Bacteria—186

CHAPTER 8 Protists and Fungi—210

CHAPTER 9 Plants—240

Plant Reproduction—272

Plant Processes—302

CONTENTS

UNIT 3 Animal Diversity—330

CHAPTER 12

Introduction to Animals—332

CHAPTER 13

Mollusks, Worms, Arthropods, Echinoderms—362

Fish, Amphibians, and Reptiles—396

Birds and Mammals—430

Animal Behavior—458

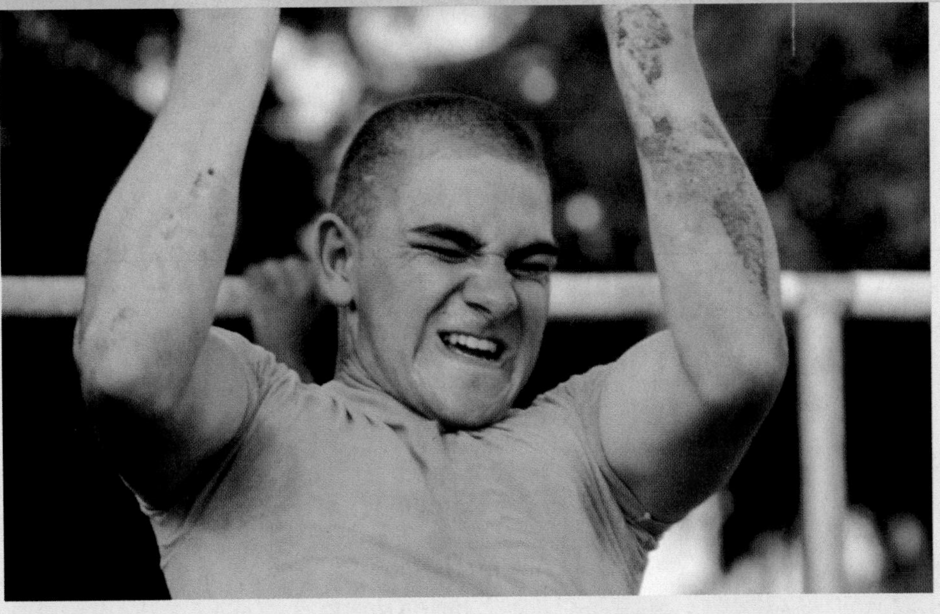

UNIT 4 Human Body Systems—486

Structure and Movement—488

Nutrients and Digestion—516

Circulation—544

Respiration and Excretion—572

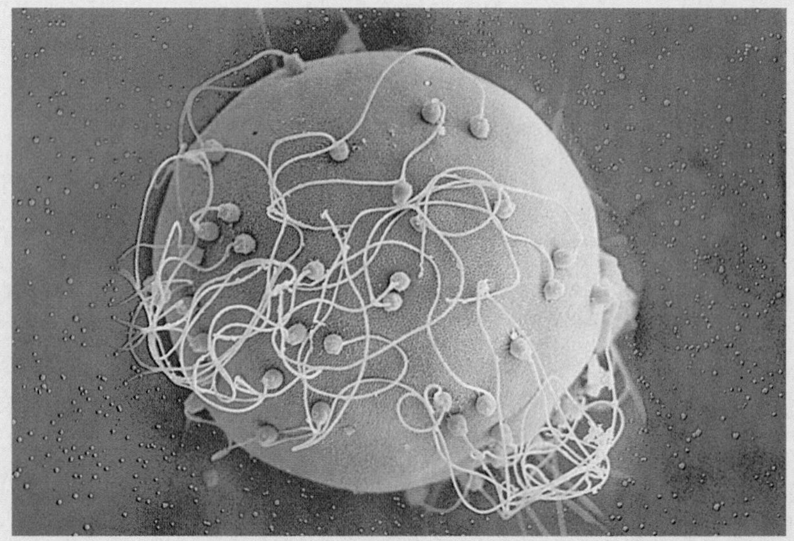

Control and Coordination—598

CHAPTER 22

Regulation and Reproduction—626

Immunity and Disease—656

UNIT 5 Ecology—688

Ecosystems—746

Conserving Resources—776

Field Guides

Skill Handbooks—832

Reference Handbooks—857

English Glossary—866

Spanish Glossary—883

Interdisciplinary Connections

NATIONAL GEOGRAPHIC Unit Openers

Feature Contents

NATIONAL GEOGRAPHIC VISUALIZING

TIME Science and Society

TIME Science and History

Oops! Accidents in Science

Science and Language Arts

Science Stats

Activities

Full Period Labs

Mini LAB

Activities

EXPLORE ACTIVITY

Problem-Solving Activities

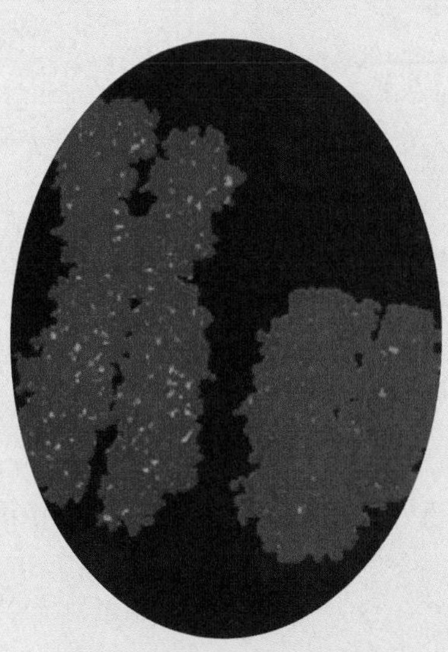

Activities

Math Skills Activities

Skill Builder Activities

Science

Math

Technology

Science INTEGRATION

SCIENCE *Online*

UNIT 1

Unit Contents

Pre-Reading Activity

Have students look through the unit for pictures of cells and identify differences among cells.

UNIT 1

Life's Structure and Function

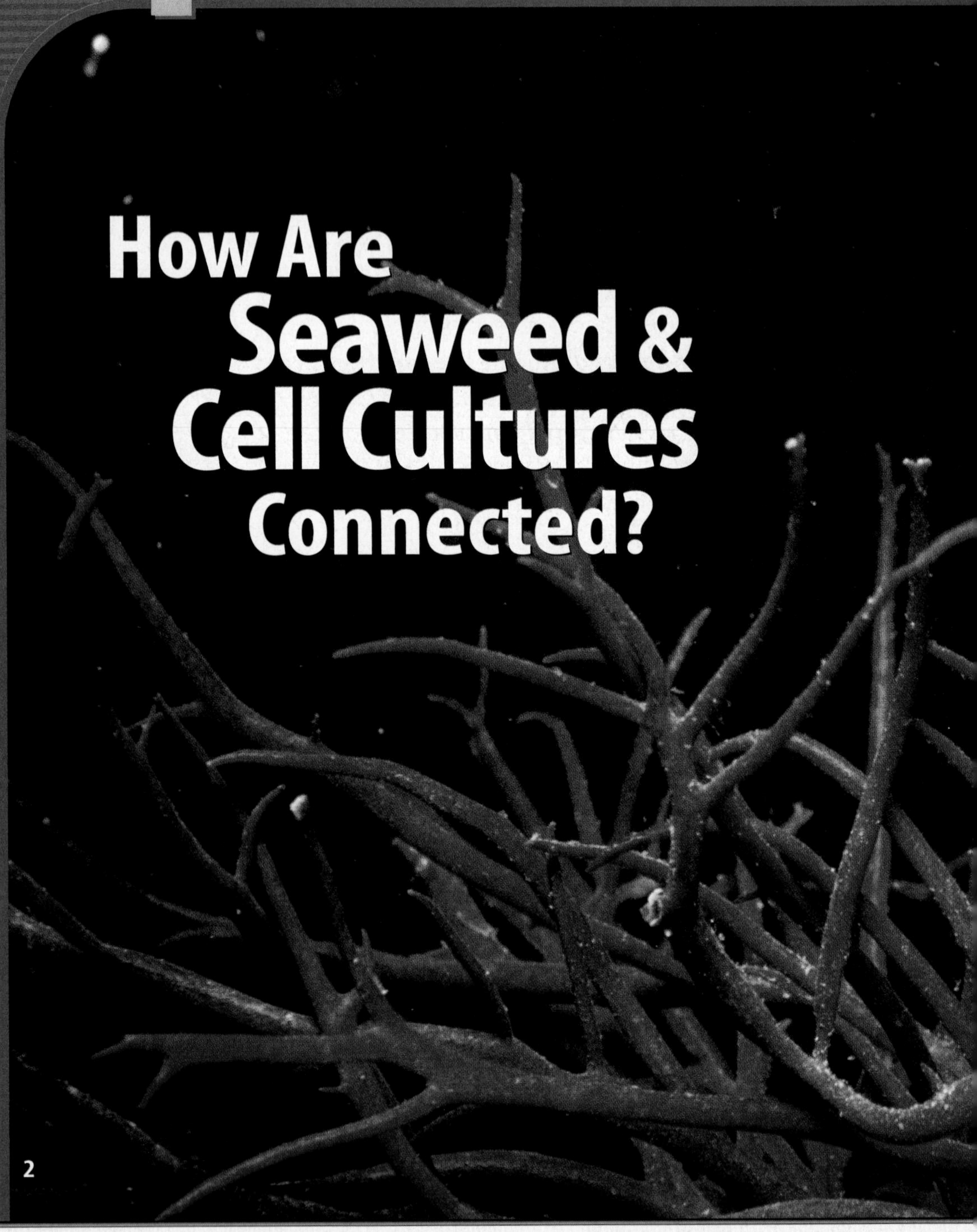

How Are Seaweed & Cell Cultures Connected?

2

Teacher to Teacher

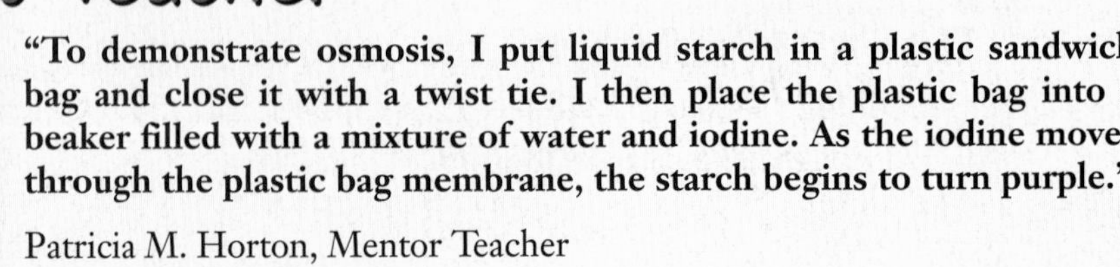

"To demonstrate osmosis, I put liquid starch in a plastic sandwich bag and close it with a twist tie. I then place the plastic bag into a beaker filled with a mixture of water and iodine. As the iodine moves through the plastic bag membrane, the starch begins to turn purple."

Patricia M. Horton, Mentor Teacher
Summit Intermediate School
Etiwanda, CA

In the 1800s, many biologists were interested in studying one-celled microorganisms. But to study them, the researchers needed to grow, or culture, large numbers of these cells. And to culture them properly, they needed a solid substance on which the cells could grow. One scientist tried using nutrient-enriched gelatin, but the gelatin had drawbacks. It melted at relatively low temperatures—and some microorganisms digested it. Fannie Eilshemius Hesse came up with a better option. She had been solidifying her homemade jellies using a substance called agar, which is derived from red seaweed (such as the one seen in the background here). It turned out that nutrient-enriched agar worked perfectly as a substance on which to culture cells. On the two types of agar in the dishes below, so many cells have grown that, together, they form dots and lines.

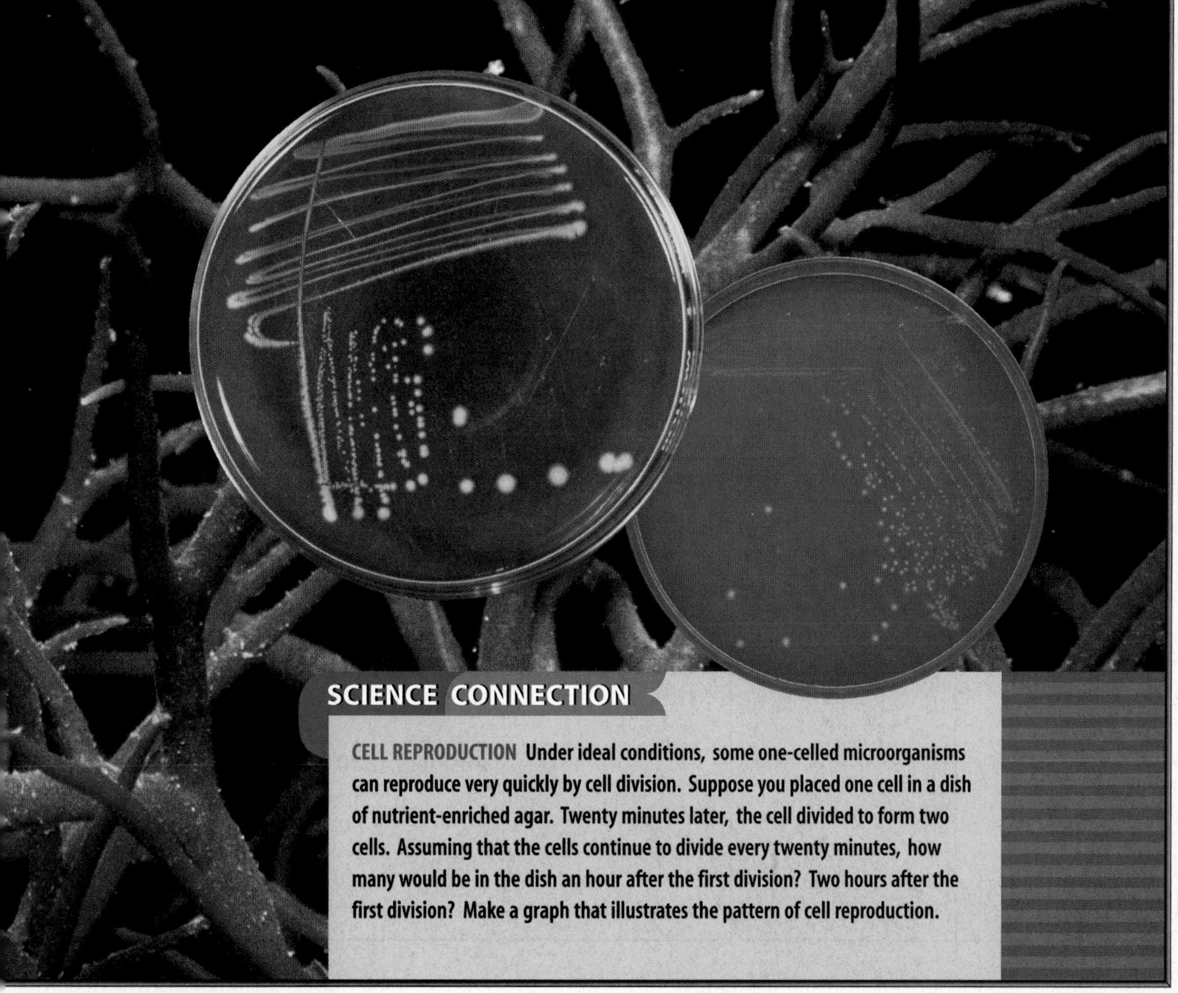

SCIENCE CONNECTION

CELL REPRODUCTION Under ideal conditions, some one-celled microorganisms can reproduce very quickly by cell division. Suppose you placed one cell in a dish of nutrient-enriched agar. Twenty minutes later, the cell divided to form two cells. Assuming that the cells continue to divide every twenty minutes, how many would be in the dish an hour after the first division? Two hours after the first division? Make a graph that illustrates the pattern of cell reproduction.

Introducing the Unit

How Are Seaweed & Cell Cultures Connected?

AGAR, a gelatin-like product, is made primarily from the algae *Gelidium* and *Gracilaria* (red seaweeds). Best known as a solidifying component of bacteriological culture media, it is used also in cosmetics; in medicines; and in dentistry. It is also used as a clarifying agent in brewing and wine making; as a thickening agent in ice cream, pastries, desserts, and salad dressings; and as a wire-drawing lubricant.

Agar is isolated from the algae as an amorphous and translucent product sold as powder, flakes, or bricks. It is produced chiefly in Japan, New Zealand, Australia, the United States, and Russia. Although agar is insoluble in cold water, it absorbs as much as 20 times its own weight. It dissolves readily in boiling water; a dilute solution is still liquid at 42° C (108° F) but solidifies at 37° C into a firm gel.

In the natural state, agar occurs as a complex cell-wall constituent containing a complex carbohydrate (polysaccharide) with sulfate and calcium. It was in 1883 that Frau Hesse came up with this medium for culturing cells. Unlike gelatin, agar could be liquefied by only a few microorganisms and does not provide a food source, thus allowing better control of the nutrient content of the medium.

SCIENCE Online

Internet Addresses

Explore the Glencoe Science Web site at **science.glencoe.com** to find out more about topics in this unit.

SCIENCE CONNECTION

Activity

If a cell divides every twenty minutes, students should find there would be eight cells at the end of one hour and 64 cells at the end of two hours. Have students compare their graphs with that of a partner.

Section/Objectives	Standards		Activities/Features
	National	State/Local	
Chapter Opener	See p. 5T for a Key to Standards.		**Explore Activity:** Use features to classify organisms, p. 5 **Before You Read,** p. 5
Section 1 What is science? 2 sessions 1 block 1. **Apply** scientific methods to problem solving. 2. **Demonstrate** how to measure using scientific units.	National Content Standards: UCP2, A1, A2, B1, G1		**Science Online,** p. 8 **MiniLAB:** Analyzing Data, p. 9 **Problem-Solving Activity:** Does temperature affect the rate of bacterial reproduction?, p. 11
Section 2 Living Things 2 sessions 1 block 1. **Distinguish** between living and nonliving things. 2. **Identify** what living things need to survive.	National Content Standards: UCP2, C1, C4		**Science Online,** p. 15 **Health Integration,** p. 17
Section 3 Where does life come from? 1 session 0.5 block 1. **Describe** experiments about spontaneous generation. 2. **Explain** how scientific methods led to the idea of biogenesis. 3. **Examine** how chemical compounds found in living things might have formed.	National Content Standards: UCP2, A2, C1, D2, G3		**Visualizing the Origins of Life,** p. 20 **Earth Science Integration,** p. 21
Section 4 How are living things classified? 3 sessions 1.5 blocks 1. **Describe** how early scientists classified living things. 2. **Explain** the system of binomial nomenclature. 3. **Demonstrate** how to use a dichotomous key.	National Content Standards: UCP1, A1, A2, C1, F5, G2, G3		**Science Online,** p. 23 **MiniLAB:** Communicating Ideas, p. 25 **Activity:** Classifying Seeds, p. 27 **Activity:** Using Scientific Methods, p. 28 **Science and Society:** Monkey Business, p. 30

NATIONAL GEOGRAPHIC

Teacher's Corner

PRODUCTS AVAILABLE FROM GLENCOE
To order call 1-800-334-7344:
Books
National Geographic Book of Mammals
Field Guide to the Birds of North America
CD-ROMs
Mammals: A Multimedia Encyclopedia
NGS PictureShow: Classifying Plants and Animals
Curriculum Kits
GeoKit: Cells and Organisms
GeoKit: Fish, Reptiles, and Amphibians
GeoKit: Plants
Transparency Set
NGS PicturePack: Classifying Plants and Animals

PRODUCTS AVAILABLE FROM NATIONAL GEOGRAPHIC SOCIETY
To order call 1-800-368-2728:
Video
Plant Classification

Activity Materials	Reproducible Resources	Section Assessment	Technology
Explore Activity: insect collection	**Chapter Resources Booklet** Foldables Worksheet, p. 15 Directed Reading Overview, p. 17 Note-taking Worksheets, pp. 33–35	Glencoe's Assessment Advantage	
MiniLAB: pan balance, sponge, water	**Chapter Resources Booklet** Transparency Activity, p. 44 MiniLAB, p. 3 Enrichment, p. 29 Reinforcement, p. 25 Lab Activity, pp. 9–10 Directed Reading, p. 18	**Portfolio** Science Journal, p. 7 **Performance** MiniLAB, p. 9 Problem-Solving Activity, p. 11 Skill Builder Activities, p. 13 **Content** Section Assessment, p. 13	Section Focus Transparency Interactive CD-ROM Guided Reading Audio Program
	Chapter Resources Booklet Transparency Activity, p. 45 Enrichment, p. 30 Reinforcement, p. 26 Directed Reading, p. 18	**Portfolio** Curriculum Connection, p. 16 **Performance** Skill Builder Activities, p. 18 **Content** Section Assessment, p. 18	Section Focus Transparency Interactive CD-ROM Guided Reading Audio Program
	Chapter Resources Booklet Transparency Activity, p. 46 Enrichment, p. 31 Reinforcement, p. 27 Directed Reading, p. 19	**Portfolio** Reteach, p. 21 **Performance** Skill Builder Activities, p. 21 **Content** Section Assessment, p. 21	Section Focus Transparency Interactive CD-ROM Guided Reading Audio Program
MiniLAB: magazine picture of a piece of furniture **Activity:** packets of seeds (10 different kinds), metric ruler, hand lens **Activity:** 3 500-mL, wide-mouthed containers; brine shrimp eggs; small plastic spoon; distilled water; weak salt solution; strong salt solution; 3 labels; hand lens	**Chapter Resources Booklet** Transparency Activity, p. 47 MiniLAB, p. 4 Enrichment, p. 32 Reinforcement, p. 28 Directed Reading, pp. 19, 20 Transparency Activity, pp. 49–50 Lab Activity, pp. 11–13 Activity Worksheets, pp. 5–6, 7–8 **Lab Management and Safety,** p. 65	**Portfolio** Assessment, p. 26 **Performance** MiniLAB, p. 25 Skill Builder Activities, p. 26 **Content** Section Assessment, p. 26	Section Focus Transparency Teaching Transparency Interactive CD-ROM Guided Reading Audio Program

Need materials? **Contact Science Kit at 1-800-828-7777 or www.sciencekit.com on the Internet.**

End of Chapter Assessment

Glencoe's Assessment Advantage

Blackline Masters	Technology	Professional Series
Chapter Resources Booklet Chapter Review, pp. 37–38 Chapter Tests, pp. 39–42 **Standardized Test Practice by The Princeton Review,** pp. 11–14	MindJogger Videoquiz Interactive CD-ROM Vocabulary PuzzleMakers ExamView Pro Test Bank Interactive Lesson Planner Interactive Teacher Edition	Performance Assessment in the Science Classroom (PASC)

Transparencies

Section Focus

Section 1 Section Focus Transparency **Do the chimpanzees ever study Dr. Goodall?**

Jane Goodall, a zoologist from England, researches chimpanzees in Gombe Stream National Park. She has described and reported many aspects of chimpanzees, including hunting, tool use, and social behaviors.

1. How was Dr. Goodall able to discover so many chimpanzee behaviors?
2. How does studying an animal in a laboratory compare with studying an animal in its natural habitat?

L2

Section 2 Section Focus Transparency **Most Enlightening**

Have you ever seen a house plant growing toward the window? Most plants grow toward the light. This bending is caused by a plant hormone that makes plant cells stretch and grow in the direction of the light source.

1. Why do plants need light?
2. What would happen if you gave the pot a half turn?
3. What does this plant need to live?

L2

Section 3 Section Focus Transparency **How About a Field Trip?**

Is there life on other planets? If there is, it probably doesn't resemble the aliens we see in the movies. Some scientists believe that Europa, one of Jupiter's moons (pictured in the center of the image below), is a candidate for supporting extraterrestrial life.

1. What general resources are needed to sustain life on Earth?
2. Is it possible that other planets or moons in our galaxy might have the resources to support life? Explain.

L2

This is a representation of key blackline masters available in the Teacher Classroom Resources. See Resource Manager boxes within the chapter for additional information.

Assessment

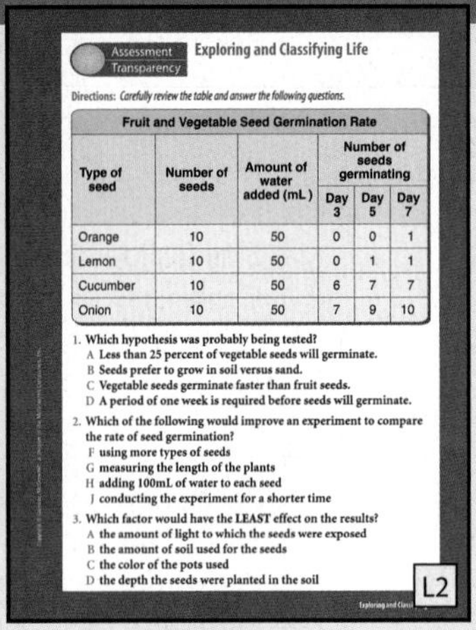
Assessment Transparency **Exploring and Classifying Life**

Directions: Carefully review the table and answer the following questions.

Fruit and Vegetable Seed Germination Rate

Type of seed	Number of seeds	Amount of water added (mL)	Number of seeds germinating Day 3	Day 5	Day 7
Orange	10	50	0	0	1
Lemon	10	50	0	1	1
Cucumber	10	50	6	7	7
Onion	10	50	7	9	10

1. Which hypothesis was probably being tested?
   A Less than 25 percent of vegetable seeds will germinate.
   B Seeds prefer to grow in soil versus sand.
   C Vegetable seeds germinate faster than fruit seeds.
   D A period of one week is required before seeds will germinate.
2. Which of the following would improve an experiment to compare the rate of seed germination?
   F using more types of seeds
   G measuring the length of the plants
   H adding 100mL of water to each seed
   J conducting the experiment for a shorter time
3. Which factor would have the LEAST effect on the results?
   A the amount of light to which the seeds were exposed
   B the amount of soil used for the seeds
   C the color of the pots used
   D the depth the seeds were planted in the soil

L2

Teaching

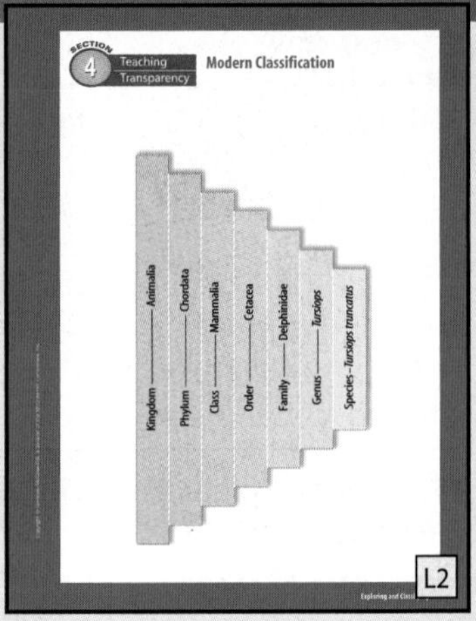
Section 4 Teaching Transparency **Modern Classification**

L2

Key to Teaching Strategies

The following designations will help you decide which activities are appropriate for your students.

- L1 Level 1 activities should be appropriate for students with learning difficulties.
- L2 Level 2 activities should be within the ability range of all students.
- L3 Level 3 activities are designed for above-average students.
- ELL ELL activities should be within the ability range of English Language Learners.
- COOP LEARN Cooperative Learning activities are designed for small group work.
- LS Multiple Learning Styles logos, as described on page 22T, are used throughout to indicate strategies that address different learning styles.
- P These strategies represent student products that can be placed into a best-work portfolio.

Hands-on Activities

Activity Worksheets

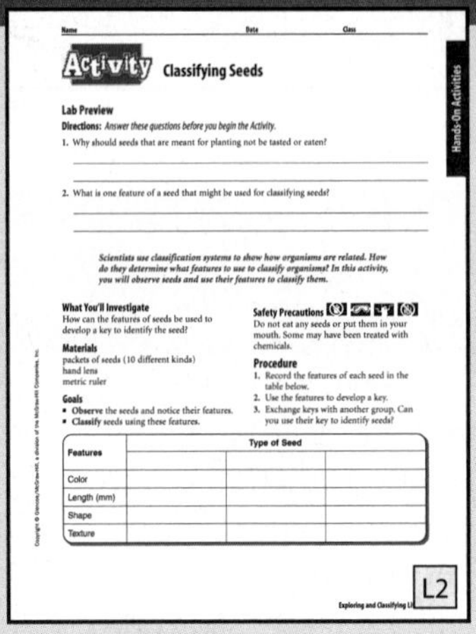
Activity **Classifying Seeds**

Lab Preview
Directions: Answer these questions before you begin the Activity.

1. Why should seeds that are meant for planting not be tasted or eaten?
2. What is one feature of a seed that might be used for classifying seeds?

Scientists use classification systems to show how organisms are related. How do they determine what features to use to classify organisms? In this activity, you will observe seeds and use their features to classify them.

What You'll Investigate
How can the features of seeds be used to develop a key to identify the seed?

Materials
packets of seeds (10 different kinds)
hand lens
metric ruler

Goals
- Observe the seeds and notice their features.
- Classify seeds using these features.

Safety Precautions
Do not eat any seeds or put them in your mouth. Some may have been treated with chemicals.

Procedure
1. Record the features of each seed in the table below.
2. Use the features to develop a key.
3. Exchange keys with another group. Can you use their key to identify seeds?

Features	Type of Seed			
Color				
Length (mm)				
Shape				
Texture				

L2

Laboratory Activities

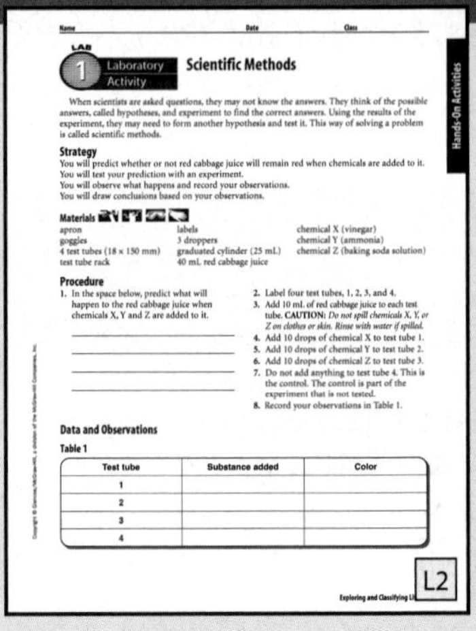
Lab 1 Laboratory Activity **Scientific Methods**

When scientists are asked questions, they may not know the answers. They think of the possible answers, called hypotheses, and experiment to find the correct answers. Using the results of the experiment, they may need to form another hypothesis and test it. This way of solving a problem is called scientific methods.

Strategy
You will predict whether or not red cabbage juice will remain red when chemicals are added to it.
You will test your prediction with an experiment.
You will observe what happens and record your observations.
You will draw conclusions based on your observations.

Materials
apron, goggles, 4 test tubes (18 × 150 mm), test tube rack, labels, 3 droppers, graduated cylinder (25 mL), 40 mL red cabbage juice, chemical X (vinegar), chemical Y (ammonia), chemical Z (baking soda solution)

Procedure
1. In the space below, predict what will happen to the red cabbage juice when chemicals X, Y and Z are added to it.
2. Label four test tubes, 1, 2, 3, and 4.
3. Add 10 mL of red cabbage juice to each test tube. CAUTION: *Do not spill chemicals X, Y, or Z on clothes or skin. Rinse with water if spilled.*
4. Add 10 drops of chemical X to test tube 1.
5. Add 10 drops of chemical Y to test tube 2.
6. Add 10 drops of chemical Z to test tube 3.
7. Do not add anything to test tube 4. This is the control. The control is part of the experiment that is not tested.
8. Record your observations in Table 1.

Data and Observations
Table 1

Test tube	Substance added	Color
1		
2		
3		
4		

L2

Meeting Different Ability Levels

Content Outline

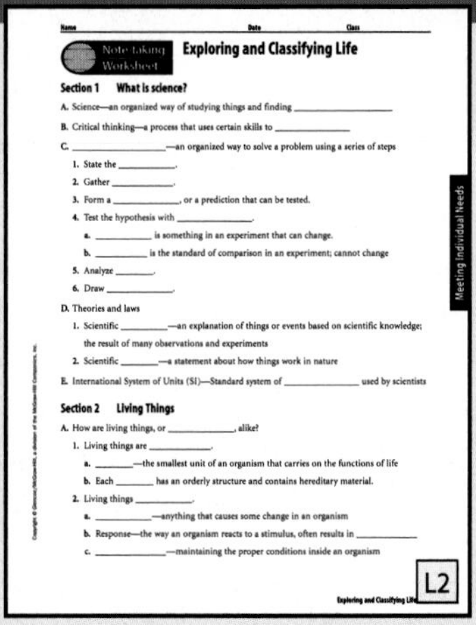
Note-taking Worksheet
Exploring and Classifying Life
Section 1 What is science?
Section 2 Living Things
L2

Reinforcement

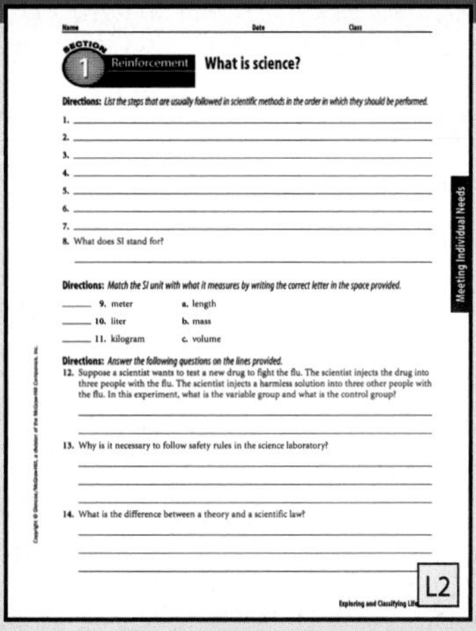
Section 1 Reinforcement
What is science?
L2

Directed Reading

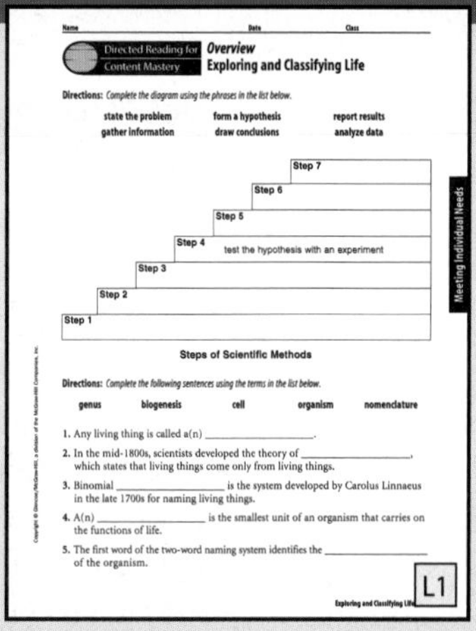
Directed Reading for Content Mastery
Overview
Exploring and Classifying Life
Steps of Scientific Methods
L1

Enrichment

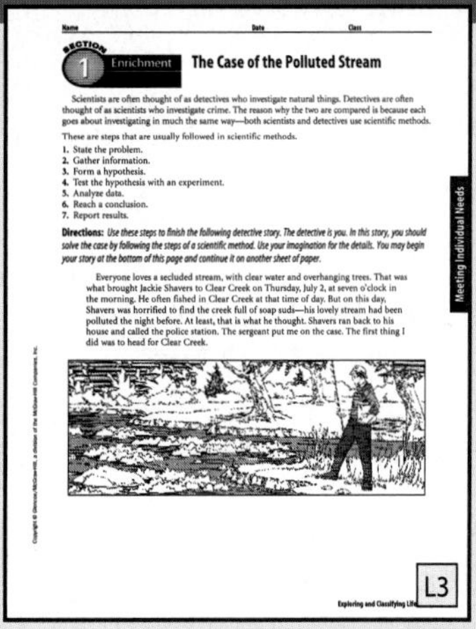
Section 1 Enrichment
The Case of the Polluted Stream
L3

Spanish Directed Reading

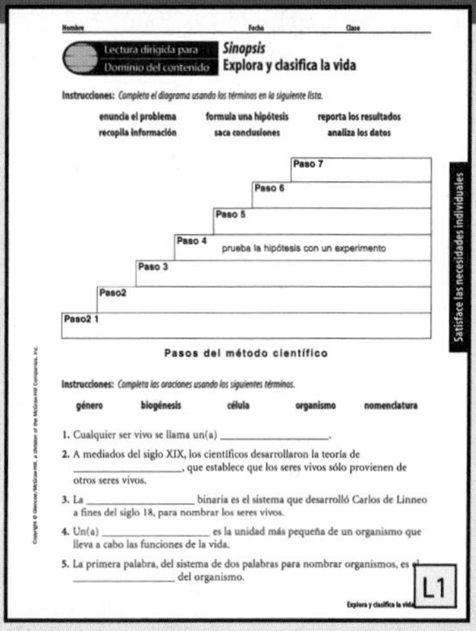
Lectura dirigida para Dominio del contenido
Sinopsis
Explora y clasifica la vida
Pasos del método científico
L1

Assessment

Chapter Tests

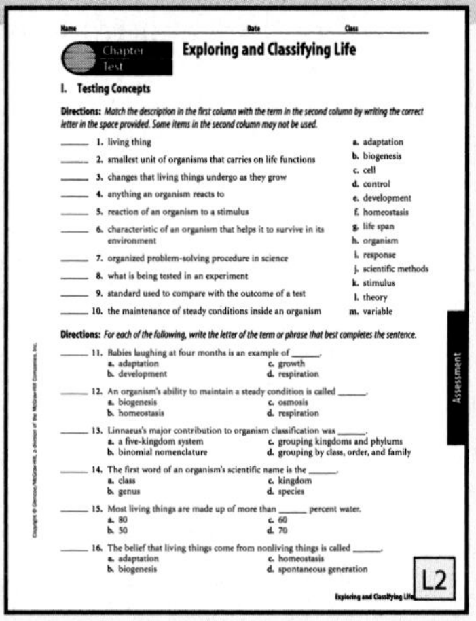
Chapter Test
Exploring and Classifying Life
I. Testing Concepts
L2

Test Practice Workbook

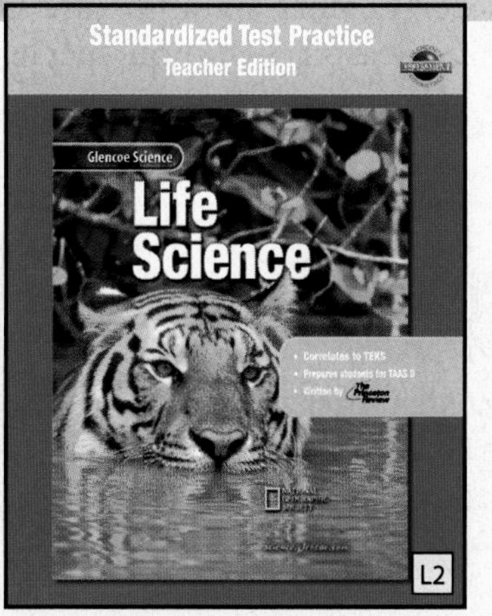
Standardized Test Practice
Teacher Edition
Glencoe Science
Life Science
L2

Chapter Review

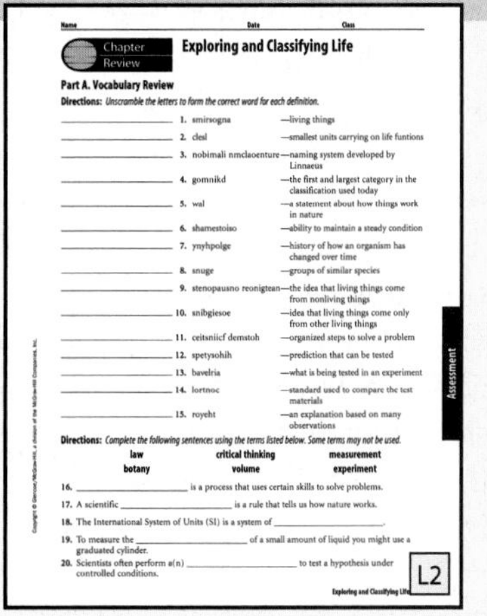
Chapter Review
Exploring and Classifying Life
Part A. Vocabulary Review
L2

Science Content Background

SECTION 2

Living Things

Living Versus Nonliving

Living organisms consist of highly organized systems that interact and are dependent upon one another. Living systems are open systems requiring a constant source of energy. All living organisms have a metabolic process by which the energy in carbohydrates is released for use. All living organisms respond to their environment in adaptive ways, including physiological responses as well as behaviors. Living organisms must also have a means of reproduction, growth, and development if their species is to continue.

Student Misconception

All things that move are alive.

Refer to the facing page for teaching strategies to address this misconception. Refer to pages 14–17 for content related to this topic.

SECTION 4

How are living things classified?

Modern Classification

This textbook uses a combination of phenetics and cladistics to classify organisms. Phenetics is based on particular features. Cladistics uses shared, derived characteristics to classify organisms. By comparing DNA nucleotide sequences between species and by measuring the amount of bonding between DNA from different species, taxonomists infer the degree of similarity between organisms. Scientists hypothesize that organisms with similar proteins are closely related. A comparison of the amino acid sequences between species' proteins provides objective, quantitative data for taxonomists because the structure of proteins is genetically determined.

Scientific Names

Most taxonomists currently divide the six-kingdom system into groups called domains. The three domains are Eubacteria, Archaea, and Eukarya. The domains Eubacteria and Archaea contain Kingdom Eubacteria and Kingdom Archaebacteria, respectively. Domain Eukarya contains four kingdoms—Kingdom Protista, Kingdom Fungi, Kingdom Plantae, and Kingdom Animalia.

The two kingdoms of prokaryotes, Kingdom Eubacteria and Kingdom Archaebacteria, differ. All eubacteria have muramic acid in their cell walls, but archaebacteria do not. The RNA sequences of eubacteria and archaebacteria are also different. Organisms that possess cells with membrane-bound organelles are eukaryotes. Several organelles—mitochondria, chloroplasts, and Golgi apparatus—are approximately the size of a prokaryotic cell.

Tools for Identifying Organisms

A system of classification avoids ambiguity among species, reflects the phylogeny (evolutionary history) of organisms, and provides clues about the organism's habits and possible features shared with similar organisms. The second word of a scientific name is called the specific epithet, usually an adjective that describes the organism, indicates the organism's place of origin, or is a Latinized surname to honor someone. Subspecies have two specific epithets. Today, species names are a mixture of Latin and Greek. At least 1.5 million species of organisms have been named.

SCIENCE Online

For additional content background on this topic, go to the Glencoe Science Web site at science.glencoe.com.

IDENTIFYING Misconceptions

Find Out What Students Think

Students may think that . . .

- **All things that move are alive.**

Students generally define "living" according to the characteristics of large animals. Hence they associate "living" with movement. Students often do not consider plants and fungi to be alive because they do not appear to move, but may classify rivers or clouds as living because they do move. Students may add other mammalian characteristics to their definitions of life such as eating, breathing, or the presence of a heartbeat.

Clouding the concept further is the confusion between "nonliving" and "dead." Students may classify both a dead animal and a rock as "nonliving" objects, even though they classify animals in general as alive.

Discussion

Place a rock, a houseplant, and a living animal (such as a caged hamster or a volunteer student) in view of the class. Ask students if they think any of the three items are alive. As students respond, ask them why the think the item is or is not alive. From this, generate a list of characteristics that students believe belong to all living organisms. Students will probably recognize that the animal is alive. Some will understand that the plant is alive, but have difficulty explaining why. Most will know that the rock is not alive.

Promote Understanding

Activity

Have the students read **Section 2** in this chapter, then review the list they generated in the discussion suggestion above. Ask the students if they want to change anything on the list.

Next, place a candle in full view of the class and light it. Ask students if they think the flame is alive. Then do the following:

- Blow gently on the flame to show that it responds.
- Light another candle or a match from the flame to show that the flame can reproduce.
- Point out that the wax of the candle is being consumed, showing that the flame uses energy.

Remind students that many nonliving things have some characteristics of living things.

- Ask the class what characteristics the candle flame lacks. Students should recognize that the flame is not highly organized, it is not made up of organic molecules, and it contains no cells.

Assess

After completing the chapter, see *Identifying Misconceptions* in the Study Guide.

CHAPTER 1

Exploring and Classifying Life

Chapter Vocabulary

scientific methods, p. 7
hypothesis, p. 8
control, p. 9
variable, p. 9
theory, p. 10
law, p. 10
organism, p. 14
cell, p. 14
homeostasis, p. 15
spontaneous generation, p. 19
biogenesis, p. 19
phylogeny, p. 23
kingdom, p. 23
binomial nomenclature, p. 24
genus, p. 24

What do you think?

Science Journal The animals in the picture are tube sponges. Tube sponges remain attached to one place. They remove oxygen and food from water that flows through a series of canals in their bodies.

CHAPTER 1

Exploring and Classifying Life

How many different living things do you see in this picture? Did your answer include the living coral? What do all living things have in common? How are they different? In this chapter, you will read the answers to these questions. You also will read how living things are classified. In the first part of the chapter, you will read how scientific methods may be used to solve many everyday and scientific problems.

What do you think?

Science Journal Look at the picture below with a classmate. Discuss what you think these might be. Here's a hint: *You could really clean up with these things.* Write your answer or best guess in your Science Journal.

4

Theme Connection

Systems and Interactions Scientists have devised systems for classifying organisms. These systems use an organism's traits, which have changed over time as a result of organisms' interactions with the environment.

Life scientists discover, describe, and name hundreds of organisms every year. How do they decide if a certain plant belongs to the iris or orchid family of flowering plants, or if an insect is more like a grasshopper or a beetle?

Use features to classify organisms

1. Observe the organisms on the opposite page or in an insect collection in your class.
2. Decide which feature could be used to separate the organisms into two groups, then sort the organisms into the two groups.
3. Continue to make new groups using different features until each organism is in a category by itself.

Observe

What features would you use to classify the living thing in the photo above? How do you think scientists classify living things? List your ideas in your Science Journal.

Before You Read

FOLDABLES Reading & Study Skills

Making a Vocabulary Study Fold **To help you study the interactions of life, make the following vocabulary Foldable. Knowing the definition of vocabulary words in a chapter is a good way to ensure you have understood the content.**

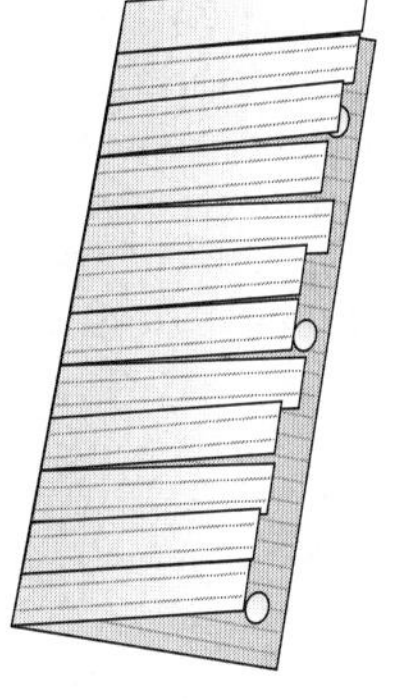

1. Place a sheet of notebook paper in front of you so that the short side is at the top. Fold the paper in half from the left to the right side.
2. Through one thickness of paper, cut along every third line from the outside edge to the center fold, forming ten tabs as shown.
3. On the front of each tab, write a vocabulary word listed on the first page of each section in this chapter. On the back of each tab, write what you think the word means. Add to or change the definitions as you read.

EXPLORE ACTIVITY

Purpose Use the Explore Activity to introduce students to classification. In this chapter students will learn how characteristics of organisms are used in classification. L2 COOP LEARN LS **Interpersonal**

Preparation Use the opening photo to promote a discussion of how organisms are classified. If insect collections are available, use them to supplement the discussion.

Materials chapter-opening photo or an insect collection

Alternate Materials collection of leaves

Teaching Strategies

- Make sure students can identify the differences between the organisms in the coral reef or in the insect collection.
- Accept any logical classification groupings devised by students.

Observe

Scientists identify the traits of an organism. They compare these traits with those of other living things. The organism is then placed into a group of living things with similar traits.

Assessment

Oral Have students explain the reasons behind the choices they made. Use **Performance Assessment in the Science Classroom,** p. 121.

Before You Read

FOLDABLES Reading & Study Skills

Dinah Zike Study Fold

Purpose Use the Activity to expose students to the chapter's content and vocabulary before they read, and to encourage a search for terms and definitions as they read. The resulting Foldable can be used as an assessment tool and study guide before, during and after reading.

For additional help, see Foldables Worksheet, p. 15 in **Chapter Resources Booklet,** or go to the Glencoe Science Web site at **science.glencoe.com.** See After You Read in the Study Guide at the end of this chapter.

SECTION

What is science?

1 Motivate

Bellringer Transparency

Display the Section Focus Transparency for Section 1. Use the accompanying Transparency Activity Master. L2 ELL

SECTION 1 Section Focus Transparency **Do the chimpanzees ever study Dr. Goodall?**

Jane Goodall, a zoologist from England, researches chimpanzees in Gombe Stream National Park. She has described and reported many aspects of chimpanzees, including hunting, tool use, and social behaviors.

1. How was Dr. Goodall able to discover so many chimpanzee behaviors?
2. How does studying an animal in a laboratory compare with studying an animal in its natural habitat?

Exploring and Classifying Life

Tie to Prior Knowledge

Students use problem-solving skills daily. Discuss how they solve everyday problems, such as deciding what outfit to wear or how to manage homework with sports schedules. Relate solving everyday problems to scientific methods.

Text Question Answer

bacteria

SECTION

What is science?

As You Read

What You'll Learn

- **Apply** scientific methods to problem solving.
- **Demonstrate** how to measure using scientific units.

Vocabulary

scientific methods, hypothesis, control, variable, theory, law

Why It's Important

Learning to use scientific methods will help you solve ordinary problems in your life.

The Work of Science

Movies and popcorn seem to go together. So before you and your friends watch a movie, sometimes you pop some corn in a microwave oven. When the popping stops, you take out the bag and open it carefully. You smell the mouthwatering, freshly popped corn and avoid hot steam that escapes from the bag. What makes the popcorn pop? How do microwaves work and make things hot? By the way, what are microwaves anyway?

Asking questions like these is one way scientists find out about anything in the world and the universe. Science is often described as an organized way of studying things and finding answers to questions.

Types of Science Many types of science exist. Each is given a name to describe what is being studied. For example, energy and matter have a relationship. That's a topic for physics. A physicist could answer most questions about microwaves.

On the other hand, a life scientist might study any of the millions of different animals, plants, and other living things on Earth. Look at the objects in **Figure 1.** What do they look like to you? A life scientist could tell you that some of the objects are living plants and some are just rocks. Life scientists who study plants are botanists, and those who study animals are zoologists. What do you suppose a bacteriologist studies?

Figure 1
Are all of these objects rocks? **Examine the picture carefully. Some of these objects are actually *Lithops* plants. They commonly are called stone plants and are native to deserts in South Africa.**

Section Assessment Planner

Portfolio
Science Journal, p. 7

Performance Assessment
MiniLAB, p. 9
Problem-Solving Activity, p. 11
Skill Builder Activities, p. 13
See page 34 for more options.

Content Assessment
Section, p. 13
Challenge, p. 13
Chapter, pp. 34–35

Critical Thinking

Whether or not you become a trained scientist, you are going to solve problems all your life. You probably solve many problems every day when you sort out ideas about what will or won't work. Suppose your CD player stops playing music. To figure out what happened, you have to think about it. That's called critical thinking, and it's the way you use skills to solve problems.

If you know that the CD player does not run on batteries and must be plugged in to work, that's the first thing you check to solve the problem. You check and the player is plugged in so you eliminate that possible solution. You separate important information from unimportant information—that's a skill. Could there be something wrong with the first outlet? You plug the player into a different outlet, and your CD starts playing. You now know that it's the first outlet that doesn't work. Identifying the problem is another skill you have.

Solving Problems

Scientists use the same types of skills that you do to solve problems and answer questions. Although scientists don't always find the answers to their questions, they always use critical thinking in their search. Besides critical thinking, solving a problem requires organization. In science, this organization often takes the form of a series of procedures called **scientific methods. Figure 2** shows one way that scientific methods might be used to solve a problem.

State the Problem Suppose a veterinary technician wanted to find out whether different types of cat litter cause irritation to cats' skin. What would she do first? The technician begins by observing something she cannot explain. A pet owner brings his four cats to the clinic to be boarded while he travels. He leaves his cell phone number so he can be contacted if any problems arise. When they first arrive, the four cats seem healthy. The next day however, the technician notices that two of the cats are scratching and chewing at their skin. By the third day, these same two cats have bare patches of skin with red sores. The technician decides that something in the cats' surroundings or their food might be irritating their skin.

Figure 2
The series of procedures shown below is one way to use scientific methods to solve a problem.

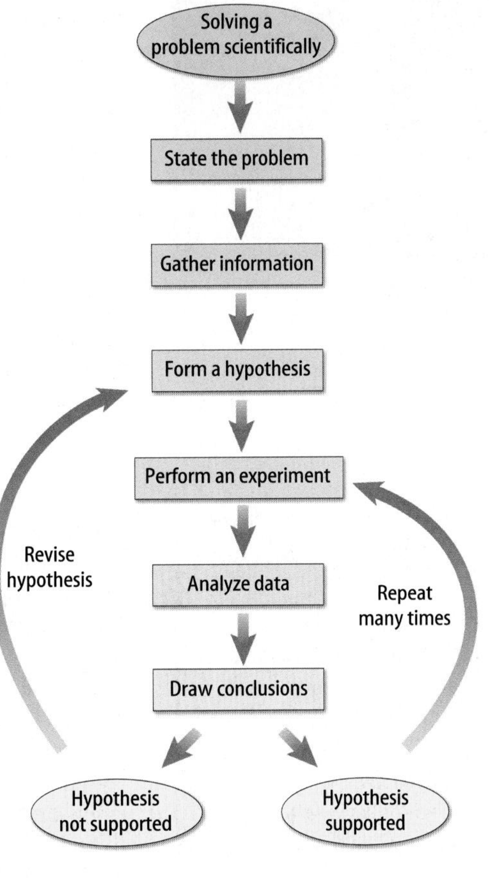

2 Teach

The Work of Science

Activity

Divide the class into small groups. Ask: **What do you think life scientists do? Where might they work?** Allow time for groups to discuss the questions and record their responses. Have each group use their results to write a Help Wanted advertisement seeking a life scientist. Ask groups to present their advertisements to the class. COOP LEARN

LS **Interpersonal**

Critical Thinking

IDENTIFYING Misconceptions

Science is often thought of as a discipline out of reach of most people. Many believe that only well-educated or specially trained people can practice science. Explain that science is a process of understanding and that anyone can use the methods of science in daily life.

Solving Problems

Visual Learning

Figure 2 Are all the steps shown here always followed in the exact same sequence? No; if a hypothesis is not supported, the scientist starts over by forming a new hypothesis. Sometimes, only a few of the steps are used.

Resource Manager

Chapter Resources Booklet

Transparency Activity, p. 44

Directed Reading for Content Mastery, pp. 17, 18

Note-taking Worksheets, pp. 33–35

Science Journal

Critical-Thinking Log Ask students to keep in their journals a log of instances in which they used critical thinking to solve problems. Logs should note the date, problem, and solution. At the end of one week, have students share their logs with classmates. Guide students in recognizing that critical thinking is a life skill.

L2 LS **Interpersonal** P

Solving Problems, continued

Quick Demo

Fill a 2-L clear container with pond water and place it in a well-lighted area. Have students hypothesize how the water will appear in ten days. Collect the written hypotheses. At the end of ten days, have students check their hypotheses against the conditions in the jar. L1

IS **Linguistic**

Teacher FYI

One of the first scientists credited with using the scientific method was Galileo. In his investigation of falling objects, the steps he used were (1) observation, (2) hypothesis, (3) mathematical analysis or deduction from hypothesis, (4)experimental test, and (5) revision of hypothesis.

Internet Addresses

Explore the Glencoe Science Web site at **science.glencoe.com** to find out more about topics in this section.

Figure 3
Observations can be made in many different settings.

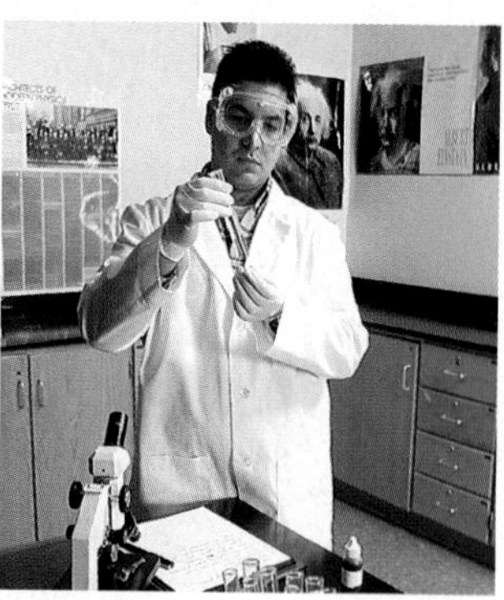

A Laboratory investigations

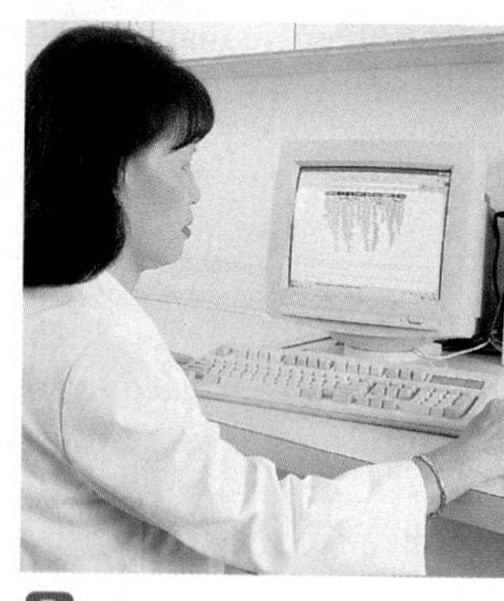

B Computer models

C Fieldwork

Gather Information Laboratory observations and experiments are ways to collect information. Some data also are gathered from fieldwork. Fieldwork includes observations or experiments that are done outside of the laboratory. For example, the best way to find out how a bird builds a nest is to go outside and watch it. **Figure 3** shows some ways data can be gathered.

The technician gathers information about the problem by watching the cats closely for the next two days. She knows that cats sometimes change their behavior when they are in a new place. She wants to see if the behavior of the cats with the skin sores seems different from that of the other two cats. Other than the scratching and chewing, all four cats' behavior seems to be the same.

The technician calls the owner and tells him about the problem. She asks him what brand of cat food he feeds his cats. Because his brand is the same one used at the clinic, she decides that food is not the cause of the skin irritation. She decides that the cats probably are reacting to something in their surroundings. There are many things in the clinic that the cats might react to. How does she decide what it is?

During her observations she notices that the cats seem to scratch and chew themselves most after using their litter boxes. The cat litter used by the clinic contains a deodorant. The technician calls the owner and finds out that the cat litter he buys does not contain a deodorant.

Research Visit the Glencoe Science Web site at **science.glencoe.com** for more information about how scientists use controlled experiments. Communicate to your class what you learn.

Form a Hypothesis Based on this information, the next thing the veterinary technician does is form a hypothesis. A **hypothesis** is a prediction that can be tested. After discussing her observations with the clinic veterinarian, she hypothesizes that something in the cat litter is irritating the cats' skin.

Test the Hypothesis with an Experiment The technician gets the owner's permission to test her hypothesis by performing an experiment. In an experiment, the hypothesis is tested using controlled conditions. The technician reads the labels on two brands of cat litter and finds that the ingredients of each are the same except that one contains a deodorant.

LAB DEMONSTRATION

Purpose to compare observations and inferences

Materials one red apple

Alternate Materials one purple grape for each student pair

Preparation Wash the fruit.

Procedure Have students record visual observations of the fruit and then classify the following statements as observations or inferences. 1. The apple's covering is red. 2. The apple is edible. 3. There are seeds inside the apple.

Expected Outcome 1 is an observation; 2 and 3 are inferences.

How are observations and inferences different? Observations are information gathered through the senses. Inferences result from past observations and knowledge.

8 CHAPTER 1 Exploring and Classifying Life

Controls The technician separates the cats with sores from the other two cats. She puts each of the cats with sores in a cage by itself. One cat is called the experimental cat. This cat is given a litter box containing the cat litter without deodorant. The other cat is given a litter box that contains cat litter with deodorant. The cat with deodorant cat litter is the control.

A **control** is the standard to which the outcome of a test is compared. At the end of the experiment, the control cat will be compared with the experimental cat. Whether or not the cat litter contains deodorant is the variable. A **variable** is something in an experiment that can change. An experiment should have only one variable. Other than the difference in the cat litter, the technician treats both cats the same.

Reading Check *How many variables should an experiment have?*

Analyze Data The veterinary technician observes both cats for one week. During this time, she collects data on how often and when the cats scratch or chew, as shown in **Figure 4.** These data are recorded in a journal. The data show that the control cat scratches and chews more often than the experimental cat does. The sores on the skin of the experimental cat begin to heal, but those on the control cat do not.

Draw Conclusions The technician then draws the conclusion—a logical answer to a question based on data and observation—that the deodorant in the cat litter probably irritated the skin of the two cats. To accept or reject the hypothesis is the next step. In this case, the technician accepts the hypothesis. If she had rejected it, new experiments would have been necessary.

Although the technician decides to accept her hypothesis, she realizes that to be surer of her results she should continue her experiment. She should switch the experimental cat with the control cat to see what the results are a second time. If she did this, the healed cat might develop new sores. She makes an ethical decision and chooses not to continue the experiment. Ethical decisions, like this one, are important in deciding what science should be done.

Analyzing Data

Procedure

1. Obtain a **pan balance.** Follow your teacher's instructions for using it.
2. Record all data in your **Science Journal.**
3. Measure and record the mass of a dry **sponge.**
4. Soak this sponge in **water.** Measure and record its mass.
5. Calculate how much water your sponge absorbed.
6. Combine the class data and calculate the average amount of water absorbed.

Analysis

What other information about the sponges might be important when analyzing the data from the entire class?

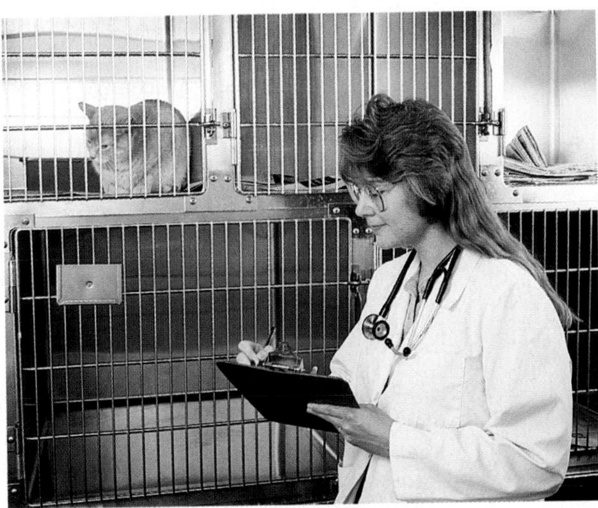

Figure 4
Collecting and analyzing data is part of scientific methods.

Discussion

Is it possible to form a hypothesis without first making observations? Explain. No; a hypothesis is formed from observations.

Reading Check

Answer one

Purpose to obtain data using a pan balance L1 IS **Logical-Mathematical**

Materials pan balance, sponge, water, Science Journal

Teaching Strategies

- Demonstrate the use of a balance.
- Review techniques for transporting a balance: be sure all riders are back to the zero point; place one hand under the balance and the other hand on the beam's support to carry the balance.

Analysis

Accept all reasonable answers. Students may suggest that the size of the sponges or how long each was soaked in water would affect results.

Assessment

Performance Have students use a meterstick to measure the length and width of their lab tables. Ask them to explain how they decided which units of measure to use. Use **PASC,** p. 97.

Resource Manager

Chapter Resources Booklet

MiniLAB, p. 3

Reinforcement, p. 25

Life Science Critical Thinking/Problem Solving, p. 4

Curriculum Connection

Language Arts Have students research a major discovery in life science and the person who made the discovery. Possible research subjects include Francesco Redi, William Harvey, Alexander Fleming, Barbara McClintock, and George Washington Carver. Have students use their findings to write newspaper articles describing their discoveries. L1 IS **Linguistic**

Developing Theories

The word *theory* is used outside of science to mean "speculation" or "an idea that is uncertain." People often use the word when they are referring to a hypothesis, for example, *I have a theory about why I didn't do well on the test*, or *I have a theory that wearing blue brings me good luck.* Reinforce that a scientific theory is an accepted fact that scientists do not usually question until new evidence is presented.

Reading Check

Answer scientific knowledge resulting from observations and experiments

Teacher FYI

Scientists use many methods of investigation. They approach problems from a variety of perspectives and structure their research based on available data, tools, and time. Observations often generate new hypotheses that lead to additional testing.

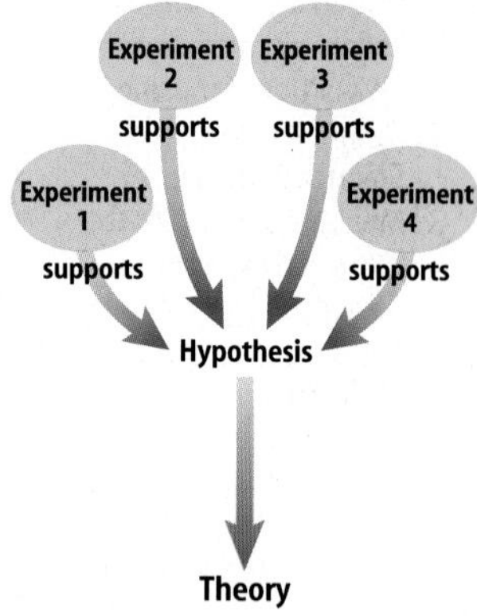

Figure 5
If data collected from several experiments over a period of time all support the hypothesis, it can finally be called a theory.

Report Results When using scientific methods, it is important to share information. The veterinary technician calls the cats' owner and tells him the results of her experiment. She tells him she has stopped using the deodorant cat litter.

The technician also writes a story for the clinic's newsletter that describes her experiment and shares her conclusions. She reports the limits of her experiment and explains that her results are not final. In science it is important to explain how an experiment can be made better if it is done again.

Developing Theories

After scientists report the results of experiments supporting their hypotheses, the results can be used to propose a scientific theory. When you watch a magician do a trick you might decide you have an idea or "theory" about how the trick works. Is your idea just a hunch or a scientific theory? A scientific **theory** is an explanation of things or events based on scientific knowledge that is the result of many observations and experiments. It is not a guess or someone's opinion. Many scientists repeat the experiment. If the results always support the hypothesis, the hypothesis can be called a theory, as shown in **Figure 5.**

Reading Check *What is a theory based on?*

A theory usually explains many hypotheses. For example, an important theory in life sciences is the cell theory. Scientists made observations of cells and experimented for more than 100 years before enough information was collected to propose a theory. Hypotheses about cells in plants and animals are combined in the cell theory.

A valid theory raises many new questions. Data or information from new experiments might change conclusions and theories can change. Later in this chapter you will read about the theory of spontaneous generation and how this theory changed as scientists used experiments to study new hypotheses.

Laws A scientific **law** is a statement about how things work in nature that seems to be true all the time. Although laws can be modified as more information becomes known, they are less likely to change than theories. Laws tell you what will happen under certain conditions but do not necessarily explain why it happened. For example, in life science you might learn about laws of heredity. These laws explain how genes are inherited but do not explain how genes work. Due to the great variety of living things, laws that describe them are few. It is unlikely that a law about how all cells work will ever be developed.

Active Reading

Metacognition Journal In this strategy, each student analyzes his or her own thought processes. Have students divide the paper in half. On the left, have them record what they have learned about a topic. On the right, have them record the reason they learned it. Have students write a Metacognition Journal about scientific methods.

Cultural Diversity

Development of Cell Theory One theory in life science that has been widely accepted by scientists is the cell theory. The cell theory originated through the work of English scientist Robert Hooke in 1665. Almost two hundred years later, the works of three German scientists—Matthias Schleiden, Theodor Schwann, and Rudolph Virchow—were incorporated to form the modern cell theory.

Scientific Methods Help Answer Questions You can use scientific methods to answer all sorts of questions. Your questions may be as simple as "Where did I leave my house key?" or as complex as "Will global warming cause the polar ice caps to melt?" You probably have had to find the answer to the first question. Someday you might try to find the answer to the second question. Using these scientific methods does not guarantee that you will get an answer. Often scientific methods just lead to more questions and more experiments. That's what science is about—continuing to look for the best answers to your questions.

Problem-Solving Activity

Does temperature affect the rate of bacterial reproduction?

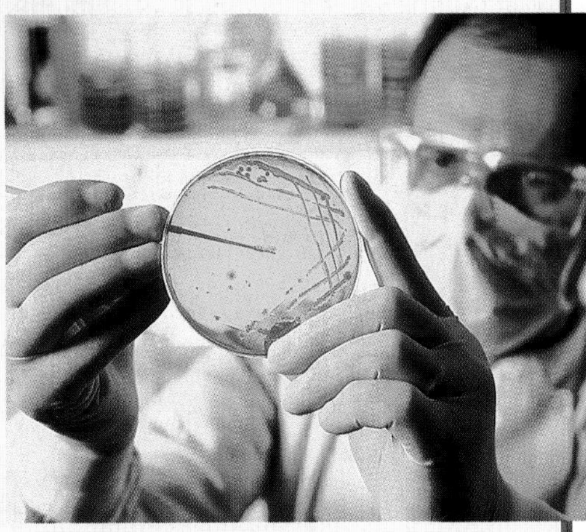

Some bacteria make you sick. Other bacteria, however, are used to produce foods like cheese and yogurt. Understanding how quickly bacteria reproduce can help you avoid harmful bacteria and use helpful bacteria. It's important to know things that affect how quickly bacteria reproduce. How do you think temperature will affect the rate of bacterial reproduction? A student makes the hypothesis that bacteria will reproduce more quickly as the temperature increases.

Identifying the Problem

The table below lists the reproduction-doubling rates at specific temperatures for one type of bacteria. A rate of 2.0 means that the number of bacteria doubled two times that hour (e.g., 100 to 200 to 400).

Bacterial Reproductive Rates

Temperature (°C)	Doubling Rate per Hour
20.5	2.0
30.5	3.0
36.0	2.5
39.2	1.2

Look at the table. What conclusions can you draw from the data?

Solving the Problem

1. Do the data in the table support the student's hypothesis?
2. How would you write a hypothesis about the relationship between bacterial reproduction and temperature?
3. Make a list of other factors that might have influenced the results in the table.
4. Are you satisfied with these data? List other things that you wish you knew.
5. Describe an experiment that would help you test these other ideas.

Activity

Have students obtain articles from science magazines, journals, or newspapers that describe scientific studies. As they read their articles, have students circle passages that describe the use of scientific methods. Ask them each to prepare an oral report that summarizes the content of the article and describes how scientific methods were used. L2
LS Logical-Mathematical

Problem-Solving Activity

National Math Standards

Correlation to Mathematics Objectives
1, 4, 5, 6, 8, 9

Answers

1. Not completely; doubling increases to a certain temperature, and then decreases.
2. Possible answer: Bacteria reproduce more quickly as temperature rises until a certain temperature is reached; then rate falls.
3. Other possible influences: Was the light always the same? Did the bacteria have the same amount of space to grow? Were the bacteria always in the same medium? Check that student's experiments test only one variable at a time.
4. Answer will vary. Accept reasonable responses.
5. Answers will vary depending on responses to question 4. Look for variables and controls in student descriptions.

Inclusion Strategies

Learning Disabled Invite students to design a bulletin board showing the steps in scientific methods using pictures from magazines. L1
LS Visual-Spatial

Resource Manager

Chapter Resources Booklet
Enrichment, p. 29

Mathematics Skill Activities, p. 33

Measuring with Scientific Units

Quick Demo

Show students a nickel and a dime. Tell them the nickel has a mass of about 5 g and the dime is 1 mm thick. Using a triple-beam balance and calipers, have students determine the mass and thickness of other coins they may have.

IDENTIFYING Misconceptions

Students may not understand that the weight of an object can vary, depending on the force of gravity. Explain that an object on the moon weighs less than an object on Earth because the pull of gravity is weaker on the moon than on Earth. However, the amount of matter (mass) that makes up the object does not change with location.

Teacher FYI

The U.S. is the only industrialized country that has not officially adopted SI. This has caused difficulties in the area of trade and commerce. To successfully compete in world markets, many products made in the U.S. are labeled in both SI and customary units. Invite students to conduct an SI measurement hunt in their homes to find five items that are marked with both types of measures.

REGULAR ORANG
473 mL
Nutrition Facts
Serv. Size 8 fl oz (240 mL)
Servings 2
Amount Per Serving
Calories 110
% Daily Value*
Total Fat 0g 0%
Sodium 25mg 1%
Potassium 480mg 14%
Total Carb 27g 9%
Sugars 24g
Protein 0g
Vitamin C 100% • Thiamin 8%
Not a significant source of fat cal., sat. fat, cholest., fiber, vitamin A, calcium and iron.
*Percent Daily Values are based on a 2,000 calorie diet.

Figure 6 Your food often is measured in metric units.

A The label of this juice bottle shows you that it contains 473 mL of juice.

B Nutritional information on the label is listed in grams or milligrams.

Measuring with Scientific Units

An important part of most scientific investigations is making accurate measurements. Think about things you use every day that are measured. Ingredients in your hamburger, hot dog, potato chips, or soft drink are measured in units such as grams and milliliters, as shown in **Figure 6.** The water you drink, the gas you use, and the electricity needed for a CD player are measured, too.

In your classroom or laboratory this year, you will use the same standard system of measurement scientists use to communicate and understand each other's research and results. This system is called the International System of Units, or SI. For example, you may need to calculate the distance a bird flies in kilometers. Perhaps you will be asked to measure the amount of air your lungs can hold in liters or the mass of an automobile in kilograms. Some of the SI units are shown in **Table 1.**

Table 1 Common SI Measurements

Measurement	Unit	Symbol	Equal to
Length	1 millimeter	mm	0.001 (1/1,000) m
	1 centimeter	cm	0.01 (1/100) m
	1 meter	m	100 cm
	1 kilometer	km	1,000 m
Volume	1 milliliter	mL	0.001 (1/1,000) L
	1 liter	L	1,000 mL
Mass	1 gram	g	1,000 mg
	1 kilogram	kg	1,000 g
	1 tonne	t	1,000 kg = 1 metric ton

Resource Manager

Chapter Resources Booklet
Lab Activity, pp. 9–10

Reading and Writing Skill Activities, pp. 17, 33

Cultural Diversity

Ancient Measurements The ancient Chinese system of weights and measures included an acoustical dimension. The quantity of content in a vessel was defined by both weight and by the pitch produced when the vessel was struck. Have students research and report on other measurement instruments and systems. Students might investigate the cubit and thermoscope or the history of the metric system.

Safety First

Doing science is usually much more interesting than just reading about it. Some of the scientific equipment that you will use in your classroom or laboratory is the same as what scientists use. Laboratory safety is important. In many states, a student can participate in a laboratory class only when wearing proper eye protection. Don't forget to wash your hands after handling materials. Following safety rules, as shown in **Figure 7,** will protect you and others from injury during your lab experiences. Symbols used throughout your text will alert you to situations that require special attention. Some of these symbols are shown below. A description of each symbol is in the Safety Symbols chart at the front of this book.

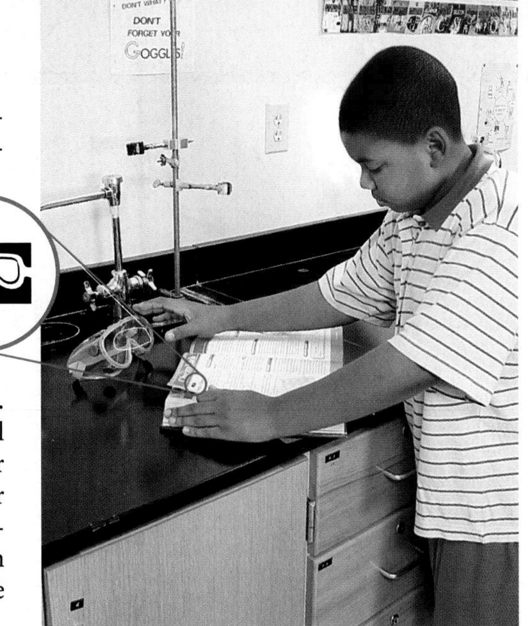

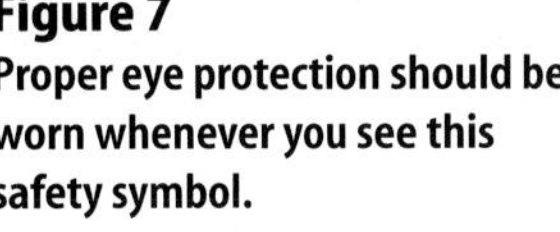

Figure 7
Proper eye protection should be worn whenever you see this safety symbol.

Section 1 Assessment

1. Identify steps that might be followed when using scientific methods.
2. Why is it important to test only one variable at a time during an experiment?
3. What SI unit would you use to measure the width of your classroom?
4. How is a theory different than a hypothesis?
5. **Think Critically** Can the veterinary technician in this section be sure that the deodorant caused the cats' skin problems? What could she change in her experiment to make it better?

Skill Builder Activities

6. **Communicating** Write a newsletter article that explains what the veterinary technician discovered from her experiment. **For more help, refer to the Science Skill Handbook.**
7. **Converting Units** Sometimes temperature is measured in Fahrenheit degrees. Normal human body temperature is 98.6°F. What is this temperature in degrees Celsius? Use the English-to-metric conversion chart at the back of this book. **For more help, refer to the Math Skill Handbook.**

Answers to Section Assessment

1. State the problem, gather information, form a hypothesis, test the hypothesis with an experiment, analyze data, and draw conclusions.
2. so the scientist can understand which condition caused the results
3. meters
4. theory—an explanation based on many observations; hypothesis—a testable prediction
5. Possible answer: Both cats may not be allergic to the same thing. She could repeat the experiment, this time giving the other cat non-deodorized litter. If the skin problem clears up, she has likely identified the problem.
6. The newspaper article should include the observations that led to stating the problem, how she gathered the information to form the hypothesis, how she tested the hypothesis with an experiment, analyzed the data, drew conclusions, and reported the results.
7. 37° C

Safety First

Discussion

What is the purpose of safety symbols? Each safety symbol alerts experimenters to a potential danger associated with a particular situation.

3 Assess

Reteach

Divide the class into groups. Give each student in a group a slip of paper labeled with a step of a scientific method. After all the papers have been distributed, have students arrange themselves in a line that shows the order in which the steps are often carried out. Have groups compare their results and discuss why each group may not necessarily have the steps in the same order.

Challenge

A scientist shares the results of her experiment with others. Three scientists repeat the experiment and get different results. **What might you conclude about the first scientist's experiment?** Possible answers: The experiment was not well designed, the procedure was not clearly stated, or variables exist that the first scientist did not identify.

Assessment

Portfolio Safety is just as important at home as it is in the laboratory. For each safety symbol in the chart at the front of the book, have students write one safety rule to follow at home in the kitchen, bathroom, or outdoors. Use **Performance Assessment in the Science Classroom,** p. 157.

SECTION

Living Things

1 Motivate

Bellringer Transparency

Display the Section Focus Transparency for Section 2. Use the accompanying Transparency Activity Master. L2 ELL

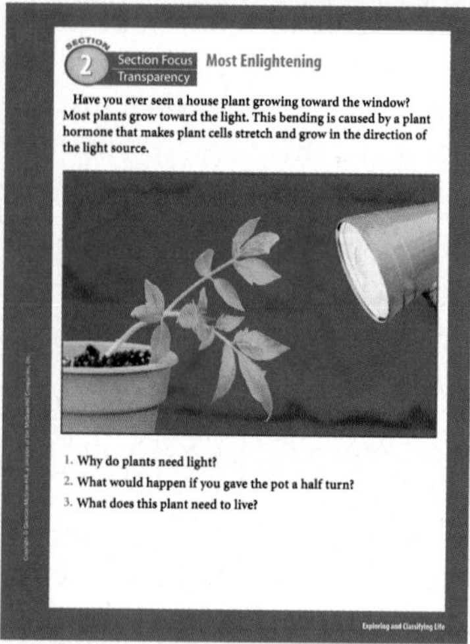

SECTION 2 Section Focus Transparency — Most Enlightening

Have you ever seen a house plant growing toward the window? Most plants grow toward the light. This bending is caused by a plant hormone that makes plant cells stretch and grow in the direction of the light source.

1. Why do plants need light?
2. What would happen if you gave the pot a half turn?
3. What does this plant need to live?

Tie to Prior Knowledge

Students will have ideas about characteristics and needs of all living things. Ask them to name traits and needs that all organisms share. Record responses on the board.

SECTION 2

Living Things

As You Read

***What* You'll Learn**

- **Distinguish** between living and nonliving things.
- **Identify** what living things need to survive.

Vocabulary

organism
cell
homeostasis

***Why* It's Important**

All living things, including you, have many of the same traits.

What are living things like?

What does it mean to be alive? If you walked down your street after a thunderstorm, you'd probably see earthworms on the sidewalk, birds flying, clouds moving across the sky, and puddles of water. You'd see living and nonliving things that are alike in some ways. For example, birds and clouds move. Earthworms and water feel wet when they are touched. Yet, clouds and water are nonliving things, and birds and earthworms are living things. Any living thing is called an **organism.**

Organisms vary in size from the microscopic bacteria in mud puddles to gigantic oak trees and are found just about everywhere. They have different behaviors and food needs. In spite of these differences, all organisms have similar traits. These traits determine what it means to be alive.

Living Things Are Organized If you were to look at almost any part of an organism, like a plant leaf or your skin, under a microscope, you would see that it is made up of small units called cells. A **cell** is the smallest unit of an organism that carries on the functions of life. Some organisms are composed of just one cell while others are composed of many cells. Cells take in materials from their surroundings and use them in complex ways. Each cell has an orderly structure and contains hereditary material. The hereditary material contains instructions for cellular organization and function. **Figure 8** shows some organisms that are made of many cells. All the things that these organisms can do are possible because of what their cells can do.

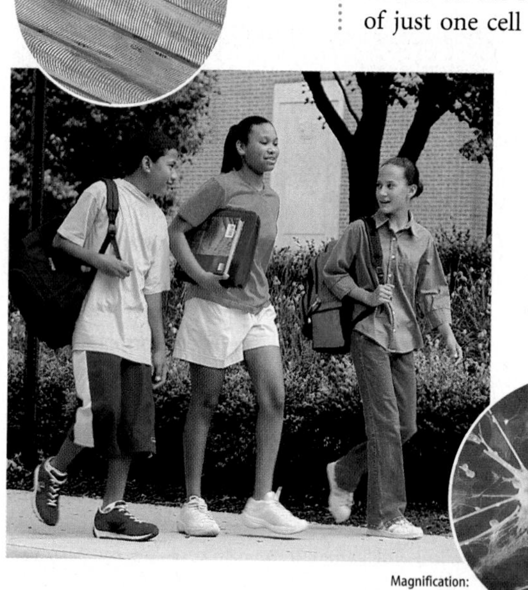

Figure 8
Your body is organized into many different types of cells. Two types are shown.

Section Assessment Planner

Portfolio
Curriculum Connection, p. 16

Performance Assessment
Skill Builder Activities, p. 18
See page 34 for more options.

Content Assessment
Section, p. 18
Challenge, p. 18
Chapter, pp. 34–35

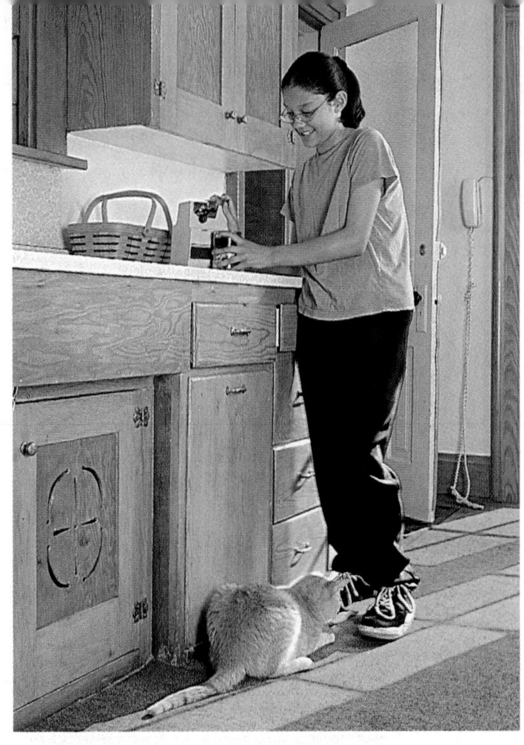

Living Things Respond Living things interact with their surroundings. Watch your cat when you use your electric can opener. Does your cat come running to find out what's happening even when you're not opening a can of cat food? The cat in **Figure 9** ran in response to a stimulus—the sound of the can opener. Anything that causes some change in an organism is a stimulus (plural, *stimuli*). The reaction to a stimulus is a response. Often that response results in movement, such as when the cat runs toward the sound of the can opener. To carry on its daily activity and to survive, an organism must respond to stimuli.

Living things also respond to stimuli that occur inside them. For example, water or food levels in organisms' cells can increase or decrease. The organisms then make internal changes to keep the right amounts of water and food in their cells. Their temperature also must be within a certain range. An organism's ability to keep the proper conditions inside no matter what is going on outside the organism is called **homeostasis.** Homeostasis is a trait of all living things.

Figure 9
Some cats respond to a food stimulus even when they are not hungry. *Why does a cat come running when it hears a can opener?*

What are some internal stimuli living things respond to?

Living Things Use Energy Staying organized and carrying on activities like homeostasis requires energy. The energy used by most organisms comes either directly or indirectly from the Sun. Plants and some other organisms use the Sun's energy and the raw materials carbon dioxide and water to make food. You and most other organisms can't use the energy of sunlight directly. Instead, you take in and use food as a source of energy. You get food by eating plants or other organisms that ate plants. Most organisms, including plants, also must take in oxygen in order to release the energy of foods.

Some bacteria live at the bottom of the oceans and in other areas where sunlight cannot reach. They can't use the Sun's energy to produce food. Instead, the bacteria use energy stored in some chemical compounds and the raw material carbon dioxide to make food. Unlike most other organisms, many of these bacteria do not need oxygen to release the energy that is found in their food.

Research Visit the Glencoe Science Web site at **science.glencoe.com** for more information about homeostasis. Communicate to your class what you learn.

2 Teach

What are living things like?

Quick Demo

Responses in plants are usually less obvious than in animals. However, if you touch a mimosa plant, all the small leaflets on the branch fold upward. Obtain a mimosa plant to demonstrate this rapid response.

Caption Answer

Figure 9 The cat is responding to the stimulus of the can opener.

Reading Check

Answer water and food levels, temperature

Use an Analogy

Compare the homeostasis that must be maintained by the body to the conditions necessary for a car to function. For example, a car must have fuel, oil, and other fluids in proper balance in order to run. In the same way, organisms must have fuel and other materials in order to remain alive.

SCIENCE Online
Internet Addresses

Explore the Glencoe Science Web site at **science.glencoe.com** to find out more about topics in this section.

Inclusion Strategies

Learning Disabled Have students choose and draw a scene on poster board or mural paper. Have them label the objects in the drawing as living or nonliving. L1 IN **Visual-Spatial**

Resource Manager

Chapter Resources Booklet
Transparency Activity, p. 45
Directed Reading for Content Mastery, p. 18

Science Inquiry Labs, p. 3

What are living things like?, continued

Discussion

How does an acorn grow and develop? An acorn sprouts and produces roots, stems, and leaves that continue to grow for years. As it grows, it takes in substances from the air and soil and changes those substances into living cells. It continues to add new cells and tissues to replace those that wear out.

Students may think that all things that move are alive. Refer to page 4F for teaching strategies that address this misconception.

Teacher FYI

Nonliving things use energy just as living things do. Windmills, solar calculators, solar panels, and thunderclouds all use energy from their environments and change it into different forms. However, living things take in energy from their environments and use it for specialized purposes such as growth, development, and reproduction.

Living Things Grow and Develop When a puppy is born, it might be small enough to hold in one hand. After the same dog is fully grown, you might not be able to hold it at all. How does this happen? The puppy grows by taking in raw materials, like milk from its female parent, and making more cells. Growth of many-celled organisms, such as the puppy, is mostly due to an increase in the number of cells. In one-celled organisms, growth is due to an increase in the size of the cell.

Organisms change as they grow. Puppies can't see or walk when they are born. In eight or nine days, their eyes open, and their legs become strong enough to hold them up. All of the changes that take place during the life of an organism are called development. **Figure 10** shows how four different organisms changed as they grew.

The length of time an organism is expected to live is its life span. Adult dogs can live for 20 years and a cat for 25 years. Some organisms have a short life span. Mayflies live only one day, but a land tortoise can live for more than 180 years. Some bristlecone pine trees have been alive for more than 4,600 years. Your life span is about 80 years.

Figure 10
Complete development of an organism can take a few days or several years. The pictures below show the development of A a dog, B a human, C a pea plant, and D a butterfly.

Science Journal

Characteristics of Living Things Have students choose an animal that they have observed. In their Science Journals, have them write an essay explaining how their observations show that the animal is a living organism. L2
LS **Linguistic**

Curriculum Connection

Math Have students obtain data that illustrates how they have changed as they have grown older. Ask them to research their heights at three different ages. (If this information is not available at home, have students obtain the data from their school records.) Then have students work in pairs to measure their current heights. Ask students to present their results as bar graphs. L2 LS **Logical-Mathematical** P

Figure 11
Living things reproduce themselves in many different ways. A A *Paramecium* reproduces by dividing into two. B Beetles, like most insects, reproduce by laying eggs. C Every spore released by these puffballs can grow into a new fungus.

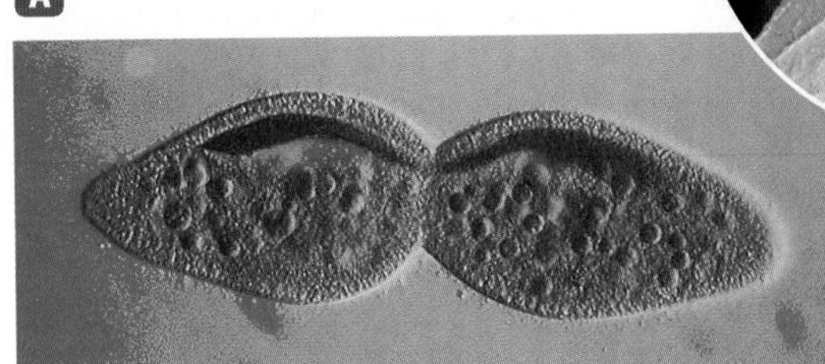

Magnification: 400×

Living Things Reproduce Cats, dogs, alligators, fish, birds, bees, and trees eventually reproduce. They make more of their own kind. Some bacteria reproduce every 20 minutes while it might take a pine tree two years to produce seeds. **Figure 11** shows some ways organisms reproduce.

Without reproduction, living things would not exist to replace those individuals that die. An individual cat can live its entire life without reproducing. However, if cats never reproduced, all cats soon would disappear.

Reading Check *Why is reproduction important?*

What do living things need?

What do you need to live? Do you have any needs that are different from those of other living things? To survive, all living things need a place to live and raw materials. The raw materials that they require and the exact place where they live can vary.

A Place to Live The environment limits where organisms can live. Not many kinds of organisms can live in extremely hot or extremely cold environments. Most cannot live at the bottom of the ocean or on the tops of mountains. All organisms also need living space in their surroundings. For example, thousands of penguins build their nests on an island. When the island becomes too crowded, the penguins fight for space and some may not find space to build nests. An organism's surroundings must provide for all of its needs.

Health INTEGRATION

Human infants can't take care of themselves at birth. Research to find out what human infants can do at different stages of development. Make a chart that shows changes from birth to one year old.

Teacher FYI

All the characteristics of living things are needed for survival of the individual, except for reproduction. Reproduction is needed for survival of the species.

Resource Manager

Chapter Resources Booklet
Enrichment, p. 30
Reinforcement, p. 26
Cultural Diversity, pp. 7, 9

Visual Learning

Figure 11 How do these organisms reproduce? Beetles lay eggs, a fungus releases spores, and a paramecium undergoes cell division to become two organisms.

Reading Check

Answer Organisms must reproduce to replace members of their species that die, or the species will become extinct.

What do living things need?

Activity

Label five sheets of paper with one of the subheads in this section. Divide the class into five groups. Give each group a sheet of paper. Ask group members to cut pictures from magazines that illustrate the subhead, to paste the pictures on the paper, and write a caption for each picture. When all groups have finished their tasks, combine the pages into a booklet titled "How Living Things Are Alike." L1 COOP LEARN

Extension

Have students name the characteristics and needs of living things that can be observed in a classroom aquarium or terrarium. L2

Health INTEGRATION

1 month: movements are clumsy, throaty sounds can be made; 3 months: can sit up with assisstance and laugh; 6 months: birth weight doubles, can roll over, sit alone and babble; 9 months: can crawl and repeat syllables; 1 year: birth weight triples, can walk and speak first words

What do living things need?, continued

Caption Answer

Figure 12 Plants take in water through their roots.

3 Assess

Reteach

Write the characteristics of living things on 3" x 5" cards. Have students draw a card and give an example of the characteristic. L1

Challenge

Which characteristic of life is important to survival of a species rather than to the organism itself? Explain. Reproduction; a living thing can survive without reproducing, but the species would not survive if none of its members reproduced.

Assessment

Process Have students heat water in a beaker and dissolve as much sugar in the beaker as they can. Tie a string around a stirring rod. Place the rod across the top of the beaker so the string is immersed in the cooled water. Leave the string in the beaker until sugar crystals begin to grow. Ask students why these crystals are not alive. They have none of the other characteristics of living things. Use **Performance Assessment in the Science Classroom,** p. 97.

Figure 12
You and a corn plant each take in and give off about 2 L of water in a day. Most of the water you take in is from water you drink or from foods you eat. *Where do plants get water to transport materials?*

Raw Materials Water is important for all living things. Plants and animals take in and give off large amounts of water each day, as shown in **Figure 12.** Organisms use homeostasis to balance the amounts of water lost with the amounts taken in. Most organisms are composed of more than 50 percent water. You are made of 60 to 70 percent water. Organisms use water for many things. For example, blood, which is about 90 percent water, transports digested food and wastes in animals. Plants have a watery sap that transports materials between roots and leaves.

Living things are made up of substances such as proteins, fats, and sugars. Animals take in most of these substances from the foods they eat. Plants and some bacteria make them using raw materials from their surroundings. These important substances are used over and over again. When organisms die, substances in their bodies are broken down and released into the soil or air. The substances can then be used again by other living organisms. Some of the substances in your body might once have been part of a butterfly or an apple tree.

At the beginning of this section, you learned that things such as clouds, sidewalks, and puddles of water are not living things. Now do you understand why? Clouds, sidewalks, and water do not reproduce, use energy, or have other traits of living things.

Section 2 Assessment

1. What is the main source of energy used by most organisms?
2. List five traits most organisms have.
3. Why would you expect to see cells if you looked at a section of a mushroom cap under a microscope?
4. In order to survive, what things do most organisms need?
5. **Think Critically** Why is homeostasis important to organisms?

Skill Builder Activities

6. **Comparing and Contrasting** What are the similarities and differences between a goldfish and the flame of a burning candle? **For more help, refer to the** Science Skill Handbook.
7. **Using a Database** Use references to find the life span of ten animals. Use your computer to make a database. Then graph the life spans from shortest to longest. **For more help, refer to the** Technology Skill Handbook.

Answers to Section Assessment

1. the Sun
2. Living things are organized, respond, take in and use energy, grow and develop, and reproduce.
3. All living things are made of cells.
4. Organisms need raw materials and a place to live.
5. Without homeostasis—the maintaining of proper conditions inside an organism regardless of external conditions—the organism would die.
6. The goldfish is made of cells, takes in and uses energy, responds, grows and develops, reproduces, and needs a place to live and raw materials. The candle flame moves, responds to wind, uses energy from the candle, gives off heat energy, produces waste products, and uses oxygen to burn.
7. Life spans will vary in different references. Sample data (in years): humans: 76; horses: 30; cows: 24; dogs: 15; cats: 12; turtles: 125; elephants: 60; penguins: 23; shrews: 1, snakes: 11; spiders: 3

SECTION 3

Where does life come from?

Life Comes from Life

You've probably seen a fish tank, like the one in **Figure 13,** that is full of algae. How did the algae get there? Before the seventeenth century, some people thought that insects and fish came from mud, that earthworms fell from the sky when it rained, and that mice came from grain. These were logical conclusions at that time, based on repeated personal experiences. The idea that living things come from nonliving things is known as **spontaneous generation.** This idea became a theory that was accepted for several hundred years. When scientists began to use controlled experiments to test this theory, the theory changed.

Reading Check *According to the theory of spontaneous generation, where do fish come from?*

Spontaneous Generation and Biogenesis From the late seventeenth century through the middle of the eighteenth century, experiments were done to test the theory of spontaneous generation. Although these experiments showed that spontaneous generation did not occur in most cases, they did not disprove it entirely.

It was not until the mid-1800s that the work of Louis Pasteur, a French chemist, provided enough evidence to disprove the theory of spontaneous generation. It was replaced with **biogenesis** (bi oh JEN uh suhs), which is the theory that living things come only from other living things.

Figure 13
The sides of this tank were clean and the water was clear when the aquarium was set up. Algal cells, which were not visible on plants and fish, reproduced in the tank. So many algal cells are present now that the water is cloudy.

As You Read

What You'll Learn

- **Describe** experiments about spontaneous generation.
- **Explain** how scientific methods led to the idea of biogenesis.
- **Examine** how chemical compounds found in living things might have formed.

Vocabulary

spontaneous generation
biogenesis

Why It's Important

You can use scientific methods to try to find out about events that happened long ago or just last week. You can even use them to predict how something will behave in the future.

Section Assessment Planner

PORTFOLIO
Reteach, p. 21

PERFORMANCE ASSESSMENT
Skill Builder Activities, p. 21
See page 34 for more options.

CONTENT ASSESSMENT
Section, p. 21
Challenge, p. 21
Chapter, pp. 34–35

SECTION 3

Where does life come from?

1 Motivate

Bellringer Transparency

Display the Section Focus Transparency for Section 3. Use the accompanying Transparency Activity Master. L2 ELL

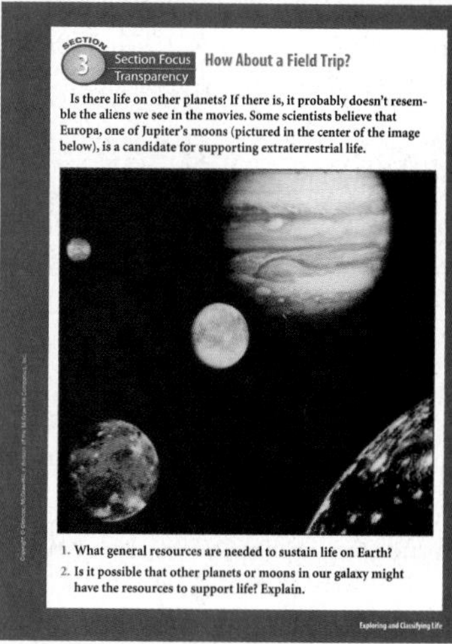

Section 3 Section Focus Transparency **How About a Field Trip?**

Is there life on other planets? If there is, it probably doesn't resemble the aliens we see in the movies. Some scientists believe that Europa, one of Jupiter's moons (pictured in the center of the image below), is a candidate for supporting extraterrestrial life.

1. What general resources are needed to sustain life on Earth?
2. Is it possible that other planets or moons in our galaxy might have the resources to support life? Explain.

Exploring and Classifying Life

Tie to Prior Knowledge

Review the characteristics and needs of living things. Elicit from volunteers their ideas on where organisms possessing such characteristics and needs came from.

Reading Check

Answer from mud

Resource Manager

Chapter Resources Booklet
Transparency Activity, p. 46
Directed Reading for Content Mastery, p. 19

NATIONAL GEOGRAPHIC

Visualizing the Origins of Life

Have students examine the pictures and read the captions. Then ask the following questions.

What are the similarities of Spallanzani's and Redi's work? Students should note that both Spallanzani and Redi did experiments that questioned the idea of spontaneous generation.

What must have been present in the neck of the S-necked flasks used by Pasteur in his experiments? The necks of the S-neck flasks must have contained microorganisms, which contaminated the broth when the flask was tilted.

Activity

Students should work in small groups to create and play a matching game based on the scientists in the this feature and their work. In the game, points should be awarded for correctly matching a scientist with his work. Have students explain the rules of their game to the class.

Extension

Have interested students research other world events that occurred in the years the experiments shown in this feature took place. These students can construct an expanded time line showing these other events, and shared their findings with the class.

NATIONAL GEOGRAPHIC **VISUALIZING THE ORIGINS OF LIFE**

Figure 14

For centuries scientists have theorized about the origins of life. As shown on this timeline, some examined spontaneous generation—the idea that nonliving material can produce life. More recently, scientists have proposed theories about the origins of life on Earth by testing hypotheses about conditions on early Earth.

1668 Francesco Redi put decaying meat in some jars, then covered half of them. When fly maggots appeared only on the uncovered meat (see below, left), Redi concluded that they had hatched from fly eggs and had not come from the meat.

1745 John Needham heated broth in sealed flasks. When the broth became cloudy with microorganisms, he mistakenly concluded that they developed spontaneously from the broth.

1768 Lazzaro Spallanzani broiled broth in sealed flasks for a longer time than Needham did. Only the ones he opened became cloudy with contamination.

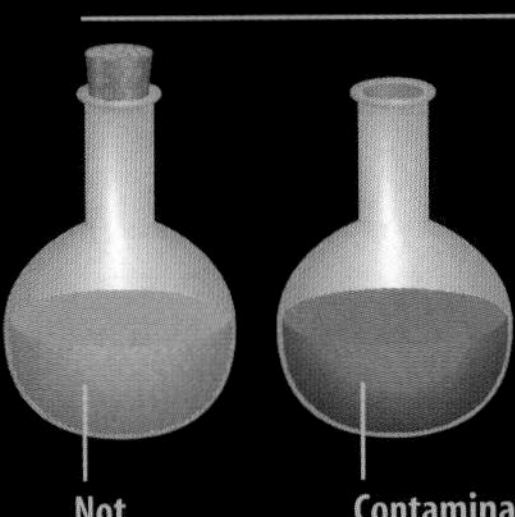

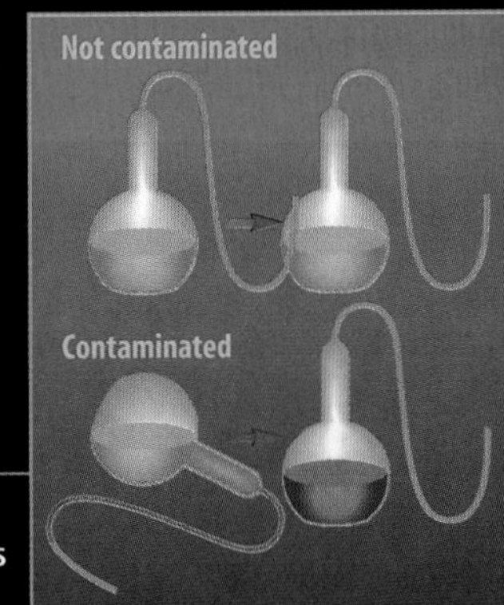

1859 Louis Pasteur disproved spontaneous generation by boiling broth in S-necked flasks that were open to the air. The broth became cloudy (see above, bottom right) only when a flask was tilted and the broth was exposed to dust in the S-neck.

Gases of Earth's early atmosphere
Electric current
Oceanlike mixture forms
Cools
Materials in present-day cells

1924 Alexander Oparin hypothesized that energy from the Sun, lightning, and Earth's heat triggered chemical reactions early in Earth's history. The newly-formed molecules washed into Earth's ancient oceans and became a part of what is often called the primordial soup.

1953 Stanley Miller and Harold Urey sent electric currents through a mixture of gases like those thought to be in Earth's early atmosphere. When the gases cooled, they condensed to form an oceanlike liquid that contained materials such as amino acids, found in present-day cells.

Resource Manager

Chapter Resources Booklet
Enrichment, p. 31
Reinforcement, p. 27

Earth Science Critical Thinking/Problem Solving, pp. 1, 12, 14

Visual Learning

Figure 14 Have students create a poster showing the progression of scientific thought on life origins, as evidenced by the experiments in this feature.

Life's Origins

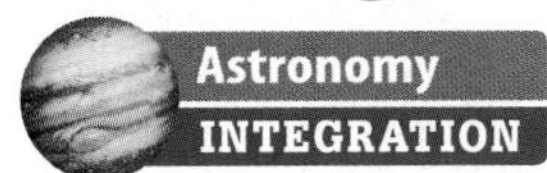

Astronomy INTEGRATION If living things can come only from other living things, how did life on Earth begin? Some scientists hypothesize that about 5 billion years ago, Earth's solar system was a whirling mass of gas and dust. They hypothesize that the Sun and planets were formed from this mass. It is estimated that Earth is about 4.6 billion years old. Rocks found in Australia that are more than 3.5 billion years old contain fossils of once-living organisms. Where did these living organisms come from?

Oparin's Hypothesis In 1924, a Russian scientist named Alexander I. Oparin suggested that Earth's early atmosphere had no oxygen but was made up of the gases ammonia, hydrogen, methane, and water vapor. Oparin hypothesized that these gases could have combined to form the more complex compounds found in living things.

Using gases and conditions that Oparin described, American scientists Stanley L. Miller and Harold Urey set up an experiment to test Oparin's hypothesis in 1953. Although the Miller-Urey experiment showed that chemicals found in living things could be produced, it did not prove that life began in this way.

For many centuries, scientists have tried to find the origins of life, as shown in **Figure 14.** Although questions about spontaneous generation have been answered, some scientists still are investigating ideas about life's origins.

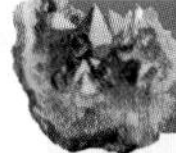

Earth Science INTEGRATION

Scientists hypothesize that Earth's oceans originally formed when water vapor was released into the atmosphere from many volcanic eruptions. Once it cooled, rain fell and filled Earth's lowland areas. Identify five lowland areas on Earth that are now filled with water. Record your answer in your Science Journal.

Section  Assessment

1. Compare and contrast spontaneous generation and biogenesis.
2. Describe three controlled experiments that helped disprove the theory of spontaneous generation.
3. List one substance that was used in the Miller-Urey experiment.
4. What were the results of the Miller-Urey experiment?
5. **Think Critically** Why was Oparin's hypothesis about the origins of life important to Miller and Urey?

Skill Builder Activities

6. **Drawing Conclusions** It was thought that in the 1768 experiment some "vital force" in the broth was destroyed. Was it? Based on this experiment, what could have been concluded about where organisms come from? **For more help, refer to the** Science Skill Handbook.
7. **Using Percentages** Earth's age is estimated at 4.6 billion years old. It is estimated that life began 3.5 billion years ago. Life has been present for what percent of Earth's age? **For more help, refer to the** Math Skill Handbook.

Answers to Section Assessment

1. spontaneous generation: living things come from nonliving matter; biogenesis: living things come only from other living things of the same kind
2. Students should describe the experiments performed by Redi, Pasteur, and Spallanzani.
3. Possible answer: ammonia
4. The experiment showed that chemicals found in living things could be produced.
5. Miller and Urey used the chemicals suggested in Oparin's hypothesis.
6. By boiling the broth, the microorganisms present in it were destroyed. It could have been concluded that organisms come from the air.
7. 76%

2 Teach

Life's Origins

Earth Science INTEGRATION

Students may list five of Earth's oceans and seas.

Teacher FYI

When Oparin first presented his hypotheses on the origins of life, they received a negative response. It was only after continued re-testing that his ideas began to be accepted.

3 Assess

Reteach

Have students make a three-column chart to summarize the experiments described in this section. Columns should be headed Experimenter, Summary of Experiment, and Conclusions. L2 P

Challenge

How did Pasteur's experiments lead to the development of pasteurization? He showed that heating could kill bacteria that caused food to spoil.

✓Assessment

Performance Have students review the results of Redi's experiment and write their interpretation. The jars that were left open to the air attracted flies, and maggots appeared on the meat. Flies could not get to the meat in the jars that were covered, and no maggots appeared. Use **Performance Assessment in the Science Classroom,** p. 99.

SECTION

How are living things classified?

1 Motivate

Bellringer Transparency

Display the Section Focus Transparency for Section 4. Use the accompanying Transparency Activity Master. L2 ELL

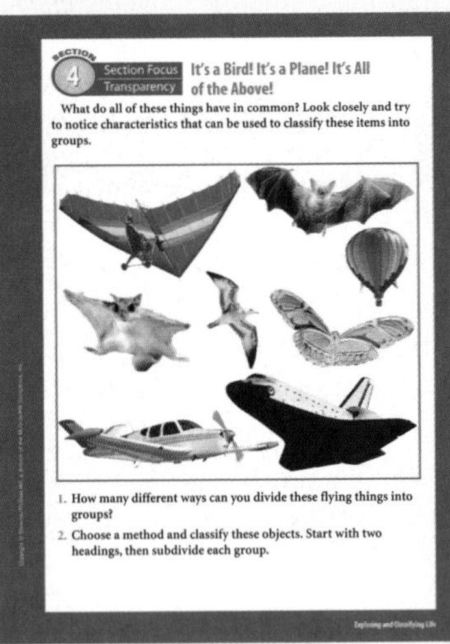

Section Focus Transparency 4 It's a Bird! It's a Plane! It's All of the Above!

What do all of these things have in common? Look closely and try to notice characteristics that can be used to classify these items into groups.

1. How many different ways can you divide these flying things into groups?
2. Choose a method and classify these objects. Start with two headings, then subdivide each group.

Exploring and Classifying Life

Tie to Prior Knowledge

Ask students to identify real-life situations in which they need to classify a group of items. Possible responses may include organizing a collection of tapes or CDs, arranging canned goods in a pantry, and sorting beads used to make jewelry. Have volunteers explain the process they use in these instances.

Caption Answer

Figure 15 Possible answer: amphibians and all invertebrates

SECTION

How are living things classified?

As You Read

***What* You'll Learn**

- **Describe** how early scientists classified living things.
- **Explain** the system of binomial nomenclature.
- **Demonstrate** how to use a dichotomous key.

Vocabulary

phylogeny
kingdom
binomial nomenclature
genus

***Why* It's Important**

Knowing how living things are classified will help you understand the relationships that exist among all living things.

Classification

If you go to a library to find a book about the life of Louis Pasteur, where do you look? Do you look for it among the mystery or sports books? You expect to find a book about Pasteur's life with other biography books. Libraries group similar types of books together. When you place similar items together, you classify them. Organisms also are classified into groups.

History of Classification When did people begin to group similar organisms together? Early classifications included grouping plants that were used in medicines. Animals were often classified by human traits such as courageous—for lions—or wise—for owls.

More than 2,000 years ago, a Greek named Aristotle observed living things. He decided that any organism could be classified as either a plant or an animal. Then he broke these two groups into smaller groups. For example, animal categories included hair or no hair, four legs or fewer legs, and blood or no blood. **Figure 15** shows some of the organisms Aristotle would have grouped together. For hundreds of years after Aristotle, no one way of classifying was accepted by everyone.

Figure 15
According to Aristotle's classification system, all animals without hair would be grouped together. *What other animals without hair would Aristotle have put in this group?*

Section Assessment Planner

PORTFOLIO
Assessment, p. 26

PERFORMANCE ASSESSMENT
Try at Home MiniLAB, p. 25
Skill Builder Activities, p. 26
See page 34 for more options.

CONTENT ASSESSMENT
Section, p. 26
Challenge, p. 26
Chapter, pp. 34–35

22 CHAPTER 1 Exploring and Classifying Life

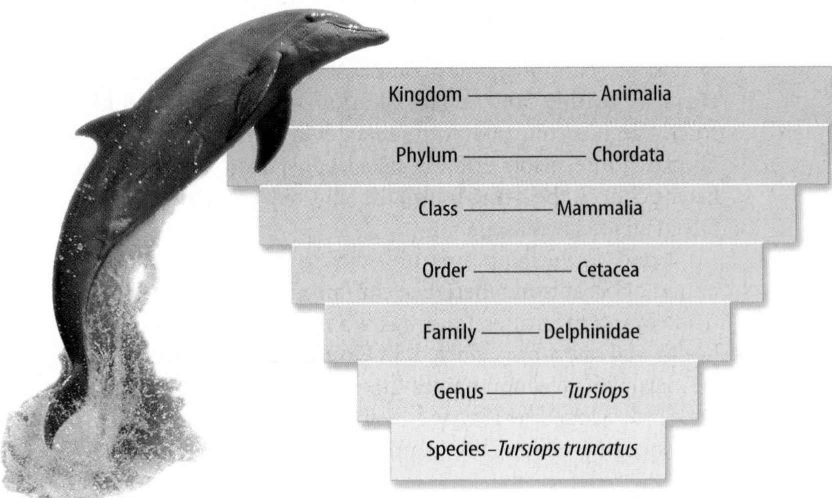

Figure 16
The classification of the bottle-nosed dolphin shows that it is in the order Cetacea. This order includes whales and porpoises.

Linnaeus In the late eighteenth century, Carolus Linnaeus, a Swedish naturalist, developed a new system of grouping organisms. His classification system was based on looking for organisms with similar structures. For example, plants that had similar flower structure were grouped together. Linnaeus's system eventually was accepted and used by most other scientists.

Modern Classification Like Linnaeus, modern scientists use similarities in structure to classify organisms. They also study fossils, hereditary information, and early stages of development. Scientists use all of this information to determine an organism's phylogeny. **Phylogeny** (fi LAH juh nee) is the evolutionary history of an organism, or how it has changed over time. Today, it is the basis for the classification of many organisms.

✔ **Reading Check** ***What information would a scientist use to determine an organism's phylogeny?***

A classification system commonly used today groups organisms into six kingdoms. A **kingdom** is the first and largest category. Refer to Student Resources, Diversity of Life at the back of your text to find characteristics that place organisms into kingdoms. Kingdoms can be divided into smaller groups. The smallest classification category is a species. Organisms that belong to the same species can mate and produce fertile offspring. To understand how an organism is classified, look at the classification of the bottle-nosed dolphin in **Figure 16.** Some scientists propose that before organisms are grouped into kingdoms, they should be placed in larger groups called domains. One proposed system groups all organisms into three domains.

SCIENCE Online

Data Update For an online update of domains, visit the Glencoe Science Web site at **science.glencoe.com** and select the appropriate chapter. Communicate to your class what you learn.

2 Teach

Classification

Quick Demo

Display a photo or an actual member of each of the six kingdoms to the class. Have students identify the kingdom each represents. L2 LS **Visual-Spatial**

Use Science Words

Word Meaning Have students compare the use of the word *kingdom* in the context of this chapter and in a Social Studies text. In science, a kingdom is the largest category of organisms. In social studies, it is a community or area governed by a king or queen. L2 LS **Linguistic**

Use an Analogy

Develop the idea that the classification system is similar to divisions that exist within your school. The entire school population is similar to all living things with each grade representing a kingdom, each classroom a phylum, and so on.

✔ **Reading Check**

Answer similar structures, fossils, hereditary information, and early stages of development

Discussion

Which classification group has the most members? Which has the fewest? Kingdom has the most; species has the fewest.

Resource Manager

Chapter Resources Booklet
Transparency Activity, p. 47
Directed Reading for Content Mastery, pp. 19, 20

SCIENCE Online
Internet Addresses

Explore the Glencoe Science Web site at **science.glencoe.com** to find out more about topics in this section.

Scientific Names

Quick Demo

Use a world map or globe to point out the Roman Empire. Tell students that Latin originated there thousands of years ago. Explain that Latin was the basis of the Romance languages—Spanish, French, Italian, and Portuguese.

Fun Fact

Scientists around the world may speak other languages but they all use Latin for scientific names.

Use an Analogy

The two-word naming system is similar to the structure of Chinese names. The first word in a Chinese name is that of the family and the second and third words are those of the individual. American and European names represent the same idea in reverse order.

Extension

Challenge students to identify an organism from its scientific name. Use *Musca domestica* (housefly), *Equus zebra* (zebra), and *Camelus dromedarius* (dromedary camel). Have students find other scientific names to present to their classmates.

Caption Answer

Figure 17B Possible answers: Sea horses are not horses that live in the sea; wolverines are not small wolves.

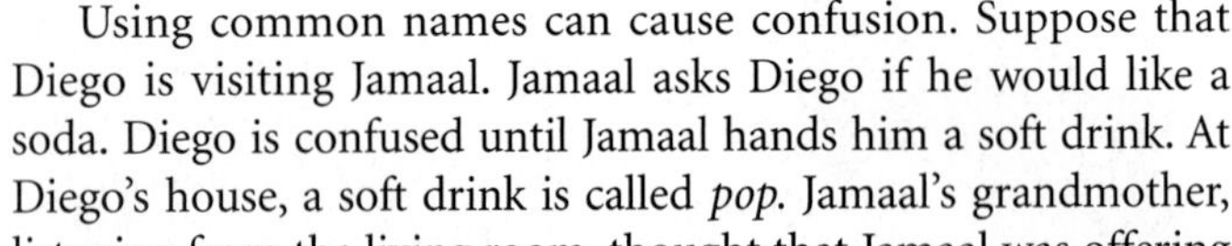

Scientific Names

Using common names can cause confusion. Suppose that Diego is visiting Jamaal. Jamaal asks Diego if he would like a soda. Diego is confused until Jamaal hands him a soft drink. At Diego's house, a soft drink is called *pop.* Jamaal's grandmother, listening from the living room, thought that Jamaal was offering Diego an ice-cream soda.

What would happen if life scientists used only common names of organisms when they communicated with other scientists? Many misunderstandings would occur, and sometimes health and safety are involved. In **Figure 17,** you see examples of animals with common names that can be misleading. A naming system developed by Linnaeus helped solve this problem. It gave each species a unique, two-word scientific name.

Figure 17
Common names can be misleading.

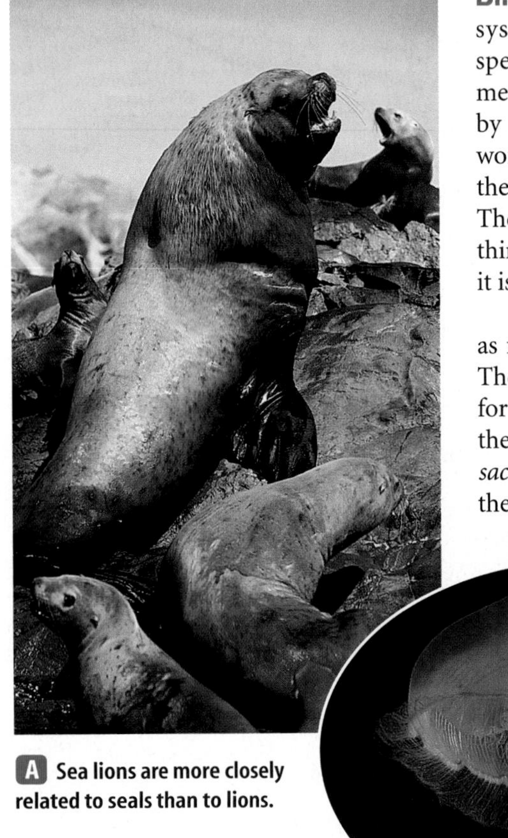

A Sea lions are more closely related to seals than to lions.

B Jellyfish are neither fish nor jelly. *Do you know a misleading common name?*

Binomial Nomenclature The two-word naming system that Linnaeus used to name the various species is called **binomial nomenclature** (bi NOH mee ul • NOH mun klay chur). It is the system used by modern scientists to name organisms. The first word of the two-word name identifies the genus of the organism. A **genus** is a group of similar species. The second word of the name might tell you something about the organism—what it looks like, where it is found, or who discovered it.

In this system, the tree species commonly known as red maple has been given the name *Acer rubrum.* The maple genus is *Acer.* The word *rubrum* is Latin for red, which is the color of a red maple's leaves in the fall. The scientific name of another maple is *Acer saccharum.* The Latin word for sugar is *saccharum.* In the spring, the sap of this tree is sweet.

Curriculum Connection

Math Ask students to explain how numbers are classified. Answers may include real and imaginary, whole numbers and fractions, decimals and percents, and rational and irrational.

Teacher FYI

Aristotle's classification system remained in use for almost two thousand years. In the 16th and 17th centuries, there was renewed interest in classification when European explorers brought back unidentified plant and animal species from other lands. In the 17th century, John Ray classified plants according to the structure of their seeds.

24 CHAPTER 1 Exploring and Classifying Life

A

B

Figure 18
These two lizards have the same common name, iguana, but are two different species.

Uses of Scientific Names Scientific names are used for four reasons. First, they help avoid mistakes. Both of the lizards shown in **Figure 18** have the name *iguana.* Using binomial nomenclature, the green iguana is named *Iguana iguana.* Someone who studied this iguana, shown in **Figure 18A,** would not be confused by information he or she read about *Dispsosaurus dorsalis,* the desert iguana, shown in **Figure 18B.** Second, organisms with similar evolutionary histories are classified together. Because of this, you know that organisms in the same genus are related. Third, scientific names give descriptive information about the species, like the maples mentioned earlier. Fourth, scientific names allow information about organisms to be organized easily and efficiently. Such information may be found in a book or a pamphlet that lists related organisms and gives their scientific names.

Reading Check *What are four functions of scientific names?*

Tools for Identifying Organisms

Tools used to identify organisms include field guides and dichotomous (di KAH tuh mus) keys. Using these tools is one way you and scientists solve problems scientifically.

Many different field guides are available. You will find some field guides at the back of this book. Most have descriptions and illustrations of organisms and information about where each organism lives. You can identify species from around the world using the appropriate field guide.

TRY AT HOME Mini LAB

Communicating Ideas

Procedure

1. Find a **magazine picture of a piece of furniture** that can be used as a place to sit and to lie down.
2. Show the picture to ten people and ask them to tell you what word they use for this piece of furniture.
3. Keep a record of the answers in your **Science Journal.**

Analysis

1. In your Science Journal, infer how using common names can be confusing.
2. How do scientific names make communication among scientists easier?

Reading Check

Answer to avoid mistakes, classify organisms with similar evolutionary histories together, give descriptive information about a species, help organize information about species

TRY AT HOME Mini LAB

Purpose Students ask people to give them the name of a common piece of furniture seen in a photo. L2

LS **Visual-Spatial**

Materials photo from magazine

Teaching Strategy Review how to collect and record data.

Analysis

1. More than one name might be used for the same object.
2. Each organism has a specific, unique name.

Assessment

Oral To further assess students' abilities to identify characteristic features, ask them to list traits of other common objects. Use **Performance Assessment in the Science Classroom,** p. 89.

Tools for Identifying Organisms

Make a Model

Have students list the characteristics of several related objects such as shoes, animals, or foods. Then have students use their lists to make a model dichotomous key.

Visual Learning

Figure 18 What traits do the desert iguana and green iguana share? clawed toes, scaly skin

Resource Manager 

Chapter Resources Booklet

Enrichment, p. 32
Reinforcement, p. 28
MiniLAB, p. 4
Transparency Activity, pp. 49–50

Tools for Identifying Organisms, continued

Activity

Pass out taxonomic keys or field guides. Ask students to describe how these tools are used. Have them use the keys to identify a particular organism. Note that students may try to skip steps in keys. Point out that skipping steps often leads to the wrong identification. L2

Text Question Answer

Microtus pinetorum

3 Assess

Reteach

Develop understanding of modern classification by asking students to name the lowest taxonomic category for the organisms described. Ask: **Which level contains a spider plant?** species **Which level contains all willow trees?** genus **Which level contains all plants?** kingdom

Challenge

Why do organisms in the same classification group have characteristics that are similar? Many probably evolved from a common ancestor.

Assessment

Performance Have students make a concept map to show how an address is like a classification system. The first step should be Country—United States. Use **Performance Assessment in the Science Classroom,** p. 161. P

Dichotomous Keys A dichotomous key is a detailed list of identifying characteristics that includes scientific names. Dichotomous keys are arranged in steps with two descriptive statements at each step. If you learn how to use a dichotomous key, you can identify and name a species.

Did you know many types of mice exist? You can use **Table 2** to find out what type of mouse is pictured to the left. Start by choosing between the first pair of descriptions. The mouse has hair on its tail, so you go to 2. The ears of the mouse are small, so you go on to 3. The tail of the mouse is less that 25 mm. What is the name of this mouse according to the key?

Table 2 Key to Some Mice of North America

1. Tail hair	**a.** no hair on tail; scales show plainly; house mouse, *Mus musculus* **b.** hair on tail, go to 2
2. Ear size	**a.** ears small and nearly hidden in fur, go to 3 **b.** ears large and not hidden in fur, go to 4
3. Tail length	**a.** less than 25 mm; woodland vole, *Microtus pinetorum* **b.** more than 25 mm; prairie vole, *Microtus ochrogaster*
4. Tail coloration	**a.** sharply bicolor, white beneath and dark above; deer mouse, *Peromyscus maniculatus* **b.** darker above than below but not sharply bicolor; white-footed mouse, *Peromyscus leucopus*

Section  Assessment

1. What is the purpose of classification?
2. What were the contributions of Aristotle and Carolus Linnaeus to classification of living things?
3. How can you identify a species using a dichotomous key?
4. Why can common names cause confusion?
5. **Think Critically** Would you expect a field guide to have common names as well as scientific names? Why or why not?

Skill Builder Activities

6. **Classifying** Create a dichotomous key that identifies types of cars. **For more help, refer to the** Science Skill Handbook.
7. **Communicating** Select a field guide for trees, insects, or mammals. Select two organisms in the field guide that closely resemble each other. Use labeled diagrams to show how they are different. **For more help, refer to the** Science Skill Handbook.

Answers to Section Assessment

1. to arrange or group things according to similarities and differences
2. Aristotle—two kingdoms: plants and animals; Linnaeus—binomial nomenclature
3. A dichotomous key contains a detailed list of identifying characteristics for species.
4. Two different organisms may have the same common name.
5. A field guide does not give as much scientific information as a key. It has pictures and descriptions that help you identify what you see, and often includes common as well as scientific names.
6. Keys will vary, but should be structured like the key shown in **Table 2.**
7. Students should be able to identify two organisms and state how they differ.

Activity

Classifying Seeds

Scientists use classification systems to show how organisms are related. How do they determine which features to use to classify organisms? In this activity, you will observe seeds and use their features to classify them.

What You'll Investigate

How can the features of seeds be used to develop a key to identify the seed?

Materials

packets of seeds (10 different kinds)
hand lens
metric ruler

Goals

- **Observe** the seeds and notice their features.
- **Classify** seeds using these features.

Safety Precautions

WARNING: Some seeds may have been treated with chemicals. Do not put them in your mouth. Wash your hands after you handle the seeds.

Procedure

1. Copy the following data table in your Science Journal and record the features of each seed. Your table will have a column for each different type of seed you observe.

Seed Data

Feature	Type of Seed		
	corn	kidney bean	wheat
Color	yellow	dark brown	light brown
Length (mm)	10	17	5
Shape	triangle	oval	oval
Texture	smooth	smooth	smooth

2. Use the features to develop a key.
3. Exchange keys with another group. Can you use their key to identify seeds?

Conclude and Apply

1. How can different seeds be classified?
2. Which feature could you use to divide the seeds into two groups?
3. **Explain** how you would classify a seed you had not seen before using your data table.
4. Why is it an advantage for scientists to use a standardized system to classify organisms? What observations did you make to support your answer?

Communicating Your Data

Compare your conclusions with those of other students in your class. **For more help, refer to the Science Skill Handbook.**

Communicating Your Data

Comparisons may or may not result in agreement. If one group can use another group's key, the second group was successful.

Resource Manager

Chapter Resources Booklet
Activity Worksheets, pp. 5–6, 7–8
Lab Activity, pp. 11–13
Lab Management and Safety, p. 65

Activity

BENCH TESTED

Purpose Students observe seed features and then classify the seeds. L2 LS **Kinesthetic**

Process Skills observing and inferring, classifying, forming operational definitions, communicating, making and using tables, comparing and contrasting

Time Required 45 minutes

Alternate Materials Any objects may be used, but biological specimens should be used if possible.

Safety Precautions Use only edible seeds, not seeds that have been treated for planting.

Teaching Strategy Prepare packets of ten different kinds of easily classified seeds, such as black-eyed peas, squash, beans (lima, kidney, pinto, black), green peas, popcorn, seed corn, and sunflower.

Answers to Questions

1. color, shape, size, texture, how they are attached to the plant
2. Answers will vary; color, shape, size, and texture are possibilities.
3. You would use the data table to categorize identifying characteristics of seeds.
4. Different classification systems could result in confusion. Answers should be based on the observation that students classified the same seeds in different ways.

Assessment

Performance Give students photocopies of ten different leaves. Have them devise and describe a classification system for the leaves. Use **PASC,** p. 121.

Activity

BENCH TESTED

Recognize the Problem

Purpose

Design and carry out an experiment using scientific methods to infer why brine shrimp live in the ocean. L1 COOP LEARN

IS Interpersonal

Process Skills

observing and inferring, comparing and contrasting, recognizing cause and effect, interpreting data, hypothesizing, communicating, making and using tables, making and using graphs, designing an experiment, separating and controlling variables, measuring in SI

Time Required

50 minutes on Day 1, 5 minutes a day for 3 days, 30 minutes to summarize

Materials

Purchase brine shrimp eggs from a pet store or a biological supply house. Do not place too many brine shrimp eggs in each container. Brine shrimp are orange-colored and swim with a jerking motion. To maintain the brine shrimp, add a pinch of yeast to the container two or three times a week.

Safety Precautions

Students should use care when working with live animals.

Form a Hypothesis

Possible Hypothesis

Brine shrimp will best grow in a strong salt solution.

Activity **Design Your Own Experiment**

Using Scientific Methods

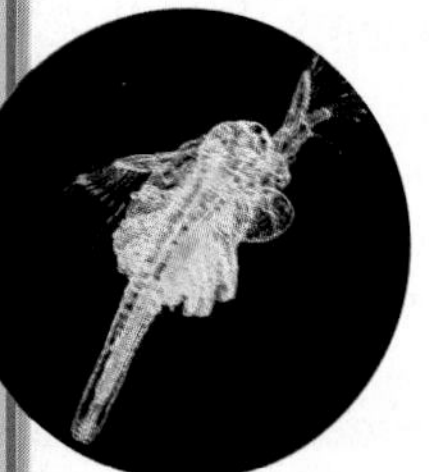

Brine shrimp

Brine shrimp are relatives of lobsters, crabs, crayfish, and the shrimp eaten by humans. They are often raised as a live food source in aquariums. In nature, they live in the oceans where fish feed on them. They can hatch from eggs that have been stored in a dry condition for many years. In this investigation, you will use scientific methods to find what factors affect their hatching and growth.

Recognize the Problem

How can you use scientific methods to determine whether salt affects the hatching and growth of brine shrimp?

Form a Hypothesis

Based on your observations, state a hypothesis about how salt affects the hatching and growth of brine shrimp.

Goals

- **Design** and carry out an experiment using scientific methods to infer why brine shrimp live in the ocean.
- **Observe** the jars for one week and notice whether the brine shrimp eggs hatch.

Possible Materials

500-mL, widemouthed containers (3)
brine shrimp eggs
small, plastic spoon
distilled water (500 mL)
weak salt solution (500 mL)
strong salt solution (500 mL)
labels (3)
hand lens

Safety Precautions

Protect eyes and clothing. Be careful when working with live organisms.

Test Your Hypothesis

Possible Procedures

The same amount of brine shrimp eggs can be added to the three solutions and observed.

Inclusion Strategies

Visually Impaired Have sighted students make paper or clay models of brine shrimp that visually impaired students can touch. Estimate the number of times the model has been enlarged so visually impaired students can have some idea of the size of brine shrimp.

Test Your Hypothesis

Plan

1. As a group, agree upon the hypothesis and decide how you will test it. Identify what results will confirm the hypothesis.
2. **List** the steps that you need to test your hypothesis. Be specific. Describe exactly what you will do in each step.
3. **List** your materials.
4. **Prepare** a data table in your Science Journal to record your data.
5. Read over your entire experiment to make sure that all planned steps are in logical order.
6. **Identify** any constants, variables, and controls of the experiment.

Do

1. Make sure your teacher approves your plan before you start.
2. Carry out the experiment as planned by your group.
3. While doing the experiment, record any observations and complete the data table in your Science Journal.
4. Use a bar graph to plot your results.

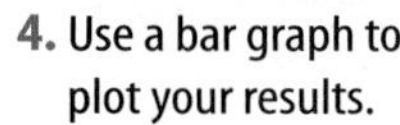

Analyze Your Data

1. **Describe** the contents of each jar after one week. Do they differ from one another? How?
2. What was your control in this experiment?
3. What were your variables?

Draw Conclusions

1. Did the results support your hypothesis? Explain.
2. **Predict** the effect that increasing the amount of salt in the water would have on the brine shrimp eggs.
3. **Compare** your results with those of other groups.

Communicating Your Data

Prepare a set of instructions on how to hatch brine shrimp to use to feed fish. Include diagrams and a step-by-step procedure.

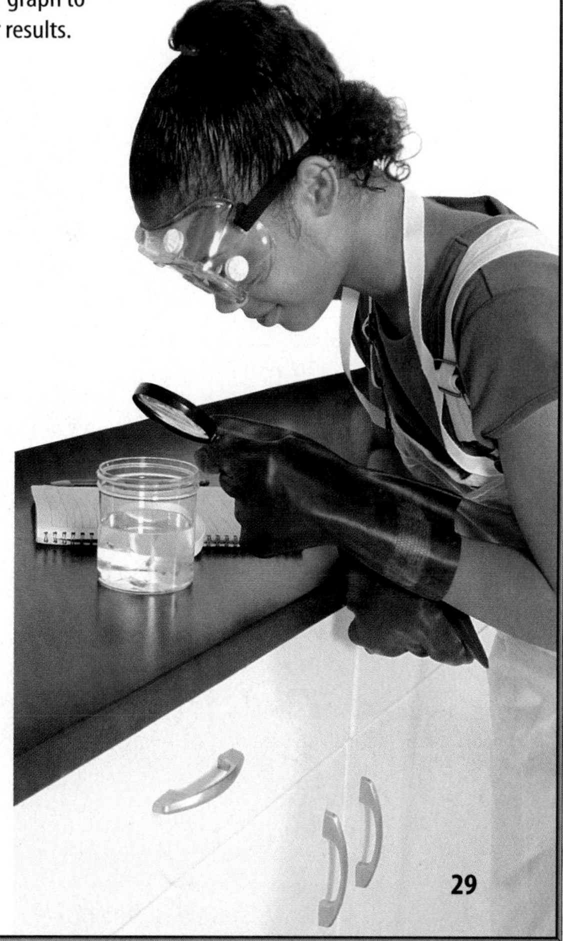

Teaching Strategies

Prepare the solutions as follows:

- Dechlorinated water: Allow tap water to stand for 48 hours.
- Weak salt solution: Add 20 mL noniodized salt to 4 L dechlorinated water. Stir until dissolved.
- Strong salt solution: Add 75 mL noniodized salt to 4 L dechlorinated water. Stir until dissolved.

Expected Outcome

Most results will reflect that the brine shrimp grew best in the strong salt solution.

Analyze Your Data

1. There were no shrimp in the distilled water or weak salt solution. There were many shrimp in the strong salt solution.
2. The dechlorinated water without salt was the control.
3. The amount of salt in the water was the variable.

Error Analysis

Have students compare their results and their hypotheses and explain any differences.

Draw Conclusions

1. Answers will be determined by students' hypotheses.
2. Answers will vary. Some may predict that more brine shrimp will hatch.
3. Results will vary.

Communicating Your Data

Instructions should include information on the amount of salt to add to the water, light conditions, and so on. Students can use word-processing software programs to write their instructions.

Assessment

Performance Have students design an experiment to determine how ocean currents affect brine shrimp. Use **Performance Assessment in the Science Classroom,** p. 95.

Content Background

The rain forests of the world are home to fifty percent of all species of plants and animals. Some insect species evolve and become extinct without ever having been seen alive by humans. This is partly a function of the fact that most rain forest species live in the forest canopy between about 18 to 46 meters (60–150 ft) above the ground. Observing wildlife in this environment is extremely difficult, particularly over long periods of time. The need for extensive study of the rain forest canopy becomes more pressing as logging and slash and burn agriculture destroys more of the forest habitat.

One method being attempted to halt the incursion of uncontrolled agriculture is the development of ecotourism. Governments, corporations and environmental groups have fostered programs intended to preserve wild areas by attracting tourists. The idea is to build an economy based on service industries, thereby relieving some of the pressure to clear more land for farming. One version of ecotourism is the canopy tour effected by means ranging from climbing harnesses to walkways and aerial tramways. One of the benefits of these operations is the establishment of permanent platforms from which canopy research can be conducted.

TIME SCIENCE AND Society

SCIENCE ISSUES THAT AFFECT YOU!

Mon

A marmoset stands in a tree. It is about the size of a squirrel.

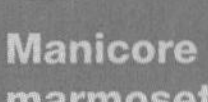

Manicore marmoset

Deep in the heart of the rain forest lives a small, furry animal. It swings from the trees, searches for food, and sleeps nestled high in the treetop canopy. What makes this animal unique is that it never had been seen by a human being. In fact, there is a whole world of creatures as yet undiscovered by humans. Many of them reside in the Amazon rain forest.

In 2000, a scientist from Brazil's Amazon National Research Institute came across two squirrel-sized monkeys in a remote and isolated corner of the rain forest, about 2,575 km from Rio de Janeiro. It turns out that the monkeys had never been seen before, or even known to exist.

The new species were spotted by a scientist who named them after two nearby rivers the Manicore and the Acari, where the animals were discovered. Both animals are marmosets, which is a type of monkey found only in Central and South America. Marmosets have claws instead of nails, live in trees, and use their extraordinarily long tail like an extra arm or leg. Small and light, both marmosets measure about 23 cm in length with a 38 cm tail, and weigh no more than 0.4 kg.

The Manicore marmoset has a silvery-white upper body, a light-gray cap on its head, a yellow-orange underbody, and a black tail.

30

Resources for Teachers and Students

Tropical Rain Forest, by Arnold Newman, New York: Facts On File, Inc., 1990.

Rain Forests of the World: Water, Fire, Earth, Air, by Art Wolfe and Sir Ghillean Prance, New York: Crown Publishers, 1998.

"New study pinpoints rain-forest destruction" by Jeff Donn, The Associated Press, *Seattle Times*, Thursday, April 8, 1999.

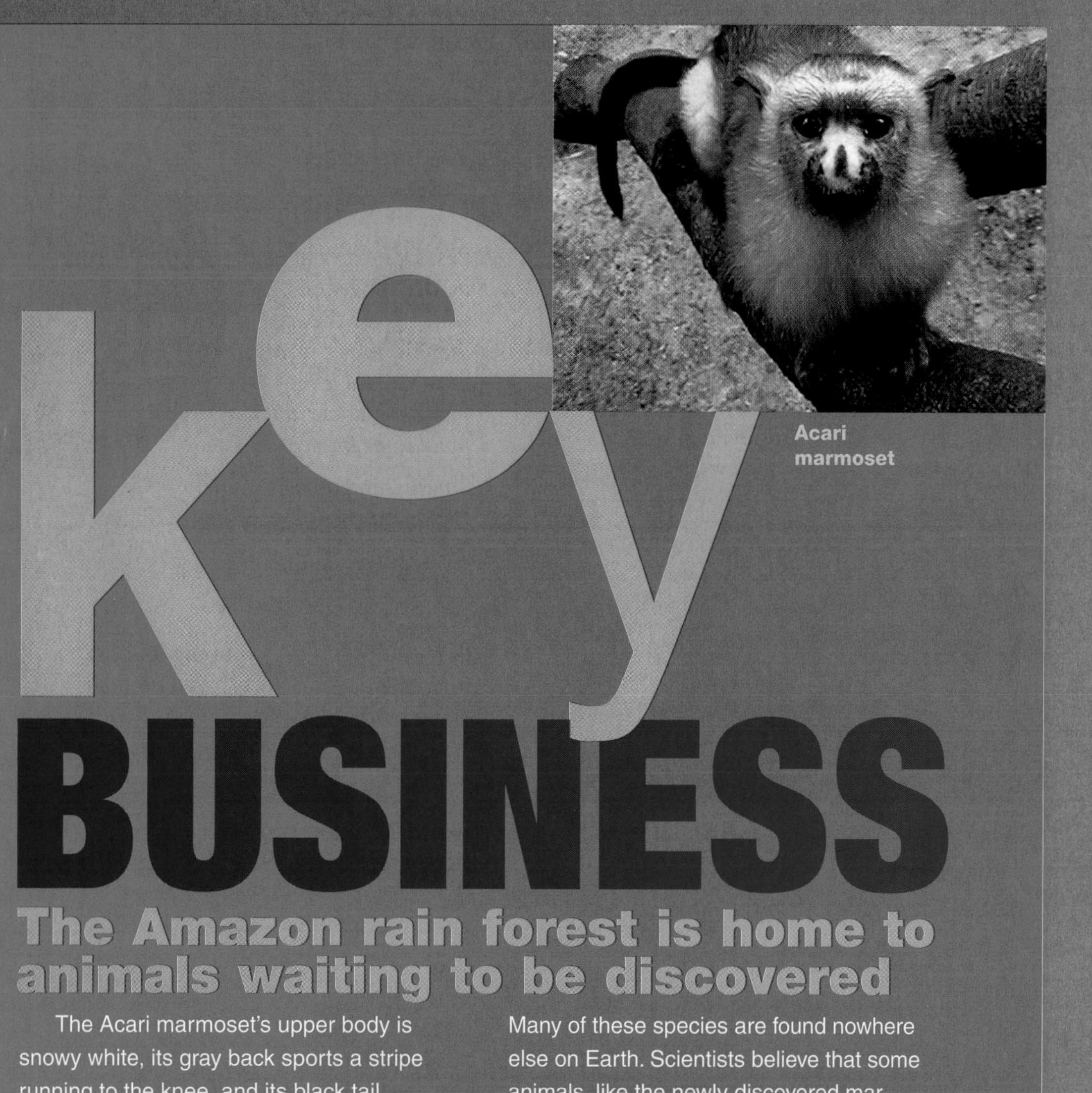

Acari marmoset

key BUSINESS

The Amazon rain forest is home to animals waiting to be discovered

The Acari marmoset's upper body is snowy white, its gray back sports a stripe running to the knee, and its black tail flashes a bright-orange tip.

Amazin' Amazon

The Amazon Basin is a treasure trove of unique species. The Amazon River is Earth's largest body of freshwater, with 1,100 smaller tributaries. And more than half of the world's plant and animal species live in its rain forest ecosystems. Many of these species are found nowhere else on Earth. Scientists believe that some animals, like the newly discovered marmosets, evolved differently from other marmosets because the rivers create natural barriers that separated the animals.

The discovery reminds people of how much we have to learn about Earth's diversity of life. Even among humans' closest relatives, the primates, there are still new species to be discovered.

CONNECTIONS Research and Report **Working in small groups, find out more about the Amazon rain forest. Which plants and animals live there? What products come from the rain forest? How does what happens in the Amazon rain forest affect you? Prepare a multimedia presentation.**

SCIENCE Online

For more information, visit science.glencoe.com

Discussion

What features of the rain forest make it possible for a large number species to remain unknown? Possible answer: The difficulty of travel and the remoteness of some areas make observation points difficult to get to. The fact that most of the species live in the canopy further complicates making accurate and wide-ranging surveys.

Activity

The Amazon is the largest river system by volume in the world, and the rain forest surrounding it regulates the flow of water into that system. Organize the class into groups and have each group construct a miniature river system, using flat disposable aluminum roasting pans, sand, and pieces of sod. Pour equal amounts of water on each group's "system" and have the group record results. Then have students remove portions of the sod and repeat the experiment. Use the results to discuss the effects of deforestation. COOP LEARN LS **Kinesthetic**

Investigate the Issue

Direct students to research the estimated number of plant and animal species worldwide and chart their distribution on a world map using colored pins. **How many species are in the rain forests? How will deforestation affect these species?**

CONNECTIONS As an extension, have students discuss the pros and cons of ecotourism in light of their research of current rain forest uses and conditions.

SCIENCE Online

Internet Addresses

Explore the Glencoe Science Web site at **science.glencoe.com** to find out more about topics in this feature.

Chapter 1 Study Guide

Reviewing Main Ideas

Preview

Students can answer the questions in their Science Journals. Discuss the answers as you go through the chapter. **LS Linguistic**

Review

Students can write their answers, then compare them with those of other students. **LS Interpersonal**

Reteach

Students can look at the illustrations and describe details that support the main ideas of the chapter. **LS Visual-Spatial**

Answers to Chapter Review

SECTION 1

1. Accept all reasonable answers.

SECTION 2

2. water

SECTION 3

2. from mosquitos

SECTION 4

3. It assigns a unique two-word name for every species of organism.

Chapter  Study Guide

Reviewing Main Ideas

Section 1 What is science?

1. Scientists investigate observations about living and nonliving things with the help of problem-solving techniques. *What problem-solving methods would this scientist use to find out how dolphins learn?*

2. Scientists use SI measurements to gather measurable data.
3. Safe laboratory practices help you learn more about science.

Section 2 Living Things

1. Organisms are made of cells, use energy, reproduce, respond, grow, and develop.
2. Organisms need energy, water, food, and a place to live. *What raw material is limited for organisms living in a desert?*

Section 3 Where does life come from?

1. Controlled experiments over many years finally disproved the theory of spontaneous generation.
2. Pasteur's experiment proved biogenesis, which is the theory that life comes from life. *Where did the mosquito larvae in this pond come from?*
3. Oparin's hypothesis is one explanation of how life began on Earth.

Section 4 How are living things classified?

1. Classification is the grouping of ideas, information, or objects based on their similar characteristics.
2. Scientists today use phylogeny to group organisms into six kingdoms.
3. All organisms are given a two word scientific name using binomial nomenclature. *How would binomial nomenclature keep scientists from confusing these two beetles?*

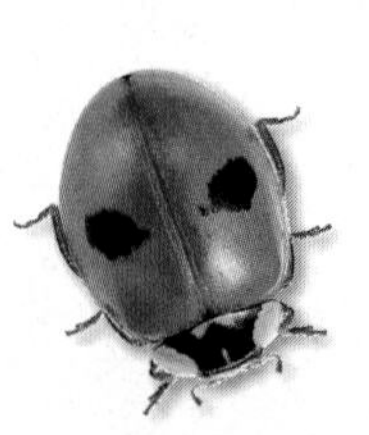

4. Dichotomous keys are used to identify specific organisms.

FOLDABLES Reading & Study Skills — After You Read

Trade vocabulary study Foldables with a classmate and quiz each other to see how many words you can define without looking under the tabs.

FOLDABLES Reading & Study Skills — After You Read

After students have read the chapter and completed the Foldable described in Before You Read, have them do the activity on the student page.

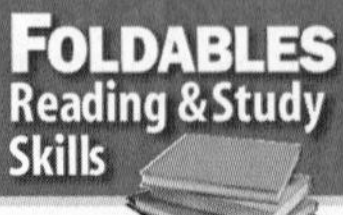

Chapter 1 Study Guide

Visualizing Main Ideas

Use the following terms to complete an events chain concept map showing the order in which you might use a scientific method: analyze data, perform an experiment, *and* form a hypothesis.

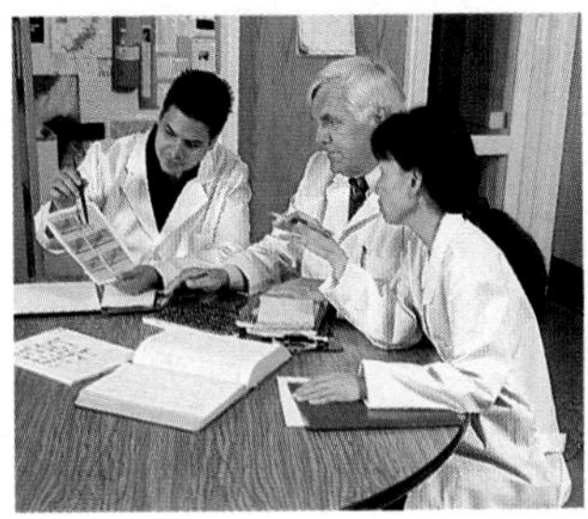

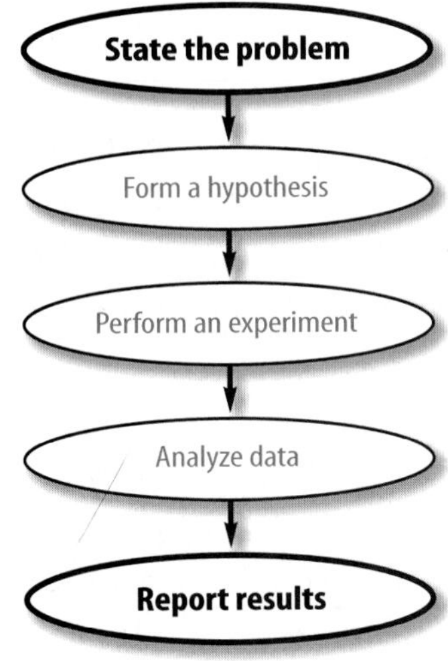

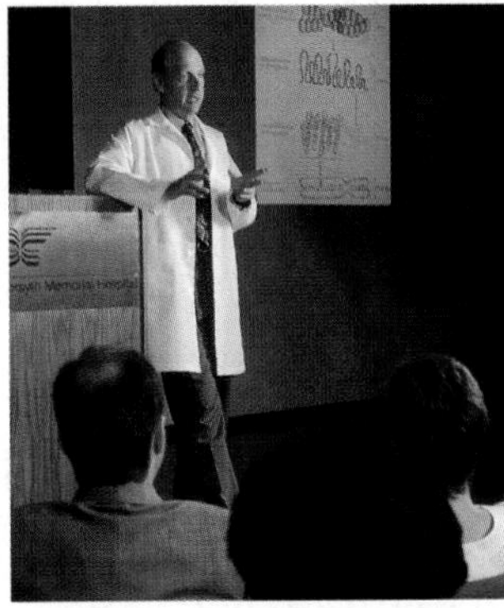

Vocabulary Review

Vocabulary Words

a. binomial nomenclature
b. biogenesis
c. cell
d. control
e. genus
f. homeostasis
g. hypothesis
h. kingdom
i. law
j. organism
k. phylogeny
l. scientific methods
m. spontaneous generation
n. theory
o. variable

THE PRINCETON REVIEW Study Tip

If you're not sure how terms in a question are related, try making a concept map of the terms. Ask your teacher to check your map.

Using Vocabulary

Explain the differences in the vocabulary words in each pair below. Then explain how they are related.

1. control, variable
2. law, theory
3. biogenesis, spontaneous generation
4. binomial nomenclature, phylogeny
5. organism, cell
6. kingdom, phylogeny
7. hypothesis, scientific methods
8. organism, homeostasis
9. kingdom, genus
10. theory, hypothesis

Chapter 1 Study Guide

Visualizing Main Ideas

See student page.

Vocabulary Review

Using Vocabulary

1. variable—condition tested; control—standard used to compare with outcome of the test
2. Theory—explanation of things or events based on many observations; law—a statement about how things work in nature.
3. The theory of spontaneous generation (living things come from nonliving things) was replaced with the theory of biogenesis (living things come only from other living things).
4. Phylogeny is the evolutionary history of an organism; binomial nomenclature—a naming system based on phylogeny.
5. A cell is the smallest unit of an organism that carries out the functions of life. All organisms are made of cells.
6. Phylogeny is the basis for placing organisms into kingdoms.
7. Forming a hypothesis is an important part of solving a problem with scientific methods.
8. Homeostasis—keeping proper internal conditions no matter what external conditions are—is a trait of all organisms.
9. A genus is a subgroup of a kingdom.
10. If the results of repeated experiments always support the same hypothesis, the hypothesis may be called a theory.

IDENTIFYING Misconceptions

Assess

Use the assessment as follow-up to page 4F after students have completed the chapter.

Assessment Show students several pictures of living and nonliving things, and have them record whether they think each item is living or nonliving and their reason.

When responses are recorded, list their ideas on the board and generate a list of characteristics that students think describe living things. Compare this list to the characteristics of life listed in **Section 2** and ask the class if they would like to make any changes in their list.

Expected Outcome Some students may persist in listing only animal-like characteristics, but most students should be forming a more sophisticated definition that includes the characteristics given in the text. They should begin to recognize that their favorite "characteristic," movement, is simply one way that some living organisms respond to the environment.

CHAPTER STUDY GUIDE 33

Chapter 1 Assessment

Checking Concepts

1. D
2. D
3. A
4. D
5. C
6. D
7. A
8. B
9. D
10. B

Thinking Critically

11. Scientists can compare and repeat experiments; they have a common tool for measurement.
12. A bird is made up of cells, uses energy to fly and breathe, moves, responds to the environment, maintains a constant body temperature, reproduces young that grow and develop, and has a life span.
13. Binomial nomenclature is a two-word naming system. It is important because scientists assign a unique name to an organism that may have many common names. This allows accurate communication between scientists and others.
14. Redi's experiment used a variable and a control.
15. The name *odoratus* tells you that the sweet pea probably has an odor.

Chapter 1 Assessment

Checking Concepts

Choose the word or phrase that best answers the question.

1. What category of organisms can mate and produce fertile offspring?
   A) family **C)** genus
   B) class **D)** species
2. What is the closest relative of *Canis lupus?*
   A) *Quercus alba* **C)** *Felis tigris*
   B) *Equus zebra* **D)** *Canis familiaris*
3. What is the source of energy for plants?
   A) the Sun **C)** water
   B) carbon dioxide **D)** oxygen
4. What makes up more than 50 percent of all living things?
   A) oxygen **C)** minerals
   B) carbon dioxide **D)** water
5. Who finally disproved the theory of spontaneous generation?
   A) Oparin **C)** Pasteur
   B) Aristotle **D)** Miller
6. What gas do some scientists think was missing from Earth's early atmosphere?
   A) ammonia **C)** methane
   B) hydrogen **D)** oxygen
7. What is the length of time an organism is expected to live?
   A) life span **C)** homeostasis
   B) stimulus **D)** theory
8. What is the part of an experiment that can be changed called?
   A) conclusion **C)** control
   B) variable **D)** data
9. What does the first word in a two-word name of an organism identify?
   A) kingdom **C)** phylum
   B) species **D)** genus
10. What SI unit is used to measure the volume of liquids?
    A) meter **C)** gram
    B) liter **D)** degree

Thinking Critically

11. How does SI help scientists in different parts of the world?
12. Using a bird as an example, explain how it has all the traits of living things.
13. Explain what binomial nomenclature is and why it is important.
14. Explain how the experiment of 1668 correctly used scientific methods to test the theory of spontaneous generation.
15. What does *Lathyrus odoratus,* the name for a sweet pea, tell you about one of its characteristics?

Developing Skills

16. **Identifying and Manipulating Variables and Controls** Design an experiment to test the effects of fertilizer on growing plants. Identify scientific methods used in your experiment.
17. **Forming Hypotheses** A lima bean plant is placed under a green light, another is placed under a red light, and a third under a blue light. Their growth is measured for four weeks to determine which light is best for plant growth. What are the variables in this experiment? State a hypothesis for this experiment.
18. **Comparing and Contrasting** What characteristics do an icicle and a plant share? How can you tell that the plant is a living thing and the icicle is not?

Chapter Assessment Planner

Portfolio Encourage students to place in their portfolios one or two items of what they consider to be their best work. Examples include:

- Science Journal, p. 7
- Curriculum Connection, p. 16
- Reteach, p. 21
- Assessment, p. 26

Performance Additional performance assessments, Performance Task Assessment Lists, and rubrics for evaluating these activities can be found in Glencoe's **Performance Assessment in the Science Classroom.**

19. **Interpreting Data** Read the following hypothesis: Babies with a birth weight of 2.5 kg have the best chance of survival. Do the data in the following graph support this hypothesis? Explain.

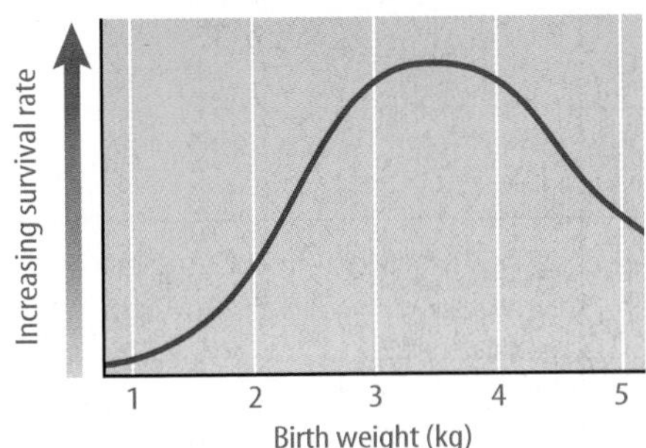

20. **Classifying** Which of these metric units—meter, kilometer, kilogram, or liter—is the best one to use when measuring each of the following?
   A) your height
   B) distance between two cities
   C) how much juice is in a pitcher
   D) your mass

Performance Assessment

21. **Bulletin Board** Interview people in your community whose jobs require a knowledge of life science. Make a Life Science Careers bulletin board. Summarize each person's job and what he or she had to study to prepare for that job.

TECHNOLOGY

Go to the Glencoe Science Web site at **science.glencoe.com** or use the **Glencoe Science CD-ROM** for additional chapter assessment.

THE PRINCETON REVIEW **Test Practice**

A science class was learning about how living things respond to stimuli. Their experiment about the response of plants to light is shown below.

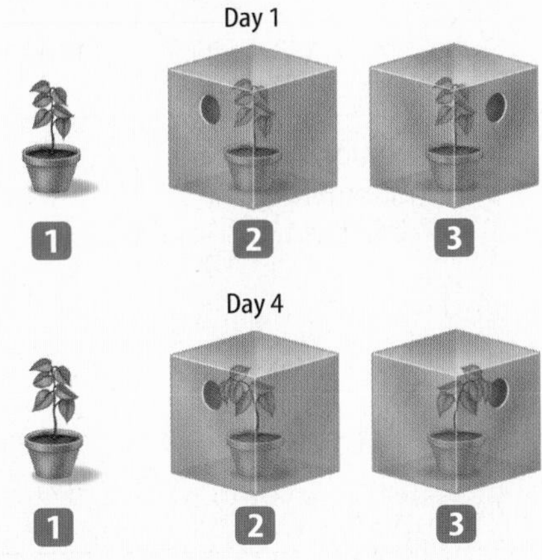

Study the experiment and answer the following questions.

1. Which hypothesis is probably being tested by this experiment?
   A) Plants grow better in full light.
   B) Plants prefer to grow in a box with one hole.
   C) Plants can grow in any direction.
   D) Plants grow toward the light.

2. After day 4, Fatima wanted to find out how plant 2 and plant 3 would grow in normal light. To do this, she would have to _____.
   F) use all new plants and boxes without holes
   G) add water to all of the pots
   H) remove the boxes over plant 2 and plant 3
   J) put holes on all sides of the boxes

Assessment Resources

Reproducible Masters

Chapter Resources Booklet
Chapter Review, pp. 37–38
Chapter Tests, pp. 39–42
Assessment Transparency Activity, p. 51

Glencoe Science Web site
Interactive Tutor
Chapter Quizzes

Glencoe Technology
Assessment Transparency
Interactive CD-ROM Chapter Quizzes
ExamView Pro Test Bank
Vocabulary PuzzleMaker Software
MindJogger Videoquiz

Chapter 1 Assessment

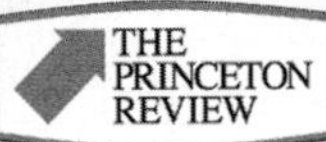

THE PRINCETON REVIEW **Test Practice**

The Test-Taking Tip was written by The Princeton Review, the nation's leader in test preparation.

1. D
2. H

Developing Skills

16. An experiment should contain a hypothesis, observations, a variable, a control, and an interpretation of results.
17. variables: the different colors of light; hypothesis might be that the green light will cause the most favorable plant growth.
18. Both respond to their surroundings and grow in size. Unlike a plant, an icicle is not made of cells and cannot take in and use energy or reproduce.
19. No; babies with a birth weight of approximately 3.5 kg have the best chance of survival.
20. a. meter b. kilometer c. liter d. kilogram

Performance Assessment

21. Careers could include farmers, produce clerks, florists, veterinary technicians, health care workers, and teachers. Use **PASC,** p. 131.

Section/Objectives	Standards		Activities/Features
	National	State/Local	
Chapter Opener	See p. 5T for a Key to Standards.		**Explore Activity:** Measure a small object, p. 37 **Before You Read,** p. 37
Section 1 Cell Structure 2 sessions 1 block 1. **Identify** names and functions of each part of a cell. 2. **Explain** how important a nucleus is in a cell. 3. **Compare** tissues, organs, and organ systems.	National Content Standards: UCP1, UCP5, A1, C1		**MiniLAB:** Modeling Cytoplasm, p. 40 **Environmental Science Integration,** p. 44 **Math Skills Activity:** Calculate the Ratio of Surface Area to Volume of Cells, p. 44 **Activity:** Comparing Cells, p. 46
Section 2 Viewing Cells 2 sessions 1 block 1. **Compare** the differences between the compound light microscope and the electron microscope. 2. **Summarize** the discoveries that led to the development of the cell theory. 3. **Relate** the cell theory to modern biology.	National Content Standards: UCP1, A1, C1		**Visualizing Microscopes,** pp. 48–49 **MiniLAB:** Observing Magnified Objects, p. 50 **Physics Integration,** p. 50
Section 3 Viruses 3 sessions 1.5 blocks 1. **Explain** how a virus makes copies of itself. 2. **Identify** the benefits of vaccines. 3. **Investigate** some uses of viruses.	National Content Standards: UCP5, A1, C1, C2, E2, F1, G3		**Science Online,** p. 53 **Science Online,** p. 54 **Activity:** Comparing Light Microscopes, pp. 56–57 **Science and History:** Cobb Against Cancer, pp. 58–59

NATIONAL GEOGRAPHIC Teacher's Corner

PRODUCTS AVAILABLE FROM GLENCOE
To order call 1-800-334-7344:
CD-ROM
NGS PictureShow: The Cell

Curriculm Kit
GeoKit: Cells and Microorganisms
Transparency Set
NGS PicturePack: The Cell

PRODUCTS AVAILABLE FROM NATIONAL GEOGRAPHIC SOCIETY
To order call 1-800-368-2728:
Videos
Discovering the Cell
Virus!

Activity Materials	Reproducible Resources	Section Assessment	Technology
Explore Activity: hand lens, metric ruler	**Chapter Resources Booklet** Foldables Worksheet, p. 17 Directed Reading Overview, p. 19 Note-taking Worksheets, pp. 33–35	Glencoe's Assessment Advantage	
MiniLAB: water, clear container, unflavored gelatin, flashlight, stirring rod **Activity:** microscope, microscope slide, coverslip, forceps, tap water, dropper, *Elodea* plant, prepared slide of human cheek cells	**Chapter Resources Booklet** Transparency Activity, p. 44 MiniLAB, p. 3 Enrichment, p. 30 Reinforcement, p. 27 Directed Reading, p. 20 Transparency Activity, pp. 47–48 Activity Worksheet, pp. 5–6 **Mathematics Skill Activities,** p. 5	Portfolio Visual Learning, p. 41 Performance MiniLAB, p. 40 Skill Builder Activities, p. 45 Content Section Assessment, p. 45	Section Focus Transparency Teaching Transparency Interactive CD-ROM Guided Reading Audio Program
MiniLAB: newspaper, clear empty glass, clear empty glass bowl, water, hand lens *Need materials?* Contact Science Kit at 1-800-828-7777 or www.sciencekit.com on the Internet.	**Chapter Resources Booklet** Transparency Activity, p. 45 MiniLAB, p. 4 Enrichment, p. 31 Reinforcement, p. 28 Directed Reading, p. 20 Lab Activity, pp. 9–12, 13–16 **Science Inquiry Labs,** p. 3	Portfolio Assessment, p. 51 Performance MiniLAB, p. 50 Skill Builder Activities, p. 51 Content Section Assessment, p. 51	Section Focus Transparency Interactive CD-ROM Guided Reading Audio Program
Activity: compound light microscope, stereomicroscope, 8 classroom items to view, microscope slides and coverslips, plastic petri dishes, distilled water, dropper	**Chapter Resources Booklet** Transparency Activity, p. 46 Enrichment, p. 32 Reinforcement, p. 29 Directed Reading, pp. 21, 22 Activity Worksheet, pp. 7–8 **Lab Management and Safety,** p. 58 **Reading and Writing Skill Activities,** p. 31	Portfolio Extension, p. 54 Performance Skill Builder Activities, p. 55 Content Section Assessment, p. 55	Section Focus Transparency Interactive CD-ROM Guided Reading Audio Program

End of Chapter Assessment

Glencoe's Assessment Advantage

Blackline Masters	Technology	Professional Series
Chapter Resources Booklet Chapter Review, pp. 37–38 Chapter Tests, pp. 39–42 **Standardized Test Practice by The Princeton Review,** pp. 15–18	MindJogger Videoquiz Interactive CD-ROM Vocabulary PuzzleMakers ExamView Pro Test Bank Interactive Lesson Planner Interactive Teacher Edition	Performance Assessment in the Science Classroom (PASC)

Transparencies

Section Focus

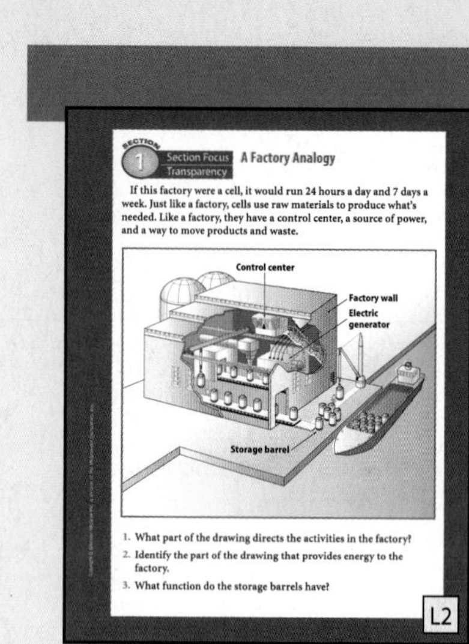
Section 1 Section Focus Transparency **A Factory Analogy**

If this factory were a cell, it would run 24 hours a day and 7 days a week. Just like a factory, cells use raw materials to produce what's needed. Like a factory, they have a control center, a source of power, and a way to move products and waste.

1. What part of the drawing directs the activities in the factory?
2. Identify the part of the drawing that provides energy to the factory.
3. What function do the storage barrels have?

L2

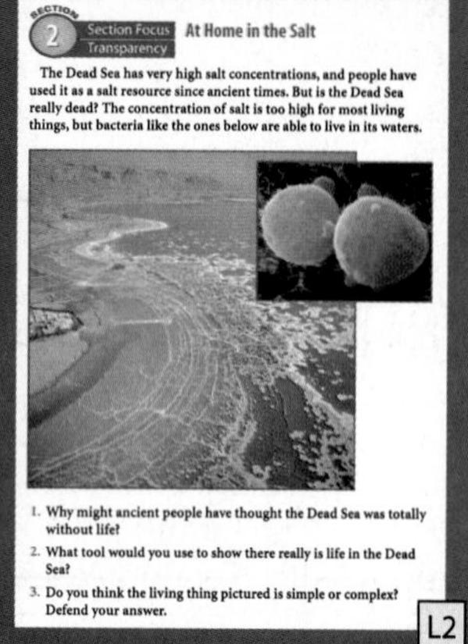
Section 2 Section Focus Transparency **At Home in the Salt**

The Dead Sea has very high salt concentrations, and people have used it as a salt resource since ancient times. But is the Dead Sea really dead? The concentration of salt is too high for most living things, but bacteria like the ones below are able to live in its waters.

1. Why might ancient people have thought the Dead Sea was totally without life?
2. What tool would you use to show there really is life in the Dead Sea?
3. Do you think the living thing pictured is simple or complex? Defend your answer.

L2

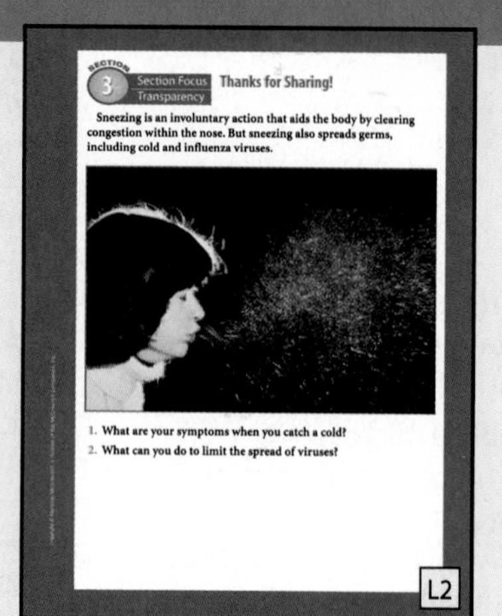
Section 3 Section Focus Transparency **Thanks for Sharing!**

Sneezing is an involuntary action that aids the body by clearing congestion within the nose. But sneezing also spreads germs, including cold and influenza viruses.

1. What are your symptoms when you catch a cold?
2. What can you do to limit the spread of viruses?

L2

This is a representation of key blackline masters available in the Teacher Classroom Resources. See Resource Manager boxes within the chapter for additional information.

Assessment

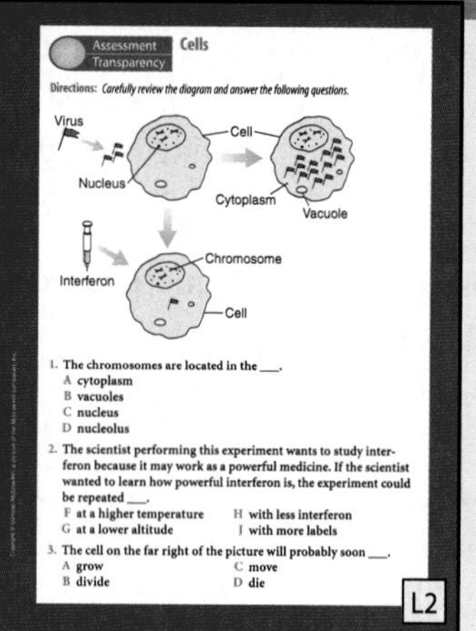
Assessment Transparency **Cells**

Directions: *Carefully review the diagram and answer the following questions.*

1. The chromosomes are located in the ___.
   A cytoplasm
   B vacuoles
   C nucleus
   D nucleolus
2. The scientist performing this experiment wants to study interferon because it may work as a powerful medicine. If the scientist wanted to learn how powerful interferon is, the experiment could be repeated ___.
   F at a higher temperature
   G at a lower altitude
   H with less interferon
   J with more labels
3. The cell on the far right of the picture will probably soon ___.
   A grow
   B divide
   C move
   D die

L2

Teaching

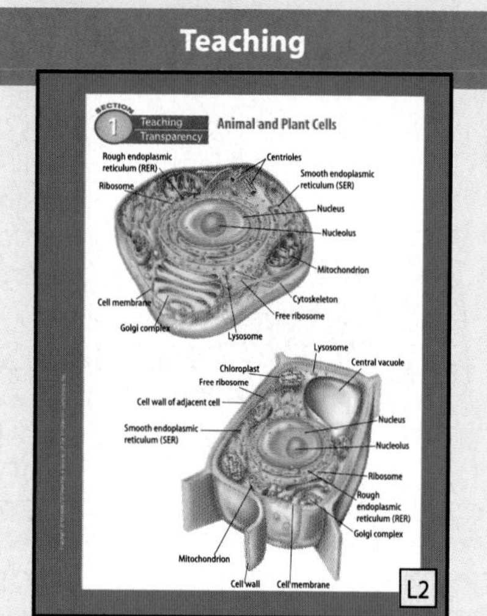
Section 1 Teaching Transparency **Animal and Plant Cells**

L2

Key to Teaching Strategies

The following designations will help you decide which activities are appropriate for your students.

- **L1** Level 1 activities should be appropriate for students with learning difficulties.
- **L2** Level 2 activities should be within the ability range of all students.
- **L3** Level 3 activities are designed for above-average students.
- **ELL** ELL activities should be within the ability range of English Language Learners.
- **COOP LEARN** Cooperative Learning activities are designed for small group work.
- **LS** Multiple Learning Styles logos, as described on page 22T, are used throughout to indicate strategies that address different learning styles.
- **P** These strategies represent student products that can be placed into a best-work portfolio.

Hands-on Activities

Activity Worksheets

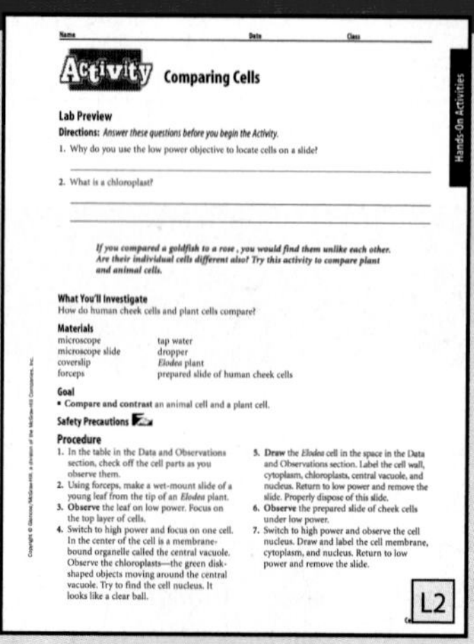
Activity **Comparing Cells**

Lab Preview

Directions: *Answer these questions before you begin the Activity.*

1. Why do you use the low power objective to locate cells on a slide?
2. What is a chloroplast?

L2

Laboratory Activities

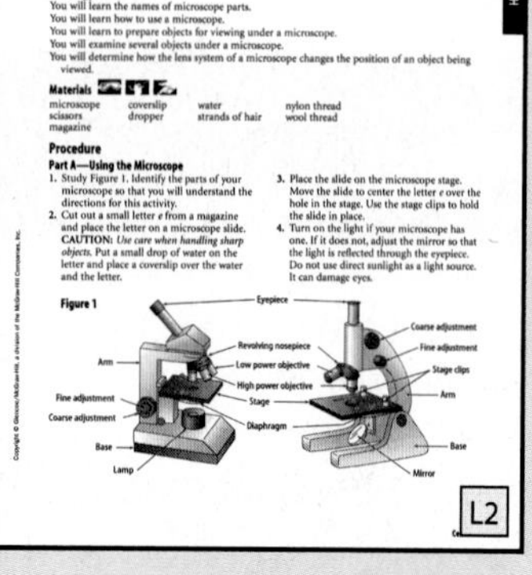
Laboratory Activity 1 **The Microscope**

L2

Meeting Different Ability Levels

Content Outline

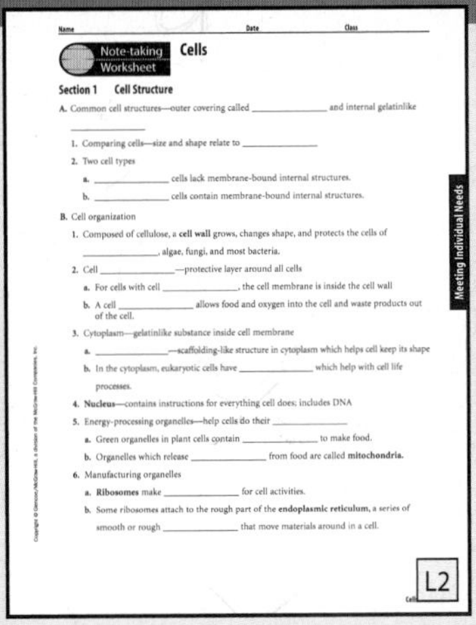

Note-taking Worksheet — Cells

Section 1 Cell Structure

A. Common cell structures—outer covering called ______ and internal gelatinlike ______

1. Comparing cells—size and shape relate to ______
2. Two cell types
   a. ______ cells lack membrane-bound internal structures.
   b. ______ cells contain membrane-bound internal structures.

B. Cell organization

1. Composed of cellulose, a **cell wall** grows, changes shape, and protects the cells of ______, algae, fungi, and most bacteria.
2. Cell ______—protective layer around all cells
   a. For cells with cell ______, the cell membrane is inside the cell wall
   b. A cell ______ allows food and oxygen into the cell and waste products out of the cell.
3. Cytoplasm—gelatinlike substance inside cell membrane
   a. ______—scaffolding-like structure in cytoplasm which helps cell keep its shape
   b. In the cytoplasm, eukaryotic cells have ______ which help with cell life processes.
4. **Nucleus**—contains instructions for everything cell does; includes DNA
5. Energy-processing organelles—help cells do their ______
   a. Green organelles in plant cells contain ______ to make food.
   b. Organelles which release ______ from food are called **mitochondria.**
6. Manufacturing organelles
   a. **Ribosomes** make ______ for cell activities.
   b. Some ribosomes attach to the rough part of the **endoplasmic reticulum,** a series of smooth or rough ______ that move materials around in a cell.

Meeting Individual Needs

L2

Reinforcement

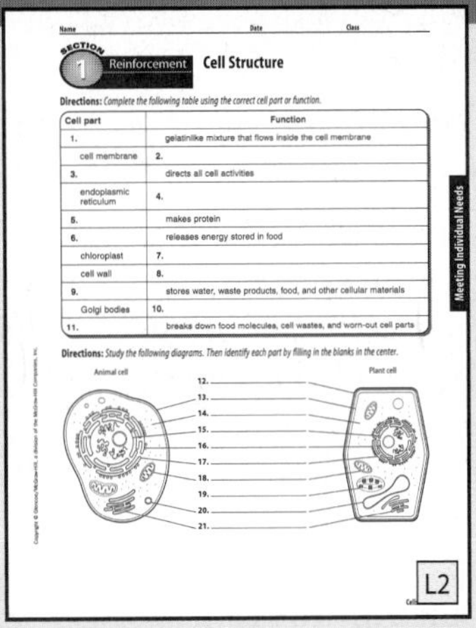

Section 1 Reinforcement — Cell Structure

Directions: Complete the following table using the correct cell part or function.

Cell part	Function
1.	gelatinlike mixture that flows inside the cell membrane
cell membrane	2.
3.	directs all cell activities
endoplasmic reticulum	4.
5.	makes protein
6.	releases energy stored in food
chloroplast	7.
cell wall	8.
9.	stores water, waste products, food, and other cellular materials
Golgi bodies	10.
11.	breaks down food molecules, cell wastes, and worn-out cell parts

Directions: Study the following diagrams. Then identify each part by filling in the blanks in the center.

Animal cell — Plant cell — 12.–21.

Meeting Individual Needs

L2

Directed Reading

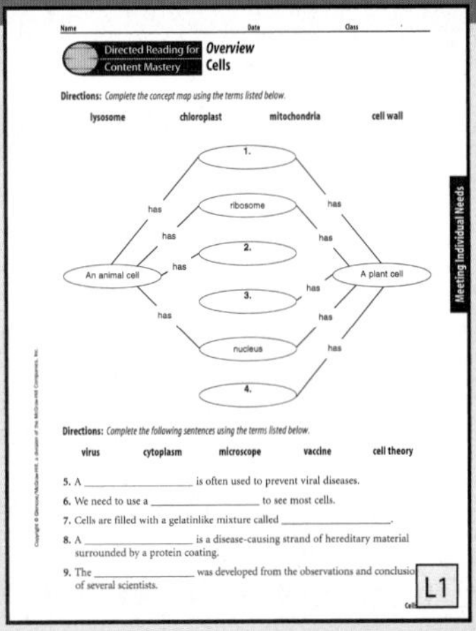

Directed Reading for Content Mastery — Overview — Cells

Directions: Complete the concept map using the terms listed below.

lysosome chloroplast mitochondria cell wall

An animal cell — A plant cell — has — ribosome — nucleus — 1. 2. 3. 4.

Directions: Complete the following sentences using the terms listed below.

virus cytoplasm microscope vaccine cell theory

5. A ______ is often used to prevent viral diseases.
6. We need to use a ______ to see most cells.
7. Cells are filled with a gelatinlike mixture called ______.
8. A ______ is a disease-causing strand of hereditary material surrounded by a protein coating.
9. The ______ was developed from the observations and conclusions of several scientists.

Meeting Individual Needs

L1

Enrichment

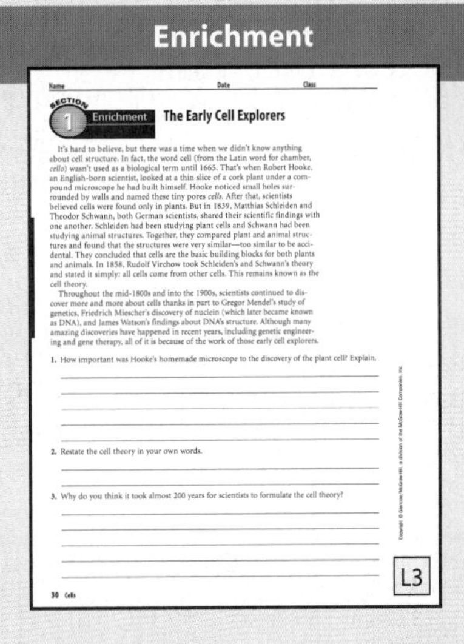

Section 1 Enrichment — The Early Cell Explorers

It's hard to believe, but there was a time when we didn't know anything about cell structure. In fact, the word cell (from the Latin word for chamber, cella) wasn't used as a biological term until 1665. That's when Robert Hooke, an English-born scientist, looked at a thin slice of a cork plant under a compound microscope he had built himself. Hooke noticed small holes surrounded by walls and named these tiny pores cells. After that, scientists believed cells were found only in plants. But in 1839, Matthias Schleiden and Theodor Schwann, both German scientists, shared their scientific findings with one another. Schleiden had been studying plant cells and Schwann had been studying animal structures. Together, they compared plant and animal structures and found that the structures were very similar—too similar to be accidental. They concluded that cells are the basic building blocks for both plants and animals. In 1858, Rudolf Virchow took Schleiden's and Schwann's theory and stated it simply: all cells come from other cells. This remains known as the cell theory.

Throughout the mid-1800s and into the 1900s, scientists continued to discover more and more about cells thanks in part to Gregor Mendel's study of genetics, Friedrich Miescher's discovery of nuclein (which later became known as DNA), and James Watson's findings about DNA's structure. Although many amazing discoveries have happened in recent years, including genetic engineering and gene therapy, all of it is because of the work of those early cell explorers.

1. How important was Hooke's homemade microscope to the discovery of the plant cell? Explain.
2. Restate the cell theory in your own words.
3. Why do you think it took almost 200 years for scientists to formulate the cell theory?

L3

Spanish Directed Reading

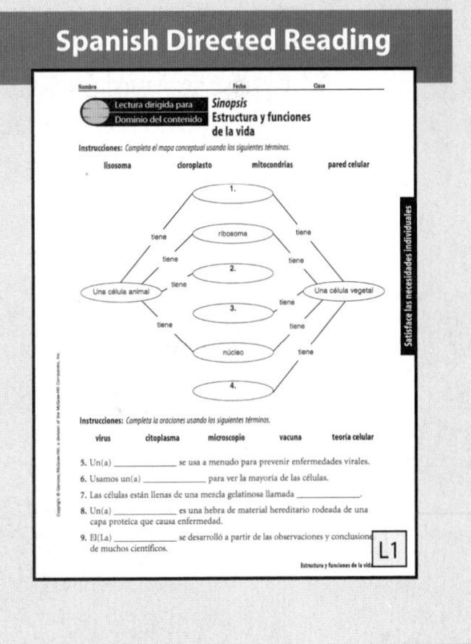

Lectura dirigida para Dominio del contenido — Sinopsis — Estructura y funciones de la vida

Instrucciones: Completa el mapa conceptual usando los siguientes términos.

lisosoma cloroplasto mitocondrias pared celular

Una célula animal — Una célula vegetal — tiene — ribosoma — núcleo — 1. 2. 3. 4.

Instrucciones: Completa las oraciones usando los siguientes términos.

virus citoplasma microscopio vacuna teoría celular

5. Un(a) ______ se usa a menudo para prevenir enfermedades virales.
6. Usamos un(a) ______ para ver la mayoría de las células.
7. Las células están llenas de una mezcla gelatinosa llamada ______.
8. Un(a) ______ es una hebra de material hereditario rodeada de una capa proteica que causa enfermedad.
9. El(La) ______ se desarrolló a partir de las observaciones y conclusiones de muchos científicos.

Satisface las necesidades individuales

L1

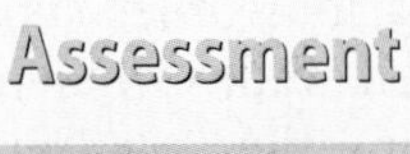

Assessment

Chapter Tests

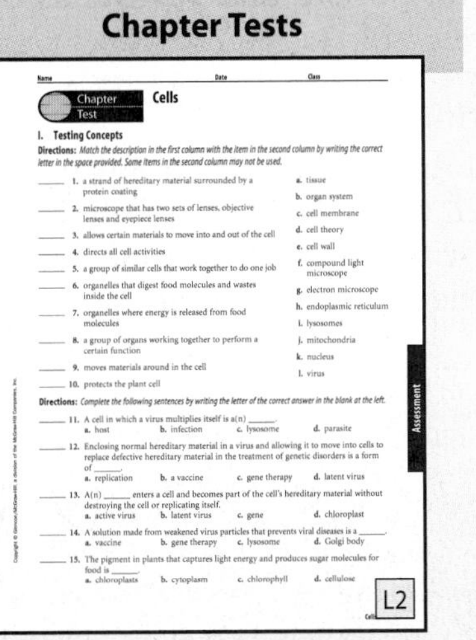

Chapter Test — Cells

I. Testing Concepts

Directions: Match the description in the first column with the item in the second column by writing the correct letter in the space provided. Some items in the second column may not be used.

1. a strand of hereditary material surrounded by a protein coating
2. microscope that has two sets of lenses, objective lenses and eyepiece lenses
3. allows certain materials to move into and out of the cell
4. directs all cell activities
5. a group of similar cells that work together to do one job
6. organelles that digest food molecules and wastes inside the cell
7. organelles where energy is released from food molecules
8. a group of organs working together to perform a certain function
9. moves materials around in the cell
10. protects the plant cell

a. tissue b. organ system c. cell membrane d. cell theory e. cell wall f. compound light microscope g. electron microscope h. endoplasmic reticulum i. lysosomes j. mitochondria k. nucleus l. virus

Directions: Complete the following sentences by writing the letter of the correct answer in the blank at the left.

11. A cell in which a virus multiplies itself is a(n) ______. a. host b. infection c. lysosome d. parasite
12. Enclosing normal hereditary material in a virus and allowing it to move into cells to replace defective hereditary material in the treatment of genetic disorders is a form of ______. a. replication b. a vaccine c. gene therapy d. latent virus
13. A(n) ______ enters a cell and becomes part of the cell's hereditary material without destroying the cell or replicating itself. a. active virus b. latent virus c. gene d. chloroplast
14. A solution made from weakened virus particles that prevents viral diseases is a ______. a. vaccine b. gene therapy c. lysosome d. Golgi body
15. The pigment in plants that captures light energy and produces sugar molecules for food is ______. a. chloroplasts b. cytoplasm c. chlorophyll d. cellulose

Assessment

L2

Test Practice Workbook

Chapter Review

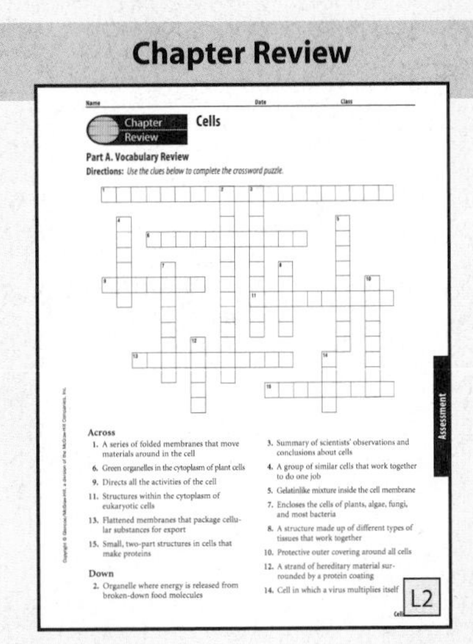

Chapter Review — Cells

Part A. Vocabulary Review

Directions: Use the clues below to complete the crossword puzzle.

Across
1. A series of folded membranes that move materials around in the cell
6. Green organelles in the cytoplasm of plant cells
9. Directs all the activities of the cell
11. Structures within the cytoplasm of eukaryotic cells
13. Flattened membranes that package cellular substances for export
15. Small, two-part structures in cells that make proteins

Down
2. Organelle where energy is released from broken-down food molecules
3. Summary of scientists' observations and conclusions about cells
4. A group of similar cells that work together to do one job
5. Gelatinlike mixture inside the cell membrane
7. Encloses the cells of plants, algae, fungi, and most bacteria
8. A structure made up of different types of tissues that work together
10. Protective outer covering around all cells
12. A strand of hereditary material surrounded by a protein coating
14. Cell in which a virus multiplies itself

Assessment

L2

Science Content Background

SECTION 1

Cell Structure

Common Cell Traits

The two kinds of cells are prokaryotes and eukaryotes. Each type is surrounded by a cell membrane and contains cytoplasm, DNA, and ribosomes. Prokaryotes have a relatively uniform cytoplasm that is not divided into separate compartments by interior membranes. The ribosomes of prokaryotes are different from those of eukaryotes. Prokaryotic DNA is a single molecule and is found floating freely in the cell's cytoplasm. The nucleus is the organelle that contains the eukaryotic cell's many molecules of DNA. All prokaryotic cells are one-celled organisms. Eukaryotic cells make up all many-celled organisms and some one-celled organisms.

Fun Fact

Scientists have found small sporelike cells in mammal tissues that are involved in tissue repair. They have been used to repair breaks in the spinal cords of rats.

Cell Wall

Although structurally they resemble plant cell walls, the walls of fungi cells are chemically quite different. Some contain cellulose, but most fungal cell walls are made up of chitin, a polysaccharide that also is found in the exoskeletons of insects. Just like cellulose in plants, the chitin is laid down in bundles of fibers that make the fungal cell walls tough and able to support the fungal body.

Bacterial cell walls are different from those found in either plants or fungi. Bacterial cell walls are composed in large part of a compound called peptidoglycan. Various other substances coat and bind to the cell wall. Other bacteria have an outer membrane that surrounds the peptidoglycan cell wall.

Cell Organization

The cytoskeleton, found only in eukaryotic cells, anchors cell organelles. This "scaffolding" cannot be seen with a normal light microscope but stands out clearly when special fluorescent

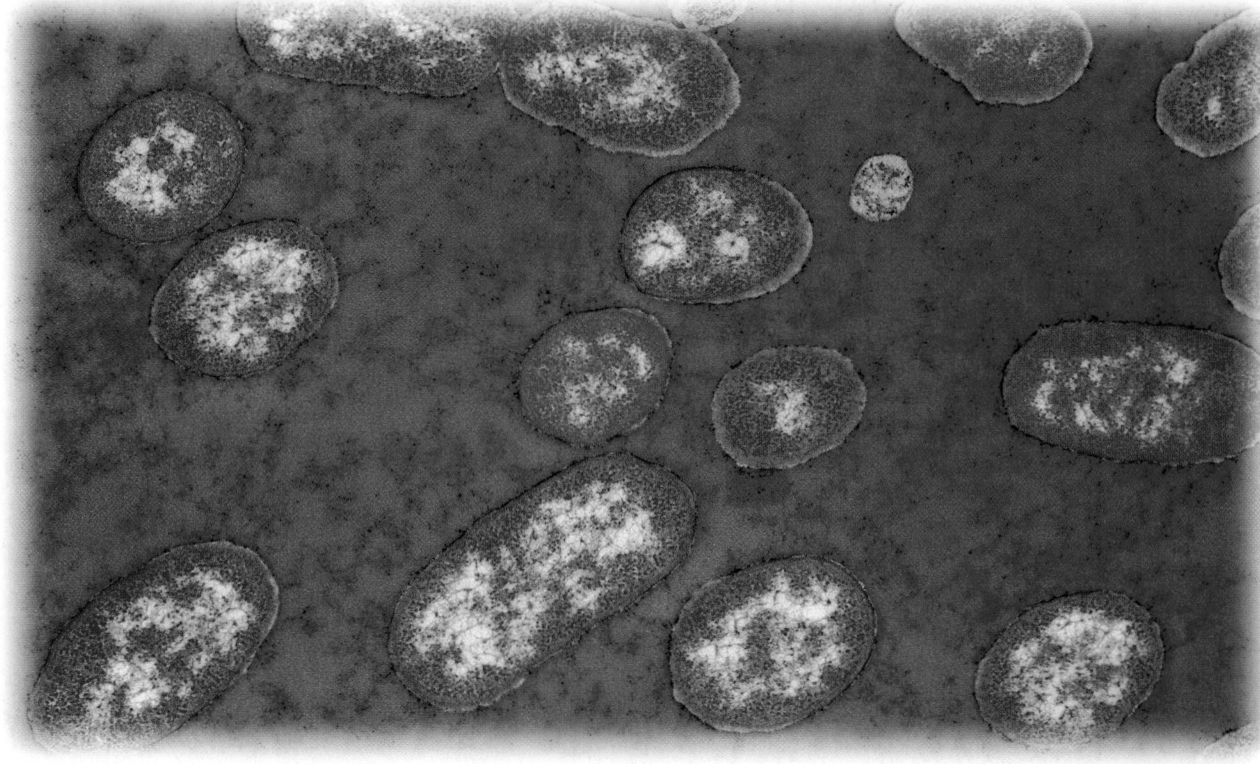

Dwight R. Kuhn/DRK Photo

dyes are used on the cell. Three different kinds of protein fibers—microfilaments, microtubules, and intermediate fibers—make up the cytoskeleton.

SECTION 2

Viewing Cells

Magnifying Cells

Microscopes enlarge the image of an object and show its details. The change of an object's apparent size is magnification. The power to show details is resolution. The resolution power of light microscopes is limited by the wavelengths of visible light. Unless the wavelength of light can pass between two objects, the objects are seen as one unit, not two. The electron microscope allows for greater resolution because it uses a beam of electrons to generate an image of the specimen. Because they move in waves that have extremely short wavelengths, electron waves can easily pass through microscopic spaces that visible light cannot enter.

Creatures 20–150 nanometers in length were found living in sandstone from the Australian seabed. They are smaller than any other known living organism. They contain DNA and distinct cell membranes.

Development of the Cell Theory

The cell theory is sometimes called the cell doctrine. Those scientists who use the term *cell doctrine* want to make it clear that extensive data support the cell theory and that it is universally accepted by biologists.

SECTION 3

Viruses

Living or Not?

To a biologist, living organisms are cellular and are able to grow and reproduce independently. The smallest organisms that satisfy these criteria are bacteria. Viruses do not meet most criteria for being a living organism.

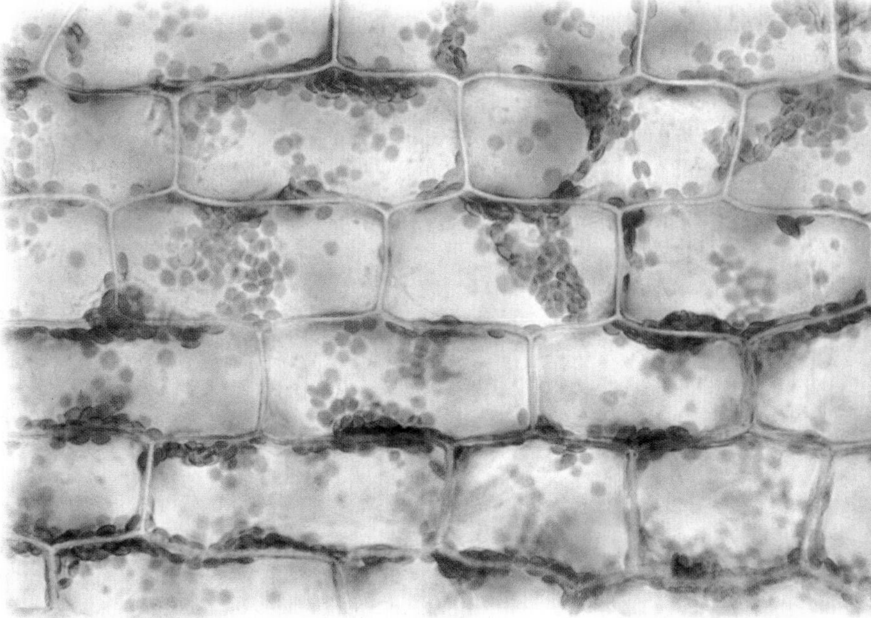

Telegraph Colour Library/FPG International

Viruses are segments of DNA or RNA wrapped in a protein coat. A membranous envelope surrounds many animal viruses. The lipids of the envelope are taken from the host cell, but the proteins are coded by the virus's genetic material. Viruses cannot reproduce on their own but multiply only within host cells using the cellular machinery of the host cell. The host cells often are destroyed when viruses multiply. For the host organism, infection by a virus may have a minor effect like a cold or may be devastating like AIDS. Several types of cancer, including some skin and cervical cancers, are now known to be caused by viruses. Viruses continue to have a major impact on the living world.

For additional content background on this topic, go to the Glencoe Science Web site at science.glencoe.com.

Cells

Chapter Vocabulary

cell membrane, p. 38
cytoplasm, p. 38
cell wall, p. 39
organelle, p. 40
nucleus, p. 40
chloroplast, p. 42
mitochondrion, p. 42
ribosome, p. 42
endoplasmic reticulum, p. 43
Golgi body, p. 43
tissue, p. 45
organ, p. 45
cell theory, p. 51
virus, p. 52
host cell, p. 52

What do you think?

Science Journal The photograph is of a virus attacking a bacterium.

CHAPTER 2

Cells

The world around you is filled with organisms that you could overlook, or even be unable to see. Some of these organisms are one-celled and some are many-celled. The monster in this photograph is a louse crawling across human skin. It can be seen in great detail with a microscope that is found in many classrooms. You can study the cells of smaller organisms with other kinds of microscopes.

What do you think?

Science Journal Look at the picture below with a classmate. Discuss what you think is happening. Here's a hint: *Not every battlefield is found on land or at sea.* Write your answer or best guess in your Science Journal.

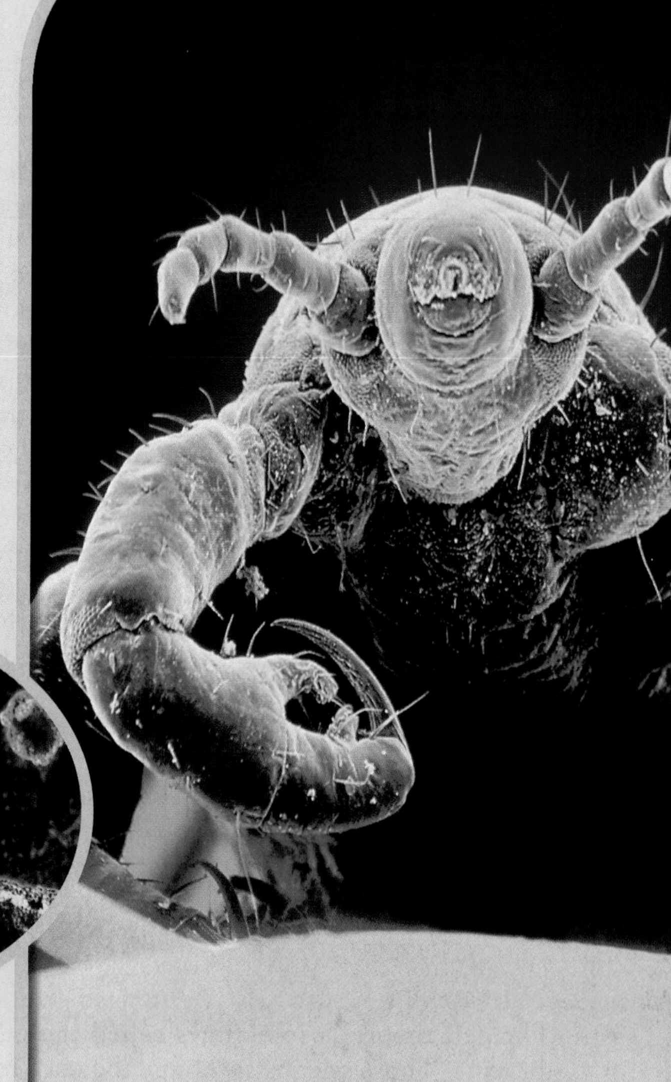

36

Theme Connection

Scale and Structure The scale and structure of cells and viruses are compared and the parts of which they are composed are described.

If you look around your classroom, you can see many things of all sizes. With the aid of a hand lens, you can see more details. You might examine a speck of dust and discover that it is a living or dead insect. In the following activity, use a hand lens to search for the smallest thing you can find in the classroom.

Measure a small object

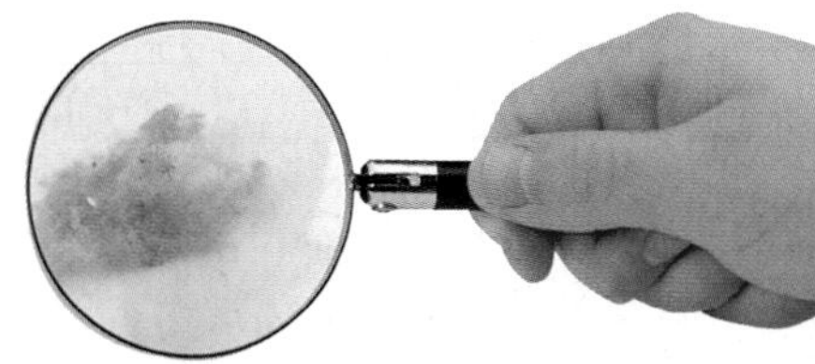

1. Obtain a hand lens from your teacher. Note its power (the number followed by ×, shown somewhere on the lens frame or handle).
2. Using the hand lens, look around the room for the smallest object you can find.
3. Measure the size of the image as you see it with the hand lens. To estimate the real size of the object, divide that number by the power. For example, if it looks 2 cm long and the power is 10×, the real length is about 0.2 cm.

Observe

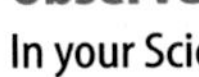

In your Science Journal, describe what you observe. Did the details become clearer? Explain.

Before You Read

FOLDABLES Reading & Study Skills

Making a Main Ideas Study Fold Make the following Foldable to help you identify the main ideas or major topics on cells.

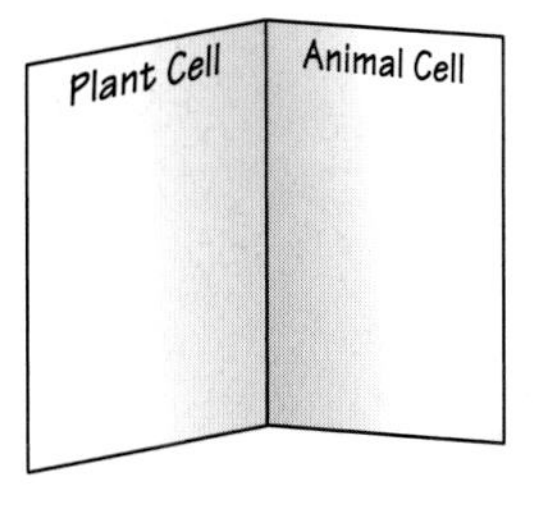

1. Place a sheet of paper in front of you so the long side is at the top. Fold the paper in half from the left side to the right side. Then unfold.
2. Label the left side of the paper *Plant Cell.* Label the right side of the paper *Animal Cell,* as shown.
3. Before you read the chapter, draw a plant cell on the left side of the paper and an animal cell on the right side of the paper.
4. As you read the chapter, change and add to your drawings.

37

Before You Read

FOLDABLES Reading & Study Skills

Dinah Zike Study Fold

Purpose Students make and use a Foldable to diagram and collect information on plant and animal cells. Students use this information to compare and contrast these two types of cells and explain how the structure of each relates to its function.

For additional help, see Foldables Worksheet, p. 17 in **Chapter Resources Booklet,** or go to the Glencoe Science Web site at **science.glencoe.com.** See After You Read in the Study Guide at the end of this chapter.

EXPLORE ACTIVITY

Purpose Students will use a hand lens to study very small objects. Students will calculate the actual size of the object from a measured size seen through the hand lens.

Preparation Obtain hand lenses and make sure the power is clearly visible on each one.

Materials hand lenses, rulers

Teaching Strategy Have some very small objects, such as grains of sand, salt, sugar, etc., available for students to study with their hand lenses.

Observe

Details of small objects will become larger and clearer when seen through a hand lens.

Assessment

Oral Have students describe aloud additional features of small objects, such as sand, salt, sugar, dust particles, etc., that they can observe through a hand lens. Use **Performance Assessment in the Science Classroom,** p. 89.

SECTION 1

Cell Structure

1 Motivate

Bellringer Transparency

Display the Section Focus Transparency for Section 1. Use the accompanying Transparency Activity Master. L2 ELL

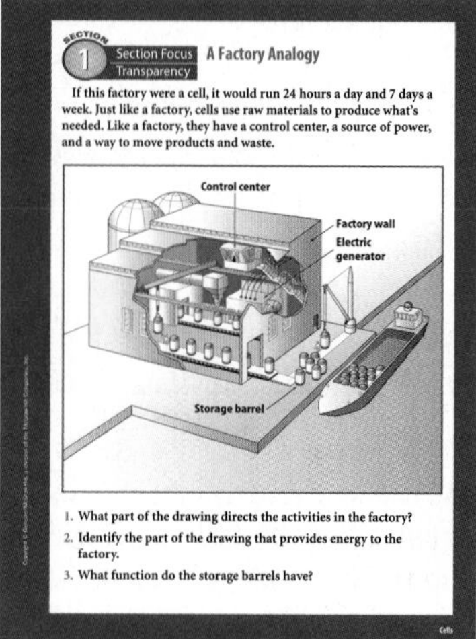

Section Focus Transparency 1 — A Factory Analogy

If this factory were a cell, it would run 24 hours a day and 7 days a week. Just like a factory, cells use raw materials to produce what's needed. Like a factory, they have a control center, a source of power, and a way to move products and waste.

1. What part of the drawing directs the activities in the factory?
2. Identify the part of the drawing that provides energy to the factory.
3. What function do the storage barrels have?

Tie to Prior Knowledge

Ask students what body systems they need to live. Write their responses on the board or overhead projector. Use this list to help students understand that the functions of life are carried out in the cell.

SECTION 1

Cell Structure

As You Read

What You'll Learn

- **Identify** names and functions of each part of a cell.
- **Explain** how important a nucleus is in a cell.
- **Compare** tissues, organs, and organ systems.

Vocabulary

cell membrane, cytoplasm, cell wall, organelle, nucleus, chloroplast, mitochondrion, ribosome, endoplasmic reticulum, Golgi body, tissue, organ

Why It's Important

If you know how organelles function, it's easier to understand how cells survive.

Common Cell Traits

Living cells are dynamic and have several things in common. A cell is the smallest unit that is capable of performing life functions. All cells have an outer covering called a **cell membrane.** Inside every cell is a gelatinlike material called **cytoplasm** (SI toh plaz uhm). In the cytoplasm of every cell is hereditary material that controls the life of the cell.

Comparing Cells Cells come in many sizes. A nerve cell in your leg could be a meter long. A human egg cell is no bigger than the dot on this **i.** A human red blood cell is about one-tenth the size of a human egg cell. A bacterium is even smaller—8,000 of the smallest bacteria can fit inside one of your red blood cells.

A cell's shape might tell you something about its function. The nerve cell in **Figure 1** has many fine extensions that send and receive impulses to and from other cells. Though a nerve cell cannot change shape, muscle cells and some blood cells can. In plant stems, some cells are long and hollow and have openings at their ends. These cells carry food and water throughout the plant.

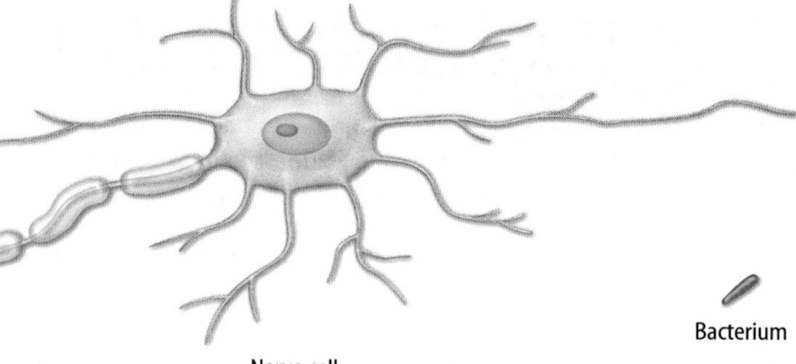

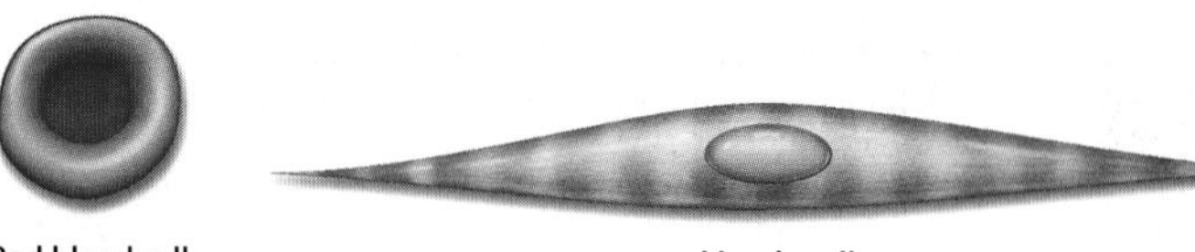

Figure 1
The shape of the cell can tell you something about its function. These cells are drawn 700 times their actual size.

Section Assessment Planner

PORTFOLIO
Visual Learning, p. 41

PERFORMANCE ASSESSMENT
MiniLAB, p. 40
Skill Builder Activities, p. 45
See page 62 for more options.

CONTENT ASSESSMENT
Section, p. 45
Challenge, p. 45
Chapter, pp. 62–63

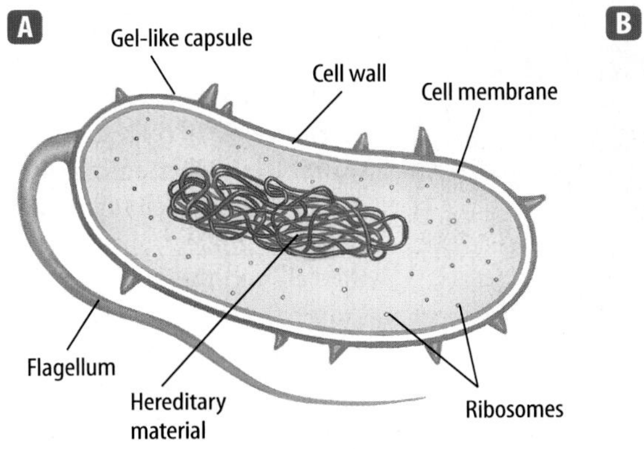

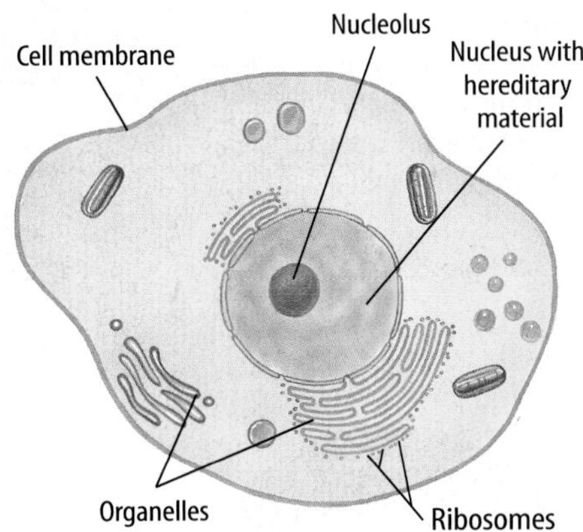

Cell Types Scientists have found that cells can be separated into two groups. One group has no membrane-bound structures inside the cell and the other group does, as shown in **Figure 2.** Cells without membrane-bound structures are called prokaryotic (proh KAYR ee yah tihk) cells. Cells with membrane-bound structures are called eukaryotic (yew KAYR ee yah tihk) cells.

Figure 2
Examine these drawings of cells. A Prokaryotic cells are only found in one-celled organisms, such as bacteria. B Protists, fungi, plants and animals are made of eukaryotic cells. *What differences do you see between them?*

Reading Check *Into what two groups can cells be separated?*

Cell Organization

Each cell in your body has a specific function. You might compare a cell to a busy delicatessen that is open 24 hours every day. Raw materials for the sandwiches are brought in often. Some food is eaten in the store, and some customers take their food with them. Sometimes food is prepared ahead of time for quick sale. Wastes are put into trash bags for removal or recycling. Similarly, your cells are taking in nutrients, secreting and storing chemicals, and breaking down substances 24 hours every day.

Cell Wall Just like a deli that is located inside the walls of a building, some cells are enclosed in a cell wall. The cells of plants, algae, fungi, and most bacteria are enclosed in a cell wall. **Cell walls** are tough, rigid outer coverings that protect the cell and give it shape.

A plant cell wall, as shown in **Figure 3,** mostly is made up of a carbohydrate called cellulose. The long, threadlike fibers of cellulose form a thick mesh that allows water and dissolved materials to pass through it. Cell walls also can contain pectin, which is used in jam and jelly, and lignin, which is a compound that makes cell walls rigid. Plant cells responsible for support have a lot of lignin in their walls.

Figure 3
The protective cell wall of a plant cell is outside the cell membrane.

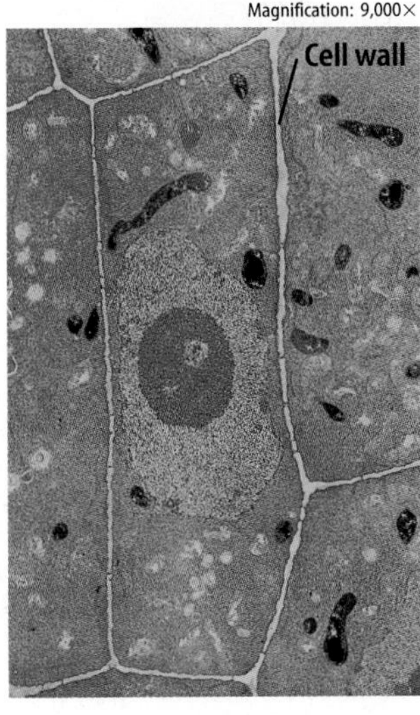

2 Teach

Common Cell Traits

Quick Demo

Use a microprojector to show prepared slides of plant, animal, and bacterial cells. Have students identify the characteristics of each cell shown. L2
LS **Visual-Spatial**

Caption Answer

Figure 2 The prokaryotic cell has no membrane-bound structures inside; the eukaryotic cell does have membrane-bound structures.

Reading Check

Answer prokaryotic and eukaryotic

Cell Organization

Use an Analogy

To show how a plant cell wall provides strength, inflate a balloon and place it inside a small cardboard box. The balloon represents the cell membrane and the box represents the cell wall.

Activity

Make a bulletin board showing unlabeled parts of an animal and plant cell. As each cell part is studied, have a student place its label beside it on the bulletin board. L1 LS **Visual-Spatial**

Discussion

How are prokaryotic and eukaryotic cells similar? Both have cell membranes, cytoplasm, and DNA as their genetic material.

Resource Manager

Chapter Resources Booklet
Transparency Activity, p. 44
Directed Reading for Content Mastery, pp. 19, 20
Note-taking Worksheets, pp. 33–35

Curriculum Connection

Health Cellulose, found in all plant cell walls, is not digestible by humans. However, it provides fiber, which is important because it helps in the elimination of wastes. Have students make a list of foods that contain fiber. Lists should include fruits, grains, and leafy vegetables. L2

Cell Organization, continued

Discussion

What would happen if the nucleus of a cell were damaged? The cell would no longer function correctly because the nucleus controls all the cell's activities. L2

Reading Check

Answer It helps the cell maintain or change its shape.

Mini LAB

Purpose Students model cytoplasm. L1 ELL LS **Kinesthetic**

Materials 250 mL beaker, unflavored gelatin (one package per student group), water, flashlight, stirring rod

Teaching Strategy Be certain students stir the gelatin well before shining the light on the beaker.

Analysis

1. particles suspended in the gelatin, which represent organelles suspended in the cytoplasm
2. A model is a representation of an abstract object that is used to help visualize and better understand it.

Assessment

Oral Have students infer how the chemical composition of cytoplasm compares to that of gelatin. Both are water-based suspensions. Cytoplasm is 80% water. Use **PASC,** p. 89.

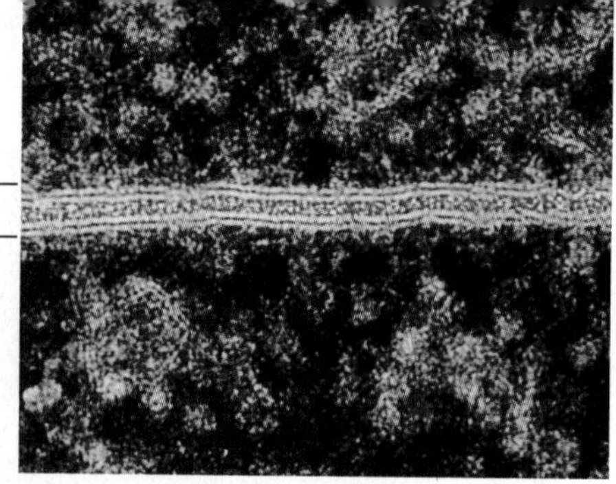

Figure 4
The cell membrane is made up of a double layer of fatlike molecules.

Cell Membrane The protective layer around all cells is the cell membrane, as shown in **Figure 4.** If cells have cell walls, the cell membrane is inside of it. The cell membrane regulates interactions between the cell and the environment. Water is able to move freely into and out of the cell through the cell membrane. Food particles and some molecules enter and waste products leave through the cell membrane.

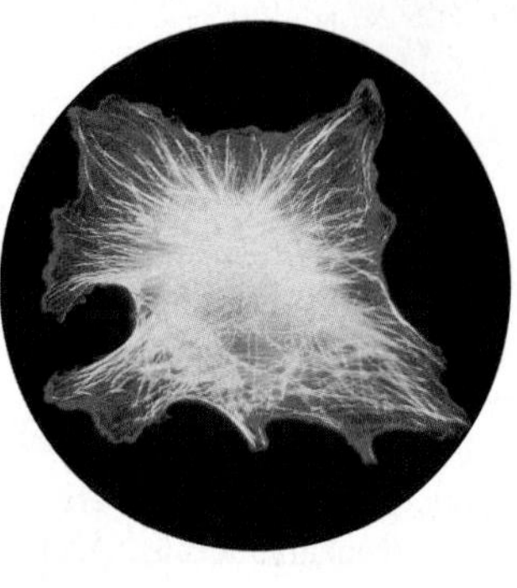

Figure 5
Cytoskeleton, a network of fibers in the cytoplasm, gives cells structure and helps them maintain shape.

Cytoplasm Cells are filled with a gelatinlike substance called cytoplasm that constantly flows inside the cell membrane. Many important chemical reactions occur within the cytoplasm.

Throughout the cytoplasm is a framework called the cytoskeleton, which helps the cell maintain or change its shape. Cytoskeletons enable some cells to move. An amoeba, for example, moves by stretching and contracting its cytoskeleton. The cytoskeleton is made up of thin, hollow tubes of protein and thin, solid protein fibers, as shown in **Figure 5.** Proteins are organic molecules made up of amino acids.

Reading Check *What is the function of the cytoskeleton?*

Most of a cell's life processes occur in the cytoplasm. Within the cytoplasm of eukaryotic cells are structures called **organelles.** Some organelles process energy and others manufacture substances needed by the cell or other cells. Certain organelles move materials, while others act as storage sites. Most organelles are surrounded by membranes. The nucleus is usually the largest organelle in a cell.

Nucleus The nucleus is like the deli manager who directs the store's daily operations and passes on information to employees. The **nucleus,** shown in **Figure 6,** directs all cell activities and is separated from the cytoplasm by a membrane. Materials enter and leave the nucleus through openings in the membrane. The nucleus contains the instructions for everything the cell does. These instructions are found on long, threadlike, hereditary material made of DNA. DNA is the chemical that contains the code for the cell's structure and activities. During cell division, the hereditary material coils tightly around proteins to form structures called chromosomes. A structure called a nucleolus also is found in the nucleus.

Mini LAB

Modeling Cytoplasm

Procedure

1. Add 100 mL of **water** to a **clear container.**
2. Add **unflavored gelatin** and stir.
3. Shine a **flashlight** through the solution.

Analysis

1. Describe what you see.
2. How does a model help you understand what cytoplasm might be like?

Teacher FYI

Before electron microscopes, scientists could only theorize about many cell structures and their makeups. Even the best compound microscope cannot reveal what can be seen with electron microscopes.

Curriculum Connection

Health Students may think that any cholesterol in the body presents a health risk. Cholesterol is an important component of the cell membrane. It creates a health risk only when it is present in high levels in the blood, where it builds up in arteries and obstructs blood flow. Ask students to investigate cholesterol to differentiate between blood cholesterol and dietary cholesterol. L3

Figure 6
Refer to these diagrams of a typical animal cell (top) and plant cell (bottom) as you read about cell structures and their functions.

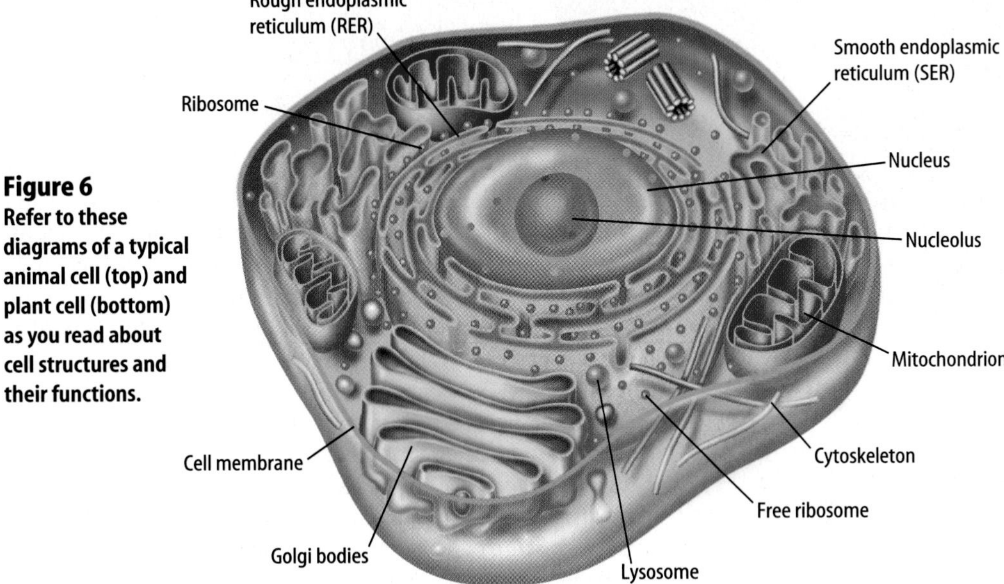

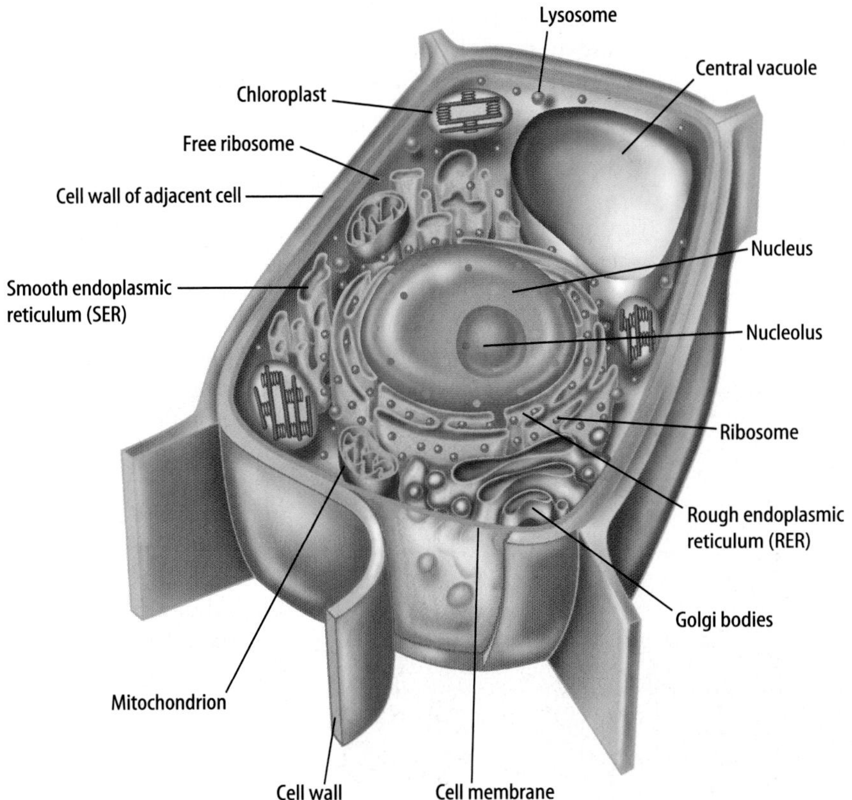

Use an Analogy

Point out that just as each part of a machine performs a different function to enable the machine to work, each organelle performs a different function in the cell.

Use Science Words

Word Origin Greek and Latin words are used in naming cell parts. Have students make a list of cell parts and use a dictionary to find the origins of the words and their meanings. L2 **LS Linguistic**

Visual Learning

Figure 6 Have students create a network tree concept map comparing and contrasting plant and animal cells. Diagrams should make clear which organelles appear in both cells, and which are specific to only one type of cell. L2 **LS Visual-Spatial** P

IDENTIFYING Misconceptions

Students may think that cells are solid. Explain that almost 80% of a cell is water. The water is enclosed in a membrane that allows certain materials to enter and leave.

Resource Manager

Chapter Resources Booklet
MiniLAB, p. 3
Enrichment, p. 30

Extension
The two cylindrical organelles at the top of the animal cell are called centrioles. Have students research the function of these organelles. Animal cells have centrioles. During mitosis and meiosis, centrioles duplicate and move to opposite ends of a cell. As they move, spindle fibers form which eventually attach to the duplicated chromosomes.

Cell Organization, continued

A liver cell has hundreds of mitochondria, which makes up about 25% of the cell's volume. The high number of mitochondria reflects the high level of energy a liver cell requires.

IDENTIFYING Misconceptions

Students may think that because plant cells carry out photosynthesis, they do not have mitochondria. Explain that plants also carry out cellular respiration.

Discussion

What color are most cells? Most cells are colorless. Photographs of cells are usually color-enhanced; prepared slides of cells are usually stained so cell parts are visible.

Text Question Answer

Mitochondria provide energy, and active cells would be more in need of energy than inactive cells.

Caption Answer

Figure 8 Possible answer: muscle cells

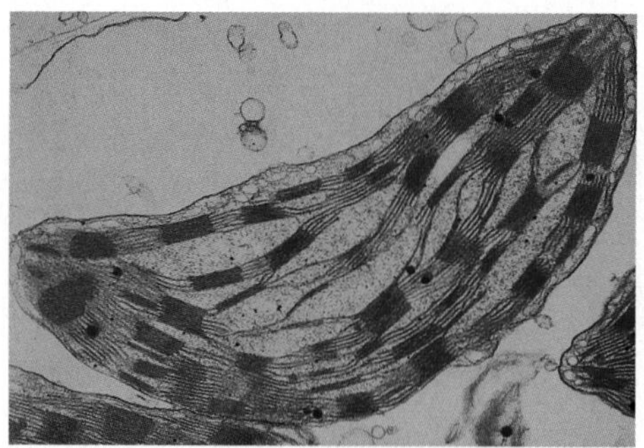

Figure 7
Chloroplasts are organelles that use sunlight to make sugar from carbon dioxide and water. They contain chlorophyll, which gives most leaves and stems their green color.

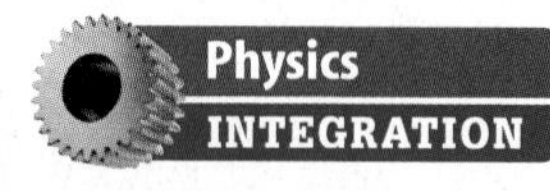

Energy-Processing Organelles Cells require a continuous supply of energy to process food, make new substances, eliminate wastes, and communicate with each other. In plant cells, food is made in green organelles in the cytoplasm called **chloroplasts** (KLOR uh plasts), as shown in **Figure 7.** Chloroplasts contain the green pigment chlorophyll, which gives leaves and stems their green color. Chlorophyll captures light energy that is used to make a sugar called glucose. Glucose molecules store the captured light energy as chemical energy. Many cells, including animal cells, do not have chloroplasts for making food. They must get food from their environment.

The energy in food is stored until it is released by the mitochondria. **Mitochondria** (mi tuh KAHN dree uh) (singular, *mitochondrion*), such as the one shown in **Figure 8,** are organelles where energy is released from breaking down food into carbon dioxide and water. Just as the gas or electric company supplies fuel for the deli, a mitochondrion releases energy for use by the cell. Some types of cells, such as muscle cells, are more active than other cells. These cells have large numbers of mitochondria. Why would active cells have more or larger mitochondria?

Figure 8
Mitochondria are known as the powerhouses of the cell because they release energy that is needed by the cell from food.
What types of cells might contain many mitochondria?

Manufacturing Organelles One substance that takes part in nearly every cell activity is protein. Proteins are part of cell membranes. Other proteins are needed for chemical reactions that take place in the cytoplasm. Cells make their own proteins on small structures called **ribosomes.** Even though ribosomes are considered organelles, they are not membrane bound. Some ribosomes float freely in the cytoplasm; and others are attached to the endoplasmic reticulum. Ribosomes are made in the nucleolus and move out into the cytoplasm. Ribosomes receive directions from the hereditary material in the nucleus on how, when, and in what order to make specific proteins.

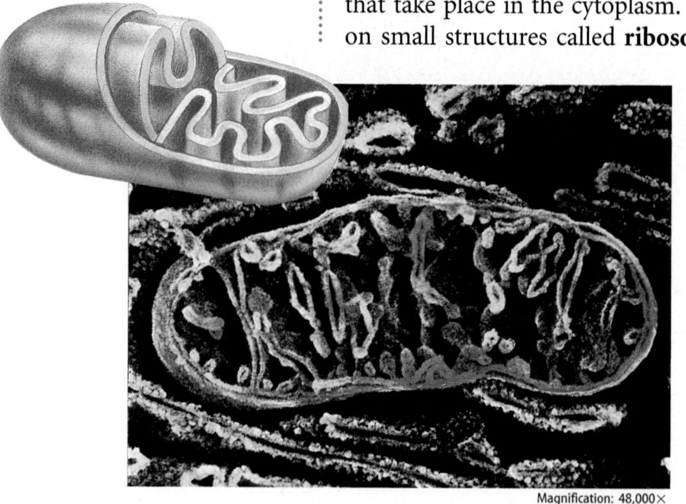

Cultural Diversity

Ernest Everett Just, an African American biologist in the early 1900s, studied cells and how they function. His research showed that all parts of the cell influence its activities, not just the nucleus, as scientists then believed. This idea changed scientific opinion concerning the basis of life. Discuss how Just's research is important to the study of cells today.

Inclusion Strategies

Learning Disabled Provide pairs of students with an unlabeled drawing of an animal cell. Have students print small stick-on labels and place them appropriately on the drawing. The labels can be folded to conceal the words and removed as the students learn the cell structures, then replaced for review. L1

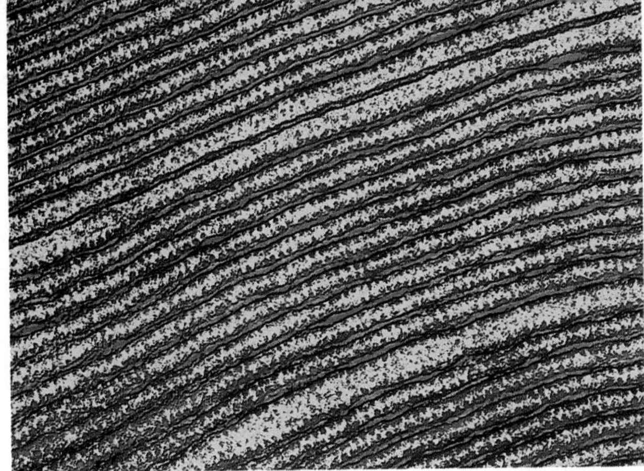

Figure 9
Endoplasmic reticulum (ER) is a complex series of membranes in the cytoplasm of the cell. *What would smooth ER look like?*

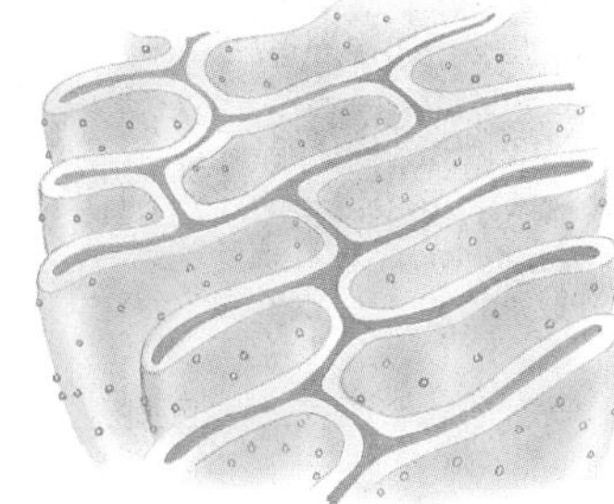

Processing, Transporting, and Storing Organelles

The **endoplasmic reticulum** (en duh PLAZ mihk • rih TIHK yuh lum) or ER, as shown in **Figure 9,** extends from the nucleus to the cell membrane. It is a series of folded membranes in which materials can be processed and moved around inside of the cell. The ER takes up a lot of space in some cells.

The endoplasmic reticulum may be "rough" or "smooth." ER that has no attached ribosomes is called smooth endoplasmic reticulum. This type of ER processes other cellular substances such as lipids that store energy. Ribosomes are attached to areas on the rough ER. There they carry out their job of making proteins that are moved out of the cell or used within the cell.

Reading Check *What is the difference between rough ER and smooth ER?*

After proteins are made in a cell, they are transferred to another type of cell organelle called the Golgi (GAWL jee) bodies. The **Golgi bodies,** as shown in **Figure 10,** are stacked, flattened membranes. The Golgi bodies sort proteins and other cellular substances and package them into membrane-bound structures called vesicles. The vesicles deliver cellular substances to areas inside the cell. They also carry cellular substances to the cell membrane where they are released to the outside of the cell.

Just as a deli has refrigerators for temporary storage of some its foods and ingredients, cells have membrane-bound spaces called vacuoles for the temporary storage of materials. A vacuole can store water, waste products, food, and other cellular materials. In plant cells, the vacuole may make up most of the cell's volume.

Figure 10
The Golgi body packages materials and moves them to the outside of the cell. *Why are materials removed from the cell?*

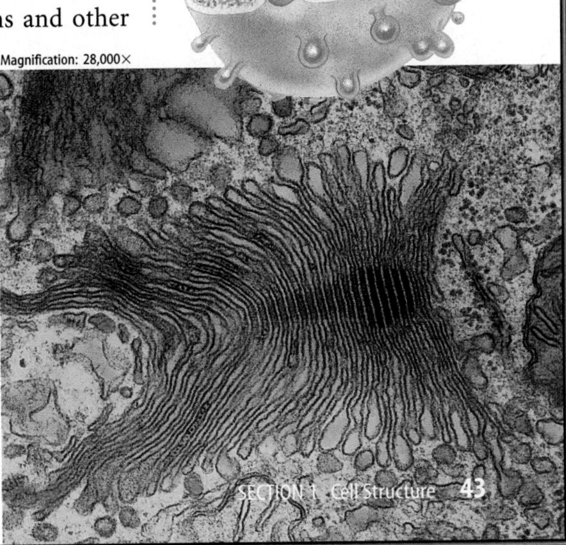

Caption Answer

Figure 9 Smooth ER looks the same as rough ER, only without ribosomes attached to it.

Make a Model

Have students make a cutaway model of a eukaryotic cell, using a clear plastic bag for the cell membrane, gelatin for cytoplasm, kidney beans for mitochondria, small seeds for ribosomes, noodles for ER and Golgi bodies, a lemon for the nucleus, and peppercorns for lysosomes. Sealed plastic bags full of water can be used for vacuoles. To make a model of a plant cell, green peas can be used for chloroplasts, and licorice for cell walls. L2 IS **Kinesthetic**

Reading Check

Answer Rough endoplasmic reticulum has ribosomes attached to it and makes proteins; smooth ER has no ribosomes and processes cellular substances.

Caption Answer

Figure 10 Materials are removed from a cell because they are waste products of the cell, or are to be used in other parts of the organism.

Extension

Have students use reference materials to find out about the work of Marcello Malpighi (1628–1694). Malpighi examined cells and tissues. His discoveries include observing and describing alveoli, capillaries, and red blood cells. He is considered the founder of the field of microscopic anatomy. L2 IS **Linguistic**

Resource Manager

Chapter Resources Booklet
Transparency Activity, pp. 47–48

Life Science Critical Thinking/ Problem Solving, p. 1

Inclusion Strategies

Gifted In 1898 Camillo Golgi, an Italian scientist, developed a silver stain for use with the light microscope and discovered the organelle that was later named for him. The Golgi body was not seriously studied until the development of the electron microscope in the 1950s. Have students use references to find electron micrographs of the Golgi body and learn about it in greater depth. L3

Cell Organization, continued

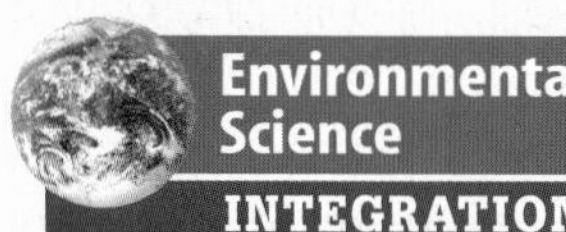

Environmental Science INTEGRATION

Posters will vary.

Reading Check

Answer to prevent digestive chemicals from leaking into the cytoplasm and destroying the cell

IDENTIFYING Misconceptions

Students may assume that the larger an organism is, the larger its cells. Explain that while cells vary in shape and size, most are only about 0.0025 cm in diameter. The number of cells, not how large they are, determines an organism's size.

Math Skills Activity

National Math Standards

Correlation to Mathematics Objectives

1, 2, 3, 4, 6, 8, 9

Answers to Practice Problems

1. $A = 2\text{ cm} \times 2\text{ cm} \times 6 = 24\text{ cm}^2$
   $V = 2\text{ cm} \times 2\text{ cm} \times 2\text{ cm} = 8\text{ cm}^3$
   $R = 24\text{ cm}^2/8\text{ cm}^3 = 3\text{ cm}^2/\text{cm}^3$
   As the size of the cube decreases, the ratio increases.
2. $A = 2(4\text{ cm} \times 4\text{ cm}) + 4(4\text{ cm} \times 8\text{ cm}) = 160\text{ cm}^2$
   $V = 4\text{ cm} \times 4\text{ cm} \times 8\text{ cm} = 128\text{ cm}^3$
   $R = 160\text{ cm}^2/128\text{ cm}^3 = 1.25\text{ cm}^2/\text{cm}^3$

Environmental Science INTEGRATION

Just like a cell, you can recycle materials. Paper, plastics, aluminum, and glass are materials that can be recycled into usable items. Make a promotional poster to encourage others to recycle.

Recycling Organelles Active cells break down and recycle substances. Organelles called lysosomes (LI suh sohmz) contain digestive chemicals that help break down food molecules, cell wastes, and worn-out cell parts. In a healthy cell, chemicals are released into vacuoles only when needed. The lysosome's membrane prevents the digestive chemicals inside from leaking into the cytoplasm and destroying the cell. When a cell dies, a lysosome's membrane disintegrates. This releases digestive chemicals that allow the quick breakdown of the cell's contents.

Reading Check *What is the function of the lysosome's membrane?*

Math Skills Activity

Calculate the Ratio of Surface Area to Volume of Cells

Example Problem

Assume that a cell is like a cube with six equal sides. Find the ratio of surface area to volume for a cube that is 4 cm high.

Solution

1. *This is what you know:* A cube has 6 equal sides of 4 cm × 4 cm.
2. *This is what you want to find:* the ratio (R) of surface area to volume for each cube
3. *These are the equations you use:* surface area (A) = width × length × 6; volume (V) = length × width × height; $R = A/V$
4. *Solve for surface area and volume, then solve for the ratio:*
   $A = 4\text{ cm} \times 4\text{ cm} \times 6 = 96\text{ cm}^2$
   $V = 4\text{ cm} \times 4\text{ cm} \times 4\text{ cm} = 64\text{ cm}^3$
   $R = 96\text{ cm}^2/64\text{ cm}^3 = 1.5\text{ cm}^2/\text{cm}^3$

Check your answer by multiplying the ratio by the volume. Do you calculate the surface area?

Practice Problems

1. Calculate the ratio of surface area to volume for a cube that is 2 cm high. What happens to this ratio as the size of the cube decreases?
2. If a 4-cm cube doubled just one of its dimensions—length, width, or height—what would happen to the ratio of surface area to volume?

For more help, refer to the Math Skills Handbook.

44 CHAPTER 2 Cells

Resource Manager

Chapter Resources Booklet
Activity Worksheet, pp. 5–6
Reinforcement, p. 27

Mathematics Skill Activities, p. 5

Active Reading

ReQuest To improve listening skills, have students listen carefully as you read an interesting article or story aloud. After the reading, have students construct discussion questions. Have students participate in a ReQuest with the chapter feature or another interesting article related to cell structure or function.

From Cell to Organism

Many one-celled organisms perform all their life functions by themselves. Cells in a many-celled organism, however, do not work alone. Each cell carries on its own life functions while depending in some way on other cells in the organism.

In **Figure 11,** you can see cardiac muscle cells grouped together to form a tissue. A **tissue** is a group of similar cells that work together to do one job. Each cell in a tissue does its part to keep the tissue alive.

Tissues are organized into organs. An **organ** is a structure made up of two or more different types of tissues that work together. Your heart is an organ made up of cardiac muscle tissue, nerve tissue, and blood tissues. The cardiac muscle tissue contracts, making the heart pump. The nerve tissue brings messages that tell the heart how fast to beat. The blood tissue is carried from the heart to other organs of the body.

Reading Check *What type of tissues make up your heart?*

A group of organs working together to perform a certain function is an organ system. Your heart, arteries, veins, and capillaries make up your cardiovascular system. In a many-celled organism, several systems work together in order to perform life functions efficiently. Your nervous, circulatory, respiratory, muscular, and other systems work together to keep you alive.

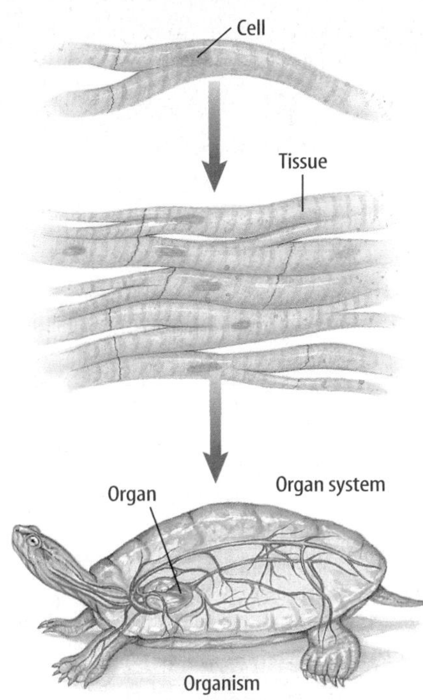

Figure 11
In a many-celled organism, cells are organized into tissues, tissues into organs, organs into systems, and systems into an organism.

Section 1 Assessment

1. Explain the important role of the nucleus in the life of a cell.
2. Compare and contrast the energy processing organelles.
3. Why are digestive enzymes in a cell enclosed in a membrane-bound organelle?
4. How are cells, tissues, organs, and organ systems related?
5. **Think Critically** How is the cell of a one-celled organism different from the cells in many-celled organisms?

Skill Builder Activities

6. **Interpreting Scientific Illustrations** Examine the illustrations of the animal cell and the plant cell in **Figure 6** and make a list of differences and similarities between them. **For more help, refer to the** Science Skill Handbook.
7. **Communicating** Your textbook compared some cell functions to that of a deli. In your Science Journal, write an essay that explains how a cell is like your school or town. **For more help, refer to the** Science Skill Handbook.

From Cell to Organism

Reading Check

Answer cardiac muscle tissue, nerve tissue, and blood tissue

3 Assess

Reteach

What are the differences between plant and animal cells? Most plant cells contain chloroplasts and cell walls; animal cells do not. **What is the difference between a prokaryotic and eukaryotic cell?** Eukaryotic cells have membrane-bound structures; prokaryotic cells do not.

Challenge

How do the cell walls, chloroplasts, and vacuoles of plant cells illustrate that cell structure is related to cell function? Cell walls, chloroplasts, and vacuoles provide the cell with protection, photosynthesis, and storage.

Assessment

Process To further assess students' abilities to compare and contrast different cell types, have them write statements in their Science Journals comparing animal and plant cells. Use **PASC,** p. 175.

Answers to Section Assessment

1. It directs the activities of the cell and stores hereditary information.
2. The chlorophyll in chloroplasts captures light energy and stores it as chemical energy in sugar molecules. Mitochondria release the energy stored in food.
3. It prevents the digestive chemicals inside from destroying the cell.
4. Organ systems are made of organs, which are made of tissues. Tissues are made of cells.
5. one-celled—performs all life functions; many-celled—cells depend on each other
6. Plant cells have chloroplasts and cell walls which animal cells do not have. Unlike plant cells, animal cells have centrioles.
7. A town or school has many parts. Different people supply services. Each person has a job. Each building has a function. All these things working together make the town or school function properly. A cell has many parts. The different parts of a cell have jobs, and each part helps the cell carry out its life processes.

Activity

BENCH TESTED

Purpose Students identify and compare the parts of a plant and animal cell. L2 ELL

LS **Visual-Spatial**

Process Skills observing, identifying, inferring, diagramming, comparing and contrasting, classifying

Time Required 45 minutes

Alternate Materials If *Elodea* is unavailable, cell parts can be seen in the thin, newest leaves of a coleus plant or similar houseplant.

Safety Precautions Caution students to use extreme care when working with a microscope and microscope slides.

Teaching Strategies

- Have students work in pairs. One student obtains and sets up the microscope while the other prepares the wet mount and obtains the cheek-cell slide. Both observe the slides and record data.
- Have students clean slides and coverslips after use.

Troubleshooting To see movement of cytoplasm, use only leaves from the tips of *Elodea.* Help students focus so they will see cell layers. Students may not be able to see the nucleus because most cell parts need to be stained to be visible. Many students may mistake the chloroplast for the cells, not realizing that the chloroplasts are *inside* the larger structure.

Answers to Questions

1. The *Elodea* cell is rectangular; the cheek cell is oval.
2. Only plant cells have a cell wall and chloroplasts.

Activity

Comparing Cells

If you compared a goldfish to a rose, you would find them unlike each other. Are their individual cells different also? Try this activity to compare plant and animal cells.

What You'll Investigate

How do human cheek cells and plant cells compare?

Materials

microscope
microscope slide
coverslip
forceps
tap water
dropper
Elodea plant
prepared slide of human cheek cells

Goal

- **Compare and contrast** an animal cell and a plant cell.

Safety Precautions

Procedure

1. Copy the data table in your Science Journal. Check off the cell parts as you observe them.

Cell Observations

Cell Part	Cheek	*Elodea*
Cytoplasm	✔	✔
Nucleus	✔	✔
Chloroplasts		✔
Cell Wall		✔
Cell Membrane	✔	✔

2. Using forceps, make a wet-mount slide of a young leaf from the tip of an *Elodea* plant.
3. **Observe** the leaf on low power. Focus on the top layer of cells.
4. Switch to high power and focus on one cell. In the center of the cell is a membrane-bound organelle called the central vacuole. Observe the chloroplasts—the green, disk-shaped objects moving around the central vacuole. Try to find the cell nucleus. It looks like a clear ball.
5. **Draw** the *Elodea* cell. Label the cell wall, cytoplasm, chloroplasts, central vacuole, and nucleus. Return to low power and remove the slide. Properly dispose of the slide.
6. **Observe** the prepared slide of cheek cells under low power.
7. Switch to high power and observe the cell nucleus. Draw and label the cell membrane, cytoplasm, and nucleus. Return to low power and remove the slide.

Conclude and Apply

1. **Compare and contrast** the shapes of the cheek cell and the *Elodea* cell.
2. What can you conclude about the differences between plant and animal cells?

Communicating Your Data

Draw the two kinds of cells on one sheet of paper. Use a green pencil to label the organelles found only in plants, a red pencil to label the organelles found only in animals, and a blue pencil to label the organelles found in both. **For more help, refer to the** Science Skill Handbook.

Assessment

Performance To further assess students' abilities to compare plant and animal cells, have them examine cells from lettuce leaves and other types of animal cells on prepared slides. Use **Performance Assessment in the Science Classroom,** p. 97.

Communicating Your Data

Chloroplasts and cell walls should be labeled in green on the plant cell. No organelles are labeled red. Cytoplasm, nuclei, and cell membranes should be labeled in blue, on plant and animal cells.

SECTION

2 Viewing Cells

Magnifying Cells

The number of living things in your environment that you can't see is much greater than the number that you can see. Many of the things that you cannot see are only one cell in size. To see most cells, you need to use a microscope.

Trying to see separate cells in a leaf, like the ones in **Figure 12,** is like trying to see individual photos in a photo mosaic picture that is on the wall across the room. As you walk toward the wall, it becomes easier to see the individual photos. When you get right up to the wall, you can see details of each small photo. A microscope has one or more lenses that enlarge the image of an object as though you are walking closer to it. Seen through these lenses, the leaf appears much closer to you, and you can see the individual cells that carry on life processes.

Early Microscopes In the late 1500s, the first microscope was made by a Dutch maker of reading glasses. He put two magnifying glasses together in a tube and got an image that was larger than the image that was made by either lens alone.

In the mid 1600s, Antonie van Leeuwenhoek, a Dutch fabric merchant, made a simple microscope with a tiny glass bead for a lens, as shown in **Figure 13.** With it, he reported seeing things in pond water that no one had ever imagined. His microscope could magnify up to 270 times. Another way to say this is that his microscope could make the image of an object 270 times larger than its actual size. Today you would say his lens had a power of 270×. Early compound microscopes were crude by today's standards. The lenses would make an image larger, but it wasn't always sharp or clear.

As You Read

***What* You'll Learn**

- **Compare** the differences between the compound light microscope and the electron microscope.
- **Summarize** the discoveries that led to the development of the cell theory.
- **Relate** the cell theory to modern biology.

Vocabulary
cell theory

***Why* It's Important**
Humans are like other living things because they are made of cells.

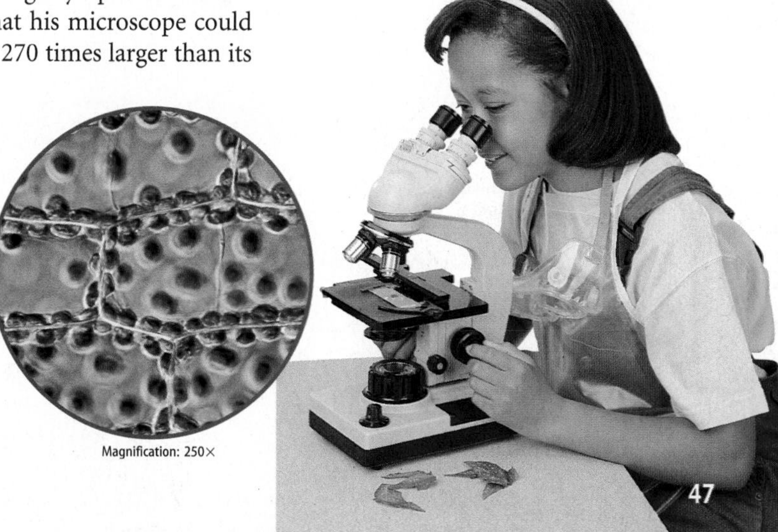

Figure 12
Individual cells become visible when a plant leaf is viewed using a microscope with enough magnifying power.

SECTION

Viewing Cells

1 Motivate

Bellringer Transparency

Display the Section Focus Transparency for Section 2. Use the accompanying Transparency Activity Master. L2 ELL

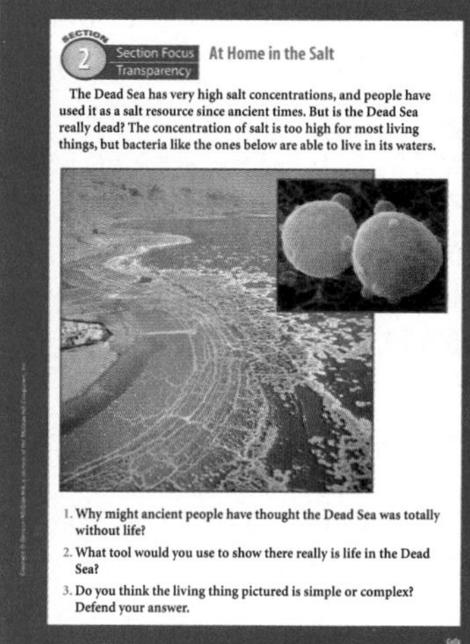

Tie to Prior Knowledge

Students may have used magnifying glasses and binoculars. Explain that a microscope magnifies in the same way.

Section *Assessment* Planner

Portfolio
Assessment, p. 51

Performance Assessment
Try at Home MiniLAB, p. 50
Skill Builder Activities, p. 51
See page 62 for more options.

Content Assessment
Section, p. 51
Challenge, p. 51
Chapter, pp. 62–63

Resource Manager

Chapter Resources Booklet
Transparency Activities, p. 45
Directed Reading for Content Mastery, p. 20

Visualizing Microscopes

Have students examine the pictures and read the captions. Then ask the following questions.

What are the similarities and differences between a fluorescence microscope and a phase-contrast microscope? Possible answers: Both microscopes magnify up to 1500x. With the fluorescence microscope, the specimen must be stained and can be viewed through the scope directly. With the phase-contrast microscope, the specimen is not stained and can only be viewed on a monitor or in a photograph. Phase-contrast microscopes are good for viewing living things.

Compare and contrast the features of a TEM and an SEM. Possible answers: Both microscope use electrons to help produce the magnified image. Also, with both microscopes the specimen can only be viewed on a monitor or in a photograph. In a TEM the electrons go through the specimen and the magnification is up to 1,000,000×. With an SEM, the electrons sweep over the surface of the specimen and a three-dimensional image is produced. The magnification of an SEM is only up to 200,000×.

Activity

Have students identify the type of microscope(s) they use in science class. Then have students view different slides under the microscope (e.g. onion slices, hair, sliver from a grass blade, comics color section of the newspaper). Have students draw what they observe. If possible, use several types of microscopes and a magnifying glass and have students compare how the same slide looks under each one. Ask students to list the similarities and differences between them, and hypothesize what accounts for these differences.

NATIONAL GEOGRAPHIC **VISUALIZING MICROSCOPES**

Figure 13

Microscopes give us a glimpse into a previously invisible world. Improvements have vastly increased their range of visibility, allowing researchers to study life at the molecular level. A selection of these powerful tools—and their magnification power—is shown here.

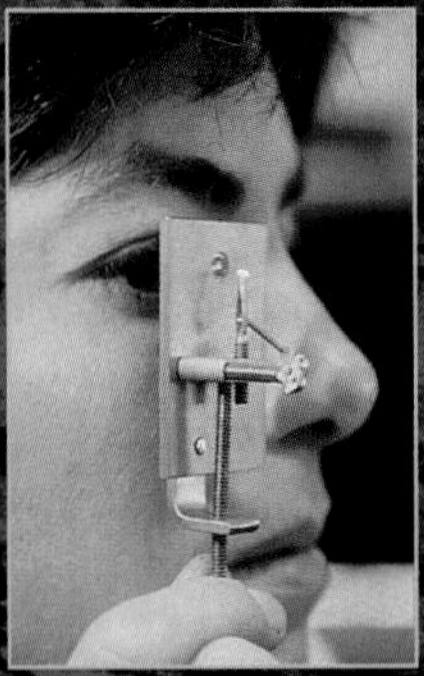

▶ **Up to 250x** LEEUWENHOEK MICROSCOPE Held by a modern researcher, this historic microscope allowed Leeuwenhoek to see clear images of tiny freshwater organisms that he called "beasties."

▼ **Up to 2,000x** BRIGHTFIELD / DARKFIELD MICROSCOPE The light microscope is often called the brightfield microscope because the image is viewed against a bright background. A brightfield microscope is the tool most often used in laboratories to study cells. Placing a thin metal disc beneath the stage, between the light source and the objective lenses, converts a brightfield microscope to a darkfield microscope. The image seen using a darkfield microscope is bright against a dark background. This makes details more visible than with a brightfield microscope. Below are images of a *Paramecium* as seen using both processes.

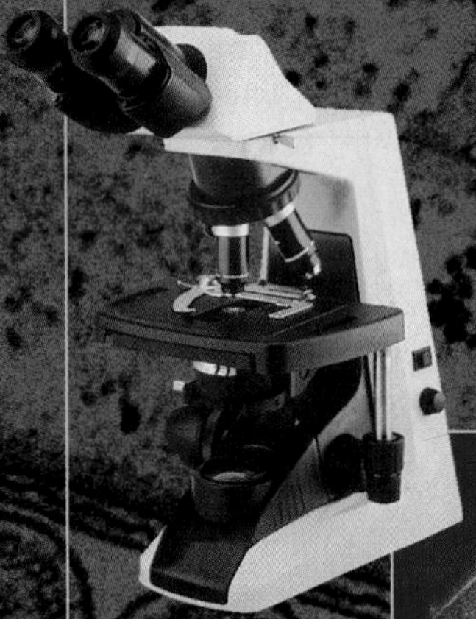

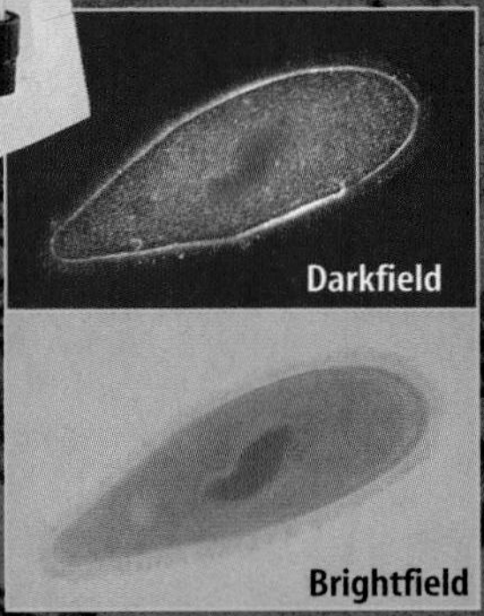

Darkfield

Brightfield

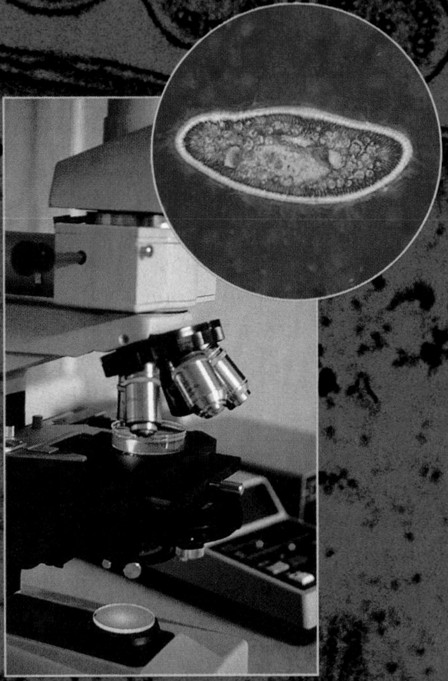

▲ **Up to 1,500x** FLUORESCENCE MICROSCOPE This type of microscope requires that the specimen be treated with special fluorescent stains. When viewed through this microscope, certain cell structures or types of substances glow, as seen in the image of a *Paramecium* above.

48 CHAPTER 2 Cells

Science Journal

Magnification Have students make a time line showing discoveries made with the light microscope, beginning with Robert Hooke (1665) identifying and drawing cells. L2

Teacher FYI

Any phenomena that occurs as a result of the fixing or staining procedure used to prepare a specimen to be viewed on a slide is called an artifact. An artifact is not a feature of the living organism. Sometimes an artifact can be a simple air bubble, other times the procedure can change the shape of a particular feature.

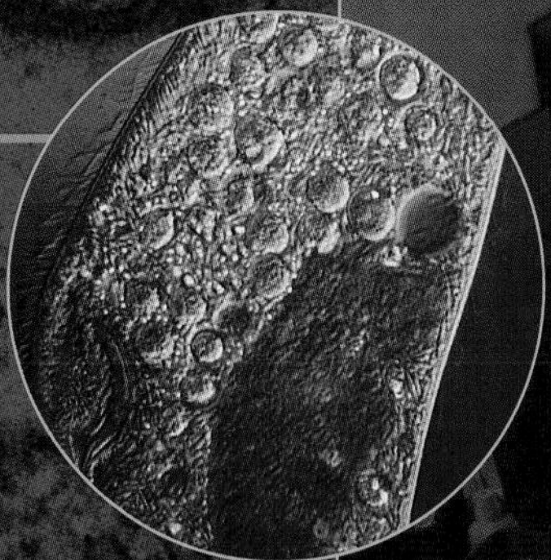

Up to 1,000,000x TRANSMISSION ELECTRON MICROSCOPE A TEM aims a beam of electrons through a specimen. Denser portions of the specimen allow fewer electrons to pass through and appear darker in the image. Organisms, such as the *Paramecium* at right, can only be seen when the image is photographed or shown on a monitor. A TEM can magnify hundreds of thousands of times.

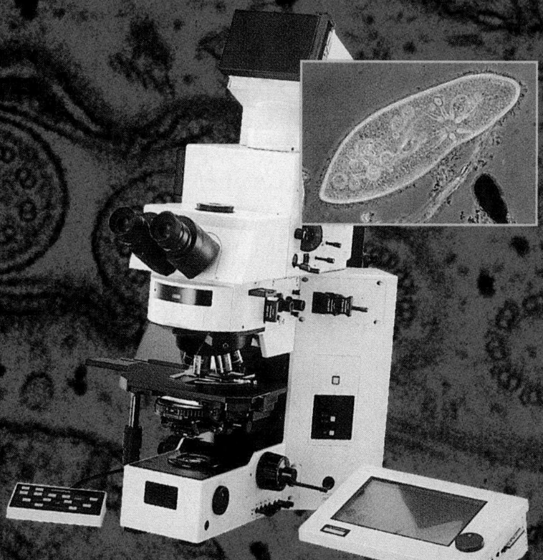

Up to 1,500x PHASE-CONTRAST MICROSCOPE A phase-contrast microscope emphasizes slight differences in a specimen's capacity to bend light waves, thereby enhancing light and dark regions without the use of stains. This type of microscope is especially good for viewing living cells, like the *Paramecium* above left. The images from a phase-contrast microscope can only be seen when the specimen is photographed or shown on a monitor.

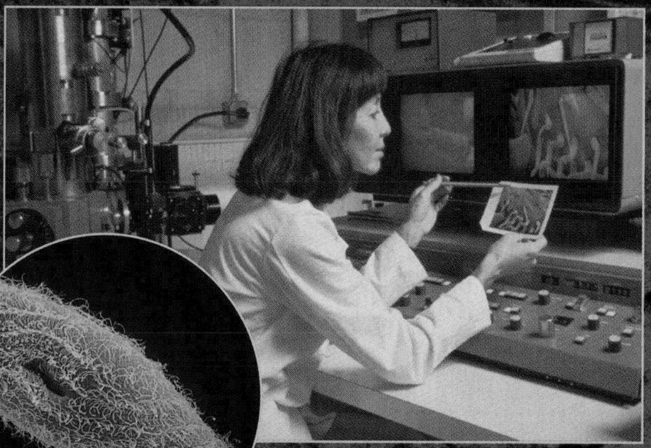

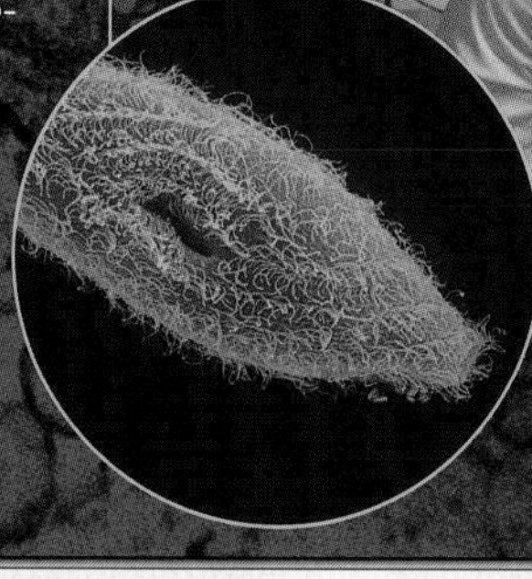

Up to 200,000x SCANNING ELECTRON MICROSCOPE An SEM sweeps a beam of electrons over a specimen's surface, causing other electrons to be emitted from the specimen. SEMs produce realistic, three-dimensional images, which can only be viewed as photographs or on a monitor, as in the image of the *Paramecium* at right. Here a researcher compares an SEM picture to a computer monitor showing an enhanced image.

SECTION 2 Viewing Cells 49

NATIONAL GEOGRAPHIC

Visualizing Microscopes

Extension

Have students do a simple experiment involving refraction. Pour a quarter cup of water into a clear glass jar or beaker. Place a ruler in the beaker so that it is leaning against the top rim. Gently pour in a quarter cup each of cooking oil and rubbing alcohol successively. Do not stir. Have students record their observations regarding the appearance of the ruler. Students should see refraction of light as it passes through the different mediums as evidenced by the ruler appearing as though it is misshapen. Have students look up the definition of refraction and relate it to what they are seeing.

Content Background

Microscopes are used by many different types of scientists including, biologists, microbiologists, botanists, geologists, and epidemiologists. In 1665, Robert Hooke was the first person to see cells through a microscope of his creation. The idea of cell theory-that all living things are made of cells- was borne from his discovery. Although Hooke could see the individual cells clearly, he did not stain any of his specimens, therefore, he would not have been able to see other single-celled organisms such as bacteria. It was Antoni van Leeuwenhoek who first examined living organisms through a simple microscope in the late seventeenth century. He found organisms in the rain water he collected, as well as in the scrapings he took from the surface of his teeth.

Resource Manager

Chapter Resources Booklet
Enrichment, p. 31
Lab Activity, pp. 9–12, 13–16

Science Inquiry Labs, p. 3

Visual Learning

Figure 13 Have students make a chart comparing and contrasting the different types of microscopes in this figure. They should include information on lenses and the uses of each. L2

 **Visual-Spatial**

2 Teach

Magnifying Cells

Purpose Students discover objects that can be used to magnify. L2 ELL LS **Kinesthetic**

Materials clear drinking glass, clear glass bowl, water, magnifying glass, newspaper pages

Teaching Strategy Try this activity with the glasses students will use. Determine beforehand the amount of water that will be needed.

Analysis

Each of the objects magnifies the newsprint.

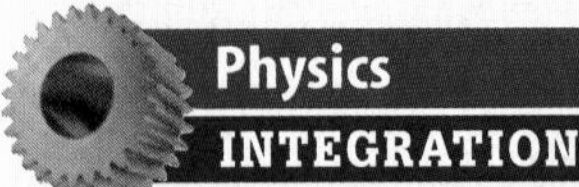

Performance Cover newsprint with clear plastic wrap. Place a drop of water on the plastic wrap. Have students explain what they see and why. The words appear magnified because the water drop acts like a convex lens. Use **Performance Assessment in the Science Classroom,** p. 97.

Physics INTEGRATION

A convex lens is thicker in the middle than at the edges. This causes the light rays to bend inward and meet at a point. Placing the object to be viewed a certain distance from the convex lens produces an enlarged image.

Observing Magnified Objects

Procedure

1. Look at a **newspaper** through the curved side and through the flat bottom of an **empty, clear glass.**
2. Look at the newspaper through a **clear glass bowl** filled with **water** and then with a **magnifying glass.**

Analysis

In your Science Journal, compare how well you can see the newspaper through each of the objects.

Modern Microscopes Scientists use a variety of microscopes to study organisms, cells, and cell parts that are too small to be seen with the human eye. Depending on how many lenses a microscope contains, it is called simple or compound. A simple microscope is similar to a magnifying glass. It has only one lens. A microscope's lens makes an enlarged image of an object and directs light toward your eye. The change in apparent size produced by a microscope is called magnification. Microscopes vary in powers of magnification. Some microscopes can make images of individual atoms.

The microscope you probably will use to study life science is a compound light microscope, similar to the one in the Reference Handbook at the back of this book. The compound light microscope has two sets of lenses—eyepiece lenses and objective lenses. The eyepiece lenses are mounted in one or two tubelike structures. Images of objects viewed through two eyepieces, or stereomicroscopes, are three-dimensional. Images of objects viewed through one eyepiece are not. Compound light microscopes usually have two to four movable objective lenses.

Magnification The powers of the eyepiece and objective lenses determine the total magnifications of a microscope. If the eyepiece lens has a power of 10× and the objective lens has a power of 43×, then the total magnification is 430× (10× times 43×). Some compound microscopes, like those in **Figure 13,** have more powerful lenses that can magnify an object up to 2,000 times its original size.

Physics INTEGRATION

A magnifying glass is a convex lens. All microscopes use one or more convex lenses. In your Science Journal, diagram a convex lens and describe its shape.

Electron Microscopes Things that are too small to be seen with other microscopes can be viewed with an electron microscope. Instead of using lenses to direct beams of light, an electron microscope uses a magnetic field in a vacuum to direct beams of electrons. Some electron microscopes can magnify images up to one million times. Electron microscope images must be photographed or electronically produced.

Several kinds of electron microscopes have been invented, as shown in **Figure 13.** Scanning electron microscopes (SEM) produce a realistic, three-dimensional image. Only the surface of the specimen can be observed using an SEM. Transmission electron microscopes (TEM) produce a two-dimensional image of a thinly-sliced specimen. Details of cell parts can be examined using a TEM. Scanning tunneling microscopes (STM) are able to show the arrangement of atoms on the surface of a molecule. A metal probe is placed near the surface of the specimen and electrons flow from the tip. The hills and valleys of the specimen's surface are mapped.

Curriculum Connection

Art Discuss the use of art in science before the camera was invented. Photocopy a picture of Hooke's drawing of cells for each student. Ask them to compare it with the photographs of cells throughout the chapter and write in their Science Journals their opinions of the advantages and disadvantages of using artwork and photography. L2 LS **Linguistic and Visual-Spatial**

Resource Manager

Chapter Resources Booklet

MiniLAB, p. 4

Reinforcement, p. 28

Development of the Cell Theory

During the seventeenth century, scientists used their new invention, the microscope, to explore the newly discovered microscopic world. They examined drops of blood, scrapings from their own teeth, and other small things. Cells weren't discovered until the microscope was improved. In 1665, Robert Hooke cut a thin slice of cork and looked at it under his microscope. To Hooke, the cork seemed to be made up of empty little boxes, which he named cells.

In the 1830s, Matthias Schleiden used a microscope to study plant parts. He concluded that all plants are made of cells. Theodor Schwann, after observing many different animal cells, concluded that all animals also are made up of cells. Eventually, they combined their ideas and became convinced that all living things are made of cells.

Several years later, Rudolf Virchow hypothesized that cells divide to form new cells. Virchow proposed that every cell came from a cell that already existed. His observations and conclusions and those of others are summarized in the **cell theory,** as described in **Table 1.**

Table 1 The Cell Theory

All organisms are made up of one or more cells.	An organism can be one cell or many cells like most plants and animals.
The cell is the basic unit of organization in organisms.	Even in complex organisms, the cell is the basic unit of structure and function.
All cells come from cells.	Most cells can divide to form two new, identical cells.

✔ Reading Check *Who made the conclusion that all animals are made of cells?*

Section  Assessment

1. Explain why the invention of the microscope was important in the study of cells.
2. What is stated in the cell theory?
3. What is the difference between a simple and a compound light microscope?
4. What was Virchow's contribution to the cell theory?
5. **Think Critically** Why would it be better to look at living cells than at dead cells?

Skill Builder Activities

6. **Concept Mapping** Using a network tree concept map, compare a compound light microscope to an electron microscope. **For more help, refer to the** Science Skill Handbook.
7. **Solving One-Step Equations** Calculate the magnifications of a microscope that has an 8× eyepiece, and 10× and 40× objectives. **For more help, refer to the** Math Skill Handbook.

Development of the Cell Theory

Teacher FYI

Hooke saw only cell walls. When plant cells die, the cell wall remains. Tree bark is dead tissue. The cork that Hooke examined comes from the bark of an oak tree.

✔ Reading Check

Answer Theodor Schwann

3 Assess

Reteach

Place a large drawing of a compound microscope on the bulletin board. Write the functions of each part on a 3 x 5 card. Have students select a card, name the part, and find it on the drawing. L1 COOP LEARN LS **Visual-Spatial**

Challenge

How does the cell theory contradict the theory that living things come from nonliving things? It shows that cells are the basic units of life, all organisms are made of one or more cells, and all cells come from existing cells.

✔ Assessment

Portfolio Have students write a paragraph describing the limitations as they understand them of each microscope presented in this section. Use **PASC,** p. 157. P

Answers to Section Assessment

1. Microscopes made cells visible, which established them as a scientific fact. This led to the understanding that all living things are made of cells.
2. All organisms are made of one or more cells. The cell is the basic unit of organization in organisms. All cells come from other cells.
3. A simple light microscope has one lens. A compound light microscope has two or more lenses.
4. Virchow proposed that every cell came from a cell that already existed.
5. Possible answer: some cell parts disintegrate when the cell dies.
6. Map should include the following information: compound light microscopes—use light, magnify up to 2000×; electron microscopes—use electrons, magnify up to 1,000,000×.
7. The low-power magnification is 80× = (8 × 10) and the high-power magnification is 320× = (8 × 40).

SECTION 3

Viruses

1 Motivate

Bellringer Transparency

Display the Section Focus Transparency for Section 3. Use the accompanying Transparency Activity Master. L2 ELL

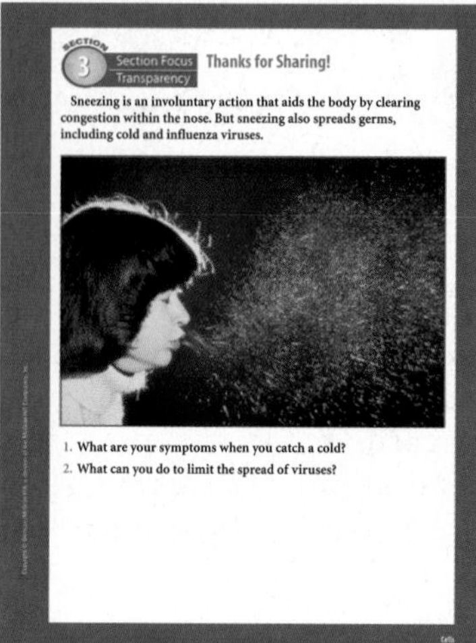
Section 3 Section Focus Transparency Thanks for Sharing!

Sneezing is an involuntary action that aids the body by clearing congestion within the nose. But sneezing also spreads germs, including cold and influenza viruses.

1. What are your symptoms when you catch a cold?
2. What can you do to limit the spread of viruses?

Tie to Prior Knowledge

Most students will be familiar with at least one viral disease (chicken pox, cold sores, the common cold). Have them list its symptoms on the board.

SECTION 3

Viruses

As You Read

***What* You'll Learn**

- **Explain** how a virus makes copies of itself.
- **Identify** the benefits of vaccines.
- **Investigate** some uses of viruses.

Vocabulary

virus
host cell

***Why* It's Important**

Viruses infect nearly all organisms, usually affecting them negatively yet sometimes affecting them positively.

What are viruses?

Cold sores, measles, chicken pox, colds, the flu, and AIDS are diseases caused by nonliving particles called viruses. A **virus** is a strand of hereditary material surrounded by a protein coating. Viruses don't have a nucleus or other organelles. They also lack a cell membrane. Viruses, as shown in **Figure 14,** have a variety of shapes. Because they are too small to be seen with a light microscope, they were discovered only after the electron microscope was invented. Before that time, scientists only hypothesized about viruses.

How do viruses multiply?

All viruses can do is make copies of themselves. However, they can't do that without the help of a living cell called a **host cell.** Crystalized forms of some viruses can be stored for years. Then, if they enter an organism, they can multiply quickly.

Once a virus is inside of a host cell, the virus can act in two ways. It can either be active or it can become latent, which is an inactive stage.

Figure 14
Viruses come in a variety of shapes.

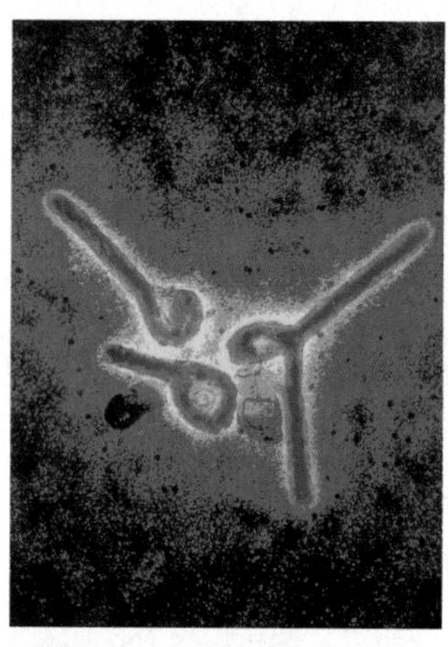
A Filoviruses do not have uniform shapes. Some of these *Ebola* viruses have a loop at one end.

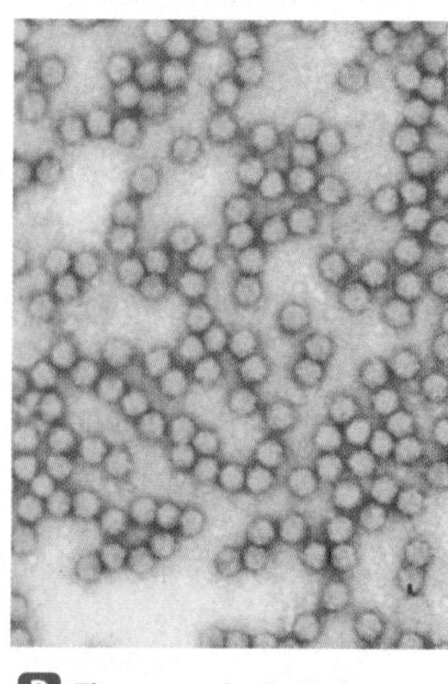
B The potato leafroll virus, *Polervirus*, damages potato crops worldwide.

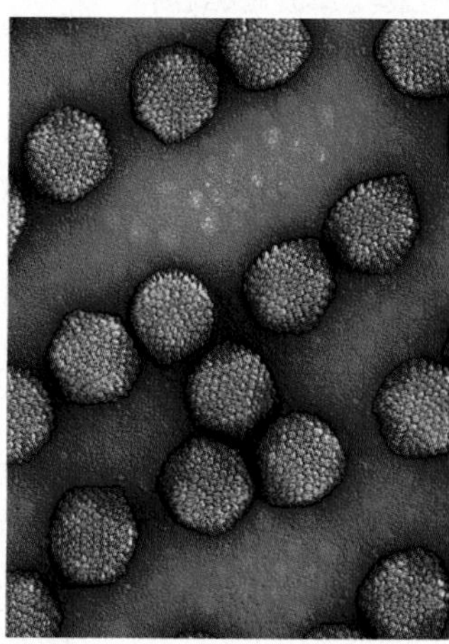
C This is just one of the many adenoviruses that can cause the common cold.

Section Assessment Planner

PORTFOLIO
Extension, p. 54

PERFORMANCE ASSESSMENT
Skill Builder Activities, p. 55
See page 62 for more options.

CONTENT ASSESSMENT
Section, p. 55
Challenge, p. 55
Chapter, pp. 62–63

Figure 15
An active virus multiplies and destroys the host cell. A The virus attaches to a specific host cell. B The virus's hereditary material enters the host cell. C The hereditary material of the virus causes the cell to make viral hereditary material and proteins. D New viruses form inside of the host cell. E New viruses are released as the host cell bursts open and is destroyed.

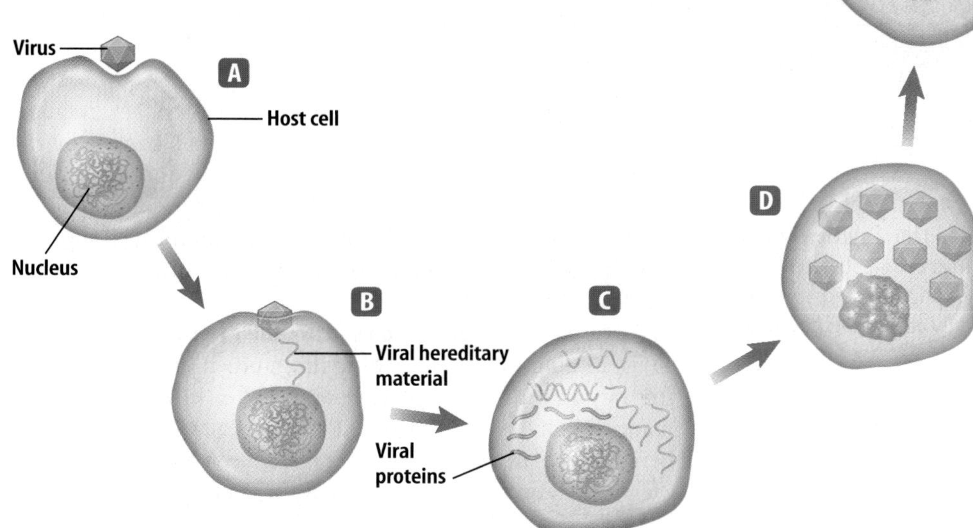

Active Viruses When a virus enters a cell and is active, it causes the host cell to make new viruses. This process destroys the host cell. Follow the steps in **Figure 15** to see one way that an active virus functions inside a cell.

Latent Viruses Some viruses can be latent. That means that after the virus enters a cell, its hereditary material can become part of the cell's hereditary material. It does not immediately make new viruses or destroy the cell. As the host cell reproduces, the viral DNA is copied. A virus can be latent for many years. Then, at any time, certain conditions, either inside or outside your body, can activate the virus.

If you have had a cold sore on your lip, a latent virus in your body has become active. The cold sore is a sign that the virus is active and destroying cells in your lip. When the cold sore disappears, the virus has become latent again. The virus is still in your body's cells, but it is hiding and doing no apparent harm.

SCIENCE Online

Research Visit the Glencoe Science Web site at **science.glencoe.com** for information on viruses. What environmental stimuli might activate a latent virus? Record your answer in your Science Journal.

2 Teach

How do viruses multiply?

Visual Learning

Figure 15 Have students make a concept map outlining the steps of viral infection and replication shown in this figure.

Explore the Glencoe Science Web site at **science.glencoe.com** to find out more about topics in this section.

Resource Manager

Chapter Resources Booklet
Transparency Activity, p. 46
Directed Reading for Content Mastery, pp. 21, 22
Enrichment, p. 32

LAB DEMONSTRATION

Purpose to model two viruses

Materials bolt, 2 nuts to fit bolt, 2 pieces #22 gauge wire cut in 14-cm lengths, polystyrene ball 4.5 cm in diameter, craft sticks cut in 2-cm lengths

Preparation Prepare the materials and provide pictures of a bacteriophage and a flu virus.

Procedure Have students use the bacteriophage picture, the bolt, nuts, and wire to make a model bacteriophage. Have them use the polystyrene ball and craft sticks to make a model flu virus.

Expected Outcome Students should observe that different viruses have different structures.

Assessment

In a real virus, what would make up the threaded part of the bolt and the wires? protein **If your flu virus were a real virus, what would you expect to find inside the ball?** hereditary material

How do viruses affect organisms?

Extension

Have students report on a specific virus. The report should give the shape of the virus, the organism infected, and symptoms of the infection. Possible viruses: hog cholera, wilt disease, HIV, Ebola, smallpox, and ringspot disease

L3 LS **Linguistic** P

Fighting Viruses

Use Science Words

Word Usage Have students use the word *vaccine* in a sentence describing its characteristics. L2 LS **Linguistic**

Extension

Have students research the use of viruses in genetic engineering to insert genes into people with genetic disorders. L3

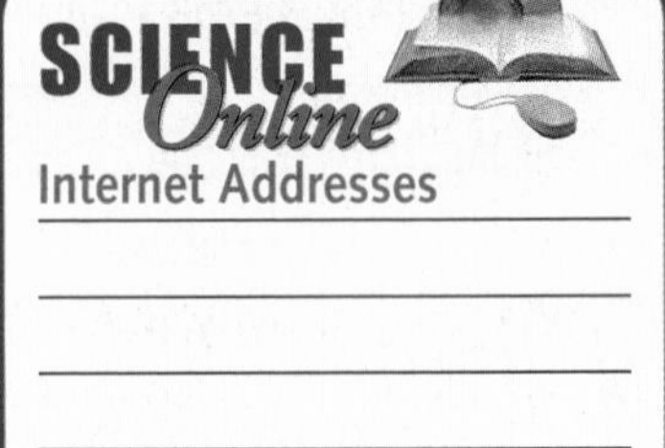

Internet Addresses

Explore the Glencoe Science Web site at **science.glencoe.com** to find out more about topics in this section.

Answer a preparation of weakened virus particles that helps prevent disease

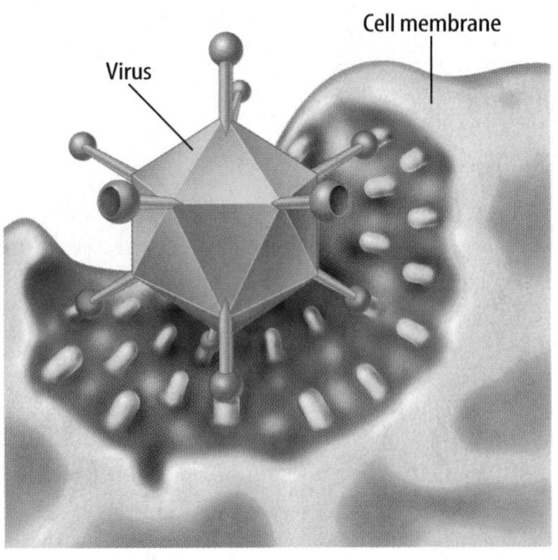

Figure 16
Viruses and the attachment sites of the host cell must match exactly. That's why most viruses infect only one kind of host cell.

How do viruses affect organisms?

Viruses attack animals, plants, fungi, protists, and all prokaryotes. Some viruses can infect only specific kinds of cells. For instance, many viruses, such as the potato leafroll virus, are limited to one host species or to one type of tissue within that species. A few viruses affect a broad range of hosts. An example of this is the rabies virus. Rabies can infect humans and many other animal hosts.

A virus cannot move by itself, but it can reach a host's body in several ways. For example, it can be carried onto a plant's surface by the wind or it can be inhaled by an animal. In a viral infection, the virus first attaches to the surface of the host cell. The virus and the place where it attaches must fit together exactly, as shown in **Figure 16.** Because of this, most viruses attack only one kind of host cell.

Viruses that infect bacteria are called bacteriophages (bak TIHR ee uh fay juhz). They differ from other kinds of viruses in the way that they enter bacteria and release their hereditary material. Bacteriophages attach to a bacterium and inject their hereditary material. The entire cycle takes about 20 min, and each virus-infected cell releases an average of 100 viruses.

SCIENCE Online

Data Update Scientists have determined that *Marburg* virus, *Ebola zaire*, and *Ebola reston* belong to the virus family Filoviridae. Visit the Glencoe Science Web site at **science.glencoe.com** for the latest information about these viruses. Share your results with your class.

Fighting Viruses

Vaccines are used to prevent disease. A vaccine is made from weakened virus particles that can't cause disease anymore. Vaccines have been made to prevent many diseases, including measles, mumps, smallpox, chicken pox, polio, and rabies.

Reading Check *What is a vaccine?*

The First Vaccine Edward Jenner is credited with developing the first vaccine in 1796. He developed a vaccine for smallpox, a disease that was still feared in the early twentieth century. Jenner noticed that people who got a disease called cowpox didn't get smallpox. He prepared a vaccine from the sores of people who had cowpox. When injected into healthy people, the cowpox vaccine protected them from smallpox. Jenner didn't know he was fighting a virus. At that time, no one understood what caused disease or how the body fought disease.

Curriculum Connection

Math A common unit of measure for viruses is the nanometer (nm), which is 1,000 times smaller than a micrometer (μm) and 1 million times smaller than a millimeter. A typical virus is 20 nm in size. What part of a millimeter is that? 0.000 02 mm A virus of 0.3 micrometers is how many nanometers? 300 nm

L2 LS **Logical-Mathematical**

Resource Manager

Chapter Resources Booklet
Reinforcement, p. 29
Reading and Writing Skill Activities, p. 31

54 CHAPTER 2 Cells

Treating and Preventing Viral Diseases Antibiotics are used to treat bacterial infections. They are ineffective against any viral disease. One way your body can stop viral infections is by making interferons. Interferons are proteins that protect cells from viruses. These proteins are produced rapidly by infected cells and move to noninfected cells in the host. They cause the noninfected cells to produce protective substances.

Antiviral drugs can be given to infected patients to help fight a virus. A few drugs show some effectiveness against viruses but some have limited use because of their adverse side effects.

Public health measures for preventing viral diseases include vaccinating people, improving sanitary conditions, quarantining patients, and controlling animals that spread the disease. Yellow fever was wiped out completely in the United States through mosquito-control programs. Annual rabies vaccinations protect humans by keeping pets and farm animals free from infection. To control the spread of rabies in wild animals such as coyotes and wolves, wildlife workers place bait containing an oral rabies vaccine, as shown in **Figure 17,** where wild animals will find it.

Figure 17
This oral rabies bait is being prepared for an aerial drop by the Texas Department of Health as part of their Oral Rabies Vaccination Program. This five-year program has prevented the expansion of rabies into Texas.

Research with Viruses

You might think viruses are always harmful. However, through research, scientists are discovering helpful uses for some viruses. One use, called gene therapy, is being tried on cells with defective genes. Normal hereditary material is substituted for a cell's defective hereditary material. The normal material is enclosed in viruses. The viruses then "infect" targeted cells, taking the new hereditary material into the cells to replace the defective hereditary material. Using gene therapy, scientists hope to help people with genetic disorders and find a cure for cancer.

Section 3 Assessment

1. Describe the structure of viruses and explain how viruses multiply.
2. How are vaccines beneficial?
3. How might some viruses be helpful?
4. How might viral diseases be prevented?
5. **Think Critically** Explain why a doctor might not give you any medication if you have a viral disease.

Skill Builder Activities

6. **Concept Mapping** Make an events chain concept map to show what happens when a latent virus becomes active. **For more help, refer to the** Science Skill Handbook.
7. **Using a Word Processor** Make an outline of the cycle of an active virus. **For more help, refer to the** Technology Skill Handbook.

Teacher FYI

Even though bacteriophages typically inject their DNA into the host cell, not all viruses invade a host cell in this way. Many animal viruses enter the host cell through endocytosis, the binding of the virus to the cell membrane. Once inside the host cell, the virus sheds its protein coat and either undergoes replication or becomes part of the host's DNA.

Research with Viruses

Use Science Words

Word Meaning Have students look up the terms *lysis*, *virion*, and *virology*. Have them write a paragraph about the relevance of each to the study of viruses. L2 LS **Linguistic**

3 Assess

Reteach

Have students write a paragraph that describes the differences between active and latent viruses. L1 LS **Linguistic**

Challenge

Some advertisements imply that their medicine will cure a cold even though it can't. **How would a real cure for the common cold work?** A cure must disrupt the replication cycle. It could prevent the virus from entering the cell or replicating.

Answers to Section Assessment

1. A virus is a particle of hereditary material surrounded by protein. Viruses are reproduced only in a host cell. The host cell is destroyed when the viruses are released.
2. Vaccines, when properly administered, help prevent many viral infections.
3. They may be used to transfer normal DNA into a cell.
4. vaccinating people, improving sanitary conditions, quarantining patients, and controlling animals that spread disease
5. No medications cure a viral disease.
6. Maps should show the following: latent virus enters cell; virus becomes part of cell's DNA; cell divides; virus reproduces as part of cell division; virus becomes active; virus forms new virus particles; cell is destroyed.
7. Outline should be similar to Figure 15.

Assessment

Oral How does a virus invade a cell? The virus's hereditary material enters the cell, which becomes infected and eventually replicates the virus. Use **PASC,** p. 143.

Activity

BENCH TESTED

Recognize the Problem

Purpose

Students will design an experiment to compare uses of stereomicroscopes and compound light microscopes. L2

COOP LEARN

LS **Logical-Mathematical**

Process Skills

observing, identifying, recognizing and using spatial relationships, classifying, communicating

Time Required

15 minutes to plan the experiment and 45 minutes to do the experiment

Safety Precautions

Caution students to use care when working with microscope slides and coverslips. Remind them to carry microscopes with both hands. Have students wash the slides and coverslips when finished.

Form a Hypothesis

Possible Hypothesis

Students may hypothesize that large items can be viewed with the stereomicroscope and small objects can be viewed with the compound light microscope.

Test Your Hypothesis

Possible Procedures

Separate items into two groups: those that can be viewed with the stereomicroscope, and those that can be viewed with the light microscope.

Teaching Strategies

- Demonstrate how to make a wet-mount.
- If microscopes have mirrors, explain how to use them.

Activity Design Your Own Experiment

Comparing Light Microscopes

You're a technician in a police forensic laboratory. You use a stereomicroscope and a compound light microscope in the laboratory. A detective just returned from a crime scene with bags of evidence. You must examine each piece of evidence under a microscope. How do you decide which microscope is the best tool to use?

Recognize the Problem

Will all of the evidence that you've collected be viewable through both microscopes?

Form a Hypothesis

Compare the items to be examined under the microscopes. Which microscope will be used for each item?

Possible Materials

compound light microscope
stereomicroscope
items from the classroom—include some living or once-living items (8)
microscope slides and coverslips
plastic petri dishes
distilled water
dropper

Goals

- **Learn** how to correctly use a stereomicroscope and a compound light microscope.
- **Compare** the uses of the stereomicroscope and compound light microscope.

Safety Precautions

Thoroughly wash your hands when you have completed this experiment.

56

Resource Manager 

Chapter Resources Booklet
Activity Worksheet, pp. 7–8

Home and Community Involvement, p. 26

Lab Management and Safety, p. 58

Test Your Hypothesis

Plan

1. As a group, decide how you will test your hypothesis.
2. **Describe** how you will carry out this experiment using a series of specific steps. Make sure the steps are in a logical order. Remember that you must place an item in the bottom of a plastic petri dish to examine it under the stereomicroscope and you must make a wet mount of any item to be examined under the compound light microscope. For more help, see the Reference Handbook.
3. If you need a data table or an observation table, design one in your Science Journal.

Do

1. Make sure your teacher approves the objects you'll examine, your plan, and your data table before you start.
2. Carry out the experiment.
3. While doing the experiment, record your observations and complete the data table.

Analyze Your Data

1. **Compare** the items you examined with those of your classmates.
2. Based on this experiment, classify the eight items you observed.

Draw Conclusions

1. **Infer** which microscope a scientist might use to examine a blood sample, fibers, and live snails.
2. **List** five careers that require people to use a stereomicroscope. List five careers that require people to use a compound light microscope. Enter the lists in your Science Journal.
3. If you examined an item under a compound light microscope and a stereomicroscope, how would the images differ?
4. Which microscope was better for looking at large, or possibly live items?

Communicating Your Data

In your Science Journal, **write** a short description of an imaginary crime scene and the evidence found there. **Sort** the evidence into two lists—items to be examined under a stereomicroscope and items to be examined under a compound light microscope. **For more help, refer to the** Science Skill Handbook.

Troubleshooting Place slides and coverslips for each group in a plastic petri dish to prevent breakage.

Expected Outcome

The stereomicroscope is used for items that are too large to fit under a coverslip on a slide. The compound light microscope reveals greater detail. Students should note that the image produced by the compound light microscope is upside down and reversed left to right.

Analyze Your Data

1. Answers will vary.
2. Large items should be classified together, and items small enough to fit on a slide should be grouped together.

Error Analysis

Have students compare their results and their hypotheses and explain why differences occurred.

Draw Conclusions

1. A scientist might use a stereomicroscope to examine live snails and a compound light microscope to examine blood and fibers.
2. Answers will vary, but may include lab technicians, forensic scientists, and cell biologists for the compound light microscope and surgeons, botanists, entomologists, geologists, and gemologists for the stereomicroscope.
3. The image under the compound light microscope will be magnified more, show greater detail, be upside down, and reversed left to right.
4. stereomicroscope

Communicating Your Data

Items small enough to fit under a coverslip should be examined with a compound light microscope; larger items should be examined with a stereomicroscope.

Assessment

Performance To further assess students' understanding of the differences in microscopes, provide other items and have students demonstrate how to use the appropriate microscope to view each item. Use **Performance Assessment in the Science Classroom,** p. 169.

Content Background

As a control, Cobb exposed cells from non-cancerous tissues to chemotherapy drugs. She hoped to discover if there was a particular drug or combination of drugs which would be effective in destroying specific types of cancer. She would also need to determine whether these drugs would also destroy healthy tissues.

Her results demonstrated that some drugs could stop the uncontrolled growth of certain types of cancer cells, but normal cells also were harmed. There were differences, however, as normal cells never showed the dramatic destruction produced in some cancer cells.

This suggested that chemotherapy was a viable approach to treatment of cancer.

Levy's research is one example of attempts to find ways to deliver high doses of cancer-killing drugs directly to a tumor while reducing the risk of damage to healthy cells.

TIME SCIENCE AND HISTORY

SCIENCE CAN CHANGE THE COURSE OF HISTORY!

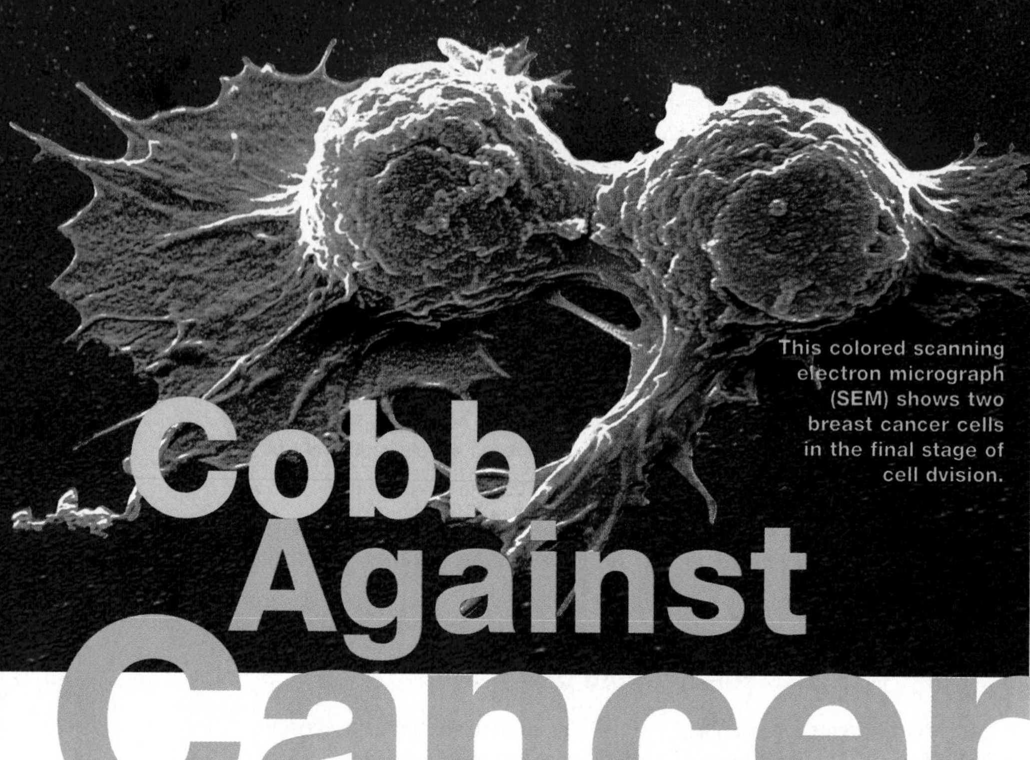

Magnification: 2,000×

This colored scanning electron micrograph (SEM) shows two breast cancer cells in the final stage of cell dvision.

Cobb Against Cancer

New York City, 1950. Jewel Plummer put yet another slide onto the stage of her microscope and clipped it into place. She switched to the high power objective, looked through the eyepiece, and turned the fine adjustment a tiny bit to bring her subject—cells from a cancerous tumor—into focus. She switched back to low power and removed the slide. She had found no change in the tumor cells. The drug that doctors had used wasn't killing or slowing the growth rate of those cancer cells. Sighing, she reached for the next slide. Maybe the slightly different drug they had used on that batch of cells would be the answer....

58

Resources for Teachers and Students

The National Cancer Institute
Public Inquiries Office
Building 31, Room 10A31
31 Center Drive
MSC 2580
Bethesda, MD 20892-2580 USA,
(301) 435-3848

Advancing Current Treatments for Cancer, by Samuel Hellman and Everett E. Vokes, Scientific American, September 1996.

How Cancer Arises, by Robert A. Weinberg, Scientific American, September 1996.

Jewel Plummer Cobb is a cell biologist who did important background research on the use of drugs against cancer. She removed cells from cancerous tumors and cultured them in the lab. Then, in a controlled study, she tried a series of different drugs against batches of the same cells. Her goal was to find the right drug to cure each patient's particular cancer. Cobb never met that goal, but her research laid the groundwork for modern chemotherapy—the use of chemicals to treat people with cancer.

Role Model

Jewel Cobb also influenced the course of science in a different way. She served as dean or president of several universities, retiring as president of the University of California at Fullerton. In her role as a college official, she was able to promote equal opportunity for students of all backgrounds, especially in the sciences.

Light Up a Cure

Vancouver, British Columbia, 2000. While Cobb herself was only able to infer what was going on inside a cell from its reactions to various drugs, her work has helped others go further. Building on Cobb's work, Professor Julia Levy and her research team at the University of British Columbia actually go inside cells and even inside organelles to work against cancer. One technique they are pioneering is the use of light to guide cancer drugs to the right cells. First, the patient is given a chemotherapy drug that reacts to light. Next, a fiber optic tube is inserted into the tumor. Finally, laser light is passed through the tube. The light activates the light-sensitive drug—but only in the tumor itself. This technique keeps healthy cells healthy but kills sick cells on the spot.

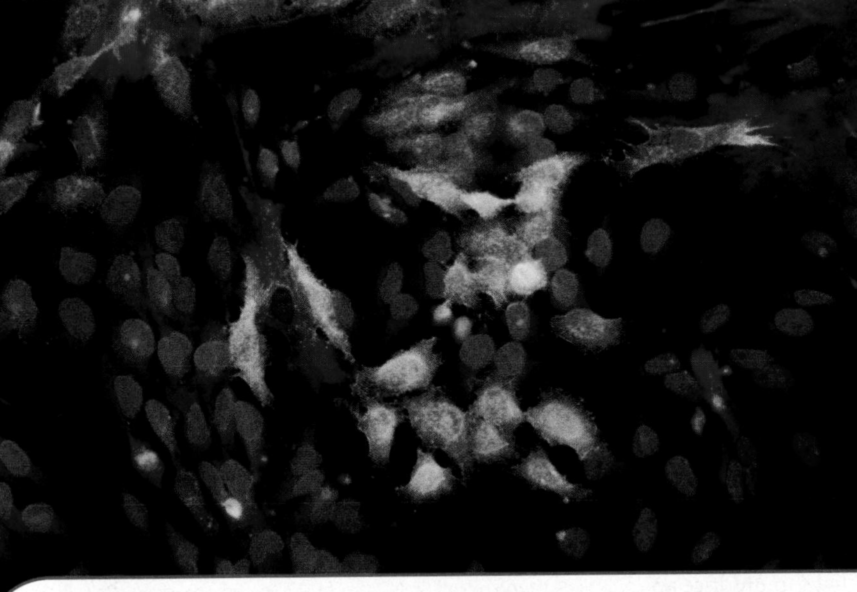

The image to the left shows human cervical cells magnified 125 times that have been attacked by cancer. The light blue areas at the center are keratin, a kind of protein. The cell nuclei are stained blue, and the red areas are fibroblasts, a kind of connective-tissue cell. These are the first human cells used to research cancer. This type of cell grows well in a lab, and is used in research worldwide.

CONNECTIONS Write **Report on Cobb's experiments on cancer cells. What were her dependent and independent variables? What would she have used as a control? What sources of error did she have to guard against? Answer the same questions about Levy's work.**

SCIENCE Online
For more information, visit science.glencoe.com

Discussion

Using Cobb's research as an example, discuss the value of experiments even if the results do not meet the researcher's specific goals. Possible answer: Science is a continuing process of discovery. Cobb's work is a necessary first step to new approaches to treatment like Levy's. **Chemotherapy treatments often result in discomfort and risk for cancer patients. Discuss why this is so.** Possible answer: All cells share the same genetic mechanisms. Treatments that affect DNA in one cell type will do so in others as well.

Historic Significance

The structure and function of DNA were not discovered until 1953. Cobb's research began shortly thereafter, long before the role of genes in the development of cancer was understood. Research like Cobb's leads to questions about how certain drugs can stop the unchecked growth of tumors. In combination with an increasing understanding of how genes work, these results allow scientists to refine the methods of administering treatments and to target the development of drugs specifically aimed at preventing the replication of DNA, a process that all cells require.

CONNECTIONS In Cobb's study the control group consisted of normal human cells that were exposed to the chemotherapeutic drugs. The independent variable was the specific drug administered to the cells. The dependent variable was the response of the cells to the treatment. Differences in these responses would allow conclusions about the effects of specific drugs, alone and in combination, on both cancerous and healthy cells.

SCIENCE Online

Internet Addresses

Explore the Glencoe Science Web site at **science.glencoe.com** to find out more about topics in this feature.

Chapter 2 Study Guide

Reviewing Main Ideas

Preview

Students can answer the questions in their Science Journals. Discuss the answers as you go through the chapter. LS **Linguistic**

Review

Students can write their answers, then compare them with those of other students. LS **Interpersonal**

Reteach

Students can look at the illustrations and describe details that support the main ideas of the chapter. LS **Visual-Spatial**

Answers to Chapter Review

Section 1

6. temporarily stores cellular material

Section 2

4. The ant is dead because specimens are placed in a vacuum to be examined with an electron microscope.

Section 3

3. They can multiply only within living cells. They do not have the cell components associated with living organisms.

Chapter 2 Study Guide

Reviewing Main Ideas

Section 1 Cell Structure

1. There are two basic cell types. Cells without membrane-bound structures are called prokaryotic cells. Cells with membrane-bound structures are called eukaryotic cells.
2. Most of the life processes of a cell occur within the cytoplasm.
3. Cell functions are performed by organelles under the control of DNA in the nucleus.
4. Organelles such as mitochondria and chloroplasts process energy.
5. Proteins take part in nearly every cell activity.
6. Golgi bodies and vacuoles transport substances, rid the cell of wastes, and store cellular materials. *What does this organelle do?*

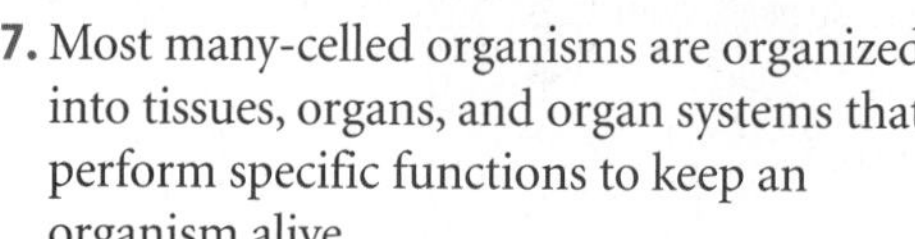

7. Most many-celled organisms are organized into tissues, organs, and organ systems that perform specific functions to keep an organism alive.

Section 2 Viewing Cells

1. A simple microscope has just one lens. A compound light microscope has eyepiece lenses and objective lenses.
2. To calculate the magnification of a microscope, multiply the power of the eyepiece by the power of the objective lens.
3. An electron microscope uses a beam of electrons instead of light to produce an image of an object.
4. Things that are too small to be viewed with a light microscope can be viewed with an electron microscope. This is an SEM of an ant. *How do you know if the ant is alive or dead?*
5. According to the cell theory, the cell is the basic unit of life. Organisms are made of one or more cells, and all cells come from other cells.

Section 3 Viruses

1. A virus is a structure containing hereditary material surrounded by a protein coating.
2. A virus can make copies of itself only when it is inside a living host cell.
3. Viruses cause diseases in animals, plants, fungi, and bacteria. *Why don't scientists consider viruses like these in the photo to be living organisms?*

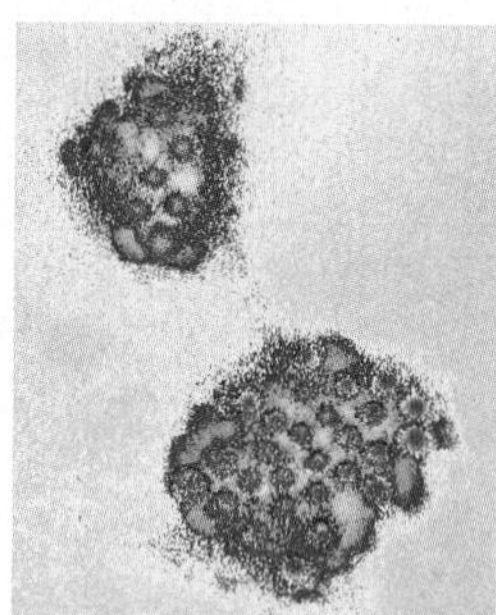

FOLDABLES Reading & Study Skills — After You Read

On the inside of the Main Ideas Study Fold you made at the beginning of the chapter describe the characteristics of each type of cell.

FOLDABLES Reading & Study Skills — After You Read

After students have read the chapter and completed the Foldable described in Before You Read, have them do the activity on the student page.

Dinah Zike

Visualizing Main Ideas

Complete the following concept map of the basic units of life.

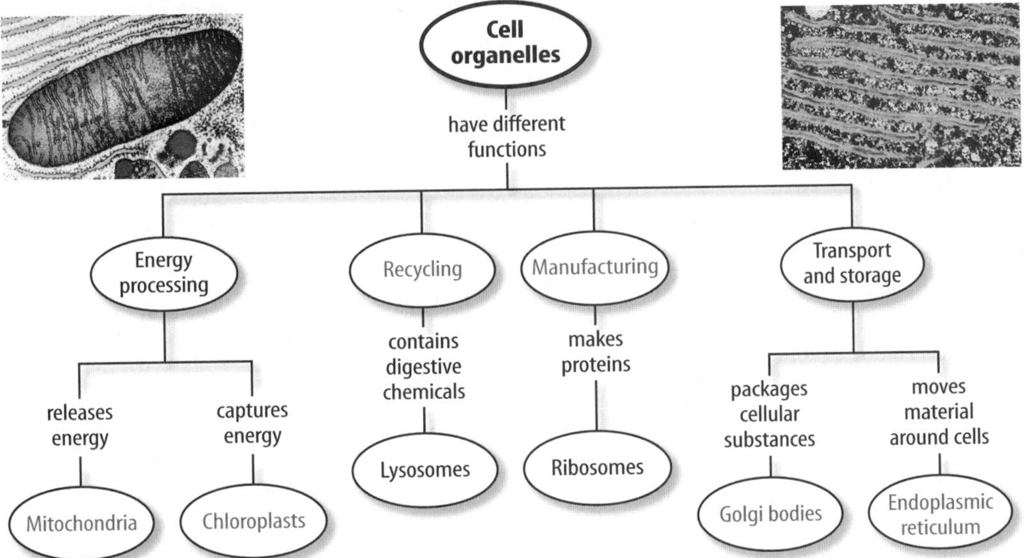

Vocabulary Review

Vocabulary Words

- **a.** cell membrane
- **b.** cell theory
- **c.** cell wall
- **d.** chloroplast
- **e.** cytoplasm
- **f.** endoplasmic reticulum
- **g.** Golgi body
- **h.** host cell
- **i.** mitochondrion
- **j.** nucleus
- **k.** organ
- **l.** organelle
- **m.** ribosome
- **n.** tissue
- **o.** virus

Study Tip

In order to understand the information that a graph is trying to communicate, write out a sentence that talks about the relationship between the *x*-axis and *y*-axis in the graph.

Using Vocabulary

Using the vocabulary words, give an example of each of the following.

1. found in every organ
2. smaller than one cell
3. a plant-cell organelle
4. part of every cell
5. powerhouse of a cell
6. used by biologists
7. contains hereditary material
8. a structure that surrounds the cell
9. can be damaged by a virus
10. made up of cells

Chapter 2 Study Guide

Visualizing Main Ideas

See student page.

Vocabulary Review

Using Vocabulary

1. n
2. d, f, g, i, j, l, m, o
3. d, f, g, j, m
4. a, e
5. i
6. b
7. e, j, o
8. a, c
9. h
10. k, n

Chapter 2 Assessment

Checking Concepts

1. B
2. A
3. D
4. A
5. C
6. C
7. B
8. C
9. A
10. A

Thinking Critically

11. Once a virus infects a cell, it uses the cell to produce more viruses. The immune system has to work to get rid of viruses because no drugs will kill them.
12. Answers may vary, but a stereomicroscope would enable you to view a large specimen as well as to look closely at the mold.
13. The plant cell would die or become dependent on other cells to provide its food.
14. No proteins could be made, and the animal cell would die.
15. If there is a cell wall and chloroplasts, it is a plant cell. A cell with no chloroplasts or cell wall is an animal cell. If no membrane-bound organelles are present, it is a bacterial cell.

Chapter 2 Assessment

Checking Concepts

Choose the word or phrase that best answers the question.

1. What structure allows only certain things to pass in and out of the cell?
   A) cytoplasm **B)** cell membrane **C)** ribosomes **D)** Golgi body
2. Which microscope uses lenses to magnify?
   A) compound light microscope
   B) scanning electron microscope
   C) transmission electron microscope
   D) atomic force microscope
3. What is made of folded membranes that move materials around inside the cell?
   A) nucleus
   B) cytoplasm
   C) Golgi body
   D) endoplasmic reticulum
4. Which scientist gave the name *cells* to structures he viewed?
   A) Hooke **B)** Schwann **C)** Schleiden **D)** Virchow
5. What organelle helps recycle old cell parts?
   A) chloroplast **B)** centriole **C)** lysosome **D)** cell wall
6. Which of the following is a viral disease?
   A) tuberculosis **B)** anthrax **C)** smallpox **D)** tetanus
7. What are structures in the cytoplasm of a eukaryotic cell called?
   A) organs **B)** organelles **C)** organ systems **D)** tissues
8. Which microscope can magnify up to a million times?
   A) compound light microscope
   B) stereomicroscope
   C) transmission electron microscope
   D) atomic force microscope
9. Which of the following is part of a bacterial cell?
   A) a cell wall **B)** lysosomes **C)** mitochondria **D)** a nucleus
10. Which of the following do groups of different tissues form?
    A) organ **B)** organelle **C)** organ system **D)** organism

Thinking Critically

11. Why is it difficult to treat a viral disease?
12. What type of microscope would be best to view a piece of moldy bread? Explain.
13. What would happen to a plant cell that suddenly lost its chloroplasts?
14. What would happen to this animal cell if it didn't have ribosomes?

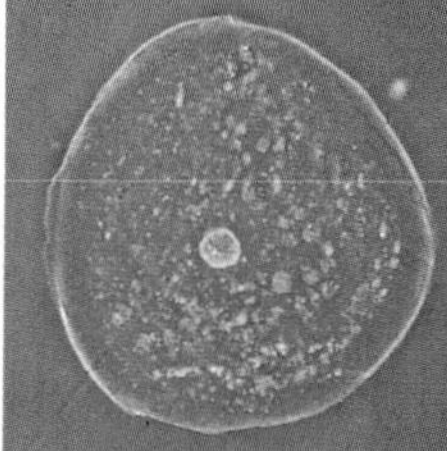

15. How would you decide whether an unknown cell was an animal cell, a plant cell, or a bacterial cell?

Developing Skills

16. **Concept Mapping** Make an events-chain concept map of the following from simple to complex: *small intestine, circular muscle cell, human,* and *digestive system.*
17. **Interpreting Scientific Illustrations** Use the illustrations in **Figure 1** to describe how the shape of a cell is related to its function.
18. **Making and Using Graphs** Use a computer to make a line graph of the following data. At 37°C there are 1.0 million viruses; at, 37.5°C, 0.5 million; at 37.8°C, 0.25 million; at 38.3°C, 0.1 million; and at 38.9°C, 0.05 million.

Chapter Assessment Planner

Portfolio Encourage students to place in their portfolios one or two items of what they consider to be their best work. Examples include:

- Visual Learning, p. 41
- Assessment, p. 51
- Extension, p. 54

Performance Additional performance assessments, Performance Task Assessment Lists, and rubrics for evaluating these activities can be found in Glencoe's **Performance Assessment in the Science Classroom.**

19. Comparing and Contrasting Complete the following table to compare and contrast the structures of a prokaryotic cell to those of a eukaryotic cell.

Cell Structures

Structure	Prokaryotic Cell	Eukaryotic Cell
Cell Membrane	Yes	Yes
Cytoplasm	Yes	Yes
Nucleus	No	Yes
Endoplasmic Reticulum	No	Yes
Golgi Bodies	No	Yes

20. Making a Model Make and illustrate a time line to show the development of the cell theory. Begin with the development of the microscope and end with Virchow. Include the contributions of Leeuwenhoek, Hooke, Schleiden, and Schwann.

Performance Assessment

21. Model Use materials that resemble cell parts or that represent their functions to make a model of a plant cell or an animal cell. Make a key to the cell parts to explain your model.

22. Poster Research the history of vaccinations. Contact your local Health Department for current information. Display your results on a poster.

Technology

Go to the Glencoe Science Web site at **science.glencoe.com** or use the **Glencoe Science CD-ROM** for additional chapter assessment.

THE PRINCETON REVIEW Test Practice

A scientist is studying living cells. Below is an image of one of the cells that is being studied. This image represents what a scientist sees when he or she uses a tool in the laboratory.

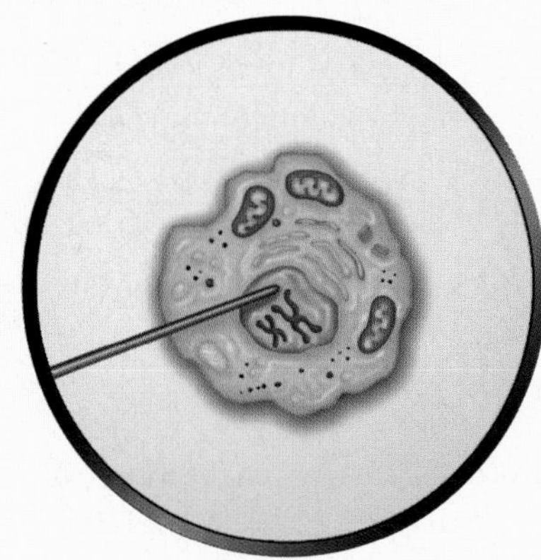

Closely examine the image above then answer the following questions.

1. If the pointer shown above with the cell is 10 micrometers in length, then about how wide is this cell?
   A) 20 micrometers
   B) 10 micrometers
   C) 5 micrometers
   D) 0.1 micrometers

2. Which of the following tools is the scientist probably using to view the living cell?
   F) telescope
   G) endoplasmic reticulum
   H) compound light microscope
   J) kaleidoscope

Chapter 2 Assessment

THE PRINCETON REVIEW Test Practice

The Test-Taking Tip was written by The Princeton Review, the nation's leader in test preparation.

1. B
2. H

Developing Skills

16. circular muscle cell, small intestine, digestive system, human
17. Answers will vary but should relate each shape to a function of the cell, such as the elongated shape of the nerve cell and its function in transmitting impulses.
18. Line graphs should show that, as temperature increases, the number of viruses decrease.
19. See student page.
20. The time line should have equal divisions of time and cover from the late 1500s to the late 1800s. Include these dates: late 1500s, microscope invented; late 1600s, Leeuwenhoek improves microscope; 1665, Hooke uses the word *cell;* 1830s, Schleiden discovers plants are made of cells; mid 1800s, Schwann discovers animals are made of cells; mid 1800s, Virchow concludes that all cells come from cells.

Performance Assessment

21. Model should include cell parts and a key to identify them. Use **PASC,** p. 123.
22. Posters should correctly show the history of vaccinations. Use **PASC,** p. 145.

Assessment Resources

 **Reproducible Masters**

Chapter Resources Booklet
Chapter Review, pp. 37–38
Chapter Tests, pp. 39–42
Assessment Transparency Activity, p. 49

Glencoe Science Web site
Interactive Tutor
Chapter Quizzes

Glencoe Technology
Assessment Transparency
Interactive CD-ROM Chapter Quizzes
ExamView Pro Test Bank
Vocabulary PuzzleMaker Software
MindJogger Videoquiz

Section/Objectives	Standards		Activities/Features
	National	State/Local	
Chapter Opener	See p. 5T for a Key to Standards.		**Explore Activity:** Demonstrate why water leaves plant cells, p. 65 **Before You Read,** p. 65
Section 1 Chemistry of Life 2 sessions 1 block 1. **List** the differences among atoms, elements, molecules, and compounds. 2. **Explain** the relationship between chemistry and life science. 3. **Discuss** how organic compounds are different from inorganic compounds.	National Content Standards: UCP2, A1, B1, C1		**Science Online,** p. 70 **MiniLAB:** Determining How Enzymes Work, p. 71 **Math Skills Activity:** Calculating the Importance of Water, p. 72
Section 2 Moving Cellular Materials 2 sessions 1 block 1. **Describe** the function of a selectively permeable membrane. 2. **Explain** how the processes of diffusion and osmosis move molecules in living cells. 3. **Explain** how passive transport and active transport differ	National Content Standards: UCP4, A1, C1, C3		**MiniLAB:** Observing Diffusion, p. 75 **Health Integration,** p. 77 **Visualizing Cell Membrane Transport,** p. 79 **Activity:** Observing Osmosis, p. 80
Section 3 Energy for Life 3 sessions 1.5 blocks 1. **List** the differences between producers and consumers. 2. **Explain** how the processes of photosynthesis and respiration store and release energy. 3. **Describe** how cells get energy from glucose through fermentation.	National Content Standards: UCP1, A1, B3, C1, C4, G1		**Chemistry Integration,** p. 83 **Science Online,** p. 84 **Activity:** Photosynthesis and Respiration, pp. 86–87 **Science and Language Arts:** Tulip, pp. 88–89

NATIONAL GEOGRAPHIC

Teacher's Corner

PRODUCTS AVAILABLE FROM GLENCOE
To order call 1-800-334-7344:

CD-ROM's
NGS PictureShow: Looking at Living Things

Curriculum Kit
GeoKit: Cells and Microorganisms

Transparency Sets
NGS PicturePack: The Cell
NGS PicturePack: Looking At Living Things

PRODUCTS AVAILABLE FROM NATIONAL GEOGRAPHIC SOCIETY
To order call 1-800-368-2728:

Videos
Photosynthesis: Life Energy

INDEX TO NATIONAL GEOGRAPHIC SOCIETY
The following articles may be used for research relating to this chapter:
"The Awesome Worlds Within a Cell," by Rick Gore, September 1976.

Activity Materials	Reproducible Resources	Section Assessment	Technology
Explore Activity: bowl, label, water (500 mL), salt (15 g), carrot sticks (6), watch or clock, beaker (250ml), balance, stirrer	**Chapter Resources Booklet** Foldables Worksheet, p. 15 Directed Reading Overview, p. 17 Note-taking Worksheets, pp. 31–33	GLENCOE'S ASSESSMENT ADVANTAGE	
MiniLAB: prepared gelatin, small cups, fresh pineapple pieces *Need materials?* Contact Science Kit at 1-800-828-7777 or www.sciencekit.com on the Internet.	**Chapter Resources Booklet** Transparency Activity, p. 42 MiniLAB, p. 3 Enrichment, p. 28 Reinforcement, p. 25 Directed Reading, p. 18 Transparency Activity, pp. 45–46 **Cultural Diversity,** p. 65	Portfolio Science Journal, p. 70 Performance MiniLAB, p. 71 Math Skills Activity, p. 72 Skill Builder Activities, p. 73 Content Section Assessment, p. 73	Section Focus Transparency Teaching Transparency Interactive CD-ROM Guided Reading Audio Program
MiniLAB: clean glasses (2 of equal size), labels, very warm water, cold water, food coloring, dropper, clock, marker or wax pencil **Activity:** unshelled egg, balance, spoon, distilled water (250 mL), light corn syrup (250 mL), 500-mL container	**Chapter Resources Booklet** Transparency Activity, p. 43 MiniLAB, p. 4 Enrichment, p. 29 Reinforcement, p. 26 Directed Reading, p. 18 Lab Activity, pp. 9–10 Activity Worksheet, pp. 5–6 **Home and Community Involvement,** p. 47	Portfolio Visual Learning, p. 79 Performance MiniLAB, p. 75 Skill Builder Activities, p. 78 Content Section Assessment, p. 78	Section Focus Transparency Interactive CD-ROM Guided Reading Audio Program
Activity: 16-mm test tubes (3), 150-mm test tubes with stoppers (4), test-tube rack, stirring rod, scissors, carbonated water (5 mL), bromothymol blue solution in dropper bottle, aged tap water (20 mL), sprig of *Elodea*	**Chapter Resources Booklet** Transparency Activity, p. 44 Enrichment, p. 30 Reinforcement, p. 27 Directed Reading, pp. 19, 20 Lab Activity, pp. 11–14 Activity Worksheet, pp. 7–8 **Lab Management and Safety,** p. 63	Portfolio Visual Learning, p. 85 Performance Skill Builder Activities, p. 85 Content Section Assessment, p. 85	Section Focus Transparency Interactive CD-ROM Guided Reading Audio Program

End of Chapter Assessment

GLENCOE'S ASSESSMENT ADVANTAGE

Blackline Masters	Technology	Professional Series
Chapter Resources Booklet Chapter Review, pp. 35–36 Chapter Tests, pp. 37–40 **Standardized Test Practice by The Princeton Review,** pp. 19–22	MindJogger Videoquiz Interactive CD-ROM Vocabulary PuzzleMakers ExamView Pro Test Bank Interactive Lesson Planner Interactive Teacher Edition	Performance Assessment in the Science Classroom (PASC)

Transparencies

Section Focus

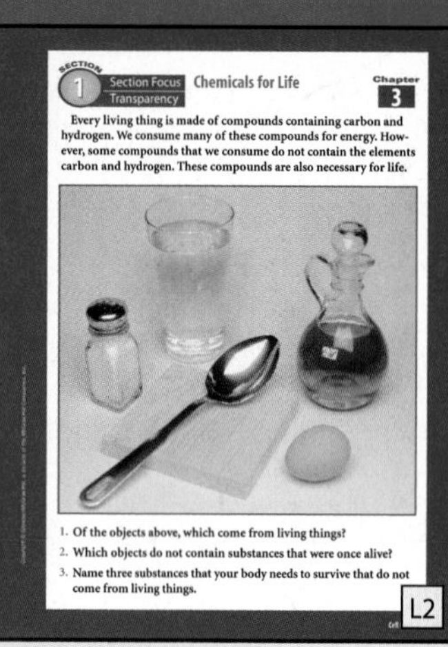
Section 1 Section Focus Transparency — Chemicals for Life — Chapter 3

Every living thing is made of compounds containing carbon and hydrogen. We consume many of these compounds for energy. However, some compounds that we consume do not contain the elements carbon and hydrogen. These compounds are also necessary for life.

1. Of the objects above, which come from living things?
2. Which objects do not contain substances that were once alive?
3. Name three substances that your body needs to survive that do not come from living things.

L2

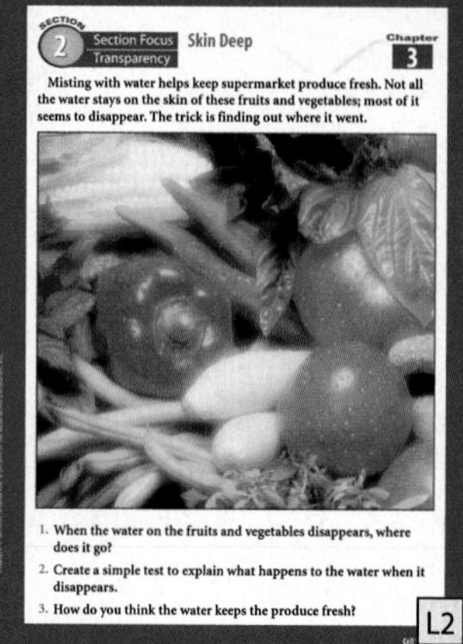
Section 2 Section Focus Transparency — Skin Deep — Chapter 3

Misting with water helps keep supermarket produce fresh. Not all the water stays on the skin of these fruits and vegetables; most of it seems to disappear. The trick is finding out where it went.

1. When the water on the fruits and vegetables disappears, where does it go?
2. Create a simple test to explain what happens to the water when it disappears.
3. How do you think the water keeps the produce fresh?

L2

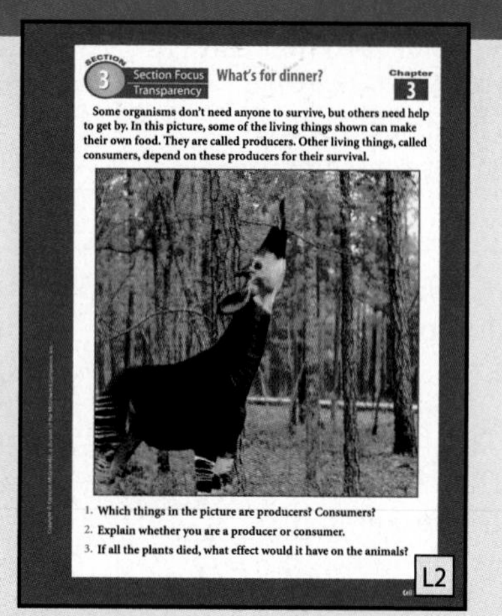
Section 3 Section Focus Transparency — What's for dinner? — Chapter 3

Some organisms don't need anyone to survive, but others need help to get by. In this picture, some of the living things shown can make their own food. They are called producers. Other living things, called consumers, depend on these producers for their survival.

1. Which things in the picture are producers? Consumers?
2. Explain whether you are a producer or consumer.
3. If all the plants died, what effect would it have on the animals?

L2

This is a representation of key blackline masters available in the Teacher Classroom Resources. See Resource Manager boxes within the chapter for additional information.

Assessment

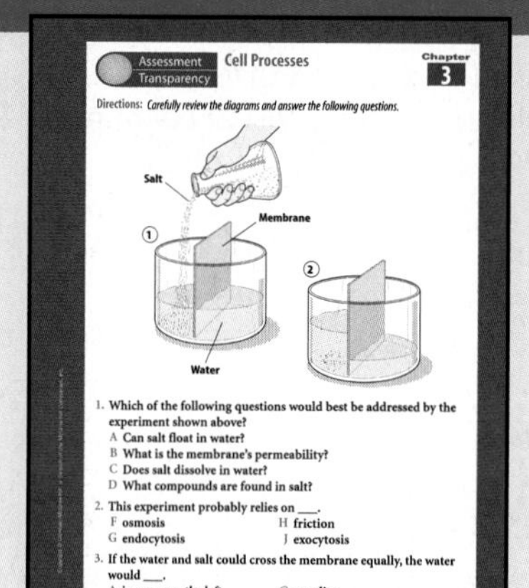
Assessment Transparency — Cell Processes — Chapter 3

Directions: *Carefully review the diagrams and answer the following questions.*

1. Which of the following questions would best be addressed by the experiment shown above?
   A Can salt float in water?
   B What is the membrane's permeability?
   C Does salt dissolve in water?
   D What compounds are found in salt?
2. This experiment probably relies on ___.
   F osmosis
   G endocytosis
   H friction
   J exocytosis
3. If the water and salt could cross the membrane equally, the water would ___.
   A increase on the left
   B increase on the right
   C equalize
   D collapse the membrane

L2

Teaching

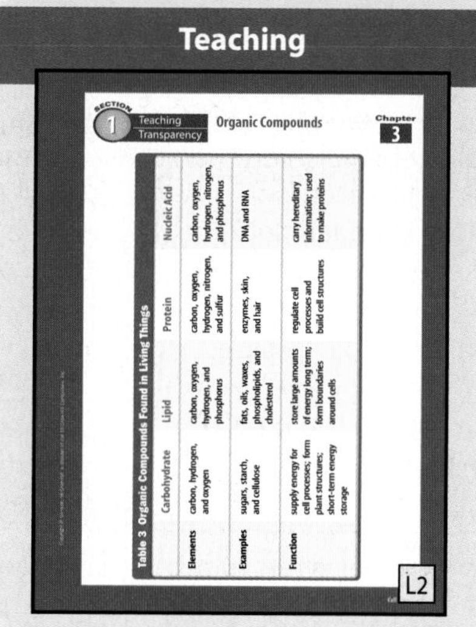
Section 1 Teaching Transparency — Organic Compounds — Chapter 3

Table 3 Organic Compounds Found in Living Things

	Carbohydrate	Lipid	Protein	Nucleic Acid
Elements	carbon, hydrogen, and oxygen	carbon, oxygen, hydrogen, and phosphorus	carbon, oxygen, hydrogen, nitrogen, and sulfur	carbon, oxygen, hydrogen, nitrogen, and phosphorus
Examples	sugars, starch, and cellulose	fats, oils, waxes, phospholipids, and cholesterol	enzymes, skin, and hair	DNA and RNA
Function	supply energy for cell processes; form plant structures; short-term energy storage	store large amounts of energy long term; form boundaries around cells	regulate cell processes and build cell structures	carry hereditary information; used to make proteins

L2

Key to Teaching Strategies

The following designations will help you decide which activities are appropriate for your students.

- L1 Level 1 activities should be appropriate for students with learning difficulties.
- L2 Level 2 activities should be within the ability range of all students.
- L3 Level 3 activities are designed for above-average students.
- ELL ELL activities should be within the ability range of English Language Learners.
- COOP LEARN Cooperative Learning activities are designed for small group work.
- LS Multiple Learning Styles logos, as described on page 22T, are used throughout to indicate strategies that address different learning styles.
- P These strategies represent student products that can be placed into a best-work portfolio.

Hands-on Activities

Activity Worksheets

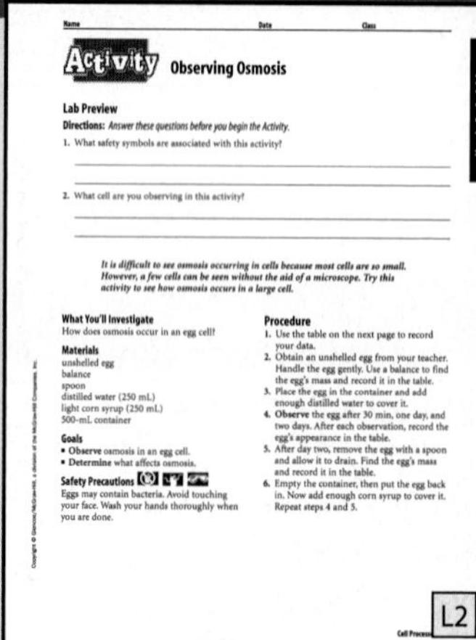
Name Date Class

Activity — Observing Osmosis

Hands-On Activities

Lab Preview

Directions: *Answer these questions before you begin the Activity.*

1. What safety symbols are associated with this activity?
2. What cell are you observing in this activity?

It is difficult to see osmosis occurring in cells because most cells are so small. However, a few cells can be seen without the aid of a microscope. Try this activity to see how osmosis occurs in a large cell.

What You'll Investigate
How does osmosis occur in an egg cell?

Materials
unshelled egg
balance
spoon
distilled water (250 mL)
light corn syrup (250 mL)
500-mL container

Goals
- **Observe** osmosis in an egg cell.
- **Determine** what affects osmosis.

Safety Precautions
Eggs may contain bacteria. Avoid touching your face. Wash your hands thoroughly when you are done.

Procedure
1. Use the table on the next page to record your data.
2. Obtain an unshelled egg from your teacher. Handle the egg gently. Use a balance to find the egg's mass and record it in the table.
3. Place the egg in the container and add enough distilled water to cover it.
4. **Observe** the egg after 30 min, one day, and two days. After each observation, record the egg's appearance in the table.
5. After day two, remove the egg with a spoon and allow it to drain. Find the egg's mass and record it in the table.
6. Empty the container, then put the egg back in. Now add enough corn syrup to cover it. Repeat steps 4 and 5.

L2

Laboratory Activities

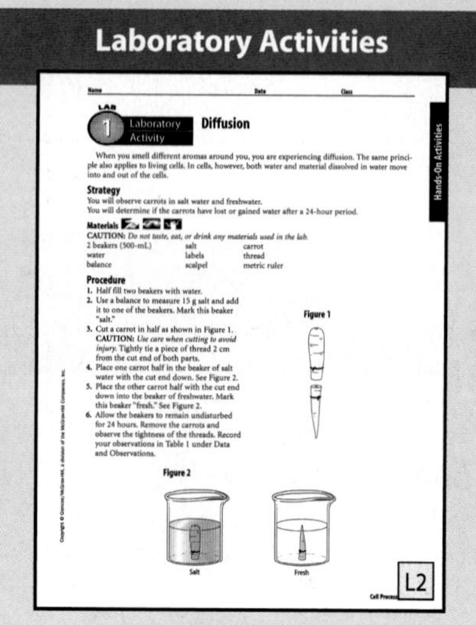
Name Date Class

Lab 1 Laboratory Activity — Diffusion

Hands-On Activities

When you smell different aromas around you, you are experiencing diffusion. The same principle also applies to living cells. In cells, however, both water and material dissolved in water move into and out of the cells.

Strategy
You will observe carrots in salt water and freshwater.
You will determine if the carrots have lost or gained water after a 24-hour period.

Materials
CAUTION: *Do not taste, eat, or drink any materials used in the lab.*

2 beakers (500-mL)	salt	carrot
water	labels	thread
balance	scalpel	metric ruler

Procedure
1. Half fill two beakers with water.
2. Use a balance to measure 15 g salt and add it to one of the beakers. Mark this beaker "salt."
3. Cut a carrot in half as shown in Figure 1. **CAUTION:** *Use care when cutting to avoid injury.* Tightly tie a piece of thread 2 cm from the cut end of both parts.
4. Place one carrot half in the beaker of salt water with the cut end down. See Figure 2.
5. Place the other carrot half with the cut end down into the beaker of freshwater. Mark this beaker "fresh." See Figure 2.
6. Allow the beakers to remain undisturbed for 24 hours. Remove the carrots and observe the tightness of the threads. Record your observations in Table 1 under Data and Observations.

Figure 1

Figure 2

L2

Meeting Different Ability Levels

Content Outline

Note-taking Worksheet — Cell Processes

Section 1 Chemistry of Life

L2

Reinforcement

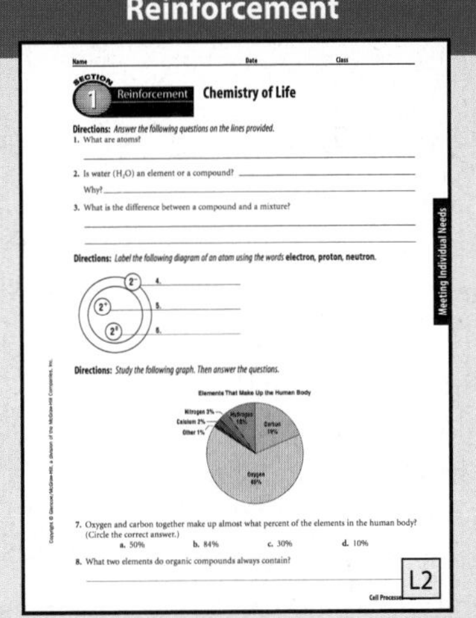

Section 1 Reinforcement — Chemistry of Life

L2

Directed Reading

Directed Reading for Content Mastery — Overview: Cell Processes

L1

Enrichment

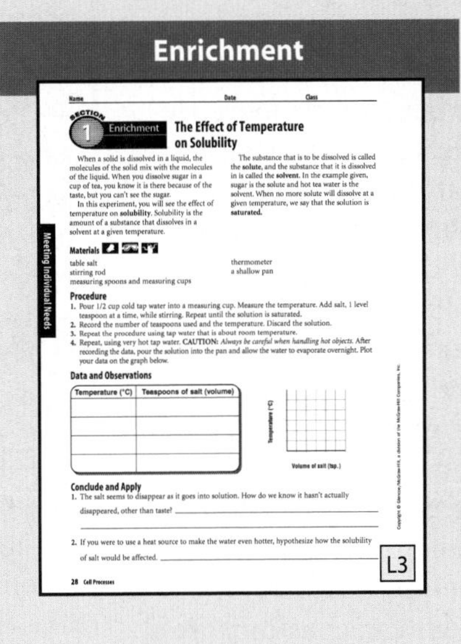

Section 1 Enrichment — The Effect of Temperature on Solubility

L3

Spanish Directed Reading

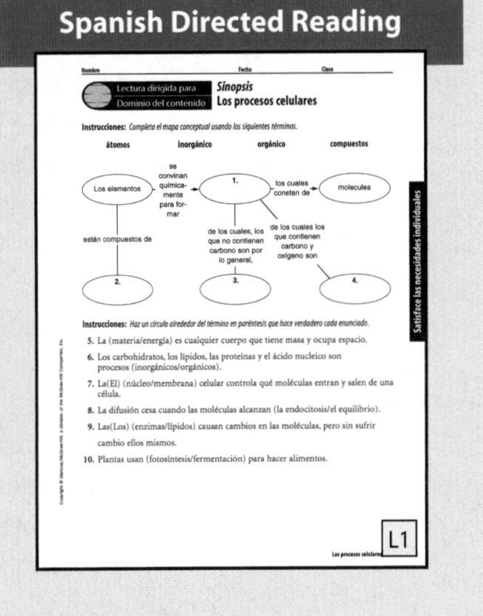

Lectura dirigida para Dominio del contenido — Sinopsis: Los procesos celulares

L1

Assessment

Chapter Tests

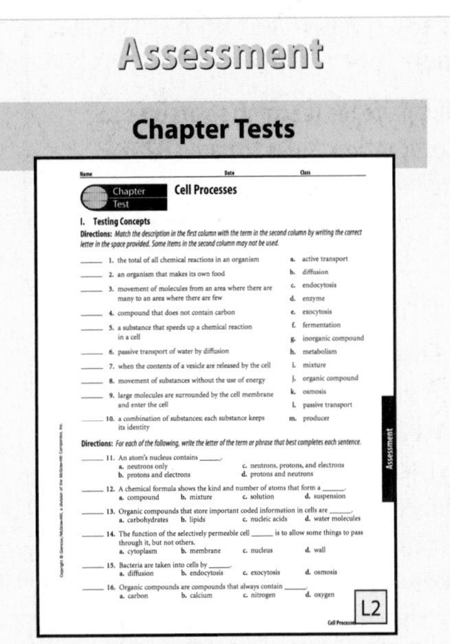

Chapter Test — Cell Processes

L2

Test Practice Workbook

Standardized Test Practice Teacher Edition — Glencoe Science Life Science

L2

Chapter Review

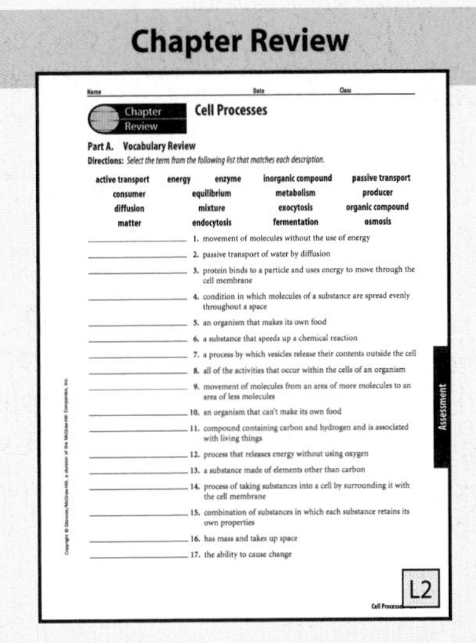

Chapter Review — Cell Processes

L2

Science Content Background

SECTION 1 Chemistry of Life

The Nature of Matter

Democritus, an ancient Greek philosopher, proposed that atoms were small, solid spheres. From the late 1800s until recently, it was thought that negatively-charged electrons orbited the positively-charged nucleus in specific paths. Quantum mechanics provide us with the current model of a positively-charged nucleus surrounded by a region in which the electrons move. The location of the electrons depends on each electron's energy level.

Compounds and Mixtures

Compounds are formed when two or more elements combine by a chemical reaction. Molecular components form when atoms share electrons. Ionic compounds form when negative and positive ions join. Organic compounds all contain carbon atoms. Most organic compounds are produced within living organisms. However, organic compounds such as plastics and synthetic fibers are constructed from organic substances such as petroleum. Inorganic compounds usually are made from elements other than carbon. Water is the most important inorganic compound.

Most things in nature are mixtures of elements. Components of homogeneous mixtures, such as solutions, cannot be distinguished from one another. The components of a heterogeneous mixture are generally visibly identifiable.

SECTION 2 Moving Cellular Materials

Maintaining Balance

The cell membrane regulates what enters and leaves a cell. The sizes, shapes, and electrical charges of molecules determine the permeability of the cell membrane. It is important for a cell to maintain its internal concentrations of substances such as water, glucose, and other nutrients while allowing elimination of waste products.

Transport

Passive transport—transport without the input of energy—depends on temperature. One form of passive transport, called diffusion, occurs when molecules move from an area where their concentration is greater into an area where they are less concentrated. Osmosis is the diffusion of water into or out of a cell. Active transport, transport with energy input, requires transport proteins.

Student Misconception

Plants do not use oxygen and do not release carbon dioxide.

Refer to the facing page for teaching strategies to address this misconception. Refer to pages 82–85 for content related to this topic.

SECTION 3 Energy for Life

Photosynthesis, Respiration, and Fermentation

During photosynthesis, plants and other producers convert light energy to chemical energy and make carbohydrates (food). During respiration, the food is broken down and the released energy can be used by the producer, other producers, and consumers. When there is a shortage of oxygen, fermentation is a process some cells can use to release energy from glucose.

For additional content background on this topic, go to the Glencoe Science Web site at science.glencoe.com.

Misconceptions

Find Out What Students Think

Students may think that . . .

- **Plants do not use oxygen and do not release carbon dioxide.**

Students may not completely understand the complementary nature of photosynthesis and respiration, especially with respect to exchange of gases.

Demonstration

Ask students to give the relationship between producers, consumers, oxygen, and carbon dioxide. Summarize students' responses on the board. If students do not explicitly respond that plants also give off carbon dioxide, don't point it out at this time. Let that understanding come from the activities below.

Promote Understanding

Activity 1

WARNING: Remind students not to suck on the straw.

Prepare a 0.1% solution of bromthymol blue.

- Have students blow through a straw into the bromthymol blue solution. The solution should turn yellow as the carbon dioxide from respiration dissolves in the solution (forming carbonic acid).
- Have students add drops of dilute ammonium hydroxide so that the solution again turns blue. Explain that the bromthymol blue is an indicator that turns yellow in an acidic solution and blue in a neutral or alkaline solution.
- Ask students what gas is given off in the process of respiration. (carbon dioxide) Explain that the carbon dioxide blown into the solution dissolves and makes the solution slightly acidic. Point out that adding the ammonium hydroxide made the solution slightly basic.

Activity 2

Acidify a large test tube of bromthymol blue by adding carbonated water to the solution. Add a sprig of *Elodea* to the tube.

- Put the test tube in sunlight or under a bright light. The solution should begin to turn blue in 30 to 45 minutes. Have students record results.
- At the same time, have students put a sprig of *Elodea* in a test tube of bromthymol blue solution that is just very slightly alkaline and thus blue and place the tube in a dark area. Within 24 hours the color of the solution should change to a pale yellow as the plant respires and releases carbon dioxide. Again have students record their results.

Discussion

- Ask why the bromthymol blue solution turned blue in the light. Ask students what evidence supports their answer. Explicitly reinforce the fact the carbon dioxide was absorbed by the plant and used in the process of photosynthesis.
- Ask students whether they think carbon dioxide was given off by the *Elodea* kept in the dark. Light-independent photosynthesis and respiration occur in the dark, so carbon dioxide is used and released. Stress that their results indicate that plants give off carbon dioxide during respiration. Point out that all living things must carry out some form of respiration.

Assess

After completing the chapter, see *Identifying Misconceptions* in the Study Guide.

CHAPTER 3

Cell Processes

Chapter Vocabulary

mixture, p. 69
organic compound, p. 70
enzyme, p. 71
inorganic compound, p. 71
passive transport, p. 74
diffusion, p. 75
equilibrium, p. 75
osmosis, p. 76
active transport, p. 77
endocytosis, p. 78
exocytosis, p. 78
metabolism, p. 81
photosynthesis, p. 82
respiration, p. 83
fermentation, p. 84

What do you think?

Science Journal The object in the picture is a mitochondrion, the place in a eukaryotic cell in which energy is released from food molecules.

CHAPTER

Cell Processes

The Sun is hot. Your back aches and your hands are sore. Weeding a garden is hard work. You are sweaty, tired, thirsty, and hungry. Are the weeds having the same reactions? You may know that plants don't sweat or get tired, but they do need water and food, just like you. How do plants take in and use water and food? In this chapter you'll find the answer to this question. You'll also find out how living things get the energy that they need to survive.

What do you think?

Science Journal Look at the picture below with a classmate. Discuss what this might be or what is happening. Here's a hint: *It's sometimes called the powerhouse of the cell.* Write your answer or best guess in your Science Journal.

64

Theme Connection

Stability and Change Living things function as a result of chemical reactions in cells. The equilibrium maintained by cells results from their selectively permeable membranes. This is critical to the life of cells and the organism as a whole.

If you forget to water a plant, it will wilt. After you water the plant, it probably will straighten up and look healthier. Why does the plant straighten? In the following activity, find out about water entering and leaving plant cells.

Demonstrate why water leaves plant cells

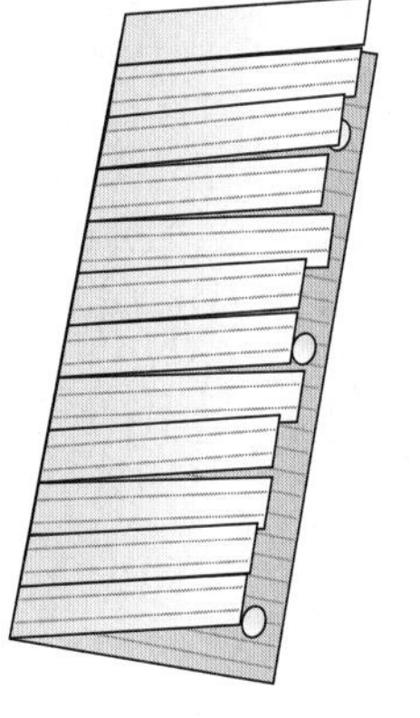

1. Label a small bowl "salt water." Pour 250 mL of water into the bowl. Then add 15 g of salt to the water and stir.
2. Pour 250 mL of water into another small bowl.
3. Place two carrot sticks into each bowl. Also, place two carrot sticks on the lab table.
4. After 30 min, remove the carrot sticks from the bowls and keep them next to the bowl they came from. Examine all six carrot sticks, then describe them in your Science Journal.

Observe

Predict what would happen if you moved the carrot sticks from the plain water to the lab table, the ones from the salt water into the plain water, and the ones from the lab table into the salt water. Now try it. Write your predictions and your results in your Science Journal.

Before You Read

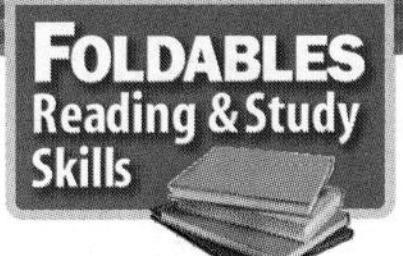

FOLDABLES Reading & Study Skills

Making a Vocabulary Study Fold **To help you study cell processes, make the following vocabulary Foldable. Knowing the definition of vocabulary words in a chapter is a good way to ensure that you have understood the content.**

1. Place a sheet of notebook paper in front of you so the short side is at the top. Fold the paper in half from the left to the right side.
2. Through the top thickness of paper, cut along every third line from the outside edge to the center fold, forming ten tabs as shown.
3. On the front of each tab, write a vocabulary word listed on the first page of each section in this chapter. On the back of each tab, define the word.

65

EXPLORE ACTIVITY

Purpose Use the Explore Activity to show students that water moves into and out of carrot cells. Explain that the materials moving into and out of cells are atoms, molecules, and compounds. L1  **Visual-Spatial**

Preparation Purchase carrots for the activity. Peel and cut the carrots into sticks.

Materials salt, 250-mL beaker, balance, 2 bowls, stirrer, 6 carrot sticks, water, label, watch or clock

Teaching Strategy Provide students with water at room temperature so the salt will dissolve more readily.

Observe

The carrot sticks in salt water and on the lab table were limp because water moved out of them. The carrot sticks in plain water were crisp because water moved into the cells that had less water. Students should predict that these conditions are reversible, depending on the relative amount of water inside and outside the carrot's cells.

Assessment

Oral Why does a wilted plant become rigid again after it has been watered? The water diffuses into the plant's cells. **Use Performance Assessment in the Science Classroom,** p. 89.

Before You Read

FOLDABLES Reading & Study Skills

Dinah Zike Study Fold

Purpose Use this activity to expose students to the chapter's content and vocabulary before they read, and to encourage a search for terms and definitions as they read. The resulting Foldable can be used as an assessment tool and study guide before, during and after reading.

For additional help, see Foldables Worksheet, p. 15 in **Chapter Resources Booklet,** or go to the Glencoe Science Web site at **science.glencoe.com.** See After You Read in the Study Guide at the end of this chapter.

SECTION 1

Chemistry of Life

1 Motivate

Bellringer Transparency

Display the Section Focus Transparency for Section 1. Use the accompanying Transparency Activity Master. L2 ELL

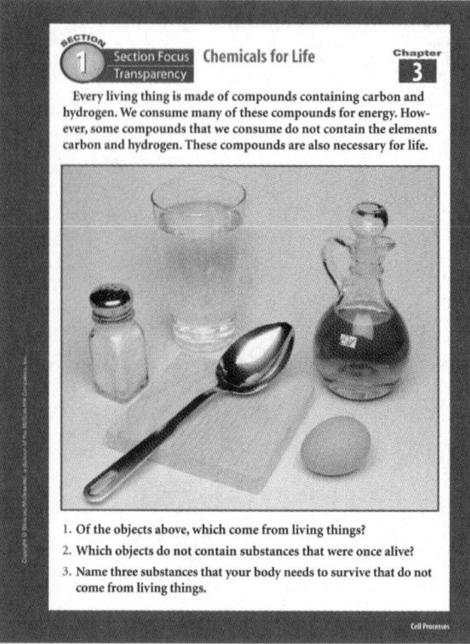
Section Focus Transparency 1 — Chemicals for Life — Chapter 3

Every living thing is made of compounds containing carbon and hydrogen. We consume many of these compounds for energy. However, some compounds that we consume do not contain the elements carbon and hydrogen. These compounds are also necessary for life.

1. Of the objects above, which come from living things?
2. Which objects do not contain substances that were once alive?
3. Name three substances that your body needs to survive that do not come from living things.

Cell Processes

Tie to Prior Knowledge

Bring in labels from foods and cleaning products. Have students use the periodic table at the back of the book to determine what elements are in the compounds contained in these products.

SECTION

Chemistry of Life

As You Read

What You'll Learn

- **List** the differences among atoms, elements, molecules, and compounds.
- **Explain** the relationship between chemistry and life science.
- **Discuss** how organic compounds are different from inorganic compounds.

Vocabulary
mixture
organic compound
enzyme
inorganic compound

Why It's Important
You grow because of chemical reactions in your body.

The Nature of Matter

Think about everything that surrounds you—chairs, books, clothing, other students, and air. What are all these things made up of? You're right if you answer "matter and energy." Matter is anything that has mass and takes up space. Energy is anything that brings about change. Everything in your environment, including you, is made of matter. Energy can hold matter together or break it apart. For example, the food you eat is matter that is held together by chemical energy. When food is cooked, energy in the form of heat can break some of the bonds holding the matter in food together. **Table 1** compares matter and energy and gives some examples of each.

Atoms Whether it is solid, liquid, or gas, matter is made of atoms. **Figure 1** shows a model of an oxygen atom. At the center of an atom is a nucleus that contains protons and neutrons. Although they have nearly equal masses, a proton has a positive charge and a neutron has no charge. Outside the nucleus are electrons, each of which has a negative charge. It takes about 1,837 electrons to equal the mass of one proton. Electrons are important because they are the part of the atom that is involved in chemical reactions. Look at **Figure 1** again and you will see that an atom is mostly empty space. Energy holds the parts of an atom together.

Figure 1
An oxygen atom model shows the placement of electrons, protons, and neutrons.

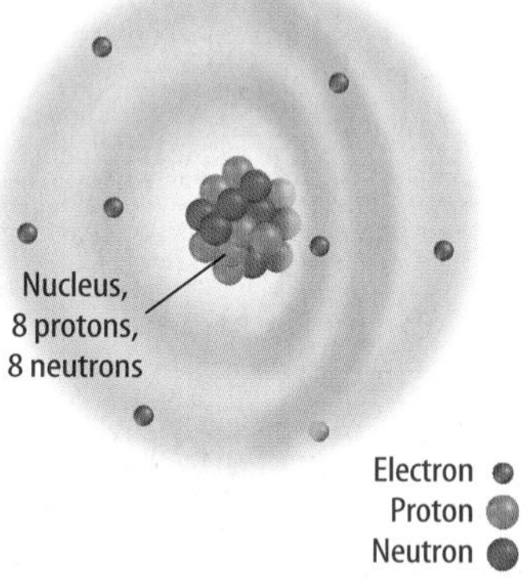

Table 1 Matter and Energy

	Definition	Examples
Matter	anything that has mass and takes up space	atoms, electrons, protons, and neutrons, living things, rocks, soil, and air
Energy	ability to cause change	sunlight, electricity, heat, chemical energy

Section Assessment Planner

PORTFOLIO
Science Journal, p. 70

PERFORMANCE ASSESSMENT
MiniLAB, p. 71
Math Skills Activity, p. 72
Skill Builder Activities, p. 73
See page 92 for more options.

CONTENT ASSESSMENT
Section, p. 73
Challenge, p. 73
Chapter, pp. 92–93

Table 2 Elements That Make Up the Human Body		
Symbol	Element	Percent
O	Oxygen	65.0
C	Carbon	18.5
H	Hydrogen	9.5
N	Nitrogen	3.2
Ca	Calcium	1.5
P	Phosphorus	1.0
K	Potassium	0.4
S	Sulfur	0.3
Na	Sodium	0.2
Cl	Chlorine	0.2
Mg	Magnesium	0.1
	Other elements	0.1

Elements When something is made up of only one kind of atom, it is called an element. An element can't be broken down into a simpler form by chemical reactions. The element oxygen is made up of only oxygen atoms, and hydrogen is made up of only hydrogen atoms. Scientists have given each element its own one- or two-letter symbol.

All elements are arranged in a chart known as the periodic table of elements. You can find this table at the back of this book. The table provides information about each element including its mass, how many protons it has, and its symbol.

Everything is made up of elements. Most things, including all living things, are made up of a combination of elements. Few things exist as pure elements. **Table 2** lists elements that are in the human body. What two elements make up most of your body?

Reading Check ***What types of things are made up of elements?***

Six of the elements listed in the table are important because they make up about 99 percent of living matter. The symbols for these elements are S, P, O, N, C, and H. Use **Table 2** to find the names of these elements.

2 Teach

The Nature of Matter

Teacher FYI

Elements are often given names by their discoverers. An element's name may reflect a property of the element. For example, chlorine, a greenish gas, comes from the Greek word *chloros*, which means "green." Some elements, such as ytterbium—discovered in Ytterby, Sweden—are named for the place where they were discovered. Other elements are named to honor someone. Einsteinium is named in honor of Albert Einstein, fermium for Enrico Fermi, and curium for Marie and Pierre Curie.

Activity

Play Tom Lehrer's *Elements Song*, which lists the elements. Have students listen to see how many elements they recognize.

Fun Fact

The symbols of many elements are derived from the first one or two letters of the Greek, Latin, or English name of the elements. Scientists worldwide use these symbols.

Text Question Answer

oxygen and carbon

Reading Check

Answer Everything is made up of elements or a combination of elements.

Resource Manager

Chapter Resources Booklet

Transparency Activity, p. 42

Directed Reading for Content Mastery, pp. 17, 18

Note-taking Worksheets, pp. 31–33

Inclusion Strategies

Visually Impaired To help visually impaired students understand the structure of an atom, make a model of an atom. Outline the nucleus and energy levels by gluing yarn to cardboard. Use marshmallows for protons, gumdrops for neutrons, and red hots for electrons. Have students feel the model to compare the sizes of the different parts.  **Kinesthetic**

The Nature of Matter, continued

Caption Answer

Figure 2 A molecule, the smallest part of a molecular compound, is a group of atoms held together by chemical bonds.

Quick Demo

To demonstrate attraction between opposite charges, run a comb through your hair. Then bring the comb close to your hair without touching it. The hair is attracted to the comb because the negative charges on the comb are attracted to the positive charges of the hair.

Discussion

Have students predict what might happen when a negatively charged ion comes in contact with a positively charged ion. The two ions may bond to form an electrically neutral compound.

Figure 2
The words *atoms, molecules,* and *compounds* are used to describe substances. *How are they related to each other?*

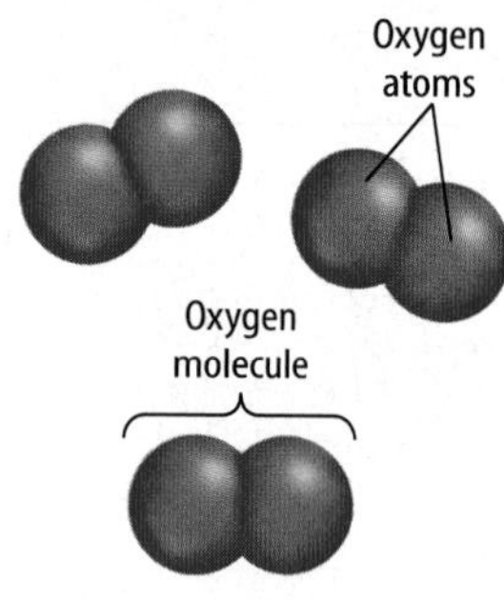

A Some elements, like oxygen, occur as molecules. These molecules contain atoms of the same element bonded together.

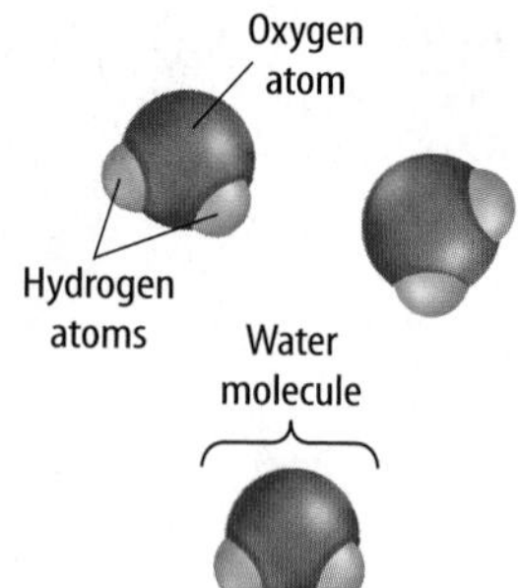

B Compounds also are composed of molecules. Molecules of compounds contain atoms of two or more different elements bonded together, as shown by these water molecules.

Compounds and Molecules

Suppose you make a pitcher of lemonade using a powdered mix and water. The water and the lemonade mix, which is mostly sugar, contain the elements oxygen and hydrogen. Yet, in one, they are part of a nearly tasteless liquid—water. In the other they are part of a sweet solid—sugar. How can the same elements be part of two materials that are so different? Water and sugar are compounds. Compounds are made up of two or more elements in exact proportions. For example, pure water, whether one milliliter of it or one million liters, is always made up of hydrogen atoms bonded to oxygen atoms in a ratio of two hydrogen atoms to one oxygen atom. Compounds have properties different from the elements they are made of. There are two types of compounds—molecular compounds and ionic compounds.

Molecular Compounds The smallest part of a molecular compound is a molecule. A molecule is a group of atoms held together by the energy of chemical bonds, as shown in **Figure 2.** When chemical reactions occur, chemical bonds break, atoms are rearranged, and new bonds form. The molecules produced are different from those that began the chemical reaction.

Molecular compounds form when different atoms share their outermost electrons. For example, two atoms of hydrogen each can share one electron on one atom of oxygen to form one molecule of water, as shown in **Figure 2B.** Water does not have the same properties as oxygen and hydrogen. Under normal conditions on Earth, oxygen and hydrogen are gases. Yet, water can be a liquid, a solid, or a gas. When hydrogen and oxygen combine, changes occur and a new substance forms.

Ions Atoms also combine because they've become positively or negatively charged. Atoms are usually neutral—they have no overall electric charge. When an atom loses an electron, it has more protons than electrons, so it becomes positively charged. When an atom gains an electron, it has more electrons than protons, so it becomes negatively charged. Electrically charged atoms—positive or negative—are called ions.

Inclusion Strategies

Hearing Impaired Provide discussion questions to hearing-impaired students before discussion. Assign another student to record the answers to the questions when they are given. L2
LS **Auditory-Musical**

Curriculum Connection

History Have students research alchemy. During the Middle Ages, alchemists searched for a way to turn common metals into gold. Though unsuccessful, they were precursors to modern chemists. Much of alchemy was based on Aristotle's idea that matter tries to reach perfection. Alchemists concluded that there must be a way to turn other metals into gold, since it was the "perfect" metal. L3 LS **Linguistic**

Ionic Compounds Ions of opposite charges attract one another to form electrically neutral compounds called ionic compounds. Table salt is made of sodium (Na) and chlorine (Cl) ions, as shown in **Figure 3B.** When they combine, a chlorine atom gains an electron from a sodium atom. The chlorine atom becomes a negatively charged ion, and the sodium atom becomes a positively charged ion. These oppositely charged ions then are attracted to each other and form the ionic compound sodium chloride, NaCl.

Ions are important in many life processes that take place in your body and in other organisms. For example, messages are sent along your nerves as potassium and sodium ions move in and out of nerve cells. Calcium ions are important in causing your muscles to contract. Ions also are involved in the transport of oxygen by your blood. The movement of some substances into and out of a cell would not be possible without ions.

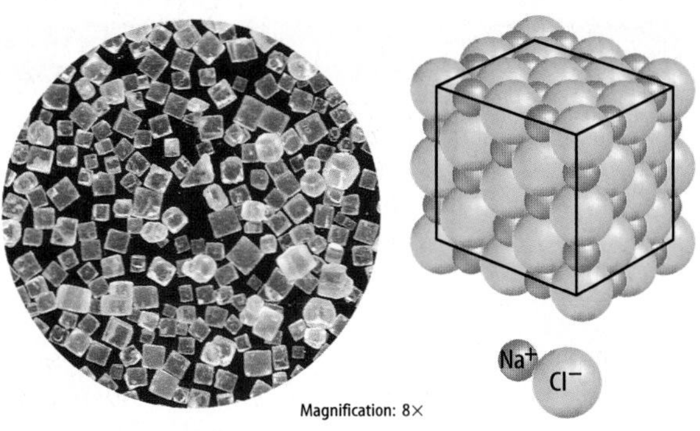

A **Magnified crystals of salt look like this.**

B **The salt crystal is held together by the attraction between sodium ions and chlorine ions.**

Figure 3
Table salt, or sodium chloride (NaCl), is a crystal composed of sodium ions and chlorine ions held together by ionic bonds.

Mixtures

Some substances, such as a combination of sugar and salt, can't change each other or combine chemically. A **mixture** is a combination of substances in which individual substances retain their own properties. Mixtures can be solids, liquids, gases, or any combination of them.

Reading Check ***Why is a combination of sugar and salt said to be a mixture?***

Most chemical reactions in living organisms take place in mixtures called solutions. You've probably noticed the taste of salt when you perspire. Sweat is a solution of salt and water. In a solution, two or more substances are mixed evenly. A cell's cytoplasm is a solution of dissolved molecules and ions.

Living things also contain mixtures called suspensions. A suspension is formed when a liquid or a gas has another substance evenly spread throughout it. Unlike solutions, the substances in a suspension eventually sink to the bottom. If blood, shown in **Figure 4,** is left undisturbed, the red blood cells and white blood cells will sink gradually to the bottom. However, the pumping action of your heart constantly moves your blood and the blood cells remain suspended.

Figure 4
When a test tube of whole blood is left standing, the blood cells sink in the watery plasma.

Teacher FYI

The two most common bonds in compounds are covalent and ionic. In covalent bonds, atoms share outermost electrons. In ionic bonds, oppositely charged ions are attracted to one another.

Mixtures

Quick Demo

Demonstrate mixtures and compounds. Mix baking soda with darker sand. Point out the different, distinct parts of the mixture. Then mix baking soda with vinegar in a clear container. The bubbles indicate that a new compound—carbon dioxide—has formed. **NOTE:** Make sure students understand that formation of bubbles does not *always* indicate that a chemical reaction has taken place. For example, the bubbles in soda indicate carbon dioxide is coming out of the mixture, not that a new substance is being formed.

Reading Check

Answer It is a combination of two substances, each of which retains its own properties when combined with the other.

Visual Learning

Figure 4 Have students identify the visibly separate parts in the test tube. **What is the transparent substance in the tube?** plasma **What is the concentrated substance at the bottom of the tube?** red and white blood cells **Describe what would happen if the tube was shaken.** The blood cells and plasma would mix, forming a suspension. This suspension is blood.

Resource Manager

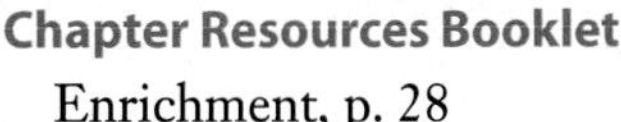

Chapter Resources Booklet
Enrichment, p. 28

Inclusion Strategies

Gifted Mark lines on a glass jar with a glass-marking pen, indicating the one-cup and two-cup levels. Pour 1 cup of hot water into the jar. Add 1 cup of sugar. Stir until the sugar dissolves. Ask why there are not two cups of solution. The sugar takes up the spaces between the particles of water. L3 LS **Logical-Mathematical**

Organic Compounds

IDENTIFYING Misconceptions

Student awareness of the emphasis on maintaining a "low-fat" diet may lead them to believe that all lipids are harmful. Explain that fats and other lipids have many useful functions in living organisms, such as energy storage, and are a vital component of cell membranes.

Activity

Display a Food Guide Pyramid and discuss the types of organic compounds represented by foods in each group. Ask students to use this information to create a bulletin board display of foods rich in carbohydrates, lipids, and proteins. Have students illustrate the display with pictures of the foods.

Fun Fact

A paste made of meat tenderizer and water is often used to treat bee and jellyfish stings. An enzyme in the meat tenderizer helps to break down the proteins in the venom, making the area less painful.

Table 3 Organic Compounds Found in Living Things

	Carbohydrates	Lipids	Proteins	Nucleic Acids
Elements	carbon, hydrogen, and oxygen	carbon, oxygen, hydrogen, and phosphorus	carbon, oxygen, hydrogen, nitrogen, and sulfur	carbon, oxygen, hydrogen, nitrogen, and phosphorus
Examples	sugars, starch, and cellulose	fats, oils, waxes, phospholipids, and cholesterol	enzymes, skin, and hair	DNA and RNA
Function	supply energy for cell processes; form plant structures; short-term energy storage	store large amounts of energy long term; form boundaries around cells	regulate cell processes and build cell structures	carry hereditary information; used to make proteins

Organic Compounds

You and all living things are made up of compounds that are classified as organic or inorganic. Rocks and other nonliving things contain inorganic compounds, but most do not contain large amounts of organic compounds. **Organic compounds** always contain carbon and hydrogen and usually are associated with living things. One exception would be nonliving things that are products of living things. For example, coal contains organic compounds because it was formed from dead and decaying plants. Organic molecules can contain hundreds or even thousands of atoms that can be arranged in many ways. **Table 3** compares the four groups of organic compounds that make up all living things—carbohydrates, lipids, proteins, and nucleic acids.

SCIENCE Online

Research Air is a mixture of many things. Weather forecasts often include information about air quality. Visit the Glencoe Science Web site at **science.glencoe.com** for more information about air quality. In your Science Journal list some things that may be measured when testing air quality.

Carbohydrates Carbohydrates are organic molecules that supply energy for cell processes. Sugars and starches are carbohydrates that cells use for energy. Some carbohydrates also are important parts of cell structures. For example, a carbohydrate called cellulose is an important part of plant cells.

Lipids Another type of organic compound found in living things is a lipid. Lipids do not mix with water. Lipids such as fats and oils store and release even larger amounts of energy than carbohydrates do. One type of lipid, the phospholipid, is a major part of cell membranes.

Science Journal

CFCs Have students research and summarize in their Science Journals the organic compounds known as chlorofluorocarbons (CFCs). Summaries should include a description of the composition of these compounds, their use as refrigerants, and a description of how the use of these substances has impacted the environment. P

Internet Addresses

Explore the Glencoe Science Web site at **science.glencoe.com** to find out more about topics in this section.

Proteins Organic compounds called proteins have many important functions in living organisms. They are made up of smaller molecules called amino acids. Proteins are the building blocks of many structures in organisms. Your muscles contain large amounts of protein. Proteins are scattered throughout cell membranes. Certain proteins called **enzymes** regulate nearly all chemical reactions in cells.

Nucleic Acids Large organic molecules that store important coded information in cells are called nucleic acids. One nucleic acid, deoxyribonucleic acid, or DNA—genetic material—is found in all cells. It carries information that directs each cell's activities. Another nucleic acid, ribonucleic acid, or RNA, is needed to make enzymes and other proteins.

Inorganic Compounds

Most **inorganic compounds** are made from elements other than carbon. Generally, inorganic molecules contain fewer atoms than organic molecules. Inorganic compounds are the source for many elements needed by living things. For example, plants take up inorganic compounds from the soil. These inorganic compounds can contain the elements nitrogen, phosphorus, and sulfur. Many foods that you eat contain inorganic compounds. **Table 4** shows some of the inorganic compounds that are important to you. One of the most important inorganic compounds for living things is water.

Mini LAB

Determining How Enzymes Work

Procedure

1. Get two small cups of **prepared gelatin** from your teacher. Do not eat or drink anything in lab.
2. On the gelatin in one of the cups, place a piece of **fresh pineapple.**
3. Let both cups stand undisturbed during your class period. Wash your hands when you are done.
4. Observe what happens to the gelatin.

Analysis

1. What effect did the piece of fresh pineapple have on the gelatin?
2. What does fresh pineapple contain that caused it to have the effect on the gelatin you observed?
3. Why do the preparation directions on a box of gelatin dessert tell you not to mix it with fresh pineapple?

Table 4 Some Inorganic Compounds Important in Humans

Compound	Use in Body
Water	makes up most of the blood; most chemical reactions occur in water
Calcium phosphate	gives strength to bones
Hydrochloric acid	breaks down foods in the stomach
Sodium bicarbonate	helps the digestion of food to occur
Salts containing sodium, chlorine, and potassium	important in sending messages along nerves

Mini LAB

Purpose to observe how enzymes affect gelatin L1
IS **Visual-Spatial**

Materials two small cups of prepared gelatin, 1 slice of fresh pineapple

Teaching Strategies

- To prepare gelatin, add only half the amount of water indicated on the gelatin package.
- After students add pineapple to one cup, allow both cups of gelatin to sit overnight.

Analysis

1. The gelatin under the fresh pineapple turned to a liquid.
2. an enzyme
3. The gelatin would not solidify if in contact with fresh pineapple.

Assessment

Performance Have students design an experiment to show conclusively that fresh pineapple contains enzymes that keep gelatin from becoming solid. They can repeat the experiment using canned pineapple. Use **PASC,** p. 95.

Inorganic Compounds

Teacher FYI

Life on Earth could not have evolved without water. Wherever life is found, water is found. Life is found in water at all temperatures. Bacteria can live under snow and in the near-boiling water of hot springs.

Resource Manager 

Chapter Resources Booklet

MiniLAB, p. 3
Reinforcement, p. 25

Curriculum Connection

Health Provide students with copies of the periodic table. Ask them to research which elements are important for good health. They can find this information on food labels, in reference books, and on the Internet. Ask students to shade each element they discover on the table and to share their results with the class. L2
IS **Interpersonal**

Inorganic Compounds, continued

Quick Demo

Display different liquids, such as a glass of fruit juice, a jar of paint, a bottle of oil, a beaker of alcohol, and a glass of water. Ask which substance is unique. Explain that water is unique, as it contains chemical and physical properties seen in no other substance. It is liquid at temperatures found on most of Earth's surface. Unlike most other substances, water expands when it freezes. In addition, water is the most common solvent in the world.
LS Visual-Spatial

Make a Model

Have students make a model of a water molecule. They may use foam balls or colored marshmallows to represent the atoms, and toothpicks to hold them together. L2 **LS Kinesthetic**

Math Skills Activity

National Math Standards

Correlation to Mathematics Objectives

1, 2, 4, 6, 8, 9

Answer to Practice Problem

Calculate the infant's water weight and the adult's water weight, then subtract to find the difference.

Infant: $78/100 = x \div 3.2$ kg
$x = (78 \times 3.2) \div 100$
$x = 2.496$ kg of water;
Adult: $60 \div 100 = x \div 95$ kg
$x = (60 \times 95) \div 100$
$x = 57$ kg of water;
Difference: 57 kg − 2.496 kg = 54.504 kg

Importance of Water Some scientists hypothesize that life began in the water of Earth's ancient oceans. Chemical reactions might have occurred that produced organic molecules. Similar chemical reactions can take place in cells in your body.

Living things are composed of more than 50 percent water and depend on water to survive. You can live for weeks without food but only for a few days without water. **Figure 5** shows where water is found in your body. Although seeds and spores of plants, fungi, and bacteria can exist without water, they must have water if they are to grow and reproduce. All the chemical reactions in living things take place in water solutions, and most organisms use water to transport materials through their bodies. For example, many animals have blood that is mostly water and moves materials. Plants use water to move minerals and sugars between the roots and leaves.

Math Skills Activity

Calculating the Importance of Water

All life on Earth depends on water for survival. Water is the most vital part of humans and other animals. It is required for all of the chemical processes that keep us alive.

Example Problem

At least 60% of an adult human body consists of water. If an adult man weighs 90 kg, how many kilograms of water does his body contain?

Solution

1. *This is what you know:* adult human body = 60% water; man = 90 kg
2. *This is what you want to find:* 60% of 90 kg
3. *This is the equation you need to use:* $60/100 = x/90$
4. *Solve the equation for* x: $x = (60 \times 90)/100$; $x = 54$ kg

Check your answer by dividing your answer by 90, then multiplying by 100. Do you get 60%?

Practice Problem

A human body at birth consists of 78% water. This percent gradually decreases to 60% in an adult. Assume a baby weighed 3.2 kg at birth, and grew into an adult weighing 95 kg. Calculate the approximate number of kilograms of water the human gained.

For more help, refer to the Math Skill Handbook.

72 CHAPTER 3 Cell Processes

Resource Manager

Chapter Resources Booklet
Transparency Activity, pp. 45–46
Mathematics Skill Activities, p. 5
Science Inquiry Labs, pp. 43, 47

Curriculum Connection

Art Have students cut out pictures from magazines that illustrate water use by organisms, in industry, and in the environment. Then, have each student make a water collage using the pictures they chose. Display collages in the classroom. L1 **LS Visual-Spatial**

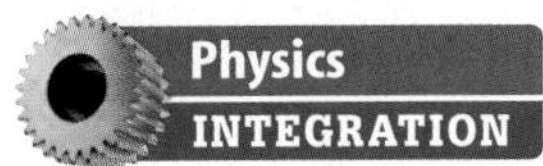

Characteristics of Water

The atoms of a water molecule are arranged in such a way that the molecule has areas with different charges. Water molecules are like magnets. The negative part of a water molecule is attracted to the positive part of another water molecule just like the north pole of a magnet is attracted to the south pole of another magnet. This attraction, or force, between water molecules is why a film forms on the surface of water. The film is strong enough to support small insects because the forces between water molecules are stronger than the force of gravity on the insect.

When heat is added to any substance, its molecules begin to move faster. Because water molecules are so strongly attracted to each other, the temperature of water changes slowly. The large percentage of water in living things acts like an insulator. The water in a cell helps keep its temperature constant, which allows life-sustaining chemical reactions to take place.

You've seen ice floating on water. When water freezes, ice crystals form. In the crystals, each water molecule is spaced at a certain distance from all the others. Because this distance is greater in frozen water than in liquid water, ice floats on water. Bodies of water freeze from the top down. The floating ice provides insulation from extremely cold temperatures and allows living things to survive in the cold water under the ice.

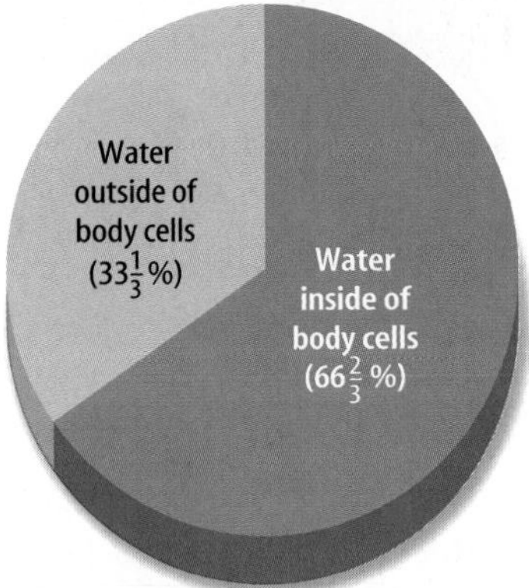

Figure 5
About two thirds of your body's water is located within your body's cells. Water helps maintain the cells' shapes and sizes. One third of your body's water is outside of your body's cells.

Section  1 Assessment

1. What are the similarities and differences between atoms and molecules?
2. What is the difference between organic and inorganic compounds? Give an example of each type of compound.
3. What are the four types of organic compounds found in all living things?
4. Why does life as we know it depend on water?
5. **Think Critically** If you mix salt, sand, and sugar with water in a small jar, will the resulting mixture be a suspension, a solution, or both?

Skill Builder Activities

6. **Interpreting Scientific Illustrations** Carefully observe **Figure 1** and determine how many protons, neutrons, and electrons an atom of oxygen has. **For more help, refer to the Science Skill Handbook.**
7. **Using an Electronic Spreadsheet** Research to find the percentage of elements that make up Earth's crust. Make a spreadsheet that includes this information and the information in **Table 2.** Create a circle graph for each set of percentages. **For more help, refer to the Technology Skill Handbook.**

Teacher FYI

Earth's distance from the Sun provides the right conditions for liquid water: temperatures between 0°C and 100°C (32°F and 212°F). Water has or would have evaporated from planets closer to the Sun.

3 Assess

Reteach

Display carbon compounds such as starch, soap, vinegar, and alcohol. Ask students to explain why these are considered to be organic compounds. They all contain carbon and hydrogen.
LS **Logical-Mathematical**

Challenge

If you were on a space mission looking for signs of life on another planet, what elements would you search for and why? Possible response: carbon, hydrogen, oxygen, nitrogen, sulfur, and phosphorus; these elements make up about 99% of all living things.

Assessment

Portfolio Have students write an essay to explain why water is important to them. Ask them to think about their family's use of water each day and what would happen if they were asked to cut their water usage. Use **Performance Assessment in the Science Classroom,** p. 157.

Answers to Section Assessment

1. Possible answer: similarities=both are made of smaller units. Atoms consist of protons, neutrons, and electrons and molecules consist of two or more atoms; differences= molecules are larger than atoms. Molecules can be formed or broken down in a chemical reaction but atoms cannot.
2. Organic compounds, such as lipids, contain carbon; most inorganic compounds, such as water, do not.
3. lipids, carbohydrates, proteins, and nucleic acids
4. Most life processes can occur only in water solutions.
5. Salt and sugar dissolve in water forming a solution; if shaken, sand will spread throughout the solution and form a suspension.
6. 8 protons, 8 neutrons, and 8 electrons
7. Human body graph: 65% oxygen, 18.5% carbon, 9.5% hydrogen, 3.2% nitrogen, 1.5% calcium, and 2.3% other elements; Earth's crust graph: 46.6% oxygen, 27.7% silicon, 8.1% aluminum, 5.0% iron, 3.6% calcium, 2.8% sodium, 2.6% potassium, 2.1% magnesium, 1.5% other elements

SECTION

Moving Cellular Materials

1 Motivate

Bellringer Transparency

Display the Section Focus Transparency for Section 2. Use the accompanying Transparency Activity Master. L2 ELL

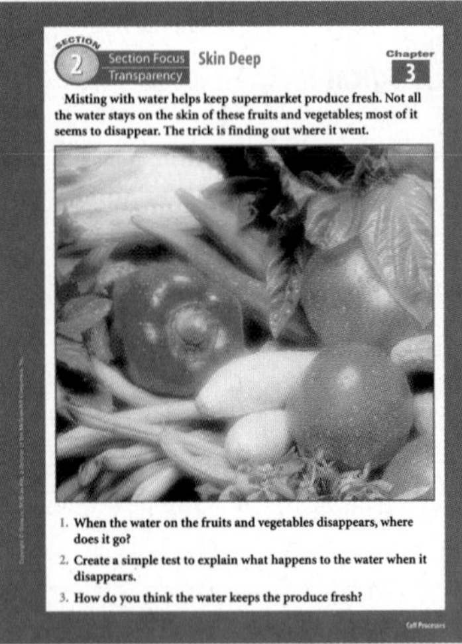

Section Focus Transparency 2 — Skin Deep — Chapter 3

Misting with water helps keep supermarket produce fresh. Not all the water stays on the skin of these fruits and vegetables; most of it seems to disappear. The trick is finding out where it went.

1. When the water on the fruits and vegetables disappears, where does it go?
2. Create a simple test to explain what happens to the water when it disappears.
3. How do you think the water keeps the produce fresh?

Tie to Prior Knowledge

Use an overhead transparency to review the parts of a cell. Point out that the cell membrane helps a cell maintain a balance between the cell and materials, such as water, salt, and sugars, in its environment.

SECTION

Moving Cellular Materials

As You Read

***What* You'll Learn**

- **Describe** the function of a selectively permeable membrane.
- **Explain** how the processes of diffusion and osmosis move molecules in living cells.
- **Explain** how passive transport and active transport differ.

Vocabulary

passive transport
diffusion
equilibrium
osmosis
active transport
endocytosis
exocytosis

***Why* It's Important**

Cell membranes control the substances that enter and leave the cells in your body.

Passive Transport

"Close that window. Do you want to let in all the bugs and leaves?" How do you prevent unwanted things from coming through the window? As seen in **Figure 6,** a window screen provides the protection needed to keep unwanted things outside. It also allows some things to pass into or out of the room like air, unpleasant odors, or smoke.

Cells take in food, oxygen, and other substances from their environments. They also release waste materials into their environments. A cell has a membrane around it that works for a cell like a window screen does for a room. A cell's membrane is selectively permeable (PUR mee uh bul). It allows some things to enter or leave the cell while keeping other things outside or inside the cell. The window screen also is selectively permeable based on the size of its openings.

Things can move through a cell membrane in several ways. Which way things move depends on the size of the molecules or particles, the path taken through the membrane, and whether or not energy is used. The movement of substances through the cell membrane without the input of energy is called **passive transport.** Three types of passive transport can occur. The type depends on what is moving through the cell membrane.

Figure 6
A cell membrane, like a screen, will let some things through more easily than others. Air gets through a screen, but insects are kept out.

Section Assessment Planner

PORTFOLIO
Visual Learning, p. 79

PERFORMANCE ASSESSMENT
Try at Home MiniLAB, p. 75
Skill Builder Activities, p. 78
See page 92 for more options.

CONTENT ASSESSMENT
Section, p. 78
Challenge, p. 78
Chapter, pp. 92–93

74 CHAPTER 3 Cell Processes

Figure 7
Like all other cells in your body, cells in your toes need oxygen.

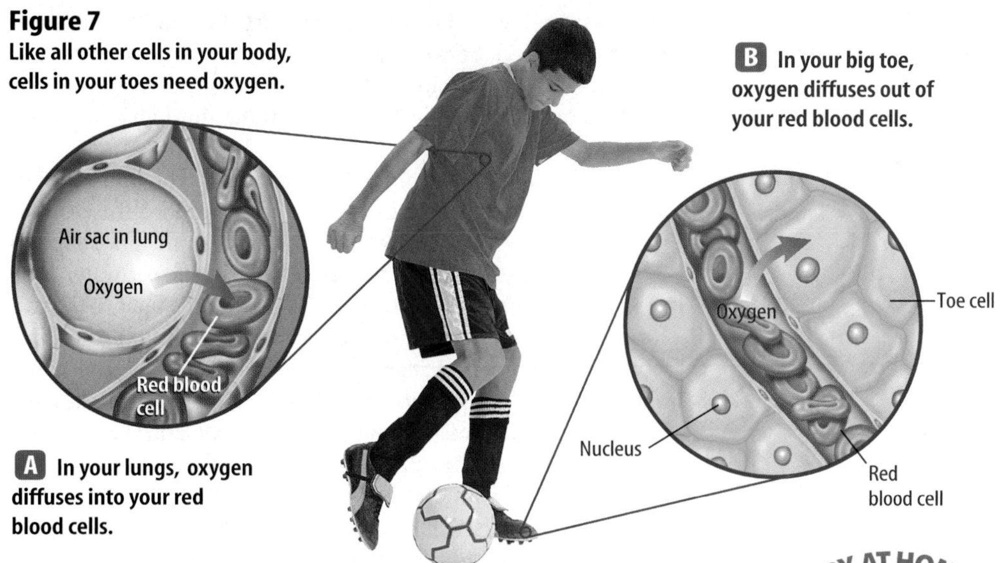

A In your lungs, oxygen diffuses into your red blood cells.

B In your big toe, oxygen diffuses out of your red blood cells.

Diffusion Molecules in solids, liquids, and gases move constantly and randomly. You might smell perfume when you sit near or as you walk past someone who is wearing it. This is because perfume molecules randomly move throughout the air. This random movement of molecules from an area where there is relatively more of them into an area where there is relatively fewer of them is called **diffusion.** Diffusion is one type of cellular passive transport. Molecules of a substance will continue to move from one area into another until the relative number of these molecules is equal in the two areas. When this occurs, **equilibrium** is reached and diffusion stops. After equilibrium occurs, it is maintained because molecules continue to move.

Reading Check *What is equilibrium?*

Every cell in your body uses oxygen. When you breathe, how does oxygen get from your lungs to cells in your big toe? Oxygen is carried throughout your body in your blood by the red blood cells. When your blood is pumped from your heart to your lungs, your red blood cells do not contain much oxygen. However, your lungs have more oxygen molecules than your red blood cells do, so the oxygen molecules diffuse into your red blood cells from your lungs, as shown in **Figure 7A.** When the blood reaches your big toe, there are more oxygen molecules in your red blood cells than in your big toe cells. The oxygen diffuses from your red blood cells and into your big toe cells, as shown in **Figure 7B.**

TRY AT HOME Mini LAB

Observing Diffusion

Procedure

1. Use **two clean glasses** of equal size. Label one "hot," then fill it until half full with **very warm water.** Label the other "cold," then fill it until half full with **cold water. WARNING:** *Do not use boiling hot water.*
2. Add one drop of **food coloring** to each glass. Carefully release the drop just at the water's surface to avoid splashing the water.
3. Observe the glasses. Record your observations immediately and again after 15 min.

Analysis

1. Describe what happens when food coloring is added to each glass.
2. How does temperature affect the rate of diffusion?

2 Teach

Passive Transport

Purpose to investigate the effect of temperature on diffusion rate L1 ELL COOP LEARN LS **Logical-Mathematical**

Materials 2 clean glasses, hot water, cold water, food coloring, dropper, marker or wax pencil, clock, labels

Teaching Strategies

- Have students record how long it takes the food coloring to diffuse evenly throughout each beaker.
- Caution students not to move the water-filled beakers.

Analysis

1. The food coloring spreads throughout the water; it spreads faster in the hot water.
2. Heat increases the rate of diffusion.

Assessment

Performance To further assess understanding of the effect of temperature on diffusion, have students repeat the activity using ice water instead of hot water. Use **PASC,** p. 105.

Reading Check

Answer when the relative number of molecules of a substance is equal in the two areas

Resource Manager

Chapter Resources Booklet

Transparency Activity, p. 43
Directed Reading for Content Mastery, p. 18
MiniLAB, p. 4

Teacher FYI

A permeable membrane allows all molecules to pass through. An impermeable membrane doesn't allow any to pass. Only some molecules can pass through a semipermeable membrane—usually only small molecules that can pass through quickly.

Passive Transport, continued

Quick Demo

To demonstrate a selectively permeable membrane, pour different substances (i.e. sand, salt, marbles, water) through a kitchen strainer. Select some substances that will pass through the strainer, and some that will not. LS **Visual-Spatial**

Discussion

Why do salty foods make you thirsty? The salt present in the food causes water to leave your cells; therefore, your body needs water to replace what your cells have lost.

Extension

Fertilizers contain chemical salts. If fertilizers are placed on plants and it doesn't rain soon after, the plants may die. Have students investigate and report on the use of fertilizers by interviewing farmers or lawn-maintenance workers. L2
LS **Interpersonal**

Reading Check

Answer Because there are relatively fewer water molecules in the salt solution around the carrot cells than inside the carrot cells, water leaves the carrot and moves into the salt solution.

Osmosis—The Diffusion of Water Remember that water makes up a large part of living matter. Cells contain water and are surrounded by water. Water molecules move by diffusion into and out of cells. The diffusion of water through a cell membrane is called **osmosis.**

If cells weren't surrounded by water that contains few dissolved substances, water inside the cells would diffuse out of them. This is why water left the carrot cells in this chapter's Explore Activity. Because there were relatively fewer water molecules in the salt solution around the carrot cells than in the carrot cells, water moved out of the cells and into the salt solution.

Losing water from inside a plant cell causes the cell membrane to come away from the cell wall, as shown in **Figure 8A.** This reduces the pressure against the cell wall, and the plant cell becomes limp. If the carrot sticks were taken out of the salt water and put in pure water, the water around the cells would move into the cells. The cells would fill with water and their cell membranes would press against their cell walls, as shown in **Figure 8B.** Pressure would increase and the plant cells would become firm. That is why the carrot sticks would be crisp again.

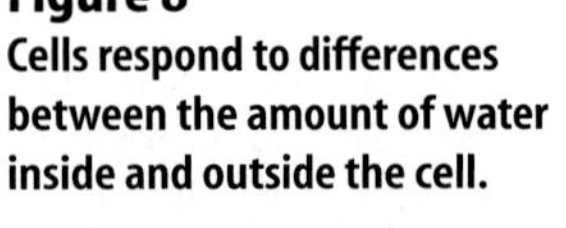

Reading Check *Why do carrots in salt water become limp?*

Osmosis also takes place in animal cells. If animal cells were placed in pure water, they too would swell up. However, animal cells are different from plant cells. Just like an overfilled water balloon, animal cells will burst if too much water enters the cell.

Figure 8
Cells respond to differences between the amount of water inside and outside the cell.

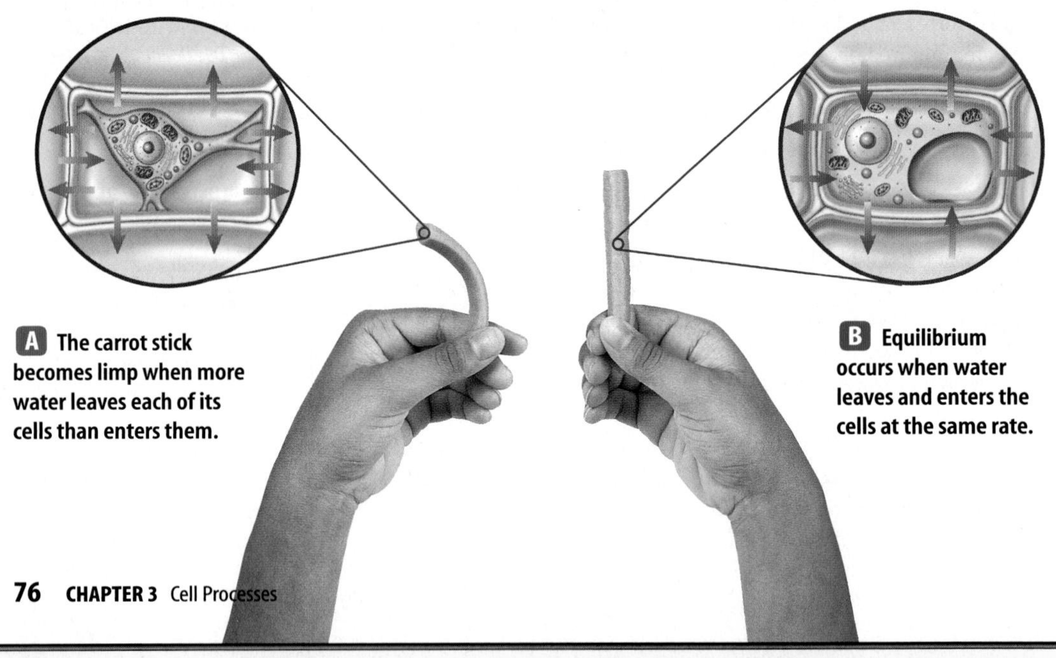

A The carrot stick becomes limp when more water leaves each of its cells than enters them.

B Equilibrium occurs when water leaves and enters the cells at the same rate.

LAB DEMONSTRATION

Purpose to observe diffusion

Materials self-sealing plastic sandwich bag, cooked rice, tincture of iodine, 8-oz. clear plastic cups, tablespoon

Preparation Half-fill the plastic cups with water and add 6 drops of tincture of iodine. Cook rice.

Procedure Seal a sandwich bag containing 2 tablespoons of rice, and place it into the water that contains iodine. Observe after 10 minutes.

Expected Outcome Iodine molecules will move through the plastic bag, turning the rice blue-black. Iodine always turns blue-black in the presence of starch.

Assessment

What did you observe? The rice inside the plastic bag turned blue-black. **Explain what occurred.** Iodine molecules diffused from an area where there was a large number of iodine molecules (outside the bag) to an area where there were few iodine molecules (inside the bag).

Facilitated Diffusion Cells take in many substances. Some substances pass easily through the cell membrane by diffusion. Other substances, such as glucose molecules, are so large that they can enter the cell only with the help of molecules in the cell membrane called transport proteins. This process, a type of passive transport, is known as facilitated diffusion. Have you ever used the drive through at a fast-food restaurant to get your meal? The transport proteins in the cell membrane are like the drive-through window at the restaurant. The window lets you get food out of the restaurant and put money into the restaurant. Similarly, transport proteins are used to move substances into and out of the cell.

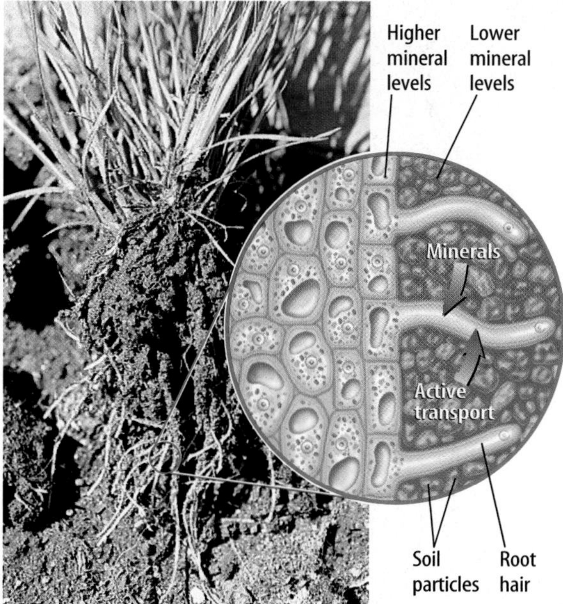

Figure 9
Some root cells have extensions called root hairs that may be 5 mm to 8 mm long. Minerals are taken in by active transport through the cell membranes of root hairs.

Active Transport

Imagine that a football game is over and you leave the stadium. As soon as you get outside of the stadium, you remember that you left your jacket on your seat. Now you have to move against the crowd coming out of the stadium to get back in to get your jacket. Which required more energy—leaving the stadium with the crowd or going back to get your jacket? Something similar to this happens in cells.

Sometimes, a substance is needed inside a cell even though the amount of that substance inside the cell is already greater than the amount outside the cell. For example, root cells require minerals from the soil. The roots of the plant in **Figure 9** already might contain more of those mineral molecules than the surrounding soil does. The tendency is for mineral molecules to move out of the root by diffusion or facilitated diffusion. But they need to move back across the cell membrane and into the cell just like you had to move back into the stadium. When an input of energy is required to move materials through a cell membrane, **active transport** takes place.

Active transport involves transport proteins, just as facilitated diffusion does. In active transport, a transport protein binds with the needed particle and cellular energy is used to move it through the cell membrane. When the particle is released, the transport protein can move another needed particle through the membrane.

Health INTEGRATION

Transport proteins are important to your health. Sometimes transport proteins are missing or do not function correctly. What would happen if proteins that transport cholesterol across membranes were missing? Cholesterol is an important lipid used by your cells. Write your ideas in your Science Journal.

Active Transport

Use an Analogy

Have students compare active and passive transport with the energy they must exert to get a bicycle to the top of a hill and then ride it back down. Students must exert energy to get the bicycle up the hill. In the same way, the cell uses energy to move substances from areas of low concentration to areas of high concentration. Students do not need to exert energy to ride the bicycle down the hill. In passive transport, cells do not have to use energy to move substances from areas of high concentration to areas of low concentration.
LS **Logical-Mathematical**

Text Question Answer

going back for the jacket

Teacher FYI

Cell membranes contain spaces through which some substances (water molecules, mineral ions, sugar molecules) can easily pass. The spaces are too small for most proteins and other large molecules to pass through. Some ions cannot pass through membranes due to their charge. These move into a cell via channels or active transport.

Health INTEGRATION

Cholesterol would not be transported to different areas of the body. Without cholesterol, the body could not synthesize bile acids, steroid hormones, or Vitamin D.

Cultural Diversity

Preserving Foods A practical use of osmosis is the drying and salting of food. Have students report on the processes and uses of dried and salted foods in Native American and other cultures. For example, the French developed a vegetable dehydrator in 1795. Both processes remove water from cells in order to preserve the food. In drying, water evaporates. In salting, a salt solution is used to remove water from cells.

Resource Manager

Chapter Resources Booklet
- Enrichment, p. 29
- Reinforcement, p. 26
- Lab Activity, pp. 9–10

Endocytosis and Exocytosis

Use Science Words

Word Meaning Have students use a dictionary to find the meanings of the prefixes *endo-* and *exo-* (*taking in* and *turning out*). Ask them to find examples of other words that make use of these prefixes, and to explain how the meaning of the prefix relates to the meaning of the word. Possible answers: endoskeleton, a skeleton that is inside the body; exoskeleton, a skeleton that is outside the body.

3 Assess

Reteach

Place two or three drops of vanilla extract inside a balloon. Blow up the balloon and tie it. Have students observe the balloon until they can smell the vanilla. Then have them explain why they smell the vanilla outside the balloon. Diffusion has taken place across the membrane.

Challenge

Have students research selectively permeable membranes. Ask them to explain why some substances but not others can pass through the cell membrane. Molecules pass through selectively permeable membranes depending upon size, chemical composition, and how quickly they can be transported.

Assessment

Oral Would a cell placed in syrup lose or gain water? Explain. It would lose water; water molecules move by diffusion from areas of high concentration to areas of low concentration. Use **Performance Assessment in the Science Classroom,** p. 93.

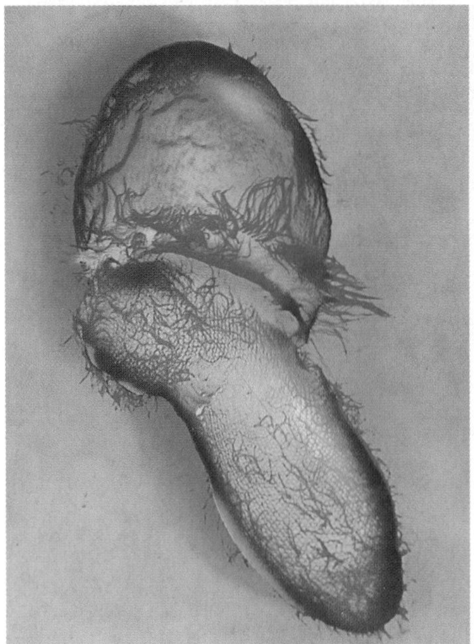

Magnification: 1400×

Figure 10
One-celled organisms like this egg-shaped one can take in other one-celled organisms using endocytosis.

Endocytosis and Exocytosis

Some molecules and particles are too large to move by diffusion or to use the cell membrane's transport proteins. Large protein molecules and bacteria, for example, can enter a cell when they are surrounded by the cell membrane. The cell membrane folds in on itself, enclosing the item in a sphere called a vesicle. Vesicles are transport and storage structures in a cell's cytoplasm. The sphere pinches off, and the resulting vesicle enters the cytoplasm. A similar thing happens when you poke your finger into a partially inflated balloon. Your finger is surrounded by the balloon in much the same way that the protein molecule is surrounded by the cell membrane. This process of taking substances into a cell by surrounding it with the cell membrane is called **endocytosis** (en duh si TOH sus). Some one-celled organisms, as shown in **Figure 10,** take in food this way.

The contents of a vesicle may be released by the cell using a process called **exocytosis** (ek soh si TOH sus). Exocytosis occurs in the opposite way that endocytosis does. The membrane of the vesicle fuses with the cell's membrane, and the vesicle's contents are released. Cells in your stomach use this process to release chemicals that help digest food. The different ways that materials may enter or leave a cell are summarized in **Figure 11.**

Section 2 Assessment

1. Explain how cell membranes are selectively permeable.
2. Compare and contrast the processes of osmosis and diffusion.
3. Identify the molecules that help substances move through the cell membrane during active transport and facilitated diffusion.
4. Why are endocytosis and exocytosis important processes to cells?
5. **Think Critically** Why are fresh fruits and vegetables sprinkled with water at produce markets?

Skill Builder Activities

6. **Concept Mapping** Make a network tree concept map to use as a study guide to help you tell the difference between passive transport and active transport. Begin with the phrase "Transport through membranes." **For more help, refer to the Science Skill Handbook.**
7. **Communicating** Seawater is saltier than tap water. In your Science Journal, explain why drinking large amounts of seawater would be dangerous to humans. **For more help, refer to the Science Skill Handbook.**

Answers to Section Assessment

1. They allow some molecules to pass through, but not others.
2. In both, molecules move from areas with many molecules to areas with few molecules. Osmosis is the diffusion of water across a cell membrane; diffusion can apply to any form of matter.
3. transport proteins
4. Molecules and particles that are too large to move by diffusion or by the cell's transport proteins can move into and out of cells using endocytosis and exocytosis.
5. Water will diffuse into the fruits and vegetables and keep them crisp.
6. Check student concept maps for accuracy.
7. The high levels of salt in seawater would cause water to move out of the cells, resulting in dehydration.

VISUALIZING CELL MEMBRANE TRANSPORT

Figure 11

A flexible yet strong layer, the cell membrane is built of two layers of lipids (gold) pierced by protein "passageways" (purple). Molecules can enter or exit the cell by slipping between the lipids or through the protein passageways. Substances that cannot enter or exit the cell in these ways may be surrounded by the membrane and drawn into or expelled from the cell.

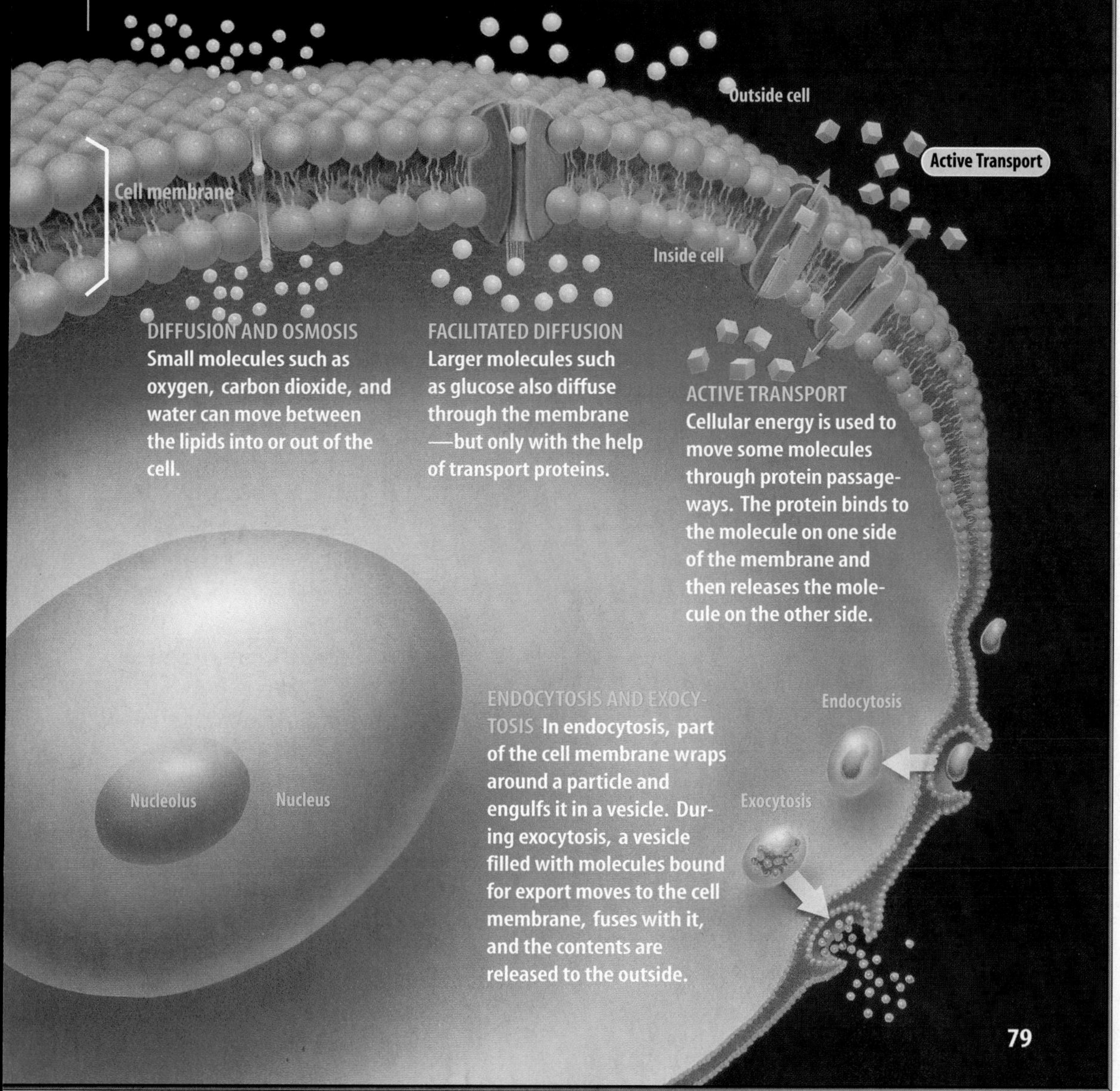

Diffusion and Osmosis

Facilitated Diffusion

Outside cell

Active Transport

Cell membrane

Inside cell

DIFFUSION AND OSMOSIS Small molecules such as oxygen, carbon dioxide, and water can move between the lipids into or out of the cell.

FACILITATED DIFFUSION Larger molecules such as glucose also diffuse through the membrane —but only with the help of transport proteins.

ACTIVE TRANSPORT Cellular energy is used to move some molecules through protein passageways. The protein binds to the molecule on one side of the membrane and then releases the molecule on the other side.

ENDOCYTOSIS AND EXOCYTOSIS In endocytosis, part of the cell membrane wraps around a particle and engulfs it in a vesicle. During exocytosis, a vesicle filled with molecules bound for export moves to the cell membrane, fuses with it, and the contents are released to the outside.

Endocytosis

Exocytosis

Nucleolus

Nucleus

79

Visual Learning

Figure 11 Have students make an outline from this figure of the steps a transport protein goes through to move substances into and out of cells. L2 LS **Visual-Spatial** P

Resource Manager

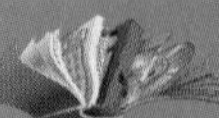

Life Science Critical Thinking/Problem Solving, p. 15

NATIONAL GEOGRAPHIC

Visualizing Cell Membrane Transport

Have students examine the pictures and read the captions. Then ask the following questions.

Why do some substances move through the cell membrane through exocytosis and endocytosis instead of one of the other transport methods? These substances, which include proteins and nucleic acids, are too large to use the other methods. For example, cholesterol enters by endocytosis; neurotransmitters exit by exocytosis.

Which transport method(s) is like floating downstream? Which is like paddling upstream? Why? In diffusion (osmosis and facilitated diffusion), a substance moves from an area of higher concentration to an area of lower concentration. This does not require energy because it goes with the flow, like floating downstream. In active transport, the substance must go against the concentration gradient which, like paddling upstream, requires energy.

Activity

Have students make a model of a cell that illustrates one type of cell membrane transport. LS **Kinesthetic**

Extension

Challenge students to investigate transport proteins and the substances each transports. Have students make a card game to teach other students what they learned. LS **Logical-Mathematical**

Activity BENCH TESTED

Purpose to observe and measure the amount of water diffusing through an egg membrane L2
LS **Logical-Mathematical**

Process Skills observing and inferring, measuring, communicating, recognizing cause and effect, forming operational definitions

Time Required 50 minutes to set up, 5 minutes each day to observe, 15 minutes to summarize

Alternate Materials Clean, empty food containers with lids may be used to hold the unshelled egg.

Teaching Strategy Cover raw eggs with vinegar. Leave undisturbed for two or three days until the shells dissolve.

Troubleshooting

- Remind students to handle unshelled eggs carefully to avoid breaking membranes.
- Thick syrup works better than thin syrup.
- Make sure students replace lids on containers when not in use.

Answers to Questions

1. water— increased in size; corn syrup—decreased in size
2. about 30 mL of water entered; about 40 mL of water left
3. The eggshell is not permeable to water and syrup.
4. cell membrane

Assessment

Performance Have students place ten dried beans in water and let them remain overnight. Direct them to explain their observations. Use **PASC,** p. 97.

Activity

Observing Osmosis

It is difficult to see osmosis occurring in cells because most cells are so small. However, a few cells can be seen without the aid of a microscope. Try this activity to see how osmosis occurs in a large cell.

What You'll Investigate

How does osmosis occur in an egg cell?

Materials

unshelled egg*	distilled water (250 mL)
balance	light corn syrup (250 mL)
spoon	500-mL container

Goals

- **Observe** osmosis in an egg cell.
- **Determine** what affects osmosis.

Safety Precautions

Eggs may contain bacteria. Avoid touching your face. Wash your hands thoroughly when you are done.

*an egg whose shell has been dissolved by vinegar

Procedure

1. Copy the table below into your Science Journal and use it to record your data.

Egg Mass Data

	Beginning Egg Mass	Egg Mass After Two Days
Distilled water	delete box show anno	delete box show anno
Corn syrup	delete box show anno	delete box show anno

2. Obtain an unshelled egg from your teacher. Handle the egg gently. Use a balance to find the egg's mass and record it in the table.
3. Place the egg in the container and add enough distilled water to cover it.
4. **Observe** the egg after 30 min, one day, and two days. After each observation, record the egg's appearance in your Science Journal.
5. After day two, remove the egg with a spoon and allow it to drain. Find the egg's mass and record it in the table.
6. Empty the container, then put the egg back in. Now add enough corn syrup to cover it. Repeat steps 4 and 5.

Conclude and Apply

1. **Explain** the difference between what happened to the egg in water and in corn syrup.
2. **Calculate** the mass of water that moved into and out of the egg.
3. **Hypothesize** why you used an unshelled egg for this investigation.
4. **Infer** what part of the egg controlled water's movement into and out of the egg.

Compare your conclusions with those of other students in your class. **For more help, refer to the** Science Skill Handbook.

Resource Manager

Chapter Resources Booklet
Activity Worksheet, pp. 5–6

Communicating Your Data

Students should discuss why their conclusions did or did not agree with those of other students.

SECTION 3

Energy for Life

Trapping and Using Energy

Think of all the energy that players use in a basketball game. Where does the energy come from? The simplest answer is "from the food they eat." The chemical energy stored in food is changed in cells into forms needed to perform all the activities necessary for life. In every cell, these changes involve chemical reactions. All of the activities of an organism involve chemical reactions in some way. The total of all chemical reactions in an organism is called **metabolism.**

The chemical reactions of metabolism need enzymes. What do enzymes do? Suppose you are hungry and decide to open a can of spaghetti. You use a can opener to open the can. Without a can opener, the spaghetti is unusable. The can of spaghetti changed because of the can opener, but the can opener did not change. The can opener can be used again later to open more cans of spaghetti. Enzymes in cells work something like can openers, as shown in **Figure 12.** The enzyme, like the can opener, causes a change, but the enzyme is not changed and is reusable. Unlike the can opener, which can only break things apart, enzymes also can cause molecules to join. Without the right enzymes, chemical reactions in cells cannot take place.

As You Read

***What* You'll Learn**

- **List** the differences between producers and consumers.
- **Explain** how the processes of photosynthesis and respiration store and release energy.
- **Describe** how cells get energy from glucose through fermentation.

Vocabulary

metabolism · respiration · photosynthesis · fermentation

***Why* It's Important**

Because of photosynthesis and respiration, you use the Sun's energy.

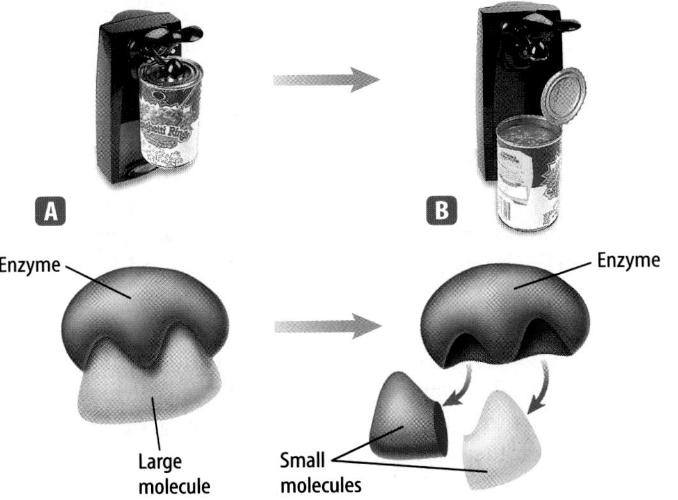

Figure 12
Enzymes are needed for most chemical reactions that take place in cells. A The enzyme attaches to the large molecule it will help change. B The enzyme causes the larger molecule to break down into two smaller molecules. Like the can opener, the enzyme is not changed and can be used again.

Section Assessment Planner

PORTFOLIO
Visual Learning, p. 85

PERFORMANCE ASSESSMENT
Skill Builder Activities, p. 85
See page 92 for more options.

CONTENT ASSESSMENT
Section, p. 85
Challenge, p. 85
Chapter, pp. 92–93

SECTION

Energy for Life

1 Motivate

Bellringer Transparency

Display the Section Focus Transparency for Section 3. Use the accompanying Transparency Activity Master. L2 ELL

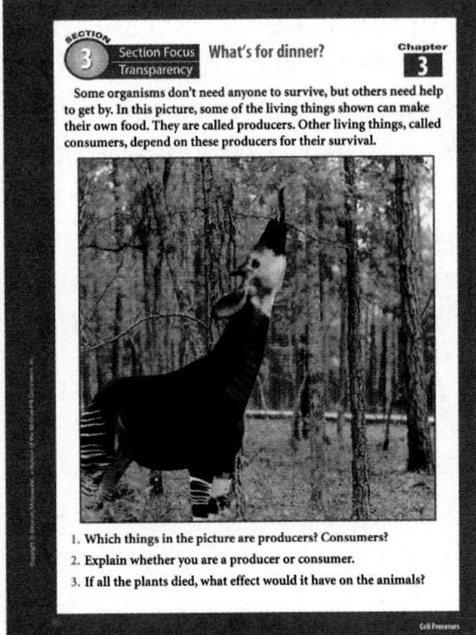

SECTION 3 Section Focus Transparency — What's for dinner? — Chapter 3

Some organisms don't need anyone to survive, but others need help to get by. In this picture, some of the living things shown can make their own food. They are called producers. Other living things, called consumers, depend on these producers for their survival.

1. Which things in the picture are producers? Consumers?
2. Explain whether you are a producer or consumer.
3. If all the plants died, what effect would it have on the animals?

Cell Processes

Tie to Prior Knowledge

Display pictures of people using energy—playing sports, gardening, working, and so on. Ask students to identify the source of this energy. chemical bonds in food Then ask where the energy in the food came from. It was derived from plants that captured the Sun's energy.

2 Teach

Trapping and Using Energy

Activity

Pick a leaf from a plant that has been exposed to sunlight for a few hours. Submerge it in water. Observe the surface of the leaf. **What forms on the leaf? Why?** Bubbles; the leaf is giving off oxygen.

Use an Analogy

Compare the construction of a house to photosynthesis. Building a house is a physical process that requires the putting together of raw materials. Photosynthesis is a chemical process of putting raw materials together. They both require raw materials and result in a usable product. LS **Logical-Mathematical**

Caption Answer

Figure 13 carbon dioxide, water, light energy, and chlorophyll

IDENTIFYING Misconceptions

Some students may think that plants obtain food from the soil. Plants take in a variety of minerals and other substances from the soil, but these are not used as food. They are dissolved in water and absorbed through the plant's roots. Once absorbed, they are transported to structures in the plant where they are needed. The food of plants—glucose—is produced by the plant from carbon dioxide, water, and radiant energy in the chloroplasts of their cells.

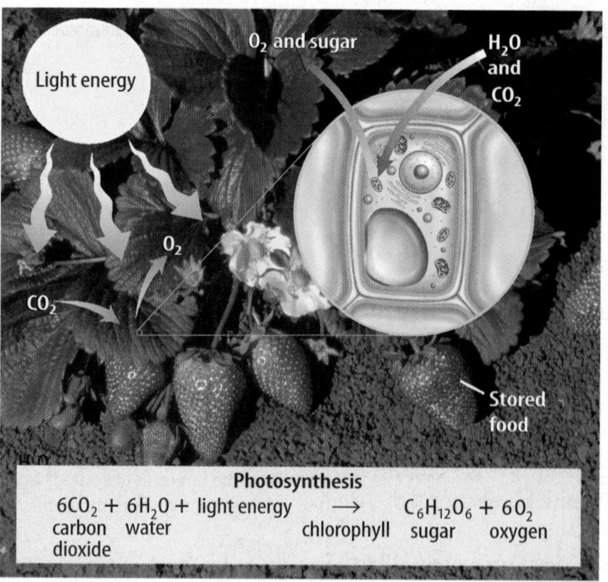

Figure 13
Plants use photosynthesis to make food. *According to the chemical equation, what raw materials would the plant pictured need for photosynthesis?*

Photosynthesis Living things are divided into two groups—producers and consumers—based on how they obtain their food. Organisms that make their own food, such as plants, are called producers. Organisms that cannot make their own food are called consumers.

If you have ever walked barefoot across a sidewalk on a sunny summer day, you probably moved quickly because the sidewalk was hot. Sunlight energy was converted into thermal energy and heated the sidewalk. Plants and many other producers can convert sunlight energy into another kind of energy—chemical energy. The process they use is called photosynthesis. During **photosynthesis,** producers use light energy to make sugars, which can be used as food.

Producing Carbohydrates Producers that use photosynthesis are usually green because they contain a green pigment called chlorophyll (KLOR uh fihl). Chlorophyll and other pigments are used in photosynthesis to capture sunlight energy. In plant cells, these pigments are found in chloroplasts.

The captured sunlight energy is used to drive chemical reactions during which the raw materials, carbon dioxide and water, are used to produce sugar and oxygen. For plants, the raw materials come from air and soil. Some of the captured sunlight energy is stored in the chemical bonds that hold the sugar molecules together. **Figure 13** shows what happens during photosynthesis in a plant. Enzymes also are needed before these reactions can occur.

Storing Carbohydrates Plants make more sugar during photosynthesis than they need for survival. Excess sugar is changed and stored as starches or used to make other carbohydrates. Plants use these carbohydrates as food for growth, maintenance, and reproduction.

Why is photosynthesis important to consumers? Do you eat apples? Apple trees use photosynthesis to produce apples. Do you like cheese? Some cheese comes from milk, which is produced by cows that eat plants. Consumers take in food by eating producers or other consumers. No matter what you eat, photosynthesis was involved directly or indirectly in its production.

Inclusion Strategies

Gifted There are certain plants such as the Indian pipe *(Monotropa uniflora)* and dodder *(Cuscuta)* that lack chlorophyll. Have students research these plants and report to the class how they obtain food. Indian pipe is a saprophyte; it lives on the remains of dead organisms. Dodder is a parasite; it absorbs nourishment from a host plant. L3

Science Journal

Energy and Photosynthesis In their Science Journals, have students list all the foods they eat in one day. Have them to divide the list into two groups: (1) foods formed directly by photosynthesis, (2) foods not formed directly by photosynthesis. Use the lists to help students see that all food energy comes from photosynthesis, whether directly or indirectly.

Respiration Imagine that you get up late for school. You dress quickly, then run three blocks to school. When you get to school, you feel hot and are breathing fast. Why? Your muscle cells use a lot of energy when you run. To get this energy, muscle cells break down food. Some of the energy from the food is used when you move and some of it becomes thermal energy, which is why you feel warm or hot. Most cells also need oxygen to break down food. You were breathing fast because your body was working to get oxygen to your muscles. Your muscle cells were using the oxygen for the process of respiration. During **respiration,** chemical reactions occur that break down food molecules into simpler substances and release their stored energy. Just as in photosynthesis, enzymes are needed for the chemical reactions of respiration.

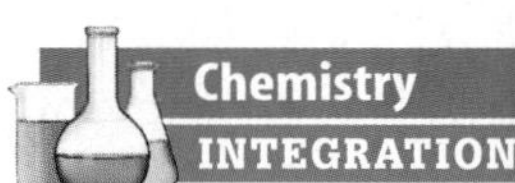

Compounds often are represented by a chemical formula. The chemical formula shows how many and what type of atoms are found in one molecule of the compound. For example, the sugar glucose has the chemical formula $C_6H_{12}O_6$. What is the total number of atoms in one glucose molecule?

Reading Check ***What must happen to food molecules for respiration to take place?***

Breaking Down Carbohydrates The type of food that is most easily broken down by cells is carbohydrates. Respiration of carbohydrates begins in the cytoplasm of the cell. The carbohydrates are broken down into glucose molecules. Each glucose molecule is broken down further into two simpler molecules. As the glucose molecules are broken down, energy is released.

The two simpler molecules are broken down again. This breakdown occurs in the mitochondria of the cells of plants, animals, fungi, and many other organisms. This process uses oxygen, releases much more energy, and produces carbon dioxide and water as wastes. When you exhale, you breathe out carbon dioxide and some of the water.

Respiration occurs in the cells of all living things. **Figure 14** shows how respiration occurs in one consumer. As you are reading this section of the chapter, millions of cells in your body are breaking down glucose, releasing energy, and producing carbon dioxide and water.

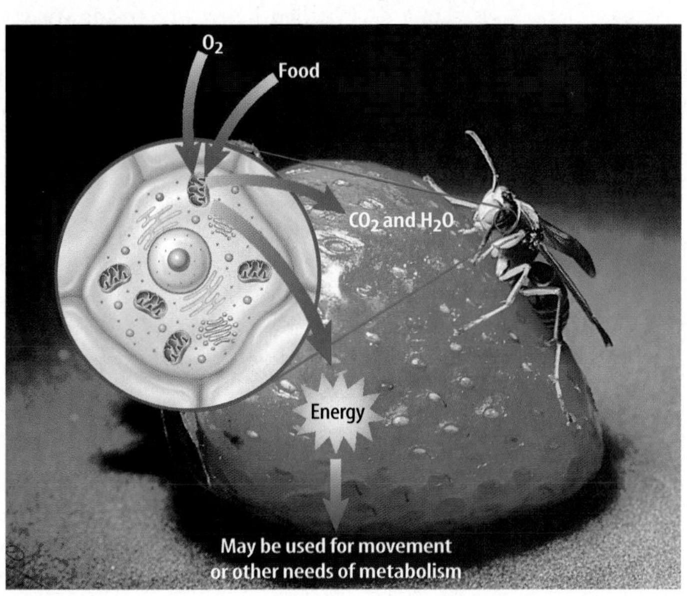

Figure 14
Producers and consumers carry on respiration that releases energy from foods.

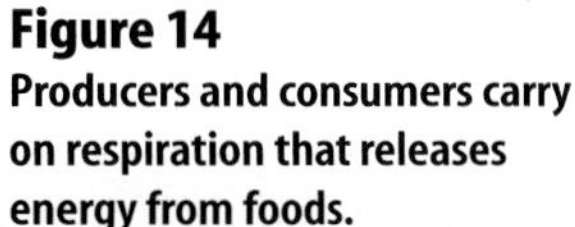

There are 24 atoms in one glucose molecule.

Use Science Words

Word Origin Have students study the parts of the word *photosynthesis*. It comes from the Greek *photo*, *syn-*, and *thesis*. Have them find the meaning of these words and word parts and describe how the word is defined. Photo: "light;" syn-: "together;" thesis: "to place;" photosynthesis uses light to place compounds together.

Reading Check

Answer They are broken down into simpler substances and their stored energy is released.

IDENTIFYING Misconceptions

Students often think that plants do not use oxygen, only that they produce oxygen and use carbon dioxide during photosynthesis. See page 64F for teaching strategies that address this misconception.

Resource Manager 

Chapter Resources Booklet
- Transparency Activity, p. 44
- Directed Reading for Content Mastery, pp. 19, 20
- Lab Activity, pp. 11–14

Active Reading

Buddy Interviews This strategy helps students understand and clarify the reading. Have students interview one another to find out what helps them to understand what they are reading, how they find answers, and how they assimilate new vocabulary terms. Have students use Buddy Interviews to help them master photosynthesis and respiration. L2

Trapping and Using Energy, continued

Explore the Glencoe Science Web site at science.glencoe.com to find out more about topics in this section.

Reading Check

Answer cytoplasm

Teacher FYI

The body of an average person running a 100-yard dash in 12 seconds would require 6 L (1.6 gal.) of air. The person's lungs could supply only about 1.2 L of air. As a result, oxygen debt would occur, and the muscles would produce lactic acid. Most athletes take in at least 10 percent more oxygen than the average person; trained marathon runners take in up to 45 percent more oxygen. They have more efficient respiratory and circulatory systems and can exert greater effort without incurring oxygen debt.

Discussion

Why do bakers use yeast for breadmaking? Yeast carry out processes that release energy in the absence of oxygen and produce carbon dioxide, which causes bread to rise.

Collect Data Visit the Glencoe Science Web site at **science.glencoe.com** for more information about how microorganisms are used to produce many useful products. In your Science Journal list three products produced by microorganisms.

Fermentation Remember imagining you were late and had to run to school? During your run, your muscle cells might not have received enough oxygen, even though you were breathing rapidly. When cells do not have enough oxygen for respiration, they use a process called **fermentation** to release some of the energy stored in glucose molecules.

Like respiration, fermentation begins in the cytoplasm. Again, as the glucose molecules are broken down, energy is released. But the simple molecules from the breakdown of glucose do not move into the mitochondria. Instead, more chemical reactions occur in the cytoplasm. These reactions release some energy and produce wastes. Depending on the type of cell, the wastes may be lactic acid, alcohol, and carbon dioxide, as shown in **Figure 15.** Your muscle cells can use fermentation to change the simple molecules into lactic acid while releasing energy. The presence of lactic acid is why your muscle cells might feel stiff and sore after you run to school.

Reading Check *Where in a cell does fermentation take place?*

Some microscopic organisms, such as bacteria, carry out fermentation and make lactic acid. Some of these organisms are used to produce yogurt and some cheeses. These organisms break down a sugar in milk to release energy. The lactic acid produced causes the milk to become more solid and gives these foods some of their flavor.

Have you ever used yeast to make bread? Yeasts are one-celled living organisms. Yeast cells use fermentation to break down sugar in bread dough. They produce alcohol and carbon dioxide as wastes. The carbon dioxide waste is a gas that makes bread dough rise before it is baked. The alcohol is lost as the bread bakes.

Figure 15
Organisms that use fermentation produce several different wastes.

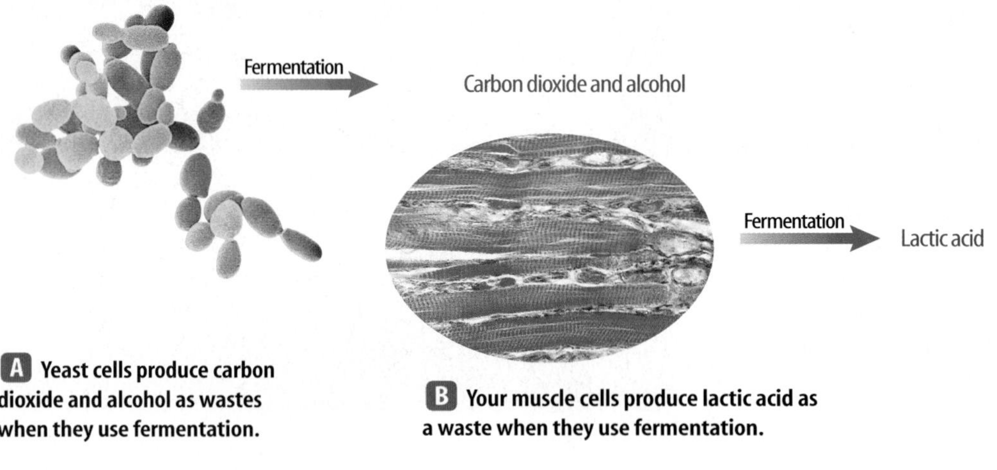

A Yeast cells produce carbon dioxide and alcohol as wastes when they use fermentation.

B Your muscle cells produce lactic acid as a waste when they use fermentation.

Resource Manager

Chapter Resources Booklet
- Enrichment, p. 30
- Reinforcement, p. 27

Life Science Critical Thinking/Problem Solving, p. 5

Cultural Diversity

Fermenting Food Lactic acid fermentation by bacteria is responsible for a number of foods from different cultures. Have students research these foods and report their findings to the class in oral reports. Possible topics: Hawaiian *poi*, Japanese soy sauce, Korean *kimchi*, German sauerkraut, yogurt. L2

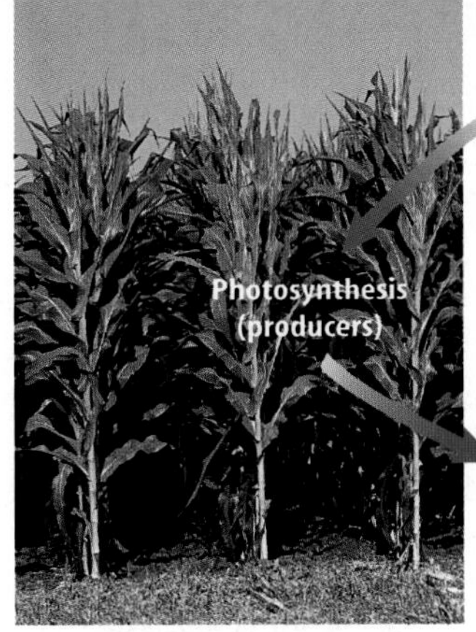

Figure 16
The chemical reactions of photosynthesis and respiration could not take place without each other.

Related Processes How are photosynthesis, respiration, and fermentation related? Some producers use photosynthesis to make food. All living things use respiration or fermentation to release energy stored in food. If you think carefully about what happens during photosynthesis and respiration, you will see that what is produced in one is used in the other, as shown in **Figure 16.** These two processes are almost the opposite of each other. Photosynthesis produces sugars and oxygen, and respiration uses these products. The carbon dioxide and water produced during respiration are used during photosynthesis. Most life would not be possible without these important chemical reactions.

Section 3 Assessment

1. Explain the difference between producers and consumers and give three examples of each.
2. Explain how the energy used by many living things on Earth can be traced back to sunlight.
3. Compare and contrast respiration and fermentation.
4. What condition must exist in cells for fermentation to occur?
5. **Think Critically** How can some indoor plants help improve the quality of air in a room?

Skill Builder Activities

6. **Identifying and Manipulating Variables and Controls** Design an experiment to show what happens to a plant when you limit sunlight or one of the raw materials for photosynthesis. Identify the control. **For more help, refer to the** Science Skill Handbook.
7. **Solving One-Step Equations** Refer to the chemical equation for photosynthesis. Calculate then compare the number of carbon, hydrogen, and oxygen atoms before and after photosynthesis. **For more help, refer to the** Math Skill Handbook.

Quick Demo

Prepare a sugar solution by mixing 1 tablespoon of sugar with 1 cup of warm water in a jar. Add some yeast to the solution a few hours before class and cover it. Have students note the odor of alcohol and the bubbles of carbon dioxide. Point out that these products result from alcoholic fermentation. L1
LS **Logical-Mathematical**

Visual Learning

Figure 16 Have students create an events chain concept map to illustrate what is occurring in each of these pictures. Producer takes in carbon dioxide and water, goes through the process of photosynthesis, and produces oxygen and sugars; other living organisms take in oxygen and sugars, go through the process of respiration, and give off carbon dioxide and water. LS **Visual-Spatial** P

3 Assess

Reteach

Have students identify organisms that photosynthesize and those that respire. Only organisms with chlorophyll photosynthesize; all organisms respire.

Challenge

Have students compare photosynthesis and respiration in regard to energy. Photosynthesis stores energy; respiration releases energy.

Assessment

Content Have students make a table to compare and contrast photosynthesis and respiration. Use **Performance Assessment in the Science Classroom,** p. 109.

Answers to Section Assessment

1. Producers make food. Consumers get energy by eating producers, food made by producers, or other consumers. Examples will vary.
2. Energy used by living things is released from food molecules during cellular respiration. Photosynthetic producers convert light energy—usually from the Sun—into the chemical energy in the sugar molecules that they produce. Consumers get this energy by eating producers or other consumers that eat producers.
3. The amount of energy released by fermentation is less than that released by respiration.
4. When oxygen is absent, fermentation occurs.
5. Plants remove carbon dioxide from the air, use it in photosynthesis, and produce oxygen.
6. Experimental designs should include a control and a variable for light, water, or carbon dioxide.
7. The number of atoms is the same before and after respiration; C = 6, H = 12, O = 18.

Activity

BENCH TESTED

What You'll Investigate

Purpose

Students observe photosynthesis and respiration in plants and infer whether the processes occur in light or darkness. L2

ELL COOP LEARN LS Visual-Spatial

Process Skills

measuring, observing, inferring, communicating, comparing and contrasting, recognizing cause and effect, separating and controlling variables, interpreting data

Time Required

50 minutes (leave overnight if using artificial light)

Safety Precautions

Students should use care when working with chemicals.

Procedure

Teaching Strategy

Tie to Prior Knowledge Most students are aware that plants use light energy to make food and that photosynthesis will occur in the tube placed near the light.

Activity

Photosynthesis and Respiration

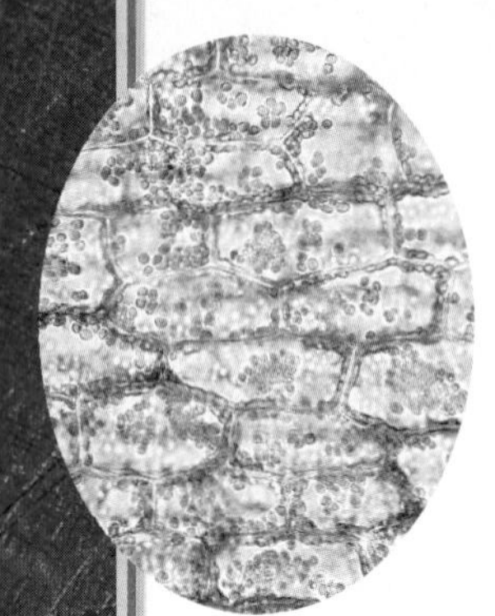

Every living cell carries on many chemical processes. Two important chemical processes are respiration and photosynthesis. All cells, including the ones in your body, carry on respiration. However, some plant cells can carry on both processes. In this experiment you will investigate when these processes occur in plant cells. How could you find out when plants were using these processes? Are the products of photosynthesis and respiration the same?

What You'll Investigate

When do plants carry on photosynthesis and respiration?

Materials

16-mm test tubes (3)
150-mm test tubes with stoppers (4)
**small, clear-glass baby food jars with lids (4)*
test-tube rack
stirring rod
scissors
carbonated water (5 mL)
bromothymol blue solution in dropper bottle
aged tap water (20 mL)
**distilled water (20 mL)*
sprig of *Elodea* (2)
**other water plants*
**Alternate materials*

Goals

- **Observe** green water plants in the light and dark.
- **Determine** whether plants carry on photosynthesis and respiration.

Safety Precautions

Wear splash-proof safety goggles to protect eyes from hazardous chemicals. Wash hands thoroughly after the activity.

Inclusion Strategies

Visually Impaired Pair students who are visually impaired with those who can describe to them the colors in the test tubes, both before and after the experiment. L2

Resource Manager

Chapter Resources Booklet
Activity Worksheet, pp. 7–8

Lab Management and Safety, p. 63

Procedure

1. Label each test tube using the numbers 1, 2, 3, and 4. Pour 5 mL of aged tap water into each test tube.
2. Add 10 drops of carbonated water to test tubes 1 and 2.
3. Add 10 drops of bromothymol blue to all of the test tubes. Bromothymol blue turns green to yellow in the presence of an acid.
4. Cut two 10-cm sprigs of *Elodea*. Place one sprig in test tube 1 and one sprig in test tube 3. Stopper all test tubes.
5. In your Science Journal, copy and complete the test-tube data table.
6. Place test tubes 1 and 2 in bright light. Place tubes 3 and 4 in the dark. Observe the test tubes for 30 min or until the color changes. Record the color of each of the four test tubes.

Test Tube Data

Test Tube	Color at Start	Color After 30 Minutes
1	yellow	blue
2	yellow	yellow
3	blue	yellow
4	blue	blue

Conclude and Apply

1. What is indicated by the color of the water in all four test tubes at the start of the activity?
2. **Infer** what process occurred in the test tube or tubes that changed color after 30 min.
3. **Describe** the purpose of test tubes 2 and 4 in this experiment.
4. Do the results of this experiment show that photosynthesis and respiration occur in plants? Explain.

Communicating Your Data

Choose one of the following activities to **communicate** your data. Prepare an oral presentation that explains how the experiment showed the differences between products of photosynthesis and respiration. Draw a cartoon strip to **explain** what you did in this experiment. Use each panel to show a different step. **For more help, refer to the** **Science Skill Handbook.**

Troubleshooting

Elodea should be kept in the dark for two days before the activity. Use sharp scissors to make a clean diagonal cut at the bottom of each stem.

Expected Outcome

Most results will reflect that plants used carbon dioxide in the light and gave off carbon dioxide in the dark.

Conclude and Apply

1. Test tubes 1 and 2 contain carbon dioxide. Tubes 3 and 4 do not.
2. They underwent photosynthesis or respiration.
3. Tubes 2 and 4 were controls.
4. Yes, the experimental results showed that both processes happen in plant cells. In test tube 1, the green plant used carbon dioxide for photosynthesis. In test tube 3, the green plant gave off carbon dioxide as a result of respiration.

Error Analysis

Have students compare their results and explain why any differences occurred.

Oral How are fermentation and respiration similar? Both processes release energy through the breakdown of other substances. Use **Performance Assessment in the Science Classroom,** p. 99.

Communicating Your Data

Students should use data from the experiment for the presentation or cartoon.

Science and Language Arts

✓ Pre-Reading Activity

This activity should help students think about the power of nature. Collect photographs that show both the beauty and the harshness of nature. Photographs by Edward Weston and Ansel Adams are good sources of these types of images. Have students work in small groups to discuss one photograph and consider what they learn about the natural world from the image.

Respond to the Reading

Active Reading Strategies

Predict At certain points in the poem, stop and have students consider what the flower might look like as it grows and whether or not they think the plant will survive. **What gives the flower the strength to break through the rubble?**

Visualize Suggest that students keep the tulip and construction site in their minds' eye as they read. Encourage them to form a mental image of the tulip as it first sprouts, and then to imagine its growth as it fights the debris. **How do you picture the contrast between the flower and the rubble?**

Answers to Questions

1. Possible answers: The tulip bulb is buried deep in the ground; the tulip is a hardy plant.
2. Possible answer: The tulip represents the rebirth of spring. The narrator herself may be experiencing a rebirth or renewal.
3. the yellow color at the base of each petal

Science and Language Arts

from "Tulip"

by Penny Harter

I watched its first green push
through bare dirt, where the builders
had dropped boards, shingles,
plaster—
killing everything.
I could not recall what grew
there,
what returned each spring,
but the leaves looked tulip,
and one morning it arrived,
a scarlet slash against the
aluminum siding.

Respond to the Reading

1. Why do you suppose the tulip survived the builders' abuse?
2. The poet chooses to write about a tulip rather than another kind of flower. Why do you think that is?
3. What is the yellow throat that the narrator is staring into?

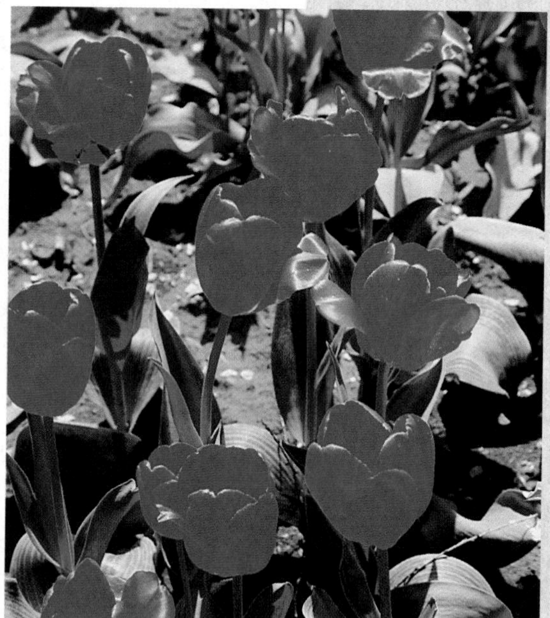

Mornings, on the way to
my car,
I bow to the still bell
of its closed petals; evenings,
it greets me, light ringing
at the end of my driveway.

Sometimes I kneel
to stare into the yellow
throat . . . .
It opens and closes my days.
It has made me weak with
love . . . .

Reading Further

Other sources on this topic include:

Tulipa: A Photographer's Botonical, by Christopher Baker (Photographer), Willem Lemmers, Emma Sweeny, and Michael Pollan, Artisan, 1999.

Methods in Plant Cell Biology, by Editors David W. Galbreth, Hans J. Bohnert, and Leslie Wilson, Academic Press, 1995.

Photosynthesis, by Krishna Rao and David O. Hall, Cambridge University Press, 1999.

Plant Identification Terminology: An Illustrated Glossary, by James G. Harris and Melinda Woolf Harris, Spring Lake Publishers, 2001.

Guide to Flowering Plant Families, by Wendy B. Zomlefer, University of North Carolina, 1995.

American Society for Microbiology, Office of Education, 1325 Massachusetts Avenue, NW, Washington, DC 20005-4171.

Personification

Understanding Literature

Personification Using human traits or emotions to describe an idea, animal, or inanimate object is called personification. When the poet writes that the tulip has a "yellow throat," she uses personification. This can make the reader think of the tulip as more than just a plant. The poet also uses personification when she states that the tulip inspires love.

Science Connection Living things are made of more than 50 percent water and depend on it for their survival. Because most chemical reactions in plants take place in water, plants must have water in order to grow. In the poem, the tulip only pushes up through the ground in the spring when the tulip's underground bulb and roots absorb enough water. The water carries nutrients and minerals from the soil into the plant.

The process of active transport allows needed nutrients to enter the roots. The cell membranes of root cells contain proteins that bind with the needed nutrients. Cellular energy is used to move these nutrients through the cell membrane.

You also learned about photosynthesis in this chapter. From reading the poem, how would you know that photosynthesis had taken place?

Linking Science and Writing

Gardener's Journal Select a plant to observe. It could be a plant that you, your family, or one of your classmates grows. Depending on the season, it could be a plant growing on the grounds of your school or in a public park. Keep a gardener's observation journal of the plant for a month. Write weekly entries in your journal, describing the plant's condition, size, health, color, and other physical qualities.

Career Connection

Microbiologist

Dr. Harold Amos is a microbiologist who has studied cell processes in bacteria and mammals over the course of his career. He studied the way that sugar is transported in normal cells and cancer cells. Dr. Amos has a medical degree and a doctorate in bacteriology and immunology, which deals with the immune system and its interaction with diseases. He also has received many awards for his scientific work and his contributions to the careers of other scientists.

SCIENCE*Online* Visit the Glencoe Science Web site at **science.glencoe.com** to learn more about careers in microbiology.

Understanding Literature

Science Connection

Plant stems play a part in the transport of materials from roots to leaves. Stems vary greatly in size and shape from one plant species to another. Some grow entirely underground and other stems can store water and nutrients. Plants often store food in their stems during their growth period. When a plant's growth stops, this stored food enables them to survive dormancy. Dormancy occurs during a cold winter or a long dry period. The dormant plant uses the stored food to begin growing when conditions again become favorable.

Linking Science and Writing

Writing Strategies

Divide the class into groups. Have each group choose a flower from those provided to study. Make study guides and plant books available for use in identification and research. Students should draw a picture of it in their Science Journals. Then by carefully pulling the flower apart, they can identify, sketch and label the petals, stamens, sepals, and carpal. As they study the flower, the group should discuss and record the role each part plays in the plant's reproduction.

Career Connection

Students interested in a career in biology should study sciences, math and Latin. Taking courses that require laboratory and field work is also advisable. A bachelor's degree is required to work in this field. For the highest professional status, a doctorate is necessary. Microbiologists study organisms of microscopic or submicroscopic size. Other scientists work to diagnose, treat, and prevent diseases.

Internet Addresses

Explore the Glencoe Science Web site at **science.glencoe.com** to find out more about topics in this feature.

Chapter 3 Study Guide

Reviewing Main Ideas

Preview

Students can answer the questions in their Science Journals. Discuss the answers as you go through the chapter. LS **Linguistic**

Review

Students can write their answers, then compare them with those of other students. LS **Interpersonal**

Reteach

Students can look at the illustrations and describe details that support the main ideas of the chapter. LS **Visual-Spatial**

Answers to Chapter Review

Section 1

4. lipds, proteins, carbohydrates, and nucleic acids

Section 2

2. Osmosis moves water into the plant's cells where it is used.

Section 3

1. Their cells do not have chlorophyll.

Chapter  Study Guide

Reviewing Main Ideas

Section 1 Chemistry of Life

1. Matter is anything that has mass and takes up space.
2. Energy in matter is in the chemical bonds that hold matter together.
3. All organic compounds contain the elements hydrogen and carbon. The organic compounds in living things are carbohydrates, lipids, proteins, and nucleic acids.
4. Organic and inorganic compounds are important to living things. *What organic compounds could be found in an elephant and a pumpkin?*

Section 2 Moving Cellular Materials

1. The selectively permeable cell membrane controls which molecules can pass into and out of the cell.
2. In diffusion, molecules move from areas where there are relatively more of them into areas where there are relatively fewer of them. Osmosis is the diffusion of water through a cell membrane. *Why might these plants use osmosis?*

3. Cells use energy to move molecules by active transport but do not use energy for passive transport.
4. Cells move large particles through cell membranes by endocytosis and exocytosis.

Section 3 Energy for Life

1. Photosynthesis is the process by which some producers change light energy into chemical energy. *Why can't cells in these humans use sunlight to make food?*

2. Respiration that uses oxygen releases the energy in food molecules and produces waste carbon dioxide and water.
3. Some one-celled organisms and cells that lack oxygen use fermentation to release small amounts of energy from glucose. Wastes such as alcohol, carbon dioxide, and lactic acid are produced.

FOLDABLES Reading & Study Skills — After You Read

Under each tab of your Vocabulary Study Fold, write a sentence about one of the cell processes using the vocabulary word on the tab.

FOLDABLES Reading & Study Skills — After You Read

After students have read the chapter and completed the Foldable described in Before You Read, have them do the activity on the student page.

Chapter 3 Study Guide

Visualizing Main Ideas

Complete the following table on energy processes.

Energy Processes

	Photosynthesis	Respiration	Fermentation
Energy Source	Sun	food (glucose)	food (glucose)
In plant and animal cells, occurs in	chloroplast	mitochondria	cytoplasm
Reactants are	water, carbon dioxide	glucose, oxygen	glucose, oxygen
Products are	glucose, oxygen	water, carbon dioxide	lactic acid, alcohol, carbon dioxide

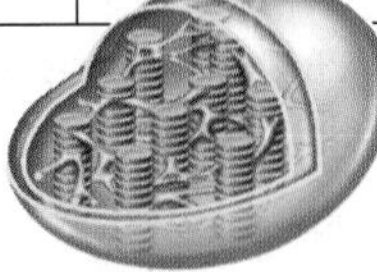

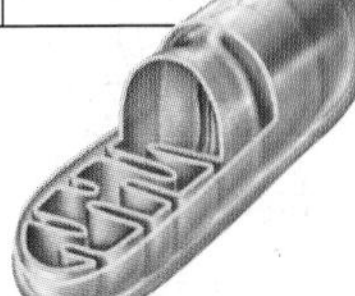

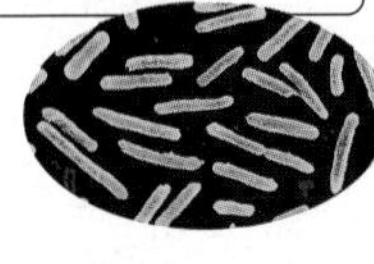

Vocabulary Review

Vocabulary Words

- **a.** active transport
- **b.** diffusion
- **c.** endocytosis
- **d.** enzyme
- **e.** equilibrium
- **f.** exocytosis
- **g.** fermentation
- **h.** inorganic compound
- **i.** metabolism
- **j.** mixture
- **k.** organic compound
- **l.** osmosis
- **m.** passive transport
- **n.** photosynthesis
- **o.** respiration

Using Vocabulary

Use what you know about the vocabulary words to answer the following questions.

1. What is the diffusion of water called?
2. What type of protein regulates nearly all chemical reactions in cells?
3. How do large food particles enter an amoeba?
4. What type of compound is water?
5. What process is used by some producers to convert light energy into chemical energy?
6. What type of compounds always contain carbon and hydrogen?
7. What process uses oxygen to break down glucose?
8. What is the total of all chemical reactions in an organism called?

THE PRINCETON REVIEW **Study Tip**

Make a note of anything you don't understand so that you'll remember to ask your teacher about it.

Chapter 3 Study Guide

Visualizing Main Ideas

See student page.

Vocabulary Review

Using Vocabulary

1. The diffusion of water is called osmosis.
2. The proteins that regulate nearly all chemical reactions in cells are enzymes.
3. Large food particles enter the amoeba by endocytosis.
4. Water is an inorganic compound.
5. Some producers convert sunlight into chemical energy by photosynthesis.
6. An organic compound always contains carbon and hydrogen.
7. Respiration uses oxygen to break down glucose.
8. The total of all chemical reactions in an organism is metabolism.

IDENTIFYING Misconceptions

Assess

Use the assessment as follow-up to page 64F after students have completed the chapter.

Discussion Do animals ever give off oxygen as a product of their metabolic activities? No **Explain.** Oxygen is given off as a product of photosynthesis, thus only organisms that can carry out photosynthesis produce this gas. Animals are not photosynthetic organisms. **What products do plants release during their metabolic processes?** both oxygen and carbon dioxide Specifically reinforce the idea that plants carry out both photosynthesis and respiration.

Expected Outcome At this point students should understand and be able to explain the complementary processes of photosynthesis and respiration in plants and animals.

Chapter 3 Assessment

Checking Concepts

1. C
2. B
3. A
4. B
5. D
6. C
7. A
8. C
9. D
10. D

Thinking Critically

11. The red blood cell would burst because water molecules would move into the cell. The water would move from an area of greater concentration (outside the cell) to an area of lesser concentration (inside the cell) in an effort to reach equilibrium.
12. Plants die as water molecules move out of the cells into the salty soil.
13. The molecules in hot water move faster than those in cold. These faster-moving molecules bump into the sugar molecules more often and more vigorously, dissolving the sugar faster.
14. Consumers would also die; they depend on producers for food.
15. The enzymes increase the rate at which protein bonds are broken; this makes the meat more tender.

Chapter 3 Assessment

Checking Concepts

Choose the word or phrase that best answers the question.

1. What is it called when cells use energy to move molecules?
   A) diffusion **C)** active transport
   B) osmosis **D)** passive transport
2. How might a cell take in a bacterium?
   A) osmosis **C)** exocytosis
   B) endocytosis **D)** diffusion
3. What occurs when the number of molecules of a substance is equal in two areas?
   A) equilibrium **C)** fermentation
   B) metabolism **D)** cellular respiration
4. Which of the following substances is an example of a carbohydrate?
   A) enzymes **C)** waxes
   B) sugars **D)** proteins
5. What is RNA an example of?
   A) carbon dioxide **C)** lipid
   B) water **D)** nucleic acid
6. What organic molecule stores the greatest amount of energy?
   A) carbohydrate **C)** lipid
   B) water **D)** nucleic acid
7. Which of these formulas is an example of an organic compound?
   A) $C_6H_{12}O_6$ **C)** H_2O
   B) NO_2 **D)** O_2
8. What are organisms that cannot make their own food called?
   A) biodegradables **C)** consumers
   B) producers **D)** enzymes
9. Which one of these cellular processes requires the presence of chlorophyll?
   A) fermentation **C)** respiration
   B) endocytosis **D)** photosynthesis
10. What kind of molecule is water?
    A) organic **C)** carbohydrate
    B) lipid **D)** inorganic

Thinking Critically

11. If you could place one red blood cell in distilled water, what would you see happen to the cell? Explain.
12. In snowy places, salt is used to melt ice on the roads. Explain what could happen to many roadside plants as a result.
13. Why does sugar dissolve faster in hot tea than in iced tea?
14. What would happen to the consumers in a lake if all the producers died?
15. Meat tenderizers contain protein enzymes. How do these enzymes affect meat?

Developing Skills

16. **Concept Mapping** Complete the events-chain concept map to sequence the following parts of matter from smallest to largest: *atom, electron,* and *compound.*

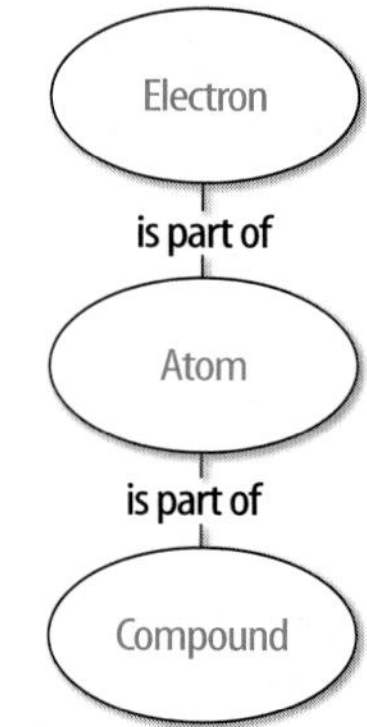

17. **Forming Hypotheses** Make a hypothesis about what will happen to wilted celery when placed in a glass of plain water.

Chapter Assessment Planner

Portfolio Encourage students to place in their portfolios one or two items of what they consider to be their best work. Examples include:
- Science Journal, p. 70
- Visual Learning, p. 79
- Visual Learning, p. 85

Performance Additional performance assessments, Performance Task Assessment Lists, and rubrics for evaluating these activities can be found in Glencoe's **Performance Assessment in the Science Classroom.**

18. Interpreting Data Water plants were placed at different distances from a light source. Bubbles coming from the plants were counted to measure the rate of photosynthesis. What can you say about how the distance from the light affected the rate?

Photosynthesis in Water Plants

Beaker Number	Distance from Light (cm)	Bubbles per Minute
1	10	45
2	30	30
3	50	19
4	70	6
5	100	1

19. Making and Using Graphs Using the data from question 18, make a line graph that shows the relationship between the rate of photosynthesis and the distance from light.

Performance Assessment

20. Puzzle Make a crossword puzzle with words describing ways substances are transported across cell membranes. Use the following words in your puzzle: *diffusion, osmosis, facilitated diffusion, active transport, endocytosis,* and *exocytosis.* Make sure your clues give good descriptions of each transport method.

TECHNOLOGY

Go to the Glencoe Science Web site at **science.glencoe.com** or use the **Glencoe Science CD-ROM** for additional chapter assessment.

Test Practice

Organic compounds called carbohydrates and proteins form many parts of a cell and also help connect cells to each other. Several organic compounds, along with their characteristics and where they are found, are listed below.

Cell Substances

Organic Compound	Flexibility	Found In
Keratin	Not very flexible	Hair and skin of mammals
Collagen	Not very flexible	Skin, bones, and tendons of mammals
Chitin	Very rigid	Tough outer shell of insects, crabs
Cellulose	Very flexible	Trees and flowers

Study the chart and answer the following questions.

1. According to this information, which organic compound is the least flexible?
A) keratin
B) collagen
C) chitin
D) cellulose

2. According to the chart, cellulose might be found in _____.
F) mammals
G) bones
H) insects
J) trees

THE PRINCETON REVIEW **Test Practice**

The Test-Taking Tip was written by The Princeton Review, the nation's leader in test preparation.

1. C
2. J

Developing Skills

16. See student page.
17. Wilted celery will become crisp as water molecules move by osmosis into its cells to reach equilibrium.
18. The closer a plant is to light, the faster its rate of photosynthesis.
19.

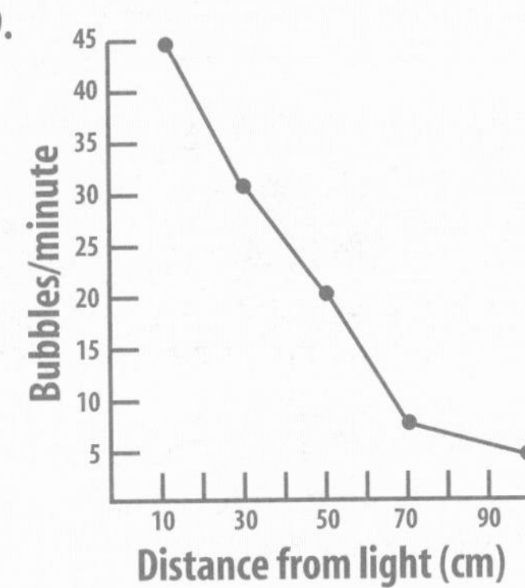

Performance Assessment

20. Definitions in the chapter for these terms can be used. Use **PASC**, p. 91.

Assessment Resources

 **Reproducible Masters**

Chapter Resources Booklet
Chapter Review, pp. 35–36
Chapter Tests, pp. 37–40
Assessment Transparency Activity, p. 47

Glencoe Science Web site
Interactive Tutor
Chapter Quizzes

Glencoe Technology
Assessment Transparency
Interactive CD-ROM Chapter Quizzes
ExamView Pro Test Bank
Vocabulary PuzzleMaker Software
MindJogger Videoquiz

Section/Objectives	Standards		Activities/Features
	National	State/Local	
Chapter Opener	See p. 5T for a Key to Standards.		**Explore Activity:** Infer about seed growth, p. 95 **Before You Read,** p. 95
Section 1 Cell Division and Mitosis 2 sessions 1 block 1. **Explain** why mitosis is important. 2. **Examine** the steps of mitosis. 3. **Compare** mitosis in plant and animal cells. 4. **List** two examples of asexual reproduction.	National Content Standards: UCP3, A1, C1		**Health Integration,** p. 97 **Science Online,** p. 97 **MiniLAB:** Modeling Mitosis, p. 101 **Activity:** Mitosis in Plant Cells, p. 103
Section 2 Sexual Reproduction and Meiosis 2 sessions 1 block 1. **Describe** the stages of meiosis and how sex cells are produced. 2. **Explain** why meiosis is needed for sexual reproduction. 3. **Name** the cells that are involved in fertilization. 4. **Explain** how fertilization occurs in sexual reproduction.	National Content Standards: UCP3, UCP4, C2		**Chemistry Integration,** p. 105 **Problem-Solving Activity:** How can chromosome numbers be predicted? p. 107 **Visualizing Polyploidy in Plants,** p. 108
Section 3 DNA 3 sessions 1.5 blocks 1. **Identify** the parts of a DNA molecule and its structure. 2. **Explain** how DNA copies itself. 3. **Describe** the structure and function of each kind of RNA.	National Content Standards: UCP3, UCP4, A1, C1, C2, E2, F5, G1		**MiniLAB:** Modeling DNA Replication, p. 111 **Science Online,** p. 113 **Science Online,** p. 115 **Activity:** Mutations, p. 116 **Oops! Accidents in Science:** A Tangled Tale, p. 118

NATIONAL GEOGRAPHIC

Teacher's Corner

PRODUCTS AVAILABLE FROM GLENCOE
To order call 1-800-334-7344:

CD-ROM
NGS PictureShow: The Cell
NGS PictureShow: Plants: What It Means to Be Green

Curriculum Kit
GeoKit: Cells and Microorganisms

Transparency Sets
NGS PicturePack: The Cell
NGS PicturePack: What It Means to Be Green

PRODUCTS AVAILABLE FROM NATIONAL GEOGRAPHIC SOCIETY
To order call 1-800-368-2728:

Video
DNA: Laboratory of Life

INDEX TO NATIONAL GEOGRAPHIC SOCIETY
The following articles may be used for research relating to this chapter:
"The Rise of Life on Earth," by Richard Monastersky, March 1998.

Activity Materials	Reproducible Resources	Section Assessment	Technology
Explore Activity: soaked bean seeds, water, paper towels, self-sealing plastic bags, hand lens	**Chapter Resources Booklet** Foldables Worksheet, p. 15 Directed Reading Overview, p. 17 Note-taking Worksheets, pp. 31–33	GLENCOE'S ASSESSMENT ADVANTAGE	
MiniLAB: colored paper, poster board, markers, toothpicks, yarn, thread, glue, scissors **Activity:** prepared slide of onion root tip, microscope	**Chapter Resources Booklet** Transparency Activity, p. 42 MiniLAB, p. 3 Enrichment, p. 28 Reinforcement, p. 25 Transparency Activity, pp. 45–46 Activity Worksheet, pp. 5–6 Directed Reading, p. 18 Lab Activity, pp. 9–10	**Portfolio** Visual Learning, p. 97 **Performance** MiniLAB, p. 101 Skill Builder Activities, p. 102 **Content** Section Assessment, p. 102 Challenge, p. 102	Section Focus Transparency Teaching Transparency Interactive CD-ROM Guided Reading Audio Program
Need materials? Contact Science Kit at 1-800-828-7777 or www.sciencekit.com on the Internet.	**Chapter Resources Booklet** Transparency Activity, p. 43 Enrichment, p. 29 Reinforcement, p. 26 Directed Reading, p. 18 **Life Science Critical Thinking/Problem Solving,** p. 19 **Mathematics Skill Activities,** p. 3 **Performance Assessment in the Science Classroom,** p. 57	**Portfolio** Make a Model, p. 107 **Performance** Skill Builder Activities, p. 109 **Content** Section Assessment, p. 109 Challenge, p. 109	Section Focus Transparency Interactive CD-ROM Guided Reading Audio Program
MiniLAB: pencil, paper **Activity:** Web sites and other resources on mutations	**Chapter Resources Booklet** Transparency Activity, p. 44 MiniLAB, p. 4 Enrichment, p. 30 Reinforcement, p. 27 Directed Reading, pp. 19, 20 Activity Worksheet, pp. 7–8 Lab Activity, pp. 11–13 **Home and Community Involvement,** p. 36 **Lab Management and Safety,** p. 58	**Portfolio** Extension, p. 113 **Performance** MiniLAB, p. 111 Skill Builder Activities, p. 115 **Content** Section Assessment, p. 115 Challenge, p. 115	Section Focus Transparency Interactive CD-ROM Guided Reading Audio Program

End of Chapter Assessment

GLENCOE'S ASSESSMENT ADVANTAGE

Blackline Masters	Technology	Professional Series
Chapter Resources Booklet Chapter Review, pp. 35–36 Chapter Tests, pp. 37–40 **Standardized Test Practice by The Princeton Review,** pp. 23–26	MindJogger Videoquiz Interactive CD-ROM Vocabulary PuzzleMakers ExamView Pro Test Bank Interactive Lesson Planner Interactive Teacher Edition	Performance Assessment in the Science Classroom (PASC)

Transparencies

Section Focus

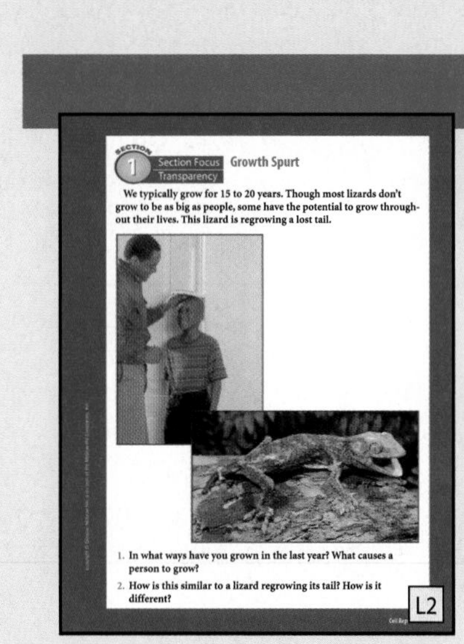

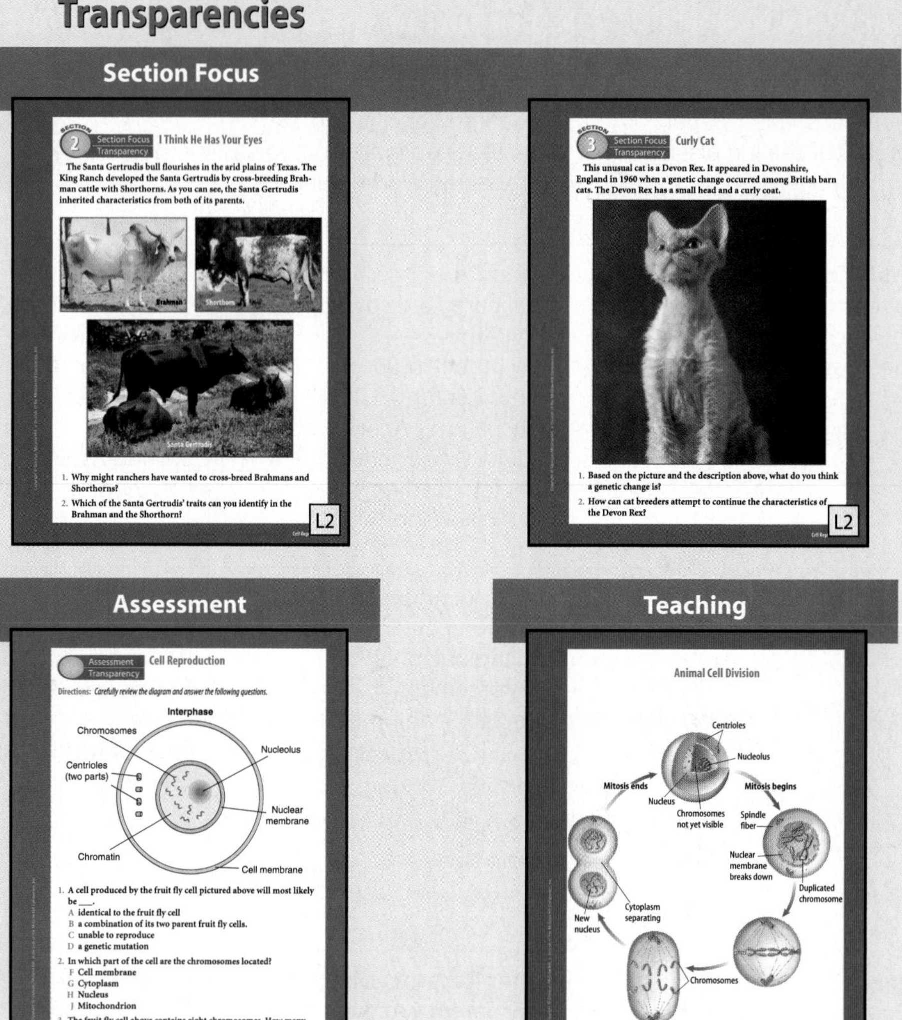

Assessment

Teaching

This is a representation of key blackline masters available in the Teacher Classroom Resources. See Resource Manager boxes within the chapter for additional information.

Key to Teaching Strategies

The following designations will help you decide which activities are appropriate for your students.

- L1 Level 1 activities should be appropriate for students with learning difficulties.
- L2 Level 2 activities should be within the ability range of all students.
- L3 Level 3 activities are designed for above-average students.
- ELL ELL activities should be within the ability range of English Language Learners.
- COOP LEARN Cooperative Learning activities are designed for small group work.
- LS Multiple Learning Styles logos, as described on page 22T, are used throughout to indicate strategies that address different learning styles.
- P These strategies represent student products that can be placed into a best-work portfolio.

Hands-on Activities

Activity Worksheets

Laboratory Activities

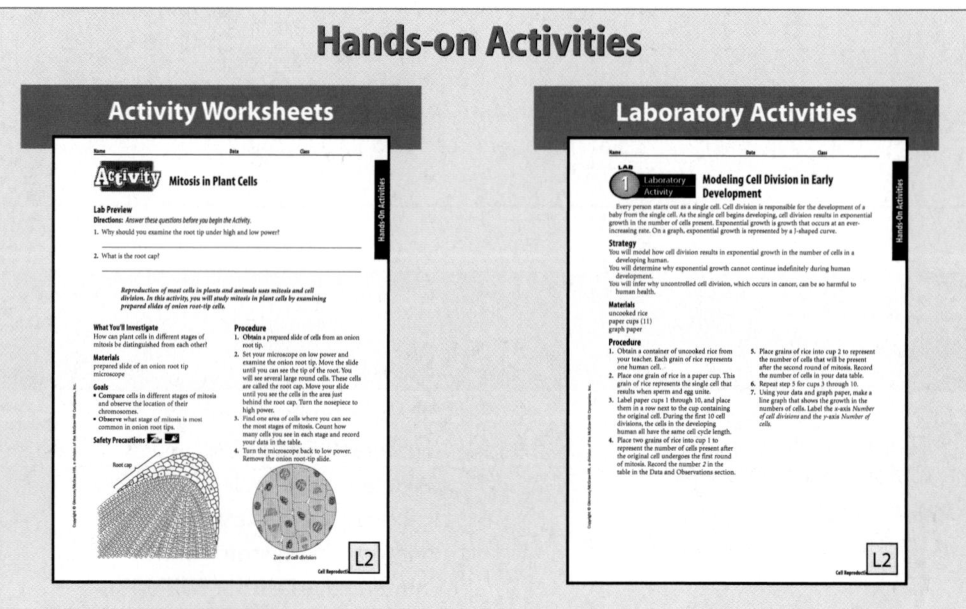

Meeting Different Ability Levels

Content Outline

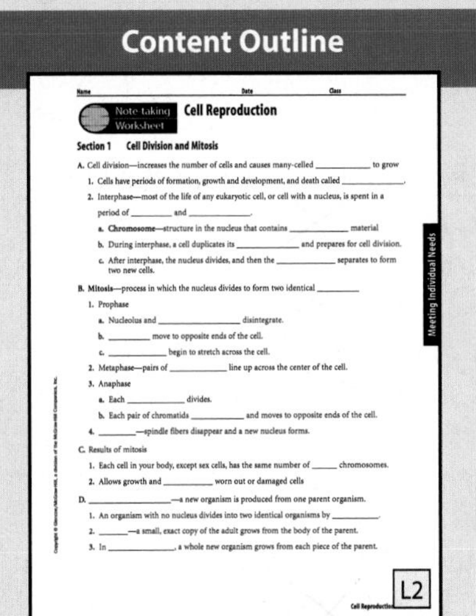

Note-taking Worksheet — Cell Reproduction

Section 1 Cell Division and Mitosis

L2

Reinforcement

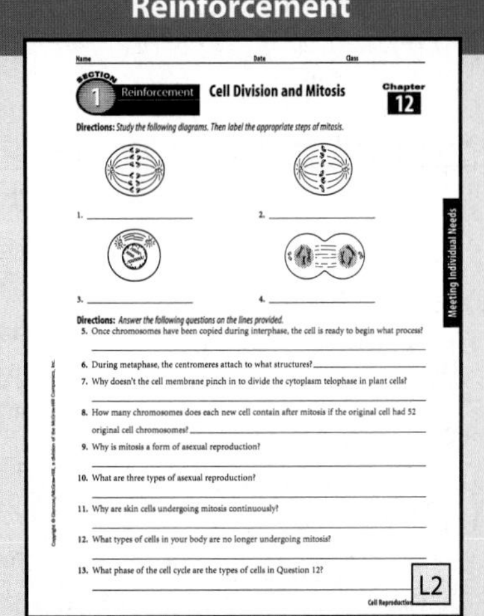

Section 1 Reinforcement — Cell Division and Mitosis — Chapter 12

L2

Directed Reading

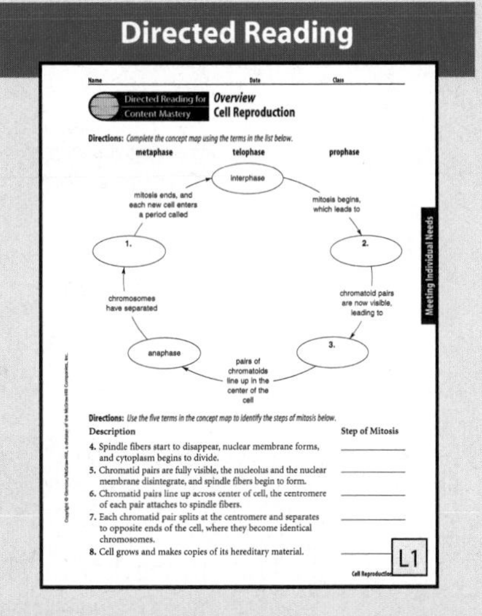

Directed Reading for Content Mastery — Overview — Cell Reproduction

L1

Assessment

Chapter Tests

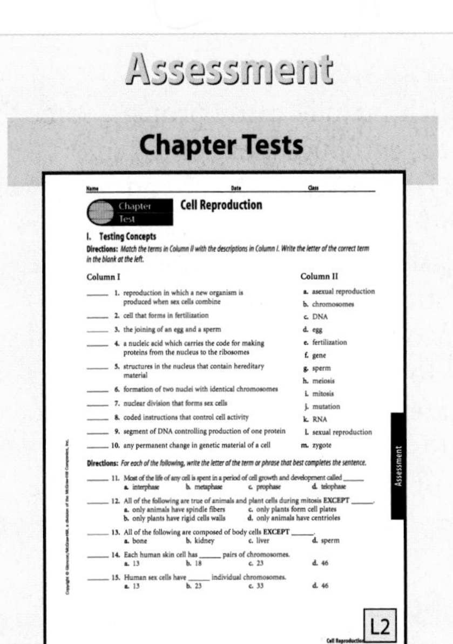

Chapter Test — Cell Reproduction

I. Testing Concepts

L2

Enrichment

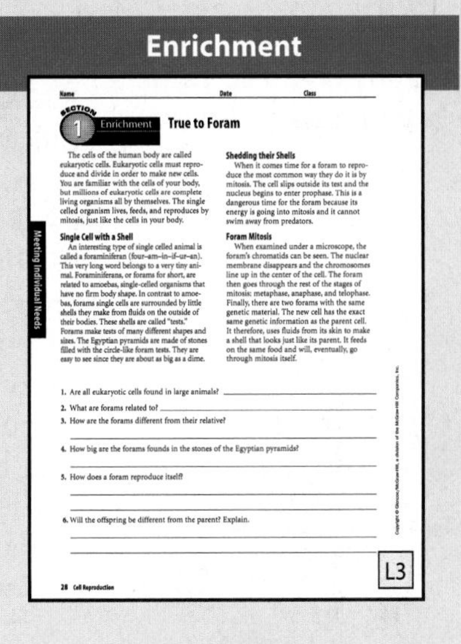

Section 1 Enrichment — True to Foram

L3

Spanish Directed Reading

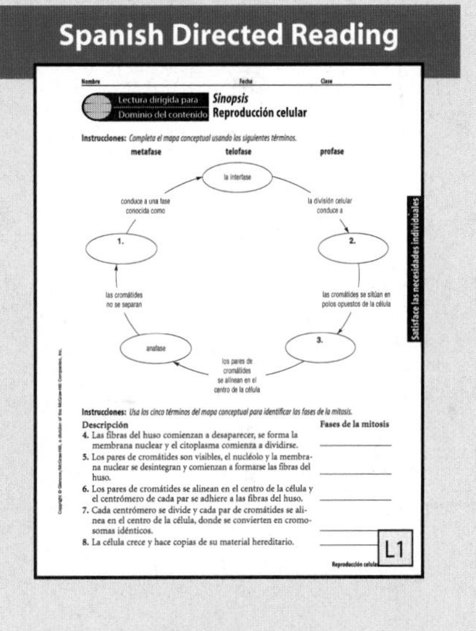

Lectura dirigida para Dominio del contenido — Sinopsis — Reproducción celular

L1

Test Practice Workbook

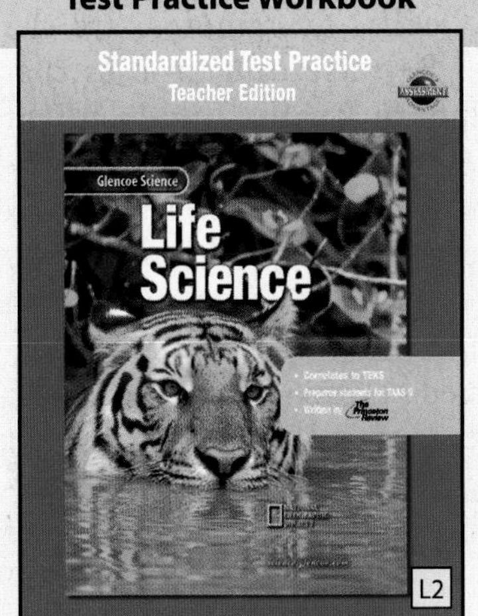

L2

Chapter Review

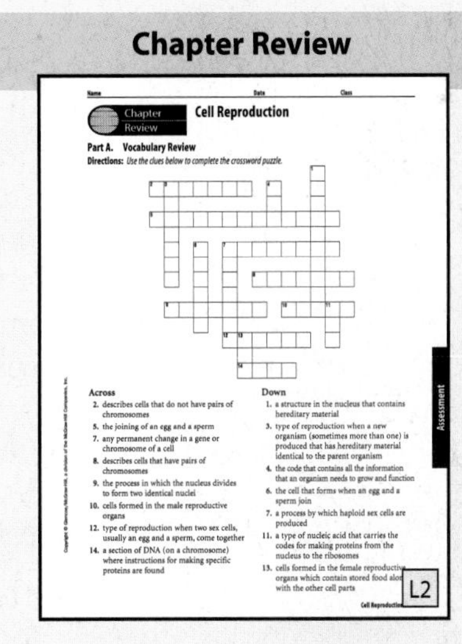

Chapter Review — Cell Reproduction

Part A. Vocabulary Review

L2

Science Content Background

SECTION 1

Cell Division and Mitosis

Results of Mitosis

Every species has a characteristic number of chromosomes in each cell. A cat has 38 chromosomes, whereas a potato and a chimpanzee each have 48 chromosomes. In all sexually reproducing organisms, chromosomes occur in homologous pairs. Except for some sex chromosomes, homologous chromosomes are of equal length and have the same genes at the same relative locations. The alleles may or may not be identical. For example, the gene for hair color would be at the same location on homologous chromosomes but may code for brunette on one chromosome and blonde on the other.

Fun Fact

The first pigs were cloned in 2000. Scientists think that organs from pigs could be transplanted into humans.

Animals and some plants have one pair of sex chromosomes. In most animals, including humans, the sex chromosomes of the female are truly homologous, whereas the male sex chromosomes are of unequal lengths and have many different genes. This is reversed in birds and butterflies, with males having the truly homologous sex chromosomes.

Asexual Reproduction

Eukaryotes, which include many protists, some fungi, and plants, reproduce asexually by mitosis. Prokaryotes, like bacteria, reproduce by fission. Depending on the organism, one or several new organisms can be created that are genetically identical to, or clones of, the original organism. Most animals do not use asexual reproduction. Recently scientists have been able to stimulate cells from adult animals to divide by mitosis and reproduce new animals that are clones of the organism from which the cells were taken.

Reuters New Media, Inc./Corbis

SECTION 2

Sexual Reproduction and Meiosis

Sexual Reproduction

Sex cells, or gametes, are the result of meiosis. Because of a process that happens at metaphase I called independent assortment, the possible combination of chromosomes for each sex cell varies every time sex cells form. When duplicated homologous chromosomes line up at a cell's center during metaphase I, there are no rules about how a particular pair is aligned relative to any other pair. The only requirement is that the alignment results in one half of each duplicated chromosome moving in one direction and the other half moving in the opposite direction during anaphase I. The offspring formed by fertilization has its own unique combination of genetic material. This produces variation between parents and offspring and may give offspring a better chance of surviving in a changing environment.

Meiosis and Sex Cells

This process is often called reduction division since the number of chromosomes in the cells produced is half that of the original cell. Meiosis provides for great diversity within a species because of the many ways the chromosomes can align during metaphase I. There are more than 8 million possible gametes that can be produced from the 23 pairs of human chromosomes.

In animals, meiosis results in haploid egg and sperm cells. In plants, meiosis results in haploid spores that later produce egg and sperm cells.

SECTION 3 DNA

What is DNA?

The information in DNA that determines what an organism will be is contained in a code dictated by the order of subunits called nucleotides. A nucleotide consists of the sugar deoxyribose, a phosphate molecule, and one of the four possible nitrogen bases. A DNA molecule is two chains of nucleotides. These two chains are antiparallel and run in opposite directions. One chain ends with a phosphate, and the other chain ends with deoxyribose. Just as the order of letters on this page determines what words you are reading, the order of nucleotides determines the message on the DNA. Because DNA is copied from one generation to the next, any change, or mutation, in a gene is also preserved. If the change occurs in cells that become gametes, it is passed on to future generations in a process called heredity.

For additional content background on this topic, go to the Glencoe Science Web site at science.glencoe.com.

A DNA Model

The process of DNA replication is directed by the enzyme called DNA polymerase. It moves along the separated DNA molecule and inserts the correct, complementary nucleotides onto the exposed nitrogen bases. This happens at many locations along the length of the DNA molecule simultaneously. Otherwise the time it would take to match up the millions of nitrogen bases would be astronomical.

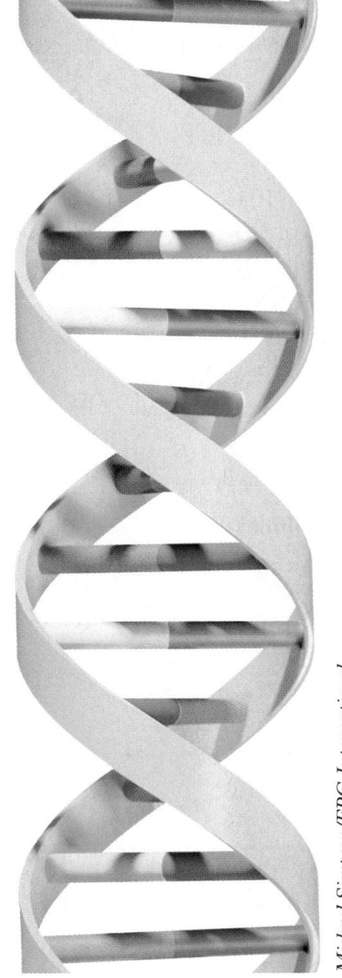

Michael Simpson/FPG International

Mutations

A change in a cell's genetic message is called a mutation. Some mutations affect the message itself, altering the sequence of DNA nucleotides. Other classes of mutations involve sequences of DNA that can move from place to place and are often called jumping genes. When a particular gene is mutated, its function is often destroyed.

Fun Fact

Barbara McClintock first published a paper on jumping genes in the 1940s. In 1983 she received the Nobel Prize for her work.

CHAPTER 4

Cell Reproduction

Chapter Vocabulary

mitosis, p. 98
chromosome, p. 98
asexual reproduction, p. 101
sexual reproduction, p. 104
sperm, p. 104
egg, p. 104
fertilization, p. 104
zygote, p. 104
diploid, p. 104
haploid, p. 105
meiosis, p. 105
DNA, p. 110
gene, p. 112
RNA, p. 112
mutation, p. 114

What do you think?

Science Journal The structures in the picture are duplicated chromosomes, which contain genetic information for the organism they belong to.

CHAPTER 4

Cell Reproduction

How does a cut on your skin heal? Why doesn't a baby chicken grow up to look like a duck? Why do turtles, like the one in the photo to the right, and most other animals need to have two parents, when a sweet potato plant can be grown from just one potato? In this chapter, you will find answers to these questions as you learn about cell reproduction. You also will learn what genetic material is and how it functions.

What do you think?

Science Journal Look at the picture below with a classmate. Discuss what you think this might be. Here is a hint: *These structures contain important information for cells.* Write your answer or best guess in your Science Journal.

94

Theme Connection

Stability and Change DNA controls all cell activities by directing the production of proteins in living organisms. Changes in DNA can result in evolutionary changes that are inherited.

Most flower and vegetable seeds sprout and grow into entire plants in just a few weeks. Although all of the cells in a seed have information and instructions to produce a new plant, only some of the cells in the seed use the information. Where are these cells in seeds? Do the following activity to find out.

Infer about seed growth

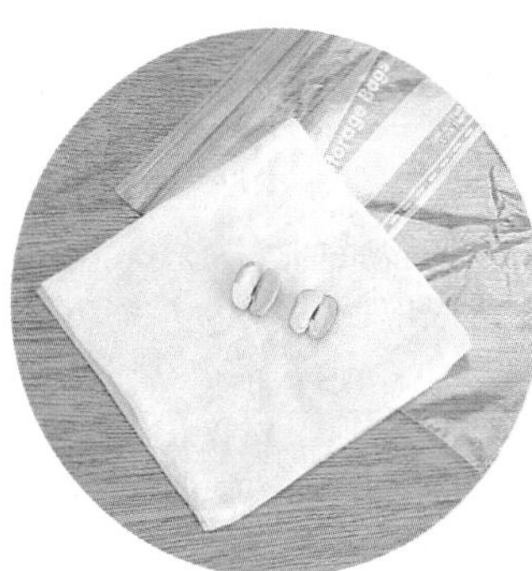

1. Carefully split open two bean seeds that have soaked in water overnight.
2. Observe both halves and record your observations.
3. Wrap all four halves in a moist paper towel. Then put them into a self-sealing, plastic bag and seal the bag. Wash your hands.
4. Make observations for a few days.

Observe

In your Science Journal, describe what you observe. Hypothesize about which cells in seeds use information about how plants grow.

Before You Read

FOLDABLES Reading & Study Skills

Making an Organizational Study Fold When information is grouped into clear categories, it is easier to make sense of what you are learning. Make the following Foldable to help you organize information about cell reproduction.

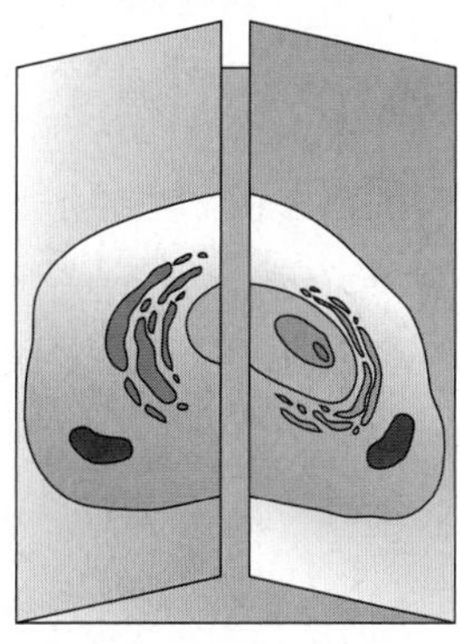

1. Place a sheet of paper in front of you so the long side is at the top. Fold the paper in half from the left side to the right side and then unfold.
2. Fold in each side to the center line to divide the paper into fourths.
3. Use a pencil to draw a cell on the front of your Foldable as shown.
4. As you read the chapter, use a pen to illustrate how the cell divides into two cells. Under the flaps, list how cells divide. In the middle section, list why cells divide.

95

Explore Activity

Purpose Use the Explore Activity to introduce students to growth; as they read the chapter, they will understand that growth is the result of mitosis. L2

Kinesthetic

Preparation Soak pinto beans or other large seeds for 24 hours.

Materials 2 soaked seeds, paper towels, self-sealing plastic bag, hand lens

Teaching Strategy After soaking, the seeds should split easily. If students have difficulty, forceps can be used to separate the seeds.

Observe

Students should observe and record the growth of a new plant from one half of each seed. They should predict that the cells of the seed embryo are able to use the information needed to grow into a plant.

Assessment

Performance Have students repeat the experiment using corn seeds and observe the new plant that grows from each seed. Use **Performance Assessment in the Science Classroom,** p. 89.

Before You Read

FOLDABLES Reading & Study Skills

Dinah Zike Study Fold

Purpose Students should use this Foldable to diagram cells and organize information on cells and cell division as they read.

For additional help, see Foldables Worksheet p. 15 in **Chapter Resources Booklet,** or go to the Glencoe Science Web site at **science.glencoe.com.** See After You Read in the Study Guide at the end of this chapter.

SECTION

Cell Division and Mitosis

1 Motivate

Bellringer Transparency

Display the Section Focus Transparency for Section 1. Use the accompanying Transparency Activity Master. L2 ELL

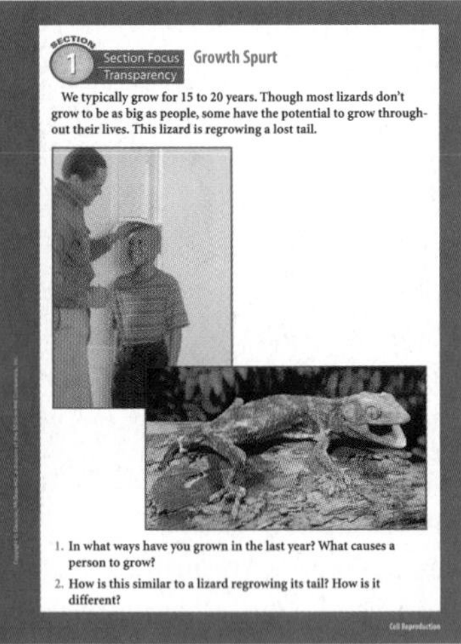

SECTION 1 Section Focus Transparency **Growth Spurt**

We typically grow for 15 to 20 years. Though most lizards don't grow to be as big as people, some have the potential to grow throughout their lives. This lizard is regrowing a lost tail.

1. In what ways have you grown in the last year? What causes a person to grow?
2. How is this similar to a lizard regrowing its tail? How is it different?

Cell Reproduction

Tie to Prior Knowledge

Use a diagram or transparency to review the parts of a cell and their functions. Explain that mitosis involves only the nucleus.

SECTION

Cell Division and Mitosis

As You Read

***What* You'll Learn**

- **Explain** why mitosis is important.
- **Examine** the steps of mitosis.
- **Compare** mitosis in plant and animal cells.
- **List** two examples of asexual reproduction.

Vocabulary

mitosis
chromosome
asexual reproduction

***Why* It's Important**

Your growth, like that of many organisms, depends on cell division.

Why is cell division important?

What do you, an octopus, and an oak tree have in common? You share many characteristics, but an important one is that you are all made of cells—trillions of cells. Where did all of those cells come from? As amazing as it might seem, many organisms start as just one cell. That cell divides and becomes two, two become four, four become eight, and so on. Many-celled organisms, including you, grow because cell division increases the total number of cells in an organism. Even after growth stops, cell division is still important. Every day, billions of red blood cells in your body wear out and are replaced. During the few seconds it takes you to read this sentence, your bone marrow produced about six million red blood cells. Cell division is important to one-celled organisms, too—it's how they reproduce themselves, as shown in **Figure 1B.** Cell division isn't as simple as just cutting the cell in half, so how do cells divide?

The Cell Cycle

A living organism has a life cycle. A life cycle begins with the organism's formation, is followed by growth and development, and finally ends in death. Right now, you are in a stage of your life cycle called adolescence, which is a period of active growth and development. Individual cells also have life cycles.

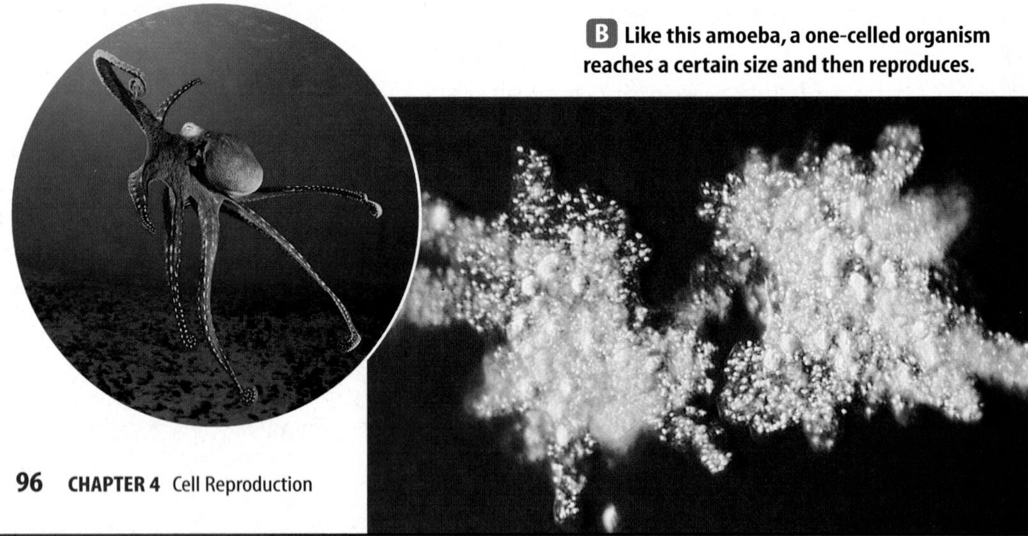

Figure 1
All organisms use cell division.

A Many-celled organisms, such as this octopus, grow by increasing the numbers of their cells.

B Like this amoeba, a one-celled organism reaches a certain size and then reproduces.

Section Assessment Planner

Portfolio
Visual Learning, p. 97

Performance Assessment
MiniLAB, p. 101
Skill Builder Activities, p. 102
See page 122 for more options.

Content Assessment
Section, p. 102
Challenge, p. 102
Chapter, pp. 122–123

Figure 2
Interphase is the longest part of the cell cycle. *When do chromosomes duplicate?*

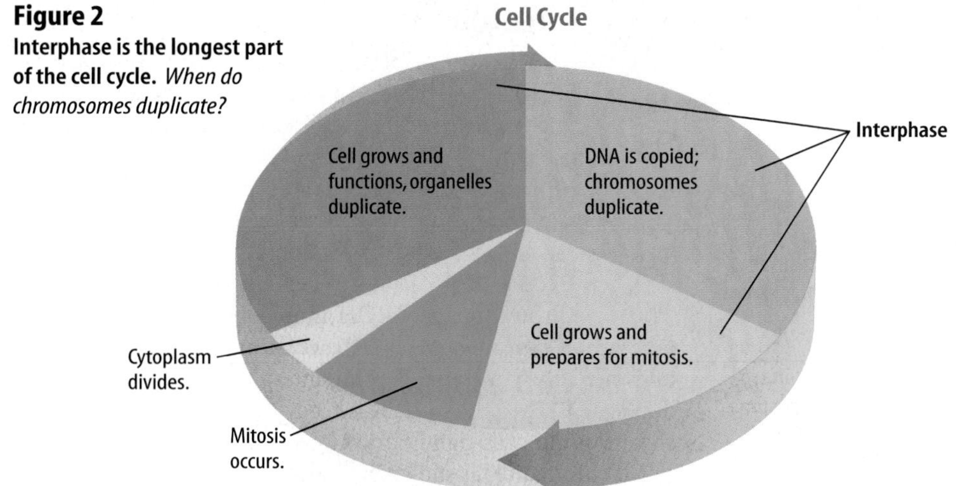
Cell Cycle
Interphase
Cell grows and functions, organelles duplicate.
DNA is copied; chromosomes duplicate.
Cell grows and prepares for mitosis.
Cytoplasm divides.
Mitosis occurs.

Length of Cycle The cell cycle, as shown in **Figure 2,** is a series of events that takes place from one cell division to the next. The time it takes to complete a cell cycle is not the same in all cells. For example, the cycle for cells in some bean plants takes about 19 h to complete. Cells in animal embryos divide rapidly and can complete their cycles is less than 20 min. In some human cells, the cell cycle takes about 16 h. Cells in humans that are needed for repair, growth, or replacement, like skin and bone cells, constantly repeat the cycle.

Interphase Most of the life of any eukaryotic cell—a cell with a nucleus—is spent in a period of growth and development called interphase. Cells in your body that no longer divide, such as nerve and muscle cells, are always in interphase. An actively dividing cell, such as a skin cell, copies its hereditary material and prepares for cell division during interphase.

Why is it important for a cell to copy its hereditary information before dividing? Imagine that you have a part in a play and the director has one complete copy of the script. If the director gave only one page to each person in the play, no one would have the entire script. Instead the director makes a complete, separate copy of the script for each member of the cast so that each one can learn his or her part. Before a cell divides, a copy of the hereditary material must be made so that each of the two new cells will get a complete copy. Just as the actors in the play need the entire script, each cell needs a complete set of hereditary material to carry out life functions.

After interphase, cell division begins. The nucleus divides, and then the cytoplasm separates to form two new cells.

Health INTEGRATION

In most cells, the cell cycle is well controlled. However, cancerous cells have uncontrolled cell division. Some cancerous cells form a mass of cells called a tumor. Find out why some tumors are harmful to an organism. Write what you find out in your Science Journal.

SCIENCE Online

Research Nerve cells in adults usually do not undergo mitosis. Visit the Glencoe Science Web site at **science.glencoe.com** for more information about nerve cell regeneration. Communicate to your class what you learn.

2 Teach

The Cell Cycle

Caption Answer

Figure 2 during interphase

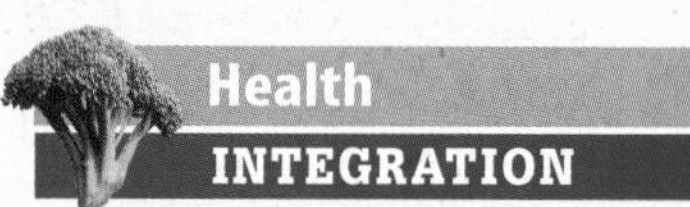
Visual Learning

Figure 2 Have students make an events chain concept map that outlines the steps of the cell cycle as illustrated in **Figure 2.** L2 LS **Visual-Spatial** P

Health INTEGRATION

Cancerous tumors grow rapidly and sometimes invade healthy tissue.

SCIENCE Online
Internet Addresses

Explore the Glencoe Science Web site at **science.glencoe.com** to find out more about topics in this section.

Resource Manager

Chapter Resources Booklet

Transparency Activity, p. 42

Directed Reading for Content Mastery, pp. 17, 18

Science Journal

Life of a Cell Have students write creative stories about the life cycle of a cell from its beginning to its end. Have them use section vocabulary as they describe what happens in the cell. L2 LS **Linguistic**

Mitosis

Students may assume that all cells divide. However, some cells do not divide at all. Red blood cells circulating in the blood vessels do not divide; they live for 90 days before they are replaced by new cells.

Use an Analogy

Compare chromosome thickening to a coiled telephone cord. When stretched out, the cord is long and thin, like chromosomes during interphase. When the cord returns to its usual position, it shortens and thickens, like chromosomes preparing to divide. L1

LS **Visual-Spatial**

Reading Check

Answer A duplicated chromosome is made up of two chromatids.

Fun Fact

Most cells are not actively engaged in mitosis. Skin cells spend 15–20 days in interphase. After infancy, nerve cells stay in interphase.

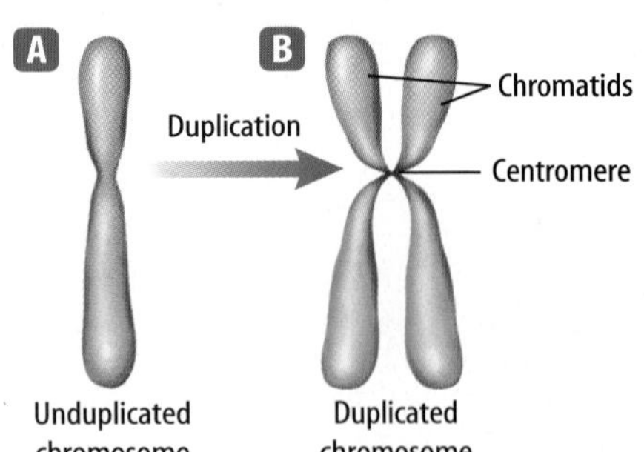

Figure 3
DNA is copied during interphase. A An unduplicated chromosome has one strand of DNA. B A duplicated chromosome has two identical DNA strands, called chromatids, that are held together at a region called the centromere.

Figure 4
The cell plate shown in this plant cell appears when the cytoplasm is being divided.

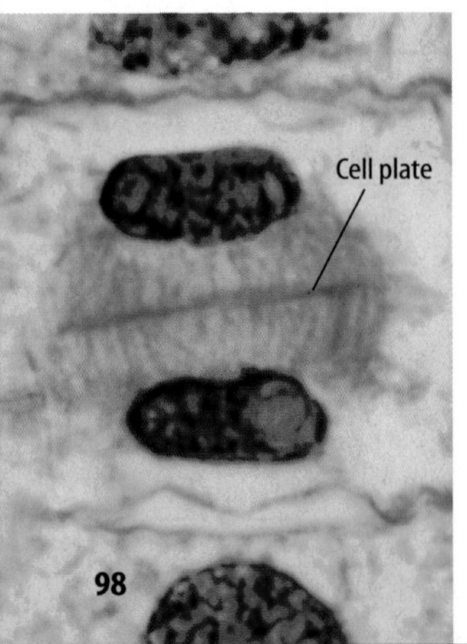

98

Mitosis

Mitosis (mi TOH sus) is the process in which the nucleus divides to form two identical nuclei. Each new nucleus also is identical to the original nucleus. Mitosis is described as a series of phases, or steps. The steps of mitosis in order are named prophase, metaphase, anaphase, and telophase.

Steps of Mitosis When any nucleus divides, the chromosomes (KROH muh sohmz) play the important part. A **chromosome** is a structure in the nucleus that contains hereditary material. During interphase, each chromosome duplicates. When the nucleus is ready to divide, each duplicated chromosome coils tightly into two thickened, identical strands called chromatids, as shown in **Figure 3.**

Reading Check *How are chromosomes and chromatids related?*

During prophase, the pairs of chromatids are fully visible when viewed under a microscope. The nucleolus and the nuclear membrane disintegrate. Two small structures called centrioles (SEN tree olz) move to opposite ends of the cell. Between the centrioles, threadlike spindle fibers begin to stretch across the cell. Plant cells also form spindle fibers during mitosis but do not have centrioles.

In metaphase, the pairs of chromatids line up across the center of the cell. The centromere of each pair usually becomes attached to two spindle fibers—one from each side of the cell.

In anaphase, each centromere divides and the spindle fibers shorten. Each pair of chromatids separates, and chromatids begin to move to opposite ends of the cell. The separated chromatids are now called chromosomes. In the final step, telophase, spindle fibers start to disappear, the chromosomes start to uncoil, and a new nucleus forms.

Division of the Cytoplasm For most cells, after the nucleus has divided, the cytoplasm separates and two new cells are formed. In animal cells, the cell membrane pinches in the middle, like a balloon with a string tightened around it, and the cytoplasm divides. In plant cells, the appearance of a cell plate, as shown in **Figure 4,** tells you that the cytoplasm is being divided. New cell walls form along the cell plate, and new cell membranes develop inside the cell walls. Following division of the cytoplasm, most new cells begin the period of growth, or interphase, again. Review cell division for an animal cell using the illustrations in **Figure 5.**

Inclusion Strategies

Visually Impaired Have selected students make three-dimensional models of mitosis on poster board. Display the posters in the classroom for visually impaired students to feel. L2

LS **Visual-Spatial**

Cultural Diversity

Historic Contributions In 1887, Edouard-Joseph-Marie van Beneden, a Belgian scientist, discovered that each species has a fixed number of chromosomes. He also observed the formation of a haploid cell. In 1956, J. Hin Tjio and Albert Levan showed that each human cell has 46 chromosomes.

Figure 5
Cell division for an animal cell is shown here. Each micrograph shown in this figure is magnified 600 times.

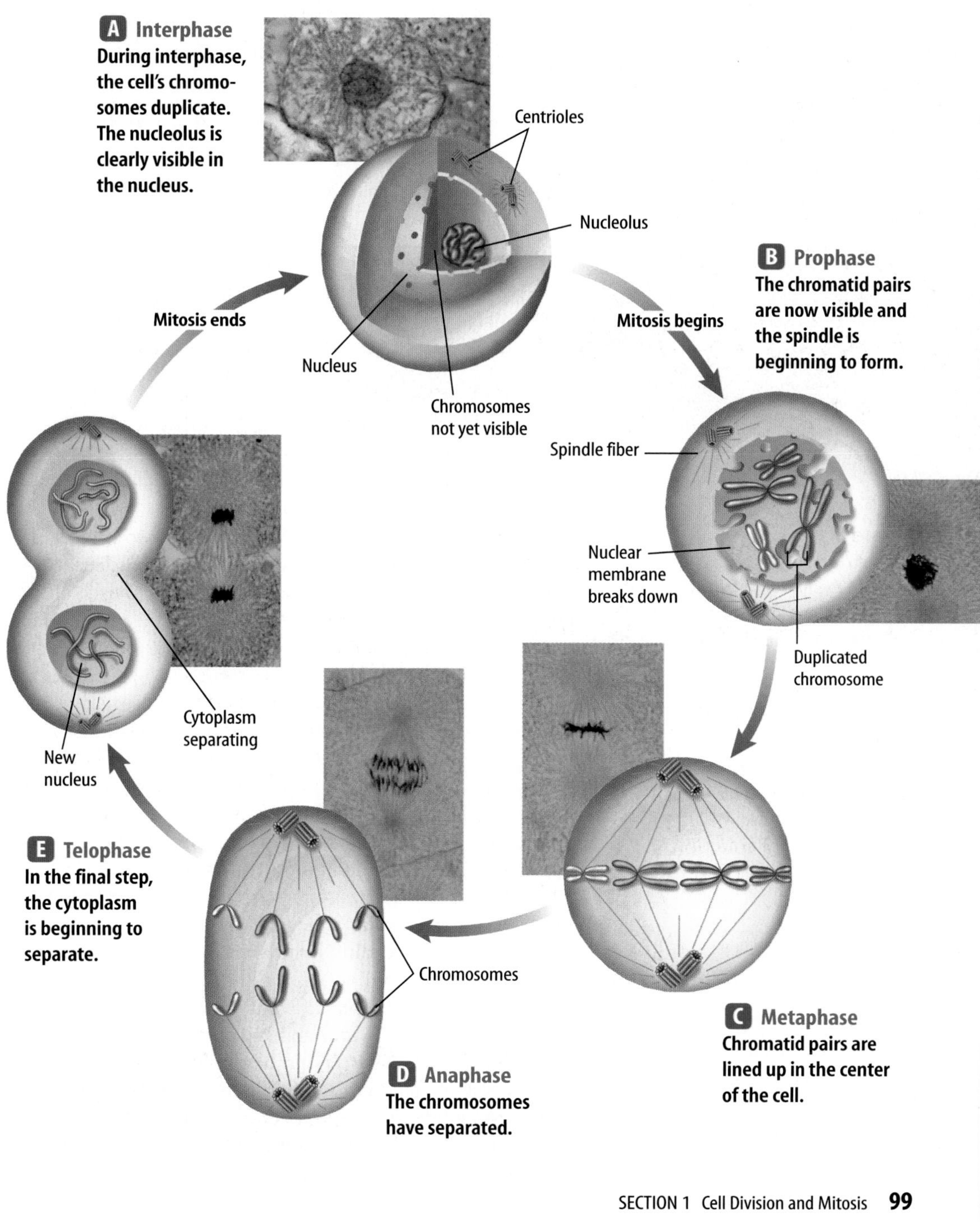
A Interphase
During interphase, the cell's chromosomes duplicate. The nucleolus is clearly visible in the nucleus.
Centrioles
Nucleolus
Nucleus
Chromosomes not yet visible
Mitosis ends
Mitosis begins
B Prophase
The chromatid pairs are now visible and the spindle is beginning to form.
Spindle fiber
Nuclear membrane breaks down
Duplicated chromosome
C Metaphase
Chromatid pairs are lined up in the center of the cell.
D Anaphase
The chromosomes have separated.
Chromosomes
E Telophase
In the final step, the cytoplasm is beginning to separate.
Cytoplasm separating
New nucleus

Quick Demo

Use a microprojector to show mitotic cell divisions in the growth of fertilized frog eggs. The increasing numbers of cells can be readily seen during the early stages of tadpole development.

Extension

Have students research and report on cancer. The report should include how cancer relates to mitosis and some of the technology used to diagnose and treat cancer. Display written reports. L2 LS **Linguistic**

Teacher FYI

The fact that chromosomes are duplicated in the nucleus during interphase has been hypothesized for more than a hundred years, but evidence for the hypothesis did not appear until 1981.

Use Science Words

Word Meaning Explain that the word *mitosis* derives from the Greek word for "thread." Have students explain the derivation. During mitosis, the replicated chromosomes—threadlike structures—separate. Then point out that *phase* is another word for "stage." Have students use a dictionary to find the meanings of the prefixes *inter-* (between), *pro-* (before), *meta-* (after), *ana-* (up), and *telo-* (end).

Resource Manager

Chapter Resources Booklet
Note-taking Worksheets, pp. 31–33
Enrichment, p. 28

Curriculum Connection

Math It takes 15 minutes for certain embryo cells to divide. Have students calculate how many cells would be produced from one embryo cell after four hours. 240 minutes divided by 15 minutes = 16 cell divisions; 2^{16} = 65,536 cells L2
LS **Logical-Mathematical**

Mitosis, continued

Discussion

Have students use their knowledge of the cell cycle to infer why even slight injuries to the brain and spinal cord can be serious and permanent. Because nerve cells do not undergo mitosis, damaged cells are not replaced, although some repair does occur.

Discussion

Many nonliving things such as icicles, stalagmites, crystals, and sand dunes appear to grow. Ask students to give examples of other nonliving things that appear to grow. Possible answers: highway systems, buildings, developments, shopping malls Have students distinguish between the processes involved in the growth of living things and the growth of nonliving things. In nonliving things, growth is caused by the surrounding environment. In living things, growth is caused by processes within the organism.

Caption Answer

Figure 6 the sex of the organism

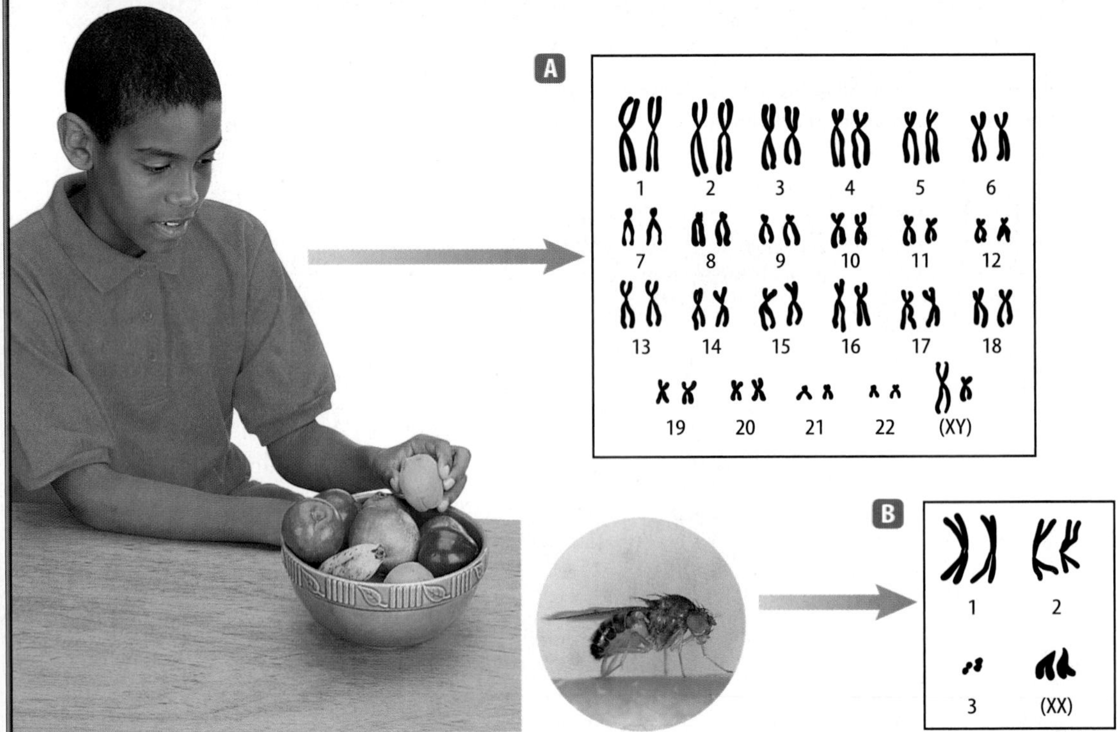

Figure 6
Pairs of chromosomes are found in the nucleus of most cells. All chromosomes shown here are in their duplicated form. A Most human cells have 23 pairs of chromosomes including one pair of chromosomes that help determine sex such as the XY pair above. B Most fruit fly cells have four pairs of chromosomes. *What do you think the XX pair in fruit flies helps determine?*

Results of Mitosis You should remember two important things about mitosis. First, it is the division of a nucleus. Second, it produces two new nuclei that are identical to each other and the original nucleus. Each new nucleus has the same number and type of chromosomes. Every cell in your body, except sex cells, has a nucleus with 46 chromosomes—23 pairs. This is because you began as one cell with 46 chromosomes in its nucleus. Skin cells, produced to replace or repair your skin, have the same 46 chromosomes as the original single cell you developed from. Each cell in a fruit fly has eight chromosomes, so each new cell produced by mitosis has a copy of those eight chromosomes. **Figure 6** shows the chromosomes found in most human cells and those found in most fruit fly cells.

Each of the trillions of cells in your body, except sex cells, has a copy of the same hereditary material. Even though all actors in a play have copies of the same script, they do not learn the same lines. Likewise, all of your cells use different parts of the same hereditary material to become different types of cells.

Cell division allows growth and replaces worn out or damaged cells. You are much larger and have more cells than a baby mainly because of cell division. If you cut yourself, the wound heals because cell division replaces damaged cells. Another way some organisms use cell division is to produce new organisms.

LAB DEMONSTRATION

Purpose to observe asexual reproduction in a sweet potato

Materials sweet potato with leaf buds, water, widemouthed glass jar, 4 toothpicks

Preparation Obtain a sweet potato that has purple leaf buds growing at its scarred end.

Procedure Fill a jar almost full of water, and place sweet potato with buds or scarred end up so at least half of the potato is in water. Toothpicks can hold the potato in place. Keep water level constant and observe for three weeks.

Expected Outcome Students should observe the formation of roots and leaf growth.

Assessment

What part of the sweet potato produced leaves and roots? Leaves developed from the buds; roots grew from the bottom half of the sweet potato. **Is this an example of sexual or asexual reproduction? Explain.** Asexual; a new organism is produced from one parent.

Asexual Reproduction

Reproduction is the process by which an organism produces others of its same kind. Among living organisms, there are two types of reproduction—sexual and asexual. Sexual reproduction usually requires two organisms. In **asexual reproduction,** a new organism (sometimes more than one) is produced from one organism. The new organism will have hereditary material identical to the hereditary material of the parent organism.

How many organisms are needed for asexual reproduction?

Cellular Asexual Reproduction Organisms with eukaryotic cells asexually reproduce by cell division. A sweet potato growing in a jar of water is an example of asexual reproduction. All the stems, leaves, and roots that grow from the sweet potato have been produced by cell division and have the same hereditary material. New strawberry plants can be reproduced asexually from horizontal stems called runners. **Figure 7** shows asexual reproduction in a potato and a strawberry plant.

Recall that mitosis is the division of a nucleus. However, bacteria do not have a nucleus so they can't use mitosis. Instead, bacteria reproduce asexually by fission. During fission, an organism whose cells do not contain a nucleus copies its genetic material and then divides into two identical organisms.

Mini LAB

Modeling Mitosis

Procedure

1. Make models of cell division using **materials supplied by your teacher.**
2. Use four chromosomes in your model.
3. When finished, arrange the models in the order in which mitosis occurs.

Analysis

1. In which steps is the nucleus visible?
2. How many cells does a dividing cell form?

Figure 7
Many plants can reproduce asexually.

A **A new potato plant can grow from each sprout on this potato.**

B *How does the genetic material in the small strawberry plant compare to the genetic material in the large strawberry plant?*

Asexual Reproduction

Reading Check

Answer one

Purpose to construct a model of mitosis L2 ELL
IS **Kinesthetic and Visual-Spatial**

Materials colored paper, poster board, markers, toothpicks, yarn, thread, glue, scissors

Teaching Strategy Student models should resemble mitosis as shown in **Figure 4.**

Analysis

1. prophase and telophase
2. two new cells

Assessment

Performance Assess students' understanding of mitosis by making flash cards of the stages and having students arrange them in the proper order. Use **PASC,** p. 163.

Caption Answer

Figure 7 They are identical.

Resource Manager

Chapter Resources Booklet

MiniLAB, p. 3
Transparency Activity, pp. 45–46
Lab Activity, pp. 9–10

Science Journal

Cloning Have students use science reference books, newspapers, and the Internet to research cloning, a process that artificially reproduces an exact duplicate of a single parent. Have students write reports in their Science Journals on the medical uses as well as the negative ethical implications of cloning technology. L2 IS **Linguistic**

Asexual Reproduction, continued

Activity

Add one package of yeast and one teaspoon of sugar to a .5 L container of warm water. Let the container stand in a warm place for a few hours. Allow students to examine microscope slides of the mixture to observe budding in yeast cells. L2

LS **Visual-Spatial**

Text Question Answers

Sea star numbers would increase because of regeneration.

3 Assess

Reteach

Have students draw the nucleus or chromosomes on cell cycle outlines and describe what is occurring at each stage. L1

ELL LS **Visual-Spatial**

Challenge

At one time, interphase was called the resting stage. Why is this not a good description of interphase? A cell in interphase is carrying out all of the life processes.

Assessment

Oral How is mitosis different from cell division? Mitosis is the division of the nucleus. Cell division includes mitosis and the division of the cytoplasm and its contents. Use **Performance Assessment in the Science Classroom,** p. 89.

Figure 8
Some organisms use cell division for budding and regeneration.

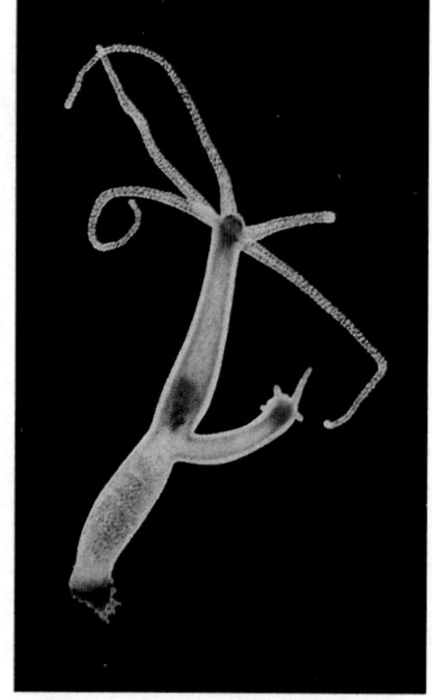

A Hydra, a freshwater animal, can reproduce asexually by budding. The bud is a small exact copy of the adult.

B Some sea stars reproduce asexually by shedding arms. Each arm can grow into a new sea star.

Budding and Regeneration Look at **Figure 8A.** A new organism is growing from the body of the parent organism. This organism, called a hydra, is reproducing by budding. Budding is a type of asexual reproduction made possible because of cell division. When the bud on the adult becomes large enough, it breaks away to live on its own.

Could you grow a new finger? Some organisms can regrow damaged or lost body parts, as shown in **Figure 8B.** Regeneration is the process that uses cell division to regrow body parts. Sponges, planaria, sea stars, and some other organisms can use regeneration for asexual reproduction. If these organisms break into pieces, a whole new organism will grow from each piece. Because sea stars eat oysters, oyster farmers dislike them. What would happen if an oyster farmer collected sea stars, cut them into pieces, and threw them back into the ocean?

Section 1 Assessment

1. What is mitosis and how does it differ in plants and animals?
2. Give two examples of asexual reproduction in many-celled organisms.
3. What happens to chromosomes before mitosis begins?
4. After a cell undergoes mitosis, how are the two new cells alike?
5. **Think Critically** Why is it important for the nuclear membrane to disintegrate during mitosis?

Skill Builder Activities

6. **Testing a Hypothesis** A piece of leaf, stem, or root can grow into a new plant. Hypothesize how you would use one of these plant parts to grow a new plant. Test your idea. **For more help, refer to the** Science Skill Handbook.
7. **Solving One-Step Equations** If a cell undergoes cell division every 5 min, how many cells will there be after 1 h? Calculate and record the answer in your Science Journal. **For more help, refer to the** Math Skill Handbook.

Answers to Section Assessment

1. A process in which a cell nucleus divides into two nuclei, each of which has the same genetic information; in animal cells, the cytoplasm divides as the cell membrane pinches in the middle of the cell. In plant cells, the appearance of the cell plate indicates that the cytoplasm is being divided.
2. Possible answers: budding and regeneration
3. The chromosomes duplicate.
4. They both have the same genetic information.
5. Otherwise, the chromosomes would not be able to move to opposite ends of the cell.
6. Hypotheses will vary. Students may separate plant parts and place them in water or soil.
7. 60 minutes divided by 5 minutes = 12 cell divisions; $2^{12} = 4{,}096$ cells

Activity

Mitosis in Plant Cells

Reproduction of most cells in plants and animals uses mitosis and cell division. In this activity, you will study mitosis in plant cells by examining prepared slides of onion root-tip cells.

What You'll Investigate

How can plant cells in different stages of mitosis be distinguished from each other?

Materials

prepared slide of an onion root tip
microscope

Goals

- **Compare** cells in different stages of mitosis and observe the location of their chromosomes.
- **Observe** what stage of mitosis is most common in onion root tips.

Safety Precautions

Procedure

1. Copy the data table in your Science Journal.
2. **Obtain** a prepared slide of cells from an onion root tip.
3. Set your microscope on low power and examine the onion root tip. Move the slide until you can see the tip of the root. You will see several large, round cells. These cells are called the root cap. Move your slide until you see the cells in the area just behind the root cap. Turn the nosepiece to high power.
4. Find one area of cells where you can see the most stages of mitosis. Count how many cells you see in each stage and record your data in the table.
5. Turn the microscope back to low power. Remove the onion root-tip slide.

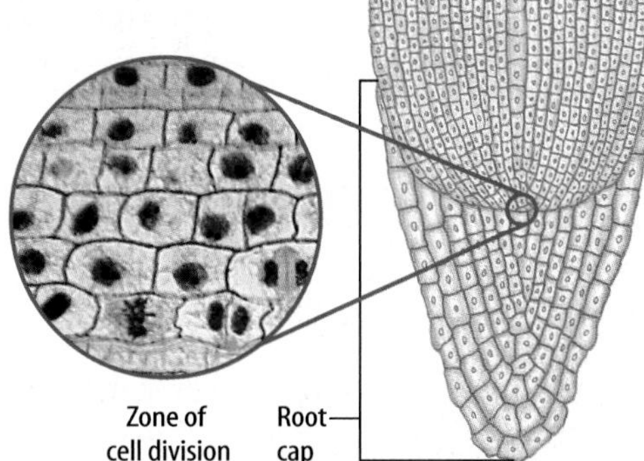

Conclude and Apply

1. **Compare** the cells in the region behind the root cap to those in the root cap.
2. **Calculate** the percent of cells found in each stage of mitosis. Infer which stage of mitosis takes the longest period of time.

Number of Root-Tip Cells Observed

Stage of Mitosis	Number of Cells Observed	Percent of Cells Observed
Prophase	78	65
Metaphase	23	19
Anaphase	12	10
Telophase	7	6
Total	120	100

Communicating Your Data

Write a story as if you were a cell in an onion root tip. Describe what changes occur as you go through mitosis. Use some of your drawings to illustrate the story. Share your story with your class. **For more help, refer to the** Science Skill Handbook.

Activity

BENCH TESTED

Purpose Students observe the stages of mitosis. L2 ELL
LS **Visual-Spatial**

Process Skills observing, inferring, comparing and contrasting

Time Required 40 minutes

Teaching Strategy Review the stages of mitosis before beginning the activity.

Troubleshooting Students may have difficulty locating all the phases. You may want to place an onion root tip slide on the microprojector and point out the phases.

Answers to Questions

1. The cells behind the root cap are smaller than those in the root cap. Mitosis occurs at a faster rate in cells behind the root cap.
2. See student page; prophase takes the longest.

Assessment

Performance To further assess students' understanding of mitosis, give each one a sheet of paper listing a stage and have them describe what comes before and after that stage. Use **Performance Assessment in the Science Classroom,** p. 163.

Resource Manager

Chapter Resources Booklet
Reinforcement, p. 25
Activity Worksheet, pp. 5–6

Communicating Your Data

The story and drawings should include the stages in mitosis.

SECTION

Sexual Reproduction and Meiosis

1 Motivate

Bellringer Transparency

Display the Section Focus Transparency for Section 2. Use the accompanying Transparency Activity Master. L2 ELL

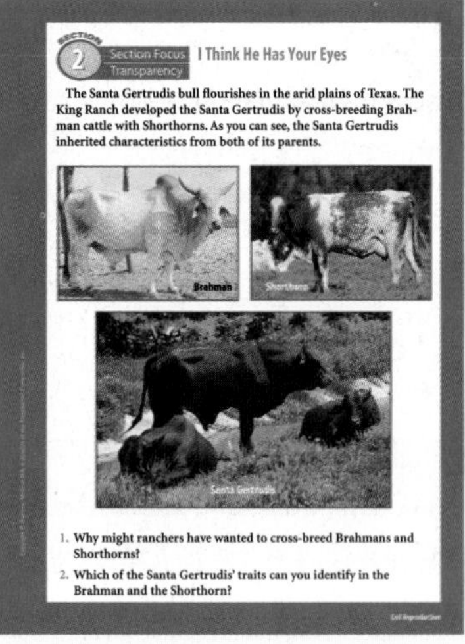
Section 2 Section Focus Transparency I Think He Has Your Eyes

The Santa Gertrudis bull flourishes in the arid plains of Texas. The King Ranch developed the Santa Gertrudis by cross-breeding Brahman cattle with Shorthorns. As you can see, the Santa Gertrudis inherited characteristics from both of its parents.

Brahman

Shorthorn

Santa Gertrudis

1. Why might ranchers have wanted to cross-breed Brahmans and Shorthorns?
2. Which of the Santa Gertrudis' traits can you identify in the Brahman and the Shorthorn?

Cell Reproduction

Tie to Prior Knowledge

As a review, ask students to describe the stages in mitosis. Then tell the students that for certain cells, the nucleus divides twice. They will learn why in this section.

SECTION

Sexual Reproduction and Meiosis

As You Read

What You'll Learn

- **Describe** the stages of meiosis and how sex cells are produced.
- **Explain** why meiosis is needed for sexual reproduction.
- **Name** the cells that are involved in fertilization.
- **Explain** how fertilization occurs in sexual reproduction.

Vocabulary

sexual reproduction, sperm, egg, fertilization, zygote, diploid, haploid, meiosis

Why It's Important

Because of meiosis and sexual reproduction, no one is exactly like you.

Sexual Reproduction

Sexual reproduction is another way that a new organism can be produced. During **sexual reproduction,** two sex cells, called an egg and a sperm, come together. Sex cells, like those in **Figure 9,** are formed from cells in reproductive organs. **Sperm** are formed in the male reproductive organs. **Eggs** are formed in the female reproductive organs. The joining of an egg and a sperm is called **fertilization,** and the cell that forms is called a **zygote** (ZI goht). Generally, the egg and the sperm come from two different organisms of the same species. Following fertilization, cell division begins. A new organism with a unique identity develops.

Diploid Cells Your body forms two types of cells—body cells and sex cells. Body cells far outnumber sex cells. Your brain, skin, bones, and other tissues and organs are formed from body cells. A typical human body cell has 46 chromosomes. Each chromosome has a mate that is similar to it in size and shape and has similar DNA. Human body cells have 23 pairs of chromosomes. When cells have pairs of similar chromosomes, they are said to be **diploid** (DIH ployd).

Figure 9
A human sperm or egg contains 23 chromosomes. The chromosomes are shown in their duplicated form.

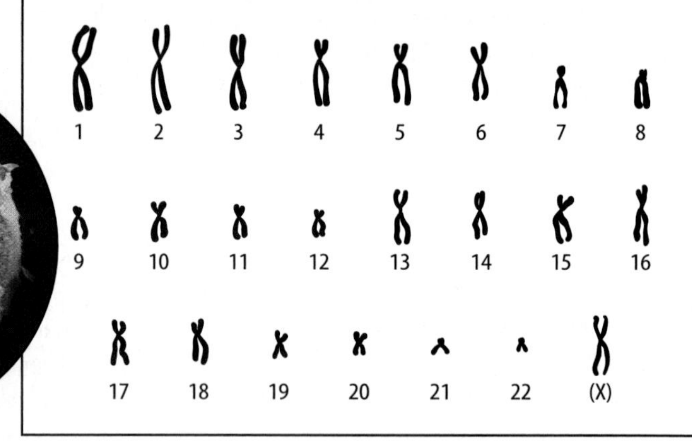

Human egg and many sperm Magnification: 790×

Section Assessment Planner

PORTFOLIO
Make a Model, p. 107

PERFORMANCE ASSESSMENT
Skill Builder Activities, p. 109
See page 122 for more options.

CONTENT ASSESSMENT
Section, p. 109
Challenge, p. 109
Chapter, pp. 122–123

Haploid Cells Because sex cells do not have pairs of chromosomes, they are said to be **haploid** (HA ployd). They have only half the number of chromosomes as body cells. *Haploid* means "single form." Human sex cells have only 23 chromosomes—one from each of the 23 pairs of similar chromosomes. Compare the chromosomes found in a sex cell, as shown in **Figure 9,** to the full set of human chromosomes seen in **Figure 6A.**

Reading Check *How many chromosomes are usually in each human sperm?*

Meiosis and Sex Cells

A process called **meiosis** (mi OH sus) produces haploid sex cells. What would happen in sexual reproduction if two diploid cells combined? The offspring would have twice as many chromosomes as its parent. Although plants with twice the number of chromosomes as the parent plants are often produced, most animals do not survive with a double number of chromosomes. Meiosis ensures that the offspring will have the same diploid number as its parent, as shown in **Figure 10.** After two haploid sex cells combine, a diploid zygote is produced that develops into a new diploid organism.

During meiosis, two divisions of the nucleus occur. These divisions are called meiosis I and meiosis II. The steps of each division have names like those in mitosis and are numbered for the division in which they occur.

Chemistry INTEGRATION

The human egg releases a chemical into the surrounding fluid that attracts sperm. Usually, only one sperm fertilizes the egg. After the sperm nucleus enters the egg, the cell membrane of the egg changes in a way that prevents other sperm from entering. What adaptation in this process guarantees that the zygote will be diploid? Write a paragraph describing your ideas in your Science Journal.

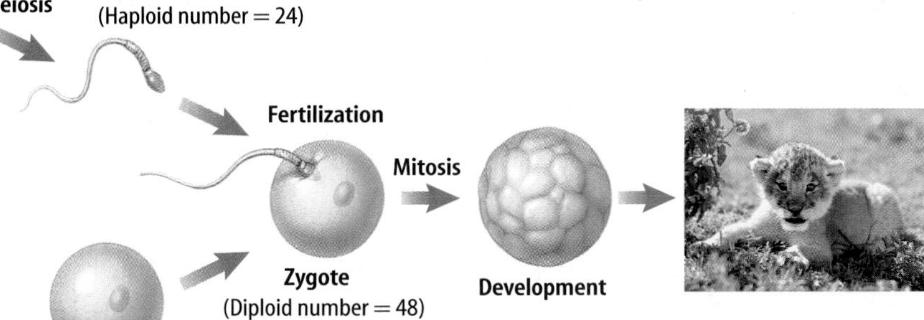

Figure 10
When sex cells join, a zygote forms. The zygote divides by cell division and develops into a new organism. Compare the number of chromosomes present in the different cells.

2 Teach

Sexual Reproduction

Reading Check

Answer 23 chromosomes

Meiosis and Sex Cells

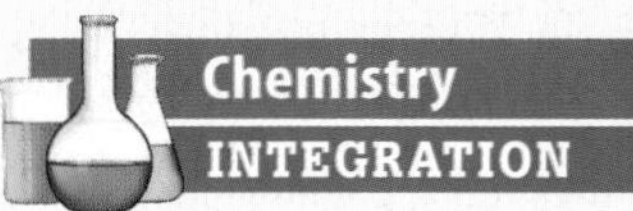

Chemistry INTEGRATION

The changes in the egg prevent fertilization by more than one sperm.

Use Science Words

Word Origin The term *meiosis* comes from a Greek word for "diminution" or becoming less. Ask students what diminishes or becomes less in meiosis. The chromosome number in each cell is diminished.

Fun Fact

With 23 pairs of chromosomes in the human body, there are more than 8 million different combinations of chromosomes possible for every human cell formed by meiosis.

Caption Answer

Figure 10 Fertilized cells have twice the number of chromosomes found in sex cells.

Resource Manager

Chapter Resources Booklet
- Transparency Activity, p. 43
- Directed Reading for Content Mastery, p. 18

Life Science Critical Thinking/Problem Solving, p. 19

Curriculum Connection

Math Have students use library references to find the number of chromosomes in the body cells of various plants and animals. Then have them determine the number of chromosomes in the sex cells of each one. The number of chromosomes in sex cells should be half the number of chromosomes in body cells. L3  **Logical-Mathematical**

Meiosis and Sex Cells, continued

Caption Answer

Figure 11 four

Teacher FYI

In vitro fertilization is a procedure that joins sperm and eggs outside the body. Fertilized eggs (actually two-day-old embryos) are then implanted into the female.

Extension

Have students research and report on the contribution of African American cell biologist Everett Anderson to the modern understanding of meiosis. Anderson is one of the leading researchers in developing electron microscopic techniques to study meiosis. L2

LS **Linguistic**

Reading Check

Answer The duplicated chromosomes of each similar pair are pulled to opposite ends of the cell.

Use Science Words

Word Meaning Have students use a dictionary to find out what *triploid* and *tetraploid* mean. Have them write an explanation of how this condition occurs. *Triploid*—each cell in the organism contains three sets of chromosomes; plant endosperm is triploid and normal. *Tetraploid* organisms have four sets of chromosomes in each cell; these conditions arise from total nondisjunction during mitosis or meiosis. L2 LS **Linguistic**

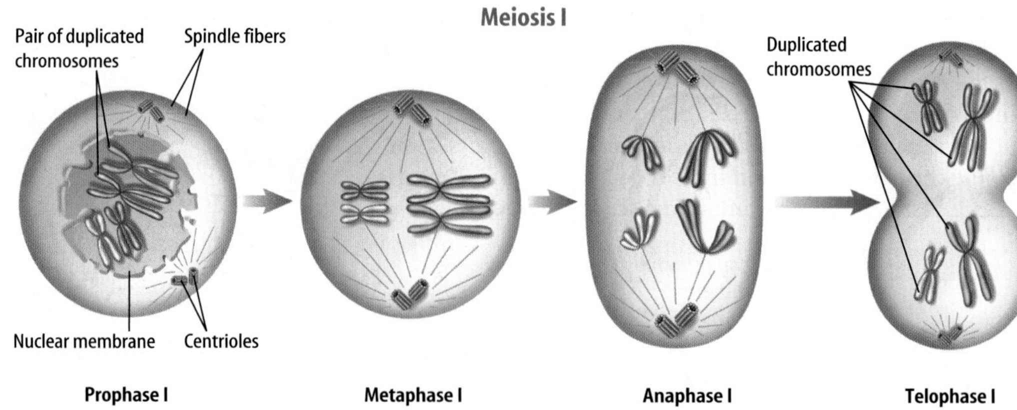

Figure 11
Meiosis has two divisions of the nucleus—meiosis I and meiosis II. *How many sex cells are finally formed after both divisions are completed?*

Meiosis I Before meiosis begins, each chromosome is duplicated, just as in mitosis. When the cell is ready for meiosis, each duplicated chromosome is visible under the microscope as two chromatids. As shown in **Figure 11,** the events of prophase I are similar to those of prophase in mitosis. In meiosis, each duplicated chromosome comes near its similar duplicated mate. In mitosis they do not come near each other.

In metaphase I, the pairs of duplicated chromosomes line up in the center of the cell. The centromere of each chromatid pair becomes attached to one spindle fiber so, the chromatids do not separate in anaphase I. The two pairs of chromatids of each similar pair move away from each other to opposite ends of the cell. Each duplicated chromosome still has two chromatids. Then, in telophase I, the cytoplasm divides, and two new cells form. Each new cell has one duplicated chromosome from each similar pair.

Reading Check *What happens to duplicated chromosomes during anaphase I?*

Meiosis II The two cells formed during meiosis I now begin meiosis II. The chromatids of each duplicated chromosome will be separated during this division. In prophase II, the duplicated chromosomes and spindle fibers reappear in each new cell. Then in metaphase II, the duplicated chromosomes move to the center of the cell. Unlike what occurs in metaphase I, each centromere now attaches to two spindle fibers instead of one. The centromere divides during anaphase II, and the chromatids separate and move to opposite ends of the cell. Each chromatid now is an individual chromosome. As telophase II begins, the spindle fibers disappear, and a nuclear membrane forms around the chromosomes at each end of the cell. When meiosis II is finished, the cytoplasm divides.

Resource Manager

Chapter Resources Booklet
Enrichment, p. 29
Mathematics Skill Activities, p. 3

Inclusion Strategies

Learning Disabled Students who are dyslexic may have trouble distinguishing between the first and second parts of meiosis. Instead of Roman numbers, as in prophase I and prophase II, use Arabic numbers for easier identification (prophase 1 and prophase 2).

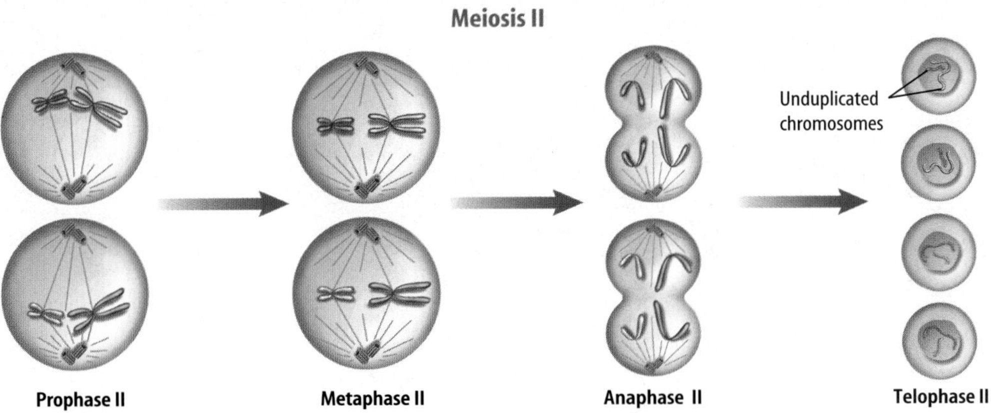

Summary of Meiosis Two cells form during meiosis I. In meiosis II, both of these cells form two cells. The two divisions of the nucleus result in four sex cells. Each has one-half the number of chromosomes in its nucleus that was in the original nucleus. From a human cell with 46 paired chromosomes, meiosis produces four sex cells each with 23 unpaired chromosomes.

Problem-Solving Activity

How can chromosome numbers be predicted?

Offspring get half of their chromosomes from one parent and half from the other. What happens if each parent has a different diploid number of chromosomes?

Identifying the Problem

A zebra and a donkey can mate to produce a zonkey. Zebras have a diploid number of 46. Donkeys have a diploid number of 62.

Solving the Problem

1. How many chromosomes would the zonkey receive from each parent?
2. What is the chromosome number of the zonkey?
3. What would happen when meiosis occurs in the zonkey's reproductive organs?
4. Predict why zonkeys are usually sterile.

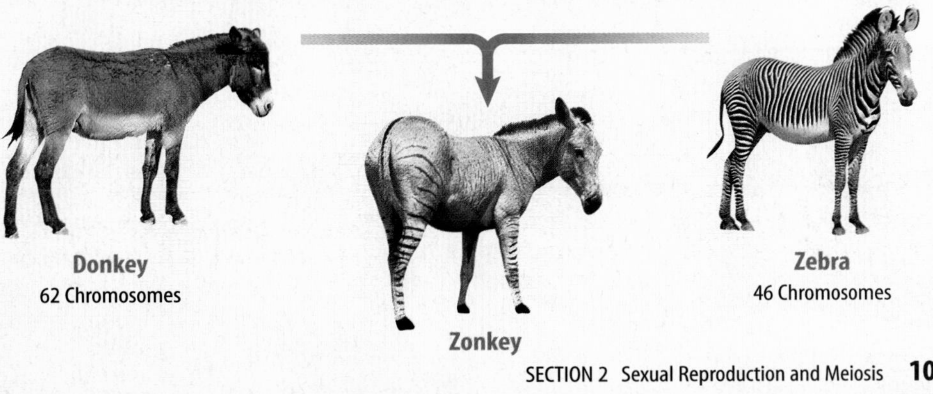

Make a Model

Have students make a model of the stages of meiosis in an organism with three pairs of chromosomes. Have them use shapes to distinguish the chromosomes. L1 LS **Kinesthetic**

Activity

Using one of their favorite songs, have students write substitute lyrics about what happens in meiosis. L2 LS **Auditory-Musical**

Problem-Solving Activity

National Math Standards

Correlation to Mathematics Objectives

1, 6, 8, 9

Answers

1. 23 from the zebra and 31 from the donkey
2. 54
3. Normal sex cells would not form because there are 8 unpaired chromosomes from the donkey.
4. Each sex cell could not have one-half the chromosomes of the original cell.

Extension

In areas throughout the world, people have similar genetically controlled traits including skin color, height, and face shape. Have students determine why. Cultures of people were unable to travel great distances for thousands of years and therefore reproduced mainly among themselves, so genetic instructions for such traits remained within given cultures. L3 LS **Logical-Mathematical**

Active Reading

Flow Chart A flow chart helps students logically sequence events. Students will write major stages of the sequence in large ovals and write substages in smaller ovals under the larger ovals. Have students design a flow chart for a concept in this section. Sample flow chart:

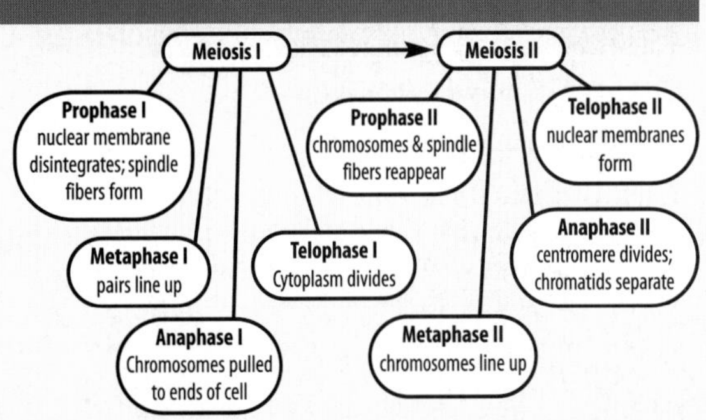

NATIONAL GEOGRAPHIC

Visualizing Polyploidy in Plants

Have students examine the pictures and read the captions. Then ask the following questions.

What kinds of mistakes in meiosis or mitosis could result in a polyploid plant? A mistake that caused chromosome sets not to separate, allowing more than one full set to be present in a cell after division to form sex cells.

What is the main advantage of bananas being triploid? Triploid plants have very small seeds, so people can eat bananas without removing seeds.

Why wouldn't you find triploid peanuts in the grocery store? The part of a peanut plant you eat is a seed, but triploid plants have little or no seeds.

Activity

Have students use pipe cleaners to model the chromosomes of one of the plants featured here. For example, a banana with 3 sets of 11 chromosomes, a strawberry with 8 sets of 7 chromosomes or a peanut with 4 sets of 10 chromosomes.

Extension

Have students research the meaning of the terms *allopolyploidy* and *autopolyploidy*. Have the students find and list some examples of plants that each term applies to.

NATIONAL GEOGRAPHIC **VISUALIZING POLYPLOIDY IN PLANTS**

Figure 12

You received a haploid (n) set of chromosomes from each of your parents, making you a diploid (2n) organism. In nature, however, many plants are polyploid—they have three (3n), four (4n), or more sets of chromosomes. We depend on some of these plants for food.

▲ TRIPLOID **Bright yellow bananas typically come from triploid (3n) banana plants. Plants with an odd number of chromosome sets usually cannot reproduce sexually and have very small seeds or none at all.**

▲ TETRAPLOID **Polyploidy occurs naturally in many plants—including peanuts and daylilies—due to mistakes in mitosis or meiosis.**

▼ HEXAPLOID **Modern cultivated strains of oats have six sets of chromosomes, making them hexaploid (6n) plants.**

▲ OCTAPLOID **Polyploid plants often are bigger than nonpolyploid plants and may have especially large leaves, flowers, or fruits. Strawberries are an example of octaploid (8n) plants.**

108

Resource Manager

Chapter Resources Booklet
Reinforcement, p. 26

Performance Assessment in the Science Classroom, p. 57

Visual Learning

Figure 13 Have students follow the unseparated chromosome pair through each stage of meiosis. **How did this error affect the sex cells?** Some had too many chromosomes; others not enough.

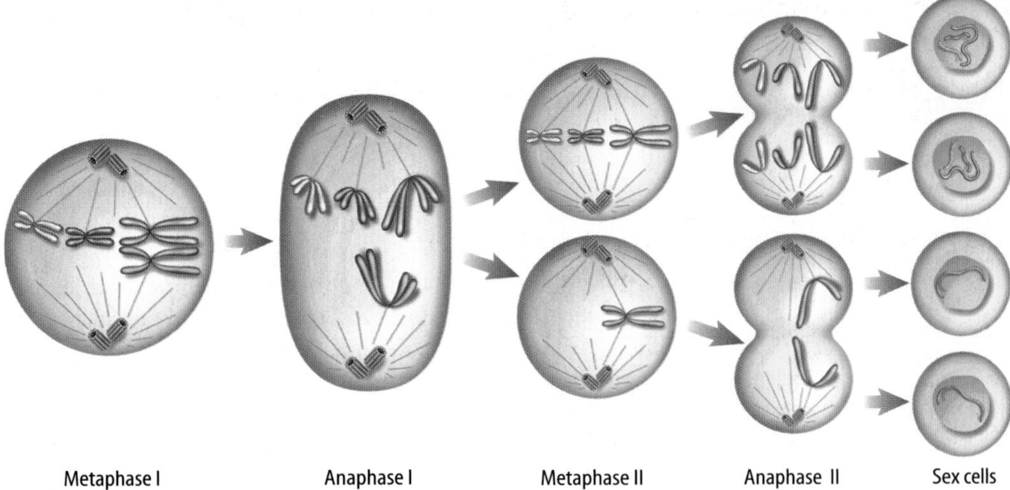

Mistakes in Meiosis Meiosis occurs many times in reproductive organs. Although mistakes in plants, as shown in **Figure 12,** are common, mistakes are less common in animals. These mistakes can produce sex cells with too many or too few chromosomes, as shown in **Figure 13.** Sometimes, zygotes produced from these sex cells die. If the zygote lives, every cell in the organism that grows from that zygote usually will have the wrong number of chromosomes. Organisms with the wrong number of chromosomes may not grow normally.

Figure 13
This diploid cell has four chromosomes. During anaphase I, one pair of duplicated chromosomes did not separate. *How many chromosomes does each sex cell usually have?*

Section  Assessment

1. Compare and contrast sexual and asexual reproduction.
2. What is a zygote, and how is it formed?
3. Give two examples of sex cells. Where are sex cells formed?
4. Compare what happens to chromosomes during anaphase I and anaphase II.
5. **Think Critically** Plants grown from runners and leaf cuttings have the same traits as the parent plant. Plants grown from seeds can vary from the parent plants in many ways. Suggest an explanation for why this can happen.

Skill Builder Activities

6. **Making and Using Tables** Make a table to compare mitosis and meiosis in humans. Vertical headings should include: *What Type of Cell (Body or Sex), Beginning Cell (Haploid or Diploid), Number of Cells Produced, End-Product Cell (Haploid or Diploid),* and *Number of Chromosomes in Cells Produced.* **For more help, refer to the Science Skill Handbook.**
7. **Communicating** Write a poem, song, or another memory device to help you remember the steps and outcome of meiosis. **For more help, refer to the Science Skill Handbook.**

Meiosis and Sex Cells, continued

Activity

Show students pictures of karyotypes with abnormal numbers of chromosomes and have them find the abnormalities. L2 ELL LS **Visual-Spatial**

Caption Answer

Figure 13 two

3 Assess

Reteach

Show the phases of meiosis out of sequence. Have students identify each phase and place the phases in order. L2 ELL LS **Visual-Spatial**

Challenge

How are the cells at the end of meiosis different from those at the beginning? The original cell is diploid, and each of the new cells is haploid.

Assessment

Content Write these chromosome numbers on the board: horse—66; pig—40; cat—38; potato—48; dog—78; corn—20. **How many chromosomes would be in a cell of each organism produced by mitosis and meiosis?** horse—66, 33; pig—40, 20; cat—38, 19; potato—48, 24; dog—78, 39; corn—20, 10 Use **PASC,** p. 101.

Answers to Section Assessment

1. Sexual reproduction: offspring is produced when sex cells combine; asexual reproduction: genetically identical offspring produced from one parent.
2. A zygote is the cell that forms when sperm fertilizes an egg.
3. sperm cells—form in male reproductive organs; egg cells—form in female reproductive organs
4. Anaphase I—duplicated chromosome pairs separate and move to opposite ends of the cell; anaphase II—chromatids separate and move to opposite ends of the cell.
5. Plants produced by asexual reproduction are the result of mitosis, which duplicates the genetic material of the parent. Plants grown from seeds have a combination of traits from their parents, because seeds are produced by sexual reproduction.
6. See table.
7. Allow students to share their memory devices with the class.

Feature	Mitosis	Meiosis
Type of cell	Body cell	Sex cell
Beginning cell	Diploid	Diploid
Number of cells produced	Two	Four
End-product	Diploid	Haploid
Number of chromosomes	Same as original cell	Half the original cell

SECTION

DNA

1 Motivate

Bellringer Transparency

Display the Section Focus Transparency for Section 3. Use the accompanying Transparency Activity Master. L2 ELL

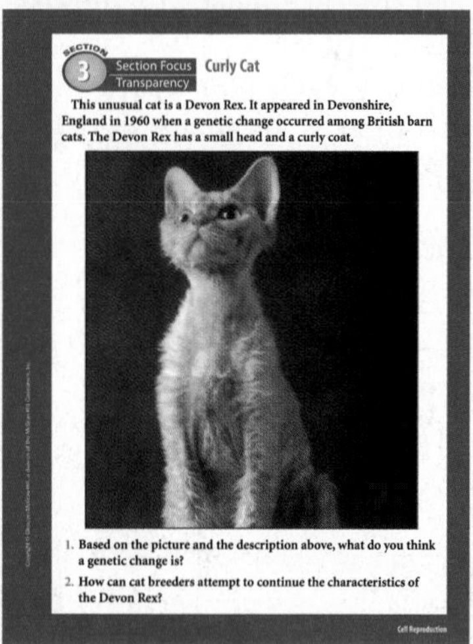

Section Focus Transparency 3 — Curly Cat

This unusual cat is a Devon Rex. It appeared in Devonshire, England in 1960 when a genetic change occurred among British barn cats. The Devon Rex has a small head and a curly coat.

1. Based on the picture and the description above, what do you think a genetic change is?
2. How can cat breeders attempt to continue the characteristics of the Devon Rex?

Cell Reproduction

Tie to Prior Knowledge

Students should be familiar with template systems, such as keys and locks and peg-and-hole games. Ask for other examples. Use this knowledge to explain that DNA in the nucleus serves as a template for RNA.

SECTION 3

DNA

As You Read

***What* You'll Learn**

- **Identify** the parts of a DNA molecule and its structure.
- **Explain** how DNA copies itself.
- **Describe** the structure and function of each kind of RNA.

Vocabulary

DNA	RNA
gene	mutation

***Why* It's Important**

DNA helps determine nearly everything your body is and does.

What is DNA?

Why was the alphabet one of the first things you learned when you started school? Letters are a code that you need to know before you learn to read. A cell also uses a code that is stored in its hereditary material. The code is a chemical called deoxyribonucleic (dee AHK sih ri boh noo klay ihk) acid, or **DNA.** It contains information for an organism's growth and function. **Figure 14** shows how DNA is stored in cells that have a nucleus. When a cell divides, the DNA code is copied and passed to the new cells. In this way, new cells receive the same coded information that was in the original cell. Every cell that has ever been formed in your body or in any other organism contains DNA.

Chemistry INTEGRATION

Discovering DNA Since the mid-1800s, scientists have known that the nuclei of cells contain large molecules called nucleic acids. By 1950, chemists had learned what the nucleic acid DNA was made of, but they didn't understand how the parts of DNA were arranged.

Figure 14
DNA is part of the chromosomes found in a cell's nucleus.

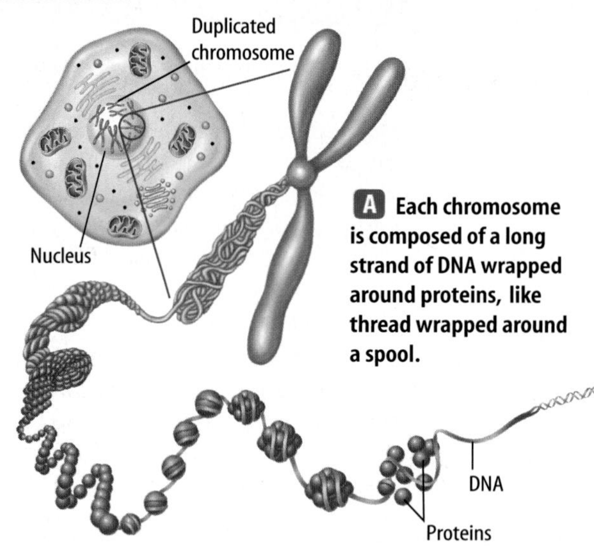

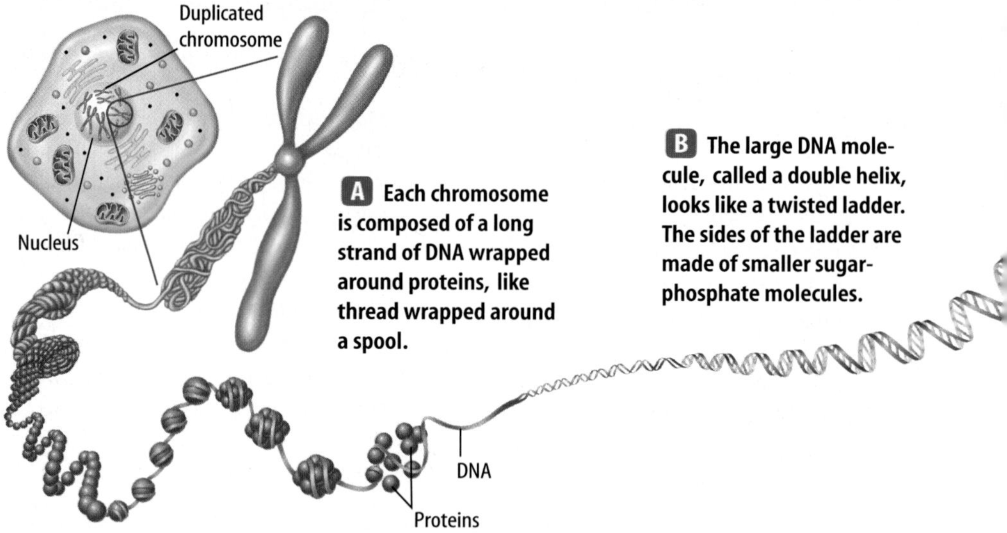

A **Each chromosome is composed of a long strand of DNA wrapped around proteins, like thread wrapped around a spool.**

B **The large DNA molecule, called a double helix, looks like a twisted ladder. The sides of the ladder are made of smaller sugar-phosphate molecules.**

Section Assessment Planner

PORTFOLIO
Extension, p. 113

PERFORMANCE ASSESSMENT
Try at Home MiniLAB, p. 111
Skill Builder Activities, p. 115
See page 122 for more options.

CONTENT ASSESSMENT
Section, p. 115
Challenge, p. 115
Chapter, pp. 122–123

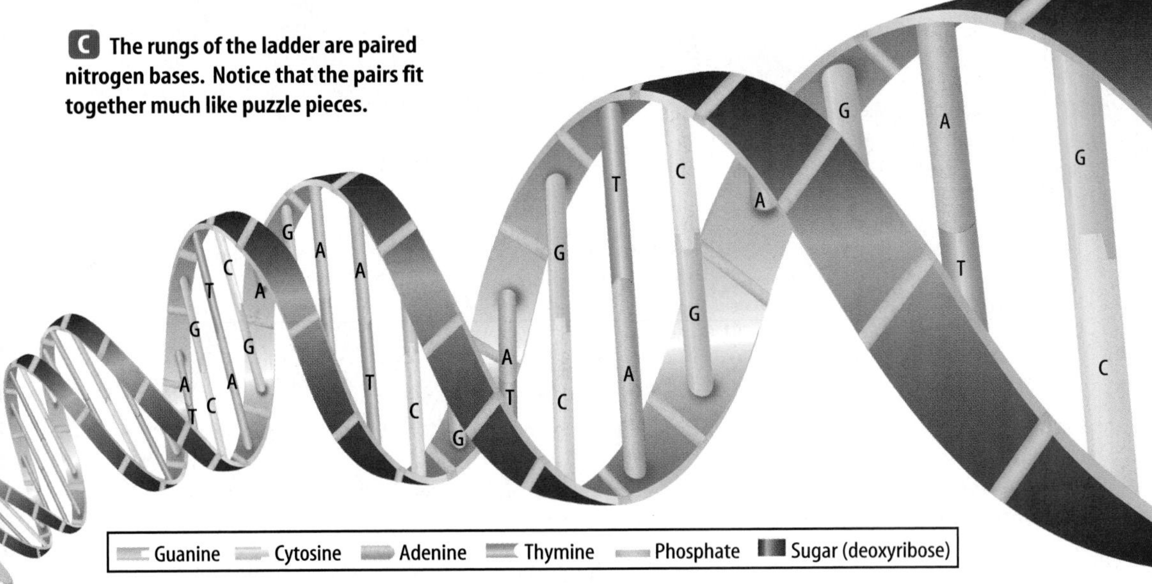

C The rungs of the ladder are paired nitrogen bases. Notice that the pairs fit together much like puzzle pieces.

DNA's Structure In 1952, scientist Rosalind Franklin discovered that DNA is two chains of molecules in a spiral form. By using an X-ray technique, Dr. Franklin showed that the large spiral was probably made up of two spirals. As it turned out, the structure of DNA is similar to a twisted ladder. In 1953, using the work of Franklin and others, scientists James Watson and Francis Crick made a model of a DNA molecule.

A DNA Model What does DNA look like? According to the Watson and Crick DNA model, each side of the ladder is made up of sugar-phosphate molecules. Each molecule consists of the sugar called deoxyribose (dee AHK sih ri bohs) and a phosphate group. The rungs of the ladder are made up of other molecules called nitrogen bases. Four kinds of nitrogen bases are found in DNA—adenine (AD un een), guanine (GWAHN een), cytosine (SITE uh seen), and thymine (THI meen). The bases are represented by the letters A, G, C, and T. The amount of cytosine in cells always equals the amount of guanine, and the amount of adenine always equals the amount of thymine. This led to the hypothesis that these bases occur as pairs in DNA. **Figure 14** shows that adenine always pairs with thymine, and guanine always pairs with cytosine. Like interlocking pieces of a puzzle, each base bonds only with its correct partner.

Reading Check *What are the nitrogen base pairs in a DNA molecule?*

Modeling DNA Replication

Procedure

1. Suppose you have a segment of DNA that is six nitrogen base pairs in length. On **paper**, using the letters A, T, C, and G, write a combination of six pairs remembering that A and T are always a pair and C and G are always a pair.
2. Duplicate your segment of DNA. On paper, diagram how this happens and show the new DNA segments.

Analysis

Compare the order of bases of the original DNA to the new DNA molecules.

2 Teach

What is DNA?

Purpose to model DNA replication L2 LS **Visual-Spatial**

Materials pencil and paper

Teaching Strategy Make sure students understand that they are to make up a sample strand of DNA, then make the complementary strand, then split the two strands and make those complementary strands, so they can see that the new strands are identical to the original.

Analysis

Answers will vary with the bases chosen, but bases should be in the same order as the original DNA.

Performance Draw and label one strand of DNA. Have students draw the complementary strand. Use **PASC,** p. 127.

Reading Check

Answer Adenine pairs with thymine, and guanine with cytosine.

Resource Manager

Chapter Resources Booklet

Transparency Activity, p. 44

MiniLAB, p. 4

Home and Community Involvement, p. 36

Inclusion Strategies

Learning Disabled Use unifix cubes to demonstrate the various bases. Have students make their own models of base pairs, using a different color for each base. L2 ELL LS **Kinesthetic**

What is DNA?
continued

Use an Analogy

Students are probably familiar with Morse code. Morse code uses only two symbols—the dot and the dash—in combinations to represent numbers and letters of the alphabet. DNA has four symbols. The order of nitrogen bases, rather than the sequence of dots and dashes, expresses the information needed for life processes.

Discussion

How can you predict the base sequence of a second strand of DNA? by knowing the base pairing rules and the sequence of the original DNA strand

Fun Fact

When students hear about the "code of life," they are hearing about the order of nitrogen bases in DNA.

Genes

Teacher FYI

An individual's complete set of genetic material is its genome. In early 2001, it was announced that a working draft of the human genome had been mapped. The knowledge gained from the project will be a basis for studying human diseases and accelerating biomedical research.

Text Question Answer

It could cause serious health problems.

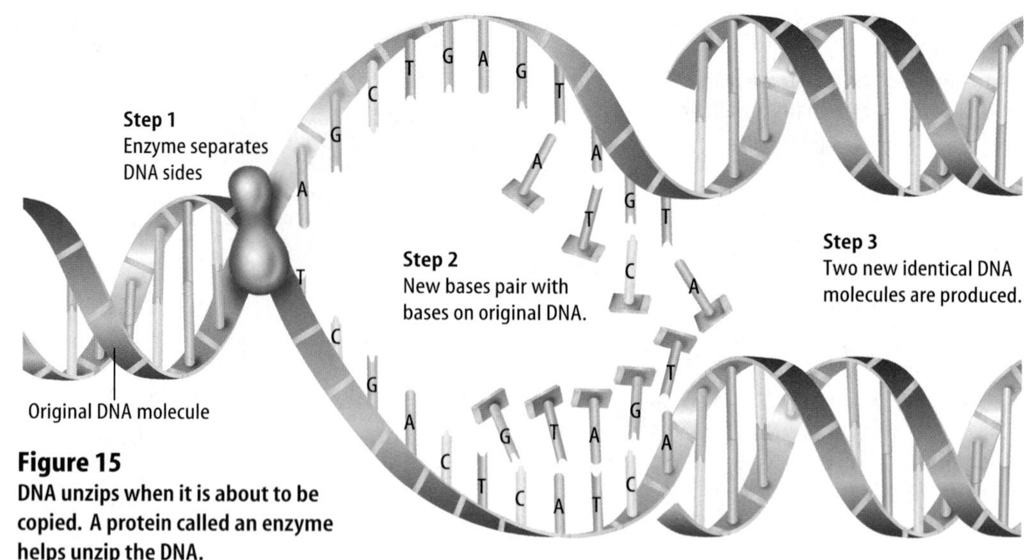

Figure 15
DNA unzips when it is about to be copied. A protein called an enzyme helps unzip the DNA.

Copying DNA When chromosomes are duplicated before mitosis or meiosis, the amount of DNA in the nucleus is doubled. The Watson and Crick model shows how this takes place. The two sides of DNA unwind and separate. Each side then becomes a pattern on which a new side forms, as shown in **Figure 15.** The new DNA has bases that are identical to those of the original DNA and are in the same order.

Genes

Most of your characteristics, such as the color of your hair, your height, and even how things taste to you, depend on the kinds of proteins your cells make. DNA in your cells stores the instructions for making these proteins.

Proteins build cells and tissues or work as enzymes. The instructions for making a specific protein are found in a **gene** which is a section of DNA on a chromosome. As shown in **Figure 16,** each chromosome contains hundreds of genes. Proteins are made of chains of hundreds or thousands of amino acids. The gene determines the order of amino acids in a protein. Changing the order of the amino acids makes a different protein. What might occur if an important protein couldn't be made or if the wrong protein was made in your cells?

Figure 16
This diagram shows just a few of the genes that have been identified on human chromosome 7. The bold print is the name that has been given to each gene.

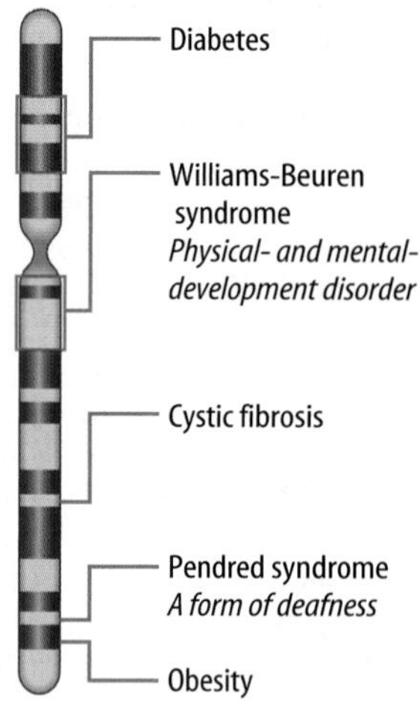

Making Proteins Genes are found in the nucleus, but proteins are made on ribosomes in cytoplasm. The codes for making proteins are carried from the nucleus to the ribosomes by another type of nucleic acid called ribonucleic acid, or **RNA.**

Science Journal

DNA as Evidence Have students research the use of DNA technology in law enforcement and write a report in their Science Journals. Have them use the Internet, news magazines, reference books, and interview forensic scientists. L2 LS **Linguistic**

Curriculum Connection

Math The DNA code is written in four "letters" and the cell "reads" the code in groups of three. Have students determine how many different ways the four "letters" (A, T, G, and C) can be arranged in groups of three. There are 64 possible combinations. L2 LS **Logical-Mathematical**

Ribonucleic Acid RNA is made in the nucleus on a DNA pattern. However, RNA is different from DNA. If DNA is like a ladder, RNA is like a ladder that has all its rungs sawed in half. Compare the DNA molecule in **Figure 14** to the RNA molecule in **Figure 17.** RNA has the bases A, G, and C like DNA but has the base uracil (U) instead of thymine (T). The sugar-phosphate molecules in RNA contain the sugar ribose, not deoxyribose.

The three main kinds of RNA made from DNA in a cell's nucleus are messenger RNA (mRNA), ribosomal RNA (rRNA), and transfer RNA (tRNA). Protein production begins when mRNA moves into the cytoplasm. There, ribosomes attach to it. Ribosomes are made of rRNA. Transfer RNA molecules in the cytoplasm bring amino acids to these ribosomes. Inside the ribosomes, three nitrogen bases on the mRNA temporarily match with three nitrogen bases on the tRNA. The same thing happens for the mRNA and another tRNA molecule, as shown in **Figure 17.** The amino acids that are attached to the two tRNA molecules bond. This is the beginning of a protein. The code carried on the mRNA directs the order in which the amino acids bond. After a tRNA molecule has lost its amino acid, it can move about the cytoplasm and pick up another amino acid just like the first one. The ribosome moves along the mRNA. New tRNA molecules with amino acids match up and add amino acids to the protein molecule.

SCIENCE Online

Data Update The Human Genome Project was begun in 1990. One of its goals is to identify all of the genes on human chromosomes. To find out how the project is progressing, visit the Glencoe Science Web site at **science.glencoe.com.** Communicate to your class what you learn.

Figure 17
Cells need DNA, RNA, and amino acids to make proteins.

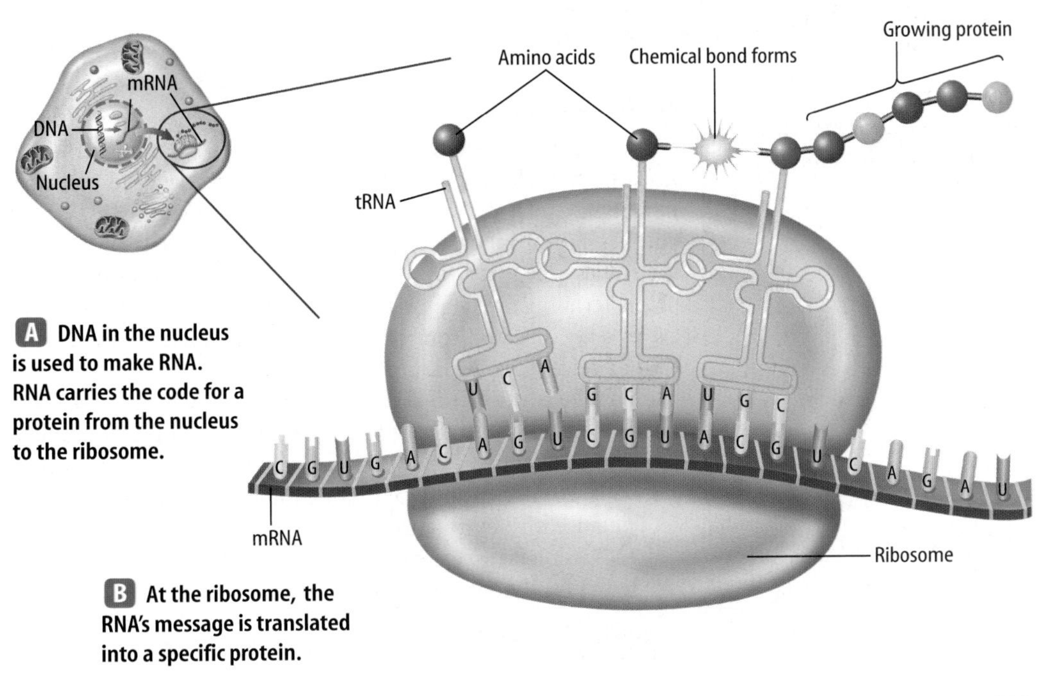

A **DNA in the nucleus is used to make RNA. RNA carries the code for a protein from the nucleus to the ribosome.**

B **At the ribosome, the RNA's message is translated into a specific protein.**

SCIENCE Online
Internet Addresses
Explore the Glencoe Science Web site at science.glencoe.com to find out more about topics in this section.

Make a Model

Have students draw a cell on poster board and make a model demonstrating protein synthesis using materials such as craft sticks, beads, yarn, and so on. L2 LS **Visual-Spatial**

Activity

On the board or an overhead transparency, write the sequence for one strand of DNA. Have students copy the sequence and write the corresponding sequence for mRNA and tRNA. L2 LS **Visual-Spatial**

Extension

Have students choose one of the following DNA pioneers for a written report: Francis Crick, James Watson, Barbara McClintock, Maurice Wilkins, Martha Chase, A.D. Hershey, Rosalind Franklin. L2 LS **Linguistic** P

Visual Learning

Figure 17 Have students make an events chain concept map to outline the stages of protein synthesis. L2 LS **Visual-Spatial**

Resource Manager

Chapter Resources Booklet

Enrichment, p. 30

Directed Reading for Content Mastery, pp. 19, 20

Cultural Diversity, p. 19

Curriculum Connection

History Have students study the history of DNA research. Then using poster board, students should draw and label a timeline showing the events of DNA research since DNA was first removed from a cell nucleus in 1869. L2 LS **Visual-Spatial and Kinesthetic**

Mutations

Teacher FYI

Any agent that can cause a change in DNA is a mutagen. Mutagens can be radiation, chemicals, or even high temperatures. Asbestos, cyanide, and formaldehyde are highly reactive compounds found in buildings and the environment that can interact with DNA and cause changes.

IDENTIFYING

Misconceptions

Students may think that any mutation that might occur during duplication is harmful. More often than not, mutations have no effect on the characteristics of the organism. Some mutations, in fact, are adaptive, providing the organism with traits that make it better suited to its environment; these mutations play a major role in evolution. An example of a beneficial mutation in bacteria is antibiotic resistance.

Reading Check

Answer when DNA is being copied

Cells in the iris of the eye produce proteins needed for eye color.
Muscle cells produce proteins that help make muscles move.
Cells in the stomach produce proteins necessary to digest food.

Figure 18
Each cell in the body produces only the proteins that are necessary to do its job.

Controlling Genes You might think that because most cells in an organism have exactly the same chromosomes and the same genes, they would make the same proteins, but they don't. In many-celled organisms like you, each cell uses only some of the thousands of genes that it has to make proteins. Just as each actor uses only the lines from the script for his or her role, each cell uses only the genes that direct the making of proteins that it needs. For example, muscle proteins are made in muscle cells, as represented in **Figure 18,** but not in nerve cells.

Cells must be able to control genes by turning some genes off and turning other genes on. They do this in many different ways. Sometimes the DNA is twisted so tightly that no RNA can be made. Other times, chemicals bind to the DNA so that it cannot be used. If the incorrect proteins are produced, the organism cannot function properly.

Mutations

Sometimes mistakes happen when DNA is being copied. Imagine that the copy of the script the director gave you was missing three pages. You use your copy to learn your lines. When you begin rehearsing for the play, everyone is ready for one of the scenes except for you. What happened? You check your copy of the script against the original and find that three of the pages are missing. Because your script is different from the others, you cannot perform your part correctly.

If DNA is not copied exactly, the proteins made from the instructions might not be made correctly. These mistakes, called **mutations,** are any permanent change in the DNA sequence of a gene or chromosome of a cell. Some mutations include cells that receive an entire extra chromosome or are missing a chromosome. Outside factors such as X rays, sunlight, and some chemicals have been known to cause mutations.

Reading Check ***When are mutations likely to occur?***

Science Journal

Effects of Mutation Have students research and write a report on mutations. Have them give examples of mutations, indicate whether the mutation is harmful, benign, or beneficial, and include the cause of the mutation. L2 LS **Linguistic**

Resource Manager

Chapter Resources Booklet
Reinforcement, p. 27
Lab Activity, pp. 11–13

Reading and Writing Skill Activities, p. 51

Figure 19
Because of a defect on chromosome 2, the mutant fruit fly has short wings and cannot fly. *Could this defect be transferred to the mutant's offspring? Explain.*

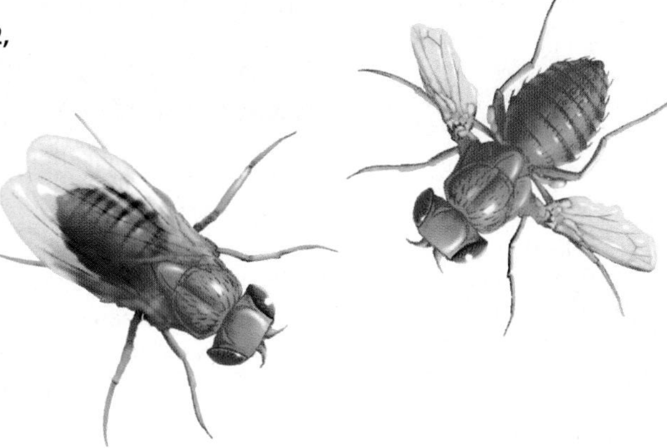

Results of a Mutation Genes control the traits you inherit. Without correctly coded proteins, an organism can't grow, repair, or maintain itself. A change in a gene or chromosome can change the traits of an organism, as illustrated in **Figure 19.**

If the mutation occurs in a body cell, it might or might not be life threatening to the organism. However, if a mutation occurs in a sex cell, then all the cells that are formed from that sex cell will have that mutation. Mutations add variety to a species when the organism reproduces. Many mutations are harmful to organisms, often causing their death. Some mutations do not appear to have any effect on the organism, and some can even be beneficial. For example, a mutation to a plant might cause it to produce a chemical that certain insects avoid. If these insects normally eat the plant, the mutation will help the plant survive.

SCIENCE Online

Research Visit the Glencoe Science Web site at **science.glencoe.com** for more information about what genes are present on the chromosomes of a fruit fly. Make a poster that shows one of the chromosomes and some of the genes found on that chromosome.

Section 3 Assessment

1. How does DNA make a copy of itself?
2. How are the codes for proteins carried from the nucleus to the ribosomes?
3. A single strand of DNA has the bases AGTAAC. Using letters, show a matching DNA strand from this pattern.
4. How is tRNA used when cells build proteins?
5. **Think Critically** You begin as one cell. Compare the DNA in one of your brain cells to the DNA in one of your heart cells.

Skill Builder Activities

6. **Concept Mapping** Using a network tree concept map, show how DNA and RNA are alike and how they are different. **For more help, refer to the** Science Skill Handbook.
7. **Using a Word Processor** Use a word processor to make an outline of the events that led up to the discovery of DNA. Use library resources to find this information. **For more help, refer to the** Technology Skill Handbook.

Answers to Section Assessment

1. The two sides unwind and separate; a complementary strand is formed for each, and the resulting double-stranded DNA has one original strand and one new strand.
2. The codes are carried by mRNA from the nucleus to the ribosome.
3. TCATTG
4. The tRNA in the cytoplasm brings amino acids to the ribosomes. There, three nitrogen bases on the mRNA template match with three bases on the tRNA. The amino acids bond, and protein synthesis begins.
5. The DNA is identical.
6. Answers should be similar to the table for question 16 in the Chapter Assessment.
7. Students should be sure to include the contributions of Miescher, Griffith, Avery, Hershey, Chase, Chargraff, Wilkins, Franklin, Crick, and Watson.

Caption Answer

Figure 19 yes, if it affects reproductive cells

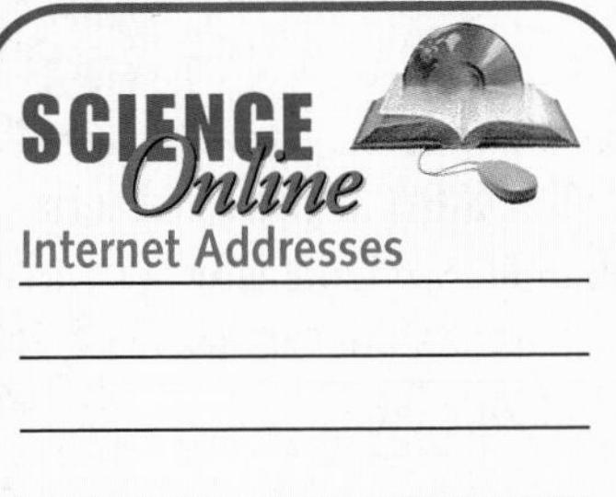

SCIENCE Online
Internet Addresses

Explore the Glencoe Science Web site at **science.glencoe.com** to find out more about topics in this section.

3 Assess

Reteach

Have students make a drawing of DNA replication and protein synthesis. L2 **Visual-Spatial**

Challenge

Why does the mutation of a sperm or egg cell have a potential for different results from that of a body cell? A mutation in a reproductive cell will affect offspring. A mutation in a body cell will affect only the individual.

Assessment

Oral What are the three kinds of RNA and their functions? Messenger RNA, transfer RNA, and ribosomal RNA; mRNA is copied from DNA and moves from the nucleus to a ribosome; tRNA carries amino acids to ribosomes; rRNA makes up ribosomes. Use **Performance Assessment in the Science Classroom,** p. 89.

Activity BENCH TESTED

Recognize the Problem

Internet Students will use Internet sites that can be accessed through the Glencoe Science Web site. They will observe genetic traits and mutations in animals.

Non-Internet Sources Collect books describing animals and their genetic traits.

Time Required

about three days

Preparation

Internet Access the Glencoe Science Web site to run through the steps that students will follow.

Non-Internet Have students use books to select an animal and one of its traits to investigate.

Form a Hypothesis

Possible Hypotheses

Most students will select a phenotype to hypothesize about. For example, a tiger's white fur is a mutation that can become a common trait.

Activity Use the Internet

Mutations

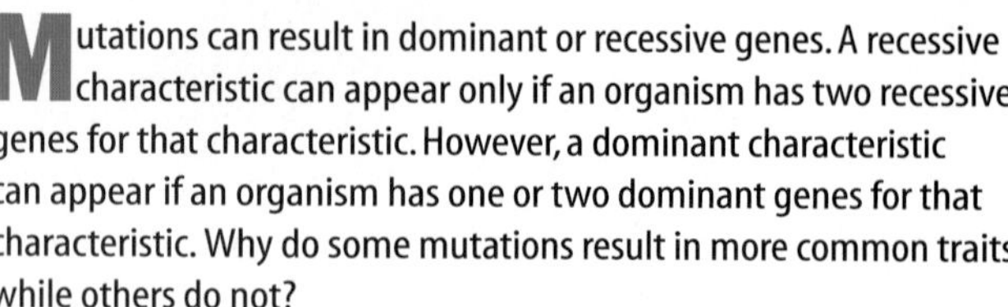

Mutations can result in dominant or recessive genes. A recessive characteristic can appear only if an organism has two recessive genes for that characteristic. However, a dominant characteristic can appear if an organism has one or two dominant genes for that characteristic. Why do some mutations result in more common traits while others do not?

Fantail Pigeon

Recognize the Problem

How can a mutation become a common trait?

Form a Hypothesis

Form a hypothesis about how a mutation can become a common trait.

Goals

- **Observe** traits of various animals.
- **Research** how mutations become traits.
- Gather data about mutations.
- Make a frequency table of your findings and communicate them to other students.

Data Source

SCIENCE*Online* Go to the Glencoe Science Web site at **science.glencoe.com** for more information on common genetic traits in different animals, recessive and dominant genes, and data from other students.

White tiger

Resource Manager

Chapter Resources Booklet
Activity Worksheet, pp. 7–8

Lab Management and Safety, p. 58

SCIENCE Online

Internet Addresses

Explore the Glencoe Science Web site at **science.glencoe.com** to find out more about topics in this activity.

Test Your Hypothesis

Plan

1. **Observe** common traits in various animals, such as household pets or animals you might see in a zoo.
2. **Learn** what genes carry these traits in each animal.
3. **Research** the traits to discover which ones are results of mutations. Are all mutations dominant? Are any of these mutations beneficial?

Do

1. Make sure your teacher approves your plan before you start.
2. Visit the Glencoe Science Web site for links to different sites about mutations and genetics.
3. **Decide** if a mutation is beneficial, harmful, or neither. Record your data in your Science Journal.

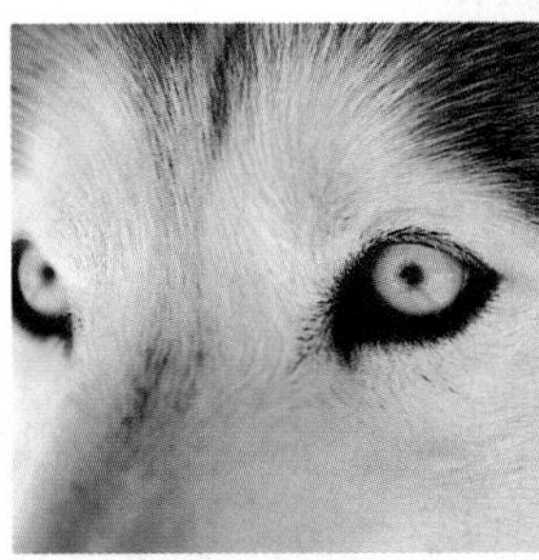

Siberian Husky's eyes

Analyze Your Data

1. **Record** in your Science Journal a list of traits that are results of mutations.
2. **Describe** an animal, such as a pet or an animal you've seen in the zoo. Point out which traits are known to be the result of a mutation.
3. Make a chart that compares recessive mutations to dominant mutations. Which are more common?
4. Share your data with other students by posting it on the Glencoe Science Web site.

Draw Conclusions

1. **Compare** your findings to those of your classmates and other data on the Glencoe Science Web site. What were some of the traits your classmates found that you did not? Which were the most common?
2. Look at your chart of mutations. Are all mutations beneficial? When might a mutation be harmful to an organism?
3. How would your data be affected if you had performed this activity when one of these common mutations first appeared? Do you think you would see more or less animals with this trait?
4. Mutations occur every day but we only see a few of them. Infer how many mutations over millions of years can lead to a new species.

Communicating Your Data

Find this *Use the Internet* activity on the Glencoe Science Web site at **science.glencoe.com. Post** your data in the table provided. Combine your data with that of other students and make a chart that shows all of the data.

Test Your Hypothesis

Teaching Strategy

Have students use animal population data to see how often that mutation is found.

Analyze Your Data

1. Answers will vary. Color can result from a mutation.
2. Answers will depend upon animals chosen.
3. Answers will vary, but dominant genes are not necessarily more common.
4. Students may need help posting data.

Draw Conclusions

1. Answers will vary. Remind students that the most common traits may be the result of mutations.
2. Answers will vary. Have students think about the mutation they are investigating and how helpful or harmful it is to the animal.
3. If you had investigated the mutation when it first appeared, you may have seen fewer animals with the trait. With the passage of time, you can determine if the mutation is beneficial.
4. Organisms with mutations may be better suited to a particular environment. These traits would be passed on to their offspring. Many mutations may lead to a new species.

Communicating Your Data

Have students use the Internet to collect pictures of the animal they are investigating. Have them find pictures that show the mutation.

Assessment

Oral Students describe mutations they researched and discuss how helpful they are to animals. Show pictures of animals with the mutation. Use **Performance Assessment in the Science Classroom,** p. 143.

Oops!

Oops! Accidents in SCIENCE

SOMETIMES GREAT DISCOVERIES HAPPEN BY ACCIDENT!

Content Background

Cytogenetics is the branch of science that studies heredity both through genetics and studies of the cell. In 1956, modern human cytogenetics began, thanks to the discovery of the number of human chromosomes present in each cell of the body. As early as 1905, scientists had determined that chromosomes are found in pairs, and in 1915, Thomas Hunt Morgan discovered that genes were found on chromosomes. It was not until 1952 that Dr. Hsu's work occurred, and 1953 when Watson and Crick used Rosalind Franklin's work to determine the structure of DNA. Studies of human chromosomes and genes have progressed at an astounding rate since that time. Scientists have determined the particular chromosome that carries the gene for many human diseases and other traits.

Discussion

Explain what type of mistake the lab technician in Dr. Hsu's lab might have made while mixing the solution that caused mysterious behavior of the chromosomes. Possible answer: The technician either added too little of the solute to a set amount of water, or too much water to a set amount of solute, causing the solution to have a higher water content than the cells.

A Tangled

How did a scientist get chromosomes to separate?

Thanks to chromosomes, each of us is unique!

118

Resources for Teachers and Students

"*Genetics and Genetic Engineering,*" by Lisa Yount, Facts on File, Inc., 1997.

The Big Idea, by Paul Strathern. New York: Doubleday, 1999.

The History of Genetics, by Robert Snedden. New York: Raintree Steck-Vaughn Publishers, 1995.

Viewed under a microscope, chromosomes in cells sometimes look a lot like tangled spaghetti. That's why during the early 1900s, scientists had such a hard time figuring out how many chromosomes are in each human cell.

Tale

Imagine then, how Dr. Tao-Chiuh Hsu (dow shew•SEW) must have felt when he looked into a microscope and saw "beautifully scattered chromosomes." The problem was, Hsu didn't know what he had done to separate the chromosomes into countable strands.

"I tried to study those slides and set up some more cultures to repeat the miracle," Hsu explained. "But nothing happened."

For three months, Hsu toiled in the lab, changing every variable he could think of to make the chromosomes separate again.

In April 1952, he reduced the amount of salt and increased the amount of water in the solution used to prepare the cells for study, and his efforts were finally rewarded. Hsu quickly realized that the chromosomes separated because of osmosis.

Osmosis is the movement of water molecules through cell membranes. This movement occurs in predictable ways. The water molecules move from areas with higher concentrations of water to areas with lower concentrations of water. In Hsu's case, the solution had a higher concentration of water than the cell did. So water moved from the solution into the cell and the cell swelled until it finally exploded. The chromosomes suddenly were visible as separate strands.

What made the cells swell the first time? Apparently, a lab technician had mixed the solution incorrectly. "Since nearly four months had elapsed, there was no way to trace who actually had prepared that particular [solution]," Hsu noted. "Therefore, this heroine must remain anonymous."

The Real Count

Although Hsu's view of the chromosomes was fairly clear, he mistakenly estimated the number of chromosomes in a human cell. He put the count at 48, which was the number that most scientists of the day accepted. By 1956, however, other scientists improved upon Hsu's techniques and concluded that there are 46 chromosomes in a human cell. Because chromosomes contain the genes that determine each person's characteristics, this discovery helped scientists better understand genetic diseases and disorders. Scientists also have a better idea of why every person, including you, is unique.

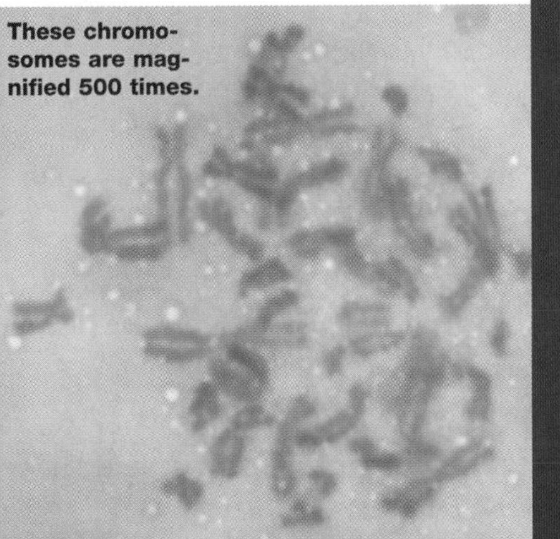
These chromosomes are magnified 500 times.

CONNECTIONS Research Until the 1950s, scientists believed that there were 48 chromosomes in a human cell. Research the developments that led scientists to the conclusion that the human cell has 46 chromosomes. Use the Glencoe Science Web site to get started.

SCIENCE Online
For more information, visit science.glencoe.com

Activity

Have students work in teams to research the major discoveries in the field of genetics. Have each team display their results on a timeline made on a long piece of paper. Students should be encouraged to include discoveries from early research until present times, and to include the names of the scientists who made the discoveries.

Analyze the Event

Ask the students to brainstorm what other positive or negative effects a mistake in making a lab solution could have. Possible answers: In some cases a mistake could result in better than expected results or a discovery that would not have otherwise been made. Negative results could include work that can't be repeated, the need to re-do the entire experiment, skewed results, or potential fire or poisoning hazards. Point out to students that because Dr. Hsu's results were due to a mistake it took him months to find the cause of the good results. In general, mistakes of this type in the lab bring only negative outcomes.

CONNECTIONS As students research the history of research on human chromosomes, have them consider the rate at which discoveries occurred then and now. Point out that the Human Genome Project has increased the knowledge of genetics at an amazing rate.

SCIENCE Online

Internet Addresses

____

____

____

Explore the Glencoe Science Web site at **science.glencoe.com** to find out more about topics in this feature.

Chapter 4 Study Guide

Reviewing Main Ideas

Preview

Students can answer the questions in their Science Journals. Discuss the answers as you go through the chapter. LS **Linguistic**

Review

Students can write their answers, then compare them with those of other students. LS **Interpersonal**

Reteach

Students can look at the illustrations and describe details that support the main ideas of the chapter. LS **Visual-Spatial**

Answers to Chapter Review

Section 1

4. Cell division produces new bone cells to replace damaged ones.

Section 2

4. 26

Section 3

4. It has a mutation that affects its number of wings.

Chapter  Study Guide

Reviewing Main Ideas

Section 1 Cell Division and Mitosis

1. The life cycle of a cell has two parts—growth and development and cell division. Cell division includes mitosis and the division of the cytoplasm.
2. In mitosis, the nucleus divides to form two identical nuclei. Mitosis occurs in four continuous steps, or phases—prophase, metaphase, anaphase, and telophase.
3. Cell division in animal cells and plant cells is similar, but plant cells do not have centrioles and animal cells do not form cell walls.
4. Organisms use cell division to grow, to replace cells, and for asexual reproduction. Asexual reproduction produces organisms with DNA identical to the parent's DNA. Fission, budding, and regeneration can be used for asexual reproduction. *How would cell division help heal this broken bone?*

Section 2 Sexual Reproduction and Meiosis

1. Sexual reproduction results when a male sex cell enters the female sex cell. This event is called fertilization, and the cell that forms is called the zygote.
2. Before fertilization, meiosis occurs in the reproductive organs, producing four haploid sex cells from one diploid cell.
3. During meiosis, two divisions of the nucleus occur.
4. Meiosis ensures that offspring produced by fertilization have the same number of chromosomes as their parents. *If the diploid number of a frog is 26, how many chromosomes does this tadpole have?*

Section 3 DNA

1. DNA—the genetic material of all organisms—is a large molecule made up of two twisted strands of sugar-phosphate molecules and nitrogen bases.
2. All cells contain DNA. The section of DNA on a chromosome that directs the making of a specific protein is a gene.
3. DNA can copy itself and is the pattern from which RNA is made. Messenger RNA, ribosomal RNA, and transfer RNA are used to make proteins.
4. Sometimes changes in DNA occur. Permanent changes in DNA are called mutations. *Why does this fruit fly have four wings instead of the normal two?*

FOLDABLES Reading & Study Skills — **After You Read**

To help you review cell reproduction, use the Organizational Study Fold about the cell you made at the beginning of the chapter.

FOLDABLES Reading & Study Skills — **After You Read**

After students have read the chapter and completed the Foldable described in Before You Read, have them do the activity on the student page.

Dinah Zike

Chapter 4 Study Guide

Visualizing Main Ideas

Think of four ways that organisms can use mitosis and fill out the spider diagram below.

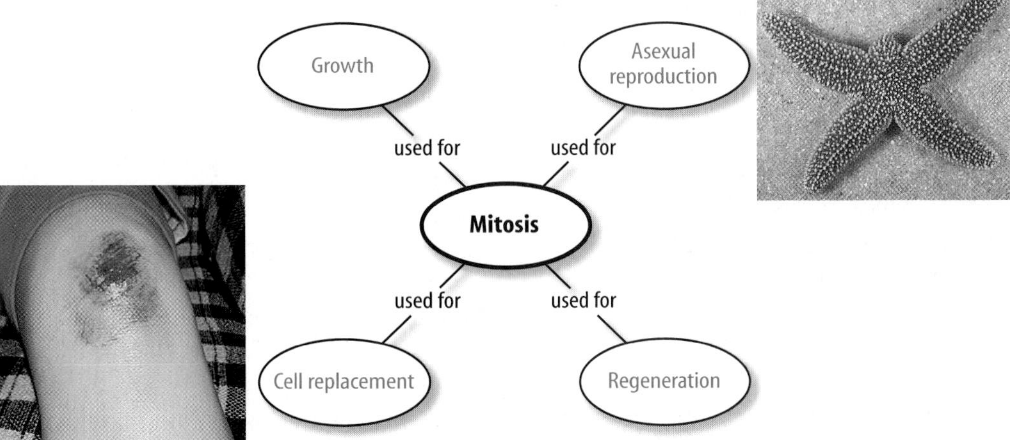

Vocabulary Review

Vocabulary Words

a. asexual reproduction
b. chromosome
c. diploid
d. DNA
e. egg
f. fertilization
g. gene
h. haploid
i. meiosis
j. mitosis
k. mutation
l. RNA
m. sexual reproduction
n. sperm
o. zygote

THE PRINCETON REVIEW Study Tip

Be a teacher—organize a group of friends and instruct each person to review a section of the chapter for the group. Teaching helps you remember and understand information thoroughly.

Using Vocabulary

Replace each underlined word in the following statements with the correct vocabulary word.

1. <u>Muscle</u> and <u>skin</u> cells are sex cells.
2. <u>Digestion</u> produces two identical cells.
3. An example of a nucleic acid is <u>sugar</u>.
4. A <u>cell</u> is the code for a protein.
5. A <u>diploid</u> sperm is formed during meiosis.
6. Budding is a type of <u>meiosis</u>.
7. A <u>ribosome</u> is a structure in the nucleus that contains hereditary material.
8. <u>Respiration</u> produces four sex cells.
9. As a result of <u>fission</u>, a new organism develops that has its own unique identity.
10. An error made during the copying of DNA is called a <u>protein</u>.

Chapter 4 Study Guide

Visualizing Main Ideas

See student page.

Vocabulary Review

Using Vocabulary

1. Egg, sperm
2. Mitosis
3. DNA or RNA
4. gene
5. haploid
6. asexual reproduction
7. chromosome
8. Meiosis
9. Fertilization, meiosis, or sexual reproduction
10. mutation

Chapter 4 Assessment

Checking Concepts

1. D
2. D
3. B
4. C
5. A
6. A
7. D
8. D
9. C
10. B

Thinking Critically

11. TAGGCAG
12. UAGGCAG
13. No; in order for a mutation to be passed to offspring, the mutation must take place in a sex cell.
14. the copying of chromosomes in interphase; the separation of the copies at anaphase; the separation of two new cells at telophase
15. This could happen if nondisjunction (failure of like chromosomes or chromatids to separate) occurs during anaphase I or II.

Chapter 4 Assessment

Checking Concepts

Choose the word or phrase that best answers the question.

1. Which of the following is a double spiral molecule with pairs of nitrogen bases?
   A) RNA **C)** protein
   B) amino acid **D)** DNA
2. What is in RNA but NOT in DNA?
   A) thymine **C)** adenine
   B) thyroid **D)** uracil
3. If a diploid tomato cell has 24 chromosomes, how many chromosomes will the tomato's sex cells have?
   A) 6 **C)** 24
   B) 12 **D)** 48
4. During a cell's life cycle, when do chromosomes duplicate?
   A) anaphase **C)** interphase
   B) metaphase **D)** telophase
5. When do chromatids separate during mitosis?
   A) anaphase **C)** metaphase
   B) prophase **D)** telophase
6. How many chromosomes are in the original cell compared to those in the new cells formed by cell division?
   A) the same amount **C)** twice as many
   B) half as many **D)** four times as many
7. What can budding, fission, and regeneration be used for?
   A) mutations
   B) sexual reproduction
   C) cell cycles
   D) asexual reproduction
8. What is any permanent change in a gene or a chromosome called?
   A) fission **C)** replication
   B) reproduction **D)** mutation
9. What does meiosis produce?
   A) cells with the diploid chromosome number
   B) cells with identical chromosomes
   C) sex cells
   D) a zygote
10. What type of nucleic acid carries the codes for making proteins from the nucleus to the ribosome?
    A) DNA **C)** protein
    B) RNA **D)** genes

Thinking Critically

11. If the sequence of bases on one side of DNA is ATCCGTC, what is the sequence on its other side?
12. A strand of RNA made using the DNA pattern ATCCGTC would have what base sequence? Look at **Figure 14** for a hint.
13. Will a mutation in a human skin cell be passed on to the person's offspring? Explain.
14. What occurs in mitosis that gives the new cells identical DNA?
15. How could a zygote end up with an extra chromosome?

Developing Skills

16. **Classifying** Copy and complete this table about DNA and RNA.

DNA and RNA

	DNA	RNA
Number of Strands	2	1
Type of Sugar	deoxyribose	ribose
Letter Names of Bases	G, A, C, T	G, A, C, U
Where Found	nucleus	nucleus & cytoplasm

Chapter Assessment Planner

Portfolio Encourage students to place in their portfolios one or two items of what they consider to be their best work. Examples include:

- Visual Learning, p. 97
- Make a Model, p. 107
- Extension, p. 113

Performance Additional performance assessments, Performance Task Assessment Lists, and rubrics for evaluating these activities can be found in Glencoe's **Performance Assessment in the Science Classroom.**

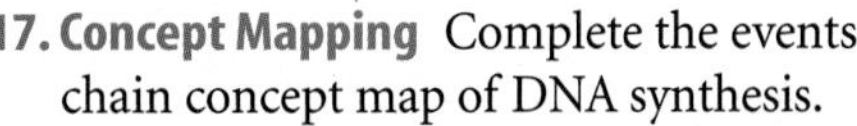

17. Concept Mapping Complete the events chain concept map of DNA synthesis.

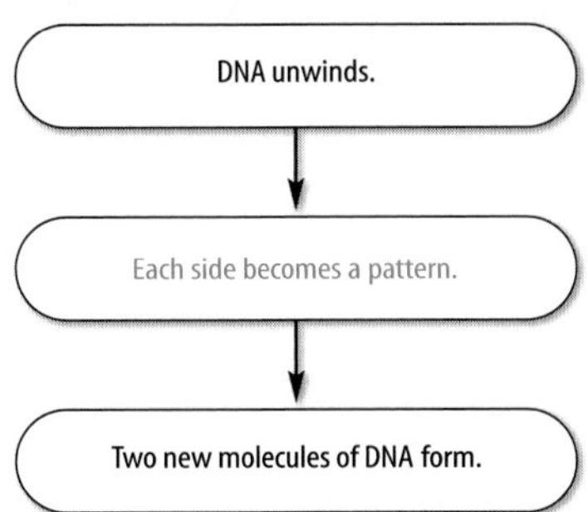
DNA unwinds.
Each side becomes a pattern.
Two new molecules of DNA form.

18. Comparing and Contrasting Meiosis is two divisions of a reproductive cell's nucleus. It occurs in a continuous series of steps. Compare and contrast the steps of meiosis I to the steps of meiosis II.

19. Forming Hypotheses Make a hypothesis about the effect of an incorrect mitotic division on the new cells produced.

20. Concept Mapping Make an events chain concept map of what occurs from interphase in the parent cell to the formation of the zygote. Tell whether the chromosome's number at each stage is haploid or diploid.

Performance Assessment

21. Flash Cards Make a set of 11 flash cards with drawings of a cell that show the different stages of meiosis. Shuffle your cards and then put them in the correct order. Give them to another student in the class to try.

Technology

Go to the Glencoe Science Web site at **science.glencoe.com** or use the **Glencoe Science CD-ROM** for additional chapter assessment.

Test Practice

A scientist studied the reproduction of human skin cells. The scientist examined several skin cells using a microscope. The table below summarizes what she learned.

Skin Cells

Cell	Phase of Division	Characteristic
1	Anaphase	Chromosome separation
2	Telophase	Cytoplasm division
3	Prophase	Visible chromosomes
4	Metaphase	Chromosomes line up

Use the information in the table to answer the following questions.

1. What process is taking place in all of the cells?
   A) cell division
   B) fertilization
   C) cytoplasm division
   D) chromosome separation

2. Which is the correct order of the stages, from first to last, in the cell division of a skin cell?
   F) 3, 4, 1, 2
   G) 1, 3, 2, 4
   H) 1, 2, 4, 3
   J) 2, 1, 3, 4

3. Since the process described in the table produces two new identical cells, before it begins the chromosomes in the cell must _____ .
   A) divide in half
   B) find a mate
   C) duplicate
   D) disintegrate

Chapter 4 Assessment

Test Practice

The Test-Taking Tip was written by The Princeton Review, the nation's leader in test preparation.

1. A
2. F
3. C

Developing Skills

16. See student page.
17. See student page.
18. Student answers should reflect the information in Section 2 and **Figure 11.**
19. Incorrect division can result in an incorrect number of chromosomes, often leading to abnormal offspring.
20. The order of events given for meiosis should reflect **Figure 11** and formation of the zygote, **Figure 10.** The cell at the beginning of meiosis is diploid. The four cells at the end of meiosis are all haploid.

Performance Assessment

21. Cards should be sequenced as shown in **Figure 11.** If interphase is included, it should come before prophase I. Use **Performance Assessment in the Science Classroom**, p. 163.

Assessment Resources

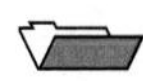

Reproducible Masters

Chapter Resources Booklet
Chapter Review, pp. 35–36
Chapter Tests, pp. 37–40
Assessment Transparency Activity, p. 47

Glencoe Science Web site
Interactive Tutor
Chapter Quizzes

Glencoe Technology
Assessment Transparency
Interactive CD-ROM Chapter Quizzes
ExamView Pro Test Bank
Vocabulary PuzzleMaker Software
MindJogger Videoquiz

CHAPTER 5 HEREDITY

Section/Objectives	Standards		Activities/Features
	National	State/Local	
Chapter Opener	See p. 5T for a Key to Standards.		**Explore Activity:** Observe dimples on faces, p. 125 **Before You Read,** p. 125
Section 1 Genetics 2 sessions 1 block 1. **Explain** how traits are inherited. 2. **Identify** Mendel's role in the history of genetics. 3. **Use** a Punnett square to predict the results of crosses. 4. **Compare and contrast** the difference between an individual's genotype and phenotype.	National Content Standards: UCP2, A1, C2, G3		**Science Online,** p. 127 **MiniLAB:** Comparing Common Traits, p. 128 **Visualizing Mendel's Experiments,** p. 129 **Math Skills Activity:** Calculating Probability Using a Punnett Square, p. 131 **Activity:** Predicting Results, p. 133
Section 2 Genetics Since Mendel 2 sessions 1 block 1. **Explain** how traits are inherited by incomplete dominance. 2. **Compare** multiple alleles and polygenic inheritance, and give examples of each. 3. **Describe** two human genetic disorders and how they are inherited. 4. **Explain** how sex-linked traits are passed to offspring.	National Content Standards: UCP2, A1, C2, F1		**Science Online,** p. 135 **MiniLAB:** Interpreting Polygenic Inheritance, p. 136 **Chemistry Integration,** p. 138
Section 3 Advances in Genetics 3 sessions 1.5 blocks 1. **Evaluate** the importance of advances in genetics. 2. **Sequence** the steps in making genetically engineered organisms.	National Content Standards: UCP2, A1, C2, E1, E2, F5, G1		**Environmental Science Integration,** p. 142 **Activity:** Tests for Color Blindness, p. 144 **Science Stats:** The Human Genome, p. 146

Activity Materials	Reproducible Resources	Section Assessment	Technology
Explore Activity: Science Journal	**Chapter Resources Booklet** Foldables Worksheets, p. 13 Directed Reading Overview, p. 15 Note-taking Worksheets, pp. 29–31	GLENCOE'S ASSESSMENT ADVANTAGE	
MiniLAB: paper and pencil **Activity:** 2 paper bags, 100 red beans, 100 white beans	**Chapter Resources Booklet** Transparency Activity, p. 40 MiniLAB, p. 3 Directed Reading, p. 16 Enrichment, p. 26 Reinforcement, p. 23 Activity Worksheet, pp. 5–6 Lab Activity, pp. 9–10, 11–12 **Mathematics Skill Activities,** p. 23 **Home and Community Involvement,** p. 36 **Performance Assessment in the Science Classroom,** p. 57	**Portfolio** Extension, p. 130 **Performance** MiniLAB, p. 128 Math Skills Activity, p. 131 Skill Builder Activities, p. 132 **Content** Section Assessment, p. 132	Section Focus Transparency Interactive CD-ROM Guided Reading Audio Program
MiniLAB: paper, pencil, ruler *Need materials?* Contact Science Kit at 1-800-828-7777 or www.sciencekit.com on the Internet.	**Chapter Resources Booklet** Transparency Activity, p. 41 MiniLAB, p. 4 Enrichment, p. 27 Reinforcement, p. 24 Directed Reading, p. 16 Transparency Activity, pp. 43–44 **Life Science Critical Thinking/ Problem Solving,** p. 19	**Portfolio** Science Journal, p. 135 **Performance** MiniLAB, p. 136 Skill Builder Activities, p. 140 **Content** Section Assessment, p. 140	Section Focus Transparency Teaching Transparency Interactive CD-ROM Guided Reading Audio Program
Activity: white paper or poster board, colored markers	**Chapter Resources Booklet** Transparency Activity, p. 42 Enrichment, p. 28 Reinforcement, p. 25 Directed Reading, pp. 17, 18 Activity Worksheet, pp. 7–8 **Lab Management and Safety,** p. 74	**Portfolio** Assessment, p. 143 **Performance** Skill Builder Activities, p. 143 **Content** Section Assessment, p. 143	Section Focus Transparency Interactive CD-ROM Guided Reading Audio Program

End of Chapter Assessment

GLENCOE'S ASSESSMENT ADVANTAGE

Blackline Masters	Technology	Professional Series
Chapter Resources Booklet Chapter Review, pp. 33–34 Chapter Tests, pp. 35–38 **Standardized Test Practice by The Princeton Review,** pp. 27–30	MindJogger Videoquiz Interactive CD-ROM Vocabulary PuzzleMakers ExamView Pro Test Bank Interactive Lesson Planner Interactive Teacher Edition	Performance Assessment in the Science Classroom (PASC)

Transparencies

Section Focus

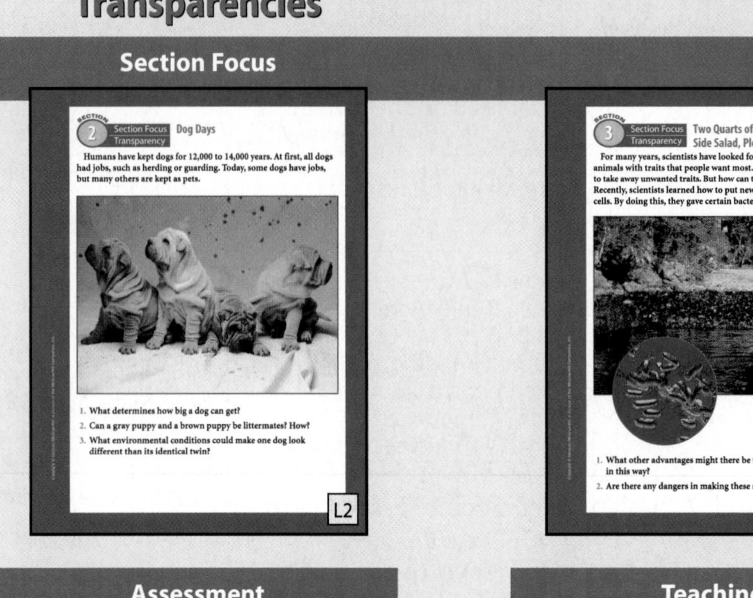

This is a representation of key blackline masters available in the Teacher Classroom Resources. See Resource Manager boxes within the chapter for additional information.

Assessment

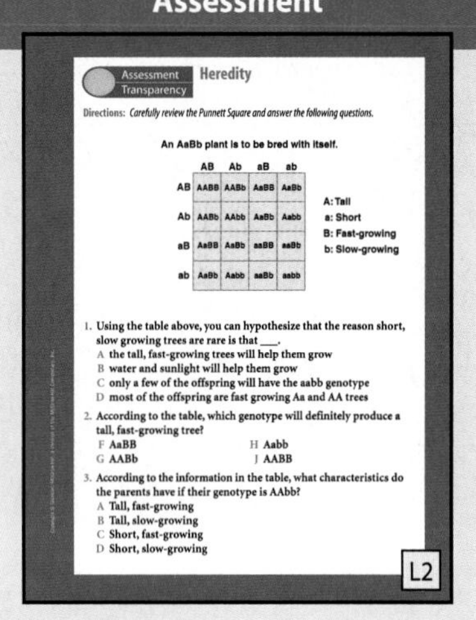

Teaching

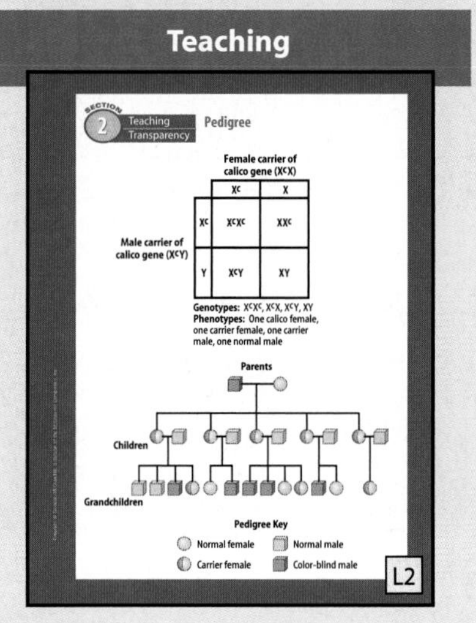

Key to Teaching Strategies

The following designations will help you decide which activities are appropriate for your students.

- L1 Level 1 activities should be appropriate for students with learning difficulties.
- L2 Level 2 activities should be within the ability range of all students.
- L3 Level 3 activities are designed for above-average students.
- ELL ELL activities should be within the ability range of English Language Learners.
- COOP LEARN Cooperative Learning activities are designed for small group work.
- LS Multiple Learning Styles logos, as described on page 22T, are used throughout to indicate strategies that address different learning styles.
- P These strategies represent student products that can be placed into a best-work portfolio.

Hands-on Activities

Activity Worksheets

Laboratory Activities

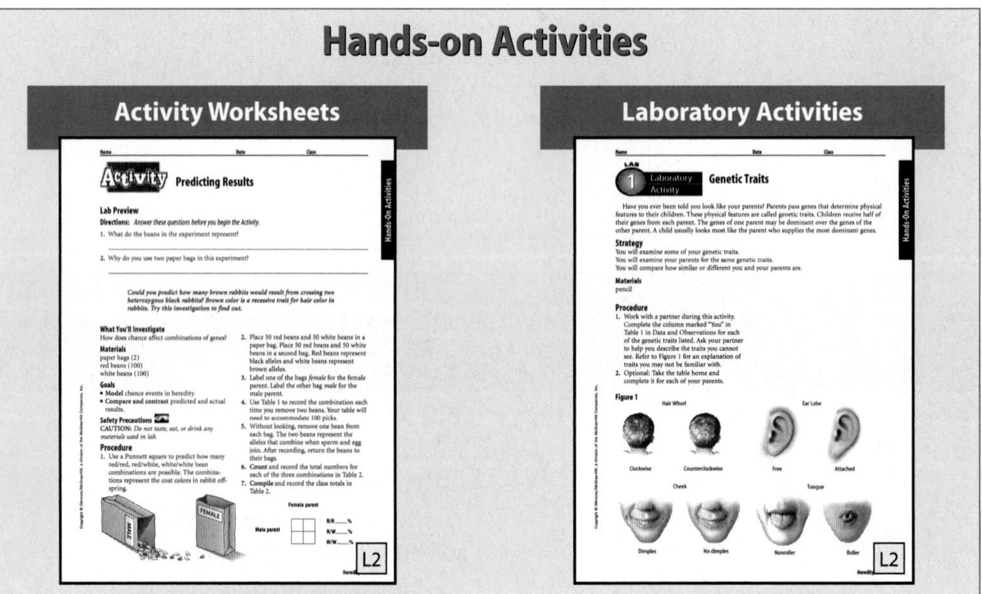

Meeting Different Ability Levels

Content Outline

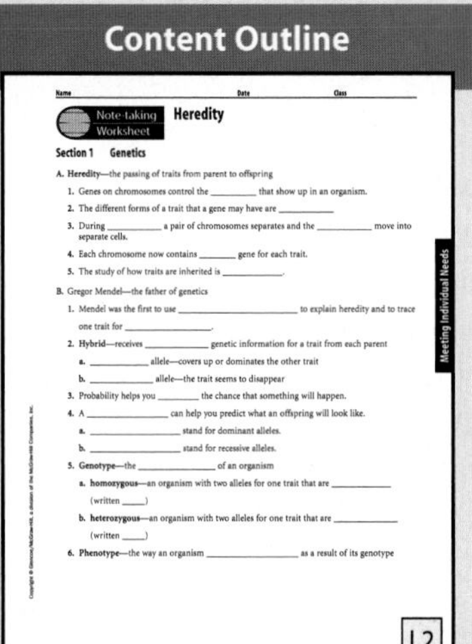

Name Date Class

Note-taking Worksheet **Heredity**

Section 1 Genetics

A. Heredity—the passing of traits from parent to offspring

1. Genes on chromosomes control the ________ that show up in an organism.
2. The different forms of a trait that a gene may have are ________.
3. During ________, a pair of chromosomes separates and the ________ move into separate cells.
4. Each chromosome now contains ________ gene for each trait.
5. The study of how traits are inherited is ________.

B. Gregor Mendel—the father of genetics

1. Mendel was the first to use ________ to explain heredity and to trace one trait for ________.
2. Hybrid—receives ________ genetic information for a trait from each parent
   a. ________ allele—covers up or dominates the other trait
   b. ________ allele—the trait seems to disappear
3. Probability helps you ________ the chance that something will happen.
4. A ________ can help you predict what an offspring will look like.
   a. ________ stand for dominant alleles.
   b. ________ stand for recessive alleles.
5. Genotype—the ________ of an organism
   a. homozygous—an organism with two alleles for one trait that are ________ (written ____)
   b. heterozygous—an organism with two alleles for one trait that are ________ (written ____)
6. Phenotype—the way an organism ________ as a result of its genotype

Meeting Individual Needs

L2

Reinforcement

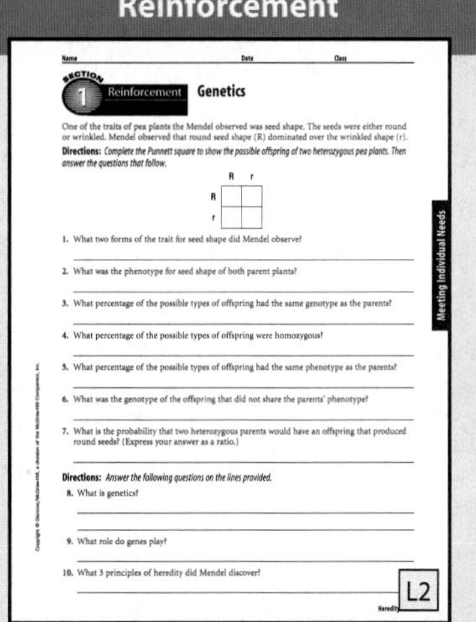

Name Date Class

Section 1 Reinforcement **Genetics**

One of the traits of pea plants the Mendel observed was seed shape. The seeds were either round or wrinkled. Mendel observed that round seed shape (R) dominated over the wrinkled shape (r).

Directions: Complete the Punnett square to show the possible offspring of two heterozygous pea plants. Then answer the questions that follow.

1. What two forms of the trait for seed shape did Mendel observe?
2. What was the phenotype for seed shape of both parent plants?
3. What percentage of the possible types of offspring had the same genotype as the parents?
4. What percentage of the possible types of offspring were homozygous?
5. What percentage of the possible types of offspring had the same phenotype as the parents?
6. What was the genotype of the offspring that did not share the parents' phenotype?
7. What is the probability that two heterozygous parents would have an offspring that produced round seeds? (Express your answer as a ratio.)

Directions: Answer the following questions on the lines provided.

8. What is genetics?
9. What role do genes play?
10. What 3 principles of heredity did Mendel discover?

Meeting Individual Needs

L2

Directed Reading

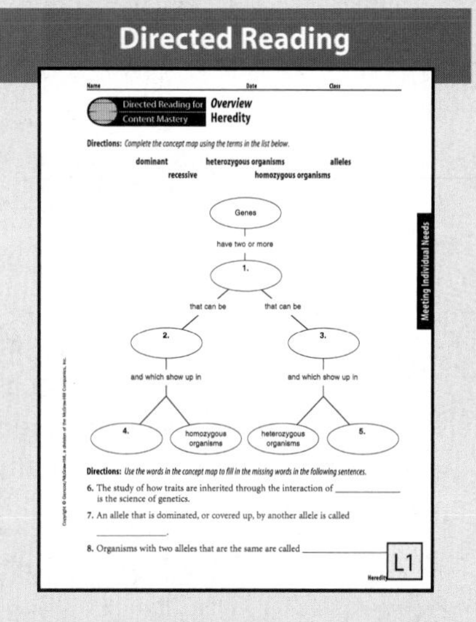

Name Date Class

Directed Reading for Content Mastery *Overview* **Heredity**

Directions: Complete the concept map using the terms in the list below.

dominant heterozygous organisms alleles recessive homozygous organisms

Genes — have two or more — 1. — that can be — that can be — 2. — 3. — and which show up in — and which show up in — 4. — homozygous organisms — heterozygous organisms — 5.

Directions: Use the words in the concept map to fill in the missing words in the following sentences.

6. The study of how traits are inherited through the interaction of ________ is the science of genetics.
7. An allele that is dominated, or covered up, by another allele is called ________.
8. Organisms with two alleles that are the same are called ________.

Meeting Individual Needs

L1

Assessment

Chapter Tests

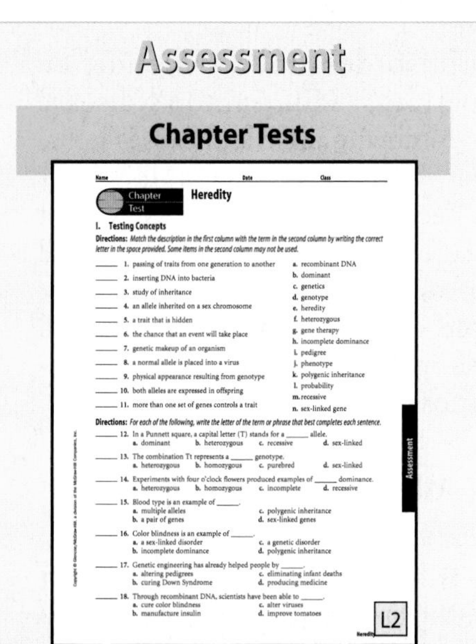

Name Date Class

Chapter Test **Heredity**

I. Testing Concepts

Directions: Match the description in the first column with the term in the second column by writing the correct letter in the space provided. Some items in the second column may not be used.

____ 1. passing of traits from one generation to another	a. recombinant DNA
____ 2. inserting DNA into bacteria	b. dominant
____ 3. study of inheritance	c. genetics
____ 4. an allele inherited on a sex chromosome	d. genotype
____ 5. a trait that is hidden	e. heredity
____ 6. the chance that an event will take place	f. heterozygous
____ 7. genetic makeup of an organism	g. gene therapy
____ 8. a normal allele is placed into a virus	h. incomplete dominance
____ 9. physical appearance resulting from genotype	i. pedigree
____ 10. both alleles are expressed in offspring	j. phenotype
____ 11. more than one set of genes controls a trait	k. polygenic inheritance
	l. probability
	m. recessive
	n. sex-linked gene

Directions: For each of the following, write the letter of the term or phrase that best completes each sentence.

____ 12. In a Punnett square, a capital letter (T) stands for a ____ allele. a. dominant b. heterozygous c. recessive d. sex-linked

____ 13. The combination Tt represents a ____ genotype. a. heterozygous b. homozygous c. purebred d. sex-linked

____ 14. Experiments with four o'clock flowers produced examples of ____ dominance. a. heterozygous b. homozygous c. incomplete d. recessive

____ 15. Blood type is an example of ____. a. multiple alleles b. a pair of genes c. polygenic inheritance d. sex-linked genes

____ 16. Color blindness is an example of ____. a. a sex-linked disorder b. incomplete dominance c. a genetic disorder d. polygenic inheritance

____ 17. Genetic engineering has already helped people by ____. a. altering pedigrees b. curing Down Syndrome c. eliminating infant deaths d. producing medicine

____ 18. Through recombinant DNA, scientists have been able to ____. a. cure color blindness b. manufacture insulin c. alter viruses d. improve tomatoes

Assessment

L2

Enrichment

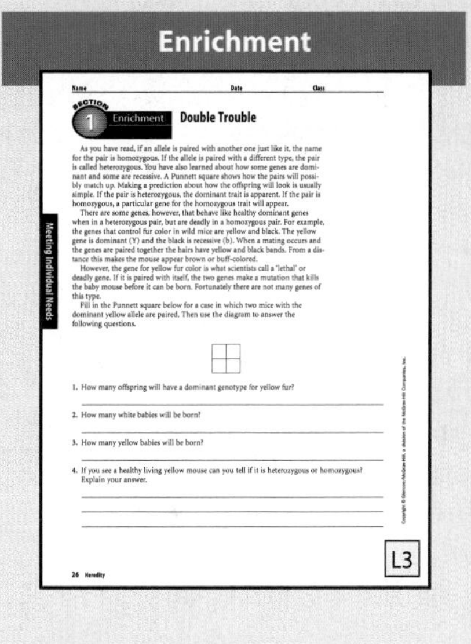

Name Date Class

Section 1 Enrichment **Double Trouble**

As you have read, if an allele is paired with another one just like it, the name for the pair is homozygous. If the allele is paired with a different type, the pair is called heterozygous. You have also learned about how some genes are dominant and some are recessive. A Punnett square shows how the pairs will possibly match up. Making a prediction about how the offspring will look is usually simple. If the pair is heterozygous, the dominant trait is apparent. If the pair is homozygous, a particular gene for the homozygous trait will appear.

There are some genes, however, that behave like healthy dominant genes when in a heterozygous pair, but are deadly in a homozygous pair. For example, the genes that control fur color in wild mice are yellow and black. The yellow gene is dominant (Y) and the black is recessive (b). When a mating occurs and the genes are paired together the hairs have yellow and black bands. From a distance this makes the mouse appear brown or buff-colored.

However, the gene for yellow fur color is what scientists call a "lethal" or deadly gene. If it is paired with itself, the two genes make a mutation that kills the baby mouse before it can be born. Fortunately there are not many genes of this type.

Fill in the Punnett square below for a case in which two mice with the dominant yellow allele are paired. Then use the diagram to answer the following questions.

1. How many offspring will have a dominant genotype for yellow fur?
2. How many white babies will be born?
3. How many yellow babies will be born?
4. If you see a healthy living yellow mouse can you tell if it is heterozygous or homozygous? Explain your answer.

26 Heredity

Meeting Individual Needs

L3

Spanish Directed Reading

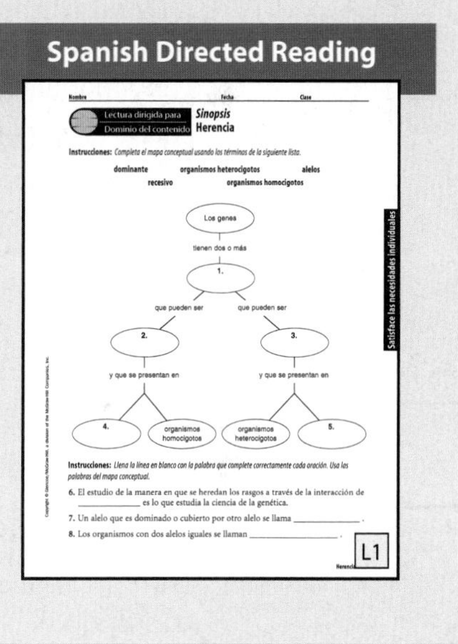

Nombre Fecha Clase

Lectura dirigida para Dominio del contenido *Sinopsis* **Herencia**

Instrucciones: Completa el mapa conceptual usando los términos de la siguiente lista.

dominante organismos heterocigotos alelos recesivo organismos homocigotos

Los genes — tienen dos o más — 1. — que pueden ser — que pueden ser — 2. — 3. — y que se presentan en — y que se presentan en — 4. — organismos homocigotos — organismos heterocigotos — 5.

Instrucciones: Llena la línea en blanco con la palabra que complete correctamente cada oración. Usa las palabras del mapa conceptual.

6. El estudio de la manera en que se heredan los rasgos a través de la interacción de ________ es lo que estudia la ciencia de la genética.
7. Un alelo que es dominado o cubierto por otro alelo se llama ________.
8. Los organismos con dos alelos iguales se llaman ________.

Satisface las necesidades individuales

L1

Test Practice Workbook

L2

Chapter Review

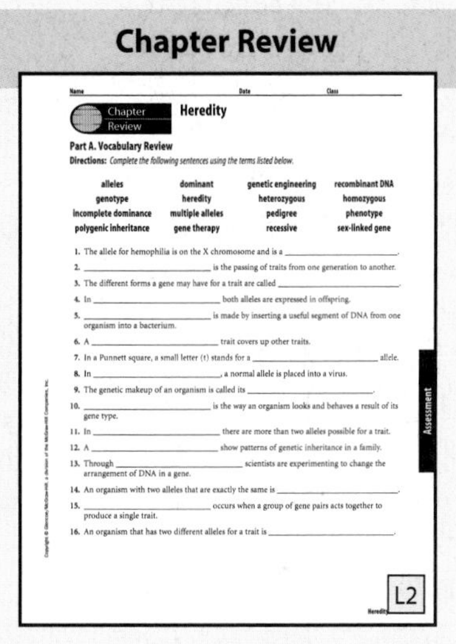

Name Date Class

Chapter Review **Heredity**

Part A. Vocabulary Review

Directions: Complete the following sentences using the terms listed below.

alleles	dominant	genetic engineering	recombinant DNA
genotype	heredity	heterozygous	homozygous
incomplete dominance	multiple alleles	pedigree	phenotype
polygenic inheritance	gene therapy	recessive	sex-linked gene

1. The allele for hemophilia is on the X chromosome and is a ________.
2. ________ is the passing of traits from one generation to another.
3. The different forms a gene may have for a trait are called ________.
4. In ________ both alleles are expressed in offspring.
5. ________ is made by inserting a useful segment of DNA from one organism into a bacterium.
6. A ________ trait covers up other traits.
7. In a Punnett square, a small letter (t) stands for a ________ allele.
8. In ________, a normal allele is placed into a virus.
9. The genetic makeup of an organism is called its ________.
10. ________ is the way an organism looks and behaves a result of its gene type.
11. In ________ there are more than two alleles possible for a trait.
12. A ________ show patterns of genetic inheritance in a family.
13. Through ________ scientists are experimenting to change the arrangement of DNA in a gene.
14. An organism with two alleles that are exactly the same is ________.
15. ________ occurs when a group of gene pairs acts together to produce a single trait.
16. An organism that has two different alleles for a trait is ________.

Assessment

L2

Science Content Background

SECTION 1

The Father of Genetics

Mendelian Inheritance

Gregor Mendel, an Austrian monk, was the first scientist to bring an experimental and quantitative approach to genetics, the study of heredity. Mendelian inheritance reflects the mathematical rules of probability.

Student Misconception

Dominant traits are those that occur most frequently, or those that will "take over" in a population.

Refer to the facing page for teaching strategies to address this misconception. Refer to pages 128–130 for content related to this topic.

Dominant and Recessive Factors

In Mendel's experiments, the inheritance patterns of traits each possessed two alleles. The law of dominance explains that one trait, the dominant trait, is expressed in homozygous and heterozygous conditions. The recessive trait is expressed only in the homozygous condition.

Using a Punnett Square

Mendel developed the law of segregation, which shows that recessive alleles are not lost during meiosis. In Mendel's experiments with pea hybridization, the recessive trait reappeared in approximately one-fourth of the offspring produced by crossing two heterozygous pea plants.

SECTION 2

Genetics Since Mendel

Other Modes of Inheritance

In incomplete dominance, the heterozygous condition results in an intermediate phenotype that appears to be a blend of the dominant and recessive traits. However, when heterozygous offspring are crossed, the next generation expresses the dominant, recessive and intermediate phenotypes. In codominance, the heterozygous condition results in a phenotype that is a mixture of both dominant alleles. Sometimes there are multiple alleles for a trait, though each individual only carries two. Polygenic inheritance occurs when a trait is produced as a result of a group of genes. Mutations and chromosome disorders are caused by changes in genes such as an error made during DNA replication.

Genetic Disorders

Many human disorders follow Mendelian inheritance patterns. Huntington's disease is carried on a dominant allele and causes lethal degeneration of the nervous system. Tay-Sachs is caused by a recessive allele and occurs most often in people of Jewish descent. Sickle-cell anemia is a recessive disorder that occurs most often in people of African descent. The red blood cells are malformed and cannot effectively transport oxygen.

SECTION 3

Advances in Genetics

Benefits of Genetic Research

Advances made in the search for the molecular basis of inheritance are phenomenal. Technology is providing new tools to aid in research, genetic testing and genetic counseling. Genetic engineering provides improved plants and efficient production of artificial chemicals such as insulin.

For additional content background on this topic, go to the Glencoe Science Web site at science.glencoe.com.

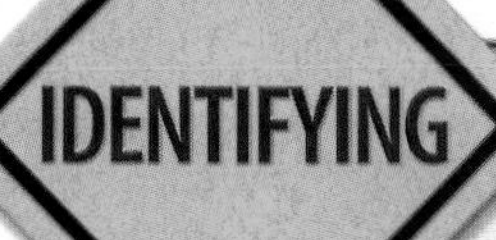

IDENTIFYING Misconceptions

Find Out What Students Think

Students may think that . . .

- **Dominant traits are the strongest, most superior, or most common traits in a population.**

Genes coding for eye color in humans comes in two alleles. The dominant allele causes brown pigment to be produced in the iris, and the recessive allele does not produce a functional protein or pigment. Each person receives two alleles of each gene, one from each parent. If a person inherits at least one "brown" allele, the person's eyes will produce pigment. If a person has only recessive alleles, no pigment is made and the eyes appear blue. Human eye color is actually somewhat more complex than this, as it is controlled by several genes (not a single pair) as opposed to simple Mendelian inheritance. The greater the number of dominant alleles a person has, the darker the eyes appear.

Discussion

Ask the class, "If brown eyes are dominant over blue eyes, does this mean that someday all people will be brown-eyed?" Let students form small discussion groups. After a set time limit, let students present their answers and supporting evidence. Their answers will reveal their preconceived notions and their reasoning.

Promote Understanding

Activity

Group students in pairs, and give each pair an envelope containing five brown and five blue squares.

- Have each student draw one brown and one blue square. These squares represent the eye color alleles of an imaginary person. Ask what color of eyes the person has (brown).
- Tell students that their two imaginary people will have a child, so each must contribute one allele. Students should randomly draw a square from the envelope. Have students lay their contributed squares side by side and determine the eye color of the child.
- Count the number of blue-eyed and brown-eyed offspring produced in the class. Ask students why some of the brown-eyed parents had a child with blue eyes.
- Poll the class to see how many students have a widow's peak hairline (dominant) versus a straight hairline (recessive), and how many have a dimple in the chin (dominant) versus no dimple in the chin (recessive). These two traits have dominant forms that are usually infrequent in a population.

Assess

After completing the chapter, see *Identifying Misconceptions* in the Study Guide.

Heredity

Chapter Vocabulary

heredity, p. 126
alleles, p. 126
genetics, p. 126
hybrid, p. 128
dominant, p. 128
recessive, p. 128
Punnett square, p. 130
genotype, p. 130
phenotype, p. 130
homozygous, p. 130
heterozygous, p. 130
incomplete dominance, p. 134
polygenic inheritance, p. 136
sex-linked gene, p. 139
genetic engineering, p. 141

What do you think?

Science Journal The cells in the picture are a human sperm and egg at the time of fertilization. The union of these cells determines a child's genetic make-up.

CHAPTER 5

Heredity

Wherever you go, look around you. You don't have the same skin color, the same kind of hair, or the same height as everyone else. Why do you resemble some people but do not look like others at all? In this chapter, you'll find out how differences are determined, and you will learn how to predict when certain traits might appear. You also will learn what causes some hereditary disorders.

What do you think?

Science Journal Look at the picture below with a classmate. Discuss what you think this might be or what is happening. Here's a hint: *The secret to why you look the way you do is found in this picture.* Write your answer or best guess in your Science Journal.

124

Theme Connection

Stability and Change Genes control stability through homeostasis at the organism level. Genetics provides background for understanding the changes involved in evolution.

You and your best friend enjoy the same sports, like the same food, and even have similar haircuts. But, there are noticeable differences between your appearances. Most of these differences are controlled by the genes you inherited from your parents. In the following activity, you will observe one of these differences.

Observe dimples on faces

1. Notice the two students in the photographs. One student has dimples when she smiles, and the other student doesn't have dimples.
2. Ask your classmates to smile naturally. In your Science Journal, record the name of each classmate and whether each one has dimples.

Observe

In your Science Journal, calculate the percentage of students who have dimples. Are facial dimples a common feature among your classmates?

Before You Read

FOLDABLES Reading & Study Skills

Making a Classify Study Fold As you read this chapter about heredity, you can use the following Foldable to help you classify characteristics. When you classify, you organize objects or events into groups based on their common features.

Personal Characteristics | Inherited | Not Inherited
eyes
hair
dimples

1. Place a sheet of paper in front of you so the short side is at the top. Fold both sides in to divide the paper into thirds. Unfold the paper so three columns show.
2. Fold the paper in half from top to bottom. Then fold it in half again two more times. Unfold all the folds.
3. Trace over all the fold lines and label the columns you created as shown: *Personal Characteristics*, *Inherited*, and *Not Inherited*. List personal characteristics down the left-hand column, as shown.
4. Before you read the chapter, predict which characteristics are inherited or not inherited. As you read the chapter, check and change the table.

Explore Activity

Purpose Use the Explore Activity to introduce students to inheritance. Inform students that they will be learning about inheritance and genetics as they read the chapter. L2 ELL COOP LEARN

LS **Logical-Mathematical**

Preparation Discuss the photograph as a class to ensure that students recognize what dimples are.

Teaching Strategy Record data for each class and have students compare their results with those of other classes.

Observe

Percentages will vary depending upon how many students in the class have and do not have dimples. Generally, the percentage of students having dimples falls between 10 and 40 percent.

Assessment

Oral Have students suggest other features that are inherited. Possible answers: hair color and texture, skin and eye color, height, shape of facial features. Use **Performance Assessment in the Science Classroom,** p. 89.

Before You Read

FOLDABLES Reading & Study Skills

Dinah Zike Study Fold

Purpose Students will define genetics by using a Foldable classification chart to record inherited and non-inherited characteristics, or traits.

For additional help, see Foldables Worksheet, p. 13 in **Chapter Resources Booklet,** or go to the Glencoe Science Web site at **science.glencoe.com.** See After You Read in the Study Guide at the end of this chapter.

SECTION

Genetics

1 Motivate

Bellringer Transparency

Display the Section Focus Transparency for Section 1. Use the accompanying Transparency Activity Master. L2 ELL

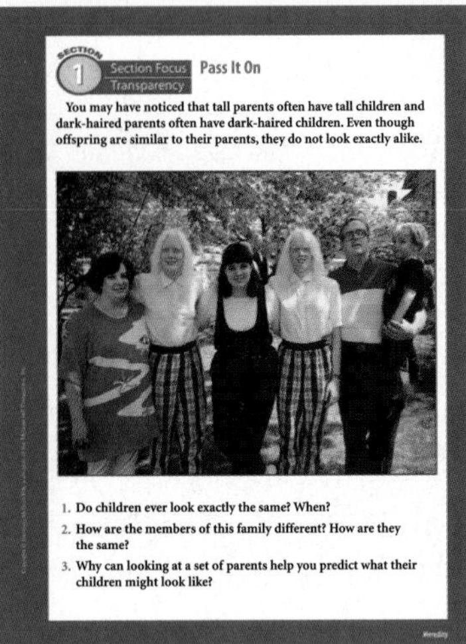

SECTION 1 Section Focus Transparency **Pass It On**

You may have noticed that tall parents often have tall children and dark-haired parents often have dark-haired children. Even though offspring are similar to their parents, they do not look exactly alike.

1. Do children ever look exactly the same? When?
2. How are the members of this family different? How are they the same?
3. Why can looking at a set of parents help you predict what their children might look like?

Tie to Prior Knowledge

Show a picture of a mother dog and her puppies (or a cat and her kittens). Have students list characteristics of the offspring they think are inherited from the parents. Lead students to understand that all of the general physical traits, such as number of legs, length and shape of ears, eye color and shape, and so on, are inherited.

SECTION 1

Genetics

As You Read

***What* You'll Learn**

- **Explain** how traits are inherited.
- **Identify** Mendel's role in the history of genetics.
- **Use** a Punnett square to predict the results of crosses.
- **Compare and contrast** the difference between an individual's genotype and phenotype.

Vocabulary

heredity, allele, genetics, hybrid, dominant, recessive, Punnett square, genotype, phenotype, homozygous, heterozygous

***Why* It's Important**

Heredity and genetics help explain why people are different.

Inheriting Traits

Do you look more like one parent or grandparent? Do you have your father's eyes? What about Aunt Isabella's cheekbones? Eye color, nose shape, and many other physical features are some of the traits that are inherited from parents, as **Figure 1** shows. An organism is a collection of traits, all inherited from its parents. **Heredity** (huh REH duh tee) is the passing of traits from parent to offspring. What controls these traits?

What is genetics? Generally, genes on chromosomes control an organism's form and function. The different forms of a trait that a gene may have are called **alleles** (uh LEELZ). When a pair of chromosomes separates during meiosis (mi OH sus), alleles for each trait also separate into different sex cells. As a result, every sex cell has one allele for each trait, as shown in **Figure 2.** The allele in one sex cell may control one form of the trait, such as having facial dimples. The allele in the other sex cell may control a different form of the trait—not having dimples. The study of how traits are inherited through the interactions of alleles is the science of **genetics** (juh NET ihks).

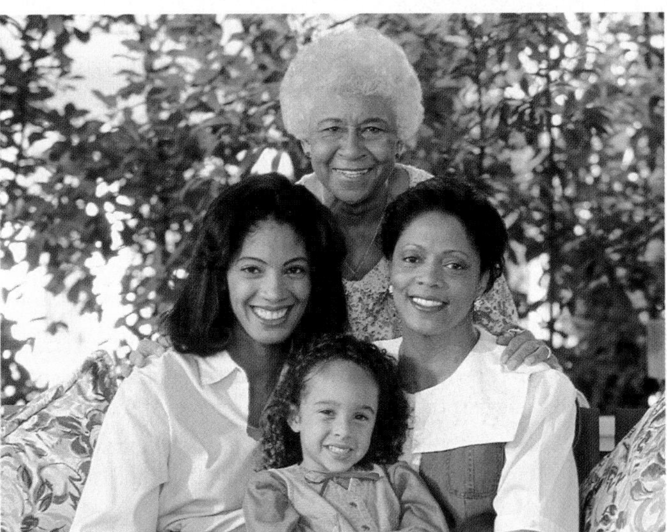

Figure 1
Note the strong family resemblance among these four generations.

Section Assessment Planner

PORTFOLIO
Extension, p. 130

PERFORMANCE ASSESSMENT
Try at Home MiniLab, p. 128
Math Skills Activity, p. 131
Skill Builder Activities, p. 132
See page 150 for more options.

CONTENT ASSESSMENT
Section, p. 132
Challenge, p. 132
Chapter, pp. 150–151

Figure 2
An allele is one form of a gene. Alleles separate into separate sex cells during meiosis. In this example, the alleles that control the trait for dimples include *D*, the presence of dimples, and *d*, the absence of dimples.

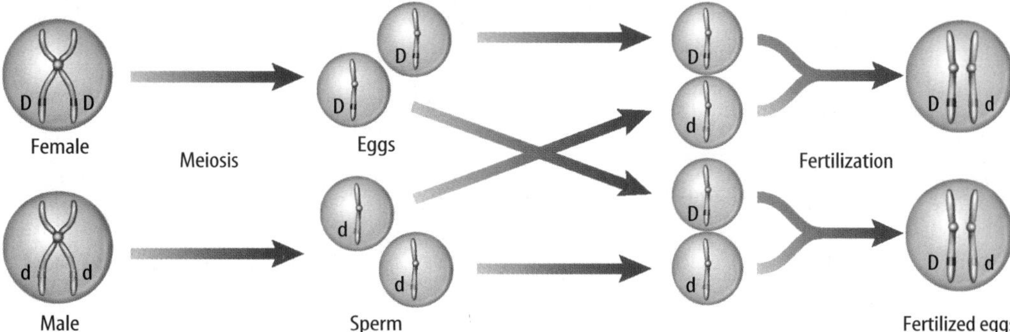

A The alleles that control a trait are located on each duplicated chromosome.

B During meiosis, duplicated chromosomes separate.

C During fertilization, each parent donates one chromosome. This results in two alleles for the trait of dimples in the new individual formed.

Mendel—The Father of Genetics

Did you know that an experiment with pea plants helped scientists understand why your eyes are the color that they are? Gregor Mendel was an Austrian monk who studied mathematics and science but became a gardener in a monastery. His interest in plants began as a boy in his father's orchard where he could predict the possible types of flowers and fruits that would result from crossbreeding two plants. Curiosity about the connection between the color of a pea flower and the type of seed that same plant produced inspired him to begin experimenting with garden peas in 1856. Mendel made careful use of scientific methods, which resulted in the first recorded study of how traits pass from one generation to the next. After eight years, Mendel presented his results with pea plants to scientists.

Before Mendel, scientists mostly relied on observation and description, and often studied many traits at one time. Mendel was the first to trace one trait through several generations. He was also the first to use the mathematics of probability to explain heredity. The use of math in plant science was a new concept and not widely accepted then. Mendel's work was forgotten for a long time. In 1900, three plant scientists, working separately, reached the same conclusions as Mendel. Each plant scientist had discovered Mendel's writings while doing his own research. Since then, Mendel has been known as the father of genetics.

SCIENCE Online

Research Visit the Glencoe Science Web site at **science.glencoe.com** for more information about early genetics experiments. Write a paragraph in your Science Journal about a scientist, other than Gregor Mendel, who studied genetics.

2 Teach

Mendel—The Father of Genetics

Teacher FYI

Mendel's experiments illustrate the scientific method. Mendel worked with a single trait at a time, conducted carefully controlled experiments, collected and analyzed data, recorded his experiments so they could be repeated, worked with large samples, and shared results with his contemporaries.

Internet Addresses

____

____

____

____

Explore the Glencoe Science Web site at **science.glencoe.com** to find out more about topics in this section.

Resource Manager 

Chapter Resources Booklet
- Transparency Activity, p. 40
- Directed Reading for Content Mastery, pp. 15, 16
- Note-taking Worksheets, pp. 29–31

Genetics in a Garden

Purpose to observe and calculate the occurrence of various traits in dogs L2 ELL

LS **Logical-Mathematical**

Teaching Strategies Make sure students understand that variations make each dog unique.

Safety Precautions Caution students not to touch or approach dogs they do not know.

Analysis

1. Answers will vary depending on dogs observed.
2. There are many variations. Each dog looks different.

Performance To further assess students' understanding of inherited traits, have volunteers observe and tabulate several traits among children, parents, and grandparents. Use **PASC,** p. 109.

Reading Check

Answer They can be relied upon to produce the same traits generation after generation.

Some students think that dominant traits are those that will "take over" in a population. Refer to page 124F for teaching strategies that address this misconception.

Table 1 Traits Compared by Mendel

Traits	Shape of Seeds	Color of Seeds	Color of Pods	Shape of Pods	Plant Height	Position of Flowers	Flower Color
Dominant Trait	Round	Yellow	Green	Full	Tall	At leaf junctions	Purple
Recessive Trait	Wrinkled	Green	Yellow	Flat, constricted	Short	At tips of branches	White

Comparing Common Traits

Procedure

1. Safely survey as many **dogs** in your neighborhood as you can for the presence of a solid color or spotted coat, short or long hair, and floppy ears or ears that stand up straight.
2. Make a data table that lists each of the traits. Record your data in the data table.

Analysis

1. Compare the number of dogs that have one form of a trait with those that have the other form. How do those two groups compare?
2. What can you conclude about the variations you noticed in the dogs?

Genetics in a Garden

Each time Mendel studied a trait, he crossed two plants with different expressions of the trait and found that the new plants all looked like one of the two parents. He called these new plants **hybrids** (HI brudz) because they received different genetic information, or different alleles, for a trait from each parent. The results of these studies made Mendel even more curious about how traits are inherited.

Garden peas are easy to breed for pure traits. An organism that always produces the same traits generation after generation is called a purebred. For example, tall plants that always produce seeds that produce tall plants are purebred for the trait of tall height. **Table 1** shows other pea plant traits that Mendel studied.

Reading Check *Why might farmers plant purebred crop seeds?*

Dominant and Recessive Factors In nature, insects randomly pollinate plants as they move from flower to flower. In his experiments, Mendel used pollen from the flowers of purebred tall plants to pollinate by hand the flowers of purebred short plants. This process is called cross-pollination. He found that tall plants crossed with short plants produced seeds that produced all tall plants. Whatever caused the plants to be short had disappeared. Mendel called the tall form the **dominant** (DAHM uh nunt) factor because it dominated, or covered up, the short form. He called the form that seemed to disappear the **recessive** (rih SES ihv) factor. Today, these are called dominant alleles and recessive alleles. What happened to the recessive form? **Figure 3** answers this question.

Resource Manager 

Chapter Resources Booklet
MiniLAB, p. 3

Home and Community Involvement, p. 36

Performance Assessment in the Science Classroom, p. 57

VISUALIZING MENDEL'S EXPERIMENTS

Figure 3

Gregor Mendel discovered that the experiments he carried out on garden plants provided an understanding of heredity. For eight years he crossed plants that had different characteristics and recorded how those characteristics were passed from generation to generation. One such characteristic, or trait, was the color of pea pods. The results of Mendel's experiment on pea pod color are shown below.

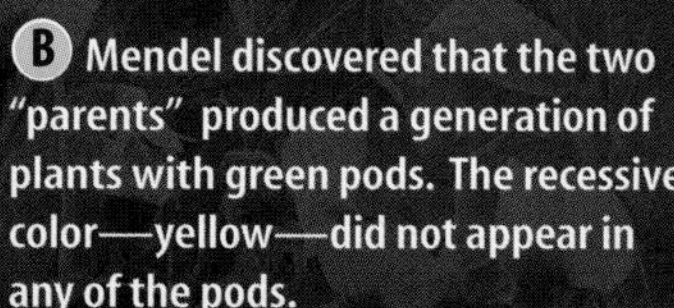

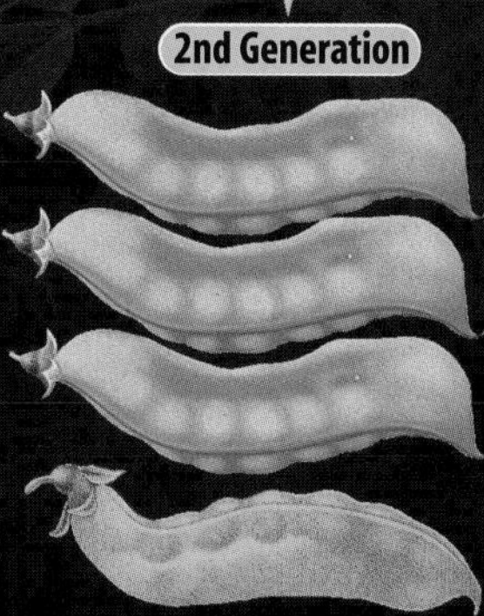

Parents

1st Generation

2nd Generation

A One of the so-called "parent plants" in Mendel's experiment had pods that were green, a dominant trait. The other parent plant had pods that were yellow, a recessive trait.

B Mendel discovered that the two "parents" produced a generation of plants with green pods. The recessive color—yellow—did not appear in any of the pods.

C Next, Mendel collected seeds from the first-generation plants and raised a second generation. He discovered that these second-generation plants produced plants with either green or yellow pods in a ratio of about three plants with green pods for every one plant with yellow pods. The recessive trait had reappeared. This 3:1 ratio proved remarkably consistent in hundreds of similar crosses, allowing Mendel to accurately predict the ratio of pod color in second-generation plants.

129

NATIONAL GEOGRAPHIC

Visualizing Mendel's Experiments

Have students examine the pictures and read the captions. Then ask the following questions:

Why is it important that Mendel based his conclusions on the results of hundreds of pea plant crosses? It's important to have as much data as possible before drawing conclusions about any experiment, and in general, the larger your sample size, the more accurate your results will be.

Would the allele for the recessive trait of yellow pea pod color be present in the first generation of pea plants? Yes, the allele would be present, but it would not be expressed because none of the plants is homozygous recessive.

Activity

Have students work in small groups. Using the example shown in the Visualizing, have the students use Mendel's ratios to determine the number of yellow pea plants in the second generation if the second generation of plants contained the following: 100 total plants (25) 300 total plants (75).

Extension

Have students learn about one of the researchers who, in 1900, rediscovered Mendel's work while analyzing their own experiments, and report their findings to the class.

Genetics in a Garden, continued

Use an Analogy

The probability of genetic events is analogous to rolling a die and other games of chance.

Make a Model

Provide students with blocks of two different colors. Have them use the blocks to model the cross involving pea plant flowers described in the text. Help them use these tools to distinguish between genotype and phenotype, and homozygous and heterozygous.

Extension

Challenge students to form Punnett squares that show the results of first- and second-generation crosses between organisms pure bred for two traits. If purebred organisms are crossed, the first generation will result in all heterozygous organisms. When these are crossed, students should obtain a 9:3:3:1 ratio, as shown below. L3 ELL COOP LEARN P

Caption Answer

Figure 4 No; if red is recessive, then the genotype is homozygous recessive (rr), but if red is dominant, then the flower could be either homozygous (RR) or heterozygous (Rr).

Reading Check

Answer Homozygous organisms carry the same two alleles for a trait. Heterozygous organisms carry two different alleles for a trait.

Using Probability to Make Predictions If you and your sister can't agree on what movie to see, you could solve the problem by tossing a coin. When you toss a coin, you're dealing with probabilities. Probability is a branch of mathematics that helps you predict the chance that something will happen. If your sister chooses tails while the coin is in the air, what is the probability that the coin will land tail-side up? Because a coin has two sides, there are two possible outcomes, heads or tails. One outcome is tails. Therefore, the probability of one side of a coin showing is one out of two, or 50 percent.

Mendel also dealt with probabilities. One of the things that made his predictions accurate was that he worked with large numbers of plants. He studied almost 30,000 pea plants over a period of eight years. By doing so, Mendel increased his chances of seeing a repeatable pattern. Valid scientific conclusions need to be based on results that can be duplicated.

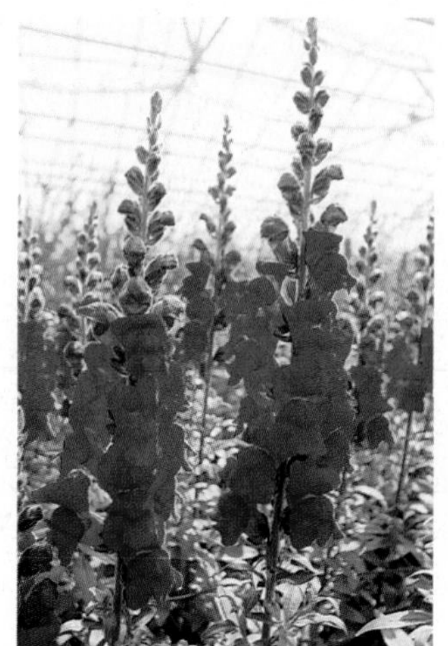

Figure 4
This snapdragon's phenotype is red. *Can you tell what the flower's genotype for color is? Explain your answer.*

Punnett Squares Suppose you wanted to know what colors of pea plant flowers you would get if you pollinated white flowers on one pea plant with pollen from purple flowers on a different plant. How could you predict what the offspring would look like without making the cross? A handy tool used to predict results in Mendelian genetics is the **Punnett** (PUN ut) **square.** In a Punnett square, letters represent dominant and recessive alleles. An uppercase letter stands for a dominant allele. A lowercase letter stands for a recessive allele. The letters are a form of code. They show the **genotype** (JEE nuh tipe), or genetic makeup, of an organism. Once you understand what the letters mean, you can tell a lot about the inheritance of a trait in an organism.

The way an organism looks and behaves as a result of its genotype is its **phenotype** (FEE nuh tipe), as shown in **Figure 4.** If you have brown hair, then the phenotype for your hair color is brown.

Alleles Determine Traits Most cells in your body have two alleles for every trait. These alleles are located on chromosomes within the nucleus of cells. An organism with two alleles that are the same is called **homozygous** (hoh muh ZI gus). For Mendel's peas, this would be written as *TT* (homozygous for the tall-dominant trait) or *tt* (homozygous for the short-recessive trait). An organism that has two different alleles for a trait is called **heterozygous** (het uh roh ZI gus). The hybrid plants Mendel produced were all heterozygous for height, *Tt.*

Reading Check ***What is the difference between homozygous and heterozygous organisms?***

Sample Punnett Square for Extension:

Parent 2 (RrYy) \ Parent 1 (RrYy)	RY	Ry	rY	ry
RY	RRYY	RRYy	RrYY	RrYy
Ry	RRYy	RRyy	RrYy	Rryy
rY	RrYY	RrYy	rrYY	rrYy
ry	RrYy	Rryy	rrYy	rryy

Making a Punnett Square In a Punnett square for predicting one trait, the letters representing the two alleles from one parent are written along the top of the grid, one letter per section. Those of the second parent are placed down the side of the grid, one letter per section. Each square of the grid is filled in with one allele donated by each parent. The letters that you use to fill in each of the squares represent the genotypes of possible offspring that the parents could produce.

Math Skills Activity

Calculating Probability Using a Punnett Square

You can determine the probability of certain traits by using a Punnett square. Letters are used to represent the two alleles from each parent and are combined to determine the possible genotypes of the offspring.

Example Problem

One dog carries heterozygous, black-fur traits (Bb), and its mate carries homogeneous, blond-fur traits (bb). Calculate the probability of the puppy having black fur.

Solution

1 *This is what you know:*
dominant allele is represented by *B*
recessive allele is represented by *b*

2 *This is what you need to find:*
the probability of a puppy's fur color being black using a Punnett square

3 *This is the diagram you need to use:*

Black dog

Blond dog	B	b
b		
b		

4 *Complete the Punnett square by taking each letter in each column and combining it with each letter from each row in the corresponding square.*

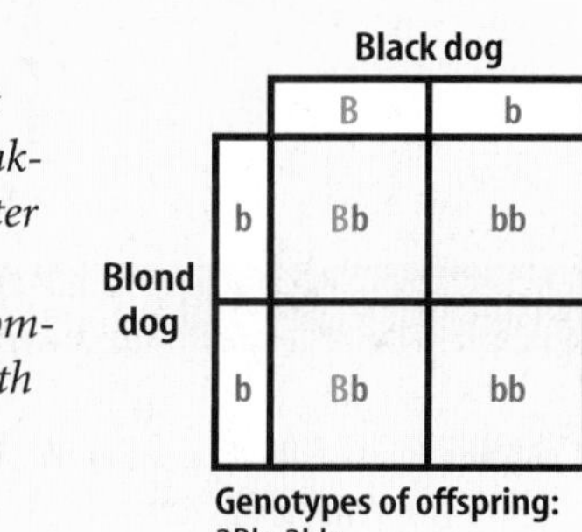

Black dog
B
b
Blond dog
b
Bb
bb
b
Bb
bb
Genotypes of offspring:
2Bb, 2bb
Phenotypes of offspring:
2 black, 2 blond

5 *Find the needed probability. There are two Bb genotypes and four possible outcomes.*

$$P(\text{black fur}) = \frac{\text{number of ways to get black fur}}{\text{number of possible outcomes}}$$

$$= \frac{2}{4} = \frac{1}{2} = 50\%$$

Practice Problem

Use a Punnett square to determine the probability of each of the offspring's genotype and phenotype when two heterozygous, tall-dominant traits (Tt) are crossed with each other.

For more help, refer to the Math Skill Handbook.

Quick Demo

Use two long strings of the large plastic beads used as a toddler's toy to demonstrate alleles along a chromosome. Explain that each different shape and color of bead represents a different trait. When the two strands are brought together, you can demonstrate homozygous and heterozygous conditions.

Math Skills Activity

National Math Standards

Correlation to Mathematics Objectives

1, 2, 4, 5, 6, 8, 9, 10

Answer to Practice Problem

Genotype: p(TT) = 25%; p(Tt) = 50%; p(tt) = 25%; Phenotype: 75% tall, 25% short

	T	t
T	TT	Tt
t	Tt	tt

Resource Manager

Chapter Resources Booklet

Enrichment, p. 26

Lab Activity, pp. 9–10

Mathematics Skill Activities, p. 23

Inclusion Strategies

Learning Disabled Have students choose one or two inherited traits (eye color, left- or right-handedness, and so on) and survey classmates to see how many of them display the characteristics. Results can be graphed. Other classrooms can be surveyed. Students can determine whether larger populations have the same ratio of the traits as subgroups. L1 COOP LEARN

IN **Interpersonal**

Genetics in a Garden, continued

Visual Learning

Table 2 Have students relate the principles of heredity to genetic examples they have studied in this section.

3 Assess

Reteach

Have students role play the alleles in a cross. Take the class to a paved portion of the school yard. Use masking tape to mark out a large Punnett square on the pavement. Assign students to be certain alleles and allow them to arrange themselves and announce the phenotypes and genotypes produced. L2 ELL
LS **Visual-Spatial**

Challenge

Have students determine the number of combinations possible in a trihybrid cross. There are 64 possibilities. L3
LS **Logical-Mathematical**

Performance Have students use a Punnett square to demonstrate their answer to Question 6. Use **PASC,** p. 97.

Principles of Heredity Even though Gregor Mendel didn't know anything about DNA, genes, or chromosomes, he succeeded in beginning to describe and mathematically represent how inherited traits are passed from parents to offspring. He realized that some factor in the pea plant produced certain traits. Mendel also concluded that these factors separated when the pea plant reproduced. Mendel arrived at his conclusions after years of detailed observation, careful analysis, and repeated experimentation. **Table 2** summarizes Mendel's principles of heredity.

What traits are cats bred for? To find out more about cat breeds, see the **Felines Field Guide** at the back of the book.

Table 2 Principles of Heredity

1	Traits are controlled by alleles on chromosomes.
2	An allele's effect is dominant or recessive.
3	When a pair of chromosomes separates during meiosis, the different alleles for a trait move into separate sex cells.

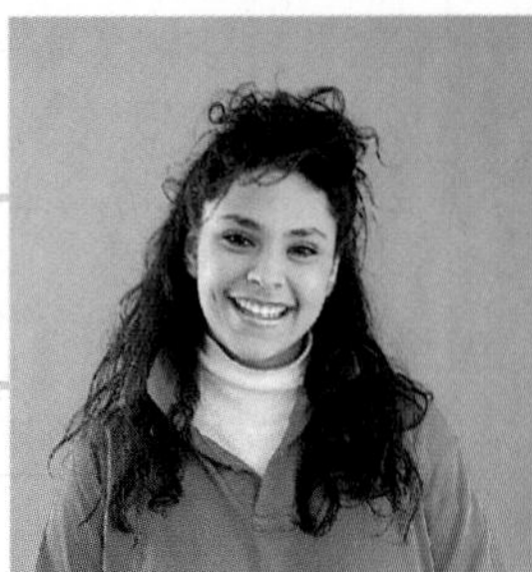

Section 1 Assessment

1. Alleles are described as being dominant or recessive. What is the difference between a dominant and a recessive allele?
2. How are dominant and recessive alleles represented in a Punnett square?
3. Explain the difference between genotype and phenotype. Give examples.
4. Gregor Mendel, an Austrian monk who lived in the 1800s, is known as the father of genetics. Explain why Mendel has been given this title.
5. **Think Critically** If an organism expresses a recessive phenotype, can you tell the genotype? Explain your answer by giving an example.

Skill Builder Activities

6. **Predicting** Hairline shape is an inherited trait in humans. The widow's peak allele is dominant, and the straight hairline allele is recessive. Predict how both parents with widow's peaks could have a child without a widow's peak hairline. **For more help, refer to the** Science Skill Handbook.
7. **Using Percentages** One fruit fly is heterozygous for long wings, and another fruit fly is homozygous for short wings. Long wings are dominant to short wings. Using a Punnett square, find out what percent of the offspring are expected to have short wings. **For more help, refer to the** Math Skill Handbook.

Answers to Section Assessment

1. A dominant allele is expressed if an allele pair is homozygous dominant or heterozygous. A recessive allele is expressed only when an allele pair is homozygous recessive.
2. Dominant alleles are represented with an uppercase letter, recessive alleles with a lowercase letter.
3. Genotype is the combination of alleles an organism contains; phenotype is the expression of the alleles in an organism. For example, a genotype might be Tt (heterozygous dominant), and the phenotype might be tall.
4. He was the first person to explain the mechanisms of heredity.
5. Yes, because two copies of the recessive allele must be present for the recessive phenotype to show up.
6. Both parents would have to be heterozygous to produce children without the widow's peak trait.
7. 50%

Activity
Predicting Results

Could you predict how many brown rabbits would result from crossing two heterozygous black rabbits? Try this investigation to find out. Brown color is a recessive trait for hair color in rabbits.

What You'll Investigate
How does chance affect combinations of genes?

Materials
paper bags (2)
white beans (100)
red beans (100)

Goals
- **Model** chance events in heredity.
- **Compare and contrast** predicted and actual results.

Safety Precautions
WARNING: *Do not taste, eat, or drink any materials used in the lab.*

Procedure
1. Use a Punnett square to predict how many red/red, red/white, and white/white bean combinations are possible. The combinations represent the coat colors in rabbit offspring.
2. Place 50 red beans and 50 white beans in a paper bag. Place 50 red beans and 50 white beans in a second bag. Red beans represent black alleles and white beans represent brown alleles.
3. Label one of the bags *female* for the female parent. Label the other bag *male* for the male parent.
4. Use a data table to record the combination each time you remove two beans. Your table will need to accommodate 100 picks.
5. Without looking, remove one bean from each bag. The two beans represent the alleles that combine when sperm and egg join. After recording, return the beans to their bags.
6. **Count** and record the total numbers for each of the three combinations in your data table.
7. **Compile** and record the class totals.

Conclude and Apply
1. Which combination occurred most often?
2. **Calculate** the ratio of red/red to red/white to white/white. What hair color in rabbits do these combinations represent?
3. **Compare** your predicted (expected) results with your observed (actual) results.
4. **Hypothesize** how you could get predicted results to be closer to actual results.

Gene Combinations

Rabbits	Red/ Red	Red/ White	White/ White
Your Total			
Class Total			

Communicating Your Data
Write a paragraph that clearly describes your results. Have another student read your paragraph. Ask if he or she could understand what happened. If not, rewrite your paragraph and have the other student read it again. **For more help, refer to the Science Skill Handbook.**

Activity
BENCH TESTED

Purpose Students use a model to investigate how the principles of heredity are related to chance. L2 ELL LS **Logical-Mathematical**

Process Skills predicting, observing, recording data, interpreting data, using numbers, making and using tables

Time Required one class period

Safety Precautions Remind students not to eat or throw the beans.

Teaching Strategies
- All the beans should be approximately the same size.
- Emphasize the importance of completing all 100 trials.
- **Troubleshooting** Explain to students that beans must be returned to the bag after each draw so that the probability of choosing the different color combinations remains the same throughout the activity.

Answers to Questions
1. red/white
2. Results should be close to 1:2:1; red/red represents a black rabbit, red/white represents a black rabbit, and white/white represents a brown rabbit.
3. Answers will vary, but should follow expected results closely.
4. A larger sample could be used or more trials done.

Performance To further assess students' knowledge of probability, have them repeat the activity using three different kinds of beans. Use the **PASC,** p. 97.

Resource Manager

Chapter Resources Booklet
Activity Worksheet, pp. 5–6
Reinforcement, p. 23
Lab Activity, pp. 11–12

Communicating Your Data
Students' paragraphs should indicate methods and results, as well as how the model relates to actual heredity principles.

SECTION

Genetics Since Mendel

1 Motivate

Bellringer Transparency

Display the Section Focus Transparency for Section 2. Use the accompanying Transparency Activity Master. L2 ELL

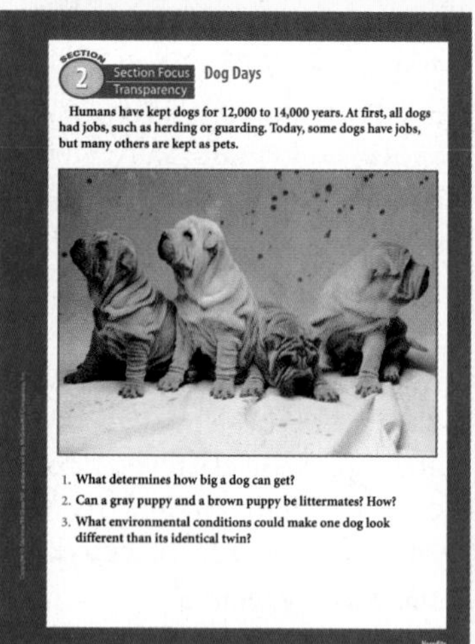

SECTION 2 Section Focus Transparency **Dog Days**

Humans have kept dogs for 12,000 to 14,000 years. At first, all dogs had jobs, such as herding or guarding. Today, some dogs have jobs, but many others are kept as pets.

1. **What determines how big a dog can get?**
2. **Can a gray puppy and a brown puppy be littermates? How?**
3. **What environmental conditions could make one dog look different than its identical twin?**

Heredity

Tie to Prior Knowledge

Ask students if any of them have eye color different from either parent. Explain that some inherited traits involve more complex patterns of inheritance, and students will learn about them in this section.

Caption Answer

Figure 5E The palomino's coat color is intermediate between its parents' coat colors.

SECTION

Genetics Since Mendel

As You Read

What **You'll Learn**

- **Explain** how traits are inherited by incomplete dominance.
- **Compare** multiple alleles and polygenic inheritance, and give examples of each.
- **Describe** two human genetic disorders and how they are inherited.
- **Explain** how sex-linked traits are passed to offspring.

Vocabulary

incomplete dominance
polygenic inheritance
sex-linked gene

Why **It's Important**

Most of your inherited traits involve more complex patterns of inheritance than Mendel discovered.

Incomplete Dominance

Not even in science do things remain the same. After Mendel's work was rediscovered in 1900, scientists repeated his experiments. For some plants, such as peas, Mendel's results proved true. However, when different plants were crossed, the results were sometimes different. One scientist crossed purebred red four-o'clock plants with purebred white four-o'clock plants. He expected to get all red flowers, but they were pink. Neither allele for flower color seemed dominant. Had the colors become blended like paint colors? He crossed the pink-flowered plants with each other, and red, pink, and white flowers were produced. The red and white alleles had not become blended. Instead, when the allele for white flowers and the allele for red flowers combined, the result was an intermediate phenotype—a pink flower. When the offspring of two homozygous parents show an intermediate phenotype, this inheritance is called **incomplete dominance.** Other examples of incomplete dominance include the feather color of some chicken breeds and the coat color of some horse breeds, as shown in **Figure 5.**

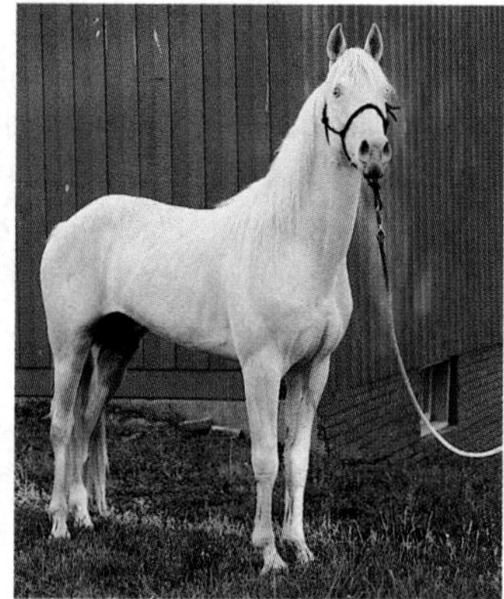

Figure 5
When A a chestnut horse is bred with B a cremello horse, all offspring will be C palomino. The Punnett square shown in D can be used to predict this result. *How does the color of the palomino horse in C show that the coat color of horses may be inherited by incomplete dominance?*

Section Assessment Planner

PORTFOLIO
Science Journal, p. 135

PERFORMANCE ASSESSMENT
MiniLAB, p. 136
Skill Builder Activities, p. 140
See page 150 for more options.

CONTENT ASSESSMENT
Section, p. 140
Challenge, p. 140
Chapter, pp. 150–151

Multiple Alleles Mendel studied traits in peas that were controlled by just two alleles. However, many traits are controlled by more than two alleles. A trait that is controlled by more than two alleles is said to be controlled by multiple alleles. Traits controlled by multiple alleles produce more than three phenotypes of that trait.

Imagine that only three types of coins are made—nickels, dimes, and quarters. If every person can have only two coins, six different combinations are possible. In this problem, the coins represent alleles of a trait. The sum of each two-coin combination represents the phenotype. Can you name the six different phenotypes possible with two coins?

Blood type in humans is an example of multiple alleles that produce only four phenotypes. The alleles for blood types are called A, B, and O. The O allele is recessive to both the A and B alleles. When a person inherits one A allele and one B allele for blood type, both are expressed—phenotype AB. A person with phenotype A blood has the genetic makeup, or genotype—AA or AO. Someone with phenotype B blood has the genotype BB or BO. Finally, a person with phenotype O blood has the genotype OO.

Reading Check *What are the six different blood type genotypes?*

Research Visit the Glencoe Science Web site at **science.glencoe.com** for information on the importance of blood types in blood transfusions. In your Science Journal, draw a chart showing which blood types can be used safely during transfusions.

C

D

Chestnut horse (CC)

Cremello horse (C'C')	C	C
C'	CC'	CC'
C'	CC'	CC'

Genotypes: All CC'
Phenotypes: All palomino horses

2 Teach

Incomplete Dominance

Discussion

Discuss why traits governed by incomplete dominance or multiple alleles might be more difficult to study. Help students see that these patterns do not conform to Mendel's prediction of a simple 3:1 ratio.

Text Question Answer

Possible combinations: nickel, dime; nickel, quarter; dime, quarter; nickel, nickel; dime, dime; quarter, quarter

Fun Fact

Blood types are important to the health profession. Matching blood types—both AB, A, B, or O and Rh—is important in transfusions. The recessive blood type, O, occurs in more than 30 percent of Americans.

Reading Check

Answer AA, AO, AB, BB, BO, OO

Genetics of Flower Color

Explain that in hibiscus flowers, red is dominant to white. Have students explain why they can tell the genotype of a red four-o'clock, but not of a red hibiscus. Four-o'clocks inherit color by incomplete dominance. A red four-o'clock must be homozygous. If it were heterozygous, it would be pink. A red hibiscus might be heterozygous or homozygous. L2 P

Resource Manager

Chapter Resources Booklet

Transparency Activity, p. 41

Directed Reading for Content Mastery, p. 16

Internet Addresses

Explore the Glencoe Science Web site at **science.glencoe.com** to find out more about topics in this section.

Polygenic Inheritance

Use Science Words

Word Origin Polygenic inheritance involves many genes. The prefix *poly-* means "many." Have students use a dictionary to find other words with this prefix and explain their meanings. Possible answers: polygon—many sided figure; polychromatic—made of many colors

Purpose to determine the inheritance pattern that controls hand span L2 ELL

LS **Logical-Mathematical**

Materials paper, pencil, ruler

Teaching Strategy It may be easier for students to have each subject place his or her hand on a piece of paper and mark the width of the hand span before measuring it.

Analysis

1. Answers will vary. Spans may range from 12.5 cm to 24 cm or more.
2. Hand spans are determined by polygenic inheritance, not by a simple Mendelian pattern.

Assessment

Oral Ask students to determine if identical twins have identical hand spans. The spans are usually very close, but not identical because of environmental factors that affect growth. Use **Performance Assessment in the Science Classroom,** p. 89.

Mini LAB

Interpreting Polygenic Inheritance

Procedure

1. Measure the hand spans of your classmates.
2. Using a **ruler,** measure from the tip of the thumb to the tip of the little finger when the hand is stretched out. Read the measurement to the nearest centimeter.
3. Record the name and hand-span measurement of each person in a data table.

Analysis

1. What range of hand spans did you find?
2. Are hand spans inherited as a simple Mendelian pattern or as a polygenic or incomplete dominance pattern? Explain.

Polygenic Inheritance

Eye color is an example of a trait that is produced by a combination of many genes. **Polygenic** (pahl ih JEHN ihk) **inheritance** occurs when a group of gene pairs acts together to produce a trait. The effects of many alleles produces a wide variety of phenotypes. For this reason, it may be hard to classify all the different shades of eye color.

Your height and the color of your eyes and skin are just some of the many human traits controlled by polygenic inheritance. It is estimated that three to six gene pairs control your skin color. Even more gene pairs might control the color of your hair and eyes. The environment also plays an important role in the expression of traits controlled by polygenic inheritance. Polygenic inheritance is common and includes such traits as grain color in wheat and milk production in cows. Egg production in chickens is also a polygenic trait.

Impact of the Environment Your environment plays a role in how some of your genes are expressed or whether they are expressed at all, as shown in **Figure 6.** Environmental influences can be internal or external. For example, most male birds are more brightly colored than females. Chemicals in their bodies determine whether the gene for brightly colored feathers is expressed.

Although genes determine many of your traits, you might be able to influence their expression by the decisions you make. Some people have genes that make them at risk for developing certain cancers. Whether they get cancer might depend on external environmental factors. For instance, if some people at risk for skin cancer limit their exposure to the Sun and take care of their skin, they might never develop cancer.

Reading Check *What environmental factors might affect the size of leaves on a tree?*

Figure 6
Himalayan rabbits have alleles for dark-colored fur. However, this allele is able to express itself only at lower temperatures. Only the areas located farthest from the rabbit's main body heat (ears, nose, feet, tail) have dark-colored fur.

Resource Manager

Chapter Resources Booklet
MiniLAB, p. 4

Life Science Critical Thinking/Problem Solving, p. 19

Active Reading

Reflective Journal In this strategy, students identify activities and what they learned and record responses to the activities. Have students divide pieces of paper into several columns. Have them record their thoughts under headings such as "What I did," "What I learned," "What questions do I have," "What surprises did I experience," and "Overall response." Have students write a Reflective Journal entry for the MiniLAB.

Human Genes and Mutations

Sometimes a gene undergoes a change that results in a trait that is expressed differently. Occasionally errors occur in the DNA when it is copied inside of a cell. Such changes and errors are called mutations. Not all mutations are harmful. They might be helpful or have no effect on an organism.

Certain chemicals are known to produce mutations in plants or animals, including humans. X rays and radioactive substances are other causes of some mutations. Mutations are changes in genes.

Chromosome Disorders In addition to individual mutations, problems can occur if the incorrect number of chromosomes is inherited. Every organism has a specific number of chromosomes. However, mistakes in the process of meiosis can result in a new organism with more or fewer chromosomes than normal. A change in the total number of human chromosomes is usually fatal to the unborn embryo or fetus, or the baby may die soon after birth.

Look at the human chromosomes in **Figure 7.** If three copies of chromosome 21 are produced in the fertilized human egg, Down's syndrome results. Individuals with Down's syndrome can be short, exhibit learning disabilities, and have heart problems. Such individuals can lead normal lives if they have no severe health complications.

Figure 7
Humans usually have 23 pairs of chromosomes. Notice that three copies of chromosome 21 are present in this photo, rather than the usual two chromosomes. This change in chromosome number results in Down's syndrome. Chris Burke, a well-known actor, has this syndrome.

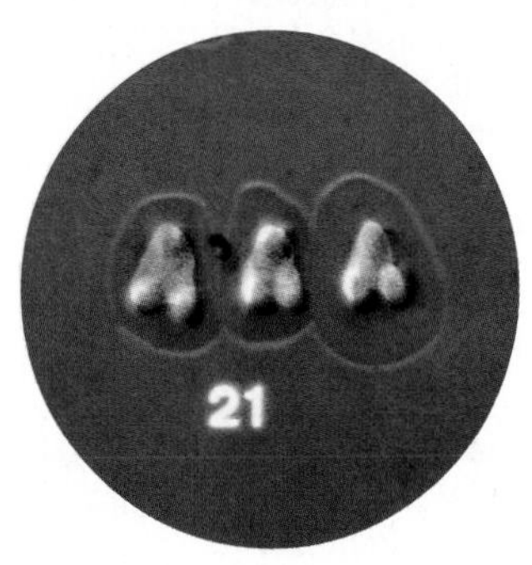

Reading Check

Answer amount of water or sunlight available, presence or absence of chemicals in soil

Human Genes and Mutations

Teacher FYI

Somatic mutations occur in body cells and can produce a localized change—e.g., the streak of white sometimes found in the hair of an otherwise normal individual. All the cells descended from the mutant body cell will carry the mutation, but it cannot be passed on to offspring. Germ cell mutations affect the sex cells (eggs or sperm) and can be transmitted to the individual's offspring.

LAB DEMONSTRATION

Purpose to show how mutations are passed to daughter cells

Materials blue and red overhead acetate, yarn, scissors, overhead projector

Preparation Cut out several 2-, 4-, and 6-cm long pairs of blue chromosomes. Cut one 4-cm long red chromosome.

Procedure Make a circle of yarn on the projector to represent a cell. Place the blue chromosome pairs in the cell. "Mutate" one chromosome from blue to red. Divide the chromosomes to make two new cells surrounded by yarn as if the cell had undergone mitosis.

Expected Outcome One daughter cell carries a mutation.

Assessment

What will happen when the cell carrying the mutation reproduces? The mutation will be reproduced. **How might this explain how a person could have a white stripe in his hair, while the rest of his hair remains black?** The mutation is in the hair cells. It is passed along when the hair cells undergo mitosis.

Recessive Genetic Disorders

Discussion

Point out that about 600 simple recessive human disorders are presently known. Genetic disorders caused by dominant alleles are more common. An example is Huntington's disease, which usually does not express itself until the person is an adult. **Why are fewer human genetic disorders recessive?** Humans with recessive genetic disorders rarely live to a reproductive age.

Reading Check

Answer Cystic fibrosis is a recessive disorder.

Caption Answer

Figure 8 The X chromosome is larger than the Y, and looks like an X. The Y chromosome looks like the V part of a Y.

If both parents are heterozygous for the trait, they have a 25 percent chance of producing an offspring with PKU with each pregnancy.

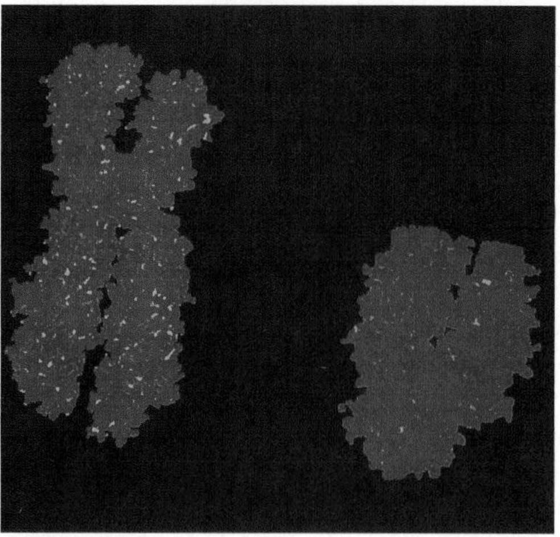

Magnification: 10,000×

Figure 8
Sex in many organisms is determined by X and Y chromosomes.
How do the X (left) and Y (right) chromosomes differ from one another in shape and size?

Recessive Genetic Disorders

Many human genetic disorders, such as cystic fibrosis, are caused by recessive genes. Some recessive genes are the result of a mutation within the gene. Many of these alleles are rare. Such genetic disorders occur when both parents have a recessive allele responsible for this disorder. Because the parents are heterozygous, they don't show any symptoms. However, if each parent passes the recessive allele to the child, the child inherits both recessive alleles and will have a recessive genetic disorder.

Reading Check *How is cystic fibrosis inherited?*

Cystic fibrosis is a homozygous recessive disorder. It is the most common genetic disorder that can lead to death among Caucasian Americans. In most people, a thin fluid is produced that lubricates the lungs and intestinal tract. People with cystic fibrosis produce thick mucus instead of this thin fluid. The thick mucus builds up in the lungs and makes it hard to breathe. This buildup often results in repeated bacterial respiratory infections. The thick mucus also reduces or prevents the flow of substances necessary for digesting food. Physical therapy, special diets, and new drug therapies have increased the life spans of patients with cystic fibrosis.

Chemistry INTEGRATION

People with PKU, a recessive disorder, cannot produce the enzyme needed for the breakdown of a substance found in some artificially sweetened drinks. Soft-drink cans must be labeled to ensure that individuals with this disorder do not unknowingly consume the substance. Explain in your Science Journal how a person can be born with PKU if neither parent has this recessive disorder.

Sex Determination

What determines the sex of an individual? Much information on sex inheritance came from studies of fruit flies. Fruit flies have only four pairs of chromosomes. Because the chromosomes are large and few in number, they are easy to study. Scientists identified one pair that contains genes that determine the sex of the organism. They labeled the pair XX in females and XY in males. Geneticists use these labels when studying organisms, including humans. You can see human X and Y chromosomes in **Figure 8.**

Each egg produced by a female normally contains one X chromosome. Males produce sperm that normally have either an X or a Y chromosome. When a sperm with an X chromosome fertilizes an egg, the offspring is a female, XX. A male offspring, XY, is the result of a Y-containing sperm fertilizing an egg. What pair of sex chromosomes is in each of your cells? Sometimes chromosomes do not separate during meiosis. When this occurs, an individual can inherit an abnormal number of sex chromosomes.

Inclusion Strategies

Learning Disabled Some students may appreciate seeing photos or videos that depict much of the information presented here. The March of Dimes and other foundations supply free or low-cost classroom materials that summarize many of these concepts. L1 LS **Visual-Spatial**

Teacher FYI

Most students will be aware of someone with a genetic disorder. Be sensitive to the possibility that students may have someone in their own family with a disorder.

138 CHAPTER 5 Heredity

Sex-Linked Disorders

Some inherited conditions are linked with the X and Y chromosomes. An allele inherited on a sex chromosome is called a **sex-linked gene.** Color blindness is a sex-linked disorder in which people cannot distinguish between certain colors, particularly red and green. This trait is a recessive allele on the X chromosome. Because males have only one X chromosome, a male with this allele on his X chromosome is color-blind. However, a color-blind female occurs only when both of her X chromosomes have the allele for this trait.

The allele for the distinct patches of three different colors found in calico cats is recessive and carried on the X chromosome. As shown in **Figure 9,** calico cats have inherited two X chromosomes with this recessive allele—one from both parents.

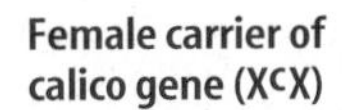

Female carrier of calico gene (X^cX)

Male carrier of calico gene (X^cY)

	X^c	X
X^c	X^cX^c	XX^c
Y	X^cY	XY

Genotypes: X^cX^c, X^cX, X^cY, XY
Phenotypes: One calico female, one carrier female, one carrier male, one normal male

Figure 9
Calico cat fur is a homozygous recessive sex-linked trait. Female cats that are heterozygous are not calico but are only carriers. Two recessive alleles must be present for this allele to be expressed. *Why aren't all the females calico?*

Pedigrees Trace Traits

How can you trace a trait through a family? A pedigree is a visual tool for following a trait through generations of a family. Males are represented by squares and females by circles. A completely filled circle or square shows that the trait is seen in that person. Half-colored circles or squares indicate carriers. A carrier is heterozygous for the trait and it is not seen. People represented by empty circles or squares do not have the trait and are not carriers. The pedigree in **Figure 10** shows how the trait for color blindness is carried through a family.

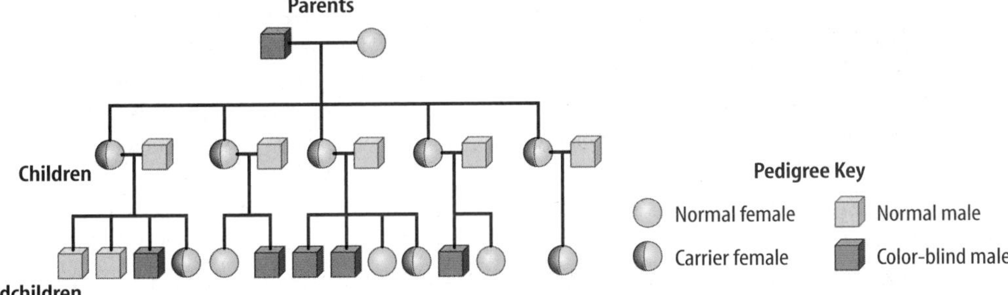

Figure 10
The symbols in this pedigree's key mean the same thing on all pedigree charts. The grandfather in this family was color-blind and married to a woman who was not a carrier of the color-blind allele. *Why are no women in this family color-blind?*

Resource Manager

Chapter Resources Booklet
Enrichment, p. 27
Transparency Activity, pp. 43–44

Sex-Linked Disorders

Quick Demo

Use Punnett squares to demonstrate inheritance patterns discussed in this section, such as the combination of X and Y chromosomes that determines the sex of an individual.

Make a Model

Have students use a set of cutouts of X and Y chromosomes to model how a sex-linked disorder can be inherited.

Caption Answer

Figure 9 All the females aren't calico because some are heterozygous.

Pedigrees Trace Traits

Visual Learning

Figure 10 Have students use this figure to answer the following questions. **How many children are carriers for color blindness?** 5 **How many grandchildren?** 3 **What percent is this of each generation?** 100% of children, 23% of grandchildren are carriers.

Extension

Have students find out the pros and cons of purebred breeding. For example, some purebred dog breeds have fragile bone structure or poor kidney functioning. Breeding with other breeds might lessen these weaknesses. L2

Caption Answer

Figure 10 Because color-blind women must inherit the allele from both mother and father, more women are carriers of color blindness than have the disorder.

Pedigrees Trace Traits, continued

Reading Check

Answer It helps him or her predict the probability of offspring showing certain traits.

3 Assess

Reteach

Have students compare the three inheritance patterns in this section by making a chart. L1

 Visual-Spatial

Challenge

Which would be more difficult to predict, the results of incomplete dominance, multiple alleles, or polygenic inheritance? The number of variations is usually much greater with polygenic inheritance than with the other two patterns.

Assessment

Process Have students prepare a table that lists types of inheritance, their descriptions, and examples of each. Use **PASC,** p. 109.

Resource Manager

Chapter Resources Booklet
Reinforcement, p. 24

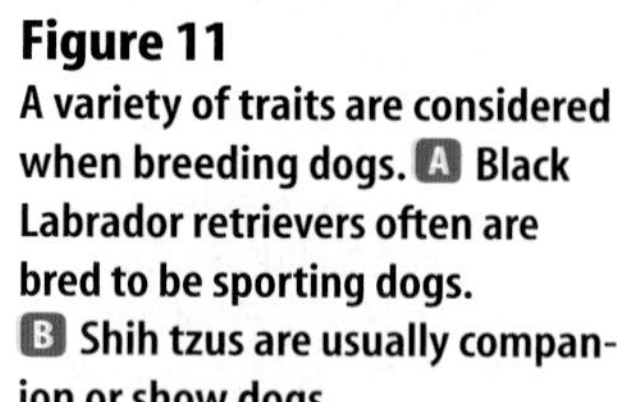

Figure 11
A variety of traits are considered when breeding dogs. A Black Labrador retrievers often are bred to be sporting dogs. B Shih tzus are usually companion or show dogs.

Using Pedigrees A pedigree is a useful tool for a geneticist. Sometimes a geneticist needs to understand who has had a trait in a family over several generations to determine its pattern of inheritance. A geneticist determines if a trait is recessive, dominant, sex-linked, or has some other pattern of inheritance. When geneticists understand how a trait is inherited, they can predict the probability that a baby will be born with a specific trait.

 Reading Check *Why is a pedigree a useful tool for a geneticist?*

Pedigrees also are important in breeding animals or plants. Because livestock and plant crops are used as sources of food, these organisms are bred to increase their yield and nutritional content. Breeders of pets and show animals, like the dogs pictured in **Figure 11,** also examine pedigrees carefully for possible desirable physical and ability traits. Issues concerning health also are considered when researching pedigrees.

Section 2 Assessment

1. Compare inheritance by multiple alleles and polygenic inheritance.
2. Explain why a trait inherited by incomplete dominance, such as the color of Appaloosa horses, is not a blend of two alleles.
3. Describe two genetic disorders and discuss how they are inherited.
4. Using a Punnett square, explain why males are affected more often than females by sex-linked genetic disorders.
5. **Think Critically** Calico male cats are rare. Explain how such a cat can exist.

Skill Builder Activities

6. **Predicting** A man with blood type B marries a woman with blood type A. Their first child has blood type O. Predict what other blood types are possible for their future children. Explain your answer using a Punnett square. **For more help, refer to the** Science Skill Handbook.
7. **Communicating** In your Science Journal, write an essay that explains why the offspring of two parents may or may not show much resemblance to either parent. **For more help, refer to the** Science Skill Handbook.

Answers to Section Assessment

1. Multiple alleles involve a single pair of genes that have more than two alleles; polygenic inheritance involves multiple pairs of genes, each with two or more alleles, all affecting the same trait.
2. The two alleles are present in the offspring, and are available to be passed on. But when combined, they produce a phenotype that is intermediate between those shown by homozygous individuals.
3. Answers will vary. Sample response: cystic fibrosis, a disease affecting the lungs and other organs, is inherited as a simple recessive trait.
4. Males only need to inherit one gene encoding for the disorder to be affected. Females must inherit two genes for the disorder to appear.
5. Possible answer: A mutation may allow a male cat to inherit an extra X chromosome in addition to a Y chromosome. Both X chromosomes may carry the recessive calico trait.
6. Children may have blood types A, B, O, or AB. The Punnett square should show heterozygous parents with the alleles AO and BO.
7. There are many genes and combinations, so an individual may look very different from either parent.

SECTION 3

Advances in Genetics

Why is genetics important?

If Mendel were to pick up a daily newspaper in any country today, he'd probably be surprised. News articles about developments in genetic research appear almost daily. The term *gene* has become a common word. The principles of heredity are being used to change the world.

Genetic Engineering

You may know that chromosomes are made of DNA and are in the nucleus of a cell. Sections of DNA in chromosomes that direct cell activities are called genes. Through **genetic engineering,** scientists are experimenting with biological and chemical methods to change the arrangement of DNA that makes up a gene. Genetic engineering already is used to help produce large volumes of medicine. Genes also can be inserted into cells to change how those cells perform their normal functions, as shown in **Figure 12.** Other research is being done to find new ways to improve crop production and quality, including the development of plants that are resistant to disease.

As You Read

***What* You'll Learn**

- **Evaluate** the importance of advances in genetics.
- **Sequence** the steps in making genetically engineered organisms.

Vocabulary
genetic engineering

***Why* It's Important**
Advances in genetics can affect your health, the foods that you eat, and your environment.

Figure 12
DNA from one organism is placed into another species. This method is used to produce human insulin, human growth hormone, and other chemicals by bacteria.

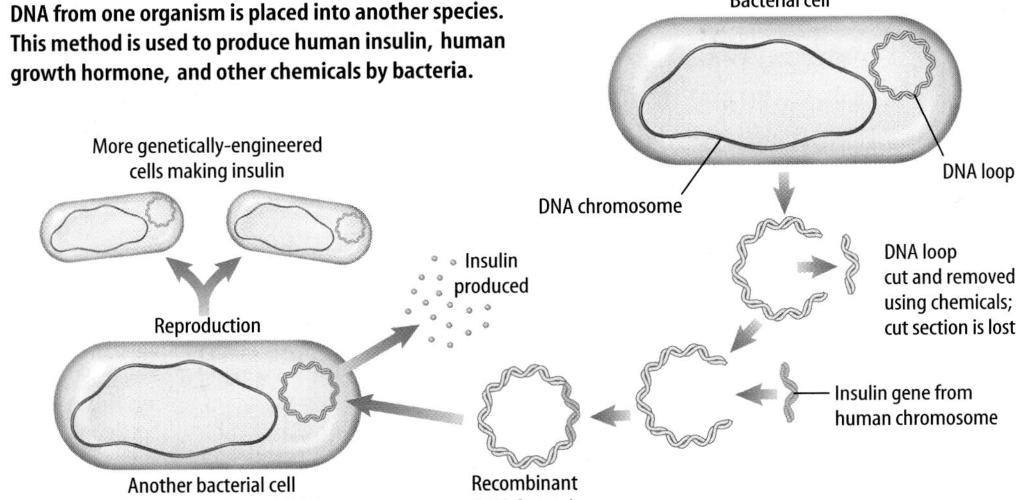

Section Assessment Planner

Portfolio
Assessment, p. 143

Performance Assessment
Skill Builder Activities, p. 143
See page 150 for more options.

Content Assessment
Section, p. 143
Challenge, p. 143
Chapter, pp. 150–151

SECTION

Advances in Genetics

1 Motivate

Bellringer Transparency

Display the Section Focus Transparency for Section 3. Use the accompanying Transparency Activity Master. L2 ELL

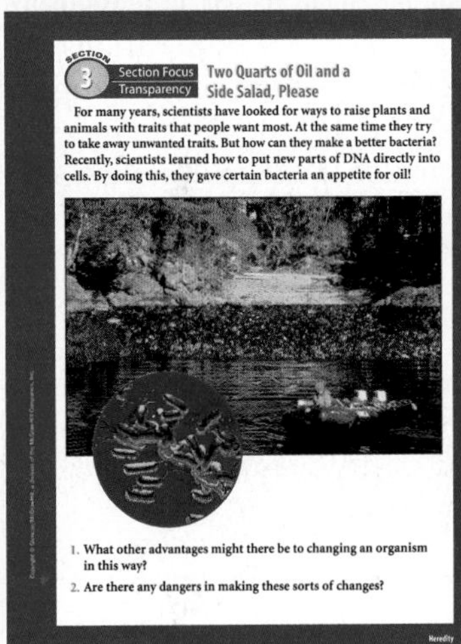

Section 3 Section Focus Transparency — Two Quarts of Oil and a Side Salad, Please

For many years, scientists have looked for ways to raise plants and animals with traits that people want most. At the same time they try to take away unwanted traits. But how can they make a better bacteria? Recently, scientists learned how to put new parts of DNA directly into cells. By doing this, they gave certain bacteria an appetite for oil!

1. What other advantages might there be to changing an organism in this way?
2. Are there any dangers in making these sorts of changes?

Heredity

Tie to Prior Knowledge

Explain that in selective breeding, specific crosses are made to accentuate a desired trait in offspring. Discuss with students how this might be advantageous to a plant breeder trying to produce a corn plant that has higher yields. Then explain that scientists are trying to find new ways to change traits without the time involved in selective breeding. They will learn about these techniques in this section.

2 Teach

Genetic Engineering

Environmental Science INTEGRATION

Possible answers: The crops may begin to grow in areas where they are not wanted; weeds might inadvertently become pesticide resistant; the plants may pollinate other fields of the same crop unintentionally.

Visual Learning

Figure 13 Explain that gene therapy is still in its infancy. As more is learned, the applications are likely to extend to many more genetic disorders. Remind students of the demonstration of a mutation in a cell being propagated by mitosis. **How is gene therapy similar to the way a mutation is propagated through body cells?** The mechanisms are similar, but in gene therapy, a mutation is corrected by the propagation, instead of spread.

Teacher FYI

Transgenesis is a genetic engineering process that involves transferring a gene from one organism into another. Using transgenesis, scientists have developed tomato plants that have increased resistance to disease and spoilage. Potato, cotton, and corn plants that have a natural resistance to insects, such as moth larvae and beetles, also have been developed.

Environmental Science INTEGRATION

Crop plants are now being genetically engineered to produce chemicals that kill specific pests that feed on them. Some of the pollen from pesticide-resistant canola crops is capable of spreading up to 8 km from the plant, while corn and potato pollen can spread up to 1 km. What might be the effects of pollen landing on other plants?

Recombinant DNA Making recombinant DNA is one method of genetic engineering. Recombinant DNA is made by inserting a useful segment of DNA from one organism into a bacterium, as illustrated in **Figure 12.** Large quantities of human insulin are made by some genetically-engineered organisms. People with Type 1 diabetes need this insulin because their pancreases produce too little or no insulin. Other uses include the production of growth hormone to treat dwarfism and chemicals to treat cancer.

Gene Therapy Gene therapy is a kind of genetic engineering. In gene therapy, a normal allele is placed in a virus, as shown in **Figure 13.** The virus then delivers the normal allele when it infects its target cell. The normal allele replaces the defective one. Scientists are conducting experiments that use this method to test ways of controlling cystic fibrosis and some kinds of cancer. More than 2,000 people already have taken part in gene therapy experiments. Gene therapy might be a method of curing several other genetic disorders in the future.

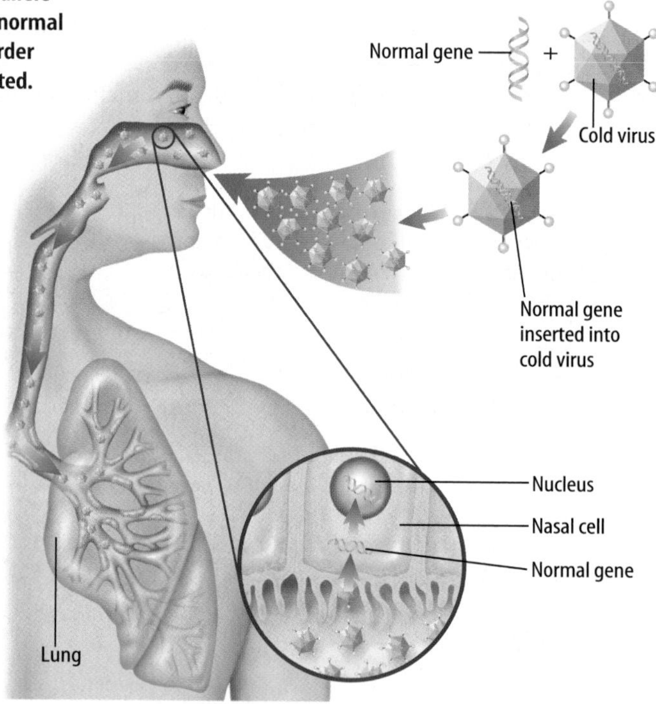

Figure 13
Gene therapy involves placing a normal allele in a cell that has a mutation. When the normal allele begins to function, a genetic disorder such as cystic fibrosis (CF) may be corrected.

Cultural Diversity

Genetic Engineering Research into genetic engineering, especially of crops, is taking place in many countries. Genetically engineered crops have already been planted in Europe, Canada, and the United States, though several countries in Europe have now banned the use of genetically engineered crops. Have students research to find out what countries could most benefit from agricultural advances involving genetic engineering. Have them research the staples of diets in those countries, and what, if any, research is being done on engineering those crops. Possible answer: Researchers at the International Rice Institute in the Philippines are working to produce new strains of rice.

Genetically Engineered Plants For thousands of years people have improved the plants they use for food and clothing even without the knowledge of genotypes. Until recently, these improvements were the results of selecting plants with the most desired traits to breed for the next generation. This process is called selective breeding. Recent advances in genetics have not replaced selective breeding. Although a plant can be bred for a particular phenotype, the genotype and pedigree of the plants also are considered.

Genetic engineering can produce improvements in crop plants, such as corn, wheat, and rice. One type of genetic engineering involves finding the genes that produce desired traits in one plant and then inserting those genes into a different plant. Scientists recently have made genetically engineered tomatoes with a gene that allows tomatoes to be picked green and transported great distances before they ripen completely. Ripe, firm tomatoes are then available in the local market. In the future, additional food crops may be genetically engineered so that they are not desirable food for insects.

What other types of traits would be considered desirable in plants?

Because some people might prefer foods that are not changed genetically, some stores label such produce, as shown in **Figure 14.** The long-term effects of consuming genetically engineered plants are unknown.

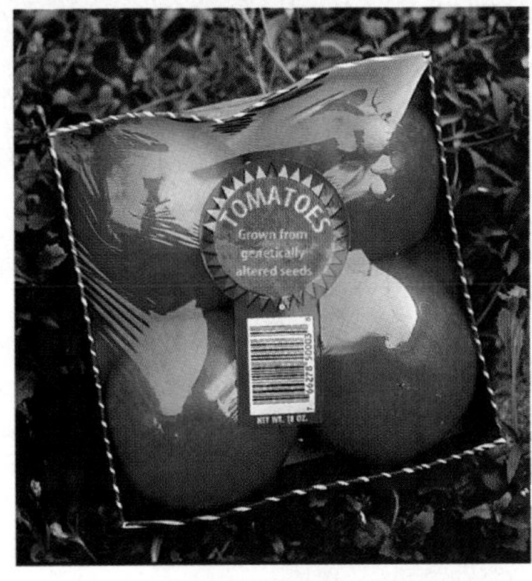

Figure 14
Genetically engineered produce is sometimes labeled. This allows consumers to make informed choices about their foods.

Section 3 Assessment

1. Give examples of areas in which advances in genetics are important.
2. Compare and contrast the technologies of using recombinant DNA and gene therapy.
3. What are some benefits of genetically engineered crops?
4. How does selective breeding differ from genetic engineering?
5. **Think Critically** Why might some people be opposed to genetically engineered plants?

Skill Builder Activities

6. **Concept Mapping** Make an events chain concept map of the steps used in making recombinant DNA. **For more help, refer to the Science Skill Handbook.**
7. **Using a Word Processor** Use a computer word processing program to write predictions about how advances in genetics might affect your life in the next ten years. **For more help, refer to the Technology Skill Handbook.**

Reading Check

Answer Possible answers: increased growth rate, increased fruit size and production, reduced need for water, improved flavor, desirable flower color

3 Assess

Reteach

Have students make flash cards that illustrate steps in the process of genetic engineering. Have students practice identifying and ordering the steps using these cards.

Challenge

Should gene therapy be made available for all genetic disorders, or only those that are most harmful? Support your answer. Individual responses will vary. Accept all responses for which students provide support.

Assessment

Performance Have students make a model that demonstrates the process of genetic engineering. Use **Performance Assessment in the Science Classroom,** p. 123. P

Resource Manager

Chapter Resources Booklet
Transparency Activity, p. 42
Reinforcement, p. 25
Directed Reading for Content Mastery, pp. 17, 18

Answers to Section Assessment

1. Answers may include agriculture, health, and medicine.
2. Recombinant DNA inserts a segment of DNA from an organism into a bacterium to produce needed substances. Gene therapy places a normal allele into a virus, which delivers the allele to its target cell. There, it replaces the defective allele.
3. They may lead to increased crop production or be pest-resistant.
4. Selective breeding relies on natural, reproductive processes. Genetic engineering may take traits from one organism and place them into another.
5. Some people are concerned about pesticide resistance in weeds or other unforeseen consequences.
6. Answers should reflect steps shown in **Figure 12.**
7. Answers may include increased food production, curing genetic disorders, or providing new medicines.

Activity

BENCH TESTED

Recognize the Problem

Purpose

Students will devise a method to test for color blindness, and administer the test to determine the percentage of affected individuals.

Process Skills

interpreting data, designing an experiment, forming a hypothesis, communicating, using numbers

Time Required

one class period

Materials

colored markers, blank white paper

Form a Hypothesis

Possible Hypothesis

Students may hypothesize that color blindness will affect more males than females.

Test Your Hypothesis

Possible Procedures

Students may choose to create a picture or number out of green circles. They can then use circles of red, orange, or yellow to surround the picture or number. Using this test, students would determine whether individuals could see the "hidden" picture or number.

Activity — Design Your Own Experiment

Tests for Color Blindness

What do color-blind people see? People who have inherited color blindness can see most colors, but they have difficulty telling the difference between two specific colors. You have three genes that help you see color. One gene lets you see red, another blue, and the third gene allows you to see green. In the most common type of color blindness, red-green color blindness, the green gene does not work properly. What percentage of people are color-blind?

Recognize the Problem

What percentages of males and females in your school are color-blind?

Form a Hypothesis

Based on your reading and your own experiences, form a hypothesis about how common color blindness is among males and females.

Goals

- **Design** an experiment that tests for a specific type of color blindness in males and females.
- **Calculate** the percentage of males and females with the disorder.

Possible Materials

white paper or poster board
colored markers: red, orange, yellow, bright green, dark green, blue
*computer and color printer

*Alternate materials

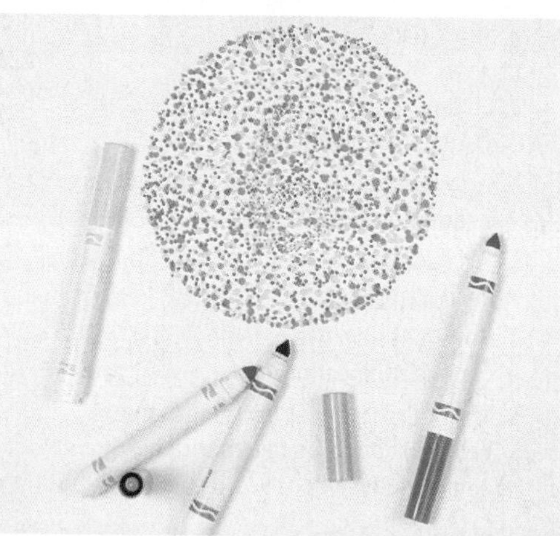

To a person with red-green color blindness, bright green appears tan in color, and dark green looks like brown. The color red also looks brown, making it difficult to tell the difference between green and red. A person without red-green color blindness will see a "6" in this test, while a red-green color-blind person will not see this number.

Resource Manager

Chapter Resources Booklet

Activity Worksheet, pp. 7–8

Enrichment, p. 28

Lab Management and Safety, p. 74

Test Your Hypothesis

Plan

1. Decide what type of color blindness you will test for—the common green-red color blindness or the more rare green-blue color blindness.
2. **List** the materials you will need and describe how you will create test pictures. Tests for color blindness use many circles of red, orange, and yellow as a background, with circles of dark and light green to make a picture or number. List the steps you will take to test your hypothesis.
3. Prepare a data table in your Science Journal to record your test results.
4. **Examine** your experiment to make sure all steps are in logical order.
5. **Identify** which pictures you will use as a control and which pictures you will use as variables.

Do

1. Make sure your teacher approves your plan before you start.
2. **Draw** the pictures that you will use to test for color blindness.
3. Carry out your experiment as planned and record your results in your data table.

Analyze Your Data

1. **Calculate** the percentage of males and females that tested positive for color blindness.
2. **Compare** the frequency of color blindness in males with the frequency of color blindness in females.

Draw Conclusions

1. Did the results support your hypothesis? Explain.
2. Use your results to explain why color blindness is called a sex-linked disorder.
3. **Infer** how common the color-blind disorder is in the general population.
4. **Predict** your results if you were to test a larger number of people.

Using a word processor, **write** a short article for the advice column of a fashion magazine about how a color-blind person can avoid wearing outfits with clashing colors. **For more help, refer to the** Technology Skill Handbook.

Teaching Strategy

Allow students to test individuals outside of class. Encourage them to test family, friends, and other teachers. Have them turn in their results after one week.

Expected Outcome

More males than females will test positive for color blindness.

Analyze Your Data

1. More males should test positive than females.
2. Males are much more likely to be color blind than females.

Error Analysis

Have students compare results to identify errors in data collection. Some possible sources of error are colors on the test pictures not being right or students overhearing the results of others so as not to give a true result.

Draw Conclusions

1. Answers will vary.
2. The allele for this trait is only located on the X chromosome. Because males only have one X chromosome, males with this allele will be color blind. A female will be color blind only when both of her X chromosomes have the color blind allele.
3. Color blindness afflicts 8 percent of males and 0.04 percent of females.
4. A larger sample will give more accurate results.

Process Have students create a similar test for another type of color blindness. After getting results, have students make a bar graph showing the percentages of individuals affected with each type of color blindness. Use **Performance Assessment in the Science Classroom,** p. 107.

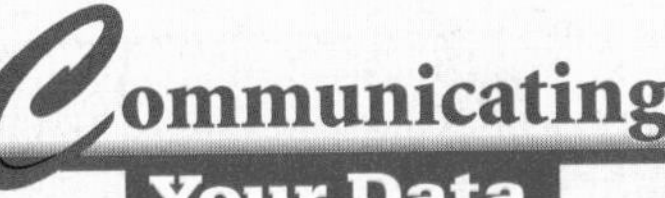

Students might suggest that matching colors be grouped in different areas of the closet, or that a tagging system be developed so that one group of matching clothing is labeled *A*, a second group is labeled *B*, and so on.

Science Stats

Content Background

The human genome project, an international, cooperative effort to sequence the human genome, is making continual contributions to our knowledge of human genetics. Scientists involved in the project are quick to point out the many things they don't know, even though the genome is complete. For example, the exact mechanism that turns genes on and off as needed, the exact function of many genes, and how some genes work together to cause disease are unknown. Students may be curious to know whose genome is being sequenced. The government and private companies working on genomes are using several anonymous donors of various racial and ethnic backgrounds.

Discussion

Mice and humans have many similar genes. What is one characteristic or function shared by mice and humans that might be coded for by similar genes? Possible answer: Both mice and humans have digestive enzymes that could be coded for by similar genes.

Activity

Have students write a story from the point of view of a human gene. Students should include details such as which chromosome the gene is located on, the function of the gene, and whether the gene functions all the time or is switched on and off. Students can either use an imaginary gene, or an actual human gene. LS **Linguistic**

Science Stats

The Human Genome

Did you know...

. . . The human genome is not very different from the genome of mice. As shown to the right, many of the genes that are found on mouse chromosome 17 are similar to genes on human chromosomes. Humans may be more closely related to other organisms than previously thought.

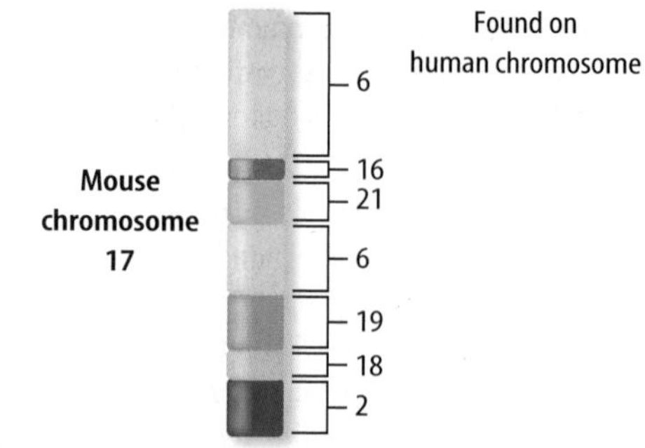

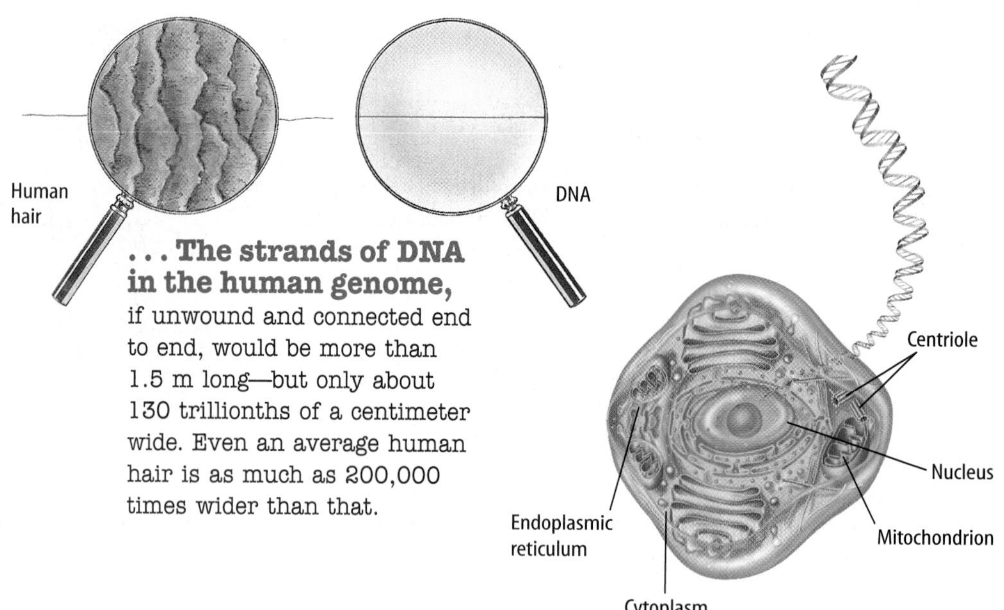

. . . The strands of DNA in the human genome, if unwound and connected end to end, would be more than 1.5 m long—but only about 130 trillionths of a centimeter wide. Even an average human hair is as much as 200,000 times wider than that.

. . . The biggest advance in genetics in years took place in February 2001. Scientists successfully mapped the human genome. There are 30,000 to 40,000 genes in the human genome. Genes are in the nucleus of each of the several trillion cells in your body.

SCIENCE Online
Internet Addresses

Explore the Glencoe Science Web site at **science.glencoe.com** to find out more about topics in this feature.

Connecting To Math

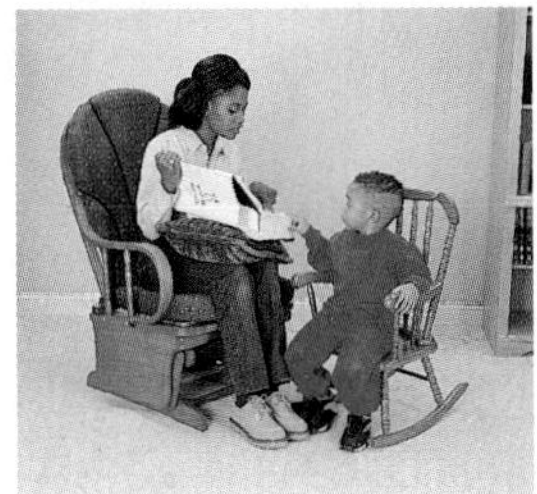

. . . It would take about nine and one-half years to read aloud without stopping the 3 billion bits of instructions (called base pairs) in your genome.

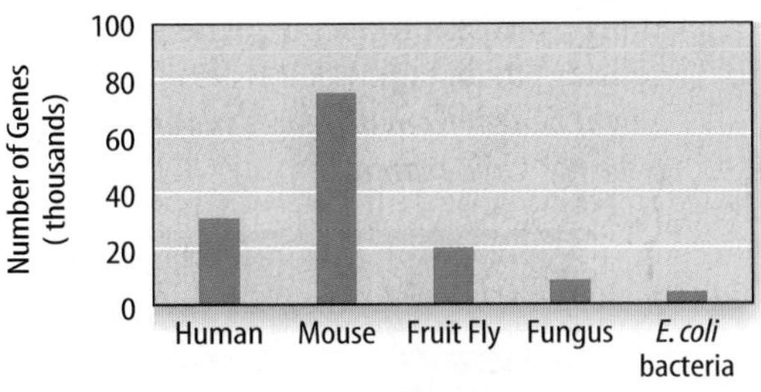

. . . Not all the DNA in your genes contains useful information. About 90 percent of it is "junk" DNA—meaningless sequences located in and between genes.

Do the Math

1. If one million base pairs of DNA take up 1 megabyte of storage space on a computer, how many gigabytes (1,024 megabytes) would the whole genome fill?
2. Consult the above graph. How many more genes are in the human genome than the genome of the fruit fly?
3. If you wrote the genetic information for each gene in the human genome on a separate sheet of 0.2-mm-thick paper and stacked the sheets, how tall would the stack be?

Go Further

By decoding the human genome scientists hope to identify the location of disease-causing genes. Research a genetic disease and share your results with your class.

Connecting To Math

Do the Math

Teaching Strategies

- Review place value for millions and billions to help students convert units in the first problem.
- Discuss what units are used to label the Y axis of the graph for the second problem.
- Remind students of the meaning of the metric prefix *milli-* (1/1000) to help them convert units for the third problem.

Answers

1. 3 gigabytes (1 million base pairs = 1 megabyte; 3 billion base pairs = 3,000 megabytes or 3 gigabytes)
2. about 10,000 genes
3. 20 m

Go Further

Have students prepare a poster with information about the genetic disease they have chosen to investigate. Children's hospitals are often an excellent source of information about genetic disorders. **LS Visual-Spatial**

Visual Learning

Genome Sizes of Various Organisms Have students examine the information in the graph and propose reasons for the large number of genes in the human genome as compared to the number of genes in the *E. coli* genome. As students discuss their ideas, point out the different levels of complexity in a human body and an *E. coli* bacterium.

Chapter 5 Study Guide

Reviewing Main Ideas

Preview

Students can answer the questions in their Science Journals. Discuss the answers as you go through the chapter. LS **Linguistic**

Review

Students can write their answers, then compare them with those of other students. LS **Interpersonal**

Reteach

Students can look at the illustrations and describe details that support the main ideas of the chapter. LS **Visual-Spatial**

Answers to Chapter Review

Section 1

4. Punnett squares can help to predict the variations and ratios of offspring.

Section 3

4. Accept all reasonable answers. Common examples may include corn, wheat, rice, and various produce.

FOLDABLES Reading & Study Skills

After You Read

After students have read the chapter and completed the Foldable described in Before You Read, have them do the activity on the student page.

Dinah Zike

Chapter 5 Study Guide

Reviewing Main Ideas

Section 1 Genetics

1. Genetics is the study of how traits are inherited. Gregor Mendel determined the basic laws of genetics.
2. Traits are controlled by alleles on chromosomes in the nuclei of cells.
3. Some alleles can be dominant and others can be recessive in action.
4. When a pair of chromosomes separates during meiosis, the different alleles for a trait move into separate sex cells. Mendel found that traits followed the laws of probability and that he could predict the outcome of genetic crosses. *How can a Punnett square help predict inheritance of traits?*

	F	f
F	FF	Ff
F	FF	Ff

Section 2 Genetics Since Mendel

1. Inheritance patterns studied since Mendel include incomplete dominance, multiple alleles, and polygenic inheritance.
2. These inheritance patterns allow a greater variety of phenotypes to be produced than would result from Mendelian inheritance.
3. Some disorders are the results of inheritance and can be harmful, even deadly, to those affected.
4. Pedigree charts help reveal patterns of the inheritance of a trait in a family. Pedigrees show that sex-linked traits are expressed more often in males than in females.

Section 3 Advances in Genetics

1. Genetic engineering uses biological and chemical methods to add or remove genes in an organism's DNA.
2. Recombinant DNA is one way genetic engineering can be performed using bacteria to make useful chemicals, including hormones.
3. Gene therapy shows promise for correcting many human genetic disorders by inserting normal alleles into cells.
4. Breakthroughs in the field of genetic engineering are allowing scientists to do many things, such as producing plants that are resistant to disease. *What types of crops might benefit from advances in genetic engineering? Give examples.*

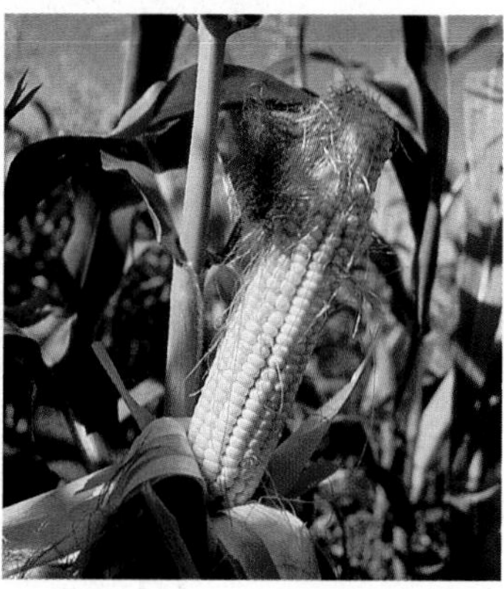

FOLDABLES Reading & Study Skills

After You Read

How many characteristics listed in your Classify Study Fold are inherited from your parents? How many are not inherited? Why are some not inherited?

Visualizing Main Ideas

Examine the following pedigree for diabetes and explain the inheritance pattern.

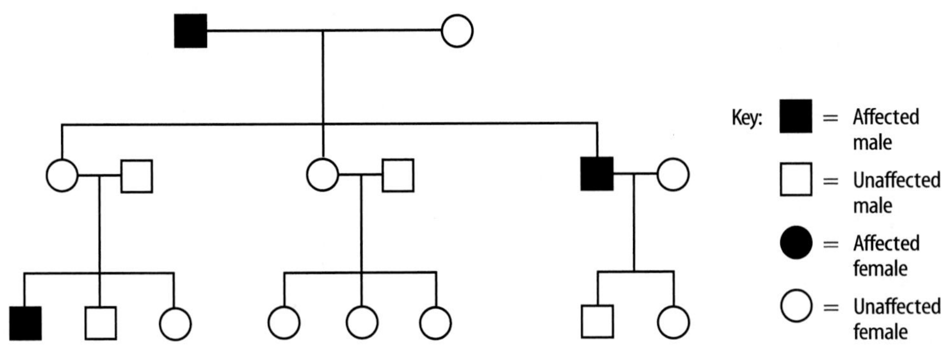

Vocabulary Review

Vocabulary Words

- **a.** allele
- **b.** dominant
- **c.** genetic engineering
- **d.** genetics
- **e.** genotype
- **f.** heredity
- **g.** heterozygous
- **h.** homozygous
- **i.** hybrid
- **j.** incomplete dominance
- **k.** phenotype
- **l.** polygenic inheritance
- **m.** Punnett square
- **n.** recessive
- **o.** sex-linked gene

Using Vocabulary

Make the sentences to the right true by replacing the underlined word with the correct vocabulary word.

Study Tip

When you encounter new vocabulary, write it down in a sentence. This will help you understand, remember, and use new vocabulary words.

1. Alternate forms of a gene are called genetics.
2. The outward appearance of a trait is a genotype.
3. Human height, eye color, and skin color are all traits controlled by sex-linked genes.
4. An allele that produces a trait in the heterozygous condition is recessive.
5. Polygenic inheritance is the branch of biology that deals with the study of heredity.
6. The actual combination of alleles of an organism is its phenotype.
7. Hybrid is moving fragments of DNA from one organism and inserting them into another organism.
8. A phenotype is a helpful device for predicting the proportions of possible genotypes.
9. Genetics is the passing of traits from parents to offspring.
10. Red-green color blindness and hemophilia are two human genetic disorders that are caused by a genotype.

Chapter 5 Study Guide

Visualizing Main Ideas

The inheritance pattern is a sex-linked trait that is expressed in males. The mother is a carrier of that trait.

Vocabulary Review

Using Vocabulary

1. alleles
2. phenotype
3. polygenic inheritance
4. dominant
5. Genetics
6. genotype
7. Genetic engineering
8. Punnett square
9. Heredity
10. sex-linked gene

IDENTIFYING Misconceptions

Assess

Use the assessment as follow-up to page 124F after students have completed the chapter.

Procedure Repeat the question: If brown eyes are dominant over blue eyes, does this mean that someday all people will be brown eyed? Have students write and diagram their answer.

Expected Outcome Students should show that brown-eyed parents can have blue-eyed children if both parents have one blue-eyed allele. Students should show that the allele is passed directly from parent to child. It does not disappear in the parent, then reappear in the child, nor does it disappear from the population. Students should show that they understand that a dominant allele is not stronger or more frequently expressed than a recessive allele.

Chapter 5 Assessment

Checking Concepts

1. A
2. C
3. A
4. C
5. C
6. B
7. D
8. A
9. A
10. B

Thinking Critically

11. DNA is a chemical; a gene contains DNA; an allele is a form of a gene specific for a trait; genes are located on chromosomes.
12. The phenotype will show the dominant trait, whether the genotype is homozygous or heterozygous, because the recessive gene does not show up in the phenotype.
13. The coat colors of some rabbits are affected by temperature differences in the environment.
14. The normal allele is usually inserted only into the cells that cause the disorder. For this reason, the reproductive cells would not be changed by gene therapy.

Chapter  Assessment

Checking Concepts

Choose the word or phrase that best answers the question.

1. Which of the following are located in the nuclei on chromosomes?
A) genes **C)** carbohydrates
B) pedigrees **D)** zygotes

2. Which of the following describes the allele that causes color blindness?
A) dominant
B) carried on the Y chromosome
C) carried on the X chromosome
D) present only in males

3. What is it called when the presence of two different alleles results in an intermediate phenotype?
A) incomplete dominance
B) polygenic inheritance
C) multiple alleles
D) sex-linked genes

4. What separates during meiosis?
A) proteins **C)** alleles
B) phenotypes **D)** pedigrees

5. What controls traits in organisms?
A) cell membrane **C)** genes
B) cell wall **D)** Punnett squares

6. Which of the following is a use for a Punnett square?
A) to dominate the outcome of a cross
B) to predict the outcome of a cross
C) to assure the outcome of a cross
D) to number the outcome of a cross

7. What term describes the inheritance of cystic fibrosis?
A) polygenic inheritance
B) multiple alleles
C) incomplete dominance
D) recessive genes

8. What type of inheritance is eye color?
A) polygenic inheritance
B) multiple alleles
C) incomplete dominance
D) recessive genes

9. What chromosome(s) did the father contribute if a normal female is produced?
A) X **C)** Y
B) XX **D)** XY

10. What type of inheritance is blood type?
A) polygenic inheritance
B) multiple alleles
C) incomplete dominance
D) recessive genes

Thinking Critically

11. Explain the relationship among DNA, genes, alleles, and chromosomes.

12. Explain how the parents and offspring represented in this Punnett square have the same phenotype.

	F	f
F	FF	Ff
F	FF	Ff

13. Explain why two rabbits with the same genes might not be colored the same if one is raised in Maine and one is raised in Texas.

14. Why would a person who receives genetic therapy for a disorder still be able to pass the disorder to his or her children?

Developing Skills

15. Predicting Two organisms were found to have different genotypes but the same phenotype. Predict what these phenotypes might be. Explain.

Chapter Assessment Planner

Portfolio Encourage students to place in their portfolios one or two items of what they consider to be their best work. Examples include:

- Extension, p. 130
- Science Journal, p. 135
- Assessment, p. 143

Performance Additional performance assessments, Performance Task Assessment Lists, and rubrics for evaluating these activities can be found in Glencoe's **Performance Assessment in the Science Classroom.**

16. **Classifying** Classify the inheritance pattern for each of the following:
   a. many different phenotypes produced by one pair of alleles;
   b. many phenotypes produced by more than one pair of alleles; two phenotypes from two alleles; three phenotypes from two alleles.

17. **Comparing and Contrasting** Compare and contrast Mendelian inheritance with incomplete dominance.

18. **Interpreting Scientific Illustrations** What were the genotypes of the parents that produced the following Punnett square?

Tt	Tt
Tt	Tt

Performance Assessment

19. **Newspaper Article** Write a newspaper article to announce a new, genetically engineered plant. Include the method of developing the plant, the characteristic changed, and the terms that you would expect to see. Read your article to the class.

Technology

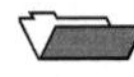

Go to the Glencoe Science Web site at **science.glencoe.com** or use the **Glencoe Science CD-ROM** for additional chapter assessment.

THE PRINCETON REVIEW Test Practice

A scientist is studying pea plants. The scientist made this Punnett square to predict the color traits of the offspring of two parent pea plants.

Parent (Yy)		Parent (Yy) Y	y
	Y	YY	Yy
	y	Yy	??

Study the Punnett square and answer the following questions.

1. Which of these genotypes will complete this Punnett square?
   A) YY
   B) Yy
   C) yy
   D) Yx

2. In peas, the color yellow (Y) is dominant to the color green (y). According to this Punnett square, most of the offspring of the two yellow pea plants probably will be _____.
   F) orange
   G) green
   H) yellow
   J) red

Chapter 5 Assessment

THE PRINCETON REVIEW Test Practice

The Test-Taking Tip was written by The Princeton Review, the nation's leader in test preparation.

1. C
2. H

Developing Skills

15. The phenotypes would be the expression of a dominant trait.
16. (a) multiple allele inheritance
(b) polygenic inheritance
17. Mendelian inheritance has two forms of an allele that produce only two phenotypes. Incomplete dominance also has two forms of an allele, but produces three phenotypes.
18. TT and tt; both were purebred, one dominant, one recessive

Performance Assessment

19. Answers will vary, but should explain genetic engineering methods and how the methods can change the traits of organisms. Use **Performance Assessment in the Science Classroom,** p.141.

Assessment Resources

Reproducible Masters

Chapter Resources Booklet
Chapter Review, pp. 33–34
Chapter Tests, pp. 35–38
Assessment Transparency Activity, p. 45

Glencoe Science Web site
Interactive Tutor
Chapter Quizzes

Glencoe Technology
Assessment Transparency
Interactive CD-ROM Chapter Quizzes
ExamView Pro Test Bank
Vocabulary PuzzleMaker Software
MindJogger Videoquiz

Section/Objectives	Standards		Activities/Features
	National	State/Local	
Chapter Opener	See p. 5T for a Key to Standards.		**Explore Activity:** Model camouflage, p. 153 **Before You Read,** p. 153
Section 1 Ideas About Evolution 2 sessions 1 block 1. **Describe** Lamarck's theory of acquired characteristics and Darwin's theory of evolution. 2. **Identify** why variations in organisms are important. 3. **Compare and contrast** gradualism and punctuated equilibrium.	National Content Standards: UCP4, A1, A2, C1, C2, C5, D2, G1, G3		**Science Online,** p. 156 **Problem-Solving Activity:** Does natural selection take place in a fish tank?, p. 157 **MiniLAB:** Relating Evolution to Species, p. 159 **Health Integration,** p. 161 **Activity:** Hidden Frogs, p. 162
Section 2 Clues About Evolution 2 sessions 1.5 blocks 1. **Identify** the importance of fossils as evidence of evolution. 2. **Explain** how relative and radiometric dating are used to estimate the age of fossils. 3. **List** examples of five types of evidence for evolution.	National Content Standards: UCP4, C1, C2, C5, D2, D1, G2, G3		**Science Online,** p. 165 **Visualizing the Geologic Time Scale,** p. 166 **Earth Science Integration,** p. 167
Section 3 The Evolution of Primates 3 sessions 2 blocks 1. **Describe** the differences among living primates. 2. **Identify** the adaptations of primates. 3. **Discuss** the evolutionary history of modern primates.	National Content Standards: UCP4, A1, C1, C2, C5, G1, G2, G3		**MiniLAB:** Living Without Thumbs, p. 171 **Activity:** Recognizing Variation in a Population, pp. 174–175 **Science and History:** Fighting the Battle Against HIV, pp. 176–177

Activity Materials	Reproducible Resources	Section Assessment	Technology
Explore Activity: classified ads from the newspaper, white paper, black paper, hole punch, watch or clock with second hand	**Chapter Resources Booklet** Foldables Worksheet, p. 15 Directed Reading Overview, p. 17 Note-taking Worksheets, pp. 31–32	GLENCOE'S ASSESSMENT ADVANTAGE	
MiniLAB: lined paper **Activity:** cardboard form of a frog, colored markers, crayons, colored pencils, glue, beads, sequins, modeling clay	**Chapter Resources Booklet** Transparency Activity, p. 42 MiniLAB, p. 3 Enrichment, p. 28 Reinforcement, p. 25 Directed Reading, p. 18 Lab Activities, pp. 9–10, 11–14 Activity Worksheet, pp. 5–6 **Cultural Diversity,** p. 19 **Earth Science Critical Thinking/ Problem Solving,** p. 14 **Mathematics Skill Activities,** p. 1	**Portfolio** Curriculum Connection, p. 159 **Performance** Problem-Solving Activity, p. 157 MiniLAB, p. 159 Skill Builder Activities, p. 161 **Content** Section Assessment, p. 161	Section Focus Transparency Interactive CD-ROM Guided Reading Audio Program
Need materials? Contact Science Kit at 1-800-828-7777 or www.sciencekit.com on the Internet.	**Chapter Resources Booklet** Transparency Activity, p. 43 Enrichment, p. 29 Reinforcement, p. 26 Directed Reading, p. 19 Transparency Activity, pp. 45–47 **Physical Science Critical Thinking/Problem Solving,** p. 11 **Life Science Critical Thinking/ Problem Solving,** p. 3	**Portfolio** Science Journal, p. 164 **Performance** Skill Builder Activities, p. 169 **Content** Section Assessment, p. 169	Section Focus Transparency Teaching Transparency Interactive CD-ROM Guided Reading Audio Program
MiniLAB: tape **Activity:** fruit and seeds from one plant species, metric ruler, hand lens, graph paper	**Chapter Resources Booklet** Transparency Activity, p. 44 MiniLAB, p. 4 Enrichment, p. 30 Reinforcement, p. 27 Directed Reading, pp. 19, 20 Activity Worksheet, pp. 7–8 **Lab Management and Safety,** p. 71	**Portfolio** MiniLAB Assessment, p. 171 **Performance** MiniLAB, p. 171 Skill Builder Activities, p. 173 **Content** Section Assessment, p. 173	Section Focus Transparency Interactive CD-ROM Guided Reading Audio Program

End of Chapter Assessment

GLENCOE'S ASSESSMENT ADVANTAGE

Blackline Masters	Technology	Professional Series
Chapter Resources Booklet Chapter Review, pp. 35–36 Chapter Tests, pp. 00–00 **Standardized Test Practice by The Princeton Review,** pp. 31–34	MindJogger Videoquiz Interactive CD-ROM Vocabulary PuzzleMakers ExamView Pro Test Bank Interactive Lesson Planner Interactive Teacher Edition	Performance Assessment in the Science Classroom (PASC)

Transparencies

Section Focus

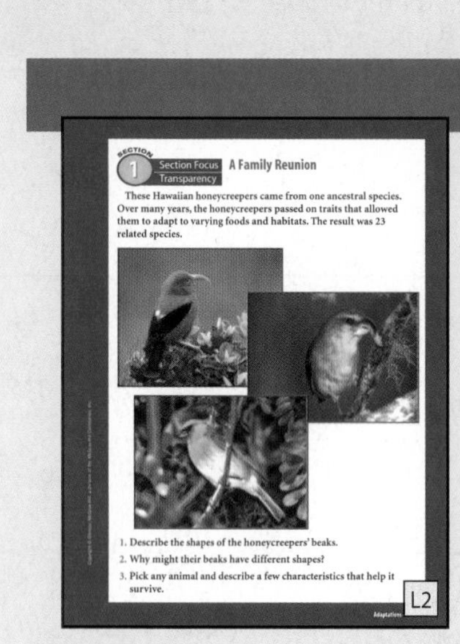

Section 1 Section Focus Transparency **A Family Reunion**

These Hawaiian honeycreepers came from one ancestral species. Over many years, the honeycreepers passed on traits that allowed them to adapt to varying foods and habitats. The result was 23 related species.

1. Describe the shapes of the honeycreepers' beaks.
2. Why might their beaks have different shapes?
3. Pick any animal and describe a few characteristics that help it survive.

L2

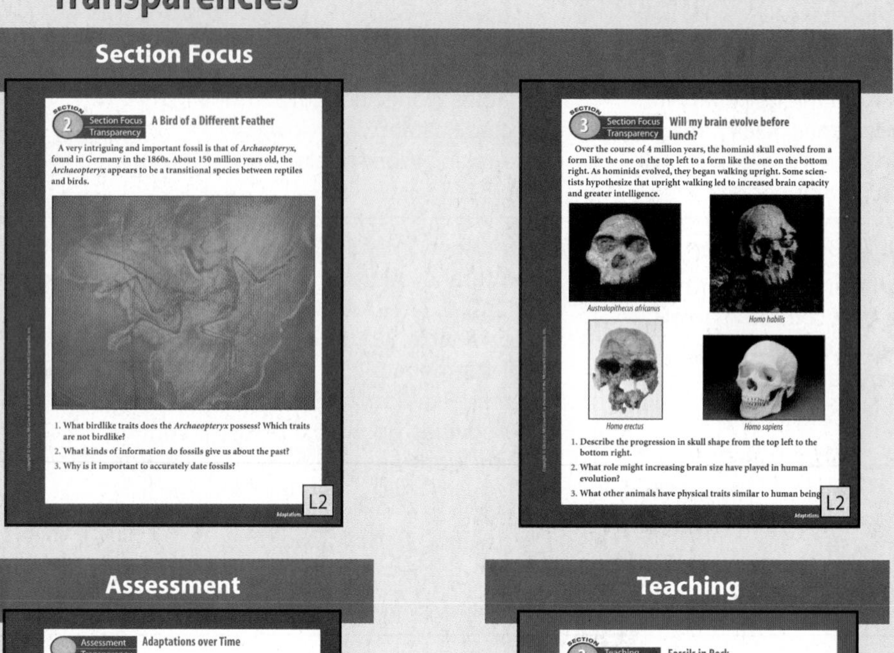

Section 2 Section Focus Transparency **A Bird of a Different Feather**

A very intriguing and important fossil is that of *Archaeopteryx*, found in Germany in the 1860s. About 150 million years old, the *Archaeopteryx* appears to be a transitional species between reptiles and birds.

1. What birdlike traits does the *Archaeopteryx* possess? Which traits are not birdlike?
2. What kinds of information do fossils give us about the past?
3. Why is it important to accurately date fossils?

L2

Section 3 Section Focus Transparency **Will my brain evolve before lunch?**

Over the course of 4 million years, the hominid skull evolved from a form like the one on the top left to a form like the one on the bottom right. As hominids evolved, they began walking upright. Some scientists hypothesize that upright walking led to increased brain capacity and greater intelligence.

Australopithecus africanus

Homo habilis

Homo erectus

Homo sapiens

1. Describe the progression in skull shape from the top left to the bottom right.
2. What role might increasing brain size have played in human evolution?
3. What other animals have physical traits similar to human beings?

L2

This is a representation of key blackline masters available in the Teacher Classroom Resources. See Resource Manager boxes within the chapter for additional information.

Assessment

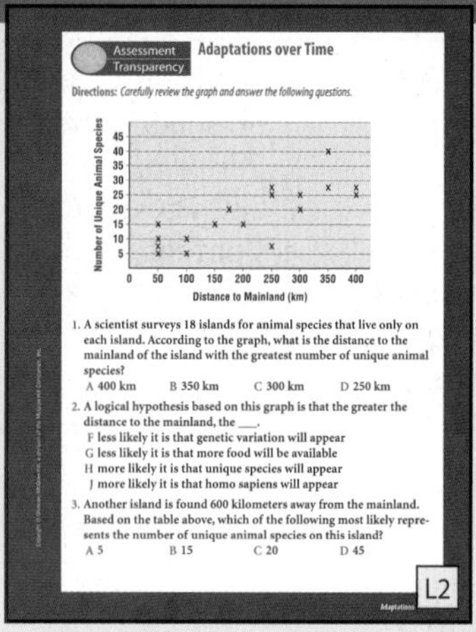

Assessment Transparency **Adaptations over Time**

Directions: Carefully review the graph and answer the following questions.

Number of Unique Animal Species (0–45) vs. Distance to Mainland (km) (0–400)

1. A scientist surveys 18 islands for animal species that live only on each island. According to the graph, what is the distance to the mainland of the island with the greatest number of unique animal species?
   A 400 km B 350 km C 300 km D 250 km
2. A logical hypothesis based on this graph is that the greater the distance to the mainland, the ___.
   F less likely it is that genetic variation will appear
   G less likely it is that more food will be available
   H more likely it is that unique species will appear
   J more likely it is that homo sapiens will appear
3. Another island is found 600 kilometers away from the mainland. Based on the table above, which of the following most likely represents the number of unique animal species on this island?
   A 5 B 15 C 20 D 45

L2

Teaching

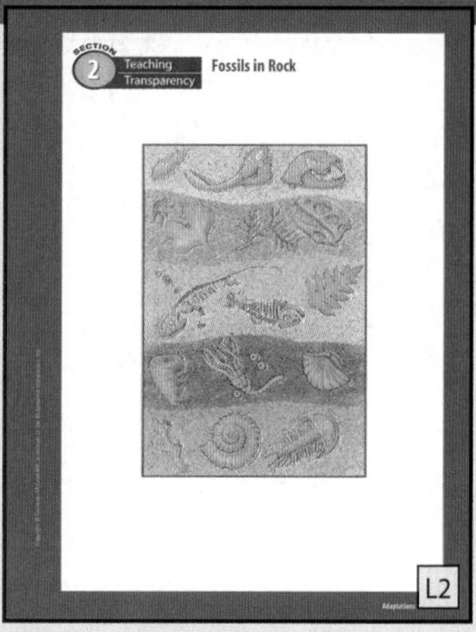

Section 2 Teaching Transparency **Fossils in Rock**

L2

Key to Teaching Strategies

The following designations will help you decide which activities are appropriate for your students.

- L1 Level 1 activities should be appropriate for students with learning difficulties.
- L2 Level 2 activities should be within the ability range of all students.
- L3 Level 3 activities are designed for above-average students.
- ELL ELL activities should be within the ability range of English Language Learners.
- COOP LEARN Cooperative Learning activities are designed for small group work.
- LS Multiple Learning Styles logos, as described on page 22T, are used throughout to indicate strategies that address different learning styles.
- P These strategies represent student products that can be placed into a best-work portfolio.

Hands-on Activities

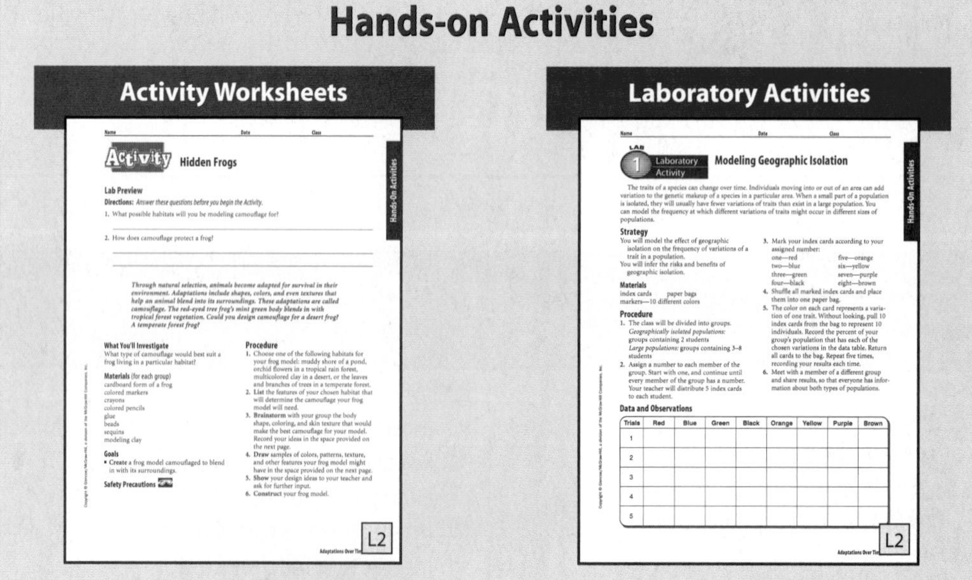

Activity Worksheets

Activity **Hidden Frogs**

Lab Preview

Directions: Answer these questions before you begin the Activity.

1. What possible habitats will you be modeling camouflage for?
2. How does camouflage protect a frog?

Through natural selection, animals become adapted for survival in their environment. Adaptations include shapes, colors, and even textures that help an animal blend into its surroundings. These adaptations are called camouflage. The red-eyed tree frog's mint green body blends in with tropical forest vegetation. Could you design camouflage for a desert frog? A temperate forest frog?

L2

Laboratory Activities

Lab 1 Laboratory Activity **Modeling Geographic Isolation**

Trials	Red	Blue	Green	Black	Orange	Yellow	Purple	Brown
1								
2								
3								
4								
5								

L2

Meeting Different Ability Levels

Content Outline

Note-taking Worksheet — **Adaptations Over Time**

Section 1 Ideas About Evolution

L2

Reinforcement

Section 1 Reinforcement — **Ideas About Evolution**

A—Bat Adaptations

B—Fish Adaptations

Figure 1 Figure 2

L2

Directed Reading

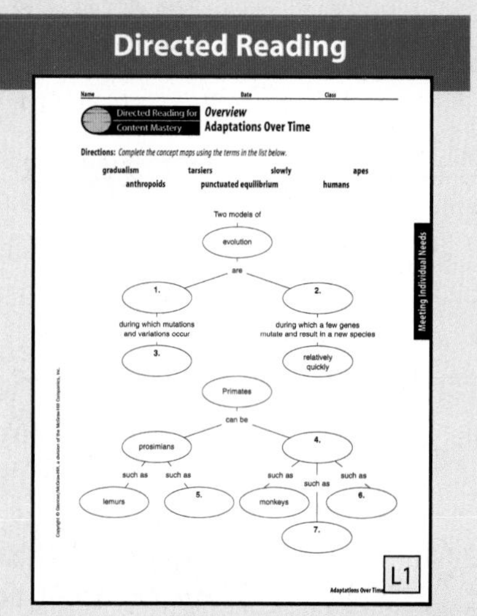

Directed Reading for Content Mastery — *Overview* **Adaptations Over Time**

Directions: Complete the concept map using the terms in the list below.

gradualism tarsiers slowly apes anthropoids punctuated equilibrium humans

L1

Enrichment

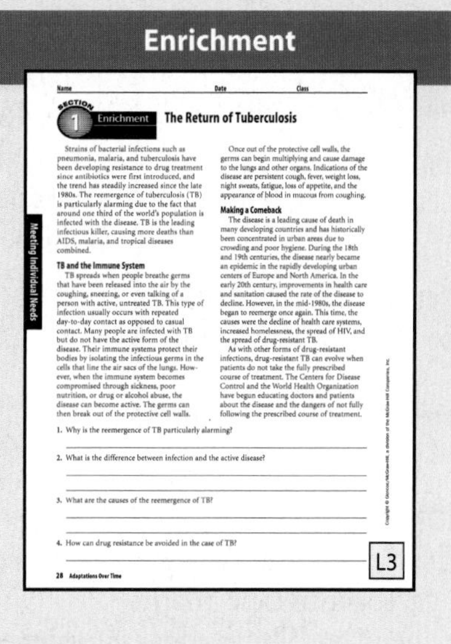

Section 1 Enrichment — **The Return of Tuberculosis**

TB and the Immune System

Making a Comeback

1. Why is the reemergence of TB particularly alarming?
2. What is the difference between infection and the active disease?
3. What are the causes of the reemergence of TB?
4. How can drug resistance be avoided in the case of TB?

L3

Spanish Directed Reading

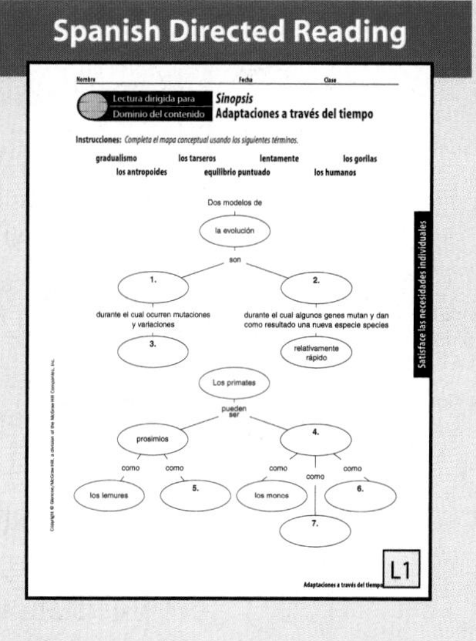

Lectura dirigida para Dominio del contenido — *Sinopsis* **Adaptaciones a través del tiempo**

Instrucciones: Completa el mapa conceptual usando los siguientes términos.

gradualismo los tarseros lentamente los gorilas los antropoides equilibrio puntuado los humanos

L1

Assessment

Chapter Tests

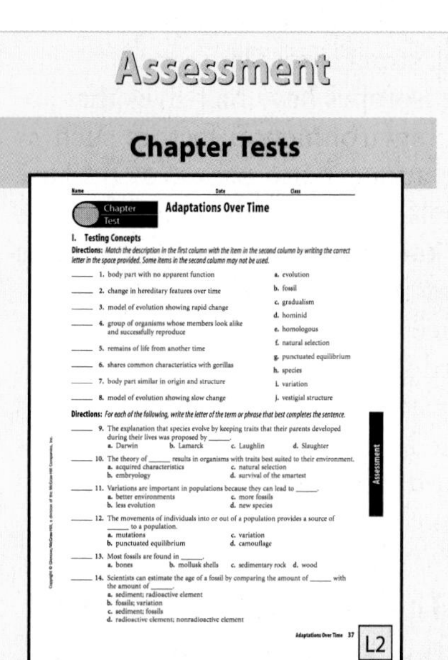

Chapter Test — **Adaptations Over Time**

I. Testing Concepts

L2

Test Practice Workbook

L2

Chapter Review

Chapter Review — **Adaptations Over Time**

Part A. Vocabulary Review

L2

Science Content Background

SECTION 1

Ideas About Evolution

Before Evolutionary Theories

Aristotle, a Greek philosopher, held a view that species were essentially perfect. Because species were considered to be well adapted, there was no discussion of evolution. Special Creation with all species fixed was the prevailing view. In addition, Carolus Linnaeus, father of taxonomy, organized the diversity of living things into a hierarchy of taxonomic categories that did not imply evolution.

Student Misconception

Environmental changes cause changes in traits that help organisms cope with the new environment.

Refer to the facing page for teaching strategies to address this misconception. Refer to page 161 for content related to this topic.

Evolution by Natural Selection

In 1858, Charles Darwin and Alfred Wallace provided enough evidence to convince many scientists that evolution occurs. Their ideas differed from the prevailing views of their time in two important ways—species change, or evolve, and natural selection is the process by which this evolution occurs.

An important point about the discussions on natural selection and evolution is Darwin's observations were not limited to those made during his trip on the HMS *Beagle*. Even as a young boy, Darwin was an avid collector of beetles and other information about natural history. By the time he became the ship's naturalist, he was already in agreement with his grandfather, Erasmus Darwin, that organisms evolve.

SECTION 2

Clues About Evolution

The Fossil Record

Some organisms which either lived for only a short time or only in a certain environment, formed fossils called index fossils. Index fossils are used by geologists to correlate rock strata across large areas.

Radioactive isotopes have half-lives that are not affected by environmental factors such as temperature or atmospheric pressure. Because the length of half-lives for radioactive isotopes of elements is known, an age estimate can be assigned to many rocks or fossils.

The evidence of evolution of species from the fossils record is compatible with other types of evidence for evolution. Transitional fossils have been located for some species, and species such as echinoderms have extensive fossil records that appear complete.

SECTION 3

The Evolution of Primates

Ongoing Research

Discoveries regarding primate evolution occur regularly. DNA comparisons have been done in an attempt to establish a date for the evolution of modern humans. Results of these tests are currently being debated, repeated, and extended.

For additional content background on this topic, go to the Glencoe Science Web site at science.glencoe.com.

Tetsu Yamazaki/International Stock

IDENTIFYING Misconceptions

Find Out What Students Think

Students may think that . . .

- **Environmental changes cause changes in traits that help organisms cope with the new environment.**

Students often form a magical view of natural selection. They know that if pesticides are applied to a crop, some insects will survive and reproduce. However, rather than understanding that the insects that survived did so because of pre-exisiting traits, students often believe that the pesticide itself caused the insects to become resistant. In the same way they may believe that antibiotics cause bacteria to form antibiotic resistance, or that organisms develop new traits because they need them to survive in a new environment (e.g., giraffes having long necks).

Activity

Have students read the section in the text that describes how bacteria become resistant to penicillin. If possible, bring in an article from a popular science journal describing the problem of antibiotic resistance. Ask students to imagine a situation in which they were required to clean their desks and the counters of the room daily with antibiotic soap to kill *Salmonella* and *Staphylococcus* bacteria. Have students write a paragraph describing what would happen to the bacteria in the room. Students should understand that resistant strains of these bacteria could be selected for and become a problem in the room. Some students, however, may persist in believing that the resistant bacteria form because of the antibacterial soaps.

Promote Understanding

Activity

Divide the class into small groups, and give each group a bowl containing 10 beans of various, distinct colors (i.e., white, black, spotted, red). Only one bean should be red. Supply each group with bags of various colors of beans. Tell students that the beans represent a colony of bacteria, and the colors represent minor genetic variations in the same species.

- On your signal have each group "multiply" their beans. Since bacteria reproduce by cell division, have students simply add one new black bean for each black bean in the bowl, one red bean for every red bean in the bowl, and so on. Have students "multiply" their beans twice (for a total of 40 beans in the bowl).
- Next, tell students that an antibiotic has been spilled in the environment. The antibiotic works by destroying the bacterial cell wall. The genes that gave the red bacteria their color also gave them a cell wall that was particularly thick and resists the action of the antibiotic. All other bacteria were killed.
- Have students remove all beans from the bowl except the red beans. Now have them "multiply" the remaining (red) beans for two or three more generations. Point out that because the red "bacteria" already had a feature that allowed them to survive the antibiotic, only red "bacteria" remain.

Assess

After completing the chapter, see *Identifying Misconceptions* in the Study Guide.

CHAPTER 

Adaptations Over Time

Chapter Vocabulary

species, p. 154
evolution, p. 154
natural selection, p. 157
variation, p. 158
adaptation, p. 158
gradualism, p. 160
punctuated equilibrium, p. 160
sedimentary rock, p. 164
radioactive element, p. 165
embryology, p. 167
homologous, p. 168
vestigial structure, p. 168
primate, p. 170
hominid, p. 171
Homo sapiens, p. 173

What do you think?

Science Journal The calico cat in this picture has a litter of kittens. The variations in offspring are because each kitten is the result of an egg and sperm joining. Fertilization is a random event that creates unique individuals and, in rare cases, can change species.

CHAPTER 

Adaptations Over Time

Are today's cockroaches different from those that lived one million years ago? How have these and other organisms survived Earth's changing environments over time? What evidence exists for changes in a species? Theories about how species change over time and some of the evidence for these changes are presented in this chapter. You also will read about primate adaptations over time.

What do you think?

Science Journal Look at the picture below with a classmate. Discuss what might be happening. Here's a hint: *This is one of the reasons species change.* Write your answer or best guess in your Science Journal.

152

Theme Connection

Stability and Change Changes that occur during evolution bring about stability by increasing variation within a population.

The cheetah is one of nature's speediest hunters, but it can run swiftly for only short distances. The cheetah's fur blends in with tall grass, making it almost invisible as it hides and waits for prey to wander close by. Then the cheetah pounces, capturing the prey before it can run away.

Model camouflage

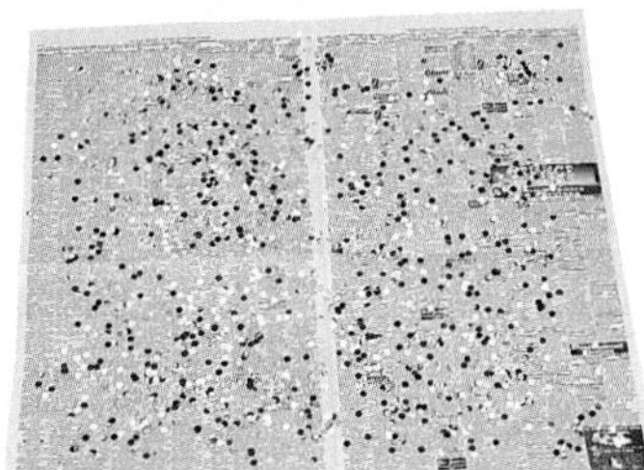

1. Spread a sheet of newspaper classified ads on the floor.
2. Using a hole puncher, punch out 100 circles from each of the following types of paper: white paper, black paper, and classified ads.
3. Scatter all the circles on the newspaper on the floor. For 10 s, pick up as many circles as possible, one at a time. Have a partner time you.

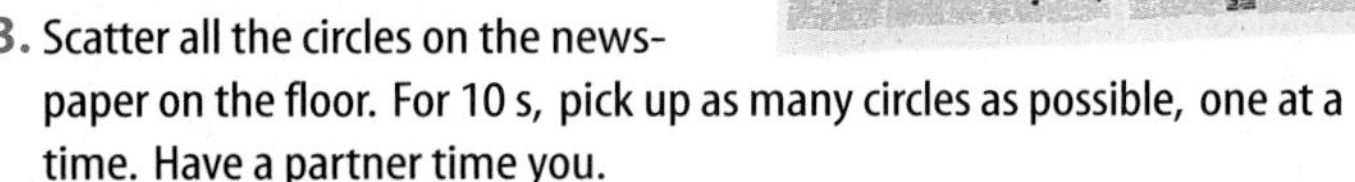

4. Count the number of each kind of paper circle that you picked up. Record your results in your Science Journal.

Observe

Which paper circles were most difficult to find? What can you infer about a cheetah's coloring from this activity? Enter your responses to these questions in your Science Journal.

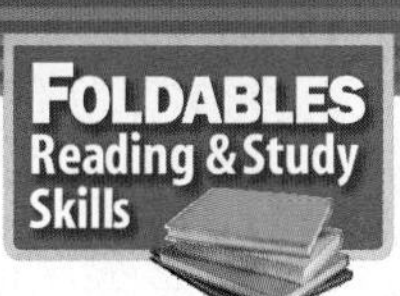

Before You Read

Making a Sequence Study Fold Make the following Foldable to help you predict what might occur next in primate adaptations over time.

1. Place a sheet of paper in front of you so the long side is at the top. Fold the paper in half from top to bottom.
2. Fold both sides in. Unfold the paper so three sections show.
3. Through the top thickness of paper, cut along each of the fold lines to the top fold, forming three tabs. Label the tabs *Past, Present,* and *Future* as shown. Title the middle tab *Primates.*
4. Before you read the chapter, write what primates have in common under the *Present* tab. As you read the chapter, write what primates were like in the past under the *Past* tab.

153

EXPLORE ACTIVITY

Purpose Students model camouflage coloration and its role in survival. L1 ELL COOP LEARN

LS **Kinesthetic**

Preparation Accumulate classified ads from the newspaper. Clear space for partners to work.

Materials newspaper classified ads, black and white paper, stopwatch or clock, hole punch

Teaching Strategies

- Show students photographs of a cheetah crouched in tall grass, and ask them to explain how the animal's markings enable it to blend in with its surroundings.
- If you find that students are picking up most of the circles within the time limit, add more circles or use less time.

Observe

Printed circles are most difficult to find. The cheetah's spotted fur blends in with the shadows and shades of dried vegetation found in tall grass.

Assessment

Process Provide students with photographs of animals that exhibit concealing coloration or patterns and have them describe how these features benefit each animal. Use **Performance Assessment in the Science Classroom,** p. 89.

FOLDABLES Reading & Study Skills

Before You Read

Dinah Zike Study Fold

Purpose Students make a Foldable to record what they know and learn about adaptations of a species over time. Students describe primates as they exist today and as they were in the past, and they use what they learn to predict what they might be like in the future.

For additional help, see Foldables Worksheet, p. 15 in **Chapter Resources Booklet,** or go to the Glencoe Science Web site at **science.glencoe.com.** See After You Read in the Study Guide at the end of this chapter.

SECTION

Ideas About Evolution

1 Motivate

Bellringer Transparency

Display the Section Focus Transparency for Section 1. Use the accompanying Transparency Activity Master. L2 ELL

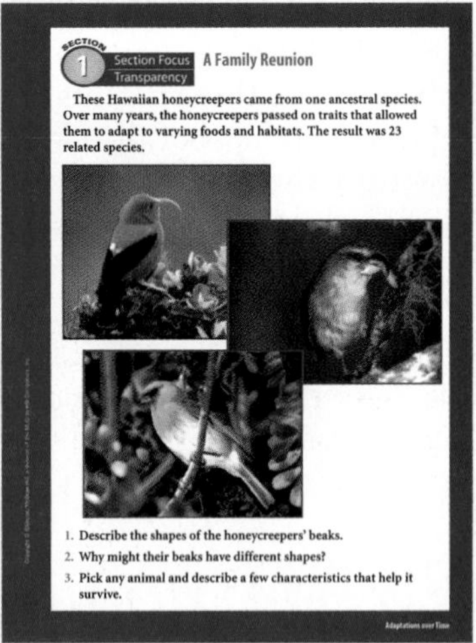

Section Focus Transparency 1 **A Family Reunion**

These Hawaiian honeycreepers came from one ancestral species. Over many years, the honeycreepers passed on traits that allowed them to adapt to varying foods and habitats. The result was 23 related species.

1. Describe the shapes of the honeycreepers' beaks.
2. Why might their beaks have different shapes?
3. Pick any animal and describe a few characteristics that help it survive.

Adaptations over Time

Tie to Prior Knowledge

Reinforce the differences between the terms *hypothesis* and *theory*. A hypothesis is a testable prediction based on observations. Explain that a theory is not a guess, but rather an accepted explanation based on a large number of tests. Scientists consider most theories to be true.

SECTION

Ideas About Evolution

As You Read

***What* You'll Learn**

- **Describe** Lamarck's theory of acquired characteristics and Darwin's theory of evolution.
- **Identify** why variations in organisms are important.
- **Compare and contrast** gradualism and punctuated equilibrium.

Vocabulary

species
evolution
natural selection
variation
adaptation
gradualism
punctuated equilibrium

***Why* It's Important**

The theory of evolution suggests why there are differences among living things.

Early Models of Evolution

Millions of species of plants, animals, and other organisms live on Earth today. Do you suppose they are exactly the same as they were when they first appeared—or have any of them changed? A **species** is a group of organisms that share similar characteristics and can reproduce among themselves to produce fertile offspring. The characteristics of a species are inherited when they pass from parent to offspring. Change in these inherited characteristics over time is **evolution. Figure 1** shows how the characteristics of the camel have changed over time.

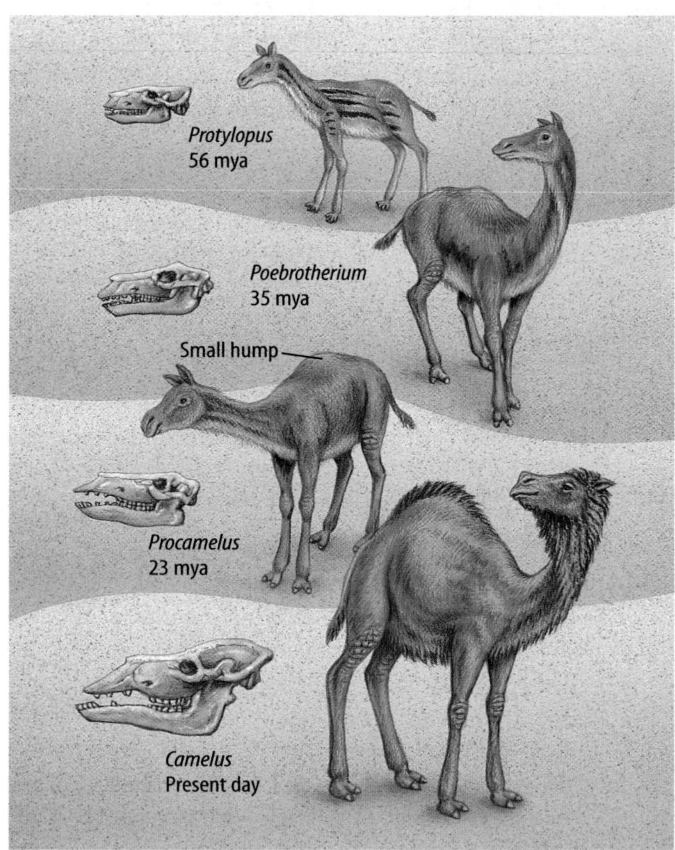

Figure 1
By studying fossils, scientists have traced the evolution of the camel. About 56 million years ago (mya), camels had a small body. Some 33 million years later, species of camels had grown larger and had a small hump. Present-day species are even larger and have a bigger hump.

Section Assessment Planner

PORTFOLIO
Curriculum Connection, p. 159

PERFORMANCE ASSESSMENT
MiniLAB, p. 159
Skill Builder Activities, p. 161
See page 180 for more options.

CONTENT ASSESSMENT
Section, p. 161
Challenge, p. 161
Chapter, pp. 180–181

154 CHAPTER 6 Adaptations Over Time

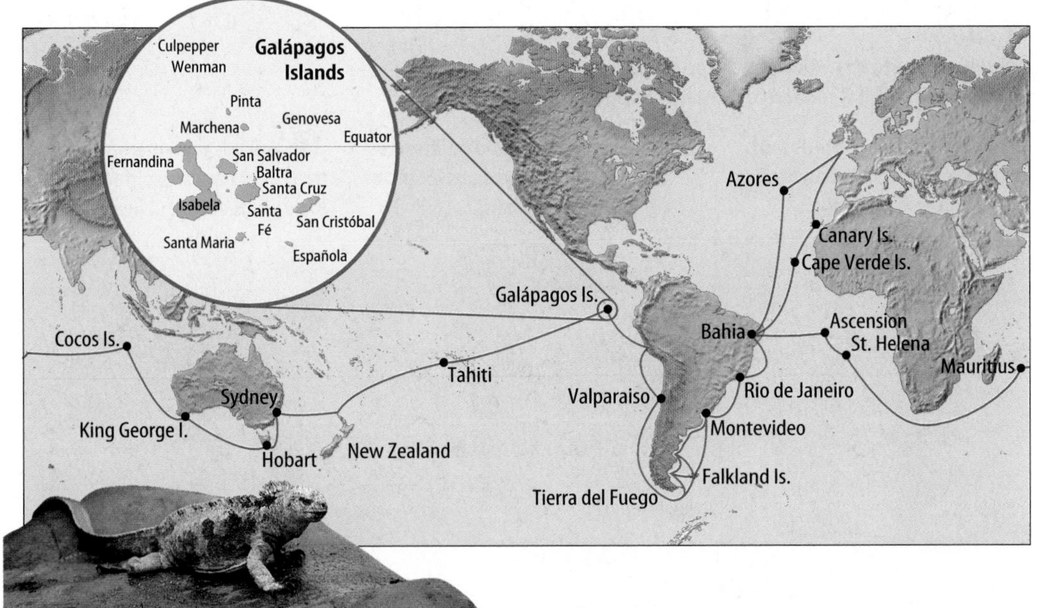

Figure 2
This map shows the route of Darwin's voyage on the HMS *Beagle*. Darwin noticed many species on the Galápagos Islands that he had not seen along the coast of South America, including the marine iguana. This species is the only lizard in the world known to enter the ocean and feed on seaweed.

Theory of Acquired Characteristics In 1809, Jean Baptiste de Lamarck proposed a hypothesis to explain how species change over time. He suggested that characteristics, or traits, developed during a parent organism's lifetime are inherited by its offspring. His hypothesis is called the theory of acquired characteristics. Scientists collected data on traits that are passed from parents to children. The data showed that traits developed during a parent's lifetime, such as large muscles built by hard work or exercise, are not passed on to offspring. The evidence did not support Lamarck's theory.

Reading Check *What was Lamarck's explanation of evolution?*

Darwin's Model of Evolution

In December 1831, the HMS *Beagle* sailed from England on a journey to explore the South American coast. On board was a young naturalist named Charles Darwin. During the journey, Darwin recorded observations about the plants and animals he saw. He was amazed by the variety of life on the Galápagos Islands, which are about 1,000 km from the coast of Ecuador. Darwin hypothesized that the plants and animals on the Galápagos Islands originally must have come from Central and South America. But the islands were home to many species he had not seen in South America, including giant cactus trees, huge land tortoises, and the iguana shown in **Figure 2.**

Resource Manager

Chapter Resources Booklet

Transparency Activity, p. 42

Directed Reading for Content Mastery, pp. 17, 18

Inclusion Strategies

Learning Disabled Allow students to use clay to make impressions of various items such as a comb, a key, etc. Plaster-of-paris can be poured into the impressions to form fossils. Place the plaster casts into a box. Allow students to try to identify the objects by reaching into the box without looking. You may use blindfolds if some students cannot resist the temptation to look.
L1  **Kinesthetic**

2 Teach

Early Models of Evolution

Visual Learning

Figure 1 Have students list the differences and similarities they observe in the modern camel and its ancestors. Possible answers: differences in teeth and leg bones; overall skull shape is similar. **How might these changes have occurred?** Environmental changes select organisms that have adapted.

Reading Check

Answer Traits developed during a parent organism's lifetime are inherited by its offspring.

IDENTIFYING Misconceptions

Ask students to list the inadequacies of Lamarck's theory. Students may agree with Lamarck until they critically examine the failures of this explanation. The primary failure of Lamarck's explanation is that acquired characteristics are not inherited.

Darwin's Model of Evolution

Visual Learning

Figure 2 Point out that Darwin suspected the process of evolution before he ever began his voyage. Ask students to explain why he was able to use evidence from his voyage to develop his theory of evolution by natural selection. Many of the species in the Galapagos are unique to the islands, but are similar to forms found on the mainland of South America.

Darwin's Model of Evolution, continued

Discussion

How are genetics and the theory of evolution related? Genetics provides the mechanism for evolution to work in a population. If traits were not inherited, there could be no evolution.

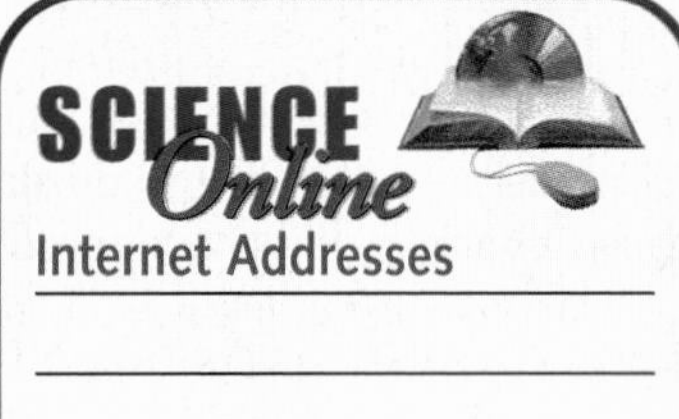

Internet Addresses

Explore the Glencoe Science Web site at **science.glencoe.com** to find out more about topics in this section.

Reading Check

Answer Darwin suggested that they all evolved from a common ancestral species in South America.

Natural Selection

Visual Learning

Table 1 Emphasize the importance of the principles of natural selection as mechanisms for evolution. **Why is overproduction of offspring important?** Overproduction assures that at least some of the offspring will survive. L2 LS **Logical-Mathematical**

Figure 3
Darwin observed that the beak shape of each species of Galápagos finch is related to its eating habits.

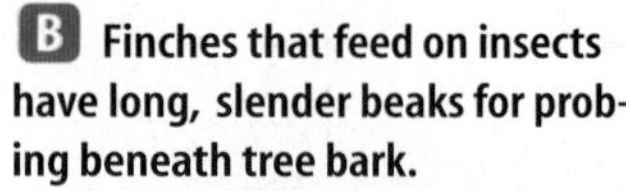

A Finches that eat nuts and seeds have short, strong beaks for breaking hard shells.

B Finches that feed on insects have long, slender beaks for probing beneath tree bark.

C Finches with medium-sized beaks eat a variety of foods including seeds and insects.

Research Visit the Glencoe Science Web site at **science.glencoe.com** for more information about the finches Darwin observed. In your Science Journal, describe the similarities and differences of any two species of Galápagos finches.

Darwin's Observations Darwin observed 13 species of finches on the Galápagos Islands. He noticed that all 13 species looked similar, except for differences in body size, beak shape, and eating habits, as shown in **Figure 3.** He also noticed that all the Galápagos finches looked similar to a finch species he had seen on the South American coast. Darwin hypothesized that all 13 Galápagos species evolved from South American species.

Competition and Survival All living organisms produce more offspring than survive. Galápagos finches lay several eggs every few months. Darwin realized that in just a few years, several pairs of finches could produce a large population. A population is made up of all the individuals of a species living in the same area. Members of a large population compete for living space, food, and other resources. Those that are best able to survive are more likely to reproduce and pass on their traits to the next generation.

Darwin reasoned that the Galápagos finches must have had to compete for food. Finches with beak shapes that allowed them to eat available food survived longer and produced more offspring than finches without those beak shapes. After many generations, these groups of finches became separate species.

Reading Check *How did Darwin explain the evolution of the different species of Galápagos finches?*

Inclusion Strategies

Gifted Students can invent their own species. They can draw it, describe its habitat and diet, and give the species a history. They should describe evolutionary changes that may have occurred within the species. Have students make a timeline showing major physical changes and ecological events that resulted in changes in the species. The species may be from the past or the future. L3 LS **Visual-Spatial**

Science Journal

Darwin and Wallace Have students research and describe in their Science Journal how the work of Alfred Wallace complemented that of Charles Darwin. Wallace and Darwin came to the same conclusion about evolution. The work of both men was presented in the same year. Darwin proposed the mechanism of natural selection to account for the conclusion. L2 LS **Linguistic**

Natural Selection

After the voyage, Charles Darwin returned to England and continued to think about his observations. He collected more evidence on inherited traits by breeding racing pigeons. He also studied breeds of dogs and varieties of flowers. In the mid 1800s, Darwin developed the theory of evolution that is accepted by most scientists today. He described his ideas in a book called *On the Origin of Species,* which was published in 1859.

Darwin's observations led many other scientists to conduct experiments on inherited characteristics. After many years, Darwin's hypothesis became known as the theory of evolution by natural selection. **Natural selection** means that organisms with traits best suited to their environment are more likely to survive and reproduce. Their traits are passed to more offspring. The principles that describe how natural selection works are listed in **Table 1.**

Over time, as new data have been gathered and reported, some changes have been made to Darwin's original ideas about evolution by natural selection. His theory remains one of the most important ideas in the study of life science.

Table 1 The Principles of Natural Selection

1. Organisms produce more offspring than can survive.
2. Differences, or variations, occur among individuals of a species.
3. Variations are passed to offspring.
4. Some variations are helpful. Individuals with helpful variations survive and reproduce better than those without these variations.
5. Over time, the offspring of individuals with helpful variations make up more of a population and eventually become a separate species.

Problem-Solving Activity

Does natural selection take place in a fish tank?

Alejandro raises tropical fish as a hobby. Could the observations that he makes over several weeks illustrate the principles of natural selection?

Identifying the Problem

Alejandro keeps a detailed journal of his observations, some of which are given in the table to the right.

Solving the Problem

Refer to **Table 1** and match each of Alejandro's journal entries with the principle(s) it demonstrates. Here's a hint: *Some entries may not match any of the principles of natural selection. Some entries may match more than one principle.*

Fish Tank Observations

Date	Observation
June 6	6 fish are placed in aquarium tank.
July 22	16 new young appear.
July 24	3 young have short or missing tail fins. 13 young have normal tail fins.
July 28	Young with short or missing tail fins die.
August 1	2 normal fish die—from overcrowding?
August 12	30 new young appear.
August 15	5 young have short or missing tail fins. 25 have normal tail fins.
August 18	Young with short or missing tail fins die.
August 20	Tank is overcrowded. Fish are divided equally into two tanks.

Discussion

Students will probably be familiar with the phrase "survival of the fittest." Have students consider this phrase in light of what they have learned about evolution. Then, have them explain what is meant by this phrase. The "fittest" are those whose adaptations make them better suited to their environments; their offspring inherit these traits, making them more likely to survive.

Problem-Solving Activity

National Math Standards

Correlation to Mathematics Objectives

5–9

Teaching Strategy

Emphasize to students that there may be several correct answers for each journal entry.

Solving the Problem

June 6: none
July 22: 1 or none
July 24: 2, 3, or 4
July 28: 4 or 5
August 1: 1, 4, or none
August 12: 1 or none
August 15: 2, 3, or 5
August 18: 2, 3, or 4
August 20: 1 or none

Quick Demo

Show students photographs of different organisms and have them list the adaptations they think are most needed for each species to survive. L2

IS Visual-Spatial

Resource Manager

Chapter Resources Booklet

Note-taking Worksheets, pp. 31–32

Mathematics Skill Activities, p. 1

Inclusion Strategies

Learning Disabled Write the five principles of natural selection on a piece of colored paper. Cut the pieces apart to make a puzzle. Allow students to put the puzzle together to reinforce what they learn about natural selection. L1

IS Visual-Spatial

Variation and Adaptation

Fun Fact

Albinism occurs in almost all species of mammals and has also been observed in other groups of plants and animals.

Caption Answers

- **Figure 4A** Neither predators nor prey can detect the scorpion fish in its natural environment.
- **Figure 4B** Predators might find it easily. Other lemurs might avoid it, preventing it from reproducing.

Activity

Display photographs of organisms that have unique adaptations such as the eye spots on the wings of moths or the thickness of a coconut husk. Have students identify the usefulness of each adaptation. Eye spots on moth wings may startle predators. Coconut husks protect the seed and allow it to travel by floating in salt water. L2 LS **Visual-Spatial**

Variation and Adaptation

Darwin's theory of natural selection emphasizes the differences among individuals of a species. These differences are called variations. A **variation** is an inherited trait that makes an individual different from other members of its species. Variations result from permanent changes, or mutations, in an organism's genes. Some gene changes produce small variations, such as differences in the shape of human hairlines. Other gene changes produce large variations, such as an albino squirrel in a population of gray squirrels or fruit without seeds. Over time, more and more individuals of the species might inherit these variations. If individuals with these variations continue to survive and reproduce over many generations, a new species can evolve. It might take hundreds, thousands, or millions of generations for a new species to evolve.

Some variations are more helpful than others. An **adaptation** is any variation that makes an organism better suited to its environment. The variations that result in an adaptation can involve an organism's color, shape, behavior, or chemical makeup. Camouflage (KA muh flahj) is an adaptation. A camouflaged organism, like the one shown in **Figure 4A,** blends into its environment and is more likely to survive and reproduce.

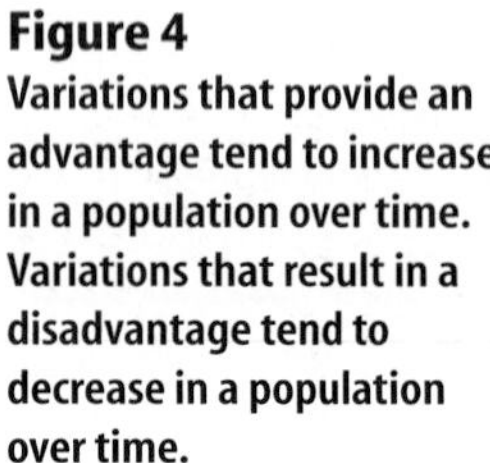

Figure 4
Variations that provide an advantage tend to increase in a population over time. Variations that result in a disadvantage tend to decrease in a population over time.

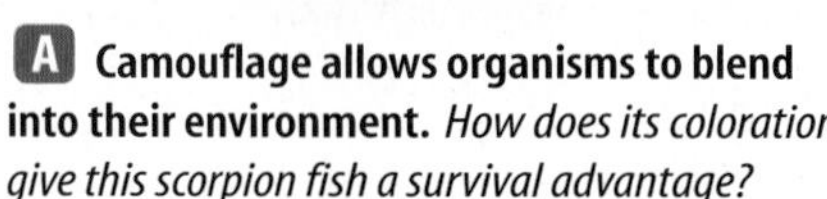

A **Camouflage allows organisms to blend into their environment.** *How does its coloration give this scorpion fish a survival advantage?*

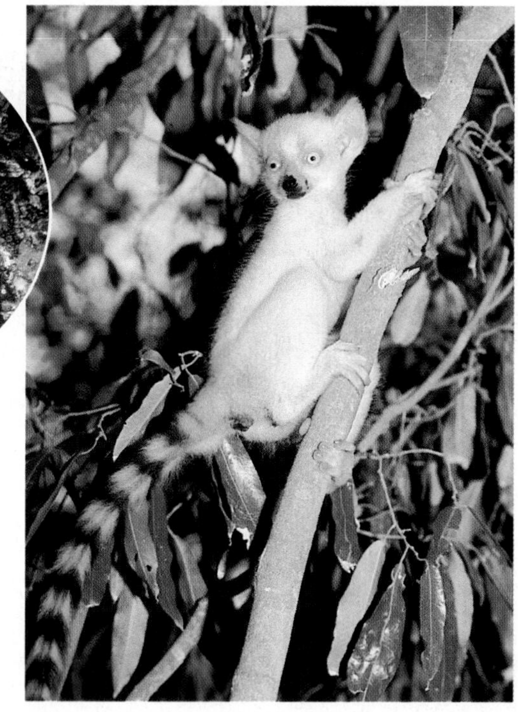

B **Albinism can prevent an organism from blending into its environment.** *What might happen to an albino lemur in its natural environment?*

LAB DEMONSTRATION

Purpose to observe variations

Materials pictures of various animal groups (i.e. cows, antelope, horses, wolves, rabbits), overhead projector

Preparation Have pictures made into transparencies. Try to find pictures that contain some obvious differences (for instance, animals of different colors).

Procedure Have students observe the pictures and list variations among the individuals in a group. Repeat for each group of animals.

Expected Outcome Students will observe variations in animals of the same species. Some variations, like size or color, will be obvious. Others, such as differences in the markings of animals, may be more subtle.

✔Assessment

What causes differences between animals in the same species? genetic variations
Do any of these variations aid in survival? If so, how? Answers will vary. Accept all reasonable answers.

158 CHAPTER 6 Adaptations Over Time

Figure 5
About 600 years ago, European rabbits were introduced to the Canary Islands from a visiting Portuguese ship. The Canary Islands are in the Atlantic Ocean off the northwest coast of Africa. Over time, the Canary Island rabbits became a separate species.

A European rabbits feed during the day and are fairly large.

B Canary Island rabbits feed during the night. *Why might large eyes be considered a helpful adaptation in Canary Island rabbits?*

Changes in the Sources of Genes Over time, the genetic makeup of a species might change its appearance. For example, as the genetic makeup of a species of seed-eating Galápagos finch changed, so did the size and shape of its beak. Many kinds of environmental factors help bring about changes. When individuals of the same species move into or out of an area, they might bring in or remove genes and variations. Suppose a family from another country moves to your neighborhood. They might bring different foods, customs, and ways of speaking with them. In a similar way, when new individuals enter an existing population, they can bring in different genes and variations.

Geographic Isolation Sometimes mountains, lakes, or other geologic features isolate a small number of individuals from the rest of a population. Over several generations, variations that do not exist in the larger population might begin to be more common in the isolated population. Also, gene mutations can occur that add variations to populations. Over time, the two populations can become so different that they no longer can breed with each other. The two populations of rabbits shown in **Figure 5** have been geographically isolated from each other for thousands of generations.

Mini LAB

Relating Evolution to Species

Procedure
1. On a piece of **lined paper,** print the alphabet in lowercase letters.
2. Organize the letters into three groups. Put all of the vowels in the first group. Place all of the letters that drop below the line into the second group. Place all of the remaining letters in the third group.

Analysis
1. How are the three groups of letters similar to each other?
2. If the letters were organisms, what traits would indicate to scientists how closely related the letters were to each other?

Caption Answer

Figure 5B Their large eyes help the rabbits see in the dark.

Purpose Students practice classifying and sequencing. L2 LS **Visual-Spatial**

Teaching Strategy Explain to students that the letters of the alphabet have changed over time. You may research and show the evolution of the letters *f* and *s* in particular. Tell how this type of evolution is different from evolution in living things.

Analysis
1. Answers will vary. Possible answers: all are letters of the alphabet; all are lowercase.
2. Letters with a characteristic in common would be the most closely related (i.e. vowels and consonants that do not drop below the line). Letters with similar characteristics would be the next closest relations (i.e. consonants that do drop below the line). Letters with no similar characteristics would be distantly related.

Performance To further assess students' understanding of evolution, have them make up and explain another hypothetical evolutionary schema using whatever shapes or materials they choose. Use **Performance Assessment in the Science Classroom,** p. 123.

Resource Manager

Chapter Resources Booklet
MiniLAB, p. 3

Curriculum Connection

History Direct students to research the mid-nineteenth century to determine what daily life was like for Darwin and his peers. Students should make posters showing technologies used, dress of the period, and religious or political events. L2 LS **Visual-Spatial** P

The Speed of Evolution

Use Science Words

Word Origin Scientists once accepted that organisms evolve according to the gradualism model. *Gradus*, meaning a step, is the Latin word from which gradualism is derived. Ask students why this word is used. Gradualism seems to occur step by step. L2 IN **Linguistic**

Discussion

Explain to students that punctuated equilibrium caused quite a bit of controversy within the scientific community when it was first postulated. **Why didn't the new evidence for a different rate of evolution destroy acceptance of the theory of evolution?** Theories are adaptable. By incorporating new evidence to explain a greater number of observations, the theory is strengthened.

Visual Learning

Figure 6 Have students use the illustration as they discuss gradualism and punctuated equilibrium. Ask why punctuated equilibrium appears to have been involved in the evolution of the bears. The diagram shows few intermediate forms. L2 IN **Visual-Spatial**

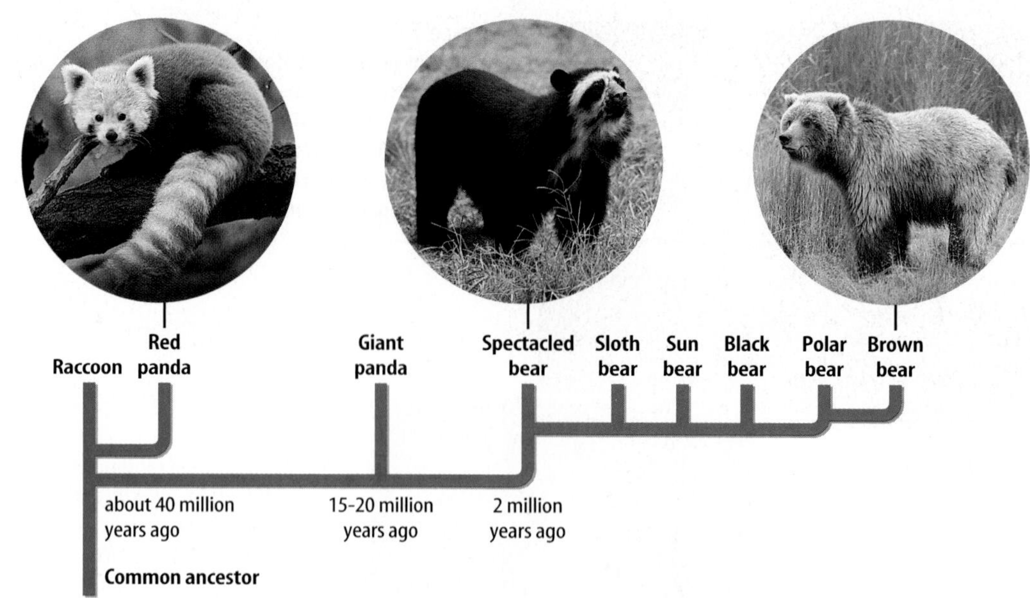

Figure 6
The evolution of bears illustrates the punctuated equilibrium model of evolution. Six distinct bear species evolved over two million years. The same series of changes would have taken many times longer according to the gradualism model of evolution.

The Speed of Evolution

Scientists do not agree on how quickly evolution occurs. Many scientists hypothesize that evolution occurs slowly, perhaps over tens or hundreds of millions of years. Other scientists hypothesize that evolution can occur quickly. Some scientists propose that evidence supports both of these models.

Gradualism Darwin hypothesized that evolution takes place slowly. The model that describes evolution as a slow, ongoing process by which one species changes to a new species is known as **gradualism.** According to the gradualism model, a continuing series of mutations and variations over time will result in a new species. Look back at **Figure 1,** which shows the evolution of the camel over tens of millions of years. Fossil evidence shows a series of intermediate forms that indicate a gradual change from the earliest camel species to today's species.

Punctuated Equilibrium Gradualism doesn't explain the evolution of all species. For some species, the fossil record shows few intermediate forms—one species suddenly changes to another. According to the **punctuated equilibrium** model, rapid evolution comes about when the mutation of a few genes results in the appearance of a new species over a relatively short period of time. The fossil record gives examples of this type of evolution, as you can see in **Figure 6.**

Resource Manager 

Chapter Resources Booklet
Enrichment, p. 28
Reinforcement, p. 26

Curriculum Connection

Art Have students make a piece of art that shows their understanding of gradualism (i.e. a drawing that shows the slow evolution of one organism to another). In art, this process is called morphing. L2 IN **Visual-Spatial**

Punctuated Equilibrium Today Evolution by the punctuated equilibrium model can occur over a few thousand or million years, and sometimes even faster. For example, many bacteria have changed in a few decades. The antibiotic penicillin originally came from the fungus shown in **Figure 7.** But many bacteria species that were once easily killed by penicillin no longer are harmed by it. These bacteria have developed resistance to the drug. Penicillin has been in use since 1943. Just four years later, in 1947, a species of bacteria that causes pneumonia and other infections already had developed resistance to the drug. By the 1990s, several disease-producing bacteria had become resistant to penicillin and many other antibiotics.

How did penicillin-resistant bacteria evolve so quickly? As in any population, some organisms have variations that allow them to survive unfavorable living conditions when other organisms cannot. When penicillin was used to kill bacteria, those with the penicillin-resistant variation survived, reproduced, and passed this trait to their offspring. Over a period of time, this bacteria population became penicillin-resistant.

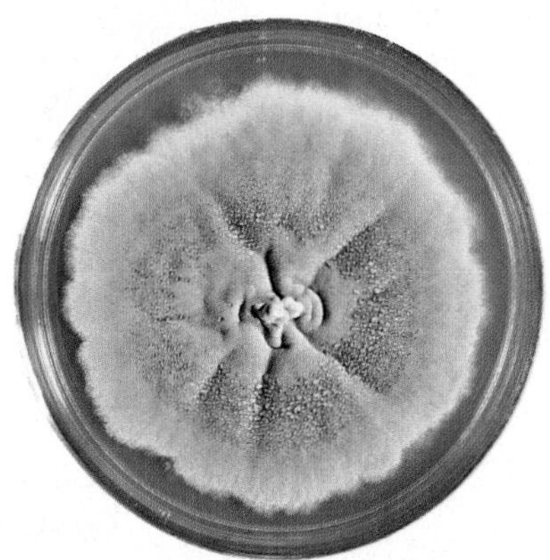

Figure 7
The fungus growing in this petri dish is *Penicillium*, the original source of penicillin. It produces an antibiotic substance that prevents the growth of certain bacteria.

Health INTEGRATION

When a doctor prescribes antibiotics, the patient is told to take the medicine every few hours for a week or more. A patient who feels better after two or three days might stop taking the medicine. But, if any of the disease-causing bacteria remain in the body, the patient could become ill again. In your Science Journal, explain why it is important to take all of the antibiotics the doctor prescribes.

Section 1 Assessment

1. Compare Lamarck's and Darwin's ideas about how evolution takes place.
2. Explain why variations are important to the survival of a population.
3. Explain how the gradualism model of evolution differs from the punctuated equilibrium model of evolution.
4. How does geographic isolation contribute to evolution?
5. **Think Critically** What adaptations would be helpful for an animal species that was moved to the arctic?

Skill Builder Activities

6. **Concept Mapping** Use information given in **Figure 6** to make a concept map that shows how raccoons, red pandas, giant pandas, polar bears, and black bears are related to a common ancestor. **For more help, refer to the Science Skill Handbook.**
7. **Using Percentages** The evolution of the camel can be traced back at least 56 million years. Use **Figure 1** to estimate the percent of this time that the modern camel has existed. **For more help, refer to the Math Skill Handbook.**

Health INTEGRATION

It's important to kill all of the disease-causing bacteria, because any surviving bacteria could reproduce and cause the illness to recur.

IDENTIFYING Misconceptions

Many students think that environmental changes cause changes in traits that help organisms cope with the new environment. Refer to page 152F for teaching strategies that address this misconception.

3 Assess

Reteach

Have students list similarities between artificial selection, such as dog breeding and natural selection. In both, specific traits are selected. L2

Challenge

Have students discuss why Darwin was impressed with the ability of humans to produce new breeds of plants and animals through artificial selection. He saw this as an analogy to the mechanism of evolution by natural selection. L2 COOP LEARN IN **Interpersonal**

Assessment

Performance To assess students' abilities to classify organisms by their variations, ask them to classify two species of birds that eat different types of foods. Use **Performance Assessment in the Science Classroom,** p. 121.

Answers to Section Assessment

1. Lamarck thought acquired traits were passed to offspring; Darwin concluded that only inherited traits were passed to offspring.
2. If a population were genetically uniform, any harmful factor that affected one of them would affect all of them. Because of variation, some individuals in a population would not be affected by the adverse factor and would survive and reproduce.
3. Gradualism—species slowly evolve to become other species; punctuated equilibrium—species suddenly become other species in a relatively short amount of time.
4. populations with different variations evolve independently, producing greater variation
5. Possible answers: lighter coat color; traits for surviving extreme cold
6. The concept maps should illustrate several species evolving from a common ancestor.
7. Two million years/56 million years $\times$ 100% = approximately 4%

Activity BENCH TESTED

Purpose Students will explore how natural selection equips organisms for survival in their environment.

Process Skills observing, analyzing, inferring, formulating, modeling

Time Required 40 minutes

Teaching Strategies:

- Obtain color photographs of frogs in natural settings to present examples of camouflage to students.
- Obtain color photographs of other camouflaged animals and ask students how natural selection has prepared them for survival in their environment.

Troubleshooting Provide students with pictures of different environments to serve as a reference.

Answers to Questions

1. Answer will vary, but students should consider the colors, patterns, and textures of the habitat.
2. Color patterns, textures, and body shapes that provide the best camouflage in an environment help those frogs avoid predators, and, through natural selection, these characteristics become dominant in a frog population.
3. The frog may not be properly camouflaged from predators in its new environment.

Assessment

Process Ask students to explain why the frog they have modeled would be not be equipped to survive in a different environment. Use **PASC,** p. 89.

Activity

Hidden Frogs

Through natural selection, animals become adapted for survival in their environment. Adaptations include shapes, colors, and even textures that help an animal blend into its surroundings. These adaptations are called camouflage. The red-eyed tree frog's mint green body blends in with tropical forest vegetation as shown in the photo on the right. Could you design camouflage for a desert frog? A temperate forest frog?

What You'll Investigate

What type of camouflage would best suit a frog living in a particular habitat?

Materials (for each group)

cardboard form of a frog	glue
colored markers	beads
crayons	sequins
colored pencils	modeling clay

Goals

- **Create** a frog model camouflaged to blend in with its surroundings.

Safety Precautions 

Procedure

1. Choose one of the following habitats for your frog model: muddy shore of a pond, orchid flowers in a tropical rain forest, multicolored clay in a desert, or the leaves and branches of trees in a temperate forest.
2. **List** the features of your chosen habitat that will determine the camouflage your frog model will need.
3. **Brainstorm** with your group the body shape, coloring, and skin texture that would make the best camouflage for your model. Record your ideas in your Science Journal.
4. **Draw** samples of colors, patterns, texture, and other features your frog model might have in your Science Journal.
5. Show your design ideas to your teacher and ask for further input.
6. **Construct** your frog model.

Conclude and Apply

1. **Explain** how the characteristics of the habitat helped you decide on the specific frog features you chose.
2. **Infer** how the color patterns and other physical features of real frogs develop in nature.
3. **Explain** why it might be harmful to release a frog into a habitat for which it is not adapted.

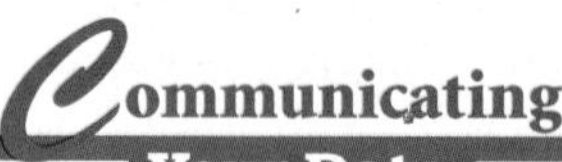

Communicating Your Data

Create a poster or other visual display that represents the habitat you chose for this activity. Use your display to show classmates how your design helps camouflage your frog model. **For more help, refer to the** Science Skill Handbook.

Communicating Your Data

Ask students to access the Glencoe Science Web site to research their information.

Resource Manager 

Chapter Resources Booklet

Activity Worksheet, pp. 5–6

Lab Activities, pp. 9–10, 11–14

SECTION 2

Clues About Evolution

Clues from Fossils

Imagine going on a fossil hunt in Wyoming. Your companions are paleontologists—scientists who study the past by collecting and examining fossils. As you climb a low hill, you notice a curved piece of stone jutting out of the sandy soil. One of the paleontologists carefully brushes the soil away and congratulates you on your find. You've discovered part of the fossilized shell of a turtle like the one shown in **Figure 8.**

The Green River Formation covers parts of Wyoming, Utah, and Colorado. On your fossil hunt, you learn that about 50 million years ago, during the Eocene Epoch, this region was covered by lakes. The water was home to fish, crocodiles, lizards, and turtles. Palms, fig trees, willows, and cattails grew on the lakeshores. Insects and birds flew through the air. How do scientists know all this? After many of the plants and animals of that time died, they were covered with silt and mud. Over millions of years, they became the fossils that have made the Green River Formation one of the richest fossil deposits in the world.

As You Read

What You'll Learn

- **Identify** the importance of fossils as evidence of evolution.
- **Explain** how relative and radiometric dating are used to estimate the age of fossils.
- **List** examples of five types of evidence for evolution.

Vocabulary

sedimentary rock
radioactive element
embryology
homologous
vestigial structure

Why It's Important

The scientific evidence for evolution helps you understand why this theory is so important to the study of biology.

The most abundant fossils are of a fresh-water herring, *Knightia oecaena,* which is Wyoming's state fossil.

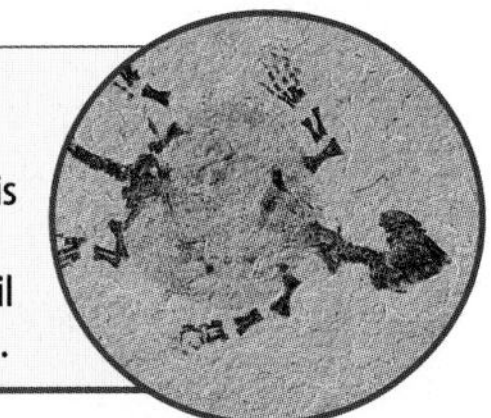

The turtle *Cisternum undatum* is from the same fossil formation.

Figure 8
The desert of the Green River Formation is home to pronghorn antelope, elks, coyotes, and eagles. Fossil evidence shows that about 50 million years ago the environment was much warmer and wetter than it is today.

Section Assessment Planner

PORTFOLIO
Science Journal, p. 164

PERFORMANCE ASSESSMENT
Skill Builder Activities, p. 169
See page 180 for more options.

CONTENT ASSESSMENT
Section, p. 169
Challenge, p. 169
Chapter, pp. 180–181

SECTION

Clues About Evolution

1 Motiva

Bellringer Transp

2 Teach

Clues from Fossils

Caption Answer

Figure 9 Imprint fossils, mineralized fossils, and cast fossils are the most common.

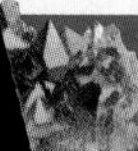

Earth Science INTEGRATION

early 75 percent of Earth's d surface is covered by sed- ntary rock. In some places, mentary rock layers may ore than a mile thick. sedimentary rocks lack ctive materials needed iometric dating.

samples of igneous, c, and sedimentary tudents to observe ces. Explain that as once molten, so uld have lived in c rock is a rock eheated, so its nged from the ls contained in Sedimentary haracteristics n of a fossil sual-Spatial

Figure 9
Examples of several different types of fossils are shown here. *Which of these would most likely be found in a layer of sedimentary rock?*

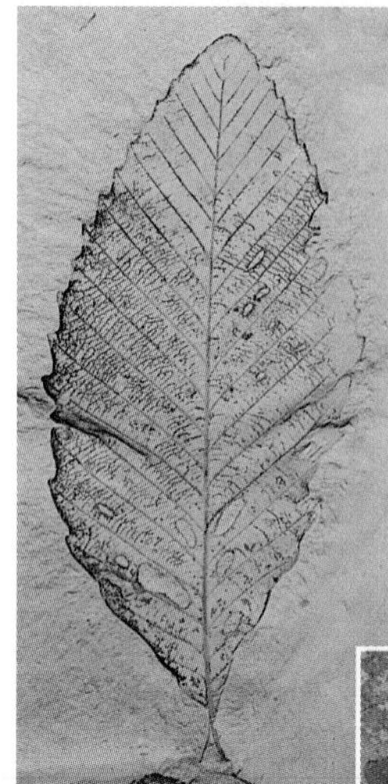

A Imprint fossils A leaf, feather, bones, or even the entire body of an organism can leave an imprint on sediment that later hardens to become rock.

B Mineralized fossils Minerals can replace wood or bone to create a piece of petrified wood as shown to the left or a mineralized bone fossil.

C Frozen fossils The remains of organisms like this mammoth can be trapped in ice that remains frozen for thousands or millions of years.

E Cast Fossils Minerals can fill in the hollows of animal tracks as shown to the right, a mollusk shell, or other parts of an organism to create a cast.

D Fossils in amber When the sticky resin of certain cone-bearing plants hardens over time, amber forms. It can contain the remains of trapped insects.

Earth Science INTEGRATION

Types of Fossils

Most of the evidence for evolution comes from fossils. A fossil is the remains, an imprint, or a trace of a prehistoric organism. Several types of fossils are shown in **Figure 9.** Most fossils are found in sedimentary rock. **Sedimentary rock** is formed when layers of sand, silt, clay, or mud are compacted and cemented together, or when minerals are deposited from a solution. Limestone, sandstone, and shale are all examples of sedimentary rock. Fossils are found more often in limestone than in any other kind of sedimentary rock. The fossil record provides evidence that living things have evolved. Other areas of study in addition to fossils also support the theory of evolution.

Teacher FYI

The fossil record has always been incomplete because most organisms never become fossils. They are either decomposed or eaten before they have an opportunity to become fossilized.

Science Journal

The Grand Canyon Few places on Earth have as many layers of exposed sedimentary rock as the Grand Canyon. Have students research the Grand Canyon by accessing the Glencoe Science Web site and prepare an essay on what they would expect to see if they visited. L2

LS **Linguistic** P

Determining a Fossil's Age

Paleontologists use detective skills to determine the age of dinosaur fossils or the remains of other ancient organisms. They can use clues provided by unique rock layers and the fossils they contain. The clues provide information about the geology, weather, and life-forms that must have been present during each geologic time period. Two basic methods—relative dating and radiometric dating—can be used, alone or together, to estimate the ages of rocks and fossils.

Relative Dating One way to find the approximate age of fossils found within a rock layer is relative dating. Relative dating is based on the idea that in undisturbed areas, younger rock layers are deposited on top of older rock layers, as shown in **Figure 10.** Relative dating provides only an estimate of a fossil's age. The estimate is made by comparing the ages of rock layers found above and below the fossil layer. For example, suppose a 50-million-year-old rock layer lies below a fossil, and a 35-million-year-old layer lies above it. According to relative dating, the fossil is probably between 35 million and 50 million years old.

Reading Check *Why can relative dating be used only to estimate the age of a fossil?*

Radiometric Dating Scientists can obtain a more accurate estimate of the age of a rock layer by using radioactive elements. A **radioactive element** gives off a steady amount of radiation as it slowly changes to a nonradioactive element. Each radioactive element gives off radiation at a different rate. Scientists can estimate the age of the rock by comparing the amount of radioactive element with the amount of nonradioactive element in the rock. This method of dating does not always produce exact results, because the original amount of radioactive element in the rock can never be determined for certain.

SCIENCE Online

Data Update Visit the Glencoe Science Web site at **science.glencoe.com** for news about recent fossil discoveries. In your Science Journal, write a brief report describing how one of these discoveries was made and what it reveals about past life on Earth.

Figure 10
In Bryce Canyon, erosion by water and wind has cut through the sedimentary rock, exposing the layers. Fossils found in lower layers of sedimentary rock are usually older than the fossils found in upper layers.

Activity

Have students research the Scopes trial and other legislation and court cases concerning the teaching of evolution. *The American Biology Teacher* published several articles detailing this history in 1998–1999. Have them report their findings to the class. L2 LS **Linguistic**

Determining a Fossil's Age

SCIENCE Online

Internet Addresses

Explore the Glencoe Science Web site at **science.glencoe.com** to find out more about topics in this section.

Reading Check

Answer Relative dating can only give a range, not an exact age.

Make a Model

Have students make a model showing how relative dating is used. Their model can show layers of sand, dirt, salt, cornmeal, or other materials in a plastic drink bottle or glass container. Several "fossils" should be placed in the model to explain their relative ages. Have each student present his or her model to the group. L2 LS **Kinesthetic and Visual-Spatial**

Activity

Have groups of students collect rocks and fossils from your area. Allow them to research the types of rocks and fossils they find. If students will donate their finds to the school, you can quickly build a school collection of fossils and rocks to display. L2 ELL COOP LEARN LS **Interpersonal**

Resource Manager

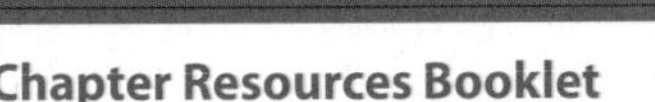

Chapter Resources Booklet

Transparency Activity, p. 43
Directed Reading for Content Mastery, p. 19

Inclusion Strategies

Visually Impaired You can explain relative dating to visually impaired students by creating layers of different materials that the student can differentiate by touch. Use stiff cardboard or foam board and glue the materials in layers. Glue easily identifiable objects as analogies to fossils.

NATIONAL GEOGRAPHIC

Visualizing The Geologic Time Scale

Have students examine the pictures and read the captions. Then ask the following questions.

In the geologic time scale, which is longer—an era or a period? Students should note that an era is a longer time than a period.

The names of the geologic eras have Greek roots. *Ceno* means "recent" and *zoic* means "life." *Paleo* means "ancient." Infer the meaning of the Greek prefix *meso*. Meso means "middle", so mesozoic means "middle life."

Activity

Have students work in teams to create a poster about one of the geologic periods shown in the feature. The poster should contain facts about the plants and animals that were alive during the period, as well as illustrations depicting the landforms and bodies of water that were present. The teams of students should present their findings to the class.

Extension

Have interested students research the Precambrian era, which accounts for about 90% of geologic time. Students should use a word processing program to prepare a short report of their findings.

NATIONAL GEOGRAPHIC **VISUALIZING THE GEOLOGIC TIME SCALE**

Figure 11

Earth is roughly 4.6 billion years old. As shown here, the vast period of time from Earth's beginning to the present day has been organized into the geologic time scale. The scale is divided into eras and periods. Dates on this scale are given as millions of years ago (mya).

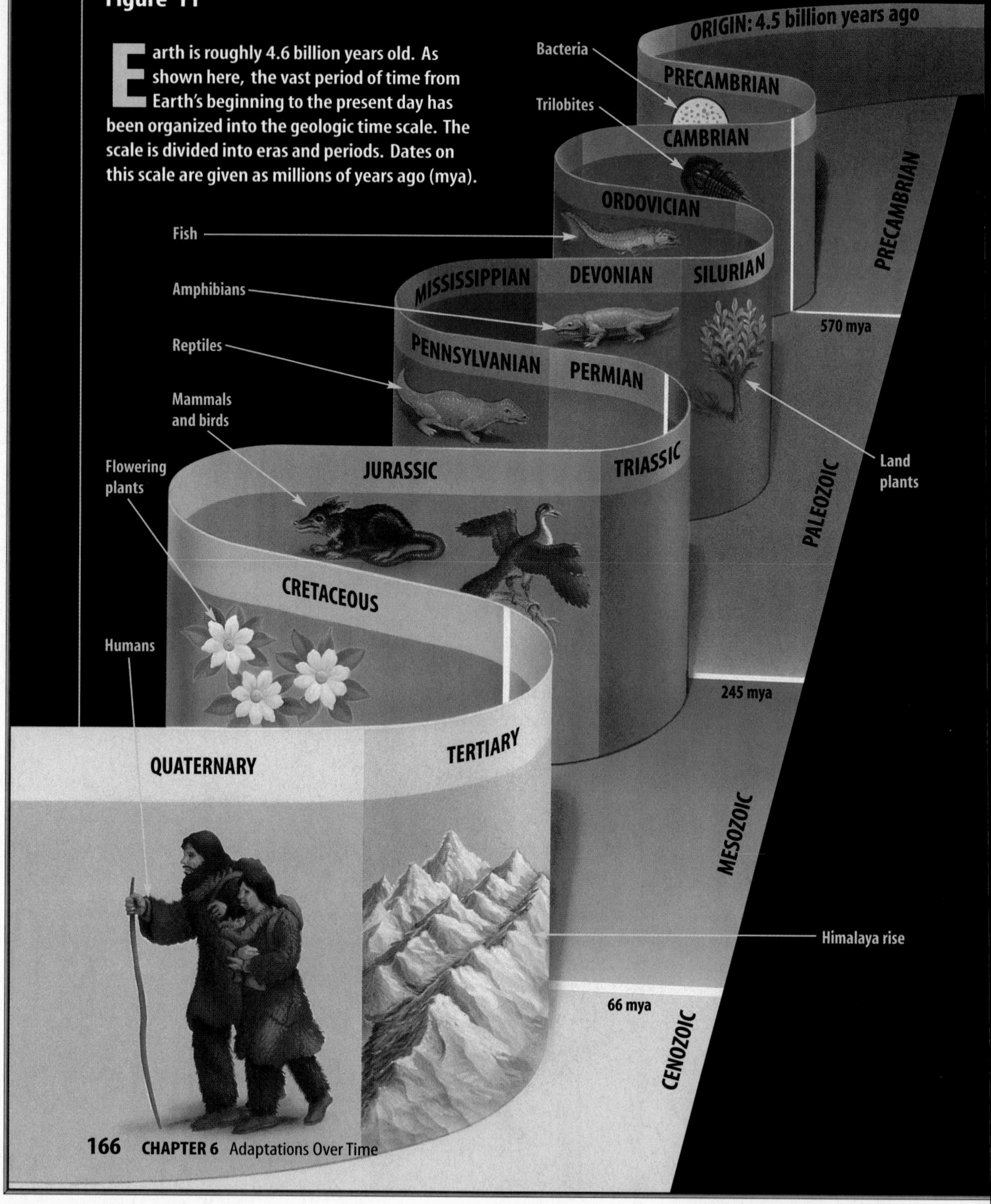

ORIGIN: 4.5 billion years ago
PRECAMBRIAN
CAMBRIAN
ORDOVICIAN
SILURIAN
DEVONIAN
MISSISSIPPIAN
PENNSYLVANIAN
PERMIAN
TRIASSIC
JURASSIC
CRETACEOUS
TERTIARY
QUATERNARY
Bacteria
Trilobites
Fish
Amphibians
Reptiles
Mammals and birds
Flowering plants
Humans
Land plants
Himalaya rise
PRECAMBRIAN
570 mya
PALEOZOIC
245 mya
MESOZOIC
66 mya
CENOZOIC

166 CHAPTER 6 Adaptations Over Time

Curriculum Connection

Math Explain the vastness of geological, or "deep" time. A million years is only 0.02 percent of the total. Have students convert the eras and periods into percentages of the entire scale. L2 **Logical-Mathematical**

Resource Manager

Chapter Resources Booklet

Transparency Activity, pp. 45–47

Fossils and Evolution

Fossils provide a record of organisms that lived in the past. However, the fossil record has gaps, much like a book with pages missing. The gaps exist because of an incomplete rock record, and because most organisms do not become fossils. This means that the fossil record will always be incomplete. By looking at fossils, scientists conclude that many simpler forms of life existed earlier in Earth's history, and more complex forms of life appeared later, as shown in **Figure 11.** Fossils provide indirect evidence that evolution has occurred on Earth.

Almost every week, fossil discoveries are made somewhere in the world. When fossils are found, they are used to help scientists understand the past. Scientists can use fossils to make models that show what the organisms might have looked like. From fossils, scientists can sometimes determine whether the organisms lived in family groups or alone, what they ate, what kind of environment they lived in, and many other things about them. Most fossils represent extinct organisms. From a study of the fossil record, scientists have concluded that more than 99 percent of all organisms that have ever existed are extinct now.

Many organisms have a history that has been preserved in sedimentary rock. Fossils show that the bones of animals such as horses and whales have become reduced in size or number over geologic time, as the species has evolved. In your Science Journal, explain what information can be gathered from changes in structures that occur over time.

More Clues About Evolution

Besides fossils, what other clues do humans have about evolution? Sometimes, evolution can be directly observed. Plant breeders observe evolution when they use cross-breeding to produce genetic changes in plants. The development of antibiotic resistance in bacteria is another direct observation of evolution. Entomologists have noted similar rapid evolution of pesticide-resistant insect species. These observations provide direct evidence that evolution occurs. Also, many examples of indirect evidence for evolution exist. They include similarities in embryo structures, the chemical makeup of organisms including DNA, and the way organisms develop into adults. Indirect evidence does not provide proof of evolution, but it does support the idea that evolution takes place over time.

Embryology The study of embryos and their development is called **embryology** (em bree AH luh jee). An embryo is the earliest growth stage of an organism. A tail and gills or gill slits are found at some point in the embryos of fish, reptiles, birds, and mammals, as **Figure 12** shows. Fish keep their gills, but the other organisms lose their gill slits as their development continues. Fish, birds, and reptiles keep their tails, but many mammals lose theirs. These similarities suggest an evolutionary relationship among all vertebrate species.

Figure 12
Similarities in the embryos of fish, chickens, and rabbits show evidence of evolution.

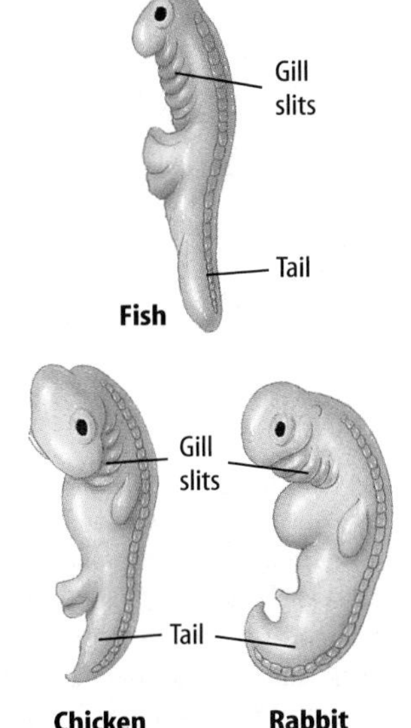

Use an Analogy

Use a length of rope or kite string as an analogy for the geologic time scale. Make knots to illustrate where the eras begin and end, and paint sections different colors to illustrate the periods. Another analogy for the geologic time scale is a clock. Use a wall clock and talk about the eras and periods as you advance the clock from 12:00. Make your conversion calculations before you begin.

Fossils and Evolution

Changes in structures often mirror changes in the environment.

Activity

Have students locate fossils in walls of local buildings and research the locations from which the building materials came. Most of the fossils will be of marine forms in limestone that may have come from other states in the U.S. or from other countries. L2 ELL
LS **Visual-Spatial**

More Clues About Evolution

Teacher FYI

Morphological and molecular studies indicate that marine mammals (e.g., whales, dolphins, porpoises) and some even-toed ungulates (e.g., hippos and cattle) share a common ancestor not shared by any other group. This implies that cattle and whales are more closely related than cattle and horses.

Active Reading

Double Entry Journal In this strategy, the student takes notes and adds his or her own reflections while reading the student text. Students are encouraged to explore ideas, make responses, and take risks in giving opinions about the reading. Have them divide a sheet of paper in half. On the left, have students identify a particular passage or quotation of significance in the reading. The reader records anything luminous, enigmatic, stimulating, or disturbing. On the right, the reader responds, questions, elaborates, makes personal connections, evaluates, reflects, analyzes, or interprets. Have students make a Double Entry Journal about evolution.

More Clues About Evolution, continued

Figure 13 Have students compare the wing of a bat and the flipper of a porpoise with a human hand. Ask students what similarities they have. Possible answers: number of bones, muscle, and blood vessels; type of bones; they are homologous. L2 IS **Visual-Spatial**

Reading Check

Answer These structures often indicate that two or more species share common ancestors.

Teacher FYI

Pesticide resistance in insects, antibiotic resistance in bacteria, and observed differences in salamanders, frogs, and birds are all examples of direct evidence for evolution.

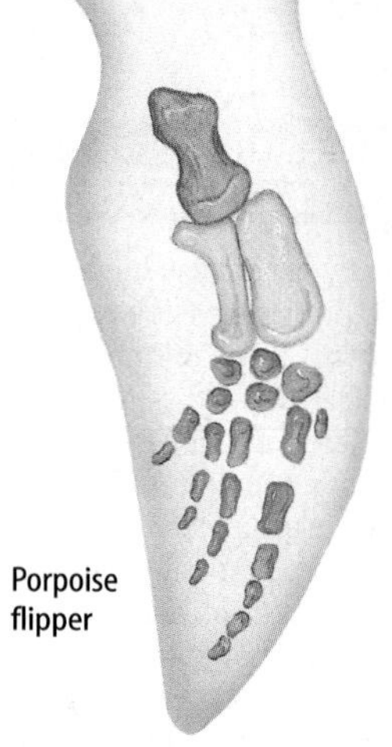

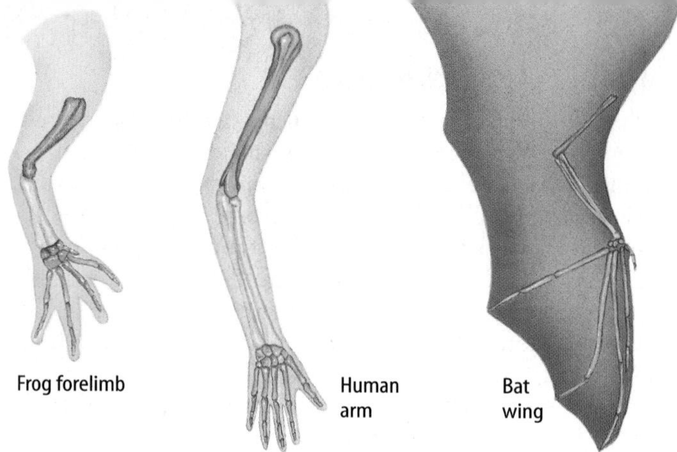

Figure 13
A porpoise flipper, frog forelimb, human arm, and bat wing are homologous. These structures show different arrangements and shapes of the bones of the forelimb. They have the same number of bones, muscles, and blood vessels, and they developed from similar tissues.

Homologous Structures What do the structures shown in **Figure 13** have in common? Although they have different functions, each of these structures is made up of the same kind of bones. Body parts that are similar in origin and structure are called **homologous** (hoh MAH luh gus). Homologous structures also can be similar in function. They often indicate that two or more species share common ancestors.

Reading Check *What do homologous structures indicate?*

Vestigial Structures The bodies of some organisms include **vestigial** (veh STIH jee ul) **structures**—structures that don't seem to have a function. Vestigial structures also provide evidence for evolution. For example, manatees, snakes, and whales no longer have back legs, but, like all animals with legs, they still have pelvic bones. The human appendix is a vestigial structure. The appendix appears to be a small version of the cecum, which is an important part of the digestive tract of many mammals. Scientists hypothesize that vestigial structures, like those shown in **Figure 14,** are body parts that once functioned in an ancestor.

Figure 14
Humans have three small muscles around each ear that are vestigial. In some mammals, such as horses, these muscles are large. They allow a horse to turn its ears toward the source of a sound. Humans cannot rotate their ears, but some people can wiggle their ears.

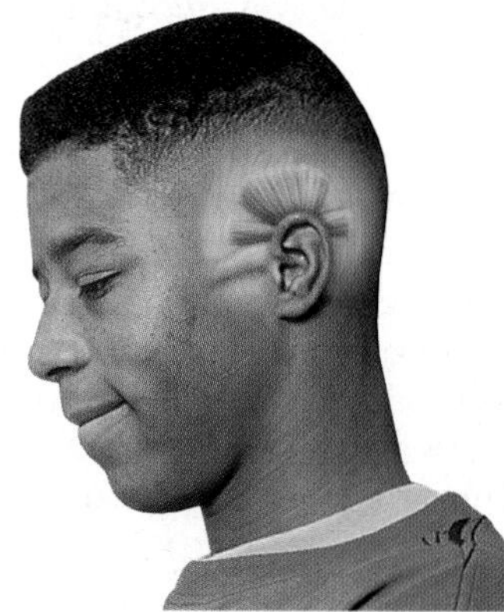

Resource Manager

Chapter Resources Booklet
Enrichment, p. 29
Reinforcement, p. 26

Cultural Diversity

Evolving Viruses The flu is an example of a sickness caused by a virus whose DNA evolves in order for it to survive. Every major flu epidemic has come from South China, where ducks, pigs, and humans are brought into daily contact. An avian flu transfers to pigs, as does a human flu variety. The viruses exchange pieces of genetic code to form a new flu strain. When the virus reinfects humans, it is different enough that antibodies made to fight the first form do not stop the new virus. That is why flu shots do not protect against all varieties.

DNA If you enjoy science fiction, you probably have read books or seen movies in which scientists re-create dinosaurs and other extinct organisms from DNA taken from fossils. DNA is the molecule that controls heredity and directs the development of every organism. In a cell with a nucleus, DNA is found in genes that make up the chromosomes. Scientists compare DNA from living organisms to identify similarities among species. Examinations of ancient DNA often provide additional evidence of how some species evolved from their extinct ancestors. By looking at DNA, scientists also can determine how closely related organisms are. For example, DNA studies indicate that dogs are the closest relatives of bears.

Figure 15
Gorillas have DNA and proteins that are similar to humans and other primates.

Similar DNA also can suggest common ancestry. Apes such as the gorillas shown in **Figure 15,** chimpanzees, and orangutans have 24 pairs of chromosomes. Humans have 23 pairs. When two of an ape's chromosomes are laid end to end, a match for human chromosome number 2 is formed. Also, similar proteins such as hemoglobin—the oxygen-carrying protein in red blood cells—are found in many primates. This can be further evidence that primates have a common ancestor.

Section  Assessment

1. How are relative dating and radiometric dating used by scientists?
2. Why are fossils important evidence of evolution? Describe five different kinds of fossils.
3. Explain how DNA can provide some evidence of evolution.
4. Describe three examples of direct evidence for evolution.
5. **Think Critically** Compare and contrast the five types of evidence that support the theory of evolution.

Skill Builder Activities

6. **Interpreting Scientific Illustrations** According to **Figure 11,** what was the longest geological era? What was the shortest era? During what period did mammals appear? **For more help, refer to the Science Skill Handbook.**
7. **Using Percentages** The Cenozoic Era represents about 66 million years. Approximately what percent of Earth's 4.6-billion-year history does this era represent? **For more help, refer to the Math Skill Handbook.**

3 Assess

Reteach

Show students examples of as many kinds of fossils as possible. Have students identify each type of fossil. L1 IN **Naturalist**

Challenge

Why isn't carbon dating used for all radiometric techniques? Carbon's half-life of approximately 5,000 years is too short.

Performance Have students prepare a poster showing the time periods in which fish, amphibians, reptiles, birds, and mammals first appeared. Use **Performance Assessment in the Science Classroom,** p. 145.

Answers to Section Assessment

1. Relative dating is used to find the approximate age of a rock layer by its position relative to other layers. Radiometric dating is used to date rocks by measuring relative amounts of radioactive and non-radioactive elements.
2. Fossils provide evidence of how species changed over time. Organisms can be frozen in ice or trapped in amber. Minerals can replace wood or bone. There are also cast fossils and imprint fossils.
3. Organisms with similar DNA may have a common ancestor.
4. antibiotic resistance in bacteria, pesticide resistance in insects, and genetic changes in plants
5. Students should compare and contrast vestigial structures, DNA, homologous structures, fossils, and embryology.
6. Precambrian; Cenozoic; Jurassic
7. 66 million years/4,600 million years $\times 100 = 1.43\%$

SECTION

The Evolution of Primates

1 Motivate

Bellringer Transparency

Display the Section Focus Transparency for Section 3. Use the accompanying Transparency Activity Master. L2 ELL

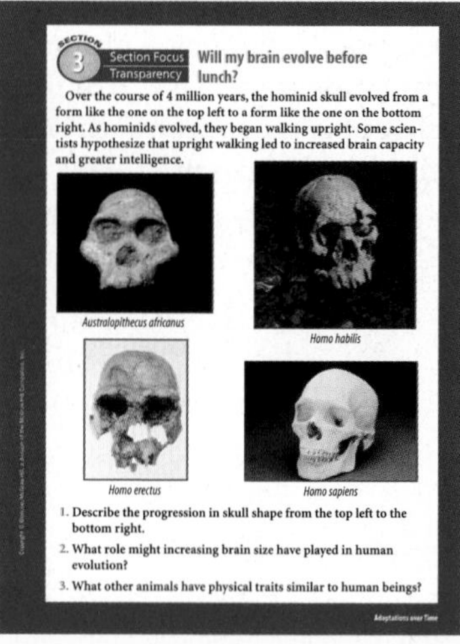

SECTION 3 Section Focus Transparency **Will my brain evolve before lunch?**

Over the course of 4 million years, the hominid skull evolved from a form like the one on the top left to a form like the one on the bottom right. As hominids evolved, they began walking upright. Some scientists hypothesize that upright walking led to increased brain capacity and greater intelligence.

Australopithecus africanus

Homo habilis

Homo erectus

Homo sapiens

1. **Describe the progression in skull shape from the top left to the bottom right.**
2. **What role might increasing brain size have played in human evolution?**
3. **What other animals have physical traits similar to human beings?**

Adaptations over Time

Tie to Prior Knowledge

Students may have questions about the relationship between species of primates. Remind students that species are classified into groups based on similarities, such as structure and DNA sequences.

SECTION 3

The Evolution of Primates

As You Read

What You'll Learn

- **Describe** the differences among living primates.
- **Identify** the adaptations of primates.
- **Discuss** the evolutionary history of modern primates.

Vocabulary

primate
hominid
Homo sapiens

Why It's Important

Studying primate evolution will help you appreciate the differences among primates.

Primates

Humans, monkeys, and apes belong to the group of mammals known as the **primates.** All primates have opposable thumbs, binocular vision, and flexible shoulders that allow the arms to rotate. These shared characteristics could indicate that all primates may have evolved from a common ancestor.

Having an opposable thumb allows you to cross your thumb over your palm and touch your fingers. This means that you can grasp and hold things with your hands. An opposable thumb allows tree-dwelling primates to hold on to branches.

Binocular vision permits you to judge depth or distance with your eyes. In a similar way, it allows tree-dwelling primates to judge the distances as they move between branches. Flexible shoulders and rotating forelimbs also help tree-dwelling primates move from branch to branch. They also allow humans to do the backstroke, as shown in **Figure 16.**

Primates are divided into two major groups. The first group, the prosimians (pro SIH mee uhnz), includes lemurs and tarsiers like those shown in **Figure 17.** The second group, the anthropoids (AN thruh poydz), includes monkeys, apes, and humans.

Figure 16
The ability to rotate the shoulder in a complete circle allows humans to swim through water and tree-dwelling primates to travel through treetops.

Section Assessment Planner

PORTFOLIO
MiniLab Assessment, p. 171

PERFORMANCE ASSESSMENT
Try at Home MiniLAB, p. 171
Skill Builder Activities, p. 173
See page 180 for more options.

CONTENT ASSESSMENT
Section, p. 173
Challenge, p. 173
Chapter, pp. 180–181

Figure 17
Tarsiers and lemurs are active at night.
A Tarsiers are commonly found in the rain forests of Southeast Asia.
B Lemurs live on Madagascar and other nearby islands.

Hominids About 4 million to 6 million years ago, humanlike primates appeared that were different from the other primates. These ancestors, called **hominids,** ate both meat and plants and walked upright on two legs. Hominids shared some characteristics with gorillas, orangutans, and chimpanzees, but a larger brain separated them from the apes.

African Origins In the early 1920s, a fossil skull was discovered in a quarry in South Africa. The skull had a small space for the brain, but it had a humanlike jaw and teeth. The fossil, named *Australopithecus,* was one of the oldest hominids discovered. An almost-complete skeleton of *Australopithecus* was found in northern Africa in 1974. This hominid fossil, shown in **Figure 18,** was called Lucy and had a small brain but is thought to have walked upright. This fossil indicates that modern hominids might have evolved from similar ancestors.

Figure 18
The fossil remains of Lucy are estimated to be 2.9 million to 3.4 million years old.

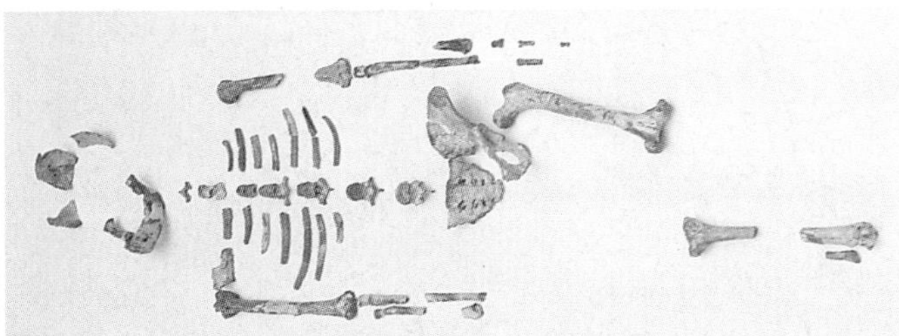

TRY AT HOME Mini LAB

Living Without Thumbs

Procedure
1. Using **tape,** fasten down each of your thumbs next to the palm of each hand.
2. Leave your thumbs taped down for at least 1 h. During this time, do the following activities: eat a meal, change clothes, and brush your teeth. Be careful not to try anything that could be dangerous.
3. Untape your thumbs, then write about your experiences in your **Science Journal.**

Analysis
1. Did not having use of your thumbs significantly affect the way you did anything? Explain.
2. Infer how having opposable thumbs could have influenced primate evolution.

2 Teach

Primates

Visual Learning

Figure 16 Have students identify other uses for rotating forelimbs in primates. Possible answers: opening doors, swinging a baseball bat, throwing a football Use the photos to discuss other common characteristics of primates. L2 LS **Visual-Spatial**

TRY AT HOME Mini LAB

Purpose Students observe the function of opposable thumbs, and infer how they may have influenced primate evolution. L1 ELL LS **Kinesthetic**

Materials tape

Teaching Strategy Tell students it will be easier for them to tape both thumbs down if they use a roll of tape, rather than tape from a dispenser.

Safety Precautions Tell students not to try anything that could be dangerous with impaired manual dexterity during this activity.

Analysis
1. Answers should indicate that students were negatively affected.
2. Possible answer: Opposable thumbs would allow for the use of tools, and tools are a foundation of modern civilization and technology.

Assessment

Performance Have students design a house with features that could be easily used by someone without thumbs. Use **PASC,** p. 123. P

Teacher FYI

Many types of primates existed in the Paleocene Epoch. More modern forms are thought to have evolved during the Eocene epoch. There are presently about 200 species of primates, although there were more in the past. Genetic studies indicate that the bonobo, chimpanzee, and gorilla are more closely related to humans than to any other primates.

Resource Manager 

Chapter Resources Booklet
Transparency Activity, p. 44
MiniLAB, p. 4

Home and Community Involvement, p. 48

Primates, continued

Teacher FYI

The African Rift Valley is an area of Africa where many human and hominid fossils have been uncovered. A rift valley occurs between geologic faults.

Activity

Using what they know about Neanderthals, have students write and illustrate an advertisement in their Science Journals for a fictional newspaper, *The Neanderthal News*. The ad should be for a modern product that Neanderthals might have been able to use. Student ads may emphasize tools for hammering and cutting. L2

LS **Linguistic**

Reading Check

Answer Because tools were found near *Homo habilis* fossils, and *Homo habilis* means "handyman."

Humans

Caption Answer

Figure 20 Neanderthal skulls have a heavier brow ridge and a smaller brain cavity.

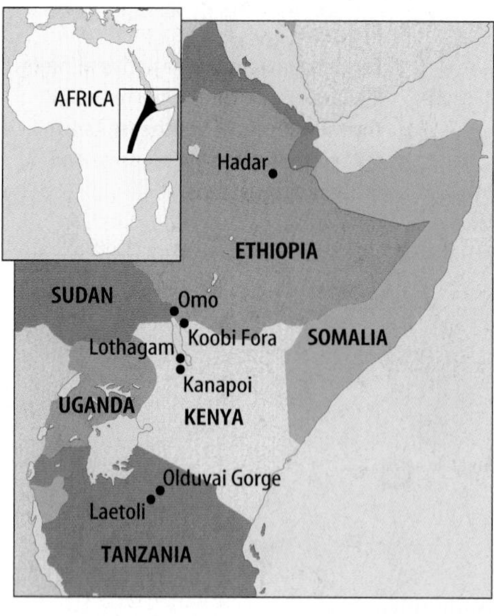

Figure 19
Many of the oldest humanlike skeletons have been found in this area of east Africa.

Early Humans In the 1960s in the region of Africa shown in **Figure 19,** a hominid fossil, which was more like present-day humans than *Australopithecus,* was discovered. The hominid was named *Homo habilis,* the handy man, because simple stone tools were found near him. *Homo habilis* is estimated to be 1.5 million to 2 million years old. Based upon many fossil comparisons, scientists have suggested that *Homo habilis* gave rise to another species, *Homo erectus,* about 1.6 million years ago. This hominid had a larger brain than *Homo habilis. Homo erectus* traveled from Africa to Southeast Asia, China, and possibly Europe. *Homo habilis* and *Homo erectus* are thought to be ancestors of humans because they had larger brains and more humanlike features than *Australopithecus.*

Reading Check *Why was* **Homo habilis** *given that name?*

Humans

The fossil record indicates that *Homo sapiens* evolved about 400,000 years ago. By about 125,000 years ago, two early human groups, Neanderthals and Cro-Magnon humans, as shown in **Figure 20,** probably lived at the same time in parts of Africa and Europe.

Neanderthals Short, heavy bodies with thick bones, small chins, and heavy browridges were physical characteristics of Neanderthals (nee AN dur tawlz). They lived in family groups in caves and used well-made stone tools to hunt large animals. Neanderthals disappeared from the fossil record about 30,000 years ago. They might represent a side branch of human evolution and might not be direct ancestors of modern humans.

Figure 20
The skull of a Neanderthal can be compared with the skull of a Cro-Magnon. *What differences can you see between these two skulls?*

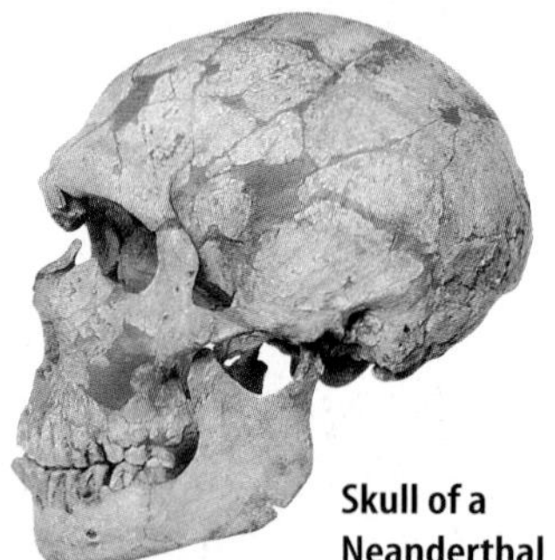

Skull of a Neanderthal

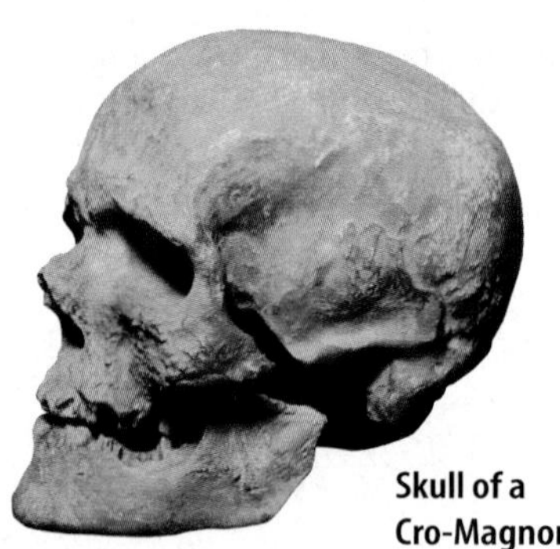

Skull of a Cro-Magnon

Cultural Diversity

Tribal Customs Use the information about fossil sites in Africa to increase students' awareness of African geography and the rich cultural heritage found there. Have students research African tribes, such as the Masai, and report on their way of life, customs, and rituals. L2

Resource Manager

Chapter Resources Booklet
- Enrichment, p. 30
- Reinforcement, p. 27
- Directed Reading for Content Mastery, pp. 19, 20

Figure 21
Paintings on cave walls have led scientists to hypothesize that Cro-Magnon humans had a well-developed culture.

Cro-Magnon Humans Cro-Magnon fossils have been found in Europe, Asia, and Australia and date from 10,000 to about 40,000 years in age. Standing about 1.6 m to 1.7 m tall, the physical appearance of Cro-Magnon people was almost the same as that of modern humans. They lived in caves, made stone carvings, and buried their dead. As shown in **Figure 21,** the oldest recorded art has been found on the walls of caves in France, where Cro-Magnon humans first painted bison, horses, and people carrying spears. Cro-Magnon humans are thought to be direct ancestors of early humans, ***Homo sapiens,*** which means "wise human." Evidence indicates that modern humans, *Homo sapiens sapiens,* evolved from *Homo sapiens.*

Section 3 Assessment

1. Describe at least three kinds of evidence that suggest that all primates might have shared a common ancestor.
2. What is the importance of *Australopithecus?*
3. Describe the differences and similarities among Neanderthals, Cro-Magnon humans, and early humans.
4. Which group do most scientists consider to be direct ancestors of modern humans?
5. **Think Critically** Propose a hypothesis about why teeth are the most abundant fossils of hominids.

Skill Builder Activities

6. **Concept Mapping** Make a concept map to show in what sequence the different groups of hominids appeared. Use the following terms: *Homo sapiens sapiens,* Neanderthal, *Homo habilis, Australopithecus, Homo sapiens,* and Cro-Magnon human. **For more help, refer to the** Science Skill Handbook.
7. **Communicating** Write a story in your Science Journal about what life would be like for you if you did not have thumbs. **For more help, refer to the** Science Skill Handbook.

Extension

Show examples of art from the caves of France and other European countries. Ask students to write a paragraph in their Science Journal explaining why this art is important to us today. Art provides insight and understanding of the artists and their lives. L2 LS **Visual-Spatial**

3 Assess

Reteach

Have students prepare a list on the board of characteristics common to primates. L1 COOP LEARN LS **Interpersonal**

Challenge

What is the difference between *Homo hablis* and *Homo erectus*? *H. hablis* is older and thought to be the ancestor of *H. erectus; H. erectus* had a larger brain and moved out of Africa 1 million years ago.

Assessment

Portfolio Have students make a timeline of the sequence of hominid evolution. Use **Performance Assessment in the Science Classroom,** p. 165.

Answers to Section Assessment

1. homologous structures; similar DNA; fossils
2. *Australopithecus,* an early hominid, had a small brain case but humanlike jaws and teeth.
3. Neanderthals had short bodies with massive bones and heavy brow ridges. Cro-Magnon humans were taller, invented art, made stone carvings, and buried their dead. Cro-Magnon humans were very similar to early humans.
4. *Homo sapiens*
5. Teeth are the hardest parts of an organism.
6. The concept map should be an events chain in the following order: *Australopithecus, Homo habilis,* Neanderthals, Cro-Magnon humans, *Homo sapiens,* and *Homo sapiens sapiens.*
7. Stories should indicate hardships that might result from being maladapted to their environment.

Activity

BENCH TESTED

Recognize the Problem

Purpose

Students design and carry out an experiment showing the variation in a population. L2 ELL COOP LEARN

LS **Logical-Mathematical**

Process Skills

forming a hypothesis, measuring in SI, using numbers, interpreting data, communicating, making and using tables, designing an experiment

Time Required

45 minutes to plan the investigation, 45 minutes to complete the investigation

Safety Precautions

Caution students not to put any materials into their mouths. Be sure students are not allergic to any plants used.

Form a Hypothesis

Possible Hypotheses

Student hypotheses will vary. Possible hypotheses include: "A sample of peanuts will exhibit variations in numbers of seeds," or "A sample of peanuts will exhibit variations in length of seeds."

Activity **Design Your Own Experiment**

Recognizing Variation in a Population

When you first observe a flock of pigeons, you might think all the birds look alike. However, if you look closer, you will notice minor differences, or variations, among the individuals. Different pigeons might have different color markings, or some might be smaller or larger than others. Individuals of the same species—whether they're birds, plants, or worms—might look alike at first, but some variations undoubtedly exist. According to the principles of natural selection, evolution could not occur without variations. What kinds of variations have you noticed among species of plants or animals?

Recognize the Problem

How can you measure variation in a plant or animal population?

Form a Hypothesis

Make a hypothesis about the amount of variation in the fruit and seeds of one species of plant.

Possible Materials

fruit and seeds from one plant species
metric ruler
magnifying glass
graph paper

Goals

- **Design** an experiment that will allow you to collect data about variation in a population.
- **Observe, measure, and analyze** variations in a population.

Safety Precautions

Do not put any fruit or seeds in your mouth. Wash your hands after handling plant parts.

Test Your Hypothesis

Possible Procedures

Procedures will vary. Most students will choose width or length to measure. Others may choose volume, number of seeds, or some other variable. Volume of fruit can be measured by water displacement. Students may want to design color charts to compare differences in fruit coloration.

Resource Manager

Chapter Resources Booklet
Activity Worksheet, pp. 7–8

Lab Management and Safety, p. 71

Test Your Hypothesis

Plan

1. As a group, agree upon and write out the hypothesis statement.
2. **List** the steps you need to take to test your hypothesis. Be specific. Describe exactly what you will do at each step. List your materials.
3. **Decide** what characteristic of fruit and seeds you will study. For example, you could measure the length of fruit and seeds or count the number of seeds per fruit.
4. **Design** a data table in your Science Journal to collect data about two variations. Use the table to record the data your group collects as you complete the experiment.
5. **Identify** any constants, variables, and controls of the experiment.
6. How many fruit and seeds will you examine? Will your data be more accurate if you examine larger numbers?
7. **Summarize** your data in a graph or chart.

Do

1. Make sure your teacher approves your plan before you start.
2. Carry out the experiment as planned.
3. While the experiment is going on, write down any observations you make and complete the data table in your Science Journal.

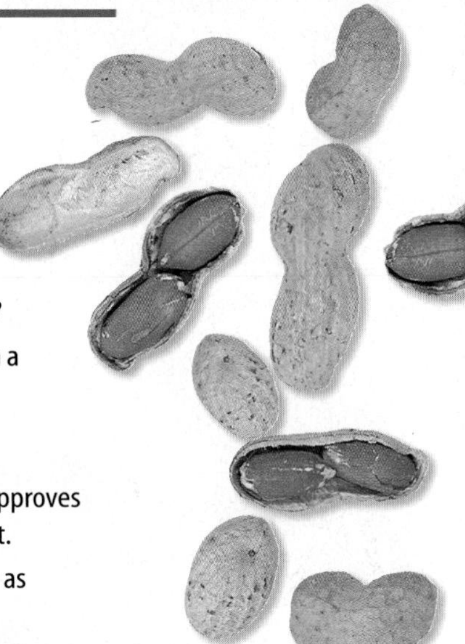

Analyze Your Data

1. **Calculate** the mean and range of variation in your experiment. The range is the difference between the largest and the smallest measurements. The mean is the sum of all the data divided by the sample size.
2. **Graph** your group's results by making a line graph for the variations you measured. Place the range of variation on the *x*-axis and the number of organisms that had that measurement on the *y*-axis.

Draw Conclusions

1. **Explain** your results in terms of natural selection.
2. What factors did you use to determine the amount of variation present?
3. Suggest reasons why one or more of the variations you observed in this activity might be helpful to the survival of the individual.

Communicating Your Data

Create a poster or other exhibit that illustrates the variations you and your classmates observed.

Teaching Strategies

- Guide students as they decide what trait to measure. Length or width of seeds will be most easily measured with the materials suggested.
- For most students, larger seeds will be easier to work with. Peanuts, lima beans, sunflower seeds, pinto beans, and peas are large enough.
- If students are physically incapable of measuring the seeds, have them work with a partner who can help.

Expected Outcome

Most students will collect data that results in a bell-shaped curve when graphed.

Analyze Your Data

1. Mean and range will vary depending on the seeds used and the variables measured.
2. Graphs will be a bell-shaped curve for most variables studied.

Error Analysis

Have students who measure the same trait share their results and explain any differences they observe.

Draw Conclusions

1. Natural selection may result in a variation that is found in many organisms within a population, but variations in the trait may also be found in smaller numbers.
2. by determining what the "norm" is and how often seeds vary from it
3. Answers will vary. Accept all reasonable answers. Possible response: Small, lightweight fruit is more easily dispersed to other areas by birds than heavier fruit.

Assessment

Performance Ask students to infer the natural selection advantage of fruits producing larger quantities of seeds. Larger seed quantities increase the chances that at least a few seeds will germinate and grow to maturity. Use **Performance Assessment in the Science Classroom,** p. 89.

Communicating Your Data

Discuss the variations observed by the class. Have students discuss why some variations are more advantageous than others.

Content Background

About the time of the 12th International Conference on AIDS in 1998, it had become clear that the powerful new drugs being used to attack HIV, called the protease inhibitors or the triple cocktail, would not bring the miracle that many had hoped they would. Between 10 and 50 percent of patients with AIDS who took protease inhibitors were later diagnosed with new and more virulent forms of HIV. As many as 4.5 percent of newly infected patients had drug-resistant strains of the virus, according to a 1999 study conducted by the Journal of the American Medical Association.

If a person contracts HIV from another person with a resistant strain, it could be as if the person got infected in 1983 when there were no antiretroviral drugs. Physicians could be starting at square one in terms of treatment.

In addition, protease inhibitors are extremely expensive and not available to everyone. This could change the HIV problem from a world problem to a problem of developing countries alone.

TIME SCIENCE AND HISTORY

SCIENCE CAN CHANGE THE COURSE OF HISTORY!

Wong-Staal was on one of the two teams that first identified HIV as the virus that causes AIDS.

Fighting

HIV particles

The first cases of AIDS, or acquired immune deficiency syndrome, in humans were reported in the early 1980s. AIDS is caused by the human immunodeficiency virus, or HIV. It is most likely that HIV first occurred in nonhuman primates, evolving into a form that could infect humans. For the first two decades of the battle against HIV and AIDS, it looked like the virus might win. Teams of scientists from many fields, and in many parts of the world, are part of the ongoing counterattack.

A major problem in AIDS research is the rapid evolution of HIV. When HIV multiplies inside a host cell, new versions of the virus are produced as well as identical copies of the virus that invaded the cell.
New versions of the virus can soon outnumber the original version. That's why HIV is so hard to fight—a treatment that works against today's HIV might not work against tomorrow's version.

176

Resources for Teachers and Students

AIDS in the World II: Global Dimensions, Social Roots, and Responses: The Global AIDS Policy Coalition, 2nd edition, edited by Jonathan Mann and Daniel J.M. Tarantola, Oxford University Press, New York and London, 1996.

AIDS and STDs: Global Perspectives, Rachel Donatelle, Pearson Custom Publishing, New York, 1999.

Confronting AIDS: Public Priorities in a Global Epidemic, edited by The World Bank, Oxford University Press, New York and London, 1999

Global Responses to AIDS, by Cristiana Bestos, Indiana University Press, Bloomington, Indiana, 1999.

These rapid changes in HIV also mean that different strains of the virus exist in different places around the world. That means most vaccines, which are still in the experimental stage, and treatments developed in the United States work only for AIDS patients who contracted the virus in the United States. This leaves AIDS sufferers in some parts of the world without effective treatments. Also, treatments might work for only a short period of time. Traditional vaccines quickly become useless. So, researchers such as geneticist Flossie Wong-Staal at the University of California in San Diego, must look for new ways to fight the evolving virus.

Working Backwards

Flossie Wong-Staal is taking a new approach. Her research focuses on how HIV uses host human cells. First, her team identifies the parts of a human cell that HIV depends on. Next, the team looks for parts of the human cell that HIV needs but the human cell doesn't need. Then the team looks for a way to remove—or inactivate—that unneeded part. This technique limits the virus's ability to multiply.

Wong-Staal's research combines three important aspects of science—a deep understanding of how cells and genes operate, great skill in the techniques of genetics, and great ideas. Understanding, skill, and great ideas are the best weapons so far in the fight to conquer HIV.

the Battle Against HIV

Scientists around the world are trying to keep up with a constantly changing virus

Adults and children living with HIV/AIDS - total: 34.3 million

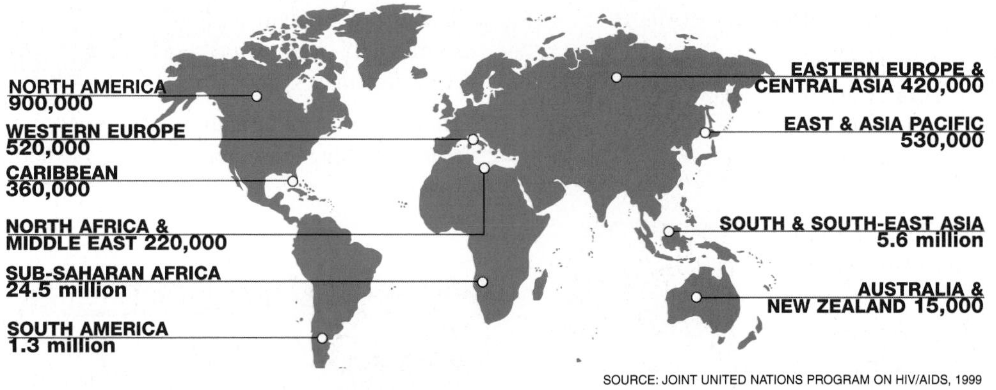

SOURCE: JOINT UNITED NATIONS PROGRAM ON HIV/AIDS, 1999

CONNECTIONS Research **Use the Glencoe Science Web site and other sources to determine which nations have the highest rates of AIDS infection. Which nation has the highest rate? Where does the U.S. rank? Next, find data from ten years ago. Have the rankings changed?**

SCIENCE *Online* For more information, visit science.glencoe.com

Discussion

How would Wong-Stall's research avoid the pitfalls of the new drugs and vaccines to treat HIV and AIDS? Possible answer: Instead of depending on suppressing the virus with drugs, this new research would prevent the virus from multiplying by changing existing cell structure. This could eliminate the daily regiment of taking multiple drugs.

Historical Significance

Even though the outbreak and spread of HIV and AIDS have a unique history, students might find useful an examination of other diseases that have had a worldwide impact and that have been "cured." Tell students that they will research the disease tuberculosis, or TB, in an effort to map the history of the disease. Provide students with copies of a world map. Then have students record on their maps the answers to these questions:

- When and where was the first known outbreak of TB?
- At the height of the TB epidemic, in what countries was the disease known to occur?
- At the height of the disease, how many people were infected with the disease?
- When did the numbers of infected people began to decline?
- When was the TB vaccine introduced?

Explain that even though there is a TB vaccine, new drug-resistant strains of TB have recently been discovered. Because of these resistant strains, scientists are interested in the TB vaccine again. Currently, in the United States, the TB vaccine is used only in special situations.

CONNECTIONS **What might account for the difference in numbers of people infected in different countries?** Possible answers: The rates vary with the availability of medicine and access to health care and with education about how HIV is transmitted. Explain that the largest number of new infections of HIV in the U.S. are among young people. Have students discuss possible reasons for this.

SCIENCE *Online*

Internet Addresses

Explore the Glencoe Science Web site at **science.glencoe.com** to find out more about topics in this feature.

Chapter 6 Study Guide

Reviewing Main Ideas

Preview

Students can answer the questions in their Science Journals. Discuss the answers as you go through the chapter. LS **Linguistic**

Review

Students can write their answers, then compare them with those of other students. LS **Interpersonal**

Reteach

Students can look at the illustrations and describe details that support the main ideas of the chapter. LS **Visual-Spatial**

Answers to Chapter Review

Section 1

4. spear-shaped bill for catching fish; long legs for wading in shallow water; eyes adapted for peering into the water

Section 2

1. Imprint fossils form when the outline of an organism is left on sediment that later becomes rock.
4. Similarities in DNA and proteins suggest ancestral relationships.

Section 3

1. opposable thumbs, binocular vision, flexible shoulders, rotating forelimbs

Chapter  Study Guide

Reviewing Main Ideas

Section 1 Ideas About Evolution

1. Evolution is one of the central ideas of biology. It is an explanation of how living things have changed in the past and a basis for predicting how they might change in the future.
2. Charles Darwin developed the theory of evolution by natural selection to explain how evolutionary changes account for the diversity of organisms on Earth.
3. Natural selection includes concepts of variation, overproduction, and competition.
4. According to natural selection, organisms with traits best suited to their environment are more likely to survive and reproduce. *What traits make this bird suited to its watery environment?*

Section 2 Clues About Evolution

1. Fossils provide evidence for evolution. *How are imprint fossils like the one to the right formed?*

2. Relative dating and radiometric dating can be used to estimate the age of fossils.
3. The evolution of antibiotic-resistant bacteria, pesticide-resistant insects, and rapid genetic changes in plant species provides direct evidence that evolution occurs.
4. Homologous structures, vestigial structures, comparative embryology, and chemical similarities in DNA and other substances provide indirect evidence of evolution. *How does DNA provide evidence of evolution?*

Section 3 The Evolution of Primates

1. Primates include monkeys, apes, and humans. Hominids are humanlike primates. *What are the common characteristics of primates?*

2. The earliest known hominid fossil is *Australopithecus.*
3. *Homo sapiens* are thought to have evolved from Cro-Magnon humans at least 400,000 years ago.

FOLDABLES Reading & Study Skills — After You Read

Using what you learned, predict how primates might change and write your ideas under the *Future* tab of your Foldable.

FOLDABLES Reading & Study Skills — After You Read

After students have read the chapter and completed the Foldable described in Before You Read, have them do the activity on the student page.

Dinah Zike

Visualizing Main Ideas

Complete the following spider map on evolution.

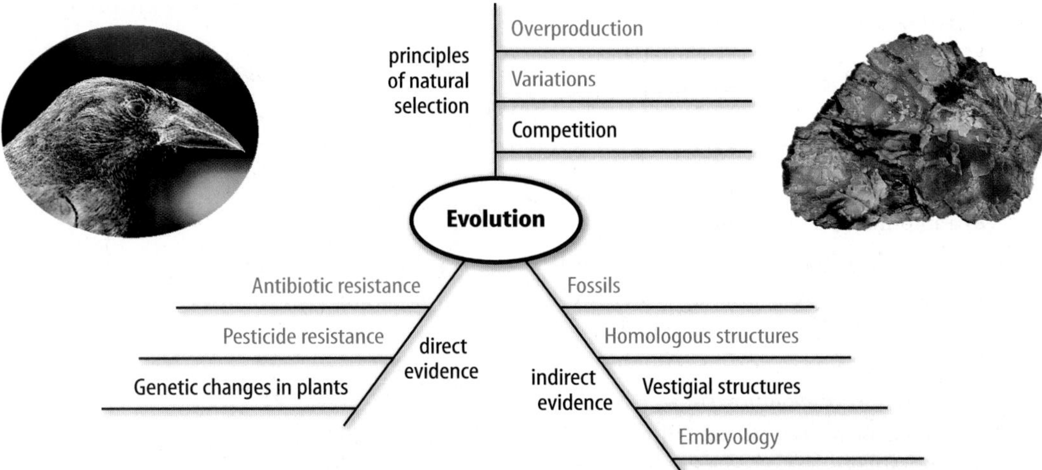

Vocabulary Review

Vocabulary Words

- **a.** adaptation
- **b.** embryology
- **c.** evolution
- **d.** gradualism
- **e.** hominid
- **f.** *Homo sapiens*
- **g.** homologous
- **h.** natural selection
- **i.** primate
- **j.** punctuated equilibrium
- **k.** radioactive element
- **l.** sedimentary rock
- **m.** species
- **n.** variation
- **o.** vestigial structure

THE PRINCETON REVIEW Study Tip

Make a plan. Before you start your homework, write a checklist of what you need to do for each subject. As you finish each item, check it off.

Using Vocabulary

Replace each underlined phrase with the correct vocabulary words.

1. Layers of deposition might contain many different kinds of fossils.
2. The muscles that move the human ear appear to be of no obvious use.
3. Forelimbs of bats, humans, and seals are similar in origin.
4. Opposable thumbs are a characteristic of this group of mammals.
5. The study of early development of species can provide evidence of evolution.
6. The principles of this mechanism of evolution include variation and competition.
7. Modern humans likely evolved directly from Cro-Magnons.

Chapter 6 Study Guide

Visualizing Main Ideas

See student page.

Vocabulary Review

Using Vocabulary

1. sedimentary rock
2. vestigial structures
3. homologous
4. primates
5. embryology
6. natural selection
7. *Homo sapiens*

IDENTIFYING Misconceptions

Assess

Use the assessment as follow-up to page 152F after students have completed the chapter.

Discussion After students complete the bean/bacteria activity, ask the following questions. Have students respond first in writing, and then discuss the answers as a class.

- Why did the red "bacteria" survive?
- Did the antibiotic cause the bacteria to have a thicker cell wall?
- When did the red bacteria's thick cell wall develop—before or after the introduction of the antibiotic?

Expected Outcome Students should understand that the red bacteria's trait of a thicker cell wall existed before the antibiotic was introduced. In the activity, genes that gave the bacterium its color also resulted in the thickened cell wall. The trait gave the bacterium an advantage that helped it survive.

Chapter 6 Assessment

Checking Concepts

1. C
2. B
3. D
4. D
5. A
6. D
7. D
8. A
9. C
10. D

Thinking Critically

11. Lamarck: Owls hunt at night and their eyes grow larger with use. The trait is passed on. Darwin: A variation in the size of owls' eyes was an advantage to survival. This inherited feature was passed on to offspring over many generations until owls became adapted for seeing prey at night with large eyes.
12. Answers will vary. Possible answer: Geographical isolation as a result of a volcanic eruption can divide a population. Two species may evolve.
13. Chameleons blend into their environment. This ability to change color helps protect them from predators.
14. The layer of rock where it was formed would be noted. Radiometric dating would be done. Comparisons to other fossils would be made.
15. Protective coloration is an adaptation. A white rabbit living in a cold climate will survive better than a brown rabbit.

Chapter 6 Assessment

Checking Concepts

Choose the word or phrase that best answers the question.

1. What is an example of adaptation?
   A) a fossil
   B) gradualism
   C) camouflage
   D) embryo
2. What method provides the most accurate estimate of a fossil's age?
   A) natural selection
   B) radiometric dating
   C) relative dating
   D) camouflage
3. What do homologous structures, vestigial structures, and fossils provide evidence of?
   A) gradualism
   B) food choice
   C) populations
   D) evolution
4. Which model of evolution shows change over a relatively short period of time?
   A) embryology
   B) adaptation
   C) gradualism
   D) punctuated equilibrium
5. What might a series of helpful variations in a species result in?
   A) adaptation
   B) fossils
   C) embryology
   D) climate change
6. What describes organisms that are adapted to their environment?
   A) homologous
   B) not reproducing
   C) forming fossils
   D) surviving and reproducing
7. What is the study of an organism's early development called?
   A) adaptation
   B) relative dating
   C) natural selection
   D) embryology
8. What animal group(s) have opposable thumbs and binocular vision?
   A) all primates
   B) hominids
   C) humans only
   D) monkeys only
9. Which of the following is a principle of natural selection?
   A) inheritance of acquired traits
   B) Unused traits become smaller.
   C) Organisms produce more offspring than can survive.
   D) the size of an organism
10. A hominid fossil has the same number of bones in its hand as a gorilla. What type of evidence for evolution does this represent?
    A) DNA
    B) embryology
    C) vestigial structures
    D) homologous structures

Thinking Critically

11. How would Lamarck and Darwin have explained the large eyes of an owl?
12. Using an example, explain how a new species of organism could evolve.
13. How is the color-changing ability of chameleons an adaptation?
14. Describe the processes a scientist would use to figure out the age of a fossil.
15. Explain how a species could adapt to its environment. Give an example.

Developing Skills

16. **Predicting** Predict what type of bird the foot pictured below would belong to. Explain your reasoning.

Chapter Assessment Planner

Portfolio Encourage students to place in their portfolios one or two items of what they consider to be their best work. Examples include:
- Curriculum Connection, p. 159
- Science Journal, p. 164
- Assessment, p. 171

Performance Additional performance assessments, Performance Task Assessment Lists, and rubrics for evaluating these activities can be found in Glencoe's **Performance Assessment in the Science Classroom.**

17. **Interpreting Data** Each letter below represents a chemical found in different species of bacteria. Which species are closely related?

Chemicals Present in Bacteria Species	
Species 1	A, G, T, C, L, E, S, H
Species 2	A, G, T, C, L, D, H
Species 3	A, G, T, C, L, D, P, U, S, R, I, V
Species 4	A, G, T, C, L, D, H

18. **Forming Hypotheses** Frog eggs are common in ponds in spring. Make a hypothesis as to why ponds are not overpopulated by frogs in summer. Use the concept of natural selection to help you.

19. **Comparing and Contrasting** Compare and contrast Cro-Magnon humans and modern humans, *Homo sapiens sapiens.*

20. **Concept Mapping** Make an events chain of the events that led Charles Darwin to his theory of evolution by natural selection.

Performance Assessment

21. **Collection** With permission, collect fossils from your area and identify them. Show your collection to your class.

22. **Brochure** Assume that you are head of an advertising company hired by Charles Darwin. Develop a brochure to explain Darwin's theory of evolution by natural selection.

TECHNOLOGY

Go to the Glencoe Science Web site at **science.glencoe.com** or use the **Glencoe Science CD-ROM** for additional chapter assessment.

Test Practice

A scientist studied a genetic variation in a large family of birds. She made the pedigree below to show how the variations within the family appeared.

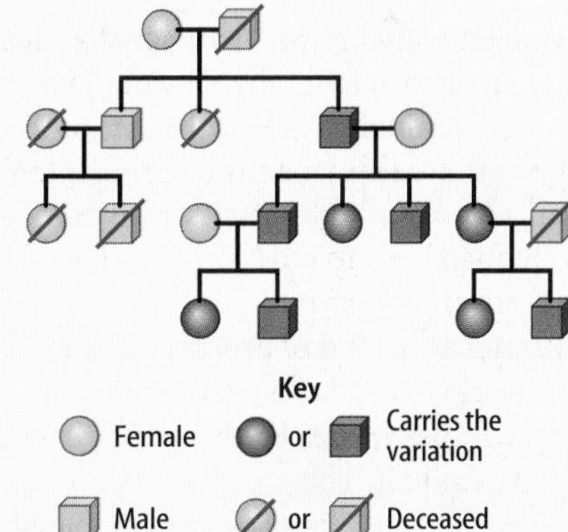

Study the pedigree and answer the following questions.

1. Which of the following is most likely the scientist's conclusion from these data?
   A) Female birds of this species die more often than the males.
   B) The variation helps the birds survive and reproduce.
   C) Birds of this species lay one or two eggs.
   D) The genetic variation only helps one of the two sexes.

2. To which offspring is this genetic variation most often passed along?
   F) all offspring
   G) some females and males
   H) only the father's daughters
   J) males only

Assessment Resources

Reproducible Masters

Chapter Resources Booklet
Chapter Review, pp. 35–36
Chapter Tests, pp. 37–40
Assessment Transparency Activity, p. 47

Glencoe Science Web site
Interactive Tutor
Chapter Quizzes

Glencoe Technology
Assessment Transparency
Interactive CD-ROM Chapter Quizzes
ExamView Pro Test Bank
Vocabulary PuzzleMaker Software
MindJogger Videoquiz

Chapter 6 Assessment

Test Practice

The Test-Taking Tip was written by The Princeton Review, the nation's leader in test preparation.

1. B
2. F

Developing Skills

16. The foot is from an aquatic bird with webbed feet for swimming.
17. Species 2 and 4 are the closest in relation; they have the same chemicals.
18. Predators and competition for resources will eliminate many frogs. Only the most adapted will survive.
19. Cro-Magnon humans and modern humans are similar physically but differ culturally.
20. Darwin did amateur studies in natural history as a boy. He became a naturalist aboard the *Beagle* and gathered information for five years. After returning to England, Darwin worked for the rest of his life to develop his theory.

Performance Assessment

21. Fossil collections will vary, depending on location. Students may get help from experts at a nearby university. Use **PASC,** p. 121.
22. The brochures should include the principles of natural selection, as found in **Table 1.** Use **PASC,** p. 129.

Standardized Test Practice

Reading Comprehension

QUESTION 1: C

Students must use the information in the passage in order to identify the best-supported conclusion.

- **Choice A** No; this is not supported by the passage.
- **Choice B** No; this is not supported by the passage.
- **Choice C** Yes; this is supported by the passage.
- **Choice D** No; this is not supported by the passage.

QUESTION 2: H

Students must use information from the passage to identify the correct cause. Students should use the clue *important to human health*.

- **Choice F** No; this is not supported by the passage.
- **Choice G** No; although this is a detail from the passage, it is not the reason enzymes are important to human health.
- **Choice H** Yes; this is the reason enzymes are important to human health.
- **Choice J** No; although this is a detail from the passage, it is not the reason enzymes are important to human health.

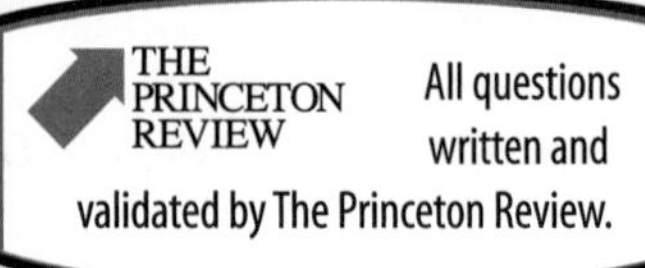

All questions written and validated by The Princeton Review.

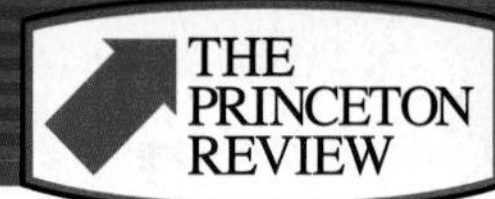

Standardized Test Practice

Reading Comprehension

Read the passage. Then read each question that follows the passage. Decide which is the best answer to each question.

Enzymes in Humans

A catalyst is a substance that makes a chemical reaction happen faster than it would happen by itself. Interestingly, it affects the rate of the reaction without permanently entering into the reaction. More than 2,000 catalysts are necessary for the human body to function well. These catalysts are called enzymes.

Enzymes are a kind of protein. How an enzyme works depends on what shape it has. Each enzyme has an area where specific chemicals can attach to it. This area is called the active site. Enzyme activity can be compared to a lock and a key. Only the correct chemicals, or keys, will fit into the enzyme, or lock. The enzyme helps chemicals come together so that they can react. This is how enzymes speed up reactions—by making the reactants come together in a more direct way than if they were left to just bump into each other randomly. One enzyme can be used over and over to activate the same reaction. In order for an enzyme to work properly, the temperature and pH must be within a certain range. Enough energy and enough reactants also must be present.

There are two main types of enzymes—metabolic and digestive. Metabolic enzymes catalyze the reactions within cells. They help phosphorus turn into bone, iron attach to red blood cells, and wounds to heal. Digestive enzymes help with the breakdown of foods, allowing nutrients to be absorbed into the blood-stream and used by the body.

Enzymes are essential for many reactions within the human body. Amylase is an enzyme found in saliva. It starts digesting certain carbohydrates in your food before you even swallow. An enzyme called carbonic anhydrase (kar BAH nihk • an HI drays) helps remove carbon dioxide from your cells. Carbonic anhydrase enzyme makes the reaction 107 times faster than if it had to happen on its own. You breathe the carbon dioxide out and replace it with oxygen. You can see how people depend on enzyme catalysts to maintain health.

Enzymes can be found in all living things. Enzymes also have been used in industry for nearly 100 years. Some of the products that depend on the action of enzymes are leather, alcohol, medications, baking products, detergents, and even fruit juice.

Test-Taking Tip Make sure that you understand what you are reading as you read a passage. If you are confused by something, stop and read the information again.

1. Based on the information in the passage, it can be concluded that _____.
   - **A)** enzymes are found only in humans
   - **B)** amylase is an enzyme that removes oxygen
   - **C)** humans have more than 2,000 enzymes
   - **D)** another word for the locks found in doors is enzyme

2. Enzymes are important to human health because they _____.
   - **F)** are used to help open locks
   - **G)** are used to make leather and fruit juice
   - **H)** speed up the reactions in human bodies
   - **J)** are found in all living things

Reasoning and Skills

Read each question and select the best answer.

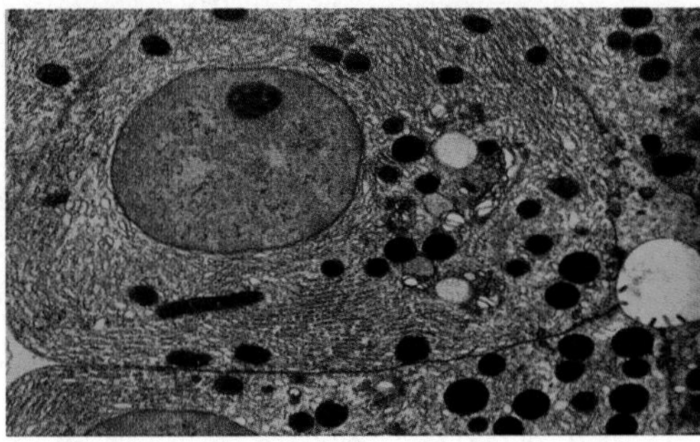

1. The object shown here is a(n) ____________ because it contains structures surrounded by membranes.
   A) prokaryotic cell
   B) mitochondrion
   C) Golgi body
   D) eukaryotic cell

Test-Taking Tip Think about the way cells are classified into groups.

A) 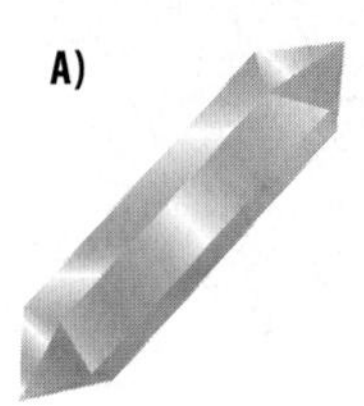

B) 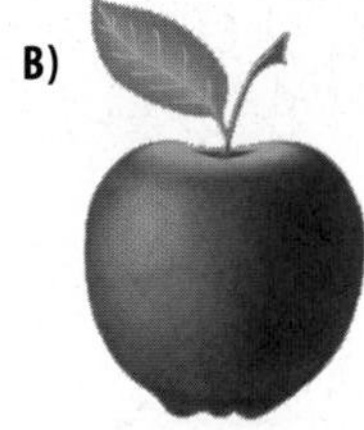

2. Item A above is different from item B because it _____.
   F) is not organized
   G) does not require energy for its formation
   H) is not composed of cells
   J) does not respond to changes in temperature or pressure

Test-Taking Tip Review the characteristics common to all living things.

3. Cattails and some other plant species can produce new plants without using seeds. What is this process called?
   A) sexual reproduction
   B) variation
   C) asexual reproduction
   D) mutation

Test-Taking Tip Think about the two types of reproduction.

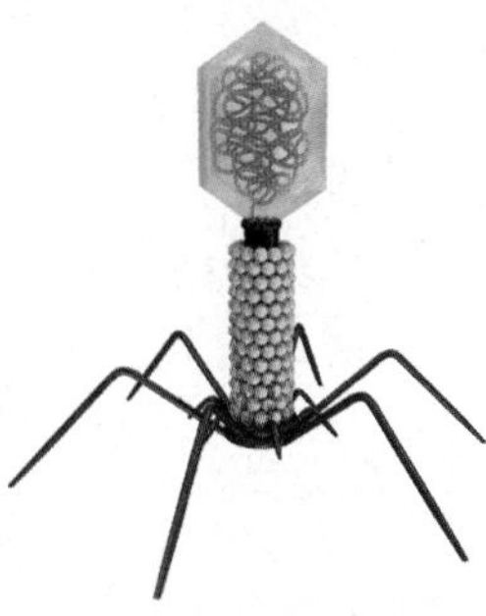

Consider this question carefully before writing your answer on a separate sheet of paper.

4. The virus particle pictured above is not inside a host cell. Give at least one good reason why it could be considered a living organism and one good reason why it could not.

Test-Taking Tip Compare the characteristics of a virus with the characteristics of living organisms.

Standardized Test Practice

Reasoning and Skills

QUESTION 1: D

Students need to understand that the structures in a *eukaryotic cell* are surrounded by membranes.

QUESTION 2: H

Students need to use their understanding of cells in order to identify the difference between Item A and Item B. Only choice H, *is not composed of cells*, correctly identifies an attribute held by Item A but not Item B.

QUESTION 3: C

Students must understand that vegetative propagation is a form of asexual reproduction.

QUESTION 4: Answers will vary.

Students should mention that viruses are not made up of cells. Furthermore, viruses cannot reproduce outside a host. On the other hand, they do have genetic material (DNA or RNA) and can multiply inside a host cell.

Teaching Tip

Suggest that students make an outline of their essays before they begin writing.

UNIT 2

Unit Contents

Pre-Reading Activity

Ask students to skim the chapter for names of one-celled and many-celled organisms. Then ask them to compare and contrast these organisms.

UNIT 2

From Bacteria to Plants

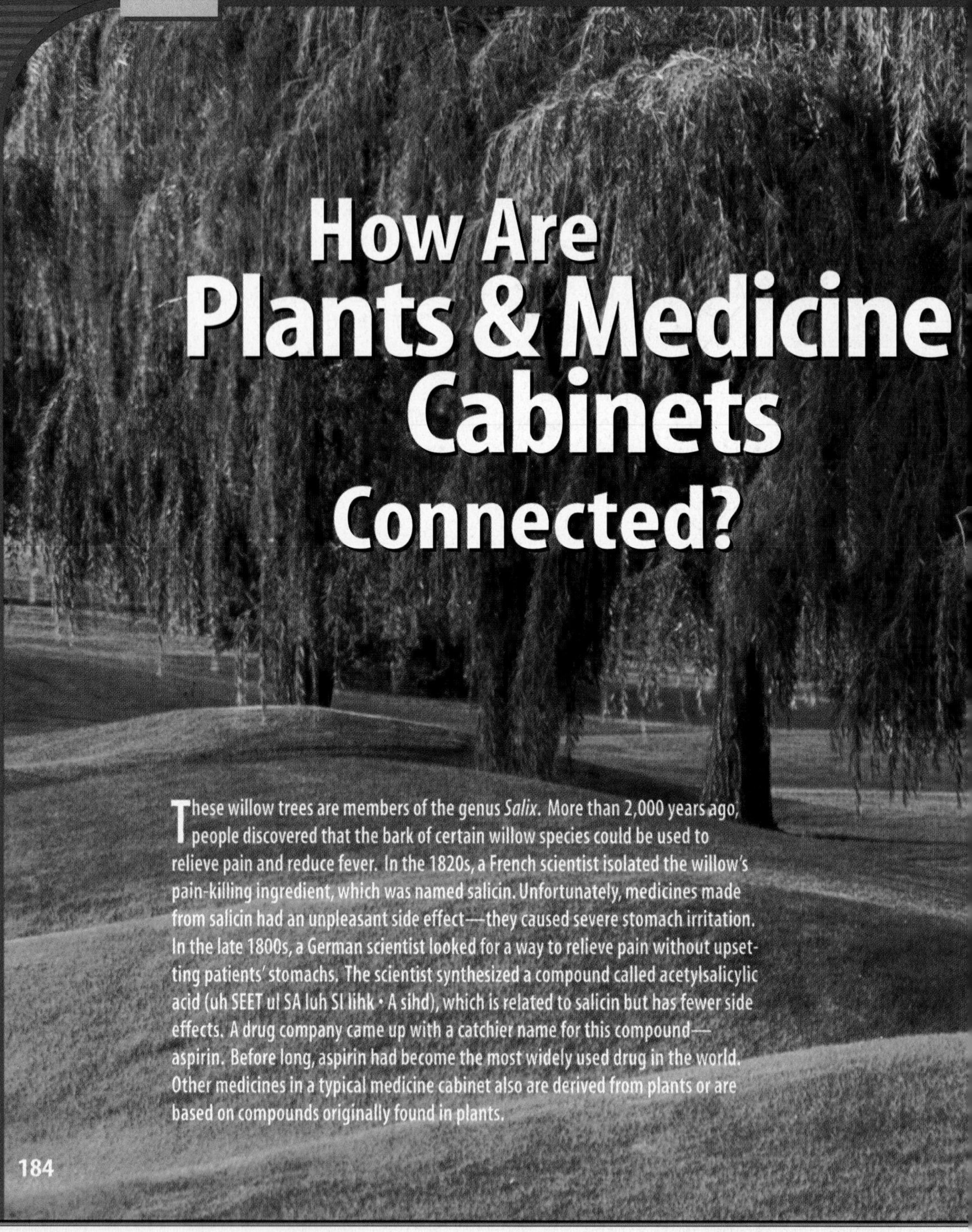

How Are Plants & Medicine Cabinets Connected?

These willow trees are members of the genus *Salix*. More than 2,000 years ago, people discovered that the bark of certain willow species could be used to relieve pain and reduce fever. In the 1820s, a French scientist isolated the willow's pain-killing ingredient, which was named salicin. Unfortunately, medicines made from salicin had an unpleasant side effect—they caused severe stomach irritation. In the late 1800s, a German scientist looked for a way to relieve pain without upsetting patients' stomachs. The scientist synthesized a compound called acetylsalicylic acid (uh SEET ul SA luh SI lihk • A sihd), which is related to salicin but has fewer side effects. A drug company came up with a catchier name for this compound—aspirin. Before long, aspirin had become the most widely used drug in the world. Other medicines in a typical medicine cabinet also are derived from plants or are based on compounds originally found in plants.

184

Teacher to Teacher

"Writing vocabulary words on large index cards and posting them above the chalkboard helps my learning disabled students. They can use these cards to spell the terms correctly on their tests and quizzes. It is like a word bank."

Catherine C. Walker, Teacher
Martin Middle School
Raleigh, NC

NATIONAL GEOGRAPHIC

SCIENCE CONNECTION

PLANT COMPOUNDS Some modern medicines contain compounds extracted directly from plants. Others contain synthetic versions of plant compounds. Among the drugs with plant origins are digitalis, vincristine, and quinine. Investigate one of these three drugs to discover what plant it comes from, how it helps people, and how its medicinal properties were first discovered. Then write a newspaper article in which you relate your findings.

SCIENCE Online

Internet Addresses

Explore the Glencoe Science Web site at **science.glencoe.com** to find out more about topics in this unit.

SCIENCE CONNECTION

Activity

Have students use a world map to plot the places of origin for the naturally derived medicines they research. Are there any obvious concentrations of these plants? What might these concentrations indicate?

Introducing the Unit

How Are Plants and Medicine Cabinets Connected?

Plants have been used as a source of curative compounds since prehistoric times. Ancient cultures usually had individuals who understood the healing properties of plants.

The development of modern chemistry in the 1800s allowed the isolation of the active compounds in medicinal plant products. Eventually it became possible to recreate the active ingredients chemically. Many drugs in use today that were originally plant derived are now only produced synthetically. Aspirin and quinine are two such drugs.

The modern reliance on synthetic compounds has brought about a decrease in formal research into the medicinal properties of plants. Only about 90 of the 250,000 known plant species are used to produce the 119 plant-derived drugs currently on the market.

Outside the industrialized world, the vast majority of people still are treated with medicines produced directly from plants. The native healers in Southeast Asia use more than 5,000 different plants to treat a wide range of diseases. Many governments have recently allocated funds to assist in surveying and cataloging the uses of their countries' native plant species.

Section/Objectives	Standards		Activities/Features
	National	State/Local	
Chapter Opener	See p. 5T for a Key to Standards.		**Explore Activity:** Model a bacterium's slime layer, p. 187 **Before You Read,** p. 187
Section 1 What are bacteria? 2 sessions 1 block 1. **Identify** the characteristics of bacteria cells. 2. **Compare and contrast** aerobic and anaerobic organisms.	National Content Standards: UCP5, A1, C1, C2, C3, C5		**MiniLAB:** Modeling Bacteria Size, p. 189 **Science Online,** p. 191 **Earth Science Integration,** p. 192 **Activity:** Observing Cyanobacteria, p. 194
Section 2 Bacteria in Your Life 3 sessions 1.5 blocks 1. **Identify** some ways bacteria are helpful. 2. **Determine** the importance of nitrogen-fixing bacteria. 3. **Explain** how some bacteria can cause human disease.	National Content Standards: UCP2, A1, C4, F1, F5, G2		**MiniLAB:** Observing Bacterial Growth, p. 196 **Visualizing Nitrogen Fixing Bacteria,** p. 197 **Chemistry Integration,** p. 198 **Science Online,** p. 199 **Problem-Solving Activity:** Controlling Bacterial Growth, p. 200 **Activity:** Composting, p. 202 **Science Stats:** Unusual Bacteria, p. 204

NATIONAL GEOGRAPHIC

Teacher's Corner

PRODUCTS AVAILABLE FROM GLENCOE
To order call 1-800-334-7344:
CD-ROM
NGS PictureShow: The Cell
Curriculum Kit
GeoKit: Cells and Microorganisms
Transparency Set
NGS PicturePack: The Cell
Videodisc
STV: The Cell

PRODUCTS AVAILABLE FROM NATIONAL GEOGRAPHIC SOCIETY
To order call 1-800-368-2728:
Videos
Bacteria; Discovering the Cell

INDEX TO NATIONAL GEOGRAPHIC SOCIETY
The following articles may be used for research relating to this chapter:
"Body Beasts" by Richard Coniff, December 1998.

Activity Materials	Reproducible Resources	Section Assessment	Technology
Explore Activity: synthetic kitchen sponge, water, hair-styling gel, plate, scissors	**Chapter Resources Booklet** Foldables Worksheet, p. 13 Directed Reading Overview, p. 15 Note-taking Worksheets, pp. 27–28	GLENCOE'S ASSESSMENT ADVANTAGE	
MiniLAB: meterstick, yarn or string **Activity:** prepared slides (or micrograph photos) of *Oscillatoria, Nostoc, Gloeocapsa,* and *Anabaena*; microscope	**Chapter Resources Booklet** Transparency Activity, p. 38 MiniLAB, p. 3 Enrichment, p. 25 Reinforcement, p. 23 Directed Reading, p. 16 Activity Worksheet, pp. 5–6 Lab Activity, pp. 9–10 Transparency Activity, pp. 41–43 **Home and Community Involvement,** p. 37 **Life Science Critical Thinking/ Problem Solving,** p. 1	Portfolio Science Journal, p. 191 Performance MiniLAB, p. 189 Skill Builder Activities, p. 193 Content Section Assessment, p. 193	Section Focus Transparency Teaching Transparency Interactive CD-ROM Guided Reading Audio Program
MiniLAB: 2–3 dried beans, distilled water, glass beaker **Activity:** 4 or more wide-mouth clear glass jars, soil, water, watering can, banana peel, apple core, scrap of newspaper, leaf, plastic candy wrapper, scrap of aluminum foil *Need materials?* Contact Science Kit at 1-800-828-7777 or www.sciencekit.com on the Internet.	**Chapter Resources Booklet** Transparency Activity, p. 39 MiniLAB, p. 4 Enrichment, p. 26 Reinforcement, p. 24 Directed Reading, pp. 17, 18 Lab Activity, pp. 11–12 Activity Worksheet, pp. 7–8 **Mathematics Skill Activities,** p. 19 **Reading and Writing Skill Activities,** p. 25 **Lab Management and Safety,** p. 58	Portfolio Cultural Diversity, p. 196 Science Journal, p. 200 Performance MiniLAB, p. 196 Problem Solving Activity, p. 200 Skill Builder Activities, p. 201 Content Section Assessment, p. 201	Section Focus Transparency Interactive CD-ROM Guided Reading Audio Program

End of Chapter Assessment

GLENCOE'S ASSESSMENT ADVANTAGE

Blackline Masters	Technology	Professional Series
Chapter Resources Booklet Chapter Review, pp. 31–32 Chapter Tests, pp. 33–36 **Standardized Test Practice by The Princeton Review,** pp. 35–38	MindJogger Videoquiz Interactive CD-ROM Vocabulary PuzzleMakers ExamView Pro Test Bank Interactive Lesson Planner Interactive Teacher Edition	Performance Assessment in the Science Classroom (PASC)

Transparencies

Section Focus

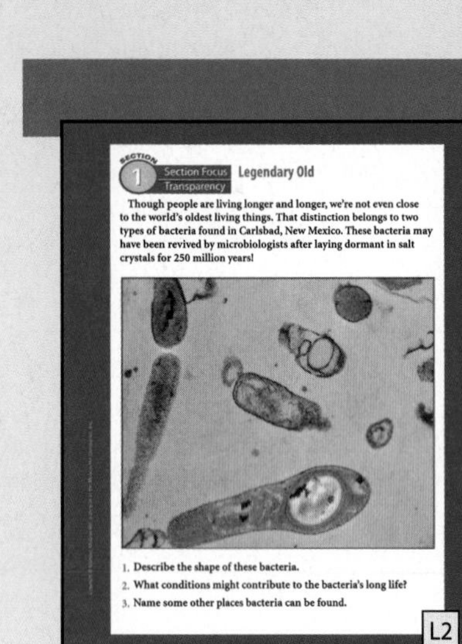
Section 1 Section Focus Transparency Legendary Old

Though people are living longer and longer, we're not even close to the world's oldest living things. That distinction belongs to two types of bacteria found in Carlsbad, New Mexico. These bacteria may have been revived by microbiologists after laying dormant in salt crystals for 250 million years!

1. Describe the shape of these bacteria.
2. What conditions might contribute to the bacteria's long life?
3. Name some other places bacteria can be found.

L2

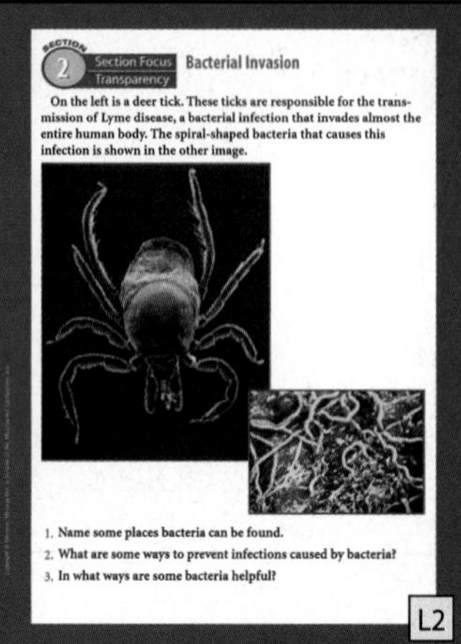
Section 2 Section Focus Transparency Bacterial Invasion

On the left is a deer tick. These ticks are responsible for the transmission of Lyme disease, a bacterial infection that invades almost the entire human body. The spiral-shaped bacteria that causes this infection is shown in the other image.

1. Name some places bacteria can be found.
2. What are some ways to prevent infections caused by bacteria?
3. In what ways are some bacteria helpful?

L2

This is a representation of key blackline masters available in the Teacher Classroom Resources. See Resource Manager boxes within the chapter for additional information.

Assessment

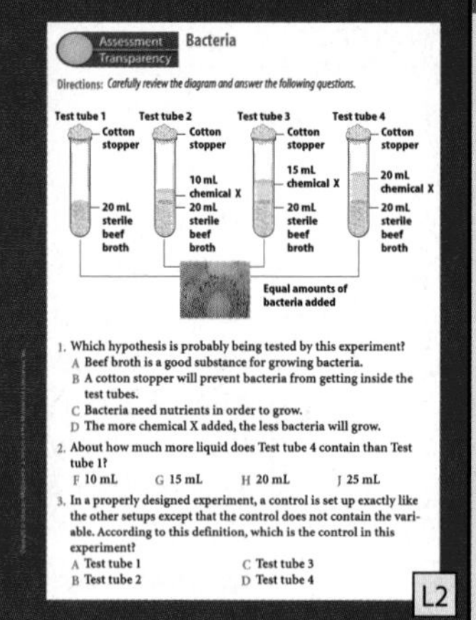
Assessment Transparency Bacteria

Directions: Carefully review the diagram and answer the following questions.

1. Which hypothesis is probably being tested by this experiment?
   A Beef broth is a good substance for growing bacteria.
   B A cotton stopper will prevent bacteria from getting inside the test tubes.
   C Bacteria need nutrients in order to grow.
   D The more chemical X added, the less bacteria will grow.
2. About how much more liquid does Test tube 4 contain than Test tube 1?
   F 10 mL G 15 mL H 20 mL J 25 mL
3. In a properly designed experiment, a control is set up exactly like the other setups except that the control does not contain the variable. According to this definition, which is the control in this experiment?
   A Test tube 1 C Test tube 3
   B Test tube 2 D Test tube 4

L2

Teaching

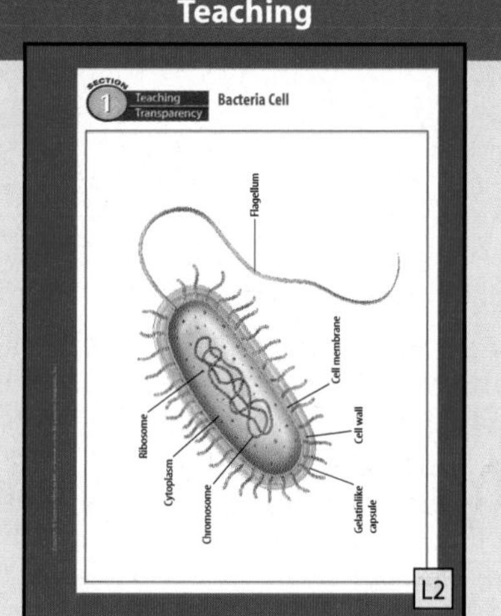
Section 1 Teaching Transparency Bacteria Cell

L2

Key to Teaching Strategies

The following designations will help you decide which activities are appropriate for your students.

L1 Level 1 activities should be appropriate for students with learning difficulties.

L2 Level 2 activities should be within the ability range of all students.

L3 Level 3 activities are designed for above-average students.

ELL ELL activities should be within the ability range of English Language Learners.

COOP LEARN Cooperative Learning activities are designed for small group work.

LS Multiple Learning Styles logos, as described on page 22T, are used throughout to indicate strategies that address different learning styles.

P These strategies represent student products that can be placed into a best-work portfolio.

Hands-on Activities

Activity Worksheets

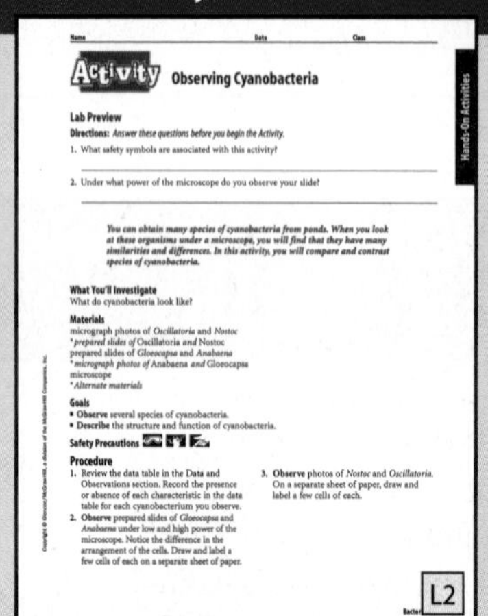
Name Date Class

Activity Observing Cyanobacteria

Lab Preview

Directions: Answer these questions before you begin the Activity.

1. What safety symbols are associated with this activity?
2. Under what power of the microscope do you observe your slide?

You can obtain many species of cyanobacteria from ponds. When you look at these organisms under a microscope, you will find that they have many similarities and differences. In this activity, you will compare and contrast species of cyanobacteria.

What You'll Investigate

What do cyanobacteria look like?

Materials

micrograph photos of Oscillatoria and Nostoc
*prepared slides of Oscillatoria and Nostoc
prepared slides of Gloeocapsa and Anabaena
*micrograph photos of Anabaena and Gloeocapsa
microscope
*Alternate materials

Goals

- Observe several species of cyanobacteria.
- Describe the structure and function of cyanobacteria.

Safety Precautions

Procedure

1. Review the data table in the Data and Observations section. Record the presence or absence of each characteristic in the data table for each cyanobacterium you observe.
2. Observe prepared slides of Gloeocapsa and Anabaena under low and high power of the microscope. Notice the difference in the arrangement of the cells. Draw and label a few cells of each on a separate sheet of paper.
3. Observe photos of Nostoc and Oscillatoria. On a separate sheet of paper, draw and label a few cells of each.

Hands-On Activities

L2

Laboratory Activities

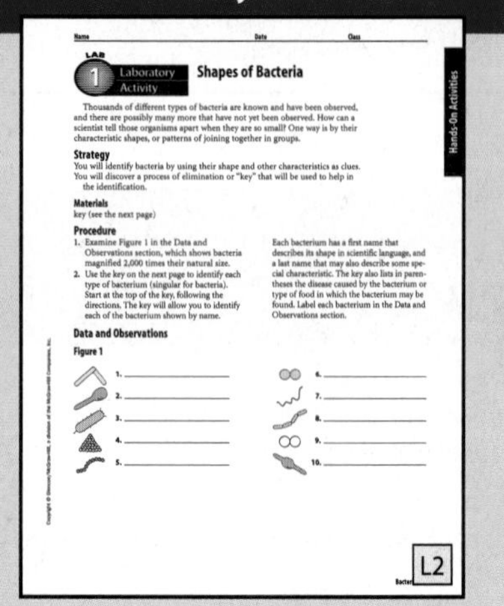
Name Date Class

Lab 1 Laboratory Activity Shapes of Bacteria

Thousands of different types of bacteria are known and have been observed, and there are possibly many more that have not yet been observed. How can a scientist tell those organisms apart when they are so small? One way is by their characteristic shapes, or patterns of joining together in groups.

Strategy

You will identify bacteria by using their shape and other characteristics as clues. You will discover a process of elimination or "key" that will be used to help in the identification.

Materials

key (see the next page)

Procedure

1. Examine Figure 1 in the Data and Observations section, which shows bacteria magnified 2,000 times their natural size.
2. Use the key on the next page to identify each type of bacterium (singular for bacteria). Start at the top of the key, following the directions. The key will allow you to identify each of the bacterium shown by name.

Each bacterium has a first name that describes its shape in scientific language, and a last name that may also describe some special characteristic. The key also lists in parentheses the disease caused by the bacterium or type of food in which the bacterium may be found. Label each bacterium in the Data and Observations section.

Data and Observations

Figure 1

1. ____ 2. ____ 3. ____ 4. ____ 5. ____ 6. ____ 7. ____ 8. ____ 9. ____ 10. ____

Hands-On Activities

L2

Meeting Different Ability Levels

Content Outline

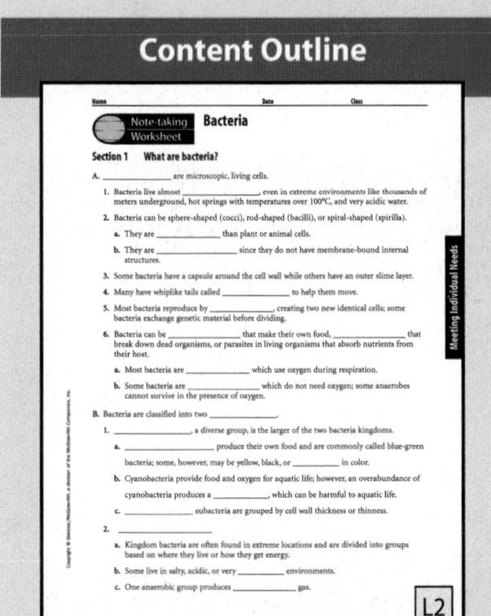

Note-taking Worksheet — Bacteria

Section 1 What are Bacteria?

L2

Reinforcement

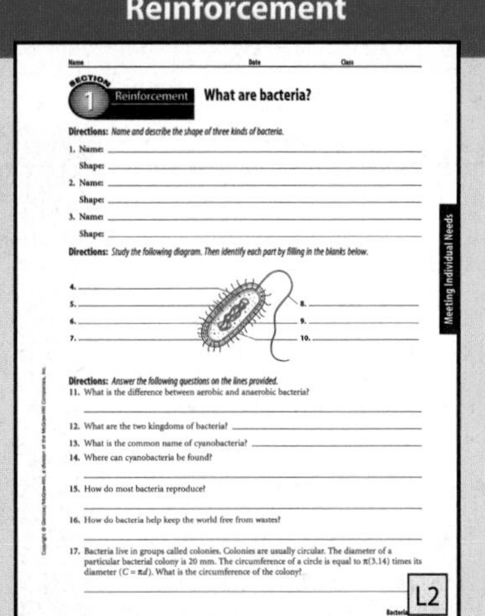

Section 1 Reinforcement — What are bacteria?

L2

Directed Reading

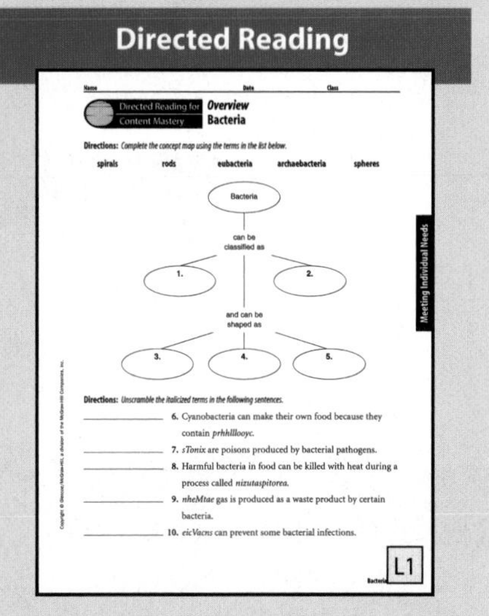

Directed Reading for Content Mastery — Overview — Bacteria

L1

Enrichment

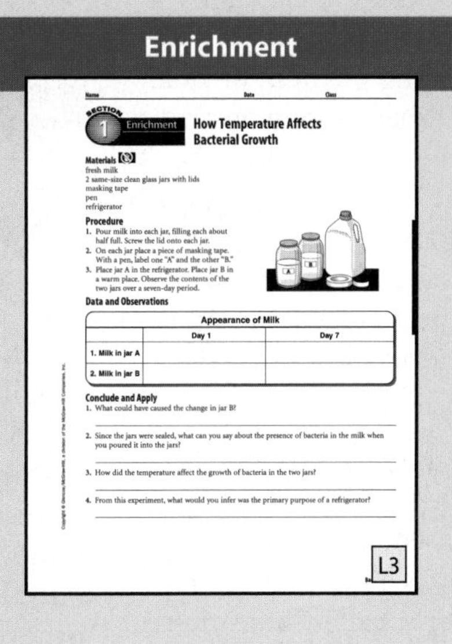

Section 1 Enrichment — How Temperature Affects Bacterial Growth

L3

Spanish Directed Reading

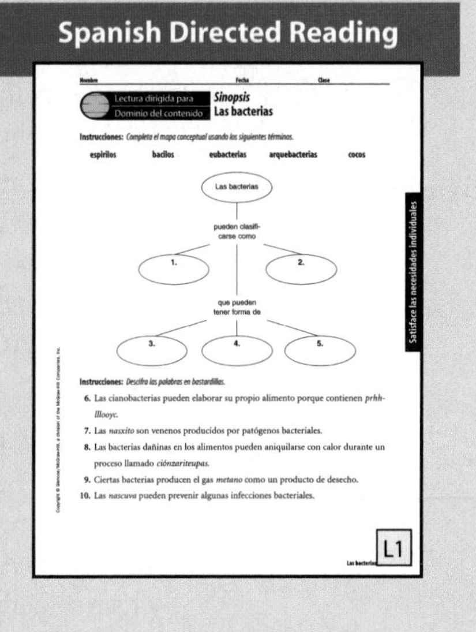

Lectura dirigida para Dominio del contenido — Sinopsis — Las bacterias

L1

Assessment

Chapter Tests

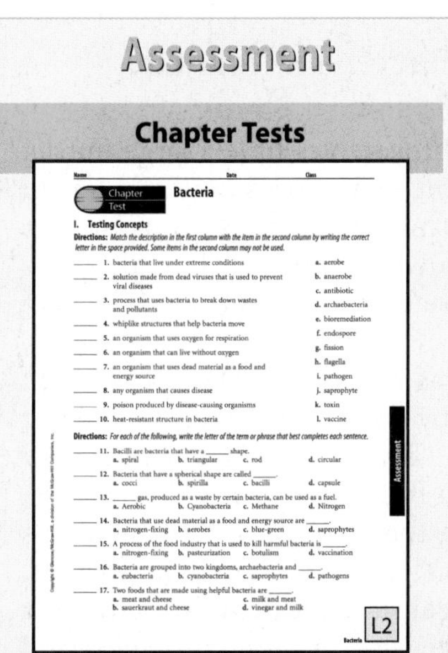

Chapter Test — Bacteria

L2

Test Practice Workbook

Chapter Review

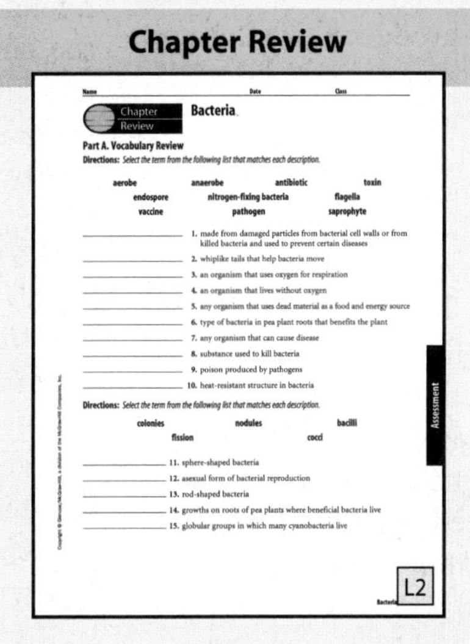

Chapter Review — Bacteria

L2

Science Content Background

SECTION 1

What are bacteria?

Characteristics

The sizes of bacteria are genetically determined and are measured in microns—1 micron (mμ)=0.001 mm. Most bacteria range from 0.2mμ to 2mμ in width and from 2 mμ to 8mμ in length. Bacteria generally have a rigid cell wall that maintains the shape of the organism. Bacterial cell walls prevent cells from bursting in environments where the pressure in the cell is greater than the pressure in the surrounding medium or fluid. Bacterial cells usually die in environments where the external pressure is greater than the pressure in the cell.

Bacteria have three basic shapes. Unlike the rod-shaped bacilli (singular, *bacillus*) and helical spirillia (singular, *spirillum*), the spherical cocci (singular, *coccus*) never possess flagella.

Fun Fact

In the late 1970s and 1980s, Carl Woese studied bacteria classification by examining sequences of genetic mutations. He determined that archaebacteria are more closely related to animals, plants, and fungi than to other bacteria.

Eubacteria

Most named bacteria are members of Kingdom Eubacteria. The five major phylogenetic groups of eubacteria are based on comparisons of their ribosomal RNA.

Cyanobacteria, formerly called blue-green algae, are bacteria that contain chlorophyll, enabling them to make their own food. This process is different from photosynthesis in plants. These organisms probably produced most of the original free oxygen in the atmosphere about 2.5 billion years ago. Cyanobacteria may be unicellular or colonial. Most live in freshwater, but some are symbiotic with fungi to form lichens.

Reproduction

Most bacteria reproduce by a process of cell division known as binary fission. In binary fission, the one or more circular chromosomes of the bacterial cell are duplicated. The duplicated chromosomes attach to the cell membrane. Continued growth of the cell separates the chromosomes, and the cell membrane eventually pinches in two as a cell wall is deposited between the daughter cells.

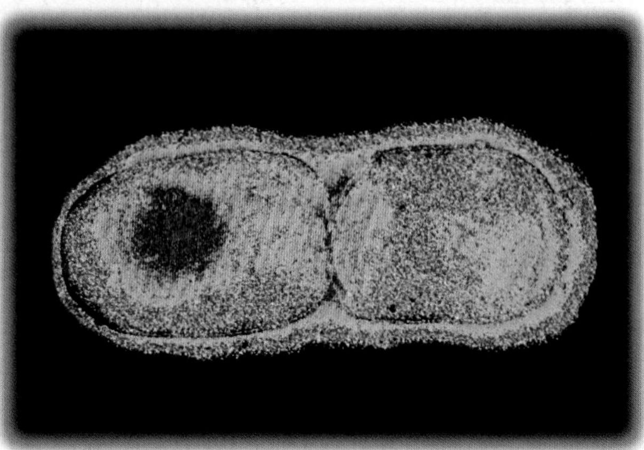

George Musil/Visuals Unlimited

SECTION 2

Bacteria in Your Life

Beneficial Bacteria

Prokaryotes have a large impact on ecology. They and fungi are the organisms primarily responsible for the decay and recycling of materials. Of these materials, carbon and nitrogen are essential.

Nitrogen gas can be used as a source of nitrogen only by some eubacteria, including cyanobacteria. These organisms not only remove nitrogen from the air for their own use, but also change the nitrogen into compounds other organisms can use. This is important, because nitrogen is necessary in order for plants and animals to make amino acids and nucleic acids. Because the nitrogen content of the environment varies considerably in quantity and kinds of nitrogen-containing compounds, it is not surprising that organisms have evolved the ability to utilize more than one nitrogen source.

Antibiotics and Vaccines

An antibiotic is a chemical that is able to kill or inhibit the growth of a microorganism. Thousands of antibiotics are known, but only a

Fun Fact

In 1939, Rene Dubos isolated the antibiotic tyrothricin from soil bacteria. This was the first antibiotic to be used successfully to treat a human disease.

few have practical uses. Many types of microorganisms including bacteria, protists, and fungi, produce antibiotics.

VCG/FPG International

The action of an antibiotic is dependent on its chemical structure. Certain antibiotics affect cell wall synthesis or destroy cell membrane permeability. Others act by inhibiting protein synthesis by causing the wrong amino acid to be inserted into the growing polypeptide chain of proteins in ribosomes. Broad spectrum antibiotics act on many different kinds of organisms. Some antibiotics, such as penicillin, act only on prokaryotes. Other antibiotics, such as cycloheximide, are active against eukaryotes but not prokaryotes.

Vaccines, on the other hand, are specific to certain bacteria or viruses. This is because a vaccine is made of damaged or killed bacterial cells or viruses. The white blood cells learn to recognize these pathogens and can respond quickly when they enter the body. It is important to note that antibiotics are taken after a bacterial pathogen enters the body, whereas a vaccine is a preventive measure.

Pasteurization

Pasteurization is achieved by passing milk continuously through a heat exchanger where its temperature quickly is raised to 71.6°C, held at that temperature for 15 s, and then quickly cooled. The process, named for Louis Pasteur, was first used to control spoilage of wine and saved the wine industry in France. Pasteurization does not kill all the microbes present and should not be confused with sterilization, which uses high heat and pressure to kill all bacteria. Although pasteurization was originally used to kill organisms that cause tuberculosis, typhoid, and brucellosis, today it is used to increase the shelf life of milk.

For additional content background on this topic, go to the Glencoe Science Web site at science.glencoe.com.

CHAPTER 7

Bacteria

Chapter Vocabulary

flagella, p. 189
fission, p. 190
aerobe, p. 190
anaerobe, p. 190
antibiotic, p. 195
saprophyte, p. 196
nitrogen-fixing bacteria, p. 196
pathogen, p. 199
toxin, p. 199
endospore, p. 199
vaccine, p. 201

What do you think?

Science Journal The photo shows bacteria on the surface of a protist. Bacteria live on surfaces or within the cells of organisms.

CHAPTER 7

Bacteria

Imagine a world of such small scale that a powerful microscope is needed to see the organisms that live there. What effects do these small organisms, some of which are bacteria, have on living things including you? In this chapter you will find the answer to this question. You also will read about many of the ways humans use bacteria, such as for composting. In addition, you will learn how the unique characteristics of bacteria help them live in almost every environment.

What do you think?

Science Journal Look at the picture below with a classmate. Discuss what you think this might be or what is happening. Here's a hint: *Bacteria can live on the surface of other organisms.* Write your answer or best guess in your Science Journal.

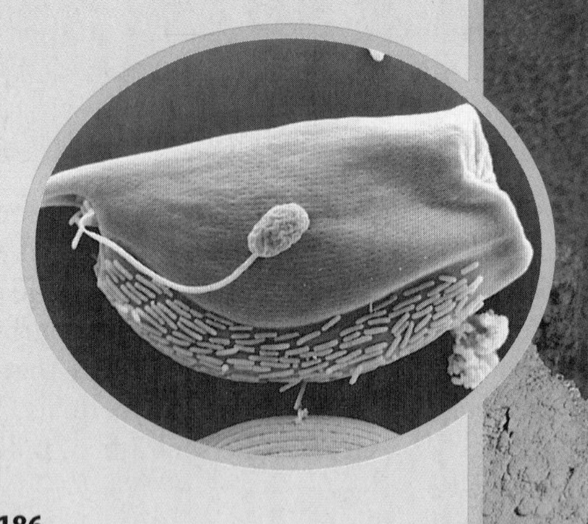

186

Theme Connection

Systems and Interactions The role of bacteria in maintaining a homeostatic balance is discussed. In addition to homeostasis, the ecological importance of bacteria is illustrated by using examples of niches filled by these organisms.

Bacterial cells have a gelatinlike, protective coating on the outside of their cell walls. In some cases, the coating is thin and is referred to as a slime layer. A slime layer helps a bacterium attach to other surfaces. Dental plaque forms when bacteria with slime layers stick to teeth and multiply there. A slime layer also can reduce water loss from a bacterium. In this activity you will make a model of a bacterium's slime layer.

Model a bacterium's slime layer

1. Cut two 2-cm-wide strips from the long side of a synthetic kitchen sponge.
2. Soak both strips in water. Remove them from the water and squeeze out the excess water. Both strips should be damp.
3. Completely coat one strip with hair-styling gel. Do not coat the other strip.
4. Place both strips on a plate (not paper) and leave them overnight.

Observe

The next day, record your observations of the two sponge strips in your Science Journal. Infer how a slime layer protects a bacterial cell from drying out. What environmental conditions are best for survival of bacteria?

Before You Read

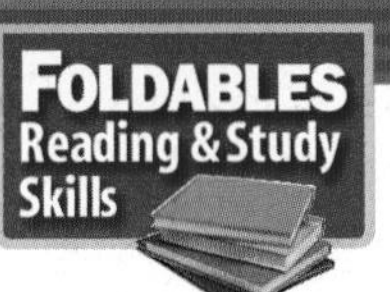

Making a Venn Diagram Study Fold **Make the following Foldable to compare and contrast the characteristics of bacteria.**

1. Place a sheet of paper in front of you so the long side is at the top. Fold the paper in half from top to bottom.
2. Fold both sides in. Unfold the paper so three sections show.
3. Through the top thickness of paper, cut along each of the fold lines to the topfold, forming three tabs. Label the tabs *Kingdom Archaebacteria, Both,* and *Kingdom Eubacteria.* Draw ovals on the front of the paper as shown.
4. As you read the chapter, list characteristics of each kingdom of bacteria under the tabs.

Explore Activity

Purpose Use this Explore Activity to help students discover how the slime layer surrounding bacterial cells helps protect them from dehydration. L2

LS **Kinesthetic**

Preparation Collect kitchen sponges, plates, and hair styling gel. Locate areas where students can leave their sponges overnight.

Materials synthetic kitchen sponge; scissors; water; hair styling gel; plate

Teaching Strategy Have students do this activity the day before you introduce the topic of bacteria slime layers. Use the activity to demonstrate the properties of a slime layer.

Observe

Students should find that the gel-treated sponge is still damp and adheres to the plate. The untreated sponge will have dried out. A slime layer seals moisture inside the bacteria cell. Bacteria cells thrive in moist, damp environmental conditions.

Assessment

Process Ask students to infer how Earth's nutrient cycles would be affected if bacteria cells did not have slime layers. Bacteria decompose dead and decaying materials into nutrients. Slime layers allow bacteria to lie dormant during drier conditions. Without slime layers, fewer bacteria would survive dry conditions, which would result in fewer nutrients being recycled. Use **PASC,** p. 89.

Before You Read

FOLDABLES Reading & Study Skills

Dinah Zike Study Fold

Purpose Have students use a Foldable Venn diagram to determine what they know about bacteria in general and to record similarities and differences between the two kingdoms of bacteria.

For additional help, see Foldables Worksheet, p. 13 in **Chapter Resources Booklet,** or go to the Glencoe Science Web site at **science.glencoe.com.** See After You Read in the Study Guide at the end of this chapter.

SECTION

What are bacteria?

1 Motivate

Bellringer Transparency

Display the Section Focus Transparency for Section 1. Use the accompanying Transparency Activity Master. L2 ELL

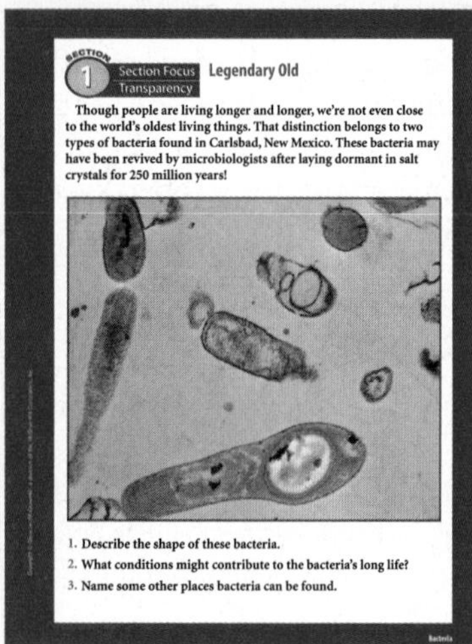
1 Section Focus Transparency — Legendary Old

Though people are living longer and longer, we're not even close to the world's oldest living things. That distinction belongs to two types of bacteria found in Carlsbad, New Mexico. These bacteria may have been revived by microbiologists after laying dormant in salt crystals for 250 million years!

1. Describe the shape of these bacteria.
2. What conditions might contribute to the bacteria's long life?
3. Name some other places bacteria can be found.

Tie to Prior Knowledge

Review with students the characteristics of living things. Emphasize that bacterial cells have all of these characteristics, although they are smaller than the more familiar cells of plants and animals.

Caption Answer

Figure 1 sphere, rod, and spiral

Resource Manager

Chapter Resources Booklet
Transparency Activity, p. 38
MiniLAB, p. 3
Directed Reading, pp. 15, 16

SECTION 1

What are bacteria?

As You Read

***What* You'll Learn**

- **Identify** the characteristics of bacterial cells.
- **Compare and contrast** aerobic and anaerobic organisms.

Vocabulary
flagella
fission
aerobe
anaerobe

***Why* It's Important**
Bacteria are found in almost all environments and affect all living things.

Characteristics of Bacteria

For thousands of years people did not understand what caused disease. They did not understand the process of decomposition or what happened when food spoiled. It wasn't until the latter half of the seventeenth century that Antonie van Leeuwenhoek, a Dutch merchant, discovered the world of bacteria. Leeuwenhoek observed scrapings from his teeth using his simple microscope. Although he didn't know it at that time, some of the tiny swimming organisms he observed were bacteria. After Leeuwenhoek's discovery, it was another hundred years before bacteria were proven to be living cells that carry on all of the processes of life.

Where do bacteria live? Bacteria are almost everywhere—in the air, in foods that you eat and drink, and on the surfaces of things you touch. They are even found thousands of meters underground and at great ocean depths. A shovelful of soil contains billions of them. Your skin has about 100,000 bacteria per square centimeter, and millions of other bacteria live in your body. Some types of bacteria live in extreme environments where few other organisms can survive. Some heat-loving bacteria live in hot springs or hydrothermal vents—places where water temperature exceeds 100°C. Others can live in cold water or soil at 0°C. Some bacteria live in very salty water, like that of the Dead Sea. One type of bacteria lives in water that drains from coal mines, which is extremely acidic at a pH of 1.

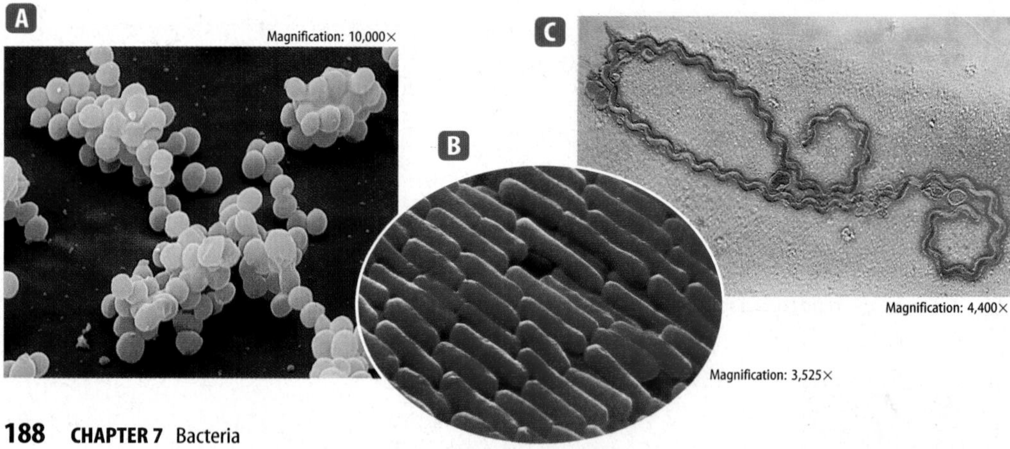

Figure 1
A Coccus-, B bacillus-, and C spirillum-shaped bacteria can be found in almost any environment. *What common terms could be used to describe these cell shapes?*

Section Assessment Planner

Portfolio
Science Journal, p. 191

Performance Assessment
Try at Home MiniLAB, p. 189
Skill Builder Activities, p. 193
See page 208 for more options.

Content Assessment
Section, p. 189
Challenge, p. 189
Chapter, pp. 208–209

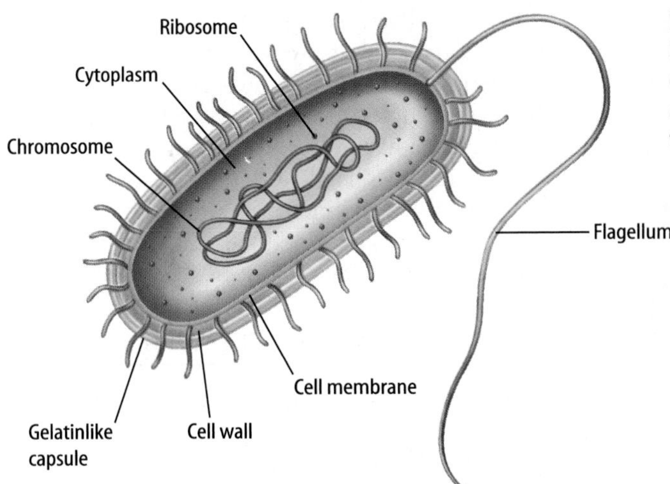

Figure 2
Bacterial cells are much smaller than eukaryotic cells. Most bacteria are about the size of some organelles found inside eukaryotic cells.

Structure of Bacterial Cells Bacteria normally have three basic shapes—spheres, rods, and spirals, as shown in **Figure 1.** Sphere-shaped bacteria are called cocci (KAH ki) (singular, *coccus*), rod-shaped bacteria are called bacilli (buh SIH li) (singular, *bacillus*), and spiral-shaped bacteria are called spirilla (spi RIH luh) (singular, *spirillum*). Bacteria are smaller than plant or animal cells. They are one-celled organisms that occur alone or in chains or groups.

A typical bacterial cell contains cytoplasm surrounded by a cell membrane and a cell wall, as shown in **Figure 2.** Bacterial cells are classified as prokaryotic because they do not contain a membrane-bound nucleus or other membrane-bound internal structures called organelles. Most of the genetic material of a bacterial cell is in its one circular chromosome found in the cytoplasm. Many bacteria also have a smaller circular piece of DNA called a plasmid. Ribosomes also are found in a bacterial cell's cytoplasm.

Special Features Some bacteria, like the type that causes pneumonia, have a thick, gelatinlike capsule around the cell wall. A capsule can help protect the bacterium from other cells that try to destroy it. The capsule, along with hairlike projections found on the surface of many bacteria, also can help them stick to surfaces. Some bacteria also have an outer coating called a slime layer. Like a capsule, a slime layer allows a bacterium to stick to surfaces and reduces water loss. Many bacteria that live in moist conditions also have whiplike tails called **flagella** to help them move.

Reading Check *How do bacteria use flagella?*

Modeling Bacteria Size

1. One human hair is about 0.1 mm wide. Use a **meterstick** to measure a piece of **yarn or string** that is 10 m long. This yarn represents the width of your hair.
2. One type of bacteria is 2 micrometers long (1 micrometer = 0.000001 m). Measure another piece of yarn or string that is 20 cm long. This piece represents the length of the bacterium.
3. Find a large area where you can lay the two pieces of yarn or string next to each other and compare them.

Analysis

1. How much smaller is the bacterium than the width of your hair?
2. In your **Science Journal** describe why a model is helpful to understand how small bacteria are.

2 Teach

Characteristics of Bacteria

Visual Learning

Figure 1 Emphasize that bacteria have three-dimensional shapes. Ask students to name common objects that are similar in shape to bacteria. Balls are similar to cocci, lengths of thick wire are similar to bacilli, and wire spirals on notebooks are similar to spirilla. **Figure 2** Emphasize that bacterial cells are small. Compare the size of a bacterium to another object you have studied. Chloroplasts and mitochondria are about the same size as a bacterium.

Purpose to model the size of bacterial cells LS **Visual-Spatial**

Materials 11 m of yarn or string; meterstick

Teaching Strategy Have students compare the size of bacteria with viruses. The diameter of the average virus is 100 nm, or 0.0000001m, which is 10 times smaller than the average bacteria.

Analysis

1. 50 times smaller
2. Using models for size comparison allows one to understand the actual size of a bacterium.

Curriculum Connection

Math Ask students whether they would rather have $10 every 20 minutes for 13 hours or start with one penny and have their money doubled every 20 minutes for 13 hours. $400 by arithmetic growth or more than $5 trillion by exponential growth Point out that the growth rate of bacteria is like that of the penny. L2 LS **Logical-Mathematical**

Assessment

Oral Explain how the size of bacteria contributes to the spread of infection. Their small size allows them to be transferred through the air when a person sneezes or coughs. Use **PASC**, p. 89.

Reading Check

Answer to help them move

Characteristics of Bacteria, continued

Students may think that bacteria are simple cells because of their appearance and lack of a membrane-bound nucleus and organelles. Explain that all living cells are very complex.

Fun Fact

Fission is also called binary fission. Binary fission is a quick and efficient means of producing many cells to utilize an energy resource.

Make a Model

Have students use objects from home to make a model of bacteria undergoing fission. For instance, two golf balls could be used to model fission in cocci. L1 LS **Kinesthetic**

Discussion

Have groups of students discuss the possible combinations of cocci, such as pairs (diplococci), strands (streptococci), and clusters (staphylococci). Explain that different species of bacteria assume all these shapes. L2 COOP LEARN LS **Interpersonal**

Magnification: 500×

Figure 3
Before dividing, these bacteria are exchanging DNA through the tubes that join them.

Reproduction Bacteria usually reproduce by fission. **Fission** is a process that produces two new cells with genetic material identical to each other and that of the original cell. It is the simplest form of asexual reproduction.

Some bacteria exchange genetic material through a process similar to sexual reproduction, as shown in **Figure 3.** Two bacteria line up beside each other and exchange DNA through a fine tube. This results in cells with different combinations of genetic material than they had before the exchange. As a result, the bacteria may acquire variations that give them an advantage for survival.

How Bacteria Obtain Food and Energy Bacteria obtain food in a variety of ways. Some make their food and others get it from the environment. Bacteria that contain chlorophyll or other pigments make their own food using energy from the Sun. Other bacteria use energy from chemical reactions to make food. Bacteria and other organisms that can make their own food are called producers.

Most bacteria are consumers. They do not make their own food. Some break down dead organisms to obtain energy. Others live as parasites of living organisms and absorb nutrients from their host.

Most organisms use oxygen when they break down food and obtain energy through a process called respiration. An organism that uses oxygen for respiration is called an **aerobe** (AY rohb). You are an aerobic organism and so are most bacteria. In contrast, an organism that is adapted to live without oxygen is called an **anaerobe** (AN uh rohb). Several kinds of anaerobic bacteria live in the intestinal tract of humans. Some bacteria, like those in **Figure 4B,** cannot survive in areas with oxygen.

Figure 4
Observing where bacteria can grow in tubes of a nutrient mixture shows you how oxygen affects different types of bacteria.

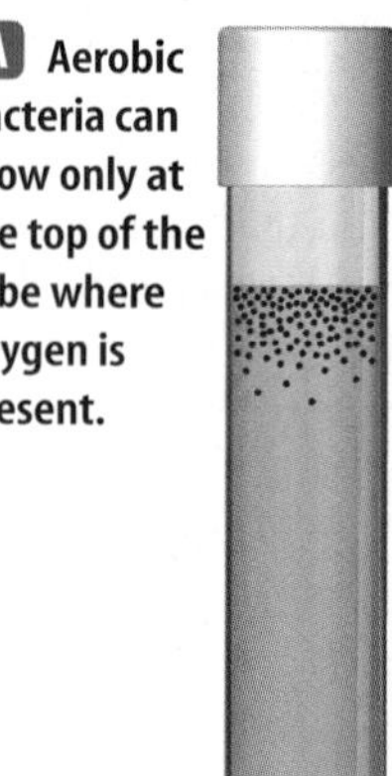

A **Aerobic bacteria can grow only at the top of the tube where oxygen is present.**

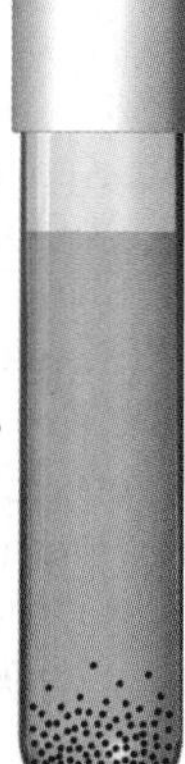

B **Some anaerobic bacteria will grow only at the bottom of the tube where there is no oxygen.**

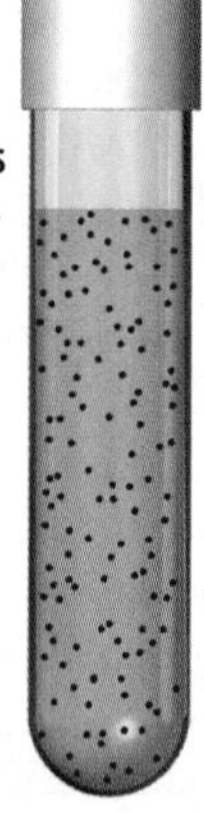

C **Other anaerobic bacteria can grow in areas with or without oxygen.**

Inclusion Strategies

Learning Disabled Have pairs of students create flash cards that have the vocabulary for this chapter on one side and the definitions on the other. Allow students to practice using the vocabulary with their flash cards until they show proficiency with the terms. Students can also use flash cards to learn the names or structures of bacteria. L1 LS **Linguistic**

Teacher FYI

Leeuwenhoek was probably not the first person to observe bacteria, but he was the first to keep convincingly accurate records of his microscopic observations. He was also the first to show fission in cells.

Figure 5
Many different bacteria can live in the intestines of humans and other animals. They often are identified based on the foods they use and the wastes they produce.

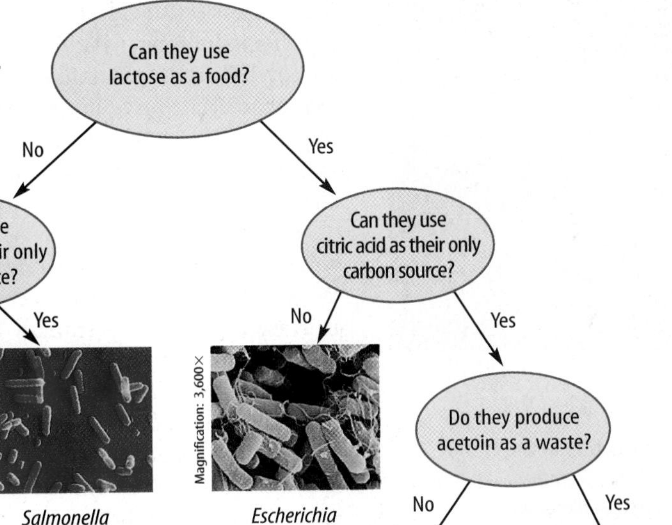

Eubacteria

Bacteria are classified into two kingdoms—eubacteria (yew bak TIHR ee uh) and archaebacteria (ar kee bak TIHR ee uh). Eubacteria is the larger of the two kingdoms. The organisms in this kingdom are diverse, and scientists must study many characteristics in order to classify eubacteria into smaller groups. Most eubacteria are grouped according to their cell shape and structure, the way they obtain food, the type of food they eat, and the wastes they produce, as shown in **Figure 5.** Other characteristics used to group eubacteria include the method used for cell movement and whether the organism is an aerobe or anaerobe. New information about their genetic material is changing how scientists classify this kingdom.

Producer Eubacteria One important group of producer eubacteria is the cyanobacteria (si an oh bak TIHR ee uh). They make their own food using carbon dioxide, water, and energy from sunlight. They also produce oxygen as a waste. Cyanobacteria contain chlorophyll and another pigment that is blue. This pigment combination gives cyanobacteria their common name—blue-green bacteria. However, some cyanobacteria are yellow, black, or red. The Red Sea gets its name from red cyanobacteria.

Reading Check *Why are cyanobacteria classified as producers?*

SCIENCE Online

Research Not all producer eubacteria use photosynthesis. Visit the Glencoe Science Web site at **science.glencoe.com** for more information about the ways that producer bacteria make food. Communicate to your class what you learn.

Visual Learning

Figure 5 After discussing the phylogeny of bacteria, explain to students that phylogeny is based on the theory that organisms change over time and on their characteristics. Ask if these bacteria could ever be re-grouped. Yes, organisms are often re-classified as new information is gained.

Use Science Words

Word Usage Have students use the words *aerobe* and *anaerobe* in sentences. An aerobe is a bacterium that requires oxygen. An anaerobe is a bacterium that lives without oxygen. L2 LS Linguistic

Eubacteria

Use Science Words

Word Origin The word *eubacteria* comes from the Greek words *eys*, meaning "good" and *bakterion*, meaning "staff." **Which group of eubacteria gave them their name?** bacilli

Reading Check

Answer They make their own food.

SCIENCE Online

Internet Addresses

Explore the Glencoe Science Web site at **science.glencoe.com** to find out more about topics in this section.

Resource Manager

Chapter Resources Booklet

- Enrichment, p. 25
- Note-taking Worksheets, pp. 27–28
- Transparency Activity, pp. 41–43

Science Journal

Bacteria in the News Ask students to find at least three newspaper or magazine articles that mention bacteria. Have them read the articles and then use **Figure 5** to classify the bacteria in the article. Have them write a paragraph about each bacteria, justifying their classification. L2 LS **Linguistic** P

Eubacteria, continued

Activity

Have students make a wet mount to observe *Oscillatoria.* Point out that swaying movements are made as the bacteria secrete a slimy substance from their cells. L2 LS **Visual-Spatial**

Earth Science INTEGRATION

Ocean vents form where two of Earth's tectonic plates are splitting apart. The conditions are hypothesized to be similar to those on early Earth. Some organisms that live near ocean vents include tube worms, clams, mussels, and bacteria.

Caption Answer

Figure 7 thick if the cells are purple or thin if the cells are pink

Quick Demo

Demonstrate the classification of bacteria through staining by allowing students to view commercially prepared slides of gram-positive and gram-negative organisms. L2 LS **Visual-Spatial**

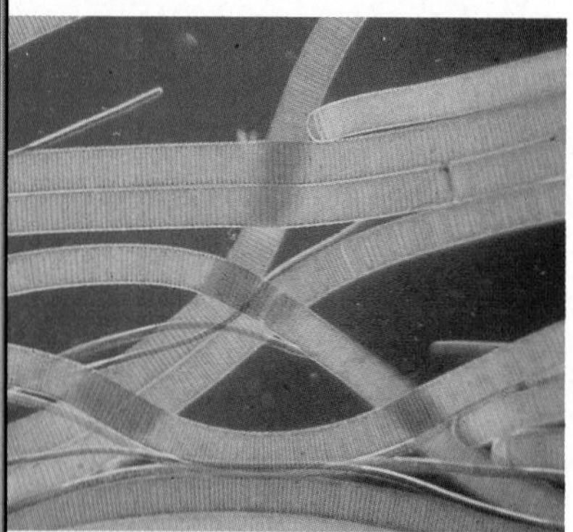

Figure 6
These colonies of the cyanobacteria *Ocillatotoria* can move by twisting like a screw.

Earth Science INTEGRATION

Ocean vents are geysers on the floor of the ocean. Research and find out how ocean vents form and what conditions are like at an ocean vent. In your Science Journal, describe organisms that have been found living around ocean vents.

Importance of Cyanobacteria Some cyanobacteria live together in long chains or filaments, as shown in **Figure 6.** Many are covered with a gelatinlike substance. This adaptation enables cyanobacteria to live in groups called colonies. They are an important source of food for some organisms in lakes, ponds, and oceans. The oxygen produced by cyanobacteria is used by all other aquatic organisms.

Cyanobacteria also can cause problems for aquatic life. Have you ever seen a pond covered with smelly, green, bubbly slime? When large amounts of nutrients enter a pond, cyanobacteria increase in number. Eventually the population grows so large that a bloom is produced. A bloom looks like a mat of bubbly green slime on the surface of the water. Available resources in the water are used up quickly and the cyanobacteria die. Other bacteria that are aerobic consumers feed on dead cyanobacteria and use up the oxygen in the water. As a result of the reduced oxygen in the water, fish and other organisms die.

Consumer Eubacteria Many of the consumer eubacteria are grouped by the type of cell wall produced—a thick cell wall or a thinner cell wall. This difference can be seen under a microscope after they are treated with certain chemicals that are called stains. As shown in **Figure 7,** thick-cell-walled bacteria stain a different color than thin-cell-walled bacteria.

The composition of the cell wall also can affect how a bacterium is affected by medicines given to treat an infection. Some medicines will be more effective against the type of bacteria with thicker cell walls than they will be against bacteria with thinner cell walls.

One group of eubacteria is unique because they do not produce cell walls. This allows them to change their shape. They are not described as coccus, bacillus, or spirillum. One type of bacteria in this group, *Mycoplasma pneumoniae,* causes a type of pneumonia in humans.

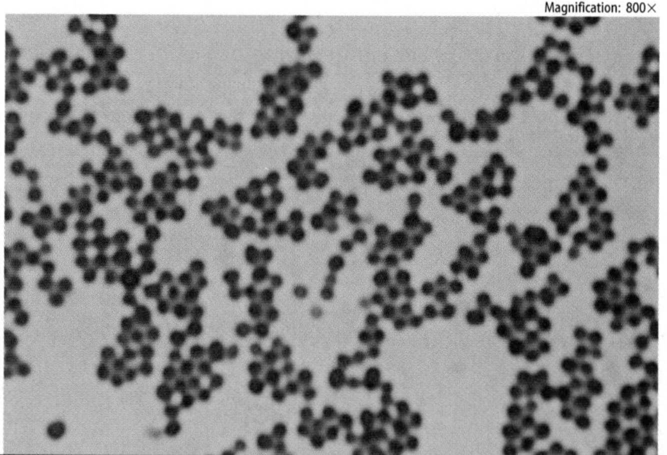

Figure 7
When stained with certain chemicals, bacteria with thin cell walls appear pink when viewed under a microscope. Those with thicker cell walls appear purple. *What type of cell walls do the coccus bacteria in this photo have?*

Inclusion Strategies

Learning Disabled If possible, bring in some pond water that has a mat of cyanobacteria on it. Place the mat in the light and ask what the bubbles are that appear in the mat. They are oxygen bubbles produced by photosynthesis. Then ask how large numbers of cyanobacteria can cause problems. When cyanobacteria die and decompose, oxygen levels drop. This can cause other organisms, such as fish, to die. L1 LS **Visual-Spatial**

Active Reading

Buddy Interviews This strategy helps students understand and clarify the reading. Have students interview one another to find out what helps them to understand what they are reading, how they find answers, and how they assimilate new vocabulary terms. Have students use Buddy Interviews to help them master concepts about bacteria.

Archaebacteria

Kingdom Archaebacteria contains certain kinds of bacteria that often are found in extreme conditions, such as hot springs. The conditions in which some archaebacteria live today are similar to conditions found on Earth during its early history. Archaebacteria are divided into groups based on where they live or how they get energy.

Salt-, Heat-, and Acid-Lovers One group of archaebacteria lives in salty environments such as the Great Salt Lake in Utah and the Dead Sea. Some of them require a habitat ten times saltier than seawater to grow.

Other groups of archaebacteria include those that live in acidic or hot environments. Some of these bacteria live near deep ocean vents or in hot springs where the temperature of the water is above 100°C.

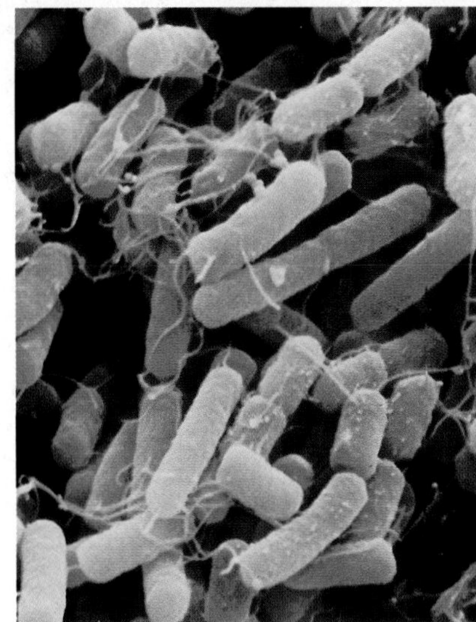
Magnification: 4,200×

Figure 8
Some methane-producing bacteria live in the digestive tracts of cattle. They help digest the plants that cattle eat.

Methane Producers Bacteria in this group of archaebacteria are anaerobic. They live in muddy swamps, the intestines of cattle, and even in you. Methane producers, as shown in **Figure 8,** use carbon dioxide for energy and release methane gas as a waste. Sometimes methane produced by these bacteria bubbles up out of swamps and marshes. These archaebacteria also are used in the process of sewage treatment. In an oxygen-free tank, the bacteria are used to break down the waste material that has been filtered from sewage water.

Section 1 Assessment

1. What are the characteristics common to all bacteria?
2. How do aerobic organisms and anaerobic organisms differ?
3. How do most bacteria reproduce?
4. Who is given credit for first discovering bacteria?
5. **Think Critically** A pond is surrounded by recently fertilized farm fields. What effect would rainwater runoff from the fields have on the organisms in the pond?

Skill Builder Activities

6. **Classifying** A scientist recently found bacteria that grow in boiling water. In what kingdom is the bacteria most likely classified? Why? **For more help, refer to the Science Skill Handbook.**
7. **Solving One-Step Equations** Some bacteria reproduce every 20 min. Suppose that you have one bacterium. How long would it take for the number of bacteria to increase to more than 1 million? **For more help, refer to the Math Skill Handbook.**

3 Assess

Reteach

To demonstrate the role of bacteria as decomposers, bring a piece of decomposing fruit to class. Have students observe the process over a few days or a week. L2 LS **Visual-Spatial**

Challenge

Have students research the cells of prokaryotes and eukaryotes to determine differences. **How are flagella of bacteria different from flagella of other organisms, such as *Euglena*?** Flagella of bacteria are simpler and are not surrounded by a membrane. L2 LS **Linguistic**

Assessment

Performance To further assess students' abilities to observe cyanobacteria, set up a practical to have them identify organisms or answer questions about them. Use **Performance Assessment in the Science Classroom,** p. 89.

Answers to Section Assessment

1. one-celled; cytoplasm surrounded by cell membrane and cell wall; single circular chromosome; ribosomes in cytoplasm; plasmid; no membrane-bound organelles
2. Aerobic: require oxygen to live; anaerobic: can live without oxygen. Oxygen kills some anaerobes.
3. Fission; some bacteria also exchange genetic material in a process similar to sexual reproduction.
4. Antonie van Leeuwenhoek
5. It could potentially kill the pond organisms as cyanobacteria flourish, die, and decompose.
6. Kingdom Archaebacteria; these organisms often live in harsh conditions.
7. 6 hours and 40 minutes (1,048,576 bacteria)

Resource Manager

Chapter Resources Booklet
Reinforcement, p. 23
Lab Activity, pp. 9–10

Activity

BENCH TESTED

Purpose to observe and record the characteristics of several cyanobacteria L2 ELL

LS **Naturalist**

Process Skills observing, classifying, interpreting data

Time Required 50 minutes

Alternate Materials In addition to the cyanobacteria listed, many others can be found in biological supply house catalogs.

Teaching Strategy Having prepared slides for use will be more interesting and visually stimulating for students than having them look at pictures.

Troubleshooting If students have trouble seeing the jellylike layer of the capsule, have them reduce the amount of light coming through the microscope's diaphragm.

Answers to Questions

1. You can infer that they are producers that carry on photosynthesis.
2. Cyanobacteria contain chlorophyll, which makes them photosynthetic eubacteria.

Assessment

Performance Have students draw, label, and describe different cyanobacteria they observe. Use **Performance Assessment in the Science Classroom**, p. 127.

Activity

Observing Cyanobacteria

You can obtain many species of cyanobacteria from ponds. When you look at these organisms under a microscope, you will find that they have similarities and differences. In this activity, compare and contrast species of cyanobacteria.

Cyanobacteria Observations

Structure	*Anabaena*	*Gloeocapsa*	*Nostoc*	*Oscillatoria*
Filament or Colony	filament	colony	filament	filament
Nucleus	no	no	no	no
Chlorophyll	yes	yes	yes	yes
Gel-Like Layer	yes	yes	yes	yes

What You'll Investigate

What do cyanobacteria look like?

Materials

micrograph photos of *Oscillatoria* and *Nostoc*
**prepared slides of* Oscillatoria *and* Nostoc
prepared slides of *Gloeocapsa* and *Anabaena*
**micrograph photos of* Anabaena *and* Gloeocapsa
microscope
**Alternate materials*

Goals

- **Observe** several species of cyanobacteria.
- **Describe** the structure and function of cyanobacteria.

Safety Precautions

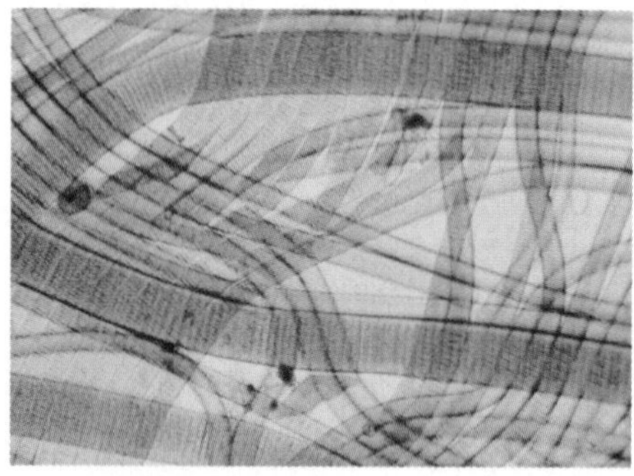

Procedure

1. Copy the data table in your Science Journal. **Record** the presence or absence of each characteristic in the data table for each cyanobacterium you observe.
2. **Observe** prepared slides of *Gloeocapsa* and *Anabaena* under low and high power of the microscope. Notice the difference in the arrangement of the cells. In your Science Journal, draw and label a few cells of each.
3. **Observe** photos of *Nostoc* and *Oscillatoria.* In your Science Journal, draw and label a few cells of each.

Conclude and Apply

1. What can you infer from the color of each cyanobacterium?
2. How can you tell by observing that a cyanobacterium is a eubacterium?

Communicating Your Data

Compare your data table with those of other students in your class. **For more help, refer to the** Science Skill Handbook.

194 CHAPTER 7 Bacteria

Communicating Your Data

Data tables should be the same for all students. Students who have differences should be prepared to explain them to others.

Resource Manager

Chapter Resources Booklet
Activity Worksheet, pp. 5–6

SECTION 2

Bacteria in Your Life

Beneficial Bacteria

When most people hear the word *bacteria,* they probably associate it with sore throats or other illnesses. However, few bacteria cause illness. Most are important for other reasons. The benefits of most bacteria far outweigh the harmful effects of a few.

Bacteria That Help You Without bacteria, you would not be healthy for long. Bacteria, like those in **Figure 9,** are found inside your digestive system. These bacteria are found in particularly high numbers in your large intestine. Most are harmless to you, and they help you stay healthy. For example, the bacteria in your intestines are responsible for producing vitamin K, which is necessary for normal blood clot formation.

Some bacteria produce chemicals called **antibiotics** that limit the growth of other bacteria. For example, one type of bacteria that is commonly found living in soil produces the antibiotic streptomycin. Another kind of bacteria, *Bacillus,* produces the antibiotic found in many nonprescription antiseptic ointments. Many diseases in humans and animals can be treated with antibiotics.

As You Read

***What* You'll Learn**

- **Identify** some ways bacteria are helpful.
- **Determine** the importance of nitrogen-fixing bacteria.
- **Explain** how some bacteria can cause human disease.

Vocabulary

antibiotic, saprophyte, nitrogen-fixing bacteria, pathogen, toxin, endospore, vaccine

***Why* It's Important**

Discovering the ways bacteria affect your life can help you understand biological processes.

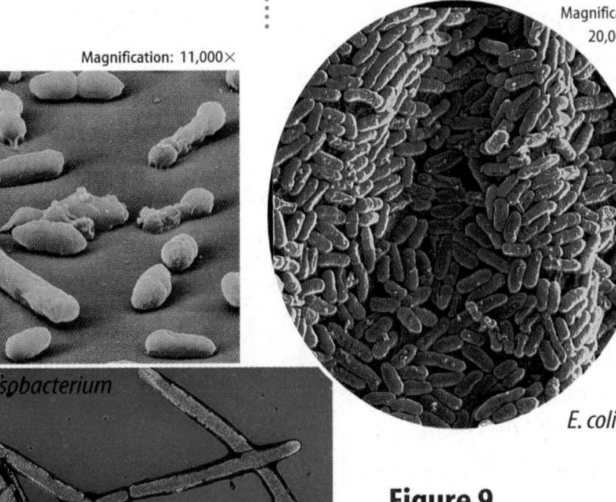

Figure 9
Many types of bacteria live naturally in your intestine. They help you digest food and produce vitamins that you need.

Section Assessment Planner

PORTFOLIO
Cultural Diversity, p. 196
Science Journal, p. 200

PERFORMANCE ASSESSMENT
MiniLAB, p. 196
Skill Builder Activities, p. 201
See page 208 for more options.

CONTENT ASSESSMENT
Section, p. 201
Challenge, p. 201
Chapter, pp. 208–209

SECTION

Bacteria in Your Life

1 Motivate

Bellringer Transparency

Display the Section Focus Transparency for Section 2. Use the accompanying Transparency Activity Master. L2 ELL

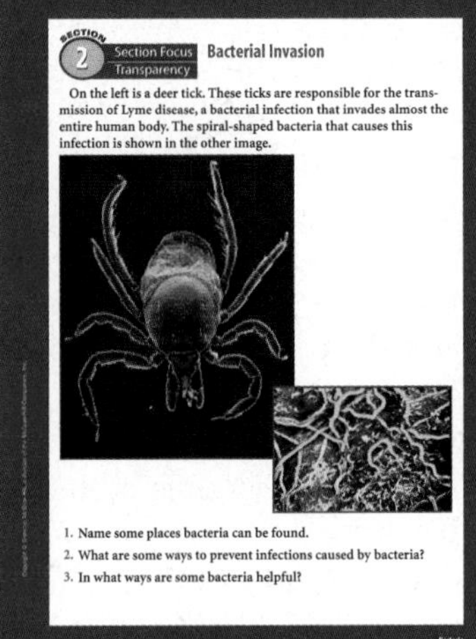

Section 2 Section Focus Transparency **Bacterial Invasion**

On the left is a deer tick. These ticks are responsible for the transmission of Lyme disease, a bacterial infection that invades almost the entire human body. The spiral-shaped bacteria that causes this infection is shown in the other image.

1. Name some places bacteria can be found.
2. What are some ways to prevent infections caused by bacteria?
3. In what ways are some bacteria helpful?

Bacteria

Tie to Prior Knowledge

Ask students if they have ever had a sore throat or eaten cheese. Explain that both of these experiences involve bacteria. In this section, they will learn about beneficial and harmful bacteria.

2 Teach

Beneficial Bacteria

Caption Answer

Figure 10 aerobes

Reading Check

Answer an organism that uses dead material as a food and energy source

Mini LAB

Purpose to observe and infer the growth rate of bacteria L1 ELL COOP LEARN LS **Kinesthetic**

Materials dried beans, distilled water, glass beaker

Teaching Strategies

- You may want to soak the beans for 24 hours prior to doing the lab, as this makes it easier for students to break them apart.
- Point out that the water's cloudiness indicates bacterial growth.

Safety Precautions Tell students to wash their hands after handling the materials and not to eat any of them.

Troubleshooting To avoid odors, caution students not to leave the beans and water in the classroom for more than five days.

Analysis

1. It usually takes 3–4 days.
2. the beans

Assessment

Process Have students hypothesize the doubling time of bacterial cells. Then have them design an experiment to test their hypothesis. Use **PASC**, p. 93.

Figure 10
Air is bubbled through the sewage in this aeration tank so that bacteria can break down much of the sewage wastes. *Are the bacteria that live in this tank aerobes or anaerobes?*

Bacteria and the Environment Without bacteria, there would be layers of dead material all over Earth deeper than you are tall. Consumer bacteria called saprophytes (SAP ruh fitz) help maintain nature's balance. A **saprophyte** is any organism that uses dead organisms as food and energy sources. Saprophytic bacteria help recycle nutrients. These nutrients become available for use by other organisms. As shown in **Figure 10,** most sewage-treatment plants use saprophytic aerobic bacteria to break down wastes into carbon dioxide and water.

Reading Check *What is a saprophyte?*

Plants and animals must take in nitrogen to make needed proteins and nucleic acids. Animals can eat plants or other animals that contain nitrogen, but plants need to take nitrogen from the soil or air. Although air is about 78 percent nitrogen, neither animals nor plants can use it directly. **Nitrogen-fixing bacteria** change nitrogen from the air into forms that plants and animals can use. The roots of some plants such as peanuts and peas develop structures called nodules that contain nitrogen-fixing bacteria, as shown in **Figure 11.** It is estimated that nitrogen-fixing bacteria save U.S. farmers millions of dollars in fertilizer costs every year. Many of the cyanobacteria also can fix nitrogen and are important in providing nitrogen in usable forms to aquatic organisms.

Bioremediation Using organisms to help clean up or remove environmental pollutants is called bioremediation. One type of bioremediation uses bacteria to break down wastes and pollutants into simpler harmless compounds. Other bacteria use certain pollutants as a food source. Every year about five percent to ten percent of all wastes produced by industry, agriculture, and cities are treated by bioremediation. Sometimes bioremediation is used at the site where chemicals, such as oil, have been spilled. Research continues on ways to make bioremediation a faster process.

Mini LAB

Observing Bacterial Growth

Procedure 

1. Obtain two or three **dried beans.**
2. Carefully break them into halves and place the halves into 10 mL of **distilled water** in a **glass beaker.**
3. Observe how many days it takes for the water to become cloudy and develop an unpleasant odor.

Analysis

1. How long did it take for the water to become cloudy?
2. What do you think the bacteria were using as a food source?

Teacher FYI

Bioremediation has been used on a wide variety of organic and toxic compounds. Cleanup of oil spills by bioremediation is likely to increase in the future.

Cultural Diversity

In a Pickle Pickling is a process of food preservation that depends on the chemical process of fermentation and the inhibition of bacterial growth in a highly acidic solution. It is found in the cuisine of many cultures. Have students research different pickling processes and prepare lists of how and what products are pickled in different cultures. L2 P

Figure 11

Although 78 percent of Earth's atmosphere is nitrogen gas (N_2), most living things are unable to use nitrogen in this form. Some bacteria, however, convert N_2 into the ammonium ion (NH_4^+) that organisms can use. This process is called nitrogen fixation. Nitrogen-fixing bacteria in soil can enter the roots of plants, such as beans, peanuts, alfalfa, and peas, as shown in the background photo. The bacteria and the plant form a relationship that benefits both of them.

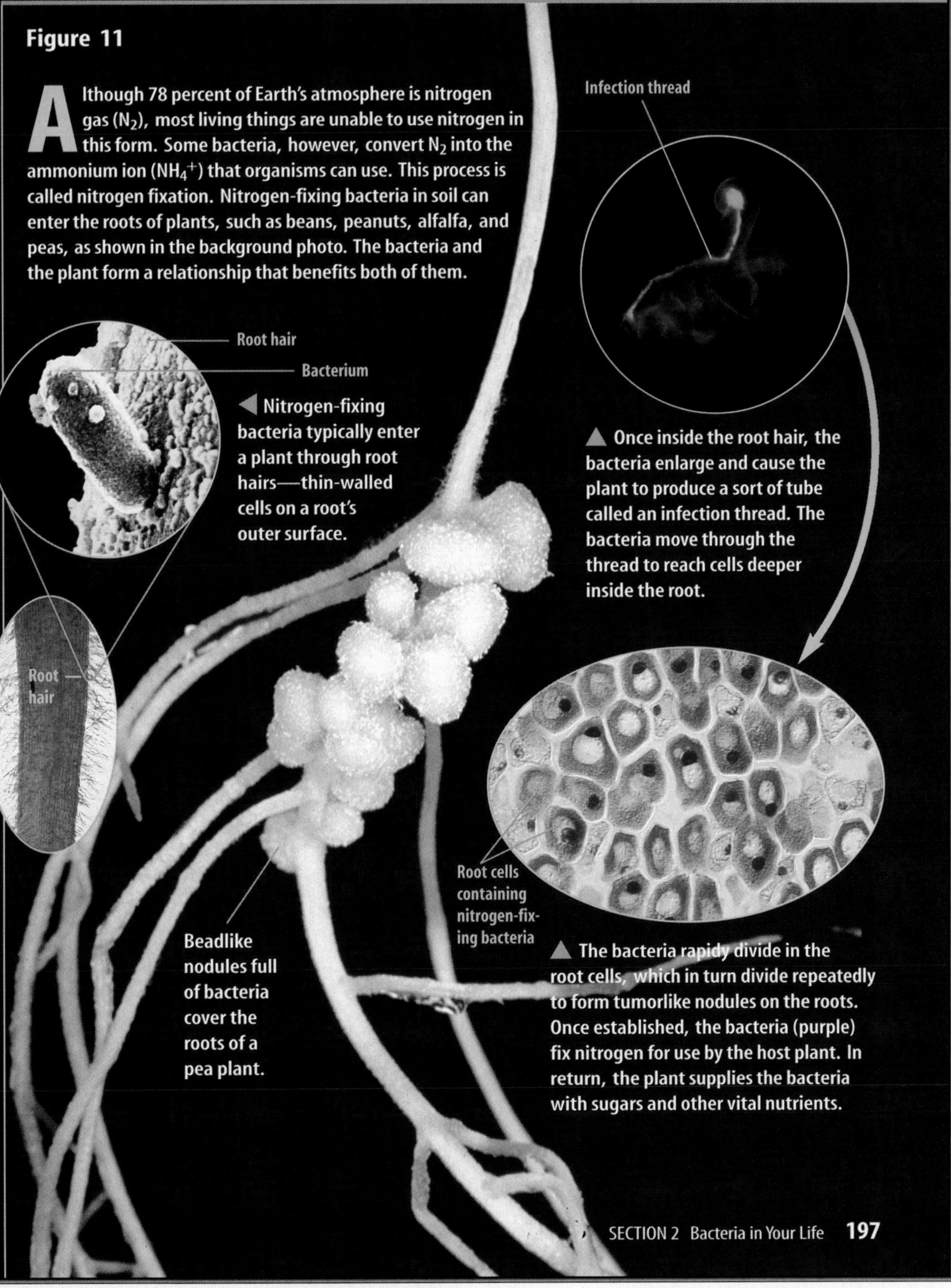

◀ Nitrogen-fixing bacteria typically enter a plant through root hairs—thin-walled cells on a root's outer surface.

▲ Once inside the root hair, the bacteria enlarge and cause the plant to produce a sort of tube called an infection thread. The bacteria move through the thread to reach cells deeper inside the root.

Beadlike nodules full of bacteria cover the roots of a pea plant.

▲ The bacteria rapidly divide in the root cells, which in turn divide repeatedly to form tumorlike nodules on the roots. Once established, the bacteria (purple) fix nitrogen for use by the host plant. In return, the plant supplies the bacteria with sugars and other vital nutrients.

Visualizing Nitrogen Fixing Bacteria

Have students examine the pictures and read the captions. Then ask the following questions.

What is the "cost" to a plant for having nitrogen-fixing bacteria in its root cells? The "cost" to the plant is that the carbohydrates it makes are used by the bacteria.

When pea plants are producing peas, the nitrogen fixation of the associated bacteria dips to a low level. What would be a logical explanation for this? When producing peas, the plant has little extra sugar for the bacteria to use, so nitrogen fixation slows.

Activity

Have students model the relationship between plants and nitrogen fixation. Designate each student as either a plant or a nitrogen-fixing bacterium. Plants should carry two index cards, one labeled "sugars" and one labeled "nutrients." Bacteria should carry two index cards, each labeled "NH_4^+." Explain that each student must have one sugar and nutrient card and one NH_4^+ card to survive. Have the students exchange cards to meet their needs. L1 IS **Interpersonal**

Extension

Direct interested students to examine the contents of different brands of garden and lawn fertilizer and infer why nitrogen is an ingredient in most of these products. Nitrogen is needed for plants to grow well. Nitrogen in the form provided by the fertilizers can be absorbed and used by plants.

Resource Manager

Chapter Resources Booklet

Transparency Activity, p. 39
MiniLAB, p. 4

Beneficial Bacteria, continued

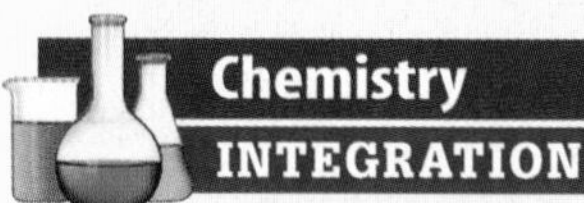

Chemistry INTEGRATION

Answers will vary, but most bacteria require a slightly acidic pH.

Science Journal

A Mutualist Relationship Have students explain in their Science Journals why "infection" of roots by nitrogen-fixing bacteria is beneficial for both plant and environment. Nitrogen gas in the atmosphere is unusable for most organisms. The bacteria fix nitrogen in a form that plants can use. After the plant dies, nitrogen is available for use by other organisms. L2 LS Linguistic

Visual Learning

Figure 12 Enhance the impact of the photo by having students taste cheese curds. You may also have students bring various cheeses from home to taste. Point out that these foods were prepared by using beneficial bacteria. Caution students who may have food allergies to avoid tasting the cheeses. L1 ELL LS Kinesthetic

Reading Check

Answer methane

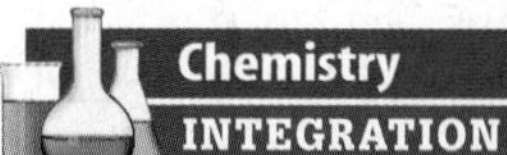

Chemistry INTEGRATION

One condition that must be monitored in a bioreactor is pH, or how acidic the conditions are in the bioreactor. Research and find out what pH levels different bacteria require for growth. In your Science Journal, write a paragraph describing what you find out about bacteria and pH levels.

Bacteria and Food Have you had any bacteria for lunch lately? Even before people understood that bacteria were involved, they were used in the production of foods. One of the first uses of bacteria was for making yogurt, a milk-based food that has been made in Europe and Asia for hundreds of years. Bacteria break down substances in milk to make many dairy products. Cheeses and buttermilk also can be produced with the aid of bacteria. Cheese making is shown in **Figure 12.**

Other foods you might have eaten also are made using bacteria. Sauerkraut, for example, is made with cabbage and a bacterial culture. Vinegar, pickles, olives, and soy sauce also are produced with the help of bacteria.

Bacteria in Industry Many industries rely on bacteria to make many products. Bacteria are grown in large containers called bioreactors. Conditions inside bioreactors are carefully controlled and monitored to allow for the growth of the bacteria. Medicines, enzymes, cleansers, and adhesives are some of the products that are made using bacteria.

Methane gas that is released as a waste by certain bacteria can be used as a fuel for heating, cooking, and industry. In landfills, methane-producing bacteria break down plant and animal material. The quantity of methane gas released by these bacteria is so large that some cities collect and burn it, as shown in **Figure 13.** Using bacteria to digest wastes and then produce methane gas could supply large amounts of fuel worldwide.

Reading Check *What waste gas produced by some bacteria can be used as a fuel?*

Figure 12
A When bacteria such as *Streptococcus lactis* are added to milk, it causes the milk to separate into curds (solids) and whey (liquids). B Other bacteria are added to the curds, which ripen into cheese. The type of cheese made depends on the bacterial species added to the curds.

LAB DEMONSTRATION

Purpose to observe the activity of bacteria

Materials plastic wastebasket, soil, paper, grass clippings, leaves, small sticks, dried food, bacteria culture, water, thermometer

Preparation Provide materials for students to see. Have them write down their expectations for mixed materials.

Procedure Mix the materials, keeping the mixture as light as possible. Add small amounts of water. Take the temperature of the mixture every couple of days and stir the compost pile. You may want to continue adding materials.

Expected Outcome Students should observe the decay of organic materials.

Assessment

Why does the temperature rise above room temperature? As bacteria respire, they release heat. **What happens to the paper and other organic material?** It decays to form compost.

Figure 13
Methane gas produced by bacteria in this landfill is burning at the top of these collection tubes.

Harmful Bacteria

As mentioned earlier, not all bacteria are beneficial. Some bacteria are known as pathogens. A **pathogen** is any organism that causes disease. If you have ever had strep throat, you have had firsthand experience with a bacterial pathogen. Other pathogenic bacteria cause anthrax in cattle, as well as diphtheria, tetanus, and whooping cough in humans.

How Pathogens Make You Sick Bacterial pathogens can cause illness and disease by several different methods. They can enter your body through a cut in the skin, you can inhale them, or they can enter in other ways. Once inside your body, they can multiply, damage normal cells, and cause illness and disease.

Some bacterial pathogens produce poisonous substances known as **toxins.** Botulism—a type of food poisoning that can result in paralysis and death—is caused by a toxin-producing bacterium. Botulism-causing bacteria are able to grow and produce toxins inside sealed cans of food. However, when growing conditions are unfavorable for their survival, some bacterial pathogens like those that cause botulism can produce thick-walled structures called **endospores.** Endospores, shown in **Figure 14,** can exist for hundreds of years before they resume growth. If the endospores of the botulism-causing bacteria are in canned food, they can grow and develop into regular bacterial cells and produce toxins again. Commercially canned foods undergo a process that uses steam under high pressure, which kills bacteria and most endospores.

Research Visit the Glencoe Science Web site at **science.glencoe.com** for more information about pathogenic bacteria and antibiotics. Communicate to your class what you learn.

Figure 14
Bacterial endospores can survive harsh winters, dry conditions, and heat. *How can endospores be destroyed?*

Magnification: 47,500×

Harmful Bacteria

Quick Demo

Burn natural gas (methane) using a Bunsen burner to emphasize to students that the product of landfill bacteria can be useful. LS **Visual-Spatial**

Extension

Tuberculosis is caused by *Mycobacterium tuberculosis*. The number of cases of this disease is on the rise in the United States and worldwide. Have students research the reasons for this increase. Answers may include population growth, spread of HIV, immigration, and drug-resistant bacteria. L2

Caption Answer

Figure 14 with long term high-heat treatment

Discussion

Have students research various pathogens to find the species of bacteria that causes each of the following diseases: cholera, strep throat, tetanus, and salmonella food poisoning. *Vibrio cholerae, Streptococcus pyogenes, Clostridium tetani, Salmonella species* Discuss each disease's symptoms and cure. L2 LS **Linguistic**

Teacher FYI

Some pathogens produce exotoxins, which are proteins secreted by bacteria. Exotoxins cause symptoms even if the bacteria aren't present. Some diseases caused by exotoxins are botulism, tetanus, and cholera. Other bacteria cause endotoxins, which cause symptoms only when bacteria are present. Some diseases caused by endotoxins are typhoid and meningitis.

Resource Manager

Chapter Resources Booklet
- Directed Reading for Content Mastery, pp. 17, 18
- Enrichment, p. 26
- Lab Activity, pp. 11–12

SCIENCE Online
Internet Addresses

Explore the Glencoe Science Web site at **science.glencoe.com** to find out more about topics in this section.

Harmful Bacteria, continued

Use an Analogy

Some antibiotics bind to fatlike molecules found in cell membranes. Just like detergents break up food and grease on dirty dishes, these antibiotics break up the fatlike molecules and destroy the cell membranes of harmful bacteria.

Science Journal

Battling TB Have students write one-page reports in their Science Journals explaining why the battle with tuberculosis and other pathogens is becoming increasingly difficult. L2 LS **Linguistic** P

Problem-Solving Activity

National Math Standards

Correlation to Mathematics Objectives
6, 8

Answers

1. Students could place disks of paper soaked in different mouthwashes in petri dishes that have bacteria growing on them.
2. Paper disks soaked in distilled water could be placed into a dish as a control.
3. Alcohol is the antiseptic. Water, glycerin, preservatives, and dyes also are listed. The dyes are solely for appearance.

Figure 15
Pasteurization lowers the amount of bacteria in foods. Dairy products, such as ice cream and yogurt, are pasteurized.

Pasteurization Unless it has been sterilized, all food contains bacteria. But heating food to sterilizing temperatures can change its taste. Pasteurization is a process of heating food to a temperature that kills most harmful bacteria but causes little change to the taste of the food. You are probably most familiar with pasteurized milk, but some fruit juices and other foods, as shown in **Figure 15,** also are pasteurized.

Problem-Solving Activity

Controlling Bacterial Growth

Bacteria can be controlled by slowing or preventing their growth, or killing them. When trying to control bacteria that affect humans, it is often desirable just to slow their growth because substances that kill bacteria or prevent them from growing can harm humans. For example, bleach often is used to kill bacteria in bathrooms or on kitchen surfaces, but it is poisonous if swallowed. *Antiseptic* is the word used to describe substances that slow the growth of bacteria.

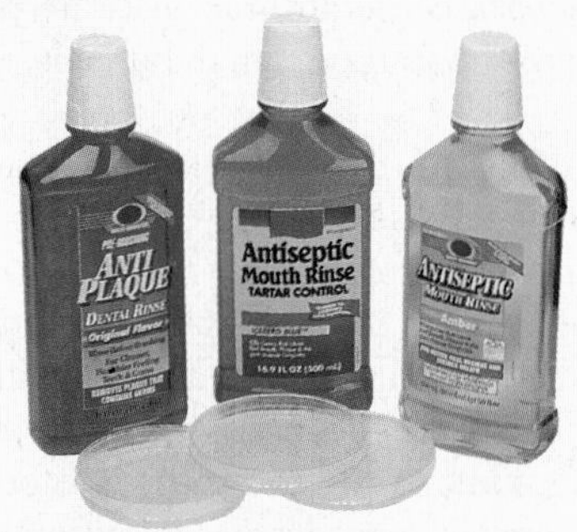

Identifying the Problem

Advertisers often claim that a substance kills bacteria, when in fact the substance only slows its growth. Many mouthwash advertisements make this claim. How could you test three mouthwashes to see which one is the best antiseptic?

Solving the Problem

1. Describe an experiment that you could do that would test which of three mouthwash products is the most effective antiseptic.
2. What control would you use in your experiment?
3. Read the ingredients label on a bottle of mouthwash. List the ingredients in the mouthwash. What ingredient do you think is the antiseptic? Explain.

Curriculum Connection

Geography Have students show on a world map where each of the major diseases discussed in this section occurs with greatest incidence. L2 LS **Visual-Spatial**

Resource Manager

Chapter Resources Booklet
Reinforcement, p. 24

Mathematics Skill Activities, p. 19

Figure 16
Each of these paper disks contains a different antibiotic. Clear areas where no bacteria are growing can be seen around some disks.
Which one of these disks would you infer contains an antibiotic that is most effective against the bacteria growing on the plate?

Health INTEGRATION

Treating Bacterial Diseases

Bacterial diseases in humans and animals usually are treated effectively with antibiotics. Penicillin, a well-known antibiotic, works by preventing bacteria from making cell walls. Without cell walls, certain bacteria cannot survive. **Figure 16** shows antibiotics at work.

Vaccines can prevent some bacterial diseases. A **vaccine** can be made from damaged particles taken from bacterial cell walls or from killed bacteria. Once the vaccine is injected, white blood cells in the blood recognize that type of bacteria. If the same type of bacteria enters the body at a later time, the white blood cells immediately attack them. Vaccines have been produced that are effective against many bacterial diseases.

Section  Assessment

1. Why are saprophytic bacteria helpful and necessary?
2. Why are nitrogen-fixing bacteria important?
3. List three uses of bacteria in food production and industry.
4. How do some bacteria cause disease?
5. **Think Critically** Why is botulism associated with canned foods and not fresh foods?

Skill Builder Activities

6. **Measuring in SI** Air can have more than 3,500 bacteria per cubic meter. How many bacteria might be in your classroom? **For more help, refer to the Science Skill Handbook.**
7. **Developing Multimedia Presentations** Prepare a presentation on how bacteria are used in industry to produce products you use. **For more help, refer to the Technology Skill Handbook.**

Caption Answer

Figure 16 The one that has the largest clear zone around it (at 10 o'clock) is most effective.

3 Assess

Reteach

Show students photographs of processes carried out by bacteria. Have students identify each process and its importance. L2
LS **Visual-Spatial**

Challenge

Have students demonstrate their understanding of the work of bacteria by bringing to class foods that are processed using bacteria or objects that show the effects of bacteria. L2

Assessment

Process Assess students' understanding of vaccines by having them make a concept map outlining what happens when someone receives a vaccination for a disease, and later is infected with that disease. The individual receives a vaccine, which allows their white blood cells to recognize and develop a defense against a particular disease-causing organism. When the organism later enters the individual's bloodstream, it is immediately recognized and killed by the white blood cells. Use **Performance Assessment in the Science Classroom,** p. 161.

Answers to Section Assessment

1. They recycle nutrients.
2. They change atmospheric nitrogen into a form that can be used by plants or animals.
3. Bacteria are used in making yogurt, sauerkraut, and other food products. Biotechnology industries use bacteria to produce medicines and other products. Methane gas can be produced in landfills.
4. Some bacteria produce toxins; others multiply in the body, damaging normal cells and causing illness and disease.
5. The bacteria that cause botulism are anaerobes, which grow in an oxygen-free environment, such as that in canned foods.
6. To calculate the answer, measure the length, width, and height of the classroom in meters. Multiply these numbers to find the volume of air in the classroom. Multiply the volume by 3,500 to obtain the number of bacteria per cubic meter.
7. Check students' work for accuracy.

Activity BENCH TESTED

Recognize the Problem

Purpose

Students design an experiment to determine the types of materials that will decompose in a compost pile. L2 LS Visual-Spatial

Process Skills

comparing, contrasting, predicting, describing, making a data table, interpreting data

Time Required

One 45-minute class period; three or four 20-minute observation periods over a period of four weeks

Form a Hypothesis

Possible Hypotheses

Most student hypotheses will reflect the knowledge that food items will decay most rapidly, but many students will not be able to identify all the biodegradable items in their experiments.

Test Your Hypothesis

Possible Procedure

Establish several compost piles in wide-mouthed jars or flat baking pans by burying food scraps, grass clippings, and leaf litter under 10 cm of soil. Water, turn, and add layers of soil to the containers regularly. After the compost is established, place test items flat on the compost and bury them under 10 cm of soil. Examine the items once a week for signs of decomposition.

Activity

Composting

Over time, landfills fill up and new places to dump trash become more difficult to find. One way to reduce the amount of trash that must be dumped in a landfill is to recycle. Composting is a form of recycling that changes plant wastes into reusable, nutrient-rich compost. How do plant wastes become compost? What types of organisms can assist in the process?

Recognize the Problem

What types of items can be composted and what types cannot?

Form a Hypothesis

Based on readings or prior knowledge, form a hypothesis about what types of items will decompose in a compost pile and which will not.

Safety Precautions

Be sure to wash your hands every time after handling the compost material.

Goals

- **Predict** which of several items will decompose in a compost pile and which will not.
- **Demonstrate** the decomposition, or lack thereof, of several items.
- **Compare** and **contrast** the speed at which various items break down.

Possible Materials

widemouthed, clear glass jars (at least 4)
soil
water
watering can
banana peel
apple core
scrap of newspaper
leaf
plastic candy wrapper
scrap of aluminum foil

202

Teaching Strategies:

- Encourage students to use common items such as polystyrene cups, aluminum cans, notebook paper, glossy magazine paper, and articles of clothing made of both natural and artificial fibers as well as biodegradable food items.
- Encourage students to bring garden gloves to school to use when unearthing their items.

Resource Manager

Chapter Resources Booklet
Activity Worksheet, pp. 11–12

Lab Management and Safety, p. 58

Test Your Hypothesis

Plan

1. **Decide** what items you are going to test. Choose some items that you think will decompose and some that you think will not.
2. **Predict** which of the items you chose will or will not decompose. Of the items that will, which do you think will decompose fastest? Slowest?
3. **Decide** how you will test whether or not the items decompose. How will you see the items? You may need to research composting in books, magazines, or on the Internet.
4. Prepare a data table in your Science Journal to record your observations.
5. **Identify** all constants, variables, and controls of the experiment.

Do

1. Make sure your teacher approves of your plan and your data table before you start.
2. Set up your experiment and collect data as planned.
3. While doing the experiment, record your observations and complete your data tables in your Science Journal.

Analyze Your Data

1. **Describe** your results. Did all of the items decompose? If not, which did and which did not?
2. Were your predictions correct? Explain.
3. Was there a difference in how fast items decomposed? If so, which items decomposed fastest and which took longer?

Draw Conclusions

1. What general statement(s) can you make about what types of items can be composted and which cannot? What about the speed of decomposition?
2. Do your results support your hypothesis?
3. What might happen to your compost pile if antibiotics were added to it? Explain.
4. **Describe** what you think happens in a landfill to items similar to those that you tested.

Write a letter to the editor of the local newspaper describing what you have learned about composting and encouraging your neighbors to do more composting.

Expected Outcome

Student results should show various degrees of decay for the food items, natural fiber clothing, and paper. Nonbiodegradable items will not show significant signs of decay.

Analyze Your Data

1. Food items, paper, and clothing made of natural fibers will show various signs of decay, but nondegradable items will not.
2. Answers will vary with results.
3. The food items will decay most rapidly, followed by clothing made of natural fibers. Moist items will decay more rapidly than drier items.

Error Analysis

To avoid confusion when examining the composted items, students should use initially new items and make a record of the appearance of each item before it is composted.

Draw Conclusions

1. Materials made of natural ingredients can be composted, but artificial items will not compost. Aerating the soil and keeping the compost moist increases decay.
2. Answers will vary.
3. Bacteria are the primary decomposing agents in compost piles. Killing bacteria would slow or stop the decay process.
4. Landfill items are frequently buried more deeply, are exposed to less moisture, and receive little or no aeration. Thus items would decay more slowly in a landfill.

Assessment

Performance With permission, have students plan and construct a school compost pile in a corner of the school property. Use **Performance Assessment in the Science Classroom,** p. 105.

Encourage students to access the Glencoe Science Web site to gather information on local landfills, compost sites, and recycling centers.

ACTIVITY 203

Science Stats

Content Background

There are many bacteria species that thrive in extreme environmental conditions. Thermophiles are bacteria that thrive at temperatures between 50°C to 60°C. Some can even live in hot springs and ocean hydrothermal vents, where temperatures can reach 110°C. Other bacteria, called psychrophiles, are most comfortable at temperatures of 15°C to 20°C. Psychrophiles that live in the soil and water of Arctic regions can survive temperatures as low as 0°C. Bacteria that live under extreme pressure are called barophiles. Barophiles that live on the ocean floor at a depth of 7 km cannot survive at atmospheric pressure. Some species of bacteria, called acidophiles, can survive in highly acidic environments. These bacteria can survive in a pH as low as 1 and are found in water that drains from coal mines, which contains high amounts of sulfuric acid and in hydrothermal vents.

Discussion

What advantages do unusual bacteria have over other types of bacteria? Possible answer: These bacteria can survive in extreme environmental conditions.

Activity

Have students research different methods of food preservation, such as refrigeration, pasteurization, sterilization, pH alteration, radiation, and chemical preservatives, and discuss how the form of preservation relates to the basic survival or environmental requirements of many bacteria.

Unusual Bacteria

Did you know...

...The hardiest bacteria, *Deinococcus radiodurans* (DE no KO kus·RA de oh DOOR anz), has a nasty odor, which has been described as similar to rotten cabbage. It might have an odor, but it can survive 3,000 times more radiation than humans because it quickly repairs damage to its DNA molecule. These bacteria were discovered in canned meat when they survived sterilization by radiation.

...The smallest bacteria, nanobes (NAN obes), are Earth's smallest living things. These miniature creatures live far below the ocean floor and are 20 to 150 nanometers long. That means, depending on their size, it would take about 6,500,000 to 50,000,000 nanobes lined up to equal 1 m!

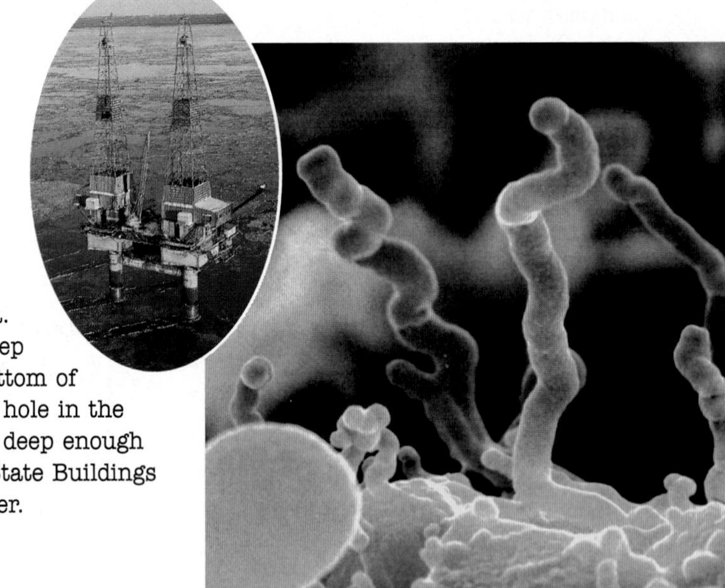

...Nanobes were discovered in ancient stone about 5 km beneath the ocean floor in petroleum exploration wells near Australia. To understand just how deep this is, first picture the bottom of the ocean. Then imagine a hole in the bottom of the ocean that's deep enough to bury about 13 Empire State Buildings stacked on top of each other.

Internet Addresses

Explore the Glencoe Science Web site at **science.glencoe.com** to find out more about topics in this feature.

Connecting To Math

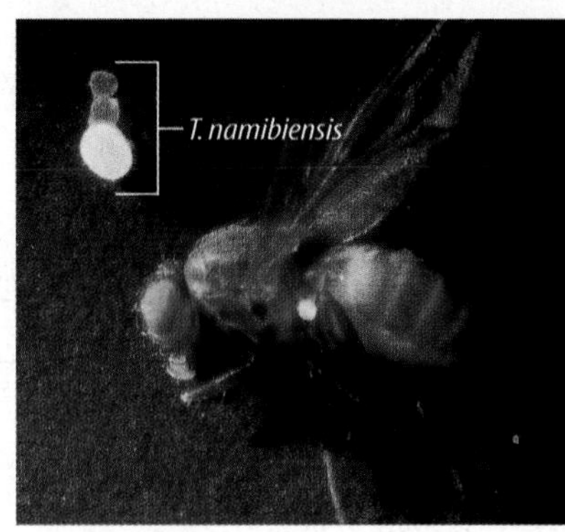

...The largest bacterium on Earth, *Thiomargarita namibiensis* (THE oh ma ga RE ta·nah ME be yen sis), is about the same size as the period at the end of this sentence. Its name means, "Sulfur Pearl of Namibia," and describes its appearance. The sulfur inside its cells reflects white light. The cells form strands that look like strings of pearls.

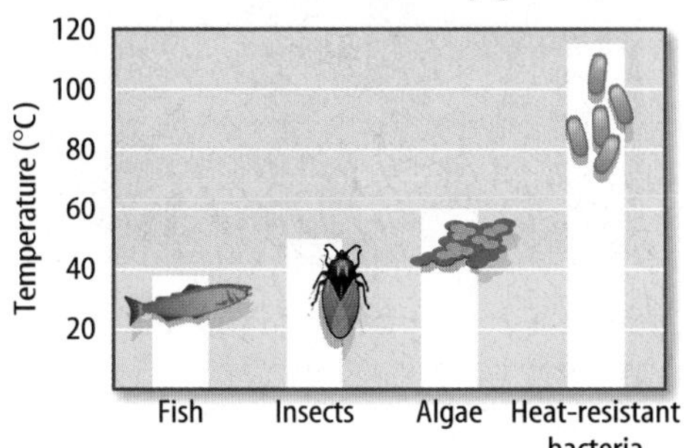

...Earth's oldest living bacteria are thought to be 250 million years old. These ancient bacteria were revived from a crystal of rock salt buried 579 m below the desert floor in New Mexico.

Do the Math

1. The smallest and the oldest bacteria were found beneath Earth's surface. Which was deeper? How many meters deeper was it found?
2. What is the difference in size between the smallest nanobe and the largest nanobe?
3. A rad is a unit for measuring radiation. *Deinococcus radiodurans* can withstand a maximum of 1.5 million rads of radiation. How many rads would be deadly to humans?

Go Further

Do library research about halophiles, the bacteria that can live in salty environments. What is the maximum salt concentration in which they can survive? How does this compare to the maximum salt concentration bacteria that are not halophiles can survive?

Connecting To Math

Do the Math

Teaching Strategies

- Have students recall how to convert km to m by multiplying km by 1000.
- Have students recall how to set up an equation to solve for an unknown variable.

Answers

1. smallest, 4421 m
2. 130 nanometers
3. 500 rads

Go Further

Have students list locations where halophiles can be found. ocean, Great Salt Lake, Dead Sea, salt licks, brine vats, salt flats Have students make a chart of the different types of halophiles, the salt concentration in which they can survive, and the number of times higher that is than the concentration in which nonhalophiles.

LS **Logical-Mathematical**

Visual Learning

How hot can they get? How much higher temperatures can heat-resistant bacteria withstand than insects? about 60°C What is the minimum temperature needed to sterilize foods such as canned goods against heat-resistant bacteria? 120°C

Chapter 7 Study Guide

Reviewing Main Ideas

Preview
Students can answer the questions in their Science Journals. Discuss the answers as you go through the chapter. LS **Linguistic**

Review
Students can write their answers, then compare them with those of other students. LS **Interpersonal**

Reteach
Students can look at the illustrations and describe details that support the main ideas of the chapter. LS **Visual-Spatial**

Answers to Chapter Review

Section 1

1. cocci
5. When cyanobacteria die, aerobic bacteria decompose them and use up all available oxygen in the water. Fish and other organisms die.

Section 2

1. Certain bacteria are able to use oil as an energy source. These bacteria could be sprayed on the spill in order to digest it.
3. Vaccinations protect you from the effects of pathogens.

Chapter 7 Study Guide

Reviewing Main Ideas

Section 1 What are bacteria?

1. Bacteria can be found almost everywhere. They have three basic shapes—cocci, bacilli, and spirilli. *What shape of bacteria is shown here?*

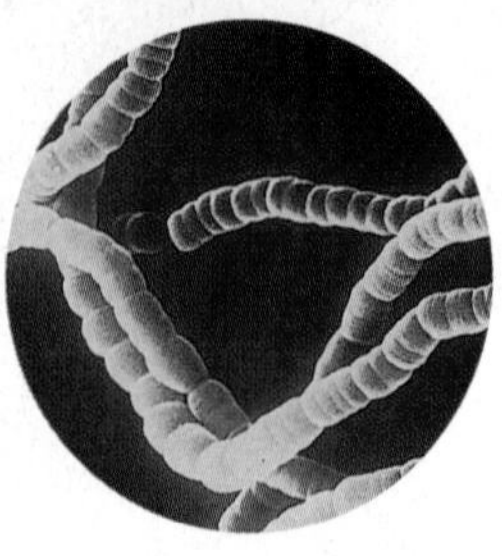

2. Bacteria are prokaryotic cells that usually reproduce by fission. All bacteria contain DNA, ribosomes, and cytoplasm but lack a membrane-bound nucleus.
3. Most bacteria are consumers, but some can make their own food. Anaerobes are bacteria that are able to live without oxygen, but aerobes need oxygen to survive.
4. Cell shape and structure, how they get food, if they use oxygen, and their waste products can be used to classify eubacteria.
5. Cyanobacteria are producer eubacteria. They are an important source of food and oxygen for some aquatic organisms. *How does a bloom of cyanobacteria affect other aquatic organisms?*

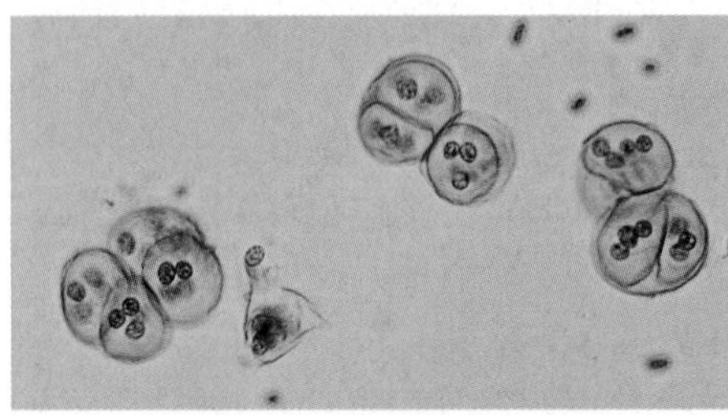

6. Archaebacteria are bacteria that often exist in extreme conditions, such as near ocean vents and in hot springs.

Section 2 Bacteria in Your Life

1. Most bacteria are helpful. They aid in recycling nutrients, fixing nitrogen, or helping in food production. They even can be used to break down harmful pollutants. *How could bacteria be used to clean up this oil spill?*

2. Some bacteria that live in your body help you stay healthy and survive.
3. Other bacteria are harmful because they can cause disease in the organisms they infect. *Why are vaccinations important to your health?*

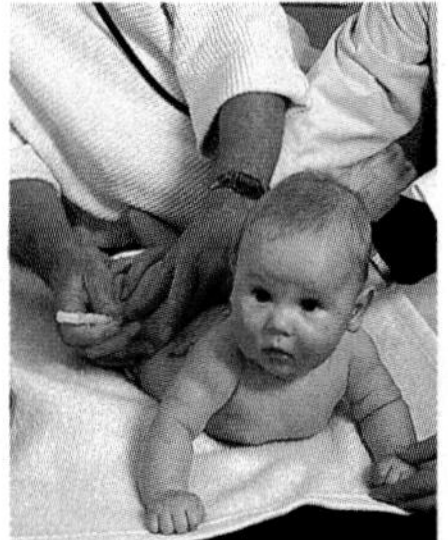

4. Pasteurization is one process that can prevent the growth of harmful bacteria in food.

After You Read

FOLDABLES Reading & Study Skills

Using the information on your Foldable, write about the characteristics these two kingdoms of bacteria have in common under the *Both* tab.

After You Read

FOLDABLES Reading & Study Skills

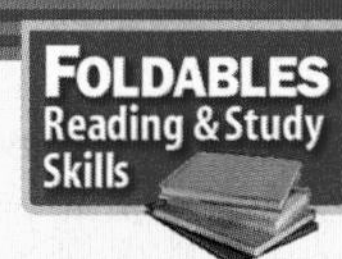

After students have read the chapter and completed the Foldable described in Before You Read, have them do the activity on the student page.

Dinah Zike

Visualizing Main Ideas

Complete the following concept map on how bacteria affect the environment.

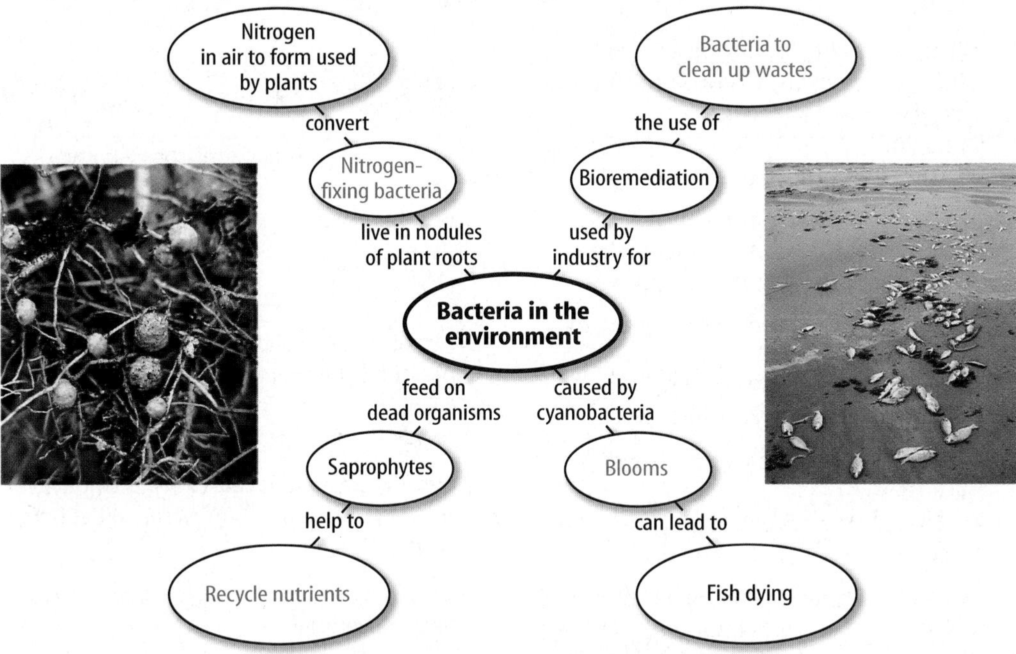

Vocabulary Review

Vocabulary Words

a. aerobe
b. anaerobe
c. antibiotic
d. endospore
e. fission
f. flagella
g. nitrogen-fixing bacteria
h. pathogen
i. saprophyte
j. toxin
k. vaccine

THE PRINCETON REVIEW — Study Tip

Make flash cards for new vocabulary words. Put the word on one side and the definition on the other. Then use them to quiz yourself.

Using Vocabulary

Replace the underlined words with the correct vocabulary word(s).

1. An aerobe uses dead organisms as a food source.
2. A toxin can prevent some bacterial diseases.
3. A saprophyte causes disease.
4. A bacterium that needs oxygen to carry out respiration is a(n) pathogen.
5. Bacteria reproduce using flagella.
6. Anaerobes are bacteria that convert nitrogen in the air to a form used by plants.
7. A(n) flagella can live without oxygen.

Chapter 7 Study Guide

Visualizing Main Ideas

See student page.

Vocabulary Review

Using Vocabulary

1. saprophyte
2. vaccine
3. pathogen
4. aerobe
5. fission
6. Nitrogen-fixing bacteria
7. anaerobe

Checking Concepts

1. D
2. B
3. A
4. D
5. A
6. A
7. B
8. C
9. D
10. A

Thinking Critically

11. Nitrogen would no longer be available in a form that plants could use; therefore, the plants would die unless fertilizer was added.
12. Bacteria can reproduce quickly, have means of moving, and can form endospores to survive extreme conditions. They can also exchange DNA, providing the population with variations that may be helpful.
13. Crops like beans, peas, and peanuts have nitrogen-fixing bacteria. These crops help to increase soil fertility.
14. spheres
15. Using fresh foods and keeping them refrigerated, washing hands and all surfaces and utensils, and properly cooking foods are ways to prevent food poisoning.

Chapter 7 Assessment

Checking Concepts

Choose the word or phrase that best answers the question.

1. What is a way of cleaning up an ecosystem using bacteria to break down harmful compounds?
   A) landfill **C)** toxic waste dumps
   B) waste storage **D)** bioremediation
2. What do bacterial cells contain?
   A) nucleus **C)** mitochondria
   B) DNA **D)** four chromosomes
3. What pigment do cyanobacteria need to make food?
   A) chlorophyll **C)** plasmids
   B) chromosomes **D)** ribosomes
4. Which of the following terms describes most bacteria?
   A) anaerobic **C)** many-celled
   B) pathogens **D)** beneficial
5. What is the name for rod-shaped bacteria?
   A) bacilli **C)** spirilla
   B) cocci **D)** colonies
6. What structure allows bacteria to stick to surfaces?
   A) capsule **C)** chromosome
   B) flagella **D)** cell wall
7. What organisms can grow as blooms in ponds?
   A) archaebacteria **C)** cocci
   B) cyanobacteria **D)** viruses
8. Which of these organisms are recyclers in the environment?
   A) producers **C)** saprophytes
   B) flagella **D)** pathogens
9. Which of the following is caused by a pathogenic bacterium?
   A) an antibiotic **C)** nitrogen fixation
   B) cheese **D)** strep throat
10. Which organisms do not need oxygen to survive?
    A) anaerobes **C)** humans
    B) aerobes **D)** fish

Thinking Critically

11. What would happen if nitrogen-fixing bacteria could no longer live on the roots of some plants?
12. Why are bacteria capable of surviving in almost all environments of the world?
13. Farmers often rotate crops such as beans, peas, and peanuts with other crops such as corn, wheat, and cotton. Why might they make such changes?
14. One organism that causes bacterial pneumonia is called pneumococcus. What is its shape?
15. What precautions can be taken to prevent food poisoning?

Developing Skills

16. **Making and Using Graphs** Graph the data from the table below. Using the graph, determine where the doubling rate would be at 20°C.

Bacterial Reproduction Rates

Temperature (°C)	Doubling Rate Per Hour
20.5	2.0
30.5	3.0
36.0	2.5
39.2	1.2

17. **Interpreting Data** What is the effect of temperature in question 16?

Chapter Assessment Planner

Portfolio Encourage students to place in their portfolios one or two items of what they consider to be their best work. Examples include:
- Science Journal, p. 191
- Cultural Diversity, p. 196
- Science Journal, p. 200

Performance Additional performance assessments, Performance Task Assessment Lists, and rubrics for evaluating these activities can be found in Glencoe's **Performance Assessment in the Science Classroom.**

18. **Concept Mapping** Complete the following events-chain concept map about the events surrounding a cyanobacteria bloom.

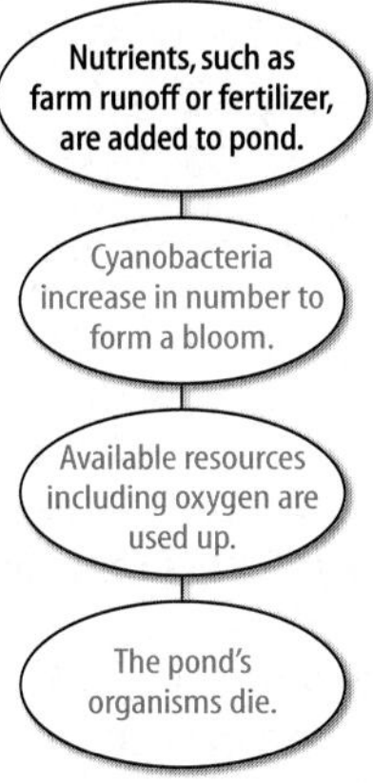
Nutrients, such as farm runoff or fertilizer, are added to pond.
Cyanobacteria increase in number to form a bloom.
Available resources including oxygen are used up.
The pond's organisms die.

19. **Identifying and Manipulating Variables and Controls** How would you decide if a kind of bacteria could grow anaerobically?

20. **Communicating** Describe the nitrogen-fixing process in your own words, using numbered steps. You will probably have more than four steps.

Performance Assessment

21. **Poster** Create a poster that illustrates the effects of bacteria. Use photos from magazines and your own drawings.

22. **Poem** Write a poem that demonstrates your knowledge of the importance of bacteria to human health.

Technology

Go to the Glencoe Science Web site at **science.glencoe.com** or use the **Glencoe Science CD-ROM** for additional chapter assessment.

Test Practice

In science class, Melissa's homework assignment was to look up five diseases that are caused by bacteria. She was to find the name of the bacterium that causes the disease and how it is transmitted to humans. The results of her research are listed in the chart below.

Infectious Diseases

Disease	Source	Bacterium
Cholera	Contaminated water	*Vibrio cholerae*
Botulism	Improperly canned foods	*Clostridium botulinum*
Legionnaires' disease	Air vents	*Legionella pneumophila*
Lyme disease	Tick bites	*Borrelia burgdorferi*
Tuberculosis	Airborne from humans	*Mycobacterium tuberculosis*

Study the chart and answer the following questions.

1. According to the chart, which disease-causing bacterium can be transmitted to humans by a bite from another animal?
   - **A)** *Vibrio cholerae*
   - **B)** *Clostridium botulinum*
   - **C)** *Borrelia burgdorferi*
   - **D)** *Legionella pneumophila*

2. Based on the information in the chart, which disease can be prevented by purifying water that is used for drinking, cooking, or washing fruits and vegetables?
   - **F)** cholera
   - **G)** botulism
   - **H)** Legionnaires'
   - **J)** tuberculosis

Assessment Resources

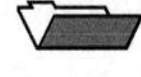

Reproducible Masters

Chapter Resources Booklet
Chapter Review, pp. 31–32
Chapter Tests, pp. 33–36
Assessment Transparency Activity, p. 43

Glencoe Science Web site
Interactive Tutor
Chapter Quizzes

Glencoe Technology
Assessment Transparency
Interactive CD-ROM Chapter Quizzes
ExamView Pro Test Bank
Vocabulary PuzzleMaker Software
MindJogger Videoquiz

Chapter 7 Assessment

Test Practice

The Test-Taking Tip was written by The Princeton Review, the nation's leader in test preparation.

1. C
2. F

Developing Skills

16. Graph should increase until a peak is reached, then decrease. Doubling rate will be almost 2.0 at 20°C.
17. Doubling rate increases until an optimal temperature of approximately 30.5 °C is reached. After this temperature, the doubling rate decreases as the temperature increases.
18. See student page.
19. Place the organism in an environment without oxygen and measure its growth rate.
20. (1) Root hairs curl before infection by nitrogen-fixing bacteria. (2) Bacteria enter roots through an infection thread. (3) Pocketlike spaces within the root form and the cells begin to grow and divide. (4) Root nodules containing nitrogen-fixing bacteria form on the roots of legumes. (5) Atmospheric nitrogen is fixed and becomes available for other living things.

Performance Assessment

21. Posters should show beneficial and harmful effects of bacteria. Use **PASC**, p. 145.
22. Poems should demonstrate knowledge of the importance of bacteria to human health. Use **PASC**, p. 157.

Section/Objectives	Standards: National	Standards: State/Local	Activities/Features
Chapter Opener	See p. 5T for a Key to Standards.		**Explore Activity:** Dissect a mushroom, p. 211 **Before You Read,** p. 211
Section 1 Protists 3 sessions 1.5 blocks 1. **Describe** the characteristics shared by all protists. 2. **Compare and contrast** the three groups of protists. 3. **List** examples of each of the three protist groups. 4. **Explain** why protists are so difficult to classify.	National Content Standards: UCP1, UCP5, A1, C1, C5		**Science Online,** p. 216 **Health Integration,** p. 219 **MiniLAB:** Observing Slime Molds, p. 220 **Problem-Solving Activity:** Is it a fungus or a protist?, p. 221 **Activity:** Comparing Algae and Protozoans, p. 223
Section 2 Fungi 4 sessions 2 blocks 1. **Identify** the characteristics shared by all fungi. 2. **Classify** fungi into groups based on their methods of reproduction. 3. **Differentiate** between the imperfect fungi and all other fungi.	National Content Standards: UCP1, UCP5, A1, C1, C2, C5, F5, G1		**Science Online,** p. 225 **MiniLAB:** Interpreting Spore Prints, p. 227 **Visualizing Lichens as Air Quality Indicators,** p. 229 **Environmental Science Integration,** p. 230 **Activity:** Creating a Fungus Field Guide, p. 232 **Science and Society:** Chocolate SOS, p. 234

NATIONAL GEOGRAPHIC

Teacher's Corner

PRODUCTS AVAILABLE FROM GLENCOE
To order call 1-800-334-7344:
CD-ROM
NGS PictureShow: The Cell
Transparency Set
NGS PicturePack: The Cell

PRODUCTS AVAILABLE FROM NATIONAL GEOGRAPHIC SOCIETY
To order call 1-800-368-2728:
Videos
Protists: Threshold of Life

INDEX TO NATIONAL GEOGRAPHIC SOCIETY
The following articles may be used for research relating to this chapter:
"Leafcutters: Gardeners of the Ant World," by Mark W. Moffet, July 1995.
"Slime Mold: The Fungus That Walks," by Douglas B. Lee, July 1981.
"The Wild World of Compost," by Cecil E. Johnson, August 1980.

Activity Materials	Reproducible Resources	Section Assessment	Technology
Explore Activity: mushroom, hand lens	**Chapter Resources Booklet** Foldables Worksheet, p. 15 Directed Reading Overview, p. 17 Note-taking Worksheets, pp. 29–30	GLENCOE'S ASSESSMENT ADVANTAGE	
MiniLAB: live specimen of *Physarum polycephaalum*, hand lens **Activity:** cultures of *Paramecium*, *Amoeba*, *Euglena*, and *Spirogyra*; prepared slide of slime mold, 4 microscope slides, 4 coverslips, microscope, dropper	**Chapter Resources Booklet** Transparency Activity, p. 40 MiniLAB, p. 3 Enrichment, p. 27 Reinforcement, p. 25 Directed Reading, p. 18 Transparency Activity, pp. 43–44 Activity Worksheet, pp. 5–6 **Cultural Diversity,** p. 3 **Science Inquiry Labs,** p. 3	Portfolio Science Journal, p. 214 Health Integration, p. 219 Performance MiniLAB, p. 220 Problem-Solving Activity, p. 221 Skill Builder Activities, p. 222 Content Section Assessment, p. 222	Section Focus Transparency Teaching Transparency Interactive CD-ROM Guided Reading Audio Program
MiniLAB: several grocery-store mushrooms, unlined white paper **Activity:** Collection jars, hand lens, microscope, microscope slides and coverslips, field guide to fungi or club fungi, art supplies	**Chapter Resources Booklet** Transparency Activity, p. 41 MiniLAB, p. 4 Enrichment, p. 28 Reinforcement, p. 26 Directed Reading, pp. 19, 20 Lab Activities, pp. 9–10, 11–13 Activity Worksheet, pp. 7–8 **Mathematics Skill Activities,** p. 5 **Reading and Writing Skill Activities,** p. 37 **Lab Management and Safety,** p. 58	Portfolio MiniLAB, p. 227 Performance MiniLAB, p. 227 Skill Builder Activities, p. 231 Content Section Assessment, p. 231	Section Focus Transparency Interactive CD-ROM Guided Reading Audio Program

End of Chapter Assessment

GLENCOE'S ASSESSMENT ADVANTAGE

Blackline Masters	Technology	Professional Series
Chapter Resources Booklet Chapter Review, pp. 33–34 Chapter Tests, pp. 35–38 **Standardized Test Practice by The Princeton Review,** pp. 39–42	MindJogger Videoquiz Interactive CD-ROM Vocabulary PuzzleMakers ExamView Pro Test Bank Interactive Lesson Planner Interactive Teacher Edition	Performance Assessment in the Science Classroom (PASC)

Transparencies

Section Focus

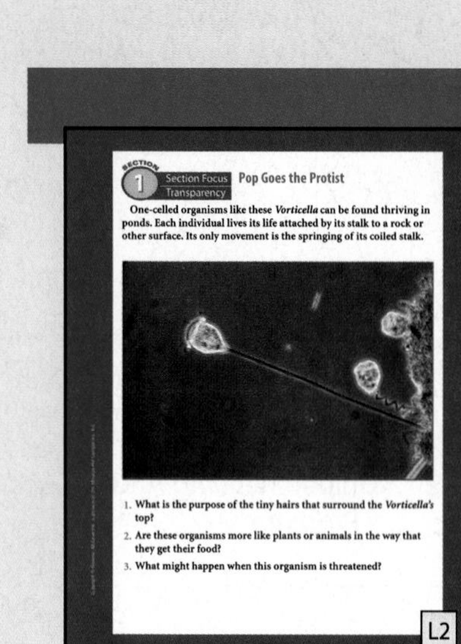
Section 1 Section Focus Transparency **Pop Goes the Protist**

One-celled organisms like these *Vorticella* can be found thriving in ponds. Each individual lives its life attached by its stalk to a rock or other surface. Its only movement is the springing of its coiled stalk.

1. What is the purpose of the tiny hairs that surround the *Vorticella's* top?
2. Are these organisms more like plants or animals in the way that they get their food?
3. What might happen when this organism is threatened?

L2

Section 2 Section Focus Transparency **Dig It**

Care for a truffle? Highly prized in Europe as a delicacy, truffles are a rare, fragrant, and flavorful variety of fungi. Because they can grow as much as 30 centimeters underground, people have trained pigs and dogs to hunt them by scent. The rarest truffles can be worth $3,000 per kilogram!

1. Do you think that truffles are classified as plants? Explain.
2. What other organisms resemble truffles?

L2

This is a representation of key blackline masters available in the Teacher Classroom Resources. See Resource Manager boxes within the chapter for additional information.

Assessment

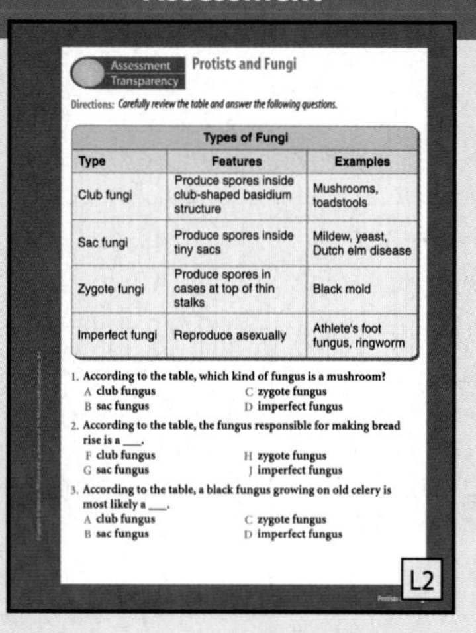
Assessment Transparency **Protists and Fungi**

Directions: *Carefully review the table and answer the following questions.*

Types of Fungi		
Type	Features	Examples
Club fungi	Produce spores inside club-shaped basidium structure	Mushrooms, toadstools
Sac fungi	Produce spores inside tiny sacs	Mildew, yeast, Dutch elm disease
Zygote fungi	Produce spores in cases at top of thin stalks	Black mold
Imperfect fungi	Reproduce asexually	Athlete's foot fungus, ringworm

1. According to the table, which kind of fungus is a mushroom?
   A club fungus C zygote fungus
   B sac fungus D imperfect fungus
2. According to the table, the fungus responsible for making bread rise is a ____.
   F club fungus H zygote fungus
   G sac fungus J imperfect fungus
3. According to the table, a black fungus growing on old celery is most likely a ____.
   A club fungus C zygote fungus
   B sac fungus D imperfect fungus

L2

Teaching

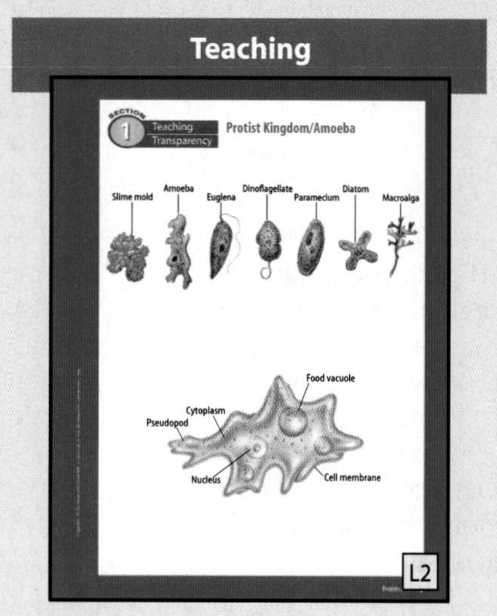

Key to Teaching Strategies

The following designations will help you decide which activities are appropriate for your students.

- L1 Level 1 activities should be appropriate for students with learning difficulties.
- L2 Level 2 activities should be within the ability range of all students.
- L3 Level 3 activities are designed for above-average students.
- ELL ELL activities should be within the ability range of English Language Learners.
- COOP LEARN Cooperative Learning activities are designed for small group work.
- LS Multiple Learning Styles logos, as described on page 22T, are used throughout to indicate strategies that address different learning styles.
- P These strategies represent student products that can be placed into a best-work portfolio.

Hands-on Activities

Activity Worksheets

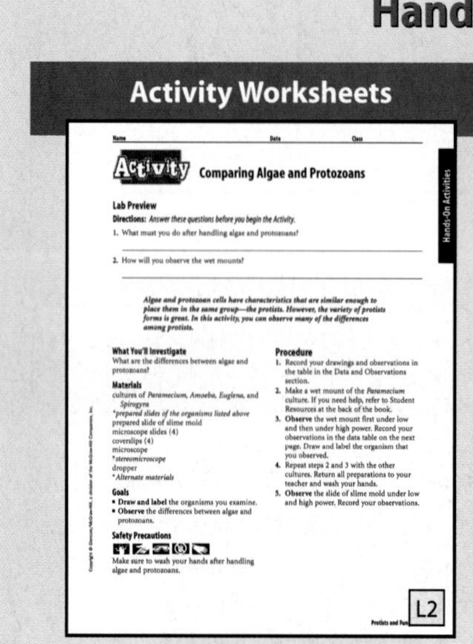
Name Date Class

Activity **Comparing Algae and Protozoans**

Hands-On Activities

Lab Preview

Directions: *Answer these questions before you begin the Activity.*

1. What must you do after handling algae and protozoans?
2. How will you observe the wet mounts?

Algae and protozoan cells have characteristics that are similar enough to place them in the same group—the protists. However, the variety of protists forms is great. In this activity, you can observe many of the differences among protists.

What You'll Investigate

What are the differences between algae and protozoans?

Materials

cultures of *Paramecium, Amoeba, Euglena,* and *Spirogyra*
**prepared slides of the organisms listed above*
prepared slide of slime mold
microscope slides (4)
coverslips (4)
microscope
**stereomicroscope*
dropper
**Alternate materials*

Goals

- **Draw and label** the organisms you examine.
- **Observe** the differences between algae and protozoans.

Safety Precautions

Make sure to wash your hands after handling algae and protozoans.

Procedure

1. Record your drawings and observations in the table in the Data and Observations section.
2. Make a wet mount of the *Paramecium* culture. If you need help, refer to Student Resources at the back of the book.
3. **Observe** the wet mount first under low and then under high power. Record your observations in the data table on the next page. Draw and label the organism that you observed.
4. Repeat steps 2 and 3 with the other cultures. Return all preparations to your teacher and wash your hands.
5. **Observe** the slide of slime mold under low and high power. Record your observations.

L2

Laboratory Activities

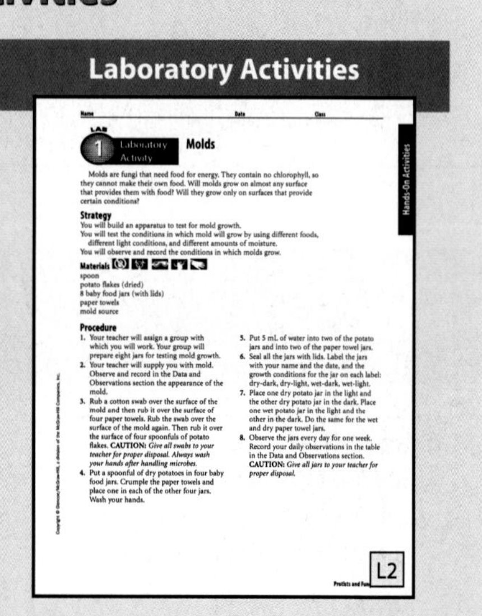
Name Date Class

Lab 1 Laboratory Activity **Molds**

Hands-On Activities

Molds are fungi that need food for energy. They contain no chlorophyll, so they cannot make their own food. Will molds grow on almost any surface that provides them with food? Will they grow only on surfaces that provide certain conditions?

Strategy

You will build an apparatus to test for mold growth.
You will test the conditions in which mold will grow by using different foods, different light conditions, and different amounts of moisture.
You will observe and record the conditions in which molds grow.

Materials

spoon
potato flakes (dried)
8 baby food jars (with lids)
paper towels
mold source

Procedure

1. Your teacher will assign a group with which you will work. Your group will prepare eight jars for testing mold growth.
2. Your teacher will supply you with mold. Observe and record in the Data and Observations section the appearance of the mold.
3. Rub a cotton swab over the surface of the mold and then rub it over the surface of four paper towels. Rub the swab over the surface of the mold again. Then rub it over the surface of four spoonfuls of potato flakes. **CAUTION:** *Give all swabs to your teacher for proper disposal. Always wash your hands after handling microbes.*
4. Put a spoonful of dry potatoes in four baby food jars. Crumple the paper towels and place one in each of the other four jars. Wash your hands.
5. Put 5 mL of water into two of the potato jars and into two of the paper towel jars.
6. Seal all the jars with lids. Label the jars with your name and the date, and the growth conditions for the jar on each label: dry-dark, dry-light, wet-dark, wet-light.
7. Place one dry potato jar in the light and the other dry potato jar in the dark. Place one wet potato jar in the light and the other in the dark. Do the same for the wet and dry paper towel jars.
8. Observe the jars every day for one week. Record your daily observations in the table in the Data and Observations section. **CAUTION:** *Give all jars to your teacher for proper disposal.*

L2

Meeting Different Ability Levels

Content Outline

Note-taking Worksheet — Protists and Fungi

Section 1 Protists

L2

Reinforcement

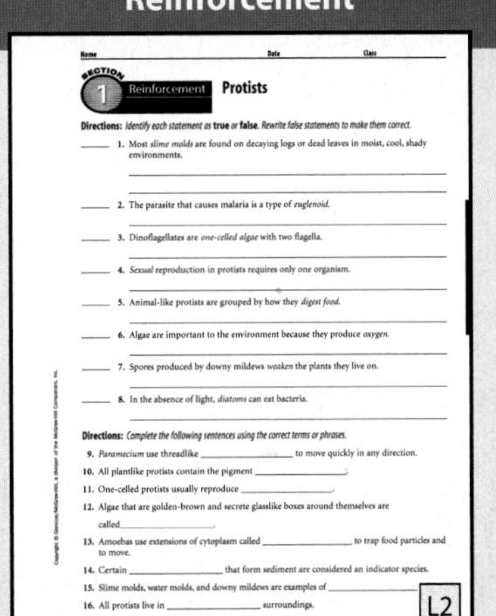
Section 1 Reinforcement — Protists

L2

Directed Reading

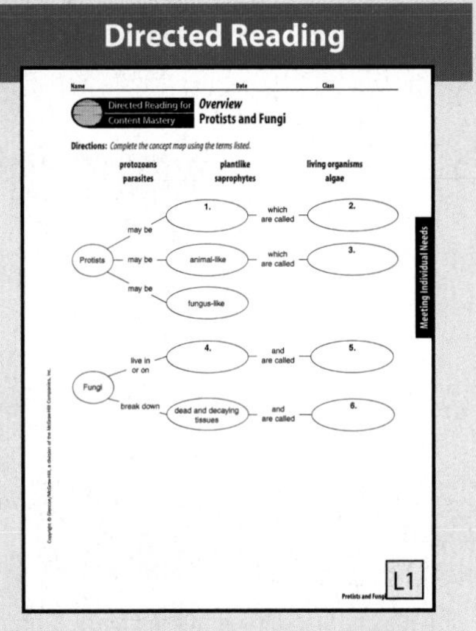
Directed Reading for Content Mastery — Overview — Protists and Fungi

L1

Enrichment

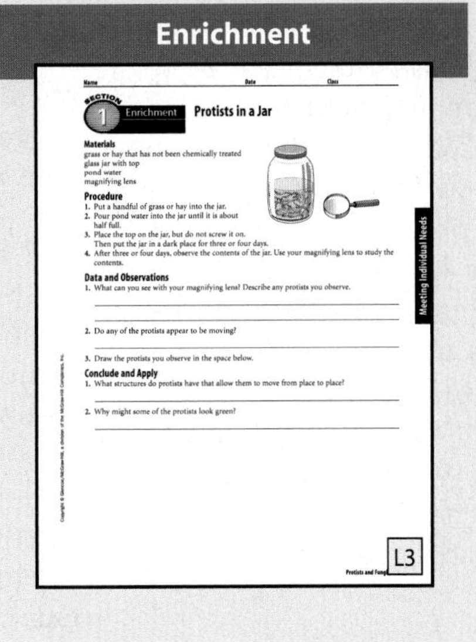
Section 1 Enrichment — Protists in a Jar

L3

Spanish Directed Reading

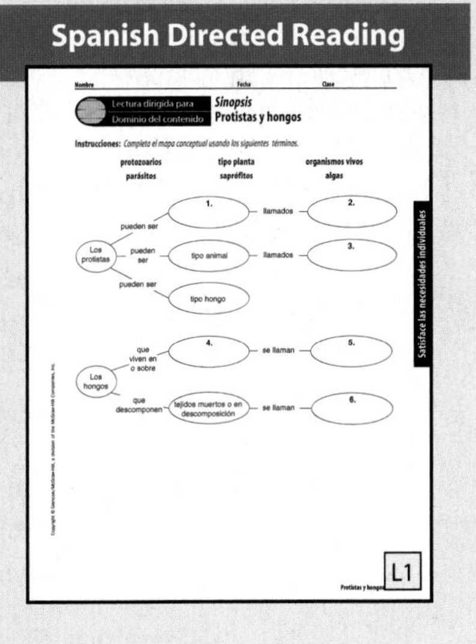
Lectura dirigida para Dominio del contenido — Sinopsis — Protistas y hongos

L1

Assessment

Chapter Tests

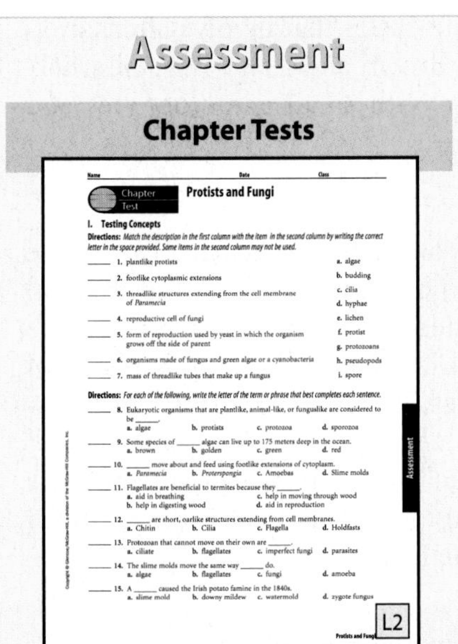
Chapter Test — Protists and Fungi

L2

Test Practice Workbook

L2

Chapter Review

Chapter Review — Protists and Fungi

Part A. Vocabulary Review

L2

Science Content Background

SECTION 1

Protists

Evolution of Protists

Convenience is the primary reason for grouping all eukaryotes that are not animals, plants, or fungi into a single kingdom. Because the phyla of Kingdom Protista appear to have evolved independently from one another, protists pose several problems for taxonomists. One of the major theories of evolution explains how eukaryotic cells evolved. According to this theory, chloroplasts evolved from a cyanobacterium taken up by an ancestor. Mitochondria and other organelles are thought to have evolved from aerobic heterotrophic prokaryotes. In these cases, the prokaryotes evolved into the organelles through symbiotic relationships in which the smaller prokaryotes lived inside larger prokaryotes. These symbiotic relationships are somewhat similar to the symbiotic relationships that exist between humans and the anaerobic protists living in the human digestive tract.

Fun Fact

A plasmodial slime mold can reach several centimeters in length and contain many nuclei, although it is one cell. A slime mold often has a web-like appearance, which allows it to increase its surface area (increasing its contact with food, water, and oxygen) and helps distribute nutrients and oxygen to different parts of the slime mold.

Plantlike Protists

The chloroplasts of diatoms in the phylum Bacillariophyta most resemble those of the brown algae and dinoflagellates. Diatoms store their food reserves as a type of oil. This oil provides buoyancy to the diatoms, keeping them near the surface of the water, and thus near sunlight. Dinoflagellates are characterized by unique chromosomes and by an unusual form of mitosis that takes place within a nucleus whose nuclear membrane does not degenerate. Dinoflagellates are widespread as symbionts of corals. In this relationship, the dinoflagellates are responsible for much of the productivity of coral reefs.

The extreme diversity of the green algae in the phylum Chlorophyta is reflected by their abundance in marine, freshwater, and damp terrestrial environments, such as on tree trunks and in soil. Red algae lack centrioles and flagellated cells. For this reason, most taxonomists hypothesize that these organisms descended from the most ancient eukaryotes. Red algae have complex life cycles that involve alternation of generations. Brown algae also have alternating generations, with small gametophytes and large sporophytes.

Fun Fact

Phylum Oomycota, the oomycetes, occur in water or as plant parasites. A member of this phylum caused the Irish potato famine of the mid-nineteenth century. Oomycotes have a filamentous structure similar to that of fungi, and they exhibit alternation of generations.

Animal-like Protists

Most flagellates are nonparasitic. But some of the parasitic flagellates can be quite harmful to humans. These harmful parasites include *Trypanosoma*, which live in the bloodstreams of many vertebrates. These protozoans cause diseases such as sleeping sickness. They protect themselves from attack by the host's immune system by changing the molecular structure of their coats frequently.

Funguslike Protists

Phylum Myxomycota contains plasmodial slime molds. These slime molds form round spore-containing capsules under unfavorable environmental conditions such as starvation. These capsules then release spores that may undergo meiosis.

For additional content background on this topic, go to the Glencoe Science Web site at science.glencoe.com.

SECTION 2

Fungi

Club Fungi

Basidiomycota includes about 25,000 species of mushrooms, puffballs, shelf fungi, and rusts. Some species of this phylum form mycorrhizae. Others are plant parasites that cause considerable damage each year. Basidiomycotes are named for club-shaped structures that form the sexual spores.

Sac Fungi

Ascomycota is the largest group of fungi accounting for 75 percent of all described fungi. These fungi are named for the sac in which their sexual spores are produced. Yeast are sac fungi that are important in baking and brewing.

Zygote Fungi

Phylum Zygomycota is made up of about 600 species of fungi, including mycorrhizae, an important group that forms mutually beneficial relationships with the roots of most species of plants. Sexual reproduction in this group occurs when appropriate mating strains grow together and produce resistant spores called zoosporangia.

Imperfect Fungi

Fungal species with no known method of sexual reproduction are classified in the phylum Deuteromycota. Some members of this phylum are responsible for producing the colors and flavors of several types of cheese.

Fun Fact

Truffles grow underground and are associated with tree roots. They are one of the most prized of edible fungi. Truffle hunters have traditionally used pigs to hunt truffles because the pigs can smell them. In more recent times, the hunters have begun to train dogs to hunt truffles because, unlike pigs, dog don't try to eat the truffles.

Antman/The Image Works

Protists and Fungi

Chapter Vocabulary

protist, p. 212
algae, p. 213
flagellum, p. 214
protozoan, p. 217
cilia, p. 217
pseudopod, p. 218
hyphae, p. 224
saprophyte, p. 224
spore, p. 225
basidium, p. 226
ascus, p. 226
budding, p. 226
sporangium, p. 227
lichen, p. 228
mycorrhizae, p. 228

What do you think?

Science Journal The picture shows the surface of a diatom, a kind of photosynthetic protist called an alga. Diatoms have intricately etched walls made of silica.

CHAPTER 8

Protists and Fungi

How many protists helped form this limestone cliff, and how did they do it? Did you know that fungi help to make hot dog buns? Some fungi can be seen only through a microscope but others are more than 100 m long. In this chapter, you will learn what characteristics separate protists and fungi from bacteria, plants, and animals. You also will learn why protists and fungi are important to you and the environment.

What do you think?

Science Journal Look at the picture below with a classmate. Discuss what you think this might be. Here's a hint: *This organism is visible only under a microscope.* Write your answer or best guess in your Science Journal.

210

Theme Connection

Systems and Interactions Changes over time and ecological relationships of protists and fungi are discussed.

It is hard to tell by a mushroom's appearance whether it is safe to eat or is poisonous. Some edible mushrooms are so highly prized that people keep their location a secret for fear that others will find their treasure. Do the activity below to learn about the parts of mushrooms.

Dissect a mushroom

WARNING: *Wash your hands after handling mushrooms. Do not eat any lab materials.*

1. Obtain a mushroom from your teacher.
2. Using a magnifying glass, observe the underside of the mushroom cap where the stalk is connected to it. Then carefully pull off the cap and observe the gills, which are the thin, tissuelike structures. Hundreds of thousands of tiny reproductive structures called spores will form on these gills.
3. Use your fingers to pull the stalk apart lengthwise. Continue this process until the pieces are as small as you can get them.

Poisonous or edible?

Observe

In your Science Journal, write a description of the parts of the mushroom, and make a labeled drawing of the mushroom and its parts.

Before You Read

FOLDABLES Reading & Study Skills

Making a Compare and Contrast Study Fold **Make the following Foldable to help you see how protists and fungi are similar and different.**

1. Place a sheet of paper in front of you so the short side is at the top. Fold the top of the paper down and the bottom up.
2. Open the paper and label the three rows *Protists, Protists and Fungi,* and *Fungi.*
3. As you read the chapter, write information about each type of organism in the appropriate row and information that they share in the middle row.

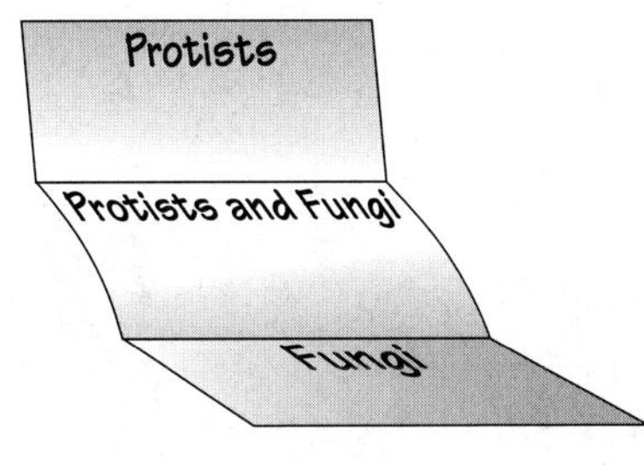

EXPLORE ACTIVITY

Purpose Use the Explore Activity to introduce students to fungi. They will learn more about fungi in this chapter. L1 ELL COOP LEARN

LS **Visual-Spatial**

Preparation Buy enough mushrooms for each student to have one.

Materials mushroom, hand lens

Teaching Strategies

- The best mushrooms to use will be those that have the membrane of the cap just separated from the stalk as opposed to those that are still tightly closed.
- Encourage students to examine the mushroom gills thoroughly with the hand lens.
- Tell students not to eat anything used in the lab.

Observe

Parts identified are cap, gills, spores, and stalk. Drawings will vary, but should include all parts.

Assessment

Oral Have students hypothesize how fungi became so widespread in the environment. Their spores are light, numerous, and easily carried by air currents. Use **Performance Assessment in the Science Classroom,** p. 93.

Before You Read

FOLDABLES Reading & Study Skills

Dinah Zike Study Fold

Purpose Students will make a Foldable for listing characteristics of protists and fungi during reading. They will use data collected to compare and contrast these forms of life after reading.

For additional help, see Foldables Worksheet, p. 15 in **Chapter Resources Booklet,** or go to the Glencoe Science Web site at **science.glencoe.com.** See After You Read in the Study Guide at the end of this chapter.

SECTION 1

Protists

1 Motivate

Bellringer Transparency

Display the Section Focus Transparency for Section 1. Use the accompanying Transparency Activity Master. L2 ELL

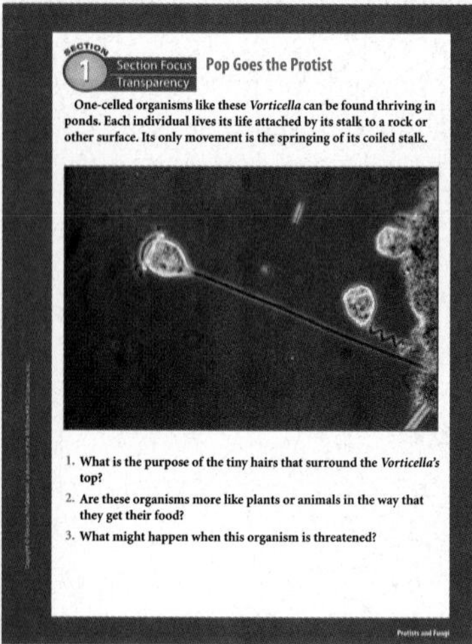
Section Focus Transparency 1 — Pop Goes the Protist

One-celled organisms like these *Vorticella* can be found thriving in ponds. Each individual lives its life attached by its stalk to a rock or other surface. Its only movement is the springing of its coiled stalk.

1. What is the purpose of the tiny hairs that surround the *Vorticella's* top?
2. Are these organisms more like plants or animals in the way that they get their food?
3. What might happen when this organism is threatened?

Tie to Prior Knowledge

Review classification with students. Explain that protists have some characteristics of animals, plants, and fungi.

SECTION 1

Protists

As You Read

What **You'll Learn**

- **Describe** the characteristics shared by all protists.
- **Compare and contrast** the three groups of protists.
- **List** examples of each of the three protist groups.
- **Explain** why protists are so difficult to classify.

Vocabulary

protist, algae, flagellum, protozoan, cilia, pseudopod

Why **It's Important**

Many protists are important food sources for other organisms.

What is a protist?

Look at the organisms in **Figure 1.** Do you see any similarities among them? As different as they appear, all of these organisms belong to one kingdom—the protist kingdom. A **protist** is a one- or many-celled organism that lives in moist or wet surroundings. All protists are made up of eukaryotic cells—cells that have a nucleus and other internal, membrane-bound structures. Some protists are plantlike. They contain chlorophyll and make their own food. Other protists are animal-like. They do not have chlorophyll and can move. Some protists have a solid or a shell-like structure on the outside of their bodies.

Protist Reproduction One-celled protists usually reproduce asexually. Asexual reproduction requires only one parent organism and occurs by the process of cell division. During cell division, the hereditary material in the nucleus is duplicated before the nucleus divides. After the nucleus divides, the cytoplasm divides. The result is two new cells that are genetically identical. In asexual reproduction of many-celled protists, parts of the large organism can break off and grow into entire new organisms by the process of cell division.

Most protists also can reproduce sexually. During sexual reproduction, the process of meiosis produces sex cells. Two sex cells join to form a new organism that is genetically different from the two organisms that were the sources of the sex cells. How and when sexual reproduction occurs depends on the specific type of protist.

Slime mold

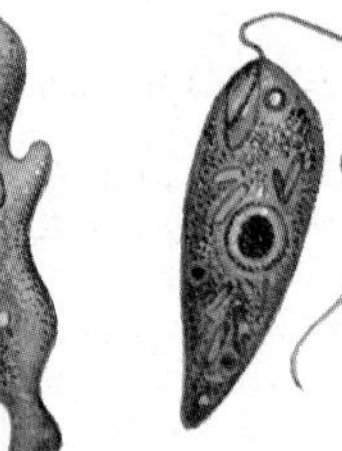

Amoeba

Euglena

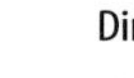

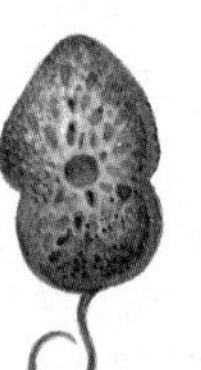

Dinoflagellate

Paramecium

Diatom

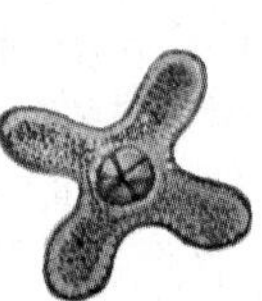

Macroalga

Figure 1
The protist kingdom is made up of a variety of organisms. Many are difficult to classify. *What characteristics do the organisms shown here have in common?*

Section Assessment Planner

PORTFOLIO
Science Journal, p. 214
Health Integration, p. 219

PERFORMANCE ASSESSMENT
MiniLAB, p. 220
Skill Builder Activities, p. 222
See page 238 for more options.

CONTENT ASSESSMENT
Section, p. 222
Challenge, p. 222
Chapter, pp. 238–239

Classification of Protists

Not all scientists agree about how to classify the organisms in this group. Protists usually are divided into three groups—plantlike, animal-like, and funguslike—based on whether they share certain characteristics with plants, animals, or fungi. **Table 1** shows some of these characteristics. As you read this section, you will understand some of the problems of grouping protists in this way.

Table 1 Characteristics of Protist Groups

Plantlike	Animal-Like	Funguslike
Contain chlorophyll and make their own food using photosynthesis	Cannot make their own food; capture other organisms for food	Cannot make their own food; absorb food from their surroundings
Have cell walls	Do not have cell walls	Some organisms have cell walls; others do not
No specialized ways to move from place to place	Have specialized ways to move from place to place	Have specialized ways to move from place to place

Evolution of Protists

Although protists that produce a hard outer covering have left many fossils, other protists lack hard parts so few fossils of these organisms have been found. But, by studying the genetic material and structure of modern protists, scientists are beginning to understand how they are related to each other and to other organisms. Scientists hypothesize that the common ancestor of most protists was a one-celled organism with a nucleus and other cellular structures. However, evidence suggests that protists with the ability to make their own food could have had a different ancestor than protists that cannot make their own food.

Plantlike Protists

Protists in this group are called plantlike because, like plants, they contain the pigment chlorophyll in chloroplasts and can make their own food. Many of them have cell walls like plants, and some have structures that hold them in place just as the roots of a plant do, but these protists do not have roots.

Plantlike protists are known as **algae** (AL jee) (singular, *alga*). As shown in **Figure 2,** some are one cell and others have many cells. Even though all algae have chlorophyll, not all of them look green. Many have other pigments that cover up their chlorophyll.

Figure 2
Algae exist in many shapes and sizes. **A** Microscopic algae are found in freshwater and salt water. **B** You can see some types of green algae growing on rocks, washed up on the beach, or floating in the water.

2 Teach

What is a protist?

Caption Answer

Figure 1 All are eukaryotic and live in a moist or wet environment.

Visual Learning

Table 1 Use information presented here to lead a discussion of the characteristics of the groups of protists. Allow students to compare and contrast the groups using these characteristics.

Plantlike Protists

Activity

Have students bring in pond water. Allow students to observe wet-mount slides of the water. They should observe a variety of algae. Use a dichotomous key to identify the algae. L2 ELL

LS **Visual-Spatial**

Make a Model

After students have looked at various algae under the microscope, have them make models to show what they look like. Materials for models might include clay, polystyrene, or plaster of paris. L2 ELL

LS **Kinesthetic**

Resource Manager

Chapter Resources Booklet
Transparency Activity, p. 40
Cultural Diversity, p. 3

Plantlike Protists, continued

Visual Learning

Figure 3 Point out to students that taxonomists use the markings on silica shells to identify individual species.

Figure 4 What advantage does having both an eyespot and a flagellum give *Euglena*? The eyespot would be useful in detecting light and the flagellum could be used to propel *Euglena* toward light.

Activity

Organize students into cooperative groups. Provide each group with about 40 buttons to arrange in a classification system. Relate this activity to the variety of protists and the difficulty in classifying them. L1 ELL COOP LEARN LS **Logical-Mathematical**

Caption Answer

Figure 4B Euglenoids are similar to animals because they do not have cell walls, they move, and they respond to light. They are similar to plants because they contain chloroplasts and can make their own food.

Fun Fact

When placed in the dark, euglenoids can lose their chloroplasts and become even more like protozoans.

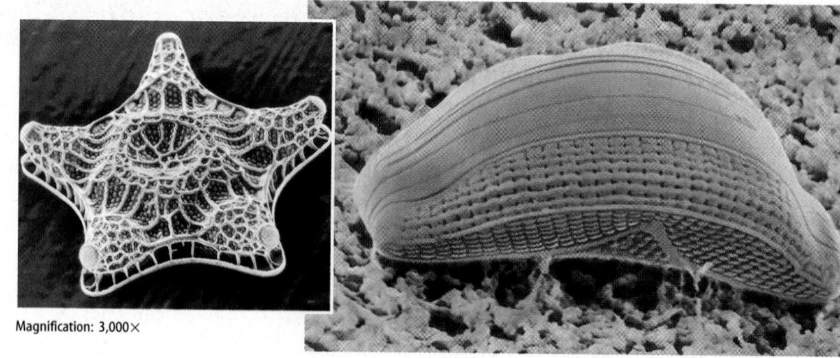

Figure 3
The cell walls of diatoms contain silica, the main element in glass. The body of a diatom is like a small box with a lid. The pattern of dots, pits, and lines on the wall's surface is different for each species of diatom.

Diatoms Extremely large populations of diatoms exist. Diatoms, shown in **Figure 3,** are found in freshwater and salt water. They have a golden-brown pigment that covers up the green chlorophyll. Diatoms secrete glasslike boxes around themselves. When the organisms die, these boxes sink. Over thousands of years, they can collect and form deep layers.

Dinoflagellates Another group of algae is called the dinoflagellates, which means "spinning flagellates." Dinoflagellates, as shown in **Figure 4A,** have two flagella. A **flagellum** (plural, *flagella*) is a long, thin, whiplike structure used for movement. One flagellum circles the cell like a belt, and another is attached to one end like a tail. As the two flagella move, they cause the cell to spin. Because many of the species in this group produce a chemical that causes them to glow at night, they are known as fire algae. Almost all dinoflagellates live in salt water. While most contain chlorophyll, some do not and must feed on other organisms.

Euglenoids Protists that have characteristics of both plants and animals are known as the euglenoids (yew GLEE noydz). Many of these one-celled algae have chloroplasts, but some do not. Those with chloroplasts, like *Euglena* shown in **Figure 4B,** can produce their own food. However, when light is not present, *Euglena* can feed on bacteria and other protists. Although *Euglena* has no cell wall, it does have a strong, flexible layer inside the cell membrane that helps it move and change shape. Many euglenoids move by whipping their flagella. An eyespot, an adaptation that is sensitive to light, helps photosynthetic euglenoids move toward light.

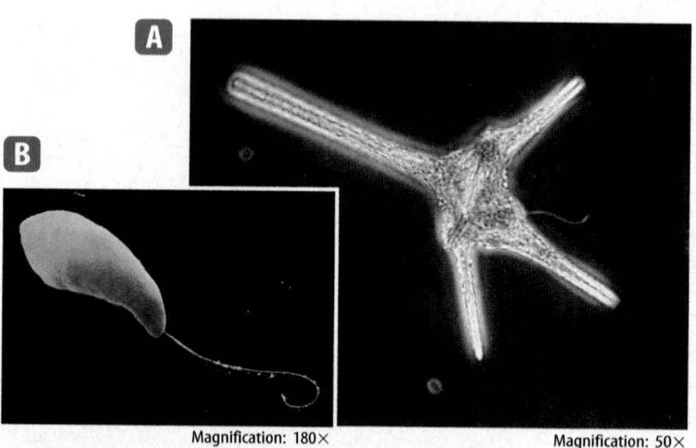

Figure 4
A Dinoflagellates usually live in the sea. Some are free living and others live in the tissues of animals like coral and giant clams.
B *How are euglenoids similar to plants and animals?*

Teacher FYI

Overlapping protein fibers in many protists, such as *Euglena*, allow them to alter their shape considerably.

Science Journal

Euglenoids Have students write a fictional story in their Science Journals to describe a day in the life of *Euglena*. Tell students to use the plantlike and animal-like characteristics of the protist in their stories. L2 LS **Linguistic** P

Red Algae Most red algae are many-celled and, along with the many-celled brown and green algae, sometimes are called seaweeds. Red algae contain chlorophyll, but they also produce large amounts of a red pigment. Some species of red algae can live up to 200 m deep in the ocean. They can absorb the limited amount of light at those depths to carry out the process of photosynthesis. **Figure 5** shows the depths at which different types of algae can live.

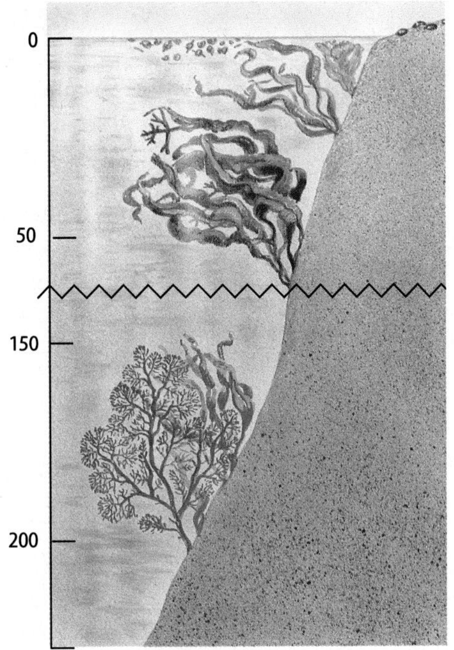

Figure 5
Green algae are found closer to the surface. Brown algae can grow from a depth of about 35 m. Red algae are found in the deepest water at 175 m to 200 m.

Green Algae Due to the diversity of their traits, about 7,000 species of green algae have been classified. These algae, shown in **Figure 6A,** contain large amounts of chlorophyll. Green algae can be one-celled or many-celled. They are the most plantlike of all the algae. Because plants and green algae are similar in their structure, chlorophyll, and how they undergo photosynthesis, some scientists hypothesize that plants evolved from ancient, many-celled green algae. Although most green algae live in water, you can observe types that live in other moist environments, including on damp tree trunks and wet sidewalks.

Brown Algae As you might expect from their name, brown algae contain a brown pigment in addition to chlorophyll. They usually are found growing in cool, saltwater environments. Brown algae are many-celled and vary greatly in size. An important food source for many fish and invertebrates is a brown alga called kelp, as shown in **Figure 6B.** Kelp forms a dense mat of stalks and leaflike blades where small fish and other animals live. Giant kelp is the largest organism in the protist kingdom and can grow to be 100 m in length.

Reading Check ***What is kelp?***

Figure 6
A Green algae often can be seen on the surface of ponds in the summer. B Giant kelp, a brown alga, can form forests like this one located off the coast of California. Extracts from kelp add to the smoothness and spreadability of products such as cheese spreads and mayonnaise.

A

B

Visual Learning

Figure 5 Red algae can photosynthesize at great depths because their red pigments are efficient at gathering the longer wavelengths of light at that depth.

Figure 6 Point out that even though some brown algae, such as kelp, may grow to great lengths, they are not plants because they do not develop the complex structures of plants.

Reading Check

Answer a brown alga that is an important food source for many fish and invertebrate

Resource Manager

Chapter Resources Booklet

Directed Reading for Content Mastery, pp. 17, 18

Life Science Critical Thinking/Problem Solving, p. 1

Cultural Diversity

Seaweed, Anyone? Algae are consumed as food by people in some cultures and used as animal food in others. Have students research the use of algae as food. Possible answers: Algae is used in pudding, ice cream, and salad dressing. L2 IS **Linguistic**

Importance of Algae

Teacher FYI

Dinoflagellates that produce red tides are a normal part of marine phytoplankton. Red tides are found in shallow marine habitats when temperatures increase and the amount of freshwater flowing into the environment decreases.

Activity

Have students research how satellites are used to capture images of red tides. L3

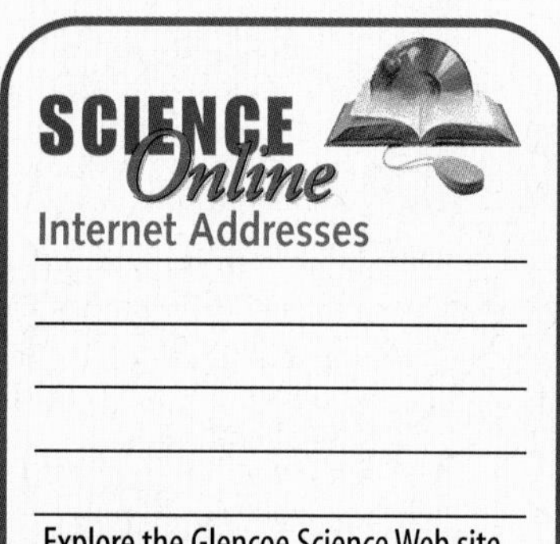

Science Online

Internet Addresses

Explore the Glencoe Science Web site at **science.glencoe.com** to find out more about topics in this section.

Extension

Each year, more than 200,000 metric tons of diatomaceous earth is mined in a quarry in California. Ask students what this means in terms of the number of diatoms it took to accumulate such a deposit and where the ocean was located at one time. This indicates that, at one time, this area may have been under water.

Reading Check

Answer Possible answer: algae is used in food and cosmetics.

Science Online

Research Visit the Glencoe Science Web site at **science.glencoe.com** for more information about red tides. Determine whether there is an area or time of year in which red tides occur more frequently. Communicate to your class what you learned.

Importance of Algae

Have you thought about how important grasses are as a food source for animals that live on land? Cattle, deer, zebras, and many other animals depend on grasses as their main source of food. Algae sometimes are called the grasses of the oceans. Most animals that live in the oceans eat either algae for food or other animals that eat algae. You might think many-celled, large algae like kelp are the most important food source, but the one-celled diatoms and dinoflagellates claim that title. Algae, such as *Euglena*, also are an important source of food for organisms that live in freshwater.

Algae and the Environment Algae are important in the environment because they produce oxygen as a result of photosynthesis. The oxygen produced by green algae is important for most organisms on Earth, including you.

Under certain conditions, algae can reproduce rapidly and develop into what is known as a bloom. Because of the large number of organisms in a bloom, the color of the water appears to change. Red tides that appear along the east and Gulf coasts of the United States are the result of dinoflagellate blooms. Toxins produced by the dinoflagellates can cause other organisms to die and can cause health problems in humans.

Algae and You People in many parts of the world eat some species of red and brown algae. You probably have eaten foods or used products made with algae. Carrageenan (kar uh JEE nuhn), a substance found in the cell walls of red algae, has gelatinlike properties that make it useful to the cosmetic and food industries. It is usually processed from the red alga Irish moss, shown in **Figure 7.** Carrageenan gives toothpastes, puddings, and salad dressings their smooth, creamy textures. Another substance, algin (AL juhn), found in the cell walls of brown algae, also has gelatinlike properties. It is used to thicken foods such as ice cream and marshmallows. Algin also is used in making rubber tires and hand lotion.

Ancient deposits of diatoms are mined and used in insulation, filters, and road paint. The cell walls of diatoms produce the sparkle that makes some road lines visible at night and the crunch you feel in toothpaste.

Figure 7
Carrageenan, a substance extracted from the red alga Irish moss, is used for thickening dairy products such as chocolate milk.

216

Reading Check *What are some uses by humans of algae?*

Curriculum Connection

Geography Have students plot on a United States map the major areas where diatomite, or diatomaceous earth, is mined. Leading producers in the United States are California, Nevada, Arizona, Washington, and Florida. L2 ELL

Science Journal

News Item Have students write in their Science Journals an item that might appear on a news program to warn people about red tides. The item should contain information about the organisms that are causing the problem and health precautions to prevent poisoning. L2
LS **Linguistic**

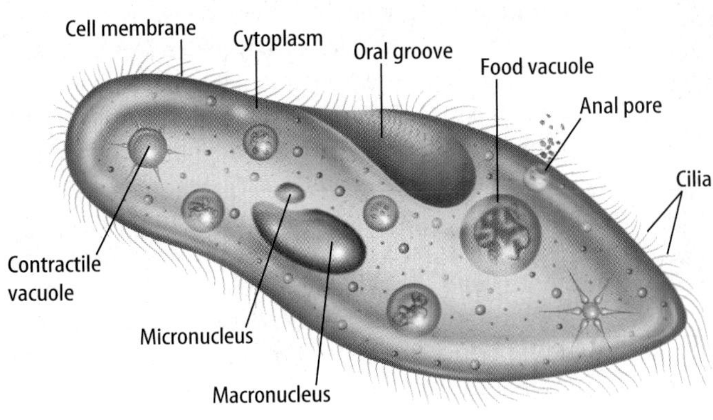

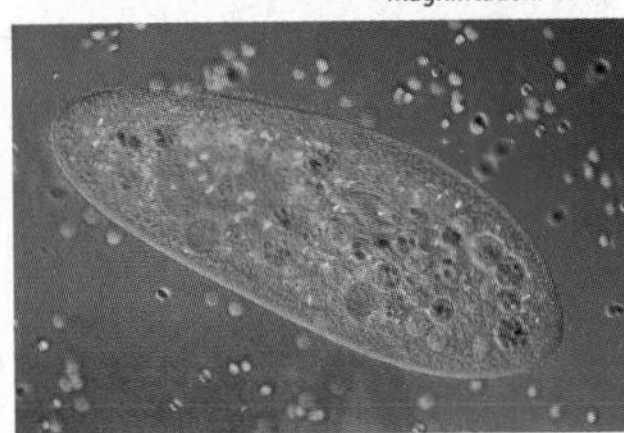

Figure 8
Paramecium **is a typical ciliate found in many freshwater environments. These rapidly swimming protists consume bacteria.** *Locate the contractile vacuoles in the photo. What is their function?*

Animal-Like Protists

One-celled, animal-like protists are known as **protozoans.** Usually protozoans are classified by how they move. These complex organisms live in or on other living or dead organisms that are found in water or soil. Many protozoans have specialized vacuoles for digesting food and getting rid of excess water.

Ciliates As their name suggests, these protists have **cilia** (SIHL ee uh)—short, threadlike structures that extend from the cell membrane. Ciliates can be covered with cilia or have cilia grouped in specific areas on the surface of the cell. The cilia beat in a coordinated way. As a result, the organism moves swiftly in any direction. Organisms in this group include some of the most complex, one-celled protists and some of the largest, one-celled protists.

A typical ciliate is *Paramecium,* shown in **Figure 8.** *Paramecium* has two nuclei—a macronucleus and a micronucleus—another characteristic of the ciliates. The micronucleus is involved in reproduction. The macronucleus controls feeding, the exchange of oxygen and carbon dioxide, the amount of water and salts entering and leaving *Paramecium,* and other functions of *Paramecium.*

Ciliates usually feed on bacteria that are swept into the oral groove by the cilia. Once the food is inside the cell, a vacuole forms around it and the food is digested. Wastes are removed through the anal pore. Freshwater ciliates, like *Paramecium,* also have a structure called the contractile vacuole that helps get rid of excess water. When the contractile vacuole contracts, excess water is ejected from the cell.

Animal-Like Protists

Caption Answer

Figure 8 The contractile vacuoles are star-shaped. Their function is to eliminate excess water from the cell.

Use Science Words

Word Meaning Have students determine the meanings of the prefix *pro-* and the suffix *-zoa* in the word *protozoan.* Ask them how these relate to the meaning of the word. *Pro-* comes from the Greek word, meaning "before," and *-zoa* comes from the Greek word for "animal." So, a protozoan is an organism that probably evolved before animals.

Use an Analogy

To help students visualize the beating of cilia, show them a photograph of a rowing crew. All members move together so that their oars are all in the same position at the same time. This propels the boat through the water as cilia propel a paramecium or other ciliate through its watery medium.

IDENTIFYING Misconceptions

Point out that the use of the words *hairlike* and *threadlike* as they refer to flagella and cilia relate to how the organelles appear. They function more like oars or propellers.

Resource Manager 

Chapter Resources Booklet
Note-taking Worksheets, pp. 29–30

Performance Assessment in the Science Classroom, p. 59

Curriculum Connection

Math A paramecium may be about 0.1 cm long. Giant kelp may be 100 m long. **How many times larger is giant kelp than a paramecium?** 0.1 cm/paramecium × 1 m/100 cm × 1 giant kelp/100 m = 100,000 times larger L2 LS **Logical-Mathematical**

Animal-Like Protists, continued

Quick Demo

Use model plant and animal cells to illustrate the organelles in common between algae and plants and between protozoans and animals. LS **Visual-Spatial**

Teacher FYI

Recent research suggests that some termite species can digest wood without their flagellated mutualists. However, wood digestion is more efficient with the mutualists than without them.

Discussion

Have groups of students research a particular parasitic protozoan such as *Plasmodium, Trypanosoma, Giardia,* or *Trichomona.* During class have them share their findings about location of outbreaks, numbers of cases, and disease symptoms. L2 COOP LEARN LS **Interpersonal**

Quick Demo

Squash a termite's abdomen in a saline solution that is isotonic for insects, making a wet mount. Allow students to observe the flagellates in the termite's gut.

Caption Answer

Figure 10 It is a one-celled consumer, has no cell wall, and moves by using pseudopods.

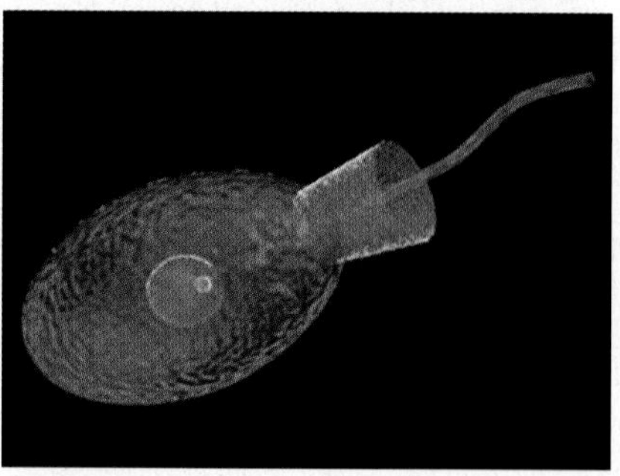

Figure 9
Proterospongia **is a rare, freshwater protist. Some scientists hypothesize that it might share an ancestor with ancient animals.**

Flagellates Protozoans called flagellates move through their watery environment by whipping their long flagella. Many species of flagellates live in freshwater, though some are parasites that harm their hosts.

Proterospongia, shown in **Figure 9,** is a member of one group of flagellates that might share an ancestor with ancient animals. These flagellates often grow in colonies of many cells that are similar in structure to cells found in animals called sponges. Like sponge cells, when *Proterospongia* cells are in colonies, they perform different functions. Moving the colony through the water and dividing which increases the colony's size, are two examples of jobs that the cells of *Proterospongia* carry out.

Movement with Pseudopods Some protozoans move through their environments and feed using temporary extensions of their cytoplasm called **pseudopods** (SEWD uh pahdz). The word *pseudopod* means "false foot." These organisms seem to flow along as they extend their pseudopods. They are found in freshwater and saltwater environments, and certain types are parasites in animals.

The amoeba shown in **Figure 10** is a typical member of this group. To obtain food, an amoeba extends the cytoplasm of a pseudopod on either side of a food particle such as a bacterium. Then the two parts of the pseudopod flow together and the particle is trapped. A vacuole forms around the trapped food. Digestion takes place inside the vacuole.

Although some protozoans of this group, like the amoeba, have no outer covering, others secrete hard shells around themselves. The white cliffs of Dover, England are composed mostly of the remains of some of these shelled protozoans. Some shelled organisms have holes in their shells through which the pseudopods extend.

Figure 10
In many areas of the world, a disease-causing species of amoeba lives in the water. If it enters a human body, it can cause dysentery—a condition that can lead to a severe form of diarrhea. *Why is an amoeba classified as a protozoan?*

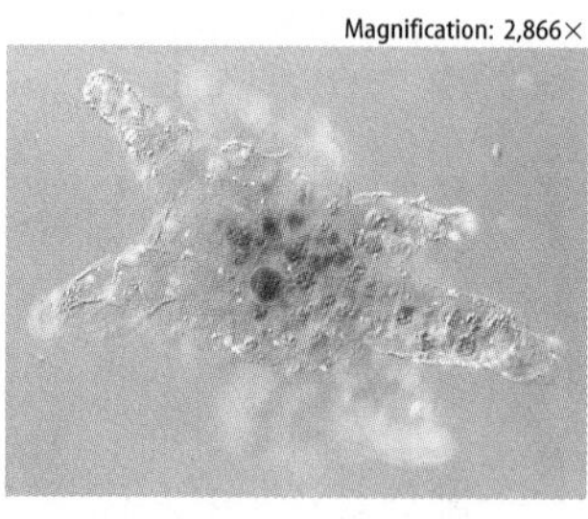

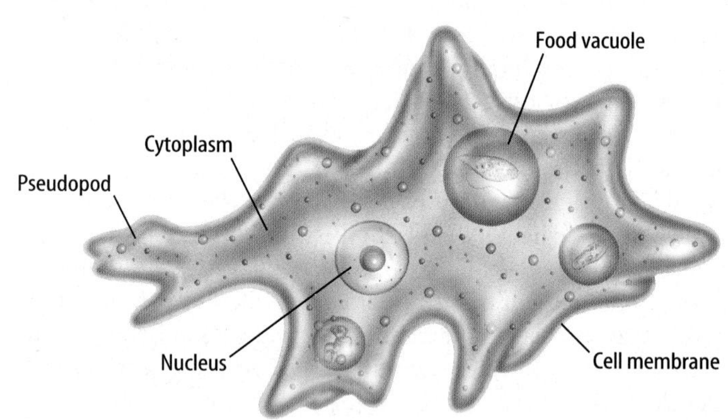

LAB DEMONSTRATION

Purpose to observe how amoebas capture prey

Materials amoeba culture, small ciliates, projecting microscope, slide and coverslip, dropper

Preparation Have all necessary equipment set up before class starts. Pre-dyed amoebas and ciliates may be helpful to obtain.

Procedure A drop of amoeba and a drop of prey per slide are sufficient. Observe under low power, then high power with the projecting microscope.

Expected Outcome Students should observe amoebas extending pseudopodia and capturing prey in food vacuoles.

Assessment

When is the organism captured? when the pseudopod completely envelopes it **Is the prey still alive after capture?** The prey lives for some time before digestive fluids kill it.

Figure 11
Asexual reproduction takes place inside a human host. Sexual reproduction takes place in the intestine of a mosquito.

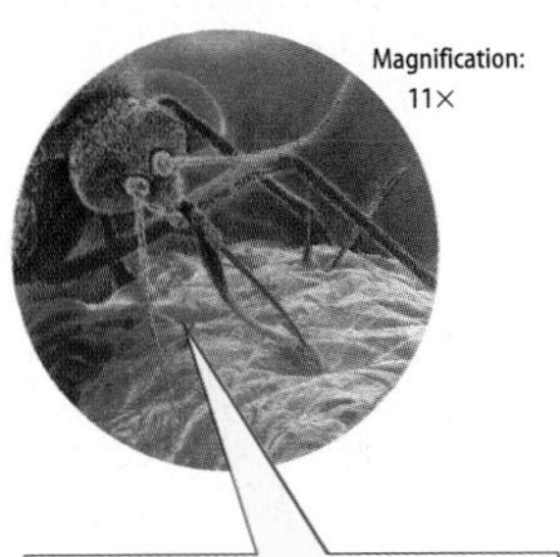
Magnification:
11×
Plasmodium lives in the salivary glands of certain female mosquitoes. The parasite can be transferred to a human's blood if an infected mosquito bites them.

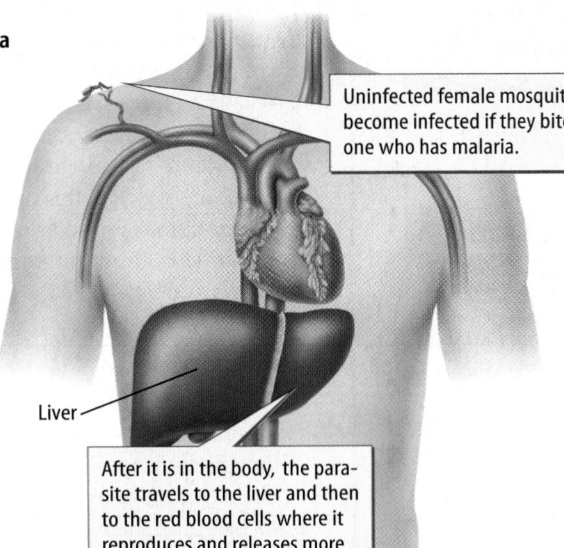
Uninfected female mosquitoes can become infected if they bite someone who has malaria.
Liver
After it is in the body, the parasite travels to the liver and then to the red blood cells where it reproduces and releases more parasites into the blood.

Other Protozoans One group of protozoans has no way of moving on their own. All of the organisms in this group are parasites of humans and other animals. These protozoans have complex life cycles that involve sexual and asexual reproduction. They often live part of their lives in one animal and part in another. The parasite that causes malaria is an example of a protozoan in this group. **Figure 11** shows the life cycle of the malaria parasite.

Importance of Protozoans

Like the algae, some protozoans are an important source of food for larger organisms. When some of the shelled protozoans die, they sink to the bottom of bodies of water and become part of the sediment. Sediment is a buildup of plant and animal remains and rock and mineral particles. The presence of these protists in sediments is used sometimes by field geologists as an indicator species. This tells them where petroleum reserves might be found beneath the surface of Earth.

Reading Check *Why are shelled protozoans important?*

One type of flagellated protozoan lives with bacteria in the digestive tract of termites. Termites feed mainly on wood. These protozoans and bacteria produce wood-digesting enzymes that help break down the wood. Without these organisms, the termites would be unable to use the chemical energy stored in wood.

Health INTEGRATION

The flagellate *Trypanosoma* is carried by the tsetse fly in Africa and causes African sleeping sickness in humans and other animals. It is transmitted to other organisms during bites from the fly. The disease affects the central nervous system. Research this disease and create a poster showing your results.

Importance of Protozoans

Health INTEGRATION

African sleeping sickness is prevalent in sub-Saharan Africa. Some regions are uninhabitable because of the risk of becoming infected. There are several varieties, caused by different species of protozoa, which differ slightly in their symptoms and severity. Early symptoms usually include fever and inflammation of the lymph nodes. More advanced symptoms may include a sensation of pain, severe headaches, mental dullness and apathy, tremors, paralysis, chorea, and profound sleepiness. These symptoms are often followed by coma and death, though in some cases the individual develops a tolerance and lives for many years as a carrier. Posters may relate the numbers of cases each year, the number of deaths, the vector, and locations of infestations. Some students may research possible cures. P

Reading Check

Answer The presence of these organisms in sediment can indicate where petroleum may be found.

Curriculum Connection

Math Have students analyze the following story by making a graph. A person who contracted malaria had the following body temperatures (°C) at the given times. Day 1: 1:00 P.M., 39.4° (chills); 6:00 P.M., 38.3° (sweating); Day 2: 1:00 A.M., 36.1°; 6:00 A.M., 36.7°; 1:00 P.M., 36.1°; 6:00 P.M, 37.2°; Day 3: 1:00 A.M., 38.3° (chills); 6:00 A.M., 39.4°; 1:00 P.M., 39.4°; 6:00 P.M., 38.3° (sweating). **When will the person have chills next?** The person will have the chills next at 1:00 P.M. on Day 5. L2 LS **Logical-Mathematical**

Resource Manager

Chapter Resources Booklet
Enrichment, p. 27
Transparency Activity, pp. 43–44

Funguslike Protists

Purpose to observe the growth of slime molds and predict the best conditions for their growth L2 LS **Visual-Spatial**

Materials slime mold specimens, magnifying glass, pencil, paper

Teaching Strategy Obtain live specimens of slime mold from a biological supply company. *Physarum polycephalum* produces good results.

Analysis

Lower temperatures and reduced humidity or the presence of food will result in the growth of the spore-producing form.

Assessment

Performance To assess students' understanding of slime molds, have them try to grow slime mold cultures on different surfaces with different nutrients. Use **Performance Assessment in the Science Classroom,** p. 97.

Caption Answer

Figure 12 Slime molds move and behave like animal-like protists during part of their life cycle, but, like fungi, they are decomposers that reproduce with spores.

Mini LAB

Observing Slime Molds

Procedure

1. Obtain live specimens of the slime mold ***Physarum polycephaalum*** from your teacher. Wash your hands.
2. Observe the mold once each day for four days.
3. Using a **magnifying glass,** make daily drawings and observations of the mold as it grows.

Analysis

Predict the growing conditions under which the slime mold will change from the amoeboid form to the spore-producing form.

Disease in Humans The protozoans that are most important to you are the ones that cause diseases in humans. In tropical areas, flies or other biting insects transmit many of the parasitic flagellates to humans. A flagellated parasite called *Giardia* can be found in water that is contaminated with wastes from humans or wild or domesticated animals. If you drink water directly from a stream, you could get this diarrhea-causing parasite.

Some amoebas also are parasites that cause disease. One parasitic amoeba, found in ponds and streams, can lead to a brain infection and death.

Funguslike Protists

Funguslike protists include several small groups of organisms such as slime molds, water molds, and downy mildews. Although all funguslike protists produce spores like fungi, most of them can move from place to place using pseudopods like the amoeba. All of them must take in food from an outside source.

Slime Molds As shown in **Figure 12,** slime molds are more attractive than their name suggests. Slime molds form delicate, weblike structures on the surface of their food supply. Often these structures are brightly colored. Slime molds have some protozoan characteristics. During part of their life cycle, slime molds move by means of pseudopods and behave like amoebas.

Most slime molds are found on decaying logs or dead leaves in moist, cool, shady environments. One common slime mold sometimes creeps across lawns and mulch as it feeds on bacteria and decayed plants and animals. When conditions become less favorable, reproductive structures form on stalks and spores are produced.

Figure 12
Slime molds come in many different forms and colors ranging from brilliant yellow or orange to rich blue, violet, pink, and jet black. *How are slime molds similar to protists and fungi?*

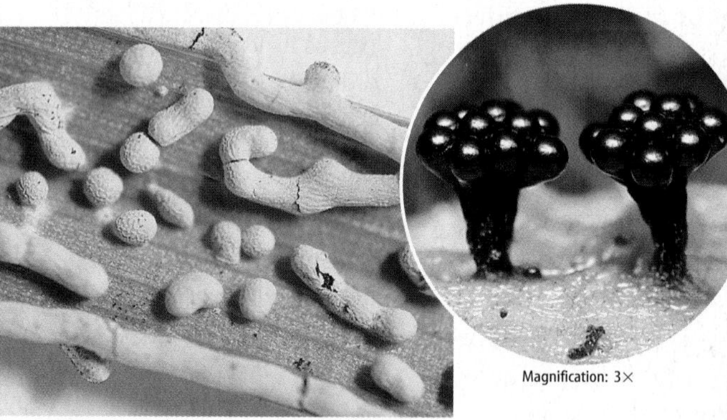

Inclusion Strategies

Learning Disabled After having students observe the movement of a slime mold under the microscope, have them perform these same movements as a group. The cytoplasm streams in one direction and then slows to a stop. Then the cytoplasm flows in the opposite direction, but not as far, before stopping. In this way, the slime mold creeps across a surface. L1 LS **Kinesthetic**

Water Molds and Downy Mildews

Most members of this large, diverse group of funguslike protists live in water or moist places. Like fungi, they grow as a mass of threads over a plant or animal. Digestion takes place outside of these protists, then they absorb the organism's nutrients. Unlike fungi, the spores these protists produce have flagella. Their cell walls more closely resemble those of plants than those of fungi.

Some water molds are parasites of plants, and others feed on dead organisms. Most water molds appear as fuzzy, white growths on decaying matter. **Figure 13** shows a parasitic water mold that grows on aquatic organisms. If you have an aquarium, you might see water molds attack a fish and cause its death. Another important type of protist is a plant parasite called downy mildew. Warm days and cool, moist nights are ideal growing conditions for them. They can live on aboveground parts of many plants. Downy mildews weaken plants and even can kill them.

Figure 13
Water mold, the threadlike material seen in the photo, grows on a dead salamander. In this case, the water mold is acting as a decomposer. This important process will return nutrients to the water.

✔ Reading Check *How do water molds affect organisms?*

Problem-Solving Activity

Is it a fungus or a protist?

Slime molds, such as the pipe cleaner slime shown in the photograph to the right, can be found covering moist wood. They can be white or bright red, yellow, or purple. If you look at a piece of slime mold on a microscope slide, you will see that the cell nuclei move back and forth as the cytoplasm streams along. This streaming of the cytoplasm is how a slime mold creeps over the wood.

Identifying the Problem

Should slime molds be classified as protists or as fungi?

Solving the Problem

1. What characteristics do slime molds share with protists? How are slime molds similar to protozoans and algae?
2. What characteristics do slime molds share with fungi? What characteristics do slime molds have that are different from fungi?
3. What characteristics did you compare to decide what group slime molds should be classified in? What other characteristics could scientists examine to help classify slime molds?

Discussion

Ask students to compare slime molds and fungi. Both are often found on decaying materials; both can reproduce by spore production.

✔ Reading Check

Answer They usually feed on organisms, sometimes causing their death.

Math Skills Activity

National Math Standards

Correlation to Mathematics Objectives
6, 8

Answers to Practice Problems

1. Slime molds are eukaryotic organisms that usually live in moist or wet surroundings. They creep across surfaces and engulf food in ways similar to amoebas.
2. Slime molds grow on decaying matter and reproduce with spores. Unlike fungi, slime molds sometimes engulf food and move.
3. Answers will vary. Scientists could examine cell structure or do a more detailed examination of physiological processes.

Resource Manager

Chapter Resources Booklet
MiniLAB, p. 3

Inclusion Strategies

Gifted Students can make a flipbook for each type of protist. On each page of the flipbook, they should show one stage of that protist's movement. When the pages are placed together and flipped through rapidly, the protist should appear to move. The book will be more interesting if it has more pages showing small sections of movement, and the organism consuming food. L3 IS **Visual-Spatial**

Importance of the Funguslike Protists

Activity

Have students make a chart listing the positive and negative effects of funguslike protists.

3 Assess

Reteach

Have students examine photographs or illustrations of various protists and identify the life cycle phase of each. L2
IS **Visual-Spatial**

Challenge

What are the causes and effects of a red tide? A red tide is caused by a population explosion of dinoflagellates. Millions of these organisms cause the water to look red. Some species release a nerve toxin that can kill fish and humans.

Assessment

Performance Have students write a statement in their Science Journals comparing the environments of slime molds and water molds. Use **Performance Assessment in the Science Classroom,** p. 175.

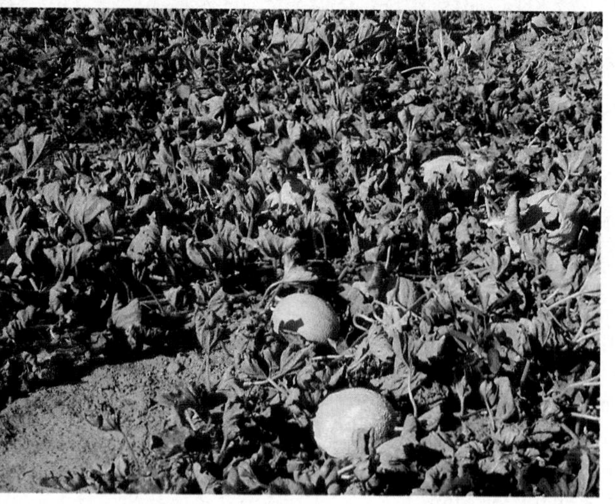

Figure 14
Downy mildews can have a great impact on agriculture and economies when they infect potatoes, sugar beets, grapes, and melons like those above.

Importance of the Funguslike Protists

Some of the organisms in this group are important because they help break down dead organisms. However, most funguslike protists are important because of the diseases they cause in plants and animals. One species of water mold that causes lesions in fish can be a problem when the number of organisms in a given area is high. Fish farms and salmon spawning in streams can be greatly affected by a water mold spreading throughout the population. Water molds cause disease in other aquatic organisms including worms and even diatoms.

Economic Effects Downy mildews can have a huge effect on economies as well as social history. A downy mildew infection of grapes in France during the 1870s nearly wiped out the entire French wine industry. One of the most well-known members of this group is a downy mildew, which caused the Irish potato famine during the 1840s. Potatoes were Ireland's main crop and the primary food source for its people. When the potato crop became infected with downy mildew, potatoes rotted in the fields, leaving many people with no food. Downy mildews, as shown in **Figure 14,** continue to infect crops such as lettuce, corn, and cabbage, as well as tropical avocados and pineapples.

Section 1 Assessment

1. What are the characteristics common to all protists?
2. Compare and contrast the different characteristics of animal-like, plantlike, and funguslike protists.
3. How are plantlike protists classified into different groups?
4. How are protozoans classified into different groups?
5. **Think Critically** Why are there few fossils of certain groups of protists?

Skill Builder Activities

6. **Making and Using Tables** Make a table of the positive and negative effects that protists have on your life and health. **For more help, refer to the** Science Skill Handbook.
7. **Using an Electronic Spreadsheet** Use a spreadsheet to make a table that compares the characteristics of the three groups of protozoans. Include *example organisms, method of transportation,* and *other characteristics.* **For more help, refer to the** Technology Skill Handbook.

Answers to Section Assessment

1. single-celled or many-celled organisms that live in moist or wet surroundings; possess membrane-bound nuclei; protists may be plant-like, animal-like, or funguslike
2. Algae are plantlike protists with chloroplasts and cell walls. Protozoans are single-celled animal-like protists that lack cell walls and cannot produce their own food. Funguslike protists are all consumers that produce spores.
3. by their structure and the pigments they contain
4. by their method of movement
5. Protists are small and do not have hard parts that are fossilized easily. The protists decay rapidly, leaving no trace of their existence.
6. Check student tables for accuracy.
7. Tables should accurately display information from this section.

Activity

Comparing Algae and Protozoans

Magnification: 50×

Algae and protozoan cells have characteristics that are similar enough to place them in the same group—the protists. However, the variety of protist forms is great. In this activity, you can observe many of the differences among protists.

What You'll Investigate

What are the differences between algae and protozoans?

Materials

cultures of *Paramecium, Amoeba, Euglena,* and *Spirogyra*
**prepared slides of the organisms listed above*
prepared slide of slime mold
microscope slides (4)
coverslips (4)
microscope
**stereomicroscope*
dropper
**Alternate materials*

Goals

- **Draw and label** the organisms you examine.
- **Observe** the differences between algae and protozoans.

Safety Precautions

Make sure to wash your hands after handling algae and protozoans.

Procedure

1. Copy the data table in your Science Journal.
2. Make a wet mount of the *Paramecium* culture. If you need help, refer to Student Resources at the back of the book.

Protist Observations

Protist	Drawing	Observations
Paramecium		
Amoeba	Student drawings	
Euglena	should resemble group features	
Spirogyra	described in this section.	
Slime mold		

3. **Observe** the wet mount first under low and then under high power. Record your observations in the data table. Draw and label the organism that you observed.
4. Repeat steps 2 and 3 with the other cultures. Return all preparations to your teacher and wash your hands.
5. **Observe** the slide of slime mold under low and high power. Record your observations.

Conclude and Apply

1. Which structure was used for movement by each organism that could move?
2. Which protists make their own food? Explain how you know that they can make their own food.
3. **Identify** the protists you observed with animal-like characteristics.

Communicating Your Data

Share the results of this activity with your classmates. **For more help, refer to the** Science Skill Handbook.

Activity

BENCH TESTED

Purpose to observe the differences between algae and protozoans L2 IN Visual-Spatial

Process Skills observing and inferring, classifying, making and using tables, comparing and contrasting

Time Required 50 minutes

Materials Prepared slides of protozoans and algae may be used. All live specimens should be obtained from a reputable supply house. No parasitic forms should be used.

Safety Precautions Remind students to be careful when plugging and unplugging the microscope. Water should be kept away from the outlet.

Teaching Strategies

- Use a videotape of the organisms to prepare students for what they will see.
- Remind students that algae and protozoans are protists.

Troubleshooting Maintain separate cultures for each organism. Prevent students from using the same dropper for more than one culture.

Answers to Questions

1. Paramecia use cilia; amoebas use pseudopods; euglenas use flagella.
2. *Spirogyra* and *Euglena* make their own food; they contain chloroplasts for photosynthesis.
3. *Paramecium, Euglena, Amoeba,* slime mold

Resource Manager

Chapter Resources Booklet
Activity Worksheet, pp. 5–6

Communicating Your Data

Students should have similar results. They may communicate by using drawings or written descriptions of their observations.

Assessment

Performance To further assess students' abilities to classify algae and protozoans, have them make and view wet mounts of scrapings from fish tanks. Use **PASC**, p. 121.

SECTION

2 Fungi

1 Motivate

Bellringer Transparency

Display the Section Focus Transparency for Section 2. Use the accompanying Transparency Activity Master. L2 ELL

2 Section Focus Transparency Dig It

Care for a truffle? Highly prized in Europe as a delicacy, truffles are a rare, fragrant, and flavorful variety of fungi. Because they can grow as much as 30 centimeters underground, people have trained pigs and dogs to hunt them by scent. The rarest truffles can be worth $3,000 per kilogram!

1. Do you think that truffles are classified as plants? Explain.
2. What other organisms resemble truffles?

Tie to Prior Knowledge

Have students relate examples of fungi they know about. Students will likely know about toadstools and fungi used in food. Explain that fungi are in a kingdom separate from other organisms.

SECTION

2 Fungi

As You Read

What You'll Learn

- **Identify** the characteristics shared by all fungi.
- **Classify** fungi into groups based on their methods of reproduction.
- **Differentiate** between the imperfect fungi and all other fungi.

Vocabulary

hyphae, saprophyte, spore, basidium, ascus, budding, sporangium, lichen, mycorrhizae

Why It's Important

Fungi are important sources of food and medicines, and they help recycle Earth's wastes.

What are fungi?

Do you think you can find any fungi in your house or apartment? You have fungi in your home if you have mushroom soup or fresh mushrooms. What about that package of yeast in the cupboard? Yeasts are a type of fungus used to make some breads and cheeses. You also might find fungus growing on a loaf of bread or mildew fungus growing on your shower curtain.

Origin of Fungi Although fossils of fungi exist, most are not useful in determining how fungi are related to other organisms. Some scientists hypothesize that fungi share an ancestor with ancient, flagellated protists and slime molds. Other scientists hypothesize that their ancestor was a green or red alga.

Structure of Fungi Most species of fungi are many-celled. The body of a fungus is usually a mass of many-celled, threadlike tubes called **hyphae** (HI fee), as shown in **Figure 15.** The hyphae produce enzymes that help break down food outside of the fungus. Then, the fungal cells absorb the digested food. Because of this, most fungi are known as saprophytes. **Saprophytes** are organisms that obtain food by feeding on dead or decaying tissues of other organisms. Other fungi are parasites. They obtain their food directly from living things.

Figure 15
The hyphae of fungi are involved in the digestion of food, as well as reproduction.

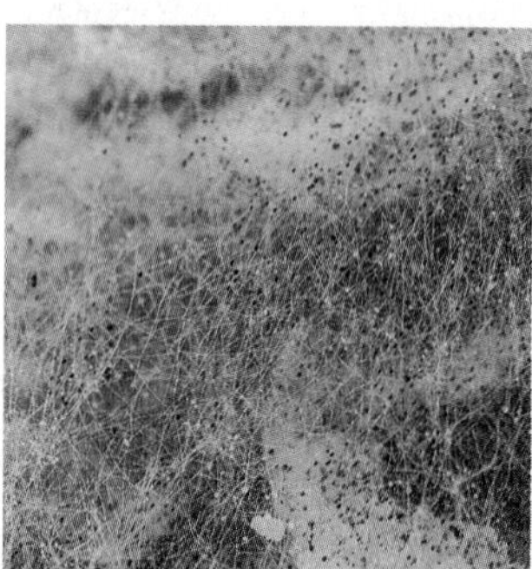
A The body of a fungus is visible to the unaided eye.

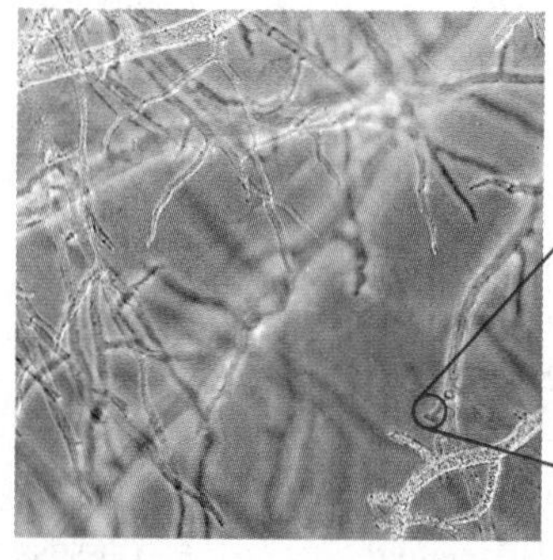
B Threadlike, microscopic hyphae make up the body of a fungus.

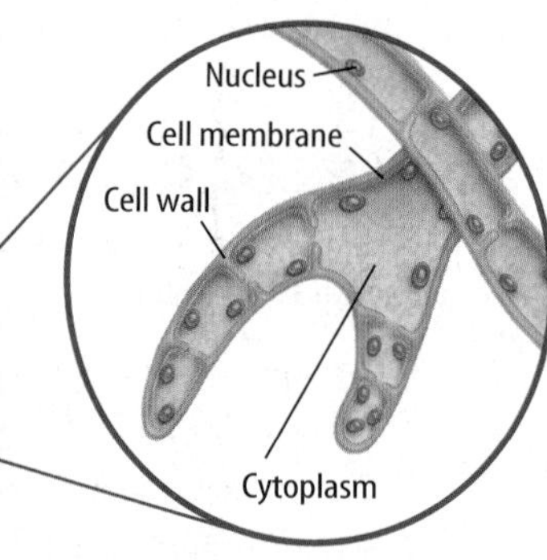

C The internal structure of hyphae.

224 CHAPTER 8 Protists and Fungi

Section Assessment Planner

PORTFOLIO
Try at Home MiniLAB, p. 227

PERFORMANCE ASSESSMENT
Try at Home MiniLAB, p. 227
Skill Builder Activities, p. 231
See page 238 for more options.

CONTENT ASSESSMENT
Section, p. 231
Challenge, p. 231
Chapter, pp. 238–239

Other Characteristics of Fungi What other characteristics do all fungi share? Because fungi grow anchored in soil and have a cell wall around each cell, fungi once were classified as plants. But fungi don't have the specialized tissues and organs of plants, such as leaves and roots. Unlike plants, fungi cannot make their own food because they don't contain chlorophyll.

Fungi grow best in warm, humid areas, such as tropical forests or between toes. You need a microscope to see some fungi, but in Michigan one fungus was found growing underground over an area of about 15 hectares. In the state of Washington, another type of fungus found in 1992 was growing throughout nearly 600 hectares of soil.

Reproduction Asexual and sexual reproduction in fungi usually involves the production of spores. A **spore** is a waterproof reproductive cell that can grow into a new organism. In asexual reproduction, cell division produces spores. These spores will grow into new fungi that are genetically identical to the fungus from which the spores came.

Fungi are not identified as either male or female. Sexual reproduction can occur when the hyphae of two genetically different fungi of the same species grow close together. If the hyphae join, a reproductive structure will grow, as shown in **Figure 16.** Following meiosis in these structures, spores are produced that will grow into fungi. These fungi are genetically different from either of the two fungi whose hyphae joined during sexual reproduction. Fungi are classified into three main groups based on the type of structure formed by the joining of hyphae.

Reading Check *How are fungi classified?*

SCIENCE Online

Research Visit the Glencoe Science Web site at **science.glencoe.com** for more information about the gigantic fungus *Armillaria ostoyae* and other unusual fungi. Communicate to your class what you learned.

A Two hyphae fuse.

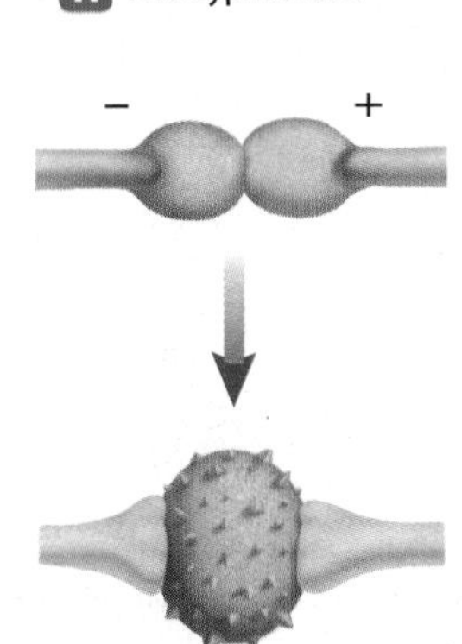

B Reproductive structure forms.

Figure 16
A When two genetically different fungi of the same species meet, B a reproductive structure, in this case a zygospore, will be formed. The new fungi will be genetically different from either of the two original fungi.

2 Teach

What are fungi?

Activity

Mix some yeast suspension with flour and water and put it in a warm place. Ask students to predict what will happen over the course of the day. The dough will rise as the yeast's respiratory processes produce carbon dioxide. L2

Discussion

Have students discuss why fungi are no longer classified as plants. Unlike plants, fungi contain no chloroplasts.

Quick Demo

Show students some food that has mold growing on it. This is best done if the food can be kept under a plastic cover as in a freezer storage bag. **Caution:** *Before beginning, ask if any students have known allergies to fungal spores. Contact the school nurse if a student shows signs of an allergic reaction to fungal spores used in demonstrations during this section. It is rare, but some students may experience breathing difficulties in the presence of fungal spores.*

Reading Check

Answer by the type of structure formed by the joining of hyphae

Resource Manager

Chapter Resources Booklet
Transparency Activity, p. 41
Directed Reading for Content Mastery, pp. 19, 20

SCIENCE Online

Internet Addresses

Explore the Glencoe Science Web site at **science.glencoe.com** to find out more about topics in this section.

Club Fungi

IDENTIFYING
Misconceptions

Point out to students that they cannot get rid of toadstools in their lawn by pulling them out. Ask why this is so. The fungi have a large mycelium underground. The fungi also spread by fungal spores that will reinvade the area if material are available to decompose.

Sac Fungi

Teacher FYI

Mycology is the study of fungi. Many fungi are useful commercially in baking and fermentation. Others, such as *Amanita* mushrooms, are poisonous. Caution students never to eat a mushroom that has not been identified by an expert or purchased from a grocery store.

A

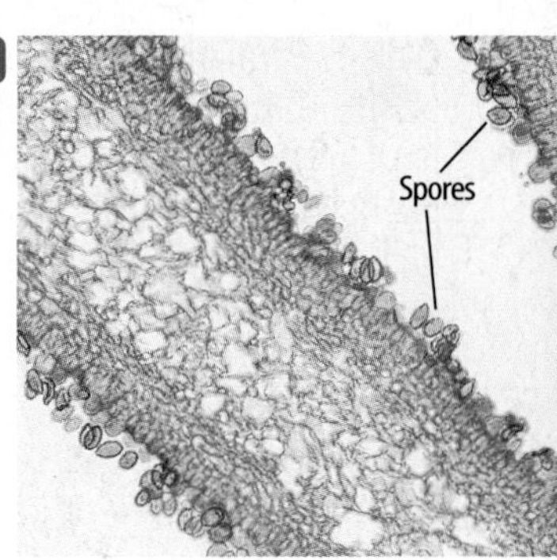
B
Spores

Figure 17
A Club fungi, like this mushroom, form a reproductive structure called a basidium. Each basidium produces four balloonlike structures called basidiospores. B Spores will be released from these as the final step in sexual reproduction.

Club Fungi

The mushrooms shown in **Figure 17** are probably the type of fungus that you are most familiar with. The mushroom is only the reproductive structure of the fungus. Most of the fungus grows as hyphae in the soil or on the surface of its food source. These fungi commonly are known as club fungi. Their spores are produced in a club-shaped structure called a **basidium** (buh SIHD ee uhm) (plural, *basidia*).

Sac Fungi

Yeasts, molds, morels, and truffles are all examples of sac fungi—a diverse group containing more than 30,000 different species. The spores of these fungi are produced in a little, saclike structure called an **ascus** (AS kus), as shown in **Figure 18A.**

Although most fungi are many-celled, yeasts are one-celled organisms. Yeasts reproduce by forming spores and reproduce asexually by budding, as illustrated in **Figure 18B. Budding** is a form of asexual reproduction in which a new organism forms on the side of an organism. The two organisms are genetically identical.

Figure 18
A The spores of a sac fungus are released when the tip of an ascus breaks open.
B Yeasts can reproduce by forming buds off their sides. A bud pinches off and forms an identical cell.

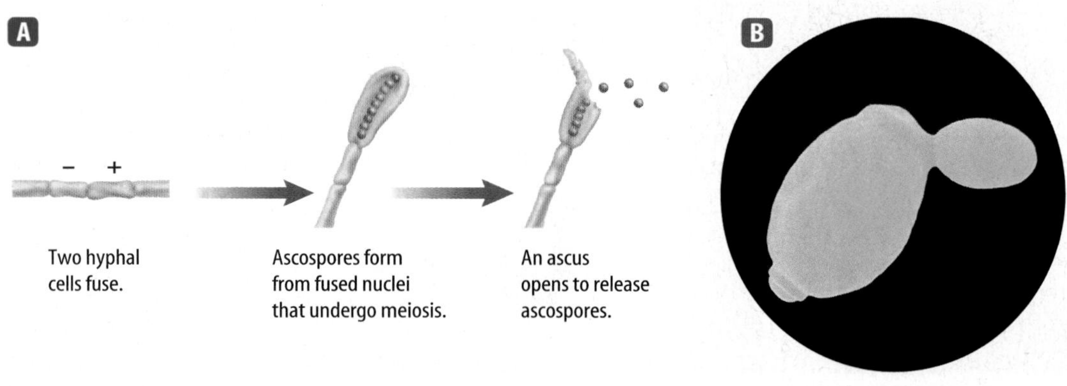
A
− +
Two hyphal cells fuse.
Ascospores form from fused nuclei that undergo meiosis.
An ascus opens to release ascospores.
B

Fun Fact

One of the largest organisms in the world is a fungus growing under acres of forest floor in Michigan. It is estimated to weigh at least 100 tons.

Curriculum Connection

Math The fairy ring toadstool (a type of mushroom) advances outward from the center at a rate of about 30 cm per year. One ring is estimated to be 150 years old. **How many meters in diameter is this fairy ring?** 150 years × 30 cm/year × 2 radii/diameter = 9,000 cm = 90 meters

L2 LS **Logical-Mathematical**

Figure 19
The black mold found growing on bread or fruit is a type of zygospore fungus.

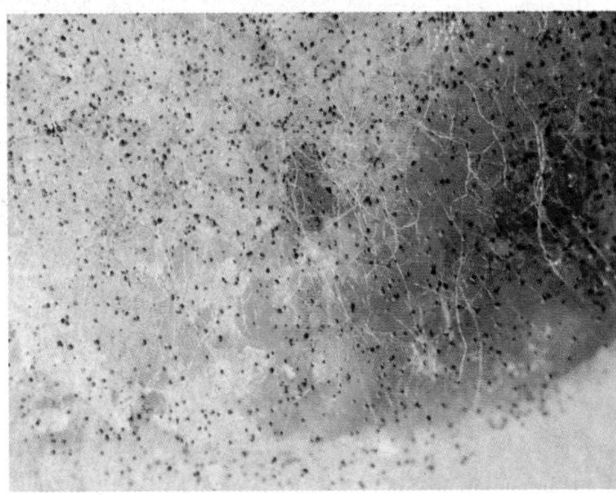

A This black mold produces zygospores during sexual reproduction.

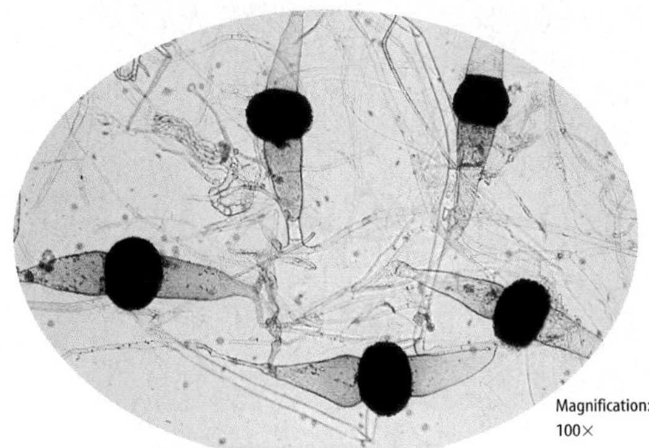

B The zygospores shown here produce sporangia that hold the individual spores.

Zygote Fungi and Other Fungi

The fuzzy black mold that you sometimes find growing on a piece of fruit or an old loaf of bread as shown in **Figure 19,** is a type of zygospore fungus. Fungi that belong to this group produce spores in a round spore case called a **sporangium** (spuh RAN jee uhm) (plural, *sporangia*) on the tips of upright hyphae. When each sporangium splits open, hundreds of spores are released into the air. Each spore will grow and reproduce if it lands in a warm, moist area that has a food supply.

Reading Check *What is a sporangium?*

Some fungi either never reproduce sexually or never have been observed reproducing sexually. Because of this, these fungi are difficult to classify. They usually are called imperfect fungi because there is no evidence that their life cycle has a sexual stage. Imperfect fungi reproduce asexually by producing spores. When the sexual stage of one of these fungi is observed, the species is classified immediately in one of the other three groups.

Penicillium is a fungus that is difficult to classify. Some scientists classify *Penicillium* as an imperfect fungi. Others believe it should be classified as a sac fungus based on the type of spores it forms during asexual reproduction. Another fungus, which causes pneumonia, has been classified recently as an imperfect fungus. Like *Penicillium,* scientists do not agree about which group to place it in.

TRY AT HOME Mini LAB

Interpreting Spore Prints

Procedure

1. Obtain several **mushrooms from the grocery store** and let them age until the undersides look brown.
2. Remove the stems. Place the mushroom caps with the gills down on a piece of **unlined white paper.** Wash your hands.
3. Let the mushroom caps sit undisturbed overnight and remove them from the paper the next day. Wash your hands.

Analysis

1. Draw and label the results in your **Science Journal.** Describe the marks on the page and what made them.
2. How could you estimate the number of new mushrooms that could be produced from one mushroom cap?

Zygote Fungi and Other Fungi

Make a Model

After students have observed bread mold with a dissecting microscope or hand lens, have them construct a model of the structures they observe. Students should show spores, hyphae, and so on. L2 LS **Kinesthetic**

Reading Check

Answer a round spore case

Purpose to observe spore prints L1 ELL LS **Visual-Spatial** P

Materials mushrooms, unlined white paper

Teaching Strategy Caution students not to disturb the mushrooms while spore prints are being made.

Safety Precautions Remind students not to eat anything used in the lab.

Analysis

1. Sketches will vary. Brown lines will be parallel or concentric rings made by falling spores.
2. Count a few spores in one area and multiply by the total area of spore production.

Assessment

Performance To further assess understanding of mushrooms, have students carefully tease apart a bit of gill from under the cap and make a wet mount of an extremely small piece. Students should draw and describe what they see in their Science Journals. Use **PASC,** p. 127.

Resource Manager

Chapter Resources Booklet
MiniLAB, p. 4
Home and Community Involvement, p. 43

Inclusion Strategies

Learning Disabled Have students make flash cards with the name of a group of fungi and a picture on one side and the characteristics and an example on the other. Allow students to practice learning the fungi by using their flash cards. L1 LS **Linguistic**

Lichens

Caption Answer

Figure 20 Possible answers: by the kind of photosynthetic cells they associate with or by their forms

Fungi and Plants

Visual Learning

Figure 22 Use the picture to point out that almost all orchid species require mycorrhizae in order to live. An important orchid to most students is the vanilla orchid. Have students research which part of the vanilla plant is useful to humans. The vanilla bean is the seedpod of the orchid plant.

✔ Reading Check

Answer The fungus helps the plant take in more nutrients than the plant can take in by itself or take in certain nutrients that the plant cannot take in without the fungus.

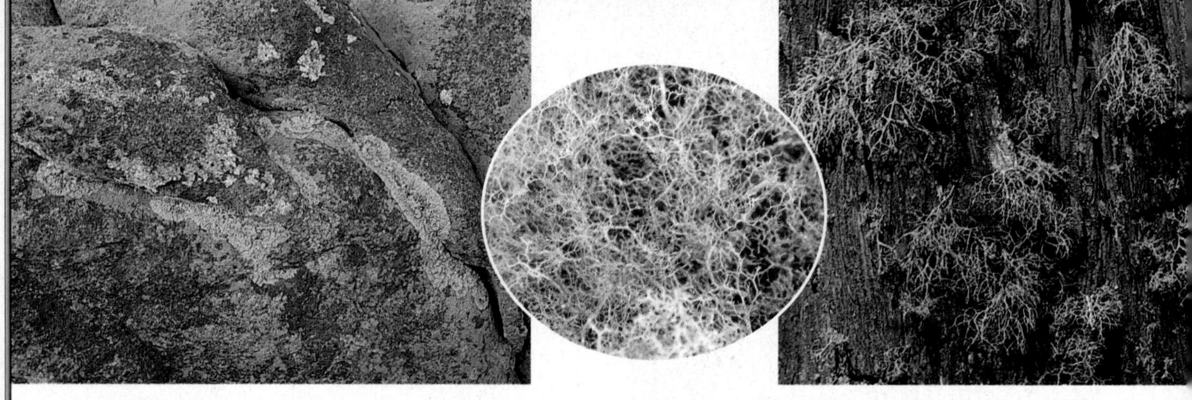

Figure 20
Lichens can look like a crust on bare rock, appear leafy, or grow upright. All three forms can grow near each other. *What is one way lichens might be classified?*

Lichens

The colorful organisms in **Figure 20** are lichens. A **lichen** (LI kun) is an organism that is made of a fungus and either a green alga or a cyanobacterium. These two organisms have a relationship in which they both benefit. The alga or cyanobacterium lives among the threadlike strands of the fungus. The fungus gets food made by the green alga or cyanobacterium. The green alga or cyanobacterium gets a moist, protected place to live.

Importance of Lichens For many animals, including caribou and musk oxen, lichens are an important food source.

Lichens also are important in the weathering process of rocks. They grow on bare rock and release acids as part of their metabolism. The acids help break down the rock. As bits of rock accumulate and lichens die and decay, soil is formed. This soil supports the growth of other species.

Scientists also use lichens as indicator organisms to monitor pollution levels, as shown in **Figure 21.** Many species of lichens are sensitive to pollution. When these organisms show a decline in their health or die quickly, it alerts scientists to possible problems for larger organisms.

Figure 22
Many plants, such as these orchids, could not survive without mycorrhizae to help absorb water and important minerals from soil.

Fungi and Plants

Some fungi interact with plant roots. They form a network of hyphae and roots known as **mycorrhizae** (mi kuh RI zee). About 80 percent of plants develop mycorrhizae. The fungus helps the plant absorb more of certain nutrients from the soil better than the roots can on their own, while the plant supplies food and other nutrients to the fungi. Some plants, like the lady's slipper orchids shown in **Figure 22,** cannot grow without the development of mycorrhizae.

✔ **Reading Check** *Why are mycorrhizae so important to plants?*

Science Journal

Erosion Have students research the importance of fungi in erosion and write a paragraph about it in their Science Journals. Wind, water, temperature changes, and living things such as fungi are the main forces of erosion. Explain that all landforms—mountains, rivers, valleys, and plains—show visible results of erosional forces. L2 LS **Linguistic**

Figure 21

Widespread, slow-growing, and long-lived, lichens come in many varieties. Lichens absorb water and nutrients mainly from the air rather than the soil. Because certain types are extremely sensitive to toxic environments, lichens make natural, inexpensive air-pollution detectors.

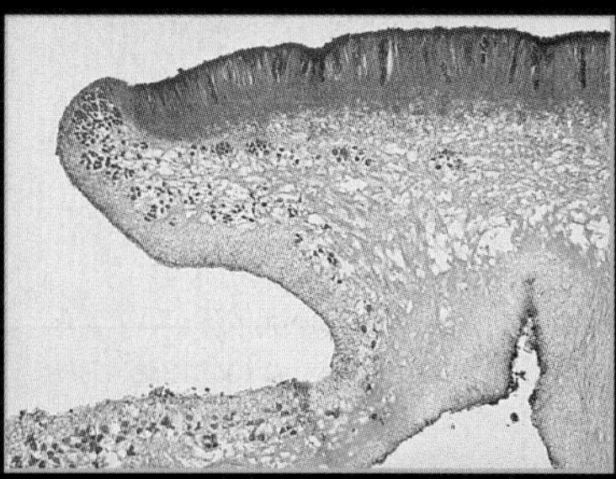

A lichen consists of a fungus and an alga or cyanobacterium living together in a partnership that benefits both organisms. In this cross section of a lichen (50x), reddish-stained bits of fungal tissue surround blue-stained algal cells.

Can you see a difference between these two red alder tree trunks? White lichens cover one trunk but not the other. Red alders are usually covered with lichens such as those seen in the photo on the left. Lichens could not survive on the tree on the right because of air pollution.

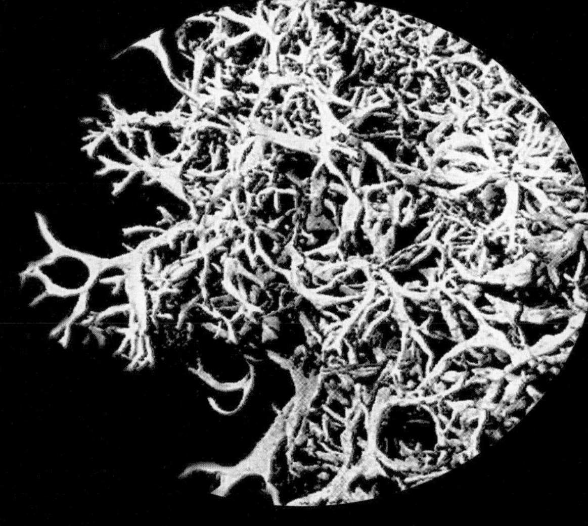

Evernia lichens, left, sicken and die when exposed to sulfur dioxide, a common pollutant emitted by coal-burning industrial plants such as the one above.

Visualizing Lichens as Air Quality Indicators

Have students examine the pictures and read the captions. Then ask the following questions.

If a tree has no lichens on its trunk, what does that indicate about the air quality in that area? Possible answer: The tree is in an area that has a source of air pollution.

Where do lichens get most of their nutrients? Lichens absorb water and nutrients from the air.

Activity

Have students make a map of the area surrounding the school. The area should encompass about 5 square km. Then have them indicate on the map which areas would most likely contain lichens. If there are no lichens in the area, have students discuss why that may be.

LS **Naturalist**

Extension

Many current studies are trying to determine the effect that air pollution has on lichens. Have students research several different species of lichens and determine whether the lichens are sensitive to certain types of air pollution.

Resource Manager

Chapter Resources Booklet

Enrichment, p. 28

Fungi and Plants, continued

Earth Science INTEGRATION

The fossilized fungus was mycorrhizae. In addition to providing evidence of how plants could have made the transition to land, the fossil also provided evidence of fungi that are scarce in the fossil record.

Importance of Fungi

Activity

Allow students to work in groups to develop and carry out interviews with local physicians concerning the role of fungi in the health field. Students will learn that fungi can cause infection in humans, but that some fungi are also used in the production of medicines. L2 COOP LEARN LS **Interpersonal**

Environmental Science INTEGRATION

Some fungi form sticky nets that can be used to trap microscopic nematodes—roundworms that can be detrimental to plants.

Environmental Science INTEGRATION

Although fungi can have negative effects on agriculture, they can be used to help farmers. Some farmers are using fungi as natural pesticides. Fungi can control a variety of pests including termites, rice weevils, tent caterpillars, aphids, and citrus mites.

Fossilized Fungus In 1999, scientists discovered a fossilized fungus in a 460 million-year-old rock. The fossil was a type of fungus that forms associations with plant roots. Scientists have known for many years that the first plants could not have survived moving from water to land alone. Early plants did not have specialized roots to absorb nutrients. Also, tubelike cells used for transporting water and nutrients to leaves were too simple.

Scientists have hypothesized that early fungi attached themselves to the roots of early plants, passing along nutrients taken from the soil. Scientists suggest that it was this relationship that allowed plants to move successfully from water onto land about 500 million years ago. Until the discovery of this fossil, no evidence had been found that this type of fungus existed at that time.

Importance of Fungi

As mentioned in the beginning of this chapter, some fungi are eaten for food. Cultivated mushrooms are an important food crop. However, wild mushrooms never should be eaten because many are poisonous. Some cheeses are produced using fungi. Yeasts are used in the baking industry. Yeasts use sugar for energy and produce alcohol and carbon dioxide as waste products. The carbon dioxide causes doughs to rise.

Agriculture Many fungi are important because they cause diseases in plants and animals. Many sac fungi are well known by farmers because they damage or destroy plant crops. Diseases caused by sac fungi are Dutch elm disease, apple scab, and ergot disease of rye. Smuts and the rust, shown in **Figure 23A,** are club fungi. They cause billions of dollars worth of damage to food crops each year.

Figure 23
A Rusts can infect the grains used to make many cereals including wheat, barley, rye, and oats. B Not all fungi are bad for agriculture. Some are natural pesticides. This grasshopper is infected with a fungal parasite.

230 CHAPTER 8 Protists and Fungi

Active Reading

Quickwrites This strategy, sometimes called freewrites, lets students use spontaneous writing to discover what they already know. Have students write a list of ideas about a topic, then share these ideas with the class. Next, have students write their ideas freely in a paragraph without worrying about punctuation, spelling, and grammar. Have students use a Quickwrite to discover what they know about the importance of fungi.

Resource Manager

Chapter Resources Booklet
Reinforcement, p. 26
Lab Activities, pp. 9–10, 11–13

Health and Medicine Fungi are responsible for causing diseases in humans and animals. Ringworm and athlete's foot are two infections of the skin caused by species of imperfect fungi. Other fungi can cause respiratory infections. The effects of fungi on health and medicine are not all negative. Some species of fungi naturally produce antibiotics that keep bacteria from growing on or near them.

The antibiotic penicillin is produced by the imperfect fungi *Penicillium.* This fungus is grown commercially, and the antibiotic is collected to use in fighting bacterial infections. Cyclosporin, an important drug used to help fight the body's rejection of transplanted organs, also is derived from a fungus. There are many more examples of breakthroughs in medicine as a result of studying and discovering new uses of fungi. In fact, there is a worldwide effort among scientists who study fungi to investigate soil samples to find more useful drugs.

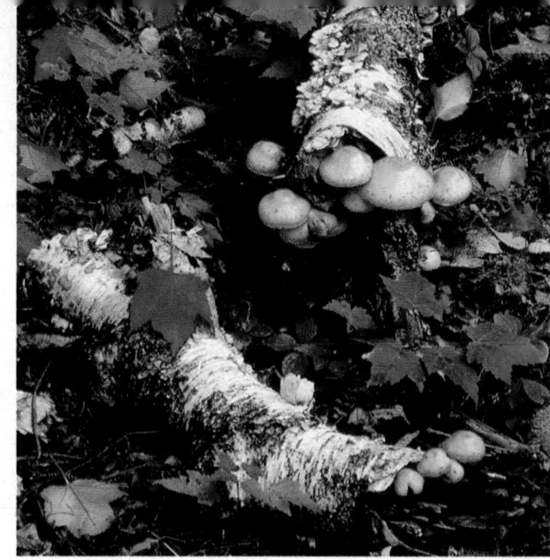

Figure 24
Fungi have an important role as decomposers in nature.

Decomposers As important as fungi are in the production of different foods and medicines, they are most important as decomposers that break down organic materials. Food scraps, clothing, and dead plants and animals are made of organic material. Often found on rotting logs, as shown in **Figure 24,** fungi break down these materials. The chemicals in these materials are returned to the soil where plants can reuse them. Fungi, along with bacteria, are nature's recyclers. They keep Earth from becoming buried under mountains of organic waste materials.

Section  Assessment

1. List characteristics common to all fungi.
2. How are fungi classified into different groups?
3. Differentiate between the imperfect fungi and all other fungi.
4. Why are lichens important to the environment?
5. **Think Critically** If an imperfect fungus were found to produce basidia under certain environmental conditions, how would the fungus be reclassified?

Skill Builder Activities

6. **Comparing and Contrasting** What are the similarities and differences among the characteristics of the four groups of fungi and lichens? **For more help, refer to the Science Skill Handbook.**
7. **Using Proportions** Of the 100,000 fungus species, approximately 30,000 are sac fungi. What percentage of fungus species are sac fungi? **For more help, refer to the Math Skill Handbook.**

3 Assess

Reteach

Show students various illustrations of fungi. Ask them to identify the parts of each fungus. L2 **Visual-Spatial**

Challenge

Why is it beneficial for fungi to reproduce both sexually and asexually? Asexual reproduction allows fungi to take full and rapid advantage of a food source. Sexual reproduction provides genetic variation for surviving in different environments.

Assessment

Oral What has never been observed in any of the imperfect fungi? a sexual stage **How do the imperfect fungi reproduce if they don't have a sexual stage?** asexual spores Use **Performance Assessment in the Science Classroom,** p. 143.

Answers to Section Assessment

1. Fungi cannot make their own food. Most fungi are many-celled saprophytes with a body made of hyphae. They grow anchored in soil and have cell walls.
2. by the structure formed by the joining of hyphae
3. Imperfect fungi have no known sexual stage in their life cycle; all other fungi do.
4. Lichens are an important food source for many animals, they help break down rocks into soil, and they are used to monitor pollution levels.
5. It would be reclassified as a club fungus belonging to division Basidiomycota.
6. Zygote fungi: round spore cases on upright stalks; sac fungi: spores grow in a protective sac; club fungi: spores grow in a club-shaped structure; imperfect fungi: no sexual stage has been observed; lichens: crusty, leafy or upright; closely associated with algae or cyanobacteria. See information in section 2 under: What are fungi?; Club fungi; Sac Fungi; Zygote Fungi and other Fungi; Lichens
7. $30,000/100,000 \times 100\% = 30\%$

Activity

BENCH TESTED

Recognize the Problem

Purpose

Students identify fungi and design a field guide for fungi in their area. LS **Kinesthetic and Visual-Spatial**

Process Skills

identifying, classifying, analyzing, and designing

Time Required

three class periods

Thinking Critically

Discussion

Tell students to think about methods for observing fungi. Have them consider features in their field guides that they would want to use to make identifying fungi easier. How will they group the organisms in the book? What type of diagrams or photographs will they include? How can they waterproof the pages of the field guide? What size should the field guide be?

Possible Materials

Provide a wide selection of containers and other collection equipment. Provide students with detailed guidebooks to help them identify their discoveries. Encourage students to use a wide variety of art mediums including color pencils, markers, pastels, charcoal, paints, and photography.

Safety Precautions

Caution students never to eat any fungi they collect and to thoroughly wash their hands after handling fungi.

Activity **Model and Invent**

Creating a Fungus Field Guide

Magnification: 18×

Cross section of club fungus

Whether they are hiking deep into a rain forest in search of rare tropical birds, diving to coral reefs to study marine worms, or peering into microscopes to identify strains of bacteria, scientists all over the world depend on reliable field guides. Field guides are books that identify and describe certain types of organisms or the organisms living in a specific environment. Scientists find field guides for a specific area especially helpful. In this activity, you will create your own field guide for the club fungi found in your area.

Recognize the Problem

How could you create a field guide for the club fungi living in your area?

Thinking Critically

What information would you include in a field guide of club fungi?

Possible Materials

collection jars
magnifying glass
microscopes
microscope slides and coverslips
field guide to fungi or club fungi
art supplies

Goals

- **Identify** the common club fungi found in the woods or grassy areas near your home or school.
- **Create** a field guide to help future science students identify these fungi.

Data Source

SCIENCE*Online* Go to the Glencoe Science Web site at **science.glencoe.com** for more information about club fungi.

Safety Precautions

Be certain not to eat any of the fungi you collect. Wash your hands after handling any fungus collected. Do not touch your face during the activity.

Internet Addresses

Explore the Glencoe Science Web site at **science.glencoe.com** to find out more about topics in this activity.

Resource Manager

Chapter Resources Booklet
Activity Worksheet, pp. 7–8
Lab Management and Safety, p. 58

Planning the Model

1. Decide on the locations where you will conduct your search.
2. Select the materials you will need to collect and survey club fungi.
3. Design a data table in your Science Journal to record the fungi you find.
4. Decide on the layout of your field guide. What information about the fungi you will include? What drawings you will use? How will you group the fungi?

Check Model Plans

1. **Describe** your plan to your teacher and ask your teacher how it could be improved.
2. **Present** your ideas for collecting and surveying fungi, and your layout ideas for your field guide to the class. Ask your classmates to suggest improvements in your plan.

Making the Model

1. Search for samples of club fungi. **Record** the organisms you find in your data table. Use a fungus field guide to identify the fungi you discover. Do not pick or touch any fungi that you find unless you have permission.
2. Using your list of organisms, complete your field guide of club fungi as planned.
3. When finished, give your field guide to a classmate to identify a club fungus.

Analyzing and Applying Results

1. **Compare** the number of fungi you found to the total number of organisms listed in the field guide you used to identify the organisms.
2. **Infer** why your field guide would be more helpful to future science students in your school than the fungus field guide you used to identify organisms.
3. **Analyze** the problems you had while collecting and identifying your fungi. Suggest steps you could take to improve your collection and identification methods.
4. **Analyze** the problems you had while creating your field guide. Suggest ways your field guide could be improved.

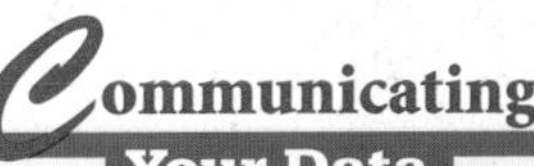

Compare your field guide with the field guides assembled by your classmates. Combine all the information on local club fungi compiled by your class to create a classroom field guide to club fungi.

Planning the Model

Teaching Strategies

- Assign each student a "buddy." Students should be responsible for staying with their buddies at all times.
- Review any poisonous fungi found in your area. Emphasize that students should not touch these organisms.

Making the Model

Expected Outcome Students will design and create a field guide that illustrates and identifies the types of fungi found in local woods and grassy areas.

Analyzing and Applying Results

Student answers will vary depending upon individual research. Accept all reasonable answers.

Assessment

Portfolio Ask students to draw a large colored picture of one of their fungi. Use **PASC**, p. 127.

Offer students who are interested the opportunity to purchase color photocopies of the classroom field guide.

ACTIVITY 233

Content Background

The cacao tree is a perennial that yields several harvests annually. It was introduced to Europe in the sixteenth century after being cultivated in South America. On average the cacao stands 20 feet tall with 12-inch long shiny leaves. The cacao tree's pods contain beans with a high level of fat and are pulverized into a residue we commonly refer to as cocoa. Other uses for the cocoa bean include medication, cosmetics, and soap.

Of the three fungi mentioned, witches' broom is the most destructive. This fungus infects the pods, making them unusable. Brazil was once the top producer of cacao beans but because of this blight has fallen into eighth place in the last five years. Hard hit by this agricultural problem are the 5 to 6 million small farmers who depend heavily on production of the cacao tree for their financial survival. The Agricultural Research Service has developed new ways of combating the effects of fungi, including spraying with copper-based fungicides, breeding trees for resistance, pruning diseased trees, and cleaning up infected pods and branches.

Chocolate SOS

Can a fungus protect cacao trees under attack?

Chocolate is made from seeds (cocoa beans) that grow in the pods of the tropical cacao tree. To grow large crops more efficiently, farmers plant only a couple of the many varieties of cacao. They also use pesticides to protect the trees from destructive insect pests. These modern farming methods have produced huge crops of cocoa beans. But they also have helped destructive fungi sweep through cacao fields. There are fewer healthy cacao trees today than there were several years ago. And unless something stops the fungi that are destroying the trees, there could be a lot less chocolate in the future.

A cacao tree plantation

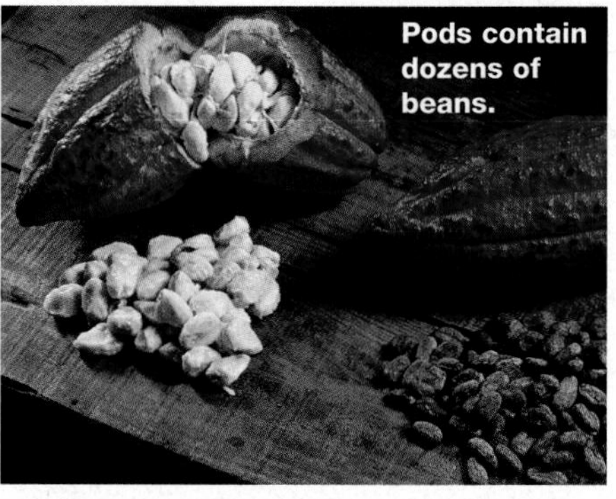
Pods contain dozens of beans.

Losing Beans

Three types of fungi (witches' broom, blackpod rot, and frosty pod rot) are now killing cacao trees. The monoculture (growing one type of crop) of modern fields helps fungi spread quickly. A disease that attacks one plant of a species in a monoculture will rapidly spread to all plants in the monoculture. If a variety of plant species is present, the disease won't spread as quickly or as far.

Resources for Teachers and Students

"Fighting a Fungal Siege on Cacao Farms." November 1999. *Agricultural Research.*

"No Fun Fungi." May 26, 2000. *St. Louis Post-Dispatch.*

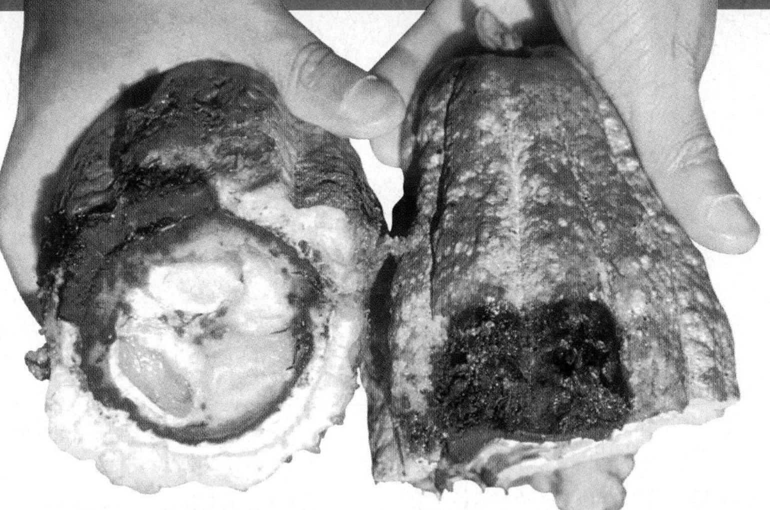
A diseased pod from a cacao tree

Since the blight began in the late 1980s and early 1990s, the world has lost 3 million tons of cocoa beans. Brazil was the top cocoa bean exporter in South America. In 1985, the United States alone bought 430,000 tons of cocoa beans from Brazil. In 1999, the whole Brazilian harvest contained just 130,000 tons, mostly because of the witches' broom fungus. The 2000 harvest was only 80,000 tons—the smallest in 30 years.

A Natural Cure

Farmers were using traditional chemical sprays to fight the fungus, but they were ineffective because in tropical regions, the sprays were washed away by rain. Now agriculture experts are working on a "natural" solution to the problem. They are using several types of "good" fungi to fight the "bad" fungi attacking the trees. When sprayed on infected trees, the good fungi (strains of *Trichoderma*) attack and stop the spread of the bad fungi. Scientists are already testing the fungal spray on trees in Brazil and Peru. The treatments have reduced the destruction of the trees by between 30 percent and 50 percent.

Don't expect your favorite chocolate bars to disappear from stores anytime soon. Right now, world cocoa bean supplies still exceed demand. But if the spread of the epidemic can't be stopped, those chocolate bars could become slightly more expensive and a little harder to find.

A fungus-infested cacao tree

CONNECTIONS Concept Map What are the steps in making chocolate—from harvesting cacao beans to packing chocolate products for sale? Use library and other sources to find out. Then draw a concept map that shows the steps. Compare your concept map with those of your classmates.

SCIENCE *Online*
For more information, visit science.glencoe.com

Discussion

What are farmers currently doing to fight the fungal attacks on the cacaos? Possible answer: Using "good" fungi called *Trichoderma* to stop the spread of the "bad" fungi that is destroying the cacao trees.

Activity

Use the Irish potato famine to illustrate how crop shortages can have devastating effects on a population. Use a team activity model. Have one group research the timetable for the famine. When did it start? Another group should focus on what caused the potatoes to become diseased and ultimately disappear as a resource. Another group should focus on the statistics of the famine. Who was affected? How many people died as a result? Another group should be responsible for an illustration representing the time period. Finally, after each group has presented, lead a discussion on how the two crop shortages are similar and how they differ.

Investigate the Issue

Lead a short discussion of the importance of each step that goes into cacao processing. To spur discussion, ask: **Would we still have easy access to chocolate bars if one group or part of the process was eliminated?**

CONNECTIONS Continue a dialogue asserting the necessity of each person in the process of making and distributing this product. Emphasize the role of the small farmers in the process. Try to convey their potential for loss if the amount of cacao that is diseased is great.

SCIENCE *Online*

Internet Addresses

Explore the Glencoe Science Web site at **science.glencoe.com** to find out more about topics in this feature.

Chapter 8 Study Guide

Reviewing Main Ideas

Preview

Students can answer the questions in their Science Journals. Discuss the answers as you go through the chapter. LS **Linguistic**

Review

Students can write their answers, then compare them with those of other students. LS **Interpersonal**

Reteach

Students can look at the illustrations and describe details that support the main ideas of the chapter. LS **Visual-Spatial**

Answers to Chapter Review

Section 1

2. Algae obtain energy through photosynthesis.
6. Downy mildews can kill plants, sometimes having a great economic impact.

Section 2

4. *Pencillium* does not appear to have a sexual stage, the primary characteristic used to classify fungi.

Chapter  Study Guide

Reviewing Main Ideas

Section 1 Protists

1. Protists are one-celled or many-celled eukaryotic organisms. They can reproduce asexually, resulting in two new cells that are genetically identical. Protists also can reproduce sexually and produce genetically different organisms.
2. The protist kingdom has members that are plantlike, animal-like, and funguslike. *How do plantlike protists like the one shown below obtain food?*

3. Protists are thought to have evolved from a one-celled organism with a nucleus and other cellular structures.
4. Plantlike protists have cell walls and contain chlorophyll.
5. Animal-like protists are separated into groups by how they move.
6. Funguslike protists have characteristics of protists and fungi. *What is the importance of funguslike protists such as the downy mildew shown below?*

Section 2 Fungi

1. Most species of fungi are many-celled. The body of a fungus consists of a mass of threadlike tubes.
2. Fungi are saprophytes or parasites—they feed off other things because they cannot make their own food.
3. Fungi reproduce using spores.
4. The three main groups of fungi are club fungi, sac fungi, and zygote fungi. Fungi that cannot be placed in a specific group are called imperfect fungi. Fungi are placed into one of these groups according to the structures in which they produce spores. *Why are fungi such as the* Penicillium *shown below so hard to classify?*

5. A lichen is an organism that consists of a fungus and a green alga or cyanobacterium.

FOLDABLES Reading & Study Skills — After You Read

Using what you have learned, write about similarities and differences of protists and fungi on the back of your Compare and Contrast Study Fold.

FOLDABLES Reading & Study Skills — After You Read

After students have read the chapter and completed the Foldable described in Before You Read, have them do the activity on the student page.

Dinah Zike

Visualizing Main Ideas

Complete the following concept map on a separate sheet of paper.

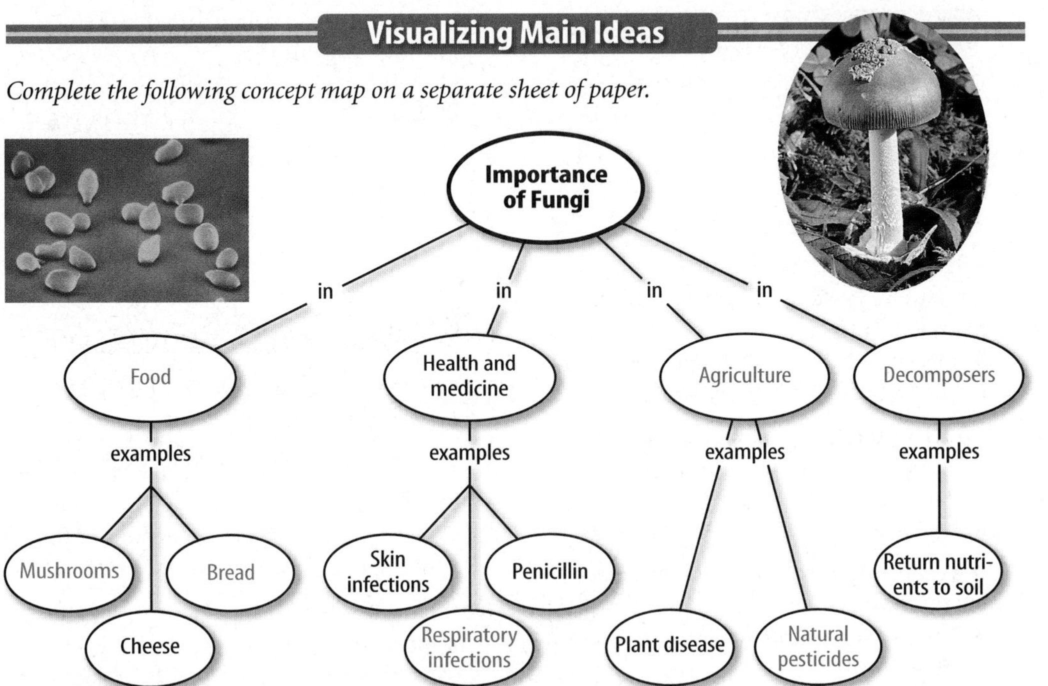

Vocabulary Review

Vocabulary Words

a. algae
b. ascus
c. basidium
d. budding
e. cilia
f. flagellum
g. hyphae
h. lichen
i. mycorrhizae
j. protist
k. protozoan
l. pseudopod
m. saprophyte
n. sporangium
o. spore

Study Tip

Make sure to read over your class notes after each lesson. Reading them will help you better understand what you've learned, as well as prepare you for the next day's lesson.

Using Vocabulary

Write the vocabulary word that matches each of these descriptions.

1. reproductive cell of a fungus
2. organisms that are animal-like, plantlike, or funguslike
3. threadlike structures used for movement
4. plantlike protists
5. organism made up of a fungus and an alga or a cyanobacterium
6. reproductive structure made by sac fungi
7. threadlike tubes that make up the body of a fungus
8. structure used for movement formed by oozing cytoplasm

Chapter 8 Study Guide

See student page.

Vocabulary Review

Using Vocabulary

1. spore
2. protist
3. cilia
4. algae
5. lichen
6. ascus
7. hyphae
8. pseudopod

CHAPTER STUDY GUIDE 237

Chapter 8 Assessment

Checking Concepts

1. D
2. B
3. D
4. D
5. B
6. A
7. D
8. B
9. B
10. C

Thinking Critically

11. no warmth, low humidity, low moisture
12. Accessory pigments help chlorophyll to be more efficient during photosynthesis.
13. Funguslike protists produce spores and take in food from an outside source like fungi. Unlike fungi, the funguslike protists usually move by using pseudopods.
14. When in association with certain mutualistic fungi, some plants are able to take in materials from their environment.
15. Fungi can digest food outside the organism. This mold secretes the enzymes, which help digest the fruit. Then the cells absorb the nutrients.

Chapter 8 Assessment

Checking Concepts

Choose the word or phrase that best answers the question.

1. Which of the following is an alga?
A) *Paramecium* **C)** *Amoeba*
B) lichen **D)** diatom

2. Which type of protist captures food, does not have cell walls, and can move from place to place?
A) algae **C)** fungi
B) protozoans **D)** lichens

3. Which of the following organisms cause red tides when found in large numbers?
A) *Euglena* **C)** *Ulva*
B) diatoms **D)** dinoflagellates

4. Algae are important for which of the following reasons?
A) They are a food source for many aquatic organisms.
B) Parts of algae are used in foods that humans eat.
C) Algae produce oxygen as a result of the process of photosynthesis.
D) all of the above

5. Which of the following moves using cilia?
A) *Amoeba* **C)** *Giardia*
B) *Paramecium* **D)** *Euglena*

6. Where would you most likely find funguslike protists?
A) on decaying logs **C)** on dry surfaces
B) in bright light **D)** on metal surfaces

7. Decomposition is an important role of which organisms?
A) protozoans **C)** plants
B) algae **D)** fungi

8. Where are spores produced in mushrooms?
A) sporangia **C)** ascus
B) basidia **D)** hyphae

9. Which of the following is used as an indicator organism?
A) club fungus **C)** slime mold
B) lichen **D)** imperfect fungus

10. Which of the following is sometimes classified as an imperfect fungus?
A) mushroom **C)** *Penicillium*
B) yeast **D)** lichen

Thinking Critically

11. What kind of environment is needed to prevent fungal growth?

12. Why do algae contain pigments other than just chlorophyll?

13. Compare and contrast the features of fungi and funguslike protists.

14. What advantages do some plants have when they form associations with fungi?

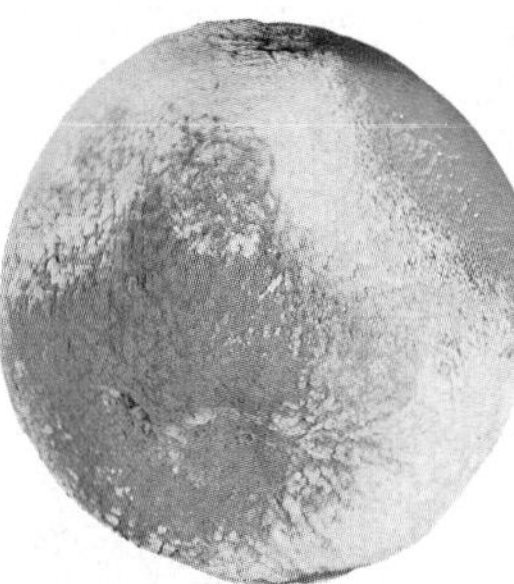

15. Explain the adaptations of fungi that enable them to get food. *How does this mold obtain food?*

Developing Skills

16. Recognizing Cause and Effect A leaf sitting on the floor of the rain forest will decompose in just six weeks. A leaf on the floor of a temperate forest, located in areas that have four seasons, will take up to a year to decompose. Explain how this is possible.

17. Classifying Classify these organisms based on their method of movement: *Euglena,* water molds, *Amoeba,* dinoflagellates, *Paramecium,* slime molds, and *Giardia.*

Chapter Assessment Planner

Portfolio Encourage students to place in their portfolios one or two items of what they consider to be their best work. Examples include:
- Science Journal, p. 214
- Health Integration, p. 219
- Try at Home MiniLAB, p. 227

Performance Additional performance assessments, Performance Task Assessment Lists, and rubrics for evaluating these activities can be found in Glencoe's **Performance Assessment in the Science Classroom.**

18. **Comparing and Contrasting** Make a chart comparing and contrasting the different ways protists and fungi can obtain food.

19. **Making and Using Tables** Complete the following table that compares the different groups of fungi.

Fungi Comparisons

Fungi Group	Structure Where Sexual Spores Are Produced	Examples
Club fungi	Basidium	Mushroom
Sac fungi	Ascus	Truffles
Zygospore fungi	Sporangium	Bread mold
Imperfect fungi	No sexual spores produced	*Penicillium*

20. **Identifying and Manipulating Variables and Controls** You find a new and unusual fungus growing in your refrigerator. Design an experiment to determine what fungus group it belongs to.

Performance Assessment

21. **Poster** Research the different types of fungi found in the area where you live. Determine to which group each fungus belongs. Create a poster to display your results and share them with your class.

22. **Poem** Write a poem about protists or fungi. Include facts about characteristics, types of movement, and ways of feeding.

Technology

Go to the Glencoe Science Web site at **science.glencoe.com** or use the **Glencoe Science CD-ROM** for additional chapter assessment.

Test Practice

Kingdom Protista includes a wide variety of organisms. Some can make their own food and others might get food from their environment. Two groups of protists are shown in the boxes below.

Group A

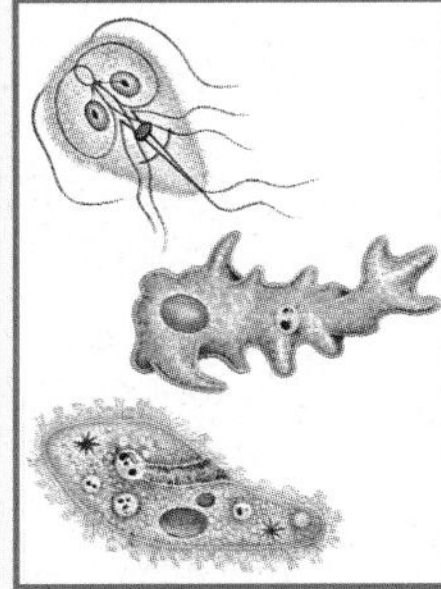

Group B

Study the pictures in the two boxes above and answer the following questions.

1. The protists in Group B are different from the protists in Group A because only the protists in Group B _____.
   A) have chlorophyll
   B) are many-celled
   C) can move
   D) have a nucleus

2. Which of the following organisms would belong in Group A above?
   F) bacteria
   G) kelp
   H) grass
   J) fish

3. Which of the following is NOT characteristic of Group A?
   A) cell membrane
   B) contain chlorophyll
   C) live in a watery environment
   D) one-celled

Chapter 8 Assessment

Test Practice

The Test-Taking Tip was written by The Princeton Review, the nation's leader in test preparation.

1. C
2. G
3. D

Developing Skills

16. Warm, moist environments such as those found in the rain forest are ideal for the growth of fungi. Therefore, fungi decompose dead organic materials more rapidly in rain forests than in cooler, drier temperate forests.
17. flagella—*Euglena*, water molds, dinoflagellates, *Giardia*; pseudopods—*Amoeba*, slime molds; cilia—*Paramecium*.
18. Check charts for accuracy.
19. See student page.
20. Design will vary. Designs should include comparing the fungus with characteristics of different fungi and observing its sexual reproduction.

Performance Assessment

21. Posters will vary. Most will have photos or drawings of various mushrooms or slime molds. Posters should contain information about the groups of fungi. Use **PASC**, p. 145.
22. Poems will vary but should indicate characteristics and types of organisms studied in this chapter. Use PASC, p. 157.

Assessment Resources

Reproducible Masters

Chapter Resources Booklet
Chapter Review, pp. 33–34
Chapter Tests, pp. 35–38
Assessment Transparency Activity, p. 45

Glencoe Science Web site
Interactive Tutor
Chapter Quizzes

Glencoe Technology
Assessment Transparency
Interactive CD-ROM Chapter Quizzes
ExamView Pro Test Bank
Vocabulary PuzzleMaker Software
MindJogger Videoquiz

Section/Objectives	Standards		Activities/Features
	National	State/Local	
Chapter Opener	See p. 5T for a Key to Standards.		**Explore Activity:** Determine how you use plants, p. 241 **Before You Read,** p. 241
Section 1 An Overview of Plants 2 sessions 1 block 1. **Identify** characteristics common to all plants. 2. **Explain** which plant adaptations make it possible for plants to survive on land. 3. **Compare and contrast** vascular and nonvascular plants.	National Content Standards: UCP1, C1, C5		**Chemistry Integration,** p. 244 **Visualizing Plant Classification,** p. 246
Section 2 Seedless Plants 2 sessions 1 block 1. **Distinguish** between characteristics of seedless nonvascular plants and seedless vascular plants. 2. **Identify** the importance of some nonvascular and vascular plants.	National Content Standards: UCP5, A1, C1, C5, F4		**MiniLAB:** Measuring Water Absorption by a Moss, p. 249 **Science Online,** p. 250 **Problem-Solving Activity:** What is the value of rain forests?, p. 250
Section 3 Seed Plants 3 sessions 1.5 blocks 1. **Identify** the characteristics of seed plants. 2. **Explain** the structures and functions of roots, stems, and leaves. 3. **Describe** the main characteristics and importance of gymnosperms and angiosperms. 4. **Compare** similarities and differences between monocots and dicots.	National Content Standards: UCP5, A1, C1, C5, E2, F5, G2		**MiniLAB:** Observing Water Moving in a Plant, p. 255 **Health Integration,** p. 257 **Science Online,** p. 261 **Activity:** Identifying Conifers, p. 263 **Activity:** Plants as Medicine, pp. 264–265 **Oops! Accidents in Science:** A Loopy Idea Inspires "Fasten-ating" Invention, pp. 266–267

NATIONAL GEOGRAPHIC

Teacher's Corner

PRODUCTS AVAILABLE FROM GLENCOE
To order call 1-800-334-7344:
CD-ROMs
NGS PictureShow: Plants: What It Means to Be Green
Curriculum Kit
GeoKit: Plants
Transparency Sets
NGS PicturePack: Plants: What It Means to Be Green
VideoDisc
STV: Plants

PRODUCTS AVAILABLE FROM NATIONAL GEOGRAPHIC SOCIETY
To order call 1-800-368-2728:
Videos
Plant Classification

Activity Materials	Reproducible Resources	Section Assessment	Technology
Explore Activity: old magazines, scissors	**Chapter Resources Booklet** Foldables Worksheet, p. 13 Directed Reading Overview, p. 15 Note-taking Worksheets, pp. 29–31	GLENCOE'S ASSESSMENT ADVANTAGE	
Need materials? Contact Science Kit at 1-800-828-7777 or www.sciencekit.com on the Internet.	**Chapter Resources Booklet** Transparency Activity, p. 40 Enrichment, p. 26 Reinforcement, p. 23 Directed Reading, p. 16 **Cultural Diversity,** p. 19 **Life Science Critical Thinking/ Problem Solving,** p. 9 **Earth Science Critical Thinking/ Problem Solving,** p. 17 **Performance Assessment in the Science Classroom,** p. 55	**Portfolio** Activity, p. 245 **Performance** Skill Builder Activities, p. 247 **Content** Section Assessment, p. 247	Section Focus Transparency Interactive CD-ROM Guided Reading Audio Program
MiniLAB: *sphagnum* moss, cheesecloth, spring scales, graduated cylinder, water, container for water	**Chapter Resources Booklet** Transparency Activity, p. 41 MiniLAB, p. 3 Enrichment, p. 27 Reinforcement, p. 24 Directed Reading, p. 17 **Home and Community Involvement,** p. 42 **Math Skill Activities,** p. 5	**Portfolio** Make a Model, p. 251 **Performance** MiniLAB, p. 249 Skill Builder Activities, p. 253 **Content** Section Assessment, p. 253	Section Focus Transparency Interactive CD-ROM Guided Reading Audio Program
MiniLAB: clear container, water, metric ruler, red food coloring, green onion, hand lens **Activity:** short branches of pine, cedar, spruce, Douglas fir, hemlock, fir, redwood, arborvitae, juniper **Activity:** no materials needed	**Chapter Resources Booklet** Transparency Activity, p. 42 MiniLAB, p. 4 Enrichment, p. 28 Reinforcement, p. 25 Directed Reading, pp. 17, 18 Activity Worksheets, pp. 5–6, 7–8 Transparency Activity, pp. 43–44 Lab Activities, pp. 9–10, 11–12 **Performance Assessment in the Science Classroom,** p. 61 **Lab Management and Safety in the Science Classroom,** p. 61	**Portfolio** Curriculum Connection, p. 257 **Performance** MiniLAB, p. 255 Skill Builder Activities, p. 262 **Content** Section Assessment, p. 262	Section Focus Transparency Teaching Transparency Interactive CD-ROM Guided Reading Audio Program

End of Chapter Assessment

GLENCOE'S ASSESSMENT ADVANTAGE

Blackline Masters	Technology	Professional Series
Chapter Resources Booklet Chapter Review, pp. 33–34 Chapter Tests, pp. 35–38 **Standardized Test Practice by The Princeton Review,** pp. 43–46	MindJogger Videoquiz Interactive CD-ROM Vocabulary PuzzleMakers ExamView Pro Test Bank Interactive Lesson Planner Interactive Teacher Edition	Performance Assessment in the Science Classroom (PASC)

Transparencies

Section Focus

Section 1 Section Focus Transparency **A Lot Can Happen in 4,000 Years**

Bristlecone pines live a very long time. The oldest one is thought to be over 4,600 years old. From the time the pyramids at Giza were built through this very moment, it has lived in a quiet spot in eastern California. Bristlecones are usually found at high altitudes where it is very dry.

1. Looking at the picture, describe the bristlecone pine's environment.
2. What might some advantages be to the bristlecone's habitat? What might be disadvantages?

L2

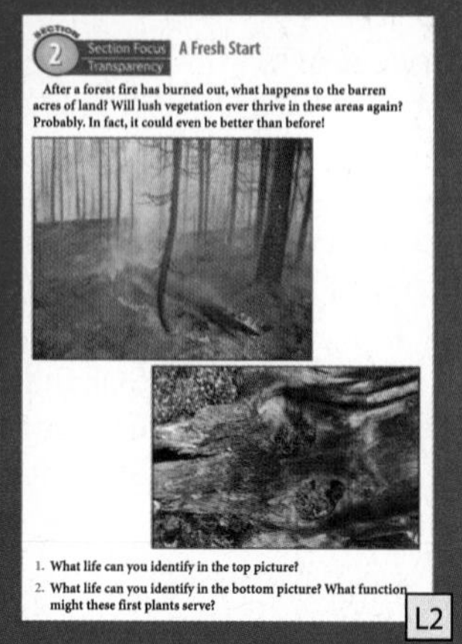
Section 2 Section Focus Transparency **A Fresh Start**

After a forest fire has burned out, what happens to the barren acres of land? Will lush vegetation ever thrive in these areas again? Probably. In fact, it could even be better than before!

1. What life can you identify in the top picture?
2. What life can you identify in the bottom picture? What function might these first plants serve?

L2

Section 3 Section Focus Transparency **Rooted in Nature**

Bonsai is an ancient method of growing trees or shrubs in small containers. The plants are kept small by pruning the branches and roots. Because some types of plants used for bonsai can live for more than 100 years, they are passed from generation to generation.

1. What are some advantages to having bonsai plants? What might some disadvantages be?
2. What qualities do you think would be important in practicing bonsai?

L2

This is a representation of key blackline masters available in the Teacher Classroom Resources. See Resource Manager boxes within the chapter for additional information.

Assessment

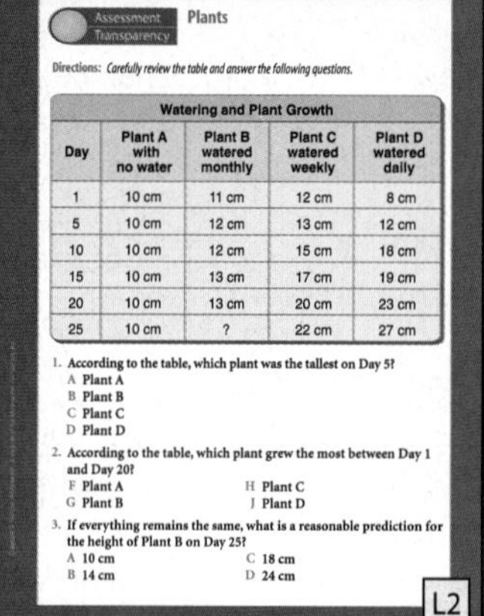
Assessment Transparency **Plants**

Directions: Carefully review the table and answer the following questions.

Watering and Plant Growth				
Day	Plant A with no water	Plant B watered monthly	Plant C watered weekly	Plant D watered daily
1	10 cm	11 cm	12 cm	8 cm
5	10 cm	12 cm	13 cm	12 cm
10	10 cm	12 cm	15 cm	18 cm
15	10 cm	13 cm	17 cm	19 cm
20	10 cm	13 cm	20 cm	23 cm
25	10 cm	?	22 cm	27 cm

1. According to the table, which plant was the tallest on Day 5?
   A Plant A
   B Plant B
   C Plant C
   D Plant D
2. According to the table, which plant grew the most between Day 1 and Day 20?
   F Plant A
   G Plant B
   H Plant C
   J Plant D
3. If everything remains the same, what is a reasonable prediction for the height of Plant B on Day 25?
   A 10 cm
   B 14 cm
   C 18 cm
   D 24 cm

L2

Teaching

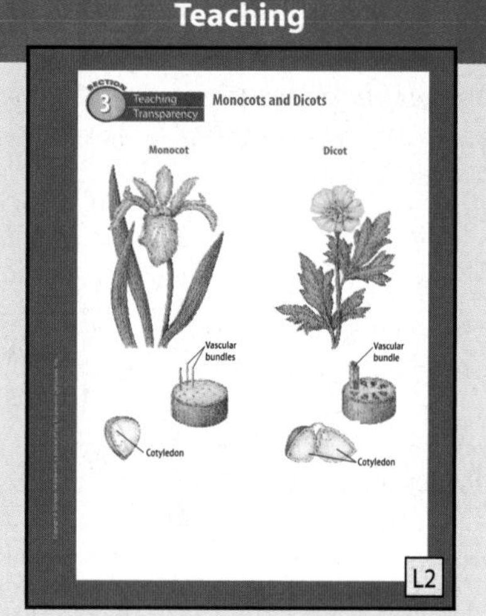
Section 3 Teaching Transparency **Monocots and Dicots**

L2

Key to Teaching Strategies

The following designations will help you decide which activities are appropriate for your students.

- **L1** Level 1 activities should be appropriate for students with learning difficulties.
- **L2** Level 2 activities should be within the ability range of all students.
- **L3** Level 3 activities are designed for above-average students.
- **ELL** ELL activities should be within the ability range of English Language Learners.
- **COOP LEARN** Cooperative Learning activities are designed for small group work.
- **LS** Multiple Learning Styles logos, as described on page 22T, are used throughout to indicate strategies that address different learning styles.
- **P** These strategies represent student products that can be placed into a best-work portfolio.

Hands-on Activities

Activity Worksheets

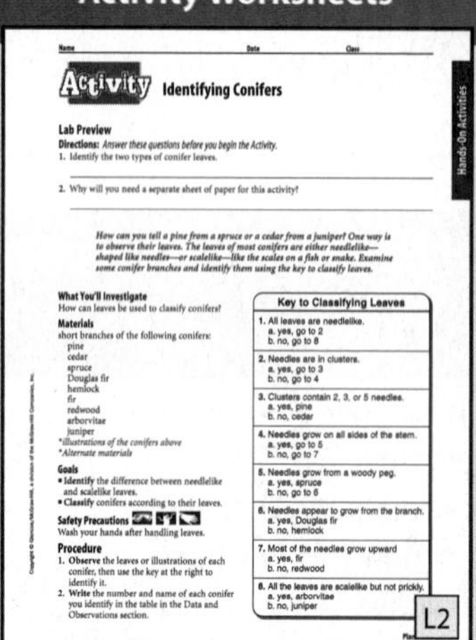
Name Date Class

Activity Identifying Conifers

Lab Preview

Directions: *Answer these questions before you begin the Activity.*

1. Identify the two types of conifer leaves.
2. Why will you need a separate sheet of paper for this activity?

How can you tell a pine from a spruce or a cedar from a juniper? One way is to observe their leaves. The leaves of most conifers are either needlelike—shaped like needles—or scalelike—like the scales on a fish or snake. Examine some conifer branches and identify them using the key to classify leaves.

What You'll Investigate
How can leaves be used to classify conifers?

Materials
short branches of the following conifers:
pine
cedar
spruce
Douglas fir
hemlock
fir
redwood
arborvitae
juniper
**illustrations of the conifers above*
**Alternate materials*

Goals
- **Identify** the difference between needlelike and scalelike leaves.
- **Classify** conifers according to their leaves.

Safety Precautions
Wash your hands after handling leaves.

Procedure
1. **Observe** the leaves or illustrations of each conifer, then use the key at the right to identify it.
2. **Write** the number and name of each conifer you identify in the table in the Data and Observations section.

Key to Classifying Leaves

1. All leaves are needlelike.
   a. yes, go to 2
   b. no, go to 8
2. Needles are in clusters.
   a. yes, go to 3
   b. no, go to 4
3. Clusters contain 2, 3, or 5 needles.
   a. yes, pine
   b. no, cedar
4. Needles grow on all sides of the stem.
   a. yes, go to 5
   b. no, go to 7
5. Needles grow from a woody peg.
   a. yes, spruce
   b. no, go to 6
6. Needles appear to grow from the branch.
   a. yes, Douglas fir
   b. no, hemlock
7. Most of the needles grow upward
   a. yes, fir
   b. no, redwood
8. All the leaves are scalelike but not prickly.
   a. yes, arborvitae
   b. no, juniper

Hands-On Activities

L2

Laboratory Activities

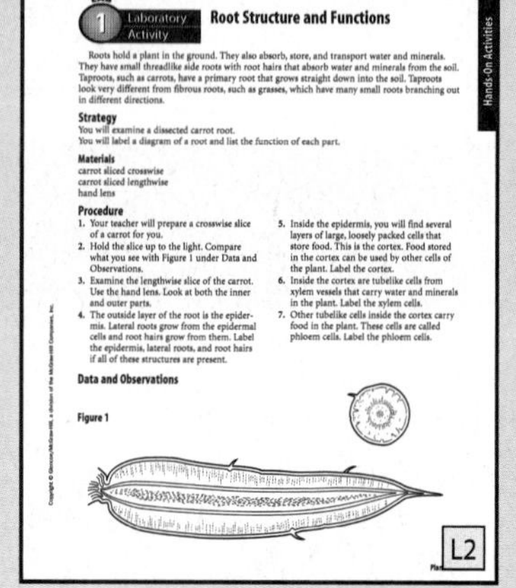
Name Date Class

Lab 1 Laboratory Activity **Root Structure and Functions**

Roots hold a plant in the ground. They also absorb, store, and transport water and minerals. They have small threadlike side roots with root hairs that absorb water and minerals from the soil. Taproots, such as carrots, have a primary root that grows straight down into the soil. Taproots look very different from fibrous roots, such as grasses, which have many small roots branching out in different directions.

Strategy
You will examine a dissected carrot root.
You will label a diagram of a root and list the function of each part.

Materials
carrot sliced crosswise
carrot sliced lengthwise
hand lens

Procedure
1. Your teacher will prepare a crosswise slice of a carrot for you.
2. Hold the slice up to the light. Compare what you see with Figure 1 under Data and Observations.
3. Examine the lengthwise slice of the carrot. Use the hand lens. Look at both the inner and outer parts.
4. The outside layer of the root is the epidermis. Lateral roots grow from the epidermal cells and root hairs grow from them. Label the epidermis, lateral roots, and root hairs if all of these structures are present.
5. Inside the epidermis, you will find several layers of large, loosely packed cells that store food. This is the cortex. Food stored in the cortex can be used by other cells of the plant. Label the cortex.
6. Inside the cortex are tubelike cells from xylem vessels that carry water and minerals in the plant. Label the xylem cells.
7. Other tubelike cells inside the cortex carry food in the plant. These cells are called phloem cells. Label the phloem cells.

Data and Observations

Figure 1

Hands-On Activities

L2

Meeting Different Ability Levels

Content Outline

Note-taking Worksheet — Plants

L2

Reinforcement

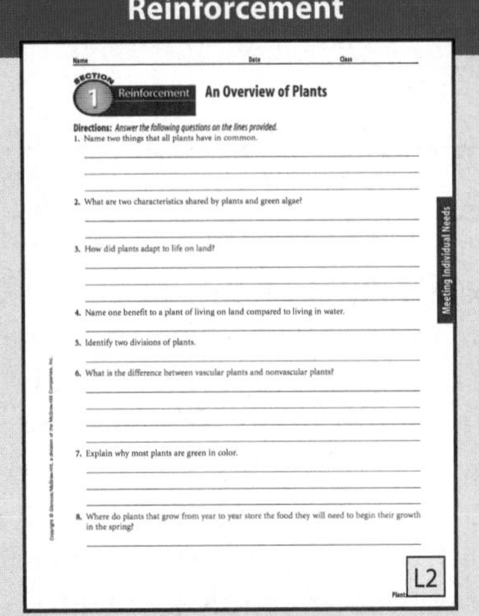

Section 1 Reinforcement — An Overview of Plants

L2

Directed Reading

Directed Reading for Content Mastery — Overview: Plants

L1

Enrichment

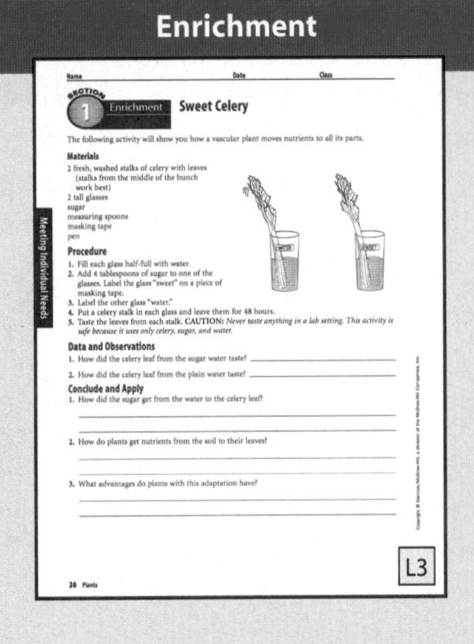

Section 1 Enrichment — Sweet Celery

L3

Spanish Directed Reading

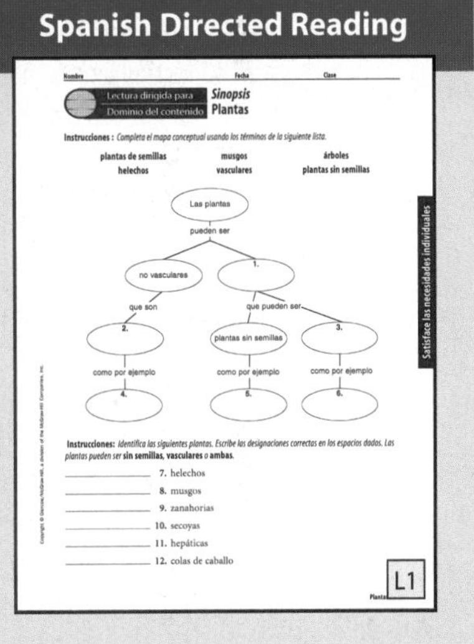

Lectura dirigida para Dominio del contenido — Sinopsis: Plantas

L1

Assessment

Chapter Tests

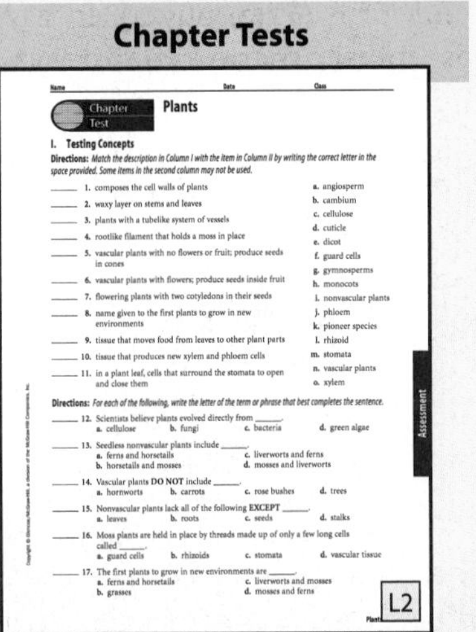

Chapter Test — Plants

L2

Test Practice Workbook

L2

Chapter Review

Chapter Review — Plants

L2

Science Content Background

SECTION 1

An Overview of Plants

Origin and Evolution of Plants

Plants probably share an ancestor with multicellular Chlorophyta, the green algae. Common characteristics of plants and green algae include pigments such as chlorophyll a and b and carotenoids, cell walls that consist primarily of cellulose, starch as the primary food-storage product, and similar cell division. Some plants, including mosses, liverworts, and ferns, have free-swimming sperm and require water for fertilization—another feature they have in common with green algae.

Fun Fact

Luminous mosses glow with a greenish light. These mosses are found in caves and have cells shaped like tiny lenses that focus small amounts of light on the chloroplast.

Adaptations to Land

Fibers are long, slender cells that are found in the vascular tissue of some plants. They usually contain an organic substance called lignin that makes the walls tough and hard. Fibers add extra support to many terrestrial plants. People weave the fibers of some plants to make products such as rope and cloth.

Classification of Plants

Classification of plants traditionally has been based on morphological characteristics such as the number and arrangement of leaves and the structure of flowers and fruit. Recently, genetic studies have been used to make minor changes in the classification of some plants. However, derived characteristics such as vascular tissue and seed formation and similar, easily observable characteristics are reliable features for classification.

For many years plants have been separated into divisions, but in 1993 the International Botanical Congress made the term *phylum* an acceptable alternative. You may wish to introduce the alternate term to your students.

SECTION 2

Seedless Plants

Less Familiar Plants

Liverworts and hornworts are leafy with creeping gametophyte forms. Mosses have distinct leaflike and stemlike structures, but because they do not contain vascular tissue, they are not homologous to the leaves and stems of vascular plants. Some liverworts produce structures called gemma cups on their surfaces. Groups of cells in these structures are washed out of the cup when it rains. These cells can grow into new liverwort plants.

Seedless vascular plants include whisk ferns (Psilophyta), club mosses (Lycopoda), horsetails (Sphenophyta), and ferns (Pterophyta). In each of these divisions, motile sperm require water to swim to the egg.

Pat Watson/The Image Works

SECTION 3

Seed Plants

Origins

Seed plants appeared suddenly about 65 million years ago at the beginning of the Cretaceous Period. These plants dominated the land. They developed sperm-containing pollen grains that could be transported from plant to plant without water. The development of an embryo inside a protective seed coat allowed seeds to survive harsh conditions for long periods. About 200,000 of the more than 260,000 species of plants in existence today are seed plants.

John Gerlach/Tom Stack & Associates

Vascular Tissue

The first vascular plants appeared no later than the early Silurian Period, some 430 million years ago. Early vascular plants had stems formed as a result of primary growth—growth from plant tips. Stems had vascular cylinders with conducting functions, as they do in modern vascular plants. Secondary growth, found in conifers and some dicots, is an important early development. It arises by mitotic divisions of cambium tissues and increases the plant's girth.

Fun Fact

An aphid drinks sap from plants by piercing the plant's phloem with its hollow mouthpart.

Xylem tissue is made of tracheids and vessel elements that carry water and dissolved minerals. Tracheids are found in all plants with vascular tissue, but vessel elements are limited almost exclusively to angiosperms. Both are long, tubelike cells that have thick cell walls. Small openings called pits allow water to seep through the cell walls from tracheid to tracheid. Vessels lack transverse end walls and are continuous pipelines through which water can flow.

Unlike xylem tissue, phloem tissue is living. It is composed mostly of sieve-tube elements and companion cells. Sieve-tube elements are cells that carry the products of photosynthesis throughout the plant. Their cell walls are thinner than those of cells found in xylem. Cytoplasm extends from one sieve-tube element to the next through structures called sieve plates. Since mature sieve-tube cells have no nuclei, companion cells help with their metabolism.

For additional content background on this topic, go to the Glencoe Science Web site at science.glencoe.com.

Plants

Chapter Vocabulary

cuticle, p. 244
cellulose, p. 244
vascular plant, p. 247
nonvascular plant, p. 247
rhizoid, p. 248
pioneer species, p. 249
stomata, p. 255
guard cell, p. 255
xylem, p. 257
phloem, p. 257
cambium, p. 257
gymnosperm, p. 258
angiosperm, p. 259
monocot, p. 260
dicot, p. 260

What do you think?

Science Journal Indian pipe is the common name of the plant in this picture. Unlike most plants, Indian pipe plants are not green.

CHAPTER 9

Plants

Go outside and look around. Where do you see plants? Plants cover almost every available surface in a tropical rain forest but only some areas of a desert. Plants are found nearly everywhere on Earth.

Take a close look at a plant. When you look at an animal, you expect to see eyes, a mouth, and maybe even legs. What do you expect to see when you look at a plant? Do all plants have leaves, roots, and flowers?

In this chapter, you'll learn what characteristics plants have and how they are classified. You'll also learn why plants are important.

What do you think?

Science Journal Look at the picture below with a classmate. Discuss what you think this might be or what is happening. Here's a hint: *Most of its relatives are green.* Write your answer or your best guess in your Science Journal.

240

Theme Connection

Stability and Change This chapter emphasizes plant adaptations that allow these organisms to adapt, survive, and reproduce in various environments.

Plants are just about everywhere—in parks and gardens, by streams, on rocks, in houses, and even on dinner plates. Do you use plants for things other than food? In the following activity, find out how plants are used. Then, in the pages that follow, learn about plant life.

Determine how you use plants

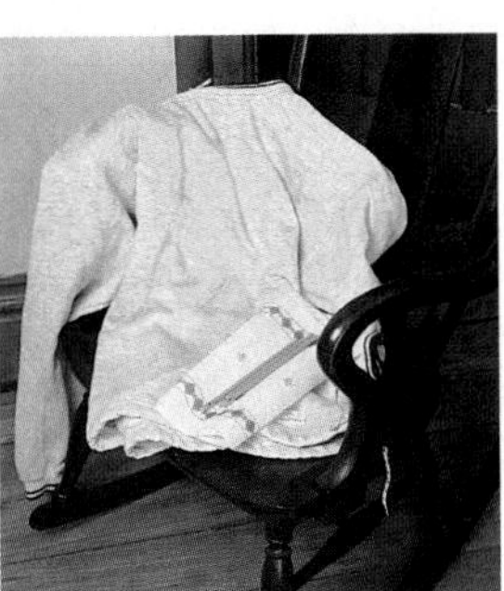

1. Brainstorm with two other classmates and make a list of everything that you use in a day that comes from plants.
2. Compare your list with those of other groups in your class.
3. Search through old magazines for images of the items on your list.
4. As a class, build a bulletin board of the magazine images.

Observe

In your Science Journal, list things that were made from plants 100 years or more ago but today are made from plastics, steel, or some other material.

Before You Read

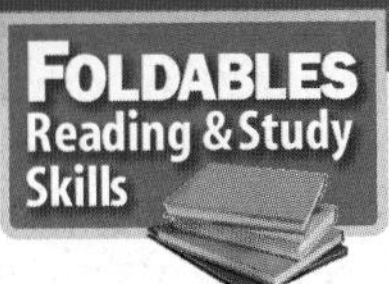

Making a Know-Want-Learn Study Fold It would be helpful to identify what you already know and what you want to know. Make the following Foldable to help you focus on reading about plants.

1. Place a sheet of paper in front of you so the long side is at the top. Fold the paper in half from top to bottom.
2. Fold both sides in to divide the paper into thirds. Unfold the paper so three columns show.
3. Through the top thickness of paper, cut along each of the fold lines to the top fold, forming three tabs.
4. Draw and label *Know, Want,* and *Learned* across the front of the paper as shown.
5. Before you read the chapter, write what you know under the left tab. Under the middle tab, write what you want to know.
6. As you read the chapter, write what you learn under the right tab.

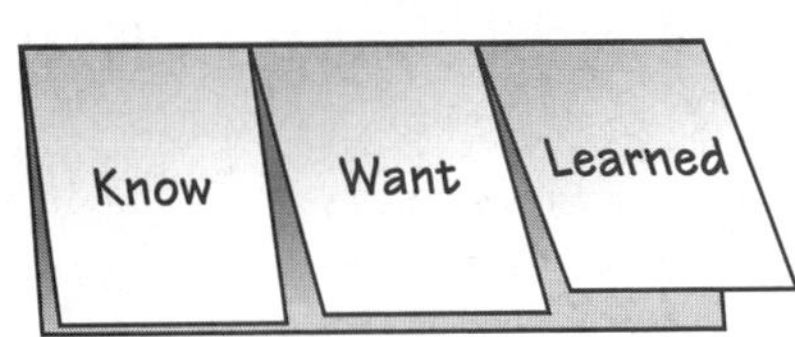

Before You Read

FOLDABLES Reading & Study Skills

Dinah Zike Study Fold

Purpose This Foldable will provide students an opportunity to review what they know about plants and make them question what they would like to know. The Foldable can be used as an assessment tool at the end of the chapter to determine what students have learned.

For additional help, see Foldables Worksheet, p. 13 in **Chapter Resources Booklet,** or go to the Glencoe Science Web site at **science.glencoe.com.** See After You Read in the Study Guide at the end of this chapter.

Explore Activity

Purpose Use the Explore Activity to introduce students to the many uses of plants. L2 COOP LEARN IS **Interpersonal**

Preparation Provide books, magazines, and other resources from which students can get ideas.

Teaching Strategy Offer suggestions of additional items from plants to students who need help.

Observe

Examples include building materials, clothing fibers, dyes, paper, resins, paints, and inks.

Assessment

Process Show students a picture of a desert succulent with plump water-filled leaves. Have them infer how desert animals might use this plant. The plant could provide water to animals in a dry environment. Use **Performance Assessment in the Science Classroom,** p. 89.

SECTION

An Overview of Plants

1 Motivate

Bellringer Transparency

Display the Section Focus Transparency for Section 1. Use the accompanying Transparency Activity Master. L2 ELL

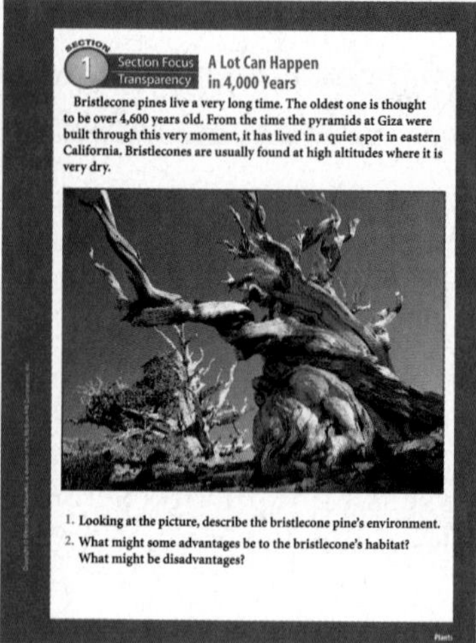

SECTION 1 Section Focus Transparency **A Lot Can Happen in 4,000 Years**

Bristlecone pines live a very long time. The oldest one is thought to be over 4,600 years old. From the time the pyramids at Giza were built through this very moment, it has lived in a quiet spot in eastern California. Bristlecones are usually found at high altitudes where it is very dry.

1. **Looking at the picture, describe the bristlecone pine's environment.**
2. **What might some advantages be to the bristlecone's habitat? What might be disadvantages?**

Plants

Tie to Prior Knowledge

Ask students to visualize a common plant and list its major parts. Students should know that most plants have the following parts in common: roots, stems, leaves, and often flowers and fruits. Display a common flowering plant, such as a geranium, and have students point out the parts they know.

SECTION 1

An Overview of Plants

As You Read

***What* You'll Learn**

- **Identify** characteristics common to all plants.
- **Explain** which plant adaptations make it possible for plants to survive on land.
- **Compare and contrast** vascular and nonvascular plants.

Vocabulary

cuticle
cellulose
vascular plant
nonvascular plant

***Why* It's Important**

Plants produce food and oxygen used by most organisms on Earth.

What is a plant?

What is the most common sight you see when you walk along nature trails in parks like the one shown in **Figure 1?** Maybe you've taken off your shoes and walked barefoot on soft, cool grass. Perhaps you've climbed a tree to see what things look like from high in its branches. In each instance, plants surrounded you.

If you named all the plants that you know, you probably would include trees, flowers, vegetables, fruits, and field crops like wheat, rice, or corn. Between 260,000 and 300,000 plant species have been discovered and identified. Scientists think more are still to be found, mainly in tropical rain forests. Some of these plants are important food sources to humans and other consumers. Without plants, most life on Earth as we know it would not be possible.

Plant Characteristics Plants range in size from microscopic water ferns to giant sequoia trees that are sometimes more than 100 m in height. Most have roots or rootlike structures that hold them in the ground or onto some other object like a rock or another plant. Plants are adapted to nearly every environment on Earth. Some grow in frigid, ice-bound polar regions and others grow in hot, dry deserts. All plants need water, but some plants cannot live unless they are submerged in either freshwater or salt water.

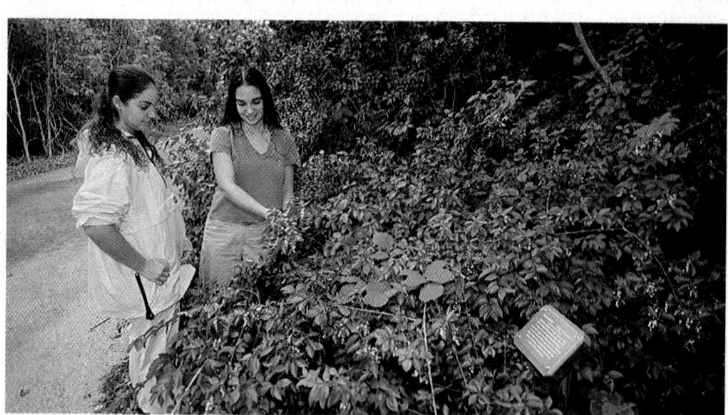

Figure 1
All plants are many-celled and nearly all contain chlorophyll. Grasses, trees, shrubs, mosses, and ferns are all plants.

Section Assessment Planner

PORTFOLIO
Activity, p. 245

PERFORMANCE ASSESSMENT
Skill Builder Activities, p. 247
See page 270 for more options.

CONTENT ASSESSMENT
Section, p. 247
Challenge, p. 247
Chapter, pp. 270–271

Plant Cells Like other living things, plants are made of cells. A plant cell has a cell membrane, a nucleus, and other cellular structures. In addition, plant cells have cell walls that make them different from animal cells. Cell walls provide structure and protection for plant cells.

Many plant cells contain the green pigment chlorophyll (KLOR uh fihl) so most plants are green. Plants need chlorophyll to make food using a process called photosynthesis. Chlorophyll is found in a cell structure called a chloroplast. Plant cells from green parts of the plant usually contain many chloroplasts.

Most plant cells have a large, membrane-bound structure called the central vacuole that takes up most of the space inside of the cell. This structure plays an important role in regulating the water content of the cell. Many substances are stored in the vacuole such as the pigments that make some flowers red, blue, or purple.

Origin and Evolution of Plants

Have plants always existed on land? The first plants that lived on land probably could survive only in damp areas. Their ancestors were probably ancient green algae that lived in the sea. Green algae are one-celled or many-celled organisms that use photosynthesis to make food. Today, plants and green algae have the same types of chlorophyll and carotenoids (kuh RAH tun oydz) in their cells. Carotenoids are red, yellow, or orange pigments that also are used for photosynthesis. This has led scientists to think that plants and green algae have a common ancestor.

Reading Check *How are plants and green algae alike?*

Fossil Record The fossil record for plants is not like that for animals. Most animals have bones or other hard parts that can fossilize. Plants usually decay before they become fossilized. But, the oldest fossil plants are about 420 million years old. **Figure 2** shows *Cooksonia,* a fossil of one of these plants. Other fossils of early plants are similar to the ancient green algae. Scientists hypothesize that some of these kinds of plants evolved into the plants that exist today.

Cone-bearing plants, such as pines, probably evolved from a group of plants that grew about 350 million years ago. Fossils of these plants have been dated to about 300 million years ago. It is estimated that flowering plants did not exist until about 120 million years ago. However, the exact origin of flowering plants is not known.

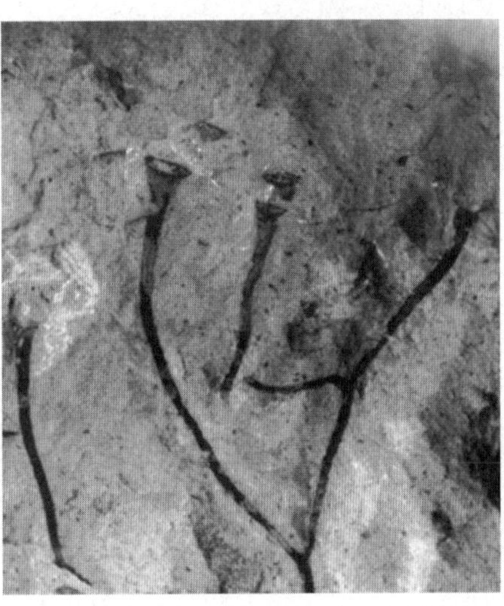

Figure 2
This is a fossil of a plant named *Cooksonia.* These plants grew about 420 million years ago and were about 2.5 cm tall.

2 Teach

What is a plant?

Visual Learning

Figure 1 Which features of the organisms in the photo suggest they are plants? They are green, grow from soil, and have leaves and stems.

IDENTIFYING Misconceptions

Students may think that all plants produce seeds in flowers. Explain that some plants are seedless and do not make seeds, others produce seeds in cones.

Origin and Evolution of Plants

Reading Check

Answer Both have similar chlorophyll and carotenoids.

Inclusion Strategies

Learning Disabled and Visually Impaired If possible, provide petrified wood or fossil casts of plants. Ask students what clues they have that these fossils were once living plants. The fossils may be shaped like plant stems or leaves. LS **Kinesthetic**

Resource Manager

Chapter Resources Booklet
Note-taking Worksheets, pp. 29–31
Transparency Activity, p. 40
Cultural Diversity, p. 19

Life on Land

Long fibers of glucose in cellulose increase structural support.

Adaptations to Land

Reading Check

Answer to slow the loss of water

Quick Demo

Use a spray mister to mist water onto a plant leaf that has a thick cuticle. Allow students to observe how the water beads up and runs off.

Activity

Set up stations around the class that contain different plant parts. Have students write the name of each plant part and important information about each as they move from one station to another. L1

LS **Visual-Spatial**

Resource Manager

Chapter Resources Booklet
Enrichment, p. 26

Life Science Critical Thinking/Problem Solving, p. 9

Earth Science Critical Thinking/Problem Solving, p. 17

Chemistry INTEGRATION

Plant cell walls are made mostly of cellulose, which is made of long chains of glucose molecules ($C_6H_{12}O_6$). More than half of the carbon in plants is found in cellulose. Raw cotton is more than 90 percent cellulose. What physical property of cellulose makes it ideal for helping plants survive on land?

Life on Land

Life on land has some advantages for plants. More sunlight and carbon dioxide—needed for photosynthesis—are available on land than in water. During photosynthesis, plants give off oxygen. Long ago, as more and more plants adapted to life on land, the amount of oxygen in Earth's atmosphere increased. This paved the way for organisms that depend on oxygen.

Adaptations to Land

What is life like for green algae, shown in **Figure 3,** as they float in a shallow pool? The water in the pool surrounds and supports them as the algae make their own food through the process of photosynthesis. Because materials can enter and leave through their cell membranes and cell walls, the algae cells have everything they need to survive as long as they have water.

Now, imagine a summer drought. The pool begins to dry up. Soon, the algae are on damp mud and are no longer supported by water. As long as the soil stays damp, materials can move in and out through the algae's cell membranes and cell walls. As the soil becomes drier and drier, the algae will lose water too because water moves through their cell membranes and cell walls from where there is more water to where there is less water. Without enough water in their environment, the algae will die.

Figure 3
The alga *Spirogyra,* like all algae, must have water to survive. If the pool where it lives dries up, it will die.

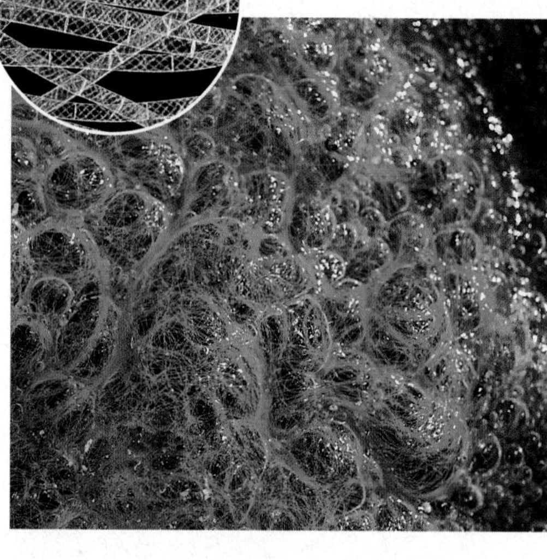

Protection and Support Water is important for plants. What adaptations would help a plant conserve water on land? Covering the stems, leaves, and flowers of many plants is a **cuticle** (KYEW tih kul)—a waxy, protective layer secreted by cells onto the surface of the plant. The cuticle slows the loss of water. The cuticle and other adaptations shown in **Figure 4** enable plants to survive on land.

What is the function of a plant's cuticle?

Supporting itself is another problem for a plant on land. Like all cells, plant cells have cell membranes, but they also have rigid cell walls outside the membrane. Cell walls contain **cellulose** (SEL yuh lohs), which is a chemical compound that plants can make out of sugar. Long chains of cellulose molecules form tangled fibers in plant cell walls. These fibers provide structure and support.

Teacher FYI

Almost all of the oxygen in our atmosphere has been produced by the release of oxygen during photosynthesis. Plants also absorb carbon dioxide from the atmosphere during photosynthesis. Thus, the destruction of vast areas of tropical forest may negatively impact the balance of these gases in the atmosphere.

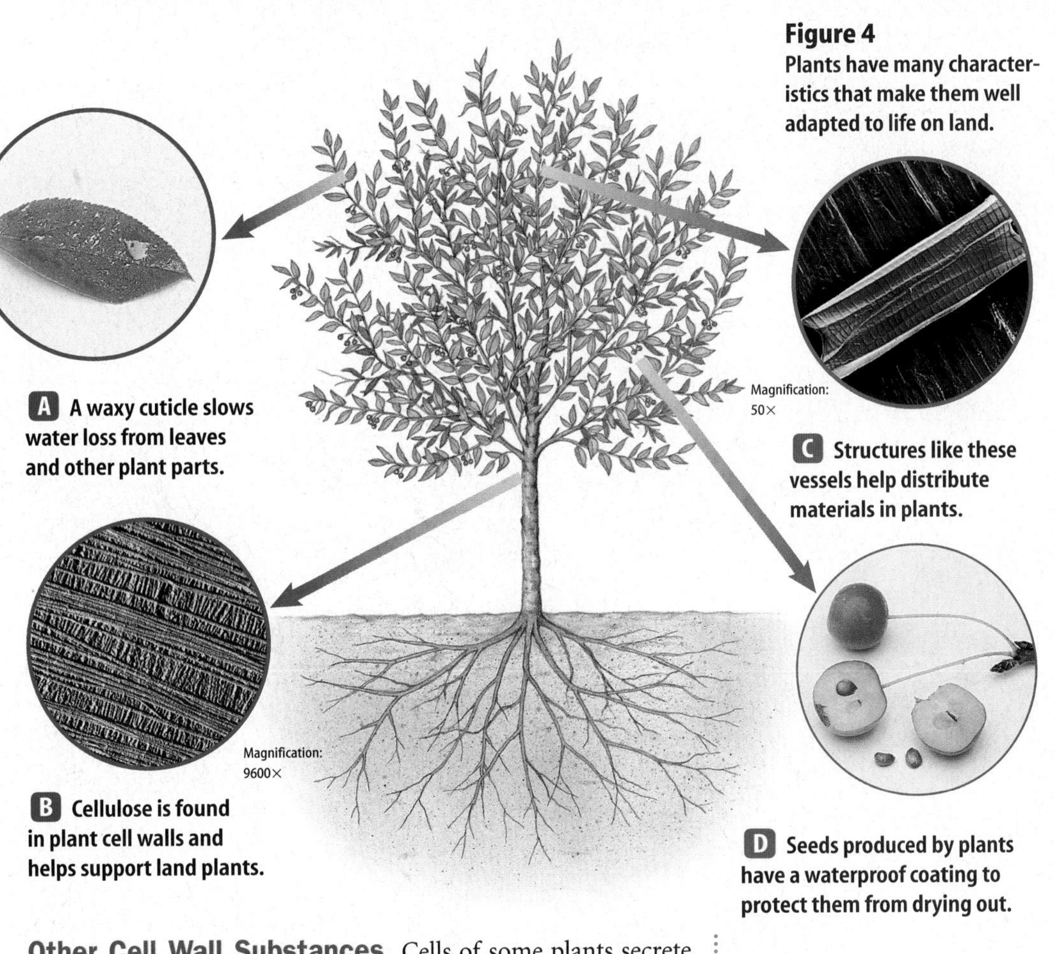

Figure 4
Plants have many characteristics that make them well adapted to life on land.

A A waxy cuticle slows water loss from leaves and other plant parts.

B Cellulose is found in plant cell walls and helps support land plants.

C Structures like these vessels help distribute materials in plants.

D Seeds produced by plants have a waterproof coating to protect them from drying out.

Other Cell Wall Substances Cells of some plants secrete other substances into the cellulose that make the cell wall even stronger. Trees, such as oaks and pines, could not grow without these strong cell walls. Wood can be used for construction mostly because of strong cell walls.

Life on land means that each plant cell is not surrounded by water. The plant cannot depend on water to move substances from one cell to the next. Through adaptations, structures developed in many plants that distribute water, nutrients, and food throughout the plant. These structures also help provide support for the plant.

Reproduction Changes in reproduction were necessary if plants were to survive on land. The presence of water-resistant spores helped some plants reproduce successfully. Other plants adapted by producing water-resistant seeds in cones or in flowers that developed into fruits.

Use Science Words

Word Meaning Have students compare the meaning of the word cuticle in relation to plants (protective layer on plant surface) and in relation to the human body (hardened skin at the base of nails). Both are derived from the Latin *cutis* meaning "skin." L2 IS **Linguistic**

Activity

Have students prepare posters that show examples of plant adaptations to life on land. L2 IS **Visual-Spatial** P

Use an Analogy

Explain that vascular tissue in plants is somewhat like the plumbing in a building. Some pipes, analogous to xylem, bring water up into the building. Other pipes, analogous to phloem, transport materials away. Reinforce that phloem does NOT carry water—it carries nutrients.

LAB DEMONSTRATION

Purpose to model the function of plant cuticles

Materials water, paper towels, wax paper, paper clips, string

Preparation Tie the string so it forms a line on which the towels can hang. Cut the towels and wax paper into 10-cm squares. Obtain a bowl of water for wetting the towels.

Procedure Wet three towel squares. Leave one uncovered. Cover one side of another with wax paper. Sandwich a third between two sheets of wax paper. Hang all three with clips. Have students observe how long it takes each towel to dry.

Expected Outcome Uncovered towels dry more quickly than covered towels.

How are towels covered with wax paper like plant leaves with cuticles? Wax paper prevents the towel from drying, as the cuticle prevents water loss from plants.

NATIONAL GEOGRAPHIC

Visualizing Plant Classification

Have students examine the pictures and read the captions. Then ask the following question.

How might an injury to the stem of a vascular plant affect the rest of the plant? Possible answer: Since the stem transports water and nutrients absorbed by the roots to the rest of the plant, an injury could result in the plant becoming dry or some leaves dying from lack of nutrients.

Activity

Provide students with hand lenses and the seeds of a variety of plants, such as sunflower, coconut, peanut, apple, orange, peach and common garden plants. Have students examine the samples to identify similarities and differences. If fern spores are available, have students compare and contrast these structures with seeds. L2 LS **Visual-Spatial**

Extension

Have students investigate how nonvascular plants transport food and water to cells. Nonvascular plants have rhizoids, rootlike structures, that collect water and nutrients from soil. The plants transport the materials throughout the rest of the body in one of two ways. Water and nutrients spread by diffusion or are carried by simple conducting tissues. Because both of these methods are very slow, plant size is limited. Usually nonvascular plants are no more than 2 cm in height.

NATIONAL GEOGRAPHIC **VISUALIZING PLANT CLASSIFICATION**

Figure 5

Scientists group plants as either vascular—those with water- and food-conducting cells in their stems—or nonvascular. Vascular plants are further divided into those that produce spores and those that make seeds.

246

Resource Manager

Chapter Resources Booklet
- Reinforcement, p. 23
- Directed Reading for Content Mastery, pp. 15, 16

Performance Assessment in the Science Classroom, p. 55

Classification of Plants

The plant kingdom is classified into major groups called divisions. A division is the same as a phylum in other kingdoms. Another way to group plants is as vascular (VAS kyuh lur) or nonvascular plants, as illustrated in **Figure 5.** **Vascular plants** have tubelike structures that carry water, nutrients, and other substances throughout the plant. **Nonvascular plants** do not have these tubelike structures and use other ways to move water and substances.

Figure 6
Although these two plants are called daisies, they are not the same species of plant. Using their binomial names helps eliminate the confusion that might come from using their common names.

Naming Plants Are biologists trying to show off when they call a pecan tree *Carya illinoiensis* or a white oak *Quercus alba?* Although it might seem so, they are just using words that accurately name the plant. In the third century B.C., most plants were grouped as trees, shrubs, or herbs and placed into smaller groups by leaf characteristics. This simple system survived until late in the eighteenth century when a Swedish botanist, Carolus Linnaeus, developed a new system. His new system used many characteristics to classify a plant. He also developed a way to name plants called binomial nomenclature (bi NOH mee ul • NOH mun klay chur). Under this system, every plant species is given a unique two-word name like the names above for the pecan tree and white oak and for the two daisies in **Figure 6.**

Section  Assessment

1. List the characteristics of plants.
2. Compare and contrast vascular and nonvascular plants.
3. Name three adaptations that allow plants to survive on land.
4. Why is binomial nomenclature used to name plants?
5. **Think Critically** If you left a board lying on the grass for a few days, what would happen to the grass underneath the board? Why?

Skill Builder Activities

6. **Forming Hypotheses** Make a hypothesis about what adaptations land plants might undergo if they lived submerged in water instead of on land. **For more help, refer to the Science Skill Handbook.**
7. **Communicating** One of the oldest surviving plant species is *Ginkgo biloba.* Research the history of this species, then write about it in your Science Journal. **For more help, refer to the Science Skill Handbook.**

3 Assess

Reteach

Obtain a sunflower with stem and leaves, or a large color photograph of one. Direct students to pick out the characteristics that would help this plant survive on land. thin cuticle that protects leaves and stem from drying out, tall stem supported by cellulose, vascular structures to distribute materials throughout the plant, seeds protected by hard covering L2

Challenge

How might animals have been affected if plants had not adapted to live on land? Life would probably not have been possible for animals on land, because plants are the foundation of all land food chains and they produce much of the atmospheric oxygen that land animals need to live.

Assessment

Oral Have students write additional questions not included in the Section Assessment and quiz each other. Use **Performance Assessment in the Science Classroom,** p. 91.

Answers to Section Assessment

1. eukaryotic cells with cell walls; pigments for photosynthesis; most have roots, stems, and leaves
2. Both have eukaryotic cells with cell walls and carry out photosynthesis. Vascular plants have tubelike structures to carry materials; nonvascular plants do not.
3. Adaptations listed may include the cuticle, vascular tissue, and seeds.
4. It gives every species of plant a unique two-word name.
5. The grass might die. Light is needed for photosynthesis.
6. Possible answers: A thicker cuticle or a system for pumping water from cells could be needed; some might have a long stem to raise leaves above the water.
7. Students' reports could include: The tree (also called the maidenhair tree) is the only surviving member of a group of plants that flourished millions of years ago. It is native to China.

SECTION

Seedless Plants

1 Motivate

Bellringer Transparency

Display the Section Focus Transparency for Section 2. Use the accompanying Transparency Activity Master. L2 ELL

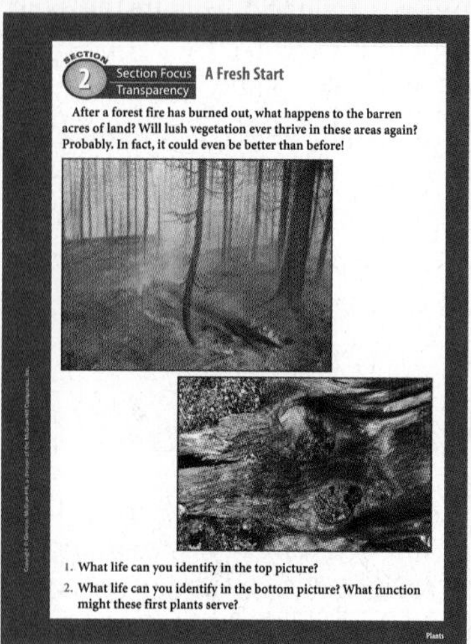

SECTION 2 Section Focus Transparency **A Fresh Start**

After a forest fire has burned out, what happens to the barren acres of land? Will lush vegetation ever thrive in these areas again? Probably. In fact, it could even be better than before!

1. **What life can you identify in the top picture?**
2. **What life can you identify in the bottom picture? What function might these first plants serve?**

Plants

Tie to Prior Knowledge

Students may already be familiar with some seedless plants. Point out that wreaths often contain club mosses, gardeners use peat moss to keep young plants from drying out, and ferns are common as house plants.

SECTION

Seedless Plants

As You Read

***What* You'll Learn**

- **Distinguish** between characteristics of seedless nonvascular plants and seedless vascular plants.
- **Identify** the importance of some nonvascular and vascular plants.

Vocabulary
rhizoid
pioneer species

***Why* It's Important**

Seedless plants are often the first to grow in damaged or disturbed environments.

Seedless Nonvascular Plants

If you were asked to name the parts of a plant, you probably would list roots, stems, leaves, and flowers. You also might know that many plants grow from seeds. However, some plants, called nonvascular plants, don't grow from seeds and they do not have all of these parts. **Figure 7** shows some common types of nonvascular plants.

Nonvascular plants are usually just a few cells thick and only 2 cm to 5 cm in height. Most have stalks that look like stems and green, leaflike growths. Instead of roots, threadlike structures called **rhizoids** (RI zoydz) anchor them where they grow. Most nonvascular plants grow in places that are damp. Therefore, water is absorbed and distributed directly through their cell membranes and cell walls. Nonvascular plants also do not have flowers or cones that produce seeds. They reproduce by spores. Mosses, liverworts, and hornworts are examples of nonvascular plants.

Mosses Most nonvascular plants are classified as mosses, like the ones in **Figure 7A.** They have green, leaflike growths arranged around a central stalk. Their rhizoids are made of many cells. Sometimes stalks with caps grow from moss plants. Reproductive cells called spores are produced in the caps of these stalks. Mosses often grow on tree trunks and rocks or the ground. Although they commonly are found in damp areas, some are adapted to living in deserts.

Figure 7
The seedless nonvascular plants include mosses, liverworts, and hornworts.

A Close-up of moss plants

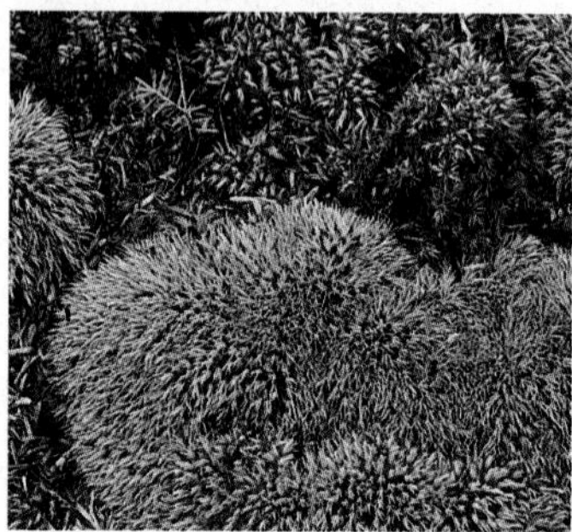

B Close-up of a liverwort

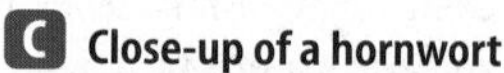

C Close-up of a hornwort

Section Assessment Planner

PORTFOLIO
Make a Model, p. 251

PERFORMANCE ASSESSMENT
MiniLab, p. 249
Skill Builder Activities, p. 253
See page 270 for more options.

CONTENT ASSESSMENT
Section, p. 253
Challenge, p. 253
Chapter, pp. 270–271

248 CHAPTER 9 Plants

Figure 8
Mosses can grow in the thin layer of soil that covers these rocks.

Liverworts In the ninth century, liverworts were thought to be useful in treating diseases of the liver. The suffix *-wort* means "herb," so the word *liverwort* means "herb for the liver." Liverworts are rootless plants with flattened, leaflike bodies, as shown in **Figure 7B.** They usually have one-celled rhizoids.

Hornworts Most hornworts are less than 2.5 cm in diameter and have a flattened body like liverworts, as shown in **Figure 7C.** Unlike other nonvascular plants, almost all hornworts have only one chloroplast in each of their cells. Hornworts get their name from their spore-producing structures, which look like tiny horns of cattle.

Nonvascular Plants and the Environment Mosses and liverworts are important in the ecology of many areas. Although they require moist conditions to grow and reproduce, many of them can withstand long, dry periods. They can grow in thin soil and in soils where other plants could not grow, as shown in **Figure 8.**

Spores of mosses and liverworts are carried by the wind. They will grow into plants if enough water is available and other growing conditions are right. Often, they are among the first plants to grow in new or disturbed environments, such as lava fields or after a forest fire. Organisms that are the first to grow in new or disturbed areas are called **pioneer species.** As pioneer plant species grow and die, decaying material builds up. This, along with the slow breakdown of rocks, builds soil. As a result, other organisms can move into the area.

Why are pioneer plant species important in disturbed environments?

Mini LAB

Measuring Water Absorption by a Moss

Procedure

1. Place a few teaspoons of ***Sphagnum* moss** on a piece of **cheesecloth.** Gather the corners of the cloth and twist, then tie them securely to form a ball.
2. Weigh the ball.
3. Put 200 mL of **water** in a **container** and add the ball.
4. After 15 min, remove the ball and drain the excess water into the container.
5. Weigh the ball and measure the amount of water left in the container.
6. Wash your hands after handling the moss.

Analysis

In your **Science Journal,** calculate how much water was absorbed by the *Sphagnum* moss.

2 Teach

Seedless Nonvascular Plants

Mini LAB

Purpose Students measure absorption capacity of *Sphagnum* moss. L2

LS **Logical-Mathematical**

Materials *Sphagnum* moss, cheesecloth, scale, graduated cylinder, beaker, water

Teaching Strategies

- Remind students that 1 mL of water has a mass of 1 g.
- Have students predict how much water the moss will hold and then check their predictions at the end.

Analysis

1. *Sphagnum* moss will soak up about 100 g (100 mL) of water.

Assessment

Performance Growers often root plants in a mix of equal parts clean sand to *Sphagnum* moss. Have students design an experiment to test this rooting method. Use **PASC,** p. 95.

Reading Check

Answer They help form soil and create conditions that allow other plants to grow.

Curriculum Connection

History Because peat mosses contain chemicals that kill germs, they were used during World War I as dressings for wounds. Have students research mosses to find out some of their other uses in the past. Possible answer: Some Native Americans used peat mosses for diapers because of their absorbency. It has also been used for lamp wicks, bedding, and stable litter. L2

Resource Manager

Chapter Resources Booklet
Transparency Activity, p. 41
MiniLAB, p. 3

Home and Community Involvement, p. 42

Seedless Vascular Plants

Quick Demo

Show a variety of fern fronds. If possible, include some with sori. Have students note differences in color, size, and location among sori.

Extension

Have motivated students read natural history books to find out why ferns have such common names as Boston fern, maidenhair fern, staghorn fern, cinnamon fern, hay-scented fern, and bracken fern. These names have to do with the shapes or scents of their leaves. L3

Problem-Solving Activity

National Math Standards

Correlation to Mathematics Objectives

5–10

Answers

1. Brazil
2. Answers should include some of the countries shaded on the map.
3. Some plants may become extinct before they can be studied.

Teacher FYI

The active ingredient in aspirin, the acetylsalicylic acid also found in willow bark, interferes with the body's production of prostaglandins. These hormonelike substances aid transmission of pain signals to the brain and help raise body temperature to fight infection. That is why taking aspirin helps dull pain and fight fever.

SCIENCE Online

Research Visit the Glencoe Science Web site at **science.glencoe.com** for more information about medicinal plants. In your Science Journal, list four medicinal plants and their uses.

Seedless Vascular Plants

The fern in **Figure 9** is growing next to some moss plants. Ferns and mosses are alike in one way. Both reproduce by spores instead of seeds. However, ferns are different from mosses because they have vascular tissue. The vascular tissue in the seedless vascular plants, like ferns, is made up of long, tubelike cells. These cells carry water, minerals, and food to cells throughout the plant. Why is having cells like these an advantage to a plant? Remember that nonvascular plants like the moss are usually only a few cells thick. Each cell absorbs water directly from its environment. As a result, these plants cannot grow large. Vascular plants, on the other hand, can grow bigger and thicker because the vascular tissue distributes water and nutrients.

Problem-Solving Activity

What is the value of rain forests?

Throughout history, cultures have used plants for medicines. Some cultures used willow bark to cure headaches. Willow bark contains salicylates (suh LIH suh layts), the main ingredient in aspirin. Heart problems were treated with foxglove, which is the main source of digitalis (dih juh TAH lus), a drug prescribed for heart problems. Have all medicinal plants been identified?

Identifying the Problem

Tropical rain forests have the largest variety of organisms on Earth. Many plant species are unknown. These forests are being destroyed rapidly. The map below shows the rate of destruction of the rain forests. Some scientists estimate that most tropical rain forests will be destroyed in 30 years.

Solving the Problem

1. What country has the most rain forest destroyed each year?
2. Where can scientists go to study rain forest plants before the plants are destroyed?
3. Predict how the destruction of rain forests might affect research on new drugs from plants.

Deforested annually (km^2)
- more than 15,000
- 2,000 to 14,800
- 100 to 1,900

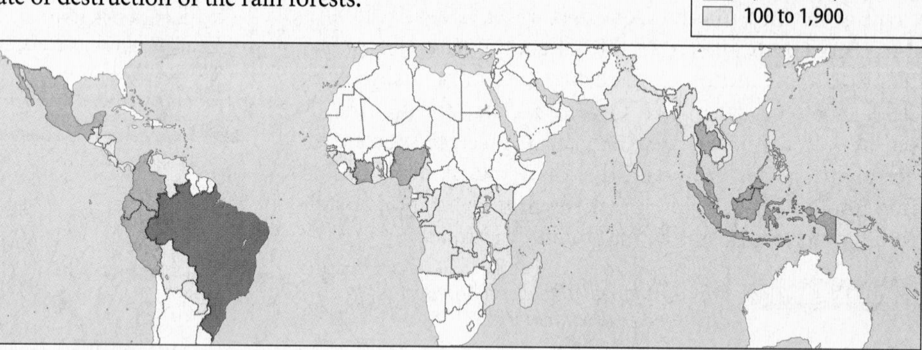

SCIENCE Online

Internet Addresses

____

____

____

Explore the Glencoe Science Web site at **science.glencoe.com** to find out more about topics in this section.

Inclusion Strategies

Visually Impaired Prepare samples of mosses, liverworts, and ferns for the class labeled with large print. Provide large magnifying glasses for closer observation of the plants.

Types of Seedless Vascular Plants

Besides ferns, seedless vascular plants include ground pines, spike mosses, and horsetails. About 1,000 species of ground pines, spike mosses, and horsetails are known to exist. Ferns are more abundant, with at least 12,000 known species. Many species of seedless vascular plants are known only from fossils. They flourished during the warm, moist period 360 million to 286 million years ago. Fossil records show that some horsetails grew 15 m tall, unlike modern species, which grow only 1 m to 2 m tall.

Figure 9
The mosses and ferns in this picture are seedless plants. *Why can the fern grow taller than the moss?*

Ferns The largest group of seedless vascular plants is the ferns. They include many different varieties, as shown in **Figure 10.** They have stems, leaves, and roots. Fern leaves are called fronds. Ferns produce spores in structures that usually are found on the underside of their fronds. Thousands of species of ferns now grow on Earth, but many more existed long ago. From clues left in rock layers, scientists know that about 360 million years ago much of Earth was tropical. Steamy swamps covered large areas. The tallest plants were species of ferns. The ancient ferns grew as tall as 25 m—as tall as the tallest fern species alive today. The tallest modern tree ferns are about 3 m to 5 m in height, as shown in **Figure 10C,** and grow in tropical areas.

Figure 10
Ferns come in many different shapes and sizes.

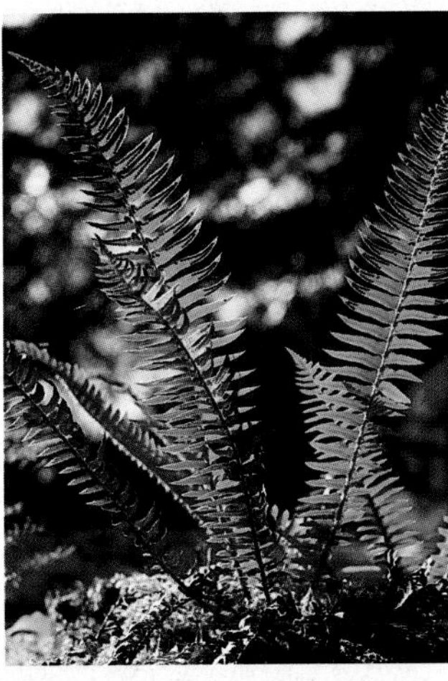

A The sword fern has a typical fern shape. Spores are produced in structures on the back of the frond.

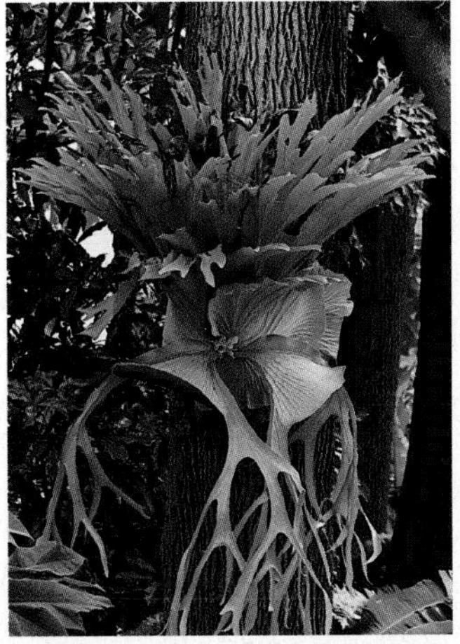

B This fern grows on other plants, not in the soil. *Why do you think it's called the staghorn fern?*

C Tree ferns, like this one in Hawaii, grow in tropical areas.

Fun Fact

The stems of tree ferns are harvested and sold as plant supports. The dry, fibrous parts of some ferns have been used as mattress stuffing.

Make a Model

Have students construct a shoe box model of what they think a tropical forest dominated by ferns may have looked like millions of years ago. L2 ELL **Kinesthetic** P

Caption Answers

- **Figure 9** Ferns have vascular tissues that transport materials and provide support; mosses do not.
- **Figure 10B** because of the shape of its leaves

Teacher FYI

Ferns are found mostly in damp shady areas in most parts of the world. In the United States, ferns are found mostly in the Southeast and the Pacific Northwest along streams in forests. In the tropics, ferns grow on tree trunks and branches. There are about 12,000 species of ferns on Earth today.

Resource Manager

Chapter Resources Booklet
Enrichment, p. 27

Mathematics Skill Activities, p. 5

Seedless Vascular Plants, continued

Discussion

How can you tell the difference between true mosses and club mosses? True mosses produce spores in capsules on stalks. Club mosses produce spores at the end of stems in structures that look like tiny pine cones.

✔ Reading Check

Answer at the ends of stems in structures that look like pine cones

Quick Demo

Obtain horsetail plants. Demonstrate (and allow students to feel) how the grittiness of the silica in the plant's cell walls could be useful for scouring. L2 LS **Kinesthetic**

Caption Answer

Figure 12 in a conelike structure at the tips of some stems

Importance of Seedless Plants

Use Science Words

Word Usage Provide each student with a list of terms that can be used to describe nonvascular and seedless vascular plants. Have students write paragraphs that compare and contrast these plants using the terms given. Terms might include *nonvascular, vascular, moss, rhizoid, moist, liverwort, ferns, leaves, roots,* and *horsetails.* L2 LS **Linguistic**

Figure 11
Photographers once used the dry, flammable spores of club mosses as flash powder. It burned rapidly and produced the light that was needed to take photographs.

Club Mosses Ground pines and spike mosses are groups of plants that often are called club mosses. They are related more closely to ferns than to mosses. These seedless vascular plants have needle-like leaves. Spores are produced at the end of the stems in structures that look like tiny pinecones. Ground pines, shown in **Figure 11,** are found from arctic regions to the tropics, but never in large numbers. In some areas, they are endangered because they have been over collected to make wreaths and other decorations.

✔ Reading Check ***Where are spores in club mosses produced?***

Spike mosses resemble ground pines. One species of spike moss, the resurrection plant, is adapted to desert conditions. When water is scarce, the plant curls up and seems dead. When water becomes available, the resurrection plant unfurls its green leaves and begins making food again. The plant can repeat this process whenever necessary.

Horsetails The stem structure of horsetails is unique among the vascular plants. The stem is jointed and has a hollow center surrounded by a ring of vascular tissue. At each joint, leaves grow out from around the stem. In **Figure 12,** you can see these joints. If you pull on a horsetail stem, it will pop apart in sections. Like the club mosses, spores from horsetails are produced in a conelike structure at the tips of some stems. The stems of the horsetails contain silica, a gritty substance found in sand. For centuries, horsetails have been used for polishing objects, sharpening tools, and scouring cooking utensils. Another common name for horsetails is scouring rush.

Figure 12
Most horsetails grow in damp areas and are less than 1 m tall.
Where would spores be produced on this plant?

Importance of Seedless Plants

When many ancient seedless plants died, they became submerged in water and mud before they decomposed. As this plant material built up, it became compacted and compressed and eventually turned into coal—a process that took millions of years.

Today, a similar process is taking place in bogs, which are poorly drained areas of land that contain decaying plants. The plants in bogs are mostly seedless plants like mosses and ferns.

Resource Manager

Chapter Resources Booklet
- Reinforcement, p. 24
- Directed Reading for Content Mastery, p. 17

Visual Learning

Figure 13 If possible, have students examine samples of peat and coal. Remind them that peat is the first stage of coal formation. **How does the appearance of peat differ from that of coal?** Peat is lighter in color and isn't as rocklike as coal.

Peat When plants die, the decay process is slow because waterlogged soil does not contain oxygen. Over time, these decaying plants are compressed into a substance called peat. Peat, which forms from the remains of sphagnum moss, is mined from bogs to use as a low-cost fuel in places such as Ireland and Russia, as shown in **Figure 13.** Peat supplies about one third of Ireland's energy requirements. Scientists hypothesize that over time, if additional layers of soil bury, compact, and compress the peat, it will become coal.

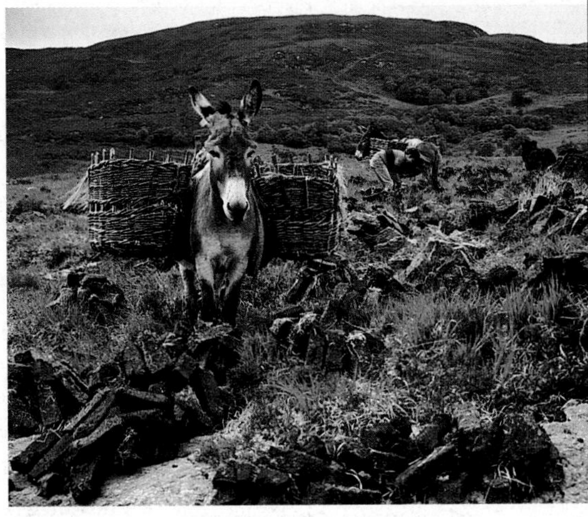

Figure 13
Peat is cut from bogs and used for a fuel in some parts of Europe.

Uses of Seedless Vascular Plants Many people keep ferns as houseplants. Ferns also are sold widely as landscape plants for shady areas. Peat and sphagnum mosses also are used for gardening. Peat is an excellent soil conditioner, and sphagnum moss often is used to line hanging baskets. Ferns also are used for weaving material and basketry.

Although most mosses are not used for food, parts of many other seedless vascular plants can be eaten. The rhizomes and young fronds of some ferns are edible. The dried stems of one type of horsetail can be ground into flour. Seedless plants have been used as folk medicines for hundreds of years. For example, ferns have been used to treat bee stings, burns, fevers, and even dandruff.

Section  Assessment

1. What are the similarities and differences between mosses and ferns?
2. What do fossil records show us about some seedless plants?
3. Under what growing conditions would you expect to find pioneer plants such as mosses and liverworts?
4. What do vascular tissues provide for plants that have them?
5. **Think Critically** The electricity that you use every day might be produced by burning coal. What is the connection between electricity production and seedless nonvascular and seedless vascular plants?

Skill Builder Activities

6. **Concept Mapping** Make a concept map showing how seedless nonvascular and seedless vascular plants are related. Include these terms in the concept map: *plant kingdom, seedless nonvascular plants, seedless vascular plants, ferns, ground pines, horsetails, liverworts, hornworts, mosses,* and *spike mosses.* **For more help, refer to the** **Science Skill Handbook.**
7. **Using Fractions** Approximately 8,000 species of liverworts and 9,000 species of mosses exist today. Estimate what fraction of these seedless nonvascular plants are mosses. **For more help, refer to the** **Math Skill Handbook.**

3 Assess

Reteach

Give pairs of students photographs or drawings of seedless nonvascular plants on 3″ × 5″ note cards. On another set of note cards, write descriptions of the plants. Have students match descriptions with pictures. L2 COOP LEARN IN **Interpersonal**

Challenge

The presence of vascular tissue allows ferns to grow taller than other seedless, nonvascular plants. **Why would this trait make them more successful than other seedless plants?** The taller a plant can grow, the more likely it is that it will receive light and thus be able to photosynthesize.

✔Assessment

Content How are ferns, club mosses, and horsetails alike? They are all seedless vascular plants. Use **Performance Assessment in the Science Classroom,** p. 89.

Answers to Section Assessment

1. alike: reproduce by spores; different: unlike mosses, ferns have vascular tissue
2. Seedless plants dominated Earth long ago and grew much larger than they grow today.
3. in disturbed or new environments
4. The vascular system carries water, minerals, and food to plant cells. This allows the plant to grow bigger and thicker. The cells of vascular tissue provide support, also.
5. Seedless plants (both vascular and nonvascular) formed ancient forests that decayed and became the coal we burn today as fuel.
6. Students should begin the concept map with *plant kingdom.* Branching from that should be *seedless nonvascular plants* and *vascular plants. Mosses, hornworts,* and *liverworts* branch from *seedless nonvascular plants. Spike mosses, ground pines, horsetails,* and *ferns* branch from *seedless vascular plants.*
7. 9/17

SECTION

Seed Plants

1 Motivate

Bellringer Transparency

Display the Section Focus Transparency for Section 3. Use the accompanying Transparency Activity Master. L2 ELL

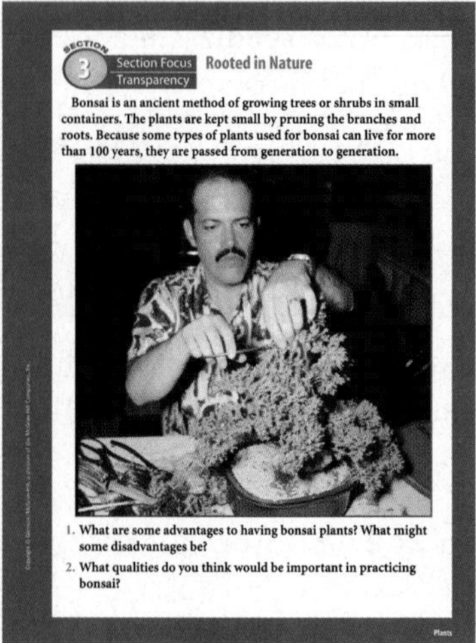
Section 3 Section Focus Transparency Rooted in Nature

Bonsai is an ancient method of growing trees or shrubs in small containers. The plants are kept small by pruning the branches and roots. Because some types of plants used for bonsai can live for more than 100 years, they are passed from generation to generation.

1. What are some advantages to having bonsai plants? What might some disadvantages be?
2. What qualities do you think would be important in practicing bonsai?

Plants

Tie to Prior Knowledge

Invite students to brainstorm a list of plant seeds that they eat or see regularly. Possible answers: any type of edible nut, sunflower seeds, sesame or poppy seeds, coconuts, seeds inside fruits

SECTION 3

Seed Plants

As You Read

What **You'll Learn**

- **Identify** the characteristics of seed plants.
- **Explain** the structures and functions of roots, stems, and leaves.
- **Describe** the main characteristics and importance of gymnosperms and angiosperms.
- **Compare** similarities and differences between monocots and dicots.

Vocabulary

stomata, guard cell, xylem, phloem, cambium, gymnosperm, angiosperm, monocot, dicot

Why **It's Important**

We depend on seed plants for food, clothing, and shelter.

Characteristics of Seed Plants

What foods from plants have you eaten today? Apples? Potatoes? Carrots? Peanut butter and jelly sandwiches? All of these foods and more come from seed plants.

Most of the plants you are familiar with are seed plants. Most seed plants have leaves, stems, roots, and vascular tissue. They produce seeds, which usually contain an embryo and stored food. The stored food is the source of energy for the embryo's early growth as it develops into a plant. Most of the plant species that have been identified in the world today are seed plants. Seed plants generally are classified into two major groups—gymnosperms (JIHM nuh spurmz) and angiosperms (AN jee uh spurmz).

Leaves Most seed plants have leaves—the organs of the plant where the food-making process—photosynthesis—usually occurs. Leaves come in many shapes, sizes, and colors. Examine the structure of a typical leaf, shown in **Figure 14.**

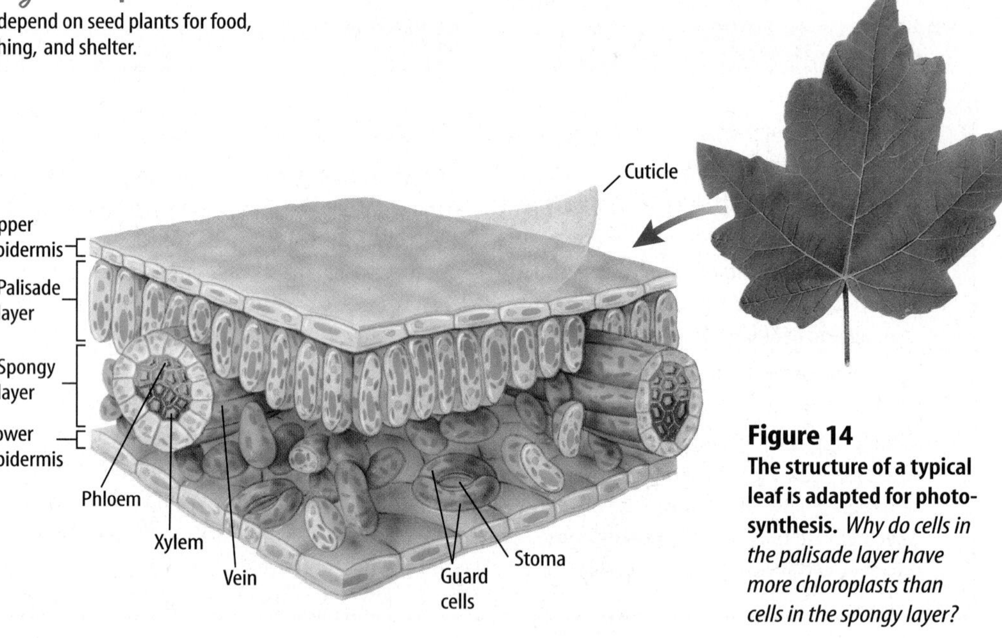

Figure 14
The structure of a typical leaf is adapted for photosynthesis. *Why do cells in the palisade layer have more chloroplasts than cells in the spongy layer?*

Section Assessment Planner

PORTFOLIO
Curriculum Connection, p. 257

PERFORMANCE ASSESSMENT
Try at Home MiniLAB, p. 255
Skill Builder Activities, p. 262
See page 270 for more options.

CONTENT ASSESSMENT
Section, p. 262
Challenge, p. 262
Chapter, pp. 270–271

254 CHAPTER 9 Plants

Leaf Cell Layers A typical leaf is made of different layers of cells. On the upper and lower surfaces of a leaf is a thin layer of cells called the epidermis, which covers and protects the leaf. A waxy cuticle coats the epidermis of some leaves. Most leaves have small openings in the epidermis called **stomata** (STOH muh tuh) (singular, *stoma*). Stomata allow carbon dioxide, water, and oxygen to enter into and exit from a leaf. Each stoma is surrounded by two **guard cells** that open and close it.

Just below the upper epidermis is the palisade layer. It consists of closely packed, long, narrow cells that usually contain many chloroplasts. Most of the food produced by plants is made in the palisade cells. Between the palisade layer and the lower epidermis is the spongy layer. It is a layer of loosely arranged cells separated by air spaces. In a leaf, veins containing vascular tissue are found in the spongy layer.

Stems The trunk of a tree is really the stem of the tree. Stems usually are located above ground and support the branches, leaves, and flowers. Materials move between leaves and roots through the vascular tissue in the stem. Stems also can have other specialized functions, as shown in **Figure 15.**

Plant stems are either herbaceous (hur BAY shus) or woody. Herbaceous stems usually are soft and green, like the stems of a tulip, while trees and shrubs have hard, rigid, woody stems. Lumber comes from woody stems.

TRY AT HOME Mini LAB

Observing Water Moving in a Plant

Procedure

1. Into a **clear container** pour **water** to a depth of 1.5 cm. Add 25 drops of **red food coloring** to the water.
2. Put the root end of a **green onion** into the container. Do not cut the onion in any way. Wash your hands.
3. The next day, examine the outside of the onion. Peel off the onion's layers and examine them. **WARNING:** *Do not eat the onion.*

Analysis

In your **Science Journal,** infer how the location of red color inside the onion might be related to vascular tissue.

Figure 15
Some plants have stems with special functions.

A **These potatos are stems that grow underground and store food for the plant.**

B **The stems of this cactus store water and can carry on photosynthesis.**

C **Some stems of this grape plant help it climb on other plants.**

2 Teach

Characteristics of Seed Plants

Caption Answer

Figure 14 This layer is more likely to be exposed to the Sun.

Purpose Students observe how water moves through vascular tissue. L2 LS **Visual-Spatial**

Materials water, clear container, red food coloring, green onion, hand lens, metric ruler

Teaching Strategy Have students predict what will happen to the green onion.

Analysis

Food coloring and water moved into the onion's roots and up through its vascular tissue.

Assessment

Performance Have students identify vascular tissue in celery. Use **Performance Assessment in the Science Classroom,** p. 89.

Teacher FYI

Leaves come in a variety of sizes and shapes. Duckweed leaves are only millimeters across, while raffia palm leaves can be 20 m long and 2.4 m wide. Maples have broad, flat leaves; conifers have needlelike leaves. Cactus spines are modified leaves that prevent water loss and protect the plant from hungry animals.

Resource Manager 

Chapter Resources Booklet

Transparency Activity, p. 42

MiniLAB, p. 4

Characteristics of Seed Plants, continued

Teacher FYI

Sweet potatoes are fleshy roots; white potatoes are fleshy underground stems (tubers). Both are structures that store food.

Quick Demo

Germinate some bean or corn seeds to demonstrate that the mass of the roots becomes larger than the rest of the plant very quickly.

Activity

Have students make posters that illustrate the different functions of roots and stems. For example, the roots of some orchids and the stems of cacti can photosynthesize. L2
LS Visual-Spatial

Caption Answer

Figure 16 to anchor the tree and to take in enough water and nutrients to support the above ground parts of the plant

Reading Check

Answer Roots take in water and nutrients from soil, anchor the plant, and store food and water. Some plants have roots that take in oxygen from the air.

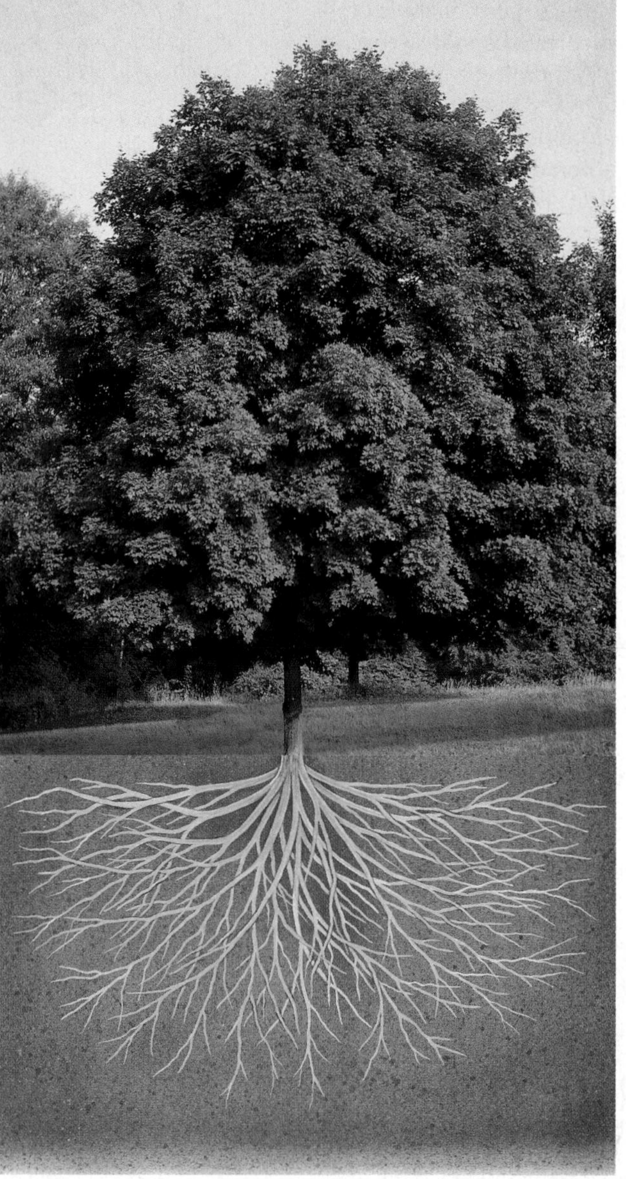

Figure 16
The root system of a tree is as long as the tree can be tall. *Why would the root system of a tree need to be so large?*

Roots Imagine a lone tree growing on top of a hill. What is the largest part of this plant? Maybe you guessed the trunk or the branches. Did you consider the roots? The root systems of most plants are as large or larger than the aboveground stems and leaves, as shown in **Figure 16.**

Roots are important to plants. Water and other substances enter a plant through its roots. Roots have vascular tissue in which water and dissolved substances move from the soil through the stems to the leaves. Roots also act as anchors, preventing plants from being blown away by wind or washed away by moving water. Each root system must support the other plant parts that are aboveground—the stem, branches, and leaves of a tree. Sometimes, part of or all of the roots are aboveground, too.

Roots can store food. When you eat carrots or beets, you eat roots that contain stored food. Plants that grow from year to year use this stored food to begin their growth in the spring. Plants that grow in dry areas often have roots that store water.

Root tissues also can perform functions such as absorbing oxygen that is used in the process of respiration. Because water does not contain as much oxygen as air does, plants that grow with their roots in water might not be able to absorb enough oxygen. Some swamp plants have roots that grow partially out of the water and take in oxygen from the air. In order to perform all these functions, the root systems of plants must be large.

 *What are several functions of roots in plants?*

Resource Manager

Chapter Resources Booklet
Enrichment, p. 28
Transparency Activity, pp. 43–44

Visual Learning

Figure 16 How could planting a large tree such as this close to a building cause a problem? Students should infer that its extensive root system could interfere with the building's foundation or pipes leading into the building.

256 CHAPTER 9 Plants

Vascular Tissue Three tissues usually make up the vascular system in a seed plant. **Xylem** (ZI lum) tissue is made up of hollow, tubular cells that are stacked one on top of the other to form a structure called a vessel. These vessels transport water and dissolved substances from the roots throughout the plant. The thick cell walls of xylem are also important because they help support the plant.

Phloem (FLOH em) is a plant tissue also made up of tubular cells that are stacked to form structures called tubes. Tubes are different from vessels. Phloem tubes move food from where it is made to other parts of the plant where it is used or stored.

In some plants, a cambium is between xylem and phloem. **Cambium** (KAM bee um) is a tissue that produces most of the new xylem and phloem cells. The growth of this new xylem and phloem increases the thickness of stems and roots. All three tissues are illustrated in **Figure 17.**

Plants have vascular tissue, and you have a vascular system. Your vascular system transports oxygen, food, and wastes through blood vessels. Instead of xylem and phloem, your blood vessels include veins and arteries. In your Science Journal write a paragraph describing the difference between veins and arteries.

Figure 17
The vascular tissue of some seed plants includes xylem, phloem, and cambium.
Which of these tissues transports food throughout the plant?

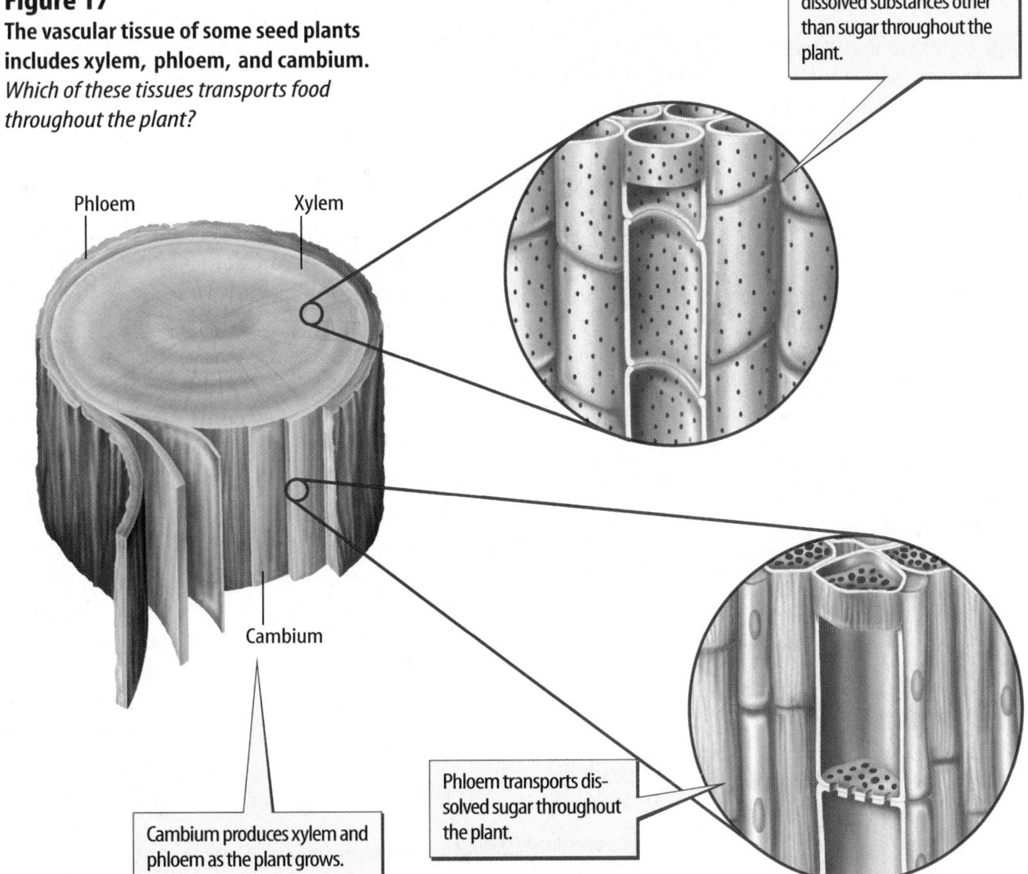

Health INTEGRATION

Arteries carry blood away from the heart; veins carry blood toward the heart. Except for those vessels going to and from the lungs, arteries carry oxygen-rich blood, and veins carry oxygen-poor blood.

Quick Demo

Demonstrate the appearance of vascular tissue in woody plants by showing students a photo of a tree trunk cross-section, or by bringing a cut woody stem to class.

Extension

Foresters measure quantities of timber in board feet. Have students research the size of this unit. A board foot is a volume measure of lumber. A board measuring 12″ × 12″ × 1″ is one board foot. Challenge students to find out how many board feet of lumber are consumed by a common activity, such as building a house or producing pulp for a certain amount of newsprint. L3

Caption Answer

Figure 17 phloem

Curriculum Connection

History Theophrastus (ca. 372–ca. 287 B.C.) is known as the father of botany. His botanical works were so complete that nearly 1,800 years passed before any new discoveries were made. Have students research the name and contributions of other botanists and compile their findings into one time line. Bauhin, Linnaeus, Bailey, Gesner, Hales, Nageli, and Ray are botanists students may name. P

Teacher FYI

The pattern of rings in tree trunks provides information about a tree's life. Good growth years produce wide rings. Slower growth, due to less favorable conditions, forms a narrower ring. If there is an extended dry period between two wet periods, two rings will be produced. Rings are wider on the sunny side of a tree.

Gymnosperms

Discussion

Is an apple tree a gymnosperm? Explain. No, it has seeds encased in fruits. **Is a maple tree whose leaves turn golden and red in fall a gymnosperm? Explain.** No, its seeds are enclosed in a dry, winged fruit.

Activity

If possible, ask each student to find and bring to class a cone from a conifer in the area. Cones may be found in yards, in parks, and along routes to and from school. Have them compare and contrast the cones in class and make sketches and written descriptions of each type of cone. Discuss how the cones are alike and different. Although they have the same basic structure, they differ in size, color, and shape. L1 LS **Visual-Spatial**

Caption Answer

Figure 18D Most gymnosperms do not lose all of their leaves in the fall.

Reading Check

Answer Cones are the reproductive structures of the plants; seeds develop on female cones.

Figure 18
The gymnosperms include four divisions of plants.

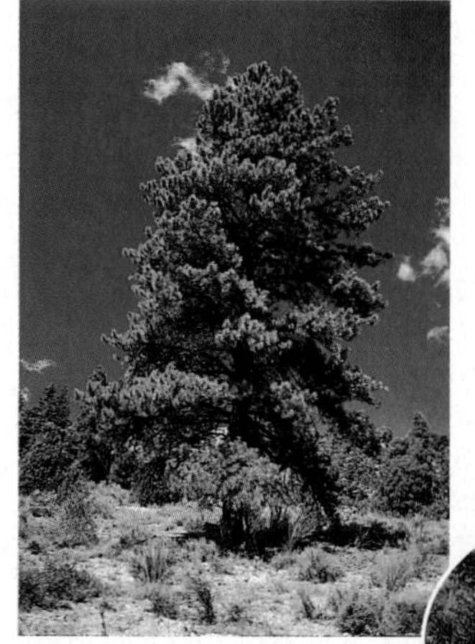

A Conifers are the largest, most diverse division. Most conifers are evergreen plants, such as this ponderosa pine.

C About 100 species of cycads exist today. Only one genus is native to the United States.

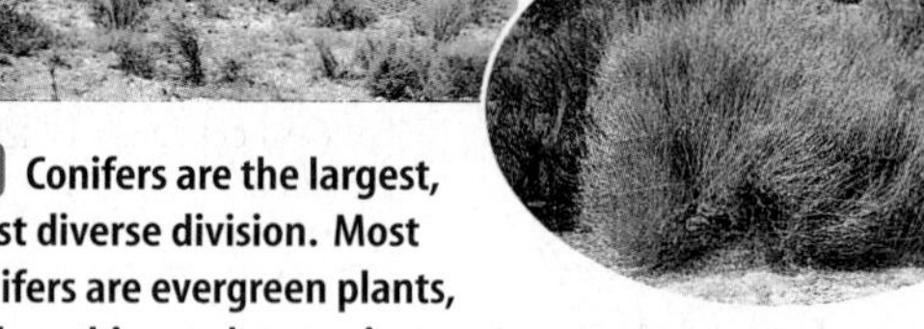

B More than half of the 70 species of gnetophytes, such as this joint fir, are in one genus.

D The ginkgoes are represented by one living species. Ginkgoes lose their leaves in the fall. *How is this different from most gymnosperms?*

Field GUIDE

Can you identify conifers by looking at their cones? To find out more about cones, see the **Cones Field Guide** at the back of the book.

Gymnosperms

The oldest trees alive are gymnosperms. A bristlecone pine tree in the White Mountains of eastern California is estimated to be 4,900 years old. **Gymnosperms** are vascular plants that produce seeds that are not protected by fruit. The word *gymnosperm* comes from the Greek language and means "naked seed." Another characteristic of gymnosperms is that they do not have flowers. Leaves of most gymnosperms are needlelike or scalelike. Many gymnosperms are called evergreens because some green leaves always remain on their branches.

Four divisions of plants—conifers, cycads, ginkgoes, and gnetophytes (NE tuh fites)—are classified as gymnosperms. **Figure 18** shows examples of the four divisions. You are probably most familiar with the division Coniferophyta (kuh NIH fur uh fi tuh), the conifers. Pines, firs, spruces, redwoods, and junipers belong to this division. It contains the greatest number of gymnosperm species. All conifers produce two types of cones—male and female. Both types usually are found on the same plant. Cones are the reproductive structures of conifers. Seeds develop on the female cone but not on the male cone.

Reading Check *What is the importance of cones to gymnosperms?*

Inclusion Strategies

Learning Disabled Bring branches from different conifers to class. Identify the branches and then have students feel the differences in texture and shape of the leaves. Encourage students to compare and contrast the smells and textures associated with each. L1 LS **Kinesthetic**

Active Reading

Think-Pair-Share This strategy encourages students to think first before discussing their ideas or thoughts about a topic. Ask students to respond to a question. After recording ideas, have partners share responses to the question. Finally, ask students to share responses with the class. Have students become involved in a Think-Pair-Share about seed plants.

Angiosperms

When people are asked to name a plant, most name an angiosperm. An **angiosperm** is a vascular plant that flowers and has a fruit that contains one or more seeds, such as the peach in **Figure 19A.** The fruit develops from a part or parts of one or more flowers. Angiosperms are familiar plants no matter where you live. They grow in parks, fields, forests, jungles, deserts, freshwater, salt water, and cracks of sidewalks. You might see them dangling from wires or other plants, and one species of orchid even grows underground. Angiosperms make up the plant division Anthophyta (AN thoh fi tuh). More than half of the known plant species belong to this division.

Flowers The flowers of angiosperms vary in size, shape, and color. Duckweed, an aquatic plant, has a flower that is only 0.1 mm long. A plant in Indonesia has a flower that is nearly 1 m in diameter and can weigh 9 kg. Nearly every color can be found in some flower, although some people would not include black. Multicolored flowers are common. Some plants have flowers that are not recognized easily as flowers, such as those shown in **Figure 19B.**

Some flower parts develop into fruit. Most fruits contain seeds, like an apple, or have seeds on their surface, like a strawberry. If you think all fruits are juicy and sweet, there are some that are not. The fruit of the vanilla orchid, as shown in **Figure 19C,** contains seeds and is dry.

Angiosperms are divided into two groups—the monocots and the dicots—shortened forms of the words *monocotyledon* (mah nuh kah tul EE dun) and *dicotyledon* (di kah tul EE dun).

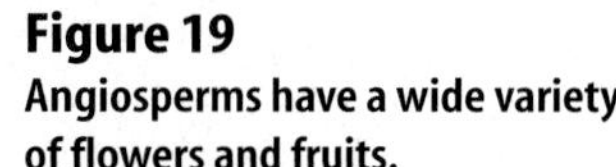

Figure 19
Angiosperms have a wide variety of flowers and fruits.

C The fruit of the vanilla orchid is the source of vanilla flavoring.

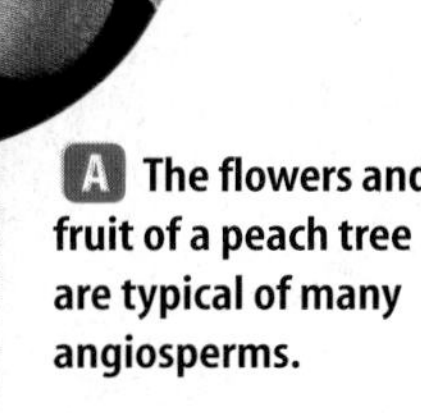

A The flowers and fruit of a peach tree are typical of many angiosperms.

B Ash flowers are not large and colorful. Their fruits are small and dry.

Angiosperms

Teacher FYI

Botanically, a fruit is any plant organ that grows from female flower parts. Therefore, tomatoes, green beans, squash, cucumbers, and peppers are fruit—although they're not necessarily sweet.

Science Journal

Nutritious Grains Have students research one of the major grains eaten in the United States and write a short report that includes what the plant looks like, what parts of it we eat, and where it is grown. Some students might also visit a supermarket to report on the number and kinds of foods containing the grain. Encourage students to include photos and diagrams in their reports, and to share their findings in class. Students could research corn, wheat, oats, or rice. L2

LS **Linguistic**

Cultural Diversity

Food for Thought People from different cultures rely on plants native to their part of the world for food. Have each student choose a country and prepare a poster that shows the main plants that are part of the diet there. After presenting each poster, encourage students to compare and contrast these foods with those that are commonly eaten in the United States.

Resource Manager

Chapter Resources Booklet

Directed Reading for Content Mastery, pp. 17, 18

Angiosperms, continued

Activity

Prepare several lab stations to demonstrate different monocot or dicot characteristics. Have students rotate through the stations, making notes and sketches of each characteristic. When everyone has completed the activity, have students discuss how monocots and dicots are similar and different. L2
LS **Interpersonal**

Teacher FYI

Grasses make up the largest of all plant families. They are also the most widespread and can be found on almost every type of land surface and in every climate region on Earth. Sugarcane is a grass that grows in tropical areas to heights of 2 to 4.6 meters. This grass supplies more than half the world's sugar. Another grass is bamboo. Its strong, woody stems are used in some parts of the world as building materials and as water pipes. Bamboo is often used to make furniture.

Extension

Have students survey the plants they find at a home and garden store, a grocery store, or a florist shop. Tell them to sketch the leaves and flowers of one monocot and one dicot and bring the sketches to class. Remind them to write down the names of the plants on the back of each sketch and whether the plant is a monocot or dicot. Have each student present his or her two sketches in class. Quiz class members on whether the plants are monocots or dicots, and have students give reasons for their choices. L1
LS **Visual-Spatial**

Monocots and Dicots A cotyledon is part of a seed often used for food storage. The prefix *mono* means "one," and *di* means "two." Therefore, **monocots** have one cotyledon inside their seeds and **dicots** have two. The flowers, leaves, and stems of monocots and dicots are shown in **Figure 20.**

Many important foods come from monocots, including corn, rice, wheat, and barley. If you eat bananas, pineapple, or dates, you are eating fruit from monocots. Lilies and orchids also are monocots.

Dicots also produce familiar foods such as peanuts, green beans, peas, apples, and oranges. You might have rested in the shade of a dicot tree. Most shade trees, such as maple, oak, and elm, are dicots.

Figure 20
By observing a monocot and a dicot, you can determine their plant characteristics.

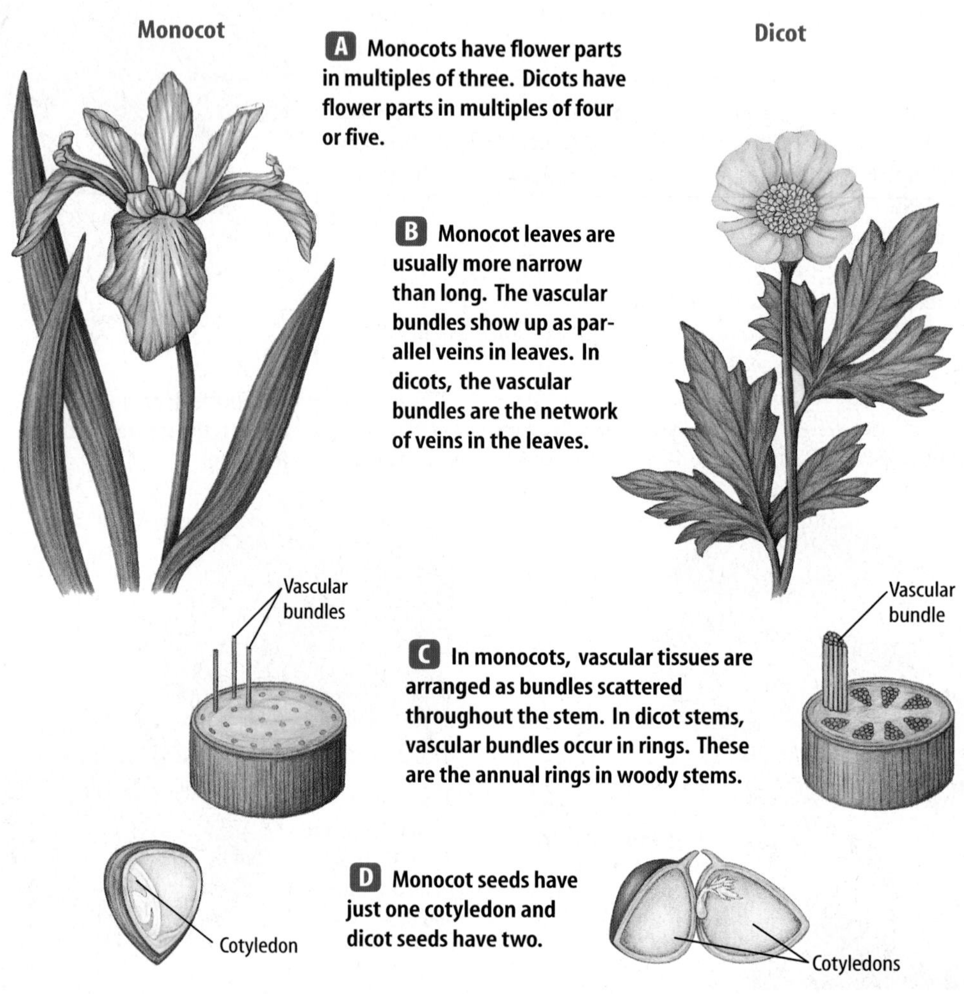
Monocot
Dicot
A Monocots have flower parts in multiples of three. Dicots have flower parts in multiples of four or five.
B Monocot leaves are usually more narrow than long. The vascular bundles show up as parallel veins in leaves. In dicots, the vascular bundles are the network of veins in the leaves.
Vascular bundles
Vascular bundle
C In monocots, vascular tissues are arranged as bundles scattered throughout the stem. In dicot stems, vascular bundles occur in rings. These are the annual rings in woody stems.
Cotyledon
D Monocot seeds have just one cotyledon and dicot seeds have two.
Cotyledons

Teacher FYI

Dandelions, chrysanthemums, and sunflowers belong to the family of plants called *Asteraceae*. What we see as a single flower is really a composite of many individual, small flowers called florets. In fact, the family name was once called *Compositae*.

A

B

C

Life Cycles of Angiosperms Flowering plants vary greatly in appearance. Their life cycles are as varied as the kinds of plants, as shown in **Figure 21.** Some angiosperms grow from seeds to mature plants with their own seeds in less than a month. The life cycles of other plants can take as long as a century. If a plant's life cycle is completed within one year, it is called an annual. These plants must be grown from seeds each year.

Plants called biennials (bi EH nee ulz) complete their life cycles within two years. Biennials such as parsley store a large amount of food in an underground root or stem for growth in the second year. Biennials produce flowers and seeds only during the second year of growth. Angiosperms that take more than two years to grow to maturity are called perennials. Herbaceous perennials such as peonies appear to die each winter but grow and produce flowers each spring. Woody perennials such as fruit trees produce flowers and fruits on stems that survive for many years.

Figure 21
Life cycles of angiosperms include annuals, biennials, and perennials. A These petunias, which are annuals, complete their life cycle in one year. B Parsley plants, which are biennials, do not produce flowers and seeds the first year. C Perennials, such as this pecan tree, flower and produce fruits year after year.

Importance of Seed Plants

What would a day at school be like without seed plants? One of the first things you'd notice is the lack of paper and books. Paper is made from pulp that comes from trees, which are seed plants. Are the desks and chairs at your school made of wood? They'll need to be made of something else if no seed plants exist. Clothing that is made from cotton would not exist because cotton comes from seed plants. When it's time for lunch, you'll have trouble finding something to eat. Bread, fruits, and potato chips all come from plants. Milk, hamburgers, and hot dogs all come from animals that eat seed plants. Unless you like to eat plants such as mosses and ferns, you'll go hungry. Without seed plants, your day at school would be different.

Research Visit the Glencoe Science Web site at **science.glencoe.com** for recent news or magazine articles about the timber industry's efforts to replant conifer trees. In your Science Journal, list the types of trees that are replanted.

Discussion

Why might it be a good idea to plant a flower garden with a mix of annuals and perennials? Students should infer that, aside from the desirability of variety in types of flowers, a garden of all annuals would be a lot of work because it would have to be replanted each year. A mix would include annuals that must be replanted and perennials that will bloom year after year.

Activity

Have the class observe the life cycle of an angiosperm by planting seeds of an annual that will germinate, grow, and bloom within a few weeks. Check with a florist or someone at a home and garden store in your area for suggestions on plants to use. L1

Discussion

Lead a discussion with students about why plants are important. You might ask each student to identify an important aspect of plants in general or the importance of a particular plant. L2

SCIENCE Online

Internet Addresses

Explore the Glencoe Science Web site at **science.glencoe.com** to find out more about topics in this section.

Resource Manager

Chapter Resources Booklet
Reinforcement, p. 25

Performance Assessment in the Science Classroom, p. 61

3 Assess

Reteach

Emphasize the important characteristics that distinguish gymnosperms from angiosperms, or monocots from dicots. Prepare flash cards with a written or visual characteristic of one of the groups on each one. Quiz students by having them quickly respond as you hold up each card. L2

Challenge

If you only know that a plant contains 12 petals, why can't you say for sure whether it is a monocot or dicot? Monocots have petals in multiples of three; dicots have petals in multiples of four or five. Since 12 is divisible by three and four, this characteristic alone won't provide the answer.

Assessment

Performance Assess students' abilities to classify food plants by plant part. Give them several common fruits and vegetables and have students classify them as roots, stems, leaves, fruits, or flowers. roots: yams, beets, carrots; stems: asparagus, white potatoes, ginger; leaves: spinach, lettuce; fruits: tomatoes, cherries; flowers: broccoli, cauliflower Use **Performance Assessment in the Science Classroom,** p. 121. ELL

Table 1 Some Products of Seed Plants

From Gymnosperms	From Angiosperms
lumber, paper, soap, varnish, paints, waxes, perfumes, edible pine nuts, medicines	foods, sugar, chocolate, cotton cloth, linen, rubber, vegetable oils, perfumes, medicines, cinnamon, flavorings (toothpaste, chewing gum, candy, etc.), dyes, lumber

Products of Seed Plants Conifers are the most economically important gymnosperms. Most of the wood used for construction and for paper production comes from conifers such as pines and spruces. Resin, a waxy substance secreted by conifers, is used to make chemicals found in soap, paint, varnish, and some medicines.

The most economically important plants on Earth are the angiosperms. They form the basis of diets for most animals. Angiosperms were the first plants that humans grew. They included grains, such as barley and wheat, and legumes, such as peas and lentils. Angiosperms are also the source of many of the fibers used in clothing. Besides cotton, linen fabrics come from plant fibers. **Table 1** shows just a few of the products of angiosperms and gymnosperms.

Section 3 Assessment

1. What are the characteristics of a seed plant?
2. Compare and contrast the characteristics of gymnosperms and angiosperms.
3. If you are looking at a flower with five petals, is it from a monocot or dicot?
4. Explain why the root system might be the largest part of a plant.
5. **Think Critically** The cuticle and epidermis of leaves are transparent. If they weren't, what might be the result?

Skill Builder Activities

6. **Forming Hypotheses** Examine the leaf diagram in **Figure 14** in this section. What cell structure is found in the guard cells but not in the other epidermal cells? Hypothesize about what guard cells might produce. **For more help, refer to the Science Skill Handbook.**
7. **Using a Word Processor** Use a word-processing program to outline the structures and functions that are associated with roots, stems, and leaves. **For more help, refer to the Technology Skill Handbook.**

Answers to Section Assessment

1. Seed plants have roots, stems, leaves, vascular tissue, and produce seeds.
2. Gymnosperms produce seeds not protected by fruit; most have needle-like, evergreen leaves. Angiosperms produce flowers that become fruits that enclose seeds.
3. It is from a dicot.
4. Roots must absorb large amounts of water and nutrients and anchor plants.
5. Less light would reach the chloroplasts, which would reduce the rate of photosynthesis.
6. Chloroplasts; guard cells produce food (sugar).
7. Answers will vary. Partial sample outline:
   I. Roots
      A. Vascular Tissue
         1. Moves water.
         2. Moves minerals.

Activity

Identifying Conifers

How can you tell a pine from a spruce or a cedar from a juniper? One way is to observe their leaves. The leaves of most conifers are either needlelike—shaped like needles—or scale-like—like the scales on a fish or snake. Examine some conifer branches and identify them using the key to classifying leaves.

What You'll Investigate

How can leaves be used to classify conifers?

Materials

short branches of the following conifers:

pine	fir
cedar	redwood
spruce	arborvitae
Douglas fir	juniper
hemlock	

**illustrations of the conifers above*

**Alternate materials*

Goals

- **Identify** the difference between needlelike and scalelike leaves.
- **Classify** conifers according to their leaves.

Safety Precautions

Wash your hands after handling leaves.

Communicating Your Data

Use the information from the key to identify any conifers that grow on your school grounds. Draw a map that locates and identifies these conifers. Post the map for other students in your school to see. **For more help, refer to the Science Skill Handbook.**

Procedure

1. **Observe** the leaves or illustrations of each conifer, then use the key below to identify it.
2. **Write** the number and name of each conifer you identify in your Science Journal.

Conclude and Apply

1. What are two traits of hemlock leaves?
2. How are pine and cedar leaves alike?

Key to Classifying Conifer Leaves
1. All leaves are needlelike. a. yes, go to 2 b. no, go to 8
2. Needles are in clusters. a. yes, go to 3 b. no, go to 4
3. Clusters contain two, three, or five needles. a. yes, pine b. no, cedar
4. Needles grow on all sides of the stem. a. yes, go to 5 b. no, go to 7
5. Needles grow from a woody peg. a. yes, spruce b. no, go to 6
6. Needles appear to grow from the branch. a. yes, Douglas fir b. no, hemlock
7. Most of the needles grow upward. a. yes, fir b. no, redwood
8. All the leaves are scalelike but not prickly. a. yes, arborvitae b. no, juniper

Activity

BENCH TESTED

Purpose Students observe and classify conifer leaves. L2 ELL

LS **Logical-Mathematical**

Process Skills observing, classifying, comparing and contrasting

Time Required 50 minutes

Safety Precautions Remind students not to eat any plant parts, and to wash their hands thoroughly after handling the leaves.

Teaching Strategy Provide hand lenses for students who want to have a closer look at the structures of the leaves.

Answers to Questions

1. Leaves are needlelike; needles grow on all sides of the stem.
2. Both have needlelike leaves with needles in clusters.

Assessment

Process Direct students to come up with a classification chart similar to the one on this page to classify several broad leaves with very different characteristics. Have students test each other's classification systems. Use **Performance Assessment in the Science Classroom,** p. 121.

Resource Manager

Chapter Resources Booklet

Lab Activities, pp. 9–10, 11–12

Activity Worksheet, pp. 5–6

Communicating Your Data

If possible, have students use a software program to draw their maps. Students can also use a word processing program to make a table that lists the types of conifers and their locations in and around the school grounds.

Activity

BENCH TESTED

Recognize the Problem

Internet Students will use Internet sites that can be accessed through the Glencoe Science Web site at **science.glencoe.com.** They will investigate plants that are used as medicine.

Non-Internet Sources Collect materials describing alternative medicines from nutritionists.

Time Required

three to six days

Preparation

Internet Access the Glencoe Science Web site at **science.glencoe.com** to run through the steps that the students will follow.

Non-Internet Collect books and brochures about plants used as medicine.

Form a Hypothesis

Possible Hypotheses

Students will identify plants that are used as medicine, then hypothesize about their effectiveness. For example, *Echinacea* eases common cold symptoms and peppermint helps an upset stomach.

Activity

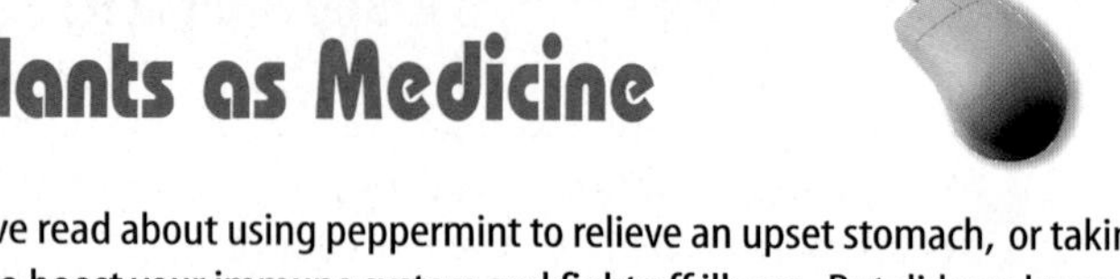

Plants as Medicine

You may have read about using peppermint to relieve an upset stomach, or taking *Echinacea* to boost your immune system and fight off illness. But did you know that pioneers brewed a cough medicine from lemon mint? In this activity, you will explore plants and their historical use in treating illness, and the benefits and risks associated with using plants as medicine.

Echinacea

Recognize the Problem

How are plants used in maintaining good health?

Form a Hypothesis

How do you know that a particular plant helps you stay healthy? If there is conflicting data, how would you evaluate the use of that plant? Form a hypothesis about how to evaluate a plant's use as a medicine.

Goals

- **Identify** two plants that can be used as a treatment for illness or as a supplement to support good health.
- **Research** the cultural and historical use of each of the two selected plants as medical treatments.
- **Review** multiple sources to understand the effectiveness of each of the two selected plants as a medical treatment.
- **Compare and contrast** the research and form a hypothesis about the medicinal effectiveness of each of the two plants.

Monarda

Data Source

SCIENCE*Online* Go to the Glencoe Science Web site at **science.glencoe.com** to get more information about plants that can be used for maintaining good health and for data collected by other students.

Resource Manager

Chapter Resources Booklet
Activity Worksheet, pp. 7–8
Lab Management and Safety, p. 61

Using Scientific Methods

Test Your Hypothesis

Plan

1. Search for information about plants that are used as medicine and identify two plants to investigate.
2. **Research** how these plants are currently recommended for use as medicine or to promote good health. Find out how each has been used historically.
3. **Explore** how other cultures used these plants as a medicine.

Do

1. Make sure your teacher approves your plan before you start.
2. **Record** data you collect about each plant in your Science Journal.

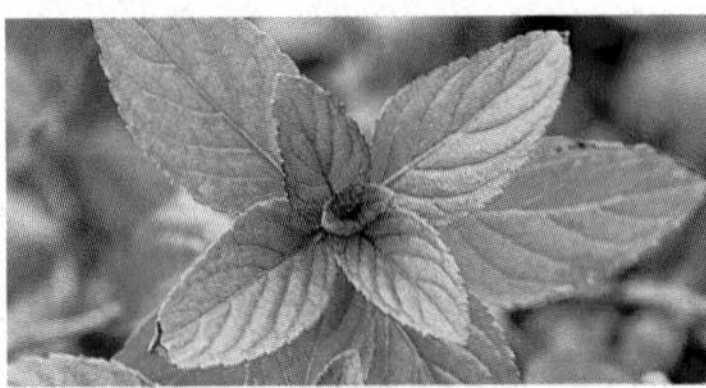

Mentha

Analyze Your Data

1. **Write** a description of how different cultures have used each plant as medicine.
2. How have the plants you investigated been used as medicine historically?
3. **Record** all the uses suggested by different sources for each plant.
4. **Record** the side effects of using each plant as a treatment.

Draw Conclusions

1. After conducting your research, what do you think are the benefits and drawbacks of using these plants as alternative medicines?
2. **Describe** any conflicting information about using each of these plants as medicine.
3. Based on your analysis, would you recommend the use of each of these two plants to treat illness or promote good health? Why or why not?
4. What would you say to someone who was thinking about using any plant-based, over-the-counter, herbal supplement?

Communicating Your Data

SCIENCE Online Find this *Use the Internet* activity on the Glencoe Science Web site at **science.glencoe.com** Post your data for the two plants you investigated in the tables provided. **Compare** your data to those of other students. Review data that other students have entered about other plants that can be used as medicine.

Test Your Hypothesis

Teaching Strategies

Students should identify plants by common names and scientific names.

Troubleshooting Remind students that they may find conflicting information among their references.

Analyze Your Data

Answers will be subjective and based on students' individual research.

Draw Conclusions

Answers will be individualized and often based on students' opinions of their research. Look for depth and quality of research performed.

Portfolio Have students create a guide describing each of the plants they investigated. The guide should include a picture of the plant, how they promote good health, and a summary of the plant's effectiveness. Use **PASC,** p. 129.

SCIENCE Online

Internet Addresses

____

____

____

Explore the Glencoe Science Web site at **science.glencoe.com** to find out more about topics in this activity.

Communicating Your Data

Suggest that students use a combination of their data and that obtained from others to draw their conclusions.

Oops!

Content Background

Hook-and-loop tape was not quickly or easily accepted as a useful invention. George deMestral faced tremendous financial difficulty and great frustration while trying to promote hook-and-loop tape to clothing manufacturers, who saw the fastener as ugly. Astronauts were some of the first to use hook-and-loop tape. It was used to attach food pouches to the walls of spacecraft and astronaut's boots to the floor of the spacecraft. Hook-and-loop tape was slowly accepted as a useful addition to sportswear and equipment. Children's clothing manufacturers then began to view hook-and-loop tape as a useful and attractive material to use.

Discussion

After deMestral had his idea for a new fastener based on the properties of cockleburs, he experimented for years to design hook-and-loop tape. Have students hypothesize why it took years for the idea to become reality. Possible answers: Scientists and inventors must find a material to build their invention with, they might have another job that keeps them from devoting long hours to their project, and many details must be worked out of any design before it takes shape as a product.

Oops! Accidents in SCIENCE

SOMETIMES GREAT DISCOVERIES HAPPEN BY ACCIDENT!

A Loopy Idea Inspires "Fasten-ating" Invention

A wild cocklebur plant inspired the hook-and-loop fastener.

The idea for a hook-and-loop fastener comes from nature

266

Resources for Teachers and Students

Why Didn't I think of That?, by Allyn Freeman and Bob Golden, John Wiley & Sons, Inc., 1997.

Mistakes that Worked, by Charlotte Foltz Jones, Doubleday, 1991.

Inventing, Inventions and Inventors: A Teaching Resource Book, by Jerry D. Flack, Teacher Ideas Press, 1989.

Scientists often spend countless hours in the laboratory dreaming up useful inventions. Sometimes, however, the best ideas hit them in unexpected places at unexpected times. That's why scientists are constantly on the lookout for things that spark their curiosity.

One day in 1948, a Swiss inventor named George deMestral strolled through a field with his dog. When they returned home, deMestral discovered that the dog's fur was covered with cockleburs, parts of a prickly plant. These burs were also stuck to deMestral's jacket and pants. Curious about what made the burs so sticky, the inventor examined one under a microscope.

DeMestral noticed that the cocklebur was covered with lots of tiny hooks. By clinging to animal fur and fabric, this plant is carried to other places. While studying these burs, he got the idea to invent a new kind of fastener that could do the work of buttons, snaps, zippers, and laces—but better!

Hook-and-loop fasteners provide fun at some amusement parks. You can attach yourself to the sticky material!

After years of experimentation, deMestral came up with a strong, durable hook-and-loop fastener made of two strips of nylon fabric. One strip has thousands of small, stiff hooks; the other strip is covered with soft, tiny loops. Today, this hook-and-loop fastening tape is used on shoes and sneakers, watchbands, hospital equipment, space suits, clothing, book bags, and more. You may have one of those hook-and-loop fasteners somewhere on you right now. They're the ones that go rippppppppp when you open them.

So, if you ever get a fresh idea that clings to your mind like a hook to a loop, stick with it and experiment! Who knows? It may lead to a fabulous invention that changes the world!

This photo provides a close-up view of a hook-and-loop fastener.

CONNECTIONS **List** Make a list of at least ten ways that hook-and-loop tape is used today. Think of three new uses for it. Since you can buy strips of hook-and-loop fastening tape in most hardware and fabric stores, you could even try out some of your favorite ideas.

SCIENCE Online

For more information, visit science.glencoe.com

Activity

Students should work in groups to examine a small sample of hook-and-loop tape with a hand lens. If possible, provide a cocklebur for the students to examine as well. Student groups should make a visual that describes the fastener with words or diagrams.

Analyze the Event

Ask students what characteristics allowed George deMestral to develop his hook-and-loop fastener. Possible answers: He was observant, he persevered through years of developing the invention, he was determined to have his invention accepted by clothing manufacturers. Stress that deMestral faced great personal difficulty while developing his product. It was financially very difficult, and many of his friends told him to give up his idea. Point out that the road from invention to finished product is not simple or easy.

CONNECTIONS Encourage students to think creatively when making their lists of uses and potential uses for hook-and-loop tape. Possible answers for today's uses of hook-and-loop tape include clothing, shoes, backpacks, toys and watches. What potential uses can students think of that don't involve clothing? How about ideas that involve automotive design, the arts, musical composition, or engineering?

SCIENCE Online

Internet Addresses

Explore the Glencoe Science Web site at **science.glencoe.com** to find out more about topics in this feature.

Chapter 9 Study Guide

Reviewing Main Ideas

Preview

Students can answer the questions in their Science Journals. Discuss the answers as you go through the chapter. LS **Linguistic**

Review

Students can write their answers, then compare them with those of other students. LS **Interpersonal**

Reteach

Students can look at the illustrations and describe details that support the main ideas of the chapter. LS **Visual-Spatial**

Answers to Chapter Review

Section 1

3. Possible answers: cuticle, vascular tissue, seeds, ability to store water, spines

Section 2

3. spores

Section 3

3. Needlelike leaves reduce water loss; seeds are produced in cones.

Chapter 9 Study Guide

Reviewing Main Ideas

Section 1 An Overview of Plants

1. Plants are made up of eukaryotic cells and vary greatly in size and shape.
2. Plants usually have some form of leaves, stems, and roots.
3. As plants evolved from aquatic to land environments, changes in structure and function occurred. Changes included how they reproduced, supported themselves, and moved substances from one part of the plant to another. *What adaptations does the plant shown above need to survive?*

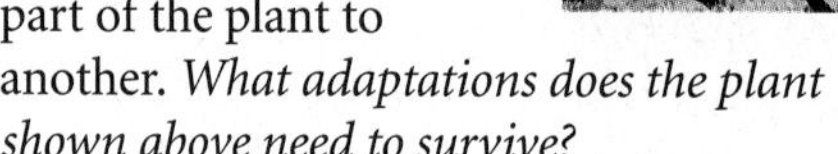

4. The plant kingdom is classified into groups called divisions.

Section 2 Seedless Plants

1. Seedless plants include nonvascular and vascular types.
2. Seedless nonvascular plants have no true leaves, stems, or roots. Reproduction usually is by spores.
3. Club mosses, horsetails, and ferns are seedless vascular plants. They have vascular tissues that move substances throughout the plant. These plants may reproduce by spores. *What is produced in these fern structures?*

4. Many ancient forms of these plants underwent a process that resulted in the formation of coal.

Section 3 Seed Plants

1. Seed plants are adapted to survive in nearly every environment on Earth.
2. Seed plants produce seeds and have vascular tissue, stems, roots, and leaves. Vascular tissues transport food, water, and dissolved substances in the roots, stems, and leaves.
3. The two major groups of seed plants are gymnosperms and angiosperms. Gymnosperms generally have needlelike leaves and some type of cone. Angiosperms are plants that flower and are classified as monocots or dicots. *What is the importance of these structures to gymnosperms?*
4. Seed plants provide food, shelter, clothing, and many other products. They are the most economically important plants on Earth.

FOLDABLES Reading & Study Skills — **After You Read**

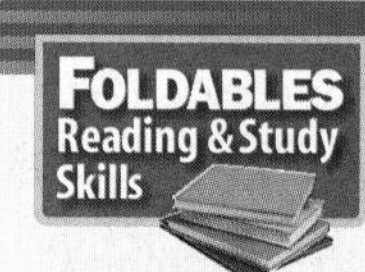

Use the information that you recorded in your Know-Want-Learned Study Fold to explain the characteristics of plants you see every day.

FOLDABLES Reading & Study Skills — **After You Read**

After students have read the chapter and completed the Foldable described in Before You Read, have them do the activity on the student page.

Dinah Zike

Visualizing Main Ideas

Complete the following concept map about the seed plants.

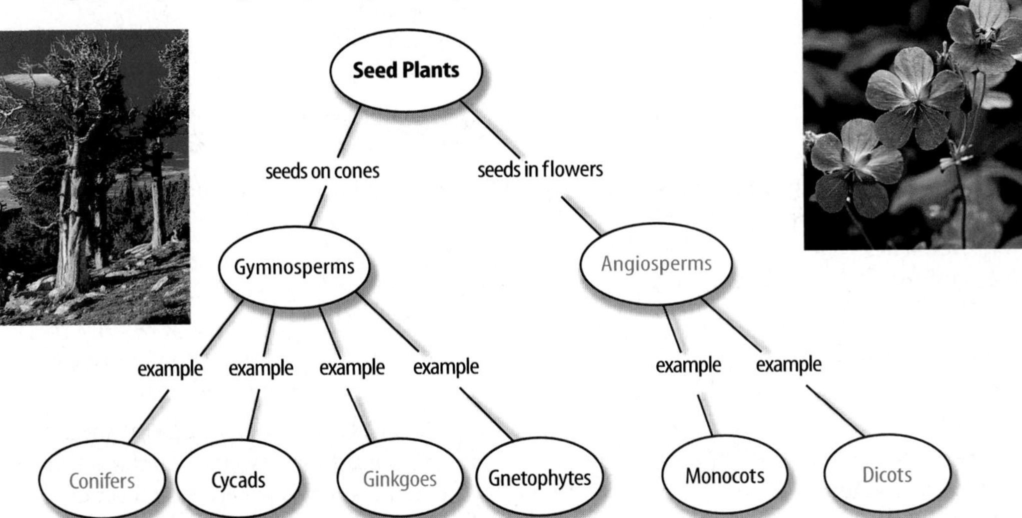

Vocabulary Review

Vocabulary Words

- **a.** angiosperm
- **b.** cambium
- **c.** cellulose
- **d.** cuticle
- **e.** dicot
- **f.** guard cell
- **g.** gymnosperm
- **h.** monocot
- **i.** nonvascular plant
- **j.** phloem
- **k.** pioneer species
- **l.** rhizoid
- **m.** stomata
- **n.** vascular plant
- **o.** xylem

Study Tip

THE PRINCETON REVIEW

Don't just memorize definitions. Write complete sentences using new vocabulary words to be certain you understand what they mean.

Using Vocabulary

Complete each analogy by providing the missing vocabulary word.

1. Angiosperm is to flower as _____ is to cone.
2. Dicot is to two seed leaves as _____ is to one seed leaf.
3. Root is to fern as _____ is to moss.
4. Phloem is to food transport as _____ is to water transport.
5. Vascular plant is to horsetail as _____ is to liverwort.
6. Cellulose is to support as _____ is to protect.
7. Fuel is to ferns as _____ is to bryophytes.
8. Cuticle is to wax as _____ is to fibers.

Chapter 9 Study Guide

Visualizing Main Ideas

See student page.

Vocabulary Review

Using Vocabulary

1. gymnosperm
2. monocot
3. rhizoid
4. xylem
5. nonvascular plant
6. cuticle
7. pioneer species
8. cellulose

Chapter 9 Assessment

Checking Concepts

1. C
2. A
3. C
4. B
5. D
6. C
7. A
8. D
9. C
10. A

Thinking Critically

11. The plant might lose so much water that it would wilt or die.
12. Flowering plants all have vascular tissue.
13. Succulents grow naturally in dry environments.
14. They must grow in moist environments because they don't have vascular tissue for water or nutrient transport. All of their cells must absorb water from the environment.
15. Pioneer species help to break down rocks and make small pockets of soil needed by other, larger plants.

Chapter 9 Assessment

Checking Concepts

Choose the word or phrase that best answers the question.

1. Which of the following is a seedless vascular plant?
   A) moss **C)** horsetail
   B) liverwort **D)** pine
2. What are the small openings in the surface of a leaf surrounded by guard cells called?
   A) stomata **C)** rhizoids
   B) cuticles **D)** angiosperms
3. What are the plant structures that anchor the plant called?
   A) stems **C)** roots
   B) leaves **D)** guard cells
4. Where is most of a plant's new xylem and phloem produced?
   A) guard cell **C)** stomata
   B) cambium **D)** cuticle
5. What group has plants that are only a few cells thick?
   A) gymnosperms **C)** ferns
   B) cycads **D)** mosses
6. Which of the following plant parts is found only on gymnosperms?
   A) flowers **C)** cones
   B) seeds **D)** fruit
7. What kinds of plants have structures that move water and other substances?
   A) vascular **C)** nonvascular
   B) protist **D)** bacterial
8. In what part of a leaf does most photosynthesis occur?
   A) epidermis **C)** stomata
   B) cuticle **D)** palisade layer
9. Which one of the following do ferns have?
   A) cones **C)** spores
   B) rhizoids **D)** seeds
10. Which of these is an advantage to life on land for plants?
    A) more direct sunlight
    B) less carbon dioxide
    C) greater space to grow
    D) less competition for food

Thinking Critically

11. What might happen if a land plant's waxy cuticle were destroyed?
12. On a walk through the woods with a friend, you find a plant neither of you has seen before. The plant is herbaceous and has yellow flowers. Your friend says it is a vascular plant. How does your friend know this?
13. Plants called succulents store large amounts of water in their leaves, stems, and roots. In what environments would you expect to find succulents growing naturally?
14. Explain why mosses are usually found in moist areas.
15. How do pioneer species change environments so that other plants can grow there?

Developing Skills

16. **Interpreting Data** What do the data in this table tell you about where gas exchange occurs in each plant leaf?

Stomata (per mm^2)		
Plant	**Upper Surface**	**Lower Surface**
Pine	50	71
Bean	40	281
Fir	0	228
Tomato	12	13

17. **Making and Using Graphs** Make two circle graphs using the table in question 16.

Chapter Assessment Planner

Portfolio Encourage students to place in their portfolios one or two items of what they consider to be their best work. Examples include:

- Activity, p. 245
- Make a Model, p. 251
- Curriculum Connection, p. 257

Performance Additional performance assessments, Performance Task Assessment Lists, and rubrics for evaluating these activities can be found in Glencoe's **Performance Assessment in the Science Classroom.**

18. **Concept Mapping** Complete this map for the seedless plants of the plant kingdom.

Seedless Plants — No transport tissue → Nonvascular plants — examples → Mosses, liverworts, and hornworts

Seedless Plants — Transport tissue → Vascular plants — example → Ferns; example → Horsetails; example → Club mosses

19. **Interpreting Scientific Illustrations** Using **Figure 20** in this chapter, compare and contrast the number of cotyledons, bundle arrangement in the stem, veins in leaves, and number of flower parts for monocots and dicots.

20. **Concept Mapping** Put the following events in order to show how coal is formed from plants: *living seedless plants, coal is formed, dead seedless plants decay,* and *peat is formed.*

Performance Assessment

21. **Poem** Choose a topic in this chapter that interests you. Look it up in a reference book, in an encyclopedia, or on a CD-ROM. Write a poem to share what you learn.

Technology

Go to the Glencoe Science Web site at **science.glencoe.com** or use the **Glencoe Science CD-ROM** for additional chapter assessment.

THE PRINCETON REVIEW Test Practice

Maria and Josh are studying how different environmental factors affect the growth of plants. They set up four pots. Each pot contains a different plant growing in a standard potting soil. They record their data in the following table.

Plant Growth Data

Type of Plant	Hours of Light	Amount of Water (mL)	Percent Growth
Moss	0	100	2%
Lettuce	4	100	15%
Tree Seedling	8	100	40%
Grape Vine	12	100	65%

Study the table and answer the following questions.

1. According to this information, which is the most likely cause of the differences in plant growth?
   A) light
   B) water
   C) plant type
   D) soil

2. How could this experiment be improved?
   F) Vary the amount of water each plant receives.
   G) Record plant growth in cm.
   H) Use only one kind of plant.
   J) Expose each plant to the same number of hours of light.

Assessment Resources

Reproducible Masters

Chapter Resources Booklet
Chapter Review, pp. 33–34
Chapter Tests, pp. 35–38
Assessment Transparency Activity, p. 45

Glencoe Science Web site
Interactive Tutor
Chapter Quizzes

Glencoe Technology
Assessment Transparency
Interactive CD-ROM Chapter Quizzes
ExamView Pro Test Bank
Vocabulary PuzzleMaker Software
MindJogger Videoquiz

THE PRINCETON REVIEW Test Practice

The Test-Taking Tip was written by The Princeton Review, the nation's leader in test preparation.

1. A
2. H

Developing Skills

16. Gas exchange for pine and tomato leaves is nearly the same on both the upper and lower surfaces because the number of stomata on each are about equal. Most of the gas exchange for bean leaves occurs on the lower surface. All gas exchange for fir needles happens on the lower surface.
17. The upper-surface graph should show 177° for pine, 141° for bean, and 42° for tomato. The lower-surface graph should show 43° for pine, 171° for bean, 138° for fir, and 8° for tomato.
18. See student page.
19. Monocots have one seed leaf, scattered vascular bundles, parallel veins in leaves, and flower parts in multiples of three. Dicots have two seed leaves, vascular bundles in rings, a network of veins in leaves, and flower parts in multiples of four or five.
20. Living seedless plants, dead seedless plants decay, peat is formed, coal is formed.

Performance Assessment

21. Have students share their poems with the class. Use **PASC**, p. 157.

CHAPTER 10 PLANT REPRODUCTION

Section/Objectives	Standards		Activities/Features
	National	State/Local	
Chapter Opener	See p. 5T for a Key to Standards.		**Explore Activity:** Predict where seeds are found, p. 273 **Before You Read,** p. 273
Section 1 Introduction to Plant Reproduction 2 sessions 1 block 1. **Distinguish** between the two types of plant reproduction. 2. **Describe** the two stages in a plant's life cycle.	National Content Standards: UCP3, A1, C1, C2		**MiniLAB:** Observing Asexual Reproduction, p. 275 **Science Online,** p. 276
Section 2 Seedless Reproduction 2 sessions 1 block 1. **Examine** the life cycles of a moss and a fern. 2. **Explain** why spores are important to seedless plants. 3. **Identify** some special structures used by ferns for reproduction.	National Content Standards: UCP5, A1, C1, C2, C5		**Physics Integration,** p. 280 **Activity:** Comparing Seedless Plants, p. 282
Section 3 Seed Reproduction 3 sessions 1.5 blocks 1. **Examine** the life cycles of typical gymnosperms and angiosperms. 2. **Describe** the structure and function of the flower. 3. **Discuss** methods of seed dispersal in seed plants.	National Content Standards: UCP5, A1, C1, C2, C5, E2, F5		**Science Online,** p. 284 **Environmental Science Integration,** p. 286 **MiniLAB:** Modeling Seed Dispersal, p. 290 **Visualizing Seed Dispersal,** p. 291 **Math Skills Activity:** Calculating the Number of Seeds That Will Germinate, p. 292 **Activity:** Germination Rate of Seeds, pp. 294–295 **Science and Society:** Genetic Engineering, pp. 296–297

NATIONAL GEOGRAPHIC

Teacher's Corner

PRODUCTS AVAILABLE FROM GLENCOE
To order call 1-800-334-7344:
CD-ROM: NGS PictureShow: *Plants: What It Means to Be Green*
Transparency Set
NGS PicturePack: *Plants: What It Means to Be Green*

PRODUCTS AVAILABLE FROM NATIONAL GEOGRAPHIC SOCIETY
To order call 1-800-368-2728:
Video: *Pollination*

INDEX TO NATIONAL GEOGRAPHIC SOCIETY
The following articles may be used for research relating to this chapter: "Bats—The Cactus Connection," by Merlin D. Tuttle, June 1991; "Hummingbirds: The Nectar Connection," by Paul W. Ewald, Feb. 1982; "The Exquisite Orchids," by Luis Marden, April 1971; "The Wasp That Plays Cupid to a Fig," by Robert F. Sisson, Nov. 1970; "Crossroads of the Insect World," by J.W. MacSwain, Dec. 1966.

Activity Materials	Reproducible Resources	Section Assessment	Technology
Explore Activity: 2 different types of grapes, plastic knife, paper towels	**Chapter Resources Booklet** Foldables Worksheet, p. 15 Directed Reading Overview, p. 17 Note-taking Worksheets, pp. 31–33	GLENCOE'S ASSESSMENT ADVANTAGE	
MiniLAB: scissors, coleus or other houseplant, cup, water, small container of soil	**Chapter Resources Booklet** Transparency Activity, p. 42 MiniLAB, p. 3 Enrichment, p. 28 Reinforcement, p. 25 Directed Reading, p. 18 **Cultural Diversity,** p. 19	**Portfolio** Assessment, p. 277 **Performance** MiniLAB, p. 275 Skill Builder Activities, p. 277 **Content** Section Assessment, p. 277	Section Focus Transparency Interactive CD-ROM Guided Reading Audio Program
Activity: live mosses, liverworts, and ferns with gametophytes and sporophytes; hand lens; forceps; dropper; microscope slide and coverslip (2); microscope; dissecting needle; pencil with eraser	**Chapter Resources Booklet** Transparency Activity, p. 43 Enrichment, p. 29 Reinforcement, p. 26 Directed Reading, p. 18 Transparency Activity, pp. 45–46 Activity Worksheet, pp. 5–6	**Portfolio** Make a Model, p. 280 **Performance** Skill Builder Activities, p. 281 **Content** Section Assessment, p. 281	Section Focus Transparency Teaching Transparency Interactive CD-ROM Guided Reading Audio Program
MiniLAB: buttons, glue, paper, string, other common materials **Activity:** seeds, water, salt, potting soil, plant trays or plastic cups, thermometer, graduated cylinder, beakers	**Chapter Resources Booklet** Transparency Activity, p. 44 MiniLAB, p. 4 Enrichment, p. 30 Reinforcement, p. 27 Directed Reading, pp. 19, 20 Lab Activity, pp. 9–12, 13–14 Activity Worksheet, pp. 7–8 **Lab Management and Safety,** p. 38	**Portfolio** Activity, p. 285 **Performance** MiniLAB, p. 290 Math Skills Activity, p. 292 Skill Builder Activities, p. 293 **Content** Section Assessment, p. 293	Section Focus Transparency Interactive CD-ROM Guided Reading Audio Program

Need materials? Contact Science Kit at 1-800-828-7777 or www.sciencekit.com on the Internet.

End of Chapter Assessment

GLENCOE'S ASSESSMENT ADVANTAGE

Blackline Masters	Technology	Professional Series
Chapter Resources Booklet Chapter Review, pp. 35–36 Chapter Tests, pp. 37–40 **Standardized Test Practice by The Princeton Review,** pp. 47–50	MindJogger Videoquiz Interactive CD-ROM Vocabulary PuzzleMakers ExamView Pro Test Bank Interactive Lesson Planner Interactive Teacher Edition	Performance Assessment in the Science Classroom (PASC)

Transparencies

Section Focus

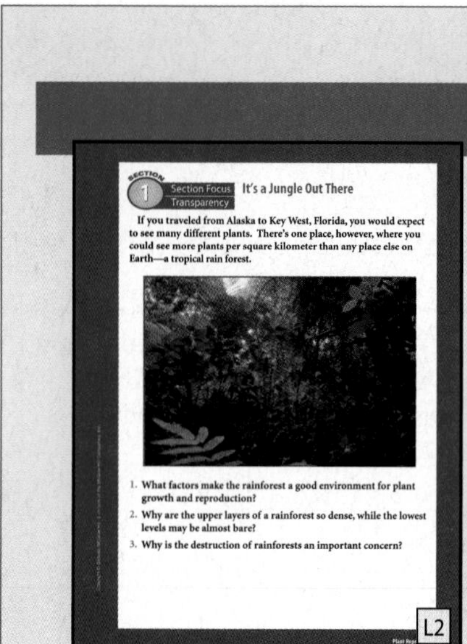
Section 1 Section Focus Transparency — It's a Jungle Out There

If you traveled from Alaska to Key West, Florida, you would expect to see many different plants. There's one place, however, where you could see more plants per square kilometer than any place else on Earth—a tropical rain forest.

1. What factors make the rainforest a good environment for plant growth and reproduction?
2. Why are the upper layers of a rainforest so dense, while the lowest levels may be almost bare?
3. Why is the destruction of rainforests an important concern?

L2

Section 2 Section Focus Transparency — It's Raining, It's Sporing

While flowering plants use seeds to reproduce, mosses use a different strategy. As seen below, one part of moss reproduction involves releasing spores into the environment. Each spore is capable of growing into a new plant.

1. Judging from the picture, how are moss spores dispersed?
2. Why does the moss produce so many spores?

L2

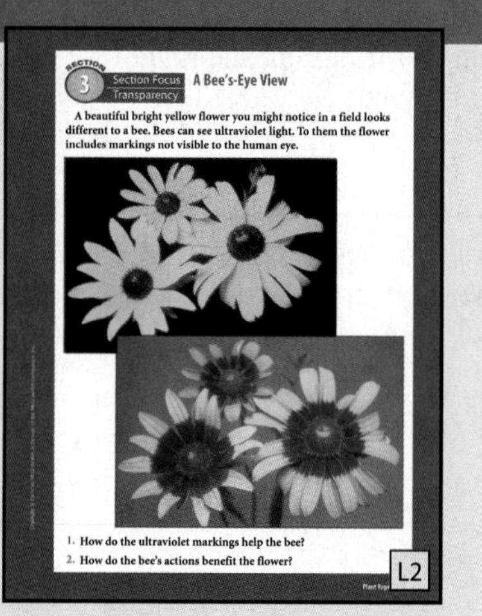
Section 3 Section Focus Transparency — A Bee's-Eye View

A beautiful bright yellow flower you might notice in a field looks different to a bee. Bees can see ultraviolet light. To them the flower includes markings not visible to the human eye.

1. How do the ultraviolet markings help the bee?
2. How do the bee's actions benefit the flower?

L2

This is a representation of key blackline masters available in the Teacher Classroom Resources. See Resource Manager boxes within the chapter for additional information.

Assessment

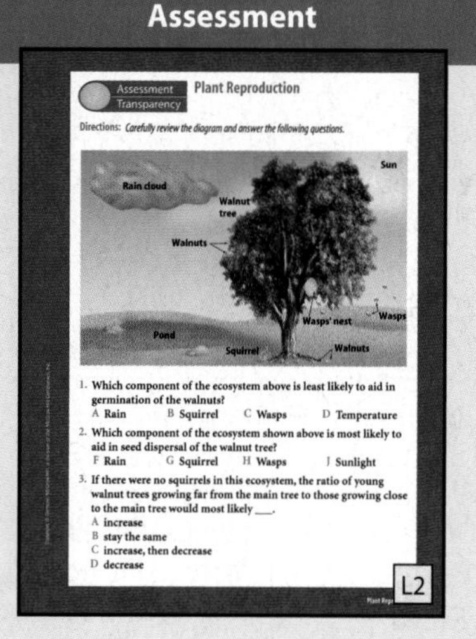
Assessment Transparency — Plant Reproduction

Directions: *Carefully review the diagram and answer the following questions.*

1. Which component of the ecosystem above is least likely to aid in germination of the walnuts?
   A Rain B Squirrel C Wasps D Temperature
2. Which component of the ecosystem shown above is most likely to aid in seed dispersal of the walnut tree?
   F Rain G Squirrel H Wasps J Sunlight
3. If there were no squirrels in this ecosystem, the ratio of young walnut trees growing far from the main tree to those growing close to the main tree would most likely ____.
   A increase
   B stay the same
   C increase, then decrease
   D decrease

L2

Teaching

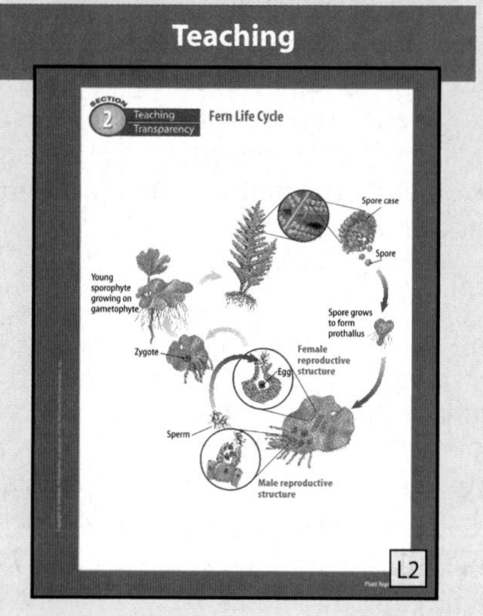
Section 2 Teaching Transparency — Fern Life Cycle

L2

Key to Teaching Strategies

The following designations will help you decide which activities are appropriate for your students.

L1 Level 1 activities should be appropriate for students with learning difficulties.

L2 Level 2 activities should be within the ability range of all students.

L3 Level 3 activities are designed for above-average students.

ELL ELL activities should be within the ability range of English Language Learners.

COOP LEARN Cooperative Learning activities are designed for small group work.

LS Multiple Learning Styles logos, as described on page 22T, are used throughout to indicate strategies that address different learning styles.

P These strategies represent student products that can be placed into a best-work portfolio.

Hands-on Activities

Activity Worksheets

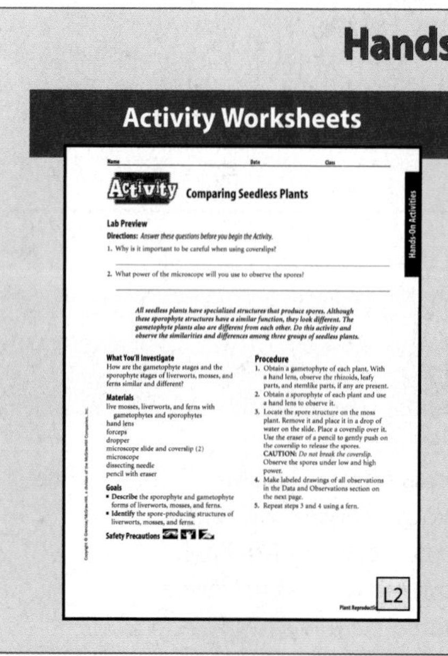
Name Date Class

Activity — Comparing Seedless Plants

Lab Preview

Directions: *Answer these questions before you begin the Activity.*

1. Why is it important to be careful when using coverslips?
2. What power of the microscope will you use to observe the spores?

All seedless plants have specialized structures that produce spores. Although these sporophyte structures have a similar function, they look different. The gametophyte plants also are different from each other. Do this activity and observe the similarities and differences among three groups of seedless plants.

What You'll Investigate

How are the gametophyte stages and the sporophyte stages of liverworts, mosses, and ferns similar and different?

Materials

live mosses, liverworts, and ferns with gametophytes and sporophytes
hand lens
forceps
dropper
microscope slide and coverslip (2)
microscope
dissecting needle
pencil with eraser

Goals

- **Describe** the sporophyte and gametophyte forms of liverworts, mosses, and ferns.
- **Identify** the spore-producing structures of liverworts, mosses, and ferns.

Safety Precautions

Procedure

1. Obtain a gametophyte of each plant. With a hand lens, observe the rhizoids, leafy parts, and stemlike parts, if any are present.
2. Obtain a sporophyte of each plant and use a hand lens to observe it.
3. Locate the spore structure on the moss plant. Remove it and place it in a drop of water on the slide. Place a coverslip over it. Use the eraser of a pencil to gently push on the coverslip to release the spores. CAUTION: *Do not break the coverslip.* Observe the spores under low and high power.
4. Make labeled drawings of all observations in the Data and Observations section on the next page.
5. Repeat steps 3 and 4 using a fern.

Hands-On Activities

L2

Plant Reproduction

Laboratory Activities

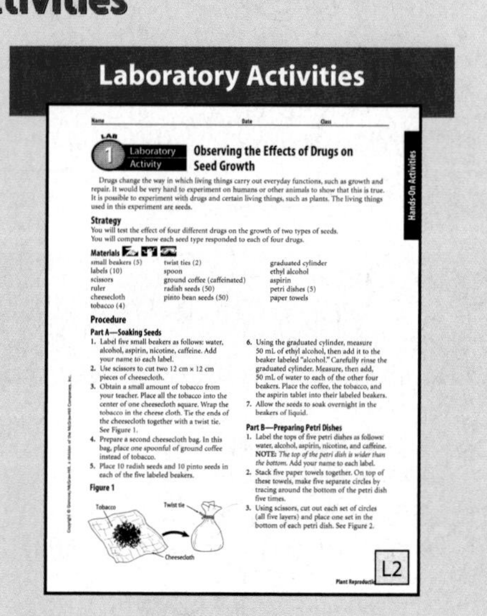
Name Date Class

Lab 1 Laboratory Activity — Observing the Effects of Drugs on Seed Growth

Drugs change the way in which living things carry out everyday functions, such as growth and repair. It would be very hard to experiment on humans or other animals to show that this is true. It is possible to experiment with drugs and certain living things, such as plants. The living things used in this experiment are seeds.

Strategy

You will test the effect of four different drugs on the growth of two types of seeds.
You will compare how each seed type responded to each of four drugs.

Materials

small beakers (5)
labels (10)
scissors
ruler
cheesecloth
tobacco (4)
twist ties (2)
spoon
ground coffee (caffeinated)
radish seeds (50)
pinto bean seeds (50)
graduated cylinder
ethyl alcohol
aspirin
petri dishes (5)
paper towels

Procedure

Part A—Soaking Seeds

1. Label five small beakers as follows: water, alcohol, aspirin, nicotine, caffeine. Add your name to each label.
2. Use scissors to cut two 12 cm × 12 cm pieces of cheesecloth.
3. Obtain a small amount of tobacco from your teacher. Place all the tobacco into the center of one cheesecloth square. Wrap the tobacco in the cheese cloth. Tie the ends of the cheesecloth together with a twist tie. See Figure 1.
4. Prepare a second cheesecloth bag. In this bag, place one spoonful of ground coffee instead of tobacco.
5. Place 10 radish seeds and 10 pinto seeds in each of the five labeled beakers.

Figure 1

Tobacco
Twist tie
Cheesecloth

6. Using the graduated cylinder, measure 50 mL of ethyl alcohol, then add it to the beaker labeled "alcohol." Carefully rinse the graduated cylinder. Measure, then add, 50 mL of water to each of the other four beakers. Place the coffee, the tobacco, and the aspirin tablet into their labeled beakers.
7. Allow the seeds to soak overnight in the beakers of liquid.

Part B—Preparing Petri Dishes

1. Label the tops of five petri dishes as follows: water, alcohol, aspirin, nicotine, and caffeine. NOTE: *The top of the petri dish is wider than the bottom.* Add your name to each label.
2. Stack five paper towels together. On top of these towels, make five separate circles by tracing around the bottom of the petri dish five times.
3. Using scissors, cut out each set of circles (all five layers) and place one set in the bottom of each petri dish. See Figure 2.

Hands-On Activities

L2

Plant Reproduction

Meeting Different Ability Levels

Content Outline

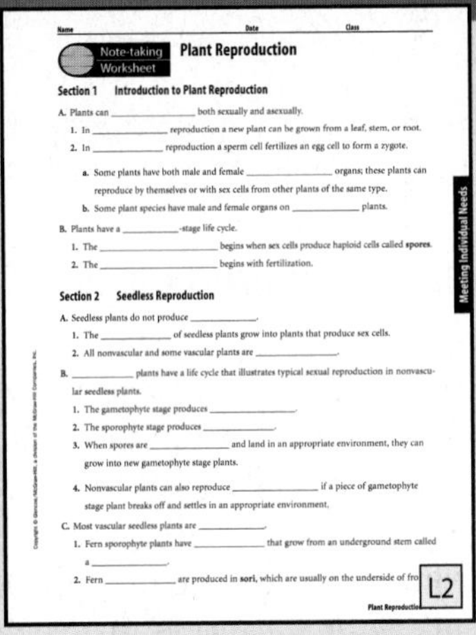
Note-taking Worksheet
Plant Reproduction
Section 1 Introduction to Plant Reproduction
Section 2 Seedless Reproduction
L2

Reinforcement

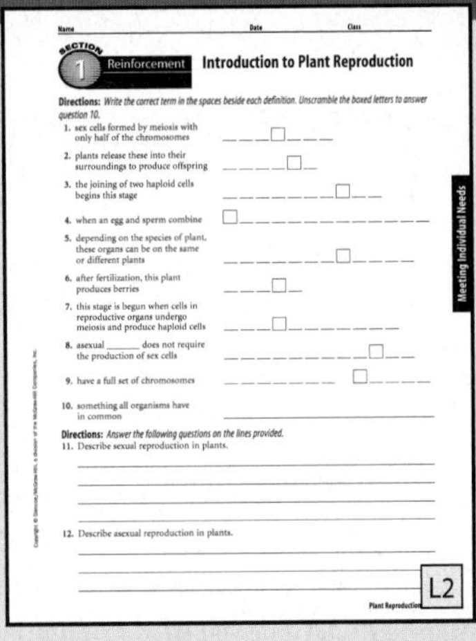
Reinforcement
Introduction to Plant Reproduction
L2

Directed Reading

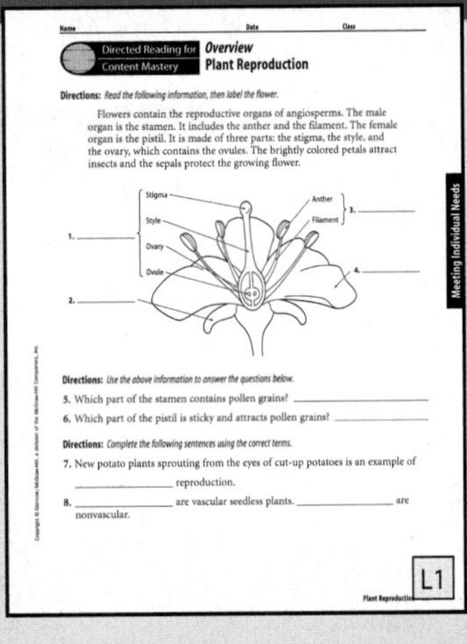
Directed Reading for Content Mastery
Overview
Plant Reproduction
L1

Enrichment

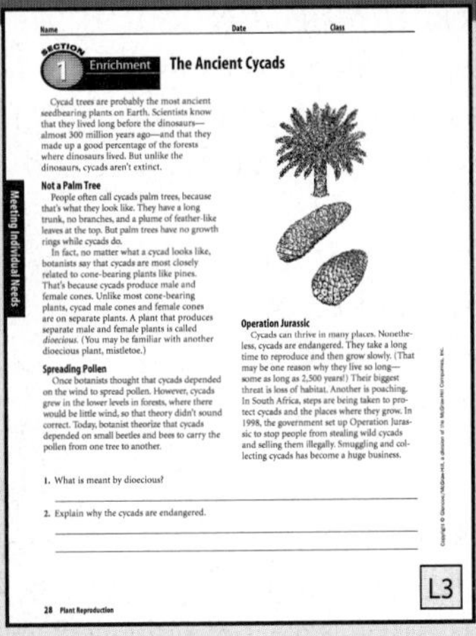
Enrichment
The Ancient Cycads
Not a Palm Tree
Spreading Pollen
Operation Jurassic
L3

Spanish Directed Reading

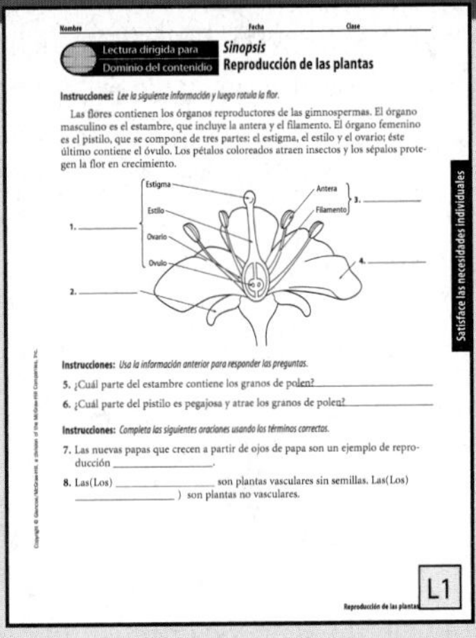
Lectura dirigida para Dominio del contenido
Sinopsis
Reproducción de las plantas
L1

Assessment

Chapter Tests

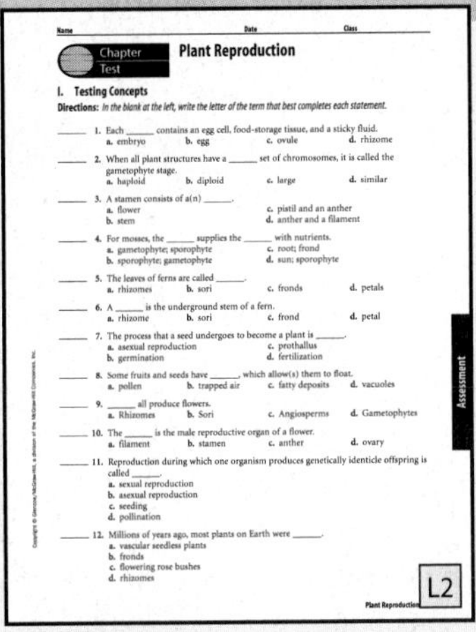
Chapter Test
Plant Reproduction
I. Testing Concepts
L2

Test Practice Workbook

Standardized Test Practice
Teacher Edition
Glencoe Science
Life Science
L2

Chapter Review

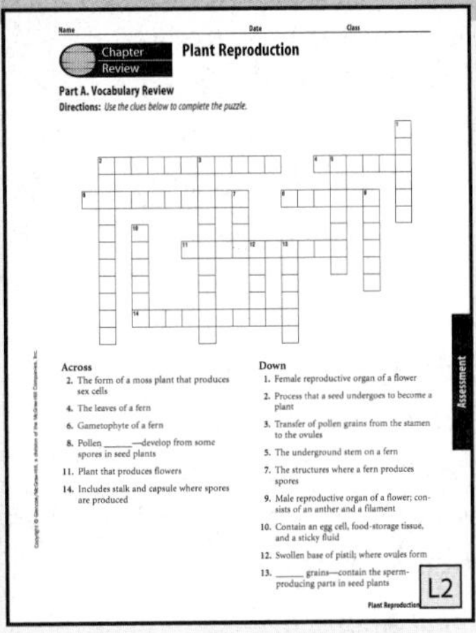
Chapter Review
Plant Reproduction
Part A. Vocabulary Review
Across
Down
L2

Science Content Background

SECTION 1 Introduction to Plant Reproduction

Types of Reproduction

Asexual reproduction is a common method of reproduction in plants. Asexual reproduction works best in appropriate environments that change little over long periods of time. The advantage of asexual reproduction is the ability to produce large numbers of offspring that have the same genetic makeup as the parent plant. Such asexual reproduction is cloning. Many commercially grown plants, such as orchids and African violets, are routinely cloned.

Fun Fact

Of the approximate 230,000 known species of flowering plants, the *Wolffia augusta* is one of the tiniest. One will easily fit through the eye of an ordinary sewing needle. Five thousand will easily fit in a sewing thimble.

The genetic diversity of plants is increased through sexual reproduction. Sexual reproduction allows plants to evolve and invade new habitats or adapt when the environment changes.

Haploid and Diploid Stages

In all plant life cycles, there are haploid and diploid stages. In some plants, the stages are separate and unique and referred to as an alternation of generations. Alternation of generations evolved with the ancestors of the plant kingdom, the ancient Chlorophyta, or green algae. A diploid sporophyte ($2n$) generation alternates with a haploid gametophyte generation (n). *Sporophyte* means "spore-producing" and *gametophyte* means "gamete-producing." These terms indicate the reproductive function of the plant. In some plants these are distinct organisms, but in others they are part of the larger organism.

Meiosis occurs in specialized cells of the sporophyte, the spore mother cells, and results in the production of spores. Spores produce the gametophyte by mitosis. In time, gametophytes produce haploid gametes. A male and a female gamete unite to form a diploid zygote, the first cell in the multicellular sporophyte.

SECTION 2 Seedless Reproduction

Seedless Plants

In mosses, liverworts, and hornworts, the gametophyte is the familiar plant that makes its own food by photosynthesis. The sporophyte generation in mosses is found at the tip of the gametophyte and consists of a stalk with a capsule in which spores are produced by meiosis.

Fern spores germinate into a filamentous

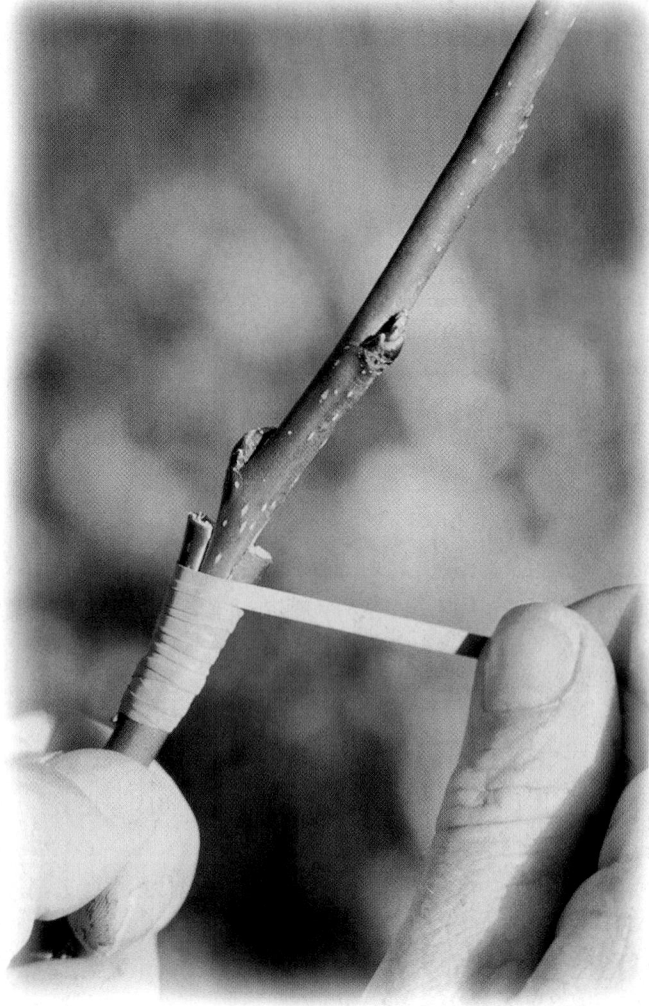

D. Cavagnaro/DRK Photo

plant that eventually grows into an inconspicuous heart-shaped gametophyte called a prothallus. The gametophyte is independent and carries on photosynthesis. Fern sporophytes have leaves called fronds. Fronds produce spores in specialized packets called sori (singular, *sorus*) that are often misidentified as a plant disease.

D. Cavagnaro/DRK Photo

SECTION 3 Seed Reproduction

Gymnosperm Reproduction

Gymnosperms are unique among seed plants because the ovules of their seeds are not completely enclosed by tissue produced by the sporophyte.

The sporophytes, or $2n$ generations of gymnosperms, are familiar trees and shrubs like pines, junipers, and spruces. Ovulate cones and pollen-bearing cones are produced on separate stems. The female cones of gymnosperms vary from the familiar woody cones to fleshy, berry-like cones. Berrylike cones are often colorful, such as the red ones on yews and the bluish ones on junipers. Many gymnosperm cones complete their life cycle in one year, but some take two or three years for maturation.

All but about 35,000 of the 235,000 species of plants today are characterized by their production of seeds.

Germination

Seeds are efficient units of dispersal for plants, and many have elaborate adaptations for moving away from the parent plant. Germination, the growth of a plant from a seed, is affected by many factors, such as temperature, amount of light, presence of moisture and presence of oxygen. Some seeds lay dormant, waiting for the appropriate set of conditions for germination.

Fun Fact

The number of seeds per fruit ranges from one—in fruits such as peaches and plums—to several hundred in pumpkins and other squashes. It has been reported that a tropical plant, *Rafflesia keithii,* produced a fruit with 273,000 seeds.

SCIENCE Online

For additional content background on this topic, go to the Glencoe Science Web site at science.glencoe.com.

CHAPTER 10

Plant Reproduction

Chapter Vocabulary

gametophyte stage, p. 277
spore, p. 277
sporophyte stage, p. 277
frond, p. 280
rhizome, p. 280
sori, p. 280
prothallus, p. 280
pollen grain, p. 283
pollination, p. 283
ovule, p. 285
stamen, p. 287
pistil, p. 287
ovary, p. 287
germination, p. 292

What do you think?

Science Journal The photo shows a flower of grass. This is not the typical showy flower most students are familiar with, but many plants have flowers of this type.

CHAPTER 10

Plant Reproduction

Saplings and other plants grow among the remains of trees that were destroyed by fire. Where did these new plants come from? Did they grow from seeds that survived the fire? Perhaps they grew from plant roots and stems that survived underground. In either case, these plants are the result of plant reproduction. In this chapter, you will learn how different groups of plants reproduce and how plants can be dispersed from place to place.

What do you think?

Science Journal Look at the picture below with a classmate. Discuss what this might be. Here's a hint: *In many plants these are colorful and have pleasant aromas.* Write your answer or best guess in your Science Journal.

Theme Connection

Systems and Interactions This chapter emphasizes the mechanisms and systems of reproduction in plants.

You might know that most plants grow from seeds. Seeds are usually found in the fruits of plants. When you eat watermelon, it can contain many small seeds. Do all fruits contain seeds? Do this activity to find out.

Predict where seeds are found

1. Obtain two grapes from your teacher. Each grape should be from a different plant.
2. Split each grape in half and examine the insides of each grape. **WARNING:** *Do not eat the grapes.*

Observe

Were seeds found in both grapes? Hypothesize how new grape plants could be grown if no seeds are produced. In your Science Journal list three other fruits you know of that do not contain seeds.

Before You Read

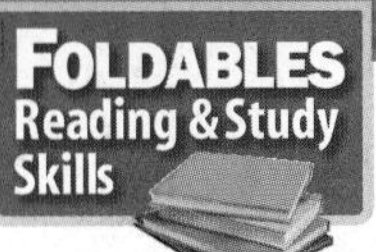

FOLDABLES Reading & Study Skills

Making a Venn Diagram Study Fold **Make the following Foldable to compare and contrast sexual and asexual characteristics of a plant.**

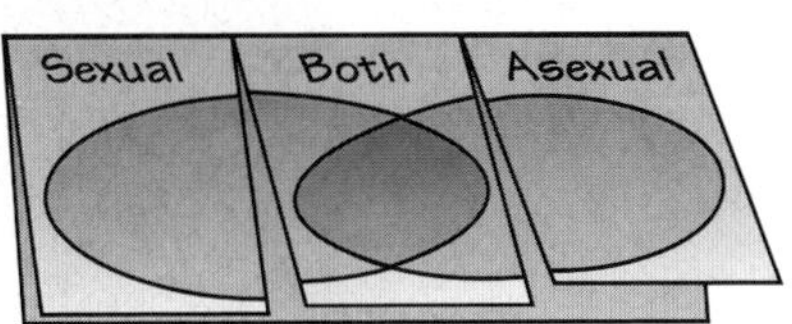

1. Place a sheet of paper in the front of you so the long side is at the top. Fold the paper in half from top to bottom.
2. Fold both sides in. Unfold the paper so three sections show.
3. Through the top thickness of the paper, cut along each of the fold lines to the top fold, forming three tabs. Label each tab *Sexual, Both,* and *Asexual* as shown.
4. Before you read the chapter, draw circles across the front of the page, as shown.
5. As you read the chapter write information about sexual and asexual reproduction under the left and right tabs.

273

Explore Activity

Purpose Use the Explore Activity to introduce students to the ideas of sexual and asexual reproduction. Inform students that they will learn more about plant reproduction in this chapter. L1 ELL LS **Visual-Spatial**

Preparation Purchase both seedless and seeded grapes.

Materials grapes, plastic knife, paper towels

Teaching Strategies

- Be sure each student has both a seedless and a seeded grape.
- Have students cover their work surfaces with a paper towel.
- Be sure students wash their hands after handling the grapes.

Observe

A seed was found in only one of the grapes. Hypotheses should indicate that some method other than seeds is responsible for producing seedless grape plants. Seedless fruits include bananas, some watermelons, and some oranges.

✓Assessment

Process Show students several fruits—some with seeds and some without. Have them classify the plants from which the fruits came as able to reproduce sexually or only asexually. Use **Performance Assessment in the Science Classroom,** p. 121.

Before You Read

FOLDABLES Reading & Study Skills

Dinah Zike Study Fold

Purpose Students make and use a Foldable to collect information on sexual and asexual reproduction in plants. They then use what they have learned to compare and contrast the two.

For additional help, see Foldables Worksheet, p. 15 in **Chapter Resources Booklet,** or go to the Glencoe Science Web site at **science.glencoe.com.** See After You Read in the Study Guide at the end of this chapter.

SECTION

Introduction to Plant Reproduction

1 Motivate

Bellringer Transparency

Display the Section Focus Transparency for Section 1. Use the accompanying Transparency Activity Master. L2 ELL

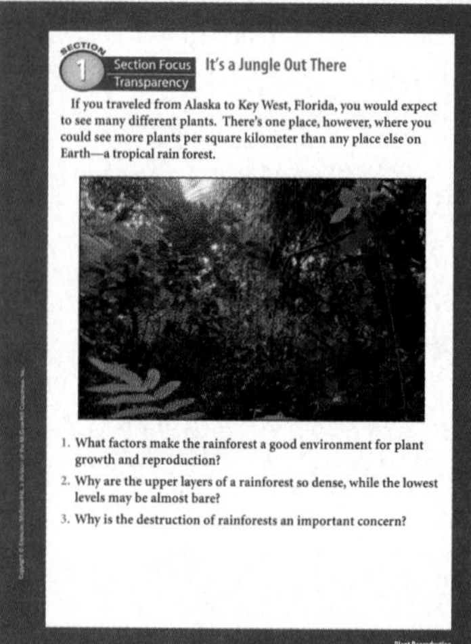

Section Focus Transparency 1 — It's a Jungle Out There

If you traveled from Alaska to Key West, Florida, you would expect to see many different plants. There's one place, however, where you could see more plants per square kilometer than any place else on Earth—a tropical rain forest.

1. What factors make the rainforest a good environment for plant growth and reproduction?
2. Why are the upper layers of a rainforest so dense, while the lowest levels may be almost bare?
3. Why is the destruction of rainforests an important concern?

Tie to Prior Knowledge

Ask students if they have ever seen a plant being rooted from a leaf cutting. Students may have seen an African violet or similar plant being propagated in this way. Explain that what they have observed is a form of asexual reproduction and that this is one way some plants reproduce.

SECTION 1

Introduction to Plant Reproduction

As You Read

***What* You'll Learn**

- **Distinguish** between the two types of plant reproduction.
- **Describe** the two stages in a plant's life cycle.

Vocabulary

spore
gametophyte stage
sporophyte stage

***Why* It's Important**

You can grow new plants without using seeds.

Types of Reproduction

Do people and plants have anything in common? You don't have leaves or roots, and a plant doesn't have a heart or a brain. Despite these differences, you are alike in many ways—you need water, oxygen, energy, and food to grow. Like humans, plants also can reproduce and make similar copies of themselves. Although humans have only one type of reproduction, most plants can reproduce in two different ways, as shown in **Figure 1.**

Sexual reproduction in plants and animals requires the production of sex cells—usually called sperm and eggs—in reproductive organs. The offspring produced by sexual reproduction are genetically different from either parent organism.

A second type of reproduction is called asexual reproduction. This type of reproduction does not require the production of sex cells. During asexual reproduction, one organism produces offspring that are genetically identical to it. Most plants have this type of reproduction, but humans and most other animals don't.

Figure 1
Many plants reproduce sexually with flowers that contain male and female parts.

A In crocus flowers, bees and other insects help get the sperm to the egg.

B Other plants can reproduce asexually. A cutting from this impatiens plant can be placed in water and will grow new roots. This new plant can then be planted in soil.

Section Assessment Planner

PORTFOLIO
Assessment, p. 277

PERFORMANCE ASSESSMENT
Try at Home MiniLAB, p. 275
Skill Builder Activities, p. 277
See page 300 for more options.

CONTENT ASSESSMENT
Section, p. 277
Challenge, p. 277
Chapter, pp. 300–301

274 CHAPTER 10 Plant Reproduction

Figure 2
Asexual reproduction in plants takes many forms.

A The eyes on these potatoes have begun to sprout. If a potato is cut into pieces, each piece that contains an eye can be planted and will grow into a new potato plant.

B The grass plants spread by reproducing asexually.

Asexual Plant Reproduction Do you like to eat oranges and grapes that have seeds, or do you like seedless fruit? If these plants do not produce seeds, how do growers get new plants? Growers can produce new plants by asexual reproduction because many plant cells have the ability to grow into a variety of cell types. New plants can be grown from just a few cells in the laboratory. Under the right conditions, an entire plant can grow from one leaf or just a portion of the stem or root. When growers use these methods to start new plants, they must make sure that the leaf, stem, or root cuttings have plenty of water and anything else that they need to survive.

Asexual reproduction has been used to produce plants for centuries. The white potatoes shown in **Figure 2A** were probably produced asexually. Many plants, such as lawn grasses shown in **Figure 2B,** can spread and cover wide areas because their stems grow underground and produce new grass plants asexually along the length of the stem.

Sexual Plant Reproduction Although plants and animals have sexual reproduction, there are differences in the way that it occurs. An important event in sexual reproduction is fertilization. Fertilization occurs when a sperm and egg combine to produce the first cell of the new organism, the zygote. How do the sperm and egg get together in plants? In some plants, water or wind help bring the sperm to the egg. For other plants, animals such as insects help bring the egg and sperm together.

Reading Check *How does fertilization occur in plants?*

Mini LAB

Observing Asexual Reproduction

Procedure
1. Using a pair of **scissors,** cut a stem with at least two pairs of leaves from a **coleus or another houseplant.**
2. Carefully remove the bottom pair of leaves.
3. Place the cut end of the stem into a **cup that is half-filled with water** for two weeks. Wash your hands.
4. Remove the new plant from the water and plant it in a small **container of soil.**

Analysis
1. Draw and label your results in your **Science Journal.**
2. Predict how the new plant and the plant from which it was taken are genetically related.

2 Teach

Types of Reproduction

Mini LAB

Purpose Students will observe the asexual reproduction of a houseplant. L2 ELL
LS **Kinesthetic**

Materials coleus plant, glass of water, scissors, container of soil

Teaching Strategy Tell students to choose a young stem rather than a tougher, older one.

Analysis
1. Drawings should show the growth of a new plant in the soil. Plants should have roots, stems, and leaves.
2. The plants are genetically identical.

Assessment

Performance Have students repeat the activity with a different plant that can be propagated from a leaf or a root. Use **PASC,** p. 97.

Quick Demo

Show students a strawberry plant with runners. Explain that runners are one means of reproducing asexually.

Extension

If there is a university nearby, arrange a field trip to see a tissue culture laboratory, or have individual students arrange such a visit and report their observations to the class.

Reading Check

Answer Wind, water, or animals may carry the sperm to the egg in plants.

Resource Manager 

Chapter Resources Booklet
Transparency Activity, p. 42
Directed Reading for Content Mastery, pp. 17, 18
MiniLAB, p. 3

Teacher FYI

Tissue culture allows many plants to be grown quickly from one plant with a desirable trait. This method also produces disease-free plants. Plants routinely cloned using tissue culture include orchids, tobacco, chrysanthemums, potatoes, strawberries, asparagus, and gladioli.

Types of Reproduction, continued

Extension

Have students research cloning as it relates to asexual reproduction of plants and write about how cloning is an important activity in tree farming.

Internet Addresses

Explore the Glencoe Science Web site at **science.glencoe.com** to find out more about topics in this section.

Plant Life Cycles

Use Science Words

Word Meaning Have students research the meanings of the prefixes and suffixes that make up the words *sporophyte* and *gametophyte*. *Spor-* is derived from a Greek word meaning "seed;" *-phyte* from a Greek word meaning "plant;" *gamet-* from a Greek word meaning "to marry." Thus the gametophytes produce sex cells that will "marry" to form the sporophyte, or seed-producing stage in a plant's life cycle. L2 LS **Linguistic**

Figure 3
Some plants can fertilize themselves. Others require two different plants before fertilization can occur.

A Flowers of pea plants contain male and female structures, and each flower can fertilize itself.

B These holly flowers contain only male reproductive structures, so they can't fertilize themselves.

C Compare the flowers of this female holly plant to those of the male plant.

Reproductive Organs A plant's female reproductive organs produce eggs and male reproductive organs produce sperm. Depending on the species, these reproductive organs can be on the same plant or on separate plants, as shown in **Figure 3.** If a plant has both organs, it usually can reproduce by itself. However, some plants that have both sex organs still must exchange sex cells with other plants of the same type to reproduce.

SCIENCE Online

Research Visit the Glencoe Science Web site at **science.glencoe.com** to find out more about male and female plants. In your Science Journal, list four plants that have male and female repoductive structures on separate plants.

In some plant species, the male and female reproductive organs are on separate plants. For example, holly plants are either female or male. For fertilization to occur, holly plants with flowers that have different sex organs must be near each other. In that case, after the eggs in female holly flowers are fertilized, berries can form.

Another difference between you and a plant is how and when plants produce sperm and eggs. You will begin to understand this difference as you examine the life cycle of a plant.

Plant Life Cycles

All organisms have life cycles. Your life cycle started when a sperm and an egg came together to produce the zygote that would grow and develop into the person you are today. A plant also has a life cycle. It can start when an egg and a sperm come together, eventually producing a mature plant.

Resource Manager

Chapter Resources Booklet
- Note-taking Worksheets, pp. 31–33
- Enrichment, p. 28
- Reinforcement, p. 25

Cultural Diversity, p. 19

Visual Learning

Figure 4 Plant life cycles can be very confusing. Help students break down the words *haploid* and *diploid* and relate them to the numbers of chromosomes contained in the cells of each plant stage. haploid—half the number of chromosomes; diploid—full number of chromosomes

Two Stages During your life cycle, all structures in your body are formed by cell division and made up of diploid cells—cells with a full set of chromosomes. However, sex cells form by meiosis and are haploid—they have half a set of chromosomes.

Plants have a two-stage life cycle, as shown in **Figure 4.** The two stages are the gametophyte (guh MEE tuh fite) stage and the sporophyte (SPOHR uh fite) stage.

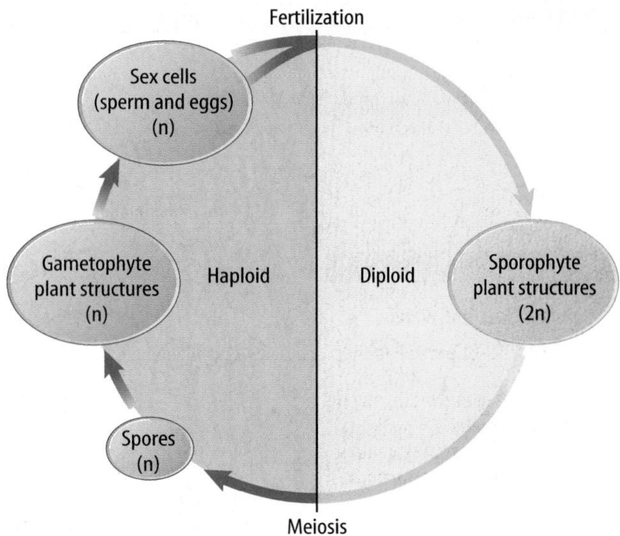

Figure 4
Plants produce diploid and haploid plant structures.

Gametophyte Stage When cells in reproductive organs undergo meiosis and produce haploid cells called **spores,** the **gametophyte stage** begins. Some plants release spores into their surroundings. Spores divide by cell division to form plant structures or an entire new plant. The cells in these structures or plants are haploid. Some of these cells undergo cell division and form sex cells.

Sporophyte Stage Fertilization—the joining of haploid sex cells—begins the **sporophyte stage.** Cells formed in this stage have the diploid number of chromosomes. Meiosis occurs in some of these plant structures to form spores, and the cycle begins again.

Section  Assessment

1. Name two types of plant reproduction.
2. Compare and contrast the gametophyte stage and the sporophyte stage.
3. Describe how plants can be grown using asexual reproduction.
4. Explain how sexual reproduction is different in plants and animals.
5. **Think Critically** You see a plant that you like and want to grow an identical one. What type of plant reproduction would you use? Why?

Skill Builder Activities

6. **Drawing Conclusions** You use a microscope to observe the nuclei of several cells from a plant. Each one has only half the number of chromosomes you would expect. What do you conclude about this stage of its life cycle? **For more help, refer to the** Science Skill Handbook.
7. **Communicating** In your Science Journal write your own analogy about the diploid and haploid stages of a plant life cycle. **For more help, refer to the** Science Skill Handbook.

3 Assess

Reteach

Have students work in small groups to prepare three multiple-choice questions about the general types of plant reproduction. Have groups take turns asking and answering each other's questions. COOP LEARN

Challenge

Work with students to make a list of the advantages and disadvantages of asexual reproduction. When the list has been compiled, have students debate this statement: Asexual reproduction has no advantages over sexual reproduction. Advantages—asexual reproduction is usually faster than sexual reproduction; it takes only one plant, so there is no need to find a "mate"; and in a stable environment, lack of genetic variation may be advantageous. Disadvantages—asexual reproduction does not provide genetic diversity because there is no genetic recombination.

✔Assessment

Portfolio Have students write a poem that includes information about sexual and asexual reproduction. Use **Performance Assessment in the Science Classroom,** p. 151. P

Answers to Section Assessment

1. asexual and sexual
2. The gametophyte stage is haploid. The sporophyte stage is diploid.
3. Some plants grow asexually from leaves, stems, roots, runners, or other plant parts.
4. In animals, only sex cells are haploid. In plants, all the cells in the gametophyte stage of the life cycle are haploid.
5. A type of asexual reproduction (stem, leaf, or tip cutting); plants produced through these methods are identical to the parent plant.
6. Based on the number of chromosomes, students should conclude that it is in the haploid stage.
7. Answers will vary. Analogies should have alternating parts such as up and down, or in and out, for example.

Seedless Reproduction

1 Motivate

Bellringer Transparency

Display the Section Focus Transparency for Section 2. Use the accompanying Transparency Activity Master. L2 ELL

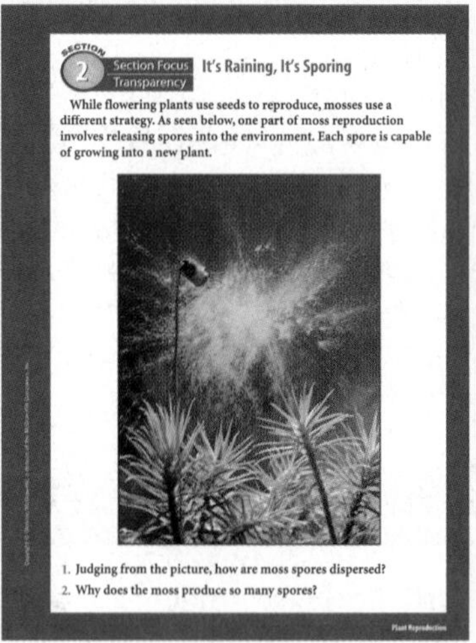

Section Focus Transparency
It's Raining, It's Sporing
While flowering plants use seeds to reproduce, mosses use a different strategy. As seen below, one part of moss reproduction involves releasing spores into the environment. Each spore is capable of growing into a new plant.
1. Judging from the picture, how are moss spores dispersed?
2. Why does the moss produce so many spores?

Tie to Prior Knowledge

Ask students to tell where they have seen mosses growing in nature. Most will indicate that they have seen these plants growing in damp places in wooded areas. Tell students that in this section, they will learn why these plants need to be in damp areas.

Seedless Reproduction

As You Read

What **You'll Learn**

- **Examine** the life cycles of a moss and a fern.
- **Explain** why spores are important to seedless plants.
- **Identify** some special structures used by ferns for reproduction.

Vocabulary

frond
rhizome
sori
prothallus

Why **It's Important**

Seedless plants have adaptations for reproduction on land.

The Importance of Spores

If you want to grow plants like ferns and moss plants, you can't go to a garden store and buy a package of seeds—they don't produce seeds. You could, however, grow them from spores. These plants produce haploid spores at the end of their sporophyte stage in structures called spore cases. When the spore case breaks open, the spores are released and spread by wind or water. The spores, shown in **Figure 5,** can grow into plants that will produce sex cells.

Seedless plants include all nonvascular plants and some vascular plants. Nonvascular plants do not have structures that transport water and substances throughout the plant. Instead, water and substances simply move from cell to cell. Vascular plants have tubelike cells that transport water and substances throughout the plant.

Nonvascular Seedless Plants

If you walked in a damp, shaded forest, you probably would see mosses covering the ground or growing on a log. Mosses, liverworts, and hornworts are all nonvascular plants.

The sporophyte stage of most nonvascular plants is so small that it can be easily overlooked. Moss plants have a life cycle that is typical of how sexual reproduction occurs in this plant group.

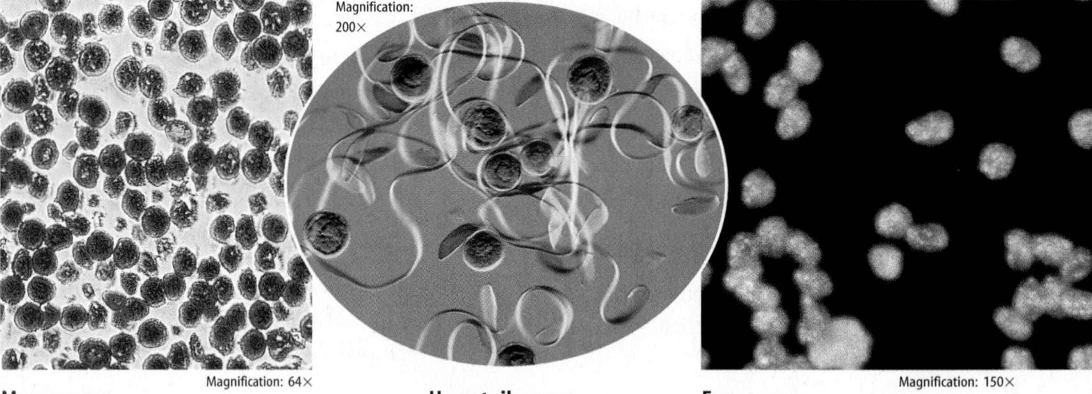

Figure 5
Spores come in a variety of shapes. All spores are small and have a waterproof coating. Some, like the horsetail spores, have winglike structures that uncoil and allow them to be blown easily by the wind.

Section Assessment Planner

Portfolio
Make a Model, p. 280

Performance Assessment
Skill Builder Activities, p. 281
See page 300 for more options.

Content Assessment
Section, p. 281
Challenge, p. 281
Chapter, pp. 300–301

The Moss Life Cycle You recognize mosses as green, low-growing masses of plants. This is the gametophyte stage, which produces the sex cells. But the next time you see some moss growing, get down and look at it closely. If you see any brownish stalks growing up from the tip of the gametophyte plants, you are looking at the sporophyte stage. The sporophyte stage does not carry on photosynthesis. It depends on the gametophyte for nutrients and water. On the tip of the stalk is a tiny capsule. Inside the capsule millions of spores have been produced. When environmental conditions are just right, the capsule opens and the spores either fall to the ground or are blown away by the wind. New moss gametophytes can grow from each spore and the cycle begins again, as shown in **Figure 6.**

Figure 6
The life cycle of a moss alternates between gametophyte and sporophyte stages. *What is produced by the gametophyte stage?*

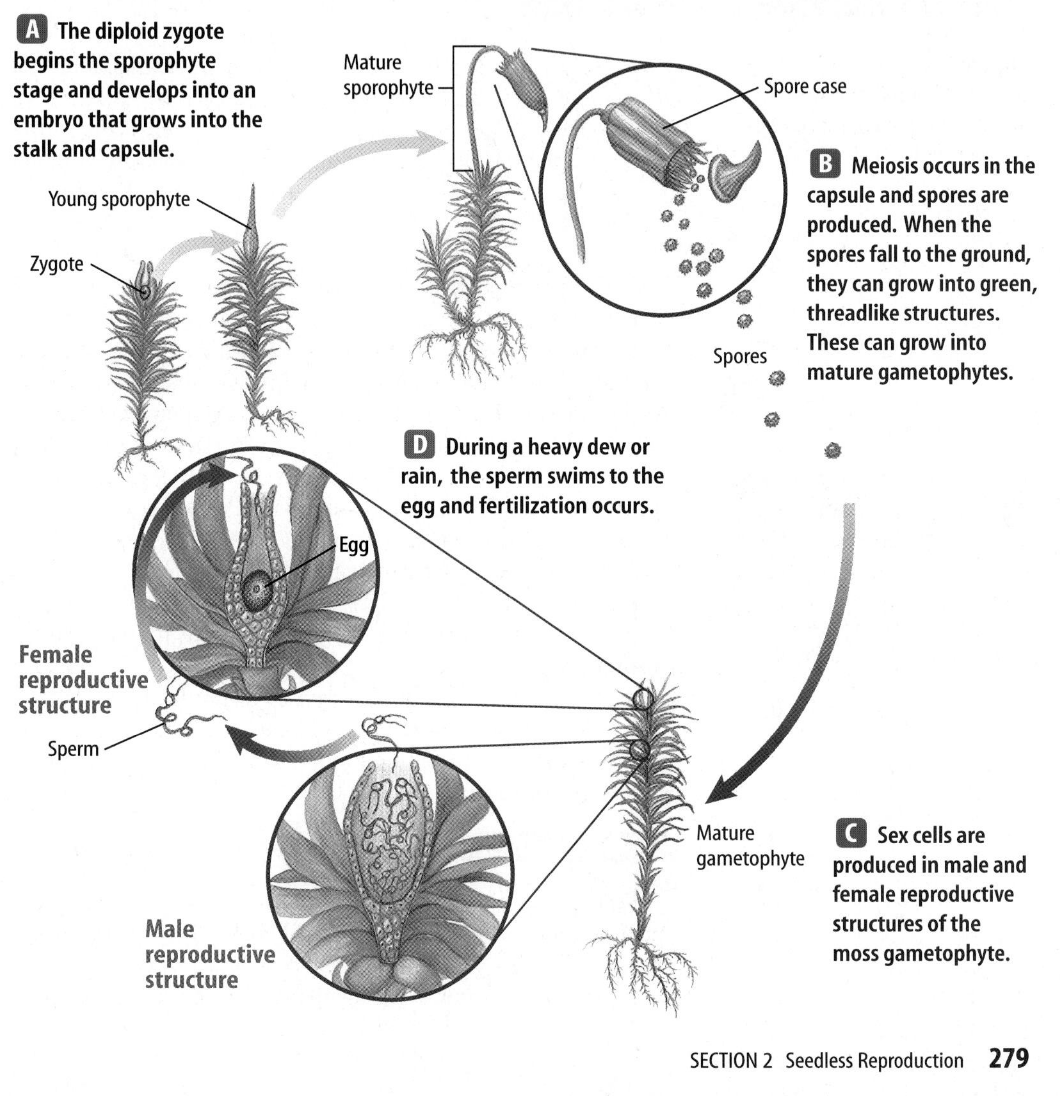

A The diploid zygote begins the sporophyte stage and develops into an embryo that grows into the stalk and capsule.
Mature sporophyte
Spore case
Young sporophyte
Zygote
B Meiosis occurs in the capsule and spores are produced. When the spores fall to the ground, they can grow into green, threadlike structures. These can grow into mature gametophytes.
Spores
D During a heavy dew or rain, the sperm swims to the egg and fertilization occurs.
Egg
Female reproductive structure
Sperm
Mature gametophyte
C Sex cells are produced in male and female reproductive structures of the moss gametophyte.
Male reproductive structure

2 Teach

Nonvascular Seedless Plants

Discussion

Explain that a single moss capsule may release 50 million spores. Ask students what advantages the production of so many spores provides to moss plants. It increases the likelihood that some spores will find a suitable environment and develop into new moss plants, thus aiding in the survival of the species.

Caption Answer

Figure 6 sex cells (eggs and sperm)

Activity

Have the class make a terrarium that includes mosses. Have students observe these plants as they grow, mature, and produce spores from their capsules.

Visual Learning

Figure 6 Have students trace the different stages in the diagram, following the arrows. Again emphasize that the gametophyte produces sex cells (egg and sperm) that unite to form the sporophyte, which produces spores. Review with students the number of chromosomes contained by cells at each stage. Then give student pairs drawings of the stages of moss life cycle on 3 × 5 cards. Have students sequence and label the drawings.

Curriculum Connection

History Have students find out how humans have used moss gametophytes historically. Have students make posters to present their findings. Mosses were once used as bandages during wars because of their absorbency and antiseptic properties.

Resource Manager

Chapter Resources Booklet
- Transparency Activity, p. 43
- Directed Reading for Content Mastery, p. 18
- Enrichment, p. 29

Teacher FYI

Some mosses possess strands of vascular tissue. This tissue is not arranged or differentiated to the extent found in other vascular plants.

Nonvascular Seedless Plants, continued

Visual Learning

Figure 7 Ask students to explain why the balls of cells that grow in the cups shown in the picture are a form of asexual reproduction. These balls of cells do not need to be fertilized in order to grow into a new plant. Thus, they are a form of asexual reproduction.

Make a Model

Have students make drawings, flowcharts, or other models to show the stages of a moss's or fern's life cycle. Their models should include both gametophyte and sporophyte generations. P

Vascular Seedless Plants

Discussion

Ask students to hypothesize how much time a plant spends in each phase of its life cycle. Allow them to explain their answers. Nonvascular plants spend most of their life cycle in the gametophyte phase. Most vascular plants spend most of their life cycle in the sporophyte stage.

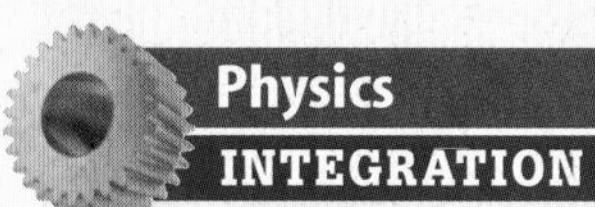

Possible answers: machines that toss tennis balls and skeet throwers

Answer prothallus

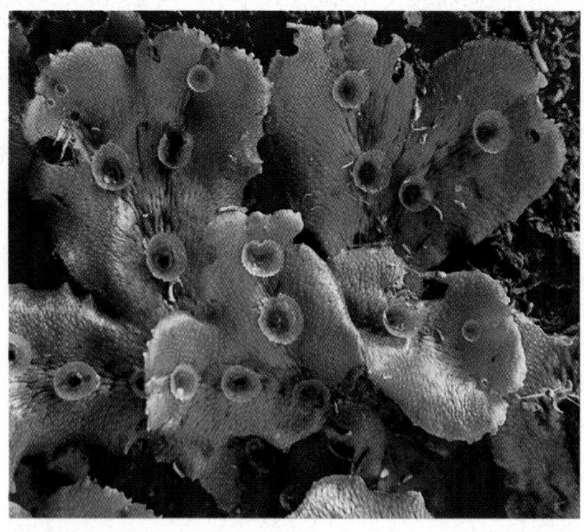

Figure 7
Small balls of cells grow in cup-like structures on the surface of the liverwort.

Nonvascular Plants and Asexual Reproduction Nonvascular plants also can reproduce asexually. For example, if a piece of a moss gametophyte plant breaks off, it can grow into a new plant. Liverworts can form small balls of cells on the surface of the gametophyte plant, as shown in **Figure 7.** These are carried away by water and grow into new gametophyte plants if they settle in a damp environment.

Vascular Seedless Plants

Millions of years ago most plants on Earth were vascular seedless plants. Today they are not as widespread.

Most vascular seedless plants are ferns. Other plants in this group include horsetails and club mosses. All of these plants have vascular tissue to transport water from their roots to the rest of the plant. Unlike the nonvascular plants, the gametophyte of vascular seedless plants is the part that is small and often overlooked.

The Fern Life Cycle The fern plants that you see in nature or as houseplants are fern sporophyte plants. Fern leaves are called **fronds.** They grow from an underground stem called a **rhizome.** Roots that anchor the plant and absorb water and nutrients also grow from the rhizome. Fern sporophytes make their own food by photosynthesis. Fern spores are produced in structures called **sori** (singular, *sorus*), usually located on the underside of the fronds. Sori can look like crusty rust-, brown-, or dark-colored bumps. Sometimes they are mistaken for a disease or for something growing on the fronds.

If a fern spore lands on damp soil or rocks, it can grow into a small, green, heart-shaped gametophyte plant called a **prothallus** (proh THA lus). A prothallus is hard to see because most of them are only about 5 mm to 6 mm in diameter. The prothallus contains chlorophyll and can make its own food. It absorbs water and nutrients from the soil. The life cycle of a fern is shown in **Figure 8.**

Physics INTEGRATION
Catapults have been used by humans for thousands of years to launch objects. The spore cases of ferns act like tiny catapults as they eject their spores. In your Science Journal list tools, toys, and other objects that use catapult technology to work.

Reading Check ***What is the gametophyte plant of a fern called?***

Ferns may reproduce asexually, also. Fern rhizomes grow and form branches. New fronds and roots develop from each branch. The new rhizome branch can be separated from the main plant. It can grow on its own and form more fern plants.

Resource Manager

Chapter Resources Booklet
Reinforcement, p. 26
Transparency Activity, pp. 45–46
Activity Worksheet, pp. 5–6

Science Journal

Using Definitions *Frond* is the name given to leaves of ferns and palms. Have students look in a dictionary to find the derivation and meaning of the word *frond* and then write a paragraph in their journals to suggest why the word is used for these leaves. *Frond* comes from the Latin word for *leaf.*

Figure 8
A fern's life cycle and a moss's are similar. However, the fern sporophyte and gametophyte are photosynthetic and can grow on their own.

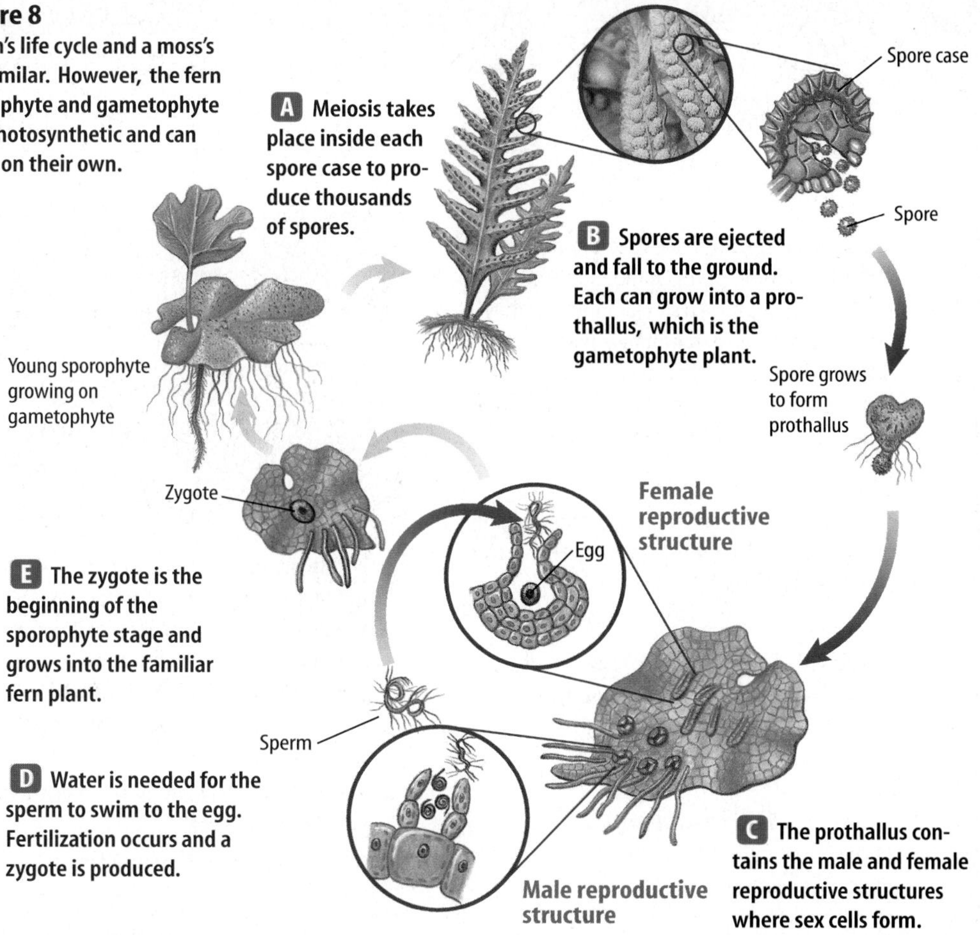

A Meiosis takes place inside each spore case to produce thousands of spores.
Spore case
Spore
B Spores are ejected and fall to the ground. Each can grow into a prothallus, which is the gametophyte plant.
Spore grows to form prothallus
Young sporophyte growing on gametophyte
Zygote
Female reproductive structure
Egg
E The zygote is the beginning of the sporophyte stage and grows into the familiar fern plant.
Sperm
D Water is needed for the sperm to swim to the egg. Fertilization occurs and a zygote is produced.
C The prothallus contains the male and female reproductive structures where sex cells form.
Male reproductive structure

Section 2 Assessment

1. Describe the life cycle of mosses.
2. Explain the stages in the life cycle of a fern.
3. Compare and contrast the gametophyte plant of the moss with the gametophyte plant of the fern.
4. List several ways that seedless plants reproduce asexually.
5. **Think Critically** Why might some seedless plants reproduce only asexually during dry times of the year?

Skill Builder Activities

6. **Concept Mapping** Use an events-chain concept map to show the events in the life cycle of either a moss or fern. **For more help, refer to the** Science Skill Handbook.
7. **Solving One-Step Equations** Moss spores are usually no more than 0.1 mm in diameter. About how many spores would it take to equal the diameter of a penny? **For more help, refer to the** Math Skill Handbook.

Visual Learning

Figure 8 Again, have students trace with their fingers the sequence of events in a fern's life cycle. This time, have students explain the difference between the sporophyte and the gametophyte generations.

3 Assess

Reteach

Provide students with a list of the terms used in this section. Have students identify each term as being part of the moss life cycle, fern life cycle, or both. L2 ELL COOP LEARN
LS **Interpersonal**

Challenge

Have students write essays that describe, compare, and contrast the life cycles of mosses and ferns. LS **Linguistic**

Assessment

Performance Give each student a 3 × 5 card on which is written a description of a fern or moss structure. Have each student identify his or her structure. Then divide the class into groups (two for each plant)—one for students whose structure is part of the sporophyte stage, and one for students whose structure is part of the gametophyte stage of their plant's life cycle. Have students work together to arrange themselves into a physical model of their plant's life cycle. Use **PASC**, p. 123.

Answers to Section Assessment

1. Spores land on the ground and grow into upright leafy gametophytes, which produce sex cells. Sperm swim in water to reach the egg, forming a zygote. The zygote grows and develops into a spore-producing sporophyte.
2. A spore grows into a heart-shaped gametophyte. The gametophyte produces sex cells that unite to form a zygote. The zygote grows into a spore-producing sporophyte.
3. A moss gametophyte is larger than the sporophyte and photosynthetic; ferns produce small, photosynthetic gametophytes.
4. Seedless plants reproduce asexually from plant parts, small balls of cells that form on the gametophyte, or from rhizomes.
5. Sexual reproduction in these plants requires water.
6. The chain should summarize **Figure 6** or **Figure 8**.
7. A penny is approximately 20 mm in diameter, so about 200 spores would be needed.

Activity
BENCH TESTED

Purpose Students will observe the stages in the life cycles of liverworts, mosses, and ferns. L2 ELL COOP LEARN IN **Visual-Spatial**

Process Skills observing, classifying, comparing and contrasting

Time Required 50 minutes

Safety Precautions Remind students not to eat any plant parts and to be careful when using microscopes.

Teaching Strategy Be sure students have properly focused their microscopes.

Troubleshooting If moss spores are not liberated using water, add an equal amount of glycerin to the water. This mixture allows the spores to come out of the capsule more easily.

Answers to Questions

1. Moss gametophyte: green, low-growing structure with leaves in a whorl around a stalk; liverwort gametophyte: green, flat, leaflike form. Sporophytes of mosses are a non-green stalk with a spore-containing capsule at the top. Liverwort sporophytes form on the gametophytes as green umbrella-like structures with spores in cases underneath. Fern gametophytes: green, heart-shaped structures; their sporophytes are familiar green plants.
2. gametophyte, sporophyte, rhizoid, spores, leaflike structures
3. Many spores do not land where conditions are right for growth. The greater the number of spores produced, the greater the chances that some will grow.

Activity

Comparing Seedless Plants

All seedless plants have specialized structures that produce spores. Although these sporophyte structures have a similar function, they look different. The gametophyte plants also are different from each other. Do this activity and observe the similarities and differences among three groups of seedless plants.

What You'll Investigate

How are the gametophyte stages and the sporophyte stages of liverworts, mosses, and ferns similar and different?

Materials

live mosses, liverworts, and ferns with gametophytes and sporophytes
hand lens
forceps
dropper
microscope slides and coverslips (2)
microscope
dissecting needle
pencil with eraser

Goals

- **Describe** the sporophyte and gametophyte forms of liverworts, mosses, and ferns.
- **Identify** the spore-producing structures of liverworts, mosses, and ferns.

Safety Precautions

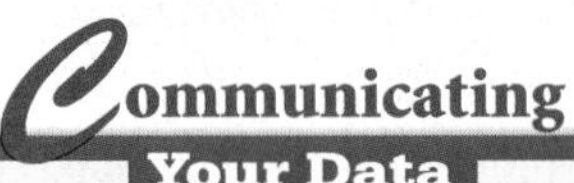

Procedure

1. Obtain a gametophyte of each plant. With a hand lens, observe the rhizoids, leafy parts, and stemlike parts, if any are present.
2. Obtain a sporophyte of each plant and use a hand lens to observe it.

3. Locate the spore structure on the moss plant. Remove it and place it in a drop of water on the slide. Place a coverslip over it. Use the eraser of a pencil to gently push on the coverslip to release the spores. **WARNING:** *Do not break the coverslip.* Observe the spores under low and high power.
4. Make labeled drawings of all observations in your Science Journal.
5. Repeat steps 3 and 4 using a fern.

Conclude and Apply

1. For each plant, compare the gametophyte's appearance to the sporophyte's appearance.
2. **List** structure(s) common to all three plants.
3. **Hypothesize** about why each plant produces a large number of spores.

Communicating Your Data

Prepare a bulletin board that shows differences between the sporophyte and gametophyte stages of liverworts, mosses, and ferns. **For more help, refer to the** Science Skill Handbook.

Communicating Your Data

The bulletin board should illustrate differences between the life cycle stages of the plants examined. Encourage students to use Internet sources to research photographs and information for the bulletin board.

Assessment

Performance Assess students' understanding of the parts of mosses, liverworts, and ferns by having them identify parts of living specimens and by describing the functions of each. Use **Performance Assessment in the Science Classroom,** p. 89.

SECTION 3

Seed Reproduction

The Importance of Pollen and Seeds

All the plants described so far have been seedless plants. However, the fruits and vegetables that you eat come from seed plants. Oak, maple, and other shade trees are also seed plants. All flowers are produced by seed plants. In fact, most of the plants on Earth are seed plants. How do you think they became such a successful group? Reproduction that involves pollen and seeds is part of the answer.

Pollen In seed plants, some spores develop into small structures called pollen grains. A **pollen grain,** as shown in **Figure 9,** has a water-resistant covering and contains gametophyte parts that can produce the sperm. The sperm of seed plants do not need to swim to the female part of the plant. Instead, they are carried as part of the pollen grain by gravity, wind, water currents, or animals. The transfer of pollen grains to the female part of the plant is called **pollination.**

After the pollen grain reaches the female part of a plant, sperm and a pollen tube are produced. The sperm moves through the pollen tube, then fertilization can occur.

As You Read

What You'll Learn

- **Examine** the life cycles of typical gymnosperms and angiosperms.
- **Describe** the structure and function of the flower.
- **Discuss** methods of seed dispersal in seed plants.

Vocabulary

pollen grain, pollination, ovule, stamen, pistil, ovary, germination

Why It's Important

Seeds from cones and flowers produce most plants on Earth.

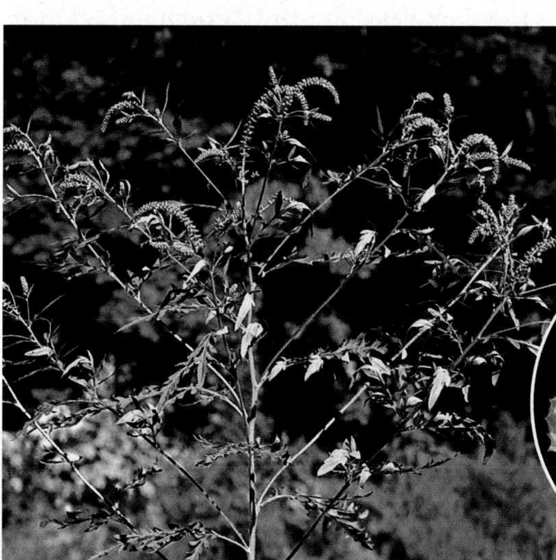

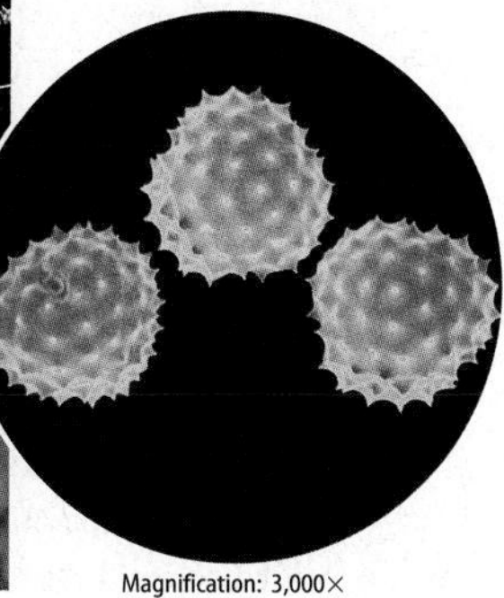

Magnification: 3,000×

Figure 9
The waterproof covering of a pollen grain is unique and can be used to identify the plant that it came from. This pollen from a ragweed plant is a common cause of hay fever.

Section Assessment Planner

Portfolio
Activity, p. 285

Performance Assessment
Try at Home MiniLAB, p. 290
Skill Builder Activities, p. 293
See page 300 for more options.

Content Assessment
Section, p. 293
Challenge, p. 293
Chapter, pp. 300–301

SECTION 3

Seed Reproduction

1 Motivate

Bellringer Transparency

Display the Section Focus Transparency for Section 3. Use the accompanying Transparency Activity Master. L2 ELL

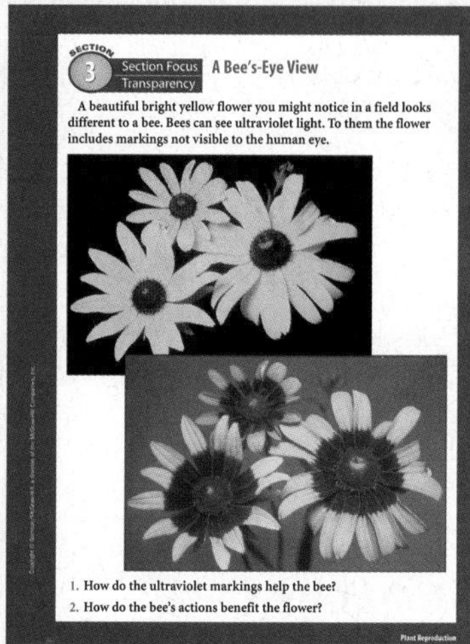

Section 3 Section Focus Transparency — A Bee's-Eye View

A beautiful bright yellow flower you might notice in a field looks different to a bee. Bees can see ultraviolet light. To them the flower includes markings not visible to the human eye.

1. How do the ultraviolet markings help the bee?
2. How do the bee's actions benefit the flower?

Plant Reproduction

Tie to Prior Knowledge

Ask students to recall a time when they dispersed seeds. One answer may be when they were eating fruit such as watermelon. Others may have actually planted seeds in a garden. Still others may have walked through a field and found seeds stuck to their clothing.

Resource Manager

Chapter Resources Booklet
Transparency Activity p. 44
Directed Reading for Content Mastery, pp. 19, 20

2 Teach

The Importance of Pollen and Seeds

IDENTIFYING Misconceptions

Many students assume that plants fertilize themselves. Point out that many plants must be cross-pollinated in order to reproduce.

Caption Answer

Figure 10 Wings allow seeds to catch the wind and be dispersed farther from the parent plant.

Answer seed coat, stored food, embryo

Internet Addresses

Explore the Glencoe Science Web site at **science.glencoe.com** to find out more about topics in this section.

Figure 10
Seeds have three main parts—a seed coat, stored food, and an embryo. This pine seed also has a wing.
What is the function of the wing?

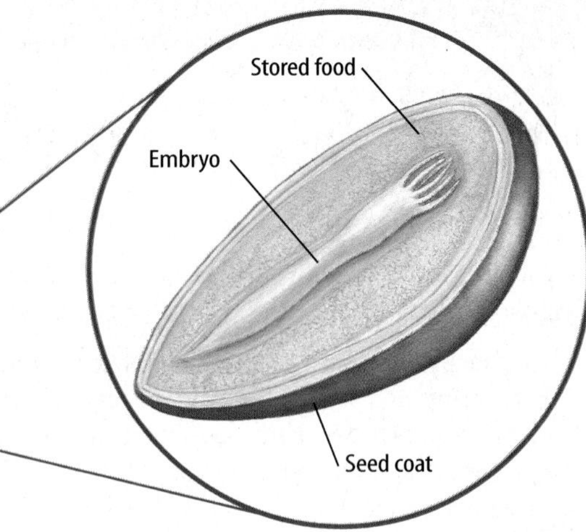

SCIENCE Online

Research Seed banks conserve seeds of many useful and endangered plants. Visit the Glencoe Science Web site at **science.glencoe.com** to find out more about seed banks. In your Science Journal list three organizations that manage seed banks.

Do all gymnosperm plants produce the same type of cones? To find out more about cones, see the **Cones Field Guide** at the back of this book.

Seeds Following fertilization, the female part can develop into a seed. A seed consists of an embryo, stored food, and a protective seed coat, as shown in **Figure 10.** The embryo has structures that eventually will produce the plant's stem, leaves, and roots. In the seed, the embryo grows to a certain stage and then stops until the seed is planted. The stored food provides energy that is needed when the plant embryo begins to grow into a plant. Because the seed contains an embryo and stored food, a new plant can develop more rapidly from a seed than from a spore.

Reading Check *What are the three parts of a seed?*

Gymnosperms (JIHM nuh spurmz) and angiosperms are seed plants. One difference between the two groups is the way seeds develop. In gymnosperms, seeds usually develop in cones—in angiosperms, seeds develop in flowers.

Gymnosperm Reproduction

If you have collected pine cones or used them in a craft project, you probably noticed that many shapes and sizes of cones exist. You probably also noticed that some cones contain seeds. Cones are the reproductive structures of gymnosperms. Each gymnosperm species has a different cone.

Gymnosperm plants include pines, firs, cedars, cycads, and ginkgoes. The pine is a familiar gymnosperm. Production of seeds in pines is typical of most gymnosperms.

Cones A pine tree or shrub is a sporophyte plant that produces male cones and female cones as shown in **Figure 11.** Male and female gametophyte structures are produced in the cones but you'd need a magnifying glass to see these structures clearly.

Curriculum Connection

Geography Gymnosperms are the dominant plant of the taiga biome. In North America, most of this area is located between 45° and 60° north latitude. Have students locate on a world map countries where taiga is the primary biome. Then have students list the climactic conditions of these areas. Canada, Norway, Sweden, and Russia are examples. These countries experience harsh winters and short summers. L2

Resource Manager

Reading and Writing Skill Activities, p. 1

Life Science Critical Thinking/Problem Solving, p. 8

A mature female cone consists of a spiral of woody scales on a short stem. At the base of each scale are two ovules. The egg is produced in the **ovule.** Pollen grains are produced in the smaller male cones. In the spring, clouds of pollen are released from the male cones. Anything near pine trees might be covered with the yellow, dustlike pollen.

Figure 11
Seed formation in pines, as in most gymnosperms, involves male and female cones.

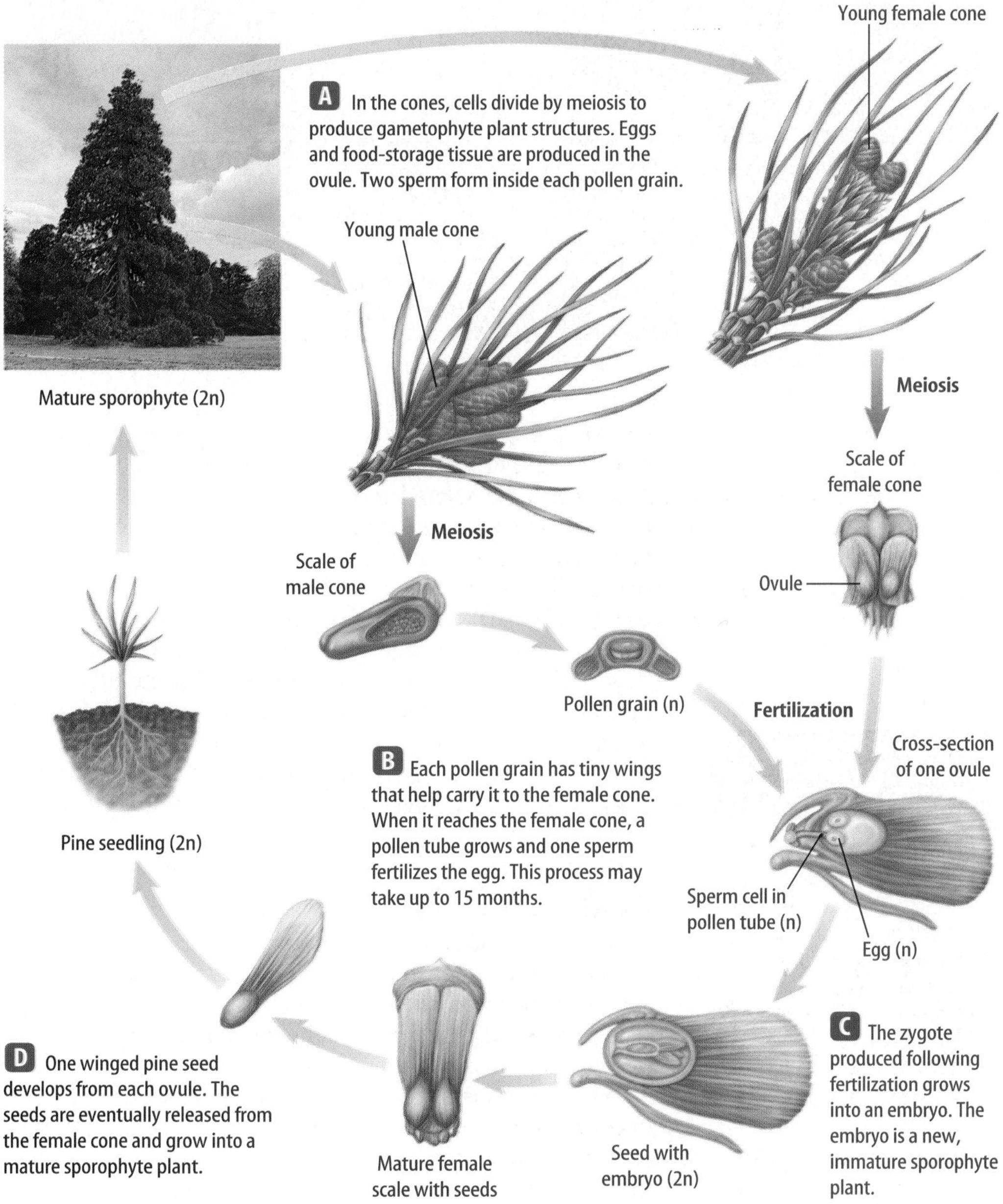

Young female cone
A In the cones, cells divide by meiosis to produce gametophyte plant structures. Eggs and food-storage tissue are produced in the ovule. Two sperm form inside each pollen grain.
Young male cone
Mature sporophyte (2n)
Meiosis
Meiosis
Scale of female cone
Scale of male cone
Ovule
Pollen grain (n)
Fertilization
Cross-section of one ovule
B Each pollen grain has tiny wings that help carry it to the female cone. When it reaches the female cone, a pollen tube grows and one sperm fertilizes the egg. This process may take up to 15 months.
Pine seedling (2n)
Sperm cell in pollen tube (n)
Egg (n)
C The zygote produced following fertilization grows into an embryo. The embryo is a new, immature sporophyte plant.
D One winged pine seed develops from each ovule. The seeds are eventually released from the female cone and grow into a mature sporophyte plant.
Mature female scale with seeds
Seed with embryo (2n)

Gymnosperm Reproduction

Visual Learning

Figure 11 Have students discuss the primary differences in the life cycles of nonseed plants and gymnosperms. In gymnosperms and other seed plants, the gametophyte stage is usually microscopic. In nonseed plants, this stage can be larger than the sporophyte.

Activity

Have students write a description of a cone for someone who is visually impaired. After reviewing all the descriptions, share the best two or three with the class. LS **Linguistic** P

Extension

Have students visit a botanical garden to identify plants from your area and around the world. Ask students to make drawings of the plants they observe and to note any unique features of the plants. Students can present their drawings and a summary of their observations in an oral presentation.

Active Reading

Double-Bubble Map This strategy utilizes two bubble maps to compare concepts. Each cluster has ideas that are unique to that idea. In the middle are connecting ideas shared by both clusters. Have students design a Double-Bubble Map summarizing gymnosperm and angiosperm reproduction. A sample is shown.

cones
flowers
gymnosperms
seeds
angiosperms
seeds not surrounded by a fruit
fruit surrounds seed

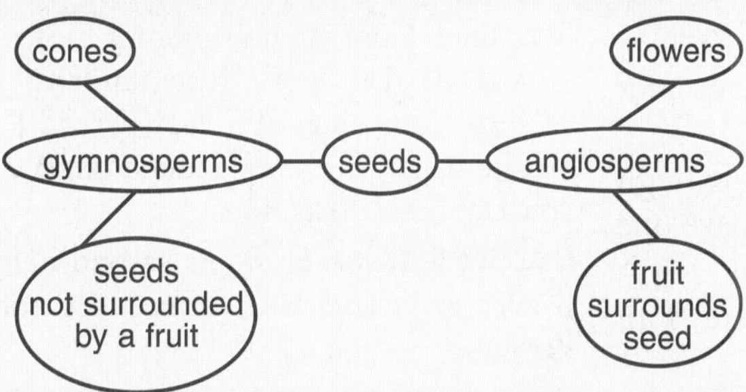

Gymnosperm Reproduction, continued

Environmental Science INTEGRATION

Without forest fires, cones would not open and new plants would not grow.

Angiosperm Reproduction

Teacher FYI

Self-pollinating plants usually produce flowers that are either not attractive to insects or have structures that hinder the movement of pollen from one plant to another. Genetic recombination in self pollinating plants generally is not as extensive as in cross pollinating plants.

Figure 12
Seed development can take more than one year in pines. The female cone looks different at various stages of the seed-production process.

Cone at pollination | Cone at the end of the first year | Mature, second-year cone

Environmental Science INTEGRATION

Some gymnosperm seeds will not germinate until the heat of a fire causes the cones to open and release the seeds. Without fires, these plants cannot reproduce. In your Science Journal, explain why some forest fires could be good for the environment.

Gymnosperm Seeds Wind usually carries the pollen from male cones to female cones. However, most of the pollen falls on other plants, the ground, and bodies of water. To be useful, the pollen has to be blown between the scales of a female cone. There it can be trapped in the sticky fluid secreted by the ovule. If the pollen grain and the female cone are the same species, fertilization and the formation of a seed can take place.

If you are near a pine tree when the female cones release their seeds, you might hear a crackling noise as the cones' scales open. It can take a long time for seeds to be released from a female pine cone. From the moment a pollen grain falls on the female cone until the seeds are released, can take two or three years, as shown in **Figure 12.** In the right environment, each seed can grow into a new pine sporophyte.

Angiosperm Reproduction

You might not know it, but you are already familiar with angiosperms. If you had cereal for breakfast or bread in a sandwich for lunch, you ate parts of angiosperms. Flowers that you send or receive for special occasions are from angiosperms. Most of the seed plants on Earth today are angiosperms.

All angiosperms have flowers. The sporophyte plant produces the flowers. Flowers are important because they contain the reproductive organs that contain gametophyte structures that produce sperm or eggs for sexual reproduction.

LAB DEMONSTRATION

Purpose to identify the parts of a flower

Materials a variety of monocot and dicot flowers, plastic knives, tape, paper

Preparation Collect or purchase enough flowers so that each student can have one flower.

Safety Caution students to be careful with the knives.

Procedure Give each student a flower to dissect. As they work, have students tape each different type of flower part in a line on the paper. Have students compare and contrast their dissections.

Expected Outcome Students should identify flower parts and note differences among flowers.

Assessment

Have students describe any differences they have observed. The numbers of flower parts vary from plant to plant. Dicot flower parts occur in fours and fives; monocot flower parts occur in threes.

The Flower When you think of a flower, you probably imagine something with a pleasant aroma and colorful petals. Although many such flowers do exist, some flowers are drab and have no aroma, like the flowers of the maple tree shown in **Figure 13.** Why do you think such variety among flowers exists?

Most flowers have four main parts—petals, sepals, stamen, and pistil—as shown in **Figure 14.** Generally, the colorful parts of a flower are the petals. Outside the petals are usually leaflike parts called sepals. Sepals form the outside of the flower bud. Sometimes petals and sepals are the same color.

Inside the flower are the reproductive organs of the plant. The **stamen** is the male reproductive organ. Pollen is produced in the stamen. The **pistil** is the female reproductive organ. The **ovary** is the swollen base of the pistil where ovules are found. Not all flowers have every one of the four parts. Remember the holly plants you learned about at the beginning of the chapter? What flower part would be missing on a flower from a male holly plant?

Reading Check *Where are ovules found in the flower?*

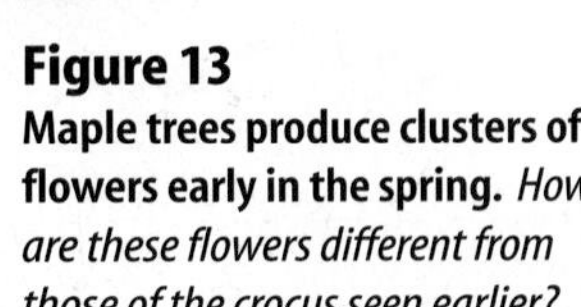

Figure 13
Maple trees produce clusters of flowers early in the spring. *How are these flowers different from those of the crocus seen earlier?*

Figure 14
The color of a flower's petals can attract insect pollinators. *What are the male and female parts of this flower?*

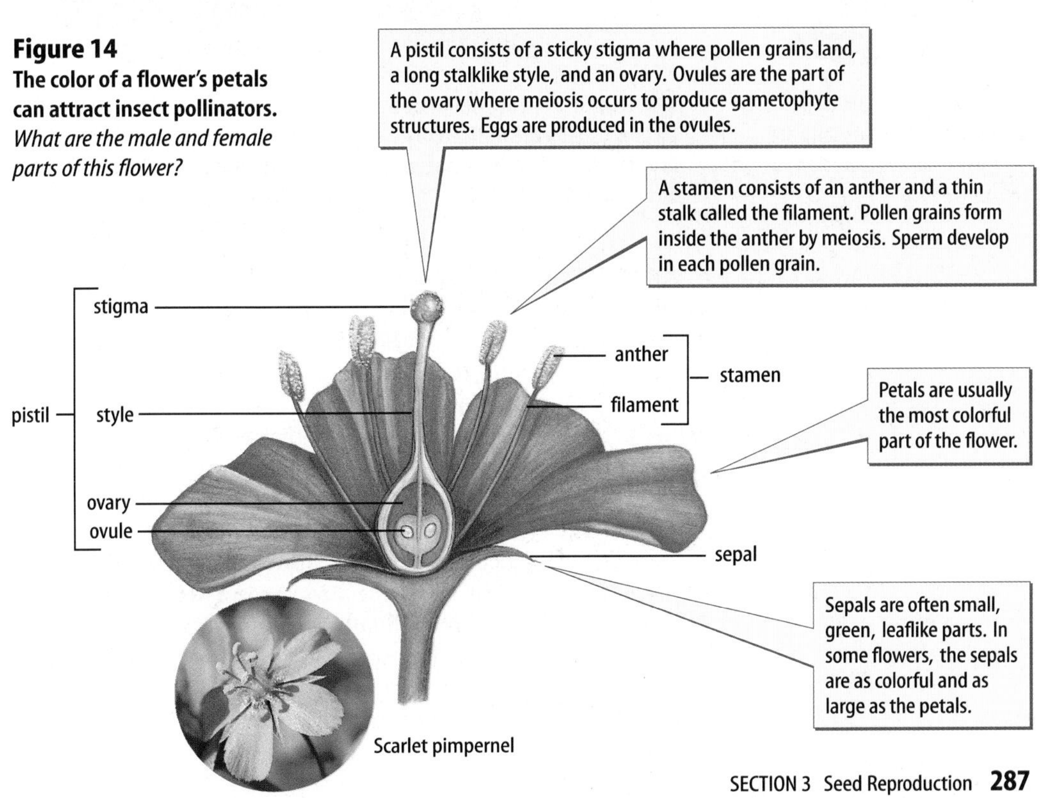

A pistil consists of a sticky stigma where pollen grains land, a long stalklike style, and an ovary. Ovules are the part of the ovary where meiosis occurs to produce gametophyte structures. Eggs are produced in the ovules.
A stamen consists of an anther and a thin stalk called the filament. Pollen grains form inside the anther by meiosis. Sperm develop in each pollen grain.
stigma
anther
stamen
filament
pistil
style
Petals are usually the most colorful part of the flower.
ovary
ovule
sepal
Sepals are often small, green, leaflike parts. In some flowers, the sepals are as colorful and as large as the petals.
Scarlet pimpernel

Text Question Answers

- Possible response: Having great variety helps flowers attract different types of insects or other animals that may aid in pollination or dispersal of seeds.
- pistil (stigma, style, and ovary)

Caption Answers

- **Figure 13** The flowers produced by the maple tree are very different from crocus flowers in appearance. The maple flower is not brightly colored.
- **Figure 14** Male parts are stamens (pollen, anthers, and filaments). Female parts are pistils (stigma, style, ovary, and ovule). Petals and sepals are neither male nor female.

Reading Check

Answer in the ovary, which is at the base of the pistil

Teacher FYI

Flowers may be perfect or imperfect. Perfect flowers possess both stamens and pistils. Imperfect flowers may be either male (if they have only stamens) or female (if they have only pistils).

Activity

Have students use **Figure 14** as a guide to make models of the structures of a flower. Allow students to select the materials from which they will make their models.

Inclusion Strategies

Visually Impaired Provide visually impaired students with large plastic models of flowers so that they can tactilely identify the flower's structures. Allow these students to smell the scents of a variety of flowers to enrich their experience. LS **Kinesthetic**

Resource Manager

Science Inquiry Labs, pp. 7, 13

Earth Science Critical Thinking/Problem Solving, p. 7

Angiosperm Reproduction, continued

Visual Learning

Figure 15 After students have studied the pollination mechanisms shown, have them work in teams to write a short story about a particular kind of flower and its pollination mechanism. The story should include a day in the life of a flower. L2 COOP LEARN LS **Linguistic**

Fun Fact

It would take more than ten million orchid seeds to equal the mass of a single coconut.

Reading Check

Answer An animal may pick up pollen as it eats the flower, its nectar, or its pollen. The pollen is then spread to other flowers that the animal visits.

Figure 15
Looking at flowers will give you a clue about how each one is pollinated.

A Honeybees are important pollinators. They are attracted to brightly colored flowers, especially blue and yellow flowers.

B Flowers that are pollinated at night, like this cactus flower being pollinated by a bat, are usually white.

C Flowers that are pollinated by hummingbirds usually are brightly colored, especially bright red and yellow.

D Flowers that are pollinated by flies usually are dull red or brown. They often have a strong odor like rotten meat.

E The flower of this wheat plant does not have a strong odor and is not brightly colored. Wind, not an animal, is the pollinator of wheat and most other grasses.

Importance of Flowers The appearance of a plant's flowers can tell you something about the life of the plant. Large flowers with brightly colored petals often attract insects and other animals, as shown in **Figure 15.** These animals might eat the flower, its nectar, or pollen. As they move about the flower, the animals get pollen on their wings, legs, or other body parts. Later, these animals spread the flower's pollen to other plants that they visit. Other flowers depend on wind, rain, or gravity to spread their pollen. Their petals can be small or absent. Flowers that open only at night, such as the cactus flower in **Figure 15B,** usually are white or yellow and have strong scents to attract animal pollinators. Following pollination and fertilization, the ovules of flowers can develop into seeds.

Reading Check *How do animals spread pollen?*

Resource Manager

Chapter Resources Booklet
Enrichment, p. 30

Home and Community Involvement, p. 41

Inclusion Strategies

Learning Disabled Play "plant bingo." Have students make a game board by writing all the bold-faced terms from this section in squares on a sheet of paper. Then read a definition of a plant term. Students who can correctly identify the term can cover that term on their board. The first student to have all terms covered wins.

288 CHAPTER 10 Plant Reproduction

Angiosperm Seeds The development of angiosperm seeds is shown in **Figure 16.** Pollen grains reach the stigma in a variety of ways. Pollen is carried by wind, rain, or animals such as insects, birds, and mammals. A flower is pollinated when pollen grains land on the sticky stigma. A pollen tube grows from the pollen grain down through the style. The pollen tube enters the ovary and reaches an ovule. The sperm then travels down the pollen tube and fertilizes the egg in the ovule. A zygote forms and grows into the plant embryo.

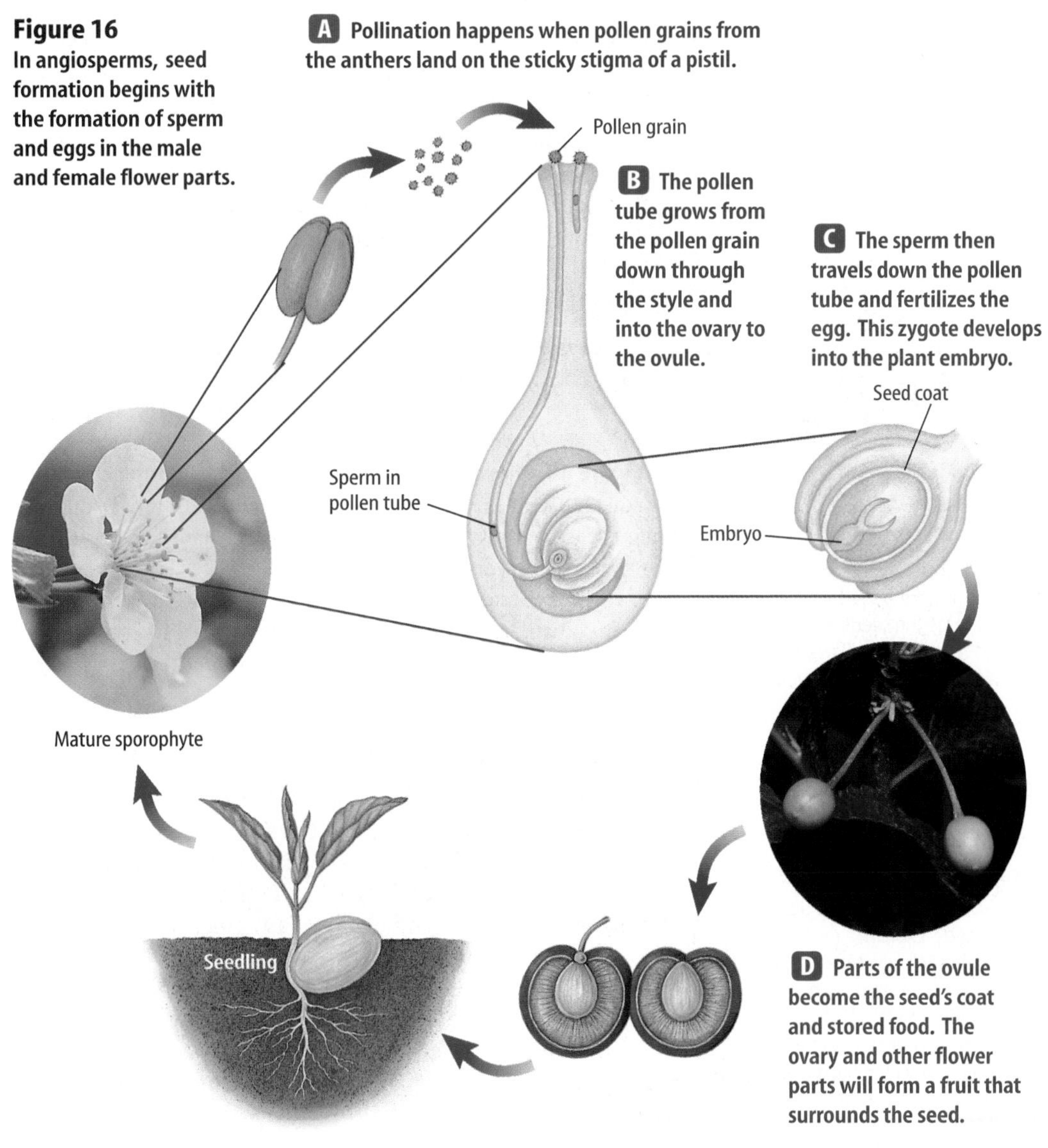

A Pollination happens when pollen grains from the anthers land on the sticky stigma of a pistil.
Pollen grain
B The pollen tube grows from the pollen grain down through the style and into the ovary to the ovule.
C The sperm then travels down the pollen tube and fertilizes the egg. This zygote develops into the plant embryo.
Seed coat
Sperm in pollen tube
Embryo
Mature sporophyte
Seedling
D Parts of the ovule become the seed's coat and stored food. The ovary and other flower parts will form a fruit that surrounds the seed.

Figure 16
In angiosperms, seed formation begins with the formation of sperm and eggs in the male and female flower parts.

Visual Learning

Figure 16 After students have read and discussed the information, have them make an events chain concept map to summarize seed formation in angiosperms. L2 LS **Visual-Spatial**

Teacher FYI

Bees and flowers have a symbiotic, or mutually beneficial, relationship. More flowers are pollinated by bees than any other kind of insect. Many flowers also have a highly complicated structure that discourages self-pollination and encourages cross-pollination of plants with single flowers. This means that while a bee is getting nectar from the flower, it is able to touch the pistil, but not the stamen. As the bee is leaving, however, it is able to touch the stamen, but not the pistil. This way, the bee leaves pollen from another flower rather than the pollen from the flower from which the bee is taking nectar.

Cultural Diversity

Drip Irrigation Crop production on a Navajo reservation in Arizona was once limited because of the scarcity of water. In 1984, David Mazigh, manager of an experimental farm in Israel, was invited to visit the reservation. Mazigh shared his knowledge of drip irrigation with the Navajos. Some Israeli farmers use drip irrigation to get water to plants in their desert lands. Water is pumped from a well and mixed with fertilizer. The fertilizer solution travels in thick pipes to thin drip lines that lie beside rows of planted seeds in the fields. Small nozzles allow the solution to drip out, providing plants with a slow and constant supply of water and fertilizer. Encourage students to visit a garden store and examine the drip irrigation systems available for home use.

Seed Dispersal

Use an Analogy

The way many seeds attach themselves to passing animals is like the way that two pieces of hook and loop tape stick together. In fact, hook and loop tape was inspired by the mechanism cocklebturs use to stick to fur and clothing.

Purpose Students infer possible methods of dispersal for a seed shaped like a button. L2 ELL LS **Logical-Mathematical**

Materials button; **Figure 18**

Teaching Strategy Divide the class into groups. Ask each group to brainstorm possible dispersal methods for imaginary seeds shaped like other common items such as safety pins, cotton swab ends, and thumb tacks.

Analysis

1. Answer will vary depending on the button chosen and methods tried.
2. Answer will vary depending on the button chosen and methods tried.

Assessment

Process Ask students to infer how the weight and shape of a seed will determine whether the wind will disperse it. Seeds capable of wind dispersal must be lightweight. Their shapes must have maximum surface area exposure and have a shape that can trap air currents. Use **Performance Assessment in the Science Classroom,** p. 89.

Reading Check

Answer Small seeds may become airborne when the plant releases them. Some seeds have structures that allow them to move with air currents.

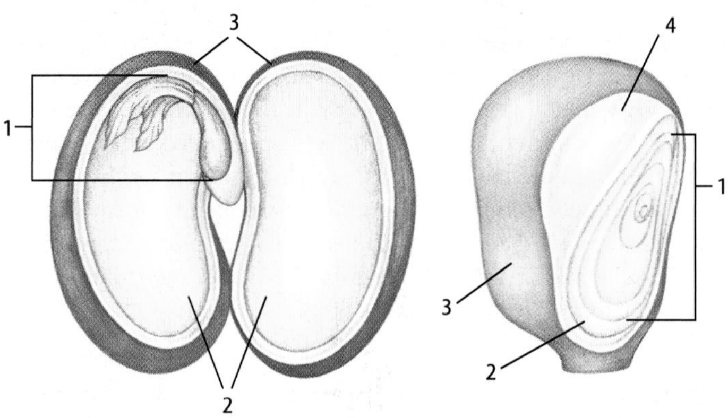

Figure 17
Seeds of land plants are capable of surviving unfavorable environmental conditions.
1. Immature plant
2. Cotyledon(s)
3. Seed coat
4. Endosperm

Seed Development Parts of the ovule develop into the stored food and the seed coat that surround the embryo, and a seed is formed, as shown in **Figure 17.** In the seeds of some plants, like beans and peanuts, the food is stored in structures called cotyledons. The seeds of other plants, like corn and wheat, have food stored in a tissue called endosperm.

Seed Dispersal

Earth Science INTEGRATION Sometimes, plants just seem to appear. They probably grew from a seed, but where did the seed come from? Plants have many ways of dispersing their seeds, as shown in **Figure 18.** Most seeds grow only when they are placed on or in soil. Do you know how seeds naturally get to the soil? For many seeds, gravity is the answer. They fall onto the soil from the parent plant on which they grew. However, in nature some seeds can be spread great distances from the parent plant.

Wind dispersal usually occurs because a seed has an attached structure that moves it with air currents. Sometimes, small seeds become airborne when released by the plant.

Reading Check *How can wind be used to disperse seeds?*

Animals can disperse many seeds. Some seeds are eaten with fruits, pass through an animal's digestive system, and are dispersed as the animal moves from place to place. Seeds can be carried great distances and stored or buried by animals. Hitchhiking on fur, feathers, and clothing is another way that animals disperse seeds.

Water also disperses seeds. Raindrops can knock seeds out of a dry fruit. Some fruits and seeds float on flowing water or ocean currents. When you touch the seedpod of an impatiens flower, it explodes. The tiny seeds are ejected and spread some distance from the plant.

Modeling Seed Dispersal

Procedure

1. Find a **button** you can use to represent a seed.
2. Examine the seeds pictured in **Figure 18** and invent a way that your button seed could be dispersed by wind, water, on the fur of an animal, or by humans.
3. Bring your button seed to class and demonstrate how it could be dispersed.

Analysis

1. Was your button seed dispersed? Explain.
2. In your **Science Journal,** write a paragraph describing your model. Also describe other ways you could model seed dispersal.

Teacher FYI

Seeds of maples, milkweed, elms, pines, cottonwoods, and other plants are dispersed by the wind.

Figure 18

Plants have many adaptations for dispersing seeds, often enlisting the aid of wind, water, or animals.

▲ Equipped with tiny hooks, burrs cling tightly to fur and feathers.

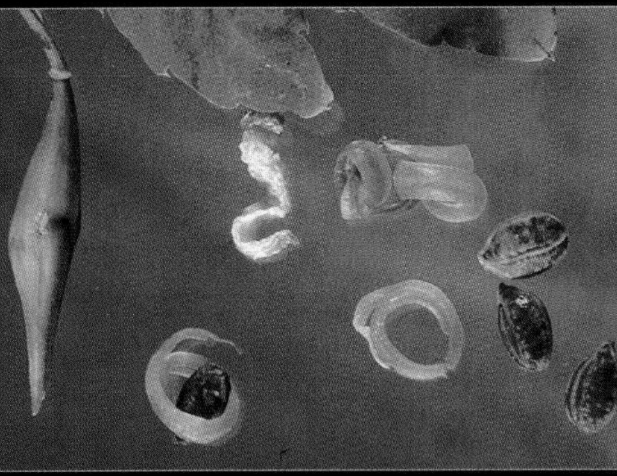

▲ Pressure builds within the seedpods of this jewelweed plant until the pod bursts, flinging seeds far and wide.

▼ Dandelion seeds are easily dislodged and sail away on a puff of wind.

▼ Some seeds buried by animals, such as this squirrel, go uneaten and sprout the next spring.

▲ Encased in a thick, buoyant husk, a coconut may be carried hundreds of kilometers by ocean currents.

▶ Blackberry seeds eaten by this white-footed mouse will pass through its digestive tract and be deposited in a new location.

NATIONAL GEOGRAPHIC

Visualizing Seed Dispersal

Have students examine the pictures and read the captions. Then ask the following question.

What advantage does wide dispersal of seeds give a plant species? Possible answers: less competition for resources between parent plant and offspring, better chance of finding a suitable environment for growth

Activity

Have students complete a chart of the different methods of seed dispersal illustrated and give more examples for each method. Sample chart:

Dispersal Method	Examples
In Fur of Animals	burdock, burr clover, foxtails, sticktights
Buried by Animals	oak
Excreted by Animals	raspberries, strawberries, tomatoes
Floating	red mangroves, sedge
Shotgun Dispersal	mistletoe, "touch-me-not" (impatiens), "squirting cucumbers" (ecballium), sandbox tree
Wind Dispersal	maple, orchids, milkweed, tumbleweeds

Extension

Have students research the importance of bats and their role in pollination and seed dispersal in rain forests around the world. Have them make posters showing their results. Possible research findings: Bats are important in seed dispersal as they excrete seeds from the fruits they consume. Bats also are important in pollination of plants in tropical areas. Plants that rely on bats for pollination only bloom at night, when bats are active.

Resource Manager

Chapter Resources Booklet
- MiniLAB, p. 4
- Lab Activity, pp. 9–12, 13–14

Mathematics Skill Activities, p. 5

Teacher FYI

Force may be defined as a push or a pull. Some dry fruits open with such great force when ripe, that their seeds are dispersed some distance from the plants. Witch hazel seeds may be propelled more than 12 m by the force of its splitting ripe fruit.

Seed Dispersal, continued

Discussion

Why might some gardeners soak their bean seeds before planting? Soaking softens the seed coat and speeds germination.

Activity

Have students collect as many different kinds of seeds as possible. Once collected, students can germinate the seeds and draw pictures of differences they note among the germinating seeds. They also can record and graph the various rates of germination. L2 ELL IS **Kinesthetic and Visual-Spatial**

Math Skills Activity

National Math Standards

Correlation to Mathematics Objectives

1, 2, 6, 8, 9

Answer to Practice Problem

$$\frac{98}{100} = \frac{x}{50}$$

$$x = \frac{98 \times 50}{100}$$

$$x = \frac{4{,}900}{100}$$

$$x = 49$$

Resource Manager

Chapter Resources Booklet
Reinforcement, p. 27
Activity Worksheet, pp. 7–8

Lab Management and Safety, p. 38

Germination A series of events that results in the growth of a plant from a seed is called **germination.** When dispersed from the plant, some seeds germinate in just a few days and other seeds take weeks or months to grow. Some seeds can stay in a resting stage for hundreds of years. In 1982, seeds of the East Indian lotus sprouted after 466 years.

Seeds will not germinate until environmental conditions are right. Temperature, the presence or absence of light, availability of water, and amount of oxygen present can affect germination. Sometimes the seed must pass through an animal's digestive system before it will germinate. Germination begins when seed tissues absorb water. This causes the seed to swell and the seed coat to break open.

Math Skills Activity

Calculating the Number of Seeds That Will Germinate

Example Problem

The label on a packet of carrot seeds says that it contains about 200 seeds. It also claims that 95 percent of the seeds will germinate. How many seeds should germinate if the packet is correct?

1. *This is what you know:*
   quantity = 200
   percentage = 95
2. *This is what you need to find:*
   95 percent of 200
3. *This is the equation you need to use:*
   $$\frac{95}{100} = \frac{x}{200}$$
4. *Solve the equation for* x:
   $$x = \frac{95 \times 200}{100}$$

Check your answer by dividing by 200 then multiplying by 100. Do you get the original percentage of 95?

Practice Problem

The label on a packet of 50 corn kernels claims that 98 percent will germinate. How many kernels will germinate if the packet is correct?

For more help, refer to the Math Skill Handbook.

Inclusion Strategies

Learning Disabled To reinforce the conditions needed for germination, have students carry out this activity. Place a sponge in a shallow dish with enough water to soak the sponge. Be sure the sponge rises above the water level. Sprinkle a small amount of birdseed on the sponge. Pat the seeds into the sponge. Place the sponge in a bright but not sunny location. Add water to keep the sponge moist. Have students use hand lenses to examine the sponge each day. Have them record their observations as drawings with explanatory labels. Be sure they note when they see cracking in the seeds and the sprouting of the embryo. In five to seven days, the seedlings can be scraped off the sponge and into a container of potting soil. Continue to have students monitor growth of the young plants. L1 ELL IS **Kinesthetic**

Figure 19
Although germination in all seeds is similar, some differences exist.

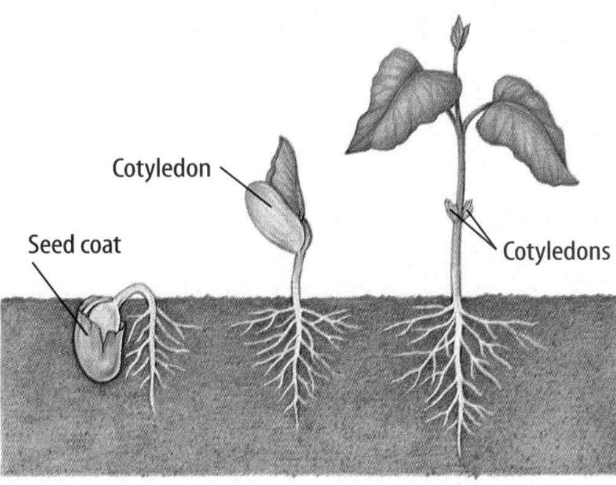

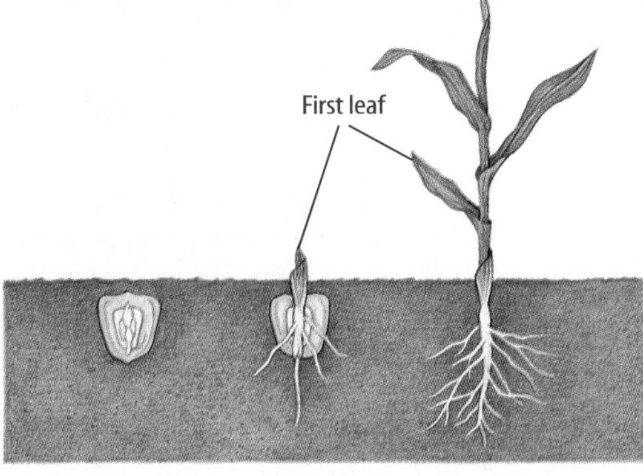

A In bean seeds, the cotyledons can be raised above the soil. As the stored food is used up, the cotyledons shrivel and fall off.

B In corn, the stored food in the endosperm remains in the soil and is gradually used up as the young plant grows.

Next, a series of chemical reactions occurs that releases energy from the stored food in the cotyledons or endosperm for growth. Eventually, a root grows from the seed, followed by a stem and leaves as shown in **Figure 19.** After the plant emerges from the soil, photosynthesis can begin. Photosynthesis provides food as the plant continues to grow.

Section 3 Assessment

1. Compare and contrast life cycles of angiosperms and gymnosperms.
2. Diagram a flower that has all four parts and label them.
3. List three methods of seed dispersal in plants.
4. Describe the three parts of a seed and give the function of each.
5. **Think Critically** Some conifers have female cones on the top half of the tree and male cones on the bottom half. Why would this arrangement of cones on a tree be important?

Skill Builder Activities

6. **Researching Information** Find out what conditions are needed for seed germination of three different garden plants, such as corn, peas, and beans. How long does each type of seed take to germinate? **For more help, refer to the Science Skill Handbook.**
7. **Communicating** Observe live specimens of several different types of flowers. In your Science Journal, describe their structures. Include numbers of petals, sepals, stamens, and pistil. **For more help, refer to the Science Skill Handbook.**

3 Assess

Reteach

Bring in plants, flowers, and seeds to demonstrate the parts of a plant's life cycle. Have students sequence a plant's life cycle by using the plants and plant parts. Reproductive structures can be obtained by dissecting a flower. A hand lens may be needed to see the flower's reproductive parts. Have students write a paragraph that details the sequence of the plant's life cycle. L2 IS **Linguistic**

Challenge

The petals and sepals of tulips are alike in color and size. Why might natural selection favor this arrangement? The greater amount of color helps attract insect pollinators and increase the chances of pollination and reproduction. L3

Assessment

Process Assess students' abilities to observe and infer by giving students flowers and having them infer how each flower may be pollinated. Use **Performance Assessment in the Science Classroom,** p. 89.

Answers to Section Assessment

1. The life cycles of angiosperms and gymnosperms are similar, except that angiosperms produce gametes in flowers and gymnosperms produce gametes in cones.
2. Students' diagrams should resemble **Figure 14.**
3. Possible responses: water, wind, animals, gravity
4. The seed coat protects the seed. The endosperm provides food for the growing embryo. The embryo contains immature leaves, stem, and root.
5. This arrangement makes self-pollination unlikely. Pollen cannot fall on the female cones if they are above the male cones. Instead, pollen will be blown to another tree where the female cones will receive the pollen.
6. Answers will vary, depending upon the seed. Many seeds germinate within a week or two, but others require months or even years to germinate.
7. Answers will vary depending on the species of flowers observed.

Activity Design Your Own Experiment

Germination Rate of Seeds

Many environmental factors affect the germination rate of seeds. Among these are soil temperature, air temperature, moisture content of soil, and salt content of soil. What happens to the germination rate when one of these variables is changed? Can you determine a way to predict the best conditions for seed germination?

Recognize the Problem

How do environmental factors affect seed germination?

Form a Hypothesis

Based on your knowledge of seed germination, state a hypothesis about how environmental factors affect germination rates.

Possible Materials

seeds
water
salt
potting soil
plant trays or plastic cups
**seedling warming cables*
thermometer
graduated cylinder
beakers

**Alternate materials*

Goals

- **Design** an experiment to test the effect of an environmental factor on seed germination rate.
- **Compare** germination rates under different conditions.

Safety Precautions

Some kinds of seeds are poisonous. Do not place any seeds in your mouth. Be careful when using any electrical equipment to avoid shock hazards.

294

Activity BENCH TESTED

Recognize the Problem

Purpose

Students design and carry out an experiment to explore how germination rate varies with an environmental factor. L2 COOP LEARN LS Logical-Mathematical

Process Skills

designing an experiment; collecting, interpreting and analyzing data; drawing conclusions; communicating; making and using tables and graphs; comparing and contrasting; recognizing cause and effect; forming a hypothesis; separating and controlling variables; measuring in SI

Time Required

one class period, plus 10 minutes per day for two weeks

Alternate Materials

Use any fast-germinating seeds. Epsom salts may be substituted for table salt. Seedling warming cables provide another variable to test.

Safety Precautions

Have students review safety symbols and precautions on the student page.

Form a Hypothesis

Possible Hypotheses

Students may predict that seeds will germinate at a higher rate with water than with salt solutions. They may predict that warmer soil will increase the rate of germination. The presence and absence of light and planting depth are other variables that may be tested.

Test Your Hypothesis

Possible Procedures

Students will plant seeds in shallow trays or plastic cups. They may test one variable in their procedure. Students using salt solutions should be encouraged to use at least two solution strengths with distilled water as the control. If students use the warming cables as a variable, then seeds without added heat will be the control. If planting depth is the variable, the control is the recommended depth.

Test Your Hypothesis

Plan

1. As a group, agree upon and write your hypothesis and decide how you will test it. Identify which results will confirm the hypothesis.
2. **List** the steps you need to take to test your hypothesis. Be specific, and describe exactly what you will do at each step. List your materials.
3. **Prepare** a data table in your Science Journal to record your observations.
4. Reread your entire experiment to make sure that all of the steps are in a logical order.
5. **Identify** all constants, variables, and controls of the experiment.

Do

1. Make sure your teacher approves your plan and your data table before you proceed.
2. Use the same type and amount of soil in each tray.
3. While the experiment is going on, record your observations accurately and complete the data table in your Science Journal.

Analyze Your Data

1. **Compare** the germination rate in the two groups of seeds.
2. **Compare** your results with those of other groups.
3. Did changing the variable affect germination rates? Explain.
4. Make a bar graph of your experimental results.

Draw Conclusions

1. **Interpret** your graph to estimate the conditions that give the best germination rate.
2. What things affect the germination rate?

Communicating Your Data

Write a short article for a local newspaper telling about this experiment. Give some ideas about when and how to plant seeds in the garden and the conditions needed for germination.

Teaching Strategy

Have students examine seed packets to gain additional information about normal germination rates.

Troubleshooting Students may confuse rate of germination (how quickly seeds germinate) with germination rate (the percent of seeds that actually germinate).

Expected Outcome

Some environmental conditions enhance seed germination; others do not.

Analyze Your Data

1. One group should have had a higher germination rate than the other.
2. Groups testing the same variable should have similar results.
3. Rates of germination and germination rates vary with environmental conditions for each variable, depending on species of plant tested.
4. Graphs should accurately reflect experimental data.

Error Analysis

Have students try to explain differences in their results from others who tested the same variable.

Draw Conclusions

1. Graphs will vary, but each should indicate a range for best germination of the variable tested.
2. Answers may include water quality, amount of water, planting depth, and other similar variables.

Assessment

Performance Have students test other temperatures, chemicals, or light conditions and compare their results to those obtained in this activity. Use **Performance Assessment in the Science Classroom,** p. 97.

Communicating Your Data

Have students include graphs in their articles.

Content Background

Genetic engineering is possible because all living organisms, from viruses and single-celled bacteria to humans, use the same genetic code. This allows the possibility of combining DNA from various organisms. The resulting product is called *recombinant DNA*. Organisms that contain DNA from different species are called *transgenic*.

Bacteria contain circular chromosomes called *plasmids*. Favorable genes can be spliced into these plasmids and replicated in great numbers as the bacteria undergo cell division. When the plasmids are introduced to other species, the new gene is transferred to the recipient's DNA, making it possible for the organism to produce a new protein with a certain desired effect. This technique is often used in transferring genes to plant species.

Viruses are little more than molecules of DNA surrounded by a protein coat. Many viruses are specialized and target specific tissues in plants and animals. Viruses work by injecting their DNA into a cell. The viral DNA then is spliced into the recipient's DNA and can be replicated in the host's body. The part of the viral DNA that causes disease can be disabled, making it non-infectious. Favorable genes are spliced into this DNA and then injected into a host. The virus will then target a specific cell type and deliver its modified DNA, allowing the cell to produce an otherwise missing protein. This technique is being developed as a potential means for curing a number of genetic disorders. Favorable results have been seen in this kind of treatment of muscular dystrophy, diabetes, and cystic fibrosis.

TIME SCIENCE AND Society

SCIENCE ISSUES THAT AFFECT YOU!

What would happen if you crossed a cactus with a rose? Well, you'd either get an extra spiky flower, or a bush that didn't need to be watered very often. Until recently, this sort of mix was the stuff science fiction was made of. But now, with the help of genetic engineering, it may be possible.

Genetic engineering is a way of taking genes from one species and giving them to another. One purpose of genetic engineering is to transfer an organism's traits. For example, scientists have changed grass by adding to it the gene from another grass species. This gene makes the grass grow so slowly, it doesn't have to be mowed very often.

How is this done? It all starts with genes—sections of DNA found in the cells of all living things. Genes produce certain characteristics, or traits, in an organism, like the color of a flower or whether a person has blond hair or black hair. Scientists have found a way to exchange genes and their traits among bacteria, viruses, plants, animals, and even humans. In 1983, the first plant was genetically modified, or changed. Since then, many crops in the U.S. have been modified in this way, including soybeans, potatoes, and tomatoes.

One common genetically engineered crop is corn. To modify it, scientists took a gene from a particular bacterium. The gene "instructed" the bacterium to produce a natural toxin that killed certain insects. This gene was placed into another bacterium, which was placed into a corn plant. This bacterial "taxi" carried the gene into the plant's DNA, giving it the new trait. The seeds from the genetically modified corn produced crops that resisted harmful insects.

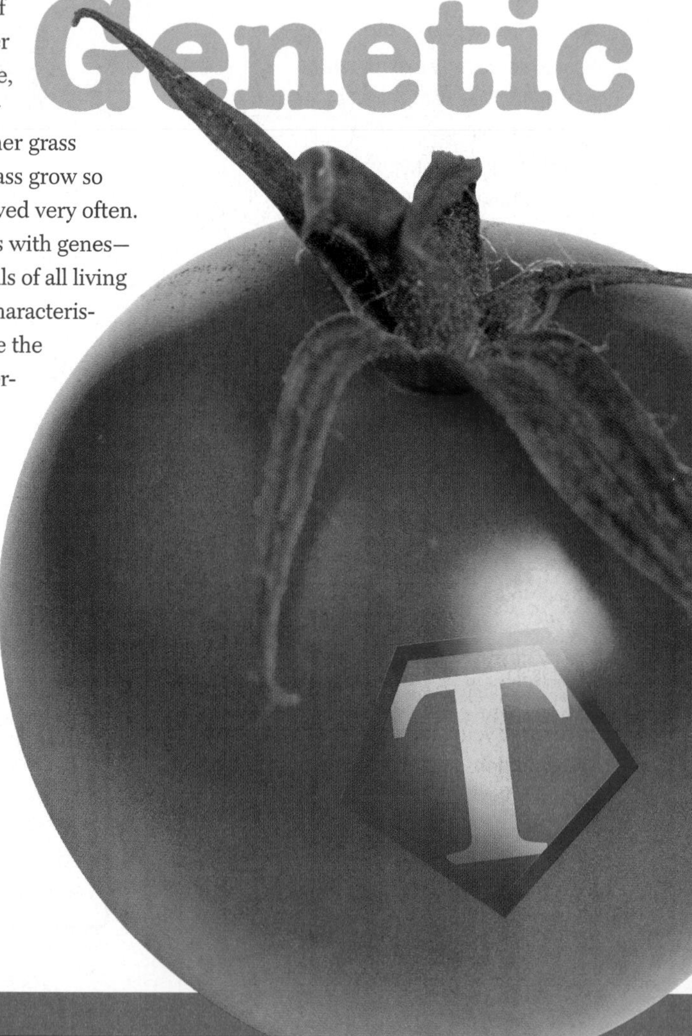

Resources for Teachers and Students

The Food Safety Educator, Available from: USDA/FSIS/Food Safety Education, Room 2944-South Building, 1400 Independence Ave., SW, Washington, DC 20250-3700

Genetic Engineering: Fast Forwarding to Future Foods, by John Henkel, April 1995, *FDA Consumer Magazine*.

"Are Bioengineered Foods Safe?," by Larry Thompson, January-February 2000, *FDA Consumer Magazine*.

"Methods For Genetically Engineering a Plant," January-February 2000, *FDA Consumer Magazine*.

Clifton Poodry: Biologist

Clifton Poodry was born in Buffalo, New York, on the Tonawanda Seneca Indian reservation. On the reservation, Native Americans took a great deal of pride in free thinking. "This way of thinking helps if you want to do scientific research," said Poodry. "As a scientist, one thing you get to do is pursue a question that is of interest to you, even if it is not of interest to someone else."

In graduate school, Poodry studied how cells were organized and how they develop structures in the human body. He was especially interested in learning how an organism develops from one cell to an organism with many different cells. He based his work on the fruit fly.

But equally exciting to Poodry was the fact that in college he shared the labs with men and women from many different ethnic backgrounds—all of whom were interested in research and science. That excitement, and the idea of many people coming together to share knowledge, led him to become a university professor. Today, he works to increase the number of minority students who go into scientific research. He heads the Division of Minority Opportunities in Research, a part of the National Institutes of Health.

Engineering

In addition to making plants resist insects, genetic engineering can make plants grow bigger and faster. Genetic engineering also has produced herbicide-resistant plants. This allows farmers to produce more crops with less chemicals. Scientists predict that genetic engineering will soon produce crops that are more nutritious and that can resist cold, heat, or even drought. This will help farmers increase their harvests and make more food available.

However, not everyone thinks genetic engineering is so great. Since it is a relatively new process, some people are worried about the long-term risks. One concern is that people might be allergic to modified foods and not realize it until it's too late. Other people say that genetic engineering is unnatural. Also, farmers must purchase the patented genetically modified seeds each growing season from the companies that make them, rather than saving and replanting the seeds from their current crops.

Genetically modified "super" tomatoes and "super" corn can resist heat, cold, drought, and insects.

People in favor of genetic engineering reply that there are always risks with new technology, but proper precautions are being taken. Each new plant is tested and then approved by U.S. governmental agencies. And they say that most "natural" crops aren't really natural. They are really hybrid plants bred by agriculturists, and they couldn't survive on their own.

As genetic engineering continues, so does the debate.

CONNECTIONS Debate Research the pros and cons of genetic engineering on the Glencoe Science Web site and in your school's media center. Decide whether you are for or against genetic engineering. Debate your conclusions with your classmates.

SCIENCE Online For more information, visit science.glencoe.com

Discussion

What other methods could be used to transfer genes from one species to another without using viruses? Possible answer: A so-called gene gun can be used to "shoot" microscopic metallic pellets coated with plasmids into a cell.

What are some of the fears associated with the technology of genetic engineering? Possible answers: Bacteria and viruses that have been disabled may regain their ability to cause disease after they are injected; some viruses that are used cause very serious diseases prior to being disabled for such a use.

Extension

Have students research which human conditions may be beneficially treated with gene therapy. Suggest students make a collage of pictures and descriptions of these disorders that demonstrates the potential benefits of genetic medicine in the future. **LS Visual-Spatial**

Investigate the Issue

Many of the fears regarding genetic engineering involve the use of this technology in altering many food items. Have students research and identify the foods that have already been subjected to this engineering. **What are the goals of this work?** Many possible answers: tomatoes with longer shelf life; corn and wheat with resistance to insects, etc. Some fears are that modified foods will produce new allergies, cause diseases, result in crop pests that are resistant to insecticides.

CONNECTIONS Students can make displays illustrating both the potential benefits and fears associated with genetic engineering technology. Help students use the results of their research to form arguments for their debate. You may wish to divide the class into two groups, one of which will defend the position that nature should not be tampered with; the other taking the position that technology can improve on natural conditions.

SCIENCE Online

Internet Addresses

Explore the Glencoe Science Web site at **science.glencoe.com** to find out more about topics in this feature.

Chapter 10 Study Guide

Reviewing Main Ideas

Preview

Students can answer the questions in their Science Journals. Discuss the answers as you go through the chapter. **LS Linguistic**

Review

Students can write their answers, then compare them with those of other students. **LS Interpersonal**

Reteach

Students can look at the illustrations and describe details that support the main ideas of the chapter. **LS Visual-Spatial**

Answers to Chapter Review

Section 1

2. They are identical.

Section 2

3. The production of many spores increases the chances that some will encounter an environment suitable for germination and growth.

Section 3

3. Orchid flowers are usually pollinated by insects.

Chapter 10 Study Guide

Reviewing Main Ideas

Section 1 Introduction to Plant Reproduction

1. Plants reproduce sexually and asexually. Sexual reproduction involves the formation of sex cells and fertilization.
2. Asexual reproduction does not involve sex cells and produces plants genetically identical to the parent plant. *How do fern plants produced from the same rhizome compare genetically?*

3. Plant life cycles include a gametophyte and a sporophyte stage. The gametophyte stage begins with meiosis. The sporophyte stage begins when the egg is fertilized by a sperm.
4. In some plant life cycles, the sporophyte and gametophyte stages are separate and not dependent on each other. In other plant life cycles, they are part of the same organism.

Section 2 Seedless Reproduction

1. For liverworts and mosses, the gametophyte stage is the familiar plant form. The sporophyte stage produces spores.
2. In ferns, the sporophyte stage, not the gametophyte stage, is the familiar plant form.
3. Seedless plants, like mosses and ferns, use sexual reproduction to produce spores. *Why do seedless plants such as these produce so many small spores?*

Section 3 Seed Reproduction

1. In seed plants the male reproductive organs produce pollen grains that eventually contain sperm. Eggs are produced in the ovules of the female reproductive organs.
2. The male and female reproductive organs of gymnosperms are called cones. Wind usually moves pollen from the male cone to the female cone for pollination.
3. The reproductive organs of angiosperms are in a flower. The male reproductive organ is the stamen, and the female reproductive organ is the pistil. Gravity, wind, rain, and animals can pollinate a flower. *How would these flowers become pollinated?*

4. Seeds of gymnosperms and angiosperms are dispersed in many ways. Wind, water, and animals spread seeds. Some plants can eject their seeds.
5. Germination is a series of events that results in the growth of a plant from a seed.

FOLDABLES Reading & Study Skills — After You Read

On the front of your Venn Diagram Study Fold where the circles overlap, write common characteristics of sexual and asexual reproduction.

FOLDABLES Reading & Study Skills — After You Read

After students have read the chapter and completed the Foldable described in Before You Read, have them do the activity on the student page.

Dinah Zike

Visualizing Main Ideas

Complete the following table that compares reproduction in different plant groups.

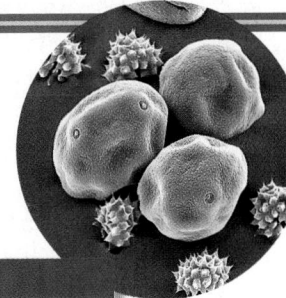

Plant Reproduction

Plant Group	Seeds?	Pollen?	Cones?	Flowers?
Mosses	No	No	No	No
Ferns	No	No	No	No
Gymnosperms	Yes	Yes	Yes	No
Angiosperms	Yes	Yes	No	Yes

Vocabulary Review

Vocabulary Words

a. frond
b. gametophyte stage
c. germination
d. ovary
e. ovule
f. pistil
g. pollen grain
h. pollination
i. prothallus
j. rhizome
k. sori
l. spore
m. sporophyte stage
n. stamen

Study Tip

Read the chapter before you go over it in class. Being familiar with the material before your teacher explains it gives you better understanding and an opportunity to ask questions.

Using Vocabulary

Replace the underlined word or phrase with the correct vocabulary word(s).

1. A <u>sori</u> is the leaf of a fern.
2. In seed plants, the <u>anther</u> contains the egg.
3. The plant structures in the <u>sporophyte stage</u> are made up of haploid cells.
4. The green, leafy moss plant is part of the <u>prothallus</u> in the moss life cycle.
5. Two parts of a sporophyte fern are <u>stamen</u> and <u>pistil</u>.
6. The female reproductive organ of the flower is the <u>rhizome</u>.
7. The <u>ovule</u> is the swollen base of the pistil.

Chapter 10 Study Guide

Visualizing Main Ideas

See student page.

Vocabulary Review

Using Vocabulary

1. frond
2. ovule
3. gametophyte stage
4. gametophyte stage
5. frond; rhizome; sori (any two)
6. pistil
7. ovary

Chapter 10 Assessment

Checking Concepts

1. A
2. A
3. A
4. A
5. A
6. C
7. C
8. D
9. D
10. D

Thinking Critically

11. Large numbers of pollen grains increase the chances that any one pollen grain will be blown to a female cone and fertilize an ovule.
12. No; the embryo is the young plant; without it, no plant can grow.
13. Nonvascular plants and ferns require water to transport the sperm to egg cells.
14. The sporophyte is not photosynthetic, so it depends on the photosynthetic gametophyte for nutrition.
15. Brightly colored structures, scents, and flower form help to ensure pollination by specialized pollinators.

Chapter 10 Assessment

Checking Concepts

Choose the word or phrase that best answers the question.

1. How are colorful flowers usually pollinated?
   A) insects **C)** clothing
   B) wind **D)** gravity
2. What type of reproduction produces plants that are genetically identical?
   A) asexual **C)** spore
   B) sexual **D)** flower
3. Which of the following terms describes the cells in the gametophyte stage?
   A) haploid **C)** diploid
   B) prokaryote **D)** missing a nucleus
4. What structures do ferns form when they reproduce sexually?
   A) spores **C)** seeds
   B) anthers **D)** flowers
5. What contains food for the plant embryo?
   A) endosperm **C)** stigma
   B) pollen grain **D)** root
6. What disperses most dandelion seeds?
   A) rain **C)** wind
   B) animals **D)** insects
7. What is the series of events that results in a plant growing from a seed?
   A) pollination **C)** germination
   B) prothallus **D)** fertilization
8. In plants, meiosis is used to produce what before fertilization?
   A) prothallus **C)** flowers
   B) seeds **D)** spores
9. Ovules and pollen grains take part in what process?
   A) germination
   B) asexual reproduction
   C) seed dispersal
   D) sexual reproduction
10. What part of the flower receives the pollen grain from the anther?
    A) sepal **C)** stamen
    B) petal **D)** stigma

Thinking Critically

11. Explain why male cones produce so many pollen grains.
12. Could a seed without an embryo germinate? Explain your answer.
13. Discuss the importance of water in the sexual reproduction of nonvascular plants and ferns.
14. In mosses, why is the sporophyte stage dependent on the gametophyte stage?
15. What features of flowers ensure pollination?

Developing Skills

16. **Making and Using Graphs** Make a bar graph for the following data table about onion seeds. Put days on the horizontal axis and temperature on the vertical axis.

Onion Seed Data

Temperature (°C)	10	15	20	25	30	35
Days to Germinate	13	7	5	4	4	13

17. **Comparing and Contrasting** Describe the differences and similarities between the fern sporophyte and gametophyte stages.

Chapter Assessment Planner

Portfolio Encourage students to place in their portfolios one or two items of what they consider to be their best work. Examples include:

- Assessment, p. 277
- Make a Model, p. 280
- Activity, p. 285

Performance Additional performance assessments, Performance Task Assessment Lists, and rubrics for evaluating these activities can be found in Glencoe's **Performance Assessment in the Science Classroom.**

18. **Predicting** Observe pictures of flowers or actual flowers and predict how they are pollinated. Explain your prediction.

19. **Interpreting Scientific Illustrations** Using **Figure 16,** sequence these events.
    pollen is trapped on the stigma
    pollen tube reaches the ovule
    fertilization
    pollen released from the anther
    pollen tube forms through the style
    a seed forms

20. **Concept Mapping** Complete this concept map of a typical plant life cycle.

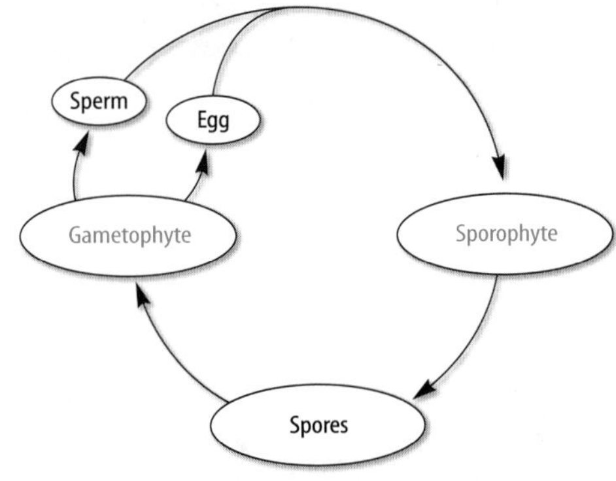

Performance Assessment

21. **Seed Mosaic** Collect several different types of seeds and use them to make a mosaic picture of a flower.

22. **Newspaper Story** Write a newspaper story to tell people about the importance of gravity, water, wind, insects, and other animals in plant life cycles.

Technology

Go to the Glencoe Science Web site at **science.glencoe.com** or use the **Glencoe Science CD-ROM** for additional chapter assessment.

THE PRINCETON REVIEW Test Practice

Four groups containing 15 plants each were set up to determine how many flowers were pollinated in a 24-h period. Each plant had five flowers. A botanist recorded the data in the following table.

Pollination Data

Plant Group (15 plants per group)	Number of Bees	Number of Birds	Number of Flowers Pollinated after 24 hrs.
1	5	1	16
2	10	1	35
3	15	1	49
4	20	1	73

Study the table and answer the following questions.

1. Which hypothesis probably is being tested in this experiment?
   A) A greater number of bees increases the rate of pollination.
   B) Birds increase the chance of pollination.
   C) A combination of birds and bees gives the best chance of successful pollination.
   D) Increasing the number of plants in a group results in increased pollination.

2. The pollination that is taking place in this experiment is part of which process?
   F) asexual reproduction
   G) sexual reproduction
   H) seed dispersal
   J) germination

Assessment Resources

 **Reproducible Masters**

Chapter Resources Booklet
Chapter Review, pp. 35–36
Chapter Tests, pp. 37–40
Assessment Transparency Activity, p. 47

Glencoe Science Web site
Interactive Tutor
Chapter Quizzes

Glencoe Technology
Assessment Transparency
Interactive CD-ROM Chapter Quizzes
ExamView Pro Test Bank
Vocabulary PuzzleMaker Software
MindJogger Videoquiz

Chapter 10 Assessment

 Test Practice

The Test-Taking Tip was written by The Princeton Review, the nation's leader in test preparation.

1. A
2. G

Developing Skills

16. Onion Seed Germination

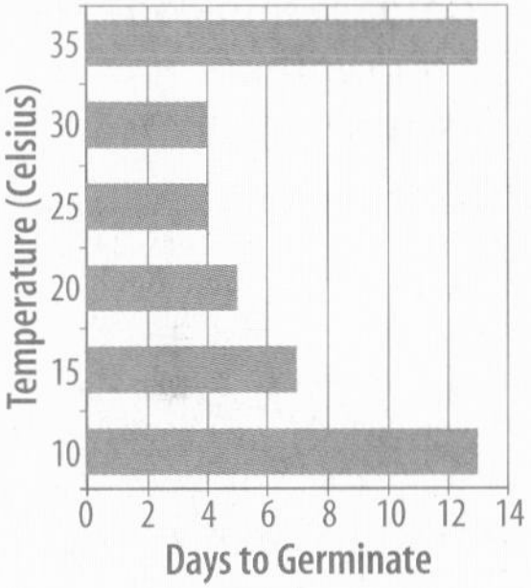

17. Haploid gametophyte stage—small and inconspicuous; diploid sporophyte stage—large and conspicuous; both stages are independent and photosynthetic.
18. Answers will vary depending on flowers observed.
19. 1—pollen is released from the anther; 2—pollen is trapped on the stigma; 3—pollen tube forms through style; 4—pollen tube reaches the ovule; 5—fertilization; 6—a seed forms
20. See student page.

Performance Assessment

21. Seed mosaics will vary depending on seed selection and flower chosen. Look for all parts of a flower in the mosaics. Use **PASC,** p. 135.
22. Stories should include information about plant life cycles and the importance of mechanisms of pollination. Use **PASC,** p. 141.

Section/Objectives	Standards		Activities/Features
	National	**State/Local**	
Chapter Opener	See p. 5T for a Key to Standards.		**Explore Activity:** Infer how plants lose water, p. 303 **Before You Read,** p. 303
Section 1 Photosynthesis and Respiration 2 sessions 1 block 1. **Explain** how plants take in and give off gases. 2. **Compare and contrast** relationships between photosynthesis and respiration. 3. **Discuss** why photosynthesis and respiration are important.	National Content Standards: UCP1, A1, C1, C3		**Health Integration,** p. 305 **MiniLAB:** Inferring What Plants Need to Produce Chlorophyll, p. 306 **Science Online,** p. 308 **Activity:** Stomata in Leaves, p. 312
Section 2 Plant Responses 3 sessions 1.5 blocks 1. **Identify** the relationship between a stimulus and a tropism in plants. 2. **Compare and contrast** long-day and short-day plants. 3. **Explain** how plant hormones and responses are related.	National Content Standards: UCP1, A1, C1, C3, G1		**Physics Integration,** p. 314 **Math Skills Activity:** Calculating Averages, p. 315 **MiniLAB:** Observing Ripening, p. 316 **Visualizing Plant Hormones,** p. 317 **Science Online,** p. 318 **Activity:** Tropism in Plants, pp. 320–321 **Science and Language Arts:** Sunkissed: An Indian Legend, pp. 322–323

NATIONAL GEOGRAPHIC

Teacher's Corner

PRODUCTS AVAILABLE FROM GLENCOE
To order call 1-800-334-7344:
CD-ROM
NGS PictureShow: Plants: What It Means to Be Green
Curriculum Kit
GeoKits: Plants

Transparency Set
NGS PicturePack: Plants: What It Means to Be Green
Videodisc
STV: Plants

PRODUCTS AVAILABLE FROM NATIONAL GEOGRAPHIC SOCIETY
To order call 1-800-368-2728:
Video
Photosynthesis: Life Energy

Activity Materials	Reproducible Resources	Section Assessment	Technology
Explore Activity: self-sealing plastic bag, aluminum foil, small potted plant	**Chapter Resources Booklet** Foldable Worksheet, p. 15 Directed Reading Overview, p. 17 Note-taking Worksheets, pp. 29–31	GLENCOE'S ASSESSMENT ADVANTAGE	
MiniLAB: black construction paper, plant with leaves, scissors, tape **Activity:** lettuce in dish of water, coverslip, microscope, microscope slide, salt solution, forceps *Need materials?* Contact Science Kit at 1-800-828-7777 or www.sciencekit.com on the Internet.	**Chapter Resources Booklet** Transparency Activity, p. 40 MiniLAB, p. 3 Enrichment, p. 27 Reinforcement, p. 25 Directed Reading, p. 18 Activity Worksheet, pp. 5–6 Transparency Activity, pp. 43–44 Lab Activity, pp. 9–10 **Science Inquiry Labs,** p. 35 **Life Science Critical Thinking/ Problem Solving,** p. 8	**Portfolio** Science Journal, p. 307 **Performance** MiniLAB, p. 307 Skill Builder Activities, p. 311 **Content** Section Assessment, p. 311	Section Focus Transparency Interactive CD-ROM Teaching Transparency Guided Reading Audio Program
MiniLAB: 2 green bananas, paper bag **Activity:** paper towel, 30 × 30-cm sheet of aluminum foil, water, mustard seeds, marking pen, 1-L clear glass or plastic jar	**Chapter Resources Booklet** Transparency Activity, p. 41 MiniLAB, p. 4 Enrichment, p. 28 Reinforcement, p. 26 Directed Reading, pp. 19, 20 Activity Worksheet, pp. 7–8 Lab Activity, pp. 11–14 **Home and Community Involvement,** p. 45 **Lab Management and Safety,** p. 58	**Portfolio** Curriculum Connection, p. 318 Reteach, p. 319 **Performance** MiniLAB, p. 316 Skill Builder Activities, p. 319 **Content** Section Assessment, p. 319	Section Focus Transparency Interactive CD-ROM Guided Reading Audio Program

GLENCOE'S ASSESSMENT ADVANTAGE

End of Chapter Assessment

Blackline Masters	Technology	Professional Series
Chapter Resources Booklet Chapter Review, pp. 33–34 Chapter Tests, pp. 35–38 **Standardized Test Practice by The Princeton Review,** pp. 51–54	MindJogger Videoquiz Interactive CD-ROM Vocabulary PuzzleMakers ExamView Pro Test Bank Interactive Lesson Planner Interactive Teacher Edition	Performance Assessment in the Science Classroom (PASC)

Transparencies

Section Focus

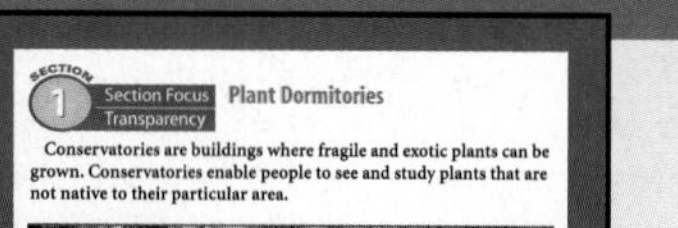
Section 1 Section Focus Transparency **Plant Dormitories**

Conservatories are buildings where fragile and exotic plants can be grown. Conservatories enable people to see and study plants that are not native to their particular area.

1. How do conservatories keep plants healthy?
2. In a conservatory, would you expect arctic plants to be found next to tropical plants? Why or why not?

L2

Section 2 Section Focus Transparency **A Bright Winter**

Here's a plant that can add a little color to your winter. It's called a Christmas cactus, and it blooms in the shorter days of the fall and winter months. Lower temperatures and drier soil also are conditions that help the Christmas cactus bloom at this time of year.

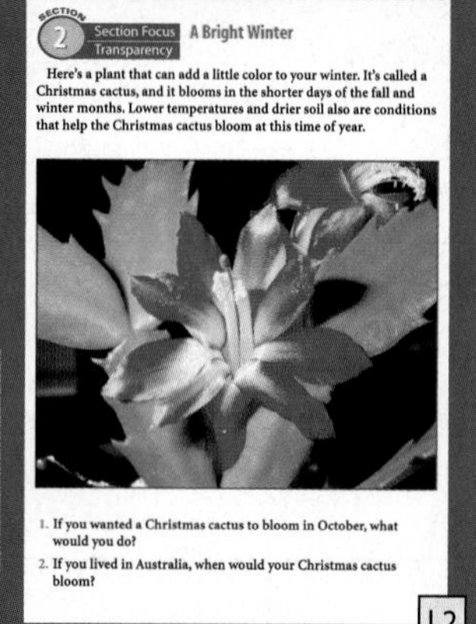

1. If you wanted a Christmas cactus to bloom in October, what would you do?
2. If you lived in Australia, when would your Christmas cactus bloom?

L2

This is a representation of key blackline masters available in the Teacher Classroom Resources. See Resource Manager boxes within the chapter for additional information.

Assessment

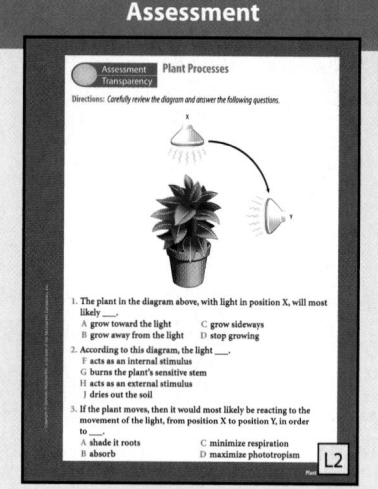

Assessment Transparency **Plant Processes**

Directions: Carefully review the diagram and answer the following questions.

1. The plant in the diagram above, with light in position X, will most likely ___.
   A grow toward the light C grow sideways
   B grow away from the light D stop growing
2. According to this diagram, the light ___.
   F acts as an internal stimulus
   G burns the plant's sensitive stem
   H acts as an external stimulus
   J dries out the soil
3. If the plant moves, then it would most likely be reacting to the movement of the light, from position X to position Y, in order to ___.
   A shade it roots C minimize respiration
   B absorb D maximize phototropism

L2

Teaching

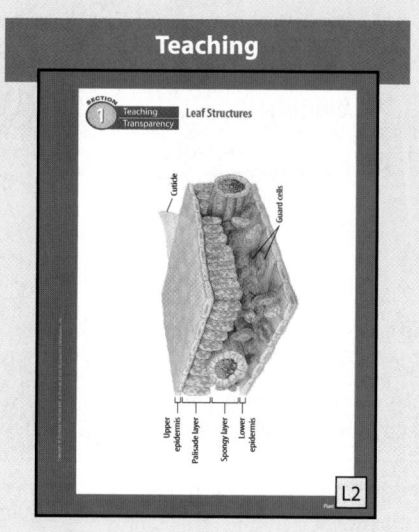

Section 1 Teaching Transparency **Leaf Structures**

Cuticle
Guard cells
Upper epidermis
Palisade layer
Spongy layer
Lower epidermis

L2

Key to Teaching Strategies

The following designations will help you decide which activities are appropriate for your students.

- L1 Level 1 activities should be appropriate for students with learning difficulties.
- L2 Level 2 activities should be within the ability range of all students.
- L3 Level 3 activities are designed for above-average students.
- ELL ELL activities should be within the ability range of English Language Learners.
- COOP LEARN Cooperative Learning activities are designed for small group work.
- LS Multiple Learning Styles logos, as described on page 22T, are used throughout to indicate strategies that address different learning styles.
- P These strategies represent student products that can be placed into a best-work portfolio.

Hands-on Activities

Activity Worksheets

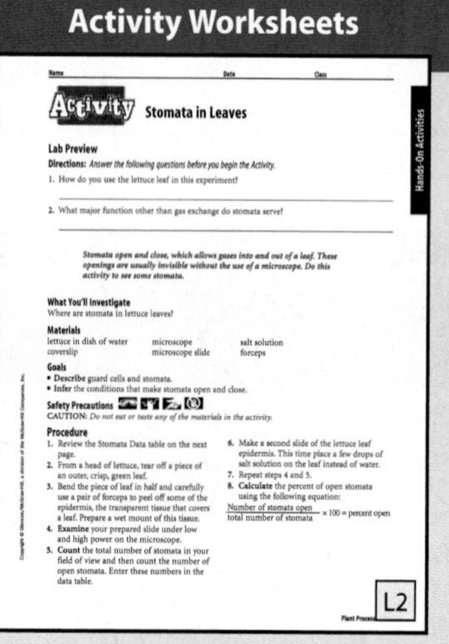
Name Date Class

Activity Stomata in Leaves

Lab Preview

Directions: *Answer the following questions before you begin the Activity.*

1. How do you use the lettuce leaf in this experiment?
2. What major function other than gas exchange do stomata serve?

Stomata open and close, which allows gases into and out of a leaf. These openings are usually invisible without the use of a microscope. Do this activity to see some stomata.

What You'll Investigate
Where are stomata in lettuce leaves?

Materials
lettuce in dish of water, coverslip, microscope, microscope slide, salt solution, forceps

Goals
- **Describe** guard cells and stomata.
- **Infer** the conditions that make stomata open and close.

Safety Precautions
CAUTION: *Do not eat or taste any of the materials in the activity.*

Procedure
1. Review the Stomata Data table on the next page.
2. From a head of lettuce, tear off a piece of an outer, crisp, green leaf.
3. Bend the piece of leaf in half and carefully use a pair of forceps to peel off some of the epidermis, the transparent tissue that covers a leaf. Prepare a wet mount of this tissue.
4. **Examine** your prepared slide under low and high power on the microscope.
5. **Count** the total number of stomata in your field of view and then count the number of open stomata. Enter these numbers in the data table.
6. Make a second slide of the lettuce leaf epidermis. This time place a few drops of salt solution on the leaf instead of water.
7. Repeat steps 4 and 5.
8. **Calculate** the percent of open stomata using the following equation:

$$\frac{\text{Number of stomata open}}{\text{total number of stomata}} \times 100 = \text{percent open}$$

Hands-On Activities

L2

Laboratory Activities

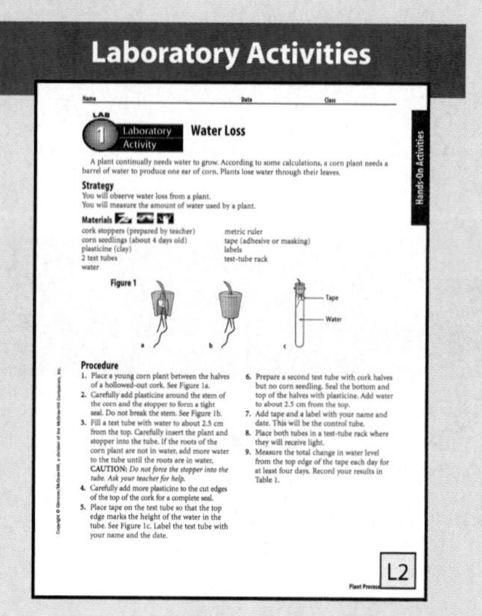
Name Date Class

Lab 1 Laboratory Activity Water Loss

A plant continually needs water to grow. According to some calculations, a corn plant needs a barrel of water to produce one ear of corn. Plants lose water through their leaves.

Strategy
You will observe water loss from a plant.
You will measure the amount of water used by a plant.

Materials
cork stoppers (prepared by teacher), corn seedlings (about 4 days old), plasticine (clay), 2 test tubes, water, metric ruler, tape (adhesive or masking), labels, test-tube rack

Figure 1

Procedure
1. Place a young corn plant between the halves of a hollowed-out cork. See Figure 1a.
2. Carefully add plasticine around the stem of the corn and the stopper to form a tight seal. Do not break the stem. See Figure 1b.
3. Fill a test tube with water to about 2.5 cm from the top. Carefully insert the plant and stopper into the tube. If the roots of the corn plant are not in water, add more water to the tube until the roots are in water. CAUTION: *Do not force the stopper into the tube. Ask your teacher for help.*
4. Carefully add more plasticine to the cut edges of the top of the cork for a complete seal.
5. Place tape on the test tube so that the top edge marks the height of the water in the tube. See Figure 1c. Label the test tube with your name and the date.
6. Prepare a second test tube with cork halves but no corn seedling. Seal the bottom and top of the halves with plasticine. Add water to about 2.5 cm from the top.
7. Add tape and a label with your name and date. This will be the control tube.
8. Place both tubes in a test-tube rack where they will receive light.
9. Measure the total change in water level from the top edge of the tape each day for at least four days. Record your results in Table 1.

Hands-On Activities

L2

Meeting Different Ability Levels

Content Outline

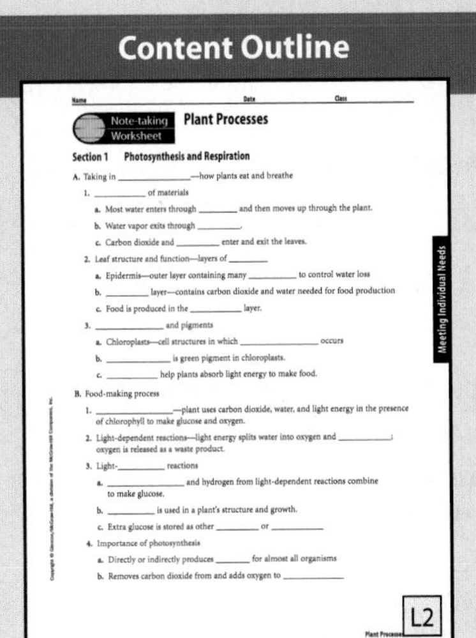

Reinforcement

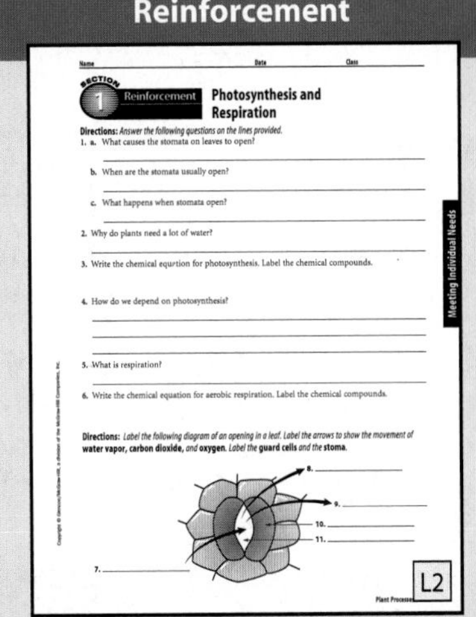

Directed Reading

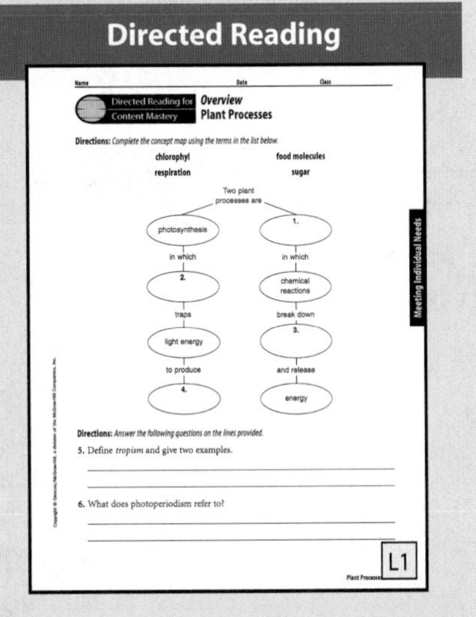

Enrichment

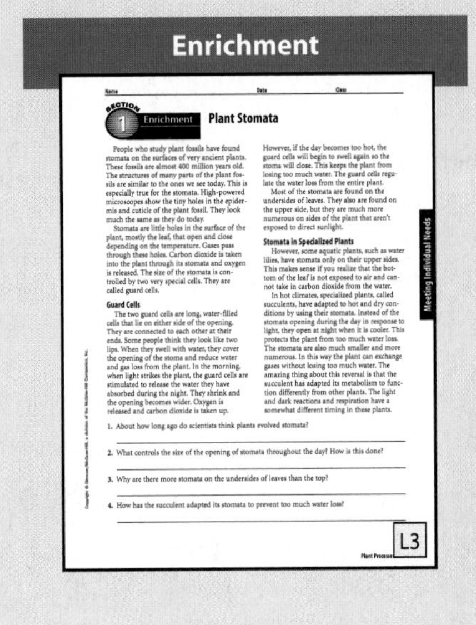

Spanish Directed Reading

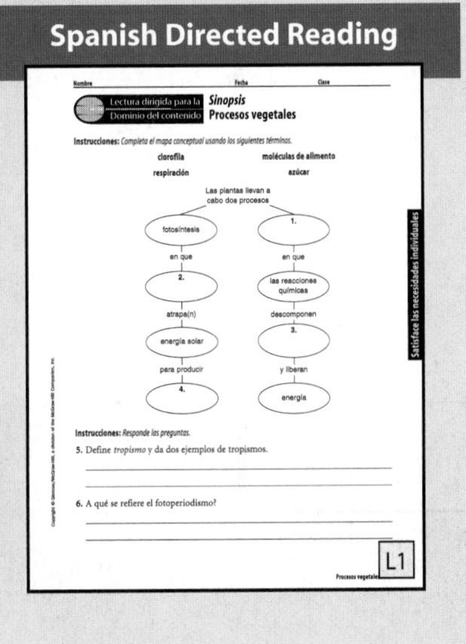

Assessment

Chapter Tests

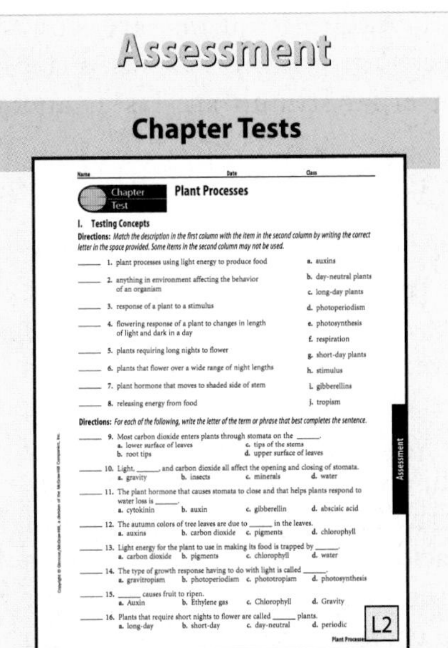

Test Practice Workbook

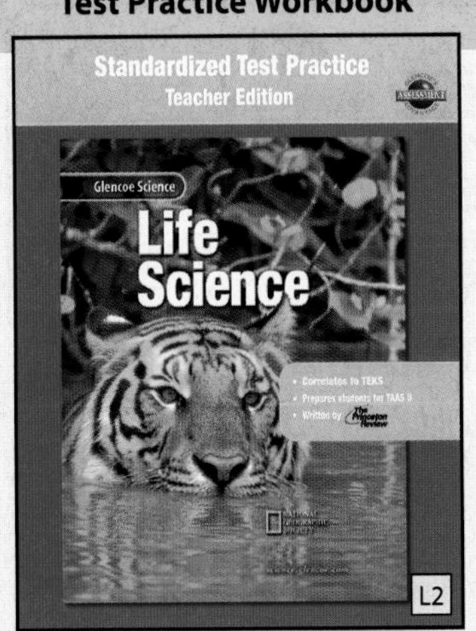

Chapter Review

Chapter Review — Plant Processes

L2

Science Content Background

SECTION 1 Photosynthesis and Respiration

The Food-Making Process

During the light-dependent cycle, a chemical reaction occurs between light and chlorophyll. Electrons from this reaction combine with hydrogen ions from water and stored chemical energy called NADPH + H+. The NADPH is the source of energy for the light-independent cycle. During this cycle, most plants utilize the NADPH energy to synthesize carbohydrates, including glucose, from carbon dioxide.

Respiration, the mechanism by which energy is released from stored fuel, is always preceded by glycolysis. Glycolysis, which occurs in cell cytoplasm, breaks down one glucose molecule into two molecules of pyruvic acid, producing only a small amount of energy. If oxygen is not required or is unavailable during respiration, the process continues as anaerobic reactions, sometimes producing lactic acid. If alcohol is produced, the process is called fermentation. These two inefficient processes extract only a small amount of energy from the pyruvic acid. Aerobic respiration uses oxygen and releases all the energy in the chemical bonds of pyruvic acid. The end products of this process are carbon dioxide, water, and energy.

Jean Paul/FPG International

Student Misconception

Plants do not take in oxygen or give off carbon dioxide.

Refer to the facing page for teaching strategies to address this misconception. Refer to pages 307–309 for content related to this topic.

SECTION 2 Plant Responses

Types of Responses

Plant responses to external stimuli, called tropisms, are slow, permanent, directed growth movements. Plant responses to internal stimuli are faster and reversible.

Plant Hormones

Plant hormones, chemicals produced in specific plant cells, are transported to other sites in the plant, where they cause physiological changes. The hormone auxin causes cell walls to become more elastic and to stretch during active cell growth, controls suppression of lateral bud growth, and prevents leaf abscission, or leaf drop. Ethylene regulates ripening of fruits. Abscisic acid, produced mainly in leaves and fruits, causes buds to become dormant. Gibberellins and cytokinins affect plant growth.

For additional content background on this topic, go to the Glencoe Science Web site at science.glencoe.com.

IDENTIFYING Misconceptions

Find Out What Students Think

Students may think that . . .

- **Plants do not take in oxygen or give off carbon dioxide.**
- **Photosynthesis is a plant's way of breathing.**

Textbooks and science activity books frequently include diagrams showing a cycle in which plants produce oxygen and take in carbon dioxide and animals take in oxygen while giving off carbon dioxide. From diagrams like these, students draw the conclusion that plants exist to give off oxygen for the benefit of animals. They also equate photosynthesis with breathing because it involves taking in one gas and giving off another. Students who do know that plants can give off carbon dioxide often believe it only occurs in the dark, when the plant cannot get sunlight.

Activity

Write the words *oxygen*, *carbon dioxide*, *plant*, *animal*, *glucose*, *light*, and *water* on the board. Ask students to copy the words and then construct concept maps showing how all these terms interrelate. Students will most likely make diagrams showing oxygen moving from plant to animal and carbon dioxide moving from animal to plant. They may not know where to place glucose and water.

Promote Understanding

Demonstrations

After students have learned that glucose is a product of photosynthesis, ask them why they think plants make glucose. A possible answer may be "Plants make glucose for animals to eat." The following demonstrations will help students understand that plants make glucose for their own use.

- Show students a soaked bean seed. Open the seed and apply iodine as a test for starch. After several minutes the starchy endosperm of the seed should turn blue-black. Use a diagram or snap-lock beads to help explain that starch molecules are chains of glucose molecules. Explain that the bean plant stored starch in the bean seed. Ask students what advantage this might have for the plant. Some students may think that the starch is food for animals, while others may understand that it is food for the embryonic plant.
- Place viable bean seeds in a flask until it is one-third full. Add enough water to completely cover the seeds. Insert a stopper with a glass tube. Attach one end of a length of rubber tubing to the glass tube. Insert the other end into a small flask of limewater. Let the apparatus sit in a warm, well-lighted place. As the seeds absorb water and begin germination, they will metabolize the stored starch in their endosperm and will give off carbon dioxide. Carbon dioxide bubbling slowly through the limewater will cause the liquid to turn cloudy.

Assess

After completing the chapter, see *Identifying Misconceptions* in the Study Guide.

CHAPTER 

Plant Processes

Chapter Vocabulary

stomata, p. 305
chlorophyll, p. 306
photosynthesis, p. 307
respiration, p. 309
tropism, p. 314
auxin, p. 316
photoperiodism, p. 318
long-day plant, p. 318
short-day plant, p. 318
day-neutral plant, p. 318

What do you think?

Science Journal The picture shows *Elodea* leaves giving off oxygen bubbles. Oxygen is a by-product of the process of photosynthesis, which requires light.

CHAPTER 11

Plant Processes

From crabgrass to giant sequoias, many plants start as small seeds. Some trees may grow to be more than 20 m tall. One tree can be cut up to produce many pieces of lumber. Where does all that wood come from? You may have seen a plant on a windowsill with all its leaves growing toward the window. Why do they grow that way? In this chapter, find the answers to these questions. In addition, learn how plants are essential to the survival of all animals on Earth—including you!

What do you think?

Science Journal Look at the picture below with a classmate. Discuss what you think this might be or what is happening. Here's a hint: *This would never happen without light.* Write your answer or best guess in your Science Journal.

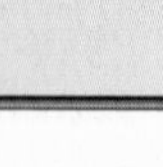

302

Theme Connection

Systems and Interactions The systems and structures involved in the processes of photosynthesis and respiration work together. Through interactions, these processes, along with the stimuli-response mechanisms discussed in the second part of the chapter, allow a plant to maintain homeostasis.

Plants are similar to other living things because they are made of cells, reproduce, make and use substances, and need water. If you forgot to water a houseplant, what do you think would happen? From your own experiences, you probably know that the houseplant would wilt. Do the following activity to discover one way plants lose water.

Infer how plants lose water 

1. Obtain a self-sealing plastic bag, some aluminum foil, and a small potted plant from your teacher.
2. Using the foil, carefully cover the soil around the plant in the pot. Place the potted plant in the plastic bag.
3. Seal the bag and place it in a sunny window. Wash your hands.
4. Look at the plant at the same time every day for a few days.

Observe

In your Science Journal, describe what happens in the bag. If enough water is lost by a plant and not replaced, predict what will happen to the plant.

Before You Read

FOLDABLES Reading & Study Skills

Making a Compare and Contrast Study Fold **As you study plant processes, use the following Foldable to help you compare and contrast plant respiration and animal respiration.**

1. Place a sheet of paper in front of you so the long side is at the top. Fold the paper in half from top to bottom.
2. Write *Respiration* across the front, as shown.
3. Unfold the paper. Draw a picture of an animal on the top half and a plant on the bottom half. Leave room to write below the drawings.
4. Before you read the chapter write what you know about animal respiration and plant respiration on the appropriate flaps.
5. As you read the chapter, add to or change your information.

Respiration

303

EXPLORE ACTIVITY

Purpose Use the Explore Activity to introduce students to plant processes. Inform students that they will be learning more about plant processes as they read the chapter. ELL LS **Kinesthetic**

Preparation The seedlings should be large enough to transpire an observable amount of water.

Materials large self-sealing plastic bags, seedling plants in pots, aluminum foil

Teaching Strategies

- Have students record their hypotheses about what will happen after the plants are sealed in the plastic bags.
- Discuss why the soil is covered with foil. to reduce evaporation from the soil

Observe

Students should explain that most of the water that gathers in the bag came from the plant. The plant will wilt or even die if it loses too much water.

Assessment

Process Have students diagram the pathway of water through a plant, drawing on prior knowledge to label their diagrams with terms such as *roots*, *stems*, *vascular tissue*, and *xylem*. Use **Performance Assessment in the Science Classroom,** p. 127.

Before You Read

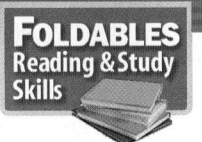

FOLDABLES Reading & Study Skills

Dinah Zike Study Fold

Purpose Students make and use a Foldable to collect information on plant respiration. Students use this information to compare and contrast plant and animal respiration. How are they the same? How do they differ?

For additional help, see Foldables Worksheet, p. 15 in **Chapter Resources Booklet,** or go to the Glencoe Science Web site at **science.glencoe.com.** See After You Read in the Study Guide at the end of this chapter.

SECTION

Photosynthesis and Respiration

1 Motivate

Bellringer Transparency

Display the Section Focus Transparency for Section 1. Use the accompanying Transparency Activity Master. L2

ELL

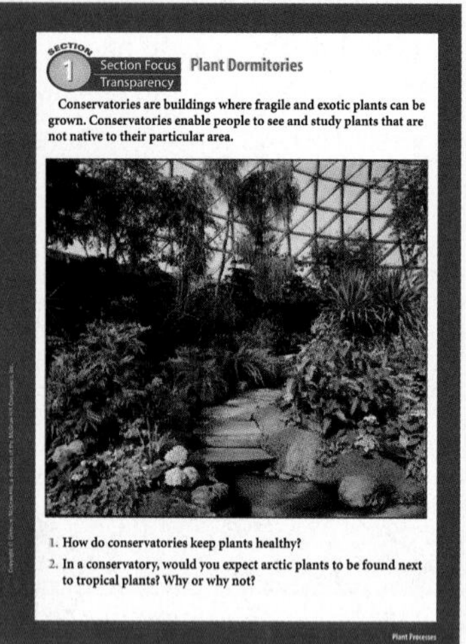

Section Focus Transparency 1 — Plant Dormitories

Conservatories are buildings where fragile and exotic plants can be grown. Conservatories enable people to see and study plants that are not native to their particular area.

1. How do conservatories keep plants healthy?
2. In a conservatory, would you expect arctic plants to be found next to tropical plants? Why or why not?

Plant Processes

Tie to Prior Knowledge

Ask if students know why plants are green. Explain that plants are green because they contain chlorophyll, a pigment that traps most of light's energy but reflects green wavelengths of light.

SECTION 1

Photosynthesis and Respiration

As You Read

***What* You'll Learn**

- **Explain** how plants take in and give off gases.
- **Compare and contrast** relationships between photosynthesis and respiration.
- **Discuss** why photosynthesis and respiration are important.

Vocabulary

stomata
chlorophyll
photosynthesis
respiration

***Why* It's Important**

Understanding photosynthesis and respiration in plants will help you understand how life is maintained on Earth.

Taking in Raw Materials

Sitting in the cool shade under a tree, you finish eating your lunch. The food you eat is one of the raw materials that you need to grow. Oxygen is another. It enters your lungs and eventually reaches every cell in your body. Your cells use oxygen to help release the energy from the food that you eat. The process that uses oxygen to release the energy from food produces carbon dioxide and water as wastes. These wastes move in your blood to your lungs where they are removed as gases when you exhale. You look up at the tree and wonder, "Does a tree need to eat? Does it use oxygen? How does a tree get rid of wastes?

Movement of Materials in Plants No one packs a sack lunch for the tree. Trees and other plants don't take in foods the way you do. Plants make their own foods using the raw materials water, carbon dioxide, and inorganic chemicals in the soil. Just like you, plants also produce waste products.

Most of the water used by plants is taken in through roots, as shown in **Figure 1.** Water moves into root cells and then up through the plant to where it is used. When you pull up a plant, some of its roots are damaged. If you replant it, the plant will need extra water until new roots grow to replace those that were damaged.

Leaves, instead of lungs, are where most gas exchange occurs in plants. Most of the water taken in through the roots exits through the leaves of a plant. Carbon dioxide, oxygen, and water vapor exit and enter the plant through the leaf. The leaf's structure helps explain how it functions in gas exchange.

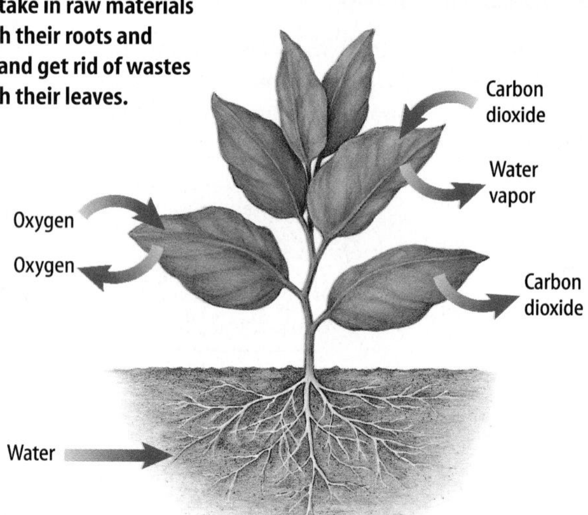

Figure 1
Plants take in raw materials through their roots and leaves and get rid of wastes through their leaves.

Section Assessment Planner

PORTFOLIO
Science Journal, p. 307

PERFORMANCE ASSESSMENT
MiniLAB, p. 307
Skill Builder Activities, p. 311
See page 326 for more options.

CONTENT ASSESSMENT
Section, p. 311
Challenge, p. 311
Chapter, pp. 326–327

Figure 2
A leaf's structure determines its function. Food is made in the inner layers. Most stomata are found on the lower epidermis.

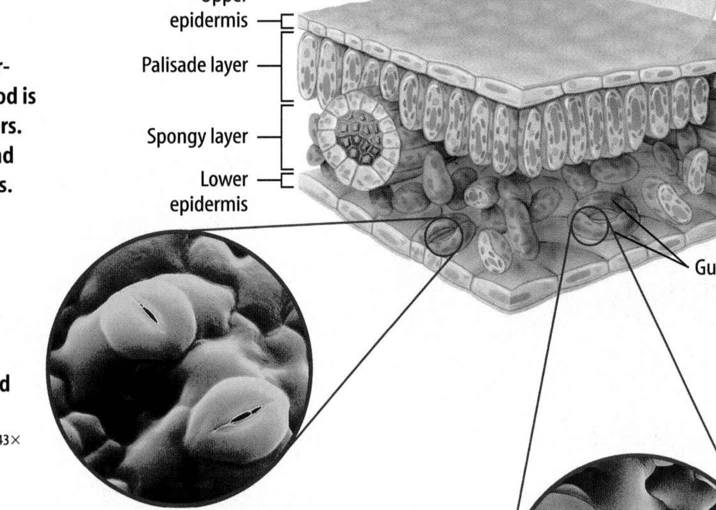

A Closed stomata
Magnification: 343×

B Open stomata
Magnification: 214×

Leaf Structure and Function A leaf is made up of many different layers, as shown in **Figure 2.** The outer cell layer of the leaf is the epidermis. A waxy cuticle that helps keep the leaf from drying out covers the epidermis. Because the epidermis is nearly transparent, sunlight—which is used to make food—reaches the cells inside the leaf. If you examine the epidermis under a microscope, you will see that it contains many small openings. These openings, called **stomata** (stoh MAH tuh) (singular, *stoma*), act as doorways for raw materials such as carbon dioxide, water vapor, and waste gases to enter and exit the leaf. Stomata also are found on the stems of many plants. More than 90 percent of the water plants take in through their roots is lost through the stomata. In one day, a growing tomato plant can lose up to 1 L of water.

Two cells called guard cells surround each stoma and control its size. As water moves into the guard cells, they swell and bend apart, opening a stoma. When guard cells lose water, they deflate, closing the stoma. **Figures 2A** and **2B** show closed and open stomata.

Stomata usually are open during the day when most plants need to take in raw materials to make food. They usually are closed at night when food making slows down. Stomata also close when a plant is losing too much water. This adaptation conserves water, because less water vapor escapes from the leaf.

Inside the leaf are two layers of cells, the spongy layer and the palisade layer. Carbon dioxide and water vapor, which are needed in the food-making process, fill the spaces of the spongy layer. Most of the food is made in the palisade layer.

Health INTEGRATION

Vitamins are substances needed for good health. You get most of the vitamins you need from the plants you eat. Research to learn about four vitamins and the plant foods you would need to eat to get them. Display your results on a poster.

2 Teach

Taking in Raw Materials

Quick Demo

Demonstrate how guard cells change shape. Show students an uninflated oblong balloon along whose length you have placed a strip of cellophane tape. Blow up the balloon, and again show it to the class. Explain that when the balloon is inflated, its shape changes just like a guard cell's shape changes when it swells with water. The guard cell takes this shape because it has a thickened cell wall on the side next to the stoma.

Make a Model

Have students use two balloons like the one in the demo above to model how two guard cells bracket a stoma. Point out the tape, which represents the thickened cell wall that adjoins the stoma.

Health INTEGRATION

Answer Answers will vary, but should include four vitamins, their sources, and their functions.

Visual Learning

Figure 2 Make sure students understand that the primary function of the stomata is to allow for the exchange of gases by the plant.

Resource Manager

Chapter Resources Booklet

Transparency Activity, p. 40
Directed Reading for Content Mastery, pp. 17, 18
Note-taking Worksheets, pp. 29–31

IDENTIFYING Misconceptions

Many students will think that all plant cells contain chlorophyll. Explain that cells deep within the plant where light does not penetrate and cells in underground plant parts lack this pigment and are not directly involved in photosynthesis. Ask: **What parts of a tree probably do not contain chlorophyll?** Woody parts that are not green, such as the stem (trunk), roots, and branches, do not contain chlorophyll.

Extension

Some students might investigate which plant pigments cause specific plant colors. Suggest that students study trees or other plants that turn particular colors in your area of the country. Anthocyanins are red; carotenoids are yellow. Leaves change color in fall because declining temperatures and short days lead to a breakdown of chlorophyll which allows other pigments to become visible. L2

Reading Check

Answer They contain a green pigment called chlorophyll.

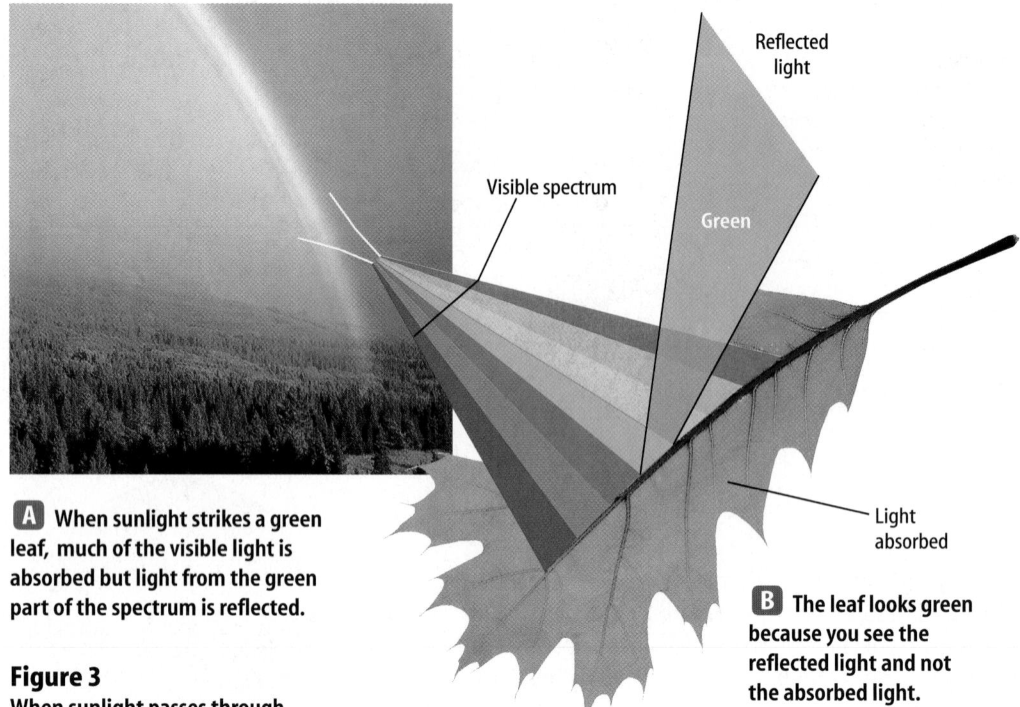

A When sunlight strikes a green leaf, much of the visible light is absorbed but light from the green part of the spectrum is reflected.

B The leaf looks green because you see the reflected light and not the absorbed light.

Figure 3
When sunlight passes through raindrops, they act like prisms. Light separates into the colors of the visible spectrum. You see a rainbow when this happens.

Chloroplasts and Plant Pigments If you look closely at the leaf in **Figure 2,** you'll see that some of the cells contain small, green structures called chloroplasts. Most leaves look green because their cells contain so many chloroplasts. Chloroplasts are green because they contain a green pigment called **chlorophyll** (KLOR uh fihl).

Reading Check *Why are chloroplasts green?*

As shown in **Figure 3,** light from the Sun contains all colors of the visible spectrum. A pigment is a substance that reflects a particular part of the visible spectrum and absorbs the rest. When you see a green leaf, you are seeing green light energy reflected from chlorophyll. Most of the other colors of the spectrum, especially red and blue, are absorbed by chlorophyll. In the spring and summer, most leaves have so much chlorophyll that it hides all other pigments. In fall, the chlorophyll in some leaves breaks down and the leaves change color as other pigments become visible. Pigments, especially chlorophyll, are important to plants because the light energy that they absorb is used to make food. For plants, this food-making process—photosynthesis—happens in the chloroplasts.

LAB DEMONSTRATION

Purpose to show that the colors we see are the colors objects reflect

Materials prism, light source, objects of different colors

Preparation Collect materials and have them grouped together to save time.

Procedure Place a prism in a bright light source so that the colors of white light entering the prism separate. Place objects of different colors in the paths of the separated beams.

Expected Outcome Objects will absorb all colors except the color they reflect.

Assessment

What would happen if you placed a red rose with green leaves in a red beam of light in a darkened room? The rose would appear red and the leaves would appear black.

The Food-Making Process

Photosynthesis (foh toh SIHN thuh suhs) is the process during which a plant's chlorophyll traps light energy and sugars are produced. In plants, photosynthesis occurs only in cells with chloroplasts. For example, photosynthesis occurs only in a carrot plant's lacy green leaves, shown in **Figure 4.** Because a carrot's root cells lack chlorophyll and normally do not receive light, they can't perform photosynthesis. But excess sugar produced in the leaves is stored in the familiar orange root that you and many animals eat.

Besides light, plants also need the raw materials carbon dioxide and water for photosynthesis. The overall chemical equation for photosynthesis is shown below. What happens to each of the raw materials in the process?

$$6CO_2 + 6H_2O + \text{light energy} \xrightarrow{\text{chlorophyll}} C_6H_{12}O_6 + 6O_2$$

carbon dioxide, water, glucose, oxygen

Light-Dependent Reactions Some of the chemical reactions that take place during photosynthesis need light but others do not. Those that need light can be called the light-dependent reactions of photosynthesis. During light-dependent reactions, chlorophyll and other pigments trap light energy that eventually will be stored in sugar molecules. Light energy causes water molecules, which were taken up by the roots, to split into oxygen and hydrogen. The oxygen leaves the plant through the stomata. This is the oxygen that you breathe. Leftover hydrogen is used in photosynthesis reactions that occur when there is no light.

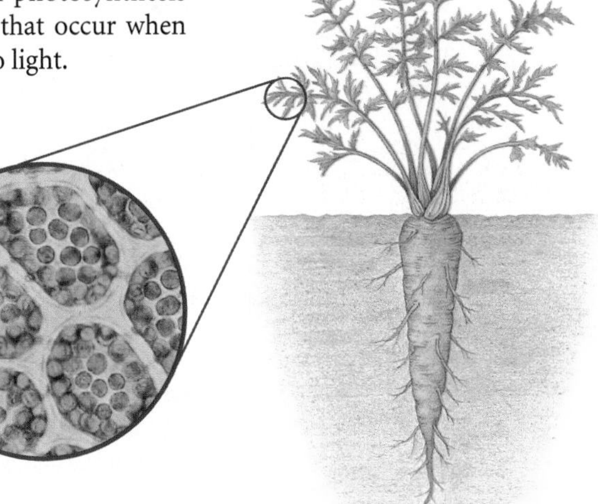

Figure 4
Because they contain chloroplasts, cells in the leaf of the carrot plant are the sites for photosynthesis.

Mini LAB

Inferring What Plants Need to Produce Chlorophyll

Procedure

1. Cut two pieces of **black construction paper** large enough so that each one completely covers one leaf on a **plant.**
2. Cut a square out of the center of each piece of paper.
3. Sandwich the leaf between the two paper pieces and **tape** the pieces together along their edges.
4. Place the plant in a sunny area. Wash your hands.
5. After seven days, carefully remove the paper and observe the leaf.

Analysis

In your **Science Journal,** describe how the color of the areas covered by paper compare to the areas not covered. Infer why this happened.

The Food-Making Process

Purpose to determine if plants require light to produce and maintain chlorophyll L2

LS **Kinesthetic**

Materials black construction paper, plant, tape, scissors

Teaching Strategy Record results immediately upon removing the construction paper.

Analysis

The covered area should be less green than the uncovered area. Light is needed in the production and maintenance of chlorophyll.

Process Have students suggest a way in which they could determine why they got their results. Use **PASC**, p. 99.

Science Journal

Carbon Dioxide Have students research how the buildup of carbon dioxide in the atmosphere might affect photosynthesis. Have them summarize their findings in their Science Journals. Increased carbon dioxide may correlate with increased photosynthesis in certain localities such as rain forests and marine environments with large amounts of plankton. L2 P

Chapter Resources Booklet
MiniLAB, p. 3
Lab Activity, pp. 9–10

Science Inquiry Labs, p. 35

The Food-Making Process, continued

Quick Demo

Place a sprig of *Elodea* in a test tube with 5 mL of water and 1 mL of bromothymol blue indicator. Have students note the yellow color. Place the tube in strong light. The solution should turn blue as *Elodea* takes up carbon dioxide in light.

Students may think that plants do not take in oxygen or give off carbon dioxide. Refer to page 302F for teaching strategies that address this misconception.

Fun Fact

A place where food is stored or used in a plant is called a sink. Depending on the plant, roots, stems, and leaves can be sinks.

Use Science Words

Word Meaning Have students look up the word *photosynthesis* and relate the meaning of its word parts to the process. *Photo-* means light; *synthesis* means the combining of parts to make a whole. So photosynthesis is the process that uses light to combine carbon dioxide and water into a larger sugar molecule.

Research Besides glucose, what other sugars do plants produce? Visit the Glencoe Science Web site at **science.glencoe.com** for more information about plant sugars. In your Science Journal list three sugars produced by plants.

Light-Independent Reactions Reactions that don't need light are called the light-independent reactions of photosynthesis. Carbon dioxide, the raw material from the air, is used in these reactions. The light energy trapped during the light-dependent reactions is used to combine carbon dioxide and hydrogen to make sugars. One important sugar that is made is glucose. The chemical bonds that hold glucose and other sugars together are stored energy. **Figure 5** compares what happens during each stage of photosynthesis.

What happens to the oxygen and glucose that were made during photosynthesis? Most of the oxygen from photosynthesis is a waste product and is released through stomata. Glucose is the main form of food for plant cells. A plant usually produces more glucose than it can use. Excess glucose is stored in plants as other sugars and starches. When you eat carrots, as well as beets, potatoes, or onions, you are eating the stored product of photosynthesis.

Glucose also is the basis of a plant's structure. You don't grow larger by breathing in and using carbon dioxide. However, that's exactly what plants do as they take in carbon dioxide gas and convert it into glucose. Cellulose, an important part of plant cell walls, is made from glucose. Leaves, stems, and roots are made of cellulose and other substances produced using glucose. The products of photosynthesis are used by plants to grow.

Figure 5
Photosynthesis includes two sets of reactions, the light-dependent reactions and the light-independent reactions.

Standard plant cell

Chloroplast

Sunlight

H_2O

O_2

CO_2

$C_6H_{12}O_6$

A During light-dependent reactions, light energy is trapped and water is split into hydrogen and oxygen. Oxygen leaves the plant.

B During light-independent reactions, energy is used to combine carbon dioxide and hydrogen to make glucose and other sugars.

Inclusion Strategies

Gifted Have students form an acrostic using the letters of the word *photosynthesis* to describe the process. L3

Internet Addresses

Explore the Glencoe Science Web site at **science.glencoe.com** to find out more about topics in this section.

Figure 6
Tropical rain forests contain large numbers of photosynthetic plants.

Importance of Photosynthesis Why is photosynthesis important to living things? First, photosynthesis produces food. Organisms that carry on photosynthesis provide food directly or indirectly for nearly all the other organisms on Earth. Second, photosynthetic organisms, like the plants in **Figure 6,** use carbon dioxide and release oxygen. This removes carbon dioxide from the atmosphere and adds oxygen to it. Most organisms, including humans, need oxygen to stay alive. As much as 90 percent of the oxygen entering the atmosphere today is a result of photosynthesis.

The Breakdown of Food

Look at the photograph in **Figure 7.** Do the fox and the plants in the photograph have anything in common? They don't look alike, but the fox and the plants are made of cells that break down food, and release energy in a process called respiration. How does this happen?

Respiration is a series of chemical reactions that breaks down food molecules and releases energy. Respiration occurs in cells of most organisms. The breakdown of food might or might not require oxygen. Respiration that uses oxygen to break down food chemically is called aerobic respiration. In plants and many organisms that have one or more cells, a nucleus, and other organelles, aerobic respiration occurs in the mitochondria (singular, *mitochondrion*). The overall chemical equation for aerobic respiration is shown below.

$$\underset{\text{glucose}}{C_6H_{12}O_6} + \underset{\text{oxygen}}{6O_2} \longrightarrow \underset{\text{carbon dioxide}}{6CO_2} + \underset{\text{water}}{6H_2O} + \text{energy}$$

Figure 7
You know that animals such as this red fox carry on respiration, but so do all the plants that surround the fox.

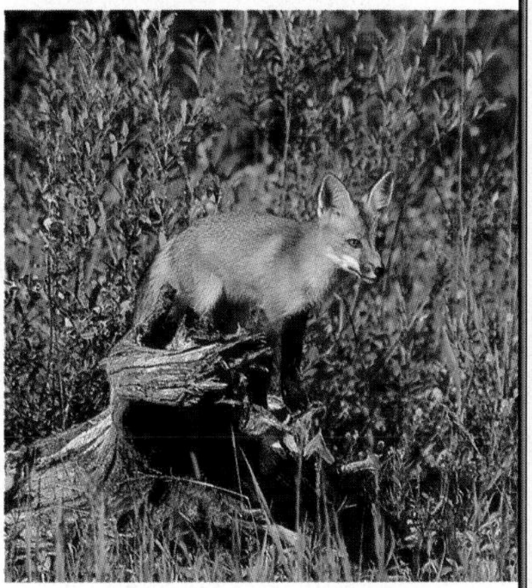

Discussion

Write the general equation for photosynthesis on the board. Use one color of chalk for the raw materials and another for the products. During the discussion, guide students to an understanding of what the equation means in terms of energy capture and conversion. L2
LS **Visual-Spatial and Interpersonal**

The Breakdown of Food

Quick Demo

Demonstrate respiration in yeast by adding 1 mL of bromothymol blue to a mixture of 1 mL sugar syrup (0.5 g of granulated sugar in 100 mL water), 5 mL water, and 2 mL yeast suspension. The color will change from blue to green and eventually to yellow as the yeasts respire and give off carbon dioxide.

Use an Analogy

Use these analogies to help clarify the processes of photosynthesis and respiration. A chloroplast where photosynthesis occurs is like a factory in which small parts are used to assemble a larger whole. A mitochondrion, in which respiration occurs, is like a powerhouse that uses fuel as an energy source for the production of goods.

Resource Manager

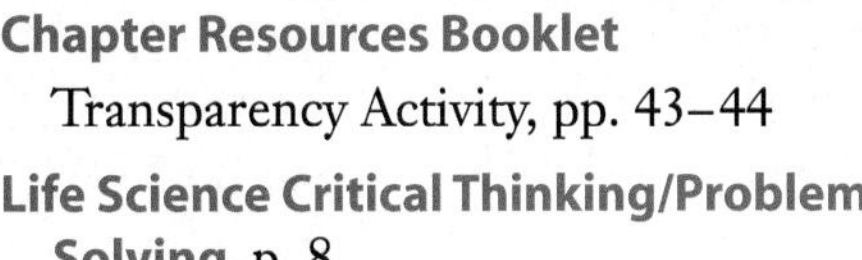

Chapter Resources Booklet
Transparency Activity, pp. 43–44
Life Science Critical Thinking/Problem Solving, p. 8

Cultural Diversity

Severo Ochoa Have students research the efforts of Spanish-American biochemist Severo Ochoa (1905–1993). He received the Nobel prize with Arthur Kornberg in 1959 for his work on RNA. Much of his scientific work was on describing the mechanisms of the citric acid cycle and identifying the functions of key enzymes. Have them present their findings in a short report to the class.

The Breakdown of Food, continued

Some students may think that plant cells contain chloroplasts, but not mitochondria. Be sure that students understand that plant cells do include mitochondria in which the breakdown of glucose produced through photosynthesis provides energy for the cell.

Reading Check

Answer all living things

Teacher FYI

Fermentation is a type of anaerobic respiration. Anaerobic means "without oxygen." It results in increased waste products that build up in cells. Also, it is a less efficient method of respiration and cannot produce as much energy as aerobic respiration. To perform the same amount of work, a cell using fermentation must consume up to 20 times more glucose per second than a cell using aerobic respiration. In the human body, if the amount of oxygen delivered to muscle cells during strenuous activity is inadequate, the cells temporarily use fermentation. The waste products that build up in the cells add to muscle fatigue.

Figure 8
Aerobic respiration takes place in the mitochondria of plant cells.

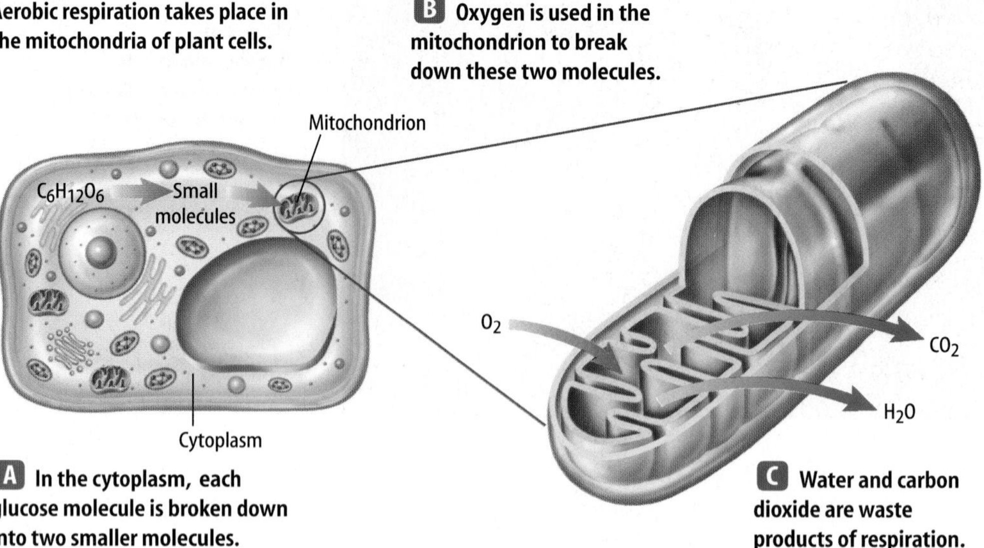

A **In the cytoplasm, each glucose molecule is broken down into two smaller molecules.**

B **Oxygen is used in the mitochondrion to break down these two molecules.**

C **Water and carbon dioxide are waste products of respiration.**

Aerobic Respiration Before aerobic respiration begins, glucose molecules are broken down into two smaller molecules. This happens in the cytoplasm. The smaller molecules then enter a mitochondrion, where aerobic respiration takes place. Oxygen is used in the reactions that break the small molecules into the waste products water and carbon dioxide. The reactions also release energy. Every cell in the organism needs this energy. **Figure 8** shows aerobic respiration in a plant cell.

Figure 9
Plants use the energy released from the respiration of food to carry out many functions.

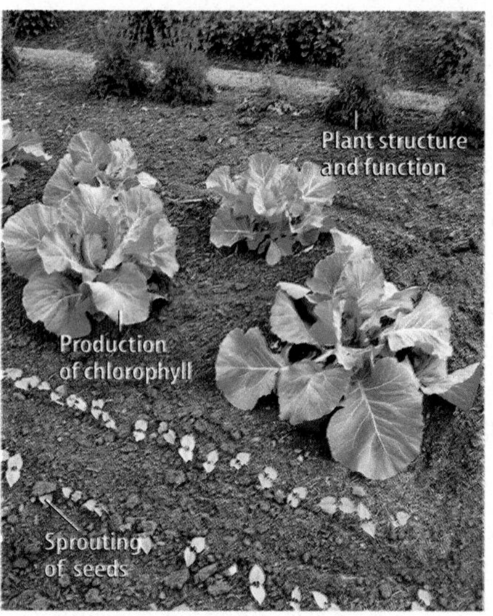

Importance of Respiration Although food contains energy, it is not in a form that can be used by cells. Respiration changes food energy into a form all cells can use. This energy drives the life processes of almost all organisms on Earth.

Reading Check *What organisms use respiration?*

Plants use energy produced by respiration to transport sugars and open and close stomata. Some of the energy is used to produce substances needed for photosynthesis, such as chlorophyll. When seeds sprout, they use energy from the respiration of stored food in the seed. **Figure 9** shows uses of energy in plants.

The waste product carbon dioxide is also important. Aerobic respiration returns carbon dioxide to the atmosphere, where it can be used again by plants and some other organisms for photosynthesis.

Resource Manager 

Chapter Resources Booklet
Enrichment, p. 27
Reinforcement, p. 25

Performance Assessment in the Science Classroom, p. 59

Visual Learning

Figure 8 Have students trace the pathways of the reactants and products of respiration in the mitochondrion. Help them understand that the arrows indicate materials moving in and out of the organelle.

Table 1 Comparing Photosynthesis and Aerobic Respiration				
	Energy	**Raw Materials**	**End Products**	**Where**
Photosynthesis	stored	water and carbon dioxide	glucose and oxygen	cells with chlorophyll
Aerobic Respiration	released	glucose and oxygen	water and carbon dioxide	cells with mitochondria

Comparison of Photosynthesis and Respiration

Look back in the chapter to find the equations for photosynthesis and aerobic respiration. Do they resemble each other? If you look closely, you can see that overall, aerobic respiration is almost the reverse of photosynthesis. Photosynthesis combines carbon dioxide and water by using light energy. The end products are glucose (food) and oxygen. During photosynthesis, energy is stored in food. Photosynthesis occurs only in cells that contain chlorophyll, such as those in the leaves of plants. Aerobic respiration combines oxygen and food to release the energy in the chemical bonds of the food. The end products of aerobic respiration are energy, carbon dioxide, and water. Because all plant cells contain mitochondria, all plant cells and any cell with mitochondria can use the process of aerobic respiration. **Table 1** compares photosynthesis and aerobic respiration.

Section  Assessment

1. Explain how a leaf exchanges carbon dioxide and water vapor.
2. Why are photosynthesis and respiration important?
3. What must happen to glucose molecules before respiration begins?
4. Compare the number of organisms that respire to those that photosynthesize.
5. **Think Critically** Humidity is water vapor in the air. How do plants contribute to the amount of humidity in the air?

Skill Builder Activities

6. **Forming Hypotheses** White potatoes sometimes have green areas on their skins. Hypothesize what process can take place in the green part but not in the white part of the potato. **For more help, refer to the Science Skill Handbook.**
7. **Solving One-Step Equations** How many CO_2 molecules result from the aerobic respiration of a glucose molecule ($C_6H_{12}O_6$)? Refer to the equation in this section. **For more help, refer to the Math Skill Handbook.**

Comparison of Photosynthesis and Respiration

Activity

Have students make up songs that include the equations for photosynthesis and respiration. Then have them sing their songs to the class.

3 Assess

Reteach

Have students place one plant in the light and another in a dark area while keeping all other variables constant. Have them observe the plants once each day for a week. Then have students explain any changes that occur.

Challenge

How many atoms of oxygen are needed to produce six molecules of glucose? 6 atoms of oxygen $\times$ 6 molecules = 36 atoms

Assessment

Performance Using molecular model kits, have groups of students make the reactants of either photosynthesis or aerobic respiration. Exchange reactants between opposite groups and have them make the products of those reactants. Students should find that the reactants of one are the products of the other. Use **Performance Assessment in the Science Classroom,** p. 123.

Answers to Section Assessment

1. Carbon dioxide and water vapor are exchanged by diffusion through the stomata on leaf surfaces.
2. Photosynthesis provides the basic food source used by most organisms on Earth, either directly or indirectly. Respiration releases the energy stored in the product of photosynthesis (glucose) for use in cells.
3. Glucose molecules must be broken down into simpler molecules in the cytoplasm before respiration can begin.
4. Only organisms that contain chlorophyll photosynthesize, but all organisms respire.
5. Plants transpire water from their leaves, contributing water vapor to the air.
6. Photosynthesis can occur in the green areas of a potato but not in the white areas.
7. For every sugar molecule respired, six carbon dioxide molecules are produced.

Activity BENCH TESTED

Purpose Students observe the activity of stomata in green plants. L2 ELL COOP LEARN
LS **Visual-Spatial**

Process Skills observing and inferring, recognizing cause and effect

Time Required 45 minutes

Alternate Materials Celery or onion epidermis may be substituted for lettuce.

Safety Precaution Emphasize that students should be careful when using microscopes.

Teaching Strategy Remind students that osmosis is diffusion of water through a semipermeable membrane.

Troubleshooting If an alternative tissue is used, try the activity beforehand to make sure observations will be appropriate.

Answers to Questions

1. the wet mount with plain water
2. Salt water causes water to leave the guard cells, causing them to become limp and close.
3. Stomata provide an entry and exit site in the leaf for gases such as carbon dioxide.

✔Assessment

Performance To further assess students' understanding of stomata, have them repeat the activity using one of the alternate materials and describe the outcome. Use **Performance Assessment in the Science Classroom**, p. 97.

Activity

Stomata in Leaves

Stomata open and close, which allows gases into and out of a leaf. These openings are usually invisible without the use of a microscope. Do this activity to see some stomata.

What You'll Investigate

Where are stomata in lettuce leaves?

Materials

lettuce in dish of water
coverslip
microscope
microscope slide
salt solution
forceps

Goals

- **Describe** guard cells and stomata.
- **Infer** the conditions that make stomata open and close.

Safety Precautions

WARNING: *Do not eat or taste any of the materials in the activity.*

Procedure

1. Copy the Stomata Data table into your Science Journal.
2. From a head of lettuce, tear off a piece of an outer, crisp, green leaf.
3. Bend the piece of leaf in half and carefully use a pair of forceps to peel off some of the epidermis, the transparent tissue that covers a leaf. Prepare a wet mount of this tissue.
4. **Examine** your prepared slide under low and high power on the microscope.
5. **Count** the total number of stomata in your field of view and then count the number of open stomata. Enter these numbers in the data table.

Stomata Data

	Wet Mount	Salt-Solution Mount
Total Number of Stomata	50	60
Number of Open Stomata	40	5
Percent Open	80	8

6. Make a second slide of the lettuce leaf epidermis. This time place a few drops of salt solution on the leaf instead of water.
7. Repeat steps 4 and 5.
8. **Calculate** the percent of open stomata using the following equation:

$$\frac{\text{number of open stomata}}{\text{total number of stomata}} \times 100 = \text{percent open}$$

Conclude and Apply

1. Determine which slide preparation had a greater percentage of open stomata.
2. **Infer** why fewer stomata were open in the salt-solution mount.
3. What can you infer about the function of stomata in a leaf?

Communicating Your Data

Collect data from other students in your class. Compare your data to the class data. Discuss any differences you find and why these differences occurred. **For more help, refer to the** Science Skill Handbook.

Communicating Your Data

Data should be similar throughout the class. Differences might occur if students don't all use the same side of the leaf tissue. Upper and lower leaf surfaces often have different numbers of stomata.

Resource Manager

Chapter Resources Booklet
Activity Worksheet, pp. 5–6

312 CHAPTER 11 Plant Processes

SECTION

Plant Responses

What are plant responses?

It's dark. You're alone in a room watching a horror film on television. Suddenly, the telephone near you rings. You jump, and your heart begins to beat faster. You've just responded to a stimulus. A stimulus is anything in the environment that causes a response in an organism. The response often involves movement either toward the stimulus or away from the stimulus. A stimulus may come from outside (external) or inside (internal) the organism. The ringing telephone is an example of an external stimulus. It caused you to jump, which is a response. Your beating heart is a response to an internal stimulus. Internal stimuli are usually chemicals produced by organisms. Many of these chemicals are hormones. Hormones are substances made in one part of an organism for use somewhere else in the organism.

All living organisms, including plants, respond to stimuli. Many different chemicals are known to act as hormones in plants. These internal stimuli have a variety of effects on plant growth and function. Plants respond to external stimuli such as touch, light, and gravity. Some responses, such as the response of the Venus's-flytrap plant in **Figure 10,** are rapid. Other plant responses are slower because they involve changes in growth.

As You Read

What You'll Learn

- **Identify** the relationship between a stimulus and a tropism in plants.
- **Compare and contrast** long-day and short-day plants.
- **Explain** how plant hormones and responses are related.

Vocabulary

tropism, auxin, photoperiodism, long-day plant, short-day plant, day-neutral plant

Why It's Important

You will be able to grow healthier plants if you understand how they respond to certain stimuli.

Figure 10
A Venus's-flytrap has three small trigger hairs on the surface of its toothed leaves. When two hairs are touched at the same time, the plant responds by closing its trap in less than 1 second.

Section Assessment Planner

Portfolio
Curriculum Connection, p. 318
Reteach, p. 319

Performance Assessment
Try at Home MiniLAB, p. 316
Skill Builder Activities, p. 319
See page 326 for more options.

Content Assessment
Section, p. 319
Challenge, p. 319
Chapter, pp. 326–327

SECTION 2

Plant Responses

1 Motivate

Bellringer Transparency

Display the Section Focus Transparency for Section 2. Use the accompanying Transparency Activity Master. L2 ELL

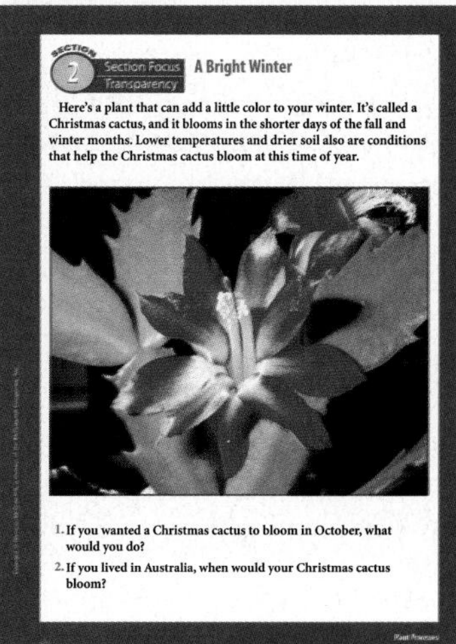

Section 2 Section Focus Transparency **A Bright Winter**

Here's a plant that can add a little color to your winter. It's called a Christmas cactus, and it blooms in the shorter days of the fall and winter months. Lower temperatures and drier soil also are conditions that help the Christmas cactus bloom at this time of year.

1. If you wanted a Christmas cactus to bloom in October, what would you do?
2. If you lived in Australia, when would your Christmas cactus bloom?

Tie to Prior Knowledge

Draw on the board a simple sketch of a flowering plant. Have students identify as many parts of the plant as they can and name the functions of those parts.

2 Teach

Plant Responses

Discussion

Have students brainstorm a list of possible ways to determine the cause of various plant responses. Lead them to understand the difference between external and internal stimuli. External stimuli include touch, light, and gravity. Internal stimuli include hormones.

Tropisms

Activity

Small groups of students can grow a pea plant from seed. As the plant begins to grow, they place a stick in the pot. The stem and tendrils will respond by growing around the stick. Have students identify the type of response this illustrates. thigmatropism Challenge students to record and graph the growth of the pea plant. L3

Quick Demo

Bring a Venus's-flytrap to class to demonstrate nastic movements. The trap of the Venus's-flytrap is triggered when three or more of the sensitive hairs on the upper surfaces of the hinged leaves are touched. Use the fine tip of a needle or pencil to manipulate the hairs.

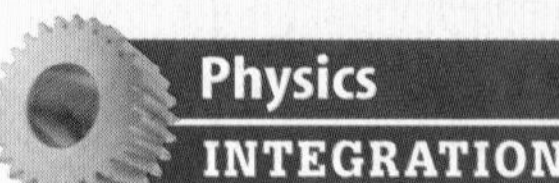

Physics INTEGRATION

Students may propose various experiments. Look for those that include a control and a method that would include a true test of the effects of gravity.

Figure 11
Tropisms are responses to external stimuli.

A The pea plant's tendrils respond to touch by coiling around things.

B This plant is growing toward the light, an example of positive phototropism.

C This plant was turned on its side. With the roots visible, you can see that they are showing positive gravitropism.

Tropisms

Some responses of a plant to an external stimuli are called tropisms. A **tropism** (TROH pih zum) can be seen as movement caused by a change in growth and can be positive or negative. For example, plants might grow toward a stimulus—a positive tropism—or away from a stimulus—a negative tropism.

Touch One stimulus that can result in a change in a plant's growth is touch. When the pea plant, shown in **Figure 11A,** touches a solid object, it responds by growing faster on one side of its stem than on the other side. As a result the stem bends and twists around any object it touches.

Light Did you ever see a plant leaning toward a window? Light is an important stimulus to plants. When a plant responds to light, the cells on the side of the plant opposite the light get longer than the cells facing the light. Because of this uneven growth, the plant bends toward the light. This response causes the leaves to turn in such a way that they can absorb more light. When a plant grows toward light it is called a positive response to light, as shown in **Figure 11B.**

Gravity Plants respond to gravity. The downward growth of plant roots is a positive response to gravity, as shown in **Figure 11C.** A stem growing upward is a negative response to gravity. Plants also may respond to electricity, temperature, and darkness.

Physics INTEGRATION

Gravity is a stimulus that affects how plants grow. Can plants grow without gravity? In space the force of gravity is low. Write a paragraph in your Science Journal that describes your idea for an experiment aboard a space shuttle to test how low gravity affects plant growth.

Visual Learning

Figure 11 Use these photographs to launch a discussion on plant responses caused by various external stimuli. **Where have you seen responses such as these? How might they help a plant meet its needs?** Answers will vary. Many of these responses help a plant grow toward the light, their source of energy.

Teacher FYI

Unlike tropisms, nastic movements are independent of the direction of the stimulus. The most common are "sleep" or nyctinastic movements. These movements position leaves of some plants horizontally during the daylight and vertically at night. This response results from turgor pressure changes in cells.

314 CHAPTER 11 Plant Processes

Plant Hormones

Hormones control the changes in growth that result from tropisms and affect other plant growth. Plants often need only millionths of a gram of a hormone to stimulate a response.

Ethylene Many plants produce the hormone ethylene (EH thuh leen) gas and release it into the air around them. This means that ethylene produced by one plant can cause a response in a nearby plant. One plant response to ethylene causes a layer of cells to form between a leaf and the stem. That's why most leaves fall from plants.

Ethylene is produced in cells of ripening fruit, which stimulates the ripening process. Commercially, fruits such as oranges and bananas are picked when they are still green. During shipping the green fruits are exposed to ethylene and they ripen.

Math Skills Activity

Calculating Averages

Example Problem

What is the average height of control bean seedlings after 14 days?

Solution

1. *This is what you know:*
   height of control seedlings after 14 days
   number of control seedlings
2. *This is what you need to find:*
   average height of control seedlings after14 days
3. *This is what you must do:*
   total the heights of all control seedlings
   $15 + 12 + 14 + 13 + 10 + 11 = 75$ cm
4. *Divide the total height by the total number of control seedlings:*
   75 cm/6
   average height of control seedlings = 12.5 cm

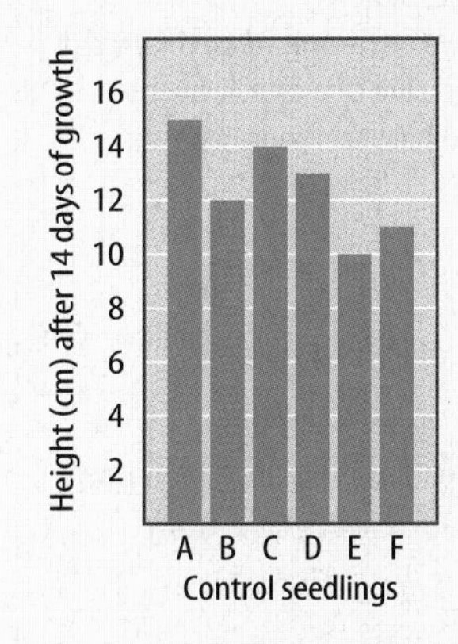

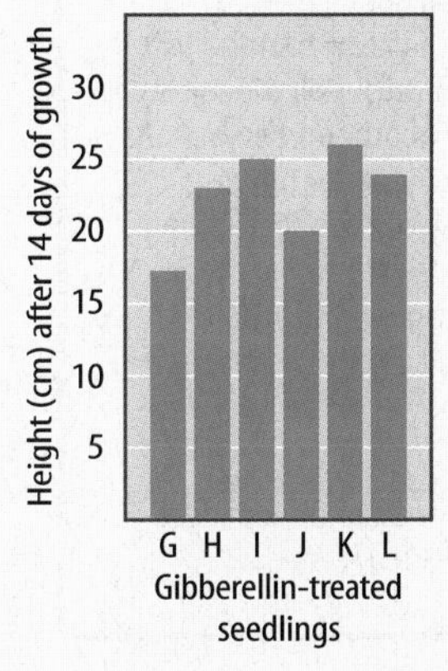

Practice Problem

Calculate the average height of seedlings treated with gibberellin.

For more help, refer to the Math Skill Handbook.

Resource Manager

Chapter Resources Booklet

Transparency Activity, p. 41

Directed Reading for Content Mastery, pp. 19, 20

Mathematics Skill Activities, p. 25

Active Reading

Quickwrites This strategy, sometimes called freewrites, lets students use spontaneous writing to discover what they already know. Have students write a list of ideas about a topic, then share these ideas with the class. Next, have students write their ideas freely in a paragraph without worrying about punctuation, spelling, and grammar. Have students use a Quickwrite to share ideas about plant responses.

Plant Hormones

Activity

Use an activity kit for rapidly growing plants of the genus *Brassica*, available from biological supply houses, to demonstrate plant responses to hormones. These plants can grow from seed to flower in about 15 days.

Discussion

Review the names of the parts of flowering plants with students. Ask if they think every structure responds equally to every stimulus. Possible answer: different parts of a flowering plant respond to different stimuli.

Math Skills Activity

National Math Standards

Correlation to Mathematics Objectives

1, 2, 4, 6, 8, 9

Teaching Suggestion:

Students may be asked to provide the following information from the graph:

a. range of heights for control seedlings
b. range of heights for gibberellin-treated seedlings
c. percent difference in height of gibberellin-treated seedlings compared to control seedlings

It may be necessary to help students interpolate the height values on the graph.

Answer to Practice Problem

135 cm ÷ 6 = 22.5 cm

Note: Students' answers may differ slightly from the answer provided. Accept answers that are reasonably close. Variation in answers may be caused by differing interpolations of seedling heights as read from the graph.

Plant Hormones, continued

Reading Check

Answer Auxin is the hormone that causes stems and leaves to exhibit positive phototropism.

Quick Demo

Obtain two coleus cuttings. Apply a rooting hormone to one cutting before planting both stems. After several days, have students observe the roots of both stems and explain the results. The cutting with the hormone should show greater root growth due to the presence of the chemical.

Purpose to observe the effects of ethylene on ripening fruit L1 ELL IS **Kinesthetic**

Materials two green bananas, paper bag

Teaching Strategies

- Tell students to choose two green bananas that are at the same stage of ripeness.
- Students may eat the bananas after use.

Analysis

The green banana in the bag; the ethylene produced by the ripening banana was trapped in the bag, causing the fruit to ripen more quickly.

Assessment

Oral Have students explain their results to the class. Use **Performance Assessment in the Science Classroom,** p. 143.

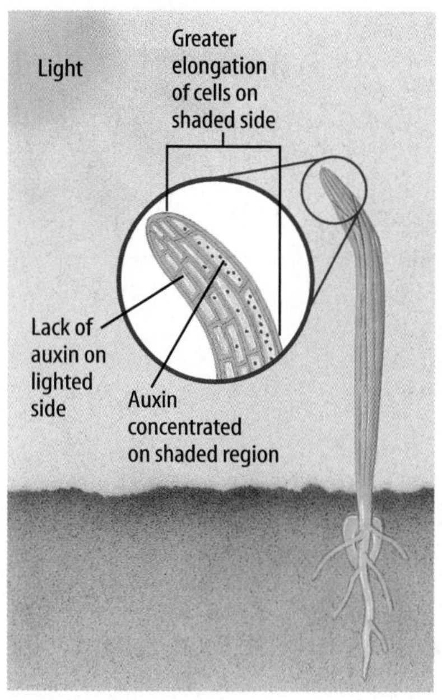

Figure 12
The concentration of auxin on the shaded side of a plant causes cells to lengthen on that side.

Auxin Scientists identified the plant hormone, **auxin** (AWK sun) more than 100 years ago. Auxin is a type of plant hormone that causes plant stems and leaves to exhibit positive response to light. When light shines on a plant from one side, the auxin moves to the shaded side of the stem where it causes a change in growth, as shown in **Figure 12.** Auxins also control the production of other plant hormones, including ethylene.

Reading Check *How are auxins and positive response to light related?*

Development of many parts of the plant, including flowers, roots, and fruit, is stimulated by auxins. Because auxins are so important in plant development, synthetic auxins have been developed for use in agriculture. Some of these synthetic auxins are used in orchards so that all plants produce flowers and fruit at the same time. Other synthetic auxins damage plants when they are applied in high doses and are used as weed killers.

Observing Ripening

Procedure

1. Place a **green banana** in a **paper bag.** Roll the top shut.
2. Place another green banana on a counter or table.
3. After two days check the bananas to see how they have ripened. **WARNING:** *Do not eat the materials used in the lab.*

Analysis

Which banana ripened more quickly? Why?

Gibberellins and Cytokinins Two other groups of plant hormones that also cause changes in plant growth are gibberellins and cytokinins. Gibberellins (jih buh REH lunz) are chemical substances that were isolated first from a fungus. The fungus caused a disease in rice plants called "foolish seedling" disease. The fungus infects the stems of plants and causes them to grow too tall. Gibberellins can be mixed with water and sprayed on plants and seeds to stimulate plant stems to grow and seeds to germinate.

Like gibberellins, cytokinins (si tuh KI nunz) also cause rapid growth. Cytokinins promote growth by causing faster cell divisions. Like ethylene, the effect of cytokinins on the plant also is controlled by auxin. Interestingly, cytokinins can be sprayed on stored vegetables to keep them fresh longer.

Abscisic Acid Because hormones that cause growth in plants were known to exist, biologists suspected that substances that have the reverse effect also must exist. Abscisic (ab SIH zihk) acid is one such substance. Many plants grow in areas that have cold winters. Normally, if seeds germinate, or buds develop on plants during the winter, they will die. Abscisic acid is the substance that keeps seeds from sprouting and buds from developing during the winter. This plant hormone also causes stomata to close and helps plants respond to water loss on hot summer days. **Figure 13** summarizes how plant hormones affect plants and how hormones are used.

Cultural Diversity

Ewiti Kurosawa Japanese scientist Ewiti Kurosawa discovered gibberellin while investigating the cause of "foolish seedling disease." He discovered that rice plants grew so tall that they fell over (thus, "foolish seedlings") after being infected with a fungus that secreted the substance. He named gibberellin after the genus of the fungus, *Gibberella fujikuroi.*

Figure 13

Chemical compounds called plant hormones help determine how a plant grows. There are five main types of hormones. They coordinate a plant's growth and development, as well as its responses to environmental stimuli, such as light, gravity, and changing seasons. Most changes in plant growth are a result of plant hormones working together, but exactly how hormones cause these changes is not completely understood.

▲ ETHYLENE By controlling the exposure of these tomatoes to ethylene, a hormone that stimulates fruit ripening, farmers are able to harvest unripe fruit and make it ripen just before it arrives at the supermarket.

◀ GIBBERELLINS The larger mustard plant in the photo at left was sprayed with gibberellins, plant hormones that stimulate stem elongation and fruit development.

◀ CYTOKININS Lateral buds do not usually develop into branches. However, if a plant's main stem is cut, as in this bean plant, naturally occurring cytokinins will stimulate the growth of lateral branches, causing the plant to grow "bushy."

▼ AUXINS Powerful growth hormones called auxins regulate responses to light and gravity, stem elongation, and root growth. The root growth on the plant cuttings, center and right, is the result of auxin treatment.

▶ ABA (ABSCISIC ACID) In plants such as the American basswood, right, abscisic acid causes buds to remain dormant for the winter. When spring arrives, ABA stops working and the buds sprout.

Resource Manager

Chapter Resources Booklet
MiniLAB, p. 4
Lab Activity, pp. 11–14
Home and Community Involvement, p. 45

Visualizing Plant Hormones

Have students examine the pictures and read the captions. Then ask the following questions.

Which of the hormones here do not stimulate plant growth? What functions do these hormones serve? ABA causes dormancy instead of growth, and ethylene stimulates fruit ripening instead of growth.

How could farmers use plant hormones to enhance their profits? By controlling plant growth, budding, dormancy periods and ripening of fruits, farmers can deliver more product to the market.

What plant hormone has most likely been studied by researchers working in space? Auxins, which control a plant's response to gravity would be of great interest to those studying a plant's response to the reduced gravity in space.

Activity

Have students work in teams to write a poem with five verses. Each verse should name a type of plant hormone, and tell the function of the hormone and the particular parts of the plant the hormone acts on.

Extension

Evidence exists that a plant hormone called florigen controls flowering in plants, but scientists haven't isolated it yet. Have students research some of the experiments scientists have done in their search for florigen. Students should report their findings to the class.

Photoperiods

Explore the Glencoe Science Web site at **science.glencoe.com** to find out more about topics in this section.

Extension

Take the class on a field trip to a commercial greenhouse. Have students interview the staff to find out how they encourage plants to flower at times other than their normal flowering seasons. Growers often plan six to twelve months ahead in order to supply plants that are blooming out of season.

Reading Check

Answer A specific amount of darkness is needed, which varies depending on the species of plant.

Photoperiods

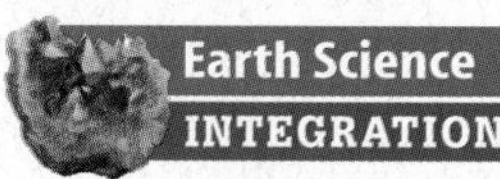

Sunflowers bloom in the summer, and cherry trees flower in the spring. Some plant species produce flowers at specific times during the year. A plant's response to the number of hours of daylight and darkness it receives daily is **photoperiodism** (foh toh PIHR ee uh dih zum).

Earth revolves around the Sun once each year. As Earth moves in its orbit, it also rotates. One rotation takes about 24 h. Because Earth is tilted about 23.5° from a line perpendicular to its orbit, the hours of daylight and darkness vary with the seasons. As you probably have noticed, the Sun sets later in summer than in winter. These changes in lengths of daylight and darkness affect plant growth.

SCIENCE Online

Research Visit the Glencoe Science Web site at **science.glencoe.com** to find out how plant pigments are involved in photoperiodism. Communicate what you learn to your class.

Darkness and Flowers Many plants require a specific length of darkness to begin the flowering process. Generally, plants that require less than 10 h to 12 h of darkness to flower are called **long-day plants.** You may be familiar with some long-day plants such as spinach, lettuce, and beets. Plants that need 12 or more hours of darkness to flower are called **short-day plants.** Some short-day plants are poinsettias, strawberries, and ragweed. **Figure 14** shows what happens when a short-day plant receives less darkness than it needs to flower.

Reading Check ***What is needed to begin the flowering process?***

Day-Neutral Plants Plants like dandelions and roses are **day-neutral plants.** They have no specific photoperiod, and the flowering process can begin within a range of hours of darkness.

In nature, photoperiodism affects where flowering plants can grow and produce flowers and fruit. Even if a particular environment has the proper temperature and other growing conditions for a plant, it will not flower and produce fruit without the correct photoperiod. **Table 2** shows how day length affects flowering in all three types of plants.

Sometimes the photoperiod of a plant has a narrow range. For example, some soybeans will flower with 9.5 h of darkness but will not flower with 10 h of darkness. Farmers must choose the variety of soybeans with a photoperiod that matches the hours of darkness in the section of the country where they plant their crop.

Figure 14
When short-day plants receive less darkness than required to produce flowers, they produce larger leaves instead.

Resource Manager

Chapter Resources Booklet
Reinforcement, p. 26
Enrichment, p. 28

Performance Assessment in the Science Classroom, p. 61

Curriculum Connection

Geography Have students research the place of origin for different plants and plot the locations on a world map. Challenge students to determine whether location of origin correlates with the length of darkness a plant needs to flower. L3 P

Table 2 Photoperiodism

	Long-Day Plants	Short-Day Plants	Day-Neutral Plants
Early Summer Noon 6 AM 6 PM Midnight			
Late Fall Noon 6 AM 6 PM Midnight			
	An iris is a long-day plant that is stimulated by short nights to flower in the early summer.	Goldenrod is a short-day plant that is stimulated by long nights to flower in the fall.	Roses are day-neutral plants and have no specific photoperiod.

Today, greenhouse growers are able to provide any length of artificial daylight or darkness. This means that you can buy short-day flowering plants during the summer and long-day flowering plants during the winter.

Section  Assessment

1. Give an example of an internal stimulus and an external stimulus in plants.
2. Compare and contrast photoperiodism and phototropism.
3. Some red raspberries produce fruit in late spring, then again in the fall. What term describes their photoperiod?
4. How do the effects of abscisic acid differ from those of gibberellins?
5. **Think Critically** What is the relationship between plant hormones and tropisms?

Skill Builder Activities

6. **Comparing and Contrasting** Different plant parts exhibit positive and negative tropisms. Compare and contrast the responses of roots and stems to gravity. **For more help, refer to the** Science Skill Handbook.
7. **Communicating** For three years a farmer in Costa Rica grew healthy strawberry plants. But the plants never produced fruit. In your Science Journal, explain why this happened. **For more help, refer to the** Science Skill Handbook.

3 Assess

Reteach

Have students make a chart describing the various tropisms. For each tropism, they should include the stimulus, the response, and the effect on the plant. P

Challenge

Some roses bloom more in the spring and fall than during the summer. **What type of photoperiod is this?** short-day

Oral Use question 6 to assess students' abilities to compare and contrast the responses of roots, stems, and leaves to light by having students explain their answers to you. Use **Performance Assessment in the Science Classroom,** p. 143.

Answers to Section Assessment

1. Possible answers: Internal stimuli include hormones; external stimuli include environmental factors such as gravity and light.
2. Photoperiodism is plant responses to the length of the period of darkness; phototropism is any growth response to light.
3. short-day
4. Abscisic acid slows growth; gibberellins speed growth in plants.
5. Plant hormones are responsible for some tropisms.
6. Roots show positive gravitropism and grow downward. Stems show negative gravitropism and grow upward.
7. Strawberries are short-day plants. Because Costa Rica is near the equator, the days are about the same length as the nights, so there are too few hours of darkness to produce flowering in strawberries.

Activity

BENCH TESTED

What You'll Investigate

Purpose

Students experiment to observe plant responses to gravity. L2 ELL LS Logical-Mathematical

Process Skills

observing and inferring, communicating, making and using tables, comparing and contrasting, recognizing cause and effect, separating and controlling variables, interpreting data, using numbers

Time Required

1 class period to set up; 20 minutes one day each week for up to two weeks

Materials

clear jar, marking pen, mustard seeds, aluminum foil, paper towel, water

Alternate Materials

Bean seeds can be substituted for mustard seeds.

Safety Precautions

Some kinds of seeds are poisonous. Do not allow students to put seeds in their mouths.

Activity: Tropism in Plants

Grapevines can climb on trees, fences, or other nearby structures. This growth is a response to the stimulus of touch. Tropisms are specific plant responses to stimuli outside of the plant. One part of a plant can respond positively while another part of the same plant can respond negatively to the same stimulus. Gravitropism is a response to gravity. Why might it be important for some plant parts to have a positive response to gravity while other plant parts have a negative response? You can design an experiment to test how some plant parts respond to the stimulus of gravity.

What You'll Investigate

Do stems and roots respond to gravity in the same way?

Materials

paper towel
30 cm × 30 cm sheet of aluminum foil
water
mustard seeds
marking pen
1-L clear glass or plastic jar

Safety Precautions

WARNING: *Some kinds of seeds are poisonous. Do not put any seed in your mouth. Wash your hands after handling the seeds.*

Goals

- **Describe** how roots and stems respond to gravity.
- **Observe** how changing the stimulus changes the growth of plants.

Inclusion Strategies

Learning Disabled Provide clear directions both orally and in writing. Assign a buddy to each student to help him or her assemble the seed packets.

Science Journal

Old Seeds Ask students if they think the age of the seeds used would make a difference in the results. Have them write their hypotheses and possible investigations in their Science Journals.

Procedure

1. Copy the following data table in your Science Journal.
2. Moisten the paper towel with water so that it's damp but not dripping. Fold it in half twice.
3. In the center of the foil, place the folded paper towel and sprinkle mustard seeds in a line across the center of the towel.
4. Fold the foil around the towel and seal each end by folding the foil over. Make sure the paper towel is completely covered by the foil.
5. Use a marking pen to draw an arrow on the foil, and place the foil package in the jar with the arrow pointing upward.
6. After five days carefully open the package and record your observations in the data table. (Note: *If no stems or roots are growing yet, reseal the package and place it back in the jar, making sure that the arrow points upward. Reopen the package in two days.*)

Response to Gravity

Position of Arrow on Foil Package	Observations of Seedling Roots	Observations of Seedling Stems
Arrow Up	Growing away from arrow	Growing toward arrow
Arrow Down	Growing toward arrow	Growing away from arrow

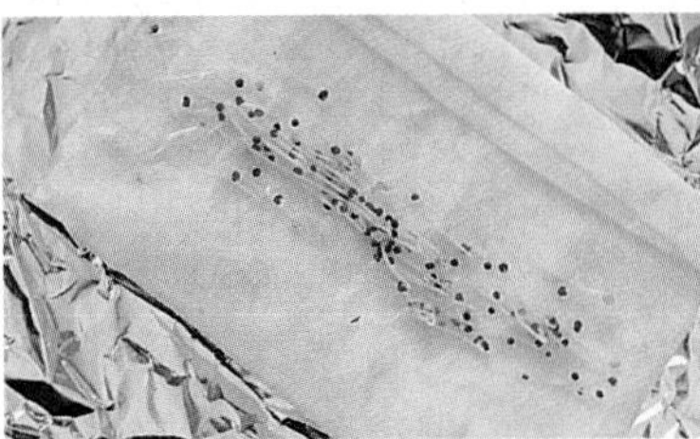

7. Reseal the foil package, being careful not to disturb the seedlings. Place it in the jar so that the arrow points downward instead of upward.
8. After five more days reopen the package and observe any new growth of the seedlings' roots and stems. Record your observations in your data table.

Conclude and Apply

1. **Classify** the responses you observed as positive or negative tropisms.
2. **Explain** why the plants' growth changed when you placed them upside down.
3. Why was it important that no light reach the seedlings during your experiment?
4. What are some other ways you could have changed the position of the foil package to test the seedlings' response?

Communicating Your Data

Use drawings to **compare** the growth of the seedlings before and after you turned the package. **Compare** your drawing with those of other students in your class. **For more help, refer to the** Science Skill Handbook.

Procedure

Teaching Strategy Explain to students that there may be more than one variable at work and that stems and roots may be responding differently to these stimuli.

Troubleshooting Be sure that students always place the seeds back in the dish with the arrow pointing up.

Expected Outcome

Roots will grow downward and shoots will grow upward.

Conclude and Apply

1. Stem growth upward is negative gravitropism; root growth downward is positive gravitropism.
2. The plants' growth continued to respond to the stimulus provided by gravity, even though the direction of this stimuli had changed.
3. If light reached the seedlings, they could have responded to it (phototropism), and results due to gravitropism would be uncertain.
4. Possible answers: The packages could have been laid flat or put on a spinning turntable.

Error Analysis

Have students compare their data with that of others and explain any differences they encounter.

Assessment

Portfolio Have students make a labeled poster of their experimental results and share it with the class. Use **Performance Assessment in the Science Classroom,** p. 145.

Resource Manager 

Chapter Resources Booklet
Activity Worksheet, pp. 7–8
Lab Management and Safety, p. 58

Communicating Your Data

Drawings will indicate that roots grow downward and shoots grow upward, notwithstanding the orientation of the seed.

Science and Language Arts

Pre-Reading Activity

Ask students what they know about the Sun before they read the retelling of this fable by the De La Fuentes. Encourage all kinds of responses, from what the Sun looks like throughout the day, to more scientific facts about the Sun such as how it helps support life on Earth. Write down student responses on the board as they are being called out.

Respond to the Reading

Active Reading Strategies

Visualize Keep the events and setting in your mind's eye as you read. Form pictures in your mind. The fable goes to great lengths to describe the natural setting of the story. **Is the setting a fictional place?**

Review Review what you have read. By looking back over several paragraphs, you can see how the information fits together. **Why do they characterize the flower as a human, or in this case, a girl?**

Answers to Questions

1. The plants need the Sun to survive and grow.
2. The flowers need water to survive and grow.
3. Student answers will vary. Some students might suggest that it does not give enough detail about photosynthesis. Others might suggest that the visual imagery of the story is enough to convey the message.

Science and Language Arts

Sunkissed: An Indian Legend

as told by Alberto and Patricia De La Fuente

Respond to the Reading

1. What does this passage tell you about the relationship between the Sun and plants?
2. What does this passage tell you about the relationship between water and the growth of flowers?
3. Do you think this passage is effective in making the reader understand the importance of light and darkness to a growing plant? Why or why not?

A long time ago, deep down in the very heart of the old Mexican forests, so far away from the sea that not even the largest birds ever had time to fly that far, there was a small, beautiful valley. A long chain of snow-covered mountains stood between the valley and the sea. . . . Each day the mountains were the first ones to tell everybody that Tonatiuh, the King of Light, was coming to the valley. The meadows would see the shining white tops of the mountains and spread out their flowery skirts for the Sun.

"Good morning, Tonatiuh!" cried a little meadow.

"Hurry up and bring us warmth and light!" sang all the wild roses along the river bank together as an opening line. . . .

The wild flowers always started their fresh new day with a kiss of golden sunlight from Tonatiuh, but it was necessary to first wash their sleepy baby faces with the dew that Metztli, the Moon, sprinkled for them out of her bucket onto the nearby leaves during the night. . . .

. . . All night long, then, Metztli Moon would walk her night-field making sure that by sun-up all flowers had the magic dew that made them feel beautiful all day long.

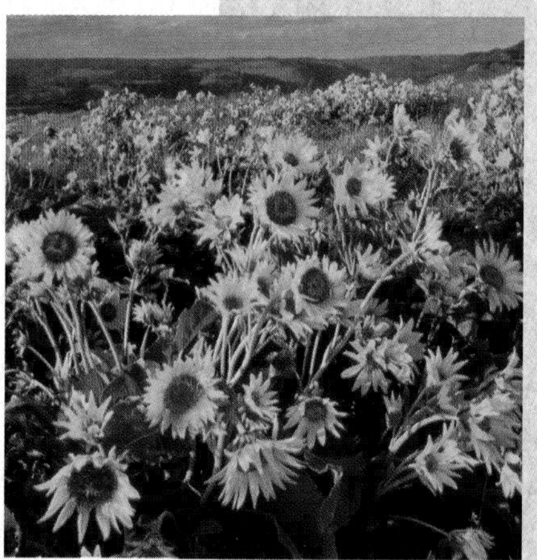

However, much as flowers love to be beautiful as long as possible, they want to be happy too. So every morning Tonatiuh himself would give each one a single golden kiss of such power that it was possible to be happy all day long after it. As you can see, then, a flower needs to feel beautiful in the first place, but if she does not feel beautiful, she will not be ready for her morning sun-kiss. If she cannot wash her little face with the magic dew, the whole day is lost.

Reading Further

American Indian Myths and Legends by Richard Erdoes (Editor) and Alfonso Ortiz (Editor), Pantheon Books, 1985.

Old Indian Legends by Zitkala-Sa, Sa Zitkala, and Angela Decora (Illustrator), University of Nebraska Press, 1985.

Understanding Literature

Legends and Oral Traditions A legend is a traditional story often told orally and believed to be based on actual people and events. Legends are believed to be true even if they cannot be proved. Sunkissed: An Indian Legend is a legend about a little flower that is changed forever by the Sun. What in this story indicates that it is a legend? This legend also is an example of an oral tradition. Oral traditions are stories or skills that are handed down by word of mouth. They can be stories about real people and events, fictional stories, recipes, or crafts.

Science Connection In this chapter, you learned about the processes of photosynthesis and respiration. The passage from Sunkissed: An Indian Legend does not teach us the details about photosynthesis or respiration. However, it does show how sunshine and water are important to plant life. The difference between the legend and the information contained in your textbook is this— photosynthesis and respiration can be proved scientifically, and the legend, although fun to read, cannot.

Linking Science and Writing

Creating Oral Traditions
Create an idea for a fictional story that explains why the sky becomes so colorful during a sunset. Write a few short notes about your story on a piece of paper. Then retell your story to your classmates using only your short notes and your imagination. When you retell your story, remember that good storytellers are enthusiastic and entertaining. An oral tradition is started because listeners want to pass the story along.

Career Connection

Horticulturist/Landscape Designer

Jill Nokes is a horticulturist who studies plants and how to grow them. Many horticulturists work in large nurseries as managers or plant breeders. Nokes works as a landscape designer, a person who creates gardens for homes and businesses. There are two important parts to a landscape designer's job. Designers must first create attractive landscapes for their clients. They also have to be plant experts so they can choose plants that will thrive in the local climate and with other plants in the design.

SCIENCE*Online* To learn more about careers in horticulture, visit the Glencoe Science Web site at **science.glencoe.com.**

Understanding Literature

Answer to Question

Answers will vary but should include that a legend is usually a fictional story relaying information about a specific culture, in this case Mexican.

Science Connection

The study of photosynthesis began in 1771, with observations made by the English chemist Joseph Priestley. Priestly had burned a candle in a closed container until the air within the container could no longer support combustion. He then placed a sprig of mint plant in the container and discovered that after several days the mint had produced some substance (later recognized as oxygen) that enabled the confined air to again support combustion. In 1779 the Dutch physician Jan Ingenhouz showed that the plant must be exposed to light if oxygen is to be restored.

Linking Science and Writing

Teaching Strategies

Lead students in brainstorming to come up with reasons that sunsets are colorful. Let them know that causes of pigment in the sky are not always natural. For example, some sky color can be caused by pollution. This exercise will give them a start on the writing activity.

Career Connection

While landscape designers design gardens, there is also the landscape architect. Landscape architecture is defined as "the art of arranging land and the objects upon it for human use and enjoyment." Landscape architecture includes site planning, land planning, master planning, urban design, and environmental planning.

Internet Addresses

Explore the Glencoe Science Web site at **science.glencoe.com** to find out more about topics in this feature.

Chapter 11 Study Guide

Reviewing Main Ideas

Preview

Students can answer the questions in their Science Journals. Discuss the answers as you go through the chapter. LS **Linguistic**

Review

Students can write their answers, then compare them with those of other students. LS **Interpersonal**

Reteach

Students can look at the illustrations and describe details that support the main ideas of the chapter. LS **Visual-Spatial**

Answers to Chapter Review

Section 1

3. They produce food for themselves and consumers.
5. Respiration provides energy the sprouting seed needs for growth and development.

Section 2

2. Gravity; some students may say light.
3. They do not depend on length of dark periods to trigger flowering.

Chapter 11 Study Guide

Reviewing Main Ideas

Section 1 Photosynthesis and Respiration

1. Carbon dioxide and water vapor gases enter and leave a plant through openings in the epidermis called stomata. Guard cells cause a stoma to open and close.
2. Photosynthesis takes place in the chloroplasts of plant cells. Light energy is used to produce glucose and oxygen from carbon dioxide and water.
3. Photosynthesis provides the food for most organisms on Earth. *Why are plants called producers?*

4. All organisms use respiration to release the energy stored in food molecules. Oxygen is used in the mitochondria to complete respiration in plant cells and many other types of cells. Energy, carbon dioxide, and water are produced.
5. The energy produced from respiration is needed by most living organisms including plants. *Why is respiration important to this sprouting seed?*

6. Photosynthesis and respiration are almost the reverse of each other. The end products of photosynthesis are the raw materials needed for aerobic respiration. The end products of aerobic respiration are the raw materials needed for photosynthesis.

Section 2 Plant Responses

1. Plants respond positively and negatively to stimuli. The response may be a movement, a change in growth, or the beginning of some process such as flowering.
2. A stimulus from outside the plant is called a tropism. Outside stimuli include such things as light, gravity, and touch. *What outside stimulus is affecting the growth of this plant?*

3. The length of darkness each day can affect flowering times of plants. *Why can day-neutral plants, such as this one, flower almost any time?*

4. Hormones control changes from inside plants. These chemicals affect plants in many ways. Some hormones cause plants to exhibit tropisms. Other hormones cause changes in plant growth.

FOLDABLES Reading & Study Skills — After You Read

Use the information in your Compare and Contrast Study Fold to compare and contrast aerobic respiration that occurs in plants and animals.

FOLDABLES Reading & Study Skills — After You Read

After students have read the chapter and completed the Foldable described in Before You Read, have them do the activity on the student page.

Dinah Zike

Chapter 11 Study Guide

Visualizing Main Ideas

Complete the following cycle concept map that shows how photosynthesis and respiration are related.

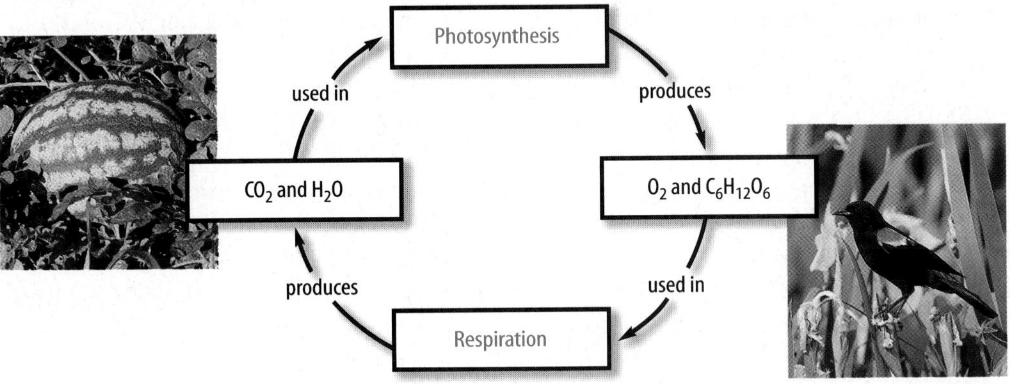

Vocabulary Review

Vocabulary Words

- **a.** auxin
- **b.** chlorophyll
- **c.** day-neutral plant
- **d.** long-day plant
- **e.** photoperiodism
- **f.** photosynthesis
- **g.** respiration
- **h.** short-day plant
- **i.** stomata
- **j.** tropism

Using Vocabulary

Replace the underlined definition with the correct vocabulary word from the list above.

1. A plant hormone causes plant stems and leaves to exhibit positive phototropism.
2. An important process of green plants is using light to make glucose and oxygen.
3. A green pigment is important in the process of photosynthesis.
4. A poinsettia, often seen flowering during December holidays, is a plant that requires long nights to flower.
5. The process of energy release from food occurs in most living things.
6. Spinach is a plant that requires only ten hours of darkness at night to flower.
7. A response of a plant to an outside stimulus can cause the plant to bend toward light.
8. Plants usually take in carbon dioxide through tiny pores in their leaves.
9. A plant's response to the number of hours of darkness it receives daily determines many plant processes.
10. Marigolds are plants that flower without regard to the length of darkness.

Study Tip

Outline the chapters to make sure that you understand the key ideas that are presented. Writing down the main points of the chapter will help you remember important details and understand larger themes.

Chapter 11 Study Guide

Visualizing Main Ideas

See student page.

Vocabulary Review

Using Vocabulary

1. Auxin
2. photosynthesis
3. Chlorophyll
4. short-day plant
5. Respiration
6. long-day plant
7. Tropism
8. stomata
9. Photoperiodism
10. day-neutral plants

IDENTIFYING Misconceptions

Assess

Use the assessment as follow-up to page 302F after students have completed the chapter.

Procedure Give the following statements, and ask students to respond with "plants," "animals," or "both plants and animals": takes in oxygen; gives off carbon dioxide; takes in carbon dioxide; gives off oxygen; make glucose; uses glucose.

Expected Outcome Students should know that both plants and animals take in oxygen, give off carbon dioxide, and use glucose. Only plants give off oxygen, take in carbon dioxide, and make glucose.

Checking Concepts

1. C
2. D
3. D
4. C
5. D
6. A
7. D
8. C
9. A
10. B

Thinking Critically

11. Put them in a brown paper bag to retain ethylene.
12. a. negative gravitropism; b. positive gravitropism; c. positive phototropism; d. positive thigmotropism
13. Oxygen is a by-product of photosynthesis. Until organisms that used carbon dioxide for photosynthesis evolved, little free oxygen was available.
14. Apple trees bloom in the spring when the days are short and nights are long. The number of dark hours in the summer is less than an apple tree's photoperiod.
15. Day-neutral plants will flower anywhere if they receive a minimum number of hours of darkness and if other environmental conditions are favorable. Long-day plants require the number of hours of darkness that occurs near the equator.

Chapter 11 Assessment

Checking Concepts

Choose the word or phrase that best answers the question.

1. What raw material needed by plants enters through open stomata?
   A) sugar **C)** carbon dioxide
   B) chlorophyll **D)** cellulose
2. What is a function of stomata?
   A) photosynthesis
   B) to guard the interior cells
   C) to allow sugar to escape
   D) to permit the release of oxygen
3. What plant process produces water, carbon dioxide, and energy?
   A) cell division **C)** growth
   B) photosynthesis **D)** respiration
4. What type of plant needs short nights in order to flower?
   A) day-neutral **C)** long-day
   B) short-day **D)** nonvascular
5. What do you call things such as light, touch, and gravity that cause plant growth responses?
   A) tropisms **C)** responses
   B) growth **D)** stimuli
6. What are the products of photosynthesis?
   A) glucose and oxygen
   B) carbon dioxide and water
   C) chlorophyll and glucose
   D) carbon dioxide and oxygen
7. What are plant substances that affect plant growth called?
   A) tropisms **C)** germination
   B) glucose **D)** hormones
8. Leaves change colors because what substance breaks down?
   A) hormone **C)** chlorophyll
   B) carotenoid **D)** cytoplasm
9. Which of these is a product of respiration?
   A) CO_2 **C)** C_2H_4
   B) O_2 **D)** H_2
10. What is a plant's response to gravity called?
    A) phototropism **C)** thigmotropism
    B) gravitropism **D)** hydrotropism

Thinking Critically

11. You buy pears at the store that are not completely ripe. What could you do to help them ripen more rapidly?
12. Name each tropism and state whether it is positive or negative.
    a. Stem grows up.
    b. Roots grow down.
    c. Plant grows toward light.
    d. A vine grows around a pole.
13. Scientists who study sedimentary rocks and fossils suggest that oxygen was not in Earth's atmosphere until plantlike, one-celled organisms appeared. Why?
14. Explain why apple trees bloom in the spring but not in the summer.
15. Why do day-neutral and long-day plants grow best in countries near the equator?

Developing Skills

16. **Forming Hypotheses** Make a hypothesis about when guard cells open and close in desert plants.
17. **Identifying and Manipulating Variables and Controls** Plan an experiment to test your hypothesis in question 16.
18. **Predicting** Make a prediction about how the number and location of stomata differ in land plants and water plants whose leaves float on the water's surface.

Chapter Assessment Planner

Portfolio Encourage students to place in their portfolios one or two items of what they consider to be their best work. Examples include:
- Science Journal, p. 307
- Curriculum Connection, p. 318
- Reteach, p. 319

Performance Additional performance assessments, Performance Task Assessment Lists, and rubrics for evaluating these activities can be found in Glencoe's **Performance Assessment in the Science Classroom.**

19. Concept Mapping Complete the following concept map about photoperiodism using the following information: flower year-round—*corn, dandelion, tomato;* flower in the spring, fall, or winter—*chrysanthemum, rice, poinsettia;* flower in summer—*spinach, lettuce, petunia.*

20. Comparing and Contrasting Compare and contrast the action of auxin and the action of ethylene on a plant.

Performance Assessment

21. Coloring Book Create a coloring book of day-neutral plants, long-day plants, and short-day plants. Use pictures from magazines and seed catalogs to get your ideas. Label the drawings with the plant's name and how it responds to darkness. Let a younger student color the flowers in your book.

Technology

Go to the Glencoe Science Web site at **science.glencoe.com** or use the **Glencoe Science CD-ROM** for additional chapter assessment.

THE PRINCETON REVIEW Test Practice

Eileen and Logan wanted to learn more about the materials that plants use during photosynthesis. They designed the following data table to record the results of their investigation.

Resources Used During Photosynthesis

Plant	Water Used	Carbon Dioxide Used	Light Absorbed	Oxygen Produced
Plant X				
Plant Y				
Plant Z				

Study the table and answer the following questions.

1. Using your knowledge of photosynthesis, which of the data columns would not be needed for recording results from the investigation?
A) water used
B) carbon dioxide used
C) light absorbed
D) oxygen produced

2. The most likely source of energy for the plants during this investigation is _____.
F) water
G) carbon dioxide
H) light
J) oxygen

Assessment Resources

Reproducible Masters

Chapter Resources Booklet
Chapter Review, pp. 33–34
Chapter Tests, pp. 35–38
Assessment Transparency Activity, p. 45

Glencoe Science Web site
Interactive Tutor
Chapter Quizzes

Glencoe Technology
Assessment Transparency
Interactive CD-ROM Chapter Quizzes
ExamView Pro Test Bank
Vocabulary PuzzleMaker Software
MindJogger Videoquiz

Chapter 11 Assessment

THE PRINCETON REVIEW Test Practice

The Test-Taking Tip was written by The Princeton Review, the nation's leader in test preparation.

1. D
2. H

Developing Skills

16. Desert plants' stomata might open at night and close during the day in order to conserve moisture. This is opposite to most other plants.
17. Experimental designs will differ but should include a comparison of several species of plants from deserts and other environments.
18. Floating water plants have stomata on the upper leaf surfaces, whereas land plants usually have more stomata on lower leaf surfaces.
19. See student page.
20. Both are hormones. Auxin makes stems grow toward light; ethylene makes fruit ripen.

Performance Assessment

21. At a minimum each plant's drawing should include its name and photoperiod. Use **Performance Assessment in the Science Classroom,** p. 133.

Standardized Test Practice

Reading Comprehension

QUESTION 1: A

Students must read carefully the context surrounding the underlined word. The fact that *there are fewer than twenty living specimens of these plants now* implies that the species is in danger of dying out. Therefore, choice A, *death of species*, is the correct answer.

Teaching Tip

Suggest that students number the paragraphs as they go through a reading passage.

QUESTION 2: H

Students must identify the main idea of the second paragraph.

- **Choice F** No; this is a detail from the third paragraph.
- **Choice G** No; this is a detail from the second paragraph.
- **Choice H** Yes; this is the main idea of the second paragraph.
- **Choice J** No; this is a detail from the second paragraph.

All questions written and validated by The Princeton Review.

Standardized Test Practice

Reading Comprehension

Read the passage carefully. Then read the questions that follow the passage. Decide which is the best answer to each question.

Medicine Plants

As part of his job, Paul Alan Cox, the director of the National Tropical Botanical Garden in Hawaii, leads teams of brave young people as they rappel down steep cliffs, hang from helicopters, and perform other daring feats. Are these people competing in an extreme sport? No, they are botanists, and they perform these daring acts with Cox in order to collect seeds from the nearly ninety Hawaiian plant species that are threatened with extinction. There are fewer than twenty living specimens of each of these plants now.

Why is Cox interested in saving plants from extinction? He knows that many plants contain medicinal, or healing, properties. For the past fifteen years, Cox has traveled all over the world to learn about the unique ways that people have been using plants to treat illnesses and to survive harsh environments. When Cox started this research, some of his colleagues thought he was throwing away his career as a scientist. Why, they wanted to know, would he be interested in what they considered nonscientific knowledge and folklore? Cox soon proved the value of his research.

Cox went to Western Samoa to record the practices of a 73-year-old woman, Epenesa Mauigoa. Epenesa gave him a detailed account of 121 herbal remedies she made from 90 different species of plants. One of those remedies she described especially caught Cox's attention. It was a preparation to fight hepatitis made from the mamala tree, or, as botanists call it, *Homolanthus nutans*.

The herbal remedy has since become the basis for an antiviral drug, prostratin. It is being studied as a drug to treat type 1 HIV.

In 1994, a study found that there are at least 119 plant-derived substances in use worldwide as medicines. Cox is on the hunt to find more.

Test-Taking Tip Consider the actions of the people in the passage.

Dr. Cox holds a branch of the mamala tree from which the antiviral drug, prostratin, is obtained.

1. What is the meaning of extinction in the context of this passage?
   A) death of a species
   B) survival
   C) ethnobotany
   D) herbal medicine
2. What is the main idea of the second paragraph?
   F) Cox discovered a preparation that could be used to fight hepatitis.
   G) Cox's colleagues thought he was throwing his career away.
   H) Cox decided to research how people use plants to treat illnesses and to survive harsh environments.
   J) Cox's colleagues thought Cox was interested in nonscientific knowledge.

Standardized Test Practice

Reasoning and Skills

Read each question and choose the best answer.

1. Which of the following chemical compounds does not influence the growth of plants?
A) cytokinins
B) gibberellins
C) auxins
D) pheromones

Test-Taking Tip Think about the roles of hormones in plants and animals.

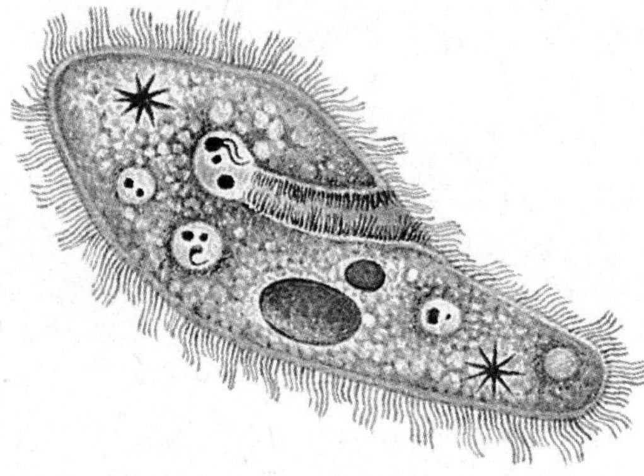

2. Protozoans are complex one-celled organisms that feed on other organisms. The four major groups of protozoans are classified primarily according to _____.
F) the presence of chlorophyll
G) their method of locomotion
H) the presence of food vacuoles
J) the types of human disease they cause

Test-Taking Tip Consider what you know about protozoans.

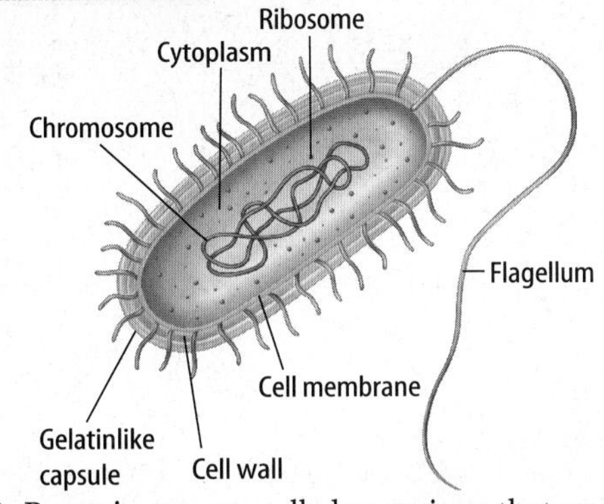

3. Bacteria are one-celled organisms that are found almost everywhere. In general, the presence of bacteria in the human body could benefit human health the most by _____.
A) decreasing the body's absorption of vitamins
B) decreasing the growth of other bacteria
C) increasing the production of vitamins
D) increasing the rate of cell division

Test-Taking Tip Consider what you know about the role of bacteria in human intestines.

Consider this question carefully before writing your answer on a separate sheet of paper.

4. Consider what you have learned about the evolution of plants. Explain how the similarities and differences between plants and algae suggest that plants originally came from the sea. You might wish to begin by making a table that summarizes characteristics of plants and algae.

Test-Taking Tip Consider the important characteristics of plants and algae before you begin writing.

Standardized Test Practice

Reasoning and Skills

QUESTION 1: D

Students must understand that choices F, G, and H are different kinds of plant hormones that affect growth.

QUESTION 2: G

Students must understand that protozoans can be classified as flagellates, amoeboids, and ciliates according to how they move.

QUESTION 3: C

Students should read the question carefully and remember that they are looking for an answer choice that shows how bacteria *benefit* human health.

- **Choice A** No; this does not benefit human health.
- **Choice B** No; this is not supported by what students should know about bacteria.
- **Choice C** Yes; this is a beneficial effect of the presence of bacteria in the human system.
- **Choice D** No; this is not supported by what students should know about bacteria.

QUESTION 4: Answers will vary.

Students should mention that plants and algae have some pigments in common and carry on photosynthesis. Adaptations that allowed plants to survive on land were the result of random mutations and natural selection.

UNIT 3

Unit Contents

Pre-Reading Activity

Have students look for pictures of familiar organisms and list what they know about them.

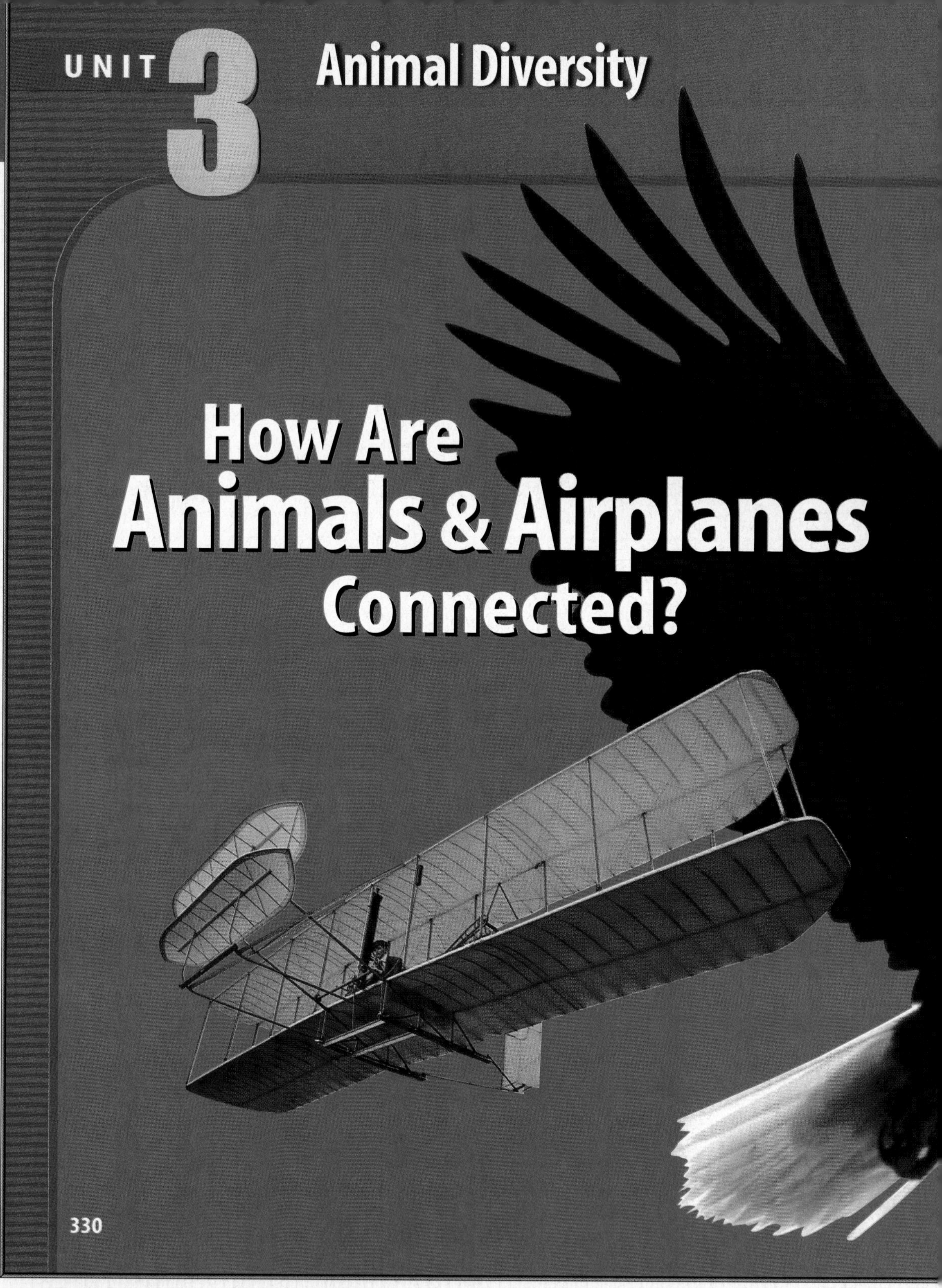

UNIT 3 Animal Diversity

How Are Animals & Airplanes Connected?

330

Teacher to Teacher

"Using everyday objects such as buttons, bolts, and letters of the alphabet is one way to introduce students to classifying. Students can easily divide objects into groups and describe the characteristics. Student-made keys help to introduce the dichotomous keys scientist use to identify organisms."

John E. Burns, Teacher
Ramona Junior High School
Chino, CA

For thousands of years, people dreamed of flying like birds. Detailed sketches of flying machines were made about 500 years ago. Many of these machines featured mechanical wings that were intended to flap like the wings of a bird. But human muscles are not powerful enough to make such wings flap. Later, inventors studied birds such as eagles, which often glide through the air on outstretched wings. Successful gliders were built in the 1800s. However, the gliders had no source of power to get them off the ground—and they were hard to control. Around 1900, two inventors studied bird flight more carefully and discovered that birds steer by changing the shape and position of their wings. The inventors built an engine-powered flying machine equipped with wires that could cause small changes in the shape and position of the wings. Though hardly as graceful as a soaring bird, the first powered, controlled flight took place in 1903, in the airplane seen here.

SCIENCE CONNECTION

FLYING ANIMALS Birds are not the only animals that fly. Bats and many insects also have wings. Investigate birds, bats, and flying insects, paying close attention to the shapes of their wings. Using black construction paper, draw and cut out "silhouettes" of 8 to 10 different flying animals with their wings outstretched. Create a mobile by suspending your silhouettes from a coat hanger or similar object with thread. In what ways are the wings similar and different?

Introducing the Unit

How Are Animals & Airplanes Connected?

Wings are complex, specialized adaptations. They enable birds to use a part of the environment not accessible to most other organisms. Their mastery of flight is reflected in the anatomical structures that allow them to modify the shape and angle of their wings. Their ability to steer and soar through the air provides them with a means of preying on other animals and of escaping predation themselves. It also allows them access to safe places for nesting. Other animals have developed anatomical adaptations for flight. Their wings are different in structure, but these species achieve the same results as birds. Some, like bats, have further adaptations allowing them to navigate through the air in darkness. As they study each chapter, ask students to identify structures, behaviors, and other adaptations that each group of organisms exhibits that allows them to survive and reproduce in diverse environments.

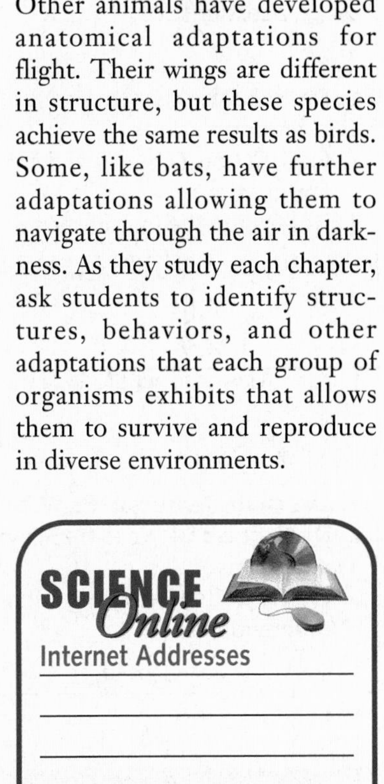

SCIENCE Online

Internet Addresses

Explore the Glencoe Science Web site at **science.glencoe.com** to find out more about topics in this unit.

SCIENCE CONNECTION

Activity

All living things, from one-celled bacteria to plants and animals, share a number of simple requirements for survival. In addition to comparing the wing structure of birds, bats, and flying insects, ask students to consider the diverse ways in which organisms meet their energy needs, reproduce, and grow and develop. While studying the diversity of organisms, have students identify the basic requirements common to all organisms, and the various adaptations organisms have for meeting them.

Section/Objectives	Standards		Activities/Features
	National	State/Local	
Chapter Opener	See p. 5T for a Key to Standards.		**Explore Activity:** Demonstrate symmetry, p. 333 **Before You Read,** p. 333
Section 1 Is it an animal? 2 sessions 1 block 1. **Identify** the characteristics common to most animals. 2. **Determine** how animals meet their needs. 3. **Distinguish** between invertebrates and vertebrates.	National Content Standards: UCP5, A1, C1, C3, C5		**Health Integration,** p. 335 **MiniLAB:** Modeling Animal Camouflage, p. 336 **Science Online,** p. 338
Section 2 Sponges and Cnidarians 2 sessions 1 block 1. **Describe** the characteristics of sponges and cnidarians. 2. **Explain** how sponges and cnidarians obtain food and oxygen. 3. **Determine** the importance of living coral reefs.	National Content Standards: UCP5, A1, C1, C3, C4, C5, F2		**Chemistry Integration,** p. 342 **Science Online,** p. 347 **Activity:** Observing a Cnidarian, p. 347
Section 3 Flatworms and Roundworms 3 sessions 1.5 blocks 1. **List** characteristics of flatworms and roundworms. 2. **Distinguish** between free-living and parasitic organisms. 3. **Identify** disease-causing flatworms and roundworms.	National Content Standards: UCP5, A1, C1, C3, C5, F1, G3		**MiniLAB:** Observing Planarian Movement, p. 350 **Math Skills Activity:** Using Percent to Calculate Number of Species, p. 351 **Visualizing Parasitic Worms,** p. 352 **Activity:** Comparing Free-Living and Parasitic Flatworms, pp. 354–355 **Science and History:** Sponges, pp. 356–357

NATIONAL GEOGRAPHIC

Teacher's Corner

PRODUCTS AVAILABLE FROM GLENCOE
To order call 1-800-334-7344:

CD-ROMs
NGS PictureShow: Classifying Plants and Animals
NGS PictureShow: Structure of Invertebrates

Transparency Sets
NGS PicturePack: Classifying Plants and Animals
NGS PicturePack: Structure of Invertebrates

INDEX TO NATIONAL GEOGRAPHIC SOCIETY
The following articles may be used for research relating to this chapter:
"The Gift of Gardening," by William S. Ellis, May 1992.
"Deception: Formula for Survival," by Robert F. Sisson, March 1980.
"Consider the Sponge," by Michael E. Long, March 1977.

Activity Materials	Reproducible Resources	Section Assessment	Technology
Explore Activity: sheet of paper, scissors	**Chapter Resources Booklet** Foldables Worksheet, p. 15 Directed Reading Overview, p. 17 Note-taking Worksheets, pp. 31–33	GLENCOE'S ASSESSMENT ADVANTAGE	
MiniLAB: assorted materials such as paper, buttons, fabric scraps, and glitter; scissors; glue	**Chapter Resources Booklet** Transparency Activity, p. 42 MiniLAB, p. 3 Lab Activity, pp. 9–12 Enrichment, p. 28 Reinforcement, p. 25 Transparency Activity, pp. 45–46 Directed Reading, p. 18 **Cultural Diversity,** p. 21 **Science Inquiry Labs,** pp. 11, 19	**Portfolio** Reteach, p. 339 **Performance** MiniLAB, p. 336 Skill Builder Activities, p. 339 **Content** Section Assessment, p. 339	Section Focus Transparency Teaching Transparency Interactive CD-ROM Guided Reading Audio Program
Activity: dropper, hydra culture, small dish, toothpick, *Daphnia* or brine shrimp, stereomicroscope *Need materials?* Contact Science Kit at 1-800-828-7777 or www.sciencekit.com on the Internet.	**Chapter Resources Booklet** Transparency Activity, p. 43 Enrichment, p. 29 Reinforcement, p. 26 Directed Reading, p. 19 Activity Worksheet, pp. 5–6 **Home and Community Involvement,** p. 38	**Portfolio** Curriculum Connection, p. 341 **Performance** Skill Builder Activities, p. 346 **Content** Section Assessment, p. 346	Section Focus Transparency Interactive CD-ROM Guided Reading Audio Program
MiniLAB: dropper, planarian culture, watch glass, water, stereomicroscope **Activity:** petri dish with planarian, compound microscope, prepared slide of a tapeworm, stereomicroscope, light source, small paintbrush, small piece of liver, dropper, water	**Chapter Resources Booklet** Transparency Activity, p. 44 MiniLAB, p. 4 Lab Activity, pp. 13–14 Enrichment, p. 30 Reinforcement, p. 27 Directed Reading, pp. 19, 20 Activity Worksheet, pp. 7–8 **Lab Management and Safety,** p. 43	**Portfolio** Science Journal, p. 350 **Performance** MiniLAB, p. 350 Math Skills Activity, p. 351 Skill Builder Activities, p. 353 **Content** Section Assessment, p. 353	Section Focus Transparency Interactive CD-ROM Guided Reading Audio Program

End of Chapter Assessment

GLENCOE'S ASSESSMENT ADVANTAGE

Blackline Masters	Technology	Professional Series
Chapter Resources Booklet Chapter Review, pp. 35–36 Chapter Tests, pp. 37–40 **Standardized Test Practice by The Princeton Review,** pp. 55–58	MindJogger Videoquiz Interactive CD-ROM Vocabulary PuzzleMakers ExamView Pro Test Bank Interactive Lesson Planner Interactive Teacher Edition	Performance Assessment in the Science Classroom (PASC)

Transparencies

Section Focus

Section 1 Section Focus Transparency — Mite Get a Bit Ugly

At the broadest level, scientists divide all living things into six kingdoms. For example, there are different kingdoms for plants, animals, and bacteria. At first, assigning a living thing to a kingdom may seem pretty easy, but sometimes it gets a little tricky. Where do you think this microscopic living thing belongs?

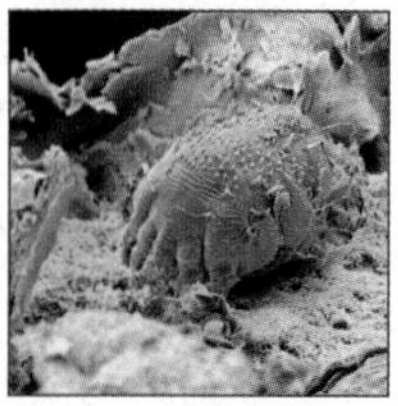

1. Describe the creature in the photo.
2. What are some characteristics that all animals share? Do you think the creature in the photo has these characteristics?
3. Where do you think this creature lives?

L2

Section 2 Section Focus Transparency — Sea-Floor Scrubbers

What you see here is the remains of a sponge called a Venus' flower basket. It is a member of a group of sponges that live in very deep water; as a consequence, relatively little is known about them. One interesting fact, though, is that the Venus' flower basket contains two shrimp in its inner chambers. The trapped shrimp and the sponge help each other survive.

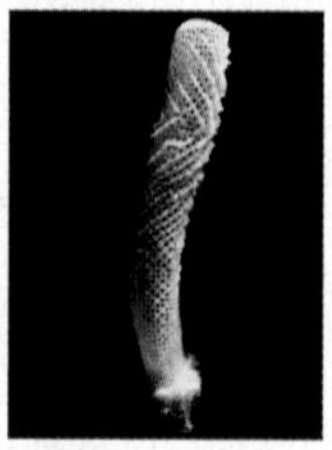

1. What are some uses of sponges?
2. Do you think a sponge is a plant or an animal? Explain.
3. How do you think the sponge and shrimp help each other?

L2

Section 3 Section Focus Transparency — Round and Round Underground

This is a microscopic roundworm. It lives in the soil. Some worms can be very destructive to crops, and scientists are finding ways to limit crop damage caused by these harmful roundworms.

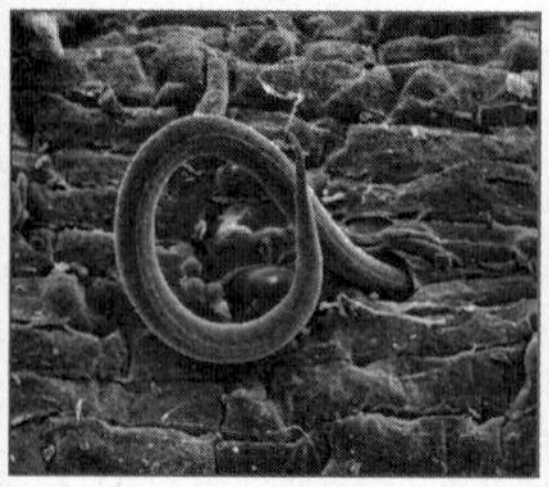

1. Some species of roundworms are parasites. What is a parasite?
2. What part of the plant do you think this worm damages?
3. How are some roundworms beneficial?

L2

Assessment

Assessment Transparency — Introduction to Animals

Directions: *Carefully review the table and answer the following questions.*

Animal Statistics

Animal	Mass (kg)	Diet	Life span (yrs)
North American black bear	up to 193	fruit, nut, meat	25.0
White-tailed deer	up to 113	twigs, fungi, grass	16.5
Reindeer	up to 180	grass, lichen, mushrooms	15.0
Coyote	up to 23	fruit, meat, insects	18.0
Mountain lion	up to 103	mostly deer	18.0

1. According to the table, a North American black bear weighs about the same as a ___.
   A mountain lion C reindeer
   B white tail deer D coyote
2. The animal that has the same life span as a coyote is a ___.
   F North American black bear H reindeer
   G white tail deer J mountain lion
3. Which of the following animals mostly eats meat?
   A White tail deer C North American black bear
   B Reindeer D Mountain lion

L2

Teaching

Section 1 Teaching Transparency — Animal Classification

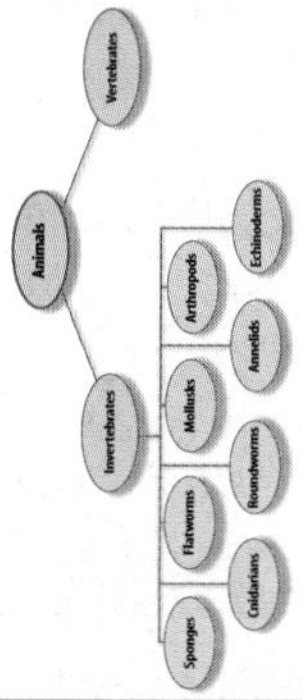

Animals; Vertebrates; Invertebrates; Sponges; Cnidarians; Flatworms; Roundworms; Mollusks; Annelids; Arthropods; Echinoderms

L2

This is a representation of key blackline masters available in the Teacher Classroom Resources. See Resource Manager boxes within the chapter for additional information.

Key to Teaching Strategies

The following designations will help you decide which activities are appropriate for your students.

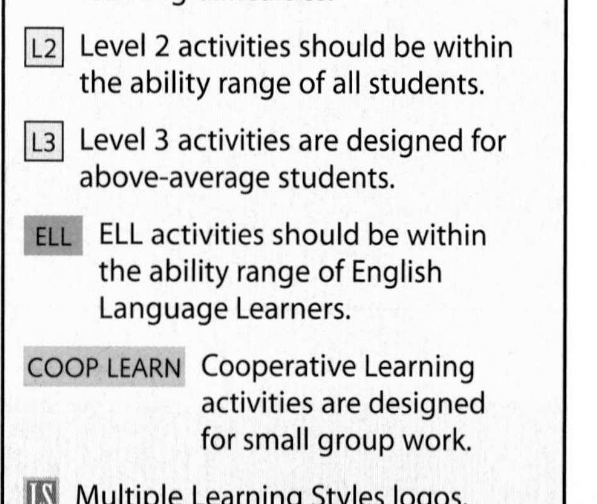

L1 Level 1 activities should be appropriate for students with learning difficulties.

L2 Level 2 activities should be within the ability range of all students.

L3 Level 3 activities are designed for above-average students.

ELL ELL activities should be within the ability range of English Language Learners.

COOP LEARN Cooperative Learning activities are designed for small group work.

LS Multiple Learning Styles logos, as described on page 22T, are used throughout to indicate strategies that address different learning styles.

P These strategies represent student products that can be placed into a best-work portfolio.

Hands-on Activities

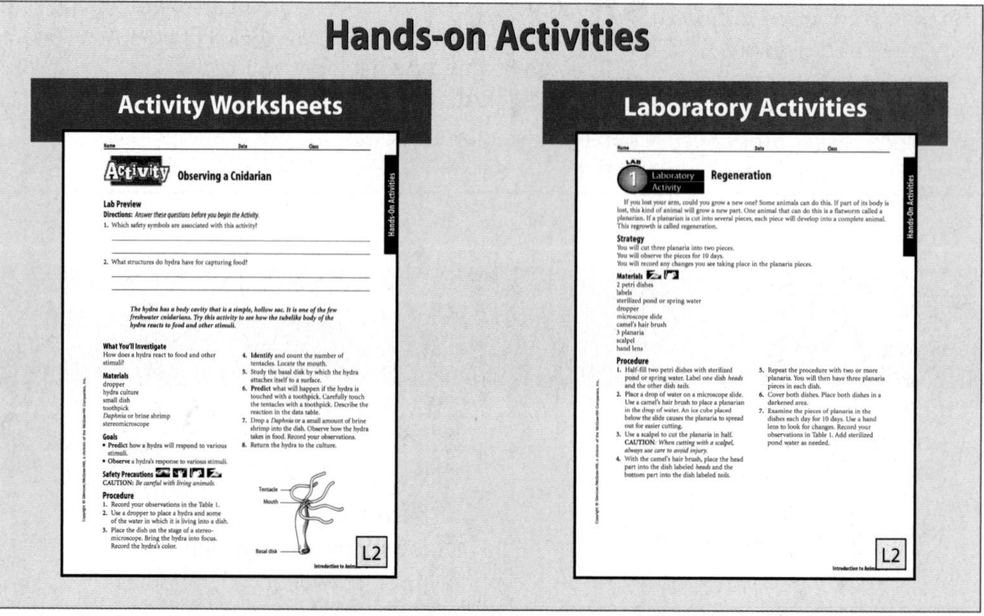

Activity Worksheets

Activity — Observing a Cnidarian

L2

Laboratory Activities

Laboratory Activity 1 — Regeneration

L2

Meeting Different Ability Levels

Content Outline

Name Date Class

Note-taking Worksheet **Introduction to Animals**

Section 1 Is it an animal?

A. Animals are diverse, but they have basic ______ in common.
1. Are made of many cells
2. Cells have a ______ and organelles.
3. Depend on other ______ things in the environment for food
4. ______ their food
5. Most animals can ______.
6. Can ______ sexually; some also can reproduce asexually

B. ______ from previous generations help individuals survive and reproduce.
1. A basic adaptation is obtaining ______ from food.
   a. ______ eat plants.
   b. ______ eat other animals.
   c. Animals that eat both plants and animals are ______.
   d. Detritivores such as beetles and millipedes eat ______ matter called detritus.
2. ______ adaptations help animals survive.
   a. Protective ______ such as shells or quills help protect animals from predators.
   b. Large ______ protects some animals.
   c. ______ or camouflage help other animals blend into the environment or confuse predators.
3. ______ is an adaptation for predators so they can sneak up on their prey.
4. ______ adaptations can help animals survive.
   a. Some animals use ______ or ink to discourage predators.
   b. ______ allows some animals to outrun predators.
   c. Traveling in ______ can assist both predators and prey.

C. Animals are ______ based on similar characteristics.
1. ______ have a backbone; ______ do not have a backbone.

Meeting Individual Needs

Introduction to Animals

L2

Reinforcement

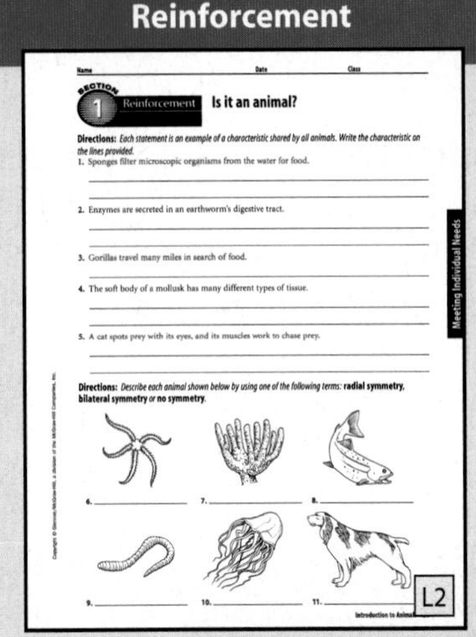

Name Date Class

Section 1 Reinforcement **Is it an animal?**

Directions: *Each statement is an example of a characteristic shared by all animals. Write the characteristic on the lines provided.*

1. Sponges filter microscopic organisms from the water for food.
2. Enzymes are secreted in an earthworm's digestive tract.
3. Gorillas travel many miles in search of food.
4. The soft body of a mollusk has many different types of tissue.
5. A cat spots prey with its eyes, and its muscles work to chase prey.

Directions: *Describe each animal shown below by using one of the following terms:* **radial symmetry, bilateral symmetry** *or* **no symmetry.**

6. ______ 7. ______ 8. ______
9. ______ 10. ______ 11. ______

Meeting Individual Needs

Introduction to Animals

L2

Directed Reading

Name Date Class

Directed Reading for Content Mastery **Overview Introduction to Animals**

Directions: *Write* **T** *if the statement is true; write* **F** *if the statement is false.*

______ 1. An animal cell has a nucleus and organelles.
______ 2. Animals depend on other organisms for food.
______ 3. Mimicry is one adaptation for escaping predators.
______ 4. About 97 percent of all animals have backbones.
______ 5. Adult sponges usually float around from place to place.
______ 6. For cnidarians, the polyp body type is usually sessile; the medusa body type is free-swimming.
______ 7. Sponges and polyps are parasitic.
______ 8. Coral reefs protect the shoreline from damage.
______ 9. Most flatworms are parasites.
______ 10. Blood flukes are harmless to people.
______ 11. Roundworms have a mouth and an anus.

Directions: *Label the following animals with the kind of symmetry each has.*

12. ______ 13. ______ 14. ______
15. ______ 16. ______ 17. ______

Meeting Individual Needs

Introduction to Animals

L1

Enrichment

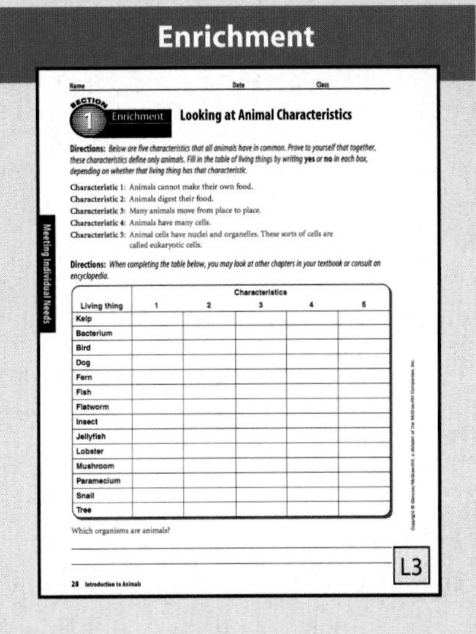

Name Date Class

Section 1 Enrichment **Looking at Animal Characteristics**

Directions: *Below are five characteristics that all animals have in common. Prove to yourself that together, these characteristics define only animals. Fill in the table of living things by writing* **yes** *or* **no** *in each box, depending on whether that living thing has that characteristic.*

Characteristic 1: Animals cannot make their own food.
Characteristic 2: Animals digest their food.
Characteristic 3: Many animals move from place to place.
Characteristic 4: Animals have many cells.
Characteristic 5: Animal cells have nuclei and organelles. These sorts of cells are called eukaryotic cells.

Directions: *When completing the table below, you may look at other chapters in your textbook or consult an encyclopedia.*

Living thing	Characteristics 1	2	3	4	5
Kelp					
Bacterium					
Bird					
Dog					
Fern					
Fish					
Flatworm					
Insect					
Jellyfish					
Lobster					
Mushroom					
Paramecium					
Snail					
Tree					

Which organisms are animals?

Meeting Individual Needs

28 Introduction to Animals

L3

Spanish Directed Reading

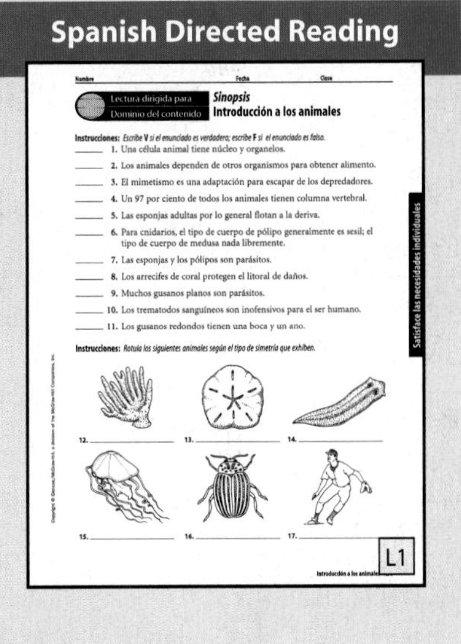

Nombre Fecha Clase

Lectura dirigida para Dominio del contenido **Sinopsis Introducción a los animales**

Instrucciones: *Escribe* **V** *si el enunciado es verdadero; escribe* **F** *si el enunciado es falso.*

______ 1. Una célula animal tiene núcleo y organelos.
______ 2. Los animales dependen de otros organismos para obtener alimento.
______ 3. El mimetismo es una adaptación para escapar de los depredadores.
______ 4. Un 97 por ciento de todos los animales tienen columna vertebral.
______ 5. Las esponjas adultas por lo general flotan a la deriva.
______ 6. Para cnidarios, el tipo de cuerpo de pólipo generalmente es sesil; el tipo de cuerpo de medusa nada libremente.
______ 7. Las esponjas y los pólipos son parásitos.
______ 8. Los arrecifes de coral protegen el litoral de daños.
______ 9. Muchos gusanos planos son parásitos.
______ 10. Los trematodos sanguíneos son inofensivos para el ser humano.
______ 11. Los gusanos redondos tienen una boca y un ano.

Instrucciones: *Rotula los siguientes animales según el tipo de simetría que exhiben.*

12. ______ 13. ______ 14. ______
15. ______ 16. ______ 17. ______

Satisface las necesidades individuales

Introducción a los animales

L1

Assessment

Chapter Tests

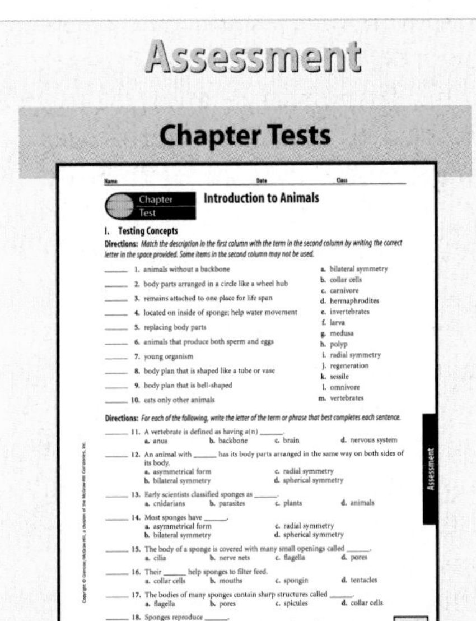

Name Date Class

Chapter Test **Introduction to Animals**

I. Testing Concepts

Directions: *Match the description in the first column with the term in the second column by writing the correct letter in the space provided. Some items in the second column may not be used.*

______ 1. animals without a backbone — a. bilateral symmetry
______ 2. body parts arranged in a circle like a wheel hub — b. collar cells
______ 3. remains attached to one place for life span — c. carnivore
______ 4. located on inside of sponge; help water movement — d. hermaphrodites
______ 5. replacing body parts — e. invertebrates
______ 6. animals that produce both sperm and eggs — f. larva
______ 7. young organism — g. medusa
______ 8. body plan that is shaped like a tube or vase — h. polyp
______ 9. body plan that is bell-shaped — i. radial symmetry
______ 10. eats only other animals — j. regeneration
k. sessile
l. omnivore
m. vertebrates

Directions: *For each of the following, write the letter of the term or phrase that best completes each sentence.*

______ 11. A vertebrate is defined as having a(n) ______. a. anus b. backbone c. brain d. nervous system
______ 12. An animal with ______ has its body parts arranged in the same way on both sides of its body. a. asymmetrical form b. bilateral symmetry c. radial symmetry d. spherical symmetry
______ 13. Early scientists classified sponges as ______. a. cnidarians b. parasites c. plants d. animals
______ 14. Most sponges have ______. a. asymmetrical form b. bilateral symmetry c. radial symmetry d. spherical symmetry
______ 15. The body of a sponge is covered with many small openings called ______. a. cilia b. nerve nets c. flagella d. pores
______ 16. Their ______ help sponges to filter food. a. collar cells b. mouths c. spongin d. tentacles
______ 17. The bodies of many sponges contain sharp structures called ______. a. flagella b. pores c. spicules d. collar cells
______ 18. Sponges reproduce ______. a. only asexually b. only with buds c. only sexually d. asexually and sexually

Assessment

Introduction to Animals

L2

Test Practice Workbook

L2

Chapter Review

Name Date Class

Chapter Review **Introduction to Animals**

Part A. Vocabulary Review

Directions: *Select the term from the following list that matches each description.*

anus	filter-feeder	larva	omnivore
cnidaria	free-living	medusa	regeneration
collar cell	hermaphrodite	polyp	sessile
camouflage	invertebrate	mimicry	tentacle
herbivore	vertebrate		

______ 1. animal with a backbone
______ 2. type of cell that lines the inside of a sponge
______ 3. a stage in development between egg and adult
______ 4. remaining attached to one place
______ 5. ability of an organism to replace body parts
______ 6. an animal that produces both sperm and eggs
______ 7. group name meaning "stinging-cells"
______ 8. armlike structure having stinging cells
______ 9. cnidarian body plan that is shaped like a tube or vase
______ 10. bell-shaped body plan of cnidarians
______ 11. organism that does not depend on another for food or a place to live
______ 12. organism that obtains food by filtering it from the water in which it lives
______ 13. animal that doesn't have a backbone
______ 14. opening at the end of digestive tract where wastes leave

Directions: *Write the correct adaptation next to its description.*

______ 15. eats plants and animals
______ 16. the non-venomous king snake looks like the venomous coral snake
______ 17. stripes help tigers hide in tall grasses
______ 18. eats only plants or parts of plants

Assessment

Introduction to Animals

L2

Science Content Background

SECTION 1

Is it an animal?

Animal Characteristics

From sponges to monkeys there is considerable diversity in the animal kingdom. Yet there are characteristics that all animals share. Animals are heterotrophic—they consume parts of other organisms for their nutritional needs. Animals are composed of eukaryotic cells, which have nuclei and have cell membranes but do not have cell walls.

Fun Fact

The lion's mane jellyfish *(Cyanea capillata)* is the largest true jellyfish. It can grow to 2.5 meters in diameter and have tentacles more than 30 meters long.

How Animals Meet Their Needs

Animals have adaptions that make them either carnivores, herbivores, or omnivores. Consider the length of the alimentary canal. Many students are surprised to learn that herbivores have a much longer alimentary canal than do carnivores. The extra length is an adaptation that helps to break down the hard-to-digest plant material, cellulose. The length of the human alimentary canal is between the lengths of herbivores and carnivores.

Another area where adaptations can be seen is with dentition. Herbivores have hard, flat molars that are used for grinding plant material. The sharp back teeth of a carnivore is for cutting and shredding meat.

Many land herbivores have eyes far apart on both sides of their head, which helps them spot predators. Land carnivores often have eyes in the front of their heads. This arrangement gives binocular vision, which better helps the predator estimate distance.

For additional content background on this topic, go to the Glencoe Science Web site at science.glencoe.com.

Ken Lucas/Visuals Unlimited

SECTION 2

Sponges and Cnidarians

Sponges

Sponges belong to the phylum Porifera, which comes from the Latin words *porus*, which means "hole," and *ferre*, which means "to carry." They have this name because sponges carry materials in through their holes. The sponges your students typically encounter are artificial sponges. As a defense against bacteria, fungi, and predators, real sponges have chemical defenses. Scientists are studying these compounds to see if they can be used to combat human diseases.

Cnidarians

These animals belong to the aquatic invertebrate phylum called Cnidaria and are also called coelenterate animals. Sea anemones are carnivores, but they have symbiotic relationships with photosynthetic organisms that produce nutrients and oxygen for the anemone. For this reason, sea anemones will not survive for long in marine aquariums unless they contain proper lighting systems.

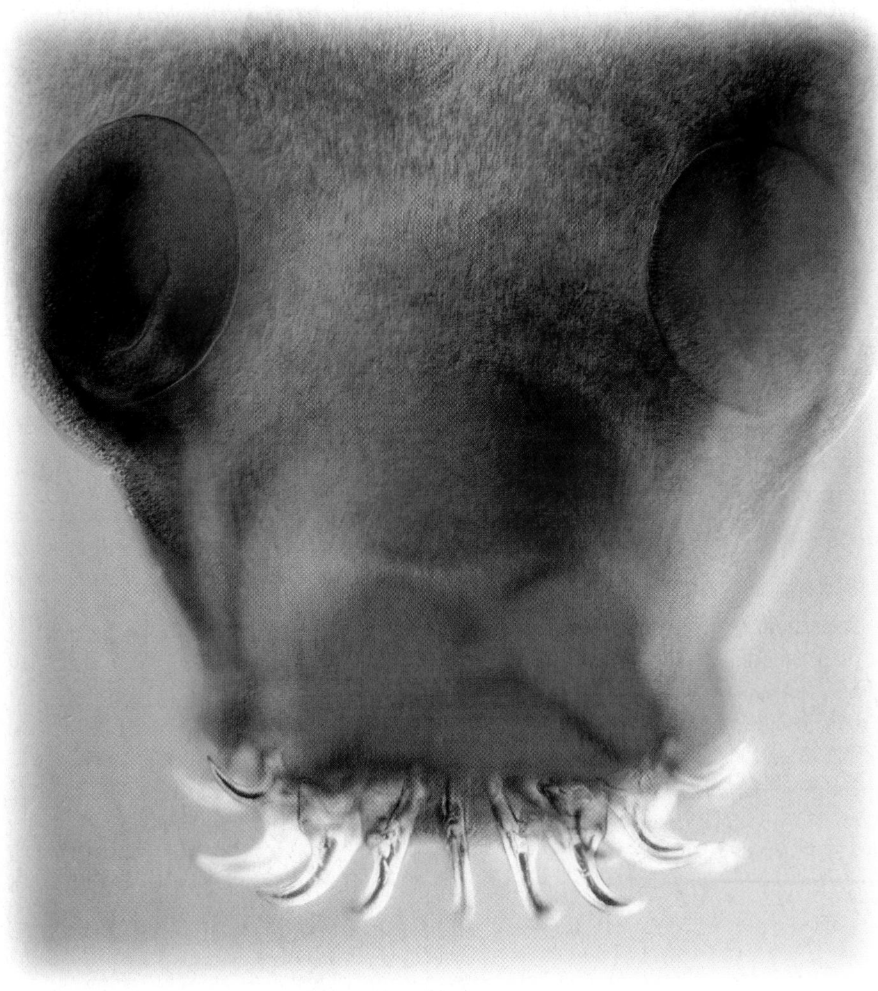

Alferd Pasieka/Science Library/Photo Researchers, Inc.

SECTION 3

Flatworms and Roundworms

Flatworms

Flatworms belong to the phylum Platyhelminthes. The name comes from the Greek word *platys*, meaning "flat" and *helminthos*, meaning "worm." There are 3,500 species of tapeworms that live in different animals. The size of the worm usually varies with the organism in which it lives. For example, a tapeworm in a sperm whale may be 30 meters long.

Roundworms

Members of the phylum Nematoda are the simplest organisms that have tubelike digestive systems starting with a mouth and ending with an anus. These are abundant animals that live in large quantities in places as diverse as soils, plants, animals, freshwater, salt water, and even vinegar.

CHAPTER 12

Introduction to Animals

Chapter Vocabulary

herbivore, p. 335
carnivore, p. 335
omnivore, p. 335
vertebrate, p. 338
invertebrate, p. 338
radial symmetry, p. 339
bilateral symmetry, p. 339
sessile, p. 341
hermaphrodite, p. 342
polyp, p. 343
medusa, p. 343
tentacle, p. 344
stinging cell, p. 344
free-living organism, p. 348
anus, p. 351

What do you think?

Science Journal The picture is of a soft coral, an invertebrate marine organism. The hard portion of the coral colony remains attached to the ocean floor or other stable object. The only movement that is noticeable is from the tiny polyps as they wave their tentacles through the water, collecting food.

CHAPTER 12

Introduction to Animals

Did you know that some cultures classified animals according to how useful or destructive they were to humans? Some animal groups were based on their roles in myths and legends. In this chapter, you will discover how animals are classified today and learn about the relationships that exist among different groups in the animal kingdom. You also will learn how some animals—such as sponges, jellyfish, roundworms, and flatworms—live and reproduce and how they are important to humans.

What do you think?

Science Journal Look at the picture below with a classmate. Discuss what you think this might be. Here's a hint: *Can these organisms move around or are they attached to the ocean floor?* Write your answer or best guess in your Science Journal.

332

Theme Connection

Stability and Change Changing environments lead to changes in the complexity of animals inhabiting these environments. The groups of animals from invertebrates to vertebrates show a trend toward increasing complexity.

The words *left* and *right* have meaning to you because your body has a left and a right side. But what is left or right to a jellyfish or sea star? How an animal's body parts are arranged is called symmetry. In the following activity, you will compare three types of symmetry found in animals.

Demonstrate symmetry

1. On a piece of paper, draw three shapes—a circle, a triangle with two equal sides, and a free-form shape—then cut them out.
2. Fold each shape through the center as many different ways as you can to make similar halves with each fold.

Observe

Which shapes can be folded into equal halves and which shapes cannot? Can any of the shapes be folded into equal halves more than one way? Record your answers in your Science Journal.

Before You Read

FOLDABLES Reading & Study Skills

Making an Organizational Study Fold

Make the following Foldable to help you organize your thoughts about your favorite animals and how they are classified.

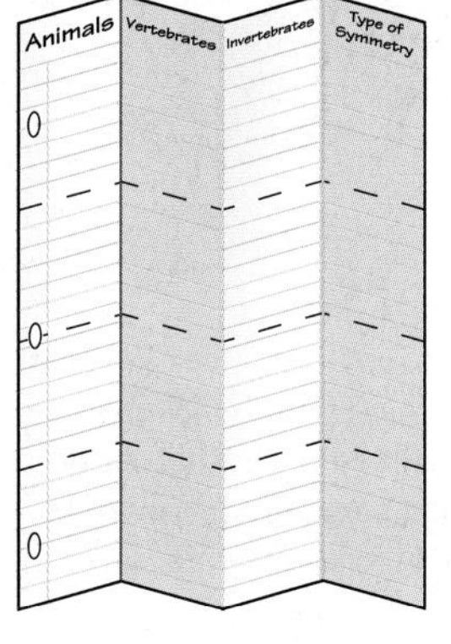

1. Place a sheet of paper in front of you so the short side is at the top. Fold the paper in half from left to right, twice.
2. Fold the paper in half from top to bottom. Then fold it in half again. Unfold all the folds and trace over the fold lines.
3. Label the columns *Animals, Vertebrates, Invertebrates,* and *Type of Symmetry* as shown.
4. Before you read the chapter, list your four favorite animals in the *Animal* column.
5. As you read the chapter, add information about how the four animals are classified to the table.

333

Explore Activity

Purpose Use this activity to introduce students to the different types of symmetry animals can have. Explain that they will be learning about different types of invertebrates during this chapter.

Preparation Cut out several shapes representing different animals with radial or bilateral symmetry such as a beetle, worm, jellyfish, human, and sea urchin. Show your cutouts to students after they have finished the activity and ask them to identify the type of symmetry of each.

Materials scissors, sheet of paper or colored construction paper

Safety Precaution Caution students to use scissors safely.

Teaching Strategy Have students compare the shapes they have made with the shapes of animals from different phyla. Ask them to classify their "animals" into a specific phylum or to devise their own phyla for classifying organisms that do not fit into any of the existing phyla of Kingdom *Animalia*.

Observe

Answers will vary, but many of the shapes will have either radial or bilateral symmetry.

Assessment

Performance Organize the class into groups and have each group make a poster display of their shapes. Similar shapes should be grouped together and classified. Use **Performance Assessment in the Science Classroom,** p. 145.

Before You Read

FOLDABLES Reading & Study Skills

Dinah Zike Study Fold

Purpose Students make and use a Foldable chart to collect information on animals as they read the chapter, and then use the data to compare and contrast the animals during and after reading.

For additional help, see Foldables Worksheet, p. 15 in **Chapter Resources Booklet,** or go to the Glencoe Science Web site at **science.glencoe.com.** See After You Read in the Study Guide at the end of this chapter.

SECTION

Is it an animal?

1 Motivate

Bellringer Transparency

Display the Section Focus Transparency for Section 1. Use the accompanying Transparency Activity Master. L2 ELL

SECTION 1 Section Focus Transparency **Mite Get a Bit Ugly**

At the broadest level, scientists divide all living things into six kingdoms. For example, there are different kingdoms for plants, animals, and bacteria. At first, assigning a living thing to a kingdom may seem pretty easy, but sometimes it gets a little tricky. Where do you think this microscopic living thing belongs?

1. Describe the creature in the photo.
2. What are some characteristics that all animals share? Do you think the creature in the photo has these characteristics?
3. Where do you think this creature lives?

Introduction to Animals

Tie to Prior Knowledge

Ask what characteristics animals have that distinguish them from other living things. They cannot make their own food, most are capable of movement. Discuss the characteristics they have in common with all living things. They are made of cells, reproduce, grow, develop, respond, and have basic needs such as energy and water.

SECTION

Is it an animal?

As You Read

What **You'll Learn**

- **Identify** the characteristics common to most animals.
- **Determine** how animals meet their needs.
- **Distinguish** between invertebrates and vertebrates.

Vocabulary

herbivore
carnivore
omnivore
vertebrate
invertebrate
radial symmetry
bilateral symmetry

Why **It's Important**

Animals provide food, medicines, and companionship in your daily life.

Animal Characteristics

From microscopic worms to giant whales, the animal kingdom includes an amazing variety of living things, but all of them have certain characteristics in common. What makes the animals in **Figure 1** different from plants? Is it because animals eat other living things? Is this enough information to identify them as animals? What characteristics do animals have?

1. Animals are made of many cells. The cells are of different kinds that carry out different functions such as sensing the environment, getting rid of wastes, and reproducing.
2. Animal cells have a nucleus and specialized structures inside the cells called organelles.
3. Animals depend on other living things in the environment for food. Some eat plants, some eat other animals, and some eat plants and animals.
4. Animals digest their food. The proteins, carbohydrates, and fats in foods are broken down into simpler molecules that can move into the animal's cells.
5. Many animals move from place to place. They can escape from their enemies and find food, mates, and places to live. Animals that move slowly or not at all have adaptations that make it possible for them to take care of these needs in other ways.
6. All animals are capable of reproducing sexually. Some animals also can reproduce asexually.

Figure 1
These organisms look like plants, but they're one of the many plantlike animals that can be found growing on shipwrecks and other underwater surfaces.

Section Assessment Planner

Portfolio
Reteach, p. 339

Performance Assessment
Try at Home MiniLAB, p. 336
Skill Builder Activities, p. 339
See page 360 for more options.

Content Assessment
Section, p. 339
Challenge, p. 339
Chapter, pp. 360–361

Figure 2
Animals eat a variety of foods.

A **Chitons eat algae from rocks.**

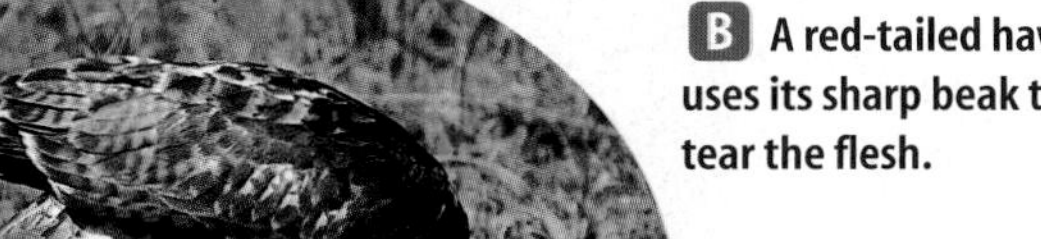

B **A red-tailed hawk uses its sharp beak to tear the flesh.**

C **Cardinal fish eat small invertebrates and some plant material.**

How Animals Meet Their Needs

Any structure, process, or behavior that helps an organism survive in its environment is an adaptation. Adaptations are inherited from previous generations. In a changing environment, adaptations determine which individuals are more likely to survive and reproduce.

Adaptations for Obtaining Energy One of the most basic needs of animals is the need for food. All animals have adaptations that allow them to obtain, eat, and digest different foods. The chiton shown in **Figure 2A,** deer, some fish, and many insects are examples of herbivores. **Herbivores** eat only plants or parts of plants. In general, herbivores eat more often and in greater amounts than other animals because plants don't supply as much energy as other types of food.

Reading Check *Why are butterflies considered to be herbivores?*

Animals that eat only other animals, like the red-tailed hawk in **Figure 2B,** are **carnivores.** Most carnivores capture and kill other animals for food. But some carnivores, called scavengers, eat only the remains of other animals. Animal flesh supplies more energy than plants do, so carnivores don't need to eat as much or as often as herbivores.

Animals that eat plants and animals or animal flesh are called **omnivores.** Bears, raccoons, robins, humans, and the cardinal fish in **Figure 2C** are examples of omnivores.

Many beetles and other animals such as millipedes feed on tiny bits of decaying matter called detritus (dih TRI tus). They are called detritivores (dih TRI tih vorz).

Health INTEGRATION

Many animals, including humans, have microorganisms in their digestive tracts. These microorganisms are helpful in preventing harmful bacteria from growing in the intestines. In your Science Journal, infer why microorganisms are important for good health in animals.

2 Teach

Animal Characteristics

Quick Demo

Have students observe the fish and plants in the classroom aquarium. Ask them to compare and contrast the two. Both are many-celled, reproduce sexually, and move. Green plants make their own food, but fish cannot. Animals can move from place to place. Plant movement is a result of growth and environmental stimulus.
LS **Visual-Spatial**

Activity

Display pictures of herbivores, carnivores, and omnivores on the bulletin board. Have students group them according to their source of obtaining energy.
L2 COOP LEARN LS **Visual-Spatial**

How Animals Meet Their Needs

Reading Check

Answer They feed on plant products.

Health INTEGRATION

Possible answer: When harmful bacteria are prevented from growing, the animal is less likely to develop disease.

Extension

Have students research the characteristics of extinct animals, such as dinosaurs, and explain why they were classified as animals. L3

Resource Manager

Chapter Resources Booklet
- Transparency Activity, p. 42
- Directed Reading for Content Mastery, pp. 17, 18
- Note-taking Worksheets, pp. 31–33

Teacher FYI

The branch of biology that deals with the study of animals is zoology. Early zoologists classified animals according to physical structure, where they lived, or economic use. Modern zoologists use cell structure and function, embryology, physiology, and genetics to classify animals.

How Animals Meet Their Needs, continued

Try at Home Mini LAB

Purpose to model camouflage
L1 IS **Logical-Mathematical**

Materials assorted materials such as paper, buttons, and fabric scraps; scissors; glue

Teaching Strategy Encourage students to make animals from various links in a food chain, and infer how camouflage assists both predator and prey in their survival.

Analysis
1. Generally, an animal will be well camouflaged in one environment and only partially camouflaged in other environments.
2. Answers will vary depending on students' designs.

Assessment

Process Have students place their animals in various locations in the room. **How does changing an animal's environment affect it chances for survival?** Most of the "animals" will no longer be camouflaged and have difficulty pursuing prey or fleeing from predators. Use **PASC**, p. 89.

Reading Check

Answer An animal can be mistaken for another type of animal. Sometimes this may save the animal's life, sometimes this may get the animal killed.

Caption Answer

Figure 4B The colors and patterns are similar. The scarlet king snake has wider, light-colored bands than does the coral snake. Remind students that the coral snake is venomous, while the king snake is not.

Figure 3
The pill bug's outer covering protects it and reduces moisture loss from its body.

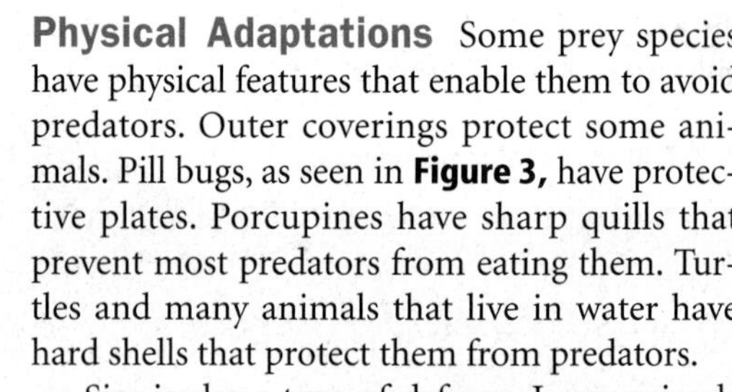

Physical Adaptations Some prey species have physical features that enable them to avoid predators. Outer coverings protect some animals. Pill bugs, as seen in **Figure 3,** have protective plates. Porcupines have sharp quills that prevent most predators from eating them. Turtles and many animals that live in water have hard shells that protect them from predators.

Size is also a type of defense. Large animals are usually safer than small animals. Few predators will attack animals such as moose or bison simply because they are so large.

Mimicry is an adaptation in which one animal closely resembles another in appearance or behavior. If predators cannot distinguish between the two, they usually will not eat either animal. The venomous coral snake and the nonvenomous scarlet king snake, shown in **Figure 4,** look alike. In some cases, this is a disadvantage for scarlet king snakes because people mistake them for coral snakes and kill them.

Reading Check *How might mimicry be an advantage and a disadvantage for an animal?*

Many animals, like the flounder in **Figure 5A,** blend into their surrounding environment, enabling them to hide from their predators. English peppered moths are brown and speckled like the lichens (LI kunz) on trees, making it difficult for their predators to see them. Many freshwater fish, like the trout in **Figure 5B,** have light bellies and dark, speckled backs that blend in with the gravelly bottoms of their habitats when they are viewed from above. Any marking or coloring that helps an animal hide from other animals is called camouflage. Some animals, like the chameleon in **Figure 5C,** have the ability to change their color depending on their surroundings.

Try at Home Mini LAB

Modeling Animal Camouflage

Procedure
1. Pretend that a room in your home is the world of some fictitious animal. From **materials you can find around your home,** build a **fictitious animal** that would be camouflaged in this world.
2. Put your animal into its world and ask someone to find it.

Analysis
1. In how many places was your animal camouflaged?
2. What changes would increase its chances of surviving in its world?

Figure 4
Mimicry helps some animals survive. Compare the colors and patterns of A the coral snake and B the scarlet king snake.
What is the difference between the two snakes?

Active Reading

Jigsaw In this collaborative learning technique, individuals become experts on a portion of a text and share their expertise with a small group, called their home group. Everyone shares responsibility for learning the assigned reading. Assign each person in each home group an expert number (1 through 5, for example). Have students gather into the expert groups that correspond to the number they were assigned. Have them read, discuss, and master chapter concepts and determine how best to teach them to their home groups. Have students return to their home groups and share the content they learned in their expert groups. Have students use the Jigsaw strategy as they study animal characteristics.

Figure 5
Many types of animals blend with their surroundings.

A **Bottom fish like this flounder, blend with the ocean floor.** *Can you see the flounder in this photo?*

B **A trout blends with the bottom of a stream.**

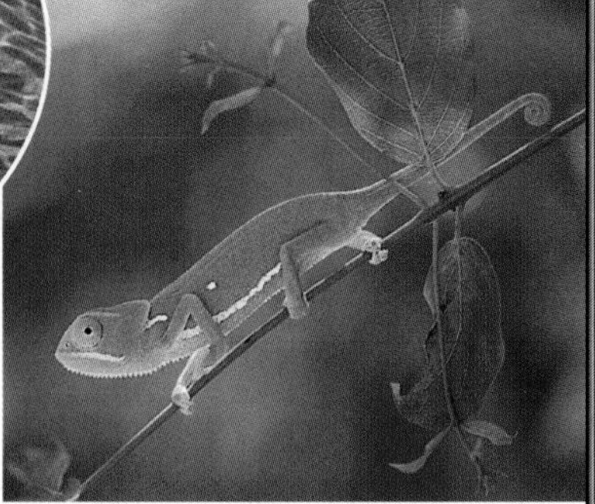

C **Chameleons can be especially difficult to find because they can change color to blend with their surroundings.**

Predator Adaptations Camouflage is an adaptation for many predators so they can sneak up on their prey. Tigers have stripes that hide them in tall grasses. Killer whales are black on their upper surface and white underneath. When seen from above, the whale blends into the darkness of the deep ocean. The killer whale's white underside appears to be nearly the same color as the bright sky overhead when viewed from below. Adaptations such as these enable predators to hunt prey more successfully.

Behavioral Adaptations In addition to physical adaptations, animals have behavioral adaptations that enable them to capture prey or to avoid predators. Chemicals are used by some animals to escape predators. Skunks spray attacking animals with a bad-smelling liquid. Some ants and beetles also use this method of defense. When squid and octopuses are threatened, they release a cloud of ink so they can escape, as shown in **Figure 6.**

Some animals are able to run faster than most of their predators. The Thomson's gazelle can run at speeds up to 80 km/h. A lion can run only about 36 km/h, so speed is a factor in the Thomson's gazelle's survival.

Traveling in groups is a behavior that is demonstrated by predators and prey. Herring swim in groups called schools that resemble an organism too large for a predator fish to attack. On the other hand, when wolves travel in packs, they can successfully hunt large prey that one predator alone could not capture.

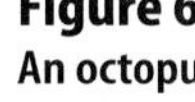

Figure 6
An octopus's cloud of ink confuses a predator long enough for the octopus to escape.

337

Caption Question Answer

Figure 5A Point out the outline of the fish.

Visual Learning

Figure 5 and 6 Have students look at the animals in these photos and list the adaptations they have for their particular environments, including those adaptations which allow them to escape predators.

Identifying Misconceptions

Students may think that chameleons change their color to match their background. However, this is not true. Each chameleon species has a particular range of color change it is capable of. Colors often include green, cream, yellow, and dark brown, often with spots of varying shades of the base color. The color change is brought about by environmental factors, such as light and temperature, as well as being threatened by a predator.

Fun Fact

Though insects make up the main portion of a chameleon's diet, large chameleons have been known to eat birds.

Resource Manager

Chapter Resources Booklet

MiniLAB, p. 3
Lab Activity, pp. 9–12
Transparency Activity, pp. 45–46

Cultural Diversity

Animal Roles Discuss the ways in which animals are viewed in the United States—pets, food, recreation. Have students research the place of animals in other cultures. L3

Animal Classification

Activity

Organize the class into nine groups. Give each group an animal picture. Each animal should be from a different phylum (or major group). Have each group make a list of traits they can see and share their findings with the class. L1 COOP LEARN

LS **Interpersonal**

IDENTIFYING Misconceptions

Students may not think of invertebrates as animals. Elicit student help in writing on the chalkboard a list of familiar invertebrates and the characteristics they share with organisms more easily recognized as animals.

Quick Demo

Compare symmetrical and asymmetrical objects. Use rocks, chalk, and other classroom objects. Have students list in their Science Journals as many asymmetrical items as they can find in the classroom. Repeat the activity with radially symmetrical and bilaterally symmetrical objects. L2 ELL LS **Visual-Spatial**

Fun Fact

Animals with radial symmetry are common in the ocean, but all land animals have bilateral symmetry.

Figure 7
Animals can be classified into two large groups. These groups can be broken down further based on different animal characteristics.

Animal Classification

Scientists have identified and named more than 1.8 million species of animals. It is estimated that there are another 3 million to 30 million more to identify and name. Animals can be classified into two major groups, as shown in **Figure 7.** All animals have common characteristics, but those in one group have more, similar characteristics because all the members of a group probably descended from a common ancestor. When a scientist finds a new animal, how does he or she begin to classify it?

Check for a Backbone To classify an animal, a scientist first looks to see whether or not the animal has a backbone. Animals with backbones are called **vertebrates.** Their backbones are made up of a stack of structures called vertebrae that support the animal. The backbone also protects and covers the spinal cord—a bundle of nerves that is connected to the brain. The spinal cord carries messages to all other parts of the body. It also carries messages from other parts of the body to the brain. Examples of vertebrates include fish, frogs, snakes, birds, and humans.

An animal without a backbone is classified as an **invertebrate.** About 97 percent of all animal species are invertebrates. Sponges, jellyfish, worms, insects, and clams are examples of invertebrates. Many invertebrates are well protected by their outer coverings. Some have a shell, some have a skeleton on the outside of their body, and others have a spiny outer covering.

SCIENCE Online

Research The classification of an animal can change as new information is learned. Visit the Glencoe Science Web site at **science.glencoe.com** to learn about a recent reclassification of an animal. Communicate to your class what you learn.

Symmetry After determining whether or not a backbone is present, a scientist might look at an animal's symmetry (SIH muh tree). Symmetry is how the body parts of an animal are arranged. Organisms that have no definite shape are called asymmetrical. Most sponges are asymmetrical animals.

Resource Manager

Chapter Resources Booklet
Enrichment, p. 28
Reinforcement, p. 25

Internet Addresses

Explore the Glencoe Science Web site at **science.glencoe.com** to find out more about topics in this section.

Figure 8
Symmetry is a characteristic of all animals.

A **Sea urchins have radial symmetry and can sense things in their environment from all directions.**

B **Most animals have bilateral symmetry like this crayfish.** *What type of symmetry do you have?*

Animals that have body parts arranged in a circle around a center point, the way spokes of a bicycle wheel are arranged, have **radial symmetry.** Hydras, jellyfish, sea urchins like the one in **Figure 8A,** and some sponges have radial symmetry.

Most animals have bilateral symmetry. Look in the mirror. Does your body look about the same on both sides? An animal with **bilateral symmetry** has its body parts arranged in a similar way on both sides. Each half is a mirror image of the other half. In Latin, the word *bilateral* means "two sides." Bilateral animals, like the one in **Figure 8B,** can be divided into right and left halves.

After an animal is classified as an invertebrate or a vertebrate and its symmetry is determined, other characteristics are identified that place it in one of the groups of animals with which it has the most characteristics in common. Sometimes a newly discovered animal is different from any existing group, and a new classification group is formed for that animal.

Section 1 Assessment

1. List five characteristics of animals.
2. Explain how herbivores, carnivores, and omnivores are different.
3. Compare invertebrates and vertebrates.
4. Name the three types of symmetry. Give an animal example for each type.
5. **Think Critically** Radial symmetry is found among species that live in water. Why might radial symmetry be an uncommon adaptation of animals that live on land?

Skill Builder Activities

6. **Concept Mapping** Using the information in this section, make an events-chain concept map that shows the steps a scientist might use to classify a new animal. **For more help, refer to the Science Skill Handbook.**
7. **Communicating** Choose an animal you are familiar with. In your Science Journal, describe the adaptations it has for getting food and avoiding predators. **For more help, refer to the Science Skill Handbook.**

Activity

Have students look through magazines to find pictures of animals. Then have them work in groups to identify each animal's symmetry. L1 COOP LEARN LS **Visual-Spatial**

Caption Answer

Figure 8B bilateral

3 Assess

Reteach

Have students make diagrams of a sea star, a butterfly, and a sponge, and label each diagram with the type of symmetry it represents. L1 LS **Visual-Spatial** P

Challenge

Where are the nerves and sense organs of animals with bilateral symmetry located? Why? In the front end; this arrangement allows animals to sense the environment as they move forward.

Assessment

Content Place a number of pictures of animals on the bulletin board. Ask students to choose one and use the section on classification to explain how they would classify that organism. Use **PASC,** p. 121.

Answers to Section Assessment

1. made of many cells, cells contain a nucleus and organelles, cannot make their own food, digest their food, most have means of movement, capable of sexual reproduction
2. Herbivores eat only plants or plant parts; carnivores eat other animals or animal remains; omnivores eat plants and animals.
3. Invertebrates do not have backbones; vertebrates do.
4. radial symmetry—sea star; bilateral symmetry—dog; asymmetry—sponge
5. An animal that lives in water may be stationary, move with the water, or move up and down in the water column. Radial symmetry allows for all of these movements in water, but such an adaptation would be less useful on land. Radial symmetry enables animals to sense their environment from all directions.
6. Determine whether the animal has a backbone; determine the animal's symmetry; compare the organism's characteristics with those of other organisms.
7. Allow students to research their chosen animal, if necessary.

SECTION

Sponges and Cnidarians

1 Motivate

Bellringer Transparency

Display the Section Focus Transparency for Section 2. Use the accompanying Transparency Activity Master. L2 ELL

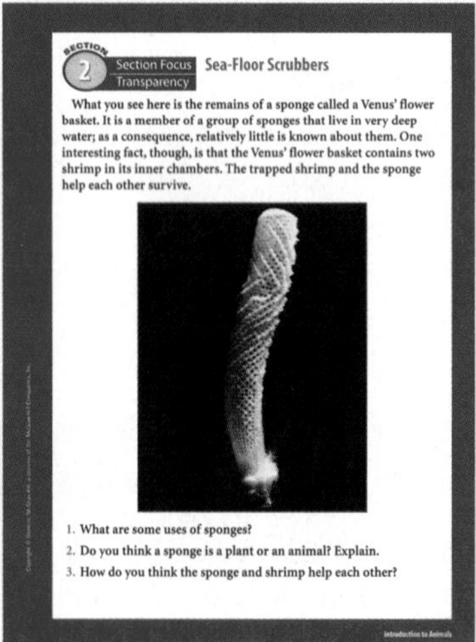

Section 2 Section Focus Transparency **Sea-Floor Scrubbers**

What you see here is the remains of a sponge called a Venus' flower basket. It is a member of a group of sponges that live in very deep water; as a consequence, relatively little is known about them. One interesting fact, though, is that the Venus' flower basket contains two shrimp in its inner chambers. The trapped shrimp and the sponge help each other survive.

1. What are some uses of sponges?
2. Do you think a sponge is a plant or an animal? Explain.
3. How do you think the sponge and shrimp help each other?

Introduction to Animals

Tie to Prior Knowledge

Review how cells are organized into tissues, organs, systems, and organisms to help students understand the differences in the body structures of sponges and cnidarians.

SECTION 2

Sponges and Cnidarians

As You Read

What You'll Learn

- **Describe** the characteristics of sponges and cnidarians.
- **Explain** how sponges and cnidarians obtain food and oxygen.
- **Determine** the importance of living coral reefs.

Vocabulary

sessile	medusa
hermaphrodite	tentacle
polyp	stinging cell

Why It's Important

Sponges and cnidarians are important to medical research because they are sources of chemicals that fight disease.

Sponges

When you think of sponges, do you think of the colorful, packaged ones that are used for cleaning or those that live in water? Natural sponges that some humans use are the remains of animals. When alive, they carried on the life processes that all animals do.

Importance of Sponges In their watery environments, sponges play many roles. They interact with many other animals such as worms, shrimp, snails, and sea stars. These animals live on, in, and under sponges. Sponges also are important as a food source for some snails, sea stars, and fish. Certain sponges contain photosynthetic bacteria and protists that provide oxygen and remove wastes for the sponge.

Only about 17 species of sponges are commercially important. Humans have long used the dried and cleaned bodies of some sponges for bathing and cleaning. Most sponges you see today are synthetic sponges or vegetable loofah sponges, but natural sea sponges like those in **Figure 9A** still are available.

Today scientists are finding other uses for sponges. Chemicals made by sponges are being tested and used to make drugs that fight disease-causing bacteria, fungi, and viruses. These chemicals also might be used to treat certain forms of arthritis.

Origin of Sponges Fossil evidence shows that sponges appeared on Earth about 600 million years ago. Because sponges have little in common with other animals, many scientists have concluded that sponges probably evolved separately from all other animals. Sponges living today have many of the same characteristics as their fossilized ancestors.

Figure 9
A Most sponges are found in salt water, but **B** a few species are found in freshwater.

Section Assessment Planner

PORTFOLIO	CONTENT ASSESSMENT
Curriculum Connection, p. 341	Section, p. 346
PERFORMANCE ASSESSMENT	Challenge, p. 346
Skill Builder Activities, p. 346	Chapter, pp. 360–361
See page 360 for more options.	

Characteristics of Sponges

Most of the 5,000 species of sponges are found in warm, shallow salt water near coastlines, although some are found at ocean depths of 8,500 m or more. A few species, like the one in **Figure 9B,** live in freshwater rivers, lakes, and streams. The colors, shapes, and sizes of sponges vary. Saltwater sponges are brilliant red, orange, yellow, or blue, while freshwater sponges are usually a dull brown or green. Some sponges have radial symmetry, but most are asymmetrical. Sponges can be smaller than a marble or larger than a compact car.

Adult sponges live attached to one place unless they are washed away by strong waves or currents. Organisms that remain attached to one place during their lifetimes are called **sessile** (SE sile). They often are found with other sponges in permanent groups called colonies. Early scientists classified sponges as plants because they didn't move. As microscopes were improved, scientists observed that sponges couldn't make their own food, so sponges were reclassified as animals.

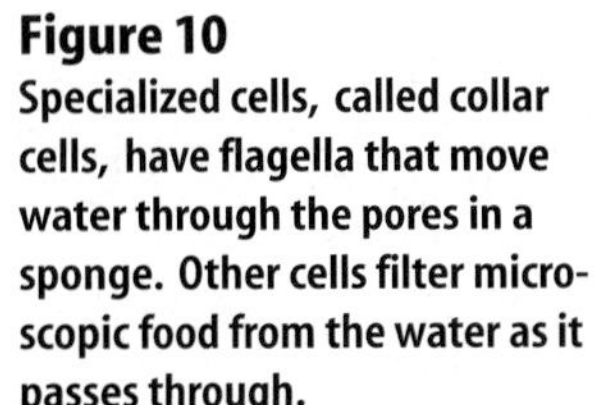

Figure 10
Specialized cells, called collar cells, have flagella that move water through the pores in a sponge. Other cells filter microscopic food from the water as it passes through.

Body Structure A sponge's body, like the one in **Figure 10,** is a hollow tube that is closed at the bottom and open at the top. The sponge has many small openings in its body. These openings are called pores.

Sponges have less complex body organization than other groups of animals. They have no tissues, organs, or organ systems. The body wall has two cell layers made up of several different types of cells. Those that line the inside of the sponge are called collar cells. The beating motion of the collar cells' flagella moves water through the sponge.

Many sponge bodies contain sharp, pointed structures called spicules (SPIH kyewlz). The soft-bodied, natural sponges that some people use for bathing or washing their cars have skeletons of a fibrous material called spongin. Other sponges contain spicules and spongin. Spicules and spongin provide support for a sponge and protection from predators.

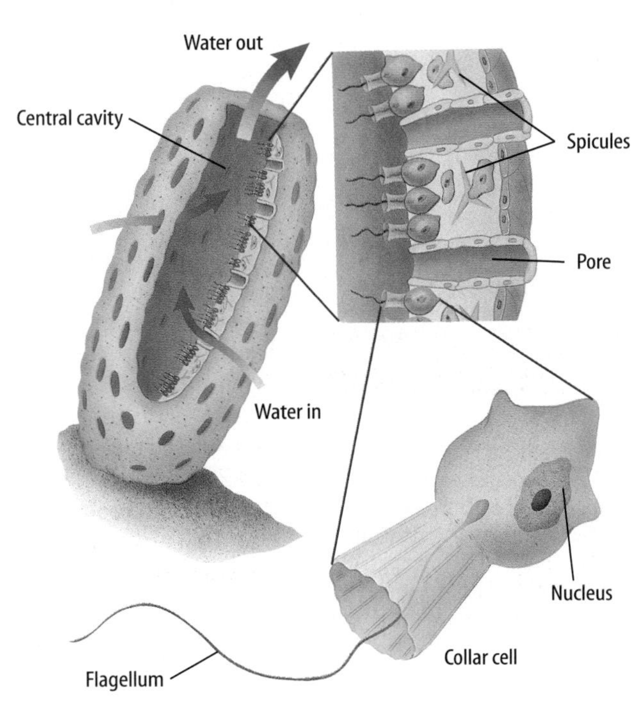

2 Teach

Sponges

Discussion

Why are there no sessile animals on land? Sessile animals get their energy from food that passes by them. Food that swims or is suspended in water often cannot avoid sessile animals because of ocean currents.

Fun Fact

Of the thousands of sponge species, only about 100 species live in freshwater.

Characteristics of Sponges

Quick Demo

To demonstrate the water-holding capacity of sponges, use a balance to weigh a dry natural sponge and a dry synthetic sponge. Record the masses on the chalkboard. Soak each in water and weigh them again. Record on the chalkboard the masses of the wet sponges. Ask students to calculate how many grams of water were absorbed by each gram of sponge.
LS **Logical-Mathematical**

Resource Manager

Chapter Resources Booklet
Transparency Activity, p. 43

Life Science Critical Thinking/Problem Solving, p. 10

Curriculum Connection

Art Artists use sponges to create unique effects in their paintings. Painters use sponges for walls. Unlike brushes, which leave evidence of strokes, sponges provide a more natural texture. Have students use sponges to create a work of art for display in the classroom. L2 ELL LS **Kinesthetic and Visual-Spatial** P

Characteristics of Sponges, continued

Visual Learning

Figure 11 Have students make an events chain concept map in which they sequence the events in sponge reproduction. L2
LS **Visual-Spatial**

Quick Demo

Mix soil and plant material in a beaker of water. Pour the water mixture through a coffee filter into a container. Let students examine the filter contents and the container to see how sponge cells might filter food particles from water.
LS **Visual-Spatial**

Students may not consider the sponge an animal. Explain that green plants can make their own food and sponges cannot. Sponges have cells with flagella that help to circulate water through the sponge so the food can be filtered out of the water.

Reading Check

Answer from water pulled in through their pores

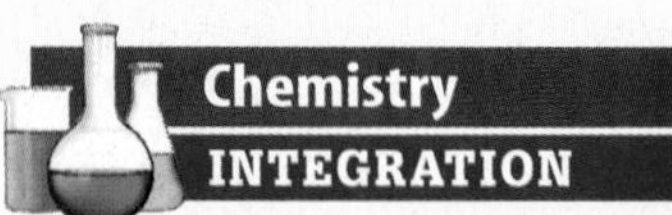

The makeup of spicules reflects the composition of the water in which they live.

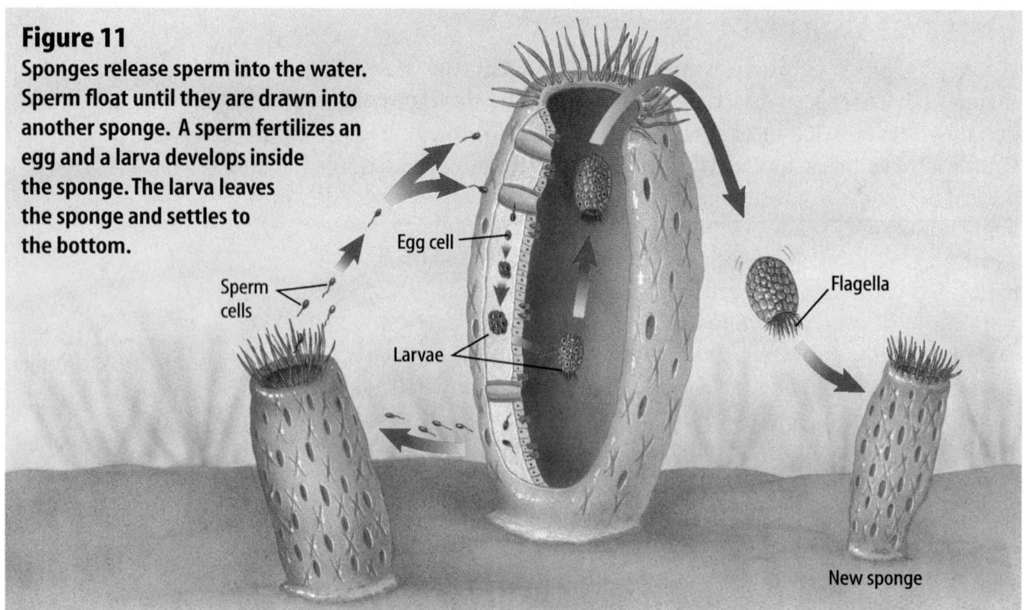

Figure 11
Sponges release sperm into the water. Sperm float until they are drawn into another sponge. A sperm fertilizes an egg and a larva develops inside the sponge. The larva leaves the sponge and settles to the bottom.

Obtaining Food and Oxygen Sponges filter microscopic food particles such as bacteria, algae, protists, and other materials from the water as it is pulled in through their pores. Oxygen also is removed from the water. The filtered water carries away wastes through an opening in the top of the sponge.

Reading Check *How do sponges get oxygen?*

Reproduction Sponges can reproduce sexually, as shown in **Figure 11.** Some species of sponges have separate sexes, but most sponge species are **hermaphrodites** (hur MA fruh dites)—animals that produce sperm and eggs in the same body. However, a sponge's sperm cannot fertilize its own eggs. After an egg is released, it might be fertilized and then develop into a larva (plural, *larvae*). The larva usually looks different from the adult form. Sponge larvae have cilia that allow them to swim. After a short time, the larvae settle down on objects where they will remain and grow into adult sponges.

Asexual reproduction occurs by budding or regeneration. A bud forms on a sponge, then drops from the parent sponge to grow on its own. New sponges also can grow by regeneration from small pieces of a sponge. Regeneration occurs when an organism grows new body parts to replace lost or damaged ones. Sponge growers cut sponges into pieces, attach weights to them, and put them back into the ocean to regenerate.

Chemistry INTEGRATION

Spicules of glass sponges are composed of silica. Other sponges have spicules of calcium carbonate. Relate the composition of spicules to the composition of the water in which the sponge lives. Write your answer in your Science Journal.

342 CHAPTER 12 Introduction to Animals

Curriculum Connection

Language Arts Have students research and report on *Xestospongi muta*, a barrel sponge that grows like a giant vase off the Cayman Islands. Sponges of this type are being tested for potential medicinal usage. L3

Cnidarians

Another group of invertebrates includes colorful corals, flowerlike sea anemones, delicate jellyfish, tiny hydras, and iridescent Portuguese man-of-wars, shown in **Figure 12.** These animals are classified as cnidarians (ni DAR ee uhnz).

Cnidarian Environments Most cnidarians live in salt water, although many types of hydras live in freshwater. Sea anemones and most jellyfish live as individual organisms, but hydras and corals tend to form colonies.

Two Body Forms Cnidarians have two different body forms. The **polyp** (PAH lup) form, shown in **Figure 13A,** is shaped like a vase and usually is sessile. Sea anemones, corals, and hydras are cnidarians that live most of their lives as polyps. The **medusa** (mih DEW suh) form, shown in **Figure 13B,** is bell-shaped and free-swimming. A jellyfish spends most of its life as a medusa floating on ocean currents. Some species of jellyfish have tentacles that grow to 30 m and trail behind the animal.

Reading Check *What are some possible benefits of having a medusa and a polyp form?*

Figure 12
The Portuguese man-of-war also is called the bluebottle. This animal is not one organism. It is four cnidarians that depend on one another for survival.

Figure 13
Cnidarians have medusa and polyp body forms.

A Adult sea anemones are polyps that grow attached to the ocean bottom, a rock, coral, or any surface. They depend on the movement of water to bring them food.

B Jellyfish can perform upward movements but must float to move downward.

Cnidarians

Quick Demo

Dissect a preserved specimen of a sea anemone so students can see the tentacles, gastrovascular cavity, and basal disc. LS **Visual-Spatial**

Use Science Words

Word Meaning The phylum name *Cnidaria* is derived from the Greek word *knide*, which means "nettle." Have students look up the word nettle in the dictionary, find its meaning, and tell how it is related to cnidarians. The nettle is a plant with stinging cells. Cnidarians have stinging tentacles. L2 LS **Linguistic**

Reading Check

Answer Possible answer: It allows more flexibility when environmental conditions change.

Make a Model

To model the difference between the medusa and the polyp, have students tape a colored plastic cup inside a colorless paper cup. Each cup represents a cell layer of an organism such as a cnidarian. It has a hollow body and only one body opening. When the mouth points downward and the cnidarian floats freely, it is called a medusa. When the mouth points upward and its base is attached to a surface, the cnidarian is called a polyp. L2 LS **Kinesthetic**

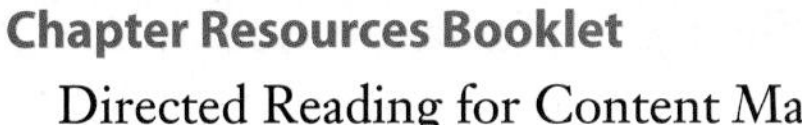

Chapter Resources Booklet

Directed Reading for Content Mastery, p. 19

Earth Science Critical Thinking/Problem Solving, p. 1

Cultural Diversity

Hydra The hydra was named for a mythical giant water monster with nine heads slain by Hercules, a Greek hero. Have students report on the Greek myth and explain how the real hydra is like the mythical one. The mythical hydra had nine heads. Each time Hercules cut off one head, it grew two back. A real hydra can be cut into pieces and each piece will generate a new hydra. L3

Cnidarians, continued

IDENTIFYING Misconceptions

Students may think the Portuguese man-of-war is a type of jellyfish. Explain that *jellyfish* is a term used for the class of cnidarians in which the medusa is the dominant form of the life cycle. A Portuguese man-of-war is a colony of four kinds of highly developed polyps.

Make a Model

Have students use lengths of string to make models of stinging cells for capturing prey. They can attach washers, adhesive tape, and toothpicks to the end of the string to model stinging cells that wrap around, stick to, or impale prey. Have them make models of small invertebrates from plastic foam to show how these types of stinging cells can be used to capture prey. L2 ELL LS Kinesthetic

SCIENCE Online

Internet Addresses

Explore the Glencoe Science Web site at **science.glencoe.com** to find out more about topics in this section.

SCIENCE Online

Data Update Visit the Glencoe Science Web site at **science.glencoe.com** for recent news and magazine articles about cnidarian ecology. Communicate to your class what you learn.

Body Structure All cnidarians have one body opening and radial symmetry. They have more complex bodies than sponges do. They have two cell layers that are arranged into tissues and a digestive cavity where food is broken down. In the two-cell-layer body plan of cnidarians, no cell is ever far from the water. In each cell, oxygen from the water is exchanged for carbon dioxide and other cell wastes.

Cnidarians have a system of nerve cells called a nerve net. The nerve net carries impulses and connects all parts of the organism. This makes cnidarians capable of some simple responses and movements. Hydras can somersault away from a threatening situation.

Armlike structures called **tentacles** (TEN tih kulz) surround the mouths of most cnidarians. Certain fish, shrimp, and other small animals live unharmed among the tentacles of large sea anemones, as shown in **Figure 14A.** The tentacles have **stinging cells.** A stinging cell has a capsule with a coiled, threadlike structure that helps the cnidarian capture food. Animals that live among an anemone's tentacles are not affected by the stinging cells. The animals are thought to help clean the sea anemone and protect it from certain predators.

Obtaining Food Cnidarians are predators. Some can stun their prey with nerve poisons produced by stinging cells. The threadlike structure in the stinging cell is sticky or barbed. When a cnidarian is touched or senses certain chemicals in its environment, the threadlike structures discharge and capture the prey. The tentacles bring the prey to the mouth, and the cnidarian ingests the food. Because cnidarians have only one body opening, undigested food goes back out through the mouth.

Figure 14
Tentacles surround the mouth of a sea anemone.

A Clown fish are protected from the sea anemone's sting by a special mucous covering. The anemone eats scraps that the fish drop, and the fish are protected from predators by the anemone's sting.

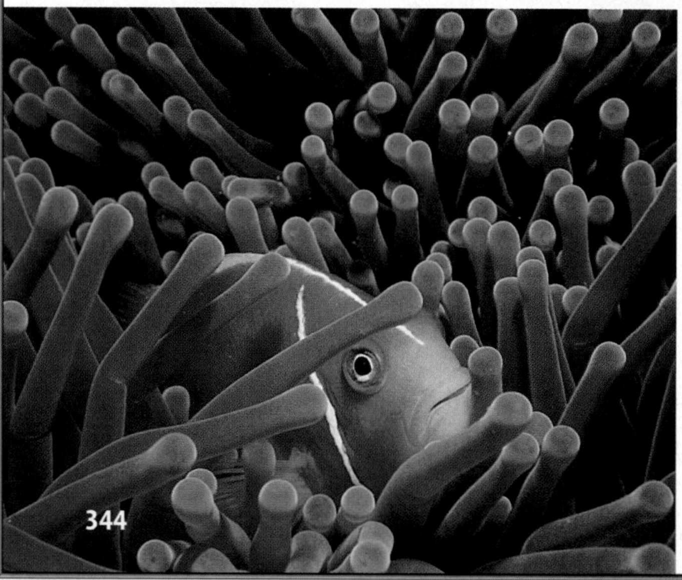

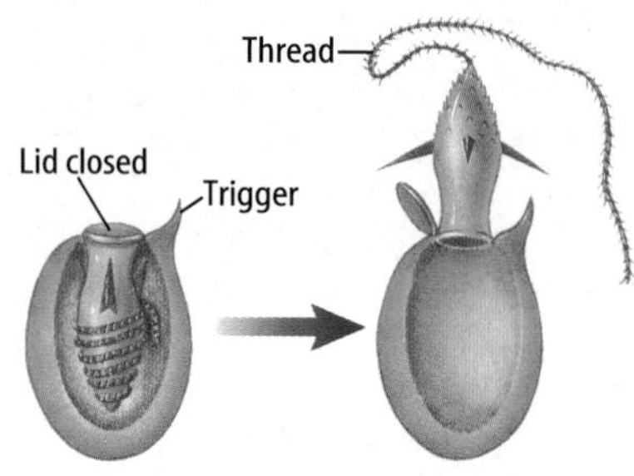

B Stinging cells have triggerlike structures. When prey brushes against the trigger, the thread is released into the prey. A poison in the stinging cell stuns the prey.

Resource Manager

Chapter Resources Booklet
Enrichment, p. 29
Reinforcement, p. 26
Cultural Diversity, p. 7

Curriculum Connection

Health Have students research and write a report on the first aid given to victims of jellyfish stings. Ask them to demonstrate the first aid procedures and explain why each procedure is performed. They should include summaries in their Science Journals. L2

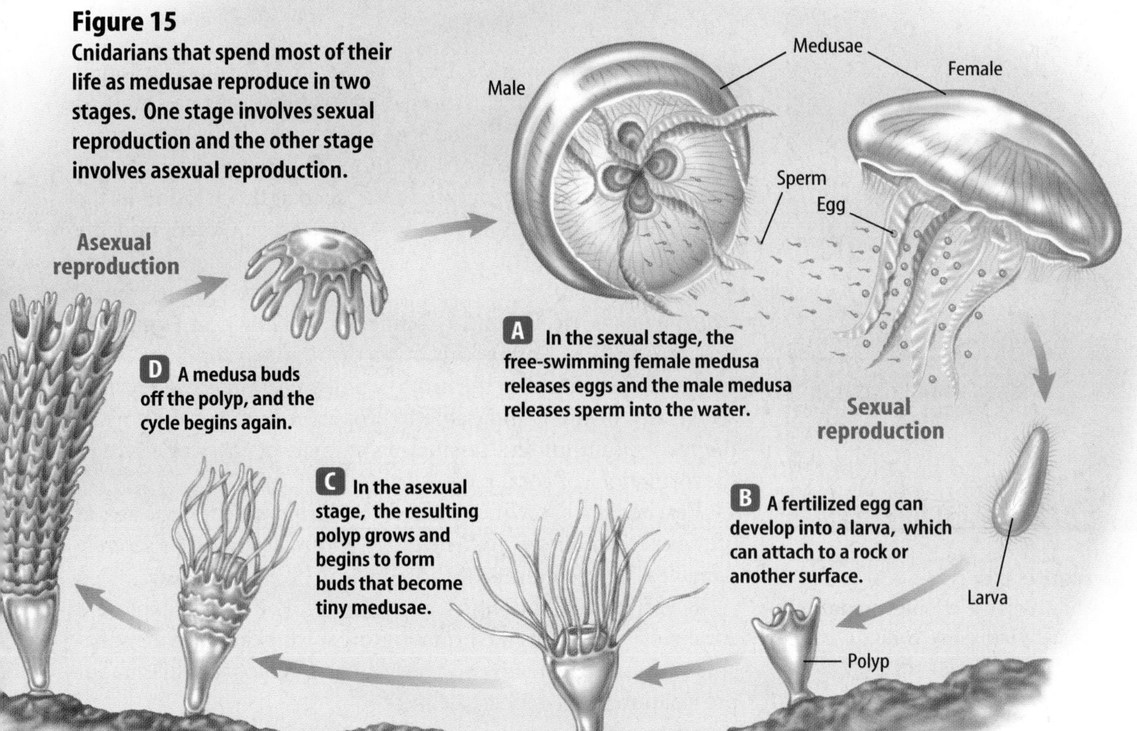
Medusae
Male
Female
Sperm
Egg
Asexual reproduction
A In the sexual stage, the free-swimming female medusa releases eggs and the male medusa releases sperm into the water.
D A medusa buds off the polyp, and the cycle begins again.
Sexual reproduction
C In the asexual stage, the resulting polyp grows and begins to form buds that become tiny medusae.
B A fertilized egg can develop into a larva, which can attach to a rock or another surface.
Larva
Polyp

Figure 15
Cidarians that spend most of their life as medusae reproduce in two stages. One stage involves sexual reproduction and the other stage involves asexual reproduction.

Reproduction Cnidarians reproduce asexually and sexually, as shown in **Figure 15.** Polyp forms reproduce asexually by producing buds that eventually fall off the cnidarian and develop into new polyps. Polyps also reproduce sexually by producing eggs or sperm. Sperm are released into the water and fertilize the eggs, which also are released into the water.

Medusa (plural, *medusae*) forms of cnidarians have two stages of reproduction—a sexual stage and an asexual stage. Free-swimming medusae produce eggs or sperm and release them into the water. The eggs are fertilized by sperm from another medusa of the same species and develop into larvae. The larvae eventually settle down and grow into polyps. When young medusae bud off the polyp, the cycle begins again.

Origin of Cnidarians

The first cnidarians might have been on Earth more than 600 million years ago. Scientists hypothesize that the medusa body was the first form of cnidarian. Polyps could have formed from larvae of medusae that became permanently attached to a surface. Most of the cnidarian fossils are corals.

Extension

Have students investigate the relationship between some species of anemones and certain types of fish, such as the clownfish and the damselfish. Students should find that these animals have symbiotic relationships. L3

Fun Fact

The giant jellyfish *Cyanea artica* is one of the largest known invertebrates. Its body is 2 meters in diameter, and its tentacles can be 36 meters long. A single jellyfish can weigh as much as 900 kilograms (1,984 lbs).

Activity

Have students make cards of all the stages in the life cycle of jellyfish and write the name of each stage on the card. Then have them scramble the cards and place them back in the correct sequence. L2
LS **Logical-Mathematical**

Origin of Cnidarians

Activity

Have students work in groups to find out how fringing reefs, barrier reefs, and atolls differ from one another. Suggest that they make models, labeled drawings, or picture collages illustrating the differences among the three types of coral reefs. L2 COOP LEARN
LS **Kinesthetic**

Teacher FYI

There are three types of coral reefs. Fringing reefs are submerged platforms of living coral that extend from the shore into the sea. Barrier reefs follow the shoreline but are separated from it by water. An atoll is a ring-shaped coral island in the open sea.

Corals

Quick Demo

Bring pieces of hard coral to class for students to observe and feel. **How do these pieces of coral differ from living coral?** Living corals have small, soft polyps that stick out from their skeletons. Explain that the skeletons of corals, like the bones and shells of other animals, provide protection and support for these organisms.

Caption Answer

Figure 16 protection

3 Assess

Reteach

Have students make drawings in their Science Journals to describe how a stinging cell is used to capture food. L1

LS **Kinesthetic**

Challenge

How do the tentacles of a jellyfish and a sea anemone differ? How is this difference an advantage to each animal? The tentacles of the jellyfish, which is free-swimming, point downward and the tentacles of the sea anemone, which is sessile, point upward. Each animal has tentacles adapted to its way of life.

Performance Have students make clay models of medusas and polyps and discuss how the two body forms are similar. Use **PASC,** p. 123. P

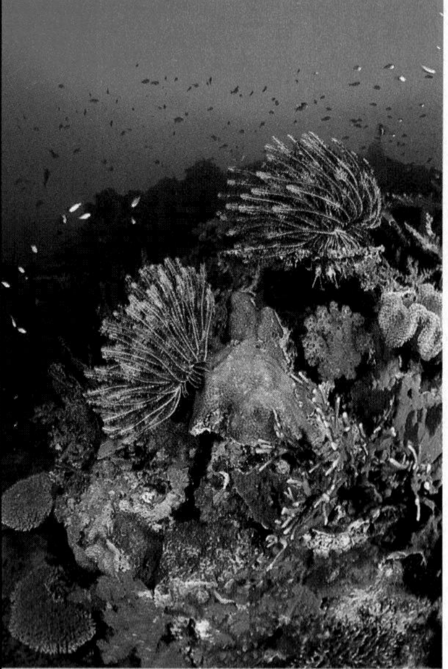

Figure 16
Coral reefs are colonies made up of many individual corals. *What benefit does living in a colony have for the corals?*

Corals

Earth Science INTEGRATION

The large coral reef formations found in shallow tropical seas are built as one generation of corals secretes their hard external skeletons on those of earlier generations. It takes millions of years for large reefs, such as those found in the waters of the Indian Ocean, the south Pacific Ocean, and the Caribbean Sea, to form.

Importance of Corals Coral reefs, as shown in **Figure 16,** are among the most productive of all ecosystems and are extremely important in the ecology of tropical waters. They have a diversity of life comparable to tropical rain forests. Some of the most beautiful and fascinating animals of the world live in the formations of coral reefs.

Beaches and shorelines are protected from much of the action of waves by coral reefs. When coral reefs are destroyed or severely damaged, large amounts of shoreline can be washed away.

If you go scuba diving or snorkeling, you might explore a coral reef. Coral reefs are home for organisms that provide valuable shells and pearls. Fossil reefs can give geologists clues about the location of oil deposits.

Like sponges, corals produce chemicals to protect themselves from diseases or to prevent other organisms from settling on them. Medical researchers are learning that some of these chemicals might provide humans with drugs to fight cancer. Some coral is even used as a permanent replacement for missing sections of bone in humans.

Section 2 Assessment

1. Why are sponges considered less complex than cnidarians?
2. How do sponges get their food?
3. Describe the two body forms of cnidarians and tell how each reproduces.
4. Why are most fossils of cnidarians coral fossils? Would you expect to find a fossil sponge? Explain.
5. **Think Critically** What effect would you expect the destruction of a large coral reef to have on other ocean life?

Skill Builder Activities

6. **Comparing and Contrasting** Compare and contrast how sponges and cnidarians obtain their food. **For more help, refer to the Science Skill Handbook.**
7. **Solving One-Step Equations** A sponge 1 cm in diameter and 10 cm tall can move 22.5 L of water through its body each day. What volume of water will it pump through its body in 1 h? In 1 min? **For more help, refer to the Math Skill Handbook.**

Answers to Section Assessment

1. Sponges are asymmetrical and have no tissues or organ systems. Cnidarians have radial symmetry, two cell layers arranged into tissues, and a digestive cavity.
2. Sponges filter microscopic particles such as bacteria, algae, protists, and other materials from the water as it is pulled through their pores.
3. polyps: vase-shaped, sessile, reproduce asexually by budding; medusas: bell-shaped, free-swimming, reproduce sexually by egg and sperm
4. Corals secrete a hard skeleton around themselves, which fossilizes easily. Fossil sponges would be rare, except for fossilized spicules.
5. There would be no homes for the animals that lived on the coral reef. Food supply would decrease.
6. Sponges: filter food out of the water; cnidarians: stinging cells on the tentacles paralyze an organism, tentacles pull the organism into the mouth.
7. The sponge will move about 0.94 L of water in one hour, and about 0.02 L of water per minute.

Activity

Observing a Cnidarian

The hydra has a body cavity that is a simple, hollow sac. It is one of the few freshwater cnidarians. Try this activity to see how the body of the hydra reacts to food and other stimuli.

What You'll Investigate

How does a hydra react to food and other stimuli?

Materials

dropper
hydra culture
small dish
toothpick
Daphnia or brine shrimp
stereomicroscope

Safety Precautions

WARNING: *Be careful with living animals.*

Goals

- **Predict** how a hydra will respond to various stimuli.
- **Observe** a hydra's responses to various stimuli.

Procedure

1. Copy the data table and use it to record your observations.

Hydra Observations	
Features	**Observations**
Color	Answers
Number of tentacles	will
Reaction to touch	vary.
Reaction to food	

2. Use a dropper to place a hydra and some of the water in which it is living into a dish.
3. Place the dish on the stage of a stereomicroscope. Bring the hydra into focus. Record the hydra's color.

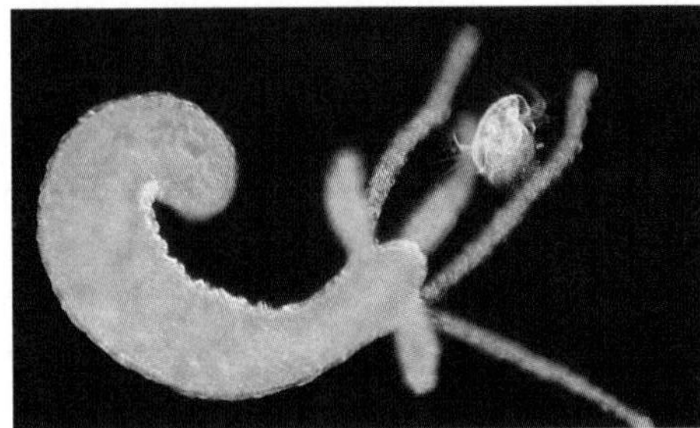

4. **Identify** and count the number of tentacles. Locate the mouth.
5. Study the basal disk by which the hydra attaches itself to a surface.
6. **Predict** what will happen if the hydra is touched with a toothpick. Carefully touch the tentacles with a toothpick. Describe the reaction in the data table.
7. Drop a *Daphnia* or a small amount of brine shrimp into the dish. Observe how the hydra takes in food. Record your observations.
8. Return the hydra to the culture.

Conclude and Apply

1. **Analyze** what happened when the hydra was touched. What happened to other areas of the animal?
2. **Describe** the advantages tentacles provide for hydra.

Communicating Your Data

Compare your results with the other students' results. **For more help, refer to the** Science Skill Handbook.

Resource Manager

Chapter Resources Booklet
Activity Worksheet, pp. 5–6

Communicating Your Data

Have students discuss their results in small groups. Then, copy the data table onto the board and fill it in as a class.

Activity

BENCH TESTED

Purpose to observe the structure and feeding method of a cnidarian L1 ELL IN **Interpersonal**

Process Skills observing and inferring, identifying, predicting, making and using tables

Time Required 40 minutes

Safety Precautions Caution students to use extreme care when working with live animals.

Teaching Strategy Assign one person to place the hydra in the dish under the stereoscopic microscope and the other to record the data.

Troubleshooting Place several coverslips into the jar the day before the hydra are needed. The hydra will probably cling to the coverslips. When you need hydra, remove the coverslips with forceps and place the coverslips directly into the dish that contains aquarium water.

Answers to Questions

1. When certain parts were touched, other parts may have responded by stretching or contracting.
2. The tentacles wrap around food and bring it into the mouth. Stinging cells stun the prey.

Assessment

Performance To further assess students' abilities to observe the structure and method of feeding in a cnidarian, have them view a short video on cnidarians and describe the cnidarians' activities. Use **Performance Assessment in the Science Classroom,** p. 89.

SECTION 3

Flatworms and Roundworms

1 Motivate

Bellringer Transparency

Display the Section Focus Transparency for Section 3. Use the accompanying Transparency Activity Master. L2 ELL

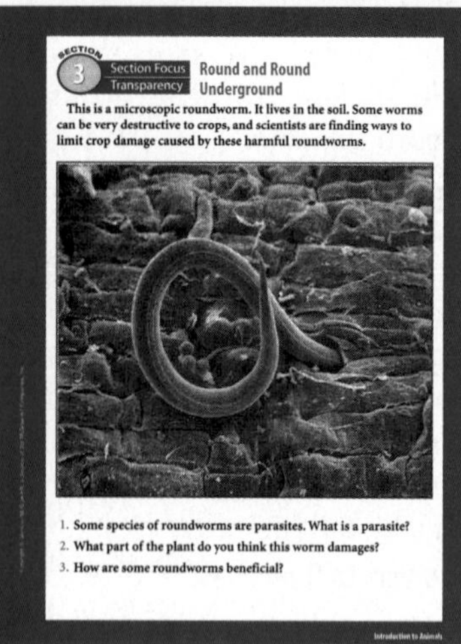
Section 3 Section Focus Transparency — Round and Round Underground

This is a microscopic roundworm. It lives in the soil. Some worms can be very destructive to crops, and scientists are finding ways to limit crop damage caused by these harmful roundworms.

1. Some species of roundworms are parasites. What is a parasite?
2. What part of the plant do you think this worm damages?
3. How are some roundworms beneficial?

Tie to Prior Knowledge

Students will be familiar with worms. Ask them to describe the appearance and shape of earthworms they have seen. Review bilateral symmetry and discuss the presence or absence of tissues in organisms in this chapter.

SECTION 3

Flatworms and Roundworms

As You Read

***What* You'll Learn**

- **List** the characteristics of flatworms and roundworms.
- **Distinguish** between free-living and parasitic organisms.
- **Identify** disease-causing flatworms and roundworms.

Vocabulary

free-living organism
anus

***Why* It's Important**

Many species of flatworms and roundworms cause disease in plants and animals.

Common Characteristics

What kind of animal do you think of when you hear the word *worm?* Is it an earthworm—the kind that crawls across pavement after a rain and is used to bait a fishing hook? You probably don't think immediately of tapeworms or any of the many other types of worms in the world. What is a worm?

Worms are invertebrates with soft bodies and bilateral symmetry. They have three tissue layers, as shown in **Figure 17,** which are organized into organs and organ systems.

Flatworms

As their name implies, flatworms have flattened bodies. Members of this group include planarians, flukes, and tapeworms. Some flatworms are free-living, but most are parasites, which means that they depend on another organism for food and a place to live. Unlike a parasite, a **free-living organism** doesn't depend on another organism for food or a place to live.

Planarians An example of a free-living flatworm is the planarian, as shown in **Figure 18A.** It has a triangle-shaped head with two eyespots. Its one body opening—a mouth—is on the underside of the body. A muscular tube called the pharynx connects the mouth and the digestive tract. A planarian feeds on small organisms and dead bodies of larger organisms. Most planarians live under rocks, on plant material, or in freshwater. They vary in length from 3 mm to 30 cm. Their bodies are covered with fine, hairlike structures called, cilia. As the cilia move, the worm is moved along in a slimy, mucous track that is secreted from the underside of the planarian.

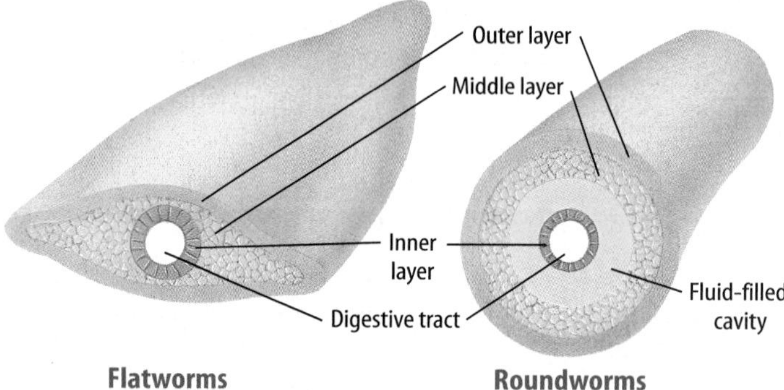

Figure 17
Worms have cells that are arranged into three specialized tissue layers and organs.

Section Assessment Planner

Portfolio
Science Journal, p. 350

Performance Assessment
MiniLAB, p. 350
Skill Builder Activities, p. 353
See page 360 for more options.

Content Assessment
Section, p. 353
Challenge, p. 353
Chapter, pp. 360–361

Figure 18
The planarian is a common freshwater flatworm.

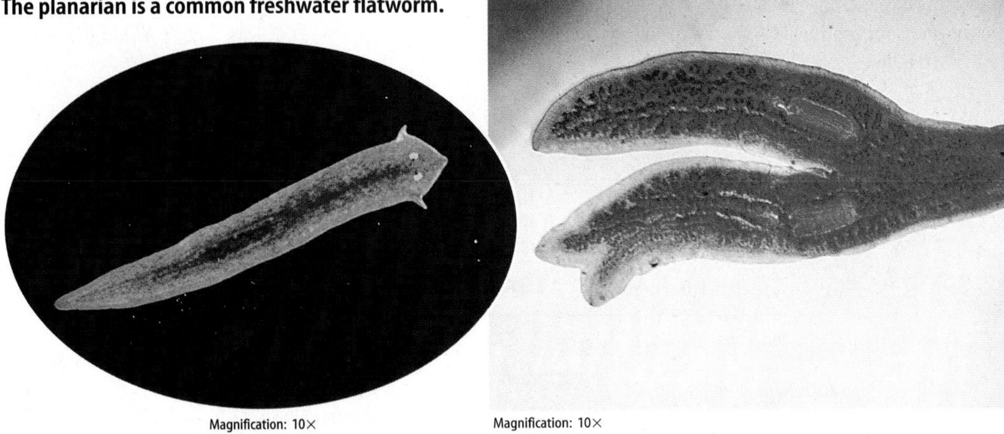

A **The planarian's eyespots sense light.**

B **Planarians can reproduce asexually by splitting, then regenerating the other half.**

Planarians reproduce asexually by dividing in two, as shown in **Figure 18B.** A planarian can be cut in two, and each piece will grow into a new worm. They also have the ability to regenerate. Planarians reproduce sexually by producing eggs and sperm. Most are hermaphrodites and exchange sperm with one another. They lay fertilized eggs that hatch in a few weeks.

Flukes All flukes are parasites with complex life cycles that require more than one host. Most flukes reproduce sexually. The male worm deposits sperm in the female worm. She lays the fertilized eggs inside the host. The eggs leave the host in its urine or feces. If the eggs end up in water, they usually infect snails. After they leave the snail, the young worms can burrow into the skin of a new host, such as a human, while he or she is standing or swimming in the water.

Of the many diseases caused by flukes, the most widespread one affecting humans is schistosomiasis (shis tuh soh MI uh sus). It is caused by blood flukes—flatworms that live in the blood, as shown in **Figure 19.** More than 200 million people, mostly in developing countries, are infected with blood flukes. It is estimated that 1 million people die each year because of them. Other types of flukes can infect the lungs, liver, eyes, and other organs of their host.

Figure 19
Female blood flukes deposit their eggs in the blood of their host. The eggs travel through the host and eventually end up in the host's digestive system.

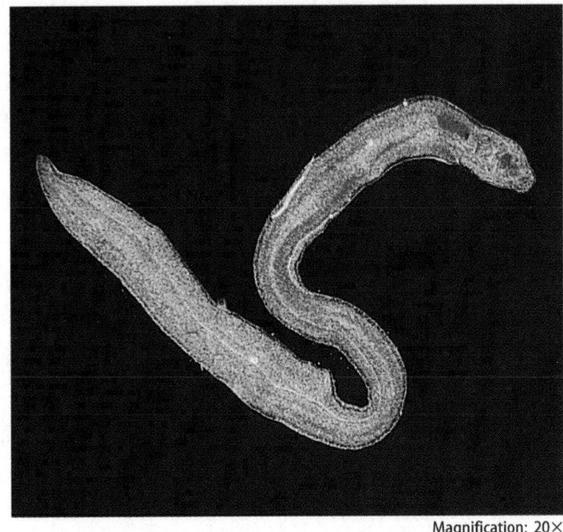

Reading Check *What is the most common disease that is caused by flukes?*

2 Teach

Common Characteristics

IDENTIFYING Misconceptions

Students may think that because a parasite harms its host, it will always eventually kill the host. This may sometimes happen, but it is not in the parasite's best interest to kill its host. This would result in the parasite losing its food source.

Flatworms

Extension

Have students research the latest figures on blood fluke infections in different regions of the world. Have students work in groups to design a poster to educate people about possible ways to eradicate the problem. L3 COOP LEARN IN **Interpersonal**

Activity

Tapeworms as long as 9 m have been found in humans. Have students use a meterstick and measure 9 m to get an understanding of just how long tapeworms can be. L1 IN **Logical-Mathematical**

Reading Check

Answer schistosomiasis

Resource Manager

Chapter Resources Booklet

Transparency Activity, p. 44

Directed Reading for Content Mastery, pp. 19, 20

Inclusion Strategies

Learning Disabled Have students select one type of worm described in this section. Have them design and construct a three-dimensional model of the worm and use the model to demonstrate its characteristics. L1 IN **Kinesthetic**

Flatworms, continued

Mini LAB

Purpose to observe planarian movement L1 ELL
LS **Kinesthetic and Visual-Spatial**

Materials planarian culture, dropper, watch glass, stereomicroscope, water

Teaching Strategy Planarians may be placed in water from the classroom aquarium.

Troubleshooting If planarians don't move, students may have to gently prod them with a small brush.

Analysis

1. Planarians ripple and flex their muscles in successive waves to propel themselves over surfaces.
2. Students may infer that movement is by means of muscular undulations on the underside of the planarian's body.
3. Planarians can move freely and are not confined within the body of another organism.

Assessment

Performance Have students feed the planarians pinhead-sized pieces of liver and describe their behavior. Use **PASC**, p. 89.

Activity

Obtain preserved tapeworm specimens from a local veterinarian or a biological supply company. Have students observe and list the characteristics of each. L1 LS **Visual-Spatial**

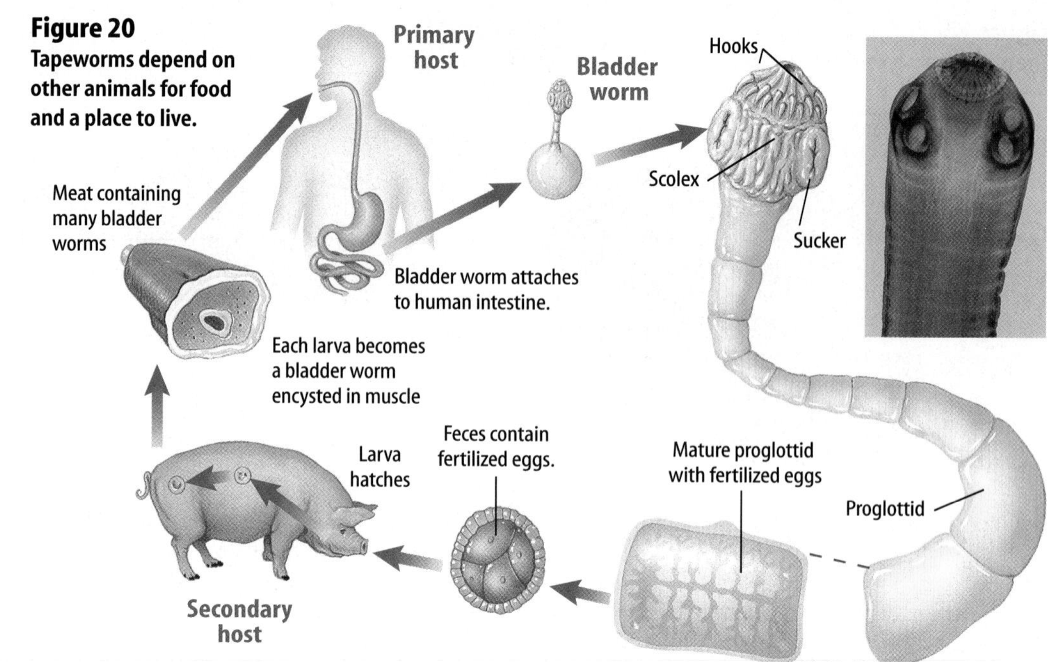

Figure 20
Tapeworms depend on other animals for food and a place to live.

Mini LAB

Observing Planarian Movement

Procedure

1. Use a **dropper** to transfer a **planarian** to a **watch glass.**
2. Add enough **water** so the planarian can move freely.
3. Place the glass under a **stereomicroscope** and observe the planarian.

Analysis

1. Describe how a planarian moves in the water.
2. What body parts appear to be used in movement?
3. Explain why a planarian is a free-living flatworm.

Tapeworms Another type of flatworm is the tapeworm. These worms are parasites. The adult form uses hooks and suckers to attach itself to the intestine of a host organism, as illustrated in **Figure 20.** Dogs, cats, humans, and other animals are hosts for tapeworms. A tapeworm doesn't have a mouth or a digestive system. Instead, the tapeworm absorbs food that is digested by the host from its host's intestine.

A tapeworm grows by producing new body segments immediately behind its head. Its ribbonlike body can grow to be 12 m long. Each body segment has both male and female reproductive organs. The eggs are fertilized by sperm in the same segment. After a segment is filled with fertilized eggs, it breaks off and passes out of the host's body with the host's wastes. If another host eats a fertilized egg, the egg hatches and develops into a new tapeworm.

Origin of Flatworms

Because of the limited fossil evidence, the evolution of flatworms is uncertain. Evidence suggests that they were the first group of animals to evolve bilateral symmetry with senses and nerves in the head region. They also were probably the first group of animals to have a third tissue layer that develops into organs and systems. Some scientists hypothesize that flatworms and cnidarians might have had a common ancestor.

Science Journal

Controlling Flukes Have students research actions taken by the Department of Agriculture to control fluke infection in this country. Ask them to write the data as an article to be published in a consumer health magazine and include the article in their Science Journals. L2 LS **Linguistic** P

Resource Manager

Chapter Resources Booklet

MiniLAB, p. 4

Roundworms

If you own a dog, you've probably had to get medicine from your veterinarian to protect it from heartworms—a type of roundworm. Roundworms are also called nematodes and make up the largest group of worms. More nematodes live on Earth than any other type of many-celled organism. It is estimated that more than a half million species of roundworms exist. They are found in soil, animals, plants, freshwater, and salt water. Many are parasitic, but most are free-living.

Roundworms are slender and tapered at both ends like the one in **Figure 21.** The body is a tube within a tube, with fluid in between. Most nematode species have male and female worms and reproduce sexually. Unlike the other animals in this chapter, nematodes have two body openings, a mouth, and an anus. The **anus** is an opening at the end of the digestive tract through which wastes leave the body.

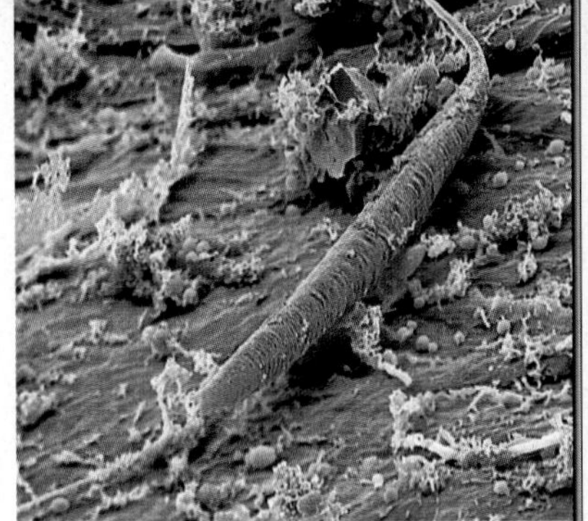

Figure 21
Some roundworms infect humans and other animals. Others infect plants, and some are free-living in the soil.

Math Skills Activity

Using Percent to Calculate Number of Species

Example Problem

In a specific deciduous forest ecosystem, 400 different species of animals exist. Scientists estimate that roundworms make up about four percent of these animal species. How many roundworms probably are present in the deciduous forest ecosystem?

Solution

1. *This is what you know:* There are 400 known species of animals. Roundworms make up four percent of all animal species.
2. *This is what you need to do:* Change four percent to a decimal.

$$\frac{4}{100} = 0.04$$

Calculate the number of roundworms using the following equation.
(total number of animal species) × (percent of species as a decimal) = number of species

3. *Substitute the known values:* $400 \times 0.04 = 16$ roundworm species

Practice Problem

Flatworms make up 1.5 percent of all animal species. How many flatworms species probably are present in the forest ecosystem?

For more help, refer to the Math Skill Handbook.

Roundworms

Discussion

How is the shape of a parasitic roundworm's body adapted to the worm's way of life? It is long and slender and has a pointed tip at either end. This shape enables it to move easily through the tissues of its host.

Extension

Health problems associated with infections by parasitic worms are often compounded by poverty, improper sanitation, and lack of governmental services to help infected people. Have students research some of the countries that are most affected by these parasites and report on what is being done to alleviate the health and social problems. L3

Math Skills Activity

National Math Standards

Correlation to Mathematics Objectives
1, 2, 6, 9

Answer to Practice Problem

6 Species

- What you know: 400 species total; 1.5% are flatworms.
- What to do: change % to a decimal. $1.5 \div 100 = 0.015$
- Calculate number of flatworms. $400 \times 0.015 = 6$ flatworm species

LAB DEMONSTRATION

Purpose to observe vinegar eels

Materials vinegar eel culture, dropper, projecting microscope, microscope slide, coverslip

Preparation Place a drop of the liquid containing vinegar eels onto a microscope slide. Gently add a coverslip.

Procedure Display vinegar eels under low power. Have students draw what they see and write a brief description.

Expected Outcome Students will observe small roundworms with jerky movements.

What is the shape of the vinegar eels? round with pointed ends **How do they move?** with jerky movements **Why are they called vinegar eels?** They live in vinegar.

NATIONAL GEOGRAPHIC

Visualizing Parasitic Worms

Have students examine the pictures and read the captions. Then ask the following questions.

Why do parasitic worms often cause weight loss in the host organism? Students should note that many of these types of worms infest the intestines, interfering with absorption of nutrients from food.

Identify one way you could reduce your chances of being infected with hookworms if you lived in a tropical climate. Hookworms usually enter through the skin of bare feet, so wearing shoes while outdoors is an effective way to reduce the risk of contracting hookworms.

Activity

Divide students into teams. Each team should research and compare the prevalence of human infestation with a specific species of parasitic worm in different parts of the world. Students should use a map when they present their findings to the class. Students should also identify any socioeconomic factors (i.e. limited access to health care) that cause certain areas to have a greater incidence of parasitic worm infestations.

Extension

Challenge students to research and diagram the complete life cycle of one of the parasitic worms shown in this feature. Students should present their diagrams to the class.
Visual-Spatial

NATIONAL GEOGRAPHIC **VISUALIZING PARASITIC WORMS**

Figure 22

Many diseases are caused by parasitic roundworms and flatworms that take up residence in the human body. Some of these diseases result in diarrhea, weight loss, and fatigue; others, if left untreated, can be fatal. Micrographs of several species of roundworms and flatworms and their magnifications are shown here.

▶ 78× BLOOD FLUKE These parasites live as larvae in lakes and rivers and penetrate the skin of people wading in the water. After maturing in the liver, the flukes settle in veins in the intestine and bladder, causing schistosomiasis (shis tuh soh MI uh sus), which damages the liver and spleen.

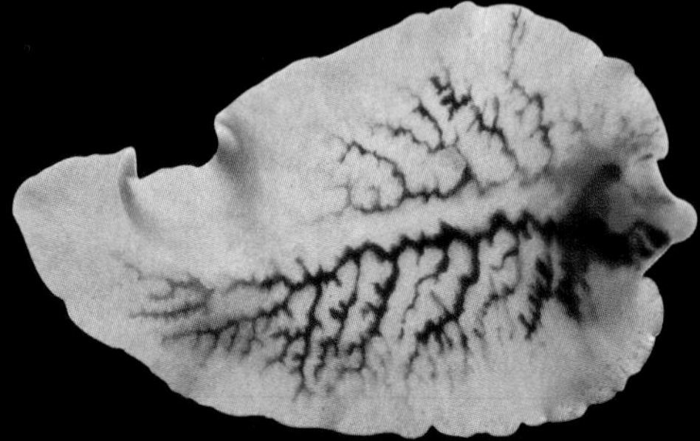

▲ 6× LIVER FLUKE Humans and other mammals ingest the larvae of these parasites by eating contaminated plant material. Immature flukes penetrate the intestinal wall and pass via the liver into the bile ducts. There they mature into adults that feed on blood and tissue.

▼ 125× PINWORMS Typically inhabiting the large intestine, the female pinworm lays her eggs near the host's anus, causing discomfort. The micrograph below shows pinworm eggs on a piece of clear tape.

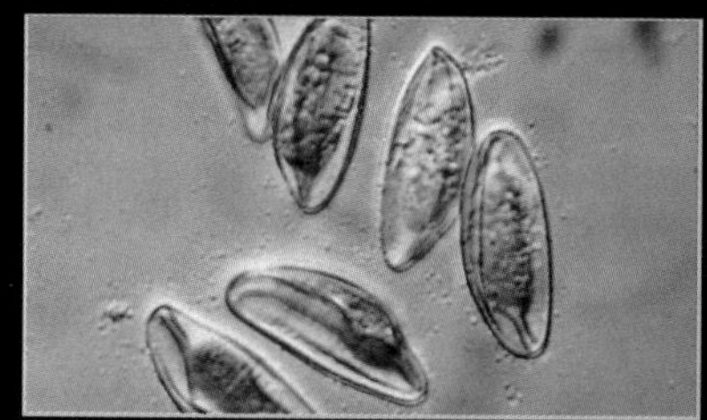

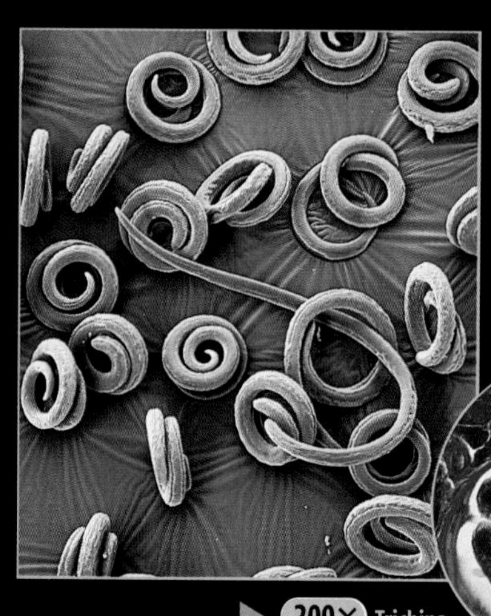

◀ 170× ROUNDWORMS The roundworms that cause the disease trichinosis (trih kuh NOH sus) are eaten as larvae in undercooked infected meat. They mature in the intestine, then migrate to muscle tissue, where they form painful cysts.

▶ 200× Trichina larvae in muscle tissue

Hookworm head 25×

▶ 4× HOOKWORM These parasites enter their human hosts as larvae by penetrating the skin of bare feet. From there, they migrate to the lungs and eventually to the intestine, where they mature.

Resource Manager

Chapter Resources Booklet
Enrichment, p. 30
Reinforcement, p. 27

Visual Learning

Figure 22 Have students create a table in which they list each of the diseases mentioned in this figure and what organism causes the disease. Students may do research to find methods of disease prevention for each listed disease. Any relevant information should be added to their table. L2 **Visual-Spatial**

Origin of Roundworms More than 550 million years ago, roundworms appeared early in animal evolution. They were the first group of animals to have a digestive system with a mouth and an anus. Scientists hypothesize that roundworms are more closely related to arthropods than to vertebrates. However, it is still unclear how roundworms fit into the evolution of animals.

Importance of Roundworms Some roundworms cause diseases in humans, as shown in **Figure 22.** Others are parasites of plants or of other animals, such as fish shown in **Figure 23**. Some nematodes cause damage to fiber, agricultural products, and food. It is estimated that the worldwide annual amount of nematode damage is in the millions of dollars.

Not all roundworms are a problem for humans, however. In fact, many species are beneficial. Some species of roundworms feed on termites, fleas, ants, beetles, and many other types of insects that cause damage to crops and human property. Some species of beneficial nematodes kill other pests. Research is being done with nematodes that kill deer ticks that cause Lyme disease.

Roundworms also are important because they are essential to the health of soil. They provide nutrients to the soil as they break down organic material. They also help in cycling nutrients such as nitrogen.

Figure 23
This fish's fin is infected with parasitic roundworms. These roundworms damage the fin, which makes it difficult for the fish to swim and escape from predators.

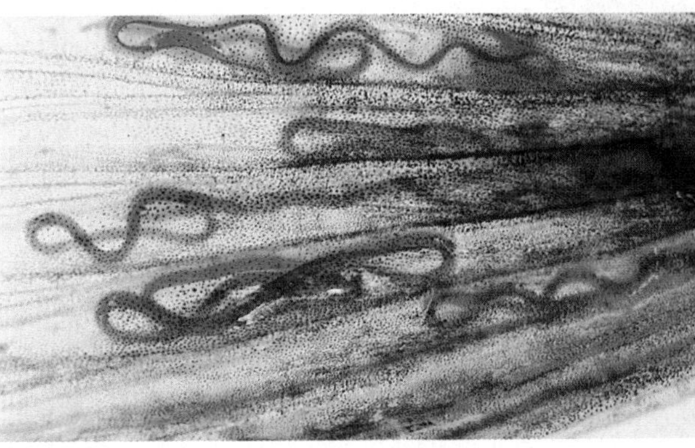

Section 3 Assessment

1. Compare the body plan of a flatworm to the body plan of a roundworm.
2. Distinguish between a free-living flatworm and a parasitic flatworm.
3. How do tapeworms get energy?
4. What are three roundworms that cause diseases in humans? How can humans prevent infection from each?
5. **Think Critically** Why is a flatworm considered to be more complex than a hydra?

Skill Builder Activities

6. **Concept Mapping** Make an events-chain concept map for tapeworm reproduction. **For more help, refer to the Science Skill Handbook.**
7. **Communicating** In your Science Journal, write a public service announcement for your local radio or television station informing the community about heartworm disease in dogs. Consult a veterinarian for information. **For more help, refer to the Science Skill Handbook.**

3 Assess

Reteach

Have each student write one short-answer question relating to flatworms and roundworms. Read the questions aloud. Ask students to respond as a group. L1 LS **Linguistic**

Challenge

Why is it an advantage to a parasite not to kill its host? A parasite depends on its host for nourishment and protection. If the parasite killed its host, the parasite would also likely die, as most adult parasites would not be able to find another host. L3

Assessment

Performance Assess students' abilities to sequence by having them sequence information on reproduction of each animal group in the chapter. Use **Performance Assessment in the Science Classroom,** p. 163.

Answers to Section Assessment

1. Flatworms have flattened bodies with one body opening, the mouth. Roundworms' bodies have a tube within a tube and fluid in between, and two body openings—a mouth and an anus.
2. Free-living flatworms find food in their environment; parasitic flatworms attach to a host and absorb food from the host.
3. They absorb food from the host's intestine.
4. Hookworm—wear shoes; *Ascaris*—don't eat contaminated food or drink contaminated water; *Trichinella*—cook pork thoroughly.
5. A hydra has two cell layers. A flatworm has three tissue layers, which are organized into organs and organ systems.
6. Student concept maps should be consistent with the information given in the text of this section.
7. Students' announcements should reflect accurate information and creativity.

Activity

BENCH TESTED

Recognize the Problem

Purpose

Students compare and contrast free-living and parasitic worms.

L2 COOP LEARN

LS **Logical-Mathematical**

Process Skills

forming a hypothesis, comparing and contrasting, observing and inferring, communicating, classifying, describing

Time Required

50 minutes

Materials

- Use prepared whole mount slides of tapeworms with heads and proglottids.
- Use a small brush to transfer the planaria from the culture to the culture dishes.
- Make sure the fed planaria are returned to a labeled dish so they will not be used again the same day.

Safety Precautions

Caution students to use extreme care when working with live animals. Soft-bodied animals are easily injured.

Form a Hypothesis

Possible Hypotheses

Most students will hypothesize that planarians have body parts for the environment in which they live and tapeworms have body parts for attaching to a host.

Activity **Design Your Own Experiment**

Comparing Free-Living and Parasitic Flatworms

Observe free-living and parasitic flatworms to determine how each type of flatworm is adapted to its particular environment.

Recognize the Problem

How are the body parts of flatworms adapted to the environment in which they live?

Form a Hypothesis

State a hypothesis about how free-living and parasitic flatworms are able to live in different environments.

Possible Materials

petri dish with a planarian
compound microscope
prepared slide of a tapeworm
stereomicroscope
light source, such as a lamp
small paintbrush
small piece of liver
dropper
water

Goals

- **Compare and contrast** the body parts and functions of free-living and parasitic flatworms.
- **Observe** how flatworms are adapted to their environments.

Safety Precautions

354

Test Your Hypothesis

Possible Procedures

One possible procedure is to observe the body structures of both free-living and parasitic worms using a hand lens or a stereomicroscope and prepared slides.

Resource Manager

Chapter Resources Booklet
Activity Worksheet, pp. 7–8
Lab Activity, pp. 13–14

Lab Management and Safety, p. 43

Test Your Hypothesis

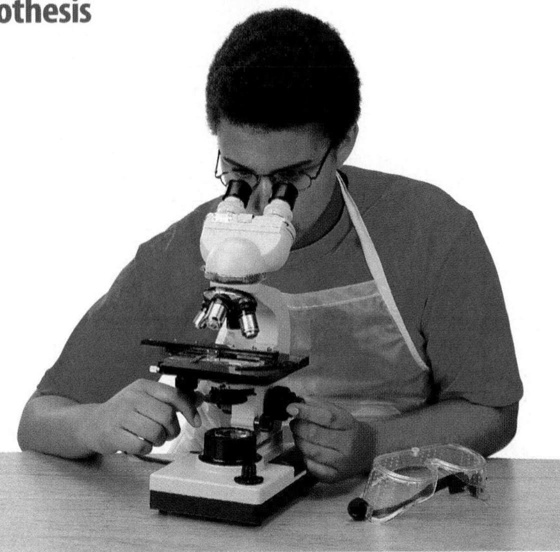

Plan

1. As a group, make a list of possible ways you might design a procedure to compare and contrast types of flatworms. Your teacher will provide you with information on handling live flatworms.
2. Choose one of the methods you described in step 1. List the steps you will need to take to follow the procedure. Be sure to describe exactly what you will do at each step of the activity.
3. **List** the materials that you will need to complete your experiment.
4. If you need a data table, design one in your Science Journal so it is ready to use when your group begins to collect data.

Do

1. Make sure your teacher approves your plan before you start.
2. Carry out the experiment according to the approved plan.
3. While the experiment is going on, record any observations that you make and complete the data table in your Science Journal.

Analyze Your Data

1. **Explain** how parasitic and free-living flatworms are similar.
2. **Describe** the differences between parasitic and free-living worms.

Draw Conclusions

1. Which body systems are more developed in free-living flatworms?
2. Which body system is more complex in parasitic flatworms?
3. What adaptations allow some flatworms to live as free-living organisms?

Communicating Your Data

Compare and **discuss** your conclusions about body design with other students. **For more help, refer to the** Science Skill Handbook.

Teaching Strategy

Tie to Prior Knowledge

Most students know that parasitic worms have body parts for attaching to a host and that free-living worms have body parts for the environment in which they live.

Expected Outcome

Students' observations of the planaria may include those already listed: planaria move with a gliding motion; the most sensitive body parts are those near the head; the tubelike structure (pharynx) pulls food into the body. Planarians have flat bodies. The mouth is on the bottom of the body. Students' observations of the tapeworm will include body parts adapted for attaching to a host and a well-developed reproductive system.

Analyze Your Data

1. Both are invertebrates, have flattened bodies, and have three tissue layers organized into organs and organ systems.
2. Parasitic worms have body parts adapted for attaching to a host. Free-living flatworms have no such parts.

Error Analysis

Have students compare their results and their hypotheses and explain why differences may have occurred.

Draw Conclusions

1. The digestive and reproductive systems are better developed in free-living flatworms.
2. The reproductive system is more complex in parasitic worms.
3. cilia, feeding organs, light-sensitive behavior

Assessment

Performance To further assess students' understanding of the differences between free-living and parasitic worms, assign them to different groups and have them use their drawings and observations to explain the differences. Assess explanations for accuracy. Use **Performance Assessment in the Science Classroom,** p. 99.

Communicating Your Data

Have students sketch the body designs of both types of worms, labeling the similarities and differences.

TIME SCIENCE AND HISTORY

Content Background

Members of the phylum Porifera are commonly called sponges. There are approximately 5,000 living sponge species. Sponges were long thought to be plants. It wasn't until scientists closely observed the way in which water was "ingested" by sponges that sponges began to be regarded as animal organisms, not plants.

Although sponges do not have mouths, they take in water through tiny pores in their outer walls. The water is pumped through the sponge by the beating of flagella that line the canals of the sponge. Certain cells in the sponge filter bacteria, other microorganisms, and organic debris out of the water that constantly passes through it. This is how the sponge eats. An enormous amount of water can pass through a sponge, sometimes 20,000 times its volume in a 24-hour period.

There are many different types of sponges. In the world's oceans, they can be quite colorful and beautiful. Sponges come in two basic types: encrusting and free-standing. Encrusting sponges typically cover hard surfaces in the same manner that mosses cover objects on land. Free-standing sponges sometimes grow into strange shapes, often reaching gigantic proportions.

TIME SCIENCE AND HISTORY

SCIENCE CAN CHANGE THE COURSE OF HISTORY!

SPONGES

A common household item contains a lot of history

Sponges and baths. They go together like hammer and nails, like burgers and fries. But sponges weren't always used just to scrub people and countertops. True, the ancient Greeks, Romans, and Egyptians did clean themselves with sponges. The Greeks and Romans also mopped floors and wiped tables with sponges. The more artistic Greeks dipped sponges into paint and dabbed it onto their artworks and crafts.

A natural sponge (above) and a synthetic sponge (right) are both used for mopping up spills.

356

Resources for Teachers and Students

Sorting out Worms and Other Invertebrates: Everything You Want to Know About Insects, Corals, Mollusks, Spruces and More, by Samuel G. Woods, Blackbirch Marketing, 1999.

Sponges: Filters of the Sea (Secrets of the Animal World), by Andreeu Llamas, Gabriel Casadevall and Ali Garousi (Ill.'s), Gareth Stevens, 1997.

In the past, sponges went to war. Greek and Roman soldiers padded their helmets with soft sponges similar to modern bike or skateboard helmets. This made them more comfortable and helped cushion blows from their enemies' weapons. For Roman soldiers, sponges also served as a lightweight canteen. During a long hot march, soldiers would dunk the sponge in a cool stream or well, soak up the water and squeeze the liquid into their mouth.

Throughout history, people have found sponges an absorbing subject. Pictures of sponges appear in the artwork of the prehistoric civilization of Crete, an island in the Aegean Sea. Medical books in the Middle Ages describe how sponges were used to clean and bathe wounds. The sponge even turns up in Shakespeare. In the play *Hamlet*, one character is described as sponging off the king.

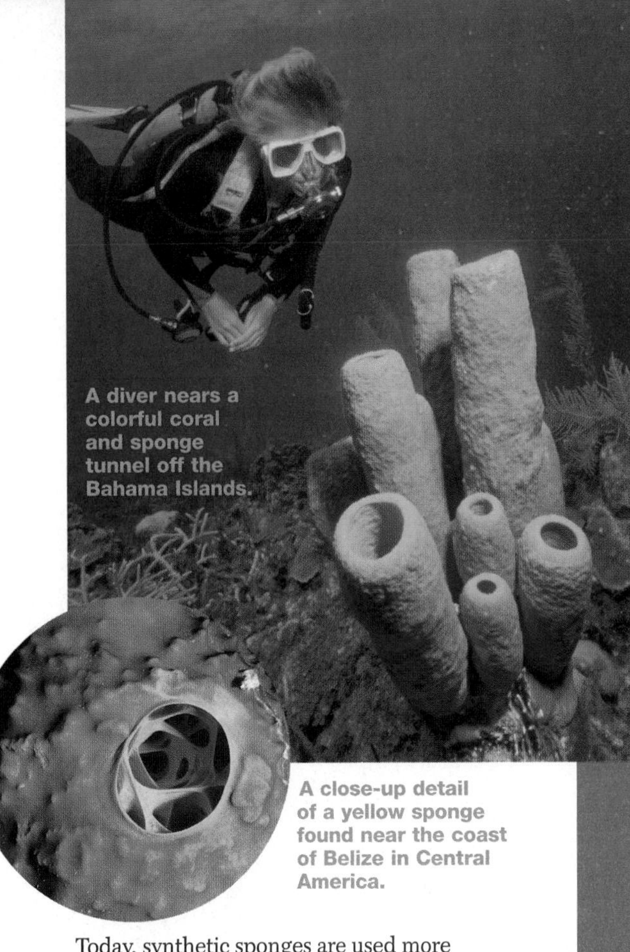
A diver nears a colorful coral and sponge tunnel off the Bahama Islands.

A close-up detail of a yellow sponge found near the coast of Belize in Central America.

How do you catch a sponge?

No matter how they're used, natural sponges have been gathered over time from the waters of the Mediterranean, the Caribbean Sea, and off the coast of Florida. In the past, divers carried up sponges from deep water. But today, sponges usually are harvested in shallower water by people in boats. They use a hook attached to a long pole to bring these marine animals to the surface. On land, the sponges are washed to remove dirt and organisms. Then they are left to dry. Eventually, the sponge's soft tissue rots away. What remains is the skeleton of the sponge. This meshlike material, called spongin, holds lots of liquid.

Today, synthetic sponges are used more than natural ones. What's their advantage? They're cheaper. There's probably no natural sponge in the "sponge" you use to clean your bathtub. Natural sponges absorb more water and last longer than the rubber or cellulose kind that most people use. They might be expensive, but natural sponges still have value. In fact, they might one day wipe away some diseases. Medical researchers hypothesize that an enzyme produced by sponges might help in curing cancer. Who says natural sponges are washed up?

CONNECTIONS Brainstorm **Work with your classmates to come up with as many sayings and phrases as you can using the word sponge. Use some of them in a story about sponges. Share your stories with the class.**

SCIENCE Online For more information, visit science.glencoe.com.

Discussion

Compare and contrast uses for sponges through history and their uses today. Possible answer: Sponges were used in more utilitarian ways, such as by the Greeks, who padded their helmets with them. They were also used to apply paint, to wipe surfaces, and to absorb liquids, just as they are today.

Historical Significance

Although the uses for sponges have stayed somewhat constant, the making of sponges for home and commercial use has changed quite a bit. While synthetic sponges nearly have replaced natural sponges for activities like housecleaning, the natural sponge still is used as a luxury item.

Ask the students to go on a fact-finding mission comparing natural to synthetic sponges. They can do this individually as a homework assignment or in class as a group activity. You might suggest that some students investigate the origin of the "loofah sponge." It is popular for bathing, but is *not* a sponge. It is actually a member of the gourd family, Cucurbitaceae. Tell students to include a visual representation of sponges in their presentations. These can include photographs, drawings, models, or real-life sponges. Each presentation should compare two types of sponges, either using a visual representation, such as a poster board presentation, or in an oral presentation to the class.

CONNECTIONS While brainstorming for the activity make use of the board to write down some of the students' suggestions. If possible use a theme related to the entire unit. Perhaps the setting of the story could be a coral reef, a salt-water aquarium, or a natural sponge retail store. Encourage students to use their imaginations for this exercise.

SCIENCE Online

Internet Addresses

Explore the Glencoe Science Web site at **science.glencoe.com** to find out more about topics in this feature.

Chapter 12 Study Guide

Reviewing Main Ideas

Preview

Students can answer the questions in their Science Journals. Discuss the answers as you go through the chapter. **LS Linguistic**

Review

Students can write their answers, then compare them with those of other students. **LS Interpersonal**

Reteach

Students can look at the illustrations and describe details that support the main ideas of the chapter. **LS Visual-Spatial**

Answers to Chapter Review

Section 1

5. bilateral

Section 2

4. cnidarians

Section 3

1. It is dependent on a host organism to get its food.

Chapter 12 Study Guide

Reviewing Main Ideas

Section 1 Is it an animal?

1. Animals are many-celled organisms that must find and digest their food.
2. Herbivores eat plants, carnivores eat animals or animal flesh, omnivores eat plants and animals, and detritivores feed on decaying plants and animals.
3. Animals have many ways to escape from predators such as speed, mimicry, protective outer coverings, and camouflage.
4. Invertebrates are animals without backbones. Animals that have backbones are called vertebrates.
5. When body parts are arranged the same way on both sides of the body, it is called bilateral symmetry. If body parts are arranged in a circle around a central point, it is known as radial symmetry. Animals without a specific central point are asymmetrical. *What kind of symmetry does the animal in the photo to the right have?*

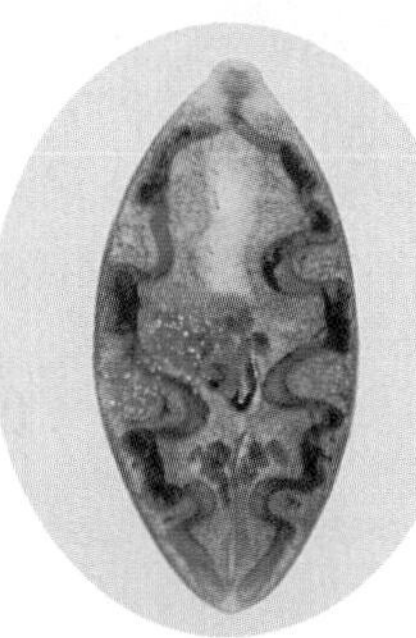

Section 2 Sponges and Cnidarians

1. Adult sponges are sessile and obtain food and oxygen by filtering water and organisms through their pores.
2. Sponges reproduce sexually and asexually.
3. Cnidarians are hollow-bodied animals with radial symmetry. Most have tentacles with stinging cells to obtain food. Jellyfish, hydras, and corals are cnidarians.
4. Coral reefs like the one in the photo below have been deposited by reef-building corals over millions of years. *Which group of animals do corals belong to?*

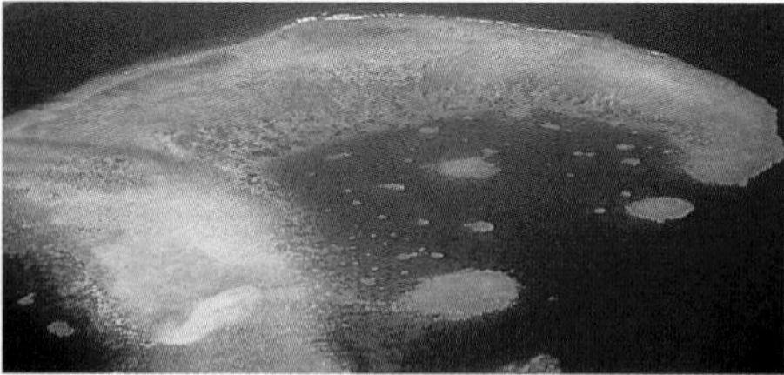

Section 3 Flatworms and Roundworms

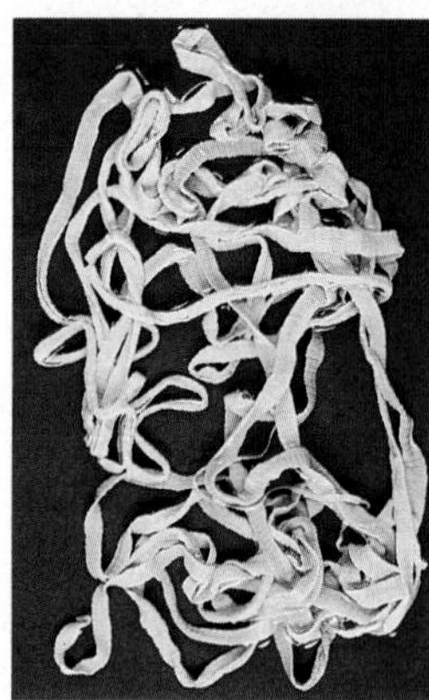

1. Flatworms have bilateral symmetry. Free-living and parasitic forms exist. *Why is a tapeworm considered to be a parasite?*
2. Flukes are parasites that have complex life cycles with multiple hosts.
3. Roundworms have a tube-within-a-tube body plan and bilateral symmetry.
4. Flatworms and roundworms have species that cause disease in humans.

FOLDABLES Reading & Study Skills — After You Read

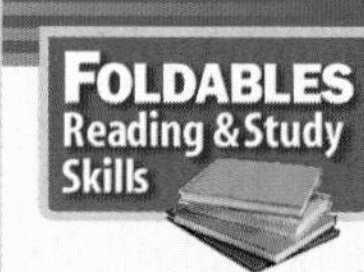

Add information about other animals to your Organizational Study Fold and then compare and contrast each animal.

FOLDABLES Reading & Study Skills — After You Read

After students have read the chapter and completed the Foldable described in Before You Read, have them do the activity on the student page.

Dinah Zike

Visualizing Main Ideas

Complete the following concept map.

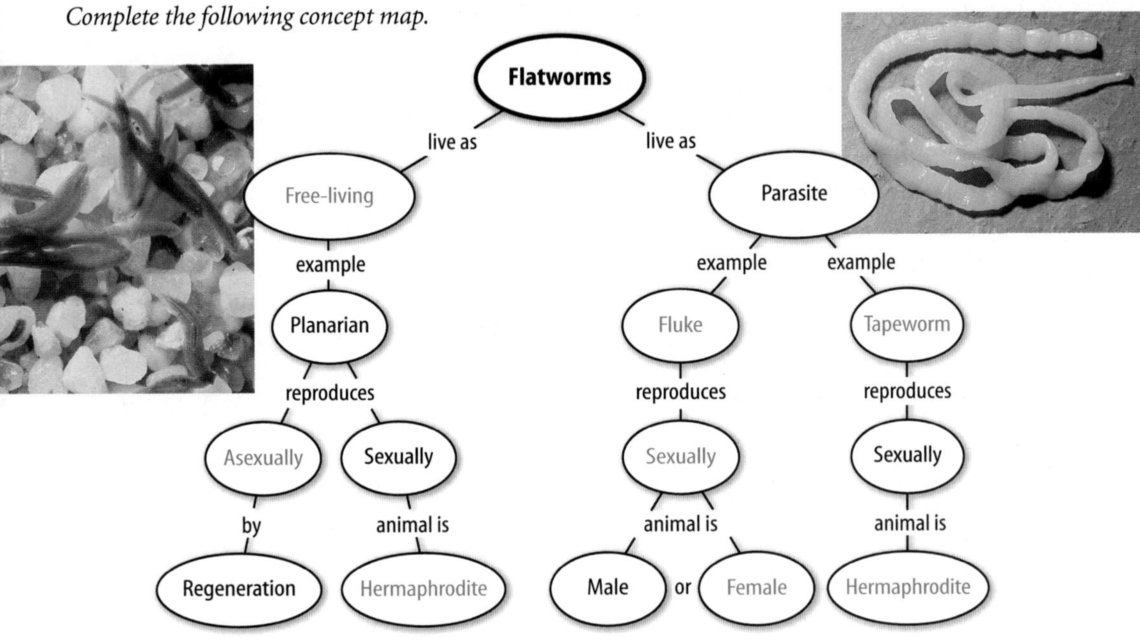

Vocabulary Review

Vocabulary Words

- a. anus
- b. bilateral symmetry
- c. carnivore
- d. free-living organism
- e. herbivore
- f. hermaphrodite
- g. invertebrate
- h. medusa
- i. omnivore
- j. polyp
- k. radial symmetry
- l. sessile
- m. stinging cell
- n. tentacle
- o. vertebrate

THE PRINCETON REVIEW **Study Tip**

Think of other possible ways that you might design an experiment to prove or disprove scientific principles.

Using Vocabulary

Replace the underlined phrases with the correct vocabulary word(s).

1. Jellyfish are <u>animals without backbones</u> and have <u>body parts arranged in a circle around a central point</u>.
2. <u>Animals that eat only other animals</u> eat less often than <u>animals that eat just plants</u>.
3. Most sponges are <u>animals that produce sperm and eggs in one body</u>.
4. Fish, humans, birds, and snakes are <u>animals with backbones</u> and <u>body parts arranged similarly on both sides of the body</u>.
5. Sea anemones are <u>vase shaped</u> and are <u>attached to one place</u>.

Chapter 12 Study Guide

Visualizing Main Ideas

See student page.

Vocabulary Review

Using Vocabulary

1. invertebrates; radial symmetry
2. Carnivores; herbivores
3. hermaphrodites
4. vertebrates; bilateral symmetry
5. polyps; sessile

Chapter 12 Assessment

Checking Concepts

1. D
2. A
3. B
4. A
5. A
6. C
7. C
8. A
9. B
10. B

Thinking Critically

11. Sponges have two cell layers, little cell organization, and are asymmetrical; flatworms have three cell layers—organized into tissues, organs, and organ systems— and are bilaterally symmetrical.
12. Being able to reproduce sexually and asexually enables them to respond to changing conditions, survive poor conditions, and take advantage of favorable conditions.
13. Sponges eat bacteria, algae, and protozoans. Hydra eat small animals they capture with their tentacles. Planarians eat smaller animals or the remains of organisms. The size of a particle is determined by the size of the opening the organism has for ingesting food.
14. The medusa stage is bell-shaped and free-swimming. The polyp stage is vase-shaped and sessile.
15. The polyp stage develops from the medusa, a free-moving form. More polyp fossils exist, possibly indicating later existence on Earth.

Chapter 12 Assessment

Checking Concepts

Choose the word or phrase that best answers the question.

1. Which of the following animals is sessile?
   A) jellyfish **C)** planarian
   B) roundworm **D)** sponge
2. What characteristic do all animals have?
   A) digest their food
   B) radial symmetry
   C) free-living
   D) polyp and medusa forms
3. Which term best describes a hydra?
   A) carnivore **C)** herbivore
   B) filter feeder **D)** parasite
4. Which animal has a mouth and an anus?
   A) roundworm **C)** planarian
   B) jellyfish **D)** tapeworm
5. What characteristic do scientists use to classify sponges?
   A) material that makes up their skeletons
   B) method of obtaining food
   C) reproduction
   D) symmetry
6. Which animal is a cnidarian?
   A) fluke **C)** jellyfish
   B) heartworm **D)** sponge
7. Which of the following invertebrate organisms is a hermaphrodite?
   A) fluke **C)** tapeworm
   B) coral **D)** roundworm
8. How do sponges reproduce asexually?
   A) budding **C)** medusae
   B) polyps **D)** eggs and sperm
9. What is the young organism that the fertilized egg of a sponge develops into?
   A) bud **C)** medusa
   B) larva **D)** polyp
10. Which group do roundworms belong to?
   A) cnidarians **C)** planarians
   B) nematodes **D)** sponges

Thinking Critically

11. Compare the body organization of a sponge to that of a flatworm.
12. What advantage does being able to reproduce sexually and asexually have for animals like sponges, cnidarians, and flatworms?
13. List the types of food that sponges, hydras, and planarians eat. Explain why each organism eats a different size of particle.
14. Compare and contrast the medusa and polyp body forms of cnidarians.
15. Why do scientists think the medusa stage was the first stage of the cnidarians?

Developing Skills

16. **Concept Mapping** Complete the following concept map about cnidarians.

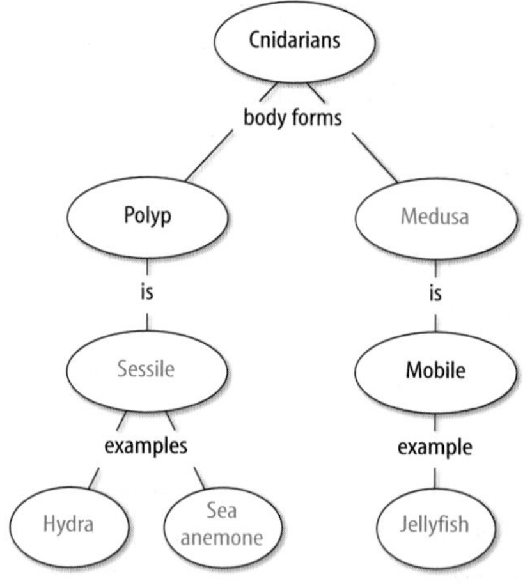

Chapter Assessment Planner

Portfolio Encourage students to place in their portfolios one or two items of what they consider to be their best work. Examples include:
- Reteach, p. 339
- Curriculum Connection, p. 341
- Science Journal, p. 350

Performance Additional performance assessments, Performance Task Assessment Lists, and rubrics for evaluating these activities can be found in Glencoe's **Performance Assessment in the Science Classroom.**

17. **Forming Hypotheses** Hypothesize why cooking pork at high temperatures prevents harmful roundworms from developing, if they are present in the uncooked meat.

18. **Predicting** What can you predict about the life of an organism that has no mouth or digestive system but has suckers and hooks on its head?

19. **Interpreting Scientific Illustrations** Look at the photograph below. This animal escapes from predators by mimicry. Where in nature might you find the animal in this photo?

20. **Identifying and Manipulating Variables and Controls** Design an experiment to test the sense of touch in a planarian. Identify variables, constants, and controls.

Performance Assessment

21. **Report** Research tapeworms and other parasitic worms that live in humans. Find out how they are able to live in the intestines without being digested by the human host. Report your findings to the class.

22. **Video Presentation** Create a video presentation using computer software or slides to illustrate the variety of sponges and cnidarians found on a coral reef.

Technology

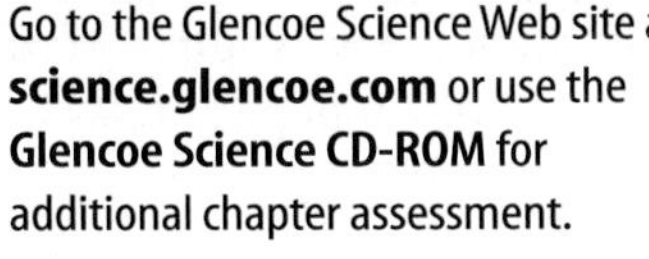

Go to the Glencoe Science Web site at **science.glencoe.com** or use the **Glencoe Science CD-ROM** for additional chapter assessment.

Test Practice

Lucas is doing a report about endangered species around the world. He found the following information about endangered animal species in various countries. He placed the information in the table below.

Endangered Species

Country	Mammal Species	Bird Species	Fish Species
Australia	58	45	37
Indonesia	128	104	60
Thailand	34	45	14
United States	35	50	123
DRC*	38	26	1

*Democratic Republic of Congo

Study the table and answer the following questions.

1. According to the information in the table, the country with the most endangered animals is _____.
   A) the United States
   B) Thailand
   C) Australia
   D) Indonesia

2. According to this information, in which country do endangered mammals account for more than half of the total number of endangered animal species?
   F) United States
   G) Indonesia
   H) Thailand
   J) DRC

Chapter 12 Assessment

Test Practice

THE PRINCETON REVIEW

The Test-Taking Tip was written by The Princeton Review, the nation's leader in test preparation.

1. D
2. J

Developing Skills

16. See student page.
17. Cysts are destroyed by heat; the worm has no protection and is killed.
18. It is a parasite.
19. on a green plant
20. From their observations of planarians, students should be able to suggest an experiment that involves touching the planarian with natural objects and observing its movement.

Performance Assessment

21. Some parasites are protected by a thick mucus. The hosts may not have the enzymes to break down the mucus. Use **PASC**, p. 159.
22. Students should be able to identify each organism in their video presentation or slide show. Use **PASC**, p. 149.

Assessment Resources

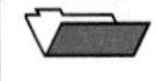

Reproducible Masters

Chapter Resources Booklet
Chapter Review, pp. 35–36
Chapter Tests, pp. 37–40
Assessment Transparency Activity, p. 47

Glencoe Science Web site
Interactive Tutor
Chapter Quizzes

Glencoe Technology
Assessment Transparency
Interactive CD-ROM Chapter Quizzes
ExamView Pro Test Bank
Vocabulary PuzzleMaker Software
MindJogger Videoquiz

MOLLUSKS, WORMS, ARTHROPODS, ECHINODERMS

Section/Objectives	Standards		Activities/Features
Chapter Opener	National See p. 5T for a Key to Standards.	State/Local	**Explore Activity:** Examine a clam's shell, p. 363 **Before You Read,** p. 363
Section 1 Mollusks 2 sessions 1 block 1. **Identify** the characteristics of mollusks. 2. **Describe** gastropods, bivalves, and cephalopods. 3. **Explain** the environmental importance of mollusks.	National Content Standards: UCP3, C1, C5, F2		**Earth Science Integration,** p. 367
Section 2 Segmented Worms 2 sessions 1 block 1. **Identify** the characteristics of segmented worms. 2. **Describe** the structures of an earthworm and how it takes in and digests its food. 3. **Explain** the importance of segmented worms.	National Content Standards: UCP3, C1, C5, F2		**Science Online,** p. 372
Section 3 Characteristics of Arthropods 2 sessions 1 block 1. **Determine** the characteristics that are used to classify arthropods. 2. **Explain** how the structure of the exoskeleton relates to its function. 3. **Distinguish** between complete and incomplete metamorphosis.	National Content Standards: UCP3, A1, C1, C2, C5		**MiniLAB:** Observing Metamorphosis, p. 376 **Health Integration,** p. 377 **Math Skills Activity:** Calculating Percent of Elasticity, p. 378 **Visualizing Arthropod Diversity,** p. 380 **Activity:** Observing a Crayfish, p. 383
Section 4 Echinoderms 3 sessions 1.5 blocks 1. **List** the characteristics of echinoderms. 2. **Explain** how sea stars obtain and digest food. 3. **Discuss** the importance of echinoderms.	National Content Standards: UCP3, A1, C1, C3, C5, F2, G1		**MiniLAB:** Modeling the Strength of Tube Feet, p. 385 **Science Online,** p. 386 **Activity:** What do worms eat?, pp. 388–389 **Science and Language Arts:** from "The Creatures on My Mind," pp. 390–391

Activity Materials	Reproducible Resources	Section Assessment	Technology
Explore Activity: hand lens, clam shell	**Chapter Resources Booklet** Foldables Worksheet, p. 15 Directed Reading Overview, p. 17 Note-taking Worksheets, pp. 33–36	GLENCOE'S ASSESSMENT ADVANTAGE	
	Chapter Resources Booklet Transparency Activity, p. 46 Enrichment, p. 29 Reinforcement, p. 25 Directed Reading, p. 18	**Portfolio** Visual Learning, p. 367 **Performance** Skill Builder Activities, p. 368 **Content** Section Assessment, p. 368	Section Focus Transparency Interactive CD-ROM Guided Reading Audio Program
	Chapter Resources Booklet Transparency Activity, p. 47 Lab Activity, pp. 9–12 Enrichment, p. 30 Reinforcement, p. 26 Transparency Activity, pp. 51–52 Directed Reading, p. 18	**Portfolio** Reteach, p. 373 **Performance** Skill Builder Activities, p. 373 **Content** Section Assessment, p. 373	Section Focus Transparency Teaching Transparency Interactive CD-ROM Guided Reading Audio Program
MiniLAB: ripe banana, jar, cheesecloth, rubber band, hand lens **Activity:** crayfish in a small aquarium, uncooked ground beef, stirrer	**Chapter Resources Booklet** Transparency Activity, p. 48 MiniLAB, p. 3 Lab Activity, pp. 13–14 Enrichment, p. 31 Reinforcement, p. 27 Directed Reading, p. 19 Activity Worksheet, pp. 5–6	**Portfolio** Activity, p. 377 **Performance** MiniLAB, p. 376 Math Skills Activity, p. 378 Skill Builder Activities, p. 382 **Content** Section Assessment, p. 382	Section Focus Transparency Interactive CD-ROM Guided Reading Audio Program
MiniLAB: heavy book, clock or watch with second hand **Activity:** skins of 5 different fruits (apple, orange, banana, kiwi, watermelon rind), 5 wide-mouth jars, potting soil, water, humus, earthworms, 5 sheets of black construction paper, masking tape, marker, 5 rubber bands	**Chapter Resources Booklet** Transparency Activity, p. 49 MiniLAB, p. 4 Enrichment, p. 32 Reinforcement, p. 28 Directed Reading, pp. 19, 20 Activity Worksheet, pp. 7–8 **Lab Management and Safety,** p. 73	**Portfolio** Visual Learning, p. 385 **Performance** MiniLAB, p. 385 Skill Builder Activities, p. 387 **Content** Section Assessment, p. 387	Section Focus Transparency Interactive CD-ROM Guided Reading Audio Program

Need materials? Contact Science Kit at 1-800-828-7777 or www.sciencekit.com on the Internet.

End of Chapter Assessment

GLENCOE'S ASSESSMENT ADVANTAGE

Blackline Masters	Technology	Professional Series
Chapter Resources Booklet Chapter Review, pp. 39–40 Chapter Tests, pp. 41–44 **Standardized Test Practice by The Princeton Review,** pp. 59–62	MindJogger Videoquiz Interactive CD-ROM Vocabulary PuzzleMakers ExamView Pro Test Bank Interactive Lesson Planner Interactive Teacher Edition	Performance Assessment in the Science Classroom (PASC)

Transparencies

Section Focus

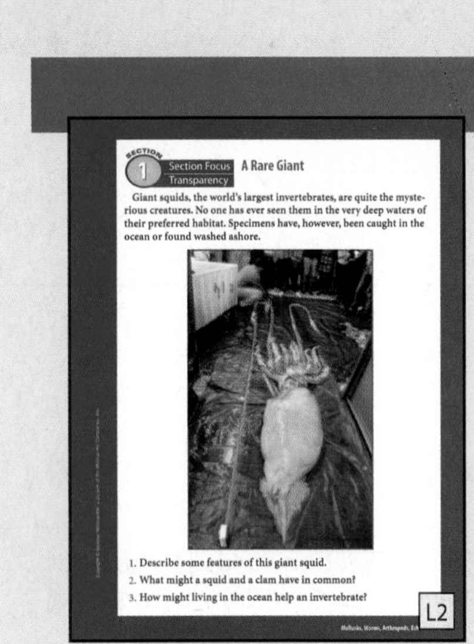
Section 1 Section Focus Transparency A Rare Giant

Giant squids, the world's largest invertebrates, are quite the mysterious creatures. No one has ever seen them in the very deep waters of their preferred habitat. Specimens have, however, been caught in the ocean or found washed ashore.

1. Describe some features of this giant squid.
2. What might a squid and a clam have in common?
3. How might living in the ocean help an invertebrate?

L2

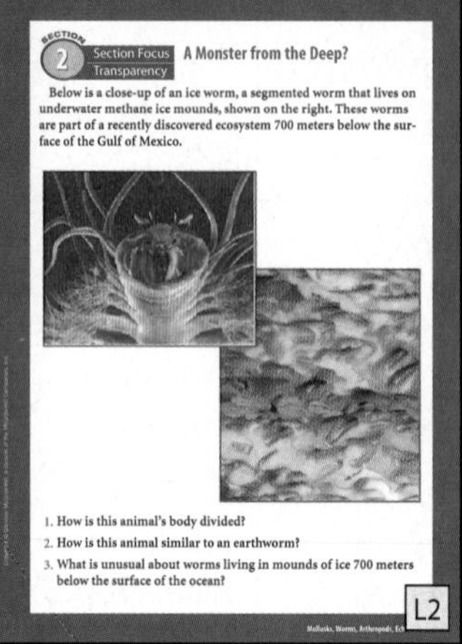
Section 2 Section Focus Transparency A Monster from the Deep?

Below is a close-up of an ice worm, a segmented worm that lives on underwater methane ice mounds, shown on the right. These worms are part of a recently discovered ecosystem 700 meters below the surface of the Gulf of Mexico.

1. How is this animal's body divided?
2. How is this animal similar to an earthworm?
3. What is unusual about worms living in mounds of ice 700 meters below the surface of the ocean?

L2

Section 3 Section Focus Transparency Natural Pest Control

The name ladybird beetle is commonly used for several different species of beetles. While a few ladybird beetles are harmful to crops, most of these beetles actually eat the pests that damage plants. This means they sometimes can be used instead of chemicals to protect crops.

1. What advantages do ladybird beetles have over chemicals for pest control?
2. Describe the appearance of this beetle. Does it look hard or soft on the outside?

L2

This is a representation of key blackline masters available in the Teacher Classroom Resources. See Resource Manager boxes within the chapter for additional information.

Assessment

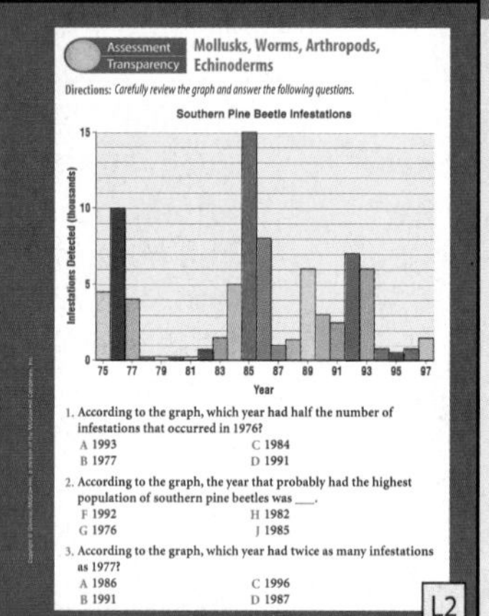
Assessment Transparency Mollusks, Worms, Arthropods, Echinoderms

Directions: Carefully review the graph and answer the following questions.

1. According to the graph, which year had half the number of infestations that occurred in 1976?
A 1993 C 1984
B 1977 D 1991
2. According to the graph, the year that probably had the highest population of southern pine beetles was ___.
F 1992 H 1982
G 1976 J 1985
3. According to the graph, which year had twice as many infestations as 1977?
A 1986 C 1996
B 1991 D 1987

L2

Teaching

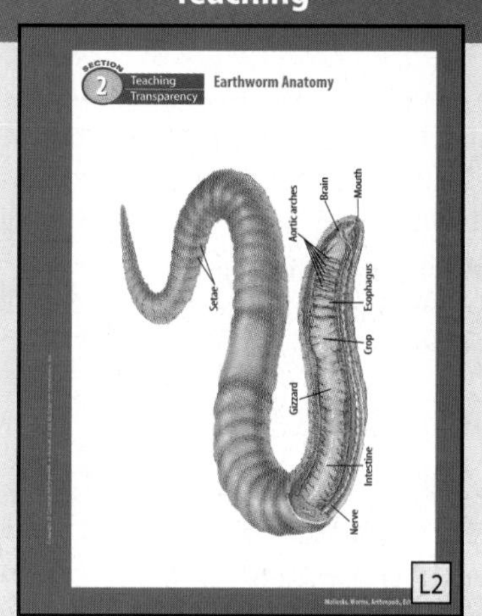
Section 2 Teaching Transparency Earthworm Anatomy

L2

Key to Teaching Strategies

The following designations will help you decide which activities are appropriate for your students.

L1 Level 1 activities should be appropriate for students with learning difficulties.

L2 Level 2 activities should be within the ability range of all students.

L3 Level 3 activities are designed for above-average students.

ELL ELL activities should be within the ability range of English Language Learners.

COOP LEARN Cooperative Learning activities are designed for small group work.

LS Multiple Learning Styles logos, as described on page 22T, are used throughout to indicate strategies that address different learning styles.

P These strategies represent student products that can be placed into a best-work portfolio.

Hands-on Activities

Activity Worksheets

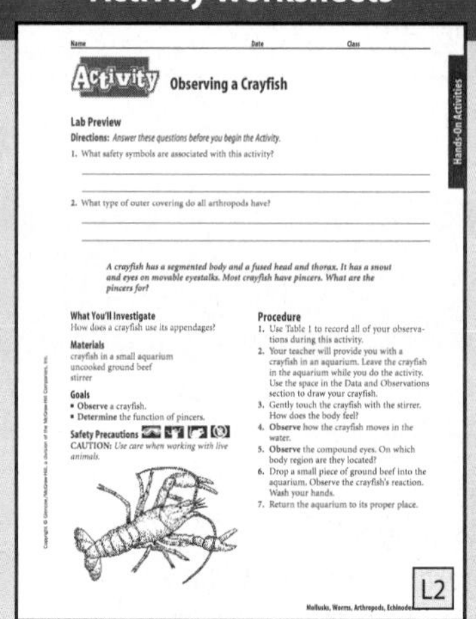
Activity Observing a Crayfish

Lab Preview

Directions: Answer these questions before you begin the Activity.

1. What safety symbols are associated with this activity?
2. What type of outer covering do all arthropods have?

A crayfish has a segmented body and a fused head and thorax. It has a snout and eyes on movable eyestalks. Most crayfish have pincers. What are the pincers for?

What You'll Investigate

How does a crayfish use its appendages?

Materials

crayfish in a small aquarium
uncooked ground beef
stirrer

Goals

- Observe a crayfish.
- Determine the function of pincers.

Safety Precautions

CAUTION: Use care when working with live animals.

Procedure

1. Use Table 1 to record all of your observations during this activity.
2. Your teacher will provide you with a crayfish in an aquarium. Leave the crayfish in the aquarium while you do the activity. Use the space in the Data and Observations section to draw your crayfish.
3. Gently touch the crayfish with the stirrer. How does the body feel?
4. Observe how the crayfish moves in the water.
5. Observe the compound eyes. On which body region are they located?
6. Drop a small piece of ground beef into the aquarium. Observe the crayfish's reaction. Wash your hands.
7. Return the aquarium to its proper place.

L2

Laboratory Activities

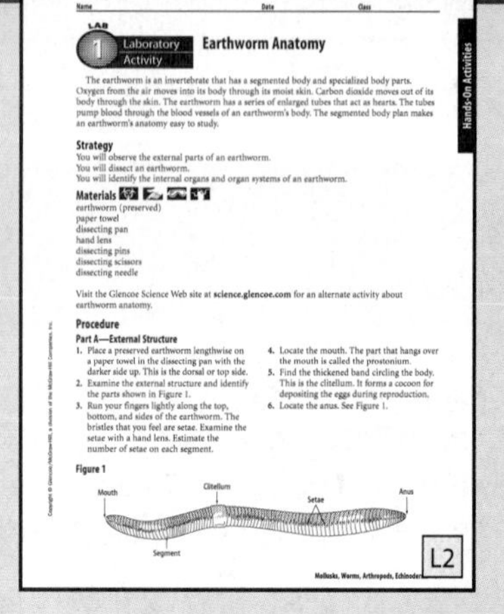
Lab 1 Laboratory Activity Earthworm Anatomy

The earthworm is an invertebrate that has a segmented body and specialized body parts. Oxygen from the air moves into its body through its moist skin. Carbon dioxide moves out of its body through the skin. The earthworm has a series of enlarged tubes that act as hearts. The tubes pump blood through the blood vessels of an earthworm's body. The segmented body plan makes an earthworm's anatomy easy to study.

Strategy

You will observe the external parts of an earthworm.
You will dissect an earthworm.
You will identify the internal organs and organ systems of an earthworm.

Materials

earthworm (preserved)
paper towel
dissecting pan
hand lens
dissecting pins
dissecting scissors
dissecting needle

Visit the Glencoe Science Web site at science.glencoe.com for an alternate activity about earthworm anatomy.

Procedure

Part A—External Structure

1. Place a preserved earthworm lengthwise on a paper towel in the dissecting pan with the darker side up. This is the dorsal or top side.
2. Examine the external structure and identify the parts shown in Figure 1.
3. Run your fingers lightly along the top, bottom, and sides of the earthworm. The bristles that you feel are setae. Examine the setae with a hand lens. Estimate the number of setae on each segment.
4. Locate the mouth. The part that hangs over the mouth is called the prostomium.
5. Find the thickened band circling the body. This is the clitellum. It forms a cocoon for depositing the eggs during reproduction.
6. Locate the anus. See Figure 1.

Figure 1

L2

Meeting Different Ability Levels

Content Outline

Name Date Class

Note-taking Worksheet **Mollusks, Worms, Arthropods, Echinoderms**

Section 1 Mollusks

A. ____________—soft-bodied invertebrates with bilateral symmetry and usually one or two shells with organs in a fluid-filled cavity

1. Thin layer of tissue called the ____________ covers the body organs.
2. Mantle cavity (between soft body and mantle) contains ____________.
3. For most mollusks, an ____________ **circulatory system** moves blood through vessels and into open spaces around body organs.
4. Well-developed head has a ____________ and some sensory organs.
5. Underside is a muscular ____________ used to move.

B. Mollusks ____________ into three common groups based on shell presence, type and foot type.

1. ____________ usually have a single shell.
   a. Use ____________ (a tongue-like organ with rows of teeth) to get food
   b. Have foot glands that secrete a layer of ____________ for sliding
   c. Include ____________, ____________, and garden slugs ____________
2. ____________ have a hinged, two-part shell and include clams, oysters, and scallops.
3. ____________ are most specialized and complex mollusks.
   a. Include squid, octopuses, and chambered nautiluses
   b. Cephalopods have a well-developed head and many ____________ for capturing prey.
   c. A ____________ **circulatory system** moves blood through the body in a series of closed vessels.
   d. Cephalopods use ____________ to move at speeds of 60 m/s.
   e. Mollusk fossils date to more than ____________ million years ago.

C. Among other uses, mollusks provide ____________ for people and other animals as well as pearls and shells for jewelry and decorations.

Meeting Individual Needs

L2

Reinforcement

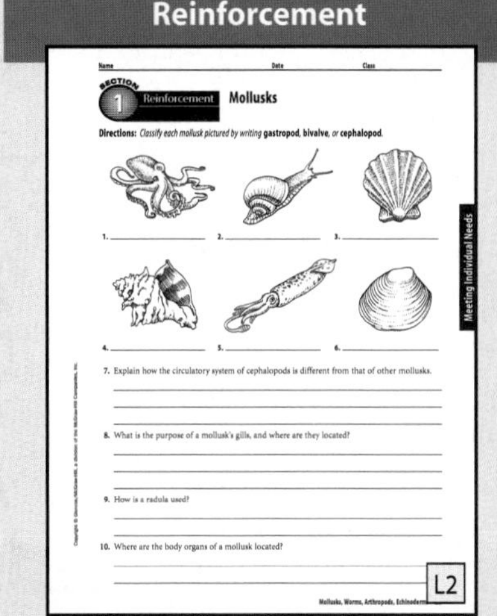

Name Date Class

Section 1 Reinforcement **Mollusks**

Directions: *Classify each mollusk pictured by writing* **gastropod, bivalve,** *or* **cephalopod.**

1. ________ 2. ________ 3. ________

4. ________ 5. ________ 6. ________

7. Explain how the circulatory system of cephalopods is different from that of other mollusks.

8. What is the purpose of a mollusk's gills, and where are they located?

9. How is a radula used?

10. Where are the body organs of a mollusk located?

Meeting Individual Needs

L2

Mollusks, Worms, Arthropods, Echinoderms

Directed Reading

Name Date Class

Directed Reading for Content Mastery *Overview* **Mollusks, Worms, Arthropods, Echinoderms**

Directions: *Using the word list below, complete this concept map that compares how some different invertebrates are adapted to obtain and eat food.*

prey shells spiders echinoderms segmented worms enzymes
earthworms tentacles soil tube feet cuttlefish

Invertebrates — include — 1. / mollusks / arthropods / 9.

such as — 2. / 4. / 7. / sea stars

which eat by taking in / which have many / which release / which use

3. / 5. / 8. / 10.

which is ground in the / for capturing / to digest food such as / to open

gizzard / 6. / insects / 11.

Meeting Individual Needs

L1

Mollusks, Worms, Arthropods, Echinoderms

Enrichment

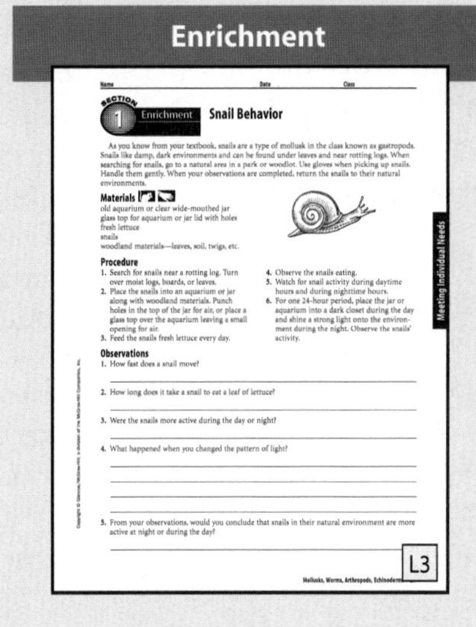

Name Date Class

Section 1 Enrichment **Snail Behavior**

As you know from your textbook, snails are a type of mollusk in the class known as gastropods. Snails like damp, dark environments and can be found under leaves and near rotting logs. When searching for snails, go to a natural area in a park or woodlot. Use gloves when picking up snails. Handle them gently. When your observations are completed, return the snails to their natural environments.

Materials
old aquarium or clear wide-mouthed jar
glass top for aquarium or jar lid with holes
fresh lettuce
snails
woodland materials—leaves, soil, twigs, etc.

Procedure
1. Search for snails near a rotting log. Turn over moist logs, boards, or leaves.
2. Place the snails into an aquarium or jar along with woodland materials. Punch holes in the top of the jar for air, or place a glass top over the aquarium leaving a small opening for air.
3. Feed the snails fresh lettuce every day.
4. Observe the snails eating.
5. Watch for snail activity during daytime hours and during nighttime hours.
6. For one 24-hour period, place the jar or aquarium into a dark closet during the day and shine a strong light onto the environment during the night. Observe the snails' activity.

Observations
1. How fast does a snail move?
2. How long does it take a snail to eat a leaf of lettuce?
3. Were the snails more active during the day or night?
4. What happened when you changed the pattern of light?
5. From your observations, would you conclude that snails in their natural environment are more active at night or during the day?

Meeting Individual Needs

L3

Mollusks, Worms, Arthropods, Echinoderms

Spanish Directed Reading

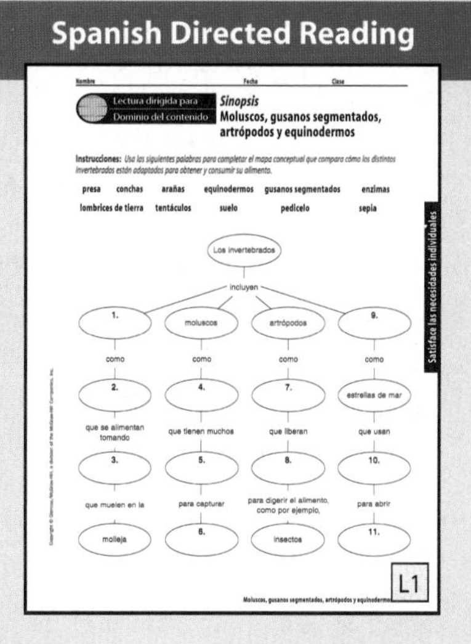

Nombre Fecha Clase

Lectura dirigida para Dominio del contenido *Sinopsis* **Moluscos, gusanos segmentados, artrópodos y equinodermos**

Instrucciones: *Usa las siguientes palabras para completar el mapa conceptual que compara cómo los distintos invertebrados están adaptados para obtener y consumir su alimento.*

presa conchas arañas equinodermos gusanos segmentados enzimas
lombrices de tierra tentáculos suelo pedicelo sepia

Los invertebrados — incluyen — 1. / moluscos / artrópodos / 9.

como — 2. / 4. / 7. / estrellas de mar

que se alimentan tomando / que tienen muchos / que liberan / que usan

3. / 5. / 8. / 10.

que muelen en la / para capturar / para digerir el alimento, como por ejemplo, / para abrir

molleja / 6. / insectos / 11.

Satisface las necesidades individuales

L1

Moluscos, gusanos segmentados, artrópodos y equinodermos

Assessment

Chapter Tests

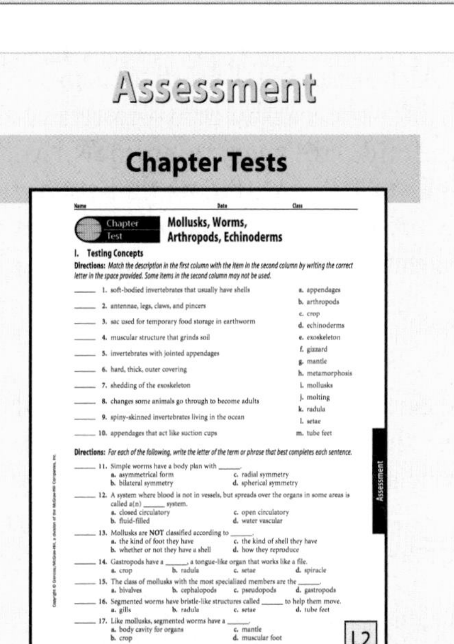

Name Date Class

Chapter Test **Mollusks, Worms, Arthropods, Echinoderms**

I. Testing Concepts

Directions: *Match the description in the first column with the item in the second column by writing the correct letter in the space provided. Some items in the second column may not be used.*

____ 1. soft-bodied invertebrates that usually have shells	a. appendages
____ 2. antennae, legs, claws, and pincers	b. arthropods
____ 3. sac used for temporary food storage in earthworm	c. crop
____ 4. muscular structure that grinds soil	d. echinoderms
____ 5. invertebrates with jointed appendages	e. exoskeleton
____ 6. hard, thick, outer covering	f. gizzard
____ 7. shedding of the exoskeleton	g. mantle
____ 8. changes some animals go through to become adults	h. metamorphosis
____ 9. spiny-skinned invertebrates living in the ocean	i. mollusks
____ 10. appendages that act like suction cups	j. molting
	k. radula
	l. setae
	m. tube feet

Directions: *For each of the following, write the letter of the term or phrase that best completes each sentence.*

____ 11. Simple worms have a body plan with ____.
a. asymmetrical form c. radial symmetry
b. bilateral symmetry d. spherical symmetry

____ 12. A system where blood is not in vessels, but spreads over the organs in some areas is called a(n) ____ system.
a. closed circulatory c. open circulatory
b. fluid-filled d. water vascular

____ 13. Mollusks are NOT classified according to ____.
a. the kind of foot they have c. the kind of shell they have
b. whether or not they have a shell d. how they reproduce

____ 14. Gastropods have a ____, a tongue-like organ that works like a file.
a. crop b. radula c. setae d. spiracle

____ 15. The class of mollusks with the most specialized members are the ____.
a. bivalves b. cephalopods c. pseudopods d. gastropods

____ 16. Segmented worms have bristle-like structures called ____ to help them move.
a. gills b. radula c. setae d. tube feet

____ 17. Like mollusks, segmented worms have a ____.
a. body cavity for organs c. mantle
b. crop d. muscular foot

Assessment

L2

Mollusks, Worms, Arthropods, Echinoderms

Test Practice Workbook

L2

Chapter Review

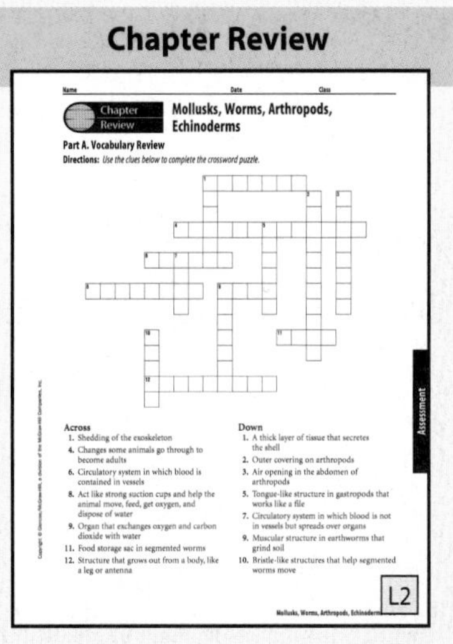

Name Date Class

Chapter Review **Mollusks, Worms, Arthropods, Echinoderms**

Part A. Vocabulary Review

Directions: *Use the clues below to complete the crossword puzzle.*

Across
1. Shedding of the exoskeleton
4. Changes some animals go through to become adults
6. Circulatory system in which blood is contained in vessels
8. Act like strong suction cups and help the animal move, feed, get oxygen, and dispose of water
9. Organ that exchanges oxygen and carbon dioxide with water
11. Food storage sac in segmented worms
12. Structure that grows out from a body, like a leg or antenna

Down
1. A thick layer of tissue that secretes the shell
2. Outer covering on arthropods
3. Air opening in the abdomen of arthropods
5. Tongue-like structure in gastropods that works like a file
7. Circulatory system in which blood is not in vessels but spreads over organs
9. Muscular structure in earthworms that grind soil
10. Bristle-like structures that help segmented worms move

Assessment

L2

Mollusks, Worms, Arthropods, Echinoderms

Science Content Background

SECTION 1

Mollusks

Characteristics of Mollusks

Mollusca is the second-largest phylum of animals. Mollusks can be found in freshwater and saltwater and on land. A mollusk is an invertebrate that has a soft-body enclosed by a mantle and a muscular organ called the foot that is generally used for locomotion. In some mollusks, the mantle secretes a hard outer shell. As the animal grows, material is added to the shell that increases its size. In the cavity between the mantle and the body are the gills. A mollusk's gills are an adaptation that increases the surface area for the absorption of oxygen and the release of carbon dioxide. Mollusks that are filter feeders also use the gills to capture food.

Classification of Mollusks

Gastropoda, Bivalvia, and Cephalopoda are three familiar classes of mollusks. The class Gastropoda includes snails and slugs and is so named because the muscular foot is below the stomach. Gastropods have distinct heads and most have a shell. Bivalves do not have distinctive heads and have a two-part shell that is hinged together. They vary in size from tiny coquinas that are several millimeters long to giant clams that can be 1.5 m wide and weigh up to 270 kg. Bivalves and cephalopods have siphons through which water can be expelled forcefully. Cephalopods use this as a means of locomotion. The foot of a cephalopod is modified into several tentacles. Each tentacle has structures—usually suction cups—that can be used for capturing prey and locomotion.

SECTION 2

Segmented Worms

Segmented Worm Characteristics

Segmented worms belong to the phylum Annelida. Although the most familiar annelid—the earthworm—is terrestrial, most annelids are marine animals. An annelid's body is made of segments that appear similar on the outside. Internally, each segment contains circulatory, excretory, and neural structures.

Earthworm Body Systems

Earthworms do not have eyes, but special sensors in their skin allow them to differentiate light and dark areas. They are negatively phototaxic, which means they move away from lighted areas.

Will Crocker/Image Bank

The first segment of an earthworm contains the mouth and the last segment contains the anus. Soil enters the mouth and then a structure called the pharynx. The pharynx acts like a pump to push soil from the mouth through the esophagus into the crop. Annelids show variety in the forms of the pharynx, which often can be pushed out through their mouths. Some pharynxes contain sharp jaws for capturing prey or for eating plant materials.

SECTION 3

Arthropods

Characteristics of Arthropods

The first arthropods are thought to have existed in the oceans over 600 million years ago. They have evolved into countless forms and varieties—all based on the same general body plan. In addition to segmented bodies with exoskeletons and jointed appendages, arthropods have open circulatory systems, a brain, and a ventral nerve cord.

Fun Fact

Only female mosquitoes "bite." The blood is used to nourish their eggs. Mosquitoes can detect you twenty feet away by the carbon dioxide you exhale. They use other sensors to make sure you are a good source of a meal, rather than a metal exhaust pipe. Their sensors detect many things including heat, lactic acid, and water vapor.

Insects

Class Insecta is the largest group of organisms on Earth and includes the only invertebrates capable of flight. Insects have evolved adaptations that allow them to live in nearly every environment.

The body of an insect is segmented. The head usually has compound eyes, antennae, and a mouth. Feeding adaptations include structures that allow insects to be carnivores, herbivores, omnivores, scavengers, or parasites. The thorax usually has legs and, if present, wings. The abdomen contains reproductive, digestive, excretory, and respiratory structures. Respiratory exchange in insects occurs in tubes called tracheae. These are connected to the outside by openings called spiracles.

While insects are commonly called bugs, entomologists, scientists who study insects, have a more restricted use of the term. The term bug is used to describe insects in the order Hemiptera. For entomologists, a cicada and a bed bug are bugs, but a fly and an ant are not.

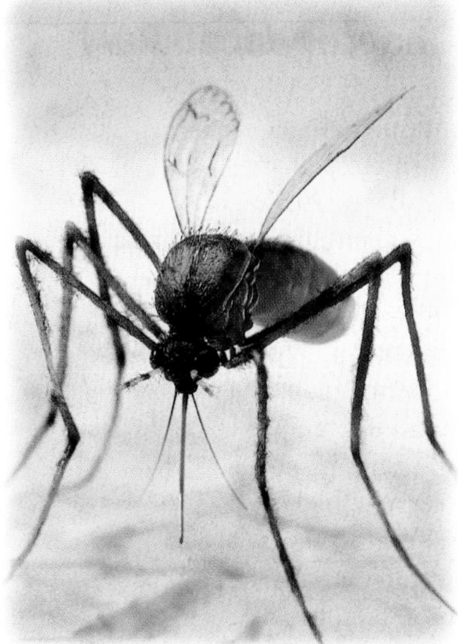

Jeff Hunter/Image Bank

Crustaceans

Most crustaceans are aquatic organisms. Unlike an insect, a crustacean has appendages on its abdomen as well as its thorax. Crustaceans are the only arthropods with two pair of antennae. They generally are classified into three groups. Decapods include lobsters, shrimp, crabs, and crawfish. The second group—the terrestrial and freshwater forms—includes sowbugs, sand fleas, and copepods. Barnacles make up the third group. They are free-swimming as larvae but sessile as adults.

SECTION 4

Echinoderms

Echinoderm Characteristics

Sea stars, sea urchins, and sand dollars are examples of echinoderms. These invertebrates are not found on land or in freshwater, they are strictly saltwater organisms. Echinoderm larvae have bilateral symmetry but adult forms have radial symmetry. They have endoskeletons and a water vascular system that is not found in any other phyla.

For additional content background on this topic, go to the Glencoe Science Web site at science.glencoe.com.

CHAPTER 13

Mollusks, Worms, Arthropods, Echinoderms

Chapter Vocabulary

mantle, p. 364
gill, p. 364
open circulatory system, p. 364
radula, p. 365
closed circulatory system, p. 366
setae, p. 369
crop, p. 370
gizzard, p. 370
appendage, p. 374
exoskeleton, p. 374
molting, p. 374
spiracle, p. 375
metamorphosis, p. 376
water-vascular system, p. 384
tube feet, p. 384

What do you think?

Science Journal This picture is of a dust mite. Dust mites are microscopic arachnids that live in upholstered furniture, pillows, mattresses, and carpets. People with dust allergies are actually reacting to proteins in the feces of dust mites, not the dust itself. The average double bed mattress contains about 2 million dust mites.

CHAPTER 13

Mollusks, Worms, Arthropods, Echinoderms

What do fiddler crabs running along the beach have in common with pill bugs and millipedes you might discover under a rock in your yard? How many mosquitoes have bitten you? These animals and more than a million other species belong to the largest, most diverse group of animals—the arthropods. In this chapter, you will learn about arthropods, as well as mollusks, worms, and echinoderms.

What do you think?

Science Journal Look at the picture below with a classmate. Discuss what you think this might be. Here's a hint: *It can be found in your house.* Write your answer or best guess in your Science Journal.

362

Theme Connection

Stability and Change and **Scale and Structure** Comparisons of the adaptations that have evolved in mollusks, segmented worms, arthropods, and echinoderms are explored.

If you've ever walked along a beach, especially after a storm, you've probably seen many seashells. They come in many different colors, shapes, and sizes. If you look closely, you will see that some shells have many rings or bands. In the following activity, find out what the bands tell you about the shell and the organism that made it.

Examine a clam's shell

1. Use a hand lens to examine a clam's shell.
2. Count the number of rings or bands on the shell. Count as number one the large, top point called the crown.
3. Compare the distances between the bands of the shell.

Observe

Do other students' shells have the same number of bands? Are all of the bands on your shell the same width? What do you think the bands represent, and why are some wider than others? Record your answers in your Science Journal.

Before You Read

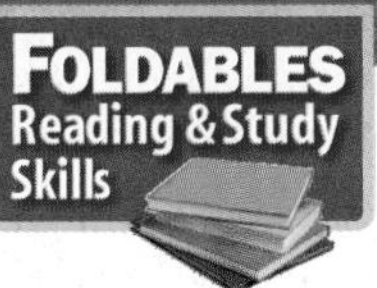

Making an Organizational Study Fold Make the following Foldable to help you organize your thoughts into clear categories about groups of invertebrates.

1. Place a sheet of paper in front of you so the long side is at the top. Fold the paper in half from the left side to the right side and then unfold.
2. Fold each side in to the centerfold line to divide the paper into fourths. Fold the paper in half from top to bottom and unfold.
3. Through the top thickness of paper, cut along both of the middle fold lines to form four tabs as shown. Label the tabs *Mollusks, Worms, Arthropods,* and *Echinoderms* as shown.
4. Before you read the chapter, write what you know about each group of invertebrate under the tab. As you read the chapter, add to and correct what you have written.

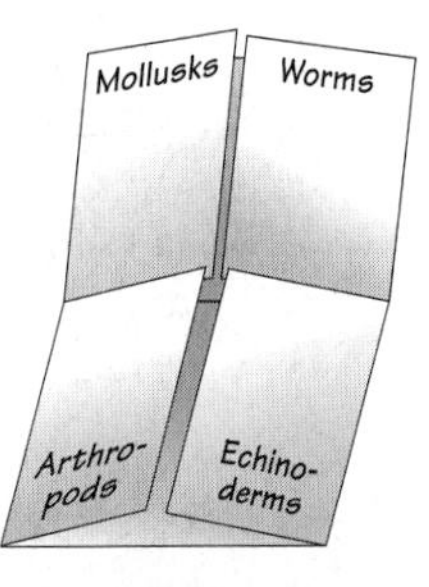

Explore Activity

Purpose Use the Explore Activity to introduce students to mollusks. Explain that they will be learning about mollusks and other complex invertebrates in the chapter. L1 IS **Visual-Spatial**

Preparation Obtain clam shells of different sizes.

Materials clam shell, hand lens, metric ruler

Teaching Strategies

- Have each pair of students count the bands and answer the questions.
- If you live near the coast, encourage students to collect shells for this activity. Freshwater clams from freshwater streams and lakes will also work.

Observe

Answers will vary. As a clam grows, so does its shell. A new ring or band shows on the shell each year. The crown is one year's growth. Food supply, water temperature, oxygen content, pollutants, and the calcium carbonate in the water affect the width of the bands.

Assessment

Oral Have students suggest ways in which the shell of a mollusk is an adaptation. It protects, conserves water, and camouflages the animal. Use **Performance Assessment in the Science Classroom**, p. 89. P

Before You Read

FOLDABLES Reading & Study Skills

Dinah Zike Study Fold

Purpose Use the Foldable to determine what students know about the four groups of invertebrates before reading the chapter. It will also provide a place to record and organize notes on the groups as they read.

For additional help, see Foldables Worksheet, p. 15 in **Chapter Resources Booklet,** or go to the Glencoe Science Web site at **science.glencoe.com.** See After You Read in the Study Guide at the end of this chapter.

Mollusks

1 Motivate

Bellringer Transparency

Display the Section Focus Transparency for Section 1. Use the accompanying Transparency Activity Master. L2 ELL

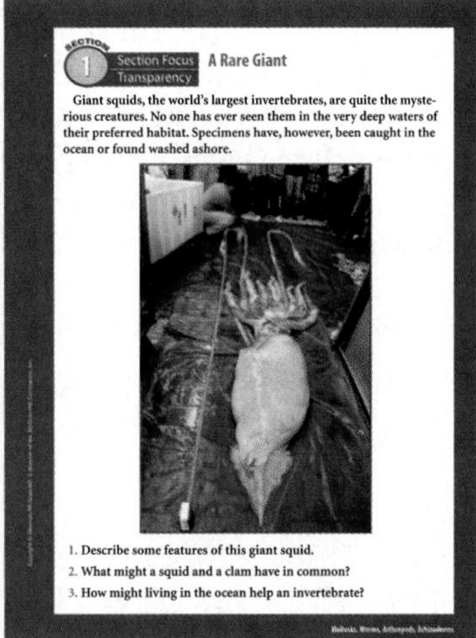

Tie to Prior Knowledge

Ask students to give examples of mollusks. Most will be familiar with mollusks such as oysters, clams, squid, garden snails, and octopuses.

SECTION 1

Mollusks

As You Read

***What* You'll Learn**

- **Identify** the characteristics of mollusks.
- **Describe** gastropods, bivalves, and cephalopods.
- **Explain** the environmental importance of mollusks.

Vocabulary

mantle
gill
open circulatory system
radula
closed circulatory system

***Why* It's Important**

Mollusks are a food source for many animals. They also filter impurities from the water.

Characteristics of Mollusks

Mollusks (MAH lusks) are soft-bodied invertebrates with bilateral symmetry and usually one or two shells. Their organs are in a fluid-filled cavity. The word *mollusk* comes from the Latin word meaning "soft." Most mollusks live in water, but some live on land. Snails, clams, and squid are examples of mollusks. More than 110,000 species of mollusks have been identified.

Body Plan All mollusks, like the one in **Figure 1,** have a thin layer of tissue called a mantle. The **mantle** covers the body organs, which are located in the visceral (VIH suh rul) mass. Between the soft body and the mantle is a space called the mantle cavity. It contains **gills**—the organs in which carbon dioxide from the mollusk is exchanged for oxygen in the water.

The mantle also secretes the shell or protects the body if the mollusk does not have a shell. The shell is made up of several layers. The inside layer is the smoothest. It is usually the thickest layer because it's added to throughout the life of the mollusk. The inside layer also protects the soft body.

The circulatory system of most mollusks is an open system. In an **open circulatory system,** the heart moves blood through vessels and out into open spaces around the body organs. The body organs are surrounded completely by blood that contains nutrients and oxygen.

Most mollusks have a well-developed head with a mouth and some sensory organs. Some mollusks, such as squid, have tentacles. On the underside of a mollusk is the muscular foot, which is used for movement.

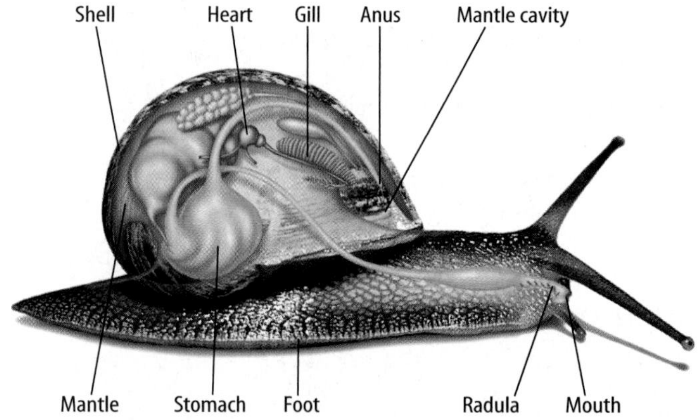

Figure 1
The general mollusk body plan is shown by this snail. Most mollusks have a head, foot, and visceral mass.

Section Assessment Planner

Portfolio
Visual Learning, p. 367

Performance Assessment
Skill Builder Activities, p. 368
See page 394 for more options.

Content Assessment
Section, p. 368
Challenge, p. 368
Chapter, pp. 394–395

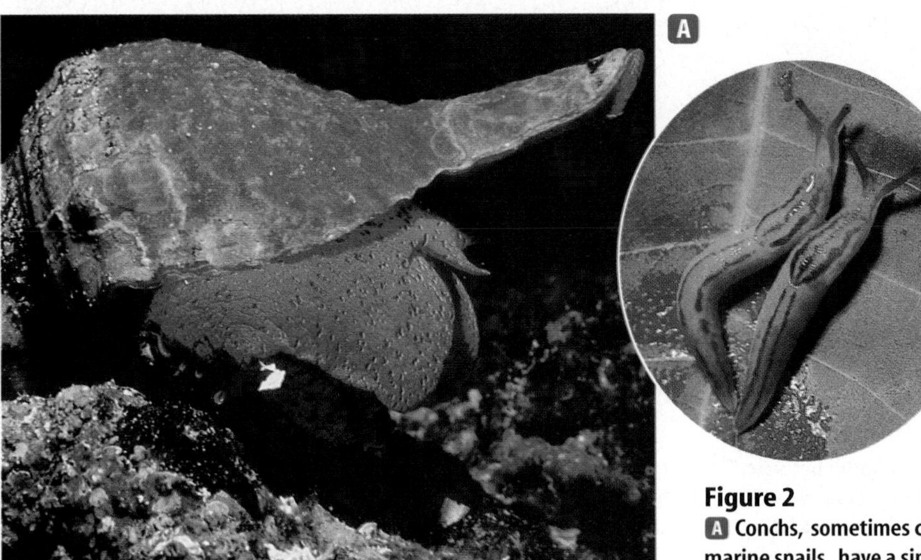

Figure 2
A Conchs, sometimes called marine snails, have a single shell covering their internal organs.
B Garden slugs are mollusks without a shell.

Classification of Mollusks

The first thing scientists look at when they classify mollusks is whether or not the animal has a shell. Mollusks that have shells are then classified by the kind of shell and kind of foot that they have. The three most common groups of mollusks are gastropods, bivalves, and cephalopods.

Gastropods The largest group of mollusks, the gastropods, includes snails, conchs like the one in **Figure 2A,** abalones, whelks, sea slugs, and garden slugs shown in **Figure 2B.** Conchs are sometimes called univalves. Except for slugs, which have no shell, gastropods have a single shell. Many have a pair of tentacles with eyes at the tips. Gastropods use a **radula** (RA juh luh)—a tonguelike organ with rows of teeth—to obtain food. The radula works like a file to scrape and tear food materials. That's why snails are helpful to have in an aquarium—they scrape the algae off the walls and keep the tank clean.

Reading Check *How do gastropods get food?*

Slugs and many snails are adapted to life on land. They move by rhythmic contractions of the muscular foot. Glands in the foot secrete a layer of mucus on which they slide. Slugs and snails are most active at night or on cloudy days when they can avoid the hot Sun. Slugs do not have shells but are protected by a layer of mucus instead, so they must live in moist places. Slugs and land snails damage plants as they eat leaves and stems.

2 Teach

Characteristics of Mollusks

Use Science Words

Word Meaning Have students look up the words *mantle* and *radula* in a dictionary. Mantle comes from a Latin word meaning "cloak" and radula is Latin for "scraper." **How is a mantle like a cloak?** It covers and helps provide protection for the mollusk's body. **How does having a scraper help a mollusk?** It allows the mollusk to scrape food. L2 IS **Linguistic**

Use an Analogy

Show students a steel file, and let them touch its surface. Use the file on a piece of scrap wood. Explain that a radula works in much the same way as the file as it scrapes algae from surfaces.

Classification of Mollusks

Reading Check

Answer They use a tonguelike organ called a radula with rows of teeth for scraping and tearing algae from rocks.

Activity

Collect snails from a local pond or purchase them from a pet shop. Have students observe how the snails move. Have them examine the snails' eyes with a hand lens. Feed lettuce to the snails so students can observe their feeding method with a hand lens. L1 ELL
IS **Visual-Spatial**

Resource Manager

Chapter Resources Booklet
- Transparency Activity, p. 46
- Directed Reading for Content Mastery, pp. 17, 18
- Note-taking Worksheets, pp. 33–36

Curriculum Connection

Literature Read Oliver Wendell Holmes' poem "The Chambered Nautilus," which was first published in 1858. The "ship of pearl" described in the poem is found in the Indian Ocean and the South Pacific Ocean. Have students draw the shell and write a report in their Science Journals about how the shell forms. L2
IS **Visual-Spatial and Linguistic**

Classification of Mollusks, continued

Identifying Misconceptions

Mussels, clams, oysters, and scallops often are called "shellfish." These animals are not fish, they belong to the phylum Mollusca.

Teacher FYI

The Mediterranean rock whelk, *Murex brandaris*, was used by the Romans to dye clothing purple. Each whelk yielded only a small amount of dye, so the dye was very expensive and only wealthy people could afford to have purple clothing. As a result, the color purple became associated with royalty.

Quick Demo

Show students a cuttlebone used in bird cages. The cuttlebone is the internal skeleton of the cuttlefish. Caged birds use the cuttlebone to sharpen their beaks. LS **Visual-Spatial**

Fun Fact

The giant clam has been known to grow up to 1.5 m (4.8 ft.) long and weigh up to 250 kg (550 lbs.).

Figure 3
Scallops force water between their valves to move away from sea stars and other predators. They can move up to 1 m with each muscular contraction.

Bivalves Mollusks that have a hinged, two-part shell joined by strong muscles are called bivalves. Clams, oysters, and scallops, as shown in **Figure 3,** are bivalve mollusks and are a familiar source of seafood. These animals pull their shells closed by contracting powerful muscles near the hinge. To open their shells, they relax these muscles.

Bivalves are well adapted for living in water. For protection, clams burrow deep into the sand by contracting and relaxing their muscular foot. Mussels and oysters attach themselves with a strong thread or cement to a solid surface. This keeps waves and currents from washing them away. Scallops escape predators by rapidly opening and closing their shells. As water is forced out, the scallop moves rapidly in the opposite direction.

Cephalopods The most specialized and complex mollusks are the cephalopods (SE fuh luh pawdz). Squid, octopuses, cuttlefish, and chambered nautiluses belong to this group. The word *cephalopod* means "head-footed" and describes the body structure of these invertebrates. Cephalopods, like the cuttlefish in **Figure 4,** have a large, well-developed head. Their foot is divided into many tentacles with strong suction cups or hooks for capturing prey. All cephalopods are predators. They feed on fish, crustaceans, worms, and other mollusks.

Squid and octopuses have a well-developed nervous system and large eyes similar to human eyes. Unlike other mollusks, cephalopods have closed circulatory systems. In a **closed circulatory system,** blood containing food and oxygen moves through the body in a series of closed vessels, just as your blood moves through your blood vessels.

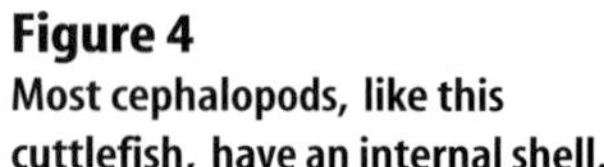

Figure 4
Most cephalopods, like this cuttlefish, have an internal shell.

366

LAB DEMONSTRATION

Purpose to observe mollusk traits

Materials squid, plastic tray, forceps, hand lens, goggles

Procedure As you demonstrate have students draw and label the body, head, eyes, tentacles, mouth, fins, beak, mantle and suction cups. Find the hard point at one end of the squid's fin (pen) and use forceps to pull it out.

Preparation Purchase squid from the supermarket. Wash the squid thoroughly before the demonstration.

Expected Outcome Students should observe mollusk traits in a squid.

Assessment

What are the suction cups used for? to capture and hold prey **What mollusk traits were observed?** soft body, head with eyes, foot divided into tentacles, internal shell (pen), beak used to tear food

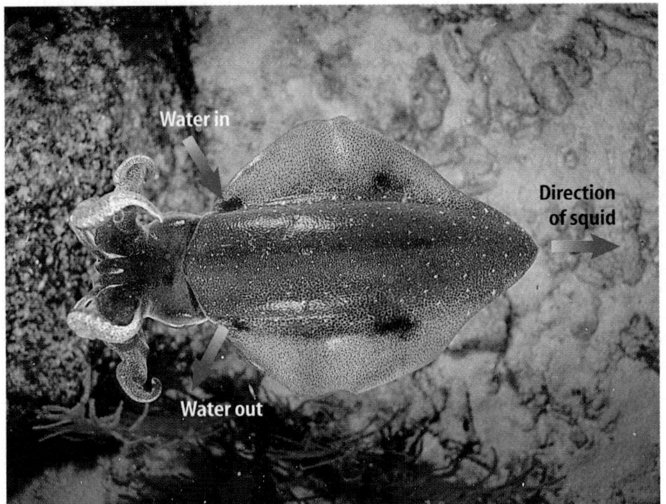

Figure 5
Squid and other cephalopods use jet propulsion to move quickly away from predators.

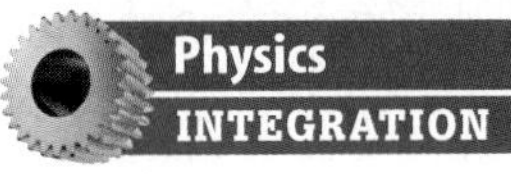

Cephalopod Propulsion All cephalopods live in oceans and are adapted for swimming. Squid and other cephalopods have a water-filled cavity between an outer muscular covering and its internal organs. When the cephalopod tightens its muscular covering, water is forced out through an opening near the head, as shown in **Figure 5.** The jet of water propels the cephalopod backwards, and it moves away quickly. According to Newton's third law of motion, when one object exerts a force on a second object, the second object exerts a force on the first that is equal and opposite in direction. The movement of cephalopods is an example of this law. Muscles exert force on water under the mantle. Water being forced out exerts a force that results in movement backwards.

A squid can propel itself at speeds of more than 6 m/s using this jet propulsion and can briefly outdistance all but whales, dolphins, and the fastest fish. A squid even can jump out of the water and reach heights of almost 5 m above the ocean's surface. It then can travel through the air as far as 15 m. However, squid can maintain their top speed for just a few pulses. Octopuses also can swim by jet propulsion, but they usually use their tentacles to creep more slowly over the ocean floor.

Origin of Mollusks Some species of mollusks, such as the chambered nautilus, have changed little from their ancestors. Mollusk fossils date back more than 500 million years. Many species of mollusks became extinct about 66 million years ago. Today's mollusks are descendants of ancient mollusks.

Earth Science INTEGRATION

By about 245 million years ago, many mollusks had become extinct. What were the major physical events of the time that could have contributed to changing the environment? Write your answers in your Science Journal.

Visual Learning

Figure 5 Using this diagram and the text, have students write a paragraph describing how jet propulsion works, and how it can help a cephalopod escape from predators. L2
LS **Visual-Spatial and Linguistic** P

Discussion

How is a squid adapted for being a predator? It has tentacles with strong suckers for capturing prey, a well-developed nervous system, large eyes, and jet propulsion for rapid movement.

IDENTIFYING Misconceptions

Students may have heard stories of giant squids battling with sperm whales, which may lead them to believe that all squids are giants. The squid most commonly sold in seafood markets, *Loligo*, is only about 30 cm (1 foot) long, and many other species are less than half that size.

Earth Science INTEGRATION

Sea levels were very low and the climate was dry.

Resource Manager

Chapter Resources Booklet
Enrichment, p. 29
Reinforcement, p. 25
Cultural Diversity, p. 3

Cultural Diversity

Contamination of Food Sources Mollusks are a food source the world over. Oysters, clams, squid, scallops, mussels, and octopuses are eaten by millions of people. In some ocean and bay fishing areas, pollution is causing problems for mollusks and the humans that eat them. Have students research the probable cultural and economic effects of pollution on mollusks and on the people who harvest them. L3

Value of Mollusks

Teacher FYI

Oyster farmers can ensure that a pearl is formed by implanting a bead of mussel shell into the oyster. This process, called seeding, increases the chances of an oyster producing a high-quality pearl. Often a small piece of mantle tissue from another oyster also is inserted.

3 Assess

Reteach

Provide students with photographs of various types of mollusks in the classes *Gastropoda*, *Bivalvia*, and *Cephalopoda*. Ask students to separate the photographs into groups. Have students describe the characteristics of mollusks in each group and explain how they classified each organism. L1
LS **Visual-Spatial**

Challenge

Why is an open circulatory system able to meet the needs of a gastropod? Gastropods move slowly and use energy at a low rate, so their needs for food and gas exchange are low. L3 LS **Logical-Mathematical**

Assessment

Process Ask students to write a paragraph comparing the muscular feet of bivalves and gastropods. A gastropod's muscular foot spreads out under its body, and a rippling motion moves it along. The foot of a bivalve is shaped and used differently. It is normally hidden inside the two shells. Some bivalves move by hooking the foot into the sand and pulling themselves along. Use **PASC,** p. 159.

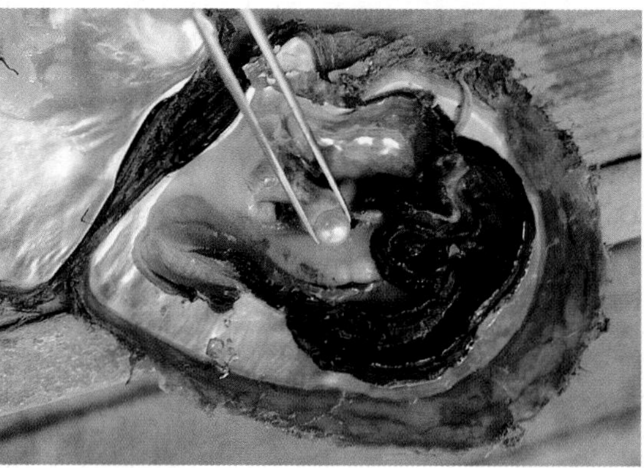

Figure 6
A pearl starts as an irritant—a grain of sand or a parasite—to an oyster. The oyster coats the irritant with a material that forms smooth, hard layers. It can take years for a pearl to form. Culturing pearls is a commercial industry in some countries.

Value of Mollusks

Mollusks have many uses. They are food for fish, sea stars, birds, and humans. Many people make their living raising or collecting mollusks to sell for food. Other invertebrates, such as hermit crabs, use empty mollusk shells as shelter. Many mollusk shells are used for jewelry and decoration. Pearls are produced by several species of mollusks, but most are made by mollusks called pearl oysters, shown in **Figure 6.** Mollusk shells also provide information about the conditions in an ecosystem, including the source and distribution of water pollutants. The internal shell of a cuttlefish is the cuttlebone, which is used in birdcages to provide birds with calcium. Squid and octopuses are able to learn tasks, so scientists are studying their nervous systems to understand how learning takes place and how memory works.

Even though mollusks are beneficial in many ways, they also can cause problems for humans. Land slugs and snails damage plants. Certain species of snails are hosts of parasites that infect humans. Shipworms, a type of bivalve, make holes in submerged wood of docks and boats, causing millions of dollars in damage each year. Because clams, oysters, and other mollusks are filter feeders, bacteria, viruses, and toxic protists from the water can become trapped in the animals. Eating these infected mollusks can result in sickness or even death.

Section 1 Assessment

1. What are the characteristics used to classify mollusks?
2. Name the three groups of mollusks. Identify a mollusk from each group, and explain why it is in that group.
3. Explain how a squid and other cephalopods can move so rapidly.
4. Describe some positive and negative ways that mollusks affect humans.
5. **Think Critically** Why is it unlikely that you would find garden slugs and land snails in a desert?

Skill Builder Activities

6. **Interpreting Scientific Illustrations** Observe the images of gastropods and bivalves in this section. Infer how bivalves are not adapted to life on land and gastropods are. **For more help, refer to the Science Skill Handbook.**
7. **Using a Word Processor** Make a data table that compares and contrasts the following for gastropods, bivalves, and cephalopods: *methods of obtaining food, movement, circulation,* and *habitat.* **For more help, refer to the Technology Skill Handbook.**

Answers to Section Assessment

1. kind of foot; presence or absence of shell; if present, kind of shell
2. gastropods—snails; except for slugs, all have a single shell and a radula; bivalves—clams; have a two-part shell and a muscular foot; cephlapods—squid; have a large, well-developed head and a foot that is divided into tentacles
3. Jet propulsion; water is ejected through the funnel or siphon in one direction, moving the animal in the opposite direction.
4. Mollusks are used for food, jewelry, and research. They damage boats and docks. Eating those that contain disease-causing organisms can cause illness.
5. The desert is too dry. Slugs and snails require a moist environment.
6. Bivalves filter food from the water. They move slowly or remain attached to one place. Gastropods use their radula and teeth to eat plants and algae.
7. Check data tables for accuracy.

SECTION 2

Segmented Worms

Segmented Worm Characteristics

The worms you see crawling across sidewalks after a rain and those used for fishing are called annelids (A nul udz). The word *annelid* means "little rings" and describes the bodies of these worms. They have tube-shaped bodies that are divided into many segments.

Have you ever watched a robin try to pull an earthworm out of the ground or tried it yourself? Why don't they slip out of the soil easily? On the outside of each body segment are bristlelike structures called **setae** (SEE tee). Segmented worms use their setae to hold on to the soil and to move. Segmented worms also have bilateral symmetry, a body cavity that holds the organs, and two body openings—a mouth and an anus. Annelids can be found in freshwater, salt water, and moist soil. Earthworms, like the one in **Figure 7,** marine worms, and leeches are examples of annelids.

Reading Check *What is the function of setae?*

As You Read

***What* You'll Learn**

- **Identify** the characteristics of segmented worms.
- **Describe** the structures of an earthworm and how it takes in and digests food.
- **Explain** the importance of segmented worms.

Vocabulary
setae
crop
gizzard

***Why* It's Important**
Earthworms condition and aerate the soil, which helps increase crop yields.

Earthworm Body Systems

The most well-known annelids are earthworms. They have a definite anterior, or front end, and a posterior, or back end. Earthworms have more than 100 body segments. The segments can be seen on the outside and the inside of the body cavity. Each body segment, except for the first and last segments, has four pairs of setae. Earthworms move by using their setae and two sets of muscles in the body wall. One set of muscles runs the length of the body, and the other set circles the body. When an earthworm contracts its long muscles, it causes some of the segments to bunch up and the setae to stick out. This anchors the worm to the soil. When the circular muscles contract, the setae are pulled in and the worm can move forward.

Figure 7
One species of earthworm that lives in Australia can grow to be 3.3 m long.

SECTION

Segmented Worms

1 Motivate

Bellringer Transparency

Display the Section Focus Transparency for Section 2. Use the accompanying Transparency Activity Master. L2 ELL

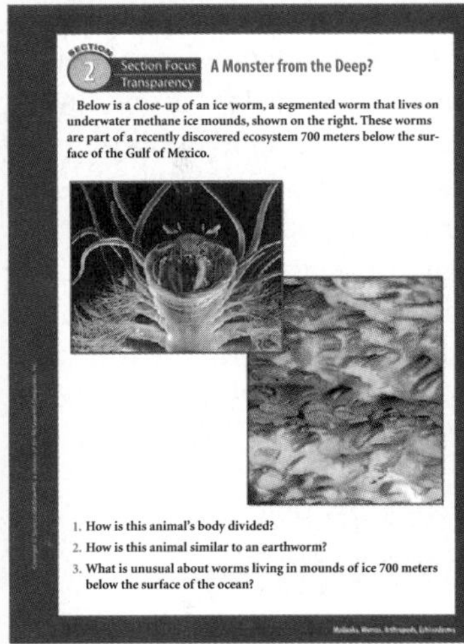

Section 2 Section Focus Transparency **A Monster from the Deep?**

Below is a close-up of an ice worm, a segmented worm that lives on underwater methane ice mounds, shown on the right. These worms are part of a recently discovered ecosystem 700 meters below the surface of the Gulf of Mexico.

1. How is this animal's body divided?
2. How is this animal similar to an earthworm?
3. What is unusual about worms living in mounds of ice 700 meters below the surface of the ocean?

Tie to Prior Knowledge

Most students have seen earthworms. Discuss their observations about worms, where worms live, and what they eat.

Reading Check

Answer to hold onto soil and move

Section Assessment Planner

PORTFOLIO
Reteach, p. 373

PERFORMANCE ASSESSMENT
Skill Builder Activities, p. 373
See page 394 for more options.

CONTENT ASSESSMENT
Section, p. 373
Challenge, p. 373
Chapter, pp. 394–395

Resource Manager

Chapter Resources Booklet
Transparency Activity, p. 47

2 Teach

Segmented Worm Characteristics

Discussion

Display specimens (or pictures on a bulletin board) of annelids (clam worms, tube worms, fan worms, leeches, *Tubifex* worms, redworms and earthworms). Have students discuss how they are similar.

Earthworm Body Systems

Activity

Have several students set up a maze in the classroom, using desks and chairs. Blindfold volunteers who have not seen the maze, and ask them to find their way through it. Use this activity to help students understand that earthworms find food and escape predators without being able to see. L2 LS **Kinesthetic**

Quick Demo

Dissect a preserved earthworm, and have students examine its digestive, circulatory, excretory, reproductive, and nervous systems. LS **Visual-Spatial**

Fun Fact

Even though earthworms do not have eyes, they have light receptors in the head and react to the presence or absence of light.

Figure 8
Earthworm castings—also called vermicompost—are used as an organic fertilizer in gardens.

Digestion and Excretion As an earthworm burrows through the soil, it takes soil into its mouth. Earthworms get energy from the bits of leaves and other organic matter found in the soil. The soil ingested by an earthworm moves to the **crop,** which is a sac used for storage. Behind the crop is a muscular structure called the **gizzard,** which grinds the soil and the bits of organic matter. This ground material passes to the intestine, where the organic matter is broken down and the nutrients are absorbed by the blood. Wastes leave the worm through the anus. When earthworms take in soil, they provide spaces for air and water to flow through it and mix the soil. Their wastes pile up at the openings to their burrows. These piles are called castings. Castings, like those in **Figure 8,** help fertilize the soil.

Circulation and Respiration Earthworms have a closed circulatory system, as shown in **Figure 9.** Two blood vessels along the top of the body and one along the bottom of the body meet in the front end of the earthworm. There, they connect to heartlike structures called aortic arches, which pump blood through the body. Smaller vessels go into each body segment.

Earthworms don't have gills or lungs. Oxygen and carbon dioxide are exchanged through their skin, which is covered with a thin film of watery mucus. It's important never to touch earthworms with dry hands or remove their thin mucous layer, because they could suffocate. But as you can tell after a rainstorm, earthworms don't survive in puddles of water either.

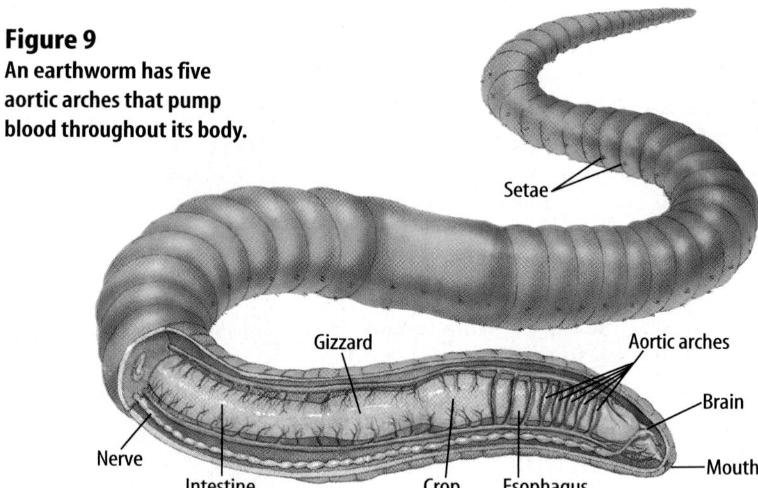

Figure 9
An earthworm has five aortic arches that pump blood throughout its body.

Inclusion Strategies

Gifted Have students research the major complex invertebrates in the chapter. Have them make identification cards of the ones in which they are most interested. On one side of the card, they can draw a picture of the invertebrate and on the other, give the name and major characteristics. A game can be played by keeping track of the number of organisms students can identify. L3

Teacher FYI

Earthworm aeration of the soil is so beneficial that their presence in hundreds or thousands per hectare is a characteristic of a productive farm. *Lumbricus terrestris* ingests its own weight in soil and decaying matter every day. Earthworms survive in thin films of water in slightly moist soil, but if the soil becomes flooded, the worms can drown.

Nerve Response and Reproduction Earthworms have a small brain in their front segment. Nerves in each segment join to form a main nerve cord that connects to the brain. Earthworms respond to light, temperature, and moisture.

Earthworms are hermaphrodites (hur MAF ruh dites)—meaning they produce sperm and eggs in the same body. Even though each worm has male and female reproductive structures, an individual worm can't fertilize its own eggs. Instead, it has to receive sperm from another earthworm in order to reproduce.

Marine Worms

More than 8,000 species of marine worms, or polychaetes, (PAH lee keets) exist, which is more than any other kind of annelid. Marine worms float, burrow, build structures, or walk along the ocean floor. Some polychaetes even produce their own light. Others, like the ice worms in **Figure 10,** are able to live 540 m deep. Polychaetes, like earthworms, have segments with setae. However, the setae occur in bundles on these worms. The word *polychaete* means "many bristles."

Sessile, bottom-dwelling polychaetes, such as the marine worms shown in **Figure 11A,** have specialized tentacles that are used for exchanging oxygen and carbon dioxide and gathering food. Some marine worms build tubes around their bodies. When these worms are startled, they retreat into their tubes. Free-swimming polychaetes, such as the bristleworm shown in **Figure 11B,** have a head with eyes; a tail; and parapodia (pur uh POH dee uh), which are paired, fleshy outgrowths on their segments. The parapodia help in feeding and locomotion.

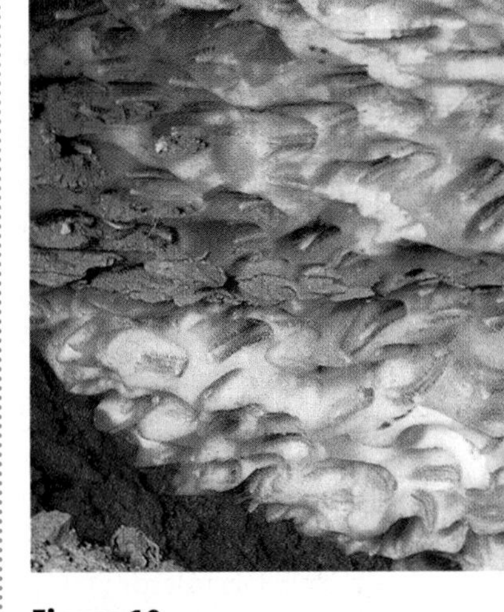

Figure 10
Ice worms, a type of marine polychaete, were discovered first in 1997 living 540 m deep in the Gulf of Mexico.

Figure 11
A These Christmas tree worms filter microorganisms from the water to eat. B Some free-swimming polychaetes swim backwards and forwards, so some have eyes at both ends of their body.

Extension

Have students research the economic importance of earthworms and how they are raised commercially. L2

Marine Worms

Teacher FYI

Polychaetes live in cracks and crevices in coral reefs, sand, mud, piles of rock, and in open water. Some build their own tube structures and burrows. Many are free-moving. Some polychaetes are brightly colored, iridescent, or even luminescent.

Visual Learning

Figure 11 Have students compare and contrast the marine worms found in this figure. L1 LS **Visual-Spatial**

Discussion

Have students discuss the meaning of "wormy" slang and colloquial expressions in the English language. Examples are: "the worm in the apple" (one bad thing in an otherwise good situation); "worm your way out of something" (get out of unpleasant situations using devious methods); describing a person as a "leech" (one who clings to another without contributing).

Resource Manager

Chapter Resources Booklet
- Directed Reading for Content Mastery, p. 18
- Transparency Activity, pp. 51–52
- Lab Activity, pp. 9–12

Inclusion Strategies

Learning Disabled Have students make a picture dictionary illustrating the meaning of key words used in each section of this chapter. Have them begin by looking up the prefixes *exo-* and *endo-* in the dictionary. L1  **Visual-Spatial**

Leeches

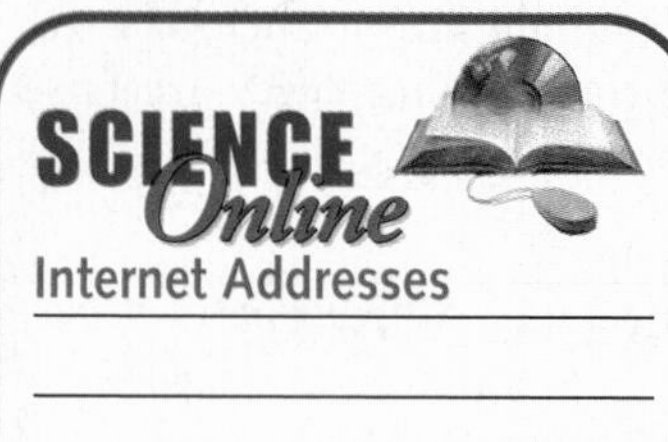

Internet Addresses

Explore the Glencoe Science Web site at **science.glencoe.com** to find out more about topics in this section.

Reading Check

Answer to keep blood flowing to the repaired area

Discussion

How do earthworms and leeches differ? Earthworms have setae; leeches do not. Leeches have anterior and posterior suckers; earthworms do not. **Why are both classified as annelids?** Each has a body cavity that holds organs and a segmented body.

Value of Segmented Worms

Extension

Have students research and report on *Hirudo medicinalis.* This leech produces the anticoagulant hirudin. *Hirudo medicinalis,* the medicinal leech, feeds primarily on the blood of mammals, but it also sucks blood from amphibians, reptiles, and fish. It has three jaws with sharp teeth that make a Y-shaped incision in the skin of the host. After it feeds, the leech detaches from its host and may not feed again for as long as 18 months. L3

Leeches

A favorite topic for scary movies is leeches. If you've ever had to remove a leech from your body after swimming in a freshwater pond, lake, or river, you know it isn't fun. Leeches are segmented worms, but their bodies are not as round or as long as earthworms are, and they don't have setae. They feed on the blood of other animals. A sucker at each end of a leech's body is used to attach itself to an animal. If a leech attaches to you, you probably won't feel it. Leeches produce many chemicals, including an anesthetic (a nus THEH tik) that numbs the wound so you don't feel its bite. Why is producing an anesthetic an advantage to a leech? After the leech has attached itself, it cuts into the animal and sucks out two to ten times its own weight in blood. Even though leeches prefer to eat blood, they can survive by eating aquatic insects and other organisms instead.

SCIENCE Online

Research Visit the Glencoe Science Web site at **science.glencoe.com** for information about the uses of chemicals from leech saliva. Communicate to your class what you learn.

Leeches and Medicine

Sometimes, leeches are used after surgery to keep blood flowing to the repaired area, as shown in **Figure 12.** For example, the tiny blood vessels in the ear quickly can become blocked with blood clots after surgery. To keep blood flowing in such places, physicians might attach leeches to the surgical site. As the leeches feed on the blood, chemicals in their saliva prevent the blood from coagulating. Besides the anti-clotting chemical, leech saliva also contains a chemical that dilates blood vessels, which improves the blood flow and allows the wound to heal more quickly. These chemicals are being studied to treat patients with heart or circulatory diseases, strokes, arthritis, or glaucoma.

Reading Check *Why are leeches sometimes used after surgery?*

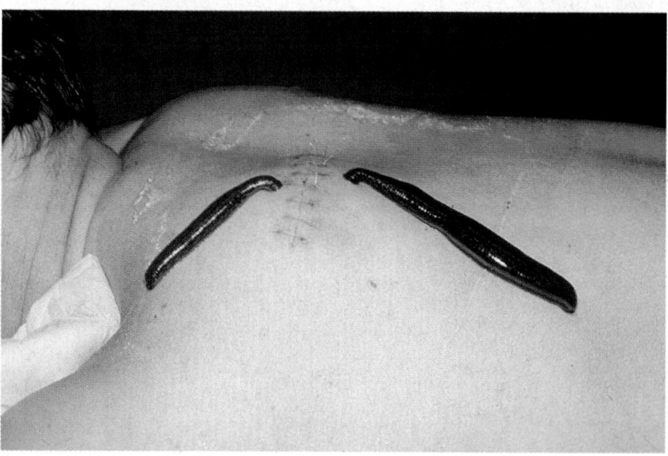

Figure 12
Medical leeches are used sometimes to prevent blood from clotting or accumulating in damaged skin.

Science Journal

Annelids Have students research and report on annelids other than earthworms and leeches. Some examples are feather worms, fanworms, peacock worms, and giant tube worms that live in deep-sea vents. Have them include the structural differences among the worms in their reports. L2 LS **Linguistic**

Resource Manager 

Chapter Resources Booklet
Enrichment, p. 31
Reinforcement, p. 27

Performance Assessment in the Science Classroom, p. 55

Value of Segmented Worms

Different kinds of segmented worms are helpful to other animals in a variety of ways. Earthworms help aerate the soil by constantly burrowing through it. By grinding and partially digesting the large amount of plant material in soil, earthworms speed up the return of nitrogen and other nutrients to the soil for use by plants.

Researchers are developing drugs based on the chemicals that come from leeches because leech saliva prevents blood clots. Small marine worms and their larvae are part of ocean plankton, which is food for many fish, invertebrates, and mammals. Bottom-dwelling marine worms are a food source for many fish.

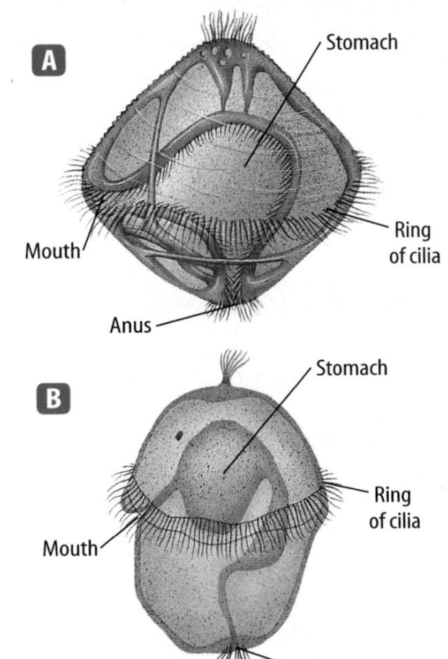

Figure 13
Some A mollusk larvae have many structures that are similar to those of some B annelid larvae.

Origin of Segmented Worms

Some scientists hypothesize that segmented worms evolved in the sea. The fossil record for segmented worms is limited because of their soft bodies. The tubes of marine worms are the most common fossils of the segmented worms. Some of these fossils date back about 620 million years.

Similarities between mollusks and segmented worms suggest that they could have a common ancestor. These groups were the first animals to have a body cavity with space for body organs to develop and function. Mollusks and segmented worms have a one-way digestive system with a separate mouth and anus. Their larvae, shown in **Figure 13,** are similar and are the best evidence that they have a common ancestor.

Section 2 Assessment

1. What is the most distinguishing characteristic of annelids?
2. How does an earthworm exchange oxygen and carbon dioxide with its environment?
3. Describe how an earthworm takes in and digests its food.
4. Why would farmers promote the use of earthworms in their fields?
5. **Think Critically** What advantages do marine worms with tubes have over free-moving polychaetes?

Skill Builder Activities

6. **Comparing and Contrasting** Compare how earthworms and marine worms obtain oxygen. **For more help, refer to the** **Science Skill Handbook.**
7. **Using Proportions** Suppose you find six earthworms in a 10-cm^3 volume of soil. Based on this sample, calculate the number of earthworms you would find in a 10-m^3 volume of soil. **For more help, refer to the** **Math Skill Handbook.**

Origin of Segmented Worms

Visual Learning

Figure 13 Have students compare the structures of the larvae.

3 Assess

Reteach

Have students make a chart that compares the structures, environment, and ways of life (free-living or parasitic) of mollusks and segmented worms. L2 P

Challenge

How does an annelid's segmentation help it move? Segmentation increases the flexibility of an earthworm because separate parts can move independently of one another.

Content Have students work in groups to list earthworm body systems, and external features. Use **PASC,** p. 169.

Answers to Section Assessment

1. body segments
2. by diffusion through its moist skin
3. It takes in soil, which moves through the digestive system. Food (plant and animal material in the soil) is removed from the soil and digested. Waste material leaves through the anus.
4. Earthworms break up hard, packed soil, allowing oxygen and water to penetrate the soil more easily to reach the roots of plants. Their wastes also help fertilize the soil.
5. Tube worms have a protective covering.
6. Earthworms obtain oxygen through their moist skin. Marine worms have specialized tentacles for obtaining oxygen.
7. 6,000 earthworms

SECTION

Arthropods

1 Motivate

Bellringer Transparency

Display the Section Focus Transparency for Section 3. Use the accompanying Transparency Activity Master. L2 ELL

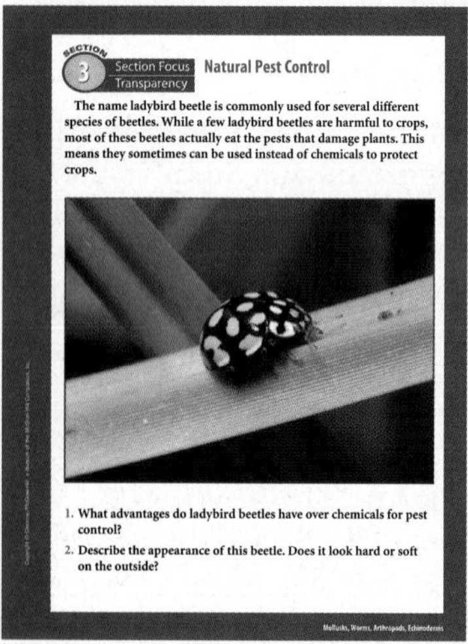

SECTION 3 Section Focus Transparency **Natural Pest Control**

The name ladybird beetle is commonly used for several different species of beetles. While a few ladybird beetles are harmful to crops, most of these beetles actually eat the pests that damage plants. This means they sometimes can be used instead of chemicals to protect crops.

1. **What advantages do ladybird beetles have over chemicals for pest control?**
2. **Describe the appearance of this beetle. Does it look hard or soft on the outside?**

Mollusks, Worms, Arthropods, Echinoderms

Tie to Prior Knowledge

Students will be familiar with many species in the phylum *Arthropoda*. Many will have eaten shrimp and lobsters. All will have some knowledge of insects and spiders. Use their knowledge of arthropods in identifying common characteristics.

SECTION 3

Arthropods

As You Read

What **You'll Learn**

- **Determine** the characteristics that are used to classify arthropods.
- **Explain** how the structure of the exoskeleton relates to its function.
- **Distinguish** between complete and incomplete metamorphosis.

Vocabulary
appendage
exoskeleton
molting
spiracle
metamorphosis

Why **It's Important**

Arthropods, such as those that carry diseases and eat crops, affect your life every day.

Characteristics of Arthropods

There are more than a million different species of arthropods, (AR thruh pahdz) making them the largest group of animals. The word *arthropoda* means "jointed foot." The jointed **appendages** of arthropods can include legs, antennae, claws, and pincers. Arthropod appendages are adapted for moving about, capturing prey, feeding, mating, and sensing their environment. Arthropods also have bilateral symmetry, segmented bodies, an exoskeleton, a body cavity, a digestive system with two openings, and a nervous system. Most arthropod species have separate sexes and reproduce sexually. Arthropods are adapted to living in almost every environment. They vary in size from microscopic dust mites to the large, Japanese spider crab, shown in **Figure 14.**

Segmented Bodies The bodies of arthropods are divided into segments similar to those of segmented worms. Some arthropods have many segments, but others have segments that are fused together to form body regions, such as those of insects, spiders, and crabs.

Exoskeletons All arthropods have a hard, outer covering called an **exoskeleton.** It covers, supports, and protects the internal body and provides places for muscles to attach. In many land-dwelling arthropods, for example insects, the exoskeleton has a waxy layer that reduces water loss from the animal.

An exoskeleton cannot grow as the animal grows. From time to time, it is shed and replaced by a new one in a process called **molting.** While the animals are molting, they are not well protected from predators because the new exoskeleton is soft. Before the new exoskeleton hardens, the animal swallows air or water to increase its exoskeleton's size. This way the new exoskeleton allows room for growth.

Figure 14
The Japanese spider crab has legs that can span more than 3 m.

Section Assessment Planner

PORTFOLIO
Activity, p. 377

PERFORMANCE ASSESSMENT
Skill Builder Activities, p. 382
MiniLAB, p. 376
See page 394 for more options.

CONTENT ASSESSMENT
Section, p. 382
Challenge, p. 382
Chapter, pp. 394–395

Insects

More species of insects exist than all other animal groups combined. More than 700,000 species of insects have been classified, and scientists identify more each year. Insects have three body regions—a head, a thorax, and an abdomen, as shown in **Figure 15.** However, it is almost impossible on some insects to see where one region stops and the next one begins.

Figure 15
One of the largest types of ants is the carpenter ant. Like all insects, it has a head, thorax, and abdomen.

Head An insect's head has a pair of antennae, eyes, and a mouth. The antennae are used for touch and smell. The eyes are simple or compound. Simple eyes detect light and darkness. Compound eyes, like those in **Figure 16,** contain many lenses and can detect colors and movement. The mouthparts of insects vary, depending on what the insect eats.

Thorax Three pairs of legs and one or two pairs of wings, if present, are attached to the thorax. Some insects, such as silverfish and fleas, don't have wings, and other insects have wings only for part of their lives. Insects are the only invertebrate animals that can fly. Flying allows insects to find places to live, food sources, and mates. Flight also helps them escape from their predators.

Reading Check *How does flight benefit insects?*

Abdomen The abdomen has neither wings nor legs but it is where the reproductive structures are found. Females lay thousands of eggs, but only a fraction of the eggs develop into adults. Think about how overproduction of eggs might ensure that each insect species will continue.

Insects have an open circulatory system that carries digested food to cells and removes wastes. However, insect blood does not carry oxygen because it does not have hemoglobin. Instead, insects have openings called **spiracles** (SPIHR ih kulz) on the abdomen and thorax through which air enters and waste gases leave the insect's body.

Figure 16
Each compound eye is made up of small lenses that fit together. Each lens sees a part of the picture to make up the whole scene. Insects can't focus their eyes. Their eyes are always open and can detect movements.

Magnification: 5×

2 Teach

Characteristics of Arthropods

Quick Demo

Provide students with live or preserved specimens of insects, crayfish, spiders, and other arthropods. Ask them to compare and contrast body segments, appendages, and other body structures. LS **Visual-Spatial**

Use an Analogy

Show students a picture of the armor worn by medieval knights. Compare the limitations of the arthropod skeleton with those of a person wearing a suit of armor. LS **Visual-Spatial**

Insects

Reading Check

Answer Flying allows insects to find places to live, find food sources, find mates, and escape from predators.

Fun Fact

The largest beetles can be up to 16.7 cm in length.

Resource Manager

Chapter Resources Booklet
Transparency Activity, p. 48

Life Science Critical Thinking/Problem Solving, p. 21

Science Journal

Insect Societies Some insects, including ants, bees, termites, and wasps, live in highly organized societies. Each member has a specific job necessary for the survival of the colony. Have students choose a social insect and describe in their Science Journals the role of each member of the society. L2 LS **Linguistic**

Purpose Students observe metamorphosis in fruit flies. L1 IS **Visual-Spatial**

Materials small piece of banana, baby food jar, cheesecloth, rubber band, hand lens

Teaching Strategy Fruit fly cultures may be purchased from a biological supply company.

Troubleshooting Be sure containers have flies at all stages of metamorphosis. Students may have a difficult time seeing the egg stage. Point out this stage to students, and have them observe the eggs with a hand lens.

Analysis

1. complete metamorphosis
2. The flies are most active in the larva and adult stages.

Assessment

Performance Have students observe mealworms over a period of five to six weeks and compare their metamorphosis with that of fruit flies. Both are complete metamorphoses. The stages are longer in mealworms. Use **PASC,** p. 99.

Observing Metamorphosis

Procedure

1. Place a 2-cm piece of ripe **banana** in a **jar** and leave it open.
2. Check the jar every day for two weeks. When you see fruit flies, cover the mouth of the jar with **cheesecloth.**
3. Identify, describe, and draw all the stages of metamorphosis that you observe.

Analysis

1. What type of metamorphosis do fruit flies undergo?
2. In which stages are the flies the most active?

From Egg to Adult Many insects go through changes in body form as they grow. This series of changes is called **metamorphosis** (meh tuh MOR fuh sus). Grasshoppers, silverfish, lice, and crickets undergo incomplete metamorphosis, shown in **Figure 17A.** The stages of incomplete metamorphosis are egg, nymph, and adult. The nymph form molts several times before becoming an adult. Many insects—butterflies, beetles, ants, bees, moths, and flies—undergo complete metamorphosis, shown in **Figure 17B.** The stages of complete metamorphosis are egg, larva, pupa, and adult. Caterpillar is the common name for the larva of a moth or butterfly. Other insect larvae are called grubs, maggots, or mealworms. Only larval forms molt.

Reading Check *When do grasshoppers molt?*

Figure 17
The two types of metamorphosis are shown here.

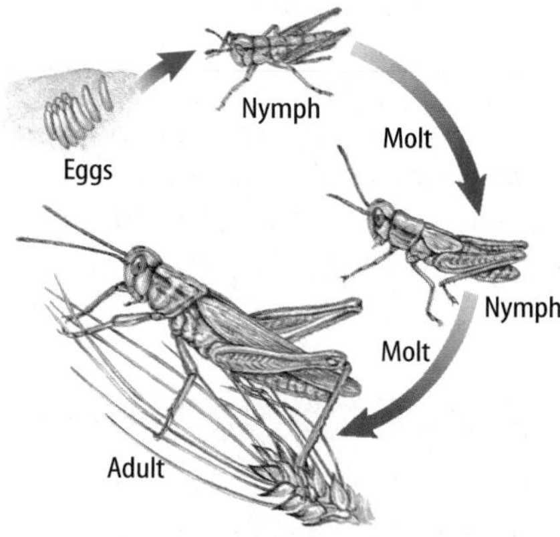

A Nymphs are smaller versions of their parents.

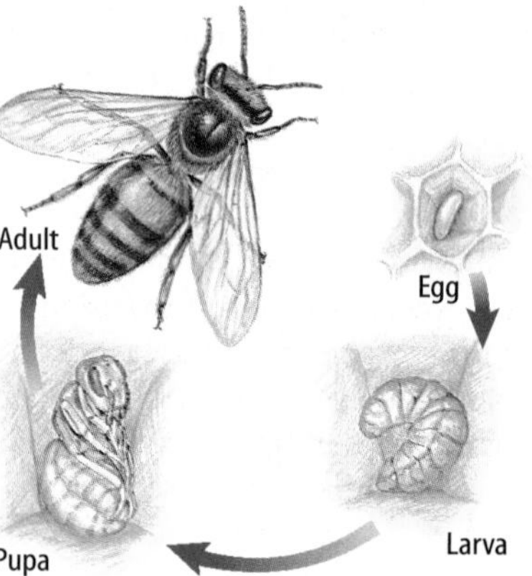

B Many insects go through complete metamorphosis.

Reading Check

Answer when in its nymph form

Visual Learning

Figure 17 Have students make a table in which they compare and contrast the two types of metamorphoses shown in this figure. L2 IS **Visual-Spatial**

Science Journal

Healing Powers Have students research the use of green bottle fly (*Lucilia sericata*) maggots to promote healing of open sores. They can use scientific and medical magazines, newspaper articles, and television programs for information. L2 IS **Linguistic**

Inclusion Strategies

Visually Impaired Purchase a variety of scientifically accurate, arthropod models. As a visually impaired student touches and describes each feature of a model, have a sighted student name the feature and record the description. Together, they should devise a classification system for the arthropod models. L2 COOP LEARN IS **Kinesthetic and Interpersonal**

Figure 18
Feeding adaptations of insects include different mouthparts.

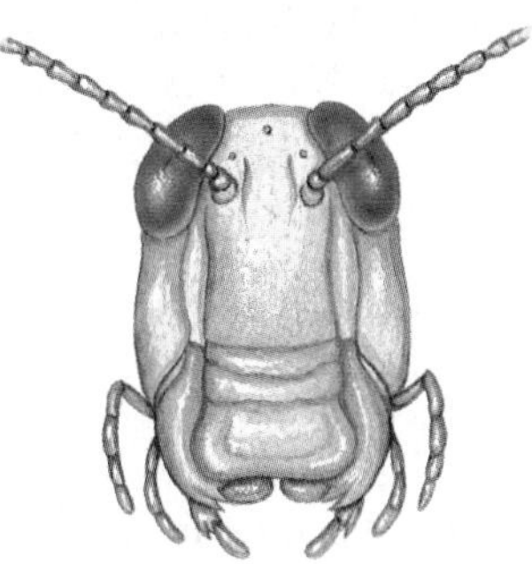

A **Grasshoppers have left and right mouthparts called mandibles that enable them to chew through tough plant tissues.**

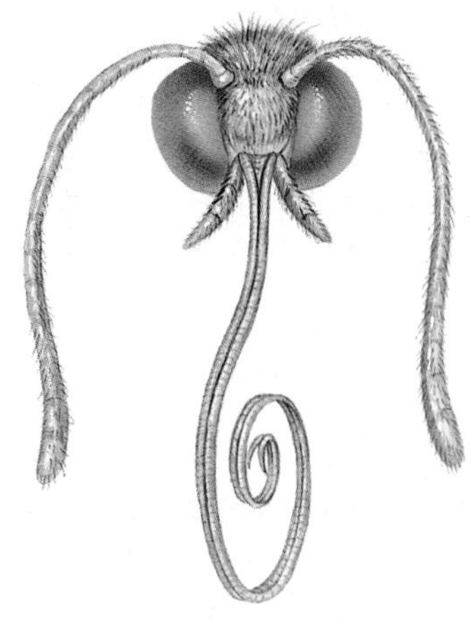

B **Butterflies and other nectar eaters have a long siphon that enables them to drink nectar from flowers.**

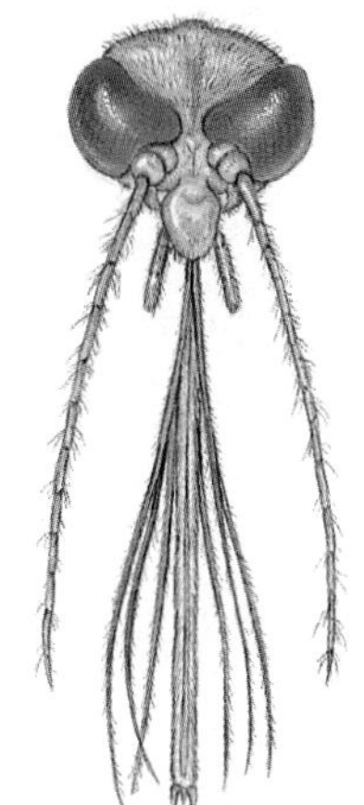

C **Mosquitoes have mouths that are adapted for piercing skin and sucking blood.**

Obtaining Food Insects feed on plants, the blood of animals, nectar, decaying materials, wood in houses, and clothes. Mouthparts of insects, as shown in **Figure 18,** are as diverse as the insects themselves. Grasshoppers and ants have large mandibles (MAN duh bulz) for chewing plant tissue. Butterflies and honeybees are equipped with siphons for lapping up nectar in flowers. Aphids and cicadas pierce plant tissues and suck out plant fluids. Praying mantises and centipedes eat other animals. External parasites, such as fleas and lice, drink the blood and body fluids of other animals. Silverfish eat things that contain starch and some moth larvae eat wool clothing.

Insect Success Because of their tough, flexible, waterproof exoskeletons; their ability to fly; rapid reproductive cycles; and small sizes, insects are extremely successful. Most insects have short life spans, so genetic traits can change more quickly in insect populations than in organisms that take longer to reproduce. Because insects generally are small, they can live in a wide range of environments and avoid their enemies. Many species of insects can live in the same area and not compete with one another for food, because many are so specialized in what they eat.

Protective coloration, or camouflage, allows insects to blend in with their surroundings. Many moths resting on trees look like tree bark or bird droppings. Walking sticks and some caterpillars resemble twigs. When a leaf butterfly folds its wings it looks like a dead leaf.

Health INTEGRATION

Some insects may carry certain diseases to humans. Some species of mosquitoes can carry malaria or yellow fever. Research to learn about one disease that is carried by an insect. Build a bulletin board of all the information that you and your classmates gather.

IDENTIFYING Misconceptions

Make sure students understand that grubs and caterpillars are not annelids. They are insects in larval stages.

Activity

Have students design a poster to increase awareness of butterflies and the need to protect them. They could use the monarch butterfly and draw a map showing the migration route of the monarch from the United States to central Mexico. The poster should also include plants that butterflies feed on and pollinate. L2

 **Visual-Spatial** P

Health INTEGRATION

Possible topics: malaria, myiasis, relapsing fever, African sleeping sickness, leishmaniasis, yellow fever, dengue fever

Fun Fact

Insects are found in every biome except the deep ocean. Some insect species can survive in extremely cold climates because they have a natural antifreeze in their body fluids. Fleas, lice, and midges are all found in extremely cold areas.

Resource Manager 

Chapter Resources Booklet
MiniLAB, p. 3
Reading and Writing Skill Activities, p. 49

Teacher FYI

Insect wings are not modified limbs as are wings in bats and birds. They are thin outgrowths of the exoskeleton. The wings of many insects are made of a double layer of chitin with a supporting network of hollow veins filled with air or blood.

Activity

Give each group a dissecting tray containing a preserved millipede, centipede, crayfish, grasshopper, and spider. Have the students list the characteristics of the animals and determine how the five organisms are similar and how they are different. L1 COOP LEARN

LS **Kinesthetic**

Arachnids

Most spider webs are made of sticky strands of silk. Students may believe that spiders' legs somehow keep them from getting stuck in their own webs. In reality, spiders weave some strands that are not sticky. They walk along these to build and repair their webs and to wrap paralyzed prey.

Math Skills Activity

National Math Standards

Correlation to Mathematics Objectives

1, 2, 6, 8, 9

Teaching Suggestion

- Silk is a naturally produced material composed of protein; nylon is a synthetic polymer formed through a chemical reaction.
- Use a rubber band to illustrate elasticity. Stretch a rubber band and it will return back to its original length. However, with nylon and silk when a certain length is reached, these fibers will no longer return to their original lengths.

Answer to Practice Problem

46.5 cm - 40 cm = 6.5 cm

6.5 cm / 40 cm × 100 = 16.25 %

A spider's silk has greater elasticity (30.7 %) than nylon (16.25 %).

Arachnids

Spiders, scorpions, mites, and ticks are examples of arachnids (uh RAK nudz). They have two body regions—a head-chest region called the cephalothorax (se fuh luh THOR aks) and an abdomen. Arachnids have four pairs of legs but no antennae. Many arachnids are adapted to kill prey with poison glands, stingers, or fangs. Others are parasites.

Scorpions Arachnids that have a sharp, poison-filled stinger at the end of their abdomen are called scorpions. The venom from the stinger paralyzes the prey. Unlike other arachnids, scorpions have a pair of well-developed appendages—pincers—with which they grab their prey. The sting of a scorpion is painful and can be fatal to humans.

Math Skills Activity

Calculating Percent of Elasticity

Example Problem

A strand of spider's silk can be stretched from 65 cm to 85 cm before it loses its elasticity—the ability to snap back to its original length. Calculate the percent of elasticity of spider's silk.

Solution

1. *This is what you know:* original length of silk strand = 65 cm; stretched length of silk strand = 85 cm
2. *This is what you need to find:* percent of elasticity
3. *This is what you must do:* Find the difference between the stretched and original length. 85 cm − 65 cm = 20 cm
4. *Use the following equation to make your calculations:*

$$\frac{\text{difference in length}}{\text{original length}} \times 100 = \text{\% of elasticity}$$

$$\frac{20\text{ cm}}{65\text{ cm}} \times 100 = 30.7\text{ \% of elasticity}$$

Practice Problem

A 40-cm strand of nylon can be stretched to a length of 46.5 cm before losing its elasticity. Calculate the percent of elasticity for nylon and compare it to that of spider's silk.

For more help, refer to the Math Skill Handbook.

Science Journal

Careers Students may be interested in careers related to arthropods. Suggest that they research different types of careers in the field of entomology and record in their Science Journals what skills and education are needed and what the jobs entail. L2 LS **Linguistic**

Cultural Diversity

Origin of Silk Silk moth cocoons are one continuous strand of sticky silk. According to Chinese legends, silk cloth originated around 3000 B.C. It is said that a cocoon accidentally fell into an empress' tea. The tea dissolved the substance that glued the cocoon together, revealing the long silk strand. Several strands were woven into a thread and, eventually, silk fabric was woven.

Spiders Because spiders can't chew their food, they release enzymes into their prey that help digest it. The spider then sucks the predigested liquid into its mouth.

Oxygen and carbon dioxide are exchanged in book lungs, illustrated in **Figure 19.** Openings on the abdomen allow these gases to move into and out of the book lungs.

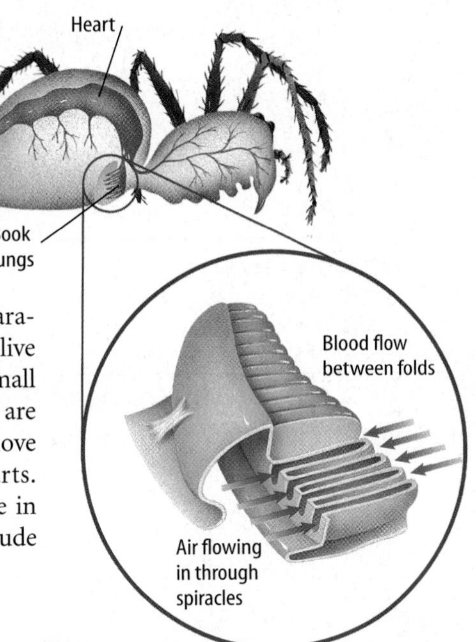

Mites and Ticks Most mites are animal or plant parasites. However, some are not parasites, like the mites that live in the follicles of human eyelashes. Most mites are so small that they look like tiny specs to the unaided eye. All ticks are animal parasites. Ticks attach to their host's skin and remove blood from their hosts through specialized mouthparts. Ticks often carry bacteria and viruses that cause disease in humans and other animals. Diseases carried by ticks include Lyme disease and Rocky Mountain spotted fever.

Centipedes and Millipedes

Two groups of arthropods—centipedes and millipedes—have long bodies with many segments, exoskeletons, jointed legs, antennae, and simple eyes. They can be found in damp environments, including in woodpiles, under vegetation, and in basements. Centipedes and millipedes reproduce sexually. They make nests for their eggs and stay with them until the eggs hatch.

Compare the centipede and millipede in **Figure 20.** How many pairs of legs does the centipede have per segment? How many pairs of legs does the millipede have per segment? Centipedes hunt for their prey, which includes snails, slugs, and worms. They have a pair of poison claws that they use to inject venom into their prey. Their pinches are painful to humans but usually aren't fatal. Millipedes feed on plants and decaying material and often are found under the damp plant material.

Figure 19
Air circulates between the moist folds of the book lungs bringing oxygen to the blood.

Figure 20
A Centipedes are predators—they capture and eat other animals. B Millipedes eat plants or decaying plant material.

Use Science Words

Word Origin Have students look up the word *arachnid* to find its origin. Arachnid comes from the Greek *arachne* meaning "spider." In Greek mythology, Athena, the goddess of wisdom, skills, and warfare, turns the girl Arachne into a spider for besting the goddess in a weaving contest.

Make a Model

Have students use plastic foam balls (or marshmallows) of the same size and toothpicks to make a model of each of the following: spider, scorpion, insect, millipede, and centipede. Tell them the balls represent body segments and the toothpicks represent appendages. The toothpicks can also be used to hold the balls together. L2
LS **Kinesthetic**

Extension

Have students prepare an illustrated report on the various hunting methods of spiders. Include the wolf spider and trap-door spider. L2
LS **Visual-Spatial**

Centipedes and Millipedes

Quick Demo

Show students the differences in centipedes and millipedes by using living or preserved specimens or photographs. Point out the number of legs per segment and the poisonous claws of the centipede. Explain that millipedes are less active and move more slowly than centipedes.
LS **Visual-Spatial**

Text Question Answer

Centipedes have one pair of legs per segment. Millipedes have two pairs of legs per segment.

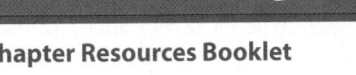

Resource Manager

Chapter Resources Booklet
Directed Reading, p. 19
Cultural Diversity, pp. 17, 21

Cultural Diversity

Insect Companions In Japan, crickets are considered pets and a source of musical pleasure. Favorite pet crickets have elaborate cages and porcelain water dishes. Delicate hand-carved brushes are used to "tickle" the crickets in order to get them to sing. In the tropics, many people allow centipedes to live in their houses to help control insect pests.

Visualizing Arthropod Diversity

Have students examine the pictures and read the captions. Then ask the following questions.

What different types of locomotion are used by arthropods? Students should note that arthropods walk, fly and swim. Barnacles usually do not move from place to place under their own power.

What characteristic of a Monarch butterfly allows it to survive the changing weather in its environment? A monarch's wings allow it to migrate to a warmer climate when temperatures become too cold.

Activity

Have students work in pairs to make a model of one of the arthropods pictured. Students should research the characteristics of the arthropod they have chosen to model, and incorporate their findings into their model. Have students present their models to the class.

Extension

Challenge students to make a Venn diagram that compares the characteristics of three of the pictured arthropods. Have students do further research to increase the number of characteristics included in their diagram.

GEOGRAPHIC VISUALIZING ARTHROPOD DIVERSITY

Figure 21

Some 600 million years ago, the first arthropods lived in Earth's ancient seas. Today, they inhabit nearly every environment on Earth. Arthropods are the most abundant and diverse group of animals on Earth. They range in size from nearly microscopic mites to spindly, giant Japanese spider crabs with legs spanning more than 3 m.

▲ LOBSTER Like crabs, lobsters are crustaceans that belong to the group called Decapoda, which means "ten legs." It's the lobster's tail, however, that interests most seafood lovers.

◀ GRASS SPIDER Grass spiders spin fine, nearly invisible webs just above the ground.

◀ GOOSENECK BARNACLE Gooseneck barnacles typically live attached to objects that float in the ocean. They use their long, feathery setae to strain tiny bits of food from the water.

▼ MONARCH BUTTERFLY Monarchs are a common sight in much of the United States during the summer. In fall, they migrate south to warmer climates.

◀ HISSING COCKROACH Most cockroaches are considered to be pests by humans, but hissing cockroaches, such as this one, are sometimes kept as pets.

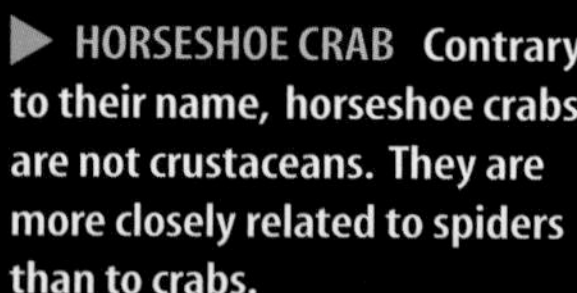

▶ HORSESHOE CRAB Contrary to their name, horseshoe crabs are not crustaceans. They are more closely related to spiders than to crabs.

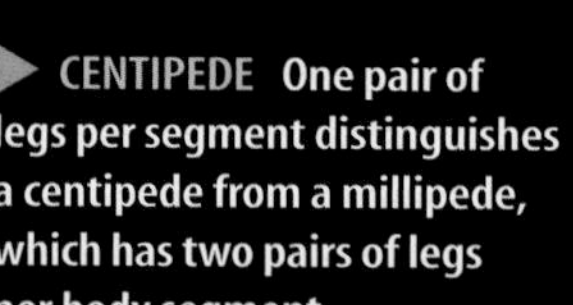

▶ CENTIPEDE One pair of legs per segment distinguishes a centipede from a millipede, which has two pairs of legs per body segment.

380

Active Reading

Jigsaw Place students in five cooperative groups. Each group is to be responsible for studying and summarizing one of the five types of arthropods discussed in this section—insects, arachnids, centipedes, millipedes, and crustaceans. Once finished, each group is to direct the discussion on the type of arthropod it was responsible for learning about. Instruct groups to include drawings and several examples of their type of arthropod. L2 COOP LEARN IN **Interpersonal**

Crustaceans

Crabs, crayfish, shrimp, barnacles, pill bugs, and water fleas are crustaceans. Crustaceans and other arthropods are shown in **Figure 21.** Crustaceans have one or two pairs of antennae and mandibles, which are used for crushing food. Most crustaceans live in water, but some, like the pill bugs shown in **Figure 22A,** live in moist environments on land. Pill bugs are common in gardens and around house foundations. They are harmless to humans.

Crustaceans, like the blue crab shown in **Figure 22B,** have five pairs of legs. The first pair of legs are claws that catch and hold food. The other four pairs are walking legs. They also have five pairs of appendages on the abdomen called swimmerets. They help the crustacean move and are used in reproduction. In addition, the swimmerets force water over the feathery gills where the oxygen and carbon dioxide are exchanged. If a crustacean loses an appendage, it will grow back, or regenerate.

Figure 22
A Pill bugs—also called roly polys—are crustaceans that live on land. *How are they similar to centipedes and millipedes?* **B The segments in some crustaceans aren't obvious because they are covered by a shieldlike structure.**

Value of Arthropods

Arthropods play several roles in the environment. They are a source of food for many animals, including humans. Some humans consider shrimp, crab, crayfish, and lobster as food delicacies. In Africa and Asia, many people eat insect larvae and insects such as grasshoppers, termites, and ants, which are excellent sources of protein.

Agriculture would be impossible without bees, butterflies, moths, and flies that pollinate crops. Bees manufacture honey, and silkworms produce silk. Many insects and spiders are predators of harmful animal species, such as stableflies. Useful chemicals are obtained from some arthropods. For example, bee venom is used to treat rheumatic arthritis.

Not all arthropods are useful to humans. Almost every cultivated crop has some insect pest that feeds on it. Many arthropods—mosquitoes, tsetse flies, fleas, and ticks—carry human and other animal diseases. In addition, weevils, cockroaches, carpenter ants, clothes moths, termites, and carpet beetles destroy food, clothing, and property.

Insects are an important part of the ecological communities in which humans live. Removing all of the insects would cause more harm than good.

Crustaceans

IDENTIFYING Misconceptions

Crustaceans—shrimp, lobsters, crayfish, and crabs— often are referred to as "shellfish." Crustaceans are not fish and they do not have shells. They have an exoskeleton that is very different from a shell.

Activity

Use sticks to lift up rocks and logs to look for isopods. Isopods are land crustaceans. There are two easily distinguishable types: the pill bug, which curls into a ball when disturbed; the sowbug, which does not. Isopods can be maintained in the classroom in a jar of moist soil with a slice of potato or oatmeal sprinkles. L2 ELL

Caption Answer

Figure 22A They have segmented bodies, exoskeletons, jointed legs, and antennae.

Value of Arthropods

Make a Model

Give two pipe cleaners, chalk dust, and moist paper towels to small groups of students. Have students use the chenille stems to model how bees help pollinate plants. (One can be moistened and bent to represent the stigma of a flower and the other can be dipped into the chalk dust, modeling how a bee's leg collects pollen.) Bees are not the only insect pollinators. Approximately two-thirds of all plants depend on insect pollination. L2 ELL COOP LEARN LS **Kinesthetic**

Cultural Diversity

Biological Controls Zhoa Jingzhao, a university vice-president in China, helped develop a technique that reduced the use of pesticides on cotton plants 80% to 90%. Spiders were used instead to control insects that damage cotton plants. Jingzhao taught farmers to dig small holes every ten paces in their fields and place spider-laden grasses in the holes and among the cotton plants.

Resource Manager

Chapter Resources Booklet
Enrichment, p. 31
Reinforcement, p. 27

Value of Arthropods, continued

Extension

Have students use the library to research and write a report on biological controls of insect pests. One specific method that shows great promise is the use of artificial insect hormones designed to prevent insects from reaching sexual maturity. Bacteria can also be used as a biological control. L3 LS **Linguistic**

3 Assess

Reteach

Have students explain why arthropods molt several times during their lives. L2 LS **Linguistic**

Challenge

How does metamorphosis contribute to the success and survival of insect species? There is no competition between larvae and adults for food; insects can survive harsh and cold weather while protected as pupae.

Assessment

Content Ask students to write in their Science Journals how incomplete and complete metamorphosis are similar and how they are different. Both are a series of changes. In complete metamorphoses, the young look very different from the adults. Use **PASC,** p. 175.

Figure 23
More than 15,000 species of trilobites have been classified. They are one of the most recognized types of fossils.

Controlling Insects One common way to control problem insects is by insecticides. However, many insecticides kill helpful insects as well as harmful ones. Because of their rapid life cycles, many insects have developed resistance to insecticides. Another problem is that many toxic substances that have been used to kill insects remain in the environment and accumulate in the bodies of animals that eat them. As other animals eat the contaminated animals, the insecticides can find their way into human food. Humans also are harmed by these toxins.

Several types of biological controls have been developed and are being tested. Different types of bacteria, fungi, and viruses are being used to control some insect pests. Natural predators and parasites of insect pests have been somewhat successful in controlling certain pests. Other biological controls involve using males that can't reproduce or naturally occurring chemicals that interfere with the reproduction or behavior of insect pests.

Origin of Arthropods Because of their hard body parts, arthropod fossils like the one in **Figure 23** are among the oldest and best-preserved fossils of many-celled animals. Some arthropod fossils are more than 500 million years old. Recall that earthworms and leeches have individual body segments. Because of this, scientists hypothesize that arthropods probably evolved from an ancestor of segmented worms. Over time, groups of body segments fused and became adapted for locomotion, feeding, and sensing the environment. The hard exoskeleton and walking legs allowed arthropods to be among the first animals to live successfully on land.

Section 3 Assessment

1. What are three characteristics of all arthropods?
2. What are the advantages and disadvantages of an exoskeleton?
3. Compare and contrast insects with arachnids.
4. Which stages of complete and incomplete metamorphosis are different?
5. **Think Critically** Choose an insect you are familiar with and explain how it is adapted to its environment.

Skill Builder Activities

6. **Concept Mapping** Make an events-chain concept map of complete metamorphosis and one of incomplete metamorphosis. **For more help, refer to the** Science Skill Handbook.
7. **Making and Using Graphs** Of the major arthropod groups, 88% are insects, 7% are arachnids, 3% are crustaceans, 1% are centipedes and millipedes, and all others make up 1%. Show these data in a circle graph. **For more help, refer to the** Science Skill Handbook.

Answers to Section Assessment

1. jointed legs, body segments, exoskeleton
2. advantages: prevents dehydration, supports and protects body; disadvantages: body outgrows exoskeleton, animal vulnerable to predators while new exoskeleton hardens
3. Insects have three body regions, three pairs of legs, one pair of antennae, spiracles, compound eyes, and most have wings. Arachnids have two body regions, four pairs of legs, and no antennae.
4. Incomplete has a nymph stage between egg and adult; complete has a larva and pupa stage between egg and adult.
5. Answers will vary. Look for understanding of insect adaptations.
6. Make sure students include all stages in both concept maps.
7. Graph segments should be proportional and labeled.

Activity

Observing a Crayfish

A crayfish has a segmented body and a fused head and thorax. It has a snout and eyes on movable eyestalks. Most crayfish have pincers. What are the pincers for?

What You'll Investigate
How does a crayfish use its appendages?

Materials
crayfish in a small aquarium
uncooked ground beef
stirrer

Goals
- **Observe** a crayfish.
- **Determine** the function of pincers.

Safety Precautions

WARNING: *Use care when working with live animals.*

Procedure
1. Copy the data table and use it to record all of your observations during this activity.

Crayfish Observations

Body Region	Number of Appendages	Function
Head	5 pairs	sense environment; hold and chew food
Thorax	5 pairs	capture food; defense; walking
Abdomen	5 pairs	create water currents to help crayfish move; reproduction

2. Your teacher will provide you with a crayfish in an aquarium. Leave the crayfish in the aquarium while you do the activity. Draw your crayfish.
3. Gently touch the crayfish with the stirrer. How does the body feel?
4. **Observe** how the crayfish moves in the water.
5. **Observe** the compound eyes. On which body region are they located?
6. Drop a small piece of ground beef into the aquarium. Observe the crayfish's reaction. Wash your hands.
7. Return the aquarium to its proper place.

Conclude and Apply
1. **Infer** how the location of the eyes is an advantage for the crayfish.
2. How does the structure of the pincers aid in getting food?
3. What can you infer about the exoskeleton and protection?

Communicating Your Data
Compare your observations with those of other students in your class. **For more help, refer to the** Science Skill Handbook.

Resource Manager

Chapter Resources Booklet
Activity Worksheet, pp. 5–6
Lab Activity, pp. 13–14

Communicating Your Data
Have students put together a bulletin board on which crayfish drawings can be displayed. Copy the data table onto the board and fill it in as a class.

Activity

BENCH TESTED

Purpose Students observe crayfish structure and determine appendage use. L2
LS **Visual-Spatial**

Process Skills observing, interpreting data, inferring, comparing and contrasting

Time Required 35 minutes

Alternate Materials Preserved crayfish may be used.

Teaching Strategy Crayfish may be obtained from a local stream or a biological supply company. If obtained locally, return them to the stream when the activity is completed.

Troubleshooting Students may not be able to count the appendages of the crayfish in the aquarium. Use a transparency of a crayfish on the overhead projector to help them.

Answers to Questions
1. Crayfish conceal themselves under rocks and in mud. The eyes at the end of stalks allow the crayfish to see without revealing their bodies.
2. The two-piece structure works like a clamp to capture prey and the serrated edges help hold prey.
3. The hard exoskeleton protects it from predators and from falling debris.

Assessment
Performance To expand students' understanding of crayfish, have them put a plastic bag containing ice cubes at one end of a long aquarium and a bag of warm water at the other end to test crayfish response to different temperatures. Then have students infer how this response is reflected in nature. Remove bags when finished. Use **PASC,** p. 89.

SECTION

Enchinoderms

1 Motivate

Bellringer Transparency

Display the Section Focus Transparency for Section 4. Use the accompanying Transparency Activity Master. L2 ELL

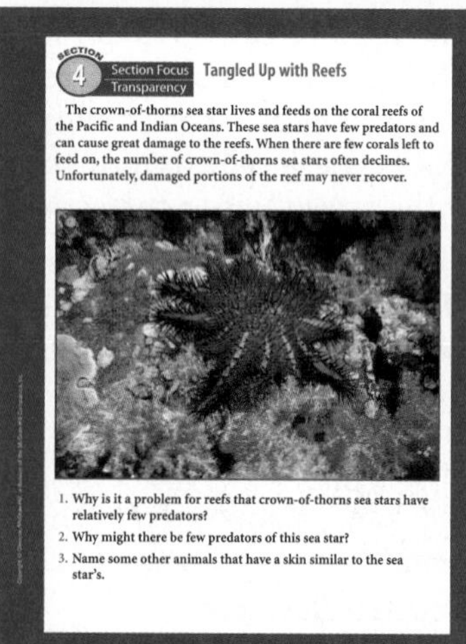

SECTION 4 Section Focus Transparency **Tangled Up with Reefs**

The crown-of-thorns sea star lives and feeds on the coral reefs of the Pacific and Indian Oceans. These sea stars have few predators and can cause great damage to the reefs. When there are few corals left to feed on, the number of crown-of-thorns sea stars often declines. Unfortunately, damaged portions of the reef may never recover.

1. Why is it a problem for reefs that crown-of-thorns sea stars have relatively few predators?
2. Why might there be few predators of this sea star?
3. Name some other animals that have a skin similar to the sea star's.

Mollusks, Worms, Arthropods, Echinoderms

Tie to Prior Knowledge

Even if students have not seen living echinoderms, they have probably seen dried sea stars and sand dollar skeletons. Use their knowledge of echinoderms to introduce this lesson.

SECTION 4

Echinoderms

As You Read

***What* You'll Learn**

- **List** the characteristics of echinoderms.
- **Explain** how sea stars obtain and digest food.
- **Discuss** the importance of echinoderms.

Vocabulary

water-vascular system
tube feet

***Why* It's Important**

Echinoderms are a group of animals that affect oceans and coastal areas.

Echinoderm Characteristics

Echinoderms are found in oceans all over the world. The term *echinoderm* is from the Greek words *echinos* meaning "spiny" and *derma* meaning "skin." Echinoderms have a hard endoskeleton covered by a thin, bumpy or spiny epidermis. They are radially symmetrical, which allows them to sense food, predators, and other things in their environment from all directions.

All echinoderms have a mouth, stomach, and intestines. They feed on a variety of plants and animals. For example, sea stars feed on worms and mollusks, and sea urchins feed on algae. Others feed on dead and decaying matter called detritus (de TRI tus) found on the ocean floor.

Echinoderms have no head or brain, but they do have a nerve ring that surrounds the mouth. They also have cells that respond to light and touch.

Water-Vascular System A characteristic unique to echinoderms is their water vascular system. It allows them to move, exchange carbon dioxide and oxygen, capture food, and release wastes. The **water-vascular system,** as shown in **Figure 24,** is a network of water-filled canals with thousands of tube feet connected to it. **Tube feet** are hollow, thin-walled tubes that each end in a suction cup. As the pressure in the tube feet changes, the animal is able to move along by pushing out and pulling in its tube feet.

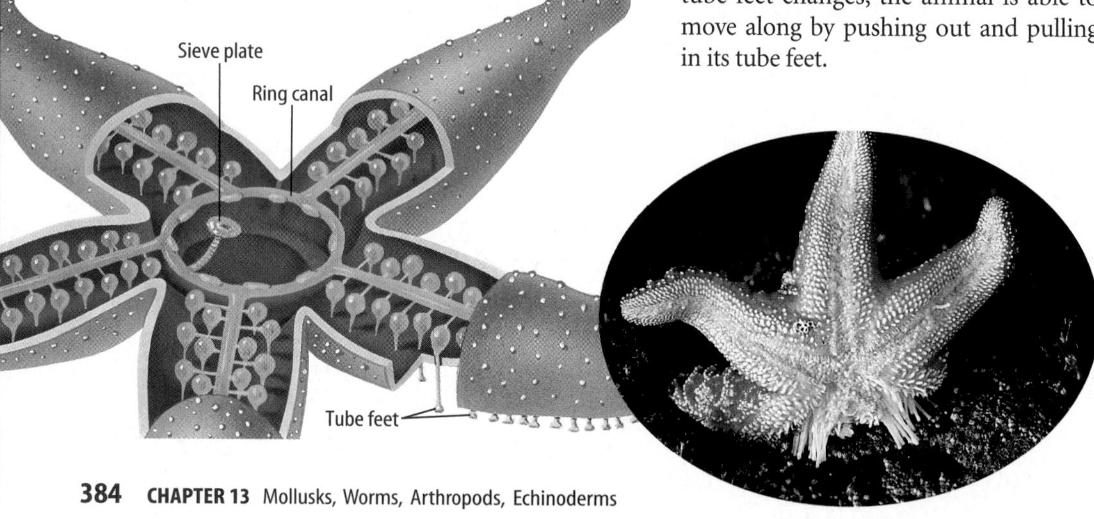

Figure 24
Sea stars alternately extend and withdraw their tube feet, enabling them to move.

Resource Manager

Chapter Resources Booklet
Transparency Activity, p. 49
MiniLAB, p. 4

Section Assessment Planner

PORTFOLIO
Visual Learning, p. 385

PERFORMANCE ASSESSMENT
Try at Home MiniLAB, p. 385
Skill Builder Activities, p. 387
See page 394 for more options.

CONTENT ASSESSMENT
Section, p. 387
Challenge, p. 387
Chapter, pp. 394–395

384 CHAPTER 13 Mollusks, Worms, Arthropods, Echinoderms

Types of Echinoderms

Approximately 6,000 species of echinoderms (ih KI nuh durmz) are living today. Of those, more than one-third are sea stars. The other groups include brittle stars, sea urchins, sand dollars, and sea cucumbers.

Sea Stars Echinoderms with at least five arms arranged around a central point are called sea stars. The arms are lined with thousands of tube feet. Sea stars use their tube feet to open the shells of their prey. When the shell is open slightly, the sea star pushes its stomach through its mouth and into its prey. The sea star's stomach surrounds the soft body of its prey and secretes enzymes that help digest it. When the meal is over, the sea star pulls its stomach back into its own body.

Reading Check *What is unusual about the way that sea stars eat their prey?*

Sea stars reproduce sexually when females release eggs and males release sperm into the water. Females can produce two million eggs in one season.

Sea stars also can repair themselves by regeneration. If a sea star loses an arm, it can grow a new one. If enough of the center disk is left attached to a severed arm, a whole new sea star can grow from that arm.

TRY AT HOME Mini LAB

Modeling the Strength of Tube Feet

Procedure

1. Hold your arm straight out, palm up.
2. Place a heavy **book** on your hand.
3. Have your partner time how long you can hold your arm up with the book on it.

Analysis

1. Describe how your arm feels after a few minutes.
2. If the book models the sea star and your arm models the clam, infer how a sea star successfully overcomes a clam to obtain food.

Brittle Stars Like the one in **Figure 25,** brittle stars have fragile, slender, branched arms that break off easily. This adaptation helps a brittle star survive attacks by predators. While the predator is eating a broken arm, the brittle star escapes. Brittle stars quickly regenerate lost parts. They live hidden under rocks or in litter on the ocean floor. Brittle stars use their flexible arms for movement instead of their tube feet. Their tube feet are used to move particles of food into their mouth.

Figure 25
A brittle star's arms are so flexible that they wave back and forth in the ocean currents. They are called brittle stars because their arms break off easily if they are grabbed by a predator.

2 Teach

Types of Echinoderms

Purpose to model how sea stars can open clam shells held closed by muscles L1
IS **Kinesthetic**

Materials heavy books, clock with a second hand

Teaching Strategies

- Make sure the books students use are heavy but not too heavy to lift.
- As students try this activity, suggest they imagine this is a life-or-death struggle as it is for the sea star and clam.

Analysis

1. arm muscles tire
2. Sea stars pull on a clam by using the suction power of their tube feet. Eventually, the muscles of the clam tire and the shell opens.

Assessment

Performance Have students wet suction cups and press them against a variety of surfaces. Ask students whether they can pick up an object with a suction cup and to compare this to tube feet. Yes; tube feet act like suction cups. Use **PASC,** p. 97.

Visual Learning

Figure 25 Have students study the brittle star in its natural environment. Then, have them make a list of its adaptations to this environment. P

Inclusion Strategies

Learning Disabled Have learning disabled students make a picture dictionary illustrating the meaning of unfamiliar terms in this chapter. Have them write their words on cards and keep the cards in alphabetical order. L1
IS **Visual-Spatial**

Reading Check

Answer They expel their stomach to eat.

Types of Echinoderms, continued

Make a Model

Have students model tube feet using an empty dropper. Have students squeeze the bulb, then place the tip firmly against one of their fingers, and then reduce the pressure on the bulb. Ask what they feel. suction L1

LS **Kinesthetic**

IDENTIFYING Misconceptions

The water vascular system of echinoderms is not directly involved in the suction of tube feet. After contact with an object, the edges of the tube foot are sealed to the object by a mucus secretion. Then, muscles in the tube foot contract causing the interior surface of the tube foot to move upward. This increases the volume of the space between the tube foot and the object and creates lower pressure or suction. The combined suction of many tube feet allows an echinoderm to move. For some, it even allows them to open shells of bivalves.

Extension

Have students find out about other echinoderm defenses such as the amount of slime produced by the sea star *Pteraster tesselatus*, the venom in the spines of the sea urchin *Asthenosoma*, and the modified poison spines that are pincerlike appendages of the sea urchin *Toxopneustes*. Also, sea cucumbers expel their internal organs as a type of defense. L3

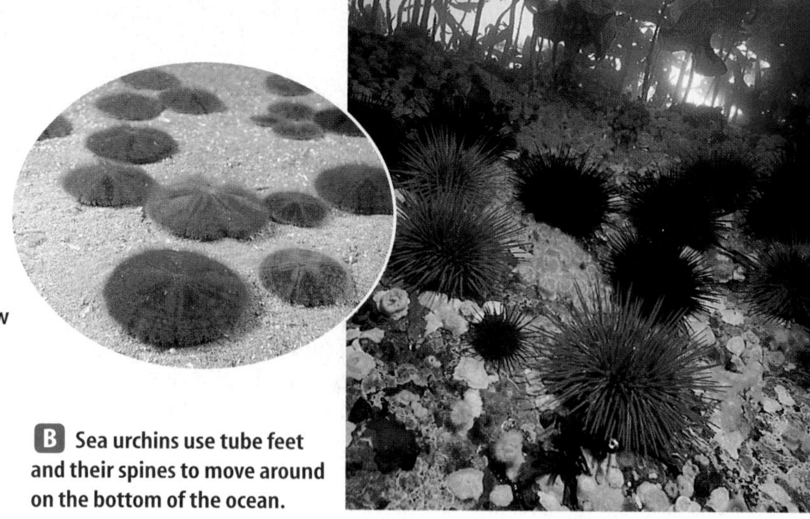

Figure 26
Like all echinoderms, sand dollars and sea urchins are radially symmetrical.

A Sand dollars live on ocean floors where they can burrow into the sand.

B Sea urchins use tube feet and their spines to move around on the bottom of the ocean.

Sea Urchins and Sand Dollars Another group of echinoderms includes sea urchins, sea biscuits, and sand dollars. They are disk- or globe-shaped animals covered with spines. They do not have arms, but sand dollars have a five-pointed pattern on their surface. Living sand dollars, like those in **Figure 26A,** are covered with stiff, hairlike spines. Sea urchins, like those in **Figure 26B,** have long, pointed spines that protect them from predators. Some have sacs near the end of the spines that contain poisonous fluid that is injected into predators. The spines also help in movement and burrowing. Sea urchins have five toothlike structures around their mouth.

SCIENCE Online

Research Visit the Glencoe Science Web site at **science.glencoe.com** for information about how echinoderms are used by humans. Communicate to your class what you learn.

Sea Cucumbers The animal shown in **Figure 27** is a sea cucumber. Sea cucumbers are soft-bodied echinoderms that have a leathery covering. They have tentacles around their mouth and rows of tube feet on their upper and lower surfaces. When threatened, sea cucumbers may expel their internal organs. These organs regenerate in a few weeks. Some sea cucumbers eat detritus, and others eat plankton.

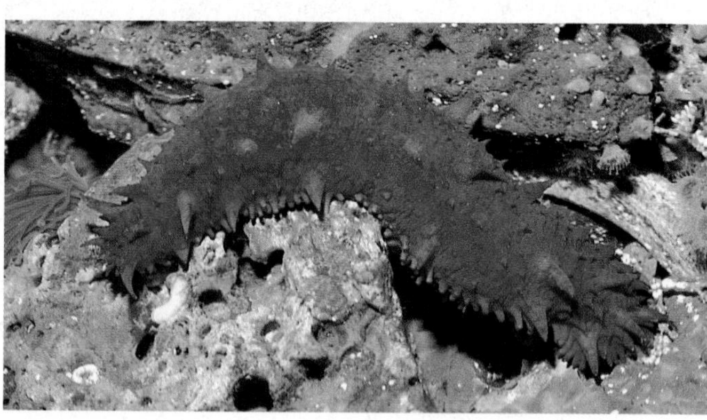

Figure 27
Sea cucumbers have short tube feet, which they use to move around.

386

Resource Manager

Chapter Resources Booklet

Directed Reading for Content Mastery, pp. 19, 20
Enrichment, p. 32
Reinforcement, p. 28

SCIENCE Online

Internet Addresses

Explore the Glencoe Science Web site at **science.glencoe.com** to find out more about topics in this section.

Value of Echinoderms

Echinoderms are important to the marine environment because they feed on dead organisms and help recycle materials. Sea urchins control the growth of algae in coastal areas. Sea urchin eggs and sea cucumbers are used for food in some places. Many echinoderms are used in research and some might be possible sources of medicines. Sea stars are important predators that control populations of other animals. However, because sea stars feed on oysters and clams, they also destroy millions of dollars' worth of mollusks each year.

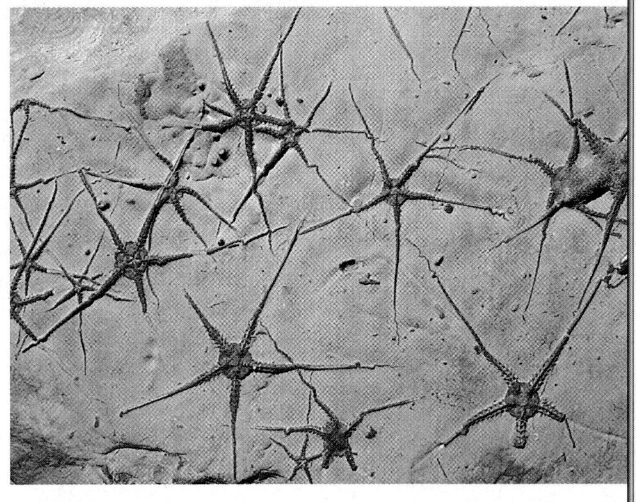

Figure 28
Ophiopinna elegans **was a brittle star that lived about 165 million years ago.**

Origin of Echinoderms Like the example in **Figure 28,** a good fossil record exists for echinoderms. Echinoderms date back more than 400 million years. The earliest echinoderms might have had bilateral symmetry as adults and may have been attached to the ocean floor by stalks. Many larval forms of modern echinoderms are bilaterally symmetrical.

Scientists hypothesize that echinoderms more closely resemble animals with backbones than any other group of invertebrates. This is because echinoderms have complex body systems and an embryo that develops the same way that the embryos of animals with backbones develop.

Section  Assessment

1. What characteristics do all echinoderms have in common?
2. How do echinoderms move and get their food?
3. How are sea urchins beneficial?
4. What methods of defense do echinoderms have to protect themselves from predators?
5. **Think Critically** Why would the ability to regenerate lost body parts be an important adaptation for sea stars, brittle stars, and other echinoderms?

Skill Builder Activities

6. **Forming Hypotheses** In your Science Journal, write a hypothesis about why echinoderms live on the ocean floor. **For more help, refer to the Science Skill Handbook.**
7. **Communicating** Choose an echinoderm that is discussed in this section and write about it in your Science Journal. Describe the following: *its appearance, how it gets food, where it lives,* and *other interesting facts.* **For more help, refer to the Science Skill Handbook.**

Value of Echinoderms

Extension

Many ancient echinoderms became extinct at the end of the Permian period. A number of factors caused the extinction, including climate changes and the formation of Pangaea. Have students research the changes that were taking place at the end of the Permian period and present the information to the class. L3 IS **Linguistic**

3 Assess

Reteach

Have students explain why echinoderms have few predators. L2 IS **Linguistic**

Challenge

How would a sea star's ability to get food be affected if it lost the water in its water-vascular system? It would be unable to use water pressure to extend and withdraw its tube feet. The tube feet are used to capture prey, so it would not be able to get food. L3 IS **Logical-Mathematical**

Oral Infer why echinoderms are bottom dwellers. The tube feet are on the ventral side. Use **PASC,** p. 89. P

Answers to Section Assessment

1. spiny skin, hard endoskeleton, water-vascular system, tube feet, radial symmetry
2. through the use of tube feet
3. They control the growth of algae. Their eggs are used as food by some people.
4. They have hard endoskeletons and spines, they regenerate rapidly, some have poison glands, and sea cucumbers can expel and regenerate their digestive systems.
5. Sea stars are dependent upon their arms (which contain tube feet) to move and obtain food. They could not survive without them.
6. With the exception of the brittle star, echinoderms have no means of movement except for their tube feet. Living on the ocean floor allows them to feed on other organisms and hide under debris.
7. Check students' work.

Activity

BENCH TESTED

What You'll Investigate

Purpose

Students experiment to determine the foods preferred by earthworms. L2 LS **Kinesthetic and Logical-Mathematical**

Process Skills

identifying and controlling variables, comparing and contrasting, observing and inferring

Time Required

one class period

Materials

Be certain students do not pack the materials into their jars tightly. Soil and humus should be sprinkled into the jar to allow sufficient air pockets to form.

Alternate Materials

Decomposing leaf litter can replace the humus, and rinds of melons or cantaloupes can be used instead of banana peels.

Safety Precautions

Students should thoroughly wash their hands after handling lab materials. Caution students not to eat foods during science class. Caution students to moisten their hands before handling earthworms and to handle them gently.

Activity

What do worms eat?

Earthworms are valuable because they improve the soil in which they live. There can be 50,000 earthworms living in one acre. Their tunnels increase air movement through the soil and improve water drainage. As they eat the decaying material in soil, their wastes can enrich the soil. Other than decaying material, what else do earthworms eat? Do they have favorite foods?

What You'll Investigate

What types of foods do earthworms eat?

Goals

- **Construct** five earthworm habitats.
- **Test** different foods to determine which ones earthworms eat.

Safety

WARNING: *Do not handle earthworms with dry hands. Do not eat any materials used in this activity.*

Materials

orange peels
apple peels
banana skin
kiwi fruit skin
watermelon rind
**skins of five different fruits*
widemouthed jars (5)
potting soil
water
humus
**peat moss*
earthworms
black construction paper (5 sheets)
masking tape
marker
rubber bands (5)

**Alternate materials*

Resource Manager 

Chapter Resources Booklet
Activity Worksheet, pp. 7–8

Lab Management and Safety, p. 73

Procedure

1. Copy the data table below in your Science Journal.
2. Pour equal amounts of soil into each of the jars. Do not pack the soil. Leave several centimeters of space at the top of each jar.
3. Sprinkle equal amounts of water into each jar to moisten the soil. Avoid pouring too much water into the jars.
4. Pour humus into each of your jars to a depth of 2 cm. The humus should be loose.
5. Add watermelon rinds to the first jar, orange peels to the second, apple peels to the third, kiwi fruit skins to the fourth, and a banana peel to the fifth jar. Each jar should have 2 cm of fruit skins on top of the layer of humus.
6. Add five earthworms to each jar.
7. Wrap a sheet of black construction paper around each jar and secure it with a rubber band.
8. Using the masking tape and marker, label each jar with the type of fruit it contains.
9. Place all of your jars in the same cool, dark place. Observe your jars every other day for a week and **record** your observations in your data table.

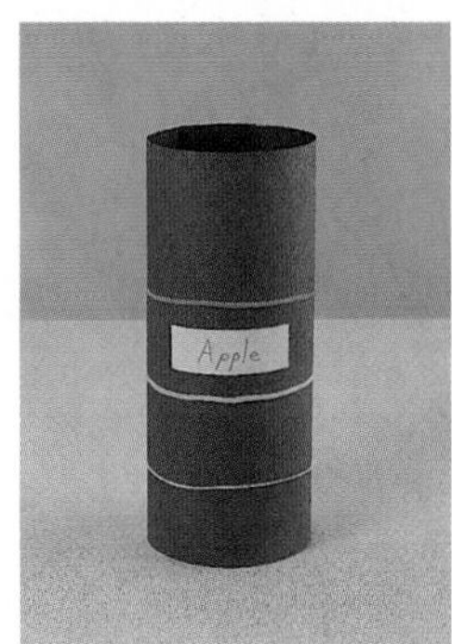

Fruit Wastes

Date	Watermelon rind	Orange peels	Apple peels	Kiwi skins	Banana peels
		Answers will	vary.		

Conclude and Apply

1. **Compare** the amount of fruit skins left in each jar.
2. **Infer** the type of food favored by earthworms.
3. **Infer** why some of the fruit skins were not eaten by the earthworms.
4. **Identify** a food source in each jar other than the fruit skins.
5. **Predict** what would happen in the jars over the next month if you continued the experiment.

Communicating Your Data

Use the results of your experiment and information from your reading to help you write a recipe for an appetizing dinner that worms would enjoy. Based on the results of your experiment, add other fruit skins or foods to your menu you think worms would enjoy.

Procedure

Teaching Strategies

- Ask students to capture worms from their home gardens or yards to be used in the activity.
- Inspect each group's jar before they start the final stages of the experiment.

Tie to Prior Knowledge Most students know that worms create rich soil by decomposing organic matter.

Expected Outcomes

Softer fruit skins such as apples and pears will be consumed by the worms first, and thicker skins will be decomposed last or possibly not at all.

Conclude and Apply

1. The apple peels will disappear during the week. The other types of fruit skins may show varying degrees of decomposition.
2. apple peels
3. Watermelon rinds, orange peels, and banana skins are thicker and difficult for earthworms to digest.
4. soil and humus
5. The less digestible fruit skins would begin to decay, enabling the earthworms to consume them.

Error Analysis

Have each student group occasionally examine the jars of other groups to compare the decay process occurring in the jars. Ask groups to list plausible explanations to explain differences in decomposition rates.

Assessment

Oral Have students explain the role earthworms play in the formation of nutrient-rich soil. Earthworms help decompose organic matter into nutrient-rich soil, and they eat soil and enrich it as it passes through their digestive systems. **Use Performance Assessment in the Science Classroom,** p. 89.

Communicating Your Data

Ask students to consult cookbooks to discover how recipe ingredients are written and arranged.

Science and Language Arts

✔ Pre-Reading Activity

Have students consider why some people fear certain insects such as the cockroach, earwig, or Japanese beetle. Ask students to choose an insect and to research its importance or the risks it poses. Ask students if their research coincides with the popular image of the insect.

Respond to the Reading

Active Reading Strategies

Question A moral dilemma is one in which the right or wrong of an action is in question. Why might the author's experience pose a moral dilemma for her?

Evaluate What would you say the author's relationship is to other living things? Do you think she is compassionate or uncaring?

Connect Connect your own experiences with insects to the authors. Have you ever felt similarly towards them?

Predict What do you think happens at the end of this story? Predict the actions the author will take.

Answers to Questions

1. Possible answer: by flying into the light fixture
2. Beetles, wood roaches, June bugs, mantises, cicadas
3. adult stage

Science and Language Arts

from "The Creatures on My Mind"

by Ursula K. Le Guin

Respond to the Reading

1. How do you suppose the beetle injured itself?
2. What kind of insects does the author fear?
3. From the author's description, in what stage of development is the beetle?

When I stayed for a week in New Orleans… I had an apartment with a balcony… But when I first stepped out on it, the first thing I saw was a huge beetle. It lay on its back directly under the light fixture. I thought it was dead, then saw its legs twitch and twitch again. Big insects horrify me. As a child I feared moths and spiders, but adolescence cured me, as if those fears evaporated in the stew of hormones. But I never got enough hormones to make me easy with the large, hard-shelled insects: wood roaches, June bugs, mantises, cicadas. This beetle was a couple of inches long; its abdomen was ribbed, its legs long and jointed; it was dull reddish brown; it was dying. I felt a little sick seeing it lie there twitching, enough to keep me from sitting out on the balcony that first day…And if I had any courage or common sense, I kept telling myself, I'd… put it out of its misery. We don't know what a beetle may or may not suffer…

Reading Further

Other works on this topic include:

Bugs: Insects, Spiders, Centipedes, Millipedes and Other Closely Related Arthropods by Frank Lowenstein and Sheryl Lechner, Black Dog & Leventhal Publishing, December 1999.

National Audubon Society Field Guide to North American Insects and Spiders by Lorus J. Milne and Susan Rayfield (Illustrator), Knopf Publishing, November 1980.

Understanding Literature

Legends and Oral Traditions In the passage you just read, the author uses her personal experience to consider her connection to other living things. A personal experience narrative is one in which the author tells a story using his or her own experience. In this piece, the author recounts a minor event in her life when she happens upon a dying beetle. The experience allows the author to pose some important questions about another species and to think about how beetles might feel when they die. How do you think the beetle is feeling?

Science Connection The author names several arthropod species in the passage, including insects and an arachnid. Beetles, June bugs, mantises, cicadas, and moths are all insects. The spider is an arachnid. Of the arthropods the author names, can you tell which ones go through a complete metamorphosis?

Linking Science and Writing

Writing a Personal Experience Narrative Write about a personal experience. Use the experience to think about an important question or topic in your life. For example, you might write about an accident you had. The accident might have made you consider the importance of good health.

Career Connection

Animal Geneticist

Edward B. Lewis was part of a genetic research team that won the 1995 Nobel Prize in Physiology or Medicine. They investigated how genes controlled the development of a fruit fly, *Drosophila,* through its various stages of development. Lewis investigated how genes of the fruit fly could control the development of specific regions into organs. Lewis also discovered that the genes were arranged on the chromosomes in the same order as the body parts that they controlled. For instance, the genes on one end of a complex strand controlled the development of the head, the genes in the middle controlled the development of the abdominal section, and the genes on the end controlled the development of the tail region. These genetic discoveries were a significant breakthrough because many of the same principles discovered in the fruit fly were found to apply in humans as well.

SCIENCE*Online* To learn more about careers in genetics, visit the Glencoe Science Web site at **science.glencoe.com.**

Understanding Literature

Answers to Questions

Answers might include that insects lack the same sensory system as do humans; others may say that there is no way of knowing how insects feel.

Science Connection

Although many people are horrified by arthropods, particularly insects, the majority of these animals are beneficial to Earth's ecosystems. Most of the world's flowering plants are pollinated by arthropods. Other arthropods, such as larger crustaceans like lobster and shrimp, are used for food. Smaller crustaceans are major components of ocean and wetland food chains.

However, some arthropods do pose threats to animals as well as to agriculture. For example, some insects can devastate crops, and others can carry diseases such as malaria, yellow fever (via mosquitoes) and typhus (via lice).

Linking Science and Writing

Teaching Strategies

Ask students to do a quick write describing a time when they feared an arthropod or other animal. What were the circumstances of the encounter? As they look back on the incident, was the danger real or imagined?

Career Connection

By studying math, chemistry, physics and biology in high school, students will have the background to pursue a career in the sciences. In college, students interested in specializing in animal genetics should major in biology or genetics. With a four-year Bachelor of Science degree in a biological science, they can become technologists, performing laboratory experiments and doing research.

SCIENCE *Online*

Internet Addresses

Explore the Glencoe Science Web site at **science.glencoe.com** to find out more about topics in this feature.

Chapter 13 Study Guide

Reviewing Main Ideas

Preview

Students can answer the questions in their Science Journals. Discuss the answers as you go through the chapter. LS **Linguistic**

Review

Students can write their answers, then compare them with those of other students. LS **Interpersonal**

Reteach

Students can look at the illustrations and describe details that support the main ideas of the chapter. LS **Visual-Spatial**

Answers to Chapter Review

Section 1

2. bivalves

Section 2

1. to filter food from the water

Section 3

2. As an insect; insects have three body segments, six legs, and a pair of antennae.

Section 4

2. with tube feet

Chapter 13 Study Guide

Reviewing Main Ideas

Section 1 Mollusks

1. Mollusks are soft-bodied invertebrates that usually are covered by a hard shell. They move using a muscular foot.

2. Mollusks with one shell are gastropods. Bivalves have two shells. Cephalopods have an internal shell and a foot that is divided into tentacles. *What group of mollusks does this animal belong to?*

Section 2 Segmented Worms

1. Segmented worms have tube-shaped bodies divided into sections, a body cavity that holds the internal organs, and bristlelike structures called setae to help them move. *How do the tube worms in the photo use their setae?*

2. An earthworm's digestive system has a mouth, crop, gizzard, intestine, and anus.

3. Leeches are parasites that attach to animals and feed on their blood.

Section 3 Arthropods

1. More than a million species of arthropods exist, which is more than any other group of animals. Most arthropods are insects.

2. Arthropods are grouped by number of body segments and appendages. *How would the arthropod shown here be grouped?*

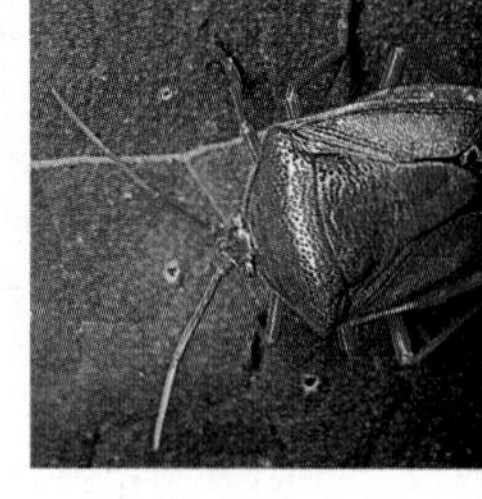

3. Exoskeletons cover, protect, and support arthropod bodies.

4. Young arthropods develop either by complete metamorphosis or incomplete metamorphosis.

Section 4 Echinoderms

1. Echinoderms have a hard, spiny exoskeleton covered by a thin epidermis. Most have a water-vascular system that enables them to move, exchange carbon dioxide and oxygen, capture food, and give off wastes.

2. Brittle stars have slender, branched arms that are fragile. Sea urchins and sand dollars are disk-shaped animals covered with spines. Sea cucumbers are soft-bodied animals that have a leathery covering. *How does the sea cucumber in the photograph move?*

FOLDABLES Reading & Study Skills — **After You Read**

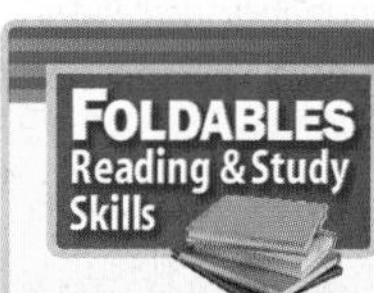

On the front of your Foldable, list characteristics of each group of invertebrates and examples of each group.

FOLDABLES Reading & Study Skills — **After You Read**

After students have read the chapter and completed the Foldable described in Before You Read, have them do the activity on the student page.

Dinah Zike

Visualizing Main Ideas

Complete the following concept map about insects.

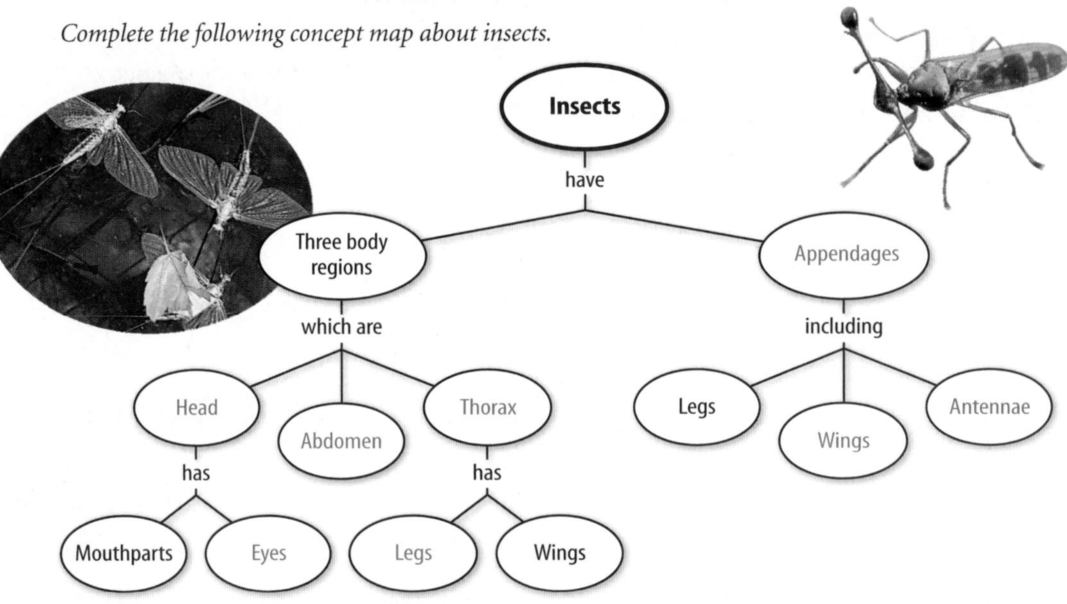

Vocabulary Review

Vocabulary Words

a. appendage
b. closed circulatory system
c. crop
d. exoskeleton
e. gill
f. gizzard
g. mantle
h. metamorphosis
i. molting
j. open circulatory system
k. radula
l. setae
m. spiracle
n. tube feet
o. water-vascular system

Study Tip

After each day's lesson, make a practice quiz for yourself. Later, when you're studying for the test, take the practice quizzes that you created.

Using Vocabulary

Using the vocabulary words, replace the underlined words with the correct science term.

1. Mollusk shells are secreted by the crop.
2. As earthworms move through soil using their appendages, they take in soil, which is stored in the gizzard.
3. The endoskeleton covers and protects arthropod bodies.
4. Insects exchange oxygen and carbon dioxide through book lungs.
5. Spines act like suction cups and help sea stars move and feed.
6. Snails use a muscular foot to get food.
7. The blood of mollusks moves in a spiracle.

Chapter 13 Study Guide

Visualizing Main Ideas

See student page.

Vocabulary Review

Using Vocabulary

1. mantle
2. setae, crop
3. exoskeleton
4. spiracles
5. Tube feet
6. radula
7. open circulatory system

CHAPTER STUDY GUIDE 393

Chapter 13 Assessment

Checking Concepts

1. C
2. D
3. A
4. C
5. D
6. B
7. B
8. A
9. B
10. B

Thinking Critically

11. Gastropods use their radula to tear plant materials and scrape algae and plant material.
12. Clams burrow into the sand; oysters attach themselves by strong sticky threads to rocks; scallops eject water and move by rapidly opening and closing their shells; a squid ejects water and escapes by jet propulsion. Oysters, clams, and scallops also have hard shells.
13. Grit in the earthworm gizzard grinds soil in the same way that teeth break up and grind food in the mouth.
14. A space in the body to hold organs is present in both groups. The larvae of both groups are similar.
15. It provides room in which to grow before the next molt.

Chapter 13 Assessment

Checking Concepts

Choose the word or phrase that best answers the question.

1. What structure covers organs of mollusks?
   A) gills **C)** mantle
   B) food **D)** visceral mass
2. What structures do echinoderms use to move and to open shells of mollusks?
   A) mantle **C)** spines
   B) calcium plates **D)** tube feet
3. Which organism has a closed circulatory system?
   A) earthworm **C)** slug
   B) octopus **D)** snail
4. What evidence suggests that arthropods might have evolved from annelids?
   A) Arthropods and annelids have gills.
   B) Both groups have species that live in salt water.
   C) Segmentation is present in both groups.
   D) All segmented worms have setae.
5. Which of the following characteristics is typical of echinoderms?
   A) an endoskeleton
   B) a mantle
   C) a segmented body
   D) a water-vascular system
6. How do millipedes differ from centipedes?
   A) Millipedes are terrestrial and segmented.
   B) Millipedes eat plants.
   C) Millipedes have only one pair of legs on each segment.
   D) Millipedes have poison fangs.
7. Of the following organisms, which have two body regions and four pairs of legs?
   A) annelids **C)** insects
   B) arachnids **D)** mollusks
8. Which is an example of an annelid?
   A) earthworm **C)** slug
   B) octopus **D)** snail
9. Which group of animals is the largest?
   A) annelids **C)** echinoderms
   B) arthropods **D)** mollusks
10. Which sequence shows incomplete metamorphosis?
    A) egg—larvae—adult
    B) egg—nymph—adult
    C) larva—pupa—adult
    D) nymph—pupa—adult

Thinking Critically

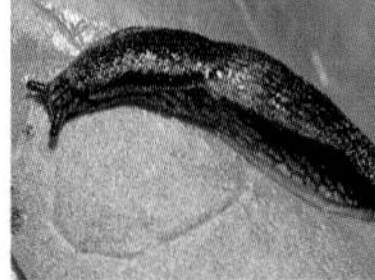

11. Describe how the slug in the photo obtains food.
12. Compare the ability of clams, oysters, scallops, and squid to protect themselves.
13. Compare an earthworm gizzard to teeth in other animals.
14. What evidence suggests that mollusks and annelids share a common ancestor?
15. After molting but before the new exoskeleton hardens, an arthropod causes its body to swell by taking in extra water or air. How does this behavior help the arthropod?

Developing Skills

16. **Classifying** Place the following animals into arthropod groups: *spider, pill bug, crayfish, grasshopper, crab, silverfish, cricket, wasp, scorpion, shrimp, barnacle, tick,* and *butterfly.*
17. **Recognizing Cause and Effect** If all the earthworms were removed from a hectare of soil, what would happen to the soil? Why?

Chapter Assessment Planner

Portfolio Encourage students to place in their portfolios one or two items of what they consider to be their best work. Examples include:
- Visual Learning, p. 367
- Reteach, p. 373
- Activity, p. 377
- Visual Learning, p. 385

Performance Additional performance assessments, Performance Task Assessment Lists, and rubrics for evaluating these activities can be found in Glencoe's **Performance Assessment in the Science Classroom.**

18. Interpreting Scientific Illustrations Using the illustrations in *Section 1,* infer why gastropods are sometimes called univalves.

19. Researching Information The suffixing -*ptera* means "wings." Research the meaning of the prefix of each insect group listed below and give an example of a member of each group.

Diptera	Homoptera
Orthoptera	Hemiptera
Coleoptera	

20. Comparing and Contrasting Complete this Venn diagram to compare arthropods to annelids. What characteristics do they have in common? How are they different?

Annelids Arthropods

Setae
Closed circulatory system
No skeleton
Bilateral symmetry
Segmented bodies
Appendages
Open circulatory system
Exoskeleton
Metamorphosis

Performance Assessment

21. Construct Choose an arthropod that develops through complete metamorphosis and construct a three-dimensional model for each of the four stages. Share your construction with your class.

Technology

Go to the Glencoe Science Web site at **science.glencoe.com** or use the **Glencoe Science CD-ROM** for additional chapter assessment.

THE PRINCETON REVIEW

Test Practice

Antonio researched mollusks and made the following circle graph, which separates mollusk species into seven living groups.

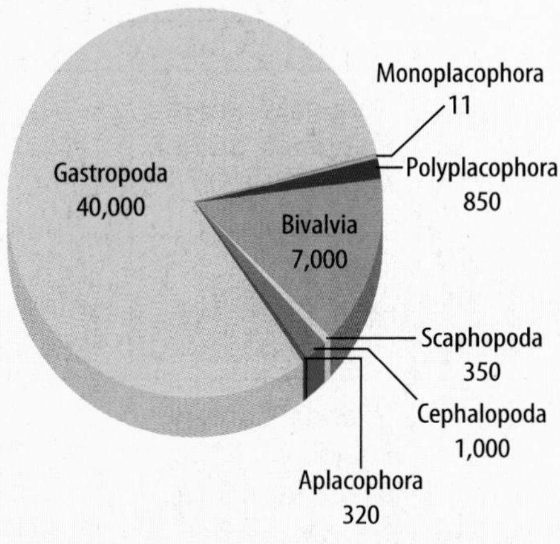

Study the circle graph and answer the following questions.

1. According to this information, approximately what percentage of mollusk species belongs to the group Gastropoda?
   A) 40 percent **C)** 80 percent
   B) 60 percent **D)** 95 percent

2. One of these groups was thought to be extinct until 1952, when marine biologists discovered some organisms living off the coast of Costa Rica. According to the graph, the group thought to be extinct is most likely the _____.
   F) Bivalvia
   G) Cephalopoda
   H) Gastropoda
   J) Monoplacophora

Chapter 13 Assessment

THE PRINCETON REVIEW

Test Practice

The Test-Taking Tip was written by The Princeton Review, the nation's leader in test preparation.

1. C
2. J

Developing Skills

16. arachnids: spider, tick, scorpion; crustaceans: pill bug, crayfish, crab, shrimp, barnacle; insects: grasshopper, silverfish, cricket, wasp, butterfly
17. The soil would become packed and hardened. It would be less fertile because of the lack of earthworm wastes.
18. Gastropods have only one shell.
19. Diptera: two wings, flies; Orthoptera: straight wings, grasshoppers; Coleoptera: shielded wings, beetles; Homoptera: whole wings, leaf hoppers; Hemiptera: half wings, water bugs
20. See student page.

Performance Assessment

21. Models will vary. Use **PASC,** p. 123.

Assessment Resources

Reproducible Masters

Chapter Resources Booklet
Chapter Review, pp. 39–40
Chapter Tests, pp. 41–44
Assessment Transparency Activity, p. 53

Glencoe Science Web site
Interactive Tutor
Chapter Quizzes

Glencoe Technology
Assessment Transparency
Interactive CD-ROM Chapter Quizzes
ExamView Pro Test Bank
Vocabulary PuzzleMaker Software
MindJogger Videoquiz

Section/Objectives	Standards		Activities/Features
	National	State/Local	
Chapter Opener	See p. 5T for a Key to Standards.		**Explore Activity:** Model how a snake hears, p. 397 **Before You Read,** p. 397
Section 1 **Chordates and Vertebrates** 2 sessions 1 block 1. **List** the characteristics of all chordates. 2. **Identify** characteristics shared by vertebrates. 3. **Differentiate** between ectotherms and endotherms.	National Content Standards: UCP3, A1, C1, C3, C5		**Activity:** Endotherms and Ectotherms, p. 402
Section 2 **Fish** 2 sessions 1 block 1. **List** the characteristics of the three classes of fish. 2. **Explain** how fish obtain food and oxygen and reproduce. 3. **Describe** the importance and origin of fish.	National Content Standards: UCP3, A1, C1, C2, C3, C4, C5		**Health Integration,** p. 406 **MiniLAB:** Modeling How Fish Adjust to Different Depths, p. 407 **Math Skills Activity:** Calculating Density, p. 408
Section 3 **Amphibians** 2 sessions 1 block 1. **Describe** the adaptations amphibians have for living in water and living on land. 2. **List** the kinds of amphibians and the characteristics of each. 3. **Explain** how amphibians reproduce and develop.	National Content Standards: UCP3, A1, C1, C2, C3, C4, C5		**Science Online,** p. 413 **MiniLAB:** Describing Frog Adaptations, p. 414
Section 4 **Reptiles** 3 sessions 1.5 blocks 1. **List** the characteristics of reptiles. 2. **Determine** how reptile adaptations enable them to live on land. 3. **Explain** the importance of the amniotic egg.	National Content Standards: UCP3, A1, C1, C2, C3, C4, C5, F5		**Science Online,** p. 417 **Visualizing Extinct Reptiles,** p. 420 **Earth Science Integration,** p. 421 **Activity:** Water Temperature and the Respiration Rate of Fish, pp. 422–423 **Science and Society:** Venom, pp. 424–425

Activity Materials	Reproducible Resources	Section Assessment	Technology
Explore Activity: tuning fork	**Chapter Resources Booklet** Foldables Worksheet, p. 17 Directed Reading Overview, p. 19 Note-taking Worksheets, pp. 35–38	Glencoe's Assessment Advantage	
MiniLAB: fiberfill, cloth, thermometer	**Chapter Resources Booklet** Transparency Activity, p. 48 Lab Activity, pp. 9–10 Enrichment, p. 31 Reinforcement, p. 27 Directed Reading, p. 20 Activity Worksheet, pp. 5–6	**Portfolio** Science Journal, p. 399 **Performance** Skill Builder Activities, p. 401 **Content** Section Assessment, p. 401	Section Focus Transparency Interactive CD-ROM Guided Reading Audio Program
MiniLAB: 2 balloons, large bowl, water	**Chapter Resources Booklet** Transparency Activity, p. 49 MiniLAB, p. 3 Enrichment, p. 32 Reinforcement, p. 28 Directed Reading, p. 20 **Mathematics Skill Activities,** p. 49	**Portfolio** Extension, p. 405 **Performance** MiniLAB, p. 407 Math Skills Activity, p. 408 Skill Builder Activities, p. 410 **Content** Section Assessment, p. 410	Section Focus Transparency Interactive CD-ROM Guided Reading Audio Program
MiniLAB: live frog, jar *Need materials?* Contact Science Kit at 1-800-828-7777 or www.sciencekit.com on the Internet.	**Chapter Resources Booklet** Transparency Activity, p. 50 MiniLAB, p. 4 Lab Activity, pp. 11–15 Enrichment, p. 33 Reinforcement, p. 29 Directed Reading, p. 21	**Portfolio** Extension, p. 414 **Performance** MiniLAB, p. 414 Skill Builder Activities, p. 415 **Content** Section Assessment, p. 415	Section Focus Transparency Interactive CD-ROM Guided Reading Audio Program
Activity: goldfish, aquarium water, small fishnet, 3 beakers (600 mL), ice, stirring rod, thermometer, aquarium	**Chapter Resources Booklet** Transparency Activity, p. 51 Enrichment, p. 34 Reinforcement, p. 30 Transparency Activity, pp. 53–54 Directed Reading, pp. 21, 22 Activity Worksheet, pp. 7–8	**Portfolio** Extension, p. 419 **Performance** Skill Builder Activities, p. 421 **Content** Section Assessment, p. 421	Section Focus Transparency Teaching Transparency Interactive CD-ROM Guided Reading Audio Program

End of Chapter Assessment

Glencoe's Assessment Advantage

Blackline Masters	Technology	Professional Series
Chapter Resources Booklet Chapter Review, pp. 41–42 Chapter Tests, pp. 43–46 **Standardized Test Practice by The Princeton Review,** pp. 63–66	MindJogger Videoquiz Interactive CD-ROM Vocabulary PuzzleMakers ExamView Pro Test Bank Interactive Lesson Planner Interactive Teacher Edition	Performance Assessment in the Science Classroom (PASC)

Transparencies

Section Focus

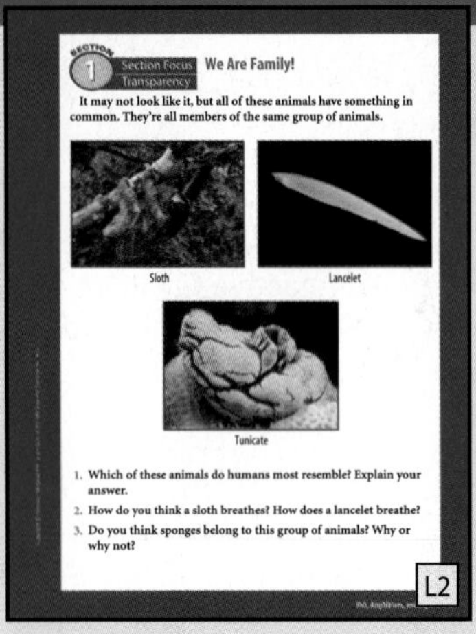

Section 1 Section Focus Transparency **We Are Family!**

It may not look like it, but all of these animals have something in common. They're all members of the same group of animals.

Sloth — Lancelet — Tunicate

1. Which of these animals do humans most resemble? Explain your answer.
2. How do you think a sloth breathes? How does a lancelet breathe?
3. Do you think sponges belong to this group of animals? Why or why not?

L2

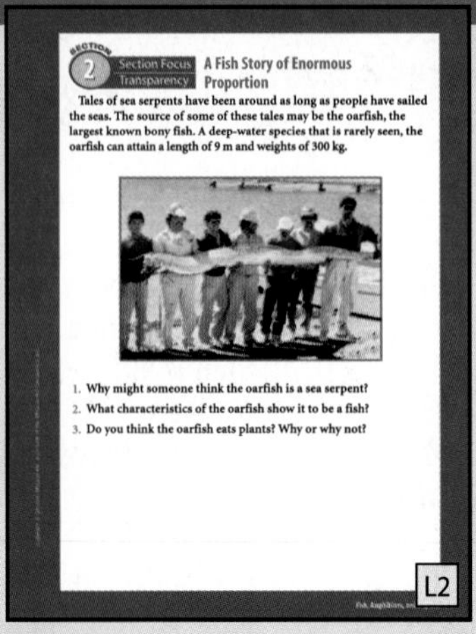

Section 2 Section Focus Transparency **A Fish Story of Enormous Proportion**

Tales of sea serpents have been around as long as people have sailed the seas. The source of some of these tales may be the oarfish, the largest known bony fish. A deep-water species that is rarely seen, the oarfish can attain a length of 9 m and weights of 300 kg.

1. Why might someone think the oarfish is a sea serpent?
2. What characteristics of the oarfish show it to be a fish?
3. Do you think the oarfish eats plants? Why or why not?

L2

Section 3 Section Focus Transparency **Sing At Your Own Risk**

When male mud-puddle frogs sing for the females, bats sometimes listen in. The bats can use the sound to locate—and eat—the frogs. This is a natural event that helps maintain a stable frog population. However, the worldwide population of frogs is declining.

1. What kind of environment do frogs live in?
2. Why might frogs be especially sensitive to pollution in the air and water?

L2

This is a representation of key blackline masters available in the Teacher Classroom Resources. See Resource Manager boxes within the chapter for additional information.

Assessment

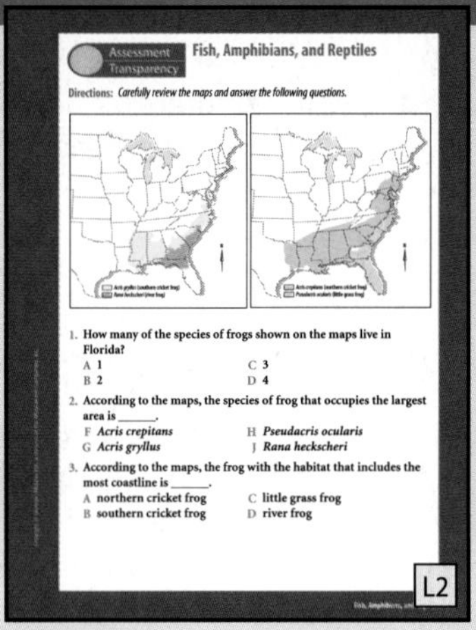

Assessment Transparency **Fish, Amphibians, and Reptiles**

Directions: *Carefully review the maps and answer the following questions.*

1. How many of the species of frogs shown on the maps live in Florida?
   A 1 C 3
   B 2 D 4
2. According to the maps, the species of frog that occupies the largest area is ______.
   F *Acris crepitans* H *Pseudacris ocularis*
   G *Acris gryllus* J *Rana heckscheri*
3. According to the maps, the frog with the habitat that includes the most coastline is ______.
   A northern cricket frog C little grass frog
   B southern cricket frog D river frog

L2

Teaching

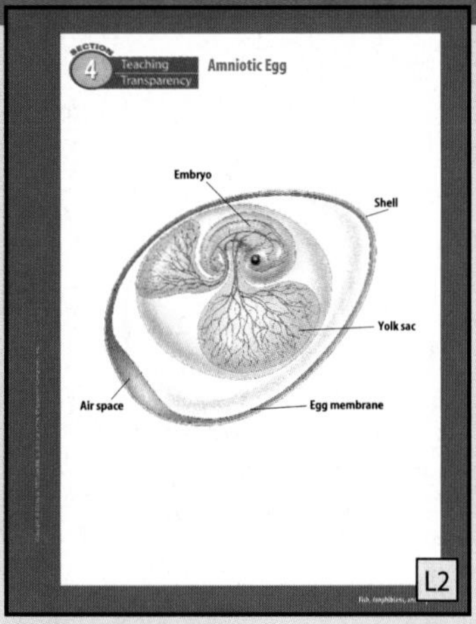

Section 4 Teaching Transparency **Amniotic Egg**

Embryo, Shell, Yolk sac, Air space, Egg membrane

L2

Key to Teaching Strategies

The following designations will help you decide which activities are appropriate for your students.

- L1 Level 1 activities should be appropriate for students with learning difficulties.
- L2 Level 2 activities should be within the ability range of all students.
- L3 Level 3 activities are designed for above-average students.
- ELL ELL activities should be within the ability range of English Language Learners.
- COOP LEARN Cooperative Learning activities are designed for small group work.
- LS Multiple Learning Styles logos, as described on page 22T, are used throughout to indicate strategies that address different learning styles.
- P These strategies represent student products that can be placed into a best-work portfolio.

Hands-on Activities

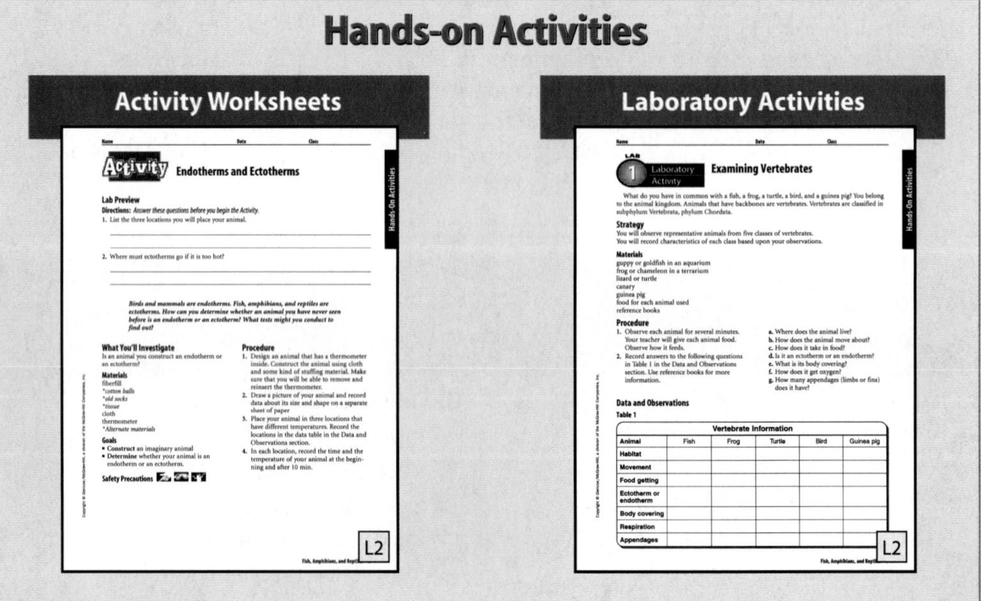

Activity Worksheets

Activity **Endotherms and Ectotherms**

L2

Laboratory Activities

Lab 1 Laboratory Activity **Examining Vertebrates**

L2

Meeting Different Ability Levels

Content Outline

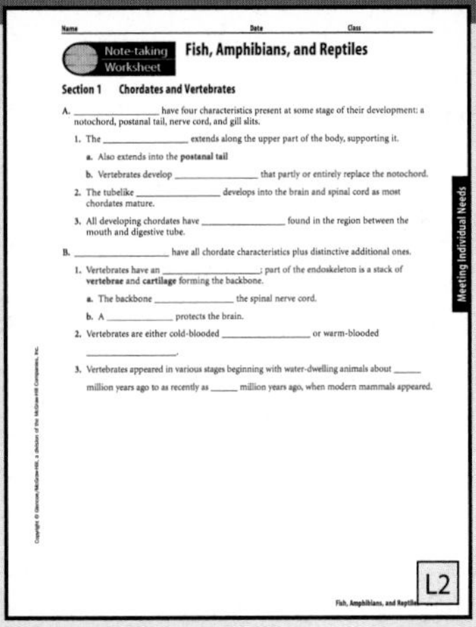

Note-taking Worksheet — Fish, Amphibians, and Reptiles

Section 1 Chordates and Vertebrates

L2

Reinforcement

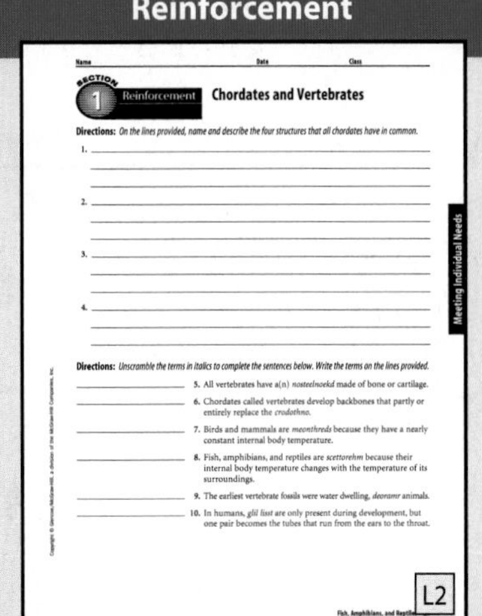

Section 1 Reinforcement — Chordates and Vertebrates

L2

Directed Reading

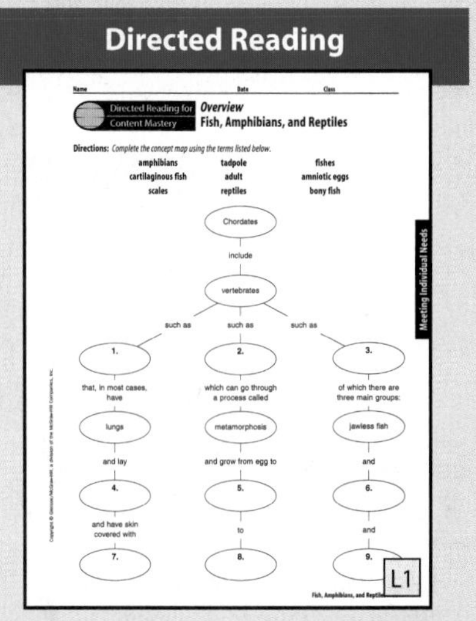

Directed Reading for Content Mastery — Overview: Fish, Amphibians, and Reptiles

L1

Enrichment

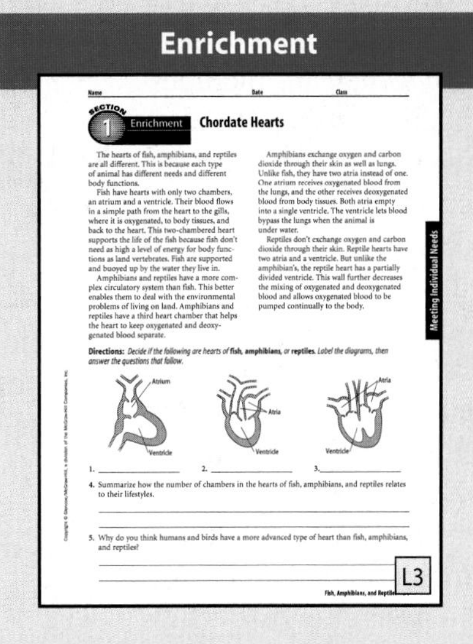

Section 1 Enrichment — Chordate Hearts

L3

Spanish Directed Reading

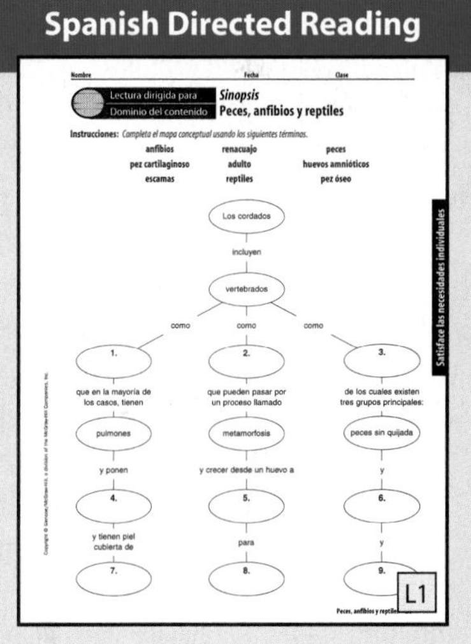

Lectura dirigida para Dominio del contenido — Sinopsis: Peces, anfibios y reptiles

L1

Assessment

Chapter Tests

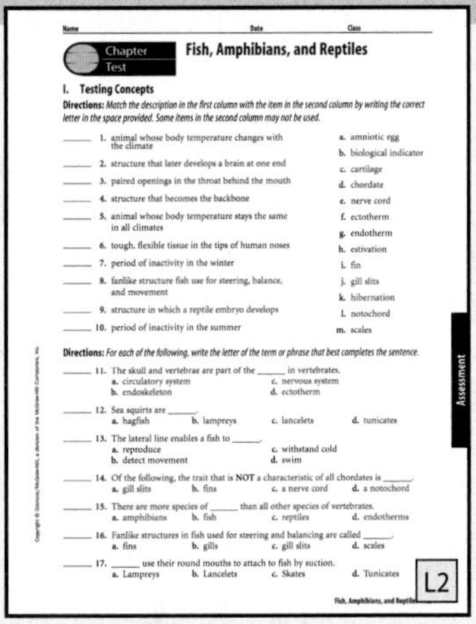

Chapter Test — Fish, Amphibians, and Reptiles

I. Testing Concepts

L2

Test Practice Workbook

L2

Chapter Review

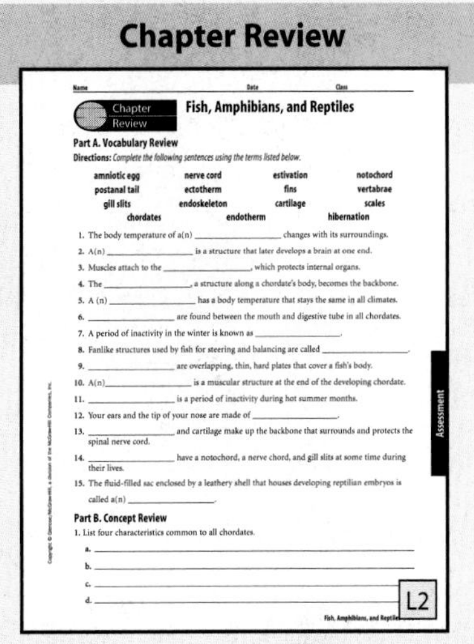

Chapter Review — Fish, Amphibians, and Reptiles

Part A. Vocabulary Review

Part B. Concept Review

L2

Science Content Background

SECTION 1

Chordates and Vertebrates

Chordate Characteristics

In Phylum *Chordata*, students are most aware of animals with backbones, such as fish and mammals, that belong to the subphylum *Vertebrata*. There are two other *Chordata* subphyla. The *Urochordata* includes sea squirts, which have a spongelike appearance. They are a very remote ancestor on the Chordata tree. Their larva, however, are similar in form to tadpoles. The *Cephalochordata* includes lancelets, which are fishlike in appearance and who spend most of their time buried in sand. In addition to having a notochord, chordates have a dorsal hollow nerve cord at some time during their life cycles.

Fun Fact

All chordates have gill slits at some time during their development. Invertebrate chordates such as the lancelets have gills their entire life. Vertebrates such as humans have gill slits only during embryonic development.

Fish, amphibians, and reptiles are ectotherms, which means their temperature varies with their surroundings. The internal temperature of ectotherms fluctuates more than it does for endotherms. The advantage for ectotherms is they spend less energy maintaining a constant body temperature. The disadvantage is that these organisms are more sluggish at cooler temperatures. Other names for ectotherms are cold-blooded animals and poikilotherms.

SECTION 2

Fish

Fish Characteristics

Most fish have fins that occur in pairs. Fish breathe with gills and reproduce sexually, usually with external fertilization. Fish circulate blood in a closed system with a two-chambered heart consisting of one atrium and one ventricle. The atrium receives blood from the body and pushes it to the ventricle. The ventricle pumps blood through the gills and then to the rest of the body. Some scientists define the fish heart as four-chambered. They include the area before the atrium and the area after the ventricle as chambers.

SECTION 3

Amphibians

Amphibian Characteristics

Amphibians were the first land animals to evolve, and they developed adaptations that allow them to spend part of their life on land. Their three-chamber heart allows better circulation of oxygenated blood. This is necessary because walking as opposed to swimming uses more energy. Lungs and moist skin provide two methods for amphibians for the exchange of oxygen and carbon dioxide. Unlike fish and other vertebrates, most amphibians undergo a metamorphosis.

Gail Shumway/FPG International

Salamanders

Having frogs and toads as the poster organisms for amphibians makes many people forget about salamanders, even though there is an abundance of species. In North America, there are more species of salamanders than in the rest of the world combined. Because they don't lose their tails as adults, they are sometimes mistaken for reptiles. Salamanders need to maintain moist skin for breathing. They lay their eggs in water, but the larva very much resemble the adult except they have gills.

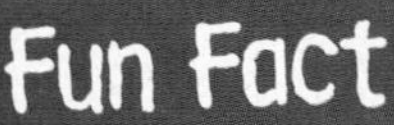

Is it a frog or a toad? Frogs have smooth, moist skin while toads have bumpy, dry skin. Frogs tend to have relatively longer hind legs than toads. This makes frogs capable of long leaps, while toads move in short hops. While toads return to water to lay their eggs, they can exist in drier terrestrial habitats than can frogs. Frogs and toads belong to the order *Anura.*

Importance of Amphibians

There is concern about the declining numbers of amphibians and the possibility of extinctions. Among the species that are endangered are the Texas Blind Salamander *(Eurycea rathbuni)*, Pine Barrens Treefrog *(Hyla andersonii)*, and Gopher frog *(Rana capito)*.

SECTION 4 Reptiles

Reptile Characteristics

Reptiles have adaptations for life away from moist environments. Their thick, dry skin is covered with scales to prevent water loss. They cannot absorb oxygen through their skin, so they have well-developed lungs for gas exchange. While most have three-chambered hearts, some reptiles evolved the more efficient four-chamber heart. Compared to amphibians, the legs of reptiles are located more directly under the animal. This increases the efficiency of movement on land. The reptile egg is an amniotic egg. It contains moisture and barriers to prevent moisture loss. It gets its name from the amnion, which is a membrane that contains fluid that cushions the embryo and prevents dehydration. So unlike the amphibian egg, the reptile egg can survive and develop in dry terrestrial environments. Without an external watery environment for sperm to swim to the egg, reptiles evolved the capability for internal fertilization.

Tom Ulrich/Stone

Lizards come in a variety of forms. While most lizards eat insects, iguanas are herbivores. The largest lizard is the Komodo dragon, which can be ten feet long and two hundred pounds. Only a couple of lizards inject poisons when biting. These are the Gila monster of the southwestern United States and the beaded lizard of Mexico.

Importance of Reptiles

The following turtles are endangered species: Kemp's Ridley Sea Turtle *(Lepidochelys kempii)* and Leatherback Sea Turtle *(Dermochelys coriacea)*.

For additional content background on this topic, go to the Glencoe Science Web site at science.glencoe.com.

CHAPTER 

Fish, Amphibians, and Reptiles

Chapter Vocabulary

chordate, p. 398
notochord, p. 398
postanal tail, p. 398
nerve cord, p. 399
gill slit, p. 399
endoskeleton, p. 399
cartilage, p. 399
vertebrate, p. 399
ectotherm, p. 401
endotherm, p. 401
fin, p. 403
scale, p. 403
hibernation, p. 411
estivation, p. 411
amniotic egg, p. 417

What do you think?

Science Journal The photograph shows a magnified view of frog eggs. Frogs are amphibians. These fertilized eggs will hatch into tadpoles. Tadpoles live in water and have structures similar to fish. As the tadpoles grow, they develop the structures that allow frogs to live on land.

CHAPTER 14

Fish, Amphibians, and Reptiles

Do you know why frogs and salamanders live near ponds or streams? How do fish "breathe" underwater? What is the difference between alligators and crocodiles? In this chapter, you will find the answers to these questions. You also will read about the characteristics of animals known as chordates and vertebrates, and how fish, amphibians, and reptiles are classified, reproduce, and develop.

What do you think?

Science Journal Look at the picture below with a classmate. Discuss what you think this might be. Here's a hint: *It can be found in a pond during the spring season.* Write your answer or best guess in your Science Journal.

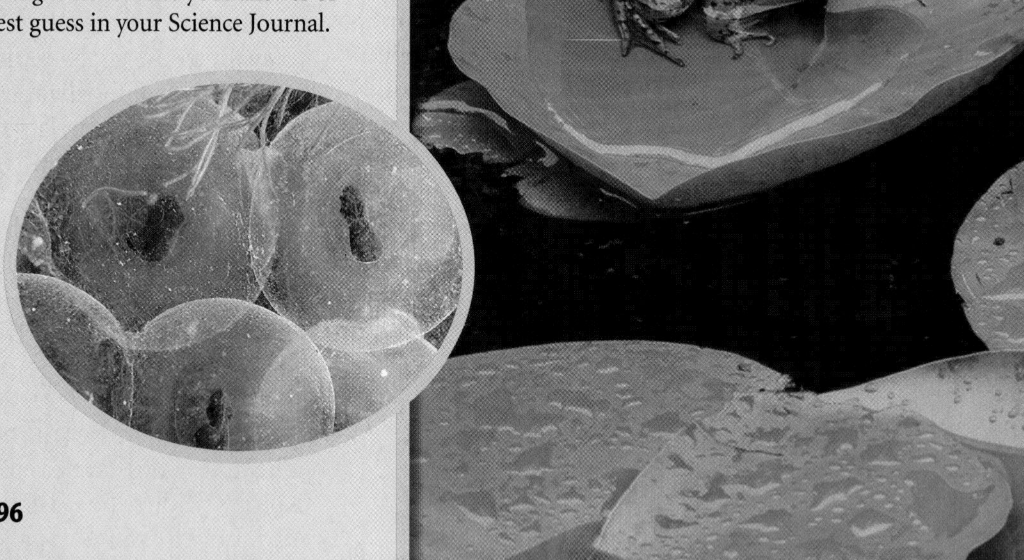

396

Theme Connection

Stability and Change The theme of stability and change is introduced in a discussion of chordates and vertebrates. The theme is developed through the discussion of adaptations that fish, amphibians, and reptiles have for living in their environments. The ecological importance of fish, amphibians, and reptiles is presented.

How much do you know about reptiles? For example, do snakes have eyelids? Why do snakes flick their tongues in and out? How can some snakes swallow animals that are larger than their own heads? Snakes don't have ears, so how do they hear? In this activity, you will discover the answer to one of these questions.

Model how a snake hears

1. Hold a tuning fork by the stem and tap it on a hard piece of rubber, such as the sole of a shoe.
2. Hold it next to your ear. What, if anything, do you hear?
3. Tap the tuning fork again. Press the base of the stem firmly against your chin. In your Science Journal, describe what happens.

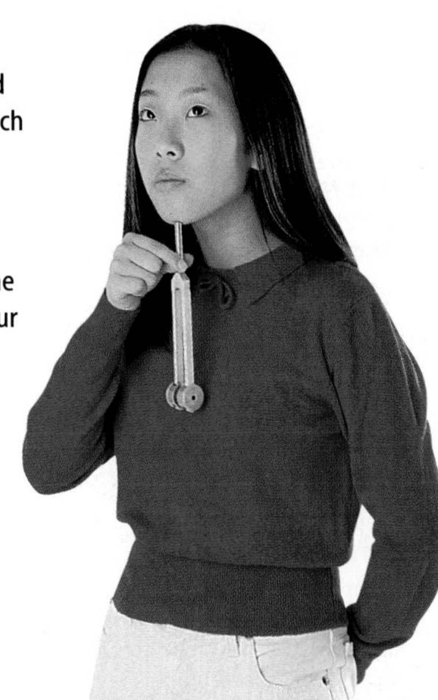

Observe

Using the results from step 3, infer how a snake detects vibrations. In your Science Journal, predict how different animals can use vibrations to hear.

Before You Read

FOLDABLES Reading & Study Skills

Making an Organizational Study Fold **Make the following Foldable to help you organize your thoughts into clear categories about fish, amphibians, and reptiles.**

1. Place a sheet of paper in front of you so the long side is at the top. Fold the paper in half from the left side to the right side two times. Unfold all the folds.
2. Fold the paper in half from top to bottom. Then fold it in half again. Unfold all the folds.
3. Trace over all the fold lines. Label the rows *Fish, Amphibians,* and *Reptiles.*
4. As you read the chapter, write characteristics about each type of animal on your Foldable chart.

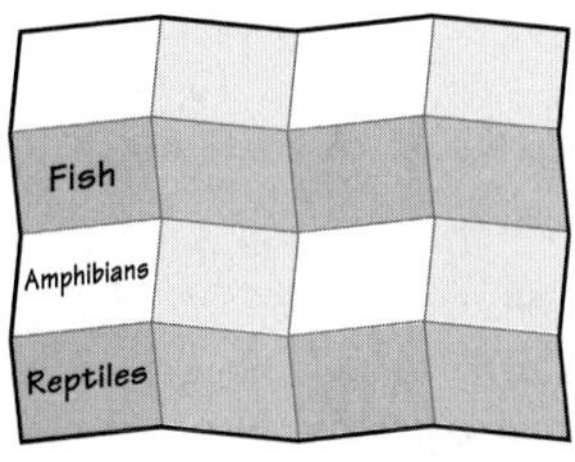

EXPLORE ACTIVITY

Purpose Use the Explore Activity to introduce students to reptiles, one of the vertebrate classes they will study in this chapter. L1 ELL IS **Auditory-Musical**

Preparation Before beginning this activity, obtain several tuning forks. You may wish to cut up a discarded rubber car floor mat for students to use as a striking pad.

Materials one tuning fork for every two students

Teaching Strategy Advise students not to touch the prongs of the tuning fork after hitting it on the piece of rubber.

Observe

Sound is heard because vibrations traveled through the bones in the jaw and skull to the fluid in the inner ear. Here, the vibrations are translated into nerve impulses and interpreted as sound by the brain. In many snakes and salamanders, the jawbone is sensitive to ground vibrations.

Assessment

Process Infer how you could best warn venomous snakes of your approach when hiking. Making heavy footsteps or striking the ground with a stick will produce vibrations to warn snakes and allow them to avoid hikers. Use **Performance Assessment in the Science Classroom,** p. 89.

Before You Read

FOLDABLES Reading & Study Skills

Dinah Zike Study Fold

Purpose Have students make and use a Foldable table to collect information on fish, amphibians, and reptiles as they read the chapter. Have them use the data they record during and after reading to compare and contrast these vertebrates.

For additional help, see Foldables Worksheet, p.17 in **Chapter Resources Booklet,** or go to the Glencoe Science Web site at **science.glencoe.com.** See After You Read in the Study Guide at the end of this chapter.

SECTION

Chordates and Vertebrates

1 Motivate

Bellringer Transparency

Display the Section Focus Transparency for Section 1. Use the accompanying Transparency Activity Master. L2 ELL

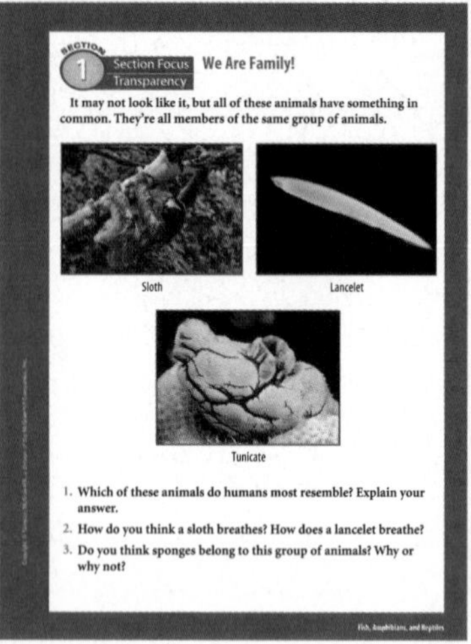

SECTION 1 Section Focus Transparency **We Are Family!**

It may not look like it, but all of these animals have something in common. They're all members of the same group of animals.

Sloth

Lancelet

Tunicate

1. Which of these animals do humans most resemble? Explain your answer.
2. How do you think a sloth breathes? How does a lancelet breathe?
3. Do you think sponges belong to this group of animals? Why or why not?

Fish, Amphibians, and Reptiles

Tie to Prior Knowledge

Vertebrates are animals that are familiar to students. Ask them to name as many kinds of vertebrates as possible. Then ask what characteristics these animals have in common.

Caption Answer

Figure 1 A sea squirt and a human are both chordates. At some stage in development all chordates have a notochord, postanal tail, nerve cord, and gill slits.

SECTION

Chordates and Vertebrates

As You Read

What You'll Learn

- **List** the characteristics of all chordates.
- **Identify** characteristics shared by vertebrates.
- **Differentiate** between ectotherms and endotherms.

Vocabulary

chordate
notochord
postanal tail
nerve cord
gill slit
endoskeleton
cartilage
vertebrae
ectotherm
endotherm

Why It's Important

Humans are vertebrates. Other vertebrates play important roles in your life because they provide food, companionship, and labor.

Chordate Characteristics

During a walk along the seashore at low tide, you often can see jellylike masses of animals clinging to rocks. Some of these animals may be sea squirts, as shown in **Figure 1,** which is one of the many types of animals known as chordates (KOR dayts). **Chordates** have four characteristics that are present at some stage of their development—a notochord (NOH tuh cord), postanal tail, nerve cord, and gill slits.

Notochord All chordates have an internal **notochord** that supports the animal and extends along the upper part of its body, as shown in **Figure 2.** The notochord is flexible but firm because it is made up of fluid-filled cells that are enclosed in a stiff covering. The notochord also extends into the **postanal tail**—a muscular structure at the end of the developing chordate. Some chordates, such as fish, amphibians, reptiles, birds, and mammals, develop backbones that partly or entirely replace the notochord. They are called vertebrates. In some chordates such as the sea squirt and other tunicates, and the lancelets, the notochord is kept into adulthood.

Reading Check *What happens to the notochord as a bat develops?*

Figure 1
Sea squirts get their name because when they're taken out of the ocean, they squirt water out of their body. *What do you have in common with a sea squirt?*

398 CHAPTER 14

Section Assessment Planner

PORTFOLIO
Science Journal, p. 399

PERFORMANCE ASSESSMENT
Skill Builder Activities, p. 401
See page 428 for more options.

CONTENT ASSESSMENT
Section, p. 401
Challenge, p. 401
Chapter, pp. 428–429

Nerve Cord Above the notochord and along the length of a developing chordate's body is a tubelike structure called the **nerve cord,** also shown in **Figure 2.** As most chordates develop, the front end of the nerve cord enlarges to form the brain and the remainder becomes the spinal cord. These two structures become the central nervous system that develops into complex systems for sensory and motor responses.

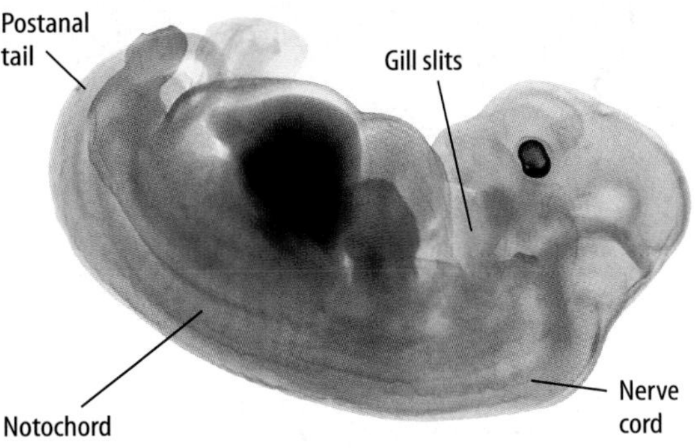

Figure 2
At some time during its development, a chordate has a notochord, postanal tail, nerve cord, and gill slits.

Gill Slits All developing chordates have **gill slits.** They are found in the region between the mouth and the digestive tube as pairs of openings to the outside. Many chordates have several pairs of gill slits. Ancient invertebrate chordates used their gill slits for filter feeding. This is still their purpose in some living chordates such as lancelets. In fish, the gill slits have developed into internal gills where oxygen and carbon dioxide are exchanged. In humans, gill slits are present only during embryonic development. However, one pair becomes the tubes that go from the ears to the throat.

Vertebrate Characteristics

Besides the characteristics common to all chordates, vertebrates have distinct characteristics. These traits set vertebrates apart from other chordates.

Structure All vertebrates have an internal framework called an **endoskeleton.** It is made up of bone and/or flexible tissue called **cartilage.** Your ears and the tip of your nose are made of cartilage. The endoskeleton provides a place for muscle attachment and supports and protects the organs. Part of the endoskeleton is a flexible, supportive column called the backbone, as shown in **Figure 3.** It is a stack of **vertebrae** alternating with cartilage. The backbone surrounds and protects the spinal nerve cord. Vertebrates also have a head with a skull that encloses and protects the brain.

Most of a vertebrate's internal organs are found in a central body cavity. A protective skin covers a vertebrate. Hair, feathers, scales, or horns sometimes grow from the skin.

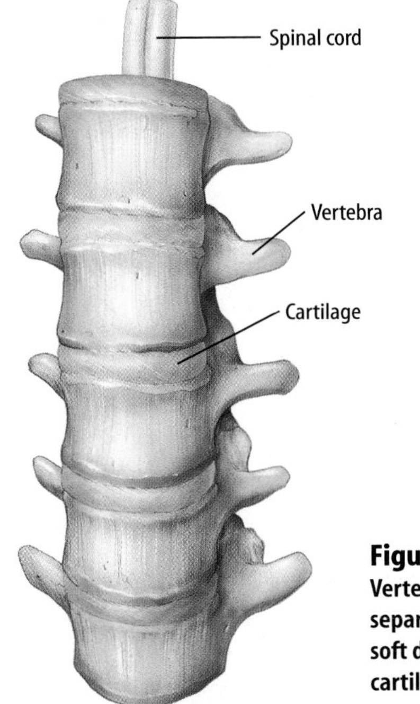

Figure 3
Vertebrae are separated by soft disks of cartilage.

2 Teach

Chordate Characteristics

Reading Check

Answer It is replaced by a backbone.

Discussion

Why are tunicates and lancelets classified as chordates? They have a notochord, postanal tail, nerve cord, and gill slits that are present at some stage of development.

Quick Demo

Display preserved specimens of a tunicate, an amphioxus, and a frog so that students can observe characteristics of the three chordate subphyla. LS **Visual-Spatial**

Vertebrate Characteristics

Quick Demo

Use a model of a human skeleton to show the vertebral column. Point out where the cartilage and spinal cord were located. In all vertebrates, the vertebral column develops from the notochord. LS **Visual-Spatial**

Resource Manager

Chapter Resources Booklet
- Transparency Activity, p. 48
- Directed Reading for Content Mastery, pp. 19, 20
- Note-taking Worksheets, pp. 35–38

Science Journal

Research Have students use the Internet and library to research tunicates and lancelets. Then ask students to write a report in their journals describing how tunicates and lancelets live and whether any are threatened or endangered. L2 LS **Linguistic** P

Vertebrate Characteristics, continued

Activity

Organize the class into seven groups. Assign each group one of the seven groups of vertebrates shown on this page. Give students time to research information about the kinds of animals in their group. Then have each group develop a game, poem, song, or short play that presents the information about the animals they researched. L2 ELL COOP LEARN

LS **Interpersonal and Linguistic**

Discussion

Lampreys and hagfish are the only jawless fish that survive today. How can you explain the small number of species in this group? Possible answers: Without paired fins, they are not good swimmers. Without jaws, they are not good predators. When jaws and paired fins evolved, species with these characteristics were more successful and became dominant.

Teacher FYI

The phylum *Chordata* includes three subphyla: *Urochordata* (tunicates), *Cephalochordata* (lancelets), and *Vertebrata*.

Visual Learning

Table 1 Have students make a circle graph from this data, showing what percentage of species belongs to each vertebrate group. L2 LS **Logical-Mathematical**

Table 1 Types of Vertebrates

Group	Estimated Number of Species	Examples
Jawless Fish	60	lamprey, hagfish
Cartilaginous Fish	500 to 590	shark, ray, skate
Bony Fish	20,000	salmon, bass, guppy, sea horse, lungfish
Amphibians	4,000	frog, toad, salamander
Reptiles	7,970	turtle, lizard, snake, crocodile, alligator
Birds	8,700	stork, eagle, sparrow, turkey, duck, ostrich
Mammals	4,600	human, whale, bat, mouse, lion, cow, otter

Resource Manager

Chapter Resources Booklet
- Enrichment, p. 31
- Reinforcement, p. 27

Earth Science Critical Thinking/Problem Solving, p. 12

Active Reading

Learning Journal Have students draw a vertical line down each page of their Learning Journals. Have them record research notes, lecture notes, or vocabulary terms in the left column, and their responses to, interpretations of, questions about, or analyses in the right column. Direct students to write a Learning Journal related to chordates and vertebrates.

400 CHAPTER 14 Fish, Amphibians, and Reptiles

Vertebrate Groups Seven main groups of vertebrates are found on Earth today, as shown in **Table 1.** Vertebrates are either ectotherms or endotherms. Fish, amphibians, and reptiles are ectotherms, also known as cold-blooded animals. An **ectotherm** has an internal body temperature that changes with the temperature of its surroundings. Birds and mammals are endotherms, which sometimes are called warm-blooded animals. An **endotherm** has a nearly constant internal body temperature.

Figure 4
Placoderms were the first fish with jaws. These predatory fish were covered with heavy armor.

Vertebrate Origins Some vertebrate fossils, like the one in **Figure 4,** are of water-dwelling, armored animals that lived about 420 million years ago (mya). Lobe-finned fish appeared in the fossil record about 395 mya. The oldest known amphibian fossils date from about 370 mya. Reptile fossils have been found in deposits about 350 million years old. One well-known group of reptiles—the dinosaurs—first appeared about 230 mya.

In 1861, a fossil imprint of an animal with scales, jaws with teeth, claws on its front limbs, and feathers was found. The 150-million-year-old fossil was an ancestor of birds, *Archaeopteryx* (ar kee AHP tuh rihks).

Mammal-like reptiles appeared about 235 mya. However, true mammals appeared about 190 mya, and modern mammals originated about 38 million years ago.

Section 1 Assessment

1. Name four characteristics that are shared by all chordates.
2. Explain the difference between a vertebra and a notocord.
3. What are characteristics of vertebrates that other chordates do not have?
4. What are some of the physical differences between ectotherm animals and endotherm animals?
5. **Think Critically** If the outside temperature decreases by 20°C, what will happen to a reptile's body temperature?

Skill Builder Activities

6. **Concept Mapping** Construct a concept map using these terms: *chordates, bony fish, amphibians, cartilaginous fish, reptiles, birds, mammals, lancelets, tunicates, invertebrate chordates, jawless fish,* and *vertebrates.* **For more help, refer to the Science Skill Handbook.**
7. **Communicating** Write a paragraph in your Science Journal comparing and contrasting the characteristics of chordates and vertebrates. **For more help, refer to the Science Skill Handbook.**

Activity

Provide a skeleton of a fish (ectothermic vertebrate) and a cat (endothermic vertebrate). Have students observe the skeletons and determine how they are similar and how they are different. L1 IN **Visual-Spatial**

3 Assess

Reteach

Have students write a paragraph explaining why vertebrates are classified as chordates, but not all chordates are classified as vertebrates. L2 IN **Linguistic**

Challenge

Ectotherms do not perspire or pant. How do they control body temperature? The temperature of an ectotherm changes with its surroundings. If an ectotherm becomes too cold, it moves to warmer surroundings. An example is a lizard on a rock in the Sun. If it becomes too warm, the ectotherm moves to cooler surroundings.

Assessment

Oral Ask students to explain temperature control in ectotherms and endotherms, comparing the way energy is absorbed and used. In ectotherms heat energy is absorbed from sunlight as opposed to chemical release of energy by digestion and respiration in endotherms. Use **Performance Assessment in the Science Classroom,** p. 143.

Answers to Section Assessment

1. notochord, postanal tail, nerve cord, gill slits
2. The notochord is made up of fluid-filled cells enclosed in a stiff covering; a vertebra is made of bone or cartilage.
3. An endosleleton of cartilage and/or bone, including a backbone with vertebrae; a skull enclosing the brain
4. The body temperature of an ectotherm changes with its surroundings. The body temperature of an endotherm remains the same regardless of its surroundings.
5. Its body temperature will decrease by about 20°.
6. Check students' concept maps to make sure they used all listed terms and classified organisms correctly.
7. chordates—notochord, postanal tail, nerve cord, and gill slits; vertebrates—backbone that protects the spinal nerve cord, an endoskeleton, head with a skull that protects the brain

Activity

BENCH TESTED

Purpose Students construct a model animal and determine if it is an endotherm or an ectotherm. L2 LS **Logical-Mathematical**

Process Skills observing and inferring, constructing, describing, comparing

Time Required 45 minutes

Alternate Materials Students can use scraps of wool clothing, cotton balls, socks, shredded paper, or tissue paper for the stuffing.

Teaching Strategy Prepare locations in the classroom that have a wide range of temperatures such as near a heating vent or radiator, on a windowsill, and in a refrigerator.

Troubleshooting Students should use only one kind of stuffing so that their results are comparable with others.

Answers to Questions

1. Answers will vary.
2. If the temperature did not change dramatically, the model represents an endotherm. If the temperature did change dramatically, it is a model of an ectotherm.
3. Thicker "animals" should maintain the temperature of their inner core better than flat "animals."
4. Answers will vary.

✓Assessment

Performance Have students build a second animal with an internal temperature opposite to the first. For example, if they first constructed an endotherm, ask them to construct an ectotherm and vice versa. Use **PASC**, p. 97.

Activity

Endotherms and Ectotherms

Birds and mammals are endotherms. Fish, amphibians and reptiles are ectotherms. How can you determine whether an animal you have never seen before is an endotherm or an ectotherm? What tests might you conduct to find the answer?

What You'll Investigate

Is an animal that you construct an endotherm or an ectotherm?

Materials

fiberfill
cotton balls
old socks
tissue
cloth
thermometer
**Alternate materials*

Goals

- **Construct** an imaginary animal.
- **Determine** whether your animal is an endotherm or an ectotherm.

Safety Precautions

Procedure

1. Design an animal that has a thermometer inside. Construct the animal using cloth and some kind of stuffing material. Make sure that you will be able to remove and reinsert the thermometer.
2. Draw a picture of your animal and record data about its size and shape.
3. Copy the data table in your Science Journal.
4. Place your animal in three locations that have different temperatures. Record the locations in the data table.
5. In each location, record the time and the temperature of your animal at the beginning and after 10 min.

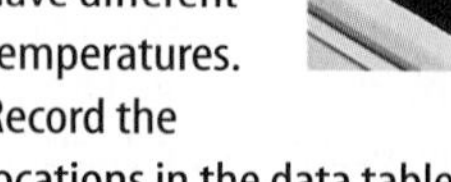

Animal Temperature

Location	Beginning Time/ Temperature	Ending Time/ Temperature
	Answers will vary	

Conclude and Apply

1. **Describe** your results. Did the animal's temperature vary depending upon the location?
2. Based on your results, is your animal an endotherm or an ectotherm? Explain.
3. **Compare** your results to those of others in your class. Were the results the same for animals of different sizes? Did the shape of the animal, such as one being flatter and another more cylindrical, matter?
4. Based on your results and information in the chapter, do you think your animal is most likely a bird, a mammal, a reptile, an amphibian, or a fish? Explain.

Communicating Your Data

Compare your conclusions with those of other students in your class. **For more help, refer to the** Science Skill Handbook.

402 **CHAPTER 14** Fish, Amphibians, and Reptiles

Communicating Your Data

Encourage students to compare the shape and contents of their animals and discuss how differences in these variables affected their results.

Resource Manager

Chapter Resources Booklet
Activity Worksheet, pp. 5–6
Lab Activity, pp. 9–10

Lab Management and Safety, p. 58

SECTION

Fish

Fish Characteristics

Did you know that more differences appear among fish than among any other vertebrate group? In fact, there are more species of fish than species of other vertebrate groups. All fish are ectotherms. They are adapted for living in nearly every type of water environment on Earth—freshwater and salt water. Some fish, such as salmon, spend part of their life in freshwater and part of it in salt water. Fish are found at depths from shallow pools to deep oceans.

A streamlined shape, a muscular tail, and fins allow most fish to move rapidly through the water. **Fins** are fanlike structures attached to the endoskeleton. They are used for steering, balancing, and moving. Paired fins on the sides allow fish to move right or left and backward or forward. Fins on the top and bottom of the body give the fish stability. Most fish secrete a slimy mucus that also helps them move through the water.

Most fish have scales. **Scales** are hard, thin plates that cover the skin and protect the body, similar to shingles on the roof of a house. Most fish scales are made of bone. **Figure 5** illustrates how they can be tooth shaped, diamond shaped, cone shaped, or round. The shape of the scales can be used to help classify fish. The age of some species can be estimated by counting the annual growth rings of the scales.

As You Read

***What* You'll Learn**

- **List** the characteristics of the three classes of fish.
- **Explain** how fish obtain food and oxygen and reproduce.
- **Describe** the importance and origin of fish.

Vocabulary
fin
scale

***Why* It's Important**

Fish are an important food source for humans as well as many other animals.

Figure 5
Four types of fish scales are shown here.

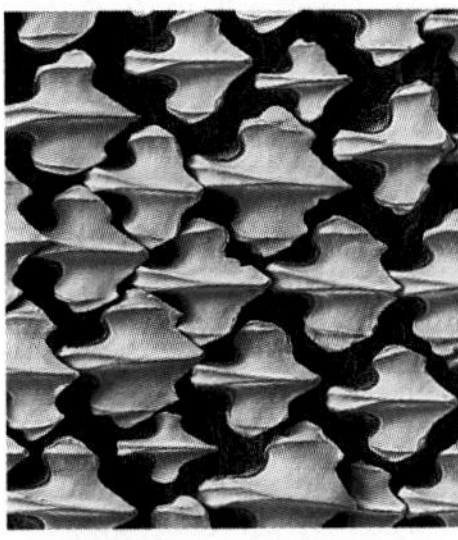

A Sharks are covered with placoid scales such as these. Shark teeth are modified forms of these scales.

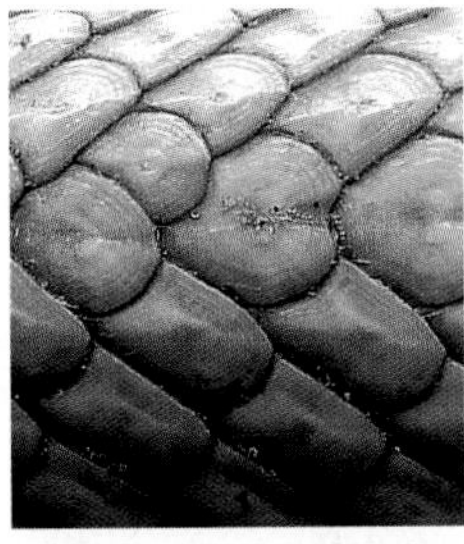

B Lobe-finned fish and gars are covered by ganoid scales. These scales don't overlap like other fish scales.

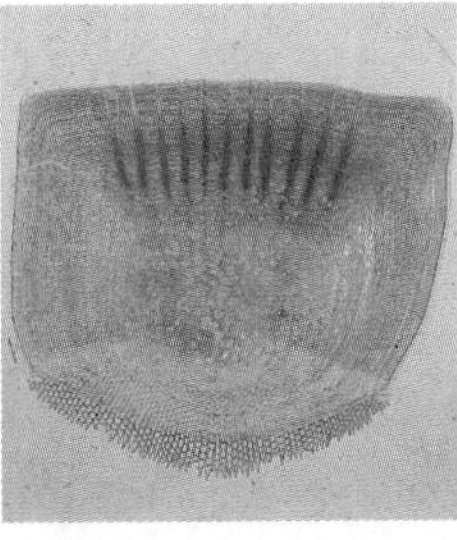

C Cycloid scales are thin and overlap, giving the fish flexibility. These scales grow as the fish grows.

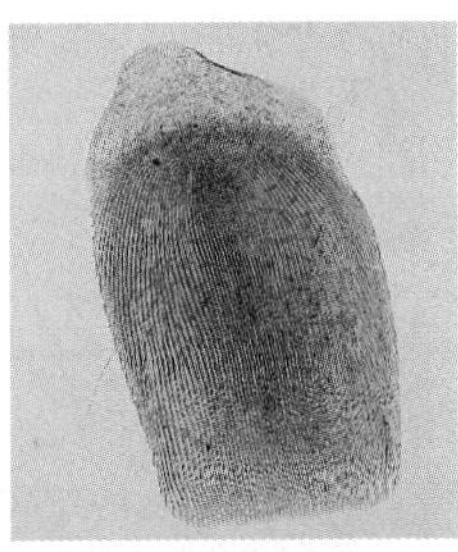

D Ctenoid (TEN oyd) scales have a rough edge, which is thought to reduce drag as the fish swims through the water.

Section Assessment Planner

PORTFOLIO
Extension, p. 405

PERFORMANCE ASSESSMENT
Try at Home MiniLAB, p. 407
Skill Builder Activities, p. 410
See page 428 for more options.

CONTENT ASSESSMENT
Section, p. 410
Challenge, p. 410
Chapter, pp. 428–429

SECTION 2

Fish

1 Motivate

Bellringer Transparency

Display the Section Focus Transparency for Section 2. Use the accompanying Transparency Activity Master. L2 ELL

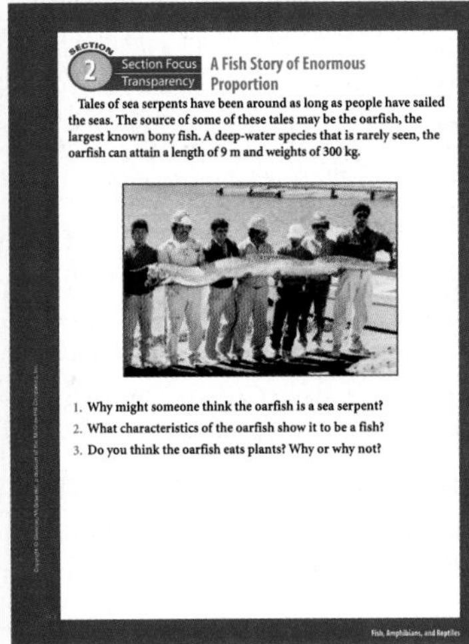

Section 2 Section Focus Transparency

A Fish Story of Enormous Proportion

Tales of sea serpents have been around as long as people have sailed the seas. The source of some of these tales may be the oarfish, the largest known bony fish. A deep-water species that is rarely seen, the oarfish can attain a length of 9 m and weights of 300 kg.

1. Why might someone think the oarfish is a sea serpent?
2. What characteristics of the oarfish show it to be a fish?
3. Do you think the oarfish eats plants? Why or why not?

Fish, Amphibians, and Reptiles

Tie to Prior Knowledge

Students will be familiar with fish. Many will have aquariums, some will have fished for recreation, and most will have eaten fish. Use their knowledge of fish to introduce fish characteristics. Most answers students give will relate to bony fish.

2 Teach

Fish Characteristics

Use an Analogy

Show students a picture of shingles on a house. Explain that most fish are covered with scales arranged much like the shingles on a roof. Scales are firmly attached to the skin tissue from which they grow. In most fish species, the outer part of each scale overlaps the next scale, like shingles on a house. The exception are ganoid scales, found on lobed-finned fish.
LS Logical-Mathematical

Activity

Organize the class into groups of four. Have each group make a table comparing the characteristics of jawless fish, cartilaginous fish, and bony fish. They should compare body shapes and coverings, placement of fins, methods of feeding, sense organs, and any other characteristics they read about. L2 COOP LEARN
LS Interpersonal

Activity

Have each student make a wet mount of a cycloid or ctenoid fish scale to observe under low power with the microscope. After observing, have students draw what they see, and write a summary identifying the type of scale and estimating the age of the fish.
L2 **LS Logical-Mathematical**

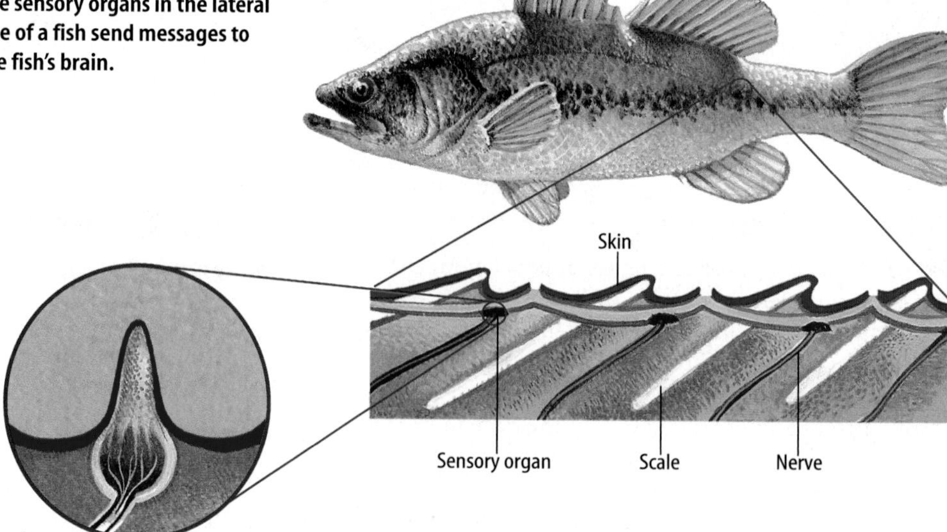

Figure 6
The sensory organs in the lateral line of a fish send messages to the fish's brain.

Body Systems All fish have highly developed sensory systems. Most fish have a lateral line system, as shown in **Figure 6.** A lateral line system is made up of a shallow, canal-like structure that extends along the length of the fish's body and is filled with sensory organs. The lateral line enables a fish to sense its environment and to detect movement. Some fish, such as sharks, also have a strong sense of smell. Sharks can detect blood in the water from several kilometers away.

Fish have a two-chambered heart in which oxygen-filled blood mixes with carbon dioxide-filled blood. A fish's blood isn't carrying as much oxygen as blood that is pumped through a three- or four-chambered heart.

Gas Exchange Most fish have organs called gills for the exchange of carbon dioxide and oxygen. Gills are located on both sides of the fish's head and are made up of feathery gill filaments that contain many tiny blood vessels. When a fish takes water into its mouth, the water passes over the gills, where oxygen from the water is exchanged with carbon dioxide in the blood. The water then passes out through slits on each side of the fish. Many fish, such as the halibut in **Figure 7,** are able to take in water while lying on the ocean floor.

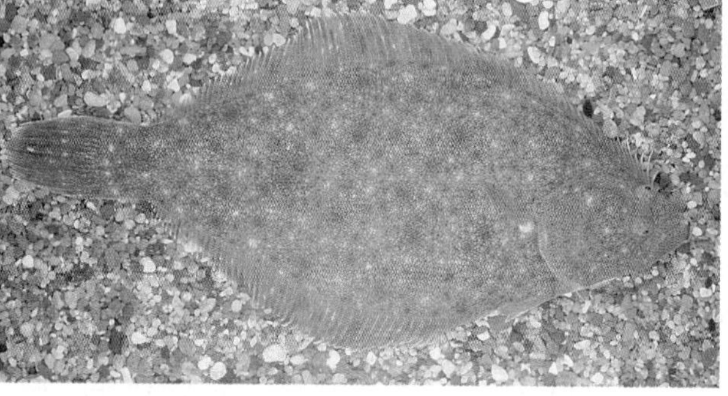

Figure 7
Even though a halibut's eyes are on one side of the fish, gills are on both sides.

LAB DEMONSTRATION

Purpose to demonstrate water flow across a fish's gill

Materials guppy or goldfish, water, food coloring, clear container.

Preparation Place guppy or goldfish in a clear container with an adequate amount of water.

Procedure Have students observe the fish as it swims, noting the opening and closing of its mouth and gill covers. Place a drop of food coloring in front of the fish's mouth.

Expected Outcome Students will see colored water come out of the fish's gills.

Assessment

How long did it take for colored water to come out of the gills? Answers will vary, but colored water should appear soon after the food coloring is added. **What does the appearance of colored water indicate?** That the water and food coloring the fish took in flowed over the fish's gills before being expelled.

Figure 8
Fish obtain food in different ways.

A **A whale shark's mouth can open to 1.4 m wide.**

B **Sawfish are rare. They use their toothed snouts to root out bottom fish to eat.**

C **Parrot fish use their hard beaks to bite off pieces of coral.**

D **Electric eels produce a powerful electric shock that stuns their prey.**

Feeding Adaptations Some of the adaptations that fish have for obtaining food are shown in **Figure 8.** Some of the largest sharks are filter feeders that take in small animals as they swim. The archerfish shoots down insects by spitting drops of water at them. Even though some fish have strong teeth, most do not chew their food. They use their teeth to capture their prey or to tear off chunks of food.

Reproduction Fish reproduce sexually. Reproduction is controlled by sex hormones. The production of sex hormones is dependent upon certain environmental factors such as temperature, length of daylight, and availability of food.

Female fish release large numbers of eggs into the water. Males then swim over the eggs and release sperm. This behavior is called spawning. The joining of the egg and sperm cells outside the female's body is called external fertilization. Certain species of sharks and rays have internal fertilization and lay fertilized eggs. Other fish, such as guppies, also have internal fertilization but do not lay eggs. The eggs develop and hatch inside the female's body. After they hatch, they leave her body.

Some species do not take care of their young. They release hundreds or even millions of eggs, which increases the chances that a few offspring will survive to become adults. Fish that care for their young lay fewer eggs. Some fish, including some catfish, hold their eggs and young in their mouths. Male sea horses keep the fertilized eggs in a pouch until they hatch.

Use an Analogy

Show students a cross section of a tree and explain its similarity to a cycloid or ctenoid fish scale. Tell students that as a fish grows, more material is added to the scales to make them larger. In temperate climates, a new layer of material is added each year, forming rings. Because one ring is added each year, scale rings can be counted to estimate the age of some fish just as tree rings can be counted to estimate the age of a tree.
IS **Logical-Mathematical**

Extension

Have students research and write a report in their Science Journals on reproduction in guppies, catfish, and sea horses.
L2 IS **Linguistic** P

Teacher FYI

Most fish are ectotherms, but tuna, mako sharks, and swordfish are exceptions. They are able to maintain their body temperatures slightly above that of the surrounding water. They can adapt to different temperatures at different ocean depths and swim faster and longer than both their competition and their prey. This allows them to hunt in much colder water than their competitors can.

Visual Learning

Figure 8 Have students make a list comparing and contrasting the fish shown.

Resource Manager

Chapter Resources Booklet
Transparency Activity, p. 48
Directed Reading for Content Mastery, p. 20
Cultural Diversity, p. 7

Fun Fact

At one time, it was believed that for every land animal there was a corresponding water animal. This is one reason for names such as catfish, sea horse, and dogfish.

Types of Fish

Use an Analogy

Fish with paired fins use them the same way airplanes use wings and propellers to generate thrust, to direct the body up and down, and to change direction.

Jawless Fish

Activity

Display pictures of the three classes of fish on the bulletin board. Have students place them in the appropriate class. Then have them examine the pictures and determine the similarities and differences in the three classes. L2 LS **Visual-Spatial**

Cartilaginous Fish

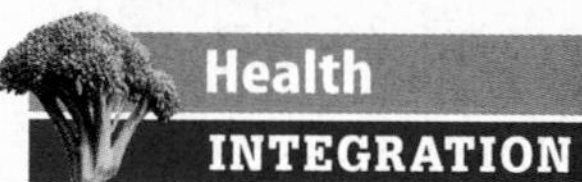

Health INTEGRATION

Accept all reasonable responses. Encourage students to use the Food Guide Pyramid as a guide for developing a healthful meal.

IDENTIFYING Misconceptions

Movies may have given students the impression that all sharks eat humans. Of the 370 known species, only 27 have been known to attack humans. Have students find out which sharks attack humans and what safety rules are used to prevent shark attacks.

Reading Check

Answer because of overfishing and the slow shark reproduction rate

Types of Fish

Fish vary in size, shape, color, living environments, and other factors. Despite their diversity, fish are grouped into only three categories—jawless fish, cartilaginous (kar tuh LA juh nuhs) fish, and bony fish.

Jawless Fish

Lampreys, along with the hagfish in **Figure 9,** are jawless fish. Jawless fish have round, toothed mouths and long, tubelike bodies covered with scaleless, slimy skin. Most lampreys are parasites. They attach to other fish with their suckerlike mouth. They then feed by removing blood and other body fluids from the host fish. Hagfish feed on dead or dying fish and other aquatic animals.

Jawless fish have flexible endoskeletons made of cartilage. Hagfish live only in salt water, but some species of lamprey live in salt water and other species live in freshwater.

Health INTEGRATION

Many fish contain oil with omega-3 fatty acids, which seems to reverse the effects of too much cholesterol. A diet rich in fish that contain this oil might prevent the formation of fatty deposits in the arteries of humans. In your Science Journal, develop a menu for a meal that includes fish.

Cartilaginous Fish

Sharks, skates, and rays are cartilaginous fish. These fish have skeletons made of cartilage like jawless fish. Unlike jawless fish, these fish have movable jaws that usually have well-developed teeth. Their bodies are covered with tiny scales that make their skins feel like fine sandpaper.

Sharks are top predators in many ocean food chains. They are efficient at finding and killing their food, which includes other fish, mammals, and some reptiles. Because of overfishing and the fact that shark reproduction is slow, shark populations are decreasing at an alarming rate.

Reading Check *Why are shark populations decreasing?*

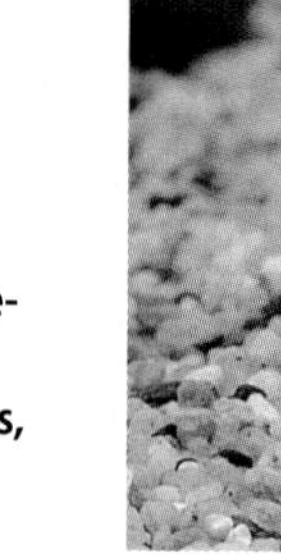

Figure 9
Hagfish have cartilaginous skeletons like sharks and rays. They feed on marine worms, mollusks, and crustaceans, in addition to dead and dying fish.

Curriculum Connection

Language Arts Divide the class into groups. Assign each group a well-known shark—great white, bull, hammerhead, or nurse. Have each group research characteristics, feeding habits, and behavior of the sharks and report back to the class. L2 COOP LEARN LS **Interpersonal**

Teacher FYI

A shark's teeth are adapted to its feeding habits. Struggles that occur while trying to capture prey can cause the loss of teeth. A shark's mouth has 6 to 20 rows of backward slanting teeth. When one tooth breaks or wears down, a replacement moves forward. A single shark may grow more than 20,000 teeth in its lifetime. Shark teeth are actually modified scales.

Figure 10
Bony fish come in many sizes, shapes, and colors. However, all bony fish have the same basic body structure.

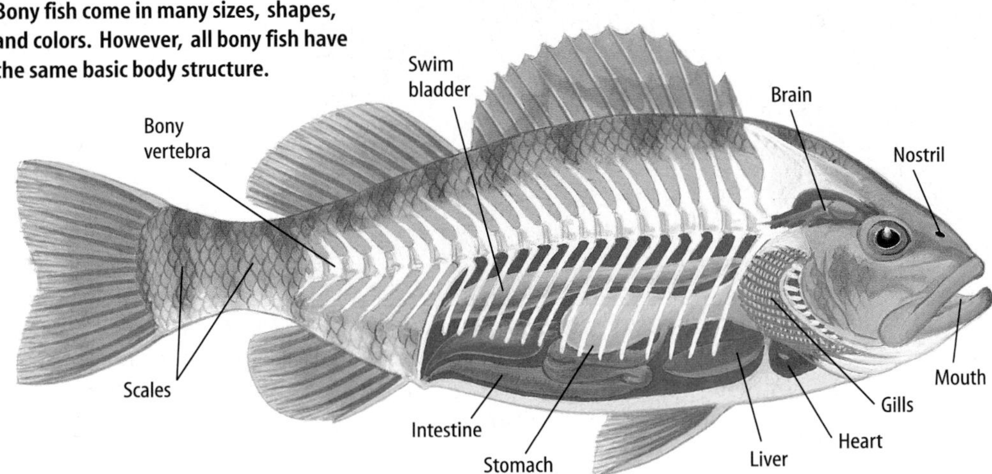

Bony Fish

About 95 percent of all species of fish are bony fish. They have skeletons made of bone. The body structure of a typical bony fish is shown in **Figure 10.** A bony flap covers and protects the gills. It closes as water moves into the mouth and over the gills. When it opens, water exits from the gills.

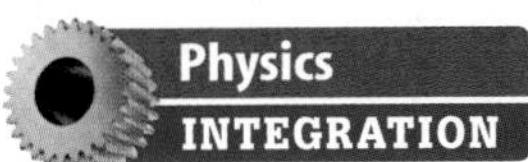

Swim Bladder An important adaptation in most bony fish is the swim bladder. It is an air sac that allows the fish to adjust its density in response to the density of the surrounding water. The density of matter is found by dividing its mass by its volume. If the density of the object is greater than that of the liquid it is in, the object will sink. If the density of the object is equal to the density of the liquid, the object will neither sink nor float to the surface. If the density of the object is less than the density of the liquid, the object will float on the liquid's surface.

The transfer of gases—mostly oxygen in deepwater fish and nitrogen in shallow-water fish—between the swim bladder and the blood causes the swim bladder to inflate and deflate. As the swim bladder fills with gases, the fish's density decreases and it rises in the water. When the swim bladder deflates, the fish's density increases and it sinks. Glands regulate the gas content in the swim bladder, enabling the fish to remain at a specific depth with little effort. Deepwater fish often have oil in their swim bladders rather than gases. Some bottom-dwelling fish and active fish that frequently change depth have no swim bladders.

Modeling How Fish Adjust to Different Depths

Procedure

1. Fill a **balloon** with air.
2. Place it in a **bowl of water.**
3. Fill another balloon partially with water, then blow air into it until it is the same size as the balloon filled only with air.
4. Place the second balloon in the bowl of water.

Analysis

1. What structure do these balloons model?
2. Compare where in the water (on the surface, or below the surface) two fish would be if they had swim bladders similar to the two balloons.

Bony Fish

Purpose Students use a model to determine how fish use a swim bladder to control their depth. L1 ELL COOP LEARN

Kinesthetic and Interpersonal

Materials 2 balloons, water, bowl

Teaching Strategies

- The bowl will need to be large enough to hold both balloons.
- Encourage students to experiment with different proportions of water and air in the balloon to simulate changes occurring within a fish's swim bladder.

Analysis

1. a swim bladder
2. A fish with a swim bladder filled with air would be near the surface; one with water and air would be farther beneath the surface.

Assessment

Process Ask students to infer the habitat of fish, such as blennies, that have no swim bladder. These fish are bottom dwellers. Use **Performance Assessment in the Science Classroom,** p. 89.

Fun Fact

The smallest freshwater fish is the dwarf pygmy goby, which measures 9 mm long. The largest living fish is the whale shark.

Resource Manager

Chapter Resources Booklet
MiniLAB, p. 3

Performance Assessment in the Science Classroom, p. 55

Cultural Diversity

Commercial Fishing Fish are a vital food source worldwide. Fishing is an important economic activity, and fish are part of the diet in many countries. Have students research the fishing industry in various countries and mark a world map to show where most commercial fishing occurs. L2 ELL **Visual-Spatial**

Bony Fish, continued

Activity

Have students research species of fish that live in the lakes and rivers of their state. Have them find or draw pictures of each species and make a bulletin board that illustrates where each species is found. L2 ELL

LS **Visual-Spatial**

Fun Fact

A swim bladder works the same way a scuba diver's buoyancy compensator does. A scuba diver adds air to his or her compensator to rise, and releases air from the compensator to sink. Also, the diver may effect small changes in depth by inhaling or exhaling.

Discussion

Bottom-dwelling fish often lack a swim bladder. What is the advantage of this? Swim bladders help fish maintain buoyancy. A bottom-dwelling fish would be at a disadvantage if were buoyant.

Math Skills Activity

National Math Standards

Correlation to Mathematics Objectives

1, 2, 4, 6, 8, 9

Answer to Practice Problem

Divide the mass of the fish (215 g) by the volume (180 cm^3). The fish will have a density of 1.19 g/cm^3. The fish will sink in salt water because it is denser than the salt water.

Figure 11
Coelacanths (SEE luh kanthz) have been found living in the Indian Ocean north of Madagascar.

Lobe-finned Fish One of the three types of bony fish is the lobe-finned fish, as shown in **Figure 11.** Lobe-finned fish have fins that are lobelike and fleshy. These organisms were thought to have been extinct for more than 70 million years. But in 1938, some South African fishers caught a lobe-finned fish in a net. Several living lobe-finned fish have been studied since. Lobe-finned fish are important because scientists hypothesize that fish similar to these were the ancestors of the first land vertebrates—the amphibians.

Math Skills Activity

Calculating Density

Example Problem

A freshwater fish has a mass of 645 g and a volume of 700 cm^3. What is the fish's density, and will it sink or float in freshwater?

Solution

1. *This is what you know:* density of freshwater = 1g/cm^3; mass of fish = 645 g; volume of fish = 700 cm^3
2. *This is what you need to find:* density of fish
3. *This is the equation you need to use:* $\frac{\text{mass of object (g)}}{\text{volume of object (cm}^3)} = \text{density of object (g/cm}^3)$
4. *Substitute the known values:* $\frac{645 \text{ g}}{700 \text{ cm}^3} = 0.92 \text{ g/cm}^3$

The fish will float in freshwater. Its density is less than that of freshwater.

Practice Problem

Calculate the density of a saltwater fish that has a mass of 215 g and a volume of 180 cm^3. Will this fish float or sink in salt water? The density of ocean salt water is about 1.025 g/cm^3.

For more help, refer to the Math Skill Handbook.

408 CHAPTER 14 Fish, Amphibians, and Reptiles

Inclusion Strategies

Learning Disabled Have students make a mobile of the different types of fish mentioned in this section (jawless, cartilaginous, and bony). Beneath each type, have them write the fact they find most interesting about it. The same thing can be done with amphibians and reptiles. L2 LS **Kinesthetic and Visual-Spatial**

Curriculum Connection

Language Arts Read aloud poems about fish. Several can be found in John Hersey's book *Blues.* Others include "The Fish" by Elizabeth Bishop, "The Red Mullet" by Robert Penn Warren, "The Lung Fish" by John Ciardi, and "Pike" by Ted Hughes. Ask students how the poet used the fish in each poem. Have them find other poems about fish to share. L2

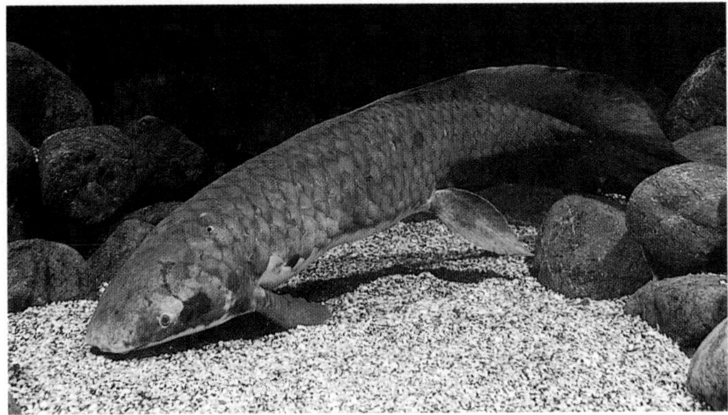

Figure 12
Australian lungfish are one of the six species of lungfish.

Lungfish A lungfish, as shown in **Figure 12,** has one lung and gills. This adaptation enables them to live in shallow waters that have little oxygen. The lung enables the lungfish to breathe air when the water evaporates. Drought conditions stimulate lungfish to burrow into the mud and cover themselves with mucus until water returns. Lungfish have been found along the coasts of South America and Australia.

Ray-Finned Fish Most bony fish have fins made of long, thin bones covered with skin. Ray-finned fish, like those in **Figure 13,** have a lot of variation in their body plans. Most predatory fish have long, flexible bodies, which enable them to pursue prey quickly. Many bottom fish have flattened bodies and mouths adapted for eating off the bottom. Fish with unusual shapes, like the sea horse and anglerfish, also can be found. Yellow perch, tuna, salmon, swordfish, and eels are ray-finned fish.

Figure 13
Bony fish have a diversity of body plans.

A **Most bony fish are ray-finned fish, like this rainbow trout.**

B **Sea horses use their tails to anchor themselves to sea grass. This prevents the ocean currents from washing them away.**

C **Anglerfish have a structure that looks like a lure to attract prey fish. When the prey comes close, the anglerfish quickly opens its mouth and captures the prey.**

Extension

Have students survey a local fish market to find out what varieties of fish are available. Have them determine the procedures that are used to ensure that fish are fresh when they are sold. L2

Teacher FYI

There is sometimes confusion about the use of the words *fish* and *fishes.* Many biologists use the following rules. When referring to a single individual of a single species, use *fish.* When referring to many individuals of a single species, the plural is also *fish.* When referring to several individuals of more than one species, the plural is *fishes.*

Extension

Have students research the different types of fishing such as fly-fishing, deep-sea fishing, spin-fishing, trolling, and downrigging. If possible, have them interview persons who participate in these sports and report their finding to the class. L2

Resource Manager

Chapter Resources Booklet
- Enrichment, p. 32
- Reinforcement, p. 38

Physical Science Critical Thinking/Problem Solving, pp. 1, 23

Cultural Diversity

Fish Appreciation Asians have long celebrated the beauty of carp and goldfish. Elaborately decorated fishbowls and kites with carp designs can be found throughout China, Japan, and Korea. Have students research other ways the beauty of carp and goldfish are used. Water gardens; Asian chefs create works of edible art that look like carp. L2

Importance and Origin of Fish

Reading Check

Answer They provide food, keep insect populations in check, keep plant growth from clogging waterways, and are kept in aquariums to admire. Fish farming and commercial fishing also are important to many economies.

3 Assess

Reteach

Ask students to explain why fish are classified into three separate classes, whereas amphibians, reptiles, birds, and mammals are not. L2 LS **Linguistic**

Challenge

Why are there more fish than any other kind of vertebrate? Answers may include that all life began in water and the water environment has undergone fewer changes than land environments. This reduced the risk of extinction because of the lack of ability to adapt to new conditions.

Assessment

Process Have students use the results of the MiniLAB in this section to determine how a submarine is able to descend and ascend in the ocean. Use **Performance Assessment in the Science Classroom,** p. 89.

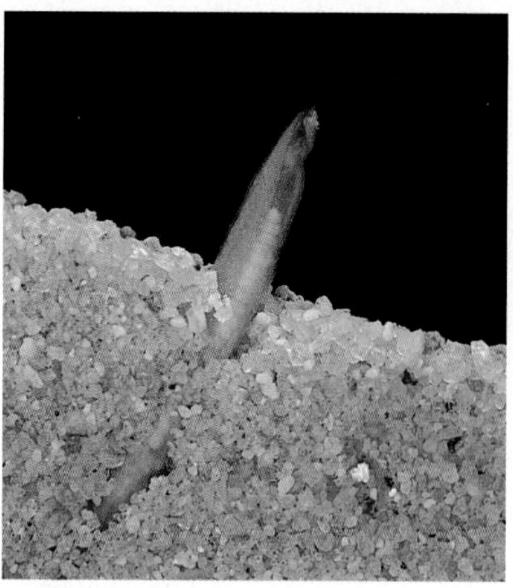

Figure 14
Lancelets are small, eel-like animals. They spend most of their time buried in the sand and mud at the bottom of the ocean.

Importance and Origin of Fish

Fish play a part in your life in many ways. They provide food for many animals, including humans. Fish farming and commercial fishing also are important to the U.S economy. Fishing is a method of obtaining food as well as a form of recreation enjoyed by many people. Many fish eat large amounts of insect larvae, such as mosquitoes, which keeps insect populations in check. Some, such as grass carp, are used to keep the plant growth from clogging waterways. Captive fish are kept in aquariums for humans to admire their bright colors and exotic forms.

Reading Check *How are fish helpful to humans?*

Most scientists agree that fish evolved from small, soft-bodied, filter-feeding organisms similar to present-day lancelets, shown in **Figure 14.** The earliest fossils of fish are those of jawless fish that lived about 450 million years ago. Fossils of these early fish usually are found where ancient streams emptied into the sea. This makes it difficult to tell whether these fish ancestors evolved in freshwater or in salt water.

Today's bony fish are probably descended from the first jawed fish called the acanthodians (a kan THOHD ee unz). They appeared in the fossil record about 410 million years ago. Another group of ancient fish—the placoderms—appeared about 400 million years ago. For about 50 million years, placoderms dominated most water ecosystems then disappeared. Modern sharks and rays are probably descended from the placoderms.

Section  Assessment

1. What are three characteristics of fish?
2. Name the three classes of fish and give an example of each.
3. How do jawless fish and cartilaginous fish take in food?
4. Describe the many ways that fish are important to humans.
5. **Think Critically** Female fish lay thousands of eggs. Why aren't lakes and oceans overcrowded with fish?

Skill Builder Activities

6. **Concept Mapping** Make an events-chain concept map to show what must take place for the fish to rise from the bottom to the surface of the lake. **For more help, refer to the** Science Skill Handbook.
7. **Using a Database** Use your computer to make a database of the characteristics of the three classes of fish. **For more help, refer to the** Technology Skill Handbook.

Answers to Section Assessment

1. Possible answers: streamlined shape, fins, muscular tail, ectotherms, two-chambered hearts
2. jawless fish—lamprey; cartilaginous fish—shark; bony fish—tuna
3. Jawless fish are parasites that attach to other fish. Cartilaginous fish are predators.
4. Possible answers: food, pets, controlling the growth of insect and plant pests
5. Many eggs are not fertilized; some eggs and young fish are eaten.
6. The sequence is as follows: A fish lying on the bottom of the lake transfers gases from the bloodstream into the swim bladder. As the swim bladder fills with gas, the fish rises in the water.
7. Database should include characteristics given in the student text.

SECTION 3

Amphibians

Amphibian Characteristics

The word *amphibian* comes from the Greek word *amphibios,* which means "double life." They are well named, because amphibians spend part of their lives in water and part on land. Frogs, toads, and the salamander shown in **Figure 15** are examples of amphibians. What characteristics do these animals have that allow them to live on land and in water?

Amphibians are ectotherms. Their body temperature changes when the temperature of their surroundings changes. In cold weather, amphibians become inactive and bury themselves in mud or leaves until the temperature warms. This period of inactivity during cold weather is called **hibernation.** Amphibians that live in hot, dry environments become inactive and hide in the ground when temperatures become too hot. Inactivity during the hot, dry months is called **estivation.**

Reading Check *How are hibernation and estivation similar?*

As You Read

***What* You'll Learn**

- **Describe** the adaptations amphibians have for living in water and living on land.
- **List** the kinds of amphibians and the characteristics of each.
- **Explain** how amphibians reproduce and develop.

Vocabulary
hibernation
estivation

***Why* It's Important**

Because amphibians are sensitive to changes in the environment, they can be used as biological indicators.

Respiration Amphibians have moist skin that is smooth, thin, and without scales. They have many capillaries directly beneath the skin and in the lining of the mouth. This makes it possible for oxygen and carbon dioxide to be exchanged through the skin and the mouth lining. Amphibians also have small, simple, saclike lungs in the chest cavity for the exchange of oxygen and carbon dioxide. Some salamanders have no lungs and breathe only through their skin.

Circulation The three-chambered heart in amphibians is an important change from the circulatory system of fish. In the three-chambered heart, one chamber receives oxygen-filled blood from the lungs and skin, and another chamber receives carbon dioxide-filled blood from the body tissues. Blood moves from both of these chambers to the third chamber, which pumps oxygen-filled blood to body tissues and carbon dioxide-filled blood back to the lungs. Limited mixing of these two bloods occurs.

Figure 15
Salamanders often are mistaken for lizards because of their shape. However, like all amphibians, they have a moist, scaleless skin that requires them to live in a damp habitat.

Section Assessment Planner

PORTFOLIO
Extension, p. 414

PERFORMANCE ASSESSMENT
MiniLAB, p. 414
Skill Builder Activities, p. 415
See page 428 for more options.

CONTENT ASSESSMENT
Section, p. 415
Challenge, p. 415
Chapter, pp. 428–429

SECTION

Amphibians

1 Motivate

Bellringer Transparency

Display the Section Focus Transparency for Section 3. Use the accompanying Transparency Activity Master. L2 ELL

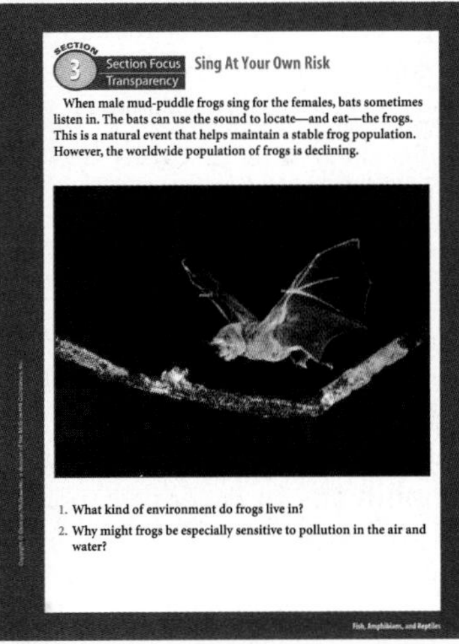

Section Focus Transparency — Sing At Your Own Risk

When male mud-puddle frogs sing for the females, bats sometimes listen in. The bats can use the sound to locate—and eat—the frogs. This is a natural event that helps maintain a stable frog population. However, the worldwide population of frogs is declining.

1. What kind of environment do frogs live in?
2. Why might frogs be especially sensitive to pollution in the air and water?

Fish, Amphibians, and Reptiles

Tie to Prior Knowledge

Discuss the characteristics of lobe-finned fish. Show students a picture of a lobe-finned fish. Ask them what adaptations would be necessary for a fish to survive on land.

Reading Check

Answer Both are periods of amphibian inactivity brought on by weather changes.

Resource Manager

Chapter Resources Booklet
Transparency Activity, p. 50
Directed Reading for Content Mastery, p. 21

2 Teach

Amphibian Characteristics

Discussion

Amphibian means "one who leads a double life." **Why is this an appropriate name for amphibians?** Many begin their lives as aquatic tadpoles and then live most of their adult lives on land.

Activity

Obtain tadpoles from a pond or a biological supply company. Place them in an aquarium in the classroom so students can observe metamorphosis in a frog. Have students observe tadpoles daily and research how to care for them.

Extension

Have students write a report on the factors that may be contributing to the worldwide decline of frogs and other amphibians in recent years. L2 LS **Linguistic**

Figure 16
Red-eyed tree frogs are found in forests of Central and South America. They eat a variety of food, including insects and even other frogs.

Reproduction Even though amphibians are adapted for life on land, they depend on water for reproduction. Because their eggs do not have a protective, waterproof shell, they can dry out easily, so amphibians must have water to reproduce.

Amphibian eggs are fertilized externally by the male. As the eggs come out of the female's body, the male releases sperm over them. In most species the female lays eggs in a pond or other body of water. However, many species have developed special reproductive adaptations, enabling them to reproduce away from bodies of water. Red-eyed tree frogs, like the ones in **Figure 16,** lay eggs in a thick gelatin on the underside of leaves that hang over water. After the tadpoles hatch, they fall into the water below, where they continue developing. The Sonoran Desert toad waits for small puddles to form in the desert during the rainy season. It takes tadpoles only two to 12 days to hatch in these temporary puddles.

Development Most amphibians go through a developmental process called metamorphosis (met uh MOR fuh sus). Fertilized eggs hatch into tadpoles, the stage that lives in water. Tadpoles have fins, gills, and a two-chambered heart similar to fish. As tadpoles grow into frogs and toads, they develop legs, lungs, and a three-chambered heart. **Figure 17** shows this life cycle.

The tadpole of some amphibian species, such as salamanders, are not much different from the adult stage. Young salamanders look like adult salamanders, but they have gills and usually a tail fin.

Figure 17
Amphibians go through metamorphosis as they develop.

B After hatching, most young amphibians, like these tadpoles, do not look like adult forms.

A Amphibian eggs are laid in a jellylike material to keep them moist.

Inclusion Strategies

Visually Impaired Use a model of a frog to help students locate and identify the function of different structures of amphibians. LS **Kinesthetic**

Curriculum Connection

Language Arts Have students read "The Celebrated Jumping Frog of Calaveras County," written by Mark Twain while he lived in California. It appeared in the *New York Saturday Press* in November 1865. Every year, frog-jumping competitions are held in Calaveras County, California. Have students find out the distance frogs can jump. L2 LS **Linguistic**

Figure 18
When a frog sees an insect flying or moving nearby, the movement stimulates the nervous system to flick the tongue out.

Frogs and Toads

Adult frogs and toads have short, broad bodies with four legs but no neck or tail. The strong hind legs are used for swimming and jumping. Bulging eyes and nostrils on top of the head let frogs and toads see and breathe while the rest of their body is submerged in water. On spring nights, they make their presence known with loud, distinctive croaking sounds. On each side of the head, just behind the eyes, are round tympanic membranes. These membranes vibrate somewhat like an eardrum in response to sounds and are used by frogs and toads to hear.

Frog and toad tongues are attached at the front of their mouths. When they see prey, their tongue flips out, as shown in **Figure 18.** Then the tongue contacts the prey. The prey gets stuck in the sticky saliva on the tongue and the tongue flips back into the mouth. Toads and frogs eat a variety of insects, worms, and spiders, and one tropical species eats berries.

Research Visit the Glencoe Science Web site at **science.glencoe.com** for more information about amphibians as biological indicators. Communicate to your class what you learn.

C Amphibians go through metamorphosis, which means they change form from larval stage to adult.

D Most adult amphibians are able to move about and live on land.

Frogs and Toads

IDENTIFYING Misconceptions

Students may believe they can get warts from touching a toad. Explain that this is a myth which probably came about because many toads have bumpy, wartlike projections on their skin.

Use an Analogy

Explain that the tongue of a frog is very sticky, like the flypaper that is used to catch flies. This increases the ability of the frog to catch flying insects.

Activity

Have students work in groups to prepare a poster showing the frog's life cycle. The poster should include drawings of each of the four stages of a frog's life cycle. Each stage should be explained with a paragraph. L2
LS **Visual-Spatial and Linguistic**

Extension

Have students work in groups to create a game or a graphic that compares and contrasts the traits of the three amphibian groups. L2 COOP LEARN
LS **Interpersonal**

Resource Manager 

Chapter Resources Booklet
Enrichment, p. 33
Reinforcement, p. 29

Life Science Critical Thinking/ Problem Solving, p. 7

SCIENCE Online
Internet Addresses

Explore the Glencoe Science Web site at **science.glencoe.com** to find out more about topics in this section.

Salamanders

Mini LAB

Purpose Students observe frog adaptations. L1 **IS Visual-Spatial**

Materials one live frog in a jar for each student group, water, magnifying lens

Teaching Strategy Obtain references on amphibians for students to use in describing frog adaptations. Caution students to avoid moving the jar abruptly.

Analysis

1. bulging eyes and nostrils at the top of the head for seeing and breathing while in water, underside coloration for camouflage, webbed feet for swimming
2. strong legs for jumping, topside coloration for camouflage, wide mouth for capturing land insects

Assessment

Oral Ask students to list the metamorphic changes tadpoles undergo to adapt to life on land. Development of legs, lungs, wide mouth, and a digestive system designed for consuming insects instead of algae. Use **PASC**, p. 99.

Teacher FYI

Zoologists divide amphibians into three groups—frogs and toads, salamanders, and caecilians. Caecilians have no legs and look like large earthworms. There are about 150 species, which are found only in tropical regions. Most caecilians live in underground burrows, but some are aquatic.

Mini LAB

Describing Frog Adaptations

Procedure

1. Carefully observe a **frog** in a **jar.** Notice the position of its legs as it sits. Record all of your observations in your **Science Journal.**
2. Observe its mouth, eyes, nostrils, and ears.
3. Observe the color of its back and belly.
4. Return the frog to your teacher.

Analysis

1. Describe the adaptations the frog has for living in water.
2. What adaptations does it have for living on land?

Salamanders

Most species of salamanders and newts live in North America. These amphibians often are mistaken for lizards because of their long, slender bodies. The short legs of salamanders and newts appear to stick straight out from the sides of their bodies.

Land-living species of salamanders and newts usually are found near water. These amphibians hide under leaf litter and rocks during the day to avoid the drying heat of the Sun. At night, they use their well-developed senses of smell and vision to find and feed on worms, crustaceans, and insects.

Many species of salamanders breed on land, where fertilization is internal. Aquatic species of salamanders and newts release and fertilize their eggs in the water.

Importance of Amphibians

Most adult amphibians are insect predators and are helpful in keeping some insect populations in check. They also are a source of food for other animals, including other amphibians. Some humans consider frog legs a delicacy.

Poison arrow frogs, like the one in **Figure 19,** produce a toxic poison that can kill large animals. They also are known as poison dart frogs. The toxin is secreted through their skin and can affect muscles and nerves of animals that come in contact with it. Native people of the Emberá Chocó in Colombia, South America, cover blowgun darts that they use for hunting with the poison of one species of these frogs. Researchers are studying the action of these toxins to learn more about how the nervous system works. Researchers also are using amphibians in regeneration studies in hopes of developing new ways of treating humans who have lost limbs or were born without limbs.

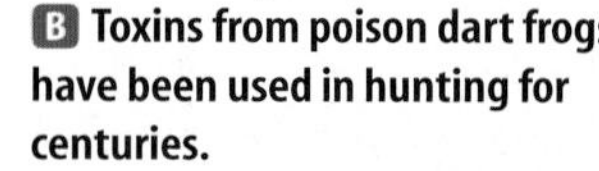

Figure 19
A Poison dart frogs are brightly colored to show potential predators that they are poisonous.
B Toxins from poison dart frogs have been used in hunting for centuries.

Inclusion Strategies

Learning Disabled Have students make flash cards of the vocabulary words in this chapter using an illustration, the phonetic spelling, and the definition of each word. L1 **IS Linguistic and Visual-Spatial**

Resource Manager

Chapter Resources Booklet
MiniLAB, p. 4
Lab Activity, pp. 11–15

Biological Indicators Because they live on land and reproduce in water, amphibians are affected directly by any chemical change in the environment, including pesticides and other poisons, soil erosion, and water pollution. Amphibians also absorb gases through their skin, making them susceptible to air pollutants. Amphibians like the one in **Figure 20** are considered to be biological indicators. Biological indicators are species whose overall health reflects the health of a particular ecosystem.

Reading Check *What is a biological indicator?*

Figure 20
Beginning in 1995, deformed frogs such as this were found in Minnesota. Concerned scientists hypothesize that an increase in the number of deformed frogs could be a warning of environmental problems for other organisms.

Origin of Amphibians The fossil record shows that ancestors of modern fish were the first vertebrates on Earth about 500 million years ago. For about 150 million years, they were the only vertebrates. Then as competition for food and space increased and the climate changed, some lobe-finned fish might have traveled across land searching for water as their ponds dried up. The lobe-finned fish had lungs and bony fins that could have supported their weight on land. Amphibians are thought to have evolved from these lobe-finned fish about 350 million years ago.

Because competition on land from other animals was minimal, evolution favored the development of amphibians. Insects, spiders, and other invertebrates were an abundant source of food on land. Land was almost free of predators, so amphibians were able to reproduce in large numbers, and many new species evolved. For 100 million years or more, amphibians were the dominant land animals.

Section 3 Assessment

1. List the adaptations amphibians have for living in water and for living on land.
2. Name three kinds of amphibians.
3. How do tadpole and frog hearts differ?
4. Describe two different environments where amphibians lay eggs.
5. **Think Critically** Why do you suppose frogs and toads seem to appear suddenly after a rain?

Skill Builder Activities

6. **Concept Mapping** Make an events-chain concept map of frog metamorphosis. Describe each stage in your Science Journal. **For more help, refer to the Science Skill Handbook.**
7. **Communicating** In your Science Journal, explain why frogs and other amphibians must live in moist or wet environments. **For more help, refer to the Science Skill Handbook.**

Importance of Amphibians

Extension

Have students research the use of amphibians in regeneration studies and report their findings to the class. L3 LS **Linguistic** P

Visual Learning

Figure 20 Have students compare this frog with a normal frog and list the differences.

Reading Check

Answer a species whose health reflects the health of their ecosystem

3 Assess

Reteach

Show pictures or slides of amphibians and have students identify each as a frog, toad, salamander, or caecilian. L1 LS **Visual-Spatial**

Challenge

Why are amphibians considered to be biological indicators? They live on land, reproduce in water, and absorb gases from the air through their skin. They are sensitive to chemical changes on land, in water, and in the air.

Assessment

Performance Assess students' understanding of metamorphosis by having them prepare a poster to compare frog metamorphosis with insect metamorphosis. Use **PASC,** p. 145.

Answers to Section Assessment

1. water: moist, smooth skin; bulging eyes and nostrils on top of the head; strong hind legs for swimming; land: lungs; strong skeleton; strong hind legs for jumping; moist, smooth skin
2. frogs, toads, and salamanders
3. Tadpoles have a two-chambered heart; frogs have a three-chambered heart.
4. Possible answers: underside of leaves in rainforest, in ponds or lakes, on the back of the female
5. They hunt food when the air is moist.
6. egg⟶legless tadpole⟶ tadpole with legs⟶young frog with developing legs⟶adult frog on land
7. Amphibians exchange oxygen and carbon dioxide through their skin, so they must keep their skin wet to survive. Most have external fertilization that requires moisture for the sperm to reach the egg.

SECTION

Reptiles

1 Motivate

Bellringer Transparency

Display the Section Focus Transparency for Section 4. Use the accompanying Transparency Activity Master. L2 ELL

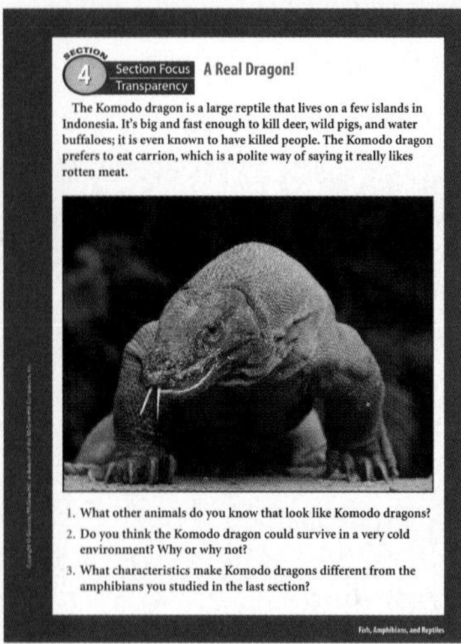

SECTION 4 Section Focus Transparency **A Real Dragon!**

The Komodo dragon is a large reptile that lives on a few islands in Indonesia. It's big and fast enough to kill deer, wild pigs, and water buffaloes; it is even known to have killed people. The Komodo dragon prefers to eat carrion, which is a polite way of saying it really likes rotten meat.

1. What other animals do you know that look like Komodo dragons?
2. Do you think the Komodo dragon could survive in a very cold environment? Why or why not?
3. What characteristics make Komodo dragons different from the amphibians you studied in the last section?

Fish, Amphibians, and Reptiles

Tie to Prior Knowledge

Ask students what animals they can identify as reptiles. Answers should include alligators, crocodiles, lizards, snakes, and chameleons. Ask what these animals have in common.

SECTION

Reptiles

As You Read

***What* You'll Learn**

- **List** the characteristics of reptiles.
- **Determine** how reptile adaptations enable them to live on land.
- **Explain** the importance of the amniotic egg.

Vocabulary
amniotic egg

***Why* It's Important**
Reptiles provide information about how body systems work during extreme weather conditions.

Reptile Characteristics

What do snakes and turtles have in common with dinosaurs? They, along with lizards, skinks like the one in **Figure 21,** crocodiles, and alligators, are reptiles. Reptiles have a variety of body shapes, but they have many characteristics in common that enable them to live on land.

Reptiles are ectotherms with a thick, dry, waterproof skin. Their skin is covered with scales that help reduce water loss and protect them from injury. Even though reptiles are ectotherms, they are able to modify their internal body temperatures by their behavior. When the weather is cold, they bask in the Sun, which is a behavior that enables them to warm up. When the weather is warm and the Sun gets too hot, they move into the shade to cool down.

Reading Check *How are reptiles able to modify their body temperature?*

Some reptiles, such as turtles, crocodiles, and lizards, move on four legs. Claws are used to dig, climb, and run. Reptiles, such as snakes and some lizards, move without legs.

Body Systems Scales on reptiles prevent the exchange of oxygen and carbon dioxide through the skin. Reptiles breathe with lungs. Even turtles and sea snakes that live in water must come to the surface to breathe.

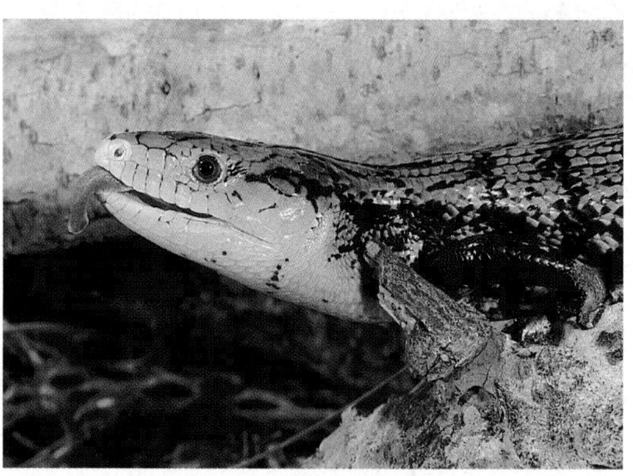

Figure 21
Some species of skinks, like this northern blue-tongue skink, don't lay eggs. The young develop inside the female and are born alive.

The circulatory system of reptiles is more highly developed than that of amphibians. Most reptiles have a three-chambered heart with a partial wall inside the main chamber. This means that less mixing of oxygen-filled blood and carbon dioxide-filled blood occurs than in amphibians. This type of circulatory system provides more oxygen to all parts of the body. Crocodiles have a four-chambered heart that completely separates the oxygen-filled blood and the carbon dioxide-filled blood and keeps them from mixing.

Section Assessment Planner

PORTFOLIO
Extension, p. 419

PERFORMANCE ASSESSMENT
Skill Builder Activities, p. 421
See page 428 for more options.

CONTENT ASSESSMENT
Section, p. 421
Challenge, p. 421
Chapter, pp. 428–429

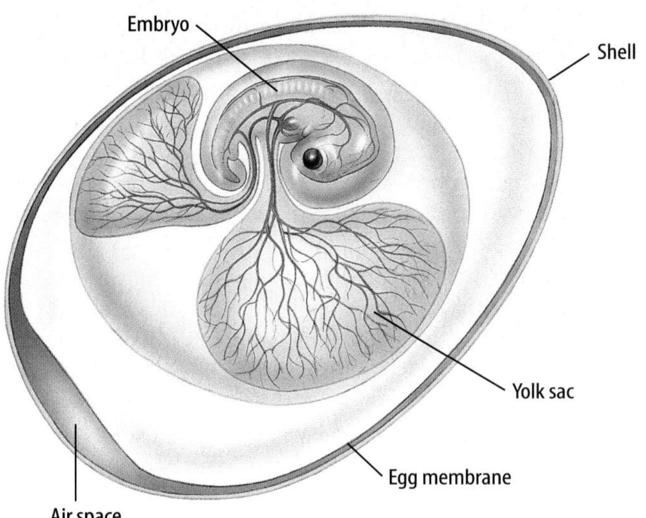

Figure 22
The development of amniotic eggs enabled reptiles to reproduce on land.

Amniotic Egg One of the most important adaptations of reptiles for living on land is the way they reproduce. Unlike the eggs of most fish and amphibians, eggs of reptiles are fertilized internally—inside the body of the female. After fertilization, the female lays eggs that are covered by tough, leathery shells. The shell prevents the eggs from drying out. This adaptation enables reptiles to lay their eggs on land.

The **amniotic egg** provides a complete environment for the embryo's development. **Figure 22** shows the structures in a reptilian egg. This type of egg contains membranes that protect and cushion the embryo and help it get rid of wastes. It also contains a large food supply—the yolk—for the embryo. Minute holes in the shell, called pores, allow oxygen and carbon dioxide to be exchanged. By the time it hatches, a young reptile looks like a small adult.

Reading Check *What is the importance of an amniotic egg?*

Types of Modern Reptiles

Reptiles live on every continent except Antarctica and in all the oceans except those in the polar regions. They vary greatly in size, shape, and color. Reticulated pythons, 10 m in length, can swallow small deer whole. Some sea turtles weigh more than 350 kg and can swim faster than humans can run. Three-horned lizards have movable eye sockets and tongues as long as their bodies. The three living groups of reptiles are lizards and snakes, turtles, and crocodiles and alligators.

Research Visit the Glencoe Science Web site at **science.glencoe.com** for recent news about the nesting sites of turtles. Communicate to your classmates what you learn.

2 Teach

Reptile Characteristics

Reading Check

Answer By their behavior; they move to locations that are warmer or cooler.

Use Science Words

The word *reptile* comes from the Latin word *repere*, meaning "to crawl." Have students use the word in a sentence describing its meaning. L2 LS **Linguistic**

Activity

Organize the class into groups of four. Give each group half of a hard-boiled chicken egg. Have students identify the three parts they observe, and tell the function of each. shell—protection, white—protects and cushions the embryo and gets rid of wastes, yolk—food supply for the embryo Explain to students that there is no embryo because commercial chicken eggs usually are not fertilized. L2 COOP LEARN LS **Interpersonal and Kinesthetic**

Reading Check

Answer It enables the reptile to lay its eggs on land.

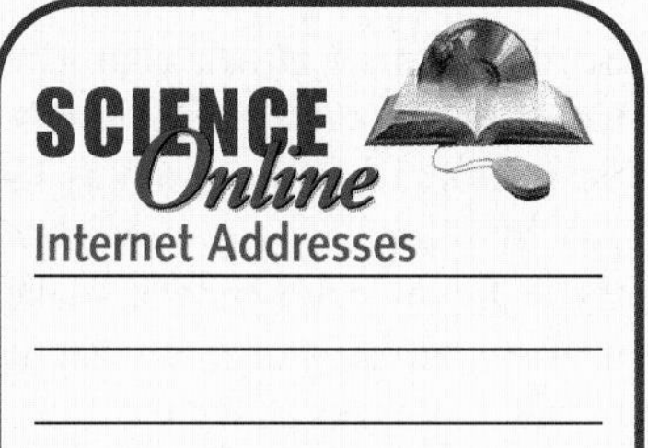

Internet Addresses

Explore the Glencoe Science Web site at **science.glencoe.com** to find out more about topics in this section.

Resource Manager

Chapter Resources Booklet
Transparency Activity, p. 51
Directed Reading for Content Mastery, pp. 21, 22

Life Science Critical Thinking/Problem Solving, pp. 11, 13

Teacher FYI

The shape of a reptile's pupil can indicate whether the animal is active during night or day. Many nocturnal reptiles have slit-like pupils, which indicate that they are active at night.

Types of Modern Reptiles

Teacher FYI

There are some 2,700 known species of snakes and only about 200 are poisonous. The only poisonous snakes in North America are the pit vipers and coral snakes. Pit vipers include rattlesnakes, water moccasins, and copperheads. Coral snakes can be recognized by their bright colors. Coral snakes and king snakes are often mistaken for one another.

Make a Model

Give each group of students plastic straws and a lump of soft clay. Ask them to find a way to move the clay through the straw to the center of the straw. (It can be moved by pinching the sides of the straw.) Use this to explain the muscular contractions of a snake to swallow and ingest food. L2 COOP LEARN

LS **Interpersonal and Kinesthetic**

IDENTIFYING Misconceptions

Students may think that the number of rattles on a rattlesnake's tail is the same as its age in years. However, a new rattle forms each time a snake molts, and molting can occur many times each year. Also, some rattles may break off during the year. Thus, there is no correlation between the number of rattles and the age of a snake.

Lizards and Snakes Animals in the largest group of reptiles—the lizards and snakes like those shown in **Figure 23A** and **23B**—have a type of jaw not found in other reptiles, like the turtle in **Figure 23C.** The jaw has a special joint that unhitches and increases the size of their mouths. This enables them to swallow their prey whole. Lizards have movable eyelids, external ears, and legs with clawed toes on each foot. They feed on other reptiles, insects, spiders, worms, and mammals.

Snakes have developed ways of moving without legs. They have poor hearing and most have poor eyesight. Recall how you could feel the vibrations of the tuning fork in the Explore Activity. Snakes do not hear sound waves in the air. They "hear" vibrations in the ground that are picked up by the lower jawbone and conducted to the bones of the snake's inner ear. From there, the vibrations are transferred to the snake's brain, where the sounds are interpreted.

Snakes are meat eaters. Some snakes wrap around and constrict their prey. Others inject their prey with venom. Many snakes feed on rodents, and as a result help control rodent populations.

Most snakes lay eggs after they are fertilized internally. In some species, eggs develop and hatch inside the female's body then leave her body shortly thereafter.

Figure 23
Examples of reptiles are shown below.

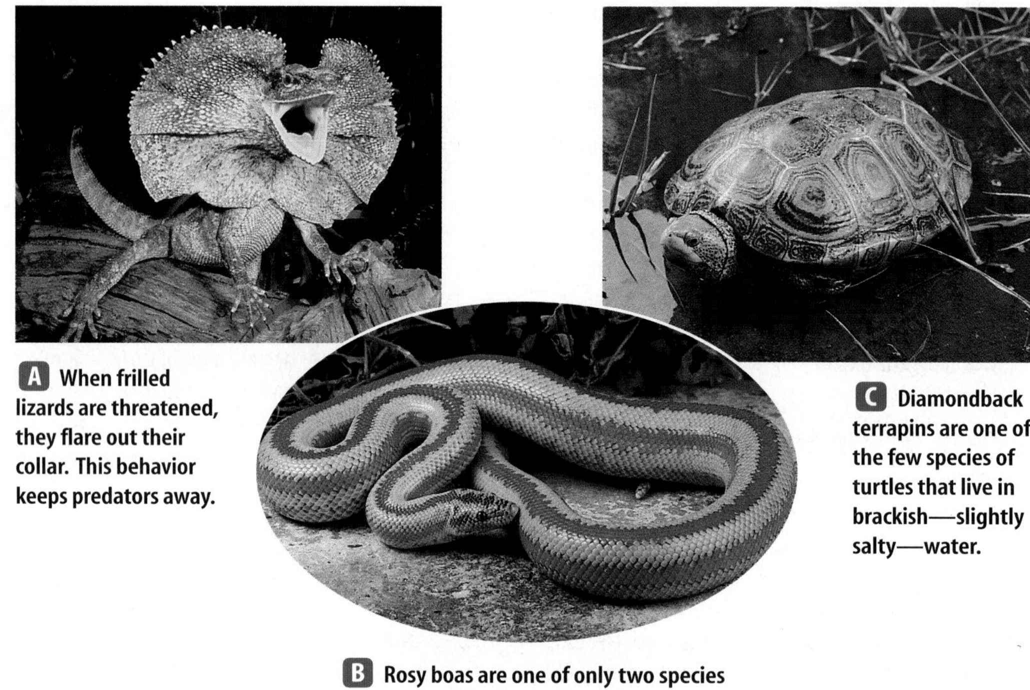

A When frilled lizards are threatened, they flare out their collar. This behavior keeps predators away.

B Rosy boas are one of only two species of boas found in the United States.

C Diamondback terrapins are one of the few species of turtles that live in brackish—slightly salty—water.

Cultural Diversity

Snakes In ancient Egypt, the poisonous asp was held in high esteem and its symbol is found in writings and artifacts. The Aztecs worshipped Quetzalcoatl, the mythical plumed serpent. In India, cobras were thought to be the reincarnated spirits of society's elite. Some cultures in Africa worship pythons. Have students find out how snakes are used in art or in celebrations in different cultures. L2

Curriculum Connection

History Have students research the impact hunting American alligators for their skin and meat had on the species early in the Twentieth Century. Ask them to find out what efforts were made to restore populations of these animals and the success of these efforts. L2

Turtles The only reptiles that have a two-part shell made of hard, bony plates are turtles. In some turtles, the shell is a tough leathery skin. The vertebrae and ribs are fused to the inside of the top part of the shell. The muscles are attached to the lower and upper part of the inside of the shell. Most turtles can withdraw their heads and legs into the shell for protection against predators.

Reading Check *What is the purpose of a turtle's shell?*

Turtles have no teeth but they do have powerful jaws with a beaklike structure used to crush food. They feed on insects, worms, fish, and plants. Turtles live in water and on land. Those that live on land are called tortoises.

Like most reptiles, turtles provide little or no care for their young. Turtles dig out a nest, deposit their eggs, cover the nest, and leave. Turtles never see their own hatchlings. Young turtles, like those in **Figure 24,** emerge from the eggs fully formed and live on their own.

Figure 24
Most turtles are eaten shortly after they hatch. Only a few sea turtles actually make it into the ocean.

Crocodiles and Alligators Found in or near water in warm climates, crocodiles and alligators are similar in appearance. They are lizardlike in shape, and their backs have large, deep scales. Crocodiles and alligators can be distinguished from each other by the shape of their heads. Crocodiles like the one in **Figure 25** have a narrow head with a triangular-shaped snout. Alligators have a broad head with a rounded snout. Crocodiles are aggressive and can attack animals as large as cattle. Alligators are less aggressive than crocodiles. They feed on fish, turtles, and waterbirds. Crocodiles and alligators are among the world's largest living reptiles.

Crocodiles and alligators are some of the few reptiles that care for their young. The female guards the nest of eggs and when the eggs hatch, the male and female protect the young. A few crocodile females have been photographed opening their nests in response to noises made by hatchlings. After the young hatch, the females carry them in their huge mouths to the safety of the water. The female crocodile continues to keep watch over the young until they can protect themselves.

Figure 25
Indian gharials are one of the rarest crocodile species on Earth. Adults are well adapted for capturing fish.

Teacher FYI

Turtles are the oldest group of living reptiles. The fossil record shows that their ancestors were around even before dinosaurs, and they have changed little over time.

Reading Check

Answer Protection

Extension

Have students research and report on a reptile in their state that is listed as threatened or endangered. Ask them to include information about the animal's history, reasons for the lower numbers, and actions being taken to help the species. L2 P

Visual Learning

Figure 24 Have students list the reptilian characteristics of this turtle.

Resource Manager

Chapter Resources Booklet
Enrichment, p. 34
Reinforcement, p. 30
Home and Community Involvement, p. 41

Science Journal

Comparison Have students find pictures of crocodiles and alligators in magazines or reference books. Ask them to study their features, especially the shape of their heads. Have them make a drawing of both on the same sheet of paper. Then have them explain how they can be distinguished from each other based on the shape of their heads. L2 LS **Visual-Spatial and Linguistic**

Visualizing Extinct Reptiles

Have students examine the pictures and read the captions. Then ask the following questions.

How did the shape of these reptiles help them catch food in their environment? Long, streamlined bodies enabled them to move quickly through the water to capture prey.

Why are these animals classified as reptiles and not fish? Possible answers: They have amniotic eggs that are internally fertilized. They can modify their internal body temperature by basking in the Sun.

Activity

Have students write a poem about extinct reptiles. Research topics such as reptile characteristics, how long ago they lived on Earth, and the location where fossils have been found. Include interesting statistics. For example, *Temnodontosaurus*, a plesiosaur, had the largest eyes of any animal that has ever lived.

Extension

Challenge students to create an illustrated book of different types of extinct reptiles. Have students classify these animals.

Figure 26

If you're like most people, the phrase "prehistoric reptiles" probably brings dinosaurs to mind. But not all ancient reptiles were dinosaurs. The first dinosaurs didn't appear until about 115 million years after the first reptiles. Paleontologists have unearthed the fossils of a variety of reptilian creatures that swam through the seas and waterways of ancient Earth. Several examples of these extinct aquatic reptiles are shown here.

▲ MOSASAUR (MOH zuh sawr) Marine-dwelling mosasaurs had snakelike bodies, large skulls, and long snouts. They also had jointed jawbones, an adaptation for grasping and swallowing large prey.

▲ ICHTHYOSAUR (IHK thee uh sawr) Ichthyosaurs resembled a cross between a dolphin and a shark, with large eyes, four paddlelike limbs, and a fishlike tail that moved from side to side. These extinct reptiles were fearsome predators with long jaws armed with numerous sharp teeth.

◀ ELASMOSAURUS (uh laz muh SAWR us) Predatory ***Elasmosaurus*** had a long neck—with as many as 76 vertebrae—topped by a small head.

▲ CHAMPOSAUR (CHAMP uh sawr) This ancient reptile looked something like a modern crocodile, with a long snout studded with razor-sharp teeth. Champosaurs lived in freshwater lakes and streams and preyed on fish and turtles.

▲ PLESIOSAUR (PLEE zee uh sawr) These marine reptiles had stout bodies, paddlelike limbs, and long necks. Plesiousaurs might have fed by swinging their heads from side to side through schools of fish.

420 CHAPTER 14 Fish, Amphibians, and Reptiles

The Importance of Reptiles

Quick Demo

Display items or pictures of items made from the skins of snakes, alligators, and crocodiles, and the shells of turtles and tortoises. Ask students how these animals are important to our world and how people threaten their survival.

Resource Manager

Chapter Resources Booklet
Transparency Activity, pp. 53–54
Activity Worksheet, pp. 7–8

Science Inquiry Labs, p. 19

The Importance of Reptiles

Reptiles are important predators in many environments. In farming areas, snakes eat rats and mice that destroy grains. Small lizards eat insects, and large lizards eat small animals that are considered pests.

Humans in many parts of the world eat reptiles and their eggs or foods that include reptiles, such as turtle soup. The number of reptile species is declining in areas where swamps and other lands are being developed for homes and recreation areas. Coastal nesting sites of sea turtles are being destroyed by development or are becoming unusable because of pollution. For years, many small turtles were collected in the wild and then sold as pets. People now understand that such practices disturb turtle populations. Today most species of turtles and their habitats are protected by law.

Origin of Reptiles Reptiles first appeared in the fossil record about 345 million years ago. The earliest reptiles did not depend upon water for reproduction. As a result, they began to dominate the land about 200 million years ago. Some reptiles even returned to the water to live, although they continued to lay their eggs on land. Dinosaurs—descendants of the early reptiles—ruled Earth during this era, then died out about 65 million years ago. Some of today's reptiles, such as alligators and crocodiles, have changed little from their ancestors, some of which are illustrated in **Figure 26.**

Earth Science INTEGRATION

Dinosaurs, reptiles that ruled Earth for 160 million years, died out about 65 million years ago. In your Science Journal, describe what changes in the environment could have caused the extinction of the dinosaurs.

Section 4 Assessment

1. What adaptations do reptiles have for living on land?
2. How do turtles differ from snakes, lizards, and alligators?
3. Why were early reptiles, including dinosaurs, so successful as a group?
4. Describe or draw the structure of an amniotic egg.
5. **Think Critically** Poisonous coral snakes and some harmless snakes have bright red, yellow, and black colors. How is this an advantage and a disadvantage to nonpoisonous snakes?

Skill Builder Activities

6. **Concept Mapping** Make a concept map showing the major characteristics of the types of reptiles. **For more help, refer to the Science Skill Handbook.**
7. **Solving One-Step Equations** Many dinosaurs were large. One large dinosaur, *Brachiosaurus,* was about 12 m tall and 22 m long. The largest land mammal now living is the elephant. The average size of an elephant is 3 m tall and 6 m long. How does the elephant compare in height to *Brachiosaurus?* **For more help, refer to the Math Skill Handbook.**

The Importance of Reptiles

Earth Science INTEGRATION

Student answers should reflect the fact that dinosaurs were ectotherms. Temperatures decreased on Earth.

3 Assess

Reteach

Prepare a quiz game with photographs or descriptions of lizards, turtles, alligators, crocodiles, snakes, frogs, and salamanders. Have students classify the animals as amphibians or reptiles and name a characteristic of each. L1

Challenge

How do you think sea turtles get the oxygen they need for respiration? Turtles are reptiles and reptiles use lungs for gas exchange. They must come to the surface to obtain oxygen.

Assessment

Oral The ability to change skin color is an adaptation in many reptiles. Ask students to explain how this adaptation may help reptiles survive. Use **PASC,** p. 177.

Answers to Section Assessment

1. a thick, dry, waterproof skin covered with scales; four legs with claws to hold the body off the ground (with the exception of snakes and some lizards); three-chambered heart; lungs; amniotic egg
2. Turtles are covered with a hard shell on both top and bottom. Most can withdraw into this shell for protection.
3. They did not depend on water for reproduction; therefore, they were able to dominate the land.
4. Drawing should resemble egg in **Figure 22.** Description: The amniotic egg contains membranes that protect and cushion the embryo and help it get rid of waste. It also contains a large food supply, the yolk, for the embryo. It has pores for the exchange of oxygen and carbon dioxide.
5. Predators think they are poisonous snakes and leave them alone. Disadvantage: non-poisonous snakes may be killed because they are thought to be venomous.
6. Check concept maps against section content.
7. The elephant is one-fourth the height of *Brachiosaurus,* and about one-third the length.

Activity

BENCH TESTED

Recognize the Problem

Purpose

Students design an experiment to determine the effect of water temperature on the respiration rate of fish. L2 IS **Visual-Spatial**

Process Skills

designing an experiment, forming a hypothesis, observing and inferring, communicating, comparing, describing, recognizing cause and effect, graphing, separating and controlling variables

Time Required

two 30-minute class periods

Materials

Large goldfish work well because their breathing is easily observed and they will not move around too much. Avoid small fish such as guppies or constantly darting fish such as minnows.

Placing a beaker with water and the fish into a large bowl of ice water will gradually lower the temperature without harming the fish.

Safety Precautions

Caution students not to handle the fish with their hands.

Form a Hypothesis

Possible Hypothesis

Students will probably be split between predicting a slowing of the respiration rate and no change in the respiration rate with a decrease in temperature. Few students will hypothesize an increase in the rate.

Activity Design Your Own Experiment

Water Temperature and the Respiration Rate of Fish

What if last summer was hot with few storms? One day after many sunny, windless days, you noticed that a lot of dead fish were floating on the surface of your neighbor's pond. What might have caused these fish to die?

Recognize the Problem

How does water temperature affect the respiration rate of fish?

Form a Hypothesis

Fish obtain oxygen from the water. State a hypothesis about how water temperature affects the respiration rate of fish.

Goals

- **Design** and carry out an experiment to measure the effect of water temperature on the rate of respiration of fish.
- **Observe** the breathing rate of fish.

Possible Materials

goldfish
aquarium water
small fishnet
600-mL beakers
container of ice water
stirring rod
thermometer
aquarium

Safety Precautions

Protect your clothing. Use the fishnet to transfer fish into beakers.

Test Your Hypothesis

Possible Procedures

Students can place the goldfish in a large beaker of room temperature water and record their first results. The respiration rate can be measured by counting the number of times the fish opens its mouth or gill covering in 20 seconds. Next, the beaker can be placed into a large bowl filled with ice water. The respiration rate of the fish can be measured each minute for 10 minutes. The beaker of water should be allowed to return to room temperature before placing it into a bath of hot water and again measuring the fish's breathing rate.

Test Your Hypothesis

Plan

1. As a group, agree upon and write out the hypothesis statement. You might form a hypothesis that relates the amount of oxygen dissolved in water to water temperature and how this affects fish.
2. As a group, list the steps that you need to take to test your hypothesis. Be specific and describe exactly what you will do at each step. List your materials.
3. How will you measure the breathing rate of fish?
4. **Explain** how you will change the water temperature in the beakers. Fish respond better to a gradual change in temperature than an abrupt change. How will you measure the response of fish to changes in water temperature?
5. What data will your group collect? Prepare a data table in your Science Journal to record the data you collect. How many times will you run your experiment?
6. Read over your entire experiment to make sure the steps are in logical order. Identify any constants, variables, and controls.

Do

1. Make sure your teacher approves your setup and your plan before you start.
2. Carry out the experiment according to the approved plan.
3. While the experiment is going on, write down any observations that you make and complete the data table in your Science Journal.

Analyze Your Data

1. **Compare** your results with the results of other groups in your class. Were the results similar?
2. What were you measuring when you counted mouth or gill cover openings?
3. **Describe** how a decrease in water temperature affects respiration rate and behavior of the fish.
4. **Explain** how your results could be used to determine the kind of environment in which a fish can live.

Draw Conclusions

1. Fish can live in water that is totally covered by ice. How is this possible?
2. What would happen to a fish if the water were to become very warm?

Communicating Your Data

Construct a graph of your data on poster board and share your results with your classmates.

Communicating Your Data

Encourage students to generate their graphs electronically.

Assessment

Performance Have students research and report on the causes and effects of eutrophication. Eutrophication occurs when excess nutrients are added to the water from farms, lawns, and other sources. The nutrients cause an explosion of algae growth, and as the alga dies off, bacteria populations increase depleting the water of oxygen and killing aquatic life. Use **PASC,** p. 137.

Teaching Strategies

Tie to Prior Knowledge

Many students will be aware that fish have gills, but many will not know that a fish opening its mouth or gill covering indicates it is breathing.

Expected Outcomes

The respiration rate of the fish should slow with a decrease in water temperature and become more rapid with an increase in water temperature.

Analyze Your Data

1. Answers will vary, but results should be similar.
2. respiration rate
3. Respiration rate decreases and movement slows as temperature decreases.
4. Similar experiments could measure the temperature range in which various species of fish can breath comfortably.

Error Analysis

Students should compare their results and hypotheses and explain any differences in their data.

Draw Conclusions

1. Ice is less dense than water, and a large body of water usually lies beneath the ice. The ice actually insulates the water, keeping the water temperature high enough for fish to breathe.
2. Warm water contains less oxygen, making it more difficult for a fish to breathe. Without enough dissolved oxygen, death could result.

Content Background

Explain that the use of venom by animals is either for subduing their prey, or for their own protection from predation. These organisms do not prey on humans, so attacks occur generally when an animal is surprised or finds itself threatened. Neurotoxins, the most dangerous venoms, work by interrupting the communication between nerves and muscles. The connection between them is called the *neuromuscular junction*. At this junction, nerve cells release a chemical called a neurotransmitter. This binds with special molecules on the muscle fibers and causes the muscle to contract.

The venom of the black widow spider causes an explosive release of this neurotransmitter. The increased amount of this chemical causes the muscles, including the muscles of respiration, to contract and prevents them from relaxing again. The result is paralysis of respiratory muscles and suffocation.

TIME SCIENCE AND Society — SCIENCE ISSUES THAT AFFECT YOU!

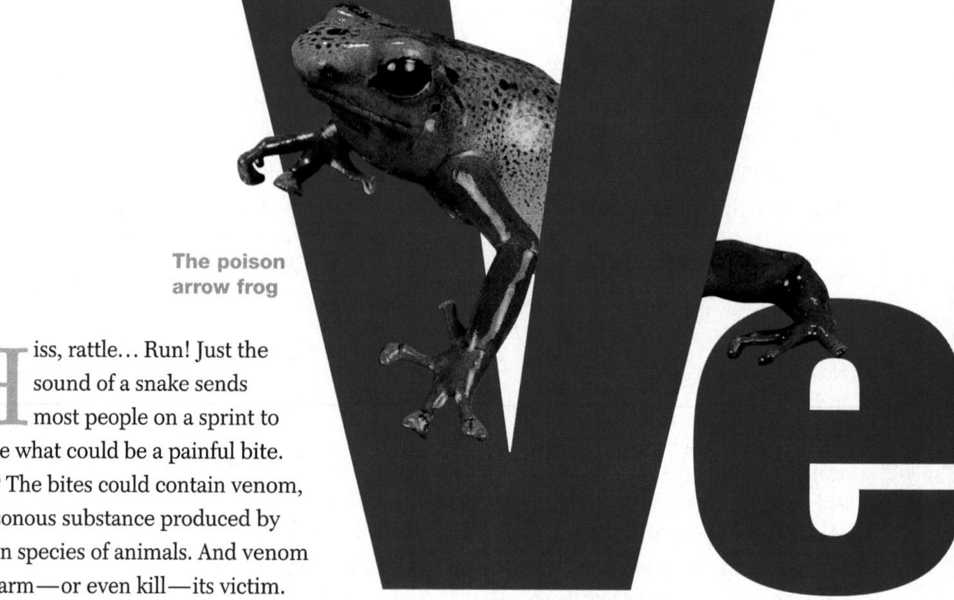

The poison arrow frog

A poison found in some animals can save lives

Hiss, rattle… Run! Just the sound of a snake sends most people on a sprint to escape what could be a painful bite. Why? The bites could contain venom, a poisonous substance produced by certain species of animals. And venom can harm—or even kill—its victim. Some venomous creatures use their poison to stun, kill, and digest their prey, while others use it as a means of protection.

Venom is produced by a gland in the body. Some fish use their sharp, bony spines to inject venom. Venomous snakes, such as pit vipers, have fangs. Poison passes through these hollow teeth into a victim's body.

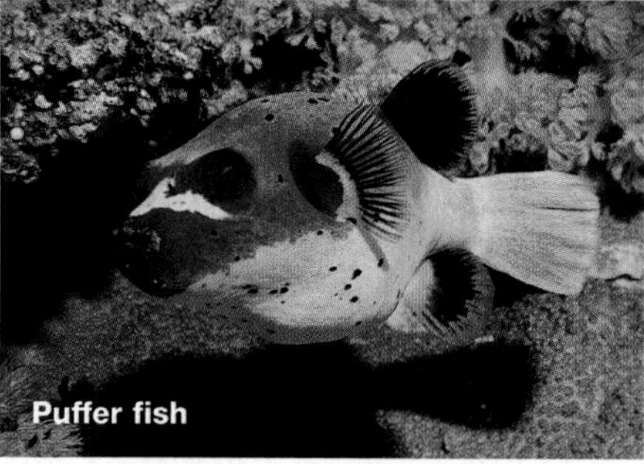

Puffer fish

The Gila monster, the largest lizard in the United States, has enlarged, grooved teeth in its lower jaw through which its venom travels. It is one of only two species of poisonous lizards. The poison arrow frog releases toxins through glands in the skin—predators immediately release these amphibians when they taste the poison. Puffer fish contain similar toxins but are only dangerous when eaten. Improper preparation of this fish can cause fatal poisoning. In some countries, chefs must be certified to prepare puffer fish.

424

Resources for Teachers and Students

Life on Earth: A Natural History, by David Attenborough, Little, Brown, 1979.

Life on Earth: A Natural History Written and Hosted by David Attenborough, 1996, British Broadcasting Corporation and BBC Enterprises, Ltd. Available through Warner Home Video.

The effects of venom on a victim can range from tingling, skin redness, and itching to paralysis and death. Some toxins cause vomiting or hallucinations. Hematoxic venom affects the blood, and can destroy cell tissue or rupture blood cells. Venoms containing neurotoxins are the most dangerous because they affect the nervous system. These toxins can paralyze the diaphragm, causing suffocation, or stop the heart from functioning.

How severely a victim is affected depends on more than the venom itself. A person's age, size, and general health play a role in the poison's effect. Also, bites and stings to fingers and toes are usually less serious than those to a person's head or body, because there's less of a chance that the venom will directly enter a blood vessel and the bloodstream.

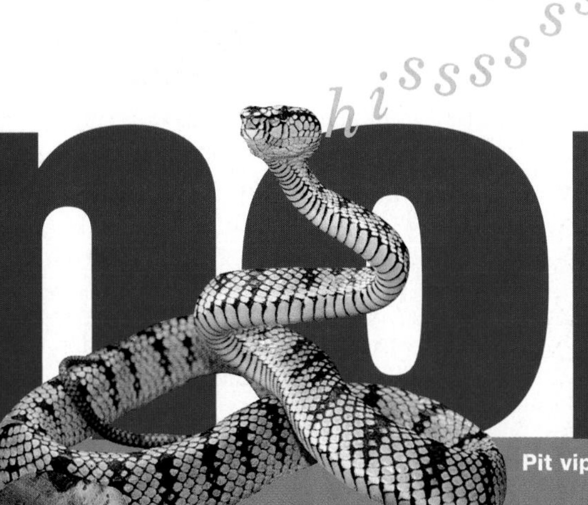

Gila monster

Pit viper

Venom as Medicine

Doctors and scientists have discovered a shocking surprise within this sometimes deadly liquid. Oddly enough, the very same poison that harms and weakens people can heal, too. In fact, doctors use the deadliest venom—that of some pit viper species—to treat certain types of heart attacks. Cobra venom has been used to soothe the effects of cancer, and other snake venoms reduce the spasms of epilepsy and asthma.

Some venoms also contain substances that help clot blood. Hemophiliacs—people whose blood will not clot naturally—rely on the medical benefits that venom-based medicines supply. Venoms also are used in biological research. For instance, venoms that affect the nervous system help doctors and researchers learn more about how nerves function.

It's still smart to steer clear of the rattle or the stinger—but it's good to know that the venom in them might someday help as many as it can hurt.

CONNECTIONS Research Besides venom, what other defenses do animals use to protect themselves or to subdue their prey? Explore how some animals that are native to your region use their built-in defenses.

SCIENCE *Online*
For more information, visit science.glencoe.com.

Discussion

There are some uses of venom as medicinal treatments that are not generally accepted. *Apitherapy*, the use of bee venom for treatment of multiple sclerosis, is particularly controversial. Many people with this disease allow themselves to be stung by bees, reporting that they experience remission of their symptoms. The use of bee venom in this manner has not been approved by any federal agencies. Ask students to discuss whether people with life-changing diseases like MS should be permitted to use unproven and controversial techniques like this, and whether doctors should encourage or discourage their use.

Activity

Most organisms that are venomous are brightly or elaborately colored. This serves as a protective measure, by making it easier for a predator to associate the colors with distasteful or painful experiences. They are likely to avoid colored prey again. Have students look through magazines for pictures of such animals, and make a collage. A good way to start would be to look for pictures of red and yellow frogs and toads, and elaborately colored venomous snakes.

Investigate the Issue

Have students look for unusual color patterns and shapes of animals. Speculate about what purposes these unusual adaptations may serve. Sort their pictures according to whether the shape or color is a warning to predators, camouflage for avoiding predators, or a way to attract their prey.

CONNECTIONS Animals use a number of strategies to attract prey or protect themselves. The viceroy butterfly, for example, is delicious to birds, but resembles, or *mimics,* the monarch butterfly, which is distasteful to them. Many insects avoid predation by being *camouflaged* and blending in with their environment. Still other organisms, like the angler fish, have developed structures that resemble worms or baitfish to attract their own prey closer to them.

SCIENCE *Online*

Internet Addresses

Explore the Glencoe Science Web site at **science.glencoe.com** to find out more about topics in this feature.

Chapter 14 Study Guide

Reviewing Main Ideas

Preview

Students can answer the questions in their Science Journals. Discuss the answers as you go through the chapter. LS **Linguistic**

Review

Students can write their answers, then compare them with those of other students. LS **Interpersonal**

Reteach

Students can look at the illustrations and describe details that support the main ideas of the chapter. LS **Visual-Spatial**

Answers to Chapter Review

Section 1

3. ectotherm

Section 2

3. to raise and lower itself in the water

Section 3

2. Its skin must be moist to exchange oxygen and carbon dioxide.

Section 4

3. thick, dry, waterproof skin covered with scales; movable eyelids; external ears; legs with clawed toes

Chapter 14 Study Guide

Reviewing Main Ideas

Section 1 Chordates and Vertebrates

1. Chordates include lancelets, tunicates, and vertebrates. Chordates have a notochord, a nerve cord, gill slits, and a postanal tail.
2. All vertebrates have an endoskeleton that includes a backbone and a skull that protects the brain.
3. An endotherm is an animal that has a nearly constant internal body temperature. An ectotherm has a body temperature that changes with the temperature of its environment. *Is the animal in the photo an endotherm or an ectotherm?*

Section 2 Fish

1. Fish are vertebrates that have a streamlined body, fins, gills for gas exchange, and a highly developed sensory system.
2. Fish are divided into three groups—jawless fish, cartilaginous fish, and bony fish.
3. The bony fish have the greatest number of known fish species. Most bony fish have scales and swim bladders. *How does this fish use its swim bladder?*

Section 3 Amphibians

1. The first vertebrates to live on land were the amphibians.
2. Amphibians have adaptations that allow them to live on land and in the water. The adaptations include moist skin, mucous glands, and lungs. Most amphibians are dependent on water to reproduce. *Why is it necessary for this frog to live in a moist habitat?*

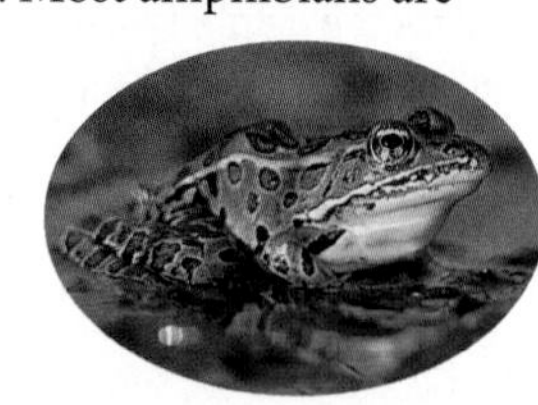

3. Most amphibians go through a metamorphosis from egg, to larva, to adult. During metamorphosis, legs develop, lungs replace gills, and the tail is lost.

Section 4 Reptiles

1. Reptiles are land animals with thick, dry, scaly skin. They lay amniotic eggs with leathery shells.
2. Turtles with tough shells, meat-eating crocodiles and alligators, and snakes and lizards make up the reptile groups.
3. Early reptiles were successful because of their adaptations to living on land. *What are some adaptations of this lizard?*

FOLDABLES Reading & Study Skills — After You Read

To help you review the characteristics of fish, amphibians, and reptiles, use the Foldable you made at the beginning of the chapter.

FOLDABLES Reading & Study Skills — After You Read

After students have read the chapter and completed the Foldable described in Before You Read, have them do the activity on the student page.

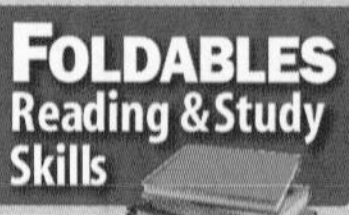

Visualizing Main Ideas

Complete the concept map below that describes chordates.

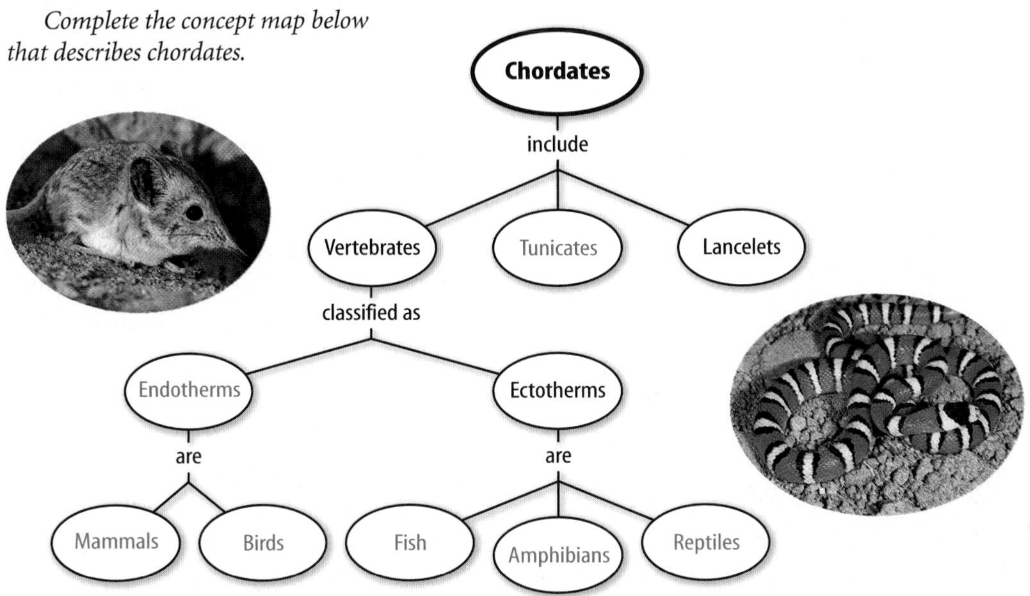

Vocabulary Review

Vocabulary Words

a. amniotic egg
b. cartilage
c. chordate
d. ectotherm
e. endoskeleton
f. endotherm
g. estivation
h. fin
i. gill slit
j. hibernation
k. nerve cord
l. notochord
m. postanal tail
n. scale
o. vertebrae

THE PRINCETON REVIEW Study Tip

Use tables and graphs to help you organize written material. For example, put the levels of biological organization in a table. Show what each level contains. Referring to a table can help you review concepts quickly.

Using Vocabulary

Replace the underlined word with the correct vocabulary word(s).

1. All chordates have a notochord, gill slits, postanal tail, and a <u>backbone</u>.
2. The inactivity of amphibians during hot, dry weather is <u>hibernation</u>.
3. All animals with a constant internal temperature are <u>vertebrates</u>.
4. Reptiles are <u>endotherms</u> with scaly skin.
5. Jawless fish have skeletons made of a tough, flexible tissue called <u>bone</u>.
6. Reptiles lay <u>eggs covered in gelatin</u>.
7. The structure that becomes the backbone in vertebrates is the <u>nerve cord</u>.

Chapter 14 Study Guide

Visualizing Main Ideas

See student page.

Vocabulary Review

Using Vocabulary

1. nerve cord
2. estivation
3. endotherms
4. ectotherms
5. cartilage
6. amniotic eggs
7. notochord

CHAPTER STUDY GUIDE 427

Checking Concepts

1. D
2. A
3. A
4. C
5. A
6. A
7. A
8. A
9. C
10. D

Thinking Critically

11. The populations of insects and other animals they eat might increase. Populations of their predators might decrease.
12. The skin of amphibians absorbs oxygen, as well as poisonous gases or chemicals in the area. They often show signs of environmental pollutants quickly. Because of this, amphibians can be considered biological indicators—species that reflect the condition of the environment.
13. They have a notochord, postanal tail, nerve cord, and gill slits in some stage of development.
14. All vertebrates have, at some time in their lives, a notochord that becomes the vertebrae in vertebrates, a postanal tail, a nerve cord, and gill slits. They also all have an endoskeleton.
15. The amniotic egg provides the developing embryo with protection from drying out and being eaten. An adequate supply of food is also provided. Reptile eggs can be laid anywhere on land, thus freeing reptiles from a reliance on water for reproduction.

Chapter 14 Assessment

Checking Concepts

Choose the word or phrase that best answers the question.

1. Which animals have fins, scales, and gills?
   A) amphibians **C)** reptiles
   B) crocodiles **D)** fish
2. Which is an example of a cartilaginous fish?
   A) hagfish **C)** perch
   B) tuna **D)** goldfish
3. What fish group has the greatest number of species?
   A) bony **C)** cartilaginous
   B) jawless **D)** amphibians
4. Which of the following is a fish with gills and lungs?
   A) shark **C)** lungfish
   B) ray **D)** perch
5. Biological indicators include which group of ectothermic vertebrates?
   A) amphibians **C)** bony fish
   B) cartilaginous fish **D)** reptiles
6. Which kinds of reptiles are included with lizards?
   A) snakes **C)** turtles
   B) crocodiles **D)** alligators
7. What term best describes eggs of reptiles?
   A) amniotic **C)** jellylike
   B) brown **D)** hard-shelled
8. Vertebrates that have lungs and moist skin belong to which group?
   A) amphibians **C)** reptiles
   B) fish **D)** lizards
9. How can crocodiles be distinguished from alligators?
   A) care of the young
   B) scales on the back
   C) shape of the head
   D) habitats in which they live
10. Which group has a notochord, nerve cord, postanal tail, and gill slits at some point in time?
    A) echinoderms **C)** arthropods
    B) mollusks **D)** chordates

Thinking Critically

11. Populations of frogs and toads are decreasing in some areas. What effects could this decrease have on other animal populations?
12. Why are some amphibians considered to be biological indicators?
13. In what ways are tunicates and lancelets similar to humans?
14. What physical features are common to all vertebrates?
15. Explain how the development of the amniotic egg led to the success of early reptiles.

Developing Skills

16. **Communicating** In your Science Journal, sequence the order in which these structures appeared in evolutionary history, then explain what type of organism had this adaptation and the advantage it provided: skin has mucous glands; skin has scales; dry, scaly skin.
17. **Comparing and Contrasting** Complete this chart that compares the features of some vertebrate groups.

Vertebrate Groups

Feature	Fish	Amphibians	Reptiles
Circulation	Two-chambered heart	Three-chambered heart	Three-chambered heart
Respiration	Gills	Skin and lungs	Two lungs
Reproduction	Requires water	Requires water	Does not require water

Chapter Assessment Planner

Portfolio Encourage students to place in their portfolios one or two items of what they consider to be their best work. Examples include:
- Science Journal, p. 399
- Extension, p. 405
- Extension, p. 413
- Extension, p. 419

Performance Additional performance assessments, Performance Task Assessment Lists, and rubrics for evaluating these activities can be found in Glencoe's **Performance Assessment in the Science Classroom.**

18. **Identifying and Manipulating Variables and Controls** Design an experiment to find out the effect of water temperature on frog egg development.

19. **Making and Using Graphs** Make a circle graph of the species of fish in the table below. What percent of the graph is accounted for by bony fish?

Fish Species

Kinds of Fish	Number of Species
Jawless	45
Cartilaginous	500
Bony	20,000

20. **Classifying** To what animal group does an animal with a two-chambered heart belong?

Performance Assessment

21. **Conduct a Survey** Many people are wary of reptiles. Write questions about reptiles to find out how people feel about these animals. Give the survey to your classmates, then graph the results and share them with your class.

22. **Display** Cut out pictures of fish from magazines and mount them on poster board. Letter the names of each fish on 3" × 5" cards. Have your classmates try to match the names of the fish with their pictures. To make this activity more challenging, use only the scientific names of each fish.

TECHNOLOGY

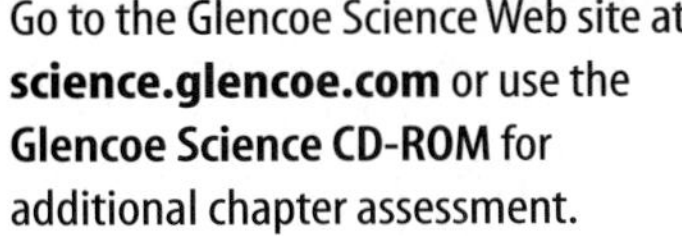

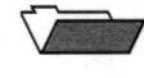

Go to the Glencoe Science Web site at **science.glencoe.com** or use the **Glencoe Science CD-ROM** for additional chapter assessment.

Test Practice

The following table shows the diversity of reptiles worldwide.

Worldwide Diversity of Reptiles

Region	Reptile Species
Africa	1,320
Asia	2,080
Australia	850
Caribbean	500
Central America	1,060
Europe	200
Indian Ocean	360
Middle East	360
North America	340
Oceania	230
South America	1,560

Study the table shown above and answer the following questions.

1. The region that has the largest number of reptile species is _____.
   A) North America
   B) Middle East
   C) Central America
   D) Asia

2. The number of classified reptile species worldwide is 7,984. The total of the table does not agree. Why?
   F) Scientists exaggerate the number of species they classify.
   G) Some areas share reptile species.
   H) Scientists keep poor records.
   J) Areas seldom share reptile species.

Chapter 14 Assessment

Test Practice

The Test-Taking Tip was written by The Princeton Review, the nation's leader in test preparation.

1. D
2. G

Developing Skills

16. Scales are present in fish, allowing them to move in water; skin with mucus glands is present in amphibians, which began to live on land; dry, scaly skin developed in reptiles that lived on land.
17. see student page
18. Students should design experiments with a control—a set temperature—and groups with higher or lower temperatures as the variables.
19. Students should find that 97.3% of the graph or 350° represents bony fish, about 2.4% or 8.6° represents cartilagenous fish, and about 0.22% or 0.8° represents jawless fish.
20. The animal is most likely a fish.

Performance Assessment

21. Student graphs will vary according to their survey audience. Use **Performance Assessment in the Science Classroom**, p. 107.
22. Students should find matching scientific names that describe the characteristics of each fish chosen. Use **Performance Assessment in the Science Classroom**, p. 145.

Assessment Resources

Reproducible Masters

Chapter Resources Booklet
Chapter Review, pp. 41–42
Chapter Tests, pp. 43–46
Assessment Transparency Activity, p. 55

Glencoe Science Web site
Interactive Tutor
Chapter Quizzes

Glencoe Technology
Assessment Transparency
Interactive CD-ROM Chapter Quizzes
ExamView Pro Test Bank
Vocabulary PuzzleMaker Software
MindJogger Videoquiz

Section/Objectives	Standards: National	Standards: State/Local	Activities/Features
Chapter Opener	See p. 5T for a Key to Standards.		**Explore Activity:** Model how a bird's gizzard works, p. 431 **Before You Read,** p. 431
Section 1 Birds 2 sessions 1 block 1. **Identify** the characteristics of birds. 2. **Identify** the adaptations birds have for flight. 3. **Explain** how birds reproduce and develop.	National Content Standards: UCP3, A1, C1, C2, C3, C5		**Astronomy Integration,** p. 433 **MiniLAB:** Modeling Feather Preening, p. 434 **Environmental Science Integration,** p. 435 **Science Online,** p. 436 **Visualizing Birds,** p. 438
Section 2 Mammals 3 sessions 1.5 blocks 1. **Identify** the characteristics of mammals and explain how they have enabled mammals to adapt to different environments. 2. **Distinguish** among monotremes, marsupials, and placentals. 3. **Explain** why many species of mammals are becoming threatened or endangered.	National Content Standards: UCP3, A1, C1, C2, C3, C4, C5, F2, G1, G3		**MiniLAB:** Inferring How Blubber Insulates, p. 442 **Problem Solving Skills:** Does a mammal's heart rate determine how long it will live?, p. 443 **Science Online,** p. 445 **Activity:** Mammal Footprints, p. 449 **Activity:** Bird Counts, pp. 450–451 **Science Stats:** Eggciting Facts, pp. 452–453

Activity Materials	Reproducible Resources	Section Assessment	Technology
Explore Activity: cracked corn, sunflower seeds, nuts, or other seeds; gravel; old sock	**Chapter Resources Booklet** Foldables Worksheet, p. 15 Directed Reading Overview, p. 17 Note-taking Worksheets, pp. 29–31	Glencoe's Assessment Advantage	
MiniLAB: cotton cloth, scissors, petroleum jelly, water *Need materials?* Contact Science Kit at 1-800-828-7777 or www.sciencekit.com on the Internet.	**Chapter Resources Booklet** Transparency Activity, p. 40 MiniLAB, p. 3 Lab Activity, pp. 9–10 Enrichment, p. 27 Reinforcement, p. 25 Directed Reading, p. 18 Transparency Activity, pp. 43–44 **Home and Community Involvement,** p. 27 **Earth Science Critical Thinking/ Problem Solving,** p. 12 **Life Science Critical Thinking/ Problem Solving,** pp. 12, 13	**Portfolio** Science Journal, p. 435 Assessment, p. 439 **Performance** MiniLAB, p. 434 Skill Builder Activities, p. 439 **Content** Section Assessment, p. 439	Section Focus Transparency Teaching Transparency Interactive CD-ROM Guided Reading Audio Program
MiniLAB: 2 self-sealing plastic bags, vegetable shortening, ice water **Activity:** diagram of mammal footprints **Activity:** Internet and other sources of information on birds	**Chapter Resources Booklet** Transparency Activity, p. 41 MiniLAB, p. 4 Lab Activity, pp. 11–14 Enrichment, p. 28 Reinforcement, p. 26 Directed Reading, pp. 19, 20 Activity Worksheets, pp. 5–6, 7–8 **Lab Management and Safety,** p. 37 **Science Inquiry Labs,** p. 37 **Mathematics Skill Activities,** p. 7 **Cultural Diversity,** p. 9	**Portfolio** Assessment, p. 442 **Performance** MiniLAB, p. 442 Problem-Solving Activity, p. 443 Skill Builder Activities, p. 448 **Content** Section Assessment, p. 448	Section Focus Transparency Interactive CD-ROM Guided Reading Audio Program

End of Chapter Assessment

Glencoe's Assessment Advantage

Blackline Masters	Technology	Professional Series
Chapter Resources Booklet Chapter Review, pp. 33–34 Chapter Tests, pp. 35–38 **Standardized Test Practice by The Princeton Review,** pp. 67–70	MindJogger Videoquiz Interactive CD-ROM Vocabulary PuzzleMakers ExamView Pro Test Bank Interactive Lesson Planner Interactive Teacher Edition	Performance Assessment in the Science Classroom (PASC)

Transparencies

Section Focus

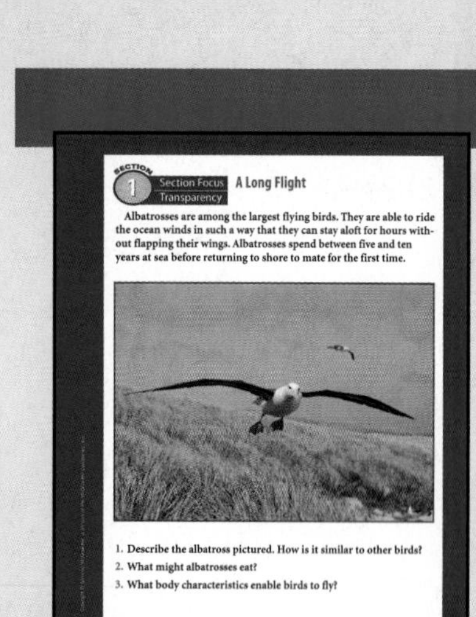
Section 1 Section Focus Transparency **A Long Flight**

Albatrosses are among the largest flying birds. They are able to ride the ocean winds in such a way that they can stay aloft for hours without flapping their wings. Albatrosses spend between five and ten years at sea before returning to shore to mate for the first time.

1. Describe the albatross pictured. How is it similar to other birds?
2. What might albatrosses eat?
3. What body characteristics enable birds to fly?

L2

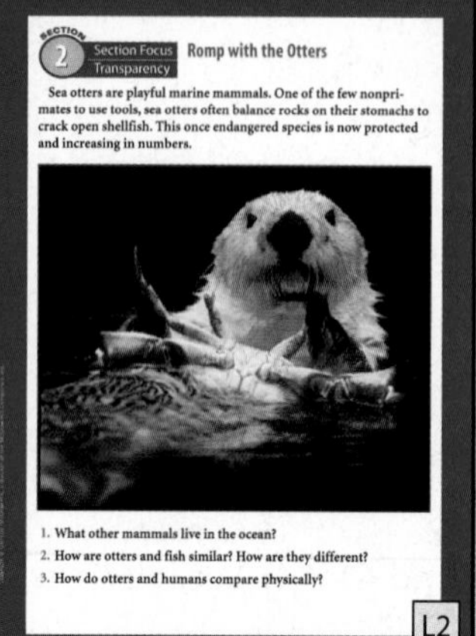
Section 2 Section Focus Transparency **Romp with the Otters**

Sea otters are playful marine mammals. One of the few nonprimates to use tools, sea otters often balance rocks on their stomachs to crack open shellfish. This once endangered species is now protected and increasing in numbers.

1. What other mammals live in the ocean?
2. How are otters and fish similar? How are they different?
3. How do otters and humans compare physically?

L2

This is a representation of key blackline masters available in the Teacher Classroom Resources. See Resource Manager boxes within the chapter for additional information.

Assessment

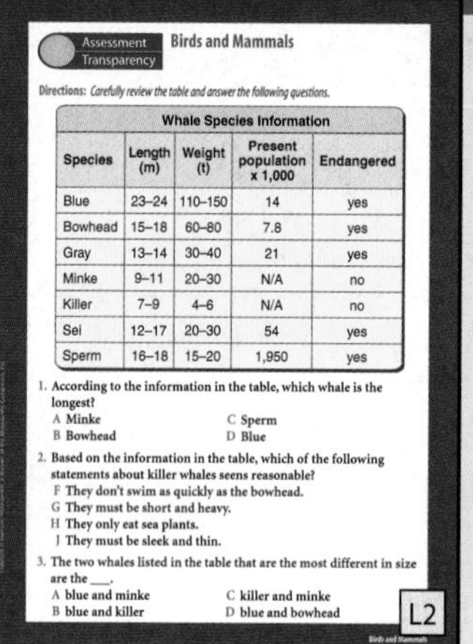
Assessment Transparency **Birds and Mammals**

Directions: Carefully review the table and answer the following questions.

Whale Species Information

Species	Length (m)	Weight (t)	Present population x 1,000	Endangered
Blue	23–24	110–150	14	yes
Bowhead	15–18	60–80	7.8	yes
Gray	13–14	30–40	21	yes
Minke	9–11	20–30	N/A	no
Killer	7–9	4–6	N/A	no
Sei	12–17	20–30	54	yes
Sperm	16–18	15–20	1,950	yes

1. According to the information in the table, which whale is the longest?
   A Minke C Sperm
   B Bowhead D Blue
2. Based on the information in the table, which of the following statements about killer whales seems reasonable?
   F They don't swim as quickly as the bowhead.
   G They must be short and heavy.
   H They only eat sea plants.
   J They must be sleek and thin.
3. The two whales listed in the table that are the most different in size are the ___.
   A blue and minke C killer and minke
   B blue and killer D blue and bowhead

L2

Teaching

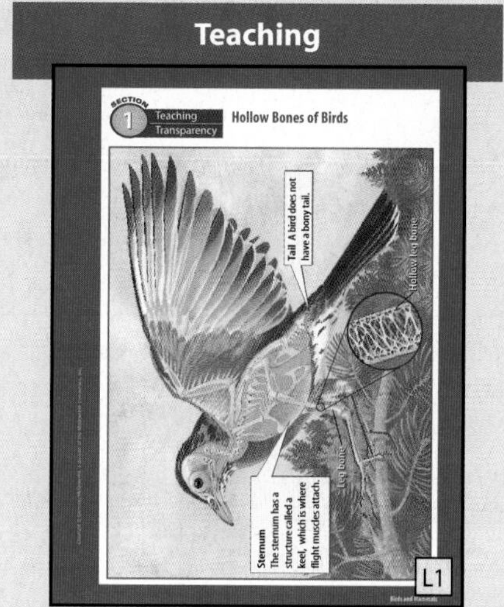
Section 1 Teaching Transparency **Hollow Bones of Birds**

L1

Key to Teaching Strategies

The following designations will help you decide which activities are appropriate for your students.

- L1 Level 1 activities should be appropriate for students with learning difficulties.
- L2 Level 2 activities should be within the ability range of all students.
- L3 Level 3 activities are designed for above-average students.
- ELL ELL activities should be within the ability range of English Language Learners.
- COOP LEARN Cooperative Learning activities are designed for small group work.
- LS Multiple Learning Styles logos, as described on page 22T, are used throughout to indicate strategies that address different learning styles.
- P These strategies represent student products that can be placed into a best-work portfolio.

Hands-on Activities

Activity Worksheets

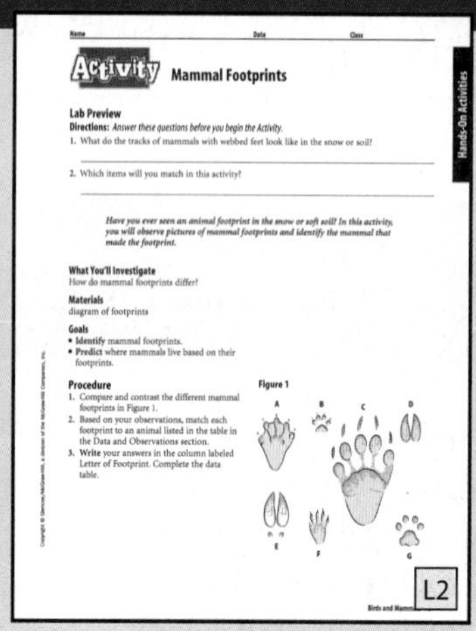
Name Date Class

Activity **Mammal Footprints**

Lab Preview
Directions: *Answer these questions before you begin the Activity.*
1. What do the tracks of mammals with webbed feet look like in the snow or soil?
2. Which items will you match in this activity?

Have you ever seen an animal footprint in the snow or soft soil? In this activity, you will observe pictures of mammal footprints and identify the mammal that made the footprint.

What You'll Investigate
How do mammal footprints differ?

Materials
diagram of footprints

Goals
- **Identify** mammal footprints.
- **Predict** where mammals live based on their footprints.

Procedure
1. Compare and contrast the different mammal footprints in Figure 1.
2. Based on your observations, match each footprint to an animal listed in the table in the Data and Observations section.
3. **Write** your answers in the column labeled Letter of Footprint. Complete the data table.

Figure 1

Hands-On Activities

L2

Laboratory Activities

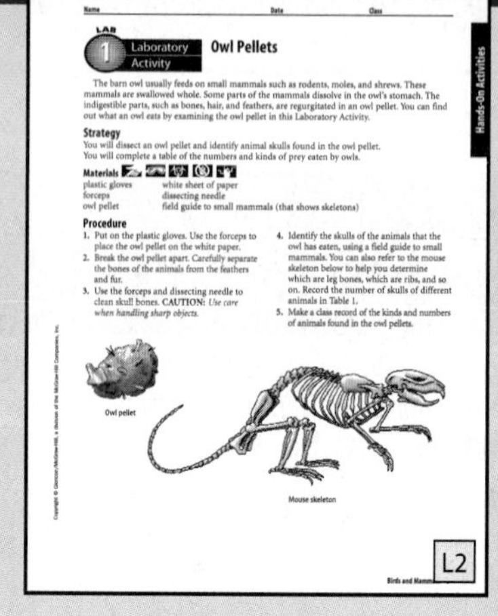
Name Date Class

Lab 1 Laboratory Activity **Owl Pellets**

The barn owl usually feeds on small mammals such as rodents, moles, and shrews. These mammals are swallowed whole. Some parts of the mammals dissolve in the owl's stomach. The indigestible parts, such as bones, hair, and feathers, are regurgitated in an owl pellet. You can find out what an owl eats by examining the owl pellet in this Laboratory Activity.

Strategy
You will dissect an owl pellet and identify animal skulls found in the owl pellet.
You will complete a table of the numbers and kinds of prey eaten by owls.

Materials
plastic gloves, white sheet of paper, forceps, dissecting needle, owl pellet, field guide to small mammals (that shows skeletons)

Procedure
1. Put on the plastic gloves. Use the forceps to place the owl pellet on the white paper.
2. Break the owl pellet apart. Carefully separate the bones of the animals from the feathers and fur.
3. Use the forceps and dissecting needle to clean skull bones. **CAUTION:** *Use care when handling sharp objects.*
4. Identify the skulls of the animals that the owl has eaten, using a field guide to small mammals. You can also refer to the mouse skeleton below to help you determine which are leg bones, which are ribs, and so on. Record the number of skulls of different animals in Table 1.
5. Make a class record of the kinds and numbers of animals found in the owl pellets.

Owl pellet

Mouse skeleton

Hands-On Activities

L2

Meeting Different Ability Levels

Content Outline

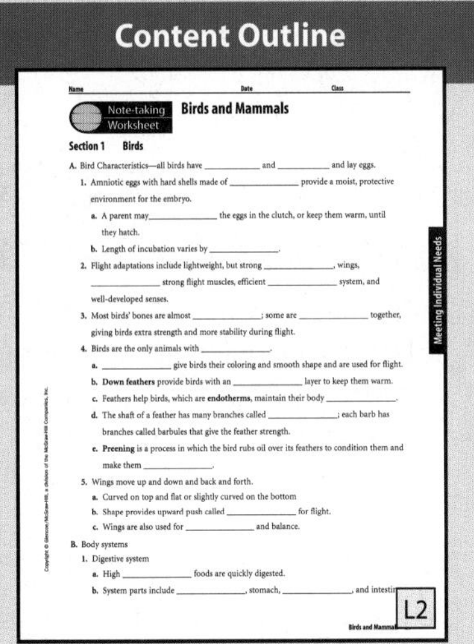

Name Date Class

Note-taking Worksheet — Birds and Mammals

Section 1 Birds

A. Bird Characteristics—all birds have ________ and ________ and lay eggs.

1. Amniotic eggs with hard shells made of ________ provide a moist, protective environment for the embryo.
   a. A parent may ________ the eggs in the clutch, or keep them warm, until they hatch.
   b. Length of incubation varies by ________.
2. Flight adaptations include lightweight, but strong ________, wings, ________ strong flight muscles, efficient ________ system, and well-developed senses.
3. Most birds' bones are almost ________; some are ________ together, giving birds extra strength and more stability during flight.
4. Birds are the only animals with ________.
   a. ________ give birds their coloring and smooth shape and are used for flight.
   b. **Down feathers** provide birds with an ________ layer to keep them warm.
   c. Feathers help birds, which are **endotherms**, maintain their body ________.
   d. The shaft of a feather has many branches called ________; each barb has branches called barbules that give the feather strength.
   e. **Preening** is a process in which the bird rubs oil over its feathers to condition them and make them ________.
5. Wings move up and down and back and forth.
   a. Curved on top and flat or slightly curved on the bottom
   b. Shape provides upward push called ________ for flight.
   c. Wings are also used for ________ and balance.

B. Body systems

1. Digestive system
   a. High ________ foods are quickly digested.
   b. System parts include ________, stomach, ________, and intestine

Meeting Individual Needs

L2

Reinforcement

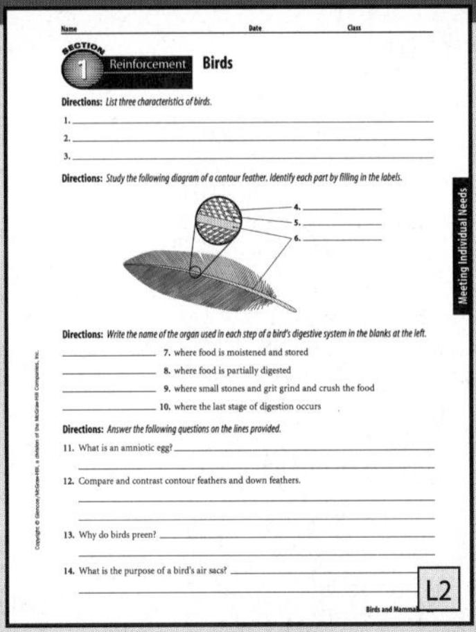

Name Date Class

Section 1 Reinforcement — Birds

Directions: List three characteristics of birds.

1. ________
2. ________
3. ________

Directions: Study the following diagram of a contour feather. Identify each part by filling in the labels.

4. ________
5. ________
6. ________

Directions: Write the name of the organ used in each step of a bird's digestive system in the blanks at the left.

________ 7. where food is moistened and stored

________ 8. where food is partially digested

________ 9. where small stones and grit grind and crush the food

________ 10. where the last stage of digestion occurs

Directions: Answer the following questions on the lines provided.

11. What is an amniotic egg? ________
12. Compare and contrast contour feathers and down feathers.
13. Why do birds preen? ________
14. What is the purpose of a bird's air sacs? ________

Meeting Individual Needs

L2

Directed Reading

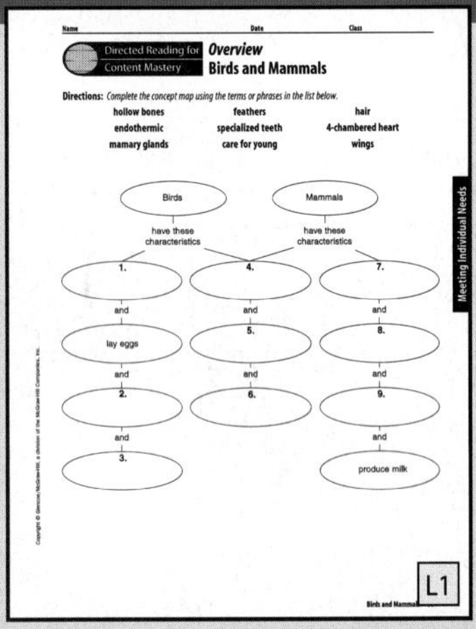

Name Date Class

Directed Reading for Content Mastery — Overview — Birds and Mammals

Directions: Complete the concept map using the terms or phrases in the list below.

hollow bones, feathers, hair, endothermic, specialized teeth, 4-chambered heart, mamary glands, care for young, wings

Birds — have these characteristics — 1. and lay eggs and 2. and 3.

Mammals — have these characteristics — 7. and 8. and 9. and produce milk

4. and 5. and 6.

Meeting Individual Needs

L1

Chapter Tests

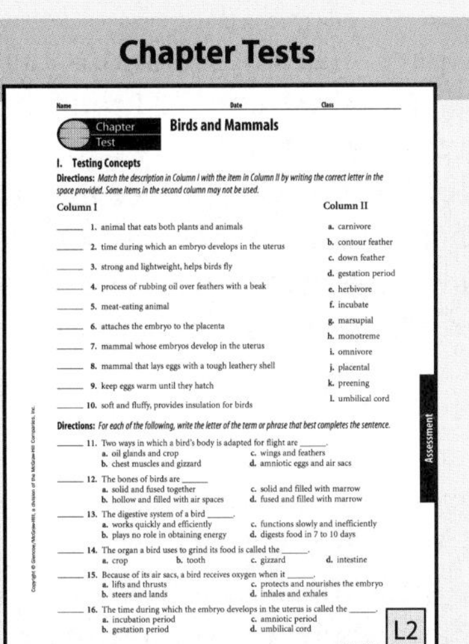

Name Date Class

Chapter Test — Birds and Mammals

I. Testing Concepts

Directions: Match the description in Column I with the item in Column II by writing the correct letter in the space provided. Some items in the second column may not be used.

Column I	Column II
____ 1. animal that eats both plants and animals	a. carnivore
____ 2. time during which an embryo develops in the uterus	b. contour feather
____ 3. strong and lightweight, helps birds fly	c. down feather
____ 4. process of rubbing oil over feathers with a beak	d. gestation period
____ 5. meat-eating animal	e. herbivore
____ 6. attaches the embryo to the placenta	f. incubate
____ 7. mammal whose embryos develop in the uterus	g. marsupial
____ 8. mammal that lays eggs with a tough leathery shell	h. monotreme
____ 9. keep eggs warm until they hatch	i. omnivore
____ 10. soft and fluffy, provides insulation for birds	j. placental
	k. preening
	l. umbilical cord

Directions: For each of the following, write the letter of the term or phrase that best completes the sentence.

____ 11. Two ways in which a bird's body is adapted for flight are ____.
a. oil glands and crop; b. chest muscles and gizzard; c. wings and feathers; d. amniotic eggs and air sacs

____ 12. The bones of birds are ____.
a. solid and fused together; b. hollow and filled with air spaces; c. solid and filled with marrow; d. fused and filled with marrow

____ 13. The digestive system of a bird ____.
a. works quickly and efficiently; b. plays no role in obtaining energy; c. functions slowly and inefficiently; d. digests food in 7 to 10 days

____ 14. The organ a bird uses to grind its food is called the ____.
a. crop; b. tooth; c. gizzard; d. intestine

____ 15. Because of its air sacs, a bird receives oxygen when it ____.
a. lifts and thrusts; b. steers and lands; c. protects and nourishes the embryo; d. inhales and exhales

____ 16. The time during which the embryo develops in the uterus is called the ____.
a. incubation period; b. gestation period; c. amniotic period; d. umbilical cord

Assessment

L2

Enrichment

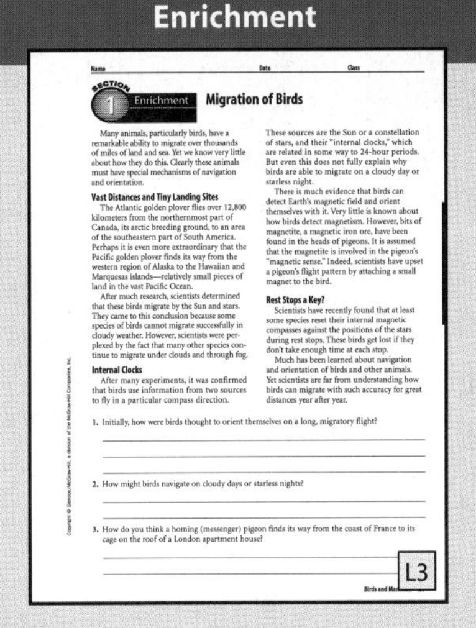

Name Date Class

Section 1 Enrichment — Migration of Birds

Many animals, particularly birds, have a remarkable ability to migrate over thousands of miles of land and sea. Yet we know very little about how they do this. Clearly these animals must have special mechanisms of navigation and orientation.

Vast Distances and Tiny Landing Sites

The Atlantic golden plover flies over 12,800 kilometers from the northernmost part of Canada, its arctic breeding ground, to an area of the southeastern part of South America. Perhaps it is even more extraordinary that the Pacific golden plover finds its way from the western region of Alaska to the Hawaiian and Marquesas islands—relatively small pieces of land in the vast Pacific Ocean.

After much research, scientists determined that these birds migrate by the Sun and stars. They came to this conclusion because some species of birds cannot migrate successfully in cloudy weather. However, scientists were perplexed by the fact that many other species continue to migrate under clouds and through fog.

Internal Clocks

After many experiments, it was confirmed that birds use information from two sources to fly in a particular compass direction. These sources are the Sun or a constellation of stars, and their "internal clocks," which are related in some way to 24-hour periods. But even this does not fully explain why birds are able to migrate on a cloudy day or starless night.

There is much evidence that birds can detect Earth's magnetic field and orient themselves with it. Very little is known about how birds detect magnetism. However, bits of magnetite, a magnetic iron ore, have been found in the heads of pigeons. It is assumed that the magnetite is involved in the pigeon's "magnetic sense." Indeed, scientists have upset a pigeon's flight pattern by attaching a small magnet to the bird.

Rest Stops a Key?

Scientists have recently found that at least some species reset their internal magnetic compasses against the positions of the stars during rest stops. These birds get lost if they don't take enough time at each stop.

Much has been learned about navigation and orientation of birds and other animals. Yet scientists are far from understanding how birds can migrate with such accuracy for great distances year after year.

1. Initially, how were birds thought to orient themselves on a long, migratory flight?
2. How might birds navigate on cloudy days or starless nights?
3. How do you think a homing (messenger) pigeon finds its way from the coast of France to its cage on the roof of a London apartment house?

L3

Spanish Directed Reading

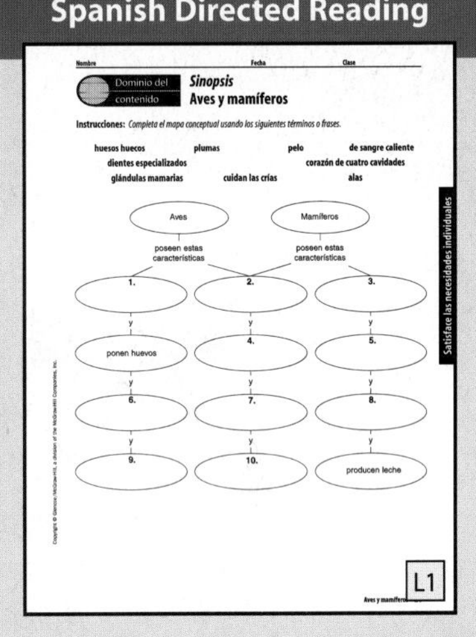

Nombre Fecha Clase

Dominio del contenido — Sinopsis — Aves y mamíferos

Instrucciones: Completa el mapa conceptual usando los siguientes términos o frases.

huesos huecos, plumas, pelo, de sangre caliente, dientes especializados, corazón de cuatro cavidades, glándulas mamarias, cuidan las crías, alas

Aves — poseen estas características — 1. y ponen huevos y 6. y 9.

Mamíferos — poseen estas características — 3. y 5. y 8. y producen leche

2. y 4. y 7. y 10.

Satisface las necesidades individuales

L1

Test Practice Workbook

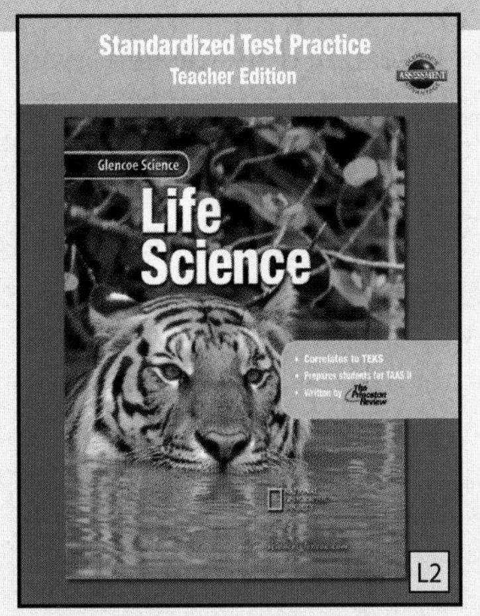

Chapter Review

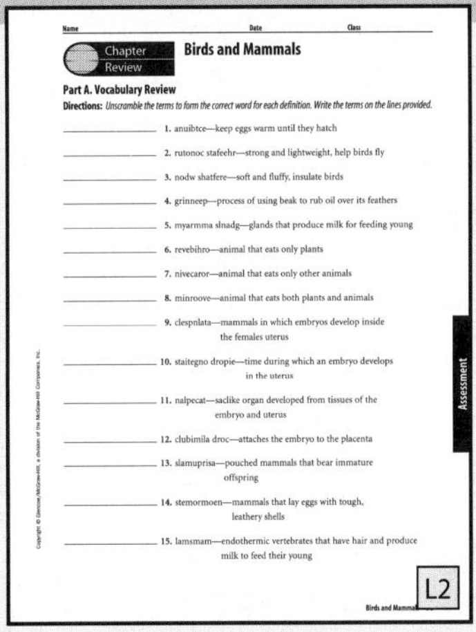

Name Date Class

Chapter Review — Birds and Mammals

Part A. Vocabulary Review

Directions: Unscramble the terms to form the correct word for each definition. Write the terms on the lines provided.

________ 1. anuibtce—keep eggs warm until they hatch

________ 2. rutootnc stafeehr—strong and lightweight, help birds fly

________ 3. nodw shatfere—soft and fluffy, insulate birds

________ 4. grinneep—process of using beak to rub oil over its feathers

________ 5. myarmma slnadg—glands that produce milk for feeding young

________ 6. revebihro—animal that eats only plants

________ 7. nivecaror—animal that eats only other animals

________ 8. minroove—animal that eats both plants and animals

________ 9. clespolata—mammals in which embryos develop inside the females uterus

________ 10. staitegno droipe—time during which an embryo develops in the uterus

________ 11. nalpecat—saclike organ developed from tissues of the embryo and uterus

________ 12. clubimila droc—attaches the embryo to the placenta

________ 13. slamuprisa—pouched mammals that bear immature offspring

________ 14. stemormoen—mammals that lay eggs with tough, leathery shells

________ 15. lamsmam—endothermic vertebrates that have hair and produce milk to feed their young

Assessment

L2

Science Content Background

Steve Lucas/International Stock

SECTION 1 Birds

Bird Characteristics

As opposed to amphibians and reptiles, birds (and mammals) are endotherms—their bodies maintain a nearly constant internal body temperature. This has two advantages—metabolic functions work optimally at certain temperature ranges, and maintaining a warm temperature prevents endotherms from being sluggish on cold days. The disadvantage is that it can take a lot of energy to maintain this temperature.

If you observe birds, you will see their preening behavior, which involves smoothing feathers and spreading oil from the uropygial gland located at the base of their tails. The oil helps keep the feathers waterproof, and smoothing feathers keeps them in their proper locations and in the proper shape. Sticky oil from oil spills hurts sea birds because their feathers get stuck in the wrong positions and they lose their water proofing. This allows cold water to contact their skin, resulting in the birds needing more energy to stay warm. In cold areas or places without enough food, this can cause death to the birds.

Fun Fact

Bird eggs come in a variety of sizes. Some hummingbird eggs are as small as a pea; some ostrich eggs are larger than softballs!

Fun Fact

The chest or pectoral muscles of birds are primarily responsible for the movement of the wings. These muscles are well developed in birds, accounting for as much as 25% of the entire mass of the bird.

Body Systems

Examinations of bird hearts reveal another way birds (and mammals) are different from all amphibians and most reptiles. Birds have a four-chambered heart. This is a more efficient pump because oxygenated and deoxygenated blood don't mix.

Some sailors have made observations that suggested that seagulls were crying. From this they inferred that they were sad or very happy to see them. Seabirds have a need to reduce the salt in their bodies that comes from eating marine organisms and drinking seawater. The tear glands in their eyes secrete the excess salt in their tears.

The Importance of Birds

Fossil evidence suggests that birds may have evolved from a group of dinosaurs. The scales on birds' feet and legs suggest their reptilian origins. In addition, birds' feathers are made of a protein called keratin, which is the same material that makes up reptile scales. Like reptiles, birds reproduce by internal fertilization and lay amniotic eggs.

Bird species are threatened by the actions of people. For example, the introduction of the brown tree snake onto the island of Guam has caused the loss of many bird species. The snake, which reproduces rapidly, climbs into trees and eats the eggs and chicks of many birds. The snake can find its way into airplanes and thus is easily spread to other islands. Nonflying birds are especially vulnerable to introduced animals. For example, about a century ago a lighthouse keeper's cat killed all the species of nonflying birds on one of New Zealand's islands.

SECTION 2

Mammals

Mammal Characteristics

Like the scales of reptiles and the feathers of birds, mammal hair is made of keratin. Hair helps these endotherms retain body heat. At times it is necessary to lose heat. Sweating and panting are two mechanisms that allow cooling of the body through evaporation of sweat from the skin or moisture from the lungs.

Body Systems

Herbivores generally have longer digestive systems than carnivores and omnivores. Many plant products, such as starches and fruits, are easy to digest. However, when a diet includes eating large amounts of leaves, large amounts of cellulose must be digested. Large molars start the digestive process by grinding the leaves into smaller pieces. Then the food moves slowly through the long digestive system where it is broken down.

While amphibians, reptiles, and birds all have red blood cells, those of mammals differ in that they don't have a nucleus in their mature state. This allows more room in the cells for hemoglobin to carry oxygen. The biconcave shape of mammalian red blood cells give them more surface area to absorb oxygen.

For additional content background on this topic, go to the Glencoe Science Web site at science.glencoe.com.

Types of Mammals

Mammals are thought to have evolved from a group of ancient reptiles called therapsids. These animals had both reptilian and mammalian characteristics.

Tree sloths (*Choloepus didactylus* and *Choloepus hoffmanni*) are one of the slowest moving mammals. They have little hope of outrunning predators so their slow movements aid in keeping them hidden. Green algae grow on their fur, which also helps them remain hidden in the branches of green trees. The slow metabolism of sloths means they don't have to eat much food, which allow a lot of time for their favorite activity—sleeping. These animals often sleep 15 hours per day.

Jeff Rotman/Stone

Birds and Mammals

Chapter Vocabulary

contour feather, p. 434
down feather, p. 434
endotherm, p. 434
preening, p. 434
mammal, p. 440
mammary gland, p. 440
omnivore, p. 441
carnivore, p. 441
herbivore, p. 441
monotreme, p. 444
marsupial, p. 444
placental, p. 445
gestation period, p. 445
placenta, p. 445
umbilical cord, p. 445

What do you think?

Science Journal The animal in the picture is a baby kangaroo. At birth, a baby kangaroo weighs only about 1 gram but can grow to 90 kilograms as an adult. The baby kangaroo finds protection and nourishment in its mother's pouch.

CHAPTER 15

Birds and Mammals

Why don't cats and dogs lay eggs? Why don't ostriches chew their food before they swallow it? Are the zebras and flamingos in the picture alike in any way? In this chapter, you will find the answers to these questions. Also presented in this chapter are the unique characteristics of birds and mammals. You will learn how birds and mammals are adapted to reproduce and live in many different environments.

What do you think?

Science Journal Look at the picture below with a classmate. Discuss what this might be or what is happening. Here's a hint: *It has found a protected place to eat and grow.* Write your answer or best guess in your Science Journal.

430

Theme Connection

Stability and Change A discussion of the adaptations of birds to life in the air and on land reinforces the steps in the evolution of different species that have moved from water to land environments. The theme of stability and change is continued in the discussion of mammal characteristics and origins. Both birds and mammals have developed homeostatic mechanisms for living on land.

You may have observed a variety of animals in your neighborhood. Maybe you have watched birds at a bird feeder. Birds don't chew their food because they don't have teeth. Instead, many birds swallow small pebbles, bits of eggshells, and other hard materials that go into the gizzard—a muscular digestive organ. Inside the gizzard, they help grind up the seeds. Do the activity below as a model of a gizzard in action.

Model how a bird's gizzard works

1. Place some cracked corn, sunflower seeds, nuts or other seeds, and some gravel in an old sock.
2. Roll the sock on a hard surface and tightly squeeze it.
3. Describe the appearance of the seeds after rolling.

Observe

Describe in your Science Journal how a bird's gizzard helps it digest food.

Before You Read

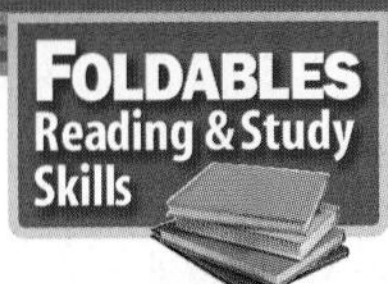

Making a Compare and Contrast Study Fold **As you study birds and mammals, use the following Foldable to help you compare and contrast their behavior.**

1. Place a sheet of paper in front of you so that the short side is at the top. Fold in the left side and then the right side to divide the paper into thirds. Unfold the paper.
2. Fold the paper into thirds from top to bottom. Then fold it from the top to bottom again and unfold.
3. Trace over all the fold lines and label the table you created with *Birds* and *Mammals* at the top, as shown. In the column on the left list: *Vertebrate/Invertebrate, Diet, Movement, Body Symmetry,* and *Young,* as shown.
4. Before you read the chapter, write what you know about birds and mammals. As you read the chapter, add information to the table.

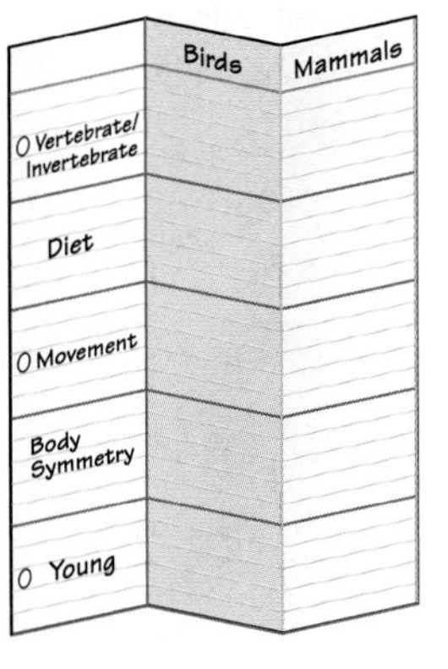

431

EXPLORE ACTIVITY

Purpose Use the Explore Activity to introduce students to characteristics of birds. Explain that they will be learning more about the external and internal characteristics of both birds and mammals in this chapter. L2 COOP LEARN LS **Kinesthetic**

Preparation Purchase packaged bird seed and mix it with corn and sunflower seeds. Collect gravel or pebbles.

Materials cracked corn, sunflower seeds, nuts, or other seeds; gravel; old sock

Teaching Strategies

- Assign one student to get the materials, one to grind the seeds, and one to record the observations.
- Have student groups compare their results. Discuss differences and similarities.

Observe

The bird's gizzard uses hard materials such as small pebbles to grind the nuts and seeds it eats.

Assessment

Performance Show students the internal structure of a bird. **Which organ grinds food?** gizzard **Hypothesize what this organ must be like.** The gizzard is very muscular in order to grind the food. Use **Performance Assessment in the Science Classroom,** p. 93.

Before You Read

FOLDABLES Reading & Study Skills

Dinah Zike Study Fold

Purpose Students make and use a Foldable table to collect information on birds and mammals as they read the chapter. Students use the data to compare and contrast these vertebrates during and after reading.

For additional help, see Foldables Worksheet, p. 15 in **Chapter Resources Booklet,** or go to the Glencoe Science Web site at **science.glencoe.com.** See After You Read in the Study Guide at the end of this chapter.

SECTION

Birds

1 Motivate

Bellringer Transparency

Display the Section Focus Transparency for Section 1. Use the accompanying Transparency Activity Master. L2 ELL

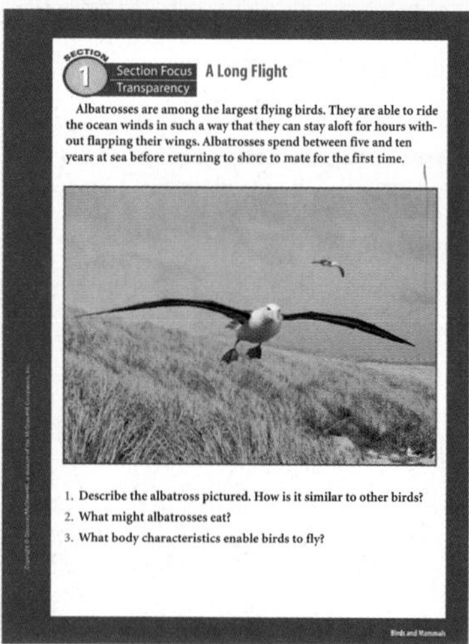

SECTION 1 Section Focus Transparency **A Long Flight**

Albatrosses are among the largest flying birds. They are able to ride the ocean winds in such a way that they can stay aloft for hours without flapping their wings. Albatrosses spend between five and ten years at sea before returning to shore to mate for the first time.

1. Describe the albatross pictured. How is it similar to other birds?
2. What might albatrosses eat?
3. What body characteristics enable birds to fly?

Birds and Mammals

Tie to Prior Knowledge

Most students will have cracked open an egg or seen someone else do so. Have them describe what they see when they crack open an egg and infer what each part is or does. yellow yolk (nourishes the embryo until it is born), clear fluid (the vitelline membrane) Many students will have seen brown eggs at the grocery store or at home. Explain that brown and white eggs taste the same, and have the same nutritional value. The color of the egg shell is determined by hen's genetic make-up.

Text Question Answer

the presence of feathers

SECTION 1

Birds

As You Read

***What* You'll Learn**

- **Identify** the characteristics of birds.
- **Identify** the adaptations birds have for flight.
- **Explain** how birds reproduce and develop.

Vocabulary

contour feather
down feather
endotherm
preening

***Why* It's Important**

Most birds demonstrate structural and behavioral adaptations for flight.

Bird Characteristics

Birds are versatile animals. Geese have been observed flying at an altitude of 9,000 m, and penguins have been seen underwater at a depth of 543 m. An ostrich might weigh 155,000 g, while a hummingbird might weigh only 2 g. Some birds can live in the tropics and others can live in polar regions. Their diets vary and include meat, fish, insects, fruit, seeds, and nectar. Birds have feathers and scales and they lay eggs. Which of these characteristics is unique to birds?

Bird Eggs Birds lay amniotic (am nee AH tik) eggs with hard shells, as shown in **Figure 1A.** This type of egg provides a moist, protective environment for the developing embryo. The hard shell is made of calcium carbonate, the same chemical that makes up seashells, limestone, and marble. The egg is fertilized internally before the shell forms around it. The female bird lays one or more eggs usually in some type of nest, as shown in **Figure 1B.** A group of eggs is called a clutch. One or both parents may keep the eggs warm, or incubate them, until they hatch. The length of time for incubation varies from species to species. The young are cared for by one or both parents.

Figure 1
A nest's materials, shape, and location are different for different species of birds. For example, this robin's round nest is built of grasses and mud in a tree.

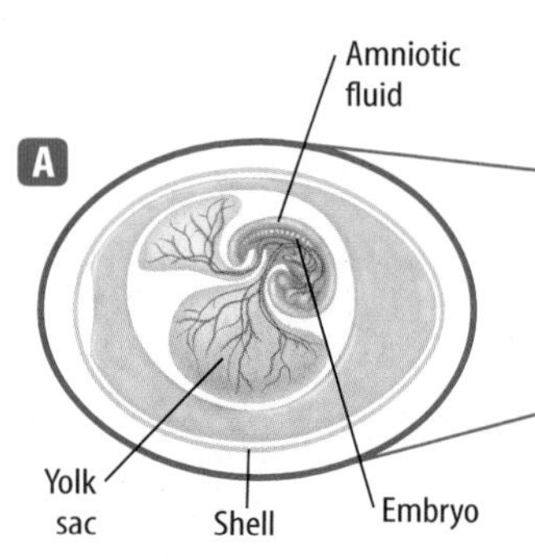

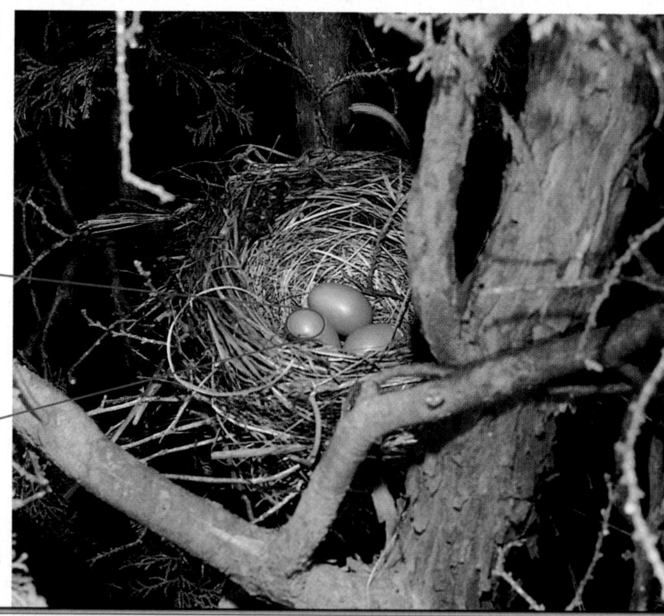

Section Assessment Planner

PORTFOLIO
Science Journal, p. 435
Assessment, p. 439

PERFORMANCE ASSESSMENT
MiniLAB, p. 434
Skill Builder Activities, p. 439
See page 456 for more options.

CONTENT ASSESSMENT
Section, p. 439
Challenge, p. 439
Chapter, pp. 456–457

Sternum The sternum has a structure called a keel, which is where flight muscles attach.
Tail A bird does not have a bony tail.
Leg bone
Hollow leg bone

Figure 2
The hollow bones of birds are an adaptation for flight. *What advantages do the thin cross braces provide?*

Flight Adaptations People have always been fascinated by the ability of birds to fly. Flight in birds is made possible by their lightweight but strong skeleton, wings, feathers, strong flight muscles, and an efficient respiratory system. Well-developed senses, especially eyesight, and tremendous amounts of energy also are needed for flight.

Hollow Bones One adaptation that birds have for flight is an internal skeleton, as shown in **Figure 2.** Many bones of a bird often are joined together. This provides more strength and more stability for flight. Most bones of birds that fly are almost hollow. These bones have thin cross braces inside that strengthen the bones without adding much weight. The hollow spaces inside of the bones are filled with air.

Reading Check *What features strengthen a bird's bones?*

A large sternum, or breastbone, supports the powerful chest muscles needed for flight. The last bones of the spine support the tail feathers, which play an important part in steering and balancing during flight and landing.

Astronomy INTEGRATION

Many theories have been proposed about how birds navigate at night. Some scientists hypothesize that star positions help night-flying birds find their way. Research the location of the North Star. In your Science Journal, infer how the North Star might help birds fly at night.

2 Teach

Bird Characteristics

Caption Answer

Figure 2 They give the bones strength and support.

Quick Demo

If someone in the class has a pet bird (canary, parakeet, parrot), ask that student to bring the bird to class so its characteristics and behavior may be observed. IS **Visual-Spatial**

Astronomy INTEGRATION

The North Star is located very close to the northern celestial pole, making its position appear relatively fixed. It is one of the brightest stars in the night sky. Because of this, it can be used in navigation.

Reading Check

Answer Many bones are joined; cross braces within hollow bones add strength.

Activity

Organize the class into pairs. Have one student keep time and count while the other holds his or her arms straight out and flaps them up and down. See how many times a student can flap his or her arms in one minute and how long it takes for the student to tire. Explain that just as our leg muscles are well developed for walking, the chest muscles of most birds are well developed for flying. L1
IS **Kinesthetic**

Inclusion Strategies

Learning Disabled Ask students to draw or take pictures of different birds found around school or their homes. They should identify the birds and start a bird diary. Have them note the time of day they saw each bird, its location, and any other interesting observations. L2
IS **Visual-Spatial and Linguistic**

Resource Manager

Chapter Resources Booklet
Transparency Activity, p. 40
Directed Reading for Content Mastery, pp. 17, 18
Note-taking Worksheets, pp. 29–31

Bird Characteristics, continued

Purpose Students use a model to discover how oil helps waterproof bird feathers. L2

LS **Kinesthetic**

Materials two 15-cm x 15-cm pieces of cotton cloth, water, petroleum jelly

Teaching Strategy To minimize the mess made, cover working space with paper towels or newspaper.

Analysis

1. The cloth without the petroleum jelly soaks up the water, but water runs off the jelly-covered cloth.
2. Oil on the feathers repels moisture, keeps the bird dry, and holds in body heat.

Assessment

Oral **Why are waterbirds more likely to preen than birds that live in trees?** Preening puts oil on the feathers and keeps them water-repellent. Use **Performance Assessment in the Science Classroom, p. 89.**

Reading Check

Answer To help maintain a constant body temperature

Mini LAB

Modeling Feather Preening

Procedure

1. Cut two 15-cm × 15-cm pieces of **cotton cloth.**
2. Apply **petroleum jelly** to one piece of the cloth.
3. Wet both pieces of the cloth with **water.**

Analysis

1. Compare the two pieces of cloth after they have been wet. In your **Science Journal,** describe what you observe. Wash your hands.
2. Infer why birds do not have to find shelter from the rain.

Feathers Birds are the only animals that have feathers. Their bodies are covered with two main types of feathers—contour feathers and down feathers. Strong, lightweight **contour feathers** give a bird its coloring and smooth shape. These are also the feathers that a bird uses when flying. The contour feathers on the wings and tail help the bird steer and keep it from spinning out of control.

Have you ever wondered how ducks can swim in a pond on a freezing cold day and keep warm? Soft, fluffy **down feathers** provide an insulating layer next to the skin of adult birds and cover the bodies of young birds. Birds are **endotherms,** meaning they maintain a constant body temperature. Feathers help birds maintain their body temperature, and grow in much the same way as your hair grows. Each feather grows from a microscopic pit in the skin called a follicle (FAHL ih kul). When a feather falls out, a new one grows in its place. As shown in **Figure 3,** the shaft of a feather has many branches called barbs. Each barb has many branches called barbules that give the feather strength.

Reading Check *Why are some young birds covered with down feathers?*

A bird has an oil gland located just above the base of its tail. Using its bill or beak, a bird rubs oil from the gland over its feathers in a process called **preening.** The oil conditions the feathers and helps make them water-repellent.

Figure 3
Down feathers help keep birds warm. Contour feathers are the feathers used for flight.

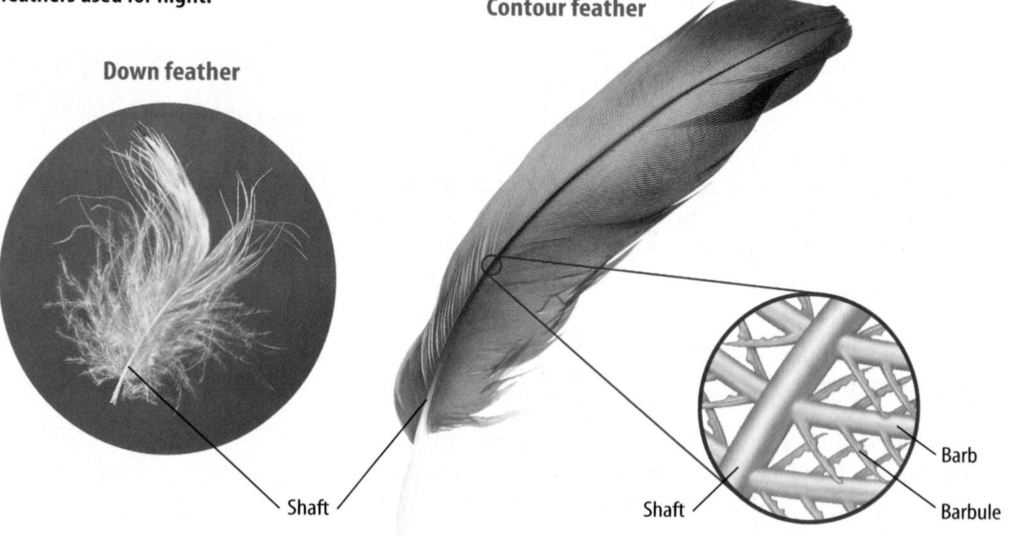

Visual Learning

Figure 3 What differences do you see between down feathers and contour feathers? Contour feathers are larger, with a more rigid shaft, and the barbs are hooked together. Down feathers are smaller, fluffier, and softer. The hairlike filaments are not hooked together, and the shaft is very flexible.

Active Reading

Reflective Journal Have students divide sheets of paper into several columns. Have them record their thoughts about an activity under headings such as "What I did," "What I learned," "What questions I have," "What surprised me," and "Overall response." Have students write a Reflective Journal entry for the MiniLAB on this page.

Figure 4
Wings provide an upward force called lift for birds and airplanes.

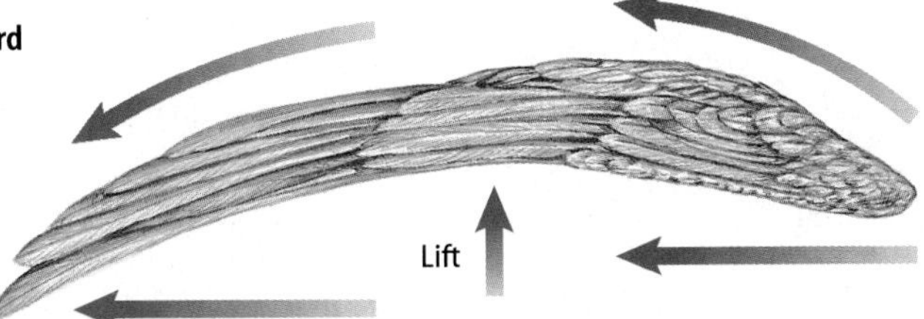

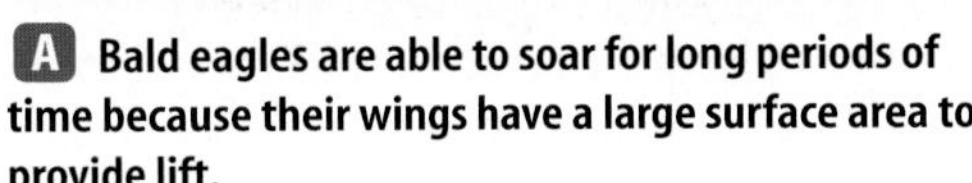
A **Bald eagles are able to soar for long periods of time because their wings have a large surface area to provide lift.**

B **This glider gets lift from its wings the same way a bald eagle gets lift.**

Physics INTEGRATION

Wings Although not all birds fly, most wings are adapted for flight. Wings are attached to powerful chest muscles. By flapping its wings, a bird attains thrust to go forward and lift to stay in the air. Its wings move up and down, as well as back and forth.

The shape of a bird's wings helps it fly. The wings are curved on top and flat or slightly curved on the bottom. Humans copied this shape to make airplane wings, as shown in **Figure 4.** When a bird flies, air moves more slowly across the bottom than across the top of its wings. Slow-moving air has greater pressure than fast-moving air, resulting in an upward push called lift. The amount of lift depends on the total surface area of the wing, the speed at which air moves over the wing, and the angle of the wing to the moving air. Once birds with large wings, such as vultures, reach high altitudes, they can soar and glide for a long time without having to beat their wings.

Wings also serve important functions for birds that don't fly. Penguins are birds that use their wings to swim underwater. Ostriches use their wings in courtship and to maintain their balance while running or walking.

Environmental Science INTEGRATION

Some birds have become pests in urban areas. Research to learn what birds are considered pests in urban areas, what effect they have on the urban environment, and what measures are taken to reduce the problems they create. Build a bulletin board showing your results.

Activity

Have students work in groups to make a paper airplane from a single sheet of paper. Then have them make a second plane from several pieces of paper, attaching separate wings and a tail to the body with transparent tape. Have groups compare the flying abilities of their planes by tossing them across the room. **Which plane stayed airborne longer?** The one made from a single sheet of paper. **Why?** Its frame is more rigid and it is lighter than the other plane. L2 LS **Kinesthetic**

Environmental Science INTEGRATION

Students may cite pigeons, crows, and Canada geese. Measures taken include relocating birds, introducing birds of prey such as falcons, and making loud noises to disturb roosting birds.

Teacher FYI

Elliptical wings are adapted for quick movements. Wings that sweep back and taper to a slender tip provide high speed. Soaring birds have broad wings.

Activity

Have students locate pictures of birds in flight. Ask them to examine the wing shapes to determine the type of flight each is suited for. L2 LS **Visual-Spatial**

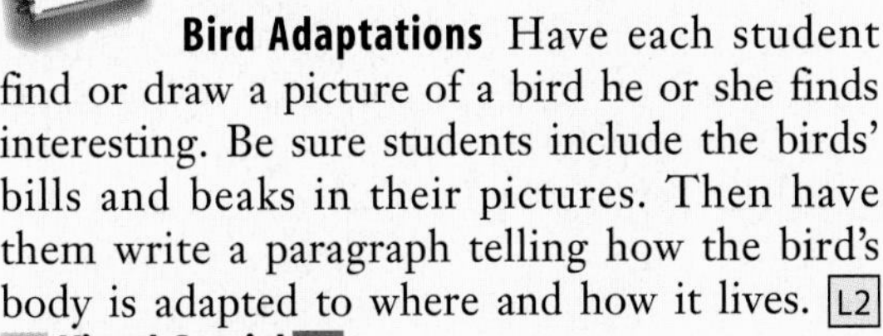

Science Journal

Bird Adaptations Have each student find or draw a picture of a bird he or she finds interesting. Be sure students include the birds' bills and beaks in their pictures. Then have them write a paragraph telling how the bird's body is adapted to where and how it lives. L2 LS **Visual-Spatial** P

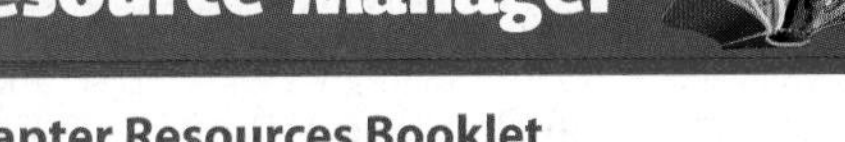

Resource Manager

Chapter Resources Booklet
MiniLAB, p. 3

Home and Community Involvement, p. 27

Body Systems

Activity

Use diagrams to show students the internal and external structures of a bird. Point out the digestive tract, oil gland, and air sacs. Have students make a list of the bird's internal and external characteristics. L2

LS **Visual-Spatial**

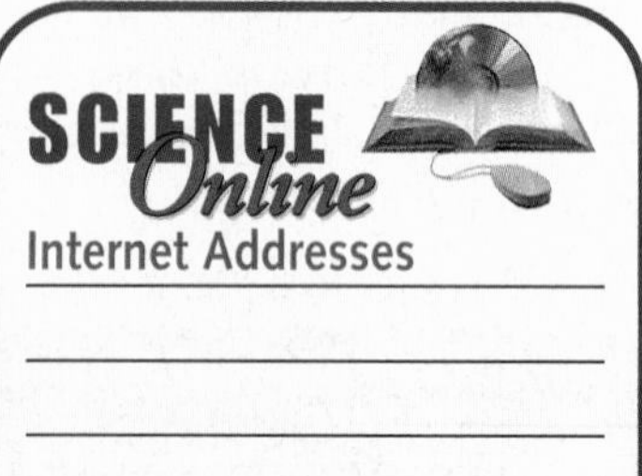

Internet Addresses

Explore the Glencoe Science Web site at **science.glencoe.com** to find out more about topics in this section.

Fun Fact

Because birds use large amounts of energy to fly, the crop and the gizzard help birds obtain maximum energy from food. The crop continuously stores and releases food. The gizzard grinds the food so it can be digested faster.

SCIENCE Online

Research Visit the Glencoe Science Web site at **science.glencoe.com** for information about homing pigeons. Make a poster to illustrate how they are used.

Body Systems

Whether they fly, swim, or run, most birds are extremely active. Their body systems are adapted for these activities.

Digestive System Because flying uses large amounts of energy, birds need large amounts of high energy foods, such as nuts, seeds, nectar, insects, and meat. Food is broken down quickly in the digestive system to supply this energy. In some birds, digestion can take less than an hour—for humans digestion can take more than a day.

From a bird's mouth, unchewed food passes into a digestive organ called the crop. The crop stores the food until it absorbs enough moisture to move on. The food enters the stomach where it is partially digested before it moves into the muscular gizzard. In the gizzard, food is ground and crushed by small stones and grit that the bird has swallowed. Digestion is completed in the intestine, and then the food's nutrients move into the bloodstream.

Figure 5
A bird's blood is circulated quickly so enough oxygen-filled blood is carried to the bird's muscles.

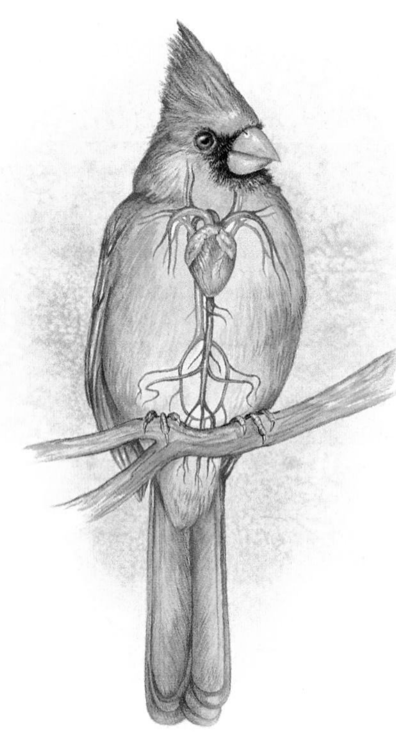

Respiratory System Body heat is generated when energy in food is combined with oxygen. A bird's respiratory system efficiently obtains oxygen, which is needed to power flight muscles and to convert food into energy. Birds have two lungs. Each lung is connected to balloonlike air sacs that reach into different parts of the body, including some of the bones. Most of the air inhaled by a bird passes into the air sacs behind the lungs. When a bird exhales, air with oxygen passes from these air sacs into the lungs. Air flows in only one direction through a bird's lungs. Unlike other vertebrates, birds receive air with oxygen when they inhale and when they exhale. This provides a constant supply of oxygen for the flight muscles.

Circulatory System A bird's circulatory system consists of a heart, arteries, capillaries, and veins, as shown in **Figure 5.** Their four-chambered heart is large compared to their body. On average, a sparrow's heart is 1.68 percent of its body weight. The average human heart is only 0.42 percent of the human's body weight. Oxygen-filled blood is kept separate from carbon dioxide-filled blood as both move through a bird's heart and blood vessels. A bird's heart beats rapidly—an active hummingbird's heart can beat more than 1,000 times per minute.

Resource Manager

Chapter Resources Booklet
Lab Activity, pp. 9–10

Earth Science Critical Thinking/Problem Solving, p. 12

Figure 6
In nature, some birds help control pests and others pollinate flowers. A Owls are birds of prey that hunt small animals, usually at night. B As a hummingbird feeds on a flower's nectar, it may pollinate the flower.

The Importance of Birds

Birds play important roles in nature. Some are sources of food and raw materials, and others are kept as pets. Some birds, like the owl in **Figure 6A,** help control pests, such as destructive rodents. Barn swallows and other birds help keep insect populations in check by eating them. Some birds, like the hummingbird in **Figure 6B,** are pollinators for many flowers. As they feed on the flower's nectar, pollen collects on their feathers and is deposited on the next flower they visit. Other birds eat fruits, then their seeds are dispersed in the birds' droppings. Seed-eating birds help control weeds. Birds can be considered pests when their populations grow too large. In cities where large numbers of birds roost, their droppings can damage buildings. Some droppings also can contain microorganisms that can cause diseases in humans.

Uses of Birds Humans have hunted birds for food and fancy feathers for centuries. Eventually, wild birds such as chickens and turkeys were domesticated and their meat and eggs became a valuable part of human diets. Feathers are used in mattresses and pillows because of their softness and ability to be fluffed over and over. Down feathers are good insulators. Even bird droppings, called guano (GWAH noh), are collected from seabird colonies and used as fertilizer.

Parakeets, parrots, and canaries often are kept as pets because many sing or can be taught to imitate sounds and human voices. Most birds sold as pets are bred in captivity, but some wild birds still are collected illegally, which threatens many species.

Use Science Words

Word Origin Birds belong to the class Aves. *Avis* is the Latin word for bird and is the root of many bird-related words. Ask students to find words with this root and explain their meanings. Aviator—pilot or member of an aircraft crew; avian—relating to birds; aviary—enclosure for breeding and rearing birds

Discussion

What is a disadvantage of being endothermic? It takes more food to maintain body temperature.

The Importance of Birds

Teacher FYI

More than 80 species of birds have become extinct in the last 300 years. Causes of extinction include habitat destruction; collecting bird parts such as feathers, beaks, and talons; illegal pet trade; competition from introduced species; and toxic effects of pesticides, oil spills, and chemical dumping.

Curriculum Connection

History Over 4,000 years ago, humans used pigeons as messengers. The first recorded use of messenger pigeons was in 1200 B.C. by Ramses III, who sent four birds out in different directions with the message that he had taken the throne. Have students research how homing pigeons find their way home. There are two hypotheses—that they use an odor map or navigate by Earth's magnetic field.

Cultural Diversity

Earliest Bird Sankar Chatterjee is best known for his 1986 discovery of *Protoavis*, a 225-million-year-old fossil that may turn out to be the earliest bird known. Have students research the work of Chatterjee.

Visualizing Birds

Have students examine the pictures and read the captions. Then ask the following questions:

How does the shape of the heron's beak help it catch food in its environment? The beak is long and helps it scoop up fish.

Why do seed-eating birds need grasping claws? They need to be able to hook onto tree limbs or hold on to tree bark.

What other adaptation do you think birds of prey must have besides sharp beaks and grasping claws? They must be able to see well so they can spot and track prey, and to fly fast so they can catch prey.

Activity

Have students research bird statistics, naming the birds with the following characteristics:

- Tallest and heaviest: ostrich
- Largest wingspan: Andean condor, albatross, marabou stork
- Earliest known: Archaeopteryx
- Smallest: hummingbird of Cuba
- Fastest: swift
- Fastest diver: peregrine falcon
- Fastest swimmer: penguin
- Largest eyes: ostrich

Have students list in a table or on the board other interesting statistics found.

Extension

Challenge students to consider birds adapted to extreme environments, such as penguins or roadrunners. Have students draw conclusions about the adaptations that allow these birds to survive, then confirm their conclusions with research.

Figure 7

There are almost 9,000 living species of birds. Birds are subdivided into smaller groups based on characteristics such as beak size and shape, foot structure, and diet. Birds belonging to several groups are shown here.

INSECT EATERS This nuthatch has a pointed beak that can pry up bark or bore into wood to find insects.

WATERBIRDS Wood ducks have webbed feet that propel them through the water.

BIRDS OF PREY This osprey has large claws that grasp and a sharp beak that tears flesh.

FLIGHTLESS BIRDS The ostrich evolved in places where there were once few mammal predators. Though they cannot fly, some flightless birds are fast runners.

WADING BIRDS The great blue heron's long legs allow it to walk in shallow water.

SEED EATERS This cardinal's thick, strong beak can crack seeds.

Resource Manager 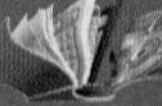

Chapter Resources Booklet

Transparency Activity, pp. 43–44
Reinforcement, p. 25
Enrichment, p. 27

Origin of Birds Birds, like those in **Figure 7,** have some characteristics of reptiles, including scales on their feet and legs. Scientists learn about the origins of most living things by studying their fossils. However, few fossils of birds have been found to study. Some scientists hypothesize that birds developed from reptiles millions of years ago.

Figure 8
A **The first *Archaeopteryx* bones were found more than 100 years ago. *Archaeopteryx* is considered a link between reptiles and birds.**
B ***Protoavis* may be an ancestor of birds.**

Archaeopteryx (ar kee AHP tuh rihks) is the oldest birdlike fossil—about 150 million years old. Although scientists do not think *Archaeopteryx* was a direct ancestor of modern birds, evidence shows that it had feathers and wings similar to today's birds. However, it had solid bones, teeth, a long bony tail, and clawed front toes, like some reptiles.

In 1991 in Texas, scientists discovered an older fossil that shows some characteristics of birds. *Protoavis* (proh toh AY vihs) had two characteristics of birds—hollow bones and a well-developed sternum with a keel. *Protoavis* lived about 225 million years ago. No fossil feathers were found with *Protoavis.* Scientists do not know if this animal was an ancestor of modern birds or a type of ground-living dinosaur. **Figure 8** shows an artist's idea of what *Archaeopteryx* and *Protoavis* may have looked like.

Section  1 Assessment

1. List four characteristics shared by all birds.
2. Explain how a bird's feathers, air sacs, and skeleton are adaptations for flight.
3. What type of feather helps birds maintain their body temperature?
4. Make a network tree concept map that details the characteristics of birds. Use the following terms in your map: *birds, beaks, hollow bones, wings, eggs, adaptations for flight, feathers,* and *air sacs.*
5. **Think Critically** Hypothesize why most birds eat nuts, berries, insects, nectar, or meat, but not grass and leaves.

Skill Builder Activities

6. **Venn Diagram** Using information in this section, draw a Venn diagram in your Science Journal that compares and contrasts the characteristics of birds that fly and birds that do not fly. **For more help, refer to the** Science Skill Handbook.
7. **Communicating** Many expressions mention birds, such as "proud as a peacock" and "wise as an owl." In your Science Journal, make a list of several of these expressions and then decide which are accurate. **For more help, refer to the** Science Skill Handbook.

The Importance of Birds, continued

Discussion

Why are fewer bird fossils found in the fossil record than those of reptiles and mammals? Their small, lightweight bones often disintegrate or are crushed before they can become fossils.

3 Assess

Reteach

Have students work together to develop a plan showing how the area near your school can be made into a more favorable habitat for a specific species of bird. L1 COOP LEARN
LS **Interpersonal**

Challenge

How does the diversity of birds help them survive? Because birds have different adaptations for different environments, they can live all over the world. If they all lived in one place, there would not be enough food or shelter. L2
LS **Logical-Mathematical**

Performance Assess students' abilities to compare and contrast birds native to your area by having them examine pictures that show the birds' beaks and feet. Students can make a model of a hypothetical bird's feet, and describe their bird's lifestyle. Use **Performance Assessment in the Science Classroom,** p.123. P

Answers to Section Assessment

1. Possible answers: endotherms, feathers, lay eggs with a hard shell, nearly hollow bones
2. Contour feathers steer and keep the bird upright. The nearly hollow bones in a bird's skeleton make the bird lighter, as do inflated air sacs, making flight easier.
3. Down feathers provide insulation that helps birds maintain body temperature.
4. The tree should begin with birds, then adaptations for flight (include lightweight bones, feathers, air sacs). Eggs, beaks, and wings should be level with adaptations for flight.
5. Because birds need so much energy, they eat high-energy foods such as nuts and berries.
6. Have students work in pairs to compare diagrams and check answers.
7. Possible answers: "Water off a duck's back" and "eagle eyes" are accurate. Others such as "eats like a bird," "wise as an owl," "happy as a lark," and "crazy as a loon" are inaccurate.

SECTION

Mammals

As You Read

What You'll Learn

- **Identify** the characteristics of mammals and explain how they have enabled mammals to adapt to different environments.
- **Distinguish** among monotremes, marsupials, and placentals.
- **Explain** why many species of mammals are becoming threatened or endangered.

Vocabulary

mammal
mammary gland
omnivore
carnivore
herbivore
monotreme
marsupial
placental
gestation period
placenta
umbilical cord

Why It's Important

Mammals, including humans, have many characteristics in common.

Characteristics of Mammals

You probably can name dozens of mammals, but can you list a few of their common characteristics? **Mammals** are endothermic vertebrates that have hair and produce milk to feed their young, as shown in **Figure 9.** Like birds, mammals care for their young. Mammals can be found almost everywhere on Earth. Each mammal species is adapted to its unique way of life.

Skin and Glands Skin covers and protects the bodies of all mammals. A mammal's skin is an organ that produces hair and in some species, horns, claws, nails, or hooves. The skin also contains different kinds of glands. One type of gland found in all mammals is the mammary gland. Female mammals have **mammary glands** that produce milk for feeding their young. Oil glands produce oil that lubricates and conditions the hair and skin. Sweat glands in some species remove wastes and help keep them cool. Many mammals have scent glands that secrete substances that can mark their territory, attract a mate, or be a form of defense.

Figure 9
Mammals, such as this moose, care for their young after they are born. *How do mammals feed their young?*

SECTION 2

Mammals

1 Motivate

Bellringer Transparency

Display the Section Focus Transparency for Section 2. Use the accompanying Transparency Activity Master. L2 ELL

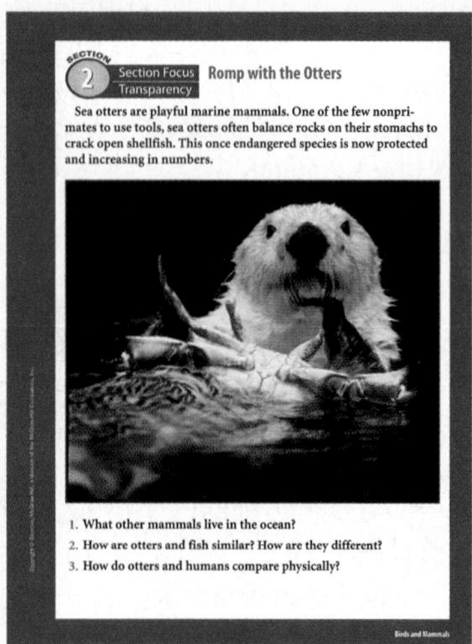

SECTION 2 Section Focus Transparency **Romp with the Otters**

Sea otters are playful marine mammals. One of the few nonprimates to use tools, sea otters often balance rocks on their stomachs to crack open shellfish. This once endangered species is now protected and increasing in numbers.

1. What other mammals live in the ocean?
2. How are otters and fish similar? How are they different?
3. How do otters and humans compare physically?

Birds and Mammals

Tie to Prior Knowledge

Most students will have had a mammal as a pet, or know someone else who has one. Remind them that dogs, cats, mice, rabbits, gerbils, hampsters, and guinea pigs are all mammals. Have students brainstorm characteristics these animals have in common. Possible answers: fur, four limbs for movement, reproduce live offspring, nurse their young

Caption Answer

Figure 9 with milk produced by the female's mammary glands

Section *Assessment* Planner

PORTFOLIO
Assessment, p. 442

PERFORMANCE ASSESSMENT
Try at Home MiniLAB, p. 442
Skill Builder Activities, p. 448
See page 456 for more options.

CONTENT ASSESSMENT
Section, p. 448
Challenge, p. 448
Chapter, pp. 456–457

Figure 10
Mammals have teeth that are shaped specifically for the food they eat.

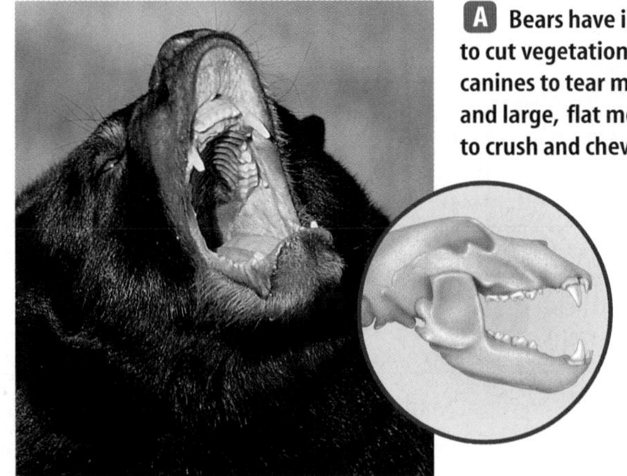

A Bears have incisors to cut vegetation, canines to tear meat, and large, flat molars to crush and chew food.

B A tiger easily can tear away the flesh of an animal because of large, sharp canine teeth and strong jaw muscles.

C A horse's back teeth, called molars, are large. *Infer how a horse chews.*

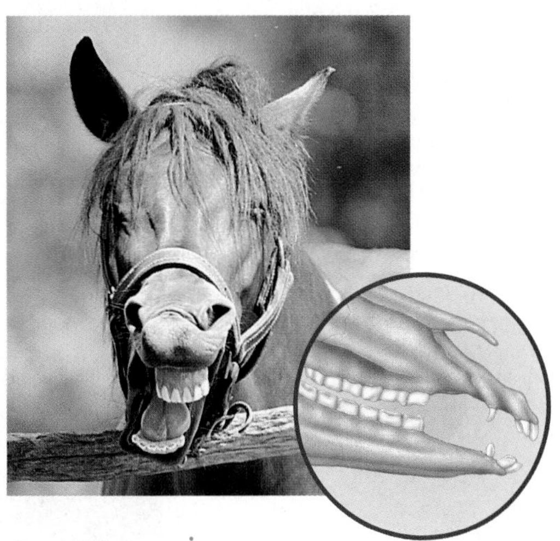

Teeth Notice that each mammal in **Figure 10** has different kinds of teeth. Almost all mammals have specialized teeth. Scientists can determine a mammal's diet by examining its teeth. Front teeth, called incisors, bite and cut. Sometimes the teeth next to the incisors, called canine teeth, are well developed to grip and tear. Premolars and molars at the back of the mouth shred, grind, and crush. Some animals, like the bear in **Figure 10A,** and humans, have all four kinds of teeth. They eat plants and other animals, so they are called **omnivores.** A **carnivore,** like the tiger in **Figure 10B,** has large canine teeth and eats only the flesh of other animals. **Herbivores,** such as the horse in **Figure 10C,** eat only plants. Their large premolars and molars grind the tough fibers in plants.

2 Teach

Characteristics of Mammals

Caption Answer

Figure 10C Horses use molars for grinding grasses.

Quick Demo

If someone in your class has a pet gerbil, hamster, or guinea pig, have that student bring the pet to class for a day. Have students observe its characteristics and behavior and record their observations. LS **Visual-Spatial**

Activity

Obtain models or pictures that show the teeth of mammals that eat different foods. A veterinarian might be a source of these models. Have students identify the incisors, canines, premolars, and molars on each model. L2 LS **Visual-Spatial**

IDENTIFYING Misconceptions

Students may not think of themselves as mammals. To help them realize that humans are classified as mammals, list the specific characteristics of mammals on the chalkboard. Include *endothermic, hair, mammary glands, oil glands, sweat glands, specialized teeth,* and *well-developed body systems* in the list. Invite volunteers to circle each characteristic possessed by humans.

Inclusion Strategies

Learning Disabled Display a wall map of the world. Ask students to affix drawings and magazine pictures of mammals to the map to show where each mammal is commonly found. Students can visit a local zoo to take pictures of mammals to add to the map. L1 LS **Visual-Spatial**

Resource Manager

Chapter Resources Booklet
Transparency Activity, p. 41
Directed Reading for Content Mastery, pp. 19, 20

Cultural Diversity, p. 9

Characteristics of Mammals, continued

Purpose Students model how fat insulates an animal. L1 ELL IS **Kinesthetic**

Materials 2 self-sealing plastic bags, vegetable shortening, bowl of ice water

Teaching Strategy Have students hold the hand in the blubber mitten under the ice water, and time how long it takes for the cold to penetrate. Point out that real blubber insulates from cold indefinitely.

Analysis

1. the hand that is bare
2. Blubber is an insulator—it traps air and protects against cold.

Assessment

Performance Ask students to design and carry out an experiment comparing the insulating properties of polyester batting and plastic foam peanuts. Use **PASC**, p. 95. P

Inferring How Blubber Insulates

Procedure

1. Fill a **self-sealing plastic bag** about one-third full with **vegetable shortening.**
2. Turn another self-sealing plastic bag inside out. Carefully place it inside the bag with the shortening so that you are able to seal one bag to the other. This is a blubber mitten.
3. Put your hand in the blubber mitten and place it in **ice water** for 5 s. Remove the blubber mitten when finished.
4. Put your bare hand in the same bowl of ice water for 5 s.

Analysis

1. Which hand seemed colder?
2. Infer how a layer of blubber provides protection against cold water.

Hair All mammals have hair on their bodies at some time during their lives. It may be thick fur that covers all or part of the animal's body. Fur traps air and helps keep the animal warm. Whales have almost no hair. They rely on a thick layer of fat under their skin, called blubber, to keep them warm. Porcupine quills and hedgehog spines are modified hairs that offer protection from predators. Whiskers located near the mouth of many mammals help them sense their environment.

Body Systems

The body systems of mammals are adapted to their activities and enable them to survive in many environments.

Mammals have four-chambered hearts that pump oxygen-filled blood directly throughout the body in blood vessels. Mammals have lungs made of millions of microscopic sacs. These sacs increase the lungs' surface area, allowing a greater exchange of carbon dioxide and oxygen.

A mammal's nervous system consists of a brain, spinal cord, and nerves. In mammals, the part of the brain involved in learning, problem solving, and remembering is larger than in other animals. Another large part of the mammal brain controls its muscle coordination.

The digestive systems of mammals vary according to the kinds of food they eat. Herbivores, like the one shown in **Figure 11,** have long digestive tracts compared to carnivores because plants take longer to digest than meat does.

Figure 11
Herbivores, like this elk, have four-chambered stomachs and long intestinal tracts that contain microorganisms, which help break down the plant material.

LAB DEMONSTRATION

Purpose to compare mammal hair

Materials samples of mammal hair (from humans, dogs, cats, gerbils, horses, and so on); glycerin, projecting microscope, microscope slides, cover slips

Preparation Place a drop of glycerin on each slide, add the animal hair, then the coverslip.

Procedure Project the hairs under low and high power. Students should draw what they see and write brief descriptions.

Expected Outcome Students observe differences in the hair of different mammals.

Assessment

How are the hairs of various mammals alike? All mammal hairs have layers and are covered by lines, blocks, or surface scales. **How are they different?** The layers have different thicknesses and different shaped lines cutting through, or no lines at all.

Reproduction and Caring for Young All mammals reproduce sexually. Most mammals give birth to live young after a period of development inside the female reproductive organ called the uterus. Many mammals are nearly helpless, and sometimes even blind, when they are born. They can't care for themselves for the first several days or even years. If you've seen newborn kittens or human babies, you know they just eat, sleep, grow, and develop. However, the young of some mammals, such as antelope, deer, and elephants, are well developed at birth and are able to travel with their constantly moving parents. These young mammals usually can stand by the time they are a few minutes old. Marine mammals, such as dolphins and whales, as shown in **Figure 12,** can swim as soon as they are born.

Is a house cat or a deer more developed at birth?

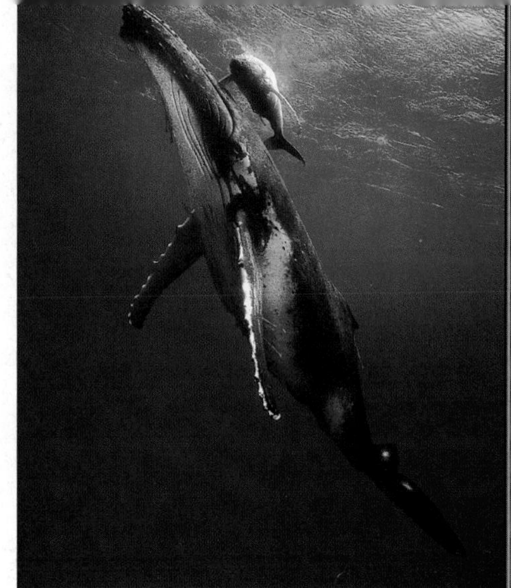

Figure 12
When a whale is born, the female whale must quickly push the newborn whale to the water's surface to breathe. Otherwise, the newborn whale will drown.

During the time that young mammals are dependent on their female parent's milk, they learn many of the skills needed for survival. Defensive skills are learned while playing with other young of their own kind. In most mammal species, only females raise the young. However, males of some species, such as wolves and humans, help provide shelter, food, and protection for their young.

Problem-Solving Activity

Does a mammal's heart rate determine how long it will live?

Some mammals live long lives, but other mammals live for only a few years. Do you think that a mammal's life span might be related to how fast its heart beats? Use your ability to interpret a data table to answer this question.

Mammal Heart Rates and Life Spans

Mammal	Heart Rate	Life Span
Mouse	400	2
Large dog	80	15
Bear	40	15-20
Elephant	25	75

Identifying the Problem

The table on the right lists the average heart rates and life spans of several different mammals. Heart rate is recorded as the number of heartbeats per minute, and life span is recorded as the average maximum years. When you examine the data, look for a relationship between the two variables.

Solving the Problem

1. Infer how heart rate and life span are related in mammals.
2. Humans have heart rates of about 70 beats per minute. Some humans may live for more than 100 years. Is this consistent with the data in the table? Explain.

Body Systems

Teacher FYI

Some birds and mammals have developed unique mutualistic relationships. Ostriches and gazelles feed near each other. Both watch for predators and can alert each other to an approaching predator. Their visual abilities differ, so each benefits from the other species' watchfulness.

Reading Check

Answer A deer is more developed, enabling it to travel with its constantly-moving parents.

Problem-Solving Activity

National Math Standards

Correlation to Mathematics Objectives
5–10

Answers
1. The greater the heart rate, the shorter the life span.
2. No; humans have advanced technology and medical procedures that extend their lifespan.

Use an Analogy

Mammals are endotherms. In the case of animals, respiration and oxidation of food are similar to the burning of fuel in a furnace to produce energy. Have students breathe onto their hands and observe that their breath is warm. L1

Science Journal

Mammal Communication Have each student choose a different mammal and investigate how the mammal communicates. Encourage students to write reports in their Science Journals that include information on both auditory signals and body language used by the mammal. L2 IS **Linguistic**

Resource Manager 

Chapter Resources Booklet
MiniLAB, p. 4

Mathematics Skill Activities, p. 7

Types of Mammals

Teacher FYI

Monotremes and marsupials make up only five percent of all mammals. Three species of monotremes—the duck-billed platypus and two species of echidnas—exist today. Monotremes live in Australia and on its nearby islands in a wide range of habitats.

Caption Answer

Figure 13 It has mammary glands.

Discussion

What advantages do the developing young marsupials have compared with the developing young monotremes? The developing young marsupials are protected in the female parent's pouch. The young monotremes are left alone while the parents seek food, making them more vulnerable to predators.

Teacher FYI

Monotreme eggs are flexible and leathery, like the eggs of reptiles, not hard and smooth like bird eggs. Female monotremes incubate their eggs. Platypuses often curl up around their eggs. Echidnas carry their eggs around with them in a pouch that develops only during breeding season.

Figure 13
A duck-billed platypus is a mammal, yet it lays eggs.
Why is it classified as a mammal?

Types of Mammals

Mammals are classified into three groups based on how their young develop. The three mammal groups are monotremes (MAHN uh treemz), marsupials (mar SEW pee ulz), and placentals (pluh SENT ulz).

Monotremes The duck-billed platypus, shown in **Figure 13,** is a monotreme. **Monotremes** are mammals that lay eggs with leathery shells. The female incubates the eggs for about ten days. After the young hatch, they nurse by licking the female's skin and hair where milk oozes from the mammary glands. Monotreme mammary glands do not have nipples.

Marsupials Many of the mammals that are classified as marsupials live in Australia, New Guinea, or South America. Only one type of marsupial, the opossum, lives in North America. **Marsupials** give birth to immature young that usually crawl into an external pouch on the female's abdomen. However, not all marsupials have pouches. Whether an immature marsupial is in a pouch or not, it instinctively crawls to a nipple. It stays attached to the nipple and feeds until it is developed. In pouched marsupials, the developed young return to the pouch for feeding and protection. Examples of marsupials are kangaroos and opossums, as shown in **Figure 14,** wallabies, koalas, bandicoots, and Tasmanian devils.

Figure 14
A Opossums are the only marsupials found in North America. B A joey, or young kangaroo, returns to its mother's pouch when danger is near.

Curriculum Connection

Language Arts Asian elephants, apes, pandas, manatees, dolphins, and rhinos are a few mammals that are likely to become extinct within 50 years due to poaching and destruction of habitat. Have students bring articles from recent newspapers and science magazines about the exploitation of mammals and the conservation efforts to save them. They can make a presentation of their findings to the class. L2

Inclusion Strategies

Hearing Impaired Place illustrations of the three types of mammals in the room for students to observe. Caption illustrations with simple, definitive sentences such as *monotremes lay eggs, most marsupials have pouches, and placentals give birth to developed young.* L1 ELL LS **Visual-Spatial**

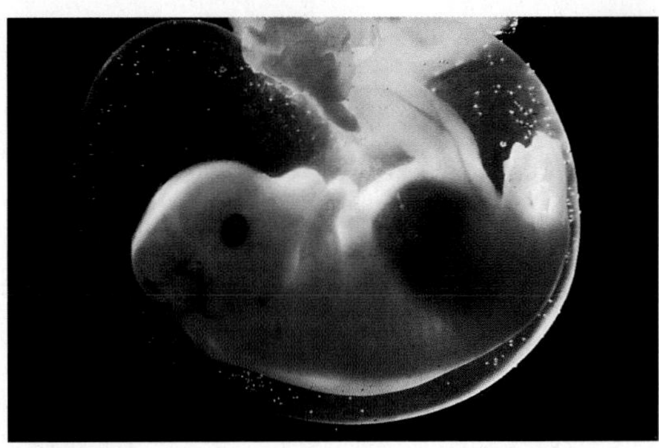

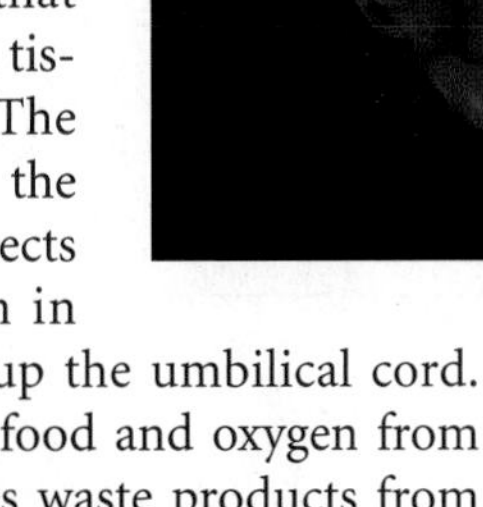

Figure 15
An unborn mammal receives nutrients and oxygen through the umbilical cord.

Placentals In **placentals,** embryos completely develop inside the female's uterus. The time during which the embryo develops in the uterus is called the **gestation period.** Gestation periods range from 16 days in hamsters to 650 days in elephants. Placentals are named for the **placenta,** an organ that develops from tissues of the embryo and tissues that line the inside of the uterus. The placenta absorbs oxygen and food from the mother's blood. An umbilical cord connects the embryo to the placenta, as shown in **Figure 15.** Several blood vessels make up the umbilical cord. Blood in the **umbilical cord** transports food and oxygen from the placenta to the embryo and removes waste products from the embryo. The female parent's blood doesn't mix with the embryo's blood. Examples of placentals are shown in **Table 1** on the following two pages.

Reading Check *How does an embryo receive the things it needs to grow?*

Some placental groups include unusual animals such as the manatee shown in **Figure 16.** Dugongs and manatees are aquatic mammals. They have no back legs, and their front legs are modified into flippers. Another group includes small, rabbitlike animals called hyraxes that have hooves and molars for grinding vegetation. The aardvark is the only member of its group. Aardvarks have tubelike teeth and dig termites for food. Many Southeast Asian islands are home to members of a group that includes gliding lemurs. Pangolins, another group of placentals, look like anteaters covered with scales.

SCIENCE Online

Research Visit the Glencoe Science Web site at **science.glencoe.com** for recent news or magazine articles about manatees and their habitats. Communicate to your class what you learn.

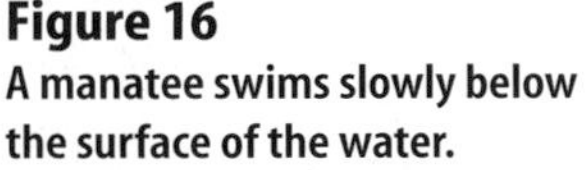

Figure 16
A manatee swims slowly below the surface of the water.

Extension

Have students research and report on gestation periods of mammals and the average number of offspring born to different species. Some gestation periods are: opossum—12 days; hamster—16 to 37 days; mouse—20 to 30 days; rabbit—30 days; dog—53 to 71 days; cat—52 days; guinea pig—63 days; human—266 days; cow—238 days; horse—340 days; giraffe—453 to 464 days; and Asian elephant—609 to 760 days.

Reading Check

Answer The umbilical cord transports food and oxygen from the placenta to the embryo.

SCIENCE Online

Internet Addresses

Explore the Glencoe Science Web site at **science.glencoe.com** to find out more about topics in this section.

Discussion

Is there a connection between the size of mammals and their gestation periods? Generally, the gestation periods of larger species are longer than those of smaller species. An exception to this rule are tigers, lions, and other large cats, who have average gestation period of 3.5 months, shorter that that of a domestic sheep.

Curriculum Connection

Geography Mammals first appeared during the Jurassic period, and diversified during the Cenozoic Era. Monotremes and marsupials developed in Australia and South America; placentals dominated North America. When North and South America joined, placentals spread southward. Australia remained separate and has a diverse population of monotremes and marsupials. Have students locate these areas on a world map. L1

Resource Manager

Chapter Resources Booklet

Enrichment, p. 28
Reinforcement, p. 26

Types of Mammals, continued

Make a Model

Have students make a mobile that shows the orders of placentals they have studied. L1 ELL **LS Kinesthetic**

Activity

Have students keep records of every placental they see for a period of three days. Then have them classify the mammals according to order. L2 **LS Logical-Mathematical**

Discussion

In what ways do retractable claws help lions and other cats to survive? They use their claws to climb trees and hold prey. The claws can be retracted, enabling the animals to walk and run faster.

IDENTIFYING Misconceptions

Students may think that camels store water in their humps. In reality, the humps contain fat, which provides energy and, when oxidized, can manufacture water. This fat helps camels survive in the desert where food and water are scarce.

Table 1 Placentals

Order	Examples	Major Characteristics
Rodentia (roh DEN chuh)	beavers, mice, rats, squirrels	one pair of chisel-like front teeth adapted for gnawing; incisors grow throughout life; herbivores
Chiroptera (ki RAHP tuh ruh)	bats	front limbs adapted for flying; active at night; different species feed on fruit, insects, fish, or other bats
Insectivora (ihn sek TIHV uh ruh)	moles, shrews, hedgehogs	small; feed on insects, earthworms, and other small animals; most have long skulls and narrow snouts; high metabolic rate
Carnivora (kar NIHV uh ruh)	cats, dogs, bears, foxes, raccoons	long, sharp canine teeth for tearing flesh; most are predators, some are omnivores
Primates (PRI maytz)	apes, monkeys, humans	arms with grasping hands and opposable thumbs; eyes are forward facing; large brains; omnivores
Artiodactyla (artee oh DAHK tih luh)	deer, moose, pigs, camels, giraffes, cows	hooves with an even number of toes; most are herbivores with large, flat molars; complex stomachs and intestines

Resource Manager

Reading and Writing Skill Activities, pp. 5, 15, 51

Life Science Critical Thinking/Problem Solving, p. 3

Teacher FYI

Examples of hibernating mammals include certain bats, echidnas, chipmunks, and woodchucks. Most scientists do not consider bears to be true hibernators because their body temperature drops only slightly. Bears go into a state called *torpor.*

Order	Examples	Major Characteristics
Cetacea (sih TAY shuh)	whales, dolphins, porpoises	one or two blowholes on top of the head for breathing; forelimbs are modified into flippers; teeth or baleen
Lagomorpha (lag uh MOR fuh)	rabbits, hares, pikas	some with long hind legs adapted for jumping and running; one pair of large, upper incisors; one pair of small, peglike incisors
Pinnipedia (pihn nih PEE dee uh)	sea lions, seals, walruses	marine carnivores; limbs modified for swimming
Edentata (ee dehn TAH tuh)	anteaters, sloths, armadillos	eat insects and other small animals; most are toothless or have tiny, peglike teeth
Perissodactyla (puh ris oh DAHK tih luh)	horses, zebras, tapirs, rhinoceroses	hooves with an odd number of toes; skeletons adapted for running; herbivores with large, grinding molars
Proboscidea (proh boh SIHD ee uh)	elephants	a long nose called a trunk; herbivores; upper incisor teeth grow to form tusks; thick, leathery skin

Visual Learning

Table 1 **Look at this table and name each animal's order. Which mammals are plant-eaters with legs adapted for running and jumping?** *Lagomorpha* **Which order has hooves with one or three toes and skeletons adapted for running?** *Perissodactyla* **Which order has blowholes for breathing?** *Cetacea* **Which mammals have front limbs adapted for flying and are most active at night?** *Chiroptera* **Which mammals have long, sharp canine teeth for tearing flesh?** *Carnivora*

Extension

Have students discuss the definition of "intelligence." Then explain that dolphins are surpassed in cerebrum-to-body mass ratio only by humans and chimpanzees. Have students research current studies investigating the intelligence of dolphins and share their findings in an oral report to the class. They should include a definition of intelligence in their reports.

Teacher FYI

Armadillos are the only members of the order *Edentata* that live in the United States. The armadillo's most distinguishing feature is its hardened skin, which is arranged in a pattern of six or nine bands around its body. The tough bands act like an armor to protect the animal from predators.

IDENTIFYING Misconceptions

Some students may think that elephants are the largest animals living today. It is true that elephants are the largest *land* animals. However, many whale species are much larger than the largest elephants. The largest elephants weigh 6,000 kg (13,000 pounds). The largest whales weigh 135,000 kg (300,000 pounds). Blue whales are the largest whales, and in fact are the largest animal to have ever lived—much larger than dinosaurs, a misconception some students may have.

Importance of Mammals

Text Question Answer

Answers may include advocating stricter hunting laws, changing to a vegetarian diet, and recycling.

3 Assess

Reteach

Label 3 x 5 cards with mammal characteristics. Have each student take a card, read the characteristics aloud, and classify the mammal described as a monotreme, marsupial, or placental. L1 LS **Logical-Mathematical**

Challenge

Have students debate which type of mammalian reproductive pattern is most successful. All strategies are successful, as they enable the species to survive. However, because the young of placental mammals are more developed when born, they may have a better chance of surviving. Accept all reasonable answers. L3

Assessment

Performance Have students make a model of a hypothetical mammal and explain how it is adapted to its environment. Use **PASC,** p. 123.

Importance of Mammals

Mammals, like other organisms, are important in maintaining a balance in the environment. Carnivores, such as lions, help control populations of other animals. Bats help pollinate flowers and control insects. Other mammals pick up plant seeds in their fur and distribute them. However, mammals and other animals are in trouble today. As millions of wildlife habitats are destroyed for shopping centers, recreational areas, housing, and roads, many mammals are left without food, shelter, and space to survive. Because humans have the ability to reason, they have a responsibility to learn that their survival is related closely to the survival of all mammals. What can you do to protect the mammals in your community?

Origin of Mammals About 65 million years ago, dinosaurs and many other organisms became extinct. This opened up new habitats for mammals, and they began to branch out into many different species. Some of these species gave rise to modern mammals. Today, more than 4,000 species of mammals have evolved from animals similar to the one in **Figure 17,** which lived about 200 million years ago.

Figure 17
The Dvinia was an ancestor of mammals.

Section 2 Assessment

1. Describe five characteristics of all mammals and explain how they allow mammals to survive in different environments.
2. Differentiate among placentals, monotremes, and marsupials.
3. Name three ways in which mammals and birds are similar. Name three ways in which they are different.
4. Compare herbivores to omnivores.
5. **Think Critically** How have humans contributed to the decrease in many wildlife populations?

Skill Builder Activities

6. **Classifying** Classify the following animals into the three mammal groups: *whales, koalas, horses, elephants, opossums, kangaroos, rabbits, bats, bears, platypuses,* and *monkeys.* Compare and contrast their characteristics. **For more help, refer to the Science Skill Handbook.**
7. **Solving One-Step Equations** The tallest land mammal is the giraffe at 5.6 m. Calculate your height in meters and determine how many of you it would take to be as tall as the giraffe. **For more help, refer to the Math Skill Handbook.**

Answers to Section Assessment

1. Hair, four-chambered hearts, well-developed lungs, relatively large brains, and functional mammary glands; these characteristics allow them to adapt to many environments.
2. In placentals, embryos develop inside the female's uterus; marsupials give birth to immature offspring that develop in their pouches; monotremes lay and incubate eggs.
3. Similar: endothermic, reproduce sexually, have an endoskeleton; mammals have hair, mammary glands, and most produce live young; birds have feathers and wings and lay eggs.
4. Both eat plants; omnivores also eat other organisms besides plants.
5. Answers will vary, but may include hunting, deforestation, and so on.
6. Placental—horses, elephants, rabbits, bats, bears, monkeys, whales; marsupials—koalas, opossums, kangaroos; monotremes—platypuses. In a table, have students compare and contrast habitat, reproduction, nutrition, and locomotion for these animals.
7. If a student is about 1.5 m tall, it would take four students to equal the height of a giraffe.

Activity

Mammal Footprints

Have you ever seen an animal footprint in the snow or soft soil? In this activity, you will observe pictures of mammal footprints and identify the mammal that made the footprint.

What You'll Investigate

How do mammal footprints differ?

Materials

diagram of footprints

Goals

- **Identify** mammal footprints.
- **Predict** where mammals live based on their footprints.

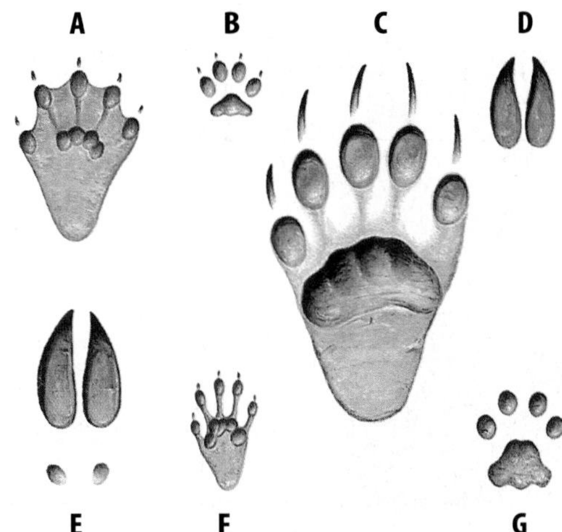

Procedure

1. Copy the following data table in your Science Journal.

Identifying Mammal Footprints		
Animal	**Letter of Footprint**	**Traits of Footprint**
Bear	C	
Beaver	A	
Cougar	G	Answers
Coyote	B	will
Deer	D	vary
Moose	E	
Raccoon	F	

2. Compare and contrast the different mammal footprints in the above diagram.
3. Based on your observations, match each footprint to an animal listed in the first column of the data table.
4. **Write** your answers in the column labeled Letter of Footprint. Complete the data table.

Conclude and Apply

1. Which mammals have hoofed feet?
2. Which mammals have clawed toes?
3. Which mammals have webbed feet?
4. **Explain** how the different feet are adapted to the areas in which these different mammals live.
5. What are the differences between track **B** and track **E**? How does that help you identify the track?

Communicating Your Data

Compare your conclusions with those of other students in your class. **For more help, refer to the Science Skill Handbook.**

Activity

BENCH TESTED

Purpose Students observe how mammal footprints differ. L2 COOP LEARN LS **Naturalist**

Process Skills observing, predicting, comparing and contrasting, inferring

Time Required 50 minutes

Teaching Strategy Have students use reference materials to help them identify the footprints. Students may think that cougars do not have claws because claws don't show in the footprint. Point out that cougars have retractable claws that they use for capturing prey and climbing. Use this as an opportunity to talk about how making a simple visual observation may be misleading and that collecting further data is sometimes necessary to reach the right conclusion.

Answers to Questions

1. deer, moose
2. coyote, bear, raccoon, beaver
3. beaver
4. Beavers use their webbed feet to swim. Deer and moose live in open, flat areas where hooves help them run. Coyotes, bears, and raccoons use their claws to dig; bears and raccoons climb trees.
5. B is an animal with paw pads and claws. E is an animal with split hooves. The size and shape of the prints help you identify the animal that left them.

Assessment

Performance Have students choose another characteristic of mammals, such as their teeth, and describe how these adaptations help them to survive. Use **Performance Assessment in the Science Classroom,** p. 89.

P

Resource Manager

Chapter Resources Booklet

Activity Worksheet, pp. 5–6

Lab Activity, pp. 11–14

Science Inquiry Labs, p. 37

Communicating Your Data

Students should discuss why their conclusions did or did not agree. They can cite their references to support their arguments.

Activity

BENCH TESTED

Recognize the Problem

Internet Students use Internet sites that can be accessed through the Glencoe Science Web site at **science.glencoe.com.** They observe birds in their neighborhoods.

Non-Internet Sources Collect materials about local birds from nature centers.

Time Required

one week to one month

Preparation

Internet Access the Glencoe Science Web site at **science.glencoe.com** to run through the steps that the students will follow.

Non-Internet Collect field guides and other materials about birds found in your area.

Form a Hypothesis

Possible Hypotheses

Students hypotheses may focus on the types of beaks most commonly observed. For example, birds with small beaks are seen most often eating from the bird feeder.

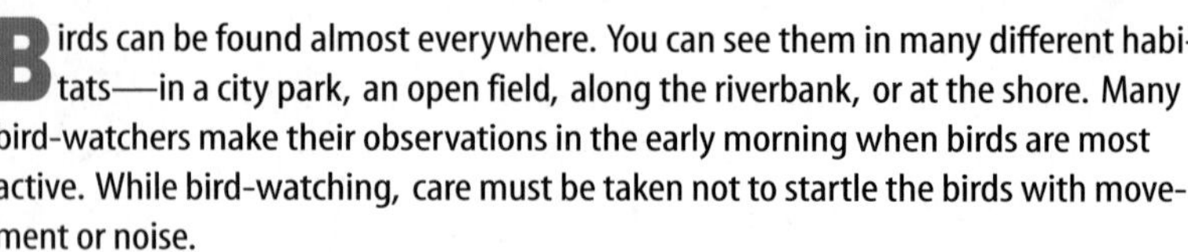

Bird Counts

American Goldfinch

Birds can be found almost everywhere. You can see them in many different habitats—in a city park, an open field, along the riverbank, or at the shore. Many bird-watchers make their observations in the early morning when birds are most active. While bird-watching, care must be taken not to startle the birds with movement or noise.

It's simple to bird-watch. You can attract birds at home or at a school by filling a bird feeder with birdseed and placing it in sight of a window.

Recognize the Problem

What is the most common bird in your neighborhood?

Form a Hypothesis

Think about the types of birds that you observe around your neighborhood. What types of food do they eat? Do all birds come to a bird feeder? Form a hypothesis about the type of bird that you think you will see most often at your bird feeder.

Cardinal

Black-capped Chickadee

Goals

- **Research** how to build a bird feeder and attract birds to it.
- **Observe** the types of birds that visit your feeder.
- **Identify** the types of birds that you observe at your bird feeder.
- **Graph** your results and then communicate them to other students.

Data Source

SCIENCE*Online* Go to the Glencoe Science Web site at **science.glencoe.com** for more information about how to build a bird feeder, hints on bird-watching, and data from other students who do this activity.

Safety Precautions

Resource Manager

Chapter Resources Booklet
Activity Worksheet, pp. 7–8

Lab Management and Safety, p. 37

Internet Addresses

Explore the Glencoe Science Web site at **science.glencoe.com** to find out more about topics in this activity.

Test Your Hypothesis

Plan

1. **Research** general information about how to attract and identify birds. Determine where you will make your observations.
2. **Search** reference sources to find out how to build a bird feeder. Do all birds eat the same types of seeds?
3. What variables can you control in this activity? For what length of time will you make your observations? Do seasonal changes or weather conditions affect your observations?
4. What will you do to identify the birds that you do not know?

Do

1. Make sure your teacher approves your plan before you start.
2. **Record** your data in your Science Journal each time you make an observation of the birds at your bird feeder.

Birds at a feeder

Analyze Your Data

1. **Write** a description of where you placed your feeder and when you made your bird observations.
2. **Record** the total number of birds you observed each day.
3. **Record** the total number of each type of bird species you observed each day.
4. **Graph** your data using a line graph, a circle graph, or a bar graph.

Draw Conclusions

1. What type of bird was most common to your feeder?
2. Did all of your classmates' data agree with yours? Why or why not?
3. Review your classmates' data and determine if the location of bird observations affected the number of birds observed.
4. Did the time of day affect the number of birds observed? Explain.
5. Many birds eat great numbers of insects. Infer what humans might do to maintain a healthy environment for birds.

Communicating Your Data

SCIENCE Online Find this *Use the Internet* activity on the Glencoe Science Web site at **science. glencoe.com.** Post your data in the table provided. **Compare** your data to those of other students. Combine your data with those of other students and **plot** the combined data on a map to recognize patterns in bird populations.

Test Your Hypothesis

Teaching Strategies

Have field guides handy for students to use near the place where they conduct their bird observations.

Analyze Your Data

1. Students should include information about nearby structures, bushes, and trees.
2. Suggest students devise a table for recording the data requested in questions 2 and 3.
4. Students may wish to make a bar graph summarizing the number of birds observed each day. Line graphs of individual species observed could also be devised. Circle graphs could be made to represent the percentage of each species observed over the course of the activity.

Draw Conclusions

1. Answers will vary. Have students describe birds' appearances in their journals.
2. Answers will vary. Data may vary because of the amount of time spent observing birds.
3. Location will likely affect the number of birds observed.
4. More birds may be observed during morning hours.
5. Possible answer: by reducing amounts of insecticides used

Assessment

Portfolio Have students make field guides for the birds they observed. In their guides, they should describe markings, beak shapes, types of food eaten, and other unique characteristics of the observed birds. Use **Performance Assessment in the Science Classroom,** p. 129.

Communicating Your Data

Have students prepare a written report that describes their findings. Include information such as days and times of observations, weather conditions, and numbers of birds counted. If they combine their data with other classes, have them add conclusions about the density and location of bird populations.

Science Stats

Content Background

Bird eggs have many adaptations that help them survive until they hatch. For example, the color of bird's eggs helps to camouflage the eggs to avoid predation. The shape of a particular species' eggs can give clues about where the nests are found. Eggs with a pointed end are common in birds that nest on ledges. These eggs tend to roll in circles when disturbed, keeping the eggs from rolling off the ledge. Other eggs have a texture that is adapted to the environment in which they are found. For example, certain species of ducks lay eggs with a greasy, water-repellent coating.

Discussion

Why must ostrich eggs be able to support a weight equal to that of an adult human? Students should infer that the ostrich that sits on the eggs to incubate them weighs about the same amount as a human adult.

Activity

Have students work in pairs to research the incubation period of the eggs of four different species of birds. Students should display their findings in a bar graph and share their graphs with the class.

Science Stats

Eggciting Facts

Did you know...

...The ostrich lays the biggest egg of all birds now living. Its egg is 15 cm to 20 cm long and 10 cm to 15 cm wide. The volume of the ostrich egg is about equal to 24 chicken eggs. It can have a mass from approximately 1 kg to a little more than 2 kg. The shell of an ostrich egg is 1.5 mm thick and can support the weight of an adult human.

Ostrich egg

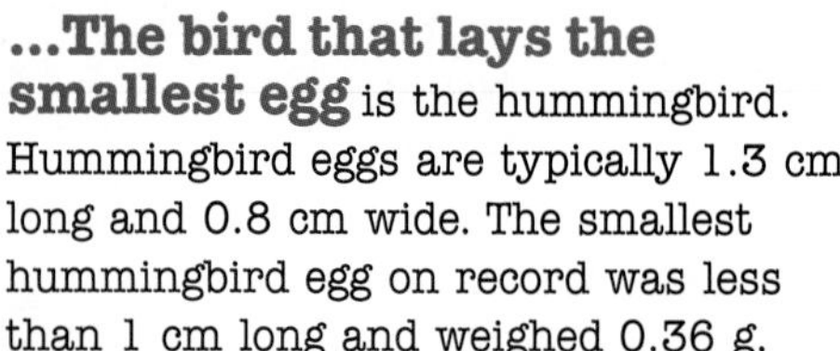

...The bird that lays the smallest egg is the hummingbird. Hummingbird eggs are typically 1.3 cm long and 0.8 cm wide. The smallest hummingbird egg on record was less than 1 cm long and weighed 0.36 g.

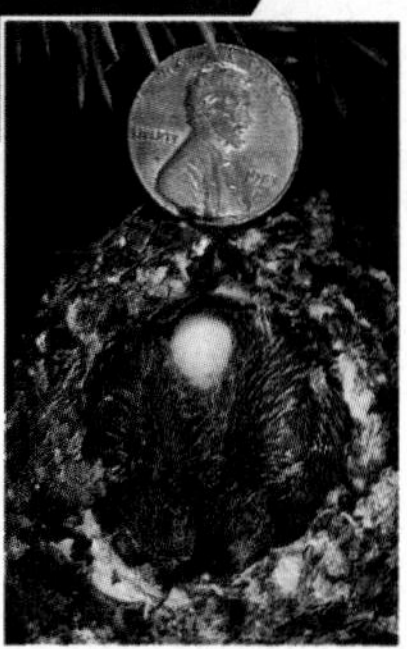

Hummingbird egg and nest

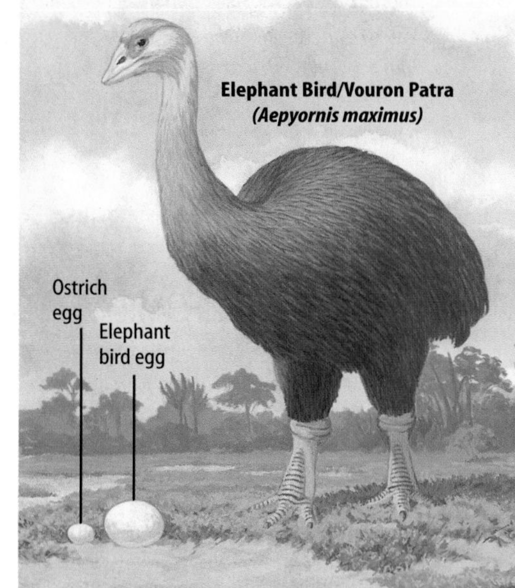

...The elephant bird, extinct within the last 1,000 years, laid an egg that was seven times larger than an ostrich egg. These eggs weighed about 12 kg. They were 30 cm long and could hold up to 8.5 L of liquid. It could hold the equivalent of 12,000 hummingbird eggs.

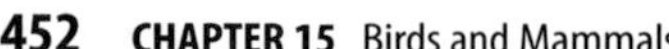

Internet Addresses

Explore the Glencoe Science Web site at **science.glencoe.com** to find out more about topics in this feature.

Connecting To Math

...The most valuable egg in the world is called the Nicholas III Equestrian Egg. It is an antique egg made of enamel, silver, and gold. The egg is worth many dollars and can be found in London, England.

...May is National Egg Month.

Eggs Eaten per Person (1997)*

Country	Eggs
Brazil	111
Ireland	163
Japan	347
Russia	198
United States	238

*Average number

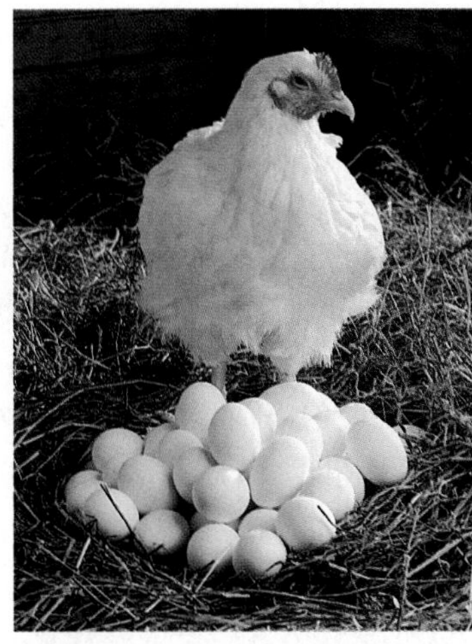

...The shell of a chicken egg can have 17,000 pores over its surface.

Do the Math

1. How many times longer is the largest ostrich egg than the smallest hummingbird egg?
2. How many elephant bird eggs would it take to equal to a dog weighing 48 kg?
3. Draw to scale an ostrich egg, a hummingbird egg, and an elephant bird egg.

Go Further

Visit the Glencoe Science Web site at **science.glencoe.com** and research the egg length of an American robin, a house sparrow, a bald eagle, and a Canada goose. Make a bar graph of this information.

Connecting To Math

Do the Math

Teaching Strategies

- Discuss which number should be the divisor to help students answer Question 1.
- Have students use 1 cm as the length of the smallest hummingbird egg.
- Review the equation that will allow students to solve for the number of elephant bird eggs asked for in Question 2.
- Provide graph paper to help students complete Question 3.

Answers

1. 20 times longer
2. 4
3. Check student drawings to make sure they are to scale.

Go Further

Have students use graph paper to make their graphs as accurate as possible. Have students research the size of these birds and make a graph of their relative sizes. Have the students determine if there is a correlation between the size of the bird and the size of the eggs it produces.

Visual Learning

Eggs Eaten Per Person (1997) Have students examine the illustration to determine many eggs each egg in the visual represents. **What is the average number of eggs eaten per week by each person in the United States?** Between 4 and 5 eggs Remind students that eggs are often an ingredient in other foods, and have them name some examples of food products that contain eggs. Have students keep a log of how many eggs they consume over a one-week period.

SCIENCE STATS 453

Chapter 15 Study Guide

Reviewing Main Ideas

Preview

Students can answer the questions in their Science Journals. Discuss the answers as you go through the chapter. **LS Linguistic**

Review

Students can write their answers, then compare them with those of other students. **LS Interpersonal**

Reteach

Students can look at the illustrations and describe details that support the main ideas of the chapter. **LS Visual-Spatial**

Answers to Chapter Review

Section 1

1. down feathers
2. They do not have wings that are shaped for flight.

Section 2

1. They have mammary glands.
4. marsupials

Chapter 15 Study Guide

Reviewing Main Ideas

Section 1 Birds

1. Birds are endothermic animals that are covered with feathers and lay eggs. *In the picture below, what type of feathers keep the goslings warm?*

2. Adaptations that enable most birds to fly include wings; feathers; a strong, lightweight skeleton; and efficient body systems. *Why can't these Emperor penguins fly?*

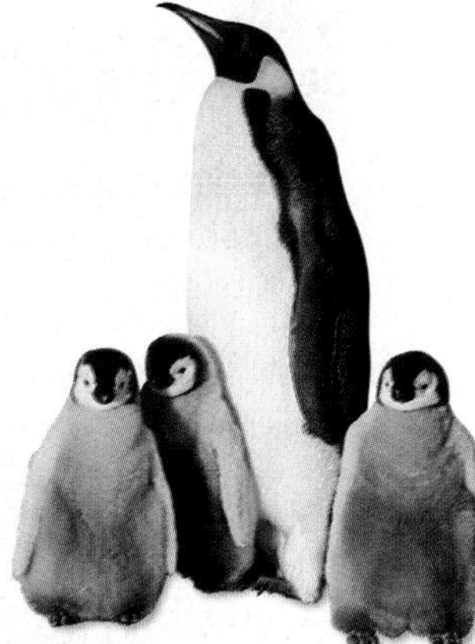

3. Birds lay eggs enclosed in hard shells. All birds' eggs are incubated until they hatch.
4. Birds help maintain a balance in nature by pollinating flowers and dispersing seeds, and by controlling animal pests and weeds.
5. Humans use birds and bird products for food, clothing, jewelry, bedding, fertilizer, and pets.

Section 2 Mammals

1. Mammals are endothermic animals with hair. *Why is this porcupine considered to be a mammal, even though it has quills?*
2. Female mammals have mammary glands that produce milk.
3. Mammals have teeth that are specialized for eating certain foods. Herbivores eat plants, carnivores eat meat, and omnivores eat plants and meat.
4. There are three groups of mammals. Monotremes lay eggs. Most marsupials have pouches for the development of their young. Placental offspring develop within a uterus and are nourished through a placenta. *The koala shown here has a pouch. To which group of mammals does it belong?*

5. Mammals, like other organisms, are important in maintaining balance in the environment. Their habitats are being destroyed.

FOLDABLES Reading & Study Skills

After You Read

Use your Compare and Contrast Study Fold that you made at the beginning of this chapter to find similarities and differences between birds and mammals. What are some common characteristics of birds and mammals?

FOLDABLES Reading & Study Skills

After You Read

After students have read the chapter and completed the Foldable described in Before You Read, have them do the activity on the student page.

Dinah Zike

Visualizing Main Ideas

Complete the following concept map on mammals.

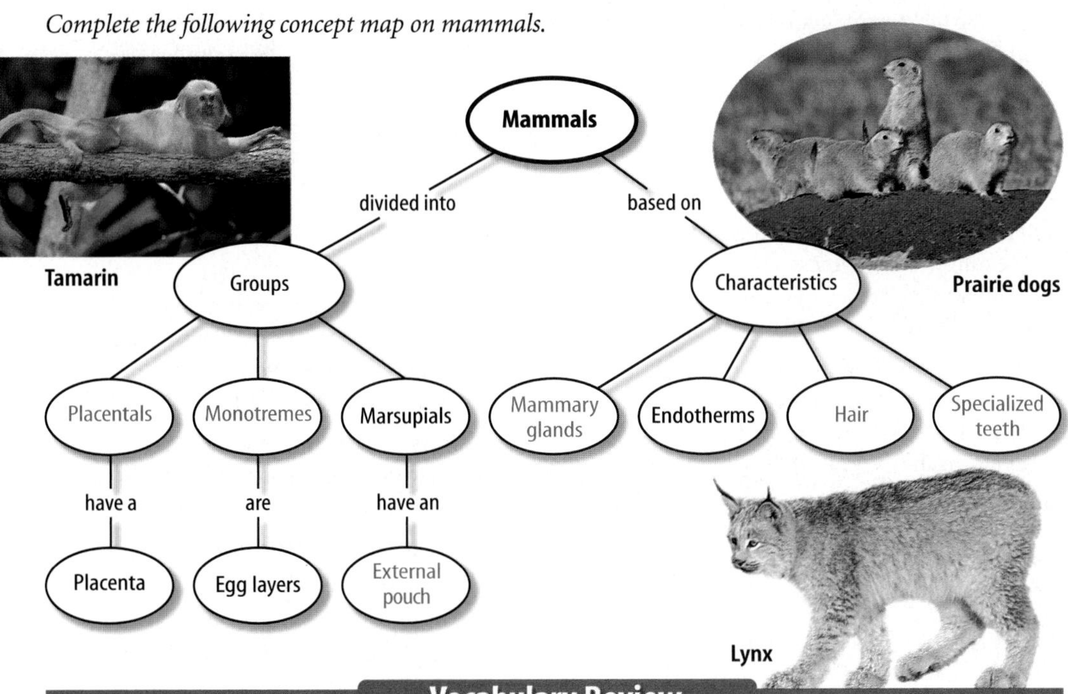

Vocabulary Review

Vocabulary Words

- **a.** carnivore
- **b.** contour feather
- **c.** down feather
- **d.** endotherm
- **e.** gestation period
- **f.** herbivore
- **g.** mammal
- **h.** mammary gland
- **i.** marsupial
- **j.** monotreme
- **k.** omnivore
- **l.** placenta
- **m.** placental
- **n.** preening
- **o.** umbilical cord

THE PRINCETON REVIEW Study Tip

Ask what kinds of questions to expect on the test. Ask for practice tests so that you can become familiar with the test-taking materials.

Using Vocabulary

Explain the difference between the vocabulary words in each of the following sets.

1. omnivore, carnivore, herbivore
2. contour feather, down feather
3. monotreme, marsupial
4. placenta, umbilical cord
5. endotherm, mammal
6. placental, monotreme
7. mammary gland, mammal
8. mammal, omnivore
9. endotherm, down feather
10. preening, down feather

Chapter 15 Study Guide

Visualizing Main Ideas

See student page.

Vocabulary Review

Using Vocabulary

1. Omnivores eat both plants and animals; carnivores eat other animals; herbivores eat plants.
2. Contour feathers are used for flight. Down feathers help insulate birds.
3. Monotremes lay eggs; marsupials give birth to immature offspring that develop in their mother's pouch.
4. The umbilical cord attaches the embryo to the placenta, a saclike organ that absorbs oxygen and food from the female's blood.
5. Endotherms maintain a constant body temperature. Mammals are endotherms.
6. Placentals are mammals in which the embryo develops inside the uterus of the female. Monotremes lay eggs.
7. A mammal is an endothermic vertebrate with hair and mammary glands that produce milk to feed its young.
8. A mammal that eats both plants and other animals is an omnivore.
9. Endotherms maintain a constant body temperature. Birds are endotherms that are covered with down feathers to conserve warmth.
10. Water birds use preening—the spreading of oil throughout the down feathers—to keep themselves warm and dry.

CHAPTER STUDY GUIDE 455

Chapter 15 Assessment

Checking Concepts

1. A
2. D
3. C
4. C
5. C
6. A
7. C
8. A
9. C
10. B

Thinking Critically

11. Both reproduce sexually; birds lay and incubate eggs; most mammals give birth to live young after a period of development in the uterus.
12. as a bird
13. Ducks have lighter bones than ostriches; ostriches do not fly and would be less likely to need this trait.
14. The amniotic egg and specialized beaks, feet, and wings allow birds to live on land.
15. This mammal eats both plants and other animals. It is an omnivore.

Chapter 15 Assessment

Checking Concepts

Choose the word or phrase that best answers the question.

1. Which of the following birds has feet adapted for moving on water?
   A) duck **C)** owl
   B) oriole **D)** rhea
2. Birds do NOT use their wings for which of the following activities?
   A) flying **C)** balancing
   B) swimming **D)** eating
3. Birds use which of the following organs to crush and grind their food?
   A) crop **C)** gizzard
   B) stomach **D)** small intestine
4. Which of the following are mammals that lay eggs?
   A) carnivores **C)** monotremes
   B) marsupials **D)** placentals
5. Which of the following mammals is classified as a marsupial?
   A) cat **C)** kangaroo
   B) human **D)** camel
6. Mammals with pouches are called what?
   A) marsupials **C)** placentals
   B) monotremes **D)** chiropterans
7. Which of the following have mammary glands without nipples?
   A) marsupials **C)** monotremes
   B) placentals **D)** omnivores
8. Teeth that are used for tearing food are called what?
   A) canines **C)** molars
   B) incisors **D)** premolars
9. Bird eggs do NOT have which of the following structures?
   A) hard shells **C)** placentas
   B) yolks **D)** membranes
10. Which of the following animals eat only plant materials?
   A) carnivores **C)** omnivores
   B) herbivores **D)** endotherms

Thinking Critically

11. Discuss the differences and similarities between bird reproduction and mammal reproduction.
12. You are a paleontologist studying fossils. One fossil appears to have hollow bones, a keeled breastbone, and a short, bony tail. How would you classify it?
13. Which type of bird would have lighter bones—a duck or an ostrich? Explain your answer.
14. What features of birds allow them to be fully adapted to life on land?
15. A mammal's teeth are similar in size and include all four types of teeth. What kind of mammal has teeth like this?

Developing Skills

16. **Classifying** Group the following mammals as herbivore, carnivore, or omnivore: *raccoon, mouse, rabbit, seal,* and *ape.*
17. **Making and Using Graphs** This table is a record of the approximate number of Canada geese that wintered at a midwestern wetland area over a five-year time period. Construct a line graph from these data.

Record of Canada Geese

Year	Number of Geese
1996	550
1997	600
1998	575
1999	750
2000	825

Chapter Assessment Planner

Portfolio Encourage students to place in their portfolios one or two items of what they consider to be their best work. Examples include:
- Science Journal, p. 435
- Assessment, p. 439
- Assessment, p. 442

Performance Additional performance assessments, Performance Task Assessment Lists, and rubrics for evaluating these activities can be found in Glencoe's **Performance Assessment in the Science Classroom.**

18. Concept Mapping Complete this concept map about birds.

Birds
Kinds
Characteristics
of bird
of all birds
Answers will vary.
Answers will vary.
Feathers
Lays eggs
Birds of prey
Answers will vary.
wings
endotherm

19. Classifying You discover three new species of placentals. The traits of each species are as follows.
Mammal 1 swims and eats meat.
Mammal 2 flies and eats fruit.
Mammal 3 runs on four legs and hunts.
Place each mammal into a correct order.

20. Comparing and Contrasting Describe the teeth of herbivores, carnivores, and omnivores. How are their types of teeth adapted to their diets?

Performance Assessment

21. Song with Lyrics Create a song about bird adaptations for flight by changing the words to a song that you know. Include in your song as many adaptations as possible.

TECHNOLOGY

Go to the Glencoe Science Web site at **science.glencoe.com** or use the **Glencoe Science CD-ROM** for additional chapter assessment.

THE PRINCETON REVIEW Test Practice

Students in Ms. Savir's science class placed five bird feeders at different locations around the school grounds. For five days, they recorded the number of each kind of bird that was attracted to the feeders. They plotted their results in the following line graph.

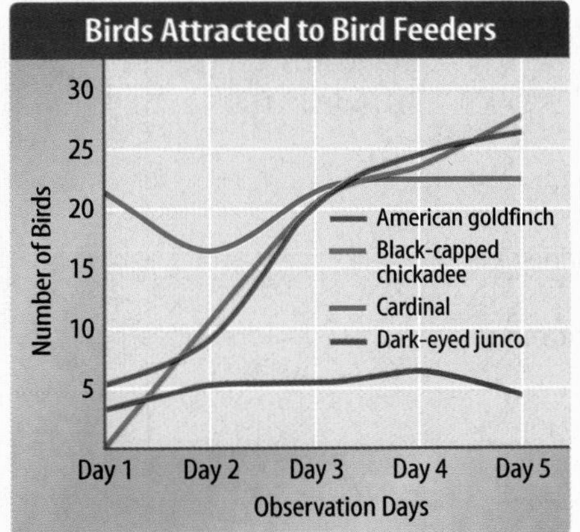

Study the graph and answer the following questions.

1. According to the graph, which bird did the students see the least?
   A) Black-capped chickadee
   B) Cardinal
   C) Dark-eyed junco
   D) American goldfinch

2. According to this information, which two birds were spotted on Day 3 the same number of times?
   F) American goldfinch and cardinal
   G) Black-capped chickadee and cardinal
   H) Dark-eyed junco and cardinal
   J) Black-capped chickadee and American goldfinch

Assessment Resources

Reproducible Masters

Chapter Resources Booklet
Chapter Review, pp. 33–34
Chapter Tests, pp. 35–38
Assessment Transparency Activity, p. 45

Glencoe Science Web site
Interactive Tutor
Chapter Quizzes

Glencoe Technology
Assessment Transparency
Interactive CD-ROM Chapter Quizzes
ExamView Pro Test Bank
Vocabulary PuzzleMaker Software
MindJogger Videoquiz

Chapter 15 Assessment

Test Practice

The Test-Taking Tip was written by The Princeton Review, the nation's leader in test preparation.

1. C
2. J

Developing Skills

16. herbivores: rabbit, mouse; carnivores: seal; omnivores: raccoon, ape
17. Graphs should show a slight increase, then slight decrease, followed by a steady, sharp increase.
18. See student page.
19. Mammal 1: *Pinnipedia;* Mammal 2: *Chiroptera;* Mammal 3: *Carnivora*
20. herbivores: large incisors for cutting off blades of grass, molars to grind plants; carnivores: small incisors, large canine teeth to grip and tear food; omnivores: canines, incisors, and molars to feed on both plants and animals

Performance Assessment

21. Songs may be simple as long as the lyrics discuss bird adaptations for flight. Use **PASC,** p.151.

CHAPTER ASSESSMENT 457

Section/Objectives	Standards		Activities/Features
	National	State/Local	
Chapter Opener	See p. 5T for a Key to Standards.		**Explore Activity:** Observe how humans communicate without using sound, p. 459 **Before You Read,** p. 459
Section 1 Types of Behavior 2 sessions 1 block 1. **Identify** the differences between innate and learned behavior. 2. **Explain** how reflexes and instincts help organisms survive. 3. **Identify** examples of imprinting and conditioning.	National Content Standards: UCP3, A1, C3, C5, G3		**Health Integration,** p. 461 **Science Online,** p. 463 **MiniLAB:** Observing Conditioning, p. 464
Section 2 Behavioral Interactions 3 sessions 1.5 blocks 1. **Explain** why behavioral adaptations are important. 2. **Describe** how courtship behavior increases reproductive success. 3. **Explain** the importance of social behavior and cyclic behavior.	National Content Standards: UCP3, A1, A2, C2, C3, C5, G1		**MiniLAB:** Demonstrating Chemical Communication, p. 469 **Chemistry Integration,** p. 470 **Visualizing Bioluminescence,** p. 471 **Science Online,** p. 472 **Problem-Solving Activity:** How can you determine which animals hibernate?, p. 473 **Activity:** Observing Earthworm Behavior, p. 475 **Activity:** Animal Habitats, p. 476 **Oops! Accidents in Science:** Going to the Dogs, p. 478

NATIONAL GEOGRAPHIC

Teacher's Corner

Products Available from Glencoe
To order call 1-800-334-7344:
CD-ROMs
Mammals: A Multimedia Encyclopedia
NGS PictureShow: Structure of Vertebrates 1
NGS PictureShow: Structure of Vertebrates 2
Transparency Sets
NGS PicturePack: Structure of Vertebrates 1
NGS PicturePack: Structure of Vertebrates 2

Products Available from National Geographic Society
To order call 1-800-368-2728:
Book
National Geographic Book of Mammals

Activity Materials	Reproducible Resources	Section Assessment	Technology
Explore Activity: Science Journal	**Chapter Resources Booklet** Foldables Worksheet, p. 15 Directed Reading Overview, p. 17 Note-taking Worksheets, pp. 29–31	GLENCOE'S ASSESSMENT ADVANTAGE	
MiniLAB: photos of different foods and landscapes *Need materials?* Contact Science Kit at 1-800-828-7777 or www.sciencekit.com on the Internet.	**Chapter Resources Booklet** Transparency Activity, p. 40 MiniLAB, p. 3 Enrichment, p. 27 Reinforcement, p. 25 Directed Reading, p. 18 Lab Activity, pp. 9–11 Transparency Activity, pp. 43–44 **Science Inquiry Labs,** p. 11 **Home and Community Involvement,** p. 44	**Portfolio** Reteach, p. 465 **Performance** MiniLAB, p. 464 Skill Builder Activities, p. 465 **Content** Section Assessment, p. 465 Challenge, p. 465	Section Focus Transparency Teaching Transparency Interactive CD-ROM Guided Reading Audio Program
MiniLAB: sample of perfume, air freshener, or flavoring oil **Activity:** scissors, shoe box with lid, flashlight, tape, paper, moist paper towels, earthworms, timer **Activity:** poster board, markers or colored pencils, materials to make a scale model	**Chapter Resources Booklet** Transparency Activity, p. 41 MiniLAB, p. 4 Enrichment, p. 28 Reinforcement, p. 26 Directed Reading, pp. 19, 20 Activity Worksheet, pp. 5–6, 7–8 Lab Activity, pp. 13–14 **Reading and Writing Skill Activities,** p. 5 **Lab Management and Safety,** p. 43	**Portfolio** Cultural Diversity, p. 470 Curriculum Connection, p. 473 **Performance** MiniLAB, p. 469 Skill Builder Activities, p. 474 **Content** Section Assessment, p. 474 Challenge, p. 474	Section Focus Transparency Interactive CD-ROM Guided Reading Audio Program

GLENCOE'S ASSESSMENT ADVANTAGE

End of Chapter Assessment

Blackline Masters	Technology	Professional Series
Chapter Resources Booklet Chapter Review, pp. 33–34 Chapter Tests, pp. 35–38 **Standardized Test Practice by The Princeton Review,** pp. 71–74	MindJogger Videoquiz Interactive CD-ROM Vocabulary PuzzleMakers ExamView Pro Test Bank Interactive Lesson Planner Interactive Teacher Edition	Performance Assessment in the Science Classroom (PASC)

Transparencies

Section Focus

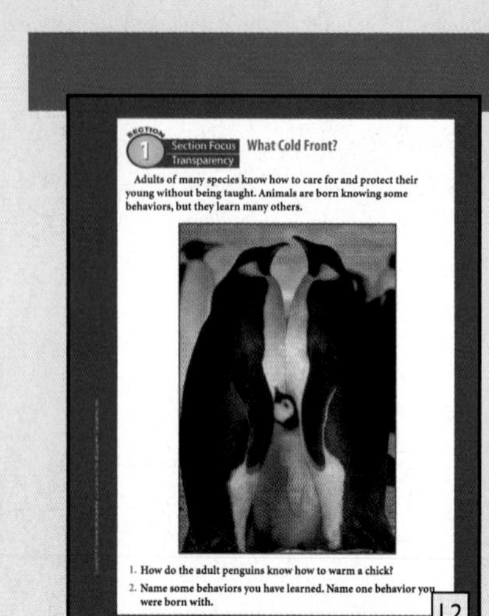
Section 1 Section Focus Transparency **What Cold Front?**

Adults of many species know how to care for and protect their young without being taught. Animals are born knowing some behaviors, but they learn many others.

1. How do the adult penguins know how to warm a chick?
2. Name some behaviors you have learned. Name one behavior you were born with.

L2

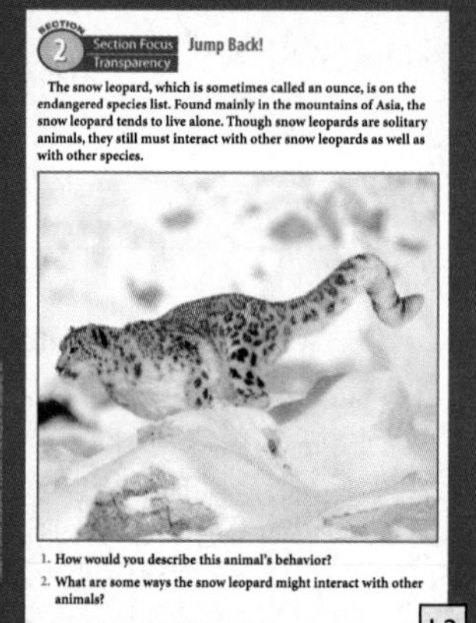
Section 2 Section Focus Transparency **Jump Back!**

The snow leopard, which is sometimes called an ounce, is on the endangered species list. Found mainly in the mountains of Asia, the snow leopard tends to live alone. Though snow leopards are solitary animals, they still must interact with other snow leopards as well as with other species.

1. How would you describe this animal's behavior?
2. What are some ways the snow leopard might interact with other animals?

L2

This is a representation of key blackline masters available in the Teacher Classroom Resources. See Resource Manager boxes within the chapter for additional information.

Assessment

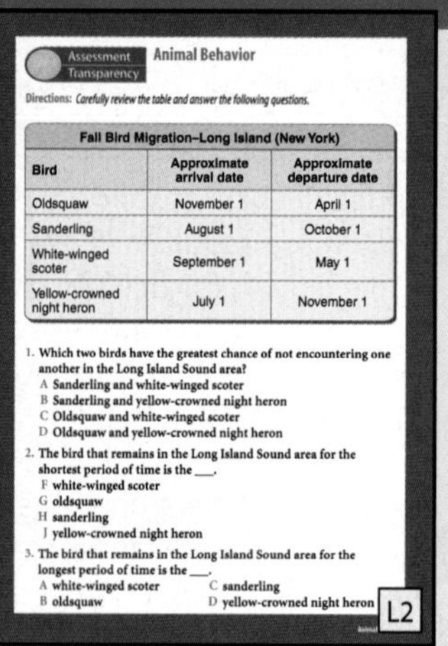
Assessment Transparency **Animal Behavior**

Directions: *Carefully review the table and answer the following questions.*

Fall Bird Migration–Long Island (New York)		
Bird	Approximate arrival date	Approximate departure date
Oldsquaw	November 1	April 1
Sanderling	August 1	October 1
White-winged scoter	September 1	May 1
Yellow-crowned night heron	July 1	November 1

1. Which two birds have the greatest chance of not encountering one another in the Long Island Sound area?
   A Sanderling and white-winged scoter
   B Sanderling and yellow-crowned night heron
   C Oldsquaw and white-winged scoter
   D Oldsquaw and yellow-crowned night heron
2. The bird that remains in the Long Island Sound area for the shortest period of time is the ___.
   F white-winged scoter
   G oldsquaw
   H sanderling
   J yellow-crowned night heron
3. The bird that remains in the Long Island Sound area for the longest period of time is the ___.
   A white-winged scoter
   B oldsquaw
   C sanderling
   D yellow-crowned night heron

L2

Teaching

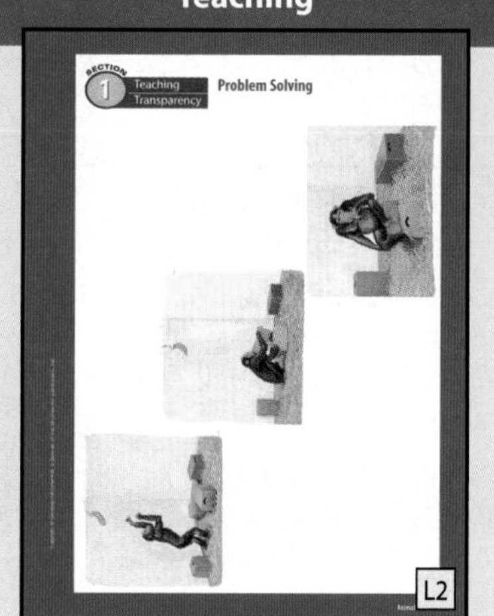
Section 1 Teaching Transparency **Problem Solving**

L2

Key to Teaching Strategies

The following designations will help you decide which activities are appropriate for your students.

- L1 Level 1 activities should be appropriate for students with learning difficulties.
- L2 Level 2 activities should be within the ability range of all students.
- L3 Level 3 activities are designed for above-average students.
- ELL ELL activities should be within the ability range of English Language Learners.
- COOP LEARN Cooperative Learning activities are designed for small group work.
- LS Multiple Learning Styles logos, as described on page 22T, are used throughout to indicate strategies that address different learning styles.
- P These strategies represent student products that can be placed into a best-work portfolio.

Hands-on Activities

Activity Worksheets

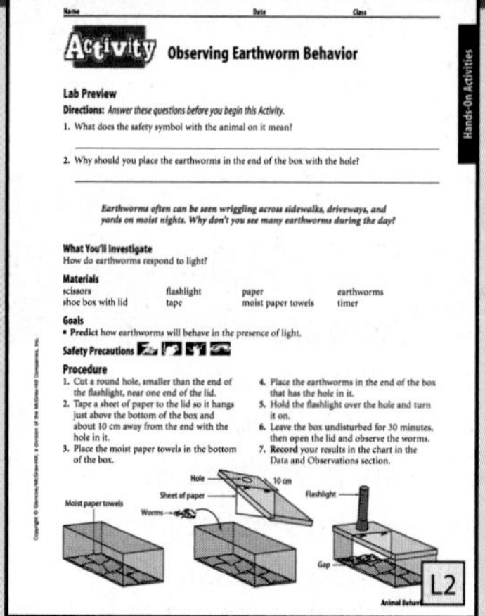
Name Date Class

Activity **Observing Earthworm Behavior**

Lab Preview
Directions: *Answer these questions before you begin this Activity.*
1. What does the safety symbol with the animal on it mean?
2. Why should you place the earthworms in the end of the box with the hole?

Earthworms often can be seen wriggling across sidewalks, driveways, and yards on moist nights. Why don't you see many earthworms during the day?

What You'll Investigate
How do earthworms respond to light?

Materials
scissors, shoe box with lid, flashlight, tape, paper, moist paper towels, earthworms, timer

Goals
- Predict how earthworms will behave in the presence of light.

Safety Precautions

Procedure
1. Cut a round hole, smaller than the end of the flashlight, near one end of the lid.
2. Tape a sheet of paper to the lid so it hangs just above the bottom of the box and about 10 cm away from the end with the hole in it.
3. Place the moist paper towels in the bottom of the box.
4. Place the earthworms in the end of the box that has the hole in it.
5. Hold the flashlight over the hole and turn it on.
6. Leave the box undisturbed for 30 minutes, then open the lid and observe the worms.
7. Record your results in the chart in the Data and Observations section.

Hands-on Activities

L2

Laboratory Activities

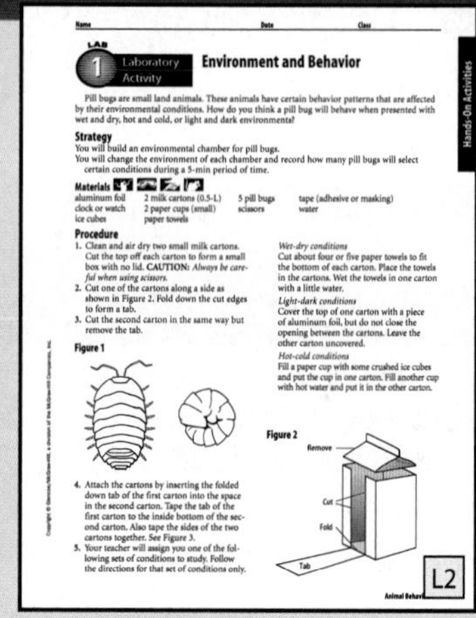
Name Date Class

LAB 1 Laboratory Activity **Environment and Behavior**

Pill bugs are small land animals. These animals have certain behavior patterns that are affected by their environmental conditions. How do you think a pill bug will behave when presented with wet and dry, hot and cold, or light and dark environments?

Strategy
You will build an environmental chamber for pill bugs.
You will change the environment of each chamber and record how many pill bugs will select certain conditions during a 5-min period of time.

Materials
aluminum foil, clock or watch, ice cubes, 2 milk cartons (0.5-L), 2 paper cups (small), paper towels, 5 pill bugs, scissors, tape (adhesive or masking), water

Procedure
1. Clean and air dry two small milk cartons. Cut the top off each carton to form a small box with no lid. CAUTION: *Always be careful when using scissors.*
2. Cut one of the cartons along a side as shown in Figure 2. Fold down the cut edges to form a tab.
3. Cut the second carton in the same way but remove the tab.
4. Attach the cartons by inserting the folded down tab of the first carton into the space in the second carton. Tape the tab of the first carton to the inside bottom of the second carton. Also tape the sides of the two cartons together. See Figure 3.
5. Your teacher will assign you one of the following sets of conditions to study. Follow the directions for that set of conditions only.

Wet-dry conditions
Cut about four or five paper towels to fit the bottom of each carton. Place the towels in the cartons. Wet the towels in one carton with a little water.

Light-dark conditions
Cover the top of one carton with a piece of aluminum foil, but do not close the opening between the cartons. Leave the other carton uncovered.

Hot-cold conditions
Fill a paper cup with some crushed ice cubes and put the cup in one carton. Fill another cup with hot water and put it in the other carton.

Figure 1

Figure 2

Hands-on Activities

L2

Meeting Different Ability Levels

Content Outline

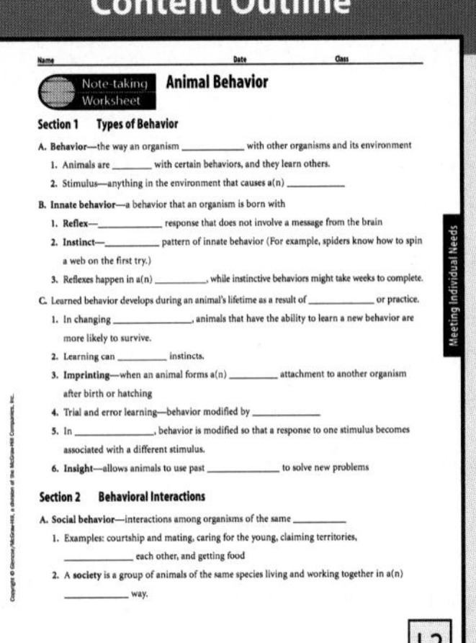

Reinforcement

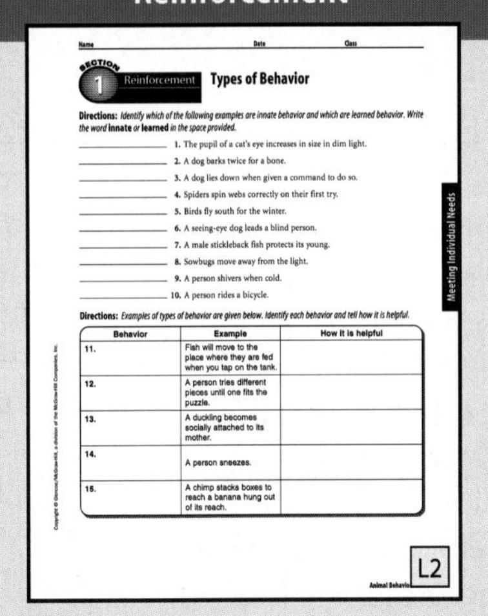

Directed Reading

Assessment

Chapter Tests

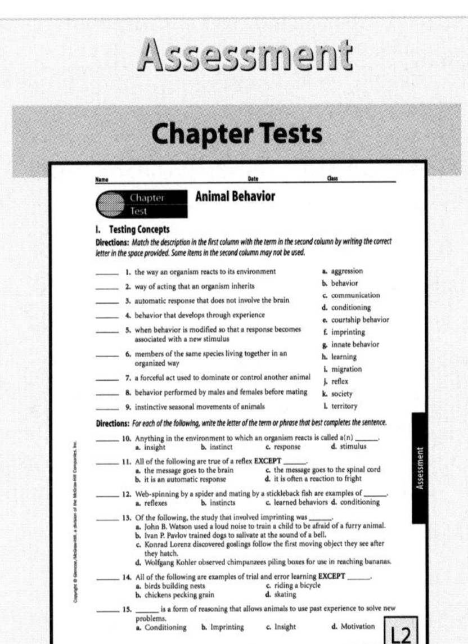

Enrichment

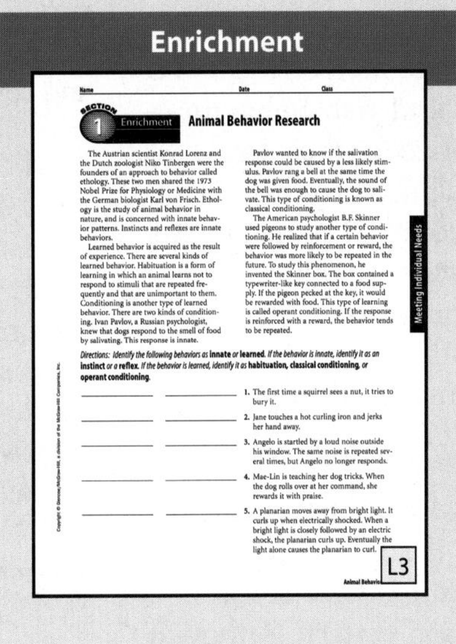

Spanish Directed Reading

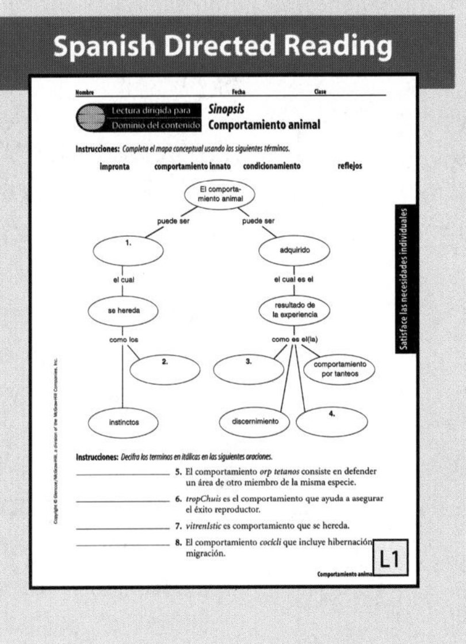

Test Practice Workbook

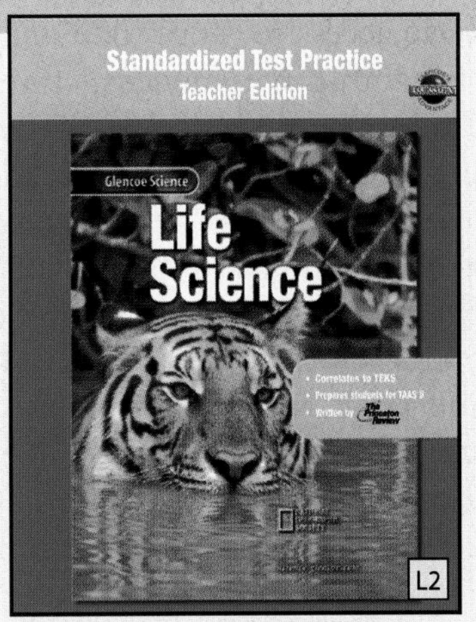

Chapter Review

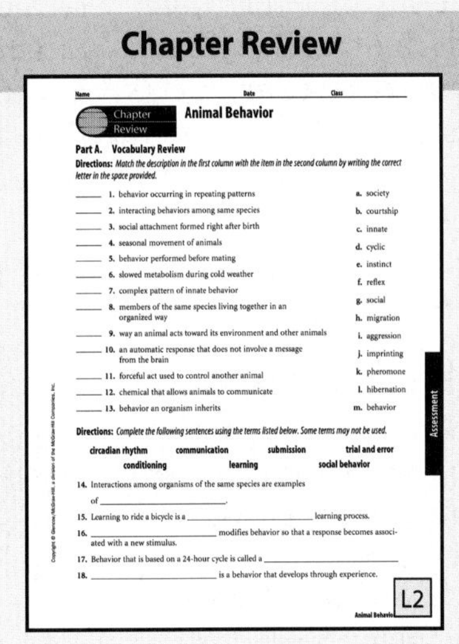

Science Content Background

SECTION 1

Types of Behavior

Ethology

The scientific study of animal behavior as it occurs in an organism's natural environment is called ethology. Konrad Z. Lorenz, a founder of ethology, studied the behavior of birds and developed a theory of animal behavior that stressed its inherited aspects. Lorenz and two other ethologists—Karl von Frisch of Austria, who studied bee communication, and Nikolaas Tinbergen of the Netherlands, who studied gull and fish behavior—received the 1973 Nobel prize for their work.

Fun Fact

Mice missing a gene that codes for a protein called oxytocin cannot learn to identify other mice. Oxytocin seems to regulate social memory.

Early ethologists thought that most behaviors were instinctual. In contrast, psychologists thought that the environment modified instinctual behavior and that learning was more important. Today, ideas from both of these groups are combined in studies of animal behavior.

Innate Behavior

Innate behavior is often also called instinctive behavior. Innate behavior is triggered by a specific environmental stimulus that triggers a behavior called a fixed action pattern. Although innate behaviors are inherited, environment plays a role in the development of the behavior. For example, young toads instinctively flick their tongues out at all dark objects, a fixed action pattern. If a toad catches a bee and gets stung it learns to avoid bees.

Learned Behavior

It is sometimes difficult to distinguish between innate behavior and learned behavior. Learned behaviors and innate behaviors involve neural and often hormonal mechanisms. The complexity of an animal's brain and nervous system is genetically determined. Animals with more complex brains receive more input from experience and exhibit learned behavior. Though learning is not instinctive, it can be automatic. For example, people learn how to use eating utensils. After a while, this action does not require conscious thought.

Habituation is learning to tune out unimportant stimuli. When animals ignore unimportant stimuli they conserve energy to deal with relevant stimuli. A person may ignore constant noises, such as traffic outside a window.

Imprinting

Goats, sheep, and the Alaskan fur seals are imprinted during the first few minutes after the birth of their offspring to recognize the offspring by their odor. The mother will accept any young that they smell during this critical period and reject any young that they did not smell.

Trial and Error

Trial and error learning also is called operant conditioning. Animals repeat behaviors that result in positive stimuli and avoid behaviors that result in negative stimuli. For example, bears soon learn by trial and error that they will catch a fish by remaining quiet rather than splashing about in the water. The toad that learned to avoid bees learned by trial and error.

SECTION 2

Social Behavior

Animal Societies

Some animal societies are organized into dominance hierarchies, such as a pecking order within a society of chickens. Animals with a high rank in the hierarchy usually have access to more food and thus have more reproductive success. The young of these dominant animals will have some of the same characteristics that helped their parents survive. If food is scarce, animals lower in the hierarchy die and the population is reduced to a number the habitat can support.

In many animal societies, reproduction occurs at the same time within the group. Having many young in a population at once ensures that some will survive to adulthood. Ethologists think that this type of behavior is more common when members of a group are related.

A group of animals is more likely to be successful in finding food than an individual alone. Some animals, like wolves and hyenas, hunt in groups so they can more easily corner prey.

Territorial Behavior

Dominant individuals are usually more successful in defending a territory. Because only individuals with territories mate, genes of the best-adapted individuals are likely to pass on to the next generation. Some territories are only large enough for mating. Other larger territories help ensure an adequate food supply for offspring.

Sound Communication

Whales "sing," and dolphins emit clicking noises that can travel more than 100 kilometers underwater. Elephants emit low-frequency sounds called infrasound. These sounds are in the same sound range as earthquakes and cannot be heard by humans. Elephants emit these sounds as warnings and female elephants "sing" at this frequency to attract mates.

Migration

Animals use a variety of navigational devices to find their way. Honeybees use polarized light. Birds use the Sun during the day or the stars at night, much as humans use a compass and map.

For additional content background on this topic, go to the Glencoe Science Web site at science.glencoe.com.

Brandon D. Cole/Corbis

CHAPTER 16

Animal Behavior

Chapter Vocabulary

behavior, p. 460
innate behavior, p. 461
reflex, p. 461
instinct, p. 462
imprinting, p. 463
conditioning, p. 464
insight, p. 465
social behavior, p. 466
society, p. 467
territory, p. 467
aggression, p. 468
courtship behavior, p. 469
pheromone, p. 469
cyclic behavior, p. 472
hibernation, p. 473
migration, p. 474

What do you think?

Science Journal The photograph shows birds waiting to be fed. This response is triggered by the arrival of the parents at the nest.

CHAPTER 16

Animal Behavior

Eye contact is made, dirt flies, and the silence is shattered. Massive horns clash as two bighorn sheep butt heads. Nearby, a spider spins a web to catch its food. Overhead, the honking of a V-shaped string of geese echoes through the valley. Do organisms learn these actions or do they occur automatically? In this chapter, you will examine the unique behaviors of animals. Also, you'll read about different types of behavior and learn about animal communication.

What do you think?

Science Journal Look at the picture below with a classmate. Discuss what you think this might be or what is happening. Here's a hint: *This instinctive reaction is triggered by their parent's arrival.* Write your answer or best guess in your Science Journal.

Theme Connection

Stability and Change Survival of a species is dependent upon the ability of its members to respond to changes in the environment by changing either themselves or their behaviors. Complex patterns of behavior have evolved in animals to help them successfully compete in a variety of environments.

Explore Activity

One way you communicate is by speaking. Other animals communicate without the use of sound. For example, a gull chick pecks at its parent's beak to get food. Try the activity below to see if you can communicate without speaking.

Observe how humans communicate without using sound

1. Form groups of students. Have one person choose an object and describe that object using gestures.
2. The other students observe and try to identify the object that is being described.
3. Each student in the group should choose an object and describe it without speaking while the others observe and identify the object.

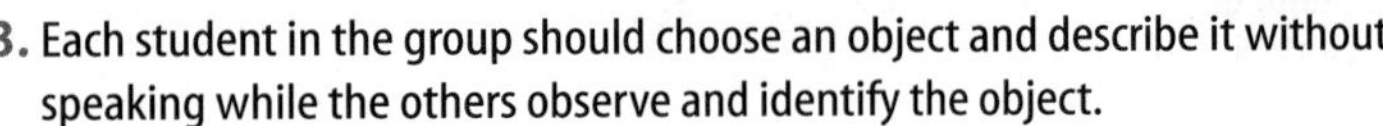

Observe

In your Science Journal, describe how you and the other students were able to communicate without speaking to one another.

Before You Read

FOLDABLES Reading & Study Skills

Making a Compare and Contrast Study Fold **As you study behaviors, make the following Foldable to help find the similarities and differences between the behaviors of two animals.**

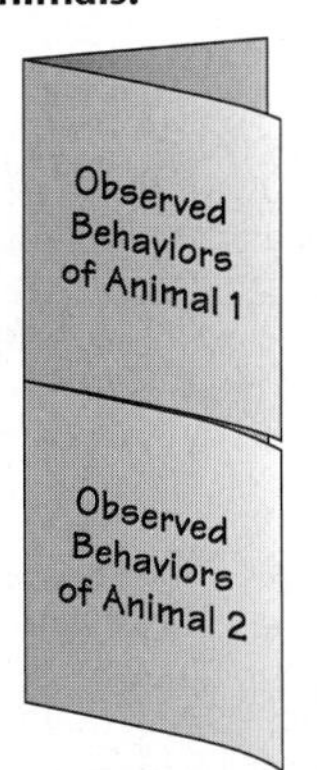

1. Place a sheet of paper in front of you so the short side is at the top. Fold the paper in half from the left to the right side. Fold top to bottom but do not crease. Then unfold.
2. Label *Observed Behaviors of Animal 1* and *Observed Behaviors of Animal 2* across the front of the paper, as shown.
3. Through one thickness of paper, cut along the middle fold line to form two tabs, as shown.
4. Before you read the chapter, choose two animals to compare.
5. As you read the chapter, list the behaviors you learn about Animal 1 and Animal 2 under the tabs.

Before You Read

FOLDABLES Reading & Study Skills

Dinah Zike Study Fold

Purpose Students make and use a Foldable to collect information on two observable animals and then use what they have learned to compare and contrast the behavior of these animals.

For additional help, see Foldables Worksheet, p. 15 in **Chapter Resources Booklet,** or go to the Glencoe Science Web site at **science.glencoe.com.** See After You Read in the Study Guide at the end of this chapter.

Explore Activity

Purpose Use this Explore Activity to demonstrate to students that humans can communicate without using sound. L1 ELL COOP LEARN IN **Kinesthetic**

Preparation Discuss how humans and other animals communicate.

Teaching Strategies

- Encourage students to choose objects with which their classmates are familiar.
- Discuss differences and similarities in their methods of communication.

Observe

Possible answers: use of hands, facial expressions, body movements, and other gestures

Assessment

Oral Ask how humans communicate with one another. Possible answers: frowning, smiling, looking perplexed or anxious, shaking hands, hugging, touching, posturing and body language in general, speaking, tone of voice. Use **Performance Assessment in the Science Classroom,** p. 89.

SECTION

Types of Behavior

1 Motivate

Bellringer Transparency

Display the Section Focus Transparency for Section 1. Use the accompanying Transparency Activity Master. L2 ELL

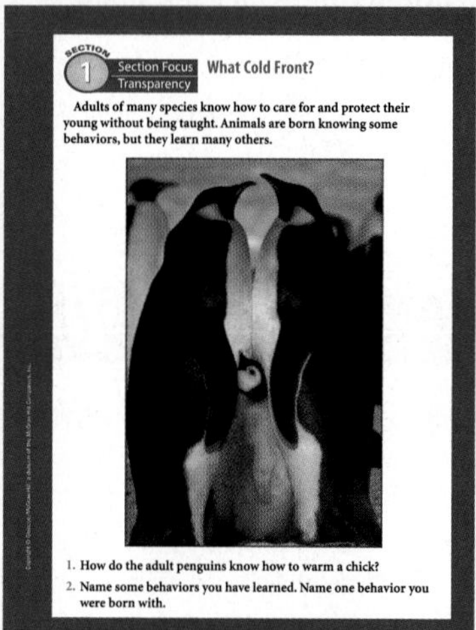

SECTION 1 Section Focus Transparency **What Cold Front?**

Adults of many species know how to care for and protect their young without being taught. Animals are born knowing some behaviors, but they learn many others.

1. **How do the adult penguins know how to warm a chick?**
2. **Name some behaviors you have learned. Name one behavior you were born with.**

Animal Behavior

Tie to Prior Knowledge

Ask students to define *communication.* Have them explain how they communicate with their pets and other animals. Invite volunteers to describe how a pet communicates with its owner.

SECTION

Types of Behavior

As You Read

***What* You'll Learn**

- **Identify** the differences between innate and learned behavior.
- **Explain** how reflexes and instincts help organisms survive.
- **Identify** examples of imprinting and conditioning.

Vocabulary
behavior
innate behavior
reflex
instinct
imprinting
conditioning
insight

***Why* It's Important**

Innate behavior helps you survive on your own.

Behavior

When you come home from school, does your dog run to meet you? Your dog barks and wags its tail as you scratch behind its ears. Sitting at your feet, it watches every move you make. Why do dogs do these things? In nature, dogs are pack animals that generally follow a leader. They have been living with people for about 12,000 years. Domesticated dogs treat people as part of their own pack, as shown in **Figure 1B.**

Animals are different from one another in their behavior. They are born with certain behaviors, and they learn others. **Behavior** is the way an organism interacts with other organisms and its environment. Anything in the environment that causes a reaction is called a stimulus. A stimulus can be external, such as a rival male entering another male's territory, or internal, such as hunger or thirst. You are the stimulus that causes your dog to bark and wag its tail. Your dog's reaction to you is a response.

Figure 1
Dogs are pack animals by nature. A This pack of wild dogs must work together to survive. B This domesticated dog has accepted a human as its leader.

B

Section Assessment Planner

PORTFOLIO
Reteach, p. 465

PERFORMANCE ASSESSMENT
MiniLAB, p. 464
Skill Builder Activities, p. 465
See page 482 for more options.

CONTENT ASSESSMENT
Section, p. 465
Challenge, p. 465
Chapter, pp. 482–483

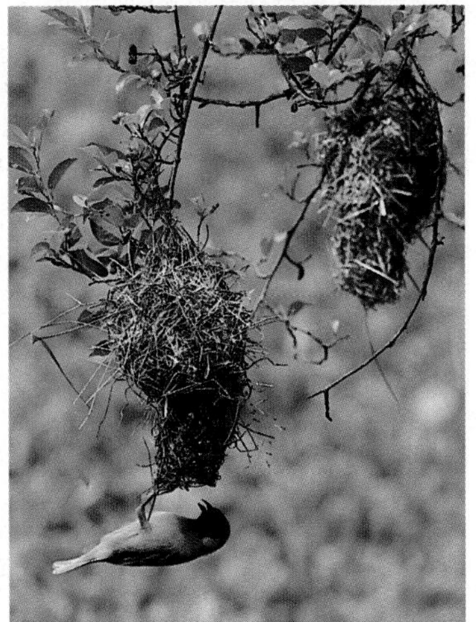

Figure 2
Bird nests come in different sizes and shapes. A Cliff swallows build nests out of mud. B Hummingbirds build delicate cup-shaped nests on branches of trees. C This male weaverbird is knotting the ends of leaves together to secure the nest.

Innate Behavior

A behavior that an organism is born with is called an **innate behavior.** These types of behaviors are inherited. They don't have to be learned.

Innate behavior patterns occur the first time an animal responds to a particular internal or external stimulus. For birds like the swallows in **Figure 2A** and the hummingbird in **Figure 2B** building a nest is innate behavior. When it's time for the female weaverbird to lay eggs, the male weaverbird builds an elaborate nest, as shown in **Figure 2C.** Although a young male's first attempt may be messy, the nest is constructed correctly.

The behavior of animals that have short life spans is mostly innate behavior. Most insects do not learn from their parents. In many cases, the parents have died or moved on by the time the young hatch. Yet every insect reacts innately to its environment. A moth will fly toward a light, and a cockroach will run away from it. They don't learn this behavior. Innate behavior allows animals to respond instantly. This quick response often means the difference between life and death.

Reflexes The simplest innate behaviors are reflex actions. A **reflex** is an automatic response that does not involve a message from the brain. Sneezing, shivering, yawning, jerking your hand away from a hot surface, and blinking your eyes when something is thrown toward you are all reflex actions.

In humans a reflex message passes almost instantly from a sense organ along the nerve to the spinal cord and back to the muscles. The message does not go to the brain. You are aware of the reaction only after it has happened. Your body reacts on its own. A reflex is not the result of conscious thinking.

Health INTEGRATION

A tap on a tendon in your knee causes your leg to stretch. This is known as the knee-jerk reflex. Abnormalities in this reflex tell doctors of a possible problem in the central nervous system. Research other types of reflexes and write a report about them in your Science Journal.

2 Teach

Behavior

Activity

Play an audiotape of animal communication sounds—whales, wolves, birds, or pet sounds. **Why do animals need to communicate with one another?** Possible answers: to warn, to locate food, to court **Can you identify the message sent by any of these sounds?** Students may distinguish some repeated sounds. **How could you determine the message?** Observe the animals in their natural habitats and note what other animals do upon hearing each sound.

Discussion

How was the survival of ancient people dependent on their knowledge of animal behavior? They had to know the habits and behavior of animals in order to hunt and fish for food and to train animals to do work.

Innate Behavior

Fun Fact

Behaviors are more likely to be innate in animals that develop without parental care.

Health INTEGRATION

Many vital body processes, such as breathing, heartbeat, diameter of blood vessels, and sweat gland secretions, are reflex actions.

Resource Manager

Chapter Resources Booklet

Transparency Activity, p. 40

Directed Reading for Content Mastery, pp. 17, 18

Note-taking Worksheets, pp. 29–31

Inclusion Strategies

Visually and Hearing Impaired Chirping is an innate behavior of crickets. Place crickets in an aquarium with moist soil and lettuce. Have hearing-impaired students observe the crickets through hand lenses to note how chirping is produced. Visually impaired students can listen to the chirps and estimate the room's temperature (°F) using this method: Count the number of chirps in 14 s, add 40. L2 IS **Auditory-Musical**

Innate Behavior, continued

Quick Demo

Reinforce students' understanding of innate behaviors by demonstrating reflex actions. The response of the pupil to light in a dark room is an automatic response.

Reading Check

Answer reflex: automatic response, does not involve the brain; instinct: complex pattern of innate behavior developed over time

Extension

Many students will find animal communication interesting. Have them research and design a project that involves tape-recording and analyzing animal sounds. L2 IS **Auditory-Musical**

Discussion

Why are reflexes important? They allow an animal to rapidly respond to sudden change.

Learned Behavior

Caption Answer

Figure 4 It protects them until they can learn to distinguish between harmful and nonthreatening organisms.

Figure 3
Spiders, like this orb weaver spider, know how to spin webs as soon as they hatch.

Instincts An **instinct** is a complex pattern of innate behavior. Spinning a web like the one in **Figure 3** is complicated, yet spiders spin webs correctly on the first try. Unlike reflexes, instinctive behaviors can take weeks to complete. Instinctive behavior begins when the animal recognizes a stimulus and continues until all parts of the behavior have been performed.

Reading Check *What is the difference between a reflex and an instinct?*

Learned Behavior

All animals have innate and learned behaviors. Learned behavior develops during an animal's lifetime. Animals with more complex brains exhibit more behaviors that are the result of learning. However, the behavior of insects, spiders, and other arthropods is mostly instinctive behavior. Fish, reptiles, amphibians, birds, and mammals all learn. Learning is the result of experience or practice.

Learning is important for animals because it allows them to respond to changing situations. In changing environments, animals that have the ability to learn a new behavior are more likely to survive. This is especially important for animals with long life spans. The longer an animal lives, the more likely it is that the environment in which it lives will change.

Learning also can modify instincts. For example, grouse and quail chicks, shown in **Figure 4,** leave their nests the day they hatch. They can run and find food, but they can't fly. When something moves above them, they instantly crouch and keep perfectly still until the danger has passed. They will crouch without moving even if the falling object is only a leaf. Older birds have learned that leaves will not harm them, but they freeze when a hawk moves overhead.

Figure 4
As they grow older, these quail chicks will learn which organisms to avoid. *Why is it important for young quail to react the same toward all organisms?*

LAB DEMONSTRATION

Purpose to observe fruit fly responses

Materials 2 vials of fruit flies, ice, black construction paper, masking tape, jars, bananas

Preparation Put 2 jars containing bananas outdoors. After fruit flies collect, wrap black paper around each jar. Invert a vial over a jar. Shine a light on the vial and insert plug after flies move into it. Do the same with the other vial and jar

Procedure Place one vial in ice. Cover half of the second vial with black paper. Leave both undisturbed for 10–15 minutes. Have students record their observations.

Expected Outcome Fruit flies in ice become sluggish. Those in the second vial move toward the light.

Assessment

How does the behavior of fruit flies help them survive? Their body processes slow when it is cold. Since fruit flies do not internally regulate their body temperatures, their positive response to light helps them stay warm and remain active.

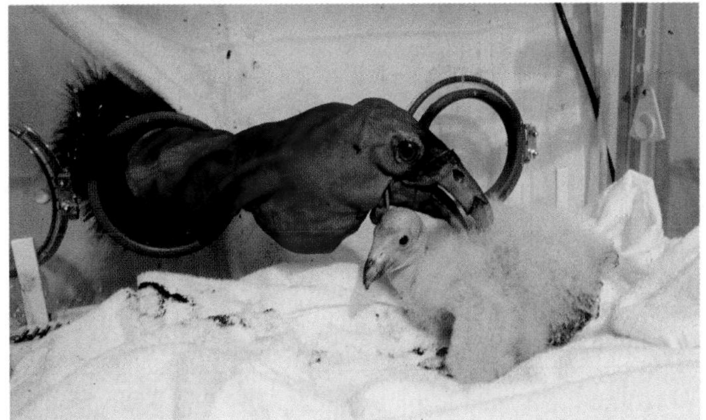

Figure 5
When feeding chicks in captivity, puppets of adult condors are used so the chicks don't associate humans with food.

Research Visit the Glencoe Science Web site at **science.glencoe.com** for the latest information about raising condors to be released into the wild. Communicate to your class what you learn.

Imprinting Learned behavior includes imprinting, trial and error, conditioning, and insight. Have you ever seen young ducks following their mother? This is an important behavior because the adult bird has had more experience in finding food, escaping predators, and getting along in the world. **Imprinting** occurs when an animal forms a social attachment, like the condor in **Figure 5,** to another organism within a specific time period after birth or hatching.

Konrad Lorenz, an Austrian naturalist, developed the concept of imprinting. Working with geese, he discovered that a gosling follows the first moving object it sees after hatching. The moving object, whatever it is, is imprinted as its parent. This behavior works well when the first moving object a gosling sees is an adult female goose. But goslings hatched in an incubator might see a human first and imprint on him or her. Animals that become imprinted toward animals of another species have difficulty recognizing members of their own species.

Trial and Error Can you remember when you learned to ride a bicycle? You probably fell many times before you learned how to balance on the bicycle. After a while you could ride without having to think about it. You have many skills that you have learned through trial and error such as feeding yourself and tying your shoes, as shown in **Figure 6.**

Behavior that is modified by experience is called trial-and-error learning. Many animals learn by trial and error. When baby chicks first try feeding themselves, they peck at many stones before they get any food. As a result of trial and error, they learn to peck only at food particles.

Figure 6
Were you able to tie your shoes on the first attempt? *What other things do you do every day that required learning?*

Activity

Separate a large puzzle into six sections. Place the disassembled pieces for each section in a paper bag. Divide the class into six groups, each with one of the bags. Have groups work together to reassemble the sections. Then, have students combine the sections to the complete puzzle. Ask students what type of behavior they demonstrated. learned L2 ELL COOP LEARN

Internet Addresses

Explore the Glencoe Science Web site at **science.glencoe.com** to find out more about topics in this section.

Caption Answer

Figure 6 Possible answers: reading, writing, brushing teeth, using the telephone, walking

Resource Manager

Chapter Resources Booklet
- Enrichment, p. 27
- Lab Activity, pp. 9–11
- Transparency Activity, pp. 43–44

Visual Learning

Figure 5 The use of puppets of adult condors ensures that expected imprinting occurs. Predict what would likely occur if puppets of adult geese had been used to feed the condor chicks. Because of imprinting, the chicks would form a social attachment to adult geese instead of to adult condors. L2

LS **Logical-Mathematical**

Purpose to observe the affects of conditioning L1 ELL
LS **Visual-Spatial**

Materials photos of food and landscapes

Teaching Strategy Have students show their partners several different types of food.

Analysis

1. Usually, staring at pictures of food causes a person to feel hungry.
2. Generally, landscape pictures remind people of places, but they do not stimulate a response or feeling. At times, landscapes can evoke feelings of nostalgia.
3. Large pictures of appetizing foods condition consumers to feel hungry and crave the food product.

Assessment

Performance Have students design another experiment in which they test for conditioning. Use **PASC,** p. 95.

Teacher FYI

Conditioning is very common in the animal kingdom. For example, birds learn to avoid certain brightly colored caterpillars that have a bad taste. Birds associate the color pattern with the bad taste. Other species of caterpillars who mimic the appearance of the bad-tasting organisms also benefit from this conditioning, as birds will avoid them also.

Reading Check

Answer Conditioning causes a response to one stimulus to become associated with a different stimulus.

Observing Conditioning

Procedure

1. Obtain several **photos of different foods and landscapes** from your teacher.
2. Show each picture to a classmate for 20 s.
3. Record how each photo made your partner feel.

Analysis

1. How did your partner feel after looking at the photos of food?
2. What effect did the landscape pictures have on your partner?
3. Infer how advertising might condition consumers to buy specific food products.

Conditioning Do you have an aquarium in your school or home? If you put your hand above the tank, the fish probably will swim to the top of the tank expecting to be fed. They have learned that a hand shape above them means food. What would happen if you tapped on the glass right before you fed them? After a while the fish probably will swim to the top of the tank if you just tap on the glass. Because they are used to being fed after you tap on the glass, they associate the tap with food.

Animals often learn new behaviors by conditioning. In **conditioning,** behavior is modified so that a response to one stimulus becomes associated with a different stimulus. There are two types of conditioning. One type introduces a new stimulus before the usual stimulus. Russian scientist Ivan P. Pavlov performed experiments with this type of conditioning. He knew that the sight and smell of food made hungry dogs secrete saliva. Pavlov added another stimulus. He rang a bell before he fed the dogs. The dogs began to connect the sound of the bell with food. Then Pavlov rang the bell without giving the dogs food. They salivated when the bell was rung even though he did not show them food. The dogs, like the one in **Figure 7,** were conditioned to respond to the bell.

In the second type of conditioning, the new stimulus is given after the affected behavior. Getting an allowance for doing chores is an example of this type of conditioning. You do your chores because you want to receive your allowance. You have been conditioned to perform an activity that you may not have done if you had not been offered a reward.

Reading Check *How does conditioning modify behavior?*

Figure 7
In Pavlov's experiment, a dog was conditioned to salivate when a bell was rung. It associated the bell with food.

Cultural Diversity

Hunting The lifestyle and survival of hunting cultures revolved around the responses of hunted animals. Have students select a Native American nation and read about its relationship with the animals it depended upon. Ask students to report on animal behaviors that were important to the cultures, such as when salmon swam upriver to spawn (Northwestern nations) or patterns of bison herd movement (Plains nations).

Resource Manager

Chapter Resources Booklet
Reinforcement, p. 25
MiniLAB, p. 3
Home and Community Involvement, p. 44

Insight How does learned behavior help an animal deal with a new situation? Suppose you have a new math problem to solve. Do you begin by acting as though you've never seen it before, or do you use what you have learned previously in math to solve the problem? If you use what you have learned, then you have used a kind of learned behavior called insight. **Insight** is a form of reasoning that allows animals to use past experiences to solve new problems. In experiments with chimpanzees, as shown in **Figure 8,** bananas were placed out of the chimpanzees' reach. Instead of giving up, they piled up boxes found in the room, climbed them, and reached the bananas. At some time in their lives, the chimpanzees must have solved a similar problem. The chimpanzees demonstrated insight during the experiment. Much of adult human learning is based on insight. When you were a baby, you learned by trial and error. As you grow older, you will rely more on insight.

Figure 8
This illustration shows how chimpanzees may use insight to solve problems.

Section  1 Assessment

1. How is innate behavior different from learned behavior?
2. Compare a reflex with an instinct.
3. What is the difference between an internal and external stimulus?
4. Compare imprinting and conditioning.
5. **Think Critically** Use what you know about conditioning to explain how the term *mouthwatering food* might have come about.

Skill Builder Activities

6. **Researching Information** How are dogs trained to sniff out certain substances? **For more help, refer to the** Science Skill Handbook.
7. **Using an Electronic Spreadsheet** Make a spreadsheet of the behaviors in this section. Sort the behaviors according to whether they are innate or learned behaviors. Then identify the type of innate or learned behavior. **For more help, refer to the** Technology Skill Handbook.

Teacher FYI

Much of human learning is based on insight. Babies first learn by trial and error. As they grow older, they rely on insight. Solving problems is an example of using insight.

3 Assess

Reteach

Have students make a concept map using all vocabulary terms in this section. L2 LS **Visual-Spatial** P

Challenge

How would a lack of innate behavior patterns affect animals? Many would not live long enough to reproduce, which could result in species eventually becoming extinct.

Assessment

Portfolio Have students write a paragraph in their Science Journals describing the type of learning that occurs when crows in a farmer's field do not react to a scarecrow that has been in place for a month. Use **Performance Assessment in the Science Classroom,** p. 99.

Answers to Section Assessment

1. innate: behavior an animal is born with; learned: develops through experience
2. reflex: automatic response, doesn't involve brain; instinct: complex pattern of innate behavior
3. An internal stimulus originates inside the body, external stimuli come from outside the body.
4. Imprinting occurs when an animal forms a social attachment to another organism within a specific time period after birth or hatching. Conditioning occurs when a response to one stimulus becomes associated with a different stimulus.
5. The response to the stimulus of food is the production of saliva. Upon conditioning, the sight, smell, or thought of food can cause the production of saliva.
6. Look for understanding of innate and learned behaviors in student responses.
7. innate: reflexes and instincts; learned: imprinting, trial and error, conditioning, and insight; An example should be provided for each

SECTION

Behavioral Interactions

1 Motivate

Bellringer Transparency

Display the Section Focus Transparency for Section 2. Use the accompanying Transparency Activity Master. L2 ELL

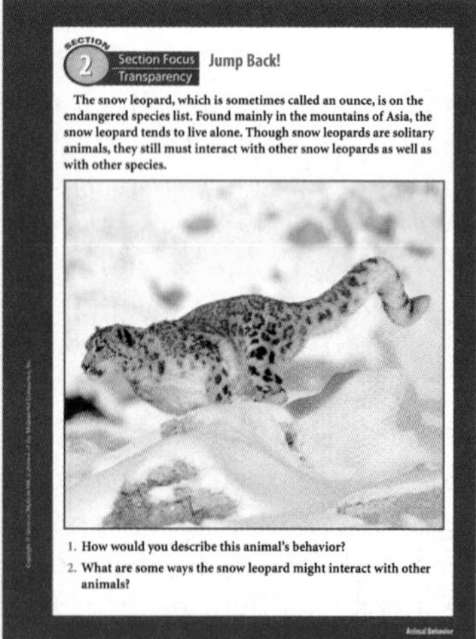

Section Focus Transparency 2 Jump Back!

The snow leopard, which is sometimes called an ounce, is on the endangered species list. Found mainly in the mountains of Asia, the snow leopard tends to live alone. Though snow leopards are solitary animals, they still must interact with other snow leopards as well as with other species.

1. How would you describe this animal's behavior?
2. What are some ways the snow leopard might interact with other animals?

Tie to Prior Knowledge

Students will be familiar with aggressive and territorial behaviors of pets and other animals. Discuss familiar examples of territorial displays and threatening behaviors.

Reading Check

Answer It provides advantages for survival of the species.

SECTION 2

Behavioral Interactions

As You Read

What You'll Learn

- **Explain** why behavioral adaptations are important.
- **Describe** how courtship behavior increases reproductive success.
- **Explain** the importance of social behavior and cyclic behavior.

Vocabulary

social behavior
society
aggression
courtship behavior
pheromone
cyclic behavior
hibernation
migration

Why It's Important

Organisms must be able to communicate with each other to survive.

Instinctive Behavior Patterns

Complex interactions of innate behaviors between organisms result in many types of animal behavior. For example, courtship and mating within most animal groups are instinctive ritual behaviors that help animals recognize possible mates. Animals also protect themselves and their food sources by defending their territories. Instinctive behavior, just like natural hair color, is inherited.

Social Behavior

Animals often live in groups. One reason, shown in **Figure 9,** is that large numbers provide safety. A lion is less likely to attack a herd of zebras than a lone zebra. Sometimes animals in large groups help keep each other warm. Also, migrating animal groups are less likely to get lost than animals that travel alone.

Interactions among organisms of the same species are examples of **social behavior.** Social behaviors include courtship and mating, caring for the young, claiming territories, protecting each other, and getting food. These inherited behaviors provide advantages that promote survival of the species.

Reading Check *Why is social behavior important?*

Figure 9
When several zebras are close together their stripes make it difficult for predators to pick out one individual.

Section Assessment Planner

PORTFOLIO
Cultural Diversity, p. 470
Curriculum Connection, p. 473

PERFORMANCE ASSESSMENT
Try at Home MiniLAB, p. 469
Skill Builder Activities, p. 474
See page 482 for more options.

CONTENT ASSESSMENT
Section, p. 474
Challenge, p. 474
Chapter, pp. 482–483

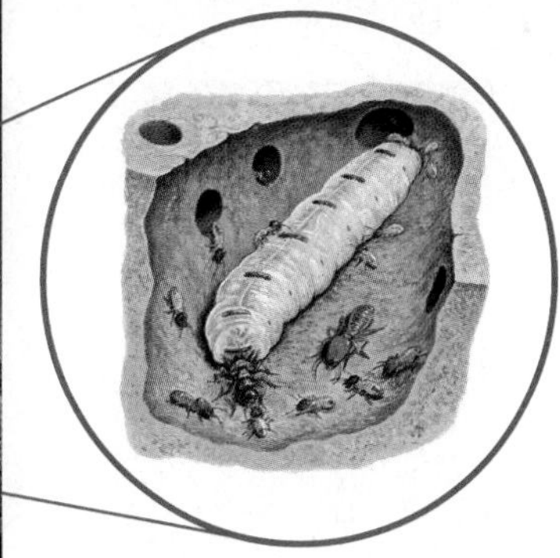

Figure 10
Termites built this large mound in Australia. The mound has a network of tunnels and chambers for the queen to deposit eggs into.

Societies Insects such as ants, bees, and the termites shown in **Figure 10,** live together in societies. A **society** is a group of animals of the same species living and working together in an organized way. Each member has a certain role. Usually a specific female lays eggs, and a male fertilizes them. Workers do all the other jobs in the society.

Some societies are organized by dominance. Wolves usually live together in packs. A wolf pack has a dominant female. The top female controls the mating of the other females. If plenty of food is available, she mates and then allows the others to do so. If food is scarce, she allows less mating. During such times, she is usually the only one to mate.

Territorial Behavior

Many animals set up territories for feeding, mating, and raising young. A territory is an area that an animal defends from other members of the same species. Ownership of a territory occurs in different ways. Songbirds sing, sea lions bellow, and squirrels chatter to claim territories. Other animals leave scent marks. Some animals, like the tiger in **Figure 11,** patrol an area and attack other animals of the same species who enter their territory. Why do animals defend their territories? Territories contain food, shelter, and potential mates. If an animal has a territory, it will be able to mate and produce offspring. Defending territories is an instinctive behavior. It improves the survival rate of an animal's offspring.

Figure 11
A tiger's territory may include several miles. It will confront any other tiger who enters it.

2 Teach

Social Behavior

Make a Model

Have students work in groups of three to make a model of animals with social behavior, such as honeybees, hornets, ants, beavers or wolves. Ask them to identify the members of the group modeled and explain their roles. L2

Discussion

How do fish benefit from forming schools? When swimming in a school, a fish is less vulnerable to attack by a predator.

Territorial Behavior

Use an Analogy

Discuss the meaning of the expression: *The best defense is a good offense.* Explain that some animals that travel together will mount an attack against predators as a means of protection. For example, some monkeys will throw sticks at an approaching leopard.

Discussion

Some male lions roar to compete for mates. Roaring takes a lot of strength. **How might roaring prevent a fight between two males?** The roar's intensity illustrates the strength of a male. A weaker male will likely leave the area rather than fight.

Resource Manager

Chapter Resources Booklet
Transparency Activity, p. 41
Directed Reading for Content Mastery, pp. 19, 20
Mathematics Skill Activities, p. 49

Visual Learning

Figure 11 What other animals defend their territories? Possible answers: songbirds, sea lions, squirrels

Territorial Behavior, continued

Identifying Misconceptions

Students may typically describe animal behavior in human terms using such words as *pain*, *emotions*, and *desire*. There is a tendency to relate all animal behavior in terms of human reactions. Caution students not to think of animal behavior in terms of their own behavior.

Use Science Words

Word Origin The term *anthropomorphism* is derived from the Greek terms *anthropos*, meaning "man," and *morphe*, meaning "form." Have students use a dictionary to find the meaning of *anthropomorphism* and use the word in a sentence. It is the application of human characteristics to anything not human.

Communication

Quick Demo

Shake a student's hand. Ask what message was communicated by the action. Have class members identify other actions that send messages. Point out that animals have many forms of nonverbal communication.

Figure 12
Young wolves roll over and make themselves as small as possible to show their submission to adult wolves.

Aggression Have you ever watched as one dog approached another dog that was eating a bone? What happened to the appearance of the dog with the bone? Did its hair on its back stick up? Did it curl its lips and make growling noises? This behavior is aggression. **Aggression** is a forceful behavior used to dominate or control another animal. Fighting and threatening are aggressive behaviors animals use to defend their territories, protect their young, or to get food.

Many animals demonstrate aggression. Some birds let their wings droop below their tail feathers. It may take another bird's perch and thrust its head forward in a pecking motion as a sign of aggression. Cats lay their ears flat, arch their backs, and hiss.

Submission Animals of the same species seldom fight to the death. Teeth, beaks, claws, and horns are used for killing prey or for defending against members of a different species.

To avoid being attacked and injured by an individual of its own species, an animal shows submission. Postures that make an animal appear smaller often are used to communicate surrender. In some animal groups, one individual is usually dominant. Members of the group show submissive behavior toward the dominant individual. This stops further aggressive behavior by the dominant animal. Young animals also display submissive behaviors toward parents or dominant animals, as shown in **Figure 12.**

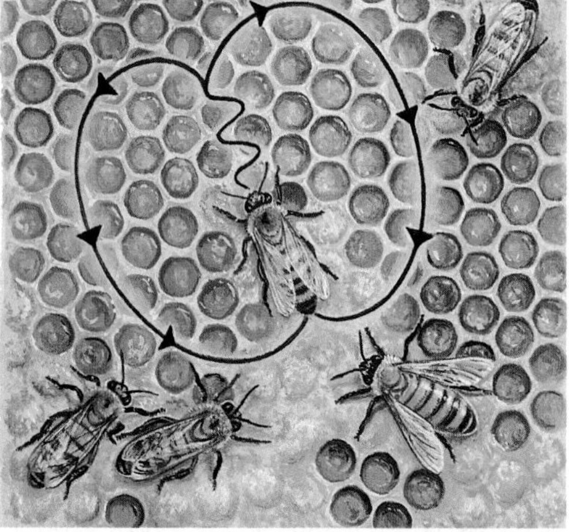

Figure 13
During the waggle dance, if the source is far from the hive, the dance takes the form of a figure eight. The angle of the waggle is equal to the angle from the hive between the Sun and nectar source.

Communication

In all social behavior, communication is important. Communication is an action by a sender that influences the behavior of a receiver. How do you communicate with the people around you? You may talk, make noises, or gesture like you did in this chapter's Explore Activity. Honeybees perform a dance, as shown in **Figure 13,** to communicate to other bees in the hive where a food source is. Animals in a group communicate with sounds, scents, and actions. Alarm calls, chemicals, speech, courtship behavior, and aggression are forms of communication.

Inclusion Strategies

Learning Disabled Write all the letters of the alphabet in random order on a sheet of paper. Provide each student three copies of the sheet and have them mark the copies 1, 2, and 3. Give students 10 seconds to find the letters and draw a line to connect them in alphabetical order. Time the students for three trials. L1 LS **Kinesthetic**

Curriculum Connection

Health Studies show that the health of hospitalized and institutionalized people often improves when they develop a relationship with an animal. Have students research capuchin monkeys or guide dogs and write reports explaining how the interaction of animals and people is thought to promote better health.

Figure 14
This male Emperor of Germany bird of paradise attracts mates by posturing and fanning its tail.

Courtship Behavior A male bird of paradise, shown in **Figure 14,** spreads its tail feathers and struts. A male sage grouse fans its tail, fluffs its feathers, and blows up its two red air sacs. These are examples of behavior that animals perform before mating. This type of behavior is called **courtship behavior.** Courtship behaviors allow male and female members of a species to recognize each other. These behaviors also stimulate males and females so they are ready to mate at the same time. This helps ensure reproductive success.

In most species the males are more colorful and perform courtship displays to attract a mate. Some courtship behaviors allow males and females to find each other across distances.

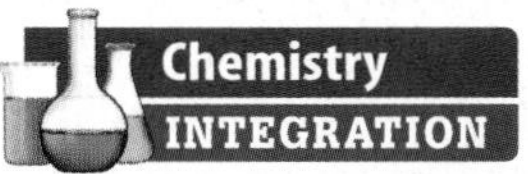

Chemical Communication Ants are sometimes seen moving single file toward a piece of food. Male dogs frequently urinate on objects and plants. Both behaviors are based on chemical communication. The ants have laid down chemical trails that others of their species can follow. The dog is letting other dogs know he has been there. In these behaviors, the animals are using a chemical called a pheromone to communicate. A **pheromone** (FER uh mohn) is a chemical that is produced by one animal to influence the behavior of another animal of the same species. They are powerful chemicals needed only in small amounts. They remain in the environment so that the sender and the receiver can communicate without being in the same place at the same time. They can advertise the presence of an animal to predators, as well as to the intended receiver of the message.

Males and females use pheromones to establish territories, warn of danger, and attract mates. Certain ants, mice, and snails release alarm pheromones when injured or threatened.

TRY AT HOME Mini LAB

Demonstrating Chemical Communication

Procedure

1. Obtain a **sample of perfume or air freshener.**
2. Spray it into the air to leave a scent trail as you move around the house or apartment to a hiding place.
3. Have someone try to discover where you are by following the scent of the substance.

Analysis

1. What was the difference between the first and last room you were in?
2. Would this be an efficient way for humans to communicate? Explain.

Teacher FYI

Courtship patterns are complex innate behaviors. The ranges of two types of woodpeckers overlap in a narrow region of Texas. Despite similarities in appearance and behavior, they do not interbreed because they use different cues in recognizing mates.

Purpose to observe a method of chemical communication

Materials perfume, air freshener, or flavoring oil

Teaching Strategy Have students choose a strong scent with a pleasant odor.

Analysis

1. The scent would be stronger in the last room.
2. Yes; a person could be located by the scent.

Assessment

Oral How do law enforcement officers help trained dogs pick up the scent of a missing person? They have the dog smell an object that belonged to the missing person. Use **Performance Assessment in the Science Classroom,** p. 143.

Resource Manager

Chapter Resources Booklet
Enrichment, p. 28
MiniLAB, p. 4

Teacher FYI

Ants make a "pheromone trail" from their nest to food sources for other ants to follow. Some female insects give off pheromones that attract males. Scientists have developed artificial pheromones for use in pest control. Traps contain the female pheromones, which attract the males to the trap.

Communication, continued

Activity
Some animals are very sensitive to changes in the environment that precede violent natural events, such as earthquakes, hurricanes, typhoons, and other storms. In China, people have learned that unusual panicky behavior by certain animals may signal an imminent earthquake. Have students research this behavior and how it can benefit people.

Quick Demo
Many students will equate communication with sound. Invite any students who know sign language to demonstrate this form of visual communication.

IDENTIFYING Misconceptions
Some students may think individual organisms evolve a structure or behavior in order to respond to their environments. In reality, traits pre-exist that may help an animal adapt. The animals that survive pass the traits to offspring. For example, if a population of flies is sprayed with a deadly chemical, some may already have a genetic makeup that causes them to be resistant to the chemical. As a result, they survive and pass the trait on to their offspring.

Figure 15
Many animals use sound to communicate.

A Frogs often croak loud enough to be heard far away.

B Pileated woodpecker calls often can be heard above everything else in the forest.

C Howler monkeys got their name because of the sounds they make.

Sound Communication Male crickets rub one forewing against the other forewing. This produces chirping sounds that attract females. Each cricket species produces several calls that are different from other cricket species. These calls are used by researchers to identify different species. Male mosquitoes have hairs on their antennae that sense buzzing sounds produced by females of their same species. The tiny hairs vibrate only to the frequency emitted by a female of the same species.

Vertebrates use a number of different forms of sound communication. Rabbits thump the ground, gorillas pound their chests, beavers slap the water with their flat tails, and frogs, like the one in **Figure 15,** croak. Do you think that sound communication in noisy environments is useful? Seabirds that live where waves pound the shore rather than in some quieter place must rely on visual signals, not sound, for communication.

Chemistry INTEGRATION

The light produced by fireflies is a particle of visible light that radiates when chemicals produce a high-energy state and then return to their normal state. Hypothesize how this helps fireflies survive. Write your hypothesis in your Science Journal.

Light Communication Certain kinds of flies, marine organisms, and beetles have a special form of communication called bioluminescence. Bioluminescence, shown in **Figure 16,** is the ability of certain living things to give off light. This light is produced through a series of chemical reactions in the organism's body. Probably the most familiar bioluminescent organisms in North America are fireflies. They are not flies, but beetles. The flash of light is produced on the underside of the last abdominal segments and is used to locate a prospective mate. Each species has its own characteristic flashing. Males fly close to the ground and emit flashes of light. Females must flash an answer at exactly the correct time to attract males.

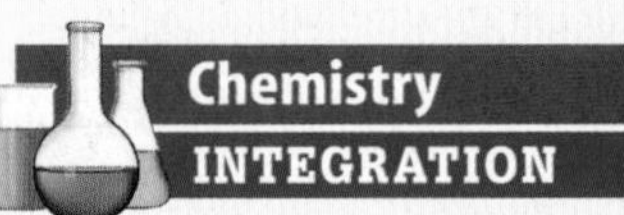

Chemistry INTEGRATION

The behavior enables females to locate males and reproduce.

Cultural Diversity
Adapting to the Environment People who live in desert areas often wear loose-fitting, lightweight, light-colored garments that reflect sunlight and heat. They may live in tents that enable them to take advantage of the smallest breezes. A tundra, rain forest, or deciduous forest would call for different cultural adaptations. Students can make posters that show the food, shelter, and clothing of different cultures. L2 IN **Kinesthetic**

Science Journal
Animal Entertainers Animals often perform in circus acts. Have students research and write reports on animals as entertainers. Have students consider whether the behaviors of animals such as dolphins, birds, and elephants should be modified for entertainment.

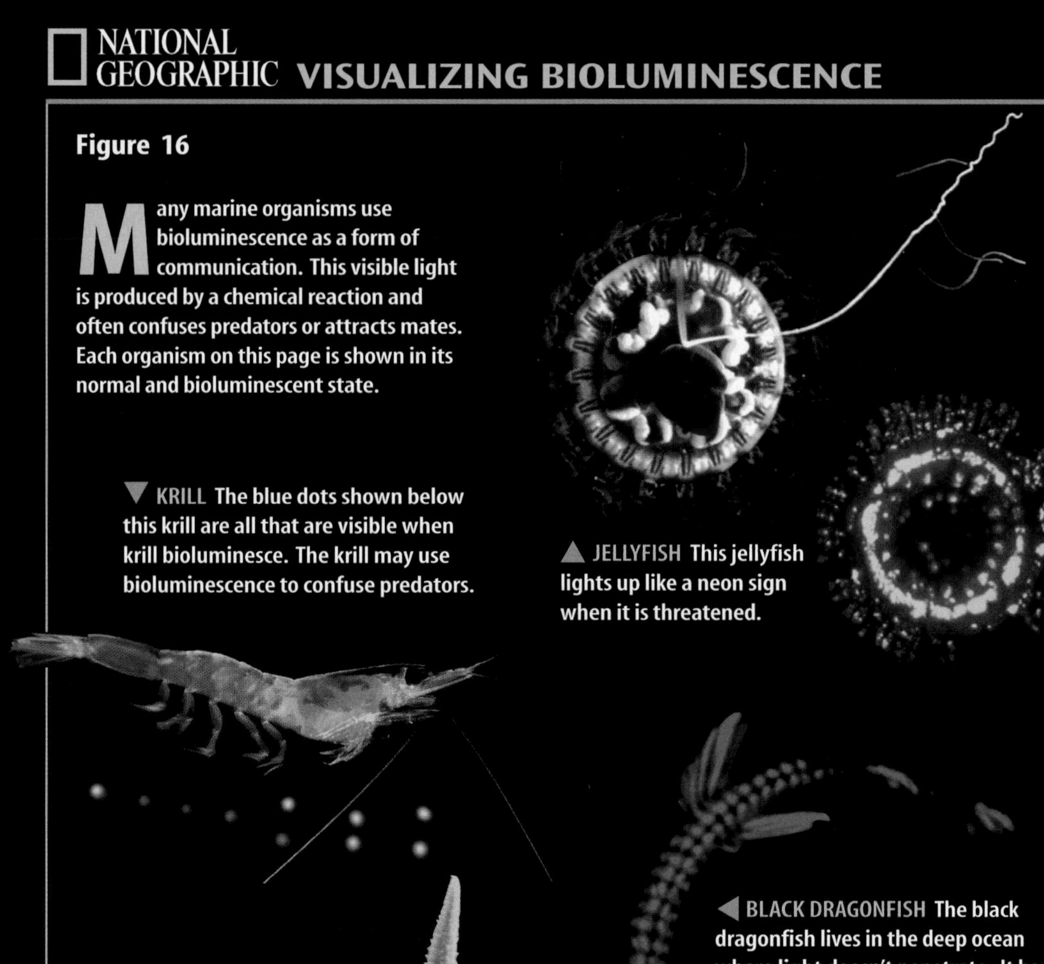

Figure 16

Many marine organisms use bioluminescence as a form of communication. This visible light is produced by a chemical reaction and often confuses predators or attracts mates. Each organism on this page is shown in its normal and bioluminescent state.

▼ KRILL The blue dots shown below this krill are all that are visible when krill bioluminesce. The krill may use bioluminescence to confuse predators.

▲ JELLYFISH This jellyfish lights up like a neon sign when it is threatened.

◀ BLACK DRAGONFISH The black dragonfish lives in the deep ocean where light doesn't penetrate. It has light organs under its eyes that it uses like a flashlight to search for prey.

▲ DEEP-SEA SEA STAR The sea star uses light to warn predators of its unpleasant taste.

Visualizing Bioluminescence

Have students examine the pictures and read the captions. Then ask the following questions.

During which times are organisms bioluminescent? Possible answers: Organisms that live near the surface are bioluminescent at night. Organisms that live in the deep sea, where there is no light, can use bioluminescence all the time.

Explain how bioluminescence can be used to attract prey. Possible answer: Prey organisms are attracted to the light, which is often coming from the mouthparts or a fleshy lure of the predator. As the unsuspecting prey approaches to investigate, it nears the mouth and is gobbled up.

Activity

Have students find examples of land animals that are bioluminescent and record where in the world they can be found living. Students can make a simple map of the world and draw in the representative bioluminescent animals found in different locations. Possible answers: fireflies are found east of the continental divide in the U.S., a type of beetle larvae called railroad worms is found in Central and South America, glowworms, which are fly larvae, can be found in caves in New Zealand, and land snails in Malaysia. Other bioluminescent land animals include some types of earthworms, centipedes and millipedes.

Resource Manager 

Chapter Resources Booklet
Lab Activity, pp. 13–14
Reading and Writing Skill Activities, p. 5

Extension

Have students investigate why there are almost no bioluminescent animals in found fresh water. Possible answer: Scientists hypothesize that the different chemical composition of fresh water may account for the lack of bioluminescence. Some essential chemical may be missing in the fresh water that will not allow the reaction to proceed.

Cyclic Behavior

Use Science Words

Word Origin The term *circadian* comes from the Latin word *circum*, meaning "around," and *dies*, meaning "day." Have students make a list of additional words derived from the Latin word *circum*. Possible answers: circuit, circulate, circumference, circumvent L2 IS **Linguistic**

Extension

Have students use encyclopedias and other resources to find out what environmental factors might trigger an animal's urge to hibernate. Examples include decreasing temperature, shorter day length, and weather conditions. L2

Internet Addresses

Explore the Glencoe Science Web site at **science.glencoe.com** to find out more about topics in this section.

Reading Check

Answer when an animal is active during the day

Caption Answer

Figure 17 cyclic behavior called nocturnal behavior

Uses of Bioluminescence Many bioluminescent animals are found deep in oceans where sunlight does not reach. The ability to produce light may serve several functions. One species of fish dangles a special luminescent organ in front of its mouth. This lures prey close enough to be caught and eaten. Deep-sea shrimp secrete clouds of a luminescent substance when disturbed. This helps them escape their predators. Patterns of luminescence on an animal's body may serve as marks of recognition similar to the color patterns of animals that live in sunlit areas.

SCIENCE Online

Research Visit the Glencoe Science Web site at **science.glencoe.com** for more information about owl behavior. Communicate to your class what you learn.

Cyclic Behavior

Why do most songbirds rest at night while some species of owls rest during the day? Some animals like the owl in **Figure 17** show regularly repeated behaviors such as sleeping in the day and feeding at night.

A **cyclic behavior** is innate behavior that occurs in a repeating pattern. It often is repeated in response to changes in the environment. Behavior that is based on a 24-hour cycle is called a circadian rhythm. Most animals come close to this 24-hour cycle of sleeping and wakefulness. Experiments show that even if animals can't tell whether it is night or day, they continue to behave in a 24-hour cycle.

Animals that are active during the day are diurnal (dy UR nul). Animals that are active at night are nocturnal. Owls are nocturnal. They have round heads, big eyes, and flat faces. Their flat faces reflect sound and help them navigate at night. Owls also have soft feathers that make them almost silent while flying.

Reading Check *What is a diurnal behavior?*

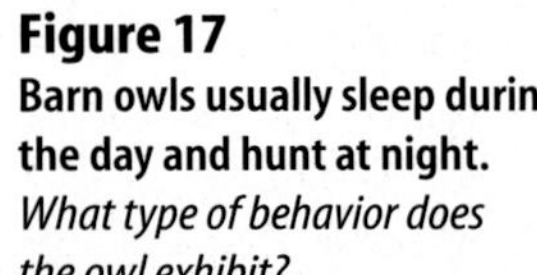

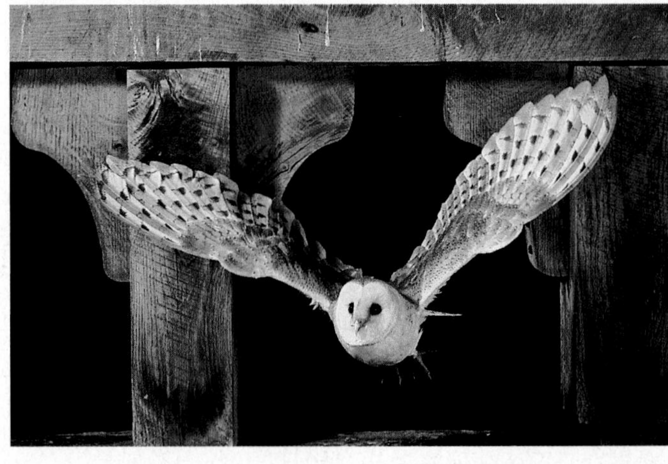

Figure 17
Barn owls usually sleep during the day and hunt at night.
What type of behavior does the owl exhibit?

Curriculum Connection

Health Point out that people function according to a circadian rhythm. The most familiar aspect of this is the sleep-wake cycle. Have students research what body changes occur during sleep and how people behave when they are deprived of sleep for several days. Sleep deprivation can cause fatigue, inability to concentrate, and visual or tactile illusions and hallucinations. L3 P

Problems in Studying Behavior Have students list some of the problems of using animals, including humans, in behavioral studies. Possible answers: Animals other than humans cannot communicate in words. Equating animal responses with those of humans may not always work.

472 CHAPTER 16 Animal Behavior

Hibernation Some cyclic behaviors also occur over long periods of time. **Hibernation** is a cyclic response to cold temperatures and limited food supplies. During hibernation, an animal's body temperature drops to near that of its surroundings, and its breathing rate is greatly reduced. Animals in hibernation, such as the bats in **Figure 18,** survive on stored body fat. The animal remains inactive until the weather becomes warm in the spring. Some mammals and many amphibians and reptiles hibernate.

Figure 18
Many bats find a frost-free place like this abandoned coal mine to hibernate for the winter when food supplies are low.

Animals that live in desert like environments also go into a state of reduced activity. This period of inactivity is called estivation. Desert animals sometimes estivate due to extreme heat, lack of food, or periods of drought.

Problem-Solving Activity

How can you determine which animals hibernate?

Many animals hibernate in the winter. During this period of inactivity, they survive on stored body fat. While they are hibernating, they undergo several physical changes. Heart rate slows down and body temperature decreases. The degree to which the body temperature decreases varies among animals. Scientists have disagreed about whether some animals truly hibernate or if they just reduce their activity and go into a light sleep. Usually, a true hibernator's body temperature will decrease significantly while it is hibernating.

Average Body Temperatures of Hibernating Animals

Animal	Normal Body Temperature (°C)	Hibernating Body Temperature (°C)
Woodchuck	37	3
Squirrel	32	4
Grizzly Bear	32–37	27–32
Whippoorwill	40	18
Hoary Marmot	37	10

Identifying the Problem

The table on the right shows the difference between the normal body temperature and the hibernating body temperature of several animals. What similarities do you notice?

Solving the Problem

1. Which animals would you classify as true hibernators and which would you classify as light sleepers? Explain.
2. Some animals such as snakes and frogs also hibernate. Why would it be difficult to record their normal body temperature on this table?
3. Which animal has the least amount of change in body temperature?

Problem-Solving Activity

National Math Standards

Correlation to Mathematics Objectives
1, 4, 5, 6, 8, 9

Answers

1. The woodchuck, squirrel, hoary marmot, and whippoorwill are "true hibernators" because their body temperatures decrease significantly during hibernation. The grizzly bear is a "light sleeper." It does not undergo significant physical changes during its period of inactivity.
2. Cold-blooded animals' body temperatures adapt to their surroundings, and therefore are in a constant state of change depending on the environment. If these animals were to be included on the chart, the physical environment would also need to be included.
3. the grizzly bear

Active Reading

Pair of Pairs This strategy encourages students as partners to respond to a question. They brainstorm together, recording on one paper their ideas. After a few minutes, they combine with another pair and share responses. Finally, groups of four share responses. Have students use the Pair of Pairs strategy on the Think Critically question in this Section Assessment.

Curriculum Connection

Social Studies Have each student research a different migrating animal and summarize his or her findings in a poster. Posters should indicate where the animal spends winters and summers, the distance between the two areas, and the animal's breeding location. Encourage students to include pictures of the animals, contrasting their appearance in summer and winter. P

Resource Manager

Earth Science Critical Thinking/Problem Solving, p. 16

Cyclic Behavior, continued

Extension

More than 100 million monarch butterflies migrate from Canada and the eastern United States to Mexico every fall. Gray whales migrate from the Bering Sea to the coastal region of California. Have students trace these routes and others on a map or globe. L1 LS **Visual-Spatial**

3 Assess

Reteach

Label 3 x 5 cards with examples of social behavior, territorial behavior, communication, and cyclic behavior. Ask students to choose a card, classify the type of behavior, and provide reasons for their responses.

Challenge

Have students research what causes jet lag. Jet lag is the temporary disruption of the body's normal biological rhythms after high-speed air travel through several time zones. People suffering from jet lag often feel fatigued and have lowered efficiency for several days after travel. This is because the body is still functioning on its "regular" time. It takes about a day per hour of time change to reset the body's clock.

Assessment

Content Have pairs of students make posters that explain social behavior, territorial behavior, communication, or cyclic behavior. Use **Performance Assessment in the Science Classroom,** p. 145.

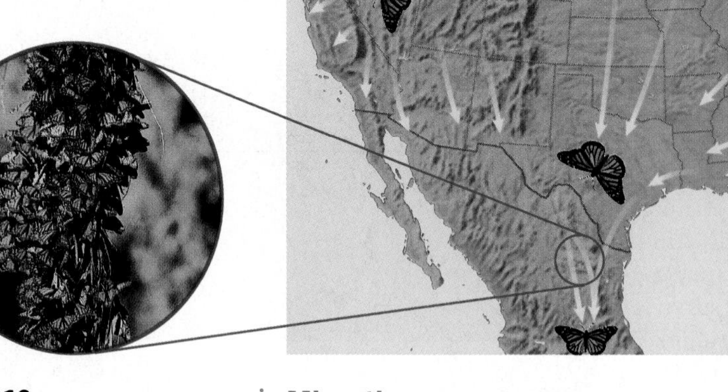

Figure 19
Many monarch butterflies travel from the United States to Mexico for the winter.

Migration Instead of hibernating, many birds and mammals move to new locations when the seasons change. This instinctive seasonal movement of animals is called **migration.** Most animals migrate to find food or reproduce in an environment that is more favorable for the survival of its offspring. Many species of birds fly for hours or days without stopping. The blackpoll warbler flies more than 4,000 km nonstop from North America to its winter home in South America. The trip takes nearly 90 hours. Monarch butterflies, shown in **Figure 19,** can migrate as much as 2,900 km. Gray whales swim from cold arctic waters to the waters off the coast of northern Mexico. After the young are born, they make the return trip.

Section 2 Assessment

1. What are some examples of courtship behavior? How does this behavior help organisms survive?
2. How are cyclic behaviors, such as hibernation, a response to stimuli in the environment?
3. Give two reasons why animals migrate.
4. What is the difference between hibernation and migration?
5. **Think Critically** Suppose a species of frog lives close to a loud waterfall. It often waves a bright blue foot in the air. What might the frog be doing?

Skill Builder Activities

6. **Testing a Hypothesis** Design an experiment that tests the hypothesis that ants leave chemical trails to show other ants where food can be found. **For more help, refer to the** Science Skill Handbook.
7. **Solving One-Step Equations** Some cicadas emerge from the ground every 17 years. The population of one type of caterpillar peaks every five years. If the peak cycle of the caterpillars and the emergence of cicadas coincided in 1990, in what year will they coincide again? **For more help, refer to the** Math Skill Handbook.

Answers to Section Assessment

1. Answers will vary. These behaviors help ensure reproductive success.
2. They are responses to changes in the environment, such as decrease in the number of daylight hours or temperature changes.
3. to find food and to reproduce in a favorable environment for offspring
4. An animal that hibernates stays in the same place and becomes inactive until environmental conditions become favorable. An animal that migrates moves to a location with favorable conditions.
5. Possible answer: signalling other frogs, either to attract a mate or to defend its territory
6. Students should identify a variable, a constant, and a control.
7. Since 17 and 5 are prime numbers, the cycles will again coincide in 17×5, or 85 years from 1990; $1990 + 85 = 2075$.

Activity

Observing Earthworm Behavior

Earthworms often can be seen wriggling across sidewalks, driveways, and yards on moist nights. Why don't you see many earthworms during the day?

What You'll Investigate

How do earthworms respond to light?

Materials

scissors	paper
shoe box with lid	moist paper towels
flashlight	earthworms
tape	timer

Goals

- **Predict** how earthworms will behave in the presence of light.

Safety Precautions

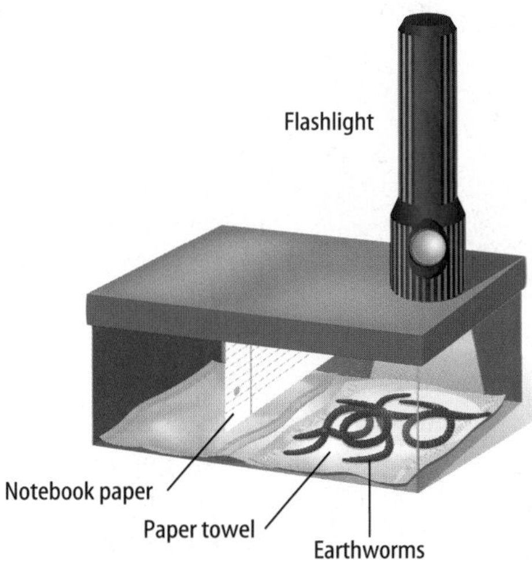

Procedure

1. Cut a round hole, smaller than the end of the flashlight, near one end of the lid.
2. Tape a sheet of paper to the lid so it hangs just above the bottom of the box and about 10 cm away from the end with the hole in it.
3. Place the moist paper towels in the bottom of the box.
4. Place the earthworms in the end of the box that has the hole in it.
5. Hold the flashlight over the hole and turn it on.
6. Leave the box undisturbed for 30 minutes, then open the lid and observe the worms.
7. **Record** the results of your experiment in your Science Journal.

Conclude and Apply

1. Which direction did the earthworms move when the light was turned on?
2. Based on your observations, what can you infer about earthworms?
3. What type of behavior did the earthworms exhibit? Explain.
4. **Predict** where you would need to go to find earthworms during the day.

Communicating Your Data

Write a story that describes a day in the life of an earthworm. List activities, dangers, and problems an earthworm can face. Include a description of its habitat. **For more help, refer to the** Science Skill Handbook.

Activity

BENCH TESTED

Purpose Students observe earthworm responses to light. L2 LS **Kinesthetic**

Process Skills observing and inferring, recognizing cause and effect

Time Required 45 minutes

Safety Precautions Caution students to wash their hands after handling earthworms.

Teaching Strategy Have students keep their hands moist while handling earthworms. Remind them to handle worms gently.

Answers to Questions

1. away from the light
2. Earthworms prefer darkness to light.
3. Innate behavior; the earthworms instinctively move away from the light and toward the darkened area.
4. in the soil

Assessment

Process Have students use their observations to list what they think an earthworm needs to survive. soil, darkness, moisture Use **Performance Assessment in the Science Classroom,** p. 89.

Inclusion Strategies

Visually Impaired Have visually impaired students dampen their hands and gently run their fingers over the body of an earthworm. Encourage them to describe both the worm's segments and its setae—bristle-like structures found on each segment that anchor the worm to the ground as it contracts its muscles for movement. L1 LS **Kinesthetic**

Communicating Your Data

Students should base their story on their knowledge of earthworms and their habitat.

Resource Manager

Chapter Resources Booklet

Activity Worksheet, pp. 5–6

Reinforcement, p. 26

Activity

BENCH TESTED

Recognize the Problem

Purpose

Students research information about animals in their natural habitats, and then design and build a model of a habitat that supports the survival of that animal. L2

LS **Logical-Mathematical**

Process Skills

making models, researching information, predicting, collecting data, measuring in SI, recognizing cause and effect, interpreting data, communicating, using proportions

Time Required

one to two weeks

Thinking Critically

Discussion Direct students to think about the types of animals with which they are familiar. **What types of food do they eat? What kind of environment do they need to survive?** Have students discuss and research other types of animals that could live in the same environments. Provide reference materials or allow students to use library resources and the Internet.

Possible Materials

Provide basic materials for making models such as modeling clay, scrap paper, scissors, and glue. Encourage reusing and recycling by having students bring in scrap materials from home.

Activity Model and Invent

Animal Habitats

Zoos, animal parks, and aquariums are safe places for wild animals. Years ago, captive animals were kept in small cages or behind glass windows. Almost no attempt was made to provide natural habitats for the animals. People who came to see the animals could not observe the animal's normal behavior. Now, most captive animals are kept in exhibit areas that closely resemble their natural habitats. These areas provide suitable environments for the animals so that they can interact with members of their same species and have healthier, longer lives.

Recognize the Problem

What types of environments are best suited for raising animals in captivity?

Thinking Critically

How can the habitats provided at an animal park affect the behavior of animals?

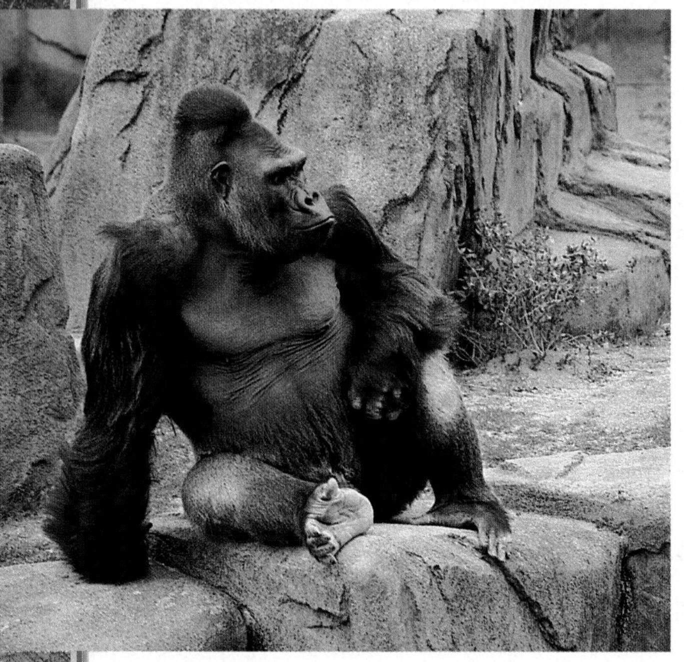

Goals

- **Research** the natural habitat and basic needs of one animal.
- **Design** and model an appropriate zoo, animal park, or aquarium environment for this animal. Working cooperatively with your classmates, design an entire zoo or animal park.

Possible Materials

poster board
markers or colored pencils
materials that can be used to make a scale model

Data Source

SCIENCE*Online* Go to the Glencoe Science Web site at **science.glencoe.com** for more information about existing zoos, animal parks, and aquariums.

Resource Manager

Chapter Resources Booklet
Activity Worksheet, pp. 7–8

Lab Management and Safety, p. 43

Internet Addresses

Explore the Glencoe Science Web site at **science.glencoe.com** to find out more about topics in this activity.

Planning the Model

1. Choose an animal to research. Find out where this animal is found in nature. What does it eat? What are its natural predators? Does it exhibit unique territorial, courtship, or other types of behavior? How is this animal adapted to its natural environment?
2. **Design** a model of a proposed habitat in which this animal can live successfully. Don't forget to include all of the things, such as shelter, food, and water, that your animal will need to survive. Will there be any other organisms in the habitat?

Check the Model Plans

1. **Research** how zoos, animal parks, or aquariums provide habitats for animals. Information may be obtained by viewing the Glencoe Science Web site and contacting scientists who work at zoos, animal parks, and aquariums.
2. **Present** your design to your class in the form of a poster, slide show, or video. Compare your proposed habitat with that of the animal's natural environment. Make sure you include a picture of your animal in its natural environment.

Making the Model

1. Using all of the information you have gathered, create a model exhibit area for your animal.
2. Indicate what other plants and animals may be present in the exhibit area.

Analyzing and Applying Results

1. **Decide** whether all of the animals studied in this activity can coexist in the same zoo or wildlife preserve.
2. **Predict** which animals could be grouped together in exhibit areas.
3. **Determine** how large your zoo or wildlife preserve needs to be. Which animals require a large habitat?
4. Using the information provided by the rest of your classmates, design an entire zoo or aquarium that could include the majority of animals studied.
5. **Analyze** problems that might exist in your design. Suggest some ways you might want to improve your design.

Communicating Your Data

Give an oral presentation to another class on the importance of providing natural habitats for captive animals. **For more help, refer to the** Science Skill Handbook.

Planning the Model

Teaching Strategies

- Distribute lists of zoo web sites.
- Encourage students to make a checklist of items they need to include in their models.

Making the Model

Expected Outcome

Students should build a model that is appropriate for their chosen animal. Area of concern might include sufficient land and water area and climate control.

Analyzing and Applying Results

Direct students to record and then discuss the answers to these questions in small groups. Decisions to combine different animals in one habitat should be based on environmental concerns such as land and water requirements and climate considerations, including temperature and amount of precipitation. In the event of unfavorable conditions, adequate shelter must be available. Animals that have predator-prey relationships must also be separated geographically.

Safety Precautions

Discuss the dangers of any materials being used, such as sharp scissors or glue with strong fumes.

Assessment

Performance Have students make pamphlets encouraging the public to visit the model animal habitats they have devised. Use **Performance Assessment in the Science Classroom,** p. 129.

Communicating Your Data

Show students how to outline their presentations as a way of organizing their ideas. Suggest that they practice several times before giving the presentation.

Oops! Accidents in SCIENCE

SOMETIMES GREAT DISCOVERIES HAPPEN BY ACCIDENT!

Content Background

Dogs can be trained to help people in many capacities. Many police departments have special K-9 units. The dogs in these units are specially trained to help the officer in a variety of ways, including searching for people or finding drugs. Dogs are often used in search and rescue after disasters such as earthquakes or avalanches. Dogs can also be used to help the hearing impaired, as well as acting as companion animals to people who are physically challenged. Guide dogs for the visually impaired learn that things like curbs and moving cars are dangerous and that they must stop for these in order to warn their master. The dogs are also trained to be aware of and lead their masters around things like trees and low-hanging obstructions such as signs and awnings. Even though the dog can walk underneath such obstacles, a person could be injured if they had no warning. Other dogs work as sled dogs, sheep or cattle herders, or even to help carry newspapers on a delivery route.

Discussion

Arrange for a patrol dog and its handler to come to the classroom. Before the guests arrive, have students make a list of questions for the officer. Questions can be about the acquisition of the dogs, information on the training procedures, at home handling, or retiring a patrol dog.

Going to the Dogs

A simple and surprising stroll showed that dogs really are humans' best friends

You've probably seen visually impaired people walking with their trusted and gentle four-legged guides—or "seeing-eye" dogs. The specially trained dogs serve as eyes for people who can't see, making it possible for them to lead independent lives. But what you probably didn't know is that about 80 years ago, a doctor and his patient discovered this canine ability entirely by accident!

Many people were killed or injured during World War I. Near the end of that war, Dr. Gerhard Stalling and his dog strolled with a patient—a German soldier who had been blinded—around hospital grounds in Germany.

German shepherds make excellent guide dogs.

478

Resources for Teachers and Students

Dogs With Jobs, by Merrily Weisbord and Kim Kachanoff, Pocket Books, 2000.

Working Dogs: Tales from Animal Planet's K-9 to 5 World, by Colleen Needles and Kit Carlson, Discovery Books, 2000.

A Dog's Gotta Do What A Dog's Gotta Do: Dogs at Work, by Marilyn Singer, Henry Holt and Company, Inc., 2000.

A dog safely guides its owner across a street.

While they were walking, the doctor was briefly called away. The dog and the soldier stayed outside. A few moments later, when the doctor returned, the dog and the soldier were gone! Searching the paths frantically, Dr. Stalling made an astonishing discovery. His pet had led the soldier safely around the hospital grounds. And together the two strolled peacefully back toward the doctor.

School for Dogs

Inspired by what his dog could do, Dr. Stalling set up the first school in the world dedicated to training dogs as guides. Dorothy Eustis, an American woman working as a dog trainer for the International Red Cross in Switzerland, traveled to Stalling's school about ten years later. A report of her visit and study of the way Stalling trained dogs appeared in a New York City newspaper in 1927.

Hearing the story, Morris Frank, a visually impaired American, became determined to get himself a guide dog. He wrote to Dorothy Eustis and asked that she train a dog for him. She accepted his request on one condition. She wanted Frank to join her in Switzerland for the training process. Frank and his guide dog Buddy returned to New Jersey in 1928. Within a year, Frank set up a training facility in New Jersey, "The Seeing Eye, Inc."

German shepherds, golden retrievers, and Labrador retrievers seem to make the best guide dogs. They learn hand gestures and simple commands to lead visually impaired people across streets and safely around obstacles. This is what scientists call "learned behavior." Animals gain learned behavior through experience. Learning happens gradually and in steps. In fact, scientists say that learning is a somewhat permanent change in behavior due to experience. But, a guide dog not only learns to respond to special commands, it must also know when *not* to obey. If its human owner urges the dog to cross the street and the dog sees that a car is approaching and refuses, the dog has learned to disobey the command. This trait, called "intelligent disobedience," ensures the safety of the owner and the dog—a sure sign that dogs are still humans' best friends.

This girl gets to help train a future guide dog for The Seeing Eye, Inc.

CONNECTIONS Write Lead a blindfolded partner around the classroom. Help your partner avoid obstacles. Then trade places. Write in your Science Journal about your experience leading and being led.

SCIENCE Online
For more information, visit science.glencoe.com

Activity

Have students investigate other capacities in which dogs can help people. Students can also research any other animals that help or have helped people in the past, such as carrier pigeons or capuchin monkeys. Students should make a poster showing their results. They could act out a story as a skit. Encourage students to share with the class any heartwarming or amazing stories that they come across in their research.

Analyze the Event

Have students discuss what elements may be involved in the training of guide dogs. **What traits should a guide dog have? How should the training progress? What should the dogs learn first? How are the dogs taught to respond to dangers such as curbs and cars?** Possible answers: The breeds of dogs usually used as guides are all described as being smart, even-tempered, and friendly animals. They are also strong and make good partners for work. During training, dogs are rewarded with praise and pats on the head when they do something correctly. When the dog needs to be corrected, the instructor says "no" loudly and may pull on the leash. The dogs are never hit or yelled at. This training is repeated many times until the dog achieves the desired goal. Simpler commands, such as "come" and "sit," are taught first. More difficult tasks such as stopping for curbs or cars are learned later.

SCIENCE Online

Internet Addresses

Explore the Glencoe Science Web site at **science.glencoe.com** to find out more about topics in this feature.

Chapter 16 Study Guide

Reviewing Main Ideas

Preview

Students can answer the questions in their Science Journals. Discuss the answers as you go through the chapter. **LS Linguistic**

Review

Students can write their answers, then compare them with those of other students. **LS Interpersonal**

Reteach

Students can look at the illustrations and describe details that support the main ideas of the chapter. **LS Visual-Spatial**

Answers to Chapter Review

Section 1

1. learned behavior

Section 2

3. courtship behavior
4. The ant has left a chemical trail that other ants can follow.

Chapter 16 Study Guide

Reviewing Main Ideas

Section 1 Types of Behavior

1. Behavior that an animal has when it's born is innate behavior. Other animal behaviors are learned through experience. *In the figure below, what type of behavior is the dog exhibiting?*

2. Reflexes are simple innate behaviors. An instinct is a complex pattern of innate behavior.
3. Learned behavior includes imprinting, in which an animal forms a social attachment immediately after birth.
4. Behavior modified by experience is learning by trial and error.
5. Conditioning occurs when the response to one stimulus becomes associated with another. Insight uses past experiences to solve new problems.

Section 2 Behavioral Interactions

1. Behavioral adaptations such as defense of territory, courtship behavior, and social behavior help species of animals survive and reproduce.
2. Courtship behaviors allow males and females to recognize each other and prepare to mate.

3. Interactions among members of the same species are social behaviors. *What type of social behavior is this male peacock displaying?*
4. Communication among organisms occurs in several ways including chemical, sound, and light. *How will other ants, like the one shown, be able to locate food that is far from their nest?*

5. Cyclic behaviors are behaviors that occur in repeating patterns. Animals that are active during the day are diurnal. Animals that are active at night are nocturnal.

FOLDABLES Reading & Study Skills — After You Read

Compare and contrast the behaviors of Animal 1 and Animal 2 listed in your foldable. How many of the behaviors you listed were innate? Learned?

FOLDABLES Reading & Study Skills — After You Read

After students have read the chapter and completed the Foldable described in Before You Read, have them do the activity on the student page.

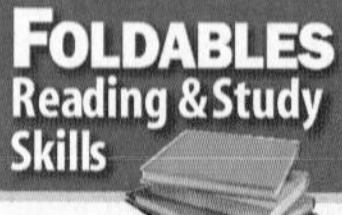

Visualizing Main Ideas

Complete the following concept map on types of behavior.

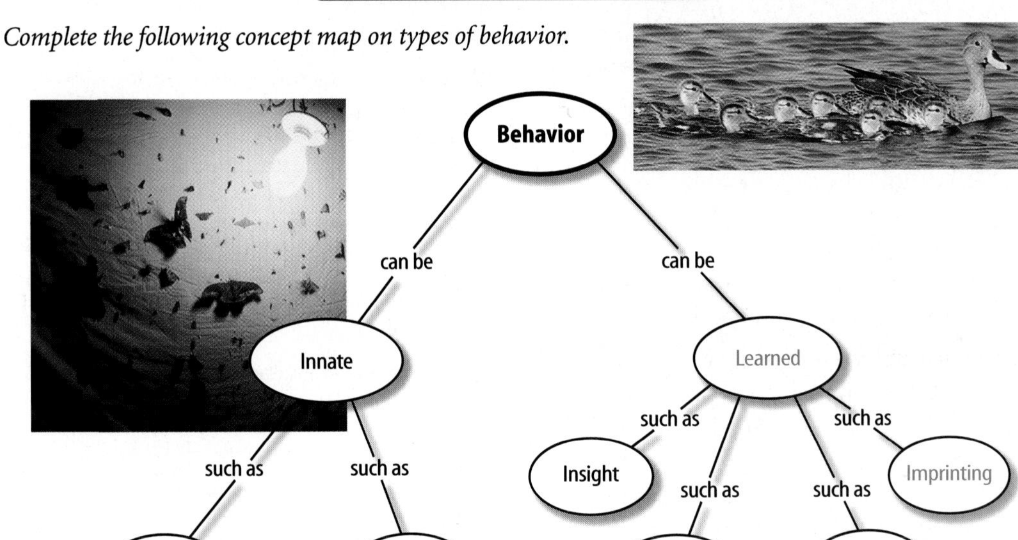

Vocabulary Review

Vocabulary Words

a. aggression
b. behavior
c. conditioning
d. courtship behavior
e. cyclic behavior
f. hibernation
g. imprinting
h. innate behavior
i. insight
j. instinct
k. migration
l. pheromone
m. reflex
n. social behavior
o. society

Study Tip

Take good notes, even during lab. Lab experiments reinforce key concepts, and looking back on these notes can help you better understand what happened and why.

Using Vocabulary

Explain the differences between the vocabulary words given below. Then explain how the words are related.

1. conditioning, imprinting
2. innate behavior, social behavior
3. insight, instinct
4. social behavior, society
5. instinct, reflex
6. hibernation, migration
7. courtship behavior, pheromone
8. cyclic behavior, migration
9. aggression, social behavior
10. behavior, reflex

Chapter 16 Study Guide

Visualizing Main Ideas

See student page.

Vocabulary Review

Using Vocabulary

1. Conditioning is modification of established behaviors. Imprinting is the formation of a new behavior. Both are learned behaviors.
2. Not all innate behaviors are social behaviors, but all social behaviors are innate behaviors.
3. Instinct is an innate behavior, and insight is a learned behavior. Both can be complex patterns of behaviors.
4. Social behavior is an innate behavior. The social behaviors within an animal population form a society.
5. Instinct: complex pattern of innate behavior; reflex: simple innate behavior.
6. Hibernation is a period of inactive behavior, and migration is the seasonal movement of an animal or animal populations. Both are cyclic behaviors.
7. Courtship behavior is a social behavior between males and females of a species. Chemicals called pheromones usually stimulate courtship behavior.
8. All migrations are cyclic behaviors, but not all cyclic behaviors are migrations.
9. Aggression is just one of the many types of social behaviors.
10. Behavior is the interaction of one organism with another organism. Some behaviors are learned and others are instinctive. Reflex is the simplest innate behavior.

CHAPTER STUDY GUIDE 481

Chapter 16 Assessment

Checking Concepts

1. A
2. D
3. C
4. B
5. C
6. B
7. C
8. A
9. C
10. A

Thinking Critically

11. Leaving the room when the bell rings is a conditioned learned response.
12. Migration allows organisms to survive changes in weather. Some organisms may not survive the long, stressful journey.
13. A habit is a learned behavior that has become automatic. A reflex is an innate behavior.
14. Behaviors that help obtain food, are protective, or are defensive help organisms survive.
15. A farmer can artificially lengthen the amount of "daylight" hens are exposed to by using lights, which stimulate the hens to lay more eggs.

Chapter 16 Assessment

Checking Concepts

Choose the word or phrase that best answers the question.

1. What is an instinct an example of?
   A) innate behavior **C)** imprinting
   B) learned behavior **D)** conditioning
2. What is a spider spinning a web an example of?
   A) conditioning **C)** learned behavior
   B) imprinting **D)** an instinct
3. Which animals depend least on instinct and most on learning?
   A) birds **C)** mammals
   B) fish **D)** amphibians
4. What is an area that an animal defends from other members of the same species called?
   A) society **C)** migration
   B) territory **D)** aggression
5. What is a forceful act used to dominate or control?
   A) courtship **C)** aggression
   B) reflex **D)** hibernation
6. Which of the following is NOT an example of courtship behavior?
   A) fluffing feathers
   B) taking over a perch
   C) singing songs
   D) releasing pheromones
7. What is an organized group of animals doing specific jobs called?
   A) community **C)** society
   B) territory **D)** circadian rhythm
8. What is the response of inactivity and slowed metabolism that occurs during cold conditions?
   A) hibernation **C)** migration
   B) imprinting **D)** circadian rhythm
9. Which of the following is a reflex?
   A) writing **C)** sneezing
   B) talking **D)** riding a bicycle
10. What are behaviors that occur in repeated patterns called?
    A) cyclic **C)** reflex
    B) imprinting **D)** society

Thinking Critically

11. Explain the type of behavior involved when the bell rings at the end of class.
12. Discuss the advantages and disadvantages of migration as a means of survival.
13. Explain how a habit such as tying your shoes, is different from a reflex.
14. Use one example to explain how behavior increases an animal's chance for survival.
15. Hens lay more eggs in the spring when the number of daylight hours increases. How can farmers use this knowledge of behavior to their advantage?

Developing Skills

16. **Testing a Hypothesis** Design an experiment to test a hypothesis about a specific response to a stimulus from an animal.
17. **Recording Observations** Make observations of a dog, cat, or bird for a week. Record what you see. How did the animal communicate with other animals and with you?

Chapter Assessment Planner

Portfolio Encourage students to place in their portfolios one or two items of what they consider to be their best work. Examples include:

- Reteach, p. 465
- Cultural Diversity, p. 470
- Curriculum Connection, p. 473

Performance Additional performance assessments, Performance Task Assessment Lists, and rubrics for evaluating these activities can be found in Glencoe's **Performance Assessment in the Science Classroom.**

18. Forming a Hypothesis Make a hypothesis about how frogs communicate with each other. How could you test your hypothesis?

19. Classifying Make a list of 25 things that you do regularly. Classify each as an innate or learned behavior. Which behaviors do you have more of?

20. Concept Mapping Complete the following concept map about communication. Use these words: *sound, chirping, bioluminescence,* and *buzzing.*

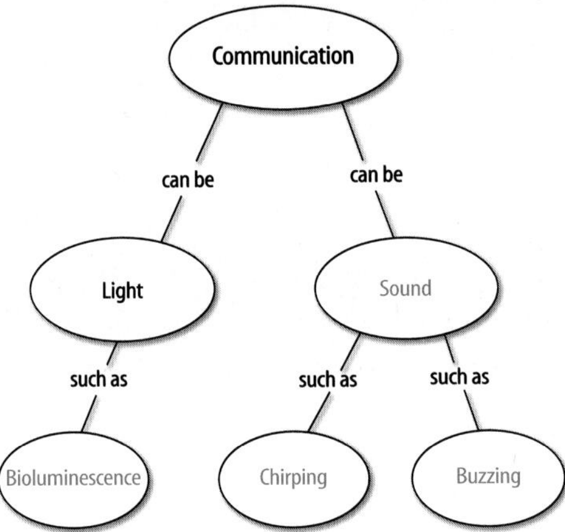

Performance Assessment

21. Poster Draw a map showing the migration route of monarch butterflies, gray whales, or blackpoll warblers.

TECHNOLOGY

Go to the Glencoe Science Web site at **science.glencoe.com** or use the **Glencoe Science CD-ROM** for additional chapter assessment.

THE PRINCETON REVIEW Test Practice

A biologist is given illustrations of different behaviors. The different types of behaviors are listed below.

Types of Behavior

Behavior	Example
1	
2	
3	
4	

Study the table and answer the following questions.

1. A reflex is an automatic response to a stimulus. Which one of the behaviors in the table is an example of a reflex?
   A) one **C)** three
   B) two **D)** four

2. Trial and error is a type of learned behavior that is modified by experience. Which of the behaviors in the table is an example of a trial-and-error behavior?
   F) one **H)** three
   G) two **J)** four

Chapter 16 Assessment

THE PRINCETON REVIEW Test Practice

The Test-Taking Tip was written by The Princeton Review, the nation's leader in test preparation.

1. A
2. H

Developing Skills

16. Answers should follow the basic plan Pavlov followed.
17. Answers will be determined by the animal the student observes.
18. Students will likely hypothesize that frogs communicate by using vocalizations. Accept all logical ways to test this hypothesis.
19. Possible answers may include: innate—sneezing, yawning, hiccups, jerking your hand away from something hot; learned—tying shoes, reading, writing, solving problems, riding a bike. Learned behaviors are probably more numerous.
20. See student page.

Performance Assessment

21. Maps should indicate both spring and fall migration routes. Use **Performance Assessment in the Science Classroom,** p. 145.

Assessment Resources

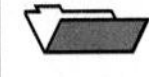 **Reproducible Masters**

Chapter Resources Booklet
Chapter Review, pp. 33–34
Chapter Tests, pp. 35–38
Assessment Transparency Activity, p. 45

Glencoe Science Web site
Interactive Tutor
Chapter Quizzes

Glencoe Technology
Assessment Transparency
Interactive CD-ROM Chapter Quizzes
ExamView Pro Test Bank
Vocabulary PuzzleMaker Software
MindJogger Videoquiz

Standardized Test Practice

Reading Comprehension

QUESTION 1: C

Students should locate the term *banned* in the passage and read the surrounding sentences looking for context clues, such as *levels of DDT decreased.*

QUESTION 2: G

Students should reread the second paragraph to determine its main idea.

- **Choice F** No; this is a detail from the second paragraph, but it is not the main idea.
- **Choice G** Yes; this is the main idea of the second paragraph.
- **Choice H** No; this is a detail from the second paragraph.
- **Choice J** No; this is a detail from the second paragraph.

Teaching Tip

Suggest that students number the paragraphs in a passage to be sure that they are referring to the correct paragraph discussed in a particular question.

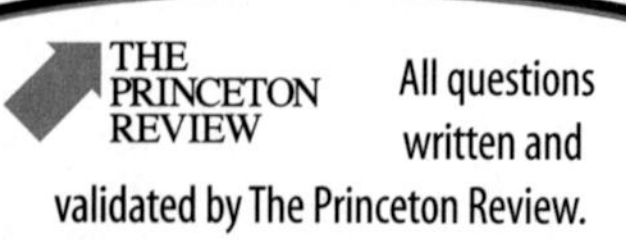

All questions written and validated by The Princeton Review.

Standardized Test Practice

Reading Comprehension

Read the passage. Then read each question that follows the passage. Decide which is the best answer to each question.

Birds and DDT

In the early 1960s, ecologists began to notice a decrease in many bird populations, particularly in the bald eagle population. Ecologists suspected that something must have changed the bald eagles' environments. They worked diligently to discover the cause of the environmental change before the bald eagle was driven to extinction.

Some ecologists thought that the birds were being hurt by something humans were doing. They looked for ways that human activities could be harming the birds. At the time, a pesticide called DDT was being used by farmers to protect their crops from pests. Ecologists realized that after farmers sprayed DDT, it was traveling into lakes and rivers and eventually was entering the groundwater. Once it was in lakes and rivers, aquatic organisms took in the DDT. Fish also became contaminated when they ate DDT-carrying organisms. After eating many DDT-carrying organisms, some fish carried a lot of DDT in their bodies. Then, birds such as the bald eagle ate these fish. Since the birds needed to eat many fish, the birds ended up carrying high levels of DDT in their bodies as well.

While studying the effects of DDT, ecologists discovered that DDT-carrying birds laid eggs with very thin shells. When the birds sat atop their eggs, they inadvertently broke them. As a result, fewer and fewer birds hatched.

Through much hard work and careful research, ecologists were able to determine what was happening to the bird populations.

As a result of their research, DDT use was banned. After several years, the levels of DDT decreased in bird habitats, and many of the bird populations returned to normal levels.

Test-Taking Tip Read the passage slowly and carefully to make sure you understand all the important details.

This drawing shows the bald eagle's food chain.

1. From the story, you can tell that when something is banned, it is _____.
   A) coated with a strip of paint
   B) used to feed baby birds
   C) made illegal
   D) used more often

2. What is the main idea of the second paragraph of this passage?
   F) Once in lakes and rivers, aquatic organisms took in the DDT.
   G) Ecologists discovered that DDT was in the food chain of birds, including the bald eagle.
   H) Fish became contaminated when they ate DDT-carrying organisms.
   J) At the time, a pesticide called DDT was being used by farmers.

Reasoning and Skills

Read each question and choose the best answer.

Group A

Group B

1. The animals in Group A are different from the animals in Group B because only the animals in Group A _____.
   A) live under water
   B) reproduce asexually
   C) feed by filtering water
   D) reproduce by budding

Test-Taking Tip Think about the different characteristics of sponges and cnidarians.

JAWLESS
CARTILAGE
SCALELESS

2. Which of the following animals have all of the characteristics that are listed above?
   F) shark
   G) tuna
   H) lamprey eel
   J) goldfish

Test-Taking Tip Review the three classes of fish: bony, jawless, and cartilaginous.

Campers dig a hole to bury their food scraps. Before they leave, they refill the hole with soil and place several large rocks on top. Later, raccoons explore the campground area, sniffing the ground. Eventually, the animals dig around and under the rocks to get to the food scraps.

3. If the raccoons do not find the food scraps, what eventually will happen to them?
   A) They will remain unchanged.
   B) Earthworms and other soil animals can break them down.
   C) The food scraps will become fungi.
   D) Other campers can reuse them.

4. The above is an example of how raccoons _____.
   F) can be affected by pheromones
   G) use insight
   H) show cyclic behavior
   J) prepare for hibernation

Test-Taking Tip Think about the definition of each type of animal behavior listed.

Consider this question carefully before writing your answer on a separate sheet of paper.

5. Recall what you know about animal behavior. Explain why most of the organisms that use bioluminescence for communication live in oceans.

Test-Taking Tip Think about the ocean environment before you answer the question.

Teaching Tip

Point out to students that in Question 1, they can eliminate choices that describe characteristics that both groups have in common. In this question, those are choices A, B, and D.

Question 5: Answers will vary.

Students should recall that bioluminescence is a means of communicating with light. In the oceans, light is an effective form of communication because the environment is dark. Also, light travels much faster through water than sound does, making it a better form of communication in the ocean. However, some animals, such as whales, do use sound to communicate.

Standardized Test Practice

Reasoning and Skills

Question 1: C

Students must understand that sponges (Group A) feed passively by filtering water, while cnidarians (Group B) use stinging cells to capture their prey.

Question 2: H

Students must identify the characteristics of the different classes of fish.

- **Choice F** No; sharks have jaws.
- **Choice G** No; bony fishes have skeletons made of bone, not cartilage.
- **Choice H** Yes; lampreys are jawless, get support from cartilage, and have smooth skin.
- **Choice J** No; goldfish are bony fish.

Question 3: B

Students should recall that earthworms feed on organic material in soil.

- **Choice A** No; all once-living substances break down over time.
- **Choice B** Yes; this is part of nature's recycling.
- **Choice C** No; fungi couldn't grow from different organisms.
- **Choice D** No; unfamiliar food should never be consumed.

Question 4: G

Students must understand how animals use previous experiences.

- **Choice F** No; pheromones are species specific.
- **Choice G** Yes; raccoons are capable of using previous experience.
- **Choice H** No; there is nothing cyclical about this behavior.
- **Choice J** No; raccoons sleep in their dens, but they do not hibernate.

UNIT 4

Unit Contents

Pre-Reading Activity

Have students look through the unit for photographs and illustrations that show relationships between body systems. They can make make a concept map that demonstrates how systems are related.

UNIT 4 Human Body Systems

How Are Chickens & Rice Connected?

486

Teacher to Teacher

"The discussion of the circulatory system provides an opportunity to integrate the sciences. Supernovas are known to produce elements found in nature. The iron bound to hemoglobin came from deep space in this manner when the planets were formed."

Edward G. Ezrailson, Ph.D.
Science Consultant
Spring, TX

NATIONAL GEOGRAPHIC

NATIONAL GEOGRAPHIC

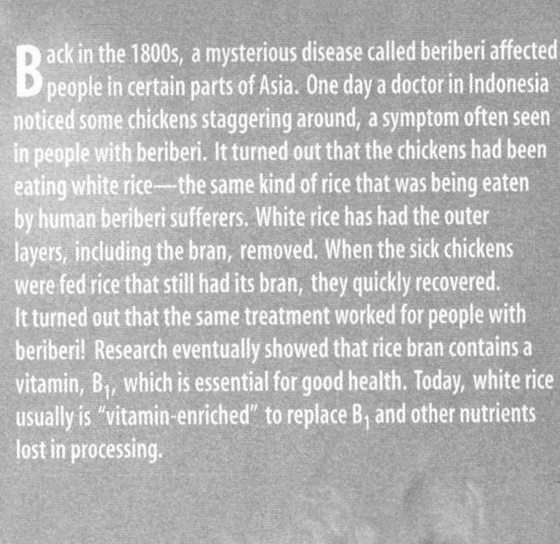

Back in the 1800s, a mysterious disease called beriberi affected people in certain parts of Asia. One day a doctor in Indonesia noticed some chickens staggering around, a symptom often seen in people with beriberi. It turned out that the chickens had been eating white rice—the same kind of rice that was being eaten by human beriberi sufferers. White rice has had the outer layers, including the bran, removed. When the sick chickens were fed rice that still had its bran, they quickly recovered. It turned out that the same treatment worked for people with beriberi! Research eventually showed that rice bran contains a vitamin, B_1, which is essential for good health. Today, white rice usually is "vitamin-enriched" to replace B_1 and other nutrients lost in processing.

SCIENCE CONNECTION

VITAMINS How does vitamin B_1 help your body and how much of this vitamin do you need? Conduct research to discover the role vitamin B_1 plays in body functions and to find out the recommended daily allowance (RDA) of this vitamin. Make a list of foods that are rich in vitamin B_1. Then create a menu for a full day's meals (breakfast, lunch, and dinner), making sure that each meal includes at least one food from your list.

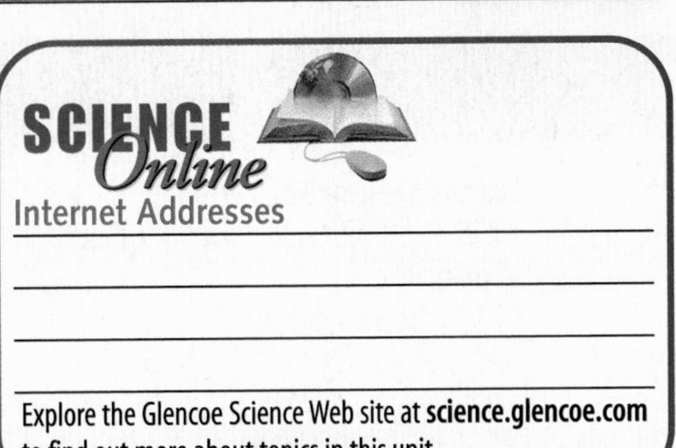

Internet Addresses

Explore the Glencoe Science Web site at **science.glencoe.com** to find out more about topics in this unit.

Introducing the Unit

How Are Chickens & Rice Connected?

Deficiencies of items like vitamin B_1 affect many human systems. This vitamin allows cells throughout the body to use many other nutrients. When B_1 is deficient, blood vessels expand in an attempt to deliver more blood and more nutrients to the cells. This in turn leads to increased work for the heart. Each body system must perform its functions in order for the other systems to do so. **How did an observation of a disease in chickens led to treatment of a human disease like beriberi?** Possible answer: All vertebrates share a common body plan and similar organ systems. Observations of animals in nature and in the laboratory provide valuable clues for an understanding of human health and biology.

SCIENCE CONNECTION

Activity

All living things must maintain a relatively constant internal environment, a condition known as homeostasis. Factors that must be controlled include body temperature, glucose levels in the blood, oxygen and carbon dioxide levels, the amount of water in the tissues, and so on. As you study each chapter, ask students to identify the variables each organ system controls, and how other organ systems are involved. Possible answer: A diet containing too much sodium can lead to increased retention of water. This can lead to high blood pressure, which can damage the circulatory and nervous systems. The kidneys must eliminate the excess salt and water.

Section/Objectives	Standards		Activities/Features
	National	State/Local	
Chapter Opener	See p. 5T for a Key to Standards.		**Explore Activity:** Observe muscle action, p. 489 **Before You Read,** p. 489
Section 1 The Skeletal System 2 sessions 1 block 1. **Identify** five functions of the skeletal system. 2. **Compare and contrast** movable and immovable joints.	National Content Standards: UCP1, A1, C1		**Science Online,** p. 492 **Math Skills Activity:** Estimating the Volume of Bones, p. 493
Section 2 The Muscular System 2 sessions 1 block 1. **Identify** the major function of the muscular system. 2. **Compare and contrast** the three types of muscles. 3. **Explain** how muscle action results in the movement of body parts.	National Content Standards: UCP1, A1, C1, F1		**Science Online,** p. 497 **Visualizing Human Body Levers,** p. 498 **MiniLAB:** Comparing Muscle Activity, p. 500
Section 3 The Skin 3 sessions 1.5 blocks 1. **Distinguish** between the epidermis and dermis of the skin. 2. **Identify** the function of the skin. 3. **Explain** how skin protects the body from disease and how it heals itself.	National Content Standards: UCP1, A1, C1, C3, F1, G1, G2		**Chemistry Integration,** p. 503 **MiniLAB:** Recognizing Why You Sweat, p. 504 **Earth Science Integration,** p. 505 **Activity:** Measuring Skin Surfaces, p. 507 **Activity:** Similar Skeletons, p. 508 **Oops! Accidents in Science:** First Aid Dolls, p. 510

NATIONAL GEOGRAPHIC

Teacher's Corner

Products Available from Glencoe
To order call 1-800-334-7344:
CD-ROM
NGS PictureShow: Human Body 1
Curriculum Kit
GeoKit: Human Body 2
Transparency Set
NGS PicturePack: Human Body 1
Videodisc
STV: Human Body

Products Available from National Geographic Society
To order call 1-800-368-2728:
Videos
Incredible Human Machine
Muscular and Skeletal System

Activity Materials	Reproducible Resources	Section Assessment	Technology
Explore Activity: table and chair	**Chapter Resources Booklet** Foldables Worksheet, p. 17 Directed Reading Overview, p. 19 Note-taking Worksheets, pp. 33–36	GLENCOE'S ASSESSMENT ADVANTAGE	
	Chapter Resources Booklet Transparency Activity, p. 46 Enrichment, p. 30 Reinforcement, p. 27 Directed Reading, p. 20 Lab Activity, pp. 9–11 **Life Science Critical Thinking/ Problem Solving,** p. 14 **Mathematics Skill Activities,** p. 17	Portfolio Visual Learning, p. 492 Performance Skill Builder Activities, p. 495 Content Section Assessment, p. 495 Challenge, p. 495	Section Focus Transparency Interactive CD-ROM Guided Reading Audio Program
MiniLAB: book, table, meterstick *Need materials?* Contact Science Kit at 1-800-828-7777 or www.sciencekit.com on the Internet.	**Chapter Resources Booklet** Transparency Activity, p. 47 MiniLAB, p. 3 Enrichment, p. 31 Reinforcement, p. 28 Directed Reading, p. 20 Transparency Activity, pp. 49–50 Lab Activity, pp. 13–16 **Home and Community Involvement,** p. 49	Portfolio Reteach, p. 501 Performance Try at Home MiniLAB, p. 500 Skill Builder Activities, p. 501 Content Section Assessment, p. 501 Challenge, p. 501	Section Focus Transparency Teaching Transparency Interactive CD-ROM Guided Reading Audio Program
MiniLAB: hand lens, clear plastic sandwich bag, tape **Activity:** large sheets of newspaper (10), scissors, tape, meterstick or ruler **Activity:** diagrams of a variety of mammal skeletons	**Chapter Resources Booklet** Transparency Activity, p. 48 MiniLAB, p. 4 Enrichment, p. 32 Reinforcement, p. 29 Directed Reading, pp. 21, 22 Activity Worksheet, pp. 5–6, 7–8 **Cultural Diversity,** p. 15 **Lab Management and Safety,** p. 67	Portfolio Visual Learning, p. 503 Performance MiniLAB, p. 504 Skill Builder Activities, p. 506 Content Section Assessment, p. 506 Challenge, p. 506	Section Focus Transparency Interactive CD-ROM Guided Reading Audio Program

End of Chapter Assessment

GLENCOE'S ASSESSMENT ADVANTAGE

Blackline Masters	Technology	Professional Series
Chapter Resources Booklet Chapter Review, pp. 39–40 Chapter Tests, pp. 41–44 **Standardized Test Practice by The Princeton Review,** pp. 75–78	MindJogger Videoquiz Interactive CD-ROM Vocabulary PuzzleMakers ExamView Pro Test Bank Interactive Lesson Planner Interactive Teacher Edition	Performance Assessment in the Science Classroom (PASC)

Transparencies

Section Focus

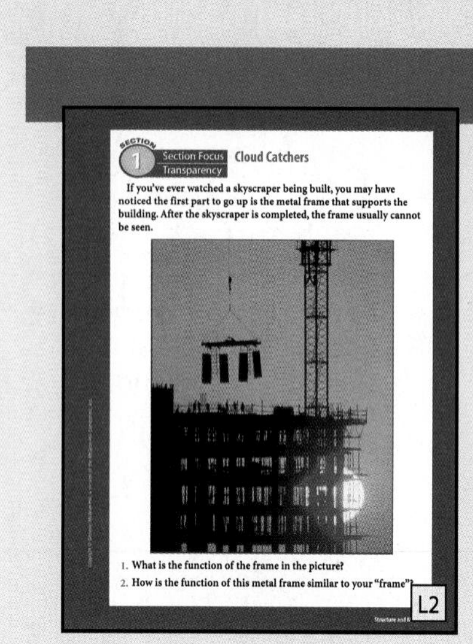
Section 1 Section Focus Transparency — Cloud Catchers

If you've ever watched a skyscraper being built, you may have noticed the first part to go up is the metal frame that supports the building. After the skyscraper is completed, the frame usually cannot be seen.

1. What is the function of the frame in the picture?
2. How is the function of this metal frame similar to your "frame"?

L2

Section 2 Section Focus Transparency — No Sweat

Just after World War II, an English neurosurgeon named Sir Ludwig Guttman organized a competition for people in wheelchairs. Today, opportunities exist for everyone to participate in a variety of sports and recreation at all levels.

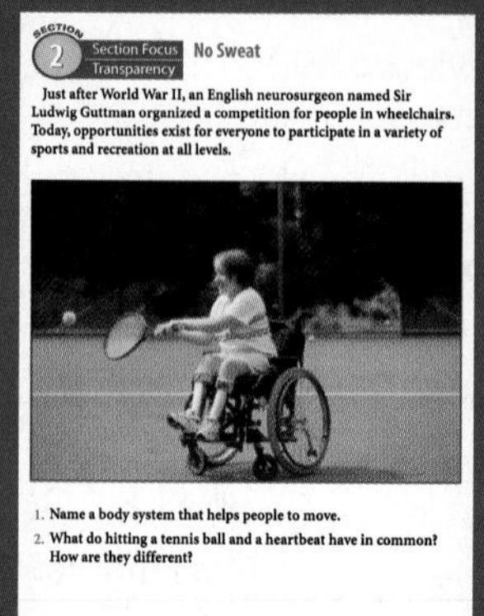

1. Name a body system that helps people to move.
2. What do hitting a tennis ball and a heartbeat have in common? How are they different?

L2

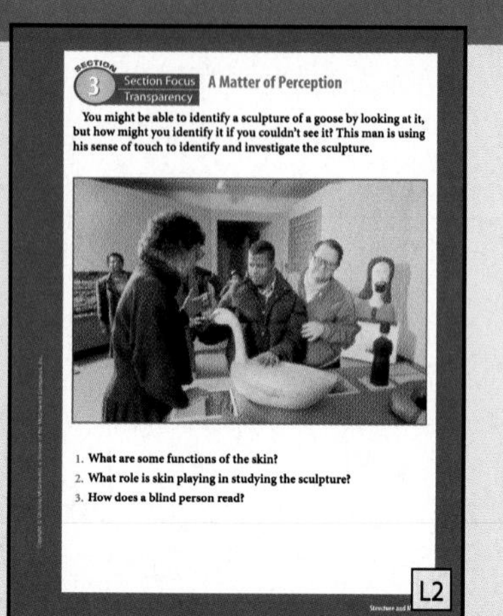
Section 3 Section Focus Transparency — A Matter of Perception

You might be able to identify a sculpture of a goose by looking at it, but how might you identify it if you couldn't see it? This man is using his sense of touch to identify and investigate the sculpture.

1. What are some functions of the skin?
2. What role is skin playing in studying the sculpture?
3. How does a blind person read?

L2

This is a representation of key blackline masters available in the Teacher Classroom Resources. See Resource Manager boxes within the chapter for additional information.

Assessment

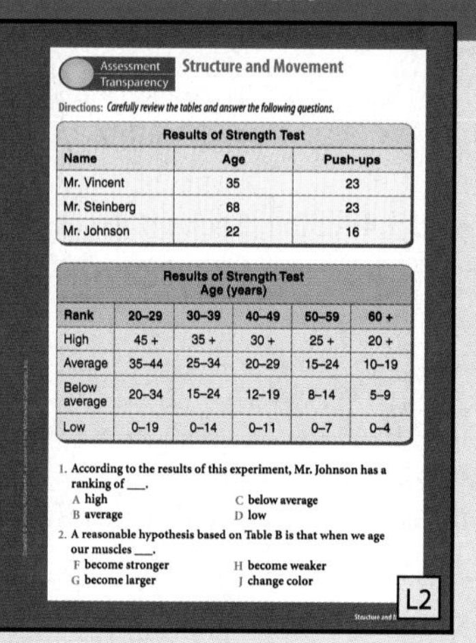
Assessment Transparency — Structure and Movement

Directions: *Carefully review the tables and answer the following questions.*

Results of Strength Test		
Name	Age	Push-ups
Mr. Vincent	35	23
Mr. Steinberg	68	23
Mr. Johnson	22	16

Results of Strength Test Age (years)					
Rank	20–29	30–39	40–49	50–59	60 +
High	45 +	35 +	30 +	25 +	20 +
Average	35–44	25–34	20–29	15–24	10–19
Below average	20–34	15–24	12–19	8–14	5–9
Low	0–19	0–14	0–11	0–7	0–4

1. According to the results of this experiment, Mr. Johnson has a ranking of ___.
   A high
   B average
   C below average
   D low
2. A reasonable hypothesis based on Table B is that when we age our muscles ___.
   F become stronger
   G become larger
   H become weaker
   J change color

L2

Teaching

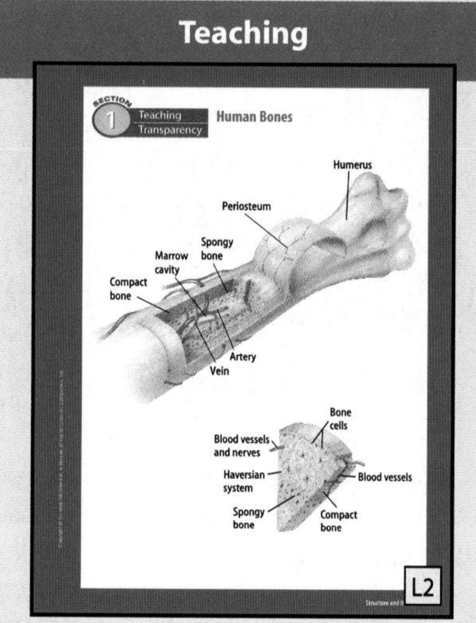
Section 1 Teaching Transparency — Human Bones

L2

Key to Teaching Strategies

The following designations will help you decide which activities are appropriate for your students.

- L1 Level 1 activities should be appropriate for students with learning difficulties.
- L2 Level 2 activities should be within the ability range of all students.
- L3 Level 3 activities are designed for above-average students.
- ELL ELL activities should be within the ability range of English Language Learners.
- COOP LEARN Cooperative Learning activities are designed for small group work.
- LS Multiple Learning Styles logos, as described on page 22T, are used throughout to indicate strategies that address different learning styles.
- P These strategies represent student products that can be placed into a best-work portfolio.

Hands-on Activities

Activity Worksheets

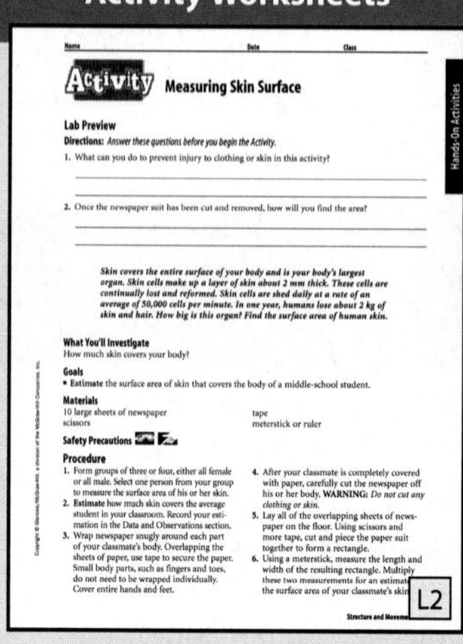
Name ___ Date ___ Class ___

Activity — Measuring Skin Surface

Hands-On Activities

Lab Preview

Directions: *Answer these questions before you begin the Activity.*

1. What can you do to prevent injury to clothing or skin in this activity?
2. Once the newspaper suit has been cut and removed, how will you find the area?

Skin covers the entire surface of your body and is your body's largest organ. Skin cells make up a layer of skin about 2 mm thick. These cells are continually lost and reformed. Skin cells are shed daily at a rate of an average of 50,000 cells per minute. In one year, humans lose about 2 kg of skin and hair. How big is this organ? Find the surface area of human skin.

What You'll Investigate
How much skin covers your body?

Goals
- **Estimate** the surface area of skin that covers the body of a middle-school student.

Materials
10 large sheets of newspaper
scissors
tape
meterstick or ruler

Safety Precautions

Procedure
1. Form groups of three or four, either all female or all male. Select one person from your group to measure the surface area of his or her skin.
2. **Estimate** how much skin covers the average student in your classroom. Record your estimation in the Data and Observations section.
3. Wrap newspaper snugly around each part of your classmate's body. Overlapping the sheets of paper, use tape to secure the paper. Small body parts, such as fingers and toes, do not need to be wrapped individually. Cover entire hands and feet.
4. After your classmate is completely covered with paper, carefully cut the newspaper off his or her body. **WARNING:** *Do not cut any clothing or skin.*
5. Lay all of the overlapping sheets of newspaper on the floor. Using scissors and more tape, cut and piece the paper suit together to form a rectangle.
6. Using a meterstick, measure the length and width of the resulting rectangle. Multiply these two measurements for an estimat[e of] the surface area of your classmate's skin

L2

Laboratory Activities

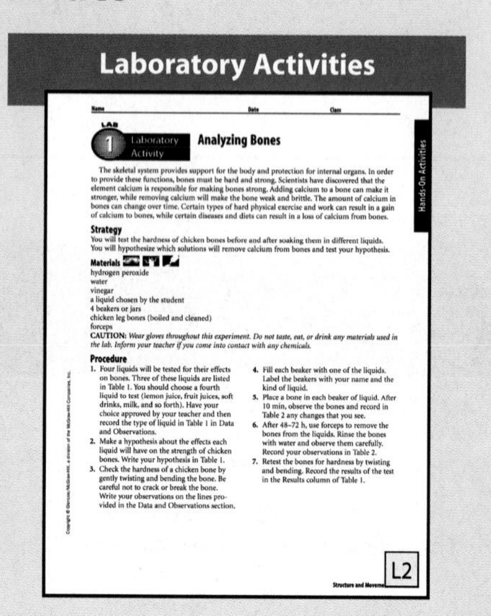
Name ___ Date ___ Class ___

Lab 1 Laboratory Activity — Analyzing Bones

Hands-On Activities

The skeletal system provides support for the body and protection for internal organs. In order to provide these functions, bones must be hard and strong. Scientists have discovered that the element calcium is responsible for making bones strong. Adding calcium to a bone can make it stronger, while removing calcium will make the bone weak and brittle. The amount of calcium in bones can change over time. Certain types of hard physical exercise and work can result in a gain of calcium to bones, while certain diseases and diets can result in a loss of calcium from bones.

Strategy
You will test the hardness of chicken bones before and after soaking them in different liquids. You will hypothesize which solutions will remove calcium from bones and test your hypothesis.

Materials
hydrogen peroxide
water
vinegar
a liquid chosen by the student
4 beakers or jars
chicken leg bones (boiled and cleaned)
forceps

CAUTION: *Wear gloves throughout this experiment. Do not taste, eat, or drink any materials used in the lab. Inform your teacher if you come into contact with any chemicals.*

Procedure
1. Four liquids will be tested for their effects on bones. Three of these liquids are listed in Table 1. You should choose a fourth liquid to test (lemon juice, fruit juices, soft drinks, milk, and so forth). Have your choice approved by your teacher and then record the type of liquid in Table 1 in Data and Observations.
2. Make a hypothesis about the effects each liquid will have on the strength of chicken bones. Write your hypothesis in Table 1.
3. Check the hardness of a chicken bone by gently twisting and bending the bone. Be careful not to crack or break the bone. Write your observations on the lines provided in the Data and Observations section.
4. Fill each beaker with one of the liquids. Label the beakers with your name and the kind of liquid.
5. Place a bone in each beaker of liquid. After 10 min, observe the bones and record in Table 2 any changes that you see.
6. After 48–72 h, use forceps to remove the bones from the liquids. Rinse the bones with water and observe them carefully. Record your observations in Table 2.
7. Retest the bones for hardness by twisting and bending. Record the results of the test in the Results column of Table 1.

L2

Meeting Different Ability Levels

Content Outline

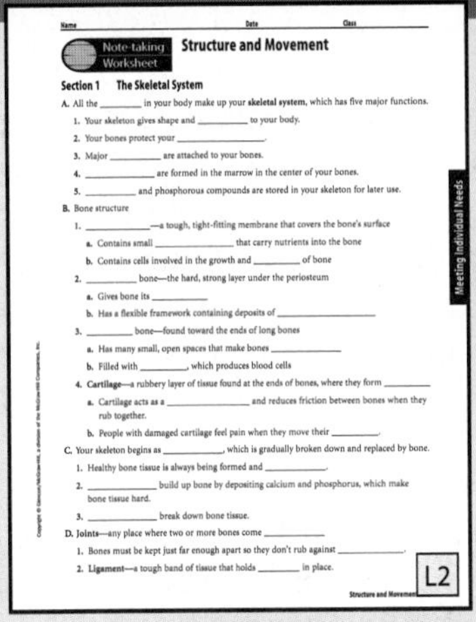

Name Date Class

Note-taking Worksheet **Structure and Movement**

Section 1 The Skeletal System

A. All the ________ in your body make up your **skeletal system**, which has five major functions.
1. Your skeleton gives shape and ________ to your body.
2. Your bones protect your ________.
3. Major ________ are attached to your bones.
4. ________ are formed in the marrow in the center of your bones.
5. ________ and phosphorous compounds are stored in your skeleton for later use.

B. Bone structure
1. ________—a tough, tight-fitting membrane that covers the bone's surface
   a. Contains small ________ that carry nutrients into the bone
   b. Contains cells involved in the growth and ________ of bone
2. ________ bone—the hard, strong layer under the periosteum
   a. Gives bone its ________
   b. Has a flexible framework containing deposits of ________
3. ________ bone—found toward the ends of long bones
   a. Has many small, open spaces that make bones ________
   b. Filled with ________, which produces blood cells
4. **Cartilage**—a rubbery layer of tissue found at the ends of bones, where they form ________
   a. Cartilage acts as a ________ and reduces friction between bones when they rub together.
   b. People with damaged cartilage feel pain when they move their ________.

C. Your skeleton begins as ________, which is gradually broken down and replaced by bone.
1. Healthy bone tissue is always being formed and ________.
2. ________ build up bone by depositing calcium and phosphorus, which make bone tissue hard.
3. ________ break down bone tissue.

D. **Joints**—any place where two or more bones come ________
1. Bones must be kept just far enough apart so they don't rub against ________.
2. **Ligament**—a tough band of tissue that holds ________ in place.

Meeting Individual Needs

L2

Reinforcement

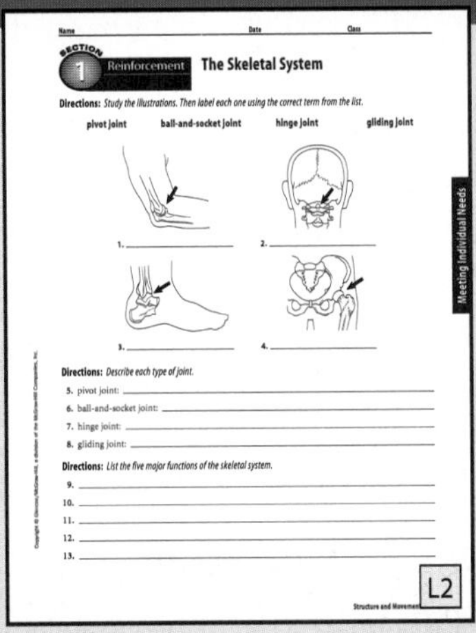

Name Date Class

SECTION 1 Reinforcement **The Skeletal System**

Directions: Study the illustrations. Then label each one using the correct term from the list.

pivot joint **ball-and-socket joint** **hinge joint** **gliding joint**

1. ________ 2. ________ 3. ________ 4. ________

Directions: Describe each type of joint.

5. pivot joint: ________
6. ball-and-socket joint: ________
7. hinge joint: ________
8. gliding joint: ________

Directions: List the five major functions of the skeletal system.

9. ________
10. ________
11. ________
12. ________
13. ________

Meeting Individual Needs

L2

Directed Reading

Name Date Class

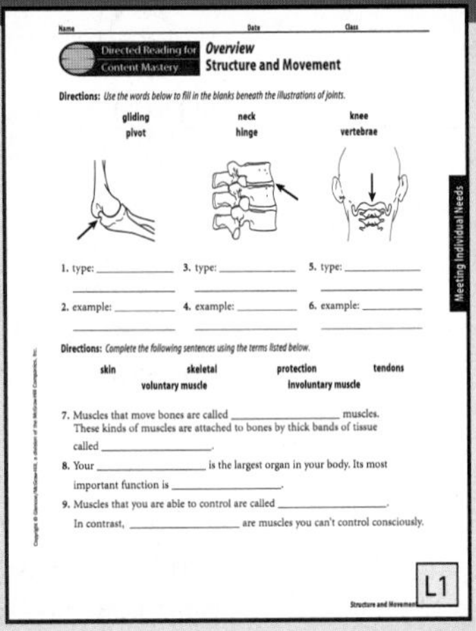

Directed Reading for Content Mastery *Overview* **Structure and Movement**

Directions: Use the words below to fill in the blanks beneath the illustrations of joints.

gliding **pivot** **neck** **hinge** **knee** **vertebrae**

1. type: ________ 3. type: ________ 5. type: ________
2. example: ________ 4. example: ________ 6. example: ________

Directions: Complete the following sentences using the terms listed below.

skin **skeletal** **protection** **tendons** **voluntary muscle** **involuntary muscle**

7. Muscles that move bones are called ________ muscles. These kinds of muscles are attached to bones by thick bands of tissue called ________.
8. Your ________ is the largest organ in your body. Its most important function is ________.
9. Muscles that you are able to control are called ________. In contrast, ________ are muscles you can't control consciously.

Meeting Individual Needs

L1

Enrichment

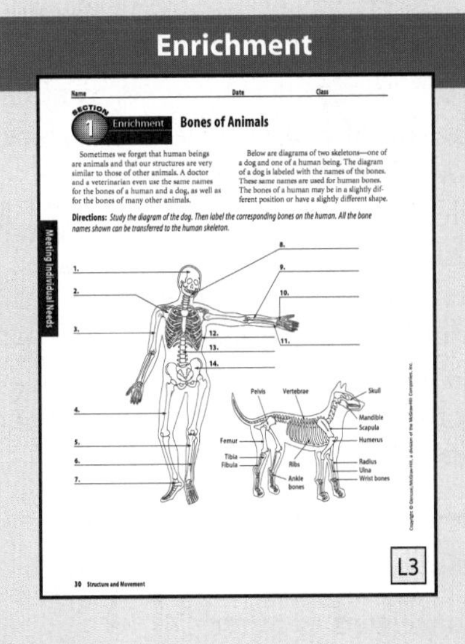

Name Date Class

SECTION 1 Enrichment **Bones of Animals**

Sometimes we forget that human beings are animals and that our structures are very similar to those of other animals. A doctor and a veterinarian even use the same names for the bones of a human and a dog, as well as for the bones of many other animals.

Below are diagrams of two skeletons—one of a dog and one of a human being. The diagram of a dog is labeled with the names of the bones. These same names are used for human bones. The bones of a human may be in a slightly different position or have a slightly different shape.

Directions: Study the diagram of the dog. Then label the corresponding bones on the human. All the bone names shown can be transferred to the human skeleton.

Meeting Individual Needs

L3

Spanish Directed Reading

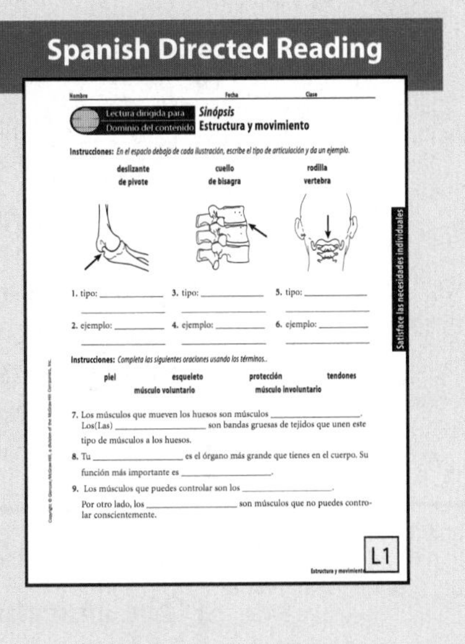

Nombre Fecha Clase

Lectura dirigida para Dominio del contenido *Sinópsis* **Estructura y movimiento**

Instrucciones: En el espacio debajo de cada ilustración, escribe el tipo de articulación y da un ejemplo.

deslizante **de pivote** **cuello** **de bisagra** **rodilla** **vertebra**

1. tipo: ________ 3. tipo: ________ 5. tipo: ________
2. ejemplo: ________ 4. ejemplo: ________ 6. ejemplo: ________

Instrucciones: Completa las siguientes oraciones usando los términos.

piel **esqueleto** **protección** **tendones** **músculo voluntario** **músculo involuntario**

7. Los músculos que mueven los huesos son músculos ________. Los(Las) ________ son bandas gruesas de tejidos que unen este tipo de músculos a los huesos.
8. Tu ________ es el órgano más grande que tienes en el cuerpo. Su función más importante es ________.
9. Los músculos que puedes controlar son los ________. Por otro lado, los ________ son músculos que no puedes controlar conscientemente.

Satisface las necesidades individuales

L1

Assessment

Chapter Tests

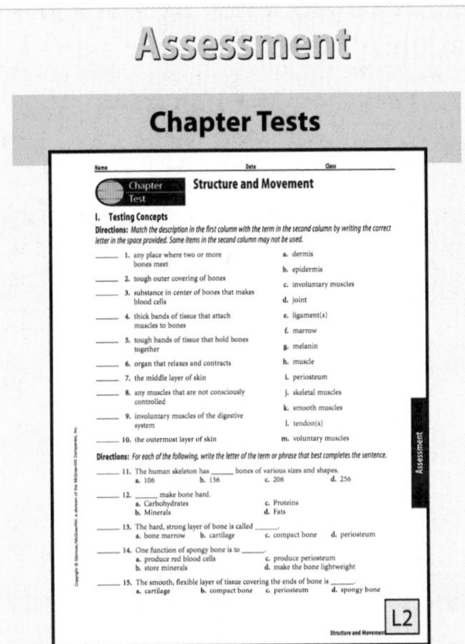

Name Date Class

Chapter Test **Structure and Movement**

I. Testing Concepts

Directions: Match the description in the first column with the term in the second column by writing the correct letter in the space provided. Some items in the second column may not be used.

____	1. any place where two or more bones meet	a. dermis
____	2. tough outer covering of bones	b. epidermis
____	3. substance in center of bones that makes blood cells	c. involuntary muscles
____	4. thick bands of tissue that attach muscles to bones	d. joint
____	5. tough bands of tissue that hold bones together	e. ligament(s)
____	6. organ that relaxes and contracts	f. marrow
____	7. the middle layer of skin	g. melanin
____	8. any muscles that are not consciously controlled	h. muscle
____	9. involuntary muscles of the digestive system	i. periosteum
____	10. the outermost layer of skin	j. skeletal muscles
		k. smooth muscles
		l. tendon(s)
		m. voluntary muscles

Directions: For each of the following, write the letter of the term or phrase that best completes the sentence.

____ 11. The human skeleton has ____ bones of various sizes and shapes.
a. 106 b. 156 c. 206 d. 256

____ 12. ____ make bone hard.
a. Carbohydrates b. Minerals c. Proteins d. Fats

____ 13. The hard, strong layer of bone is called ____.
a. bone marrow b. cartilage c. compact bone d. periosteum

____ 14. One function of spongy bone is to ____.
a. produce red blood cells b. store minerals c. produce periosteum d. make the bone lightweight

____ 15. The smooth, flexible layer of tissue covering the ends of bone is ____.
a. cartilage b. compact bone c. periosteum d. spongy bone

Assessment

L2

Test Practice Workbook

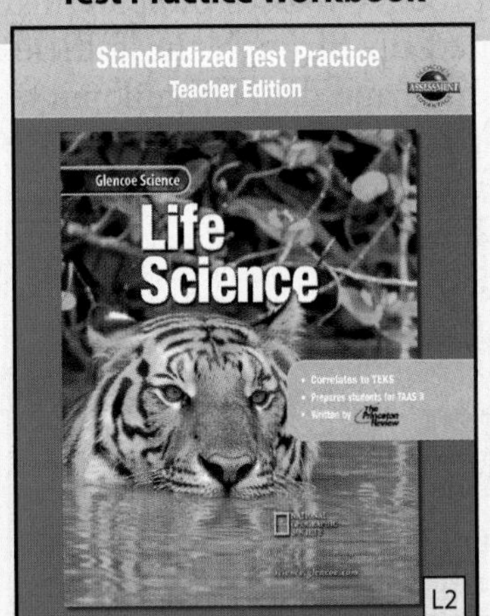

L2

Chapter Review

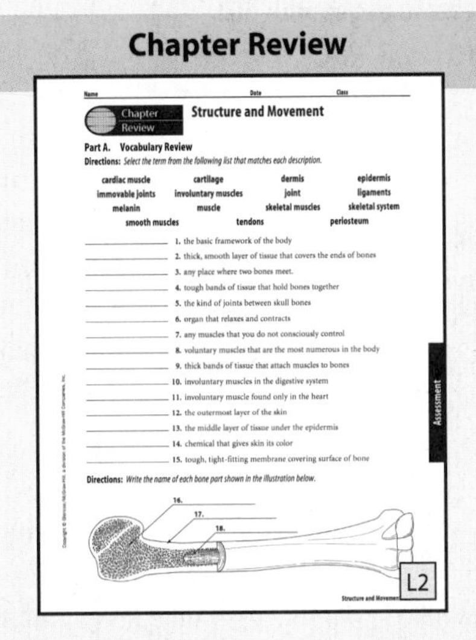

Name Date Class

Chapter Review **Structure and Movement**

Part A. Vocabulary Review

Directions: Select the term from the following list that matches each description.

cardiac muscle	cartilage	dermis	epidermis
immovable joints	involuntary muscles	joint	ligaments
melanin	muscle	skeletal muscles	skeletal system
smooth muscles	tendons	periosteum	

________ 1. the basic framework of the body
________ 2. thick, smooth layer of tissue that covers the ends of bones
________ 3. any place where two bones meet.
________ 4. tough bands of tissue that hold bones together
________ 5. the kind of joints between skull bones
________ 6. organ that relaxes and contracts
________ 7. any muscles that you do not consciously control
________ 8. voluntary muscles that are the most numerous in the body
________ 9. thick bands of tissue that attach muscles to bones
________ 10. involuntary muscles in the digestive system
________ 11. involuntary muscle found only in the heart
________ 12. the outermost layer of the skin
________ 13. the middle layer of tissue under the epidermis
________ 14. chemical that gives skin its color
________ 15. tough, tight-fitting membrane covering surface of bone

Directions: Write the name of each bone part shown in the illustration below.

16. 17. 18.

Assessment

L2

Science Content Background

SECTION 1 The Skeletal System

Human Skeletons

Human bodies have endoskeletons, skeletons located inside the body. The skeleton is divided into the appendicular skeleton and the axial skeleton. The appendicular skeleton is made up of the bones of arms and legs and the girdler that attaches these bones to the rest of the body. The axial skeleton is made up of the skull, backbone, ribs, and breastbone.

SECTION 2 The Muscular System

Muscle Contractions

The contraction of a muscle cell involves a chemical called acetylcholine, which is released by the ends of the motor neurons. This action sends an impulse over the surface and into the interior of the muscle fiber. Calcium ions are released, which results in muscle contraction. The energy required for the contraction is supplied by molecules of adenosine triphosphate (ATP).

Student Misconception

The muscular system is unrelated to other body systems.

Refer to the facing page for teaching strategies to address this misconception. Refer to pages 500–501 for content related to this topic.

SECTION 3 The Skin

The skin is stretchable, tough, and selectively permeable. The epidermis is only about 30 to 60 cells thick. The dermis varies from 1 to 3 mm in thickness. The surface area of the skin is nearly 1.2 m^2 for an adolescent.

The Dermis

The dermis has two layers. The upper papillary layer is composed of connective tissue and has many small blood vessels and nerves. The folding of this layer produces ridges on the skin's surface, including fingerprints. The lower reticular layer is made of dense connective tissue with many collagen fibers. This layer also contains the sweat glands, oil glands, and hair follicles.

Sweat Glands

Sweat glands can be found in large numbers on the hands, feet, chest, and neck. Perspiration is similar to weak urine. The oil (sebaceous) glands secrete a substance composed of fats, salts, proteins, and water. The oil lubricates the skin and reduces evaporation of water from the skin's surface.

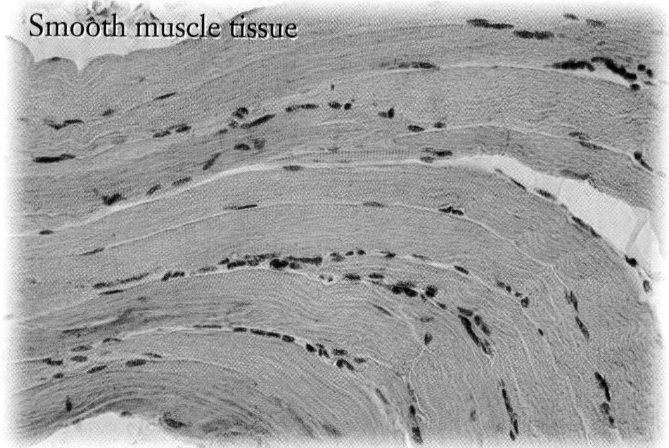
Smooth muscle tissue

Fred Hossler/Visuals Unlimited, Inc.

Hair

The hair follicles produce masses of epidermal cells that are pushed up through the follicle. These cells then flatten and die. The amount of melanin in the cells gives hair its color. Because hair comes from the skin, it is considered an appendage of the skin.

For additional content background on this topic, go to the Glencoe Science Web site at science.glencoe.com.

IDENTIFYING Misconceptions

Find Out What Students Think

Students may think that . . .

- **The muscular system is unrelated to other body systems.**

When asked about the structure and function of muscles, most students tend to think only about the importance of muscles in movement. Often they don't understand the importance of muscles in the functioning of other systems or the role of the nervous system in controlling the muscular system.

Discussion

Ask students to explain what muscles do. Most will note the importance of muscles in gross motor movement. Record their responses on the board or on the overhead projector. Then ask students to consider other roles muscles play in the body. For example, shivering is a result of muscle contractions. These contractions release heat, which helps warm the body. Have students speculate on other processes that might depend on the movement of muscles.

Promote Understanding

Activity

Show students how to take a pulse by lightly placing two fingers on the major artery on the neck and counting the number of pulses in 6 seconds. By adding a zero to this number, the number of beats per minute (heart rate) can be determined. A similar process can be used to determine the respiration rate.

- Have students determine and record their at-rest pulse and respiration rates.
- Have those who are able exercise vigorously for 30 seconds. You might have students jump up and down or jog in place.
- When you call time, again have students determine and record their pulse and respiration rates.

Have students compare their at-rest and after-exercise pulse and respiration rates. Emphasize that the data they have collected illustrate that the muscular system is related to both the circulatory and respiratory systems. As muscle activity increased, so too did pulse and respiration rate. Remind students that increased breathing brings needed oxygen into the body and expels waste carbon dioxide. The increase in heart rate quickly moves this oxygen to working muscles. Explain that it is the nervous system that causes these increased rates. As the nervous system senses a buildup of carbon dioxide and other waste products in muscle cells, it causes the body to increase breathing and heart rate.

As an extension, discuss with students how muscles support other systems. An example of this would be muscles aiding in digestion by moving food and undigested material through the digestive track.

Summing

Ask students to describe activities that would cause heart rate to increase. If necessary, ask students what happens to their heart rates when they are frightened. Again point out the connections between the muscular system and the cardiovascular and nervous systems.

Assess

After completing the chapter, see *Identifying Misconceptions* in the Study Guide.

CHAPTER 17

Structure and Movement

Chapter Vocabulary

skeletal system, p. 490
periosteum, p. 491
cartilage, p. 492
joint, p. 493
ligament, p. 493
muscle, p. 496
voluntary muscle, p. 497
involuntary muscle, p. 497
skeletal muscle, p. 499
tendon, p. 499
cardiac muscle, p. 499
smooth muscle, p. 499
epidermis, p. 502
melanin, p. 503
dermis, p. 503

What do you think?

Science Journal These are the tiny bones of the middle ear. They transfer sound waves from the eardrum to the inner ear.

CHAPTER 17

Structure and Movement

A calm, misty morning's silence is broken when a huge, snarling *Tyrannosaurus rex* rushes to pounce on its prey. Without an internal skeleton, the *T. rex* would be a large, formless mass of flesh. Movement would be impossible. Its internal organs would not be protected. In this chapter, learn about the internal structures that support you.

What do you think?

Science Journal Look at the picture below with a classmate. Discuss what you think this might be or what is happening. Here's a hint: *They help you avoid dangerous situations.* Write your answer or best guess in your Science Journal.

488

Theme Connection

Energy When the skeletal and muscular systems work to produce movement, energy is used and work is done. Food is processed by the digestive system and converted into glucose. The chemical energy in glucose is used by muscles and transformed into mechanical energy.

The expression "Many hands make light work" is also true when it comes to muscles in your body. In fact, hundreds of muscles and bones work together to bring about smooth, easy movement. Muscle interactions enable you to pick up a penny or lift a 10-kg weight. Try the following activity to see and feel how your muscles work in pairs.

Observe muscle action

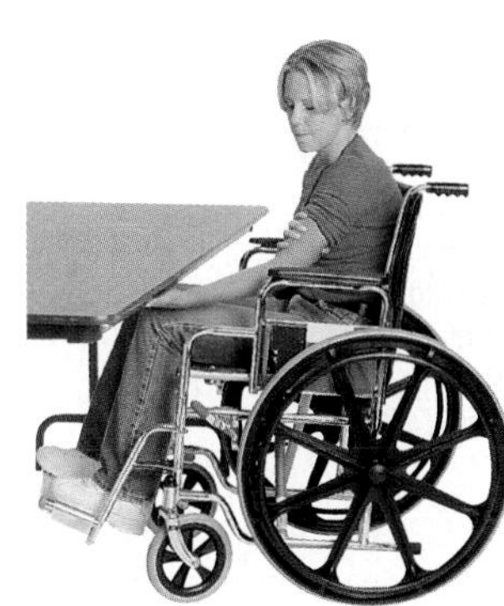

1. Sit on a chair at an empty table and place the palm of one hand under the edge of the table.
2. Push your hand up against the table. Do not push too hard.
3. Use your other hand to feel the muscles located on both sides of your upper arm, as shown in the photo.
4. Next, place your palm on the top of the table and push down. Again, feel the muscles in your upper arm.

Observe

Which muscles felt harder when pushing up on the table? When pushing down on the table? Describe in your Science Journal how the different muscles in your upper arm were working during each movement.

Before You Read

FOLDABLES Reading & Study Skills

Making a Main Ideas Study Fold **Make the following Foldable to help you identify the main topics about structure and movement.**

1. Stack two sheets of paper in front of you so the short side of both sheets is at the top.
2. Slide the top sheet up so that about 4 cm of the bottom sheet show.
3. Fold both sheets top to bottom to form four tabs and staple along the top fold as shown.
4. Label the flaps *Skin, Muscle, Bone,* and *Structure and Movement* as shown. Before you read the chapter, list the things you know about each on the back of each flap.
5. As you read the chapter, write about the changes that occur in the skin, muscle, and bone on their flap.

Skin
Muscle
Bone
Structure and Movement

489

EXPLORE ACTIVITY

Purpose Use the Explore Activity to introduce students to muscles. L2 ELL COOP LEARN

LS **Kinesthetic**

Preparation Clear tables of anything that could spill or break before students begin activity.

Materials table, chair

Teaching Strategy Inform students that they will learn more about the muscular and skeletal systems as they read the chapter. This activity may also be done by student pairs.

Observe

Possible answers: When pushing up on the table, the top of the upper arm muscles feel hard. When pushing down, the muscles on the back of the upper arm feel hard.

Assessment

Process Ask students to observe and decide where the largest muscles in their bodies are located. The largest muscles are located where they can move the limbs and other large parts of the body, such as the buttocks. Use **Performance Assessment in the Science Classroom,** p. 89.

Before You Read

FOLDABLES Reading & Study Skills

Dinah Zike Study Fold

Purpose Students display what they know about structure and movement before reading the chapter. A Foldable is provided for recording and organizing notes on skin, muscle, and bone as students read.

For additional help, see Foldables Worksheet, p. 17 in **Chapter Resources Booklet,** or go to the Glencoe Science Web site at **science.glencoe.com.** See After You Read in the Study Guide at the end of this chapter.

SECTION

1 The Skeletal System

As You Read

What You'll Learn

- **Identify** five functions of the skeletal system.
- **Compare and contrast** movable and immovable joints.

Vocabulary

skeletal system
periosteum
cartilage
joint
ligament

Why It's Important

You'll begin to understand how each of your body parts moves and what happens that allows you to move them.

Living Bones

Often in a horror movie, a mad scientist works frantically in his lab with a complete human skeleton hanging silently in the corner. When looking at a skeleton, you might think that bones are dead structures made of rocklike material. Although these bones are no longer living, the bones in your body are very much alive. Each is a living organ made of several different tissues. Like all the other living tissues in your body, bone tissue is made of cells that take in nutrients and use energy. Bone cells have the same needs as other body cells.

Functions of Your Skeletal System All the bones in your body make up your **skeletal system.** Like the framework of the building in **Figure 1,** the skeletal system is the framework of your body and has five major functions.

1. The skeleton gives shape and support to your body.
2. Bones protect your internal organs. For example, ribs surround the heart and lungs, and the skull encloses the brain.
3. Major muscles are attached to bone and help them move.
4. Blood cells are formed in the center of many bones in soft tissue called red marrow.
5. Major quantities of calcium and phosphorous compounds are stored in the skeleton for later use. Calcium and phosphorus make bones hard.

Figure 1
Nonliving structures—like cars, houses, and this building—require some type of framework for support, as does your body.

SECTION

The Skeletal System

1 Motivate

Bellringer Transparency

Display the Section Focus Transparency for Section 1. Use the accompanying Transparency Activity Master. L2 ELL

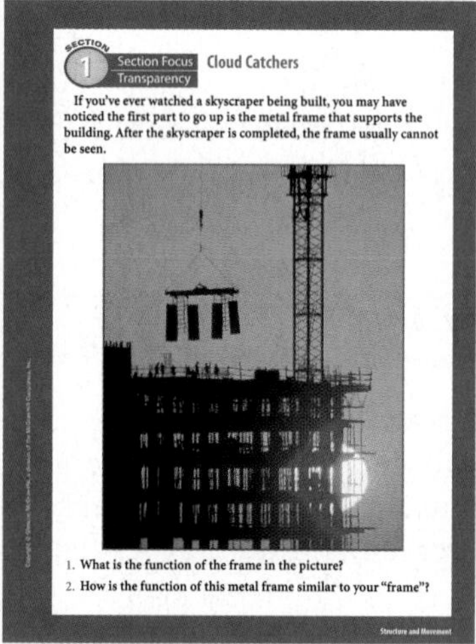

SECTION 1 Section Focus Transparency **Cloud Catchers**

If you've ever watched a skyscraper being built, you may have noticed the first part to go up is the metal frame that supports the building. After the skyscraper is completed, the frame usually cannot be seen.

1. What is the function of the frame in the picture?
2. How is the function of this metal frame similar to your "frame"?

Structure and Movement

Tie to Prior Knowledge

Show students an illustration of the human skeleton. Point out that the skeletal system is made up of bones of various sizes and shapes. Have them identify in the picture examples of these sizes and shapes, such as flat bones of ribs and skull, short bones of wrists and ankles, and long bones of arms and legs.

Section Assessment Planner

Portfolio
Visual Learning, p. 492

Performance Assessment
Skill Builder Activities, p. 495
See page 514 for more options.

Content Assessment
Section, p. 495
Challenge, p. 495
Chapter, pp. 514–515

Bone Structure

Several characteristics of bones are noticeable. The most obvious, as seen in **Figure 2,** are the differences in their sizes and shapes. The shapes of bones are inherited. However, a bone's shape can change when the attached muscles are used.

Looking at bone through a magnifying glass will show you that it isn't smooth. Bones have bumps, edges, round ends, rough spots, and many pits and holes. Muscles and ligaments attach to some of the bumps and pits. In your body blood vessels and nerves enter and leave through the holes. Internal characteristics, how a bone looks from the inside, and external characteristics, how the same bone looks from the outside, are shown in **Figure 3.**

A living bone's surface is covered with a tough, tight-fitting membrane called the **periosteum** (pur ee AHS tee um). Small blood vessels in the periosteum carry nutrients into the bone. Cells involved in the growth and repair of bone also are found in the periosteum. Under the periosteum are two different types of bone tissue—compact bone and spongy bone.

Compact Bone Directly under the periosteum is a hard, strong layer called compact bone. Compact bone gives bones strength. It has a framework containing deposits of calcium phosphate. These deposits make the bone hard. Bone cells and blood vessels also are found in this layer. This framework is living tissue and even though it's hard, it keeps bone from being too rigid, brittle, or easily broken.

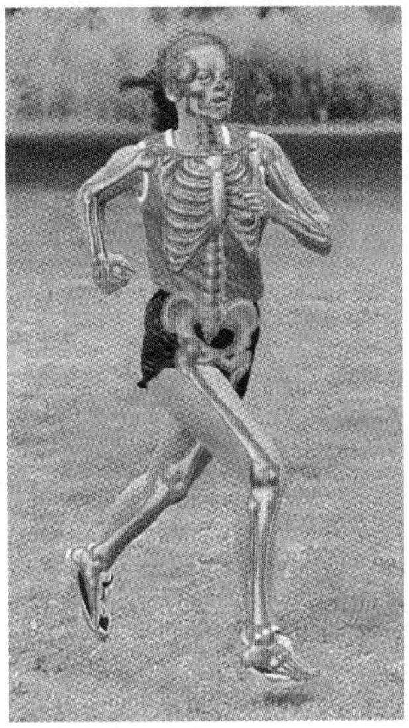

Figure 2
The 206 bones of the body are connected, forming a framework called the skeleton.

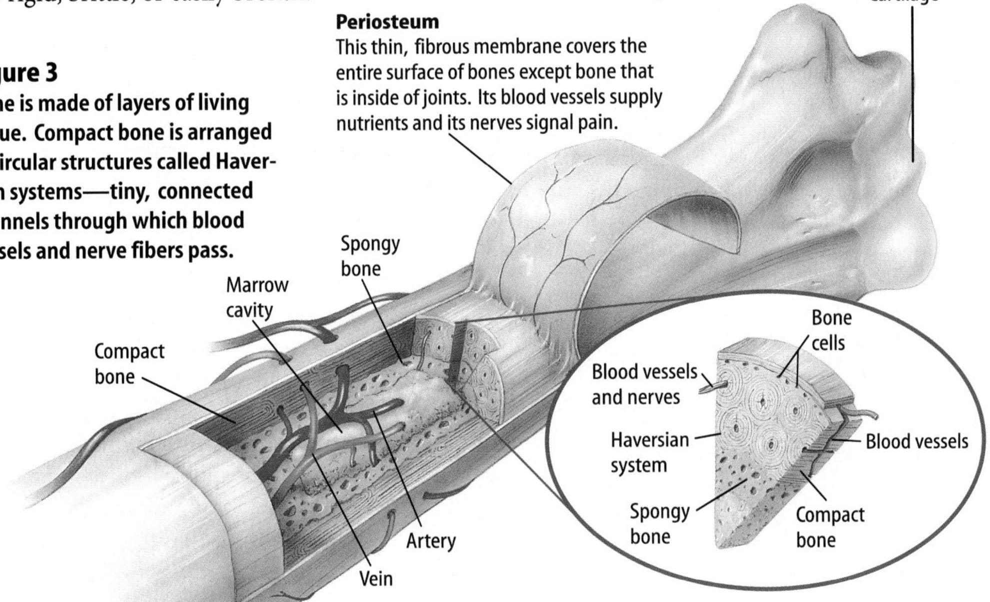

Figure 3
Bone is made of layers of living tissue. Compact bone is arranged in circular structures called Haversian systems—tiny, connected channels through which blood vessels and nerve fibers pass.

Periosteum
This thin, fibrous membrane covers the entire surface of bones except bone that is inside of joints. Its blood vessels supply nutrients and its nerves signal pain.

Cartilage
Spongy bone
Marrow cavity
Compact bone
Artery
Vein
Bone cells
Blood vessels and nerves
Haversian system
Blood vessels
Spongy bone
Compact bone

2 Teach

Living Bones

Quick Demo

Use 4×6 cards and tape to make one rectangular column and one cylindrical tube. Stand the structures on a flat surface and balance books on top of each one. Have students note which structure collapses first. Relate this strength to the long, round bones of the human body.

Bone Structure

Use Science Words

Word Usage Have students find nonscientific meanings of the use of the word *skeleton*. Refer to such idioms as *skeleton outline*, *skeleton crew*, and *skeleton structure*.

Teacher FYI

Osteoporosis is a condition in which bones become porous and thin, resulting in reduced bone mass. Factors that increase the risk of this condition include being female, being Caucasian, having chronic low calcium intake, lacking exercise, being underweight, and smoking.

Resource Manager

Chapter Resources Booklet

Transparency Activity, p. 46

Note-taking Worksheets, pp. 33–36

Life Science Critical Thinking/Problem Solving, p. 14

Curriculum Connection

Health Fractures are breaks or cracks in bones. When the broken bone isn't completely separated, it is called a greenstick fracture. Complete fractures occur when the broken bone is completely separated, but the broken ends do not pierce the skin. Compound, or open, fractures occur when the ends of the broken bone pierce the skin. Have students find out how each type of fracture is treated. L2

Bone Structure, continued

Activity

Have students place clean chicken bones in jars of 5% white vinegar for several days. Then have them remove the bones and examine them. Students should note how the mineral salts have dissolved, leaving only elastic tissue. Have them compare how the bone originally felt with how it feels now. L2 ELL LS **Visual-Spatial**

Reading Check

Answer a smooth, thick, flexible layer of tissue at the ends of bones

Bone Formation

Caption Answer

Figure 4 osteoblasts

IDENTIFYING Misconceptions

Students may think that the cartilage of a fetus hardens into bone. Explain that the fibrous part of cartilage calcifies over time, and eventually osteocytes begin to be produced, replacing cartilage cells.

Visual Learning

Figure 4 Have students make an events chain concept map of the process depicted in this figure. P

Research Visit the Glencoe Science Web site at **science.glencoe.com** for information on new techniques for treating bone fractures. Using captions, illustrate one technique in your Science Journal.

Spongy Bone Spongy bone is located toward the ends of long bones such as those in your thigh and upper arm. Spongy bone has many small, open spaces that make bones lightweight. If all your bones were completely solid, you'd have greater mass. In the centers of long bones are large openings called cavities. These cavities and the spaces in spongy bone are filled with a substance called marrow. Some marrow is yellow and is composed of fat cells. Red marrow produces red blood cells at an incredible rate of 2 million to 3 million cells per second.

Cartilage The ends of bones are covered with a smooth, slippery, thick layer of tissue called **cartilage.** Cartilage does not contain blood vessels or minerals. It is flexible and important in joints because it acts as a shock absorber. It also makes movement easier by reducing friction that would be caused by bones rubbing together. Cartilage can be damaged because of disease, injury, or years of use. People with damaged cartilage experience pain when they move.

Reading Check *What is cartilage?*

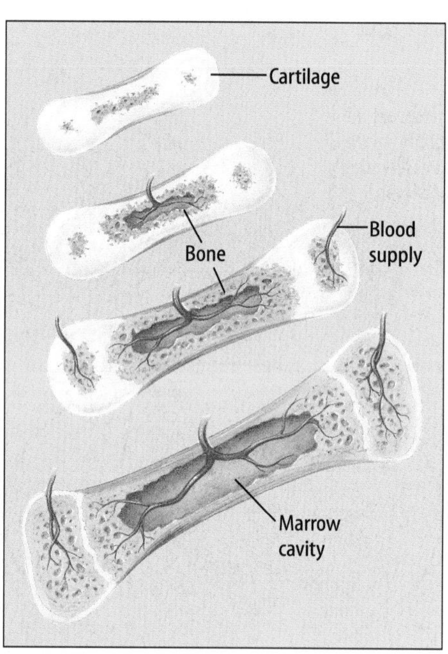

Figure 4
Cartilage is replaced slowly by bone as solid tissue grows outward. Over time, the bone reshapes to include blood vessels, nerves, and marrow. *What type of bone cell builds up bone?*

Bone Formation

Although your bones have some hard features, they have not always been this way. Months before your birth, your skeleton was made of cartilage. Gradually the cartilage broke down and was replaced by bone, as illustrated in **Figure 4.** Bone-forming cells called osteoblasts (AHS tee oh blasts) deposit the minerals calcium and phosphorus in bones, making the bone tissue hard. At birth, your skeleton was made up of more than 300 bones. As you developed, some bones fused, or grew together, so that now you have only 206 bones.

Healthy bone tissue is always being formed and re-formed. Osteoblasts build up bone. Another type of bone cell, called an osteoclast, breaks down bone tissue in other areas of the bone. This is a normal process in a healthy person. When osteoclasts break bone down, they release calcium and phosphorus into the bloodstream. This process maintains the elements calcium and phosphorus in your blood at about the levels they need to be. These elements are necessary for the working of your body, including the movement of your muscles.

Internet Addresses

Explore the Glencoe Science Web site at **science.glencoe.com** to find out more about topics in this section.

Inclusion Strategies

Visually Impaired Have students gently manipulate their ears and the ends of their noses and note the flexibility. Discuss the advantages of these body extremities being flexible and strong. The resiliency of this material makes it difficult to break these body parts. L1

492 CHAPTER 17 Structure and Movement

Joints

What will you do during your lunch break today? You may sit at a table, pick up a sandwich, bite off a piece of a carrot and chew it, or walk to class. All of these motions are possible because your skeleton has joints.

Any place where two or more bones come together is a **joint.** The bones in healthy joints are kept far enough apart by a thin layer of cartilage so that they do not rub against each other as they move. The bones are held in place at these joints by a tough band of tissue called a **ligament.** Many joints, such as your knee, are held together by more than one ligament. Muscles move bones by moving joints.

What would you do if you sprained your ankle? To find out more about what to do in emergency situations, see the **Emergencies Field Guide** at the back of the book.

Math Skills Activity

Estimating the Volume of Bones

Example Problem

The Haversian systems found in the cross section of your bones are arranged in long cylinders. This cylindrical shape allows your bones to withstand great pressure. Although bones are not perfectly shaped, many of them are cylinder shaped. Estimate the volume of a bone that is 36 cm long and is 7 cm in diameter.

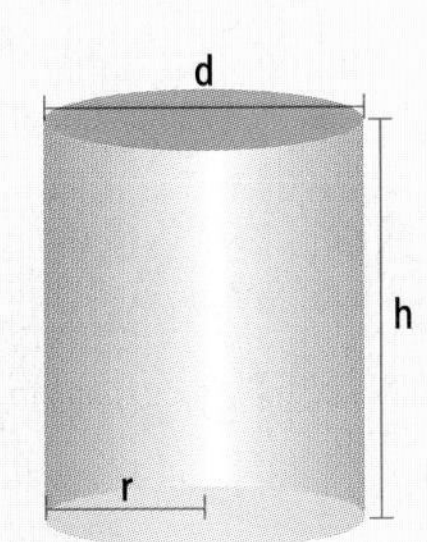

Solution

1. *This is what you know:* The bone has a shape of a cylinder whose height, *h*, measures 36 cm and whose diameter is 7.0 cm.
2. *This is what you want to find:* volume of the cylinder
3. *This is the equation you need to use:* Volume = $\pi \times (\text{radius})^2 \times$ height, or $V = \pi \times r^2 \times h$
   A radius is one-half the diameter $(\frac{1}{2} \times 7)$, *so* $r = 3.5$, $h = 36$, *and* $\pi = 3.14$.
4. *Substitute the values for* π, *radius, and height into the equation and solve for V:* $V = 3.14 \times (3.5)^2 \times 36$
   $V = 1{,}384.74$
   The volume of the bone is 1,384.74 cm^3.

To check your answer, first divide it by 3.14 and then divide that number by $(3.5)^2$. *This number should be the height of the bone.*

Practice Problem

Find the volume of a bone that has a height of 12 cm and a diameter of 2.4 cm.

Joints

Make a Model

Use two cardboard paper towel tubes and rubber bands to model how ligaments hold bones together at a joint. L2 ELL LS **Visual-Spatial**

Teacher FYI

During arthroscopic surgery, an arthroscope (surgical instrument used to visually examine the interior of a joint) is inserted through an incision and the surgeon looks around inside the joint. Repair of the joint is done through the incision by means of instruments designed to be used with the arthroscope.

Math Skills Activity

National Math Standards

Correlation to Mathematics Objectives

1–4, 6, 9

Use equations to determine time from average speed and distance measurements.

Use division to find unit rates and ratios in proportional relationships such as speed, density, price, and recipes.

Answer to Practice Problem

54 cm^3

Resource Manager

Chapter Resources Booklet

Directed Reading for Content Mastery, pp. 19, 20

Mathematics Skill Activities, p. 17

Curriculum Connection

Language Arts Have students look up *periosteum* and *osteoblast* in the dictionary. Have volunteers explain how the root of the word reflects its meaning. The root word *osteo* means "bone"; the root word *peri* means "surrounding"; the root word *blast* means "bud" or "germ." The periosteum surrounds the bone; the osteoblasts are bone-forming cells. L2 LS **Linguistic**

Joints, continued

Caption Answer

Figure 5 Possible answers: hitting a baseball, jumping rope

Use an Analogy

Moving parts of machines require protection from friction. Lubricants such as oil and grease and other coatings serve to reduce the wear of the parts. Moving parts of the body at bone joints have spaces between the bones. These spaces have lubricants called synovial fluids and sacs of fluids—the bursae and synovial sheaths—to reduce friction between bone surfaces.

Teacher FYI

The joints between the bones of the skull are called sutures. In an infant, the bones are held together by fibrous connective tissue and there is some flexibility between the bones. In later years, the tissue is replaced by bone and the skull becomes a hard, solid protective case for the brain.

Extension

Have students write a brief report on the hyoid bone located in the anterior part of the neck. It is the only bone in the body that is not part of a joint with another bone. L2

Immovable Joints Refer to **Figure 5** as you learn about different types of joints. Joints are broadly classified as immovable or movable. An immovable joint allows little or no movement. The joints of the bones in your skull and pelvis are classified as immovable joints.

Movable Joints All movements, including somersaulting and working the controls of a video game, require movable joints. A movable joint allows the body to make a wide range of motions. There are several types of movable joints—pivot, ball and socket, hinge, and gliding. In a pivot joint, one bone rotates in a ring of another bone that does not move. Turning your head is an example of a pivot movement.

A ball-and-socket joint consists of a bone with a rounded end that fits into a cuplike cavity on another bone. A ball-and-socket joint provides a wider range of motion than a pivot joint does. That's why your legs and arms can swing in almost any direction.

A third type of joint is a hinge joint. This joint has a back-and-forth movement like hinges on a door. Elbows, knees, and fingers have hinge joints. Hinge joints have a smaller range of motion than the ball-and-socket joint. They are not dislocated as easily, or pulled apart, as a ball-and-socket joint can be.

A fourth type of joint is a gliding joint in which one part of a bone slides over another bone. Gliding joints also move in a back-and-forth motion and are found in your wrists and ankles and between vertebrae. Gliding joints are used the most in your body. You can't write a word, use a joy stick, or take a step without using a gliding joint.

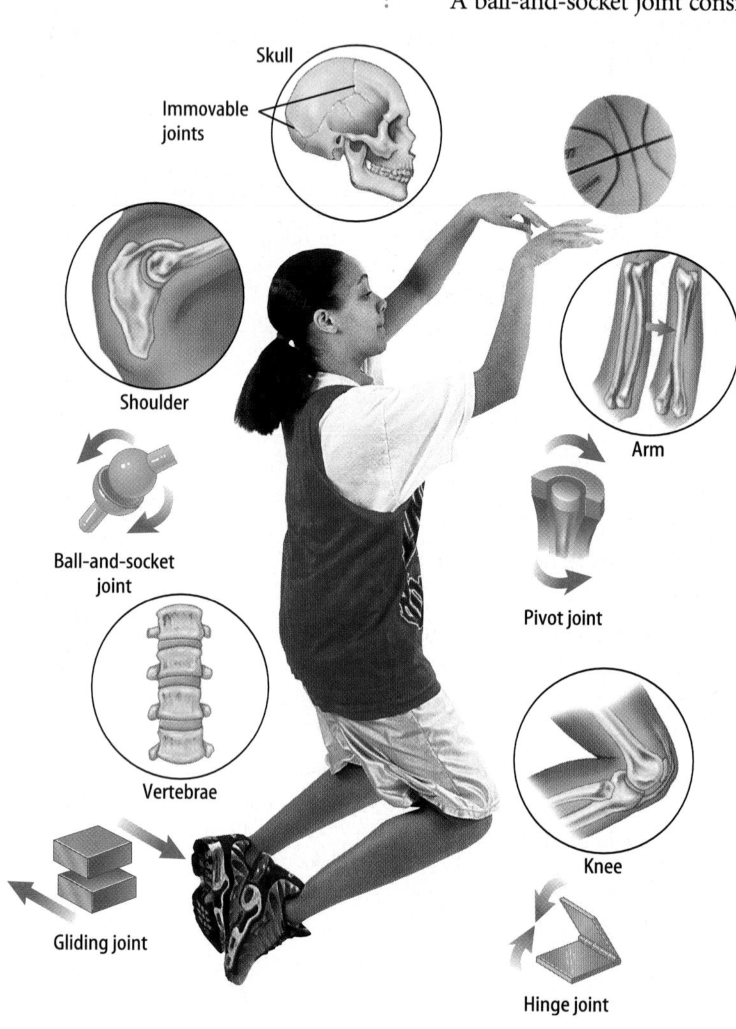

Figure 5
When a basketball player shoots a ball, several types of joints are in action. *What other activities use several types of joints?*

Science Journal

Mechanical Joints at Home Have students make lists in their Science Journals of mechanical joints found at and around the home that are similar to joints found in the body. Examples include: door hinge—elbow; swivel chair—wrist; and wind vane—skull on vertebra. L2 LS **Visual-Spatial**

Resource Manager

Chapter Resources Booklet
Enrichment, p. 30
Reinforcement, p. 27

Moving Smoothly When you rub two pieces of chalk together, their surfaces begin to wear away, and they get reshaped. Without the protection of the cartilage at the end of your bones, they also would wear away at the joints. Cartilage helps make joint movement easier. It reduces friction and allows bones to slide more easily over each other. Shown in **Figure 6,** pads of cartilage, called disks, are located between the vertebrae in your back. They act as a cushion and prevent injury to your spinal cord. A fluid that comes from nearby blood vessels also lubricates the joint.

Your skeleton is a living framework of bones. Bones support the body and supply it with minerals and blood cells. Joints make the framework flexible.

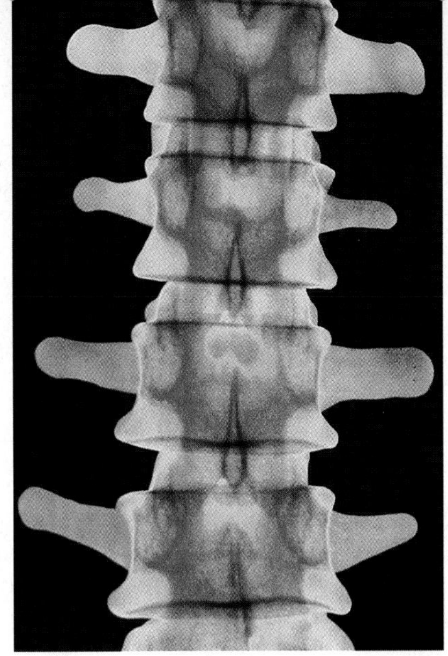

Figure 6
A colored X ray of the human backbone shows disks of cartilage between the vertebrae.

Common Joint Problems Arthritis is the most common joint problem. The term *arthritis* describes more than 100 different diseases that can damage the joints. About one out of every seven people in the United States suffers from arthritis. All forms of arthritis begin with the same symptoms: pain, stiffness, and swelling of the joints.

Two common types of arthritis include osteoarthritis and rheumatoid arthritis. Older people often suffer from osteoarthritis, in which cartilage breaks down because of years of use. Rheumatoid arthritis occurs in both young and older adults. This disorder is an ongoing condition in which the body's immune system tries to destroy its own tissues.

Section 1 Assessment

1. What are the five major functions of the skeletal system?
2. Name and give an example of both a movable joint and an immovable joint.
3. What are the functions of cartilage in your skeletal system?
4. What are ligaments?
5. **Think Critically** A thick band of bone forms around a broken bone as it heals. In time, the thickened band disappears. Explain how this extra bone can disappear over time.

Skill Builder Activities

6. **Making and Using Tables** Use a table to classify the bones of the human body as follows: *long, short, flat,* and *irregular.* **For more help, refer to the Science Skill Handbook.**
7. **Using Graphics Software** Using graphics software, make a circle graph that shows how an adult's bones are distributed: *29 skull bones, 26 vertebrae, 25 ribs, four shoulder bones, 60 arm and hand bones, two hip bones,* and *60 leg and feet bones.* **For more help, refer to the Technology Skill Handbook.**

3 Assess

Reteach

Bring in the leg and wing bones of cooked chicken or turkey and allow students to examine the ends of the bones for cartilage. Have them note the smooth and slippery surface that facilitates movement, but also notice the firmness needed for support. L2 ELL
LS **Visual-Spatial**

Challenge

If your hand had no joints, how would this affect you? Possible answer: You would not be able to pick up, hold, or turn objects.

Assessment

Oral Have students infer the functions of a fluid-filled cavity between two cartilage surfaces. The cavity cushions the cartilage and keeps the surfaces from rubbing against each other. Use **Performance Assessment in the Science Classroom,** p. 89.

Answers to Section Assessment

1. gives shape and support; protects internal organs; provides place for muscle attachment; produces blood cells; stores minerals
2. movable joint: base of skull, shoulder, hip, elbow, knee, finger, wrist, and ankle; immovable joint: skull and pelvis
3. provides padding; also provides shape for ears and nose
4. tough bands of tissue that hold bones in place
5. Osteoclasts break down the extra bone material.
6. Have students work in pairs to compare their classification tables.
7. Circle graph should show these approximate percentages: skull–14% (50°), vertebral column–13% (47°), rib cage–12% (43°), shoulder–7% (2°), arms and hands–30% (108°), hip–1% (4°), legs and feet–30% (108°).

SECTION

The Muscular System

1 Motivate

Bellringer Transparency

Display the Section Focus Transparency for Section 2. Use the accompanying Transparency Activity Master. L2 ELL

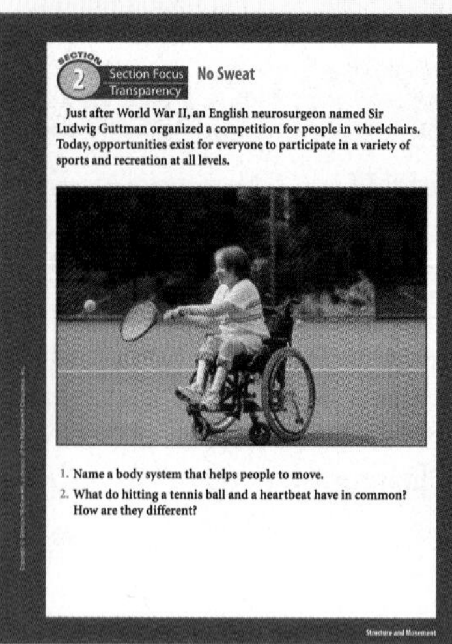

SECTION 2 Section Focus Transparency **No Sweat**

Just after World War II, an English neurosurgeon named Sir Ludwig Guttman organized a competition for people in wheelchairs. Today, opportunities exist for everyone to participate in a variety of sports and recreation at all levels.

1. Name a body system that helps people to move.
2. What do hitting a tennis ball and a heartbeat have in common? How are they different?

Structure and Movement

Tie to Prior Knowledge

Everyone has had sore, overworked muscles. Have students discuss why they think this happens.

Resource Manager

Chapter Resources Booklet
Transparency Activity, p. 47
Directed Reading for Content Mastery, p. 20

SECTION 2

The Muscular System

As You Read

What You'll Learn

- **Identify** the major function of the muscular system.
- **Compare and contrast** the three types of muscles.
- **Explain** how muscle action results in the movement of body parts.

Vocabulary

muscle
voluntary muscle
involuntary muscle
skeletal muscle
tendon
cardiac muscle
smooth muscle

Why It's Important

The muscular system is responsible for how you move and the production of heat in your body. Muscles also give your body its shape.

Movement of the Human Body

The golfer looks down the fairway and then at the golf ball. With intense concentration and muscle coordination, the golfer swings the club along a graceful arc and connects with the ball. The ball sails through the air, landing inches away from the flag. The crowd applauds. A few minutes later, the final putt is made and the tournament is won. The champion has learned how to use controlled muscle movement to bring success.

Muscles help make all of your daily movements possible. **Figure 7** shows which muscles connect some of the bones in your body. A **muscle** is an organ that can relax, contract, and provide the force to move your body parts. In the process, energy is used and work is done. Imagine how much energy the more than 600 muscles in your body use each day. No matter how still you might try to be, some muscles in your body are always moving. You're breathing, your heart is beating, and your digestive system is working.

Figure 7
Your muscles come in many shapes and sizes. Even simple movements require the coordinated use of several muscles. The muscles shown here are only those located directly under the skin. Beneath these muscles are middle and deep layers of muscles.

Section Assessment Planner

PORTFOLIO
Reteach, p. 501

PERFORMANCE ASSESSMENT
Try at Home MiniLAB, p. 500
Skill Builder Activities, p. 501
See page 514 for more options.

CONTENT ASSESSMENT
Section, p. 501
Challenge, p. 501
Chapter, pp. 514–515

496 CHAPTER 17 Structure and Movement

A

B

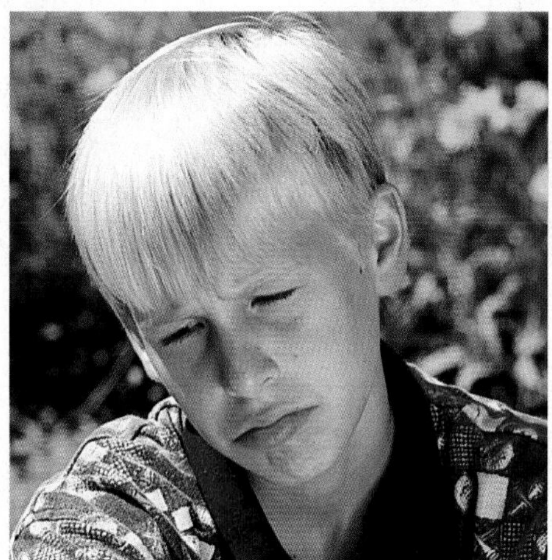

Muscle Control Your hand, arm, and leg muscles are voluntary. So are the muscles of your face, shown in **Figure 8.** You can choose to move them or not to move them. Muscles that you are able to control are called **voluntary muscles.** In contrast, **involuntary muscles** are muscles you can't control consciously. They go on working all day long, all your life. Blood gets pumped through blood vessels, and food is moved through your digestive system by the action of involuntary muscles.

Figure 8
Facial expressions generally are controlled by voluntary muscles. It takes only 13 muscles to smile, but 43 muscles to frown.

Reading Check ***What is another body activity that is controlled by involuntary muscles?***

Your Body's Simple Machines—Levers

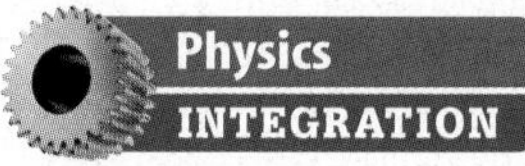

Physics INTEGRATION

Your skeletal system and muscular system work together when you move, in the same way that the parts of a bicycle work together when it moves. A machine, such as a bicycle, is any device that makes work easier. A simple machine does work with only one movement, like a hammer. The hammer is a type of simple machine called a lever, which is a rod or plank that pivots or turns about a point. This point is called a fulcrum. The action of muscles, bones, and joints working together is like a lever. In your body, bones are rods, joints are fulcrums, and contraction and relaxation of muscles provide the force to move body parts. Levers are classified into three types—first class, second class, and third class. Examples of the three types of levers that are found in the human body are shown in **Figure 9.**

SCIENCE Online

Research Visit the Glencoe Science Web site at **science.glencoe.com** for recent news or magazine articles about replacing diseased joints. Communicate to your class what you learn.

SCIENCE Online
Internet Addresses

Explore the Glencoe Science Web site at **science.glencoe.com** to find out more about topics in this section.

Curriculum Connection

History Archimedes was a scientist and mathematician in ancient Greece. He was the first to explain the math and science involved in levers. He is quoted as saying, "Give me but a place to stand, and I will move the world." Have students discuss the meaning of this saying. Archimedes implied that with a long enough bar and a place to stand, even something as large as a planet could be moved with a first class-lever.

2 Teach

Movement of the Human Body

Discussion

Why is it important that some muscles are involuntary? It would be impossible for a person to think about all the body functions that require muscle action—breathing, heart beating, stomach churning, and so on.

Reading Check

Answer breathing

Your Body's Simple Machines—Levers

Teacher FYI

Levers are one kind of simple machine. Machines make work easier by decreasing the amount of force, transferring the amount of force, or changing the direction of force. The three classes of levers can be demonstrated by the movements of the foot: first-class—the movement when the ball of the foot presses on the brake pedal of a car; second-class—the movement of the foot when rising on tiptoe; third-class—the movement of the foot when rising on the heels.

Activity

Have students experiment using a ruler and a small block of wood to become familiar with the placement of the fulcrum and the movement of the lever in each of the three classes of levers. L2 ELL

NATIONAL GEOGRAPHIC

Visualizing Human Body Levers

Have students examine the pictures and read the captions. Then ask the following questions.

Which type of lever moves the load in the opposite direction of the effort force? First-class levers move the load in a direction opposite to the effort force.

How could the tennis racquet in the picture be thought of as an extension of a lever arm? If the fulcrum is the shoulder and the load is the tennis ball being struck, then the player's arm and racquet together form the lever arm.

Activity

Have students work in small groups to conduct a search through the classroom, or, if possible, the school building for first-, second- and third-class levers. Have each group prepare a visual to list the different examples of levers they found. Have the students include a diagram of one of the examples.

Extension

There are other examples of levers within the human body. Have students research to find out which parts of the human ear work as a lever, and write a paragraph explaining their findings to the class.

NATIONAL GEOGRAPHIC **VISUALIZING HUMAN BODY LEVERS**

Figure 9

All three types of levers—first-class, second-class, and third-class—are found in the human body. In the photo below, a tennis player prepares to serve a ball. As shown in the accompanying diagrams, the tennis player's stance demonstrates the operation of all three classes of levers in the human body.

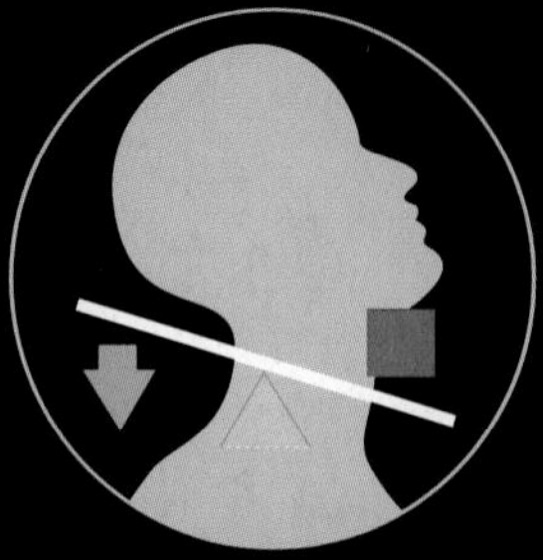

FIRST-CLASS LEVER
The fulcrum lies between the effort force and the load. This happens when the tennis player uses his neck muscles to tilt his head back.

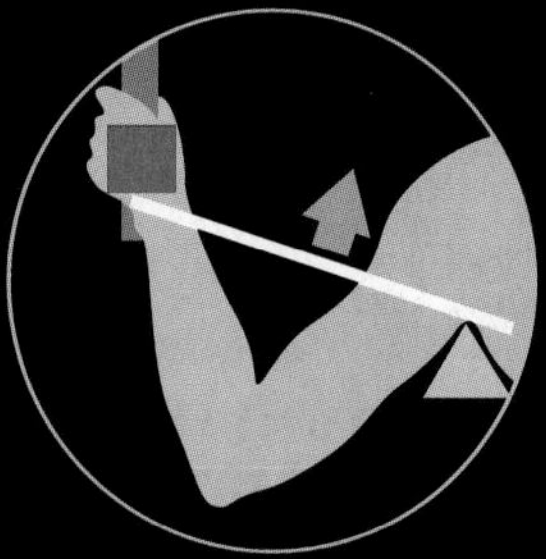

THIRD-CLASS LEVER
The effort force is between the fulcrum and the load. This happens when the tennis player flexes the muscles in his arm and shoulder.

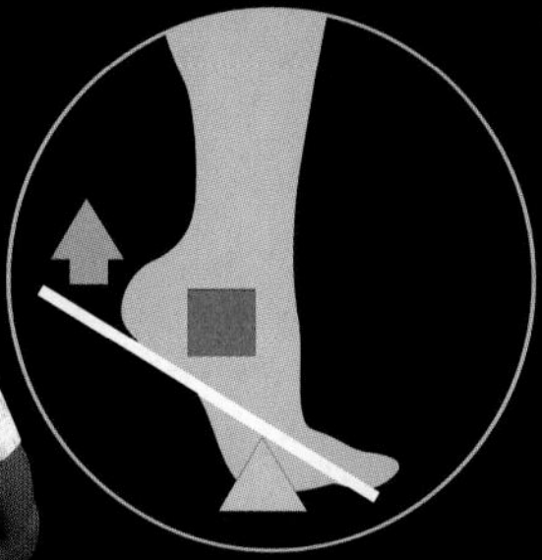

SECOND-CLASS LEVER
The load lies between the fulcrum and the effort force. This happens when the tennis player's calf muscles lift the weight of his body up on his toes.

498

Resource Manager

Chapter Resources Booklet
- Enrichment, p. 31
- Transparency Activity, pp. 49–50
- Lab Activity, pp. 9–11

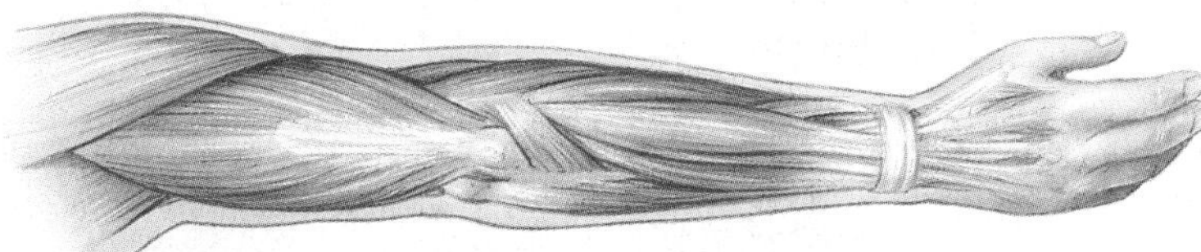

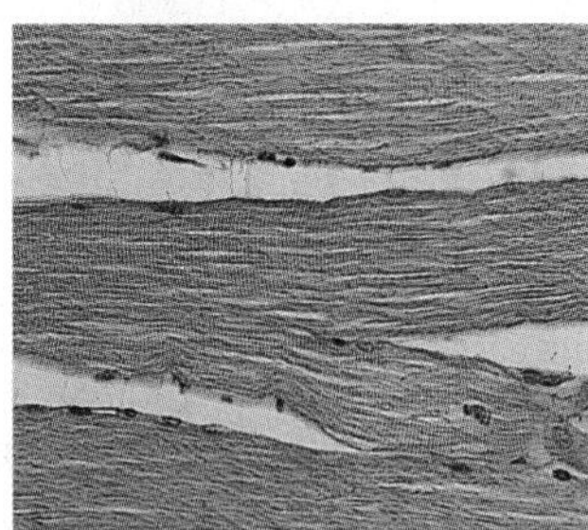

A Skeletal muscles move bones. The muscle tissue appears striped, or striated, and is attached to bone.

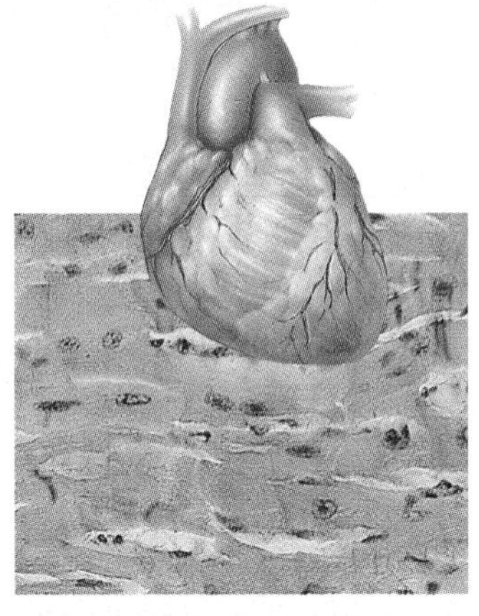

B Cardiac muscle is found only in the heart. The muscle tissue has striations.

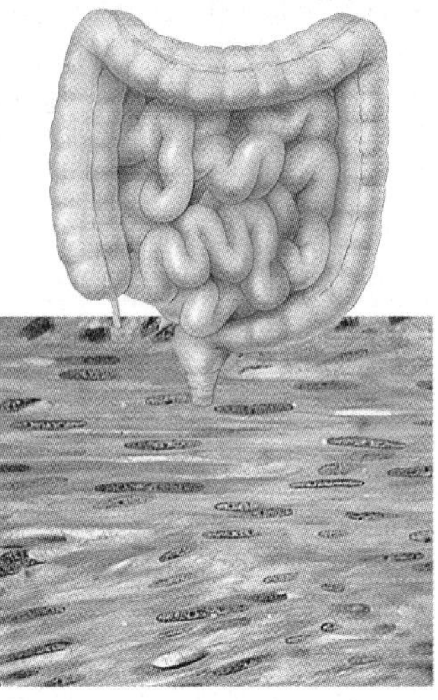

C Smooth muscle is found in many of your internal organs, such as the digestive tract. This muscle tissue is nonstriated.

Figure 10
The three types of muscle tissue are skeletal muscle, cardiac muscle, and smooth muscle.

Classification of Muscle Tissue

All the muscle tissue in your body is not the same. The three types of muscles are skeletal, smooth, and cardiac. **Skeletal muscles** are the muscles that move bones. They are more common than other muscle types and are attached to bones by thick bands of tissue called **tendons.** When viewed under a microscope, skeletal muscle cells look striped, or striated (STRI ayt ud). You can see the striations in **Figure 10A.** Skeletal muscles are voluntary muscles. You choose when to walk or when not to walk. Skeletal muscles tend to contract quickly and tire more easily than involuntary muscles do.

The remaining two types of muscles are shown in **Figures 10B** and **10C. Cardiac muscle** is found only in the heart. Like skeletal muscle, cardiac muscle is striated. This type of muscle contracts about 70 times per minute every day of your life. **Smooth muscles** are found in your intestines, bladder, blood vessels, and other internal organs. They are nonstriated, involuntary muscles that slowly contract and relax. Internal organs are made of one or more layers of smooth muscles.

Classification of Muscle Tissue

Visual Learning

Figure 10 Have students study the photographs and illustrations of each muscle type. Then ask riddle-type questions and have students identify which muscle type (or types) you are describing. For example: **I have striations and am attached to bones. What am I?** skeletal muscle **I have no striations. What am I?** smooth muscle

Fun Fact

You have the same number of muscle fibers now as when you were born. Muscle fibers grow in length and width, but not in number.

Teacher FYI

Structures within muscle fibers contain thick filaments of the protein myosin and thin filaments of the protein actin. When a muscle is activated, the chemical adenosine triphosphate (ATP) is broken down, resulting in the release of large amounts of energy. The energy causes the actin and myosin filaments to slide over each other and the muscle contracts.

LAB DEMONSTRATION

Purpose to observe the coordinated work of muscle pairs

Materials chart of arm muscles

Procedure Have students feel the muscles in their upper arms as they pump their lower arms out and back. Have them use the chart of arm muscles to determine which upper arm muscles are involved.

Expected Outcome Students should note that the biceps and triceps are involved in the action.

Assessment

Which muscle contracted to bring the forearm closer to the shoulder? The biceps contracted. **Which muscle relaxed to allow this action?** The triceps relaxed.

Working Muscles

Caption Answer

Figure 11 first-class lever

Purpose Students feel the effects of muscle fatigue. L1 ELL LS **Kinesthetic**

Materials book, table, meterstick

Teaching Strategy Students can work with a family member. One person can do the activity while the other holds the meterstick vertically.

Analysis

1. Arm muscles become tired after a relatively short period of activity, heart muscles work continuously.
2. Heart muscles do not tire, but work continuously throughout one's life.

Oral Have students infer why muscle contractions of the heart must be rhythmic. Use **PASC,** p. 89.

Some students think that the muscular system is unrelated to other body systems. Refer to page 488F for teaching strategies that address this misconception.

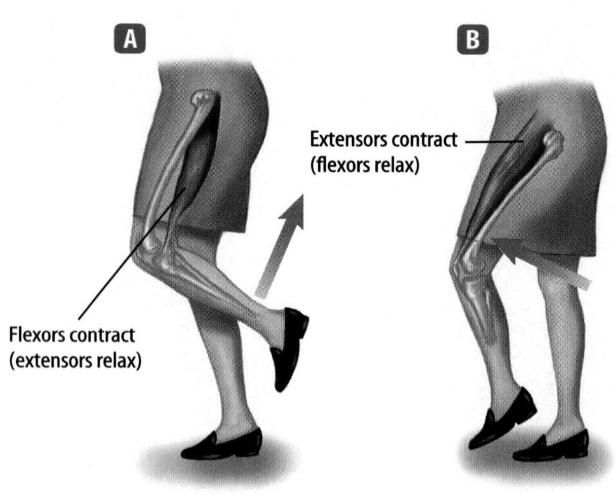

Figure 11
A When the flexor (hamstring) muscles of your thigh contract, the lower leg is brought toward the thigh. B When the extensor (quadriceps) muscles contract, the lower leg is straightened.
What class of lever is shown here?

Working Muscles

How do muscles allow you to move your body? You move because pairs of skeletal muscles work together. When one muscle of a pair contracts, the other muscle relaxes, or returns to its original length, as shown in **Figure 11.** Muscles always pull. They never push. When the muscles on the back of your upper leg contract, they shorten and pull your lower leg back and up. When you straighten your leg, the back muscles lengthen and relax, and the muscles on the front of your upper leg contract. Compare how the muscles of your legs work with how the muscles of your arms work.

Changes in Muscles Over a period of time, muscles can become larger or smaller, depending on whether or not they are used. Skeletal muscles that do a lot of work, such as those in your writing hand, become strong and large. For example, many soccer and basketball players have noticeably larger, defined leg muscles. Muscles that are given regular exercise respond quickly to stimuli. Some of this change in muscle size is because of an increase in the number of muscle cells. However, most of this change in muscle size is because individual muscle cells become larger.

In contrast, if you participate only in nonactive pastimes such as watching television or playing computer games, your muscles will become soft and flabby and will lack strength. Muscles that aren't exercised become smaller in size. When someone is paralyzed, his or her muscles become smaller due to lack of exercise.

TRY AT HOME Mini LAB

Comparing Muscle Activity

Procedure

1. Hold a light **book** in your outstretched hand over a dining or kitchen **table.**
2. Lift the book from this position to a height of 30 cm from the table 20 times.

Analysis

1. Compare your arm muscle activity to the continuous muscle activity of the heart.
2. Infer whether heart muscles become tired.

Resource Manager

Chapter Resources Booklet
MiniLAB, p. 3
Reinforcement, p. 28
Home and Community Involvement, p. 49

Cultural Diversity

Acupuncture Acupuncture originated in China more than 2,500 years ago. It is the system of inserting thin needles into the skin at specific body points. Acupuncture has been used to treat a variety of disorders. Have students find out some modern uses of acupuncture. Possible answers: to anesthetize patients for surgery, to cure disease, to relieve pain, to improve health L2

How Muscles Move Your muscles need energy to contract and relax. Your blood carries energy-rich molecules to your muscle cells where the chemical energy stored in these molecules is released. As the muscle contracts, this released energy changes to mechanical energy (movement) and thermal energy (heat), as shown in **Figure 12.** When the supply of energy-rich molecules in a muscle is used up, the muscle becomes tired and needs to rest. During this resting period, your blood supplies more energy-rich molecules to your muscle cells. The heat produced by muscle contractions helps keep your body temperature constant.

Figure 12
Chemical energy is needed for muscle activity. During activity, chemical energy supplied by food is changed into mechanical energy (movement) and thermal energy (heat).

Section  Assessment

1. What is the function of muscles?
2. Compare and contrast the three types of muscle tissue.
3. What type of muscle tissue is found in your heart?
4. Describe how a muscle attaches to a bone.
5. **Think Critically** What happens to your upper arm muscles when you bend your arm at the elbow?

Skill Builder Activities

6. **Concept Mapping** Using a concept map, sequence the activities that take place when you bend your leg at the knee. **For more help, refer to the** Science Skill Handbook.
7. **Communicating** Write a paragraph in your Science Journal about the three forms of energy involved in a muscle contraction. **For more help, refer to the** Science Skill Handbook.

Fun Fact

Skeletal muscles form a large proportion of the body's mass. Therefore, even at rest they produce about 40 percent of body heat. Shivering and physical exercise can increase the production of heat to double that amount.

3 Assess

Reteach

Have students make flash cards with names of body organs that require muscle action. On the reverse side of each card, have them identify the type of muscle (skeletal, smooth, or cardiac) involved. L2 P

Challenge

How can you tell whether a muscle is voluntary? Possible answer: The muscle can be moved by thinking about it. Name muscles and have students tell whether they are voluntary or involuntary.

Assessment

Process Have students view illustrations of robots at work. Have them describe the similarities and differences in how the robots move and how the human body moves. Use **Performance Assessment in the Science Classroom,** p. 89.

Answers to Section Assessment

1. movement
2. Skeletal (voluntary) and cardiac (involuntary) have striations; smooth muscle (involuntary) has no striations.
3. cardiac
4. Thick bands of tissue called tendons attach muscles to bones.
5. Muscles in the front (biceps) contract, while muscles in the back (triceps) relax.
6. The muscles on the underside of your thigh contract, and the bottom part of your leg is drawn toward the thigh. At the same time, the muscles on the top of the thigh relax and lengthen.
7. Entries should list the three forms of energy as chemical, mechanical, and thermal. It is the thermal energy of muscle contractions that helps maintain the constant body heat of warm-blooded animals.

SECTION

The Skin

1 Motivate

Bellringer Transparency

Display the Section Focus Transparency for Section 3. Use the accompanying Transparency Activity Master. L2 ELL

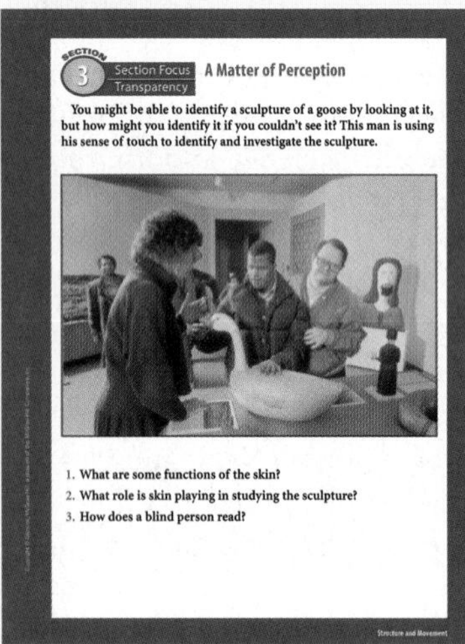

SECTION 3 Section Focus Transparency A Matter of Perception

You might be able to identify a sculpture of a goose by looking at it, but how might you identify it if you couldn't see it? This man is using his sense of touch to identify and investigate the sculpture.

1. What are some functions of the skin?
2. What role is skin playing in studying the sculpture?
3. How does a blind person read?

Tie to Prior Knowledge

Recall how an adult may have felt your forehead if he or she suspected you had a fever. Because the skin permits excess internal heat to escape from the body, touching the skin serves as a quick way to determine whether you have a high temperature.

SECTION 3

The Skin

As You Read

***What* You'll Learn**

- **Distinguish** between the epidermis and dermis of the skin.
- **Identify** the functions of the skin.
- **Explain** how skin protects the body from disease and how it heals itself.

Vocabulary
epidermis
melanin
dermis

***Why* It's Important**

Skin plays a vital role in protecting your body against injury and disease.

Your Largest Organ

What is the largest organ in your body? When you think of an organ, you might imagine your heart, stomach, lungs, or brain. However, your skin is the largest organ of your body. Much of the information you receive about your environment comes through your skin. You can think of your skin as your largest sense organ.

Skin Structures

Skin is made up of three layers of tissue—the epidermis, the dermis, and a fatty layer—as shown in **Figure 13.** Each layer of skin is made of different cell types. The **epidermis** is the outer, thinnest layer of your skin. The epidermis's outermost cells are dead and water repellent. Thousands of epidermal cells rub off every time you take a shower, shake hands, blow your nose, or scratch your elbow. New cells are produced constantly at the base of the epidermis. These new cells move up and eventually replace those that are rubbed off.

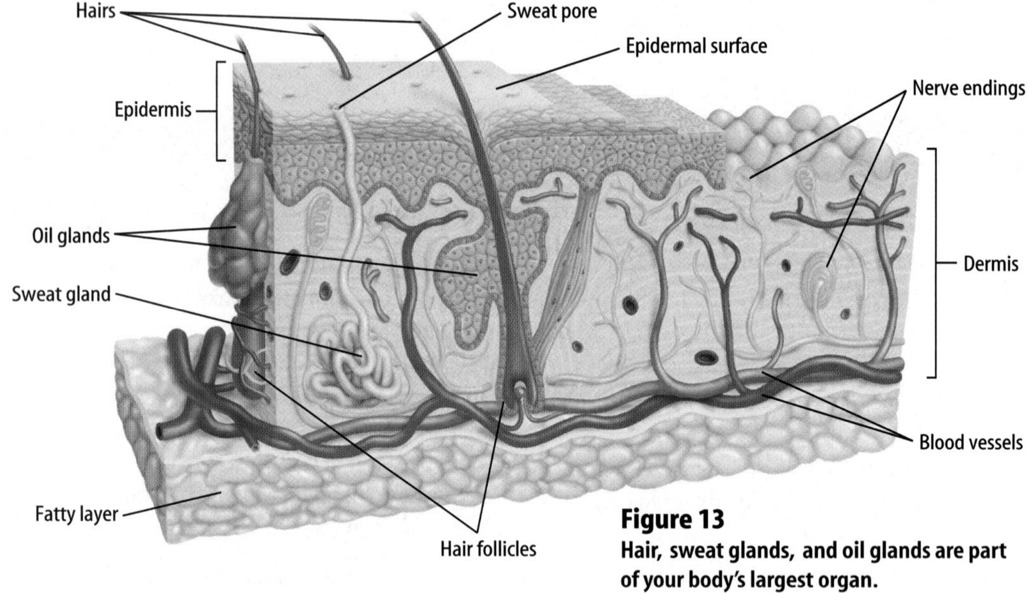

Figure 13
Hair, sweat glands, and oil glands are part of your body's largest organ.

Section Assessment Planner

PORTFOLIO
Visual Learning, p. 504

PERFORMANCE ASSESSMENT
MiniLAB, p. 504
Skill Builder Activities, p. 506
See page 514 for more options.

CONTENT ASSESSMENT
Section, p. 506
Challenge, p. 506
Chapter, pp. 514–515

Melanin Cells in the epidermis produce the chemical melanin (MEL uh nun). **Melanin** is a pigment that protects your skin and gives it color. The different amounts of melanin produced by cells result in differences in skin color, as shown in **Figure 14.** When your skin is exposed to ultraviolet rays, melanin production increases and your skin becomes darker. Lighter skin tones have less protection from the Sun. Such skin burns more easily and may be more susceptible to skin cancer.

Other Skin Layers The **dermis** is the layer of cells directly below the epidermis. This layer is thicker than the epidermis and contains many blood vessels, nerves, muscles, oil and sweat glands, and other structures. Below the dermis is a fatty region that insulates the body. This is where much of the fat is deposited when a person gains weight.

Skin Functions

Your skin is not only the largest organ of your body, it also carries out several major functions, including protection, sensory response, formation of vitamin D, regulation of body temperature, and ridding the body of wastes. The most important function of the skin is protection. The skin forms a protective covering over the body that prevents physical and chemical injury. Some bacteria and other disease-causing organisms cannot pass through the skin as long as it is unbroken. Glands in the skin secrete fluids that can damage or destroy some bacteria. The skin also slows down water loss from body tissues.

Specialized nerve cells in the skin detect and relay information to the brain, making the skin a sensory organ, too. Because of these cells, you are able to sense the softness of a cat, the sharpness of a pin, or the heat of a frying pan.

Earth Science INTEGRATION

Research the effects of ultraviolet radiation on skin. Mountain climbers risk becoming severely sunburned even in freezing temperatures due to increased ultraviolet (UV) radiation. Why is UV radiation stronger on top of mountains? Record your answers in your Science Journal.

Figure 14
Melanin gives skin and eyes their color. The more melanin that is present, the darker the color is. This pigment provides protection from damage caused by harmful light energy.

2 Teach

Skin Structures

Earth Science INTEGRATION

At higher altitudes the atmosphere is thinner and fewer of the Sun's ultraviolet rays are blocked. Therefore, the skin is exposed to more harmful radiation.

Skin Functions

Extension

Have students find out how various animals thermoregulate (maintain or regulate their body temperature). Students might investigate dogs panting, elephants fanning ears, and desert lizards escaping into burrows. L3

Use an Analogy

The hypothalamus in the brain acts like a thermostat on a furnace. A furnace's thermostat senses the temperature of the air and turns the furnace on and off to maintain a constant temperature in a home. The hypothalamus receives temperature readings from the skin and relays messages to body parts to maintain a constant temperature.

Teacher FYI

Dandruff flakes are batches of old epidermal cells that are being shed from the surface of the scalp. Batches of the dead cells may harbor bacteria. Scratching the scalp accelerates the formation of new cells to replace the cells that are flaking away.

Inclusion Strategies

Learning Disabled Have students pat a wet cotton ball onto their wrists. Then have them gently blow on the wet surface. The evaporation removes body heat. Relate this experience to the evaporation of perspiration from the skin during hot weather. L1

Resource Manager

Chapter Resources Booklet
Transparency Activity, p. 48
Directed Reading for Content Mastery, pp. 21, 22
Cultural Diversity, p. 15

Skin Functions, continued

Purpose to observe water evaporation from skin L1 ELL
LS **Kinesthetic**

Materials clear plastic bag, tape, hand lens

Teaching Strategy Use tape on a roll, rather than from a dispenser. It will be easier for students to manage with one hand.

Safety Precautions Caution students not to wrap the tape too tightly. To prevent skin injury when removing the tape, tape only the bag, not the skin.

Analysis

1. water; from the skin
2. Evaporation of water from the skin cools the skin and helps the body maintain a constant temperature.

Performance Have students predict the relative amounts of sweat that would accumulate in the bag under a variety of conditions. Have them design experiments to test their predictions. Use **PASC,** p. 95.

Reading Check

Answer to regulate body temperature and excrete wastes

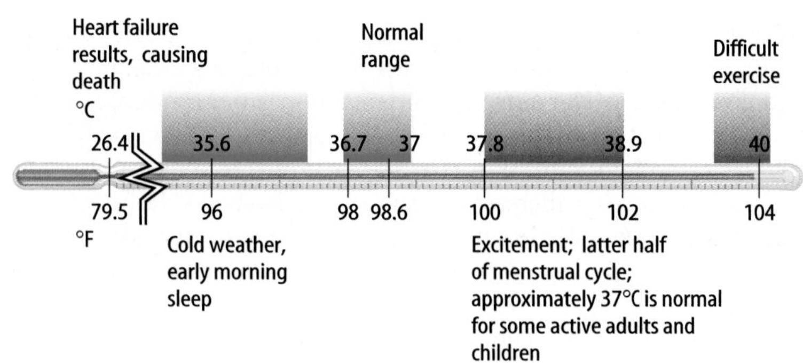

Figure 15
Normal human body temperature is about 37°C. Temperature varies throughout the day. The highest body temperature is reached at about 11 A.M. and the lowest at around 4 A.M. At 43°C (109.5°F) fatal bleeding results, causing death.

MiniLAB

Recognizing Why You Sweat

Procedure

1. Examine the epidermis and the pores of your skin using a **hand lens.**
2. Place a **clear-plastic sandwich bag** on your hand. Use **tape** to seal the bag around your wrist. **WARNING:** *Do not wrap the tape too tightly.*
3. Quietly study your **text** for 10 min, then look at your hand. Remove the bag.
4. Describe what happened to your hand while it was inside the bag.

Analysis

1. Identify what formed inside the bag. Where did this substance come from?
2. Why does this substance form even when you are not active?

Vitamin D Formation Another important function of skin is the formation of vitamin D. Small amounts of this vitamin are produced in the presence of ultraviolet light from a fatlike molecule in your epidermis. Vitamin D is essential for good health because it helps your body absorb calcium into your blood from food in your digestive tract.

Heat and Waste Exchange Humans can withstand a limited range of body temperatures, as shown in **Figure 15.** Your skin plays an important role in regulating your body temperature. Blood vessels in the skin can help release or hold heat. If the blood vessels expand, or dilate, blood flow increases and heat is released. In contrast, less heat is released when the blood vessels constrict. Think of yourself after running—are you flushed red or pale and shivering?

The adult human dermis has about 3 million sweat glands. These glands help regulate the body's temperature and excrete wastes. When the blood vessels dilate, pores open in the skin that lead to the sweat glands. Perspiration, or sweat, moves out onto the skin. Heat transfers from the body to the sweat on the skin. Eventually, this sweat evaporates, removing the heat and cooling the skin. This system eliminates excess heat produced by muscle contractions.

Reading Check *What are two functions of sweat glands?*

As your cells use nutrients for energy, they produce wastes. Such wastes, if not removed from your body, can act as poisons. In addition to helping regulate your body's temperature, sweat glands release water, salt, and other waste products. If too much water and salt are released by sweating during periods of extreme heat or physical exertion, you might feel light-headed or even faint.

Visual Learning

Figure 15 Have students practice interpreting scientific illustrations by studying this graph and writing a paragraph rephrasing the information it contains. L2 LS **Linguistic and Visual-Spatial** P

Active Reading

Synthesis Journal In this strategy, students reflect on a project, a paper, or a performance in light of their own experiences and plan for personal application. Have each student divide a piece of paper into three sections. Have them record "What I did," "What I learned," and "How I can use it." Have students write a Synthesis Journal entry related to the MiniLAB on this page.

504 CHAPTER 17 Structure and Movement

Skin Injuries and Repair

Your skin often is bruised, scratched, burned, ripped, and exposed to harsh conditions like cold and dry air. In response, the skin produces new cells in its epidermis and repairs tears in the dermis. When the skin is injured, disease-causing organisms can enter the body rapidly. An infection often results.

Bruises Bruises are common, everyday events. Playing sports or working around your house often results in small injuries. What is a bruise and how does your body repair it?

When you have a bruise, your skin is not broken but the tiny blood vessels underneath the skin have burst. Red blood cells from these broken blood vessels leak into the surrounding tissue. These blood cells then break down, releasing a chemical called hemoglobin. The hemoglobin gradually breaks down into its components, called pigments. The color of these pigments causes the bruised area to turn shades of blue, red, and purple, as shown in **Figure 16.** Swelling also may occur. As the injury heals, the bruise eventually turns yellow as the pigment in the red blood cells is broken down even more and reenters the bloodstream. After all of the pigment is absorbed into the bloodstream, the bruise disappears and the skin looks normal again.

Reading Check *What is the source of the yellow color of a bruise that is healing?*

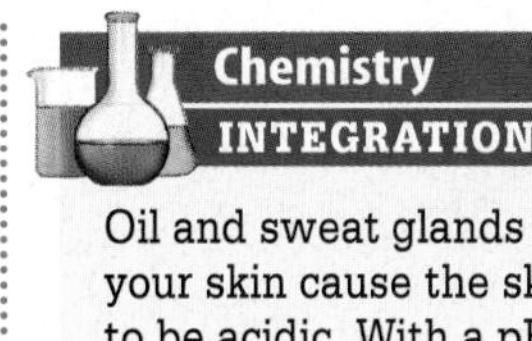

Oil and sweat glands in your skin cause the skin to be acidic. With a pH between 3 and 5, the growth of potential disease-causing micro-organisms on your skin is reduced. What does pH mean? What common substances around your home have a pH value similar to that of your skin? Research to find these answers and then record them in your Science Journal.

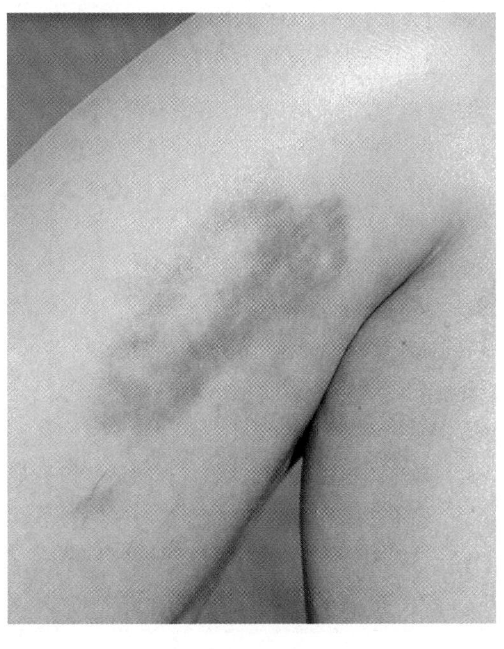

Figure 16
Bruising occurs when tiny blood vessels beneath the skin burst.

Cuts Any tear in the skin is called a cut. Blood flows out of the cut until a clot forms over it. A scab then forms, preventing bacteria from entering the body. Cells in the surrounding blood vessels fight infection while the skin cells beneath the scab grow to fill the gap in the skin. In time, the scab falls off, leaving the new skin behind. If the cut is large enough, a scar may develop because of the large amounts of thick tissue fibers that form.

The body generally can repair bruises and small cuts. What happens when severe burns, some diseases, and surgeries result in injury to large areas of skin? Sometimes, not enough skin cells are left that can divide to replace this lost layer. If not treated, this can lead to rapid water loss from skin and muscle tissues, leading to infection and possible death. Skin grafts can prevent such problems. What are skin grafts?

Skin Injuries and Repair

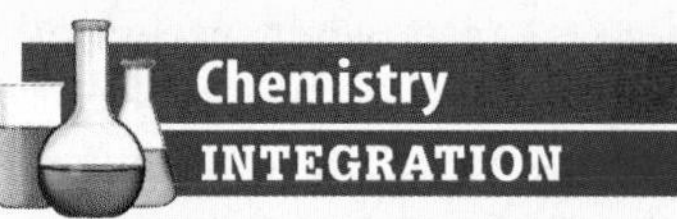

pH is a symbol for the measure of acidity or alkalinity of a solution. Substances with pH similar to that of your skin are apples, bananas, cherries, oranges, grapes, and tomatoes.

Discussion

How would humans receive information about environmental conditions if they did not have skin? Possible answer: They would have to have other tissues or organs for sensing environmental conditions in order to survive.

Reading Check

Answer the breakdown of pigment in red blood cells

Teacher FYI

Contact with certain plants such as poison ivy, poison oak, and poison sumac may produce an inflammation of the skin due to an allergic reaction to the plants. The skin becomes red and itchy, and small blisters develop. Scratching the affected area will cause the blisters to open and may allow infections to develop.

Inclusion Strategies

Gifted Have students do research to find out about the use of artificial skin for burn victims. Have them note particularly the properties of the artificial skin that help the patient heal. Artificial skin is a combination of human skin cells and biodegradable polymers. Currently used in treatment of severe burns, artificial skin provides an interactive bandage that covers the wound until a real skin graft can be grown. L3

Resource Manager

Chapter Resources Booklet
MiniLAB, p. 4
Enrichment, p. 32
Reinforcement, p. 29

Teacher FYI

Acne is a common skin disorder. It starts when excess oil combines with dead skin cells to clog pores. Bacterial infection within the pore can cause a red, inflamed pimple, a blackhead, or a white, pus-filled pimple. Rupture of the pimple may cause the bacteria to infect nearby follicles. About 80% of teenagers suffer from acne.

3 Assess

Reteach

Have students prepare an outline of skin functions correlated with the skin layers. L1

Challenge

Have students find out what happens to the skin when it is sunburned. They should write a list of ways to prevent damage to the skin from the sun or from other sources. L2

Assessment

Content Have students make a concept map to describe the steps the body goes through as it heals a cut. Use **Performance Assessment in the Science Classroom**, p. 163.

A

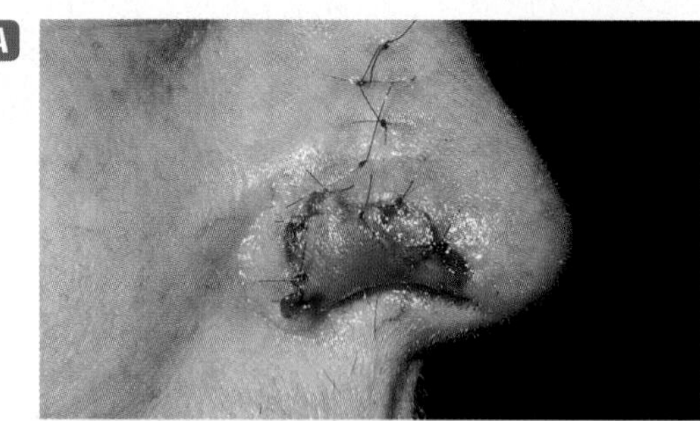

B

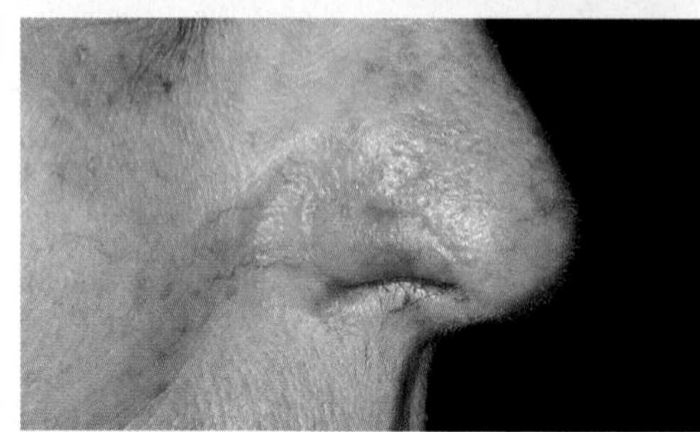

Figure 17
A cancerous growth was removed from the nose of a 69-year-old woman. A A piece of skin removed from her scalp was grafted onto her nose to replace the lost skin. B The skin graft is healing after only one month.

Skin Grafts Pieces of skin that are cut from one part of a person's body and then moved to the injured or burned area where there is no skin are called skin grafts. This new graft of skin is kept alive by nearby blood vessels and soon becomes part of the surrounding skin. Successful skin grafts, shown in **Figure 17,** must be taken from the victim's own body or possibly an identical twin. Skin transplants from other sources are rejected in about three weeks.

What can be done for severe burn victims who have little healthy skin left? Since the 1880s, doctors have used the skin of dead individuals, called cadavers, to treat such burns temporarily. However, the body usually rejects this skin, so the skin must be replaced continually until the burn heals.

A recent advancement in skin repair uses temporary grafts from cadavers to prevent immediate infections, while scientists grow large sheets of epidermis from small pieces of the burn victim's healthy skin. After 19 to 21 days, the cadaver skin patch is removed and the new epidermis is applied. With new technologies, severe cases of skin loss or damage that cannot be repaired may no longer be fatal.

Section 3 Assessment

1. Compare and contrast the epidermis and dermis.
2. List the major functions of the body's largest organ, skin.
3. How does skin help prevent disease in the body?
4. Describe one way doctors are able to repair severe skin damage from burns, injuries, or surgeries.
5. **Think Critically** Why is a person who has been severely burned in danger of dying from loss of water?

Skill Builder Activities

6. **Concept Mapping** Make an events chain concept map to show how skin helps keep body temperature constant. **For more help, refer to the Science Skill Handbook.**
7. **Solving One-Step Equations** Your skin varies in thickness. The thin, almost transparent eyelids are 0.5 mm thick. On the palms of your hand and soles of your feet, skin is up to 0.4 cm thick. How many times thicker is the skin on the soles of your feet compared to your eyelids? **For more help, refer to the Math Skill Handbook.**

Answers to Section Assessment

1. epidermis—thin outer layer of the skin, contains melanin; dermis—under the epidermis, is thicker, contains many blood vessels, nerves, and sweat glands
2. protects, regulates body temperature, excretes wastes, serves as sensory organ, forms vitamin D
3. As long as it is unbroken, skin prevents pathogens from entering the body. Glands in the skin secrete fluids that destroy bacteria.
4. A graft of skin from another part of the person's body is moved to the injured area. The graft eventually becomes part of the surrounding skin.
5. The person has lost the skin's protection from loss of water.
6. the body becomes warm → blood vessels expand → sweat moves out onto the skin → the body cools as sweat evaporates
7. 8 times

Activity

Measuring Skin Surface

Skin covers the entire surface of your body and is your body's largest organ. Skin cells make up a layer of skin about 2 mm thick. These cells are continually lost and re-formed. Skin cells are shed daily at a rate of an average of 50,000 cells per minute. In one year, humans lose about 2 kg of skin and hair. How big is this organ? Find the surface area of human skin.

What You'll Investigate

How much skin covers your body?

Goals

- **Estimate** the surface area of skin that covers the body of a middle-school student.

Materials

10 large sheets of newspaper
scissors
tape
meterstick or ruler

Safety Precautions

Procedure

1. Form groups of three or four, either all female or all male. Select one person from your group to measure the surface area of his or her skin.
2. **Estimate** how much skin covers the average student in your classroom. In your Science Journal, record your estimation.
3. Wrap newspaper snugly around each part of your classmate's body. Overlapping the sheets of paper, use tape to secure the paper. Small body parts, such as fingers and toes, do not need to be wrapped individually. Cover entire hands and feet.
4. After your classmate is completely covered with paper, carefully cut the newspaper off his or her body. **WARNING:** *Do not cut any clothing or skin.*
5. Lay all of the overlapping sheets of newspaper on the floor. Using scissors and more tape, cut and piece the paper suit together to form a rectangle.
6. Using a meterstick, measure the length and width of the resulting rectangle. Multiply these two measurements for an estimate of the surface area of your classmate's skin.

Conclude and Apply

1. Was your estimation correct? Explain.
2. How accurate are your measurements of your classmate's skin surface area? How could your measurements be improved?
3. Calculate the volume of your classmate's skin, using 2 mm as the average thickness and your calculated surface area from this activity.

Communicating Your Data

Using a table, record the estimated skin surface area from all the groups in your class. Find the average surface areas for both males and females. Discuss any differences in these two averages. **For more help, refer to the** Math Skill Handbook.

Activity

BENCH TESTED

Purpose Students will estimate the surface area of skin covering a middle school student.

Process Skills collecting data, predicting, measuring in SI, analyzing results, drawing conclusions

Time Required 40 minutes

Safety Precautions Students should use care when cutting the newspaper model off of the student.

Teaching Strategy Provide printless paper if possible, so the ink does not rub off onto students.

Answers to Questions

1. Answers will vary.
2. Measurements are estimates only. Improvement suggestions will vary.
3. Answers will vary.

Assessment

Performance Today scientists are researching methods for producing synthetic skin. This is especially important for burn victims that lose large portions of their skin. Research this topic and report to your class the results of your search. Use **Performance Assessment in the Science Classroom,** p. 143.

Inclusion Strategies

Physically Disabled Have these students do the data recording for the group. All students should assist in estimating the volume of the skin.

Communicating Your Data

Students may want to use a spreadsheet program to record their results.

Resource Manager

Chapter Resources Booklet
Lab Activity, pp. 13–16
Activity Worksheet, pp. 5–6

Activity

BENCH TESTED

Recognize the Problem

Internet Students will gather data from the Internet sites that can be accessed through the Glencoe Science Web site at **science.glencoe.com.** Students can post their findings on the site and get information from other schools around the country about similar skeletal structures among humans and other mammals.

Non-Internet Sources Bring books to class that describe the physical structures among different mammals.

Time Required

two days

Preparation

Internet Access the Glencoe Science Web site at **science.glencoe.com** to run through the steps that students will follow.

Non-Internet Sources Collect books about mammals. Find realistic models of different mammals to display in the classroom.

Form a Hypothesis

Possible Hypothesis

Student hypotheses may focus on similar skeletal structures found in mammal limbs. For example, the human hand and the fruit bat wing have similar skeletal structures.

Activity Use the Internet

Similar Skeletons

Humans and other mammals share many similar characteristics, including similar skeletal structures. Think about all the different types of mammals you have seen or read about. Tigers, dogs, and household cats are meat-eating mammals. Whales and dolphins live in water. Primates, which include gorillas, chimpanzees, and humans, walk on two legs. Mammals live in different environments, eat different types of food, and even look different, but they all have hair, possess the ability to maintain fairly constant body temperatures, and have similar skeletal structures.

Recognize the Problem

Which skeletal structures are similar among humans and other mammals? How many bones do you have in your hand? What types of bones are they? Do other mammals have similar skeletal structures?

Form a Hypothesis

Make a hypothesis about the skeletal structures that humans and other mammals have in common.

Goals

- **Identify** a skeletal structure in the human body.
- **Write** a list of mammals with which you are familiar.
- **Compare** the identified human skeletal structure to a skeletal structure in each of the mammals.
- **Determine** if the mammal skeletal structure that you selected is similar to the human skeletal structure you identified.
- **Describe** how the mammal skeletal structure is similar to or different from the skeletal structure in a human.

Data Source

SCIENCE *Online*

Visit the Glencoe Science Web site at **science.glencoe.com** to get more information about skeletal structures and for data collected by other students.

508 **CHAPTER 17** Structure and Movement

Resource Manager

Chapter Resources Booklet
Activity Worksheet, pp. 7–8

Lab Management and Safety, p. 67

Internet Addresses

Explore the Glencoe Science Web site at **science.glencoe.com** to find out more about topics in this activity.

Test Your Hypothesis

Plan

1. Choose a specific part of the human skeletal structure to study, such as your hand, foot, skull, leg, or arm.
2. List four to six different mammals.
3. Do these mammals possess skeletal structures similar to the human skeleton? Remember, the mammals' skeletons can be similar to that of the human, but the structures can have different functions.
4. **Compare and contrast** the mammal and human skeletal structures. Are the types of bone similar? Is the number of bones the same? Where are these structures located?

Do

1. Make sure your teacher approves your plan before you start.
2. Go to the Glencoe Science Web site at **science.glencoe.com** to post your data.

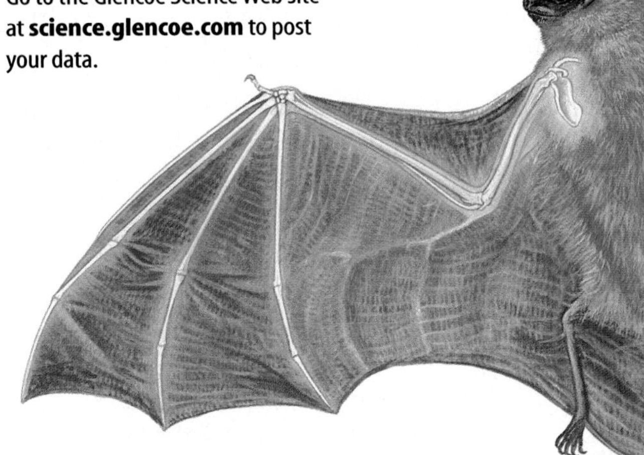

Analyze Your Data

1. Is each mammal's skeletal structure similar to or different from the human skeletal structure you chose?
2. In the data table provided on the Web site, describe how the structures are alike or different.

Draw Conclusions

1. Go to the Glencoe Science Web site at **science.glencoe.com** and compare your data to that of other students. Do other students agree with your conclusions?
2. Do the structures studied have similar function in the human and the mammals you researched?

Communicating Your Data

SCIENCE Online Find this *Use the Internet* activity on the Glencoe Science Web site at **science.glencoe. com** and post your data in the table provided. **Compare** your data with that posted by other students.

Test Your Hypothesis

Teaching Strategies

Have students focus on similar features among humans and mammals. Encourage them to think about human hands, feet, legs, and arms. Have students determine which mammals have similar limb structures to humans.

Troubleshooting While students can compare mammal skeletal structure to skeletal structure for other non-mammals, be sure to have students compare human skeletal structures to other mammals to draw comparisons.

Analyze Your Data

1. Answers will vary. Have students compare specific human bones to specific mammal bones to determine whether they are alike or different.
2. Answers will vary. Students should describe how a particular skeletal structure, such as a foot, is similar between a human and a mammal. To do this, they might describe the function of that structure in humans and for that mammal.

Draw Conclusions

Answers will be individualized and often based on the student's opinion of his or her research. Look for depth and quality of research performed.

Assessment

Content Have students make drawings of the skeletal structures they investigated. Make separate drawings for the human structure and the mammal's structure. Have them label the bones and other physical features in both drawings. Use **PASC,** p. 127.

Communicating Your Data

Have students use a word processing program to create a two-column table describing how the human structure and the mammal structure are similar or different. Include descriptions of the labels that are featured on students' drawings of skeletal structures.

Content Background

Artificial body parts, or prostheses, have been used since ancient times. In fact, Egyptian mummies have been found with prostheses. Improving the look, function, and comfort of prosethic devices is a constant concern for the scientists who develop artificial body parts. Innovations include myoelectric arms, which are powered by batteries and remaining arm muscles. Bionics connect a prosthesis with the brain through a combination of computer sensors in the prosthesis and nerve cells in the remainder of the limb. Bionics allow limited reactions to some stimuli. Special limbs, such as a sprinting leg, have also been developed for individuals who have lost a limb and wish to participate in sports.

Discussion

Imagine the steps involved with selecting your lunch in the school cafeteria, paying for it, and eating it. How would artificial fingers without flexible joints make these tasks difficult? How would a flexible finger help? Possible answers: Difficulty in picking up trays and food, difficulty holding and sorting money and holding eating utensils. In every case, flexibility in the fingers would make these tasks easier.

Oops! Accidents in SCIENCE

SOMETIMES GREAT DISCOVERIES HAPPEN BY ACCIDENT!

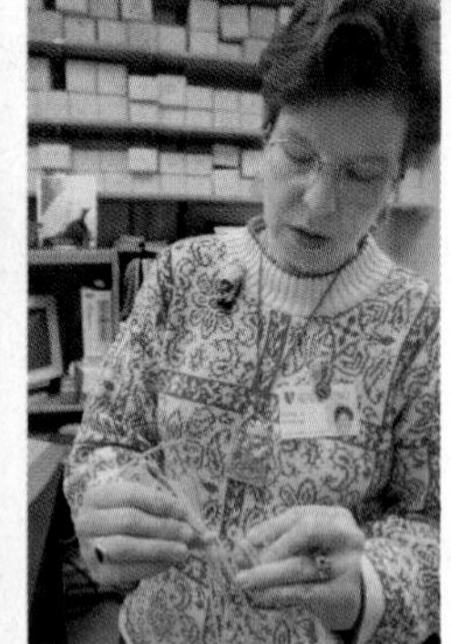

First

A fashion doll is doing her part for medical science! It turns out that the plastic joints that make it possible for one type of doll's legs to bend make good joints in prosthetic (artificial) fingers in humans.

Jane Bahor (photo above) works at Duke University Medical Center in Durham, North Carolina. She makes lifelike body parts for people who have lost legs, arms, or fingers. A few years ago, she met a patient named Jennifer Jordan, an engineering student who'd lost a finger. The artificial finger that Bahor made looked real, but it couldn't bend. She and Jordan began to discuss the problem.

"If only the finger could bend, like a doll's legs bend," said Bahor. "It would be so much more useful to you!"

Jordan's eyes lit up. "That's it!" Jordan said. The engineer went home and borrowed one of her sister's dolls. Returning with it to Bahor's office, she and Bahor did "surgery." They operated on the fashion doll's legs and removed the knee joints from their vinyl casings.

"It turns out that the doll's knee joints flexed the same way that human finger joints do," says Bahor. "We could see that using these joints would allow patients more use and flexibility with their 'new' fingers."

Holding On

The new, fake, flexible fingers can bend in the same way that a doll's legs bend. A person can use his or her other hand to bend and straighten the joint. When the joint bends, it makes a sound similar to a cracking knuckle.

Being able to bend prosthetic fingers allows wearers to hold a pen, pick up a cup, or grab a steering wheel. These are tasks that were impossible before the plastic knee joints were implanted in the artificial fingers. "We've even figured out how to insert three joints in each finger, so that now its wearer can almost make a fist," adds Bahor. Just like the doll's legs, the prosthetic fingers stay bent until the wearer straightens them.

Bahor removes a knee joint from a doll. The joint will soon be in a human's finger!

510

Resources for Teachers and Students

"Lending a Helping Leg," by Diane Martindale, *Scientific American*, May 2000.

"Barbie Lends a Leg," by Sharon Guynup, *Science World*, Sept. 2000.

"Rebuilding the Body," by Alexander Newman, *National Geographic World*, February 2000.

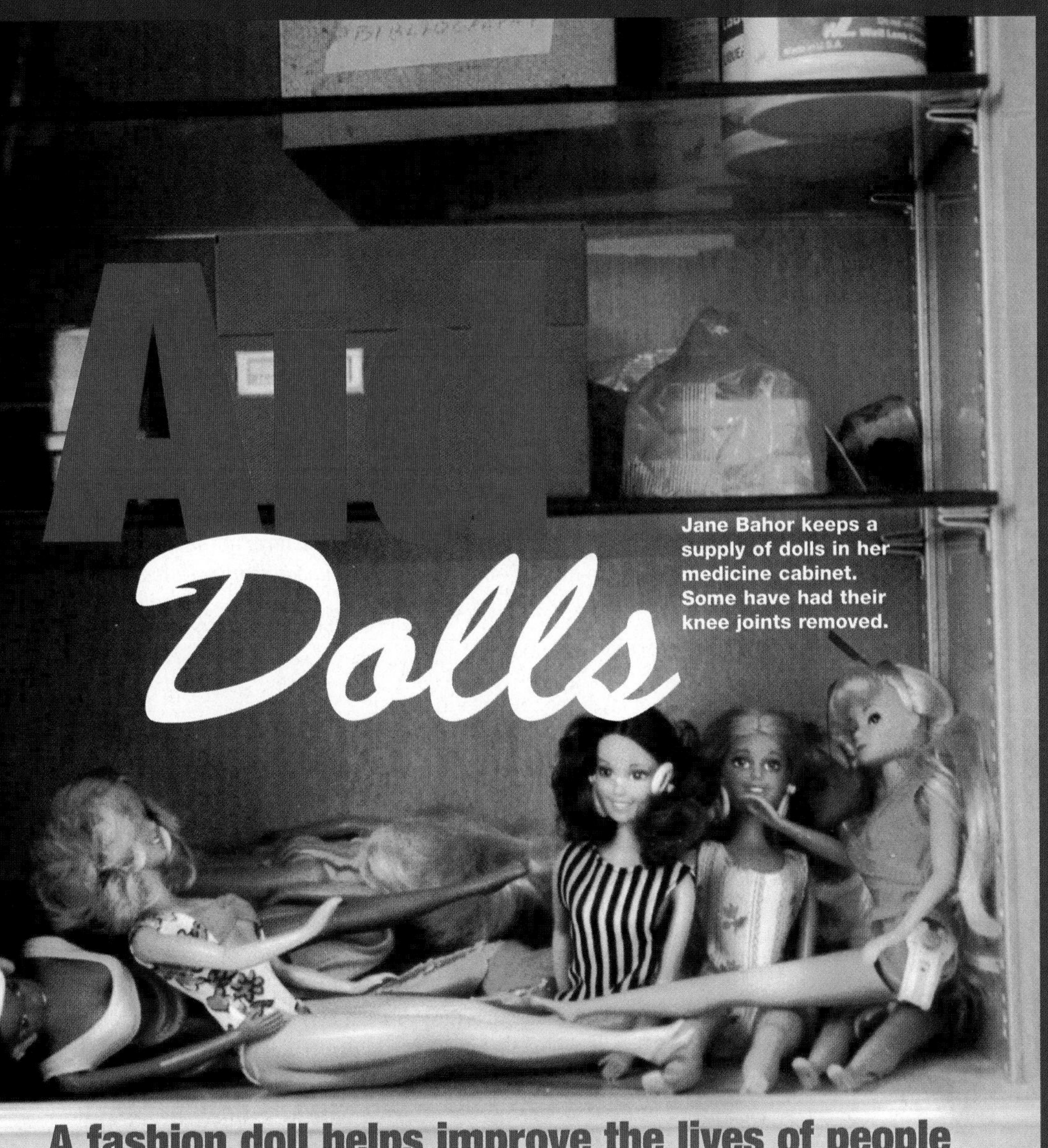

Jane Bahor keeps a supply of dolls in her medicine cabinet. Some have had their knee joints removed.

A fashion doll helps improve the lives of people

Bahor called the company that makes the fashion doll and shared the surprising discovery. The toymaker was so impressed that Bahor now has a ten-year supply of plastic knee joints—free of charge!

But supplies come from other sources, too. "A Girl Scout troop in New Jersey just sent me a big box of donated dolls for the cause," reports Bahor. "It's really great to have kids' support in this effort."

CONNECTIONS **Invent** Choose a "problem" you can solve. Need a better place to store your notebooks in your locker, for instance? Use what Bahor calls "commonly found materials" to solve the problem. Then make a model or a drawing of the problem-solving device.

SCIENCE Online
For more information, visit science.glencoe.com

CONNECTIONS **How People Responded**

Encourage students to first brainstorm the problem they wish to solve, then work on a creative solution, rather than trying to come up with a problem and solution together. Direct students to solve a problem that will impact their everyday lives—something that is important to them. A display or box with a variety of everyday items that might be used to solve problems could provide some inspiration to students. Instruct students that they are not limited to using items in the display or box. The more variety, the better!

Activity

Organize the class into several groups. Each group should research innovations and uses of prostheses in a certain time period: ancient times, the 1800s, 1900–1950, 1950–present, the future. Each group should report their findings to the class, including the limitations of each prosthesis type.

Analyze the Event

Have students analyze why a conversation between an anaplastologist and an engineering student who used an artificial finger was a likely place for an innovation to occur. Possible answers: An anaplastologist is an expert at making artificial limbs, and a person needing a prosthetic finger is very motivated to have a functional prosthesis. Point out to students that this innovation happened because Jane Bahor and Jennifer Jordan were able to think creatively about a problem that needed to be solved, and use unconventional materials to solve the problem.

SCIENCE Online

Internet Addresses

Explore the Glencoe Science Web site at **science.glencoe.com** to find out more about topics in this feature.

Chapter 17 Study Guide

Reviewing Main Ideas

Preview

Students can answer the questions in their Science Journals. Discuss the answers as you go through the chapter. LS **Linguistic**

Review

Students can write their answers, then compare them with those of other students. LS **Interpersonal**

Reteach

Students can look at the illustrations and describe details that support the main ideas of the chapter. LS **Visual-Spatial**

Answers to Chapter Review

Section 1

2. The shape of long bones can support weight. Small and irregular bones are shaped to allow for movement. Flat bones give shape and protection to the body.

Section 2

3. by thick bands of tissue called tendons

Section 3

2. sweat glands and blood vessels

Chapter 17 Study Guide

Reviewing Main Ideas

Section 1 The Skeletal System

1. Bones are living structures that protect, support, make blood, store minerals, and provide for muscle attachment.
2. The skull and pelvic joints in adults do not move and are classified as immovable. *How does the shape of bones relate to their function?*

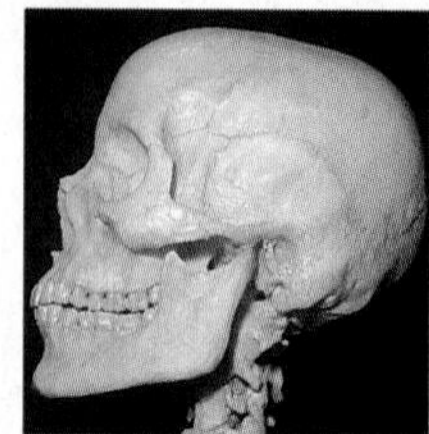

3. Movable joints move freely. Types of movable joints include pivot, hinge, ball-and-socket, and gliding joints.

Section 2 The Muscular System

1. Muscles contract to move bones and body parts.
2. Skeletal muscle is voluntary and moves bones. Smooth muscle is involuntary and controls movement of internal organs. Cardiac muscle is involuntary and located only in the heart.
3. Muscles contract—they pull, not push, to move body parts. Skeletal muscles work in pairs—when one contracts, the other relaxes. *How are skeletal muscles attached to the bones that they move?*

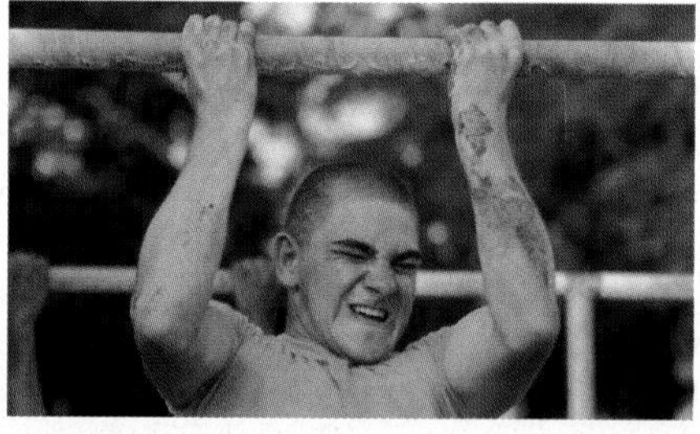

Section 3 The Skin

1. The epidermis has dead cells on its surface. Melanin is produced in the epidermis. Cells at the base of the epidermis produce new skin cells. The dermis is the inner layer where nerves, sweat and oil glands, and blood vessels are located.
2. The functions of skin include protection, reduction of water loss, production of vitamin D, and maintenance of body temperature. *What structures in the skin help maintain an even body temperature?*
3. Glands in the epidermis produce substances that destroy bacteria.

4. Severe damage to skin, including injuries and burns, can lead to infection and death if it is not treated. Advances in technology continue to provide different ways to repair such damage.

FOLDABLES Reading & Study Skills — **After You Read**

Use the information in your Main Ideas Study Fold to review what you learned about skin, muscle, bone, and structure and movement from the chapter.

FOLDABLES Reading & Study Skills — **After You Read**

After students have read the chapter and completed the Foldable described in Before You Read, have them do the activity on the student page.

Dinah Zike

Visualizing Main Ideas

Complete the following concept map on body movement.

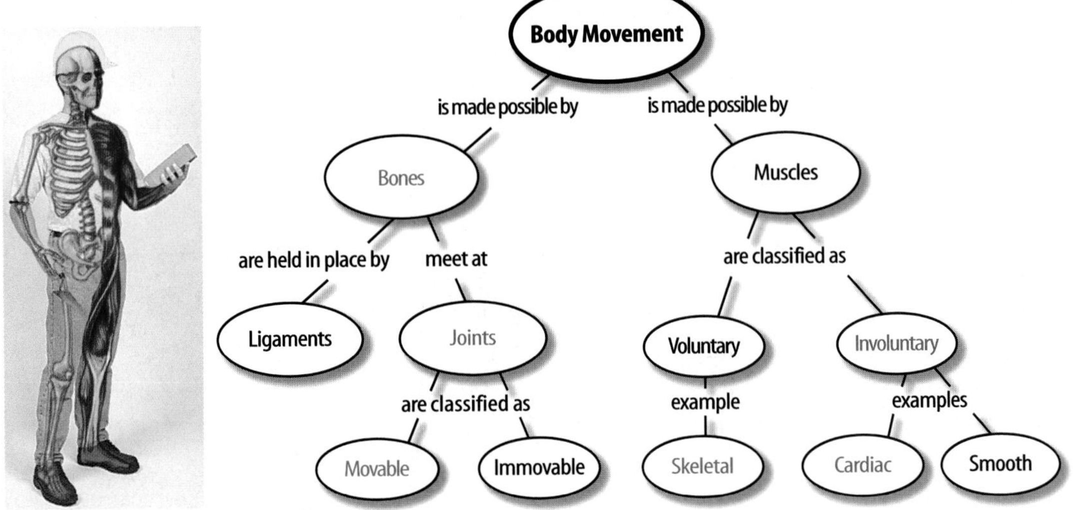

Vocabulary Review

Vocabulary Words

a. cardiac muscle
b. cartilage
c. dermis
d. epidermis
e. involuntary muscle
f. joint
g. ligament
h. melanin
i. muscle
j. periosteum
k. skeletal muscle
l. skeletal system
m. smooth muscle
n. tendon
o. voluntary muscle

THE PRINCETON REVIEW Study Tip

Find a quiet place to study, whether at home or school. Turn off the television or radio, and give your full attention to your lessons.

Using Vocabulary

Match the definitions with the correct vocabulary word.

1. tough outer covering of bone
2. internal framework of the body
3. outer layer of skin
4. thick band of tissue that attaches muscle to a bone
5. muscle found in the heart
6. a tough band of tissue that holds two bones together
7. organ that can relax and contract to aid in the movement of the body
8. a muscle that you control

Chapter 17 Study Guide

Visualizing Main Ideas

See student page.

Vocabulary Review

Using Vocabulary

1. periosteum
2. skeletal system
3. epidermis
4. tendons
5. cardiac muscle
6. ligaments
7. muscles
8. voluntary muscles

IDENTIFYING Misconceptions

Assess

Use the assessment as follow-up to page 488F after students have completed the chapter.

Procedure Put students in pairs. Have one student initiate a knee-jerk reflex by striking the knee of the second student. Have the students note the strength of the reaction as measured by the height of the jerk. Then tell students to lock their right and left hands together and pull vigorously as in an isometric exercise. Have the second student again strike the knee and measure the strength of the reflex. The strength of the reflex as measured by the height of the knee jerk should be greater the second time. This is an example of the interaction of the nervous system and the muscular system.

Expected Outcome Students should understand the interaction of the muscular system with other systems and be able to cite examples of other interactions.

Chapter 17 Assessment

Checking Concepts

1. A
2. D
3. A
4. A
5. D
6. B
7. C
8. C
9. B
10. C

Thinking Critically

11. If there is not enough exposure to sunlight, not enough vitamin D is produced.
12. the severity and size of the burn and the general health of the patient
13. Bones lacking calcium become too flexible and misshapen. They also break more easily.
14. Smooth muscle is made of individual, spindle-shaped cells in layers; skeletal muscle is made of striped fibers; cardiac muscle is a branching, fiberlike structure.
15. Novocaine numbs the nerves so your skin can no longer sense stimuli such as pressure or pain. Novocaine numbs nerves in the dermis.

Chapter 17 Assessment

Checking Concepts

Choose the word or phrase that best answers the question.

1. Which of the following is the most solid form of bone?
   A) compact **C)** spongy
   B) periosteum **D)** marrow
2. Where are blood cells made?
   A) compact bone **C)** cartilage
   B) periosteum **D)** marrow
3. Where are minerals stored?
   A) bone **C)** muscle
   B) skin **D)** blood
4. What are the ends of bones covered with?
   A) cartilage **C)** ligaments
   B) tendons **D)** muscle
5. Where are immovable joints found in the human body?
   A) at the elbow **C)** in the wrist
   B) at the neck **D)** in the skull
6. What kind of joints are the knees, toes, and fingers?
   A) pivot **C)** gliding
   B) hinge **D)** ball and socket
7. Which vitamin is made in the skin?
   A) A **C)** D
   B) B **D)** K
8. Where are dead skin cells found?
   A) dermis **C)** epidermis
   B) marrow **D)** periosteum
9. Which of the following is found in bone?
   A) iron **C)** vitamin D
   B) calcium **D)** vitamin K
10. Which of the following structures helps retain fluids in the body?
    A) bone **C)** skin
    B) muscle **D)** a joint

Thinking Critically

11. When might skin not be able to produce enough vitamin D?
12. What factors might a doctor consider before choosing a method of skin repair for a severe burn victim?
13. What would lack of calcium do to bones?
14. How can you distinguish among these three muscle types?

A
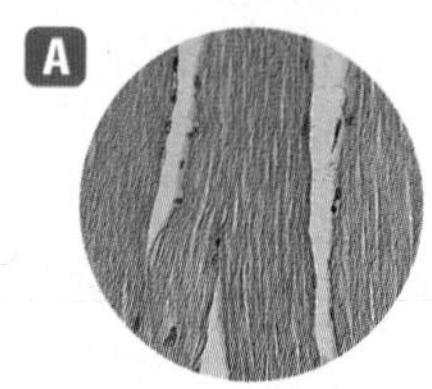

B
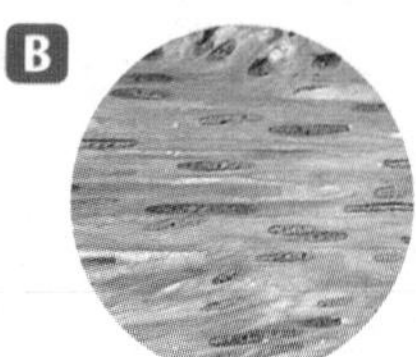

C
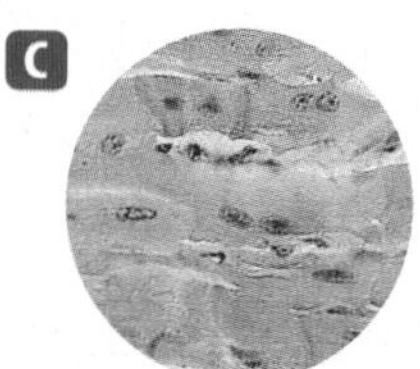

15. What function of your lower lip's skin changes when a dentist gives you novocaine before filling a bottom tooth? Why?

Developing Skills

16. **Drawing Conclusions** The joints in the skull of a newborn baby are flexible, but those of a teenager have fused together and are immovable. Conclude why the infant's skull joints are flexible.
17. **Predicting** Predict what would happen if a person's sweat glands didn't produce sweat.
18. **Comparing and Contrasting** Compare and contrast the functions of ligaments and tendons.

Chapter Assessment Planner

Portfolio Encourage students to place in their portfolios one or two items of what they consider to be their best work. Examples include:
- Visual Learning, p. 492
- Reteach, p. 501
- Visual Learning, p. 504

Performance Additional performance assessments, Performance Task Assessment Lists, and rubrics for evaluating these activities can be found in Glencoe's **Performance Assessment in the Science Classroom.**

19. **Forming Hypotheses** Your body has about 3 million sweat glands. Make a hypothesis about where these sweat glands are on your body. Are they distributed evenly throughout your body?

20. **Concept Mapping** Complete the following concept map that describes the types and functions of bone cells.

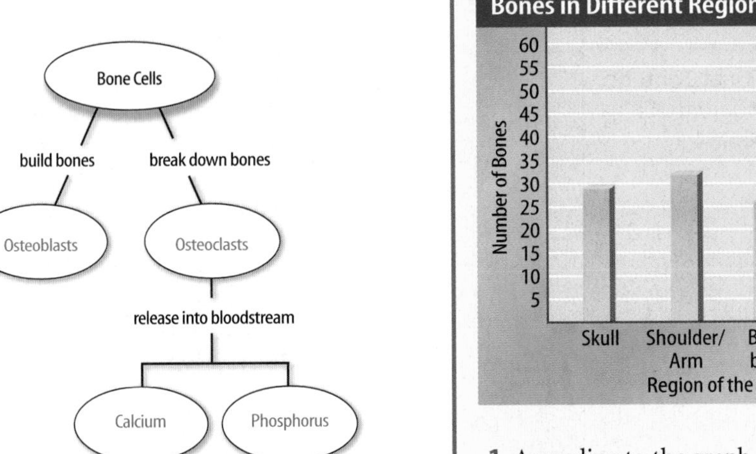

Performance Assessment

21. **Display** Research the differences among first-, second-, and third-degree burns. A local hospital's burn unit or fire department is a possible source of information about burns. Display pictures of each type of burn and descriptions of treatments on a three-sided, free-standing poster.

TECHNOLOGY

Go to the Glencoe Science Web site at **science.glencoe.com** or use the **Glencoe Science CD-ROM** for additional chapter assessment.

THE PRINCETON REVIEW Test Practice

Mia has researched the number of bones in different regions of the body. She placed her results in the following bar graph.

Bones in Different Regions of the Body

Number of Bones: 5, 10, 15, 20, 25, 30, 35, 40, 45, 50, 55, 60

Region of the Body: Skull, Shoulder/Arm, Backbone, Lower Body

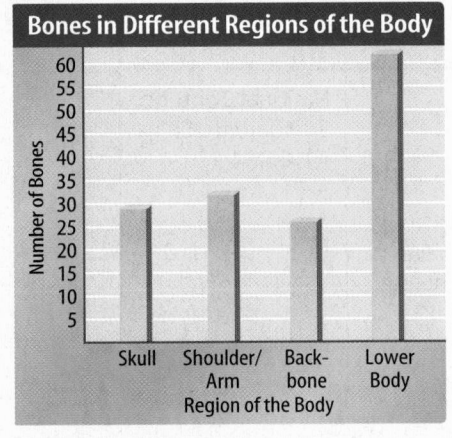

1. According to the graph, the region of the body that has the greatest number of bones is the ______.
   A) backbone
   B) skull
   C) shoulder/arm
   D) lower body

2. The total number of bones in the human body is 206. Approximately what percentage of bones is located in the backbone?
   F) 2%
   G) 12%
   H) 50%
   J) 75%

Chapter 17 Assessment

THE PRINCETON REVIEW Test Practice

The Test-Taking Tip was written by The Princeton Review, the nation's leader in test preparation.

1. D
2. G

Developing Skills

16. Accept all reasonable answers. Flexible joints are thought to be helpful during the birthing process.
17. The person would not be able to maintain a constant body temperature or release certain wastes through the skin.
18. Ligaments hold bones in place at joints. Tendons attach muscle to bones.
19. Possible answer: Sweat glands are not evenly distributed on the skin. This is known because when a person exercises, more sweat is found in some areas (face, underarms) than others.
20. See student page.

Performance Assessment

21. First-degree burns involve only the epidermis; second-degree burns involve the epidermis and dermis; and third-degree burns extend beyond the dermis into the muscle and bone. Use **Performance Assessment in the Science Classroom,** p. 145.

Assessment Resources

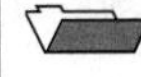 **Reproducible Masters**

Chapter Resources Booklet
Chapter Review, pp. 39–40
Chapter Tests, pp. 41–44
Assessment Transparency Activity, p. 51

Glencoe Science Web site
Interactive Tutor
Chapter Quizzes

Glencoe Technology
Assessment Transparency
Interactive CD-ROM Chapter Quizzes
ExamView Pro Test Bank
Vocabulary PuzzleMaker Software
MindJogger Videoquiz

Section/Objectives	Standards		Activities/Features
	National	State/Local	
Chapter Opener	See p. 5T for a Key to Standards.		**Explore Activity:** Model the digestive tract, p. 517 **Before You Read,** p. 517
Section 1 Nutrition 2 sessions 1 block 1. **Distinguish** among the six classes of nutrients. 2. **Identify** the importance of each type of nutrient. 3. **Explain** the relationships between diet and health.	National Content Standards: UCP3, A1, C1, F1		**Science Online,** p. 520 **MiniLAB:** Comparing the Fat Content of Foods, p. 521 **Problem-Solving Activity,** Is it unhealthy to snack between meals? p. 522 **Visualizing Vitamins,** p. 523 **Earth Science Integration,** p. 525 **Activity:** Identifying Vitamin C Content, p. 528
Section 2 The Digestive System 3 sessions 1.5 blocks 1. **Distinguish** the differences between mechanical digestion and chemical digestion. 2. **Identify** the organs of the digestive system and what takes place in each. 3. **Explain** how homeostasis is maintained in digestion.	National Content Standards: UCP1, A1, C1, C3, E2, F1		**Science Online,** p. 532 **MiniLAB:** Modeling Absorption in the Small Intestine, p. 534 **Environmental Science Integration,** p. 535 **Activity:** Particle Size and Absorption, pp. 536–537 **Science and Society:** Eating Well, pp. 538–539

NATIONAL GEOGRAPHIC

Teacher's Corner

Products Available from Glencoe
To order call 1-800-334-7344:
CD-ROM
NGS PictureShow: Human Body 2
Curriculum Kit
GeoKit: Human Body 1
Transparency Set
NGS PicturePack: Human Body 2
Videodisc
STV: Human Body

Products Available from National Geographic Society
To order call 1-800-368-2728:
Videos
Bacteria; Digestive System (The Human Body Series); Incredible Human Machine; Nutrition: Eating Well

Activity Materials	Reproducible Resources	Section Assessment	Technology
Explore Activity: index cards, marker, masking tape, meterstick	**Chapter Resources Booklet** Foldables Worksheet, p. 17 Directed Reading Overview, p. 19 Note-taking Worksheets, pp. 31–33	GLENCOE'S ASSESSMENT ADVANTAGE	
MiniLAB: 3 potato chips, pretzels, peanuts; small cubes of fruits, cheese, vegetables, meat; brown grocery bag **Activity:** 4 test tubes, test-tube rack, masking tape, 13 wooden stirrers, graduated cylinder, 2% tincture of iodine, dropper, cornstarch, triple-beam balance, weighing paper, water, glass-marking pencil, 4 types of orange juice in dropper bottles	**Chapter Resources Booklet** Transparency Activity, p. 42 MiniLAB, p. 3 Enrichment, p. 29 Reinforcement, p. 27 Directed Reading, p. 20 Activity Worksheet, pp. 5–6 Lab Activity, pp. 9–11 Transparency Activity, pp. 45–46 **Cultural Diversity,** pp. 6, 23 **Mathematics Skill Activities,** p. 47 **Life Science Critical Thinking/Problem Solving,** pp. 15, 16 **Performance Assessment in the Science Classroom,** p. 66	Portfolio Activity, p. 526 Performance MiniLAB, p. 521 Problem-Solving Activity, p. 522 Skill Builder Activities, p. 527 Content Section Assessment, p. 527	Section Focus Transparency Teaching Transparency Interactive CD-ROM Guided Reading Audio Program
MiniLAB: smooth cotton cloth (25 × 25 cm), cotton terry cloth (25 × 25 cm), bowl, water, measuring cup, 2 containers **Activity:** 3 beakers or jars, 3 thermometers, sugar granules, mortar and pestle, triple-beam balance, stirring rod, sugar cubes, weighing paper, warm water, stopwatch	**Chapter Resources Booklet** Transparency Activity, p. 43 MiniLAB, p. 4 Enrichment, p. 30 Reinforcement, p. 28 Directed Reading, pp. 21, 22 Activity Worksheet, pp. 7–8 Lab Activity, pp. 13–15 **Lab Management and Safety,** p. 52 **Science Inquiry Labs,** p. 17 **Home and Community Involvement,** p. 41	Portfolio Science Journal, p. 532 Reteach, p. 535 Performance MiniLAB, p. 534 Skill Builder Activities, p. 535 Content Section Assessment, p. 535	Section Focus Transparency Interactive CD-ROM Guided Reading Audio Program

End of Chapter Assessment

GLENCOE'S ASSESSMENT ADVANTAGE

Blackline Masters	Technology	Professional Series
Chapter Resources Booklet Chapter Review, pp. 35–36 Chapter Tests, pp. 37–40 **Standardized Test Practice by The Princeton Review,** pp. 79–82	MindJogger Videoquiz Interactive CD-ROM Vocabulary PuzzleMakers ExamView Pro Test Bank Interactive Lesson Planner Interactive Teacher Edition	Performance Assessment in the Science Classroom (PASC)

Transparencies

Section Focus

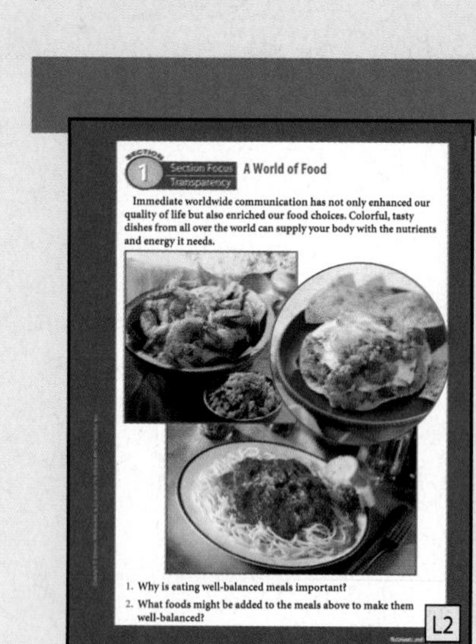
Section Focus Transparency 1 — A World of Food

Immediate worldwide communication has not only enhanced our quality of life but also enriched our food choices. Colorful, tasty dishes from all over the world can supply your body with the nutrients and energy it needs.

1. Why is eating well-balanced meals important?
2. What foods might be added to the meals above to make them well-balanced?

L2

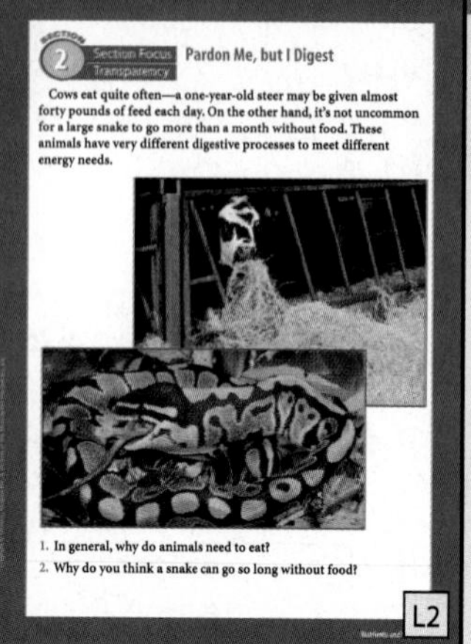
Section Focus Transparency 2 — Pardon Me, but I Digest

Cows eat quite often—a one-year-old steer may be given almost forty pounds of feed each day. On the other hand, it's not uncommon for a large snake to go more than a month without food. These animals have very different digestive processes to meet different energy needs.

1. In general, why do animals need to eat?
2. Why do you think a snake can go so long without food?

L2

This is a representation of key blackline masters available in the Teacher Classroom Resources. See Resource Manager boxes within the chapter for additional information.

Assessment

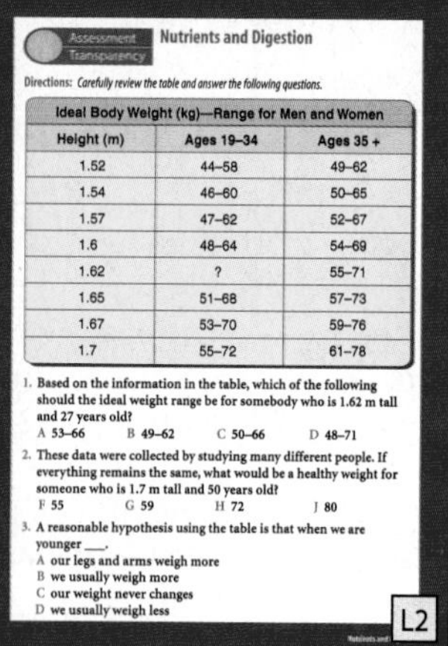
Assessment Transparency — Nutrients and Digestion

Directions: *Carefully review the table and answer the following questions.*

Ideal Body Weight (kg)—Range for Men and Women		
Height (m)	Ages 19–34	Ages 35 +
1.52	44–58	49–62
1.54	46–60	50–65
1.57	47–62	52–67
1.6	48–64	54–69
1.62	?	55–71
1.65	51–68	57–73
1.67	53–70	59–76
1.7	55–72	61–78

1. Based on the information in the table, which of the following should the ideal weight range be for somebody who is 1.62 m tall and 27 years old?
   A 53–66 B 49–62 C 50–66 D 48–71
2. These data were collected by studying many different people. If everything remains the same, what would be a healthy weight for someone who is 1.7 m tall and 50 years old?
   F 55 G 59 H 72 J 80
3. A reasonable hypothesis using the table is that when we are younger ___.
   A our legs and arms weigh more
   B we usually weigh more
   C our weight never changes
   D we usually weigh less

L2

Teaching

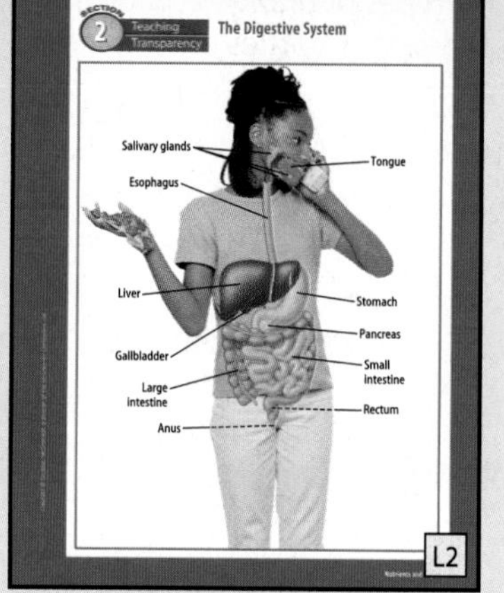
Teaching Transparency 2 — The Digestive System

L2

Key to Teaching Strategies

The following designations will help you decide which activities are appropriate for your students.

- **L1** Level 1 activities should be appropriate for students with learning difficulties.
- **L2** Level 2 activities should be within the ability range of all students.
- **L3** Level 3 activities are designed for above-average students.
- **ELL** ELL activities should be within the ability range of English Language Learners.
- **COOP LEARN** Cooperative Learning activities are designed for small group work.
- **LS** Multiple Learning Styles logos, as described on page 22T, are used throughout to indicate strategies that address different learning styles.
- **P** These strategies represent student products that can be placed into a best-work portfolio.

Hands-on Activities

Activity Worksheets

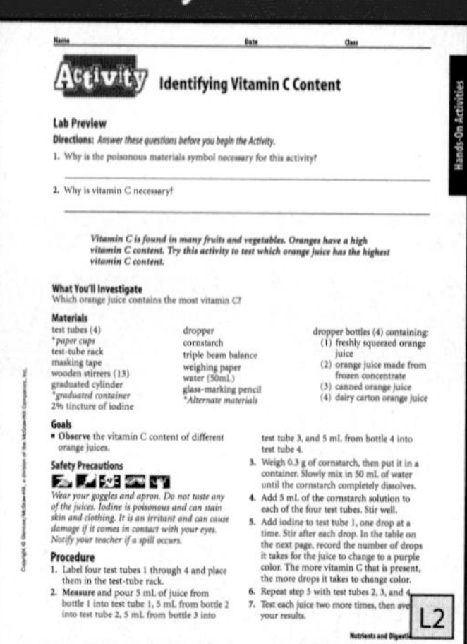
Name Date Class

Activity — Identifying Vitamin C Content

Hands-On Activities

Lab Preview

Directions: *Answer these questions before you begin the Activity.*

1. Why is the poisonous materials symbol necessary for this activity?
2. Why is vitamin C necessary?

Vitamin C is found in many fruits and vegetables. Oranges have a high vitamin C content. Try this activity to test which orange juice has the highest vitamin C content.

What You'll Investigate
Which orange juice contains the most vitamin C?

Materials
test tubes (4)
*paper cups
test-tube rack
masking tape
wooden stirrers (13)
graduated cylinder
*graduated container
2% tincture of iodine
dropper
cornstarch
triple beam balance
weighing paper
water (50mL)
glass-marking pencil
*Alternate materials
dropper bottles (4) containing:
(1) freshly squeezed orange juice
(2) orange juice made from frozen concentrate
(3) canned orange juice
(4) dairy carton orange juice

Goals
- **Observe** the vitamin C content of different orange juices.

Safety Precautions

Wear your goggles and apron. Do not taste any of the juices. Iodine is poisonous and can stain skin and clothing. It is an irritant and can cause damage if it comes in contact with your eyes. Notify your teacher if a spill occurs.

Procedure
1. Label four test tubes 1 through 4 and place them in the test-tube rack.
2. **Measure** and pour 5 mL of juice from bottle 1 into test tube 1, 5 mL from bottle 2 into test tube 2, 5 mL from bottle 3 into test tube 3, and 5 mL from bottle 4 into test tube 4.
3. Weigh 0.3 g of cornstarch, then put it in a container. Slowly mix in 50 mL of water until the cornstarch completely dissolves.
4. Add 5 mL of the cornstarch solution to each of the four test tubes. Stir well.
5. Add iodine to test tube 1, one drop at a time. Stir after each drop. In the table on the next page, record the number of drops it takes for the juice to change to a purple color. The more vitamin C that is present, the more drops it takes to change color.
6. Repeat step 5 with test tubes 2, 3, and 4.
7. Test each juice two more times, then ave[rage] your results.

L2

Laboratory Activities

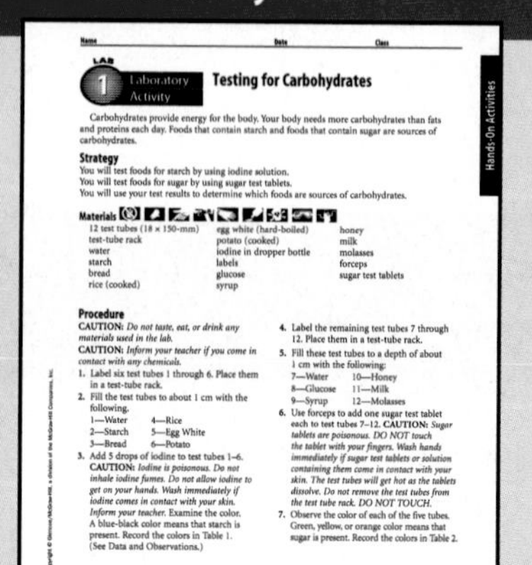
Name Date Class

Lab 1 Laboratory Activity — Testing for Carbohydrates

Hands-On Activities

Carbohydrates provide energy for the body. Your body needs more carbohydrates than fats and proteins each day. Foods that contain starch and foods that contain sugar are sources of carbohydrates.

Strategy
You will test foods for starch by using iodine solution.
You will test foods for sugar by using sugar test tablets.
You will use your test results to determine which foods are sources of carbohydrates.

Materials
12 test tubes (18 × 150-mm)
test-tube rack
water
starch
bread
rice (cooked)
egg white (hard-boiled)
potato (cooked)
iodine in dropper bottle
labels
glucose
syrup
honey
milk
molasses
forceps
sugar test tablets

Procedure
CAUTION: *Do not taste, eat, or drink any materials used in the lab.*
CAUTION: *Inform your teacher if you come in contact with any chemicals.*
1. Label six test tubes 1 through 6. Place them in a test-tube rack.
2. Fill the test tubes to about 1 cm with the following.
   1—Water 4—Rice
   2—Starch 5—Egg White
   3—Bread 6—Potato
3. Add 5 drops of iodine to test tubes 1–6. **CAUTION:** *Iodine is poisonous. Do not inhale iodine fumes. Do not allow iodine to get on your hands. Wash immediately if iodine comes in contact with your skin. Inform your teacher.* Examine the color. A blue-black color means that starch is present. Record the colors in Table 1. (See Data and Observations.)
4. Label the remaining test tubes 7 through 12. Place them in a test-tube rack.
5. Fill these test tubes to a depth of about 1 cm with the following:
   7—Water 10—Honey
   8—Glucose 11—Milk
   9—Syrup 12—Molasses
6. Use forceps to add one sugar test tablet each to test tubes 7–12. **CAUTION:** *Sugar tablets are poisonous. DO NOT touch the tablet with your fingers. Wash hands immediately if sugar test tablets or solution containing them come in contact with your skin. The test tubes will get hot as the tablets dissolve. Do not remove the test tubes from the test tube rack. DO NOT TOUCH.*
7. Observe the color of each of the five tubes. Green, yellow, or orange color means that sugar is present. Record the colors in Table 2.

L2

Meeting Different Ability Levels

Content Outline

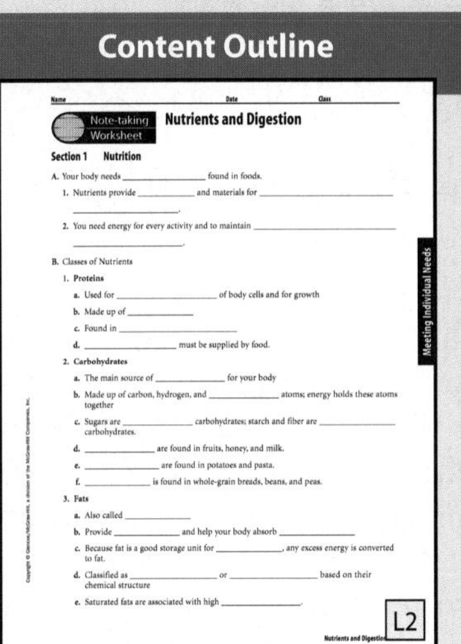

Name Date Class

Note-taking Worksheet **Nutrients and Digestion**

Section 1 Nutrition

A. Your body needs __________ found in foods.
1. Nutrients provide __________ and materials for __________
2. You need energy for every activity and to maintain __________

B. Classes of Nutrients
1. **Proteins**
   a. Used for __________ of body cells and for growth
   b. Made up of __________
   c. Found in __________
   d. __________ must be supplied by food.
2. **Carbohydrates**
   a. The main source of __________ for your body
   b. Made up of carbon, hydrogen, and __________ atoms; energy holds these atoms together
   c. Sugars are __________ carbohydrates; starch and fiber are __________ carbohydrates.
   d. __________ are found in fruits, honey, and milk.
   e. __________ are found in potatoes and pasta.
   f. __________ is found in whole-grain breads, beans, and peas.
3. **Fats**
   a. Also called __________
   b. Provide __________ and help your body absorb __________
   c. Because fat is a good storage unit for __________, any excess energy is converted to fat.
   d. Classified as __________ or __________ based on their chemical structure
   e. Saturated fats are associated with high __________.

Meeting Individual Needs

L2

Reinforcement

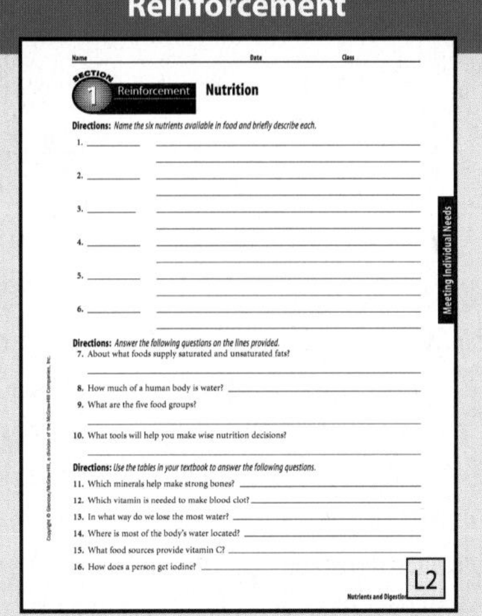

Name Date Class

Section 1 Reinforcement **Nutrition**

Directions: Name the six nutrients available in food and briefly describe each.

1. __________
2. __________
3. __________
4. __________
5. __________
6. __________

Directions: Answer the following questions on the lines provided.

7. About what foods supply saturated and unsaturated fats?
8. How much of a human body is water?
9. What are the five food groups?
10. What tools will help you make wise nutrition decisions?

Directions: Use the tables in your textbook to answer the following questions.

11. Which minerals help make strong bones?
12. Which vitamin is needed to make blood clot?
13. In what way do we lose the most water?
14. Where is most of the body's water located?
15. What food sources provide vitamin C?
16. How does a person get iodine?

Meeting Individual Needs

L2

Directed Reading

Name Date Class

Directed Reading for Content Mastery *Overview* **Nutrients and Digestion**

Directions: Complete the concept map using the terms listed below.

vitamins	fats	repairs	proteins
cell development	minerals	growth	carbohydrates

1. 2. 3. 4. 5. 6. 7. 8. — nutrients — provide — for

Directions: Circle the organs that are involved in each of the three processes named below. Note that a process may involve more than one organ.

9. **ingestion**
   stomach — small intestine — mouth
   pancreas — large intestine — liver
10. **digestion**
   stomach — small intestine — mouth
   pancreas — large intestine — liver
11. **absorption**
   stomach — small intestine — mouth
   pancreas — large intestine — liver

Meeting Individual Needs

L1

Assessment

Chapter Tests

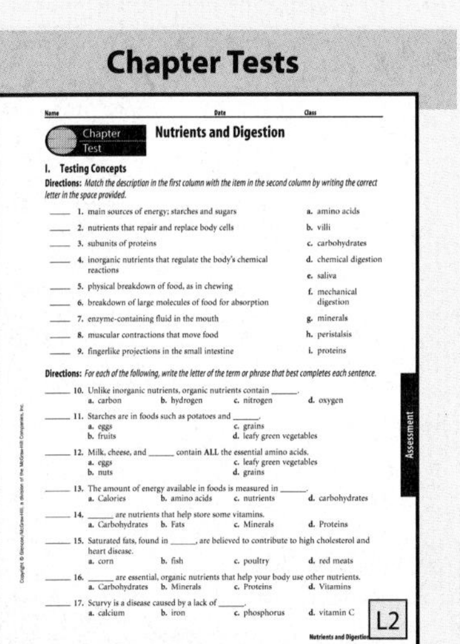

Name Date Class

Chapter Test **Nutrients and Digestion**

I. Testing Concepts

Directions: Match the description in the first column with the item in the second column by writing the correct letter in the space provided.

____ 1. main sources of energy; starches and sugars — a. amino acids
____ 2. nutrients that repair and replace body cells — b. villi
____ 3. subunits of proteins — c. carbohydrates
____ 4. inorganic nutrients that regulate the body's chemical reactions — d. chemical digestion
____ 5. physical breakdown of food, as in chewing — e. saliva
____ 6. breakdown of large molecules of food for absorption — f. mechanical digestion
____ 7. enzyme-containing fluid in the mouth — g. minerals
____ 8. muscular contractions that move food — h. peristalsis
____ 9. fingerlike projections in the small intestine — i. proteins

Directions: For each of the following, write the letter of the term or phrase that best completes each sentence.

____ 10. Unlike inorganic nutrients, organic nutrients contain ____. a. carbon b. hydrogen c. nitrogen d. oxygen
____ 11. Starches are in foods such as potatoes and ____. a. eggs b. fruits c. grains d. leafy green vegetables
____ 12. Milk, cheese, and ____ contain ALL the essential amino acids. a. eggs b. nuts c. leafy green vegetables d. grains
____ 13. The amount of energy available in foods is measured in ____. a. Calories b. amino acids c. nutrients d. carbohydrates
____ 14. ____ are nutrients that help store some vitamins. a. Carbohydrates b. Fats c. Minerals d. Proteins
____ 15. Saturated fats, found in ____, are believed to contribute to high cholesterol and heart disease. a. corn b. fish c. poultry d. red meats
____ 16. ____ are essential, organic nutrients that help your body use other nutrients. a. Carbohydrates b. Minerals c. Proteins d. Vitamins
____ 17. Scurvy is a disease caused by a lack of ____. a. calcium b. iron c. phosphorus d. vitamin C

Assessment

L2

Enrichment

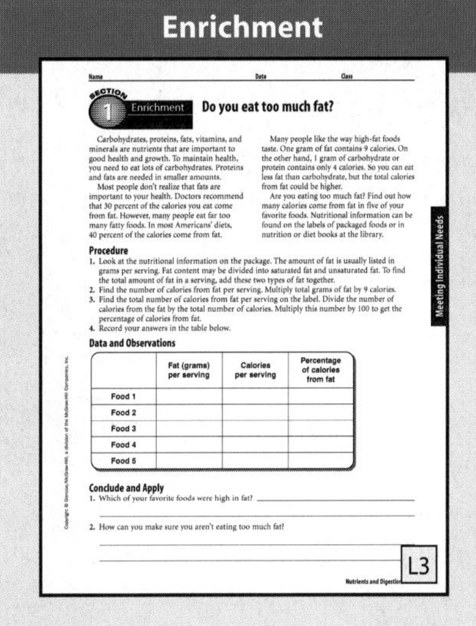

Name Date Class

Section 1 Enrichment **Do you eat too much fat?**

Carbohydrates, proteins, fats, vitamins, and minerals are nutrients that are important to good health and growth. To maintain health, you need to eat lots of carbohydrates. Proteins and fats are needed in smaller amounts.

Most people don't realize that fats are important to your health. Doctors recommend that 30 percent of the calories you eat come from fat. However, many people eat far too many fatty foods. In most Americans' diets, 40 percent of the calories come from fat.

Many people like the way high-fat foods taste. One gram of fat contains 9 calories. On the other hand, 1 gram of carbohydrate or protein contains only 4 calories. So you can eat less fat than carbohydrate, but the total calories from fat could be higher.

Are you eating too much fat? Find out how many calories come from fat in five of your favorite foods. Nutritional information can be found on the labels of packaged foods or in nutrition or diet books at the library.

Procedure

1. Look at the nutritional information on the package. The amount of fat is usually listed in grams per serving. Fat content may be divided into saturated fat and unsaturated fat. To find the total amount of fat in a serving, add these two types of fat together.
2. Find the number of calories from fat per serving. Multiply total grams of fat by 9 calories.
3. Find the total number of calories from fat per serving on the label. Divide the number of calories from the fat by the total number of calories. Multiply this number by 100 to get the percentage of calories from fat.
4. Record your answers in the table below.

Data and Observations

	Fat (grams) per serving	Calories per serving	Percentage of calories from fat
Food 1			
Food 2			
Food 3			
Food 4			
Food 5			

Conclude and Apply

1. Which of your favorite foods were high in fat?
2. How can you make sure you aren't eating too much fat?

Meeting Individual Needs

L3

Spanish Directed Reading

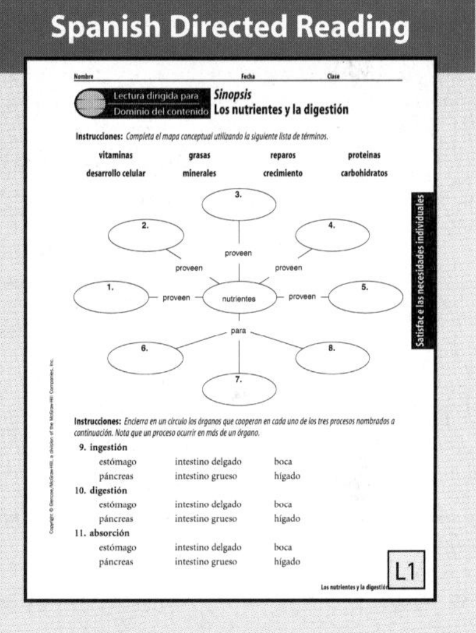

Nombre Fecha Clase

Lectura dirigida para Dominio del contenido *Sinopsis* **Los nutrientes y la digestión**

Instrucciones: Completa el mapa conceptual utilizando la siguiente lista de términos.

vitaminas	grasas	reparos	proteínas
desarrollo celular	minerales	crecimiento	carbohidratos

1. 2. 3. 4. 5. 6. 7. 8. — nutrientes — proveen — para

Instrucciones: Encierra en un círculo los órganos que cooperan en cada uno de los tres procesos nombrados a continuación. Nota que un proceso ocurrir en más de un órgano.

9. **ingestión**
   estómago — intestino delgado — boca
   páncreas — intestino grueso — hígado
10. **digestión**
   estómago — intestino delgado — boca
   páncreas — intestino grueso — hígado
11. **absorción**
   estómago — intestino delgado — boca
   páncreas — intestino grueso — hígado

Satisfac e las necesidades individuales

L1

Test Practice Workbook

Chapter Review

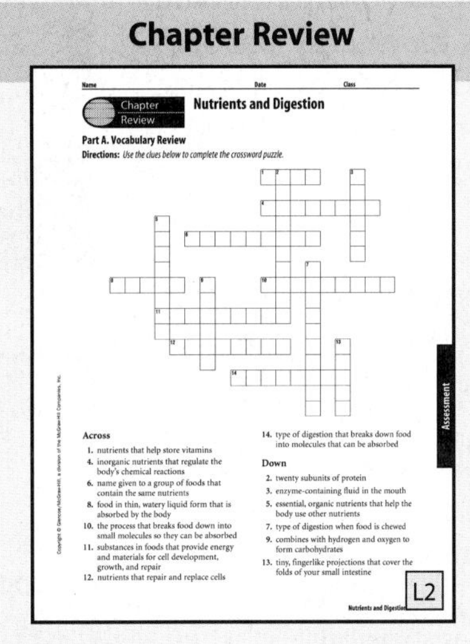

Name Date Class

Chapter Review **Nutrients and Digestion**

Part A. Vocabulary Review

Directions: Use the clues below to complete the crossword puzzle.

Across

1. nutrients that help store vitamins
4. inorganic nutrients that regulate the body's chemical reactions
6. name given to a group of foods that contain the same nutrients
8. food in thin, watery liquid form that is absorbed by the body
10. the process that breaks food down into small molecules so they can be absorbed
11. substances in foods that provide energy and materials for cell development, growth, and repair
12. nutrients that repair and replace cells
14. type of digestion that breaks down food into molecules that can be absorbed

Down

2. twenty subunits of protein
3. enzyme-containing fluid in the mouth
5. essential, organic nutrients that help the body use other nutrients
7. type of digestion when food is chewed
9. combines with hydrogen and oxygen to form carbohydrates
13. tiny, fingerlike projections that cover the folds of your small intestine

Assessment

L2

Science Content Background

SECTION 1

Nutrition

Calorie Needs

The rate at which the body consumes energy when at rest is termed the basal metabolic rate. The basal metabolic rate and the physical activity metabolic rate are two of the factors that help determine the number of Calories a person's body requires each day. Other factors include age, weight, size, sex, endocrine gland activity, and external temperature.

Student Misconception

Energy is released directly from food.

Refer to the facing page for teaching strategies to address this misconception. Refer to pages 518–525 for content related to this topic.

Carbohydrates

Carbohydrates and proteins supply about four Calories per gram, and fats supply about nine Calories per gram. Excess sugar is stored in the liver and muscles in the form of glycogen. When energy is required, a series of activities involving the brain, nerves, and adrenal glands brings about the conversion of glycogen to glucose. The amino acids of protein can be converted into carbohydrates, and then these can be utilized for energy production. Excess fat stored in the body can oxidize and supply energy. This reaction produces a great deal of heat as a waste product.

Vitamins

The role of vitamins as nutrients was not recognized until the early 1900s. During the early years of research, each new vitamin that was identified was given a letter designation. This method proved to be inadequate to correctly classify the substances. Vitamins then were called by their chemical names. Niacin is an example of a vitamin that goes by its chemical name rather than a letter designation.

SECTION 2

The Digestive System

Digestion

The process of transforming foods into usable nutrients is called digestion. This extracellular process takes place in the digestive system, specifically in the stomach and small intestine. Enzymes that serve as catalysts for chemical reactions often require precise environmental conditions, including the proper temperature, pH, and substrate, to be active. For example, the enzyme pepsin, which is found in the stomach, is only active in a medium having a pH of 1.5 to 2.2 and only helps digest proteins.

Palmer/The Stock Market

For additional content background on this topic, go to the Glencoe Science Web site at science.glencoe.com.

IDENTIFYING Misconceptions

Find Out What Students Think

Students may think that . . .

- **Energy comes directly from the food they eat.**

Students often think that digestion is a process in which usable energy is released directly from food. Many students do not understand that food must be broken down into other substances in the digestive tract and then transported to various parts of the body in order to be re-formed into other substances or broken down for energy release.

Discussion

Have students describe the process of digestion, including what happens to the food they eat, where it goes, and how it is used. Record their ideas on the board or on the overhead projector next to an outline of the digestive system. Keep track of misconceptions, but do not attempt to correct them at this time.

Promote Understanding

Activity

Preparation Prepare a 0.1% starch solution by heating 1 mL soluble starch in 1 L water. Prepare a 0.2% diastase solution by dissolving 2 mL diastase in 1 L water. (Diastase can be purchased from most biological supply houses.)

Procedure Tell students they are going to simulate the digestion of starch in the body. Starch is found in foods such as crackers, rice, and potatoes.

- Have students place two drops of starch solution on each end of a clean glass slide. (One of the sets of drops will serve as a control.)
- Have students add two drops of dilute Lugol's solution to each of the sets of drops. Both sets of drops should turn a pale blue.
- Add one drop of the diastase solution to one of the sets of drops. The diastase will cause the blue of the solution to disappear.

John Paul Endress/The Stock Market

Ask students why they think the color disappeared. After some discussion, explain that the changes they observed here are similar to the way starch is affected by amylase in the body. Starches are broken down into simple sugars and then transported to the different parts of the body where they are used. Emphasize that these simple sugars also may be reassembled in the liver and stored as a more complex substance, glycogen, or they may be converted into fat molecules and stored throughout the body.

As an extension, have students brainstorm a list of other examples of foods that are broken down and then reassembled into another substance. For example, proteins can be broken down into amino acids, which are then assembled in the cells to form new proteins. Explain that many of these processes will be described in this chapter.

Assess

After completing the chapter, see *Identifying Misconceptions* in the Study Guide.

CHAPTER 18

Nutrients and Digestion

Chapter Vocabulary

nutrient, p. 518
protein, p. 519
amino acid, p. 519
carbohydrate, p. 520
fat, p. 521
vitamin, p. 522
mineral, p. 524
food group, p. 526
digestion, p. 529
mechanical digestion, p. 529
chemical digestion, p. 529
enzyme, p. 530
peristalsis, p. 532
chyme, p. 533
villi, p. 534

What do you think?

Science Journal The picture is of the gallbladder and part of the liver. The gallbladder secretes bile, a substance that physically breaks up the fats in foods.

CHAPTER 18

Nutrients and Digestion

You may think the photograph on the right is a view of a pile of potatoes or a heap of loaves of bread, but it is a close-up of your small intestine. The wall of the small intestine has many fingerlike projections that absorb, or soak up, substances from digested food. Other organs in your body also help break down the food you eat.

What do you think?

Science Journal Look at this picture with a classmate. What part of the digestive system do you think it is? Here's a hint: *The fluid from this organ acts like soapy water does on a greasy pan.* Write your answer or best guess in your Science Journal.

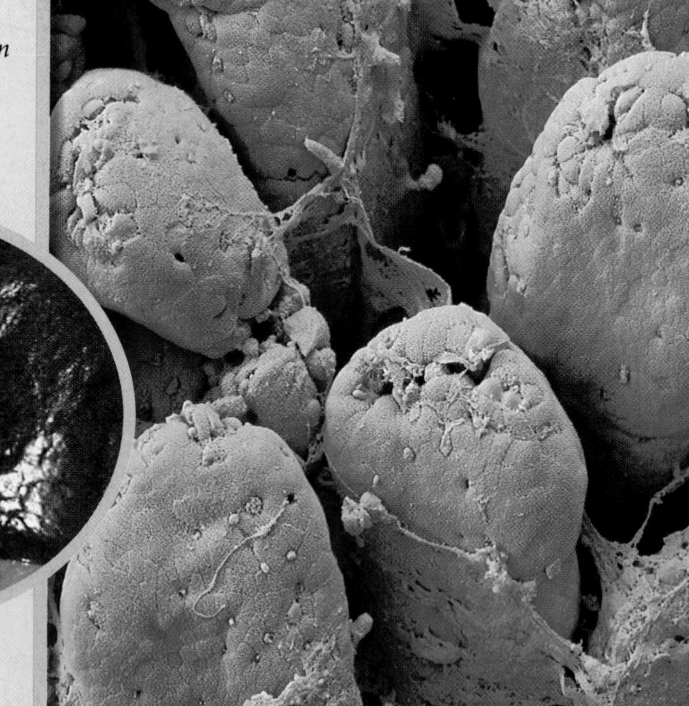

516

Theme Connection

Energy Energy is a major theme of this chapter. Nutrients contain chemical energy. During digestion, complex food molecules are broken down into simpler forms that body cells can use for metabolism. This process transforms chemical energy into thermal and mechanical energy.

Think about your favorite food. Now imagine yourself taking a bite of it. When you eat, your body breaks down food to release energy. How long does it take for the food to go through the entire process?

Model the digestive tract

1. Make a label for each of the major organs of the digestive tract listed here. Include the organ's name, its length, and the time it takes for food to pass through it.
2. Working with a partner, place a piece of masking tape that is 6.5 m long on the classroom floor.
3. Beginning at one end of the tape, and in the same order as they are listed in the table, mark the length for each organ. Place each label next to its section.

Organs of the Digestive System

Organ	Length	Time
Mouth	8 cm	5 s to 30 s
Pharynx and Esophagus	25 cm	10 s
Stomach	16 cm	2 h to 4 h
Small Intestine	4.75 m	3 h
Large Intestine	1.25 m	2 days

Observe

In your Science Journal, suggest reasons why the food that you eat spends a different amount of time in each of the organs. What factors might change the amount of time digestion takes?

Before You Read

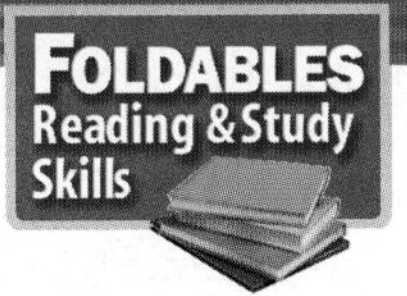

Making a Classify Study Fold **Make the following Foldable to help you organize foods based on the nutrients that they contain.**

1. Place a sheet of paper in front of you so the short side is at the top. Fold the top of the paper down and the bottom up to divide the paper into thirds. Then fold the paper in half from top to bottom.
2. Open the paper and label the six columns as shown: *Proteins, Carbohydrates, Lipids, Water, Vitamins,* and *Minerals*.
3. As you read the chapter, list foods you eat that provide each of these nutrients in the proper columns.

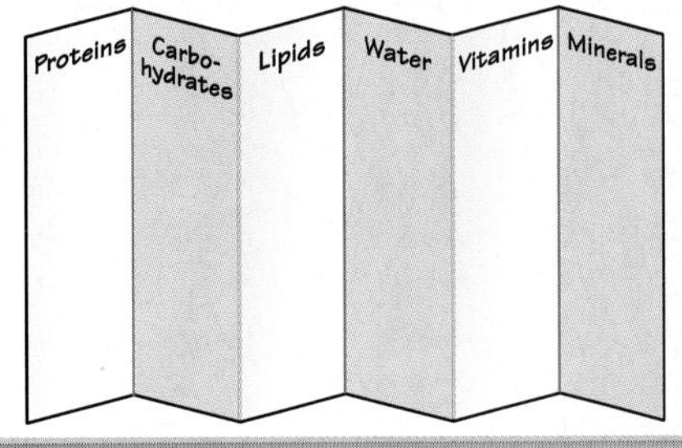

Explore Activity

Purpose Use the Explore Activity to introduce students to the digestive system. L2 COOP LEARN

LS **Visual-Spatial**

Preparation Find an area where students can work undisturbed during the activity.

Materials index cards, marking pens, masking tape, meter stick or measuring tape

Teaching Strategy

- Explain that the length of time food spends in the digestive tract varies among individuals and can depend on health conditions.
- After the complete length of the digestive system has been marked off, encourage students to infer how something that long can fit inside their bodies.

Observe

The amount of digestion time depends on the type of food. Different foods undergo different chemical processes as they are digested.

Assessment

Process Have students predict what symptoms an infant might exhibit if a birth defect caused a constriction in a portion of the digestive tract. Use **Performance Assessment in the Science Classroom,** p. 93.

Before You Read

FOLDABLES Reading & Study Skills

Dinah Zike Study Fold

Purpose Students will demonstrate what they know about the six classes of nutrients available in food by listing examples of foods that provide these nutrients in a Foldable chart.

For additional help, see the Foldables Worksheet, p.17 in **Chapter Resources Booklet,** or go to the Glencoe Science Web site at **science.glencoe.com.** See After You Read in the Study Guide at the end of this chapter.

SECTION

Nutrition

1 Motivate

Bellringer Transparency

Display the Section Focus Transparency for Section 1. Use the accompanying Transparency Activity Master. L2 ELL

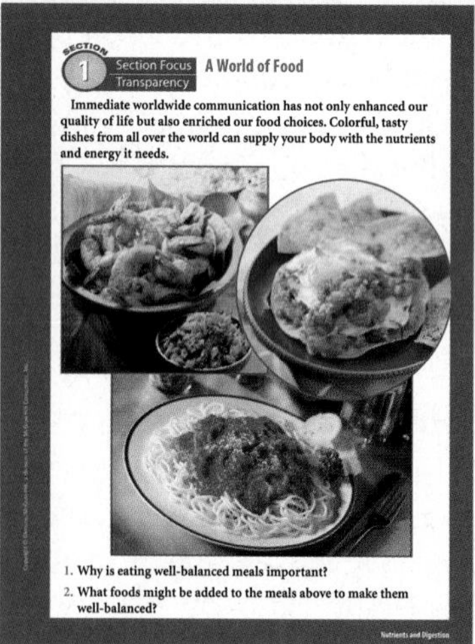

SECTION 1 Section Focus Transparency **A World of Food**

Immediate worldwide communication has not only enhanced our quality of life but also enriched our food choices. Colorful, tasty dishes from all over the world can supply your body with the nutrients and energy it needs.

1. Why is eating well-balanced meals important?
2. What foods might be added to the meals above to make them well-balanced?

Nutrients and Digestion

Tie to Prior Knowledge

Have students discuss what they know about eating a "balanced" diet.

SECTION 1

Nutrition

As You Read

What **You'll Learn**

- **Distinguish** among the six classes of nutrients.
- **Identify** the importance of each type of nutrient.
- **Explain** the relationship between diet and health.

Vocabulary

nutrient, protein, amino acid, carbohydrate, fat, vitamin, mineral, food group

Why **It's Important**

You can make healthful food choices if you know what nutrients your body uses daily.

Why do you eat?

You're listening to a favorite song on the radio, maybe even singing along. Then all of a sudden, the music stops. You examine the radio to see what happened. The batteries died. You hunt for more batteries and quickly put in the new ones. In the same way that the radio needs batteries to work, you need food to carry out your daily activities—but not just any food. When you are hungry, you probably choose food based on taste and the amount of time you have to eat it. However, as much as you don't want to admit it, the nutritional value of the food you choose is more important than the taste. A chocolate-iced donut might be tasty and quick to eat, yet it provides few of the nutrients your body needs. **Nutrients** (NEW tree unts) are substances in foods that provide energy and materials for cell development, growth, and repair.

Energy Needs Your body needs energy for every activity that it performs. Muscle activities such as the beating of your heart, blinking your eyes, and lifting your backpack require energy. Your body also uses energy to maintain a steady internal temperature of about 37°C (98.6°F). This energy comes from the foods you eat. The amount of energy available in food is measured in Calories. A Calorie (Cal) is the amount of heat necessary to raise the temperature of 1 kg of water 1°C. As shown in **Figure 1,** different foods contain different numbers of Calories. A raw carrot may have 30 Cal. This means that when you eat a carrot, your body has 30 Cal of energy available to use. A slice of cheese pizza might have 170 Cal, and one hamburger might have 260 Cal. The number of Calories varies due to the kinds of nutrients a food provides.

Figure 1
Foods vary in the number of Calories they contain. A hamburger has the same number of Calories as 8.5 average-sized carrots.

Section Assessment Planner

Portfolio
Activity, p. 526

Performance Assessment
MiniLAB, p. 521
Problem-Solving Activity, p. 522
Skill Builder Activities, p. 527
See page 542 for more options.

Content Assessment
Section, p. 527
Challenge, p. 527
Chapter, pp. 542–543

Classes of Nutrients

Six kinds of nutrients are available in food—proteins, carbohydrates, fats, vitamins, minerals, and water. Proteins, carbohydrates, vitamins, and fats all contain carbon and are called organic nutrients. In contrast, inorganic nutrients, such as water and minerals, do not contain carbon. Foods containing carbohydrates, fats, and proteins need to be digested or broken down before your body can use them. Water, vitamins, and minerals don't require digestion and are absorbed directly into your bloodstream.

Figure 2
Meats, poultry, eggs, fish, peas, beans, and nuts are all rich in protein.

Proteins Your body uses proteins for replacement and repair of body cells and for growth. **Proteins** are large molecules that contain carbon, hydrogen, oxygen, nitrogen and sometimes sulfur. A molecule of protein is made up of a large number of smaller units, or building blocks, called **amino acids.** In **Figure 2** you can see some sources of proteins. Different foods contain different amounts of protein, as shown in **Figure 3.**

Your body needs only 20 amino acids in various combinations to make the thousands of proteins used in your cells. Most of these amino acids can be made in your body's cells, but eight of them cannot. These eight are called essential amino acids. They have to be supplied by the foods you eat. Complete proteins provide all of the essential amino acids. Eggs, milk, cheese, and meat contain complete proteins. Incomplete proteins are missing one or more of the essential amino acids. If you are a vegetarian, you can get all of the essential amino acids by eating a wide variety of protein-rich vegetables, fruits, and grains.

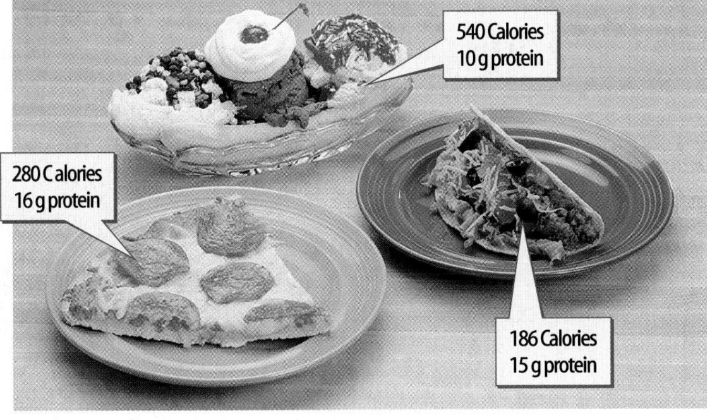

Figure 3
The amount of protein in a food is not the same as the number of Calories in the food. A taco has nearly the same amount of protein as a slice of pizza, but it usually has about 100 fewer Calories.

2 Teach

Why do you eat?

Discussion

Are you what you eat? The food you eat supplies materials for the production of new cells, which become part of your body. It also supplies energy, which allows you to do the things you like to do.

Teacher FYI

When cells need energy, they oxidize fuels such as carbohydrates and fats. This process results in the formation of carbon dioxide and water, the same products that are formed when a fuel such as gasoline is burned in an engine. Energy is released in this reaction.

Classes of Nutrients

Fun Fact

The average rate of protein synthesis is estimated at 500 g per day. This usually is greater than an individual's daily intake and is possible because amino acids are recycled.

Resource Manager 

Chapter Resources Booklet
- Transparency Activity, p. 42
- Directed Reading for Content Mastery, pp. 19, 20
- Note-taking Worksheets, pp. 31–33

Curriculum Connection

Health Have the school lunchroom manager or a hospital dietitian discuss with students how a balanced diet can be achieved with a variety of foods. Have students work in pairs to list what they ate during the last 24 hours and then evaluate the variety of their diets. L2 COOP LEARN

Classes of Nutrients, continued

Internet Addresses

Explore the Glencoe Science Web site at **science.glencoe.com** to find out more about topics in this section.

Extension

Have students research unique sources of proteins and carbohydrates used in different countries. Make labels with the food names and place them in the proper geographic locations on a world map. Examples include amaranth in South America and Africa and taro root in the Pacific Islands. L1 LS **Visual-Spatial**

Quick Demo

Burn a Brazil nut, pecan, or whole peanut to illustrate the amount of energy contained in fats. As you present this demo, follow safety precautions for sharp objects, flames, eye safety, and clothing protection. Insert the sharp end of a needle into the nut. Push the eye of the needle into a cork. Stand the entire apparatus in a metal pan. Ignite the nut and have students observe the length of time the nut burns. Repeat with several types of nuts, and have students compare burning times.

Research Visit the Glencoe Science Web site at **science.glencoe.com** for recent news or magazine articles about the importance of fiber in your diet. In your Science Journal, classify your favorite foods into two groups—Good source of fiber and Little or no fiber.

Carbohydrates Study the nutrition label on several boxes of cereal. You'll notice that the number of grams of carbohydrates found in a typical serving of cereal is higher than the amounts of the other nutrients. **Carbohydrates** (kar boh HI drayts) usually are the main sources of energy for your body. Each carbohydrate molecule is made of carbon, hydrogen, and oxygen atoms. Energy holds the atoms together. When carbohydrates are broken down in the presence of oxygen in your cells, this energy is released for use by your body.

Three types of carbohydrates are sugar, starch, and fiber, as shown in **Figure 4.** Sugars are called *simple carbohydrates.* You're probably most familiar with table sugar. However, fruits, honey, and milk also contain forms of sugar. Your cells break down glucose, a simple sugar. The other two types of carbohydrates—starch and fiber—are called *complex carbohydrates.* Starch is found in potatoes and foods made from grains such as pasta. Starches are made up of many simple sugars in long chains. Fiber, such as cellulose, is found in the cell walls of plant cells. Foods like whole-grain breads and cereals, beans, peas, and other vegetables and fruits are good sources of fiber. Because different types of fiber are found in foods, you should eat a variety of fiber-rich plant foods. You cannot digest fiber, but it is needed to keep your digestive system running smoothly.

Nutritious snacks can help your body get the nutrients it needs, especially when you are growing rapidly and are physically active. Choose snacks that provide nutrients such as complex carbohydrates, proteins, and vitamins, as well as fiber. Foods high in sugar and fat can have lots of Calories that supply energy, but they provide only some of the nutrients your body needs.

Figure 4
These foods contain carbohydrates that provide energy for all the things that you do.

IDENTIFYING Misconceptions

Some students think that energy is released directly from food. Refer to page 516F for teaching strategies that address this misconception.

Inclusion Strategies

Learning Disabled Ask students to list the simple and complex carbohydrates they ate during the last 24 hours. Ask each student to analyze the length of the two lists and write answers to these questions: **Do I eat more simple or complex carbohydrates? How could I improve my diet?** Eat fewer simple carbohydrates. L1 LS **Linguistic**

Curriculum Connection

History The extraction of sugar from sugarcane is an ancient practice. Sugarcane grass was first discovered either in the South Pacific or in India. It most likely spread to Europe via Chinese and Arab traders. Have students research how and when sugarcane was brought to the Americas.

Figure 5
Fat is stored in certain cells in your body. A The cytoplasm and nucleus are pushed to the edge of the cell by the fat deposits. B Some foods you might choose for lunch or snacks that are high in fat are outlined in red.

Fats The term fat has developed a negative meaning for some people. However, **fats,** also called lipids, are necessary because they provide energy and help your body absorb vitamins. Fat tissue cushions your internal organs. A major part of every cell membrane is made up of fat. A gram of fat can release more than twice as much energy as a gram of carbohydrate can. During the digestion process, fat is broken down into smaller molecules called fatty acids and glycerol (GLIHS ur awl). Because fat is a good storage unit for energy, excess energy from the foods you eat is converted to fat and stored for later use, as shown in **Figure 5A.**

Reading Check *Why is fat a good storage unit for energy?*

Fats are classified as unsaturated or saturated based on their chemical structure. Unsaturated fats are usually liquid at room temperature. Vegetable oils as well as fats found in seeds are unsaturated fats. Saturated fats are found in meats, animal products, and some plants and are usually solid at room temperature. Although fish contains saturated fat, it also has some unsaturated fats that your body needs. Saturated fats have been associated with high levels of blood cholesterol. Your body makes cholesterol in your liver. Cholesterol is part of the cell membrane in all of your cells. However, a diet high in cholesterol may result in deposits forming on the inside walls of blood vessels. These deposits can block the blood supply to organs and increase blood pressure. This can lead to heart disease and strokes.

Mini LAB

Comparing the Fat Content of Foods

Procedure

1. Collect three pieces of each of the following foods: **potato chips; pretzels; peanuts;** and **small cubes of fruits, cheese, vegetables, and meat.**
2. Place the food items on a piece of **brown grocery bag.** Label the paper with the name of each food. Do not taste the foods.
3. Allow foods to sit for 30 min.
4. Remove the items, properly dispose of them, and observe the paper.

Analysis

1. Which items left a translucent (greasy) mark? Which left a wet spot?
2. How are the foods that left a greasy spot on the paper alike?
3. Use this test to determine which other foods contain fats. A greasy mark means the food contains fat. A wet mark means the food contains a lot of water.

Reading Check

Answer A gram of fat can release twice as much energy as a gram of carbohydrate.

Mini LAB

Purpose Students test for fats in foods. L1 ELL LS **Kinesthetic**

Materials 3 potato chips, pretzels, and peanuts; small cubes of fruits, cheeses, vegetables, and meat; brown craft paper or brown paper bag

Teaching Strategy Point out the difference between a water spot and a greasy spot.

Safety Precaution Use only cooked meat.

Analysis

1. Potato chips, peanuts, cheeses, and meat will leave a translucent spot. Pretzels may leave a greasy spot if they are fresh. Fruits and vegetables will leave a wet spot.
2. They have some fat content.
3. Other foods that contain fat include butter, oils, and many crackers and chips.

Assessment

Process Have students test an unknown food item for fat. Use **Performance Assessment in the Science Classroom,** p. 97.

Resource Manager

Chapter Resources Booklet
MiniLAB, p. 3
Mathematics Skill Activities, p. 47
Cultural Diversity, p. 6

Curriculum Connection

Math Have students calculate the percentage of fat in foods. First have them note the grams of fat in a serving, and then multiply this number by 9, the number of Calories released when fat is oxidized. Divide this number by the total number of Calories in a serving. This yields the percent of Calories from fat. Recommendations are that no more than 30 percent of your Calorie intake should come from fat. L2

Classes of Nutrients, continued

Discussion

Is milk the perfect food? Milk does supply many nutrients but it is not a perfect food, as it lacks certain essential vitamins and minerals. LS **Interpersonal**

IDENTIFYING Misconceptions

Students may have the notion that if vitamins are good for you, more is better. Some vitamins should not be taken in high doses. An excess of vitamin A can cause liver and skin problems. Too much vitamin D can cause an imbalance of blood calcium, resulting in digestive, urinary, and nervous system disorders.

Problem-Solving Activity

National Math Standards

Correlation to Mathematics Objectives
1,5,6,7,8,9

Answers

1. Of the snack foods listed, pretzels are the lowest in fat. Other snack foods could be brought into the classroom to compare their fat contents. Students can discuss the difference between fried and baked snacks, and healthier alternatives to their favorite snack foods.
2. Most frozen pizzas are prepared using cheese and pepperoni, which are both high in fat. Ways to make pizza healthier include preparing it fresh at home using low-fat cheese, homemade tomato sauce, turkey pepperoni, and a variety of fresh vegetables.

Vitamins Those organic nutrients needed in small quantities for growth, regulating body functions, and preventing some diseases are called **vitamins.** For instance, your bone cells need vitamin D to use calcium, and your blood needs vitamin K in order to clot.

Most foods supply some vitamins, but no food has them all. Some people feel that taking extra vitamins is helpful, while others feel that eating a well-balanced diet usually gives your body all the vitamins it needs.

Vitamins are classified into two groups, as shown in **Figure 6.** Some vitamins dissolve easily in water and are called water-soluble vitamins. They are not stored by your body so you have to take them daily. Other vitamins dissolve only in fat and are called fat-soluble vitamins. These vitamins are stored by your body. Although you eat or drink most vitamins, some are made by your body. Vitamin D is made when your skin is exposed to sunlight. Some vitamin K and two of the B vitamins are made with the help of bacteria that live in your large intestine.

Problem-Solving Activity

Is it unhealthy to snack between meals?

Most children eat three meals each day accompanied by snacks in between. Grabbing a bite to eat to satisfy you until your next meal is a common occurrence in today's society, and 20% of our energy and nutrient needs comes from snacking. While it would be best to select snacks consisting of fruits and vegetables, most children prefer to eat a bag of chips or a candy bar. Although these quick snacks are highly convenient, many times they are high in fat, as well.

Identifying the Problem

The table on the right lists several snack foods that are popular among adolescents. They are listed alphabetically, and the grams of fat per individual serving is shown. As you examine the chart, can you conclude which snacks would be a healthier choice based on their fat content?

Fat in Snack Foods

One Serving	Fat (g)
Candy bar	12
Frozen pizza	30
Ice cream	8
Potato chips	10
Pretzels	1

1. Looking at the data, what can you conclude about the snack foods you eat? What other snack foods do you eat that are not listed on the chart? How do you think they compare in nutritional value? Which snack foods are healthiest?
2. Pizza appears to be the unhealthiest choice on the chart because of the amount of the fat it contains. Why do you think pizza contains so much fat? List at least three ways to make pizza a healthier snack food.

Inclusion Strategies

Gifted Have students research and report on a particular vitamin deficiency. Their reports should include information about how the vitamin was discovered, the symptoms of a deficiency, and foods that are high in the vitamin. Have students work together to present their findings on a "Vitamins for Good Health" bulletin board. L3 COOP LEARN LS **Linguistic**

Science Journal

Taking Your Vitamins Have students write a paragraph about why it might be a disadvantage to substitute vitamin pills for a proper diet. Their entries should indicate an understanding that other nutrients besides vitamins are needed for maintaining health. A well-balanced diet supplies the range of needed vitamins. L2 LS **Logical-Mathematical** P

Figure 6

Vitamins come in two groups—water-soluble, which should be replaced daily, and fat-soluble, which can be stored in the body. The sources and benefits of both groups are shown below.

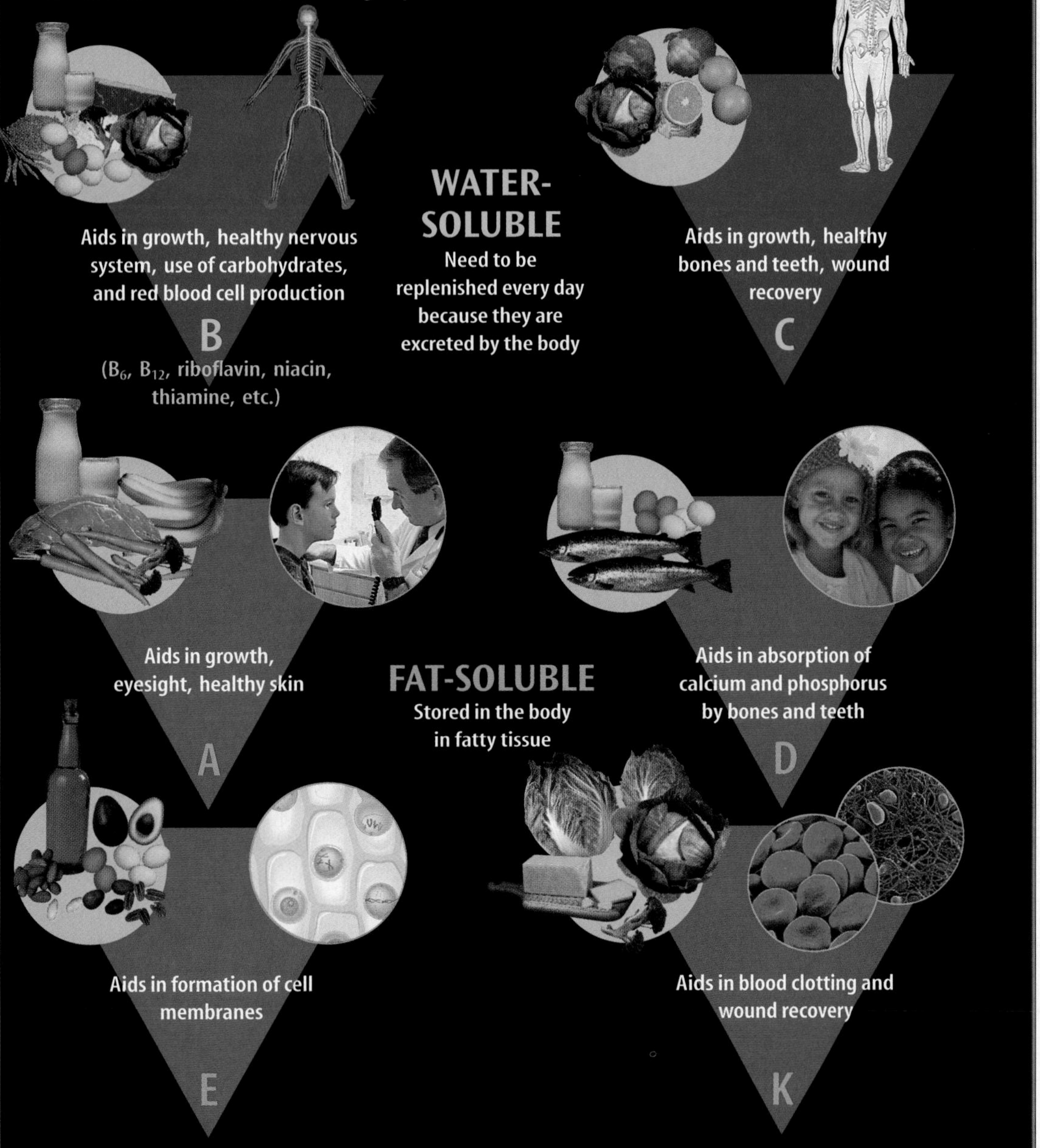

WATER-SOLUBLE
Need to be replenished every day because they are excreted by the body

B — Aids in growth, healthy nervous system, use of carbohydrates, and red blood cell production (B_6, B_{12}, riboflavin, niacin, thiamine, etc.)

C — Aids in growth, healthy bones and teeth, wound recovery

FAT-SOLUBLE
Stored in the body in fatty tissue

A — Aids in growth, eyesight, healthy skin

D — Aids in absorption of calcium and phosphorus by bones and teeth

E — Aids in formation of cell membranes

K — Aids in blood clotting and wound recovery

523

NATIONAL GEOGRAPHIC

Visualizing Vitamins

Have students examine the pictures and read the captions. Then ask the following questions.

Why is it important to eat foods containing vitamin K? A deficiency can lead to excessive bleeding when you are injured and it may take longer for the wound to heal.

What role does vitamin D have in healthy bones? It aids in the absorption of calcium, which is a necessary component of bone tissue.

Activity

Have students define the following terms: *beriberi*, *rickets*, *scurvy*, *pellagra*, *night blindness*. Be sure to have students include which vitamin is deficient in each condition and how the deficiency affects the body.

Extension

Have students research the dangers of vitamin overdose. **What effects can high doses of vitamins such as A, C, or E have on the body?** Have students answer the question: **Why do the Inuit people choose not to eat polar bear liver?** Possible answer: Polar bear liver contains a high amount of vitamin A. As much as 12 times the minimum daily requirement of vitamin A can be found in one gram of polar bear liver. Ingestion of too much vitamin A results in a host of ailments and can even be deadly.

Resource Manager

Chapter Resources Booklet
Transparency Activity, pp. 45–46

Life Science Critical Thinking/Problem Solving, p. 15

Classes of Nutrients, continued

Teacher FYI

In addition to the minerals listed in **Table 1,** other minerals found in significant amounts in body tissue (macrominerals) include chlorine, magnesium, and sulfur. Chlorine is found in all foods and table salt; magnesium is found in green vegetables, whole grains, soybeans, and beef; and sulfur is found in all protein-containing foods.

Reading Check

Answer It is needed by the body only in small amounts.

Discussion

Why is salt iodized? Potassium iodide is added to salt to prevent the enlarged thyroid gland condition known as a goiter.

Visual Learning

Table 1 Have students study the food sources listed for the different minerals. Discuss what problems a vegetarian might have in obtaining adequate amounts of some minerals. Have students use the table to identify alternative foods that could help support a balanced vegetarian diet.

Minerals Inorganic nutrients—nutrients that lack carbon and regulate many chemical reactions in your body—are called **minerals.** Your body uses about 14 minerals. Minerals build cells, take part in chemical reactions in cells, send nerve impulses throughout your body, and carry oxygen to body cells. In **Figure 7,** you can see how minerals can get from the soil into your body. Of the 14 minerals, calcium and phosphorus are used in the largest amounts for a variety of body functions. One of these functions is the formation and maintenance of bone. Some minerals, called trace minerals, are required only in small amounts. Copper and iodine usually are listed as trace minerals. Several minerals, what they do, and some food sources for them are listed in **Table 1.**

Reading Check *Why is copper considered a trace mineral?*

Figure 7
The roots of the wheat take in phosphorus from the soil. Then the mature wheat is harvested and used in bread and cereal. Your body gets phosphorus when you eat the cereal.

Phosphorus

Wheat being harvested

Table 1 Minerals

Mineral	Health Effect	Food Sources
Calcium	strong bones and teeth, blood clotting, muscle and nerve activity	dairy products, eggs, green leafy vegetables, soy
Phosphorus	strong bones and teeth, muscle contraction, stores energy	cheese, meat, cereal
Potassium	balance of water in cells, nerve impulse conduction, muscle contraction	bananas, potatoes, nuts, meat, oranges
Sodium	fluid balance in tissues, nerve impulse conduction	meat, milk, cheese, salt, beets, carrots, nearly all foods
Iron	oxygen is transported in hemoglobin by red blood cells	red meat, raisins, beans, spinach, eggs
Iodine (trace)	thyroid activity, metabolic stimulation	seafood, iodized salt

Resource Manager

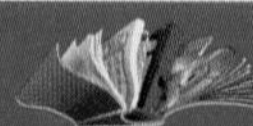

Chapter Resources Booklet
Enrichment, p. 29
Lab Activity, pp.9–11

Performance Assessment in the Science Classroom, p. 66

Science Journal

Mineral Intake Encourage students to keep track in their science journals of everything they eat for one day. Then have students use the data they collect to analyze their mineral intake. L2 IN **Logical-Mathematical**

524 CHAPTER 18 Nutrients and Digestion

Figure 8
About two thirds of your body water is located within your body cells. Water helps maintain the cells' shapes and sizes. The water that is lost through perspiration and respiration must be replaced.

Water Loss	
Method of Loss	**Amount (mL/day)**
Exhaled air	350
Feces	150
Skin (mostly as sweat)	500
Urine	1,500

Water Have you ever gone on a bike ride on a hot summer day without a bottle of water? You probably were thirsty and maybe you even stopped to get some water. Water is important for your body. Next to oxygen, water is the most important factor for survival. Different organisms need different amounts of water to survive. You could live for a few weeks without food but for only a few days without water because your cells need water to carry out their work. Most of the nutrients you have studied in this chapter can't be used by your body unless they are carried in a solution. This means that they have to be dissolved in water. In cells, chemical reactions take place in solutions.

The human body is about 60 percent water by weight. About two thirds of your body water is located in your body cells. Water also is found around cells and in body fluids such as blood. As shown in **Figure 8,** your body loses water as perspiration. When you exhale, water leaves your body as water vapor. Water also is lost every day when your body gets rid of wastes. To replace water lost each day, you need to drink about 2 L of liquids. However, drinking liquids isn't the only way to supply cells with water. Most foods have more water than you realize. An apple is about 80 percent water, and many meats are 90 percent water.

Earth Science INTEGRATION

The mineral halite is processed to make table salt. In the United States, most salt comes from underground mines. Research to find the locations of these mines, then label them on a map.

Use an Analogy

Perspiration of water from the body is like the transpiration of water from plants. In both animals and plants, excessive water loss can have profoundly negative effects on the health of the organism.

Discussion

What are other sources of water in your diet in addition to drinking water? Other sources include fruits and vegetables. Water is also a by-product of the breakdown of molecules in the process of respiration.

Extension

Have students keep track of all the foods and liquids they consume in one day. Have them estimate how much water they took in and compare that number with the 2 L or so of water lost daily. L2 ELL  **Logical-Mathematical**

Earth Science INTEGRATION

Salt-producing regions in the United States are found in New York, Ohio, Michigan, Louisiana, Texas, and Kansas.

LAB DEMONSTRATION

Purpose to measure the water content of food

Materials pan balance, 250-mL beaker, sliced celery, tray

Preparation Use the pan balance to find the mass of the beaker.

Procedure Fill the beaker with celery and find its mass. Spread the celery on the tray to dry for 2 or 3 days. Again mass the celery.

Expected Outcome Students should find that dried celery has a mass much less than fresh celery. Have them calculate the percentage of celery that is water.

✔Assessment

Why was the beaker massed when empty? so its mass could be subtracted from the mass of the beaker and celery **Infer how much water might be in other fresh vegetables.** Answers will vary. Leafy vegetables have more water than hard vegetables such as broccoli.

Food Groups

Make a Model

Have students work together to make a three-dimensional display of the food pyramid using packages of representative food items. L2 ELL COOP LEARN
LS Kinesthetic

Activity

Have students draw a food pyramid that illustrates the foods they have eaten during one day. Be sure they include snacks. Place the name or drawing of each food item in its proper level within the pyramid. In addition, have them identify any food items that are high in fats, sugars, and salt. Encourage students to reflect on any changes in their diet that would make it more closely meet the recommended number of servings for each level. L2
LS Visual-Spatial P

Caption Answer

Figure 9 from the fats, oils, and sweets group at the top of the pyramid

Why do you get thirsty? Your body is made up of systems that operate together. When your body needs to replace lost water, messages are sent to your brain that result in a feeling of thirst. Drinking water satisfies your thirst and usually restores the body's homeostasis (hoh mee oh STAY sus). Homeostasis is the regulation of the body's internal environment, such as temperature and amount of water. When homeostasis is restored, the signal to the brain stops and you no longer feel thirsty.

Food Groups

Because no naturally occurring food has every nutrient, you need to eat a variety of foods. Nutritionists have developed a simple system, called the food pyramid, shown in **Figure 9,** to help people select foods that supply all the nutrients needed for energy and growth.

Foods that contain the same type of nutrient belong to a **food group.** Foods have been divided into five groups—bread and cereal, vegetable, fruit, milk, and meat. The recommended daily amount for each food group will supply your body with the nutrients it needs for good health. Using the food pyramid to make choices when you eat will help you maintain good health.

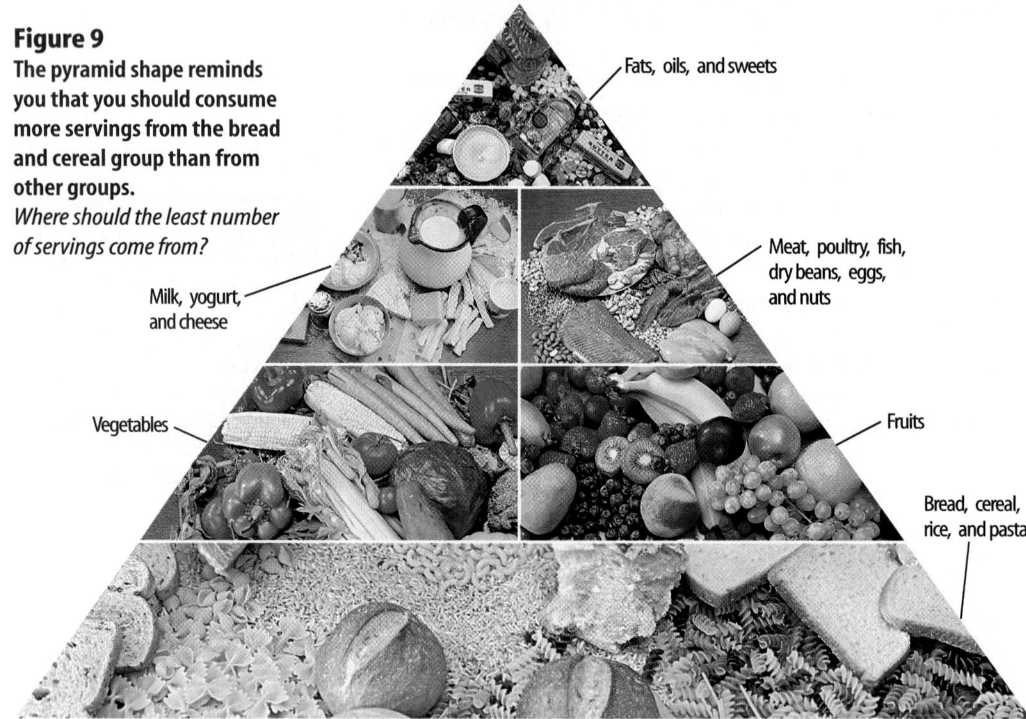

Figure 9
The pyramid shape reminds you that you should consume more servings from the bread and cereal group than from other groups.
Where should the least number of servings come from?

Cultural Diversity

Diet and Disease Certain cultures have diets that contain little animal fat. Such diets typically result in low intake of fats and cholesterol. These diets may include large amounts of vegetables, fruits, and grains. People of Asia have a lower incidence of heart disease than people in the United States, possibly as a result of having a diet that is lower in fat.

Resource Manager

Chapter Resources Booklet
Reinforcement, p. 27

Cultural Diversity, p. 23

Daily Servings Each day you should eat six to eleven servings from the bread and cereal group, three to five servings from the vegetable group, two to four servings from the fruit group, two to three servings from the milk group, and two to three servings from the meat and beans group. Only small amounts of fats, oils, and sweets should be consumed.

The size of a serving is different for different foods. For example, a slice of bread or one ounce of ready-to-eat cereal is a bread-and-cereal group serving. One cup of raw leafy vegetables or one-half cup of cooked or chopped raw vegetables make a serving from the vegetable group. One medium apple, banana, or orange is a fruit serving. A serving from the milk group can be one cup of milk or yogurt. Two ounces of cooked lean meat, one-half cup of cooked dry beans, or one egg counts as a serving from the meat and beans group.

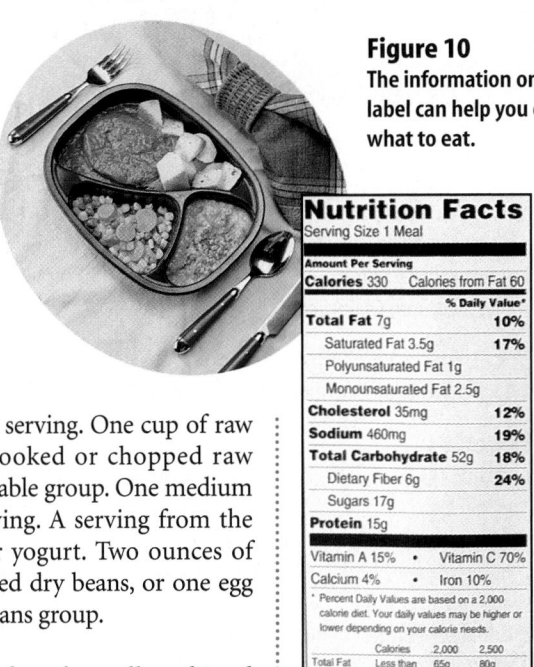

Figure 10
The information on a food label can help you decide what to eat.

Nutrition Facts
Serving Size 1 Meal

Amount Per Serving	% Daily Value*
Calories 330 Calories from Fat 60	
Total Fat 7g	**10%**
Saturated Fat 3.5g	**17%**
Polyunsaturated Fat 1g	
Monounsaturated Fat 2.5g	
Cholesterol 35mg	**12%**
Sodium 460mg	**19%**
Total Carbohydrate 52g	**18%**
Dietary Fiber 6g	**24%**
Sugars 17g	
Protein 15g	

Vitamin A 15% • Vitamin C 70%
Calcium 4% • Iron 10%

* Percent Daily Values are based on a 2,000 calorie diet. Your daily values may be higher or lower depending on your calorie needs.

	Calories	2,000	2,500
Total Fat	Less than	65g	80g
Sat Fat	Less than	20g	25g
Cholesterol	Less than	300mg	300mg
Sodium	Less than	2,400mg	2,400mg
Total Carbohydrate		300g	375g
Dietary Fiber		25g	30g

Food Labels The nutritional facts found on all packaged foods make it easier to make healthful food choices. These labels, as shown in **Figure 10,** can help you plan meals that supply the daily recommended amounts of nutrients and meet special dietary requirements (for example, a low-fat diet).

Section 1 Assessment

1. List six classes of nutrients that your body needs and give one example of a food source for each.
2. Describe a major function of each class of nutrient.
3. Discuss how food choices can positively and negatively affect your health.
4. Explain the importance of water in the body.
5. **Think Critically** What foods from each food group would provide a balanced breakfast? Explain.

Skill Builder Activities

6. **Interpreting Data** Nutritional information can be found on the labels of most foods. Interpret the labels found on three different types of food products. **For more help, refer to the** Science Skill Handbook.
7. **Using an Electronic Spreadsheet** Make a spreadsheet of the minerals listed in **Table 1.** Use reference books to gather information about minerals and add these to the table: *sulfur, magnesium, copper, manganese, cobalt,* and *zinc*. **For more help, refer to the** Technology Skill Handbook.

Activity

Have students read the labels of canned and packaged foods. Discuss the major sources of various nutrients in the foods they eat each day. L2
LS **Logical-Mathematical**

3 Assess

Reteach

Have students make flash cards with names of fruits or vegetables. On the reverse side, have them identify the major vitamin content of each food. Students can test each other using the flash cards. L1
LS **Visual-Spatial**

Challenge

Vitamins may be toxic in very large doses. Challenge students to find out how excessive amounts of vitamins K and D can affect the body. Excessive intake of vitamin K can cause anemia, jaundice, and gastrointestinal problems; megadoses of vitamin D can result in nausea and vomiting, calcification of soft tissues, and kidney failure.

Assessment

Performance Assess students' abilities to make and use tables by having them use **Figure 8** to determine how much water (in liters) is lost through the skin. Use **Performance Assessment in the Science Classroom,** p. 109.

Answers to Section Assessment

1. carbohydrates: bread; proteins: fish; fats: butter; vitamins: fruit; minerals: vegetables; water: juice
2. carbohydrates: source of energy; proteins: growth of cells; fats: source of energy; vitamins: growth; minerals: nerve activity; water: enables chemical reactions to occur
3. An unbalanced diet can be detrimental to your health. For example, an inadequate intake of certain vitamins and minerals can hinder your body's energy supply and functions. Another example is a diet high in cholesterol can result in deposits in blood vessels which may lead to blockages and possibly heart disease.
4. dissolves and carries nutrients, removes wastes, enables chemical reactions to occur
5. Students should be able to support their answers with information from Figure 9.
6. Have pairs of students compare their interpretations.
7. **sulfur**—all protein-rich foods; **magnesium**—green vegetables, milk, meats, nuts; **copper**—liver, legumes, shellfish, seeds, whole grains; **manganese**—legumes, whole grains, nuts, dark green vegetables, chocolate; **cobalt**—leafy vegetables, shellfish, liver, milk, red meat; **zinc**—oysters, seafood, meat, dairy products

Activity

BENCH TESTED

Purpose Students test orange juices for vitamin C content. L2 ELL COOP LEARN

Process Skills observing, measuring, predicting, interpreting data, experimenting, communicating, comparing and contrasting

Time Required 50 minutes

Safety Precautions Remind students not to consume any substances used in the lab.

Teaching Strategy Have students practice making uniform drops using water before they begin adding drops of iodine to the test tubes. Remind students to rinse test tubes after each trial.

Troubleshooting Warn students not to mix up the test-solution droppers as they are preparing the test tubes.

Answers to Questions

1. Answers should reflect student results.
2. Results may vary because of freshness, exposure to heat or air, and amount of vitamin C added.

Assessment

Performance To further assess students' abilities to identify vitamin C content, have them test water in which shredded lettuce or shredded cabbage cores have been soaked overnight. Use **Performance Assessment in the Science Classroom, p. 97.**

Activity

Identifying Vitamin C Content

Vitamin C is found in many fruits and vegetables. Oranges have a high vitamin C content. Try this activity to test which orange juice has the highest vitamin C content.

What You'll Investigate

Which orange juice contains the most vitamin C?

Materials

test tube (4)
paper cups
test-tube rack
masking tape
wooden stirrer (13)
graduated cylinder
graduated container
2% tincture of iodine
dropper
cornstarch
triple-beam balance
weighing paper
water (50 mL)
glass-marking pencil

dropper bottles (4) containing:
(1) freshly squeezed orange juice
(2) orange juice made from frozen concentrate
(3) canned orange juice
(4) dairy carton orange juice

** Alternate materials*

Goals

- **Observe** the vitamin C content of different orange juices.

Safety Precautions

Wear your goggles and apron. Do not taste any of the juices. Iodine is poisonous and can stain skin and clothing. It is an irritant and can cause damage if it comes in contact with your eyes. Notify your teacher if a spill occurs.

Procedure

1. Make a data table like the example shown to record your observations.

Drops of Iodine Needed to Change Color				
Juice	Trial			Average
	1	2	3	
1 Fresh Juice	8	7	8	8
2 Frozen Juice	7	8	8	8
3 Canned Juice	6	6	6	6
4 Carton Juice	14	12	10	12

2. Label four test tubes 1 through 4 and place them in the test-tube rack.
3. **Measure** and pour 5 mL of juice from bottle 1 into test tube 1, 5 mL from bottle 2 into test tube 2, 5 mL from bottle 3 into test tube 3, and 5 mL from bottle 4 into test tube 4.
4. Measure 0.3 g of cornstarch, then put it in a container. Slowly mix in 50 mL of water until the cornstarch completely dissolves.
5. Add 5 mL of the cornstarch solution to each of the four test tubes. Stir well.
6. Add iodine to test tube 1, one drop at a time. Stir after each drop. Record the number of drops it takes for the juice to change to a purple color. The more vitamin C that is present, the more drops it takes to change color.
7. Repeat step 6 with test tubes 2, 3, and 4.
8. Empty and clean the test tubes. Repeat steps 3 through 7 two more times, then average your results.

Conclude and Apply

1. **Compare and contrast** the amount of vitamin C in the orange juices tested.
2. If the amount of vitamin C varied in the orange juices, suggest a reason why. Check the labels of the containers.

Communicating Your Data

Have students check the labels of the containers to see how much vitamin C each claims to contain. Have students use a spreadsheet program to enter the comparison between their tests and the information on the labels.

Resource Manager

Chapter Resources Booklet
Activity Worksheet, pp. 5–6

SECTION 2

The Digestive System

Functions of the Digestive System

You are walking through a park on a cool, autumn afternoon. Birds are searching in the grass for insects. A squirrel is eating an acorn. Why are the animals so busy? Like you, they need food to supply their bodies with energy. Food is processed in your body in four stages—ingestion, digestion, absorption, and elimination. Whether it is a piece of fruit or an entire meal, all the food you eat is treated to the same processes in your body. As soon as food enters your mouth, or is ingested as shown in **Figure 11,** breakdown begins. **Digestion** is the process that breaks down food into small molecules so that they can be absorbed and moved into the blood. From the blood, food molecules are transported across the cell membrane to be used by the cell. Unused molecules pass out of your body as wastes.

Digestion is mechanical and chemical. **Mechanical digestion** takes place when food is chewed, mixed, and churned. **Chemical digestion** occurs when chemical reactions occur that break down large molecules of food into smaller ones.

As You Read

***What* You'll Learn**

- **Distinguish** the differences between mechanical digestion and chemical digestion.
- **Identify** the organs of the digestive system and what takes place in each.
- **Explain** how homeostasis is maintained in digestion.

Vocabulary

digestion, mechanical digestion, chemical digestion, enzyme, peristalsis, chyme, villi

***Why* It's Important**

The processes of the digestive system make the food you eat available to your cells.

Figure 11
Humans have to chew solid foods before swallowing them, but snakes have adaptations that allow them to swallow their food whole.

SECTION

The Digestive System

1 Motivate

Bellringer Transparency

Display the Section Focus Transparency for Section 2. Use the accompanying Transparency Activity Master. L2 ELL

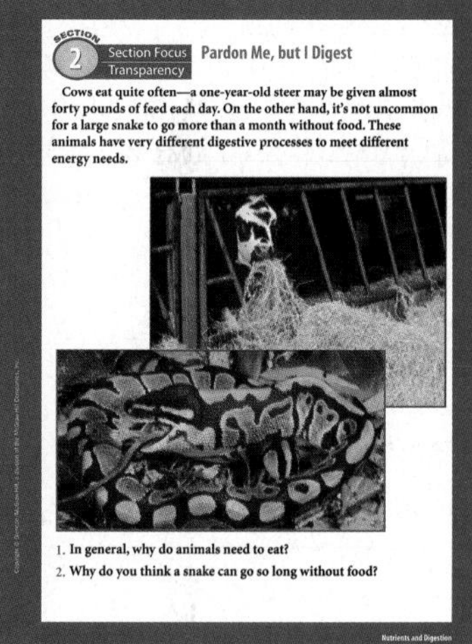

Section Focus Transparency 2 — Pardon Me, but I Digest

Cows eat quite often—a one-year-old steer may be given almost forty pounds of feed each day. On the other hand, it's not uncommon for a large snake to go more than a month without food. These animals have very different digestive processes to meet different energy needs.

1. In general, why do animals need to eat?
2. Why do you think a snake can go so long without food?

Nutrients and Digestion

Tie to Prior Knowledge

Remind students that one feature of living things is that they use energy. Discuss with students that food is the source of energy for cell activities, but that it must be processed into usable molecules. This is the function of the digestive system.

Section Assessment Planner

PORTFOLIO
Science Journal, p. 532
Reteach, p. 535

PERFORMANCE ASSESSMENT
Try at Home MiniLAB, p. 534
Skill Builder Activities, p. 535
See page 542 for more options.

CONTENT ASSESSMENT
Section, p. 535
Challenge, p. 535
Chapter, pp. 542–543

Resource Manager

Chapter Resources Booklet
Transparency Activity, p. 43
Directed Reading for Content Mastery, pp. 21, 22

2 Teach

Enzymes

Quick Demo

Meat tenderizers often contain the enzyme papain, which is made from papaya juice. Sprinkle some meat tenderizer on a small cube of beef. On another cube of beef, sprinkle some sugar. Heat both pieces in an oven at 250°F until brown. When cooled, have students examine both pieces and probe with a plastic fork to compare tenderness.

Use Science Words

Word Meaning The names of many enzymes are designated with the suffix *-ase*. For example, the enzyme that is responsible for the conversion of sucrose is called *sucrase*. Have students determine the enzymes for lactose (lactase), lipids (lipase), and amylose (amylase).

Caption Answer

Figure 12 It is free to join with another molecule in another reaction.

Discussion

What characteristics of enzymes enable them to affect chemical reactions within the body? Enzymes remain unchanged by their activity; they are effective in small amounts; they speed up chemical change; and they are specific in the chemicals they affect. LS **Linguistic**

Reading Check

Answer Enzymes speed up the rate of chemical digestion.

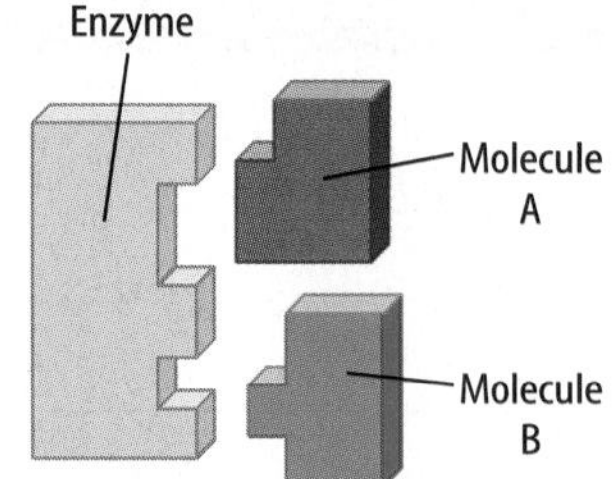

A The surface shape of an enzyme fits the shape of specific molecules that take part in the reaction.

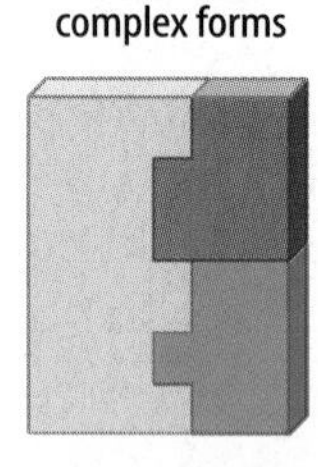

B The enzyme and the molecules join and the reaction occurs between the two molecules.

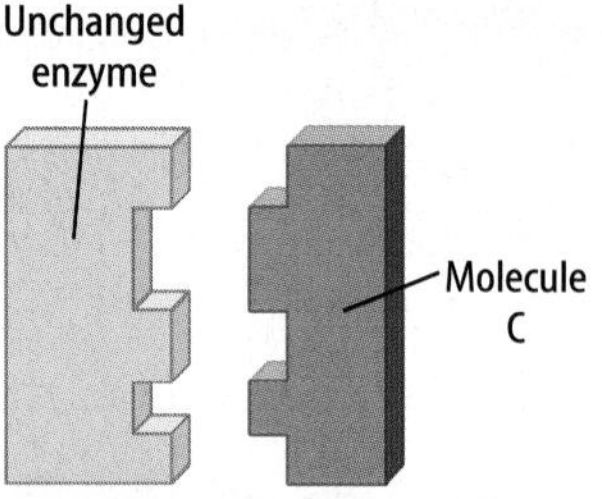

C Following the reaction, the enzyme and the new molecule separate. The enzyme is not changed by the reaction. The resulting new molecule has a new chemical structure.

Figure 12
Enzymes speed up the rate of certain body reactions. During these reactions, the enzymes are not used up or changed in any way.
What happens to the enzyme after it separates from the new molecule?

Enzymes

Chemical digestion is possible only because of enzymes (EN zimez). An **enzyme** is a type of protein that speeds up the rate of a chemical reaction in your body. One way enzymes speed up reactions is by reducing the amount of energy necessary for a chemical reaction to begin. If enzymes weren't there to help, the rate of chemical reactions would slow down. Some might not even happen at all. As shown in **Figure 12,** enzymes work without being changed or used up.

Enzymes in Digestion Many enzymes help you digest carbohydrates, proteins, and fats. Amylase (AM uh lays) is an enzyme produced by glands near the mouth. This enzyme helps speed up the breakdown of complex carbohydrates, such as starch, into simpler carbohydrates—sugars. In your stomach, the enzyme pepsin aids the chemical reactions that break down complex proteins into less complex proteins. In your small intestine, a number of other enzymes continue to speed up the breakdown of proteins into amino acids. The pancreas, an organ on the back side of the stomach, releases several enzymes through a tube into the small intestine. Some of these enzymes continue to aid the process of starch breakdown that started in the mouth. The resulting sugars are turned into glucose and are used by your body's cells. Different enzymes from the pancreas are involved in the breakdown of fats into fatty acids. Others help in the reactions that break down proteins.

Reading Check *What is the role of enzymes in the chemical digestion of food?*

Teacher FYI

Nearly every bodily chemical reaction involves enzymes. There is an intricate relationship among enzymes, vitamins, and minerals. Often enzymes cannot function in the absence of specific vitamins or minerals.

Inclusion Strategies

Visually Impaired and Learning Disabled Cut from foam-core board pairs of shapes that fit together as shown in **Figure 12.** Mix up several pairs, and have students find the enzyme for each molecule by matching the shapes. Compare the matching of shapes to a key fitting in a lock or pieces of a puzzle fitting together. L1 LS **Kinesthetic**

Other Enzyme Actions Enzyme-aided reactions are not limited to the digestive process. Enzymes also help speed up chemical reactions responsible for building your body. They are involved in the energy production activities of your muscle and nerve cells. Enzymes also aid in the blood-clotting process. Without enzymes, the chemical reactions of your body would not happen. In fact, you would not exist.

Organs of the Digestive System

Your digestive system has two parts—the digestive tract and the accessory organs. The major organs of your digestive tract—mouth, esophagus (ih SAH fuh guhs), stomach, small intestine, large intestine, rectum, and anus—are shown in **Figure 13.** Food passes through all of these organs. The tongue, teeth, salivary glands, liver, gallbladder, and pancreas, also shown in **Figure 13,** are the accessory organs. Although food doesn't pass through them, they are important in mechanical and chemical digestion. Your liver, gallbladder, and pancreas produce or store enzymes and chemicals that help break down food as it passes through the digestive tract.

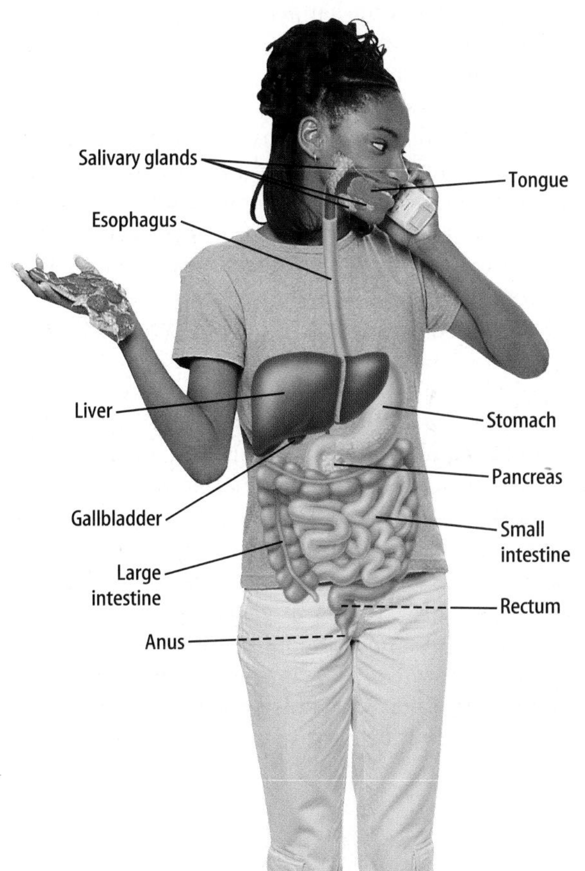

Figure 13
The human digestive system can be described as a tube divided into several specialized sections. If stretched out, an adult's digestive system is 6 m to 9 m long.

Organs Of the Digestive System

Visual Learning

Figure 13 Have students review the chart accompanying the Explore Activity and use this diagram to reinforce how organs of these lengths can be contained within the body.

Teacher FYI

Our teeth are designed for specific jobs in mechanically digesting food. The incisors are used for cutting, the canines for tearing, and the premolars for crushing and grinding. Most carnivores have large canines and specialized molars. Most herbivores lack canines, but often have large incisors and molars.

Resource Manager

Chapter Resources Booklet
Enrichment, p. 30

Curriculum Connection

Language Arts In one of Robert Frost's poems, he describes a rotting woodpile as the "smokeless burning of decay." Have students compare this to the oxidation of foods that is part of the digestive system. L3 LS **Linguistic**

Organs of the Digestive System, continued

Caption Answer

Figure 14 You begin to salivate.

IDENTIFYING Misconceptions

Students may think that peristalsis cannot occur in the "weightless" environment of a spacecraft. Because peristalsis is an action controlled by muscles, the lack of gravity does not affect swallowing and the movement of food through the digestive system.

Teacher FYI

The digestive systems of various animals are reflective of their lifestyles and diets. Birds have a specialized stomach chamber, the gizzard, that contains small stones. These stones aid in grinding food—a process that is needed in the absence of teeth. Mammals that subsist on grasses have stomach storage pouches or more than one stomach in which their food is ground more thoroughly for subsequent bacterial action.

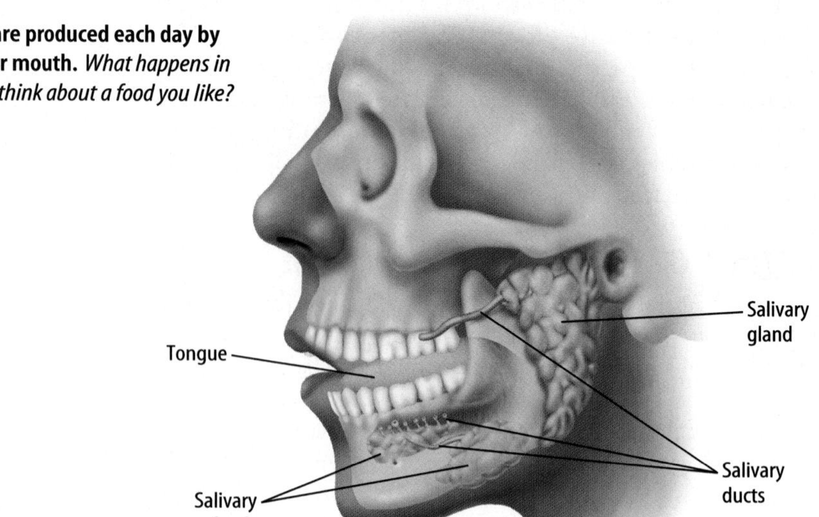

Figure 14
About 1.5 L of saliva are produced each day by salivary glands in your mouth. *What happens in your mouth when you think about a food you like?*

The Mouth Mechanical and chemical digestion begin in your mouth. Mechanical digestion happens when you chew your food with your teeth and mix it with your tongue. Chemical digestion begins with the addition of a watery substance called saliva (suh LIVE uh). As you chew, your tongue moves food around and mixes it with saliva. Saliva is produced by three sets of glands near your mouth, as shown in **Figure 14.** Although saliva is mostly water, it also contains mucus and an enzyme that aids in the breakdown of starch into sugar. Food mixed with saliva becomes a soft mass and is moved to the back of your mouth by your tongue. It is swallowed and passes into your esophagus. Now ingestion is complete, but the process of digestion continues.

SCIENCE Online

Research Visit the Glencoe Science Web site at **science.glencoe.com** for more information about the role of the stomach during digestion. Communicate to your class what you learned.

The Esophagus Food moving into the esophagus passes over the epiglottis (ep uh GLAHT us). This structure automatically covers the opening to the windpipe to prevent food from entering it, otherwise you would choke. Your esophagus is a muscular tube about 25 cm long. It takes about 4 s to 10 s for food to move down the esophagus to the stomach. No digestion takes place in the esophagus. Mucous glands in the wall of the esophagus keep the food moist. Smooth muscles in the wall move food downward with a squeezing action. These waves of muscle contractions, called **peristalsis** (per uh STAHL sus), move food through the entire digestive tract.

Science Journal

Cavities Have interested students research information about the relationship between sugars in the mouth and cavity-causing bacteria. Have them record in their journals information on the formation of tooth cavities. Some students might like to include diagrams showing the stages of tooth decay. L2

LS **Linguistic** P

SCIENCE Online

Internet Addresses

Explore the Glencoe Science Web site at **science.glencoe.com** to find out more about topics in this section.

The Stomach The stomach, shown in **Figure 15,** is a muscular bag. When empty, it is somewhat sausage shaped with folds on the inside. As food enters from the esophagus, the stomach expands and the folds smooth out. Mechanical and chemical digestion take place in the stomach. Mechanically, food is mixed in the stomach by peristalsis. Chemically, food is mixed with enzymes and strong digestive solutions, such as hydrochloric acid, to help break it down.

Specialized cells in the walls of the stomach release about 2 L of hydrochloric acid each day. The acid works with the enzyme pepsin to digest protein. Hydrochloric acid has another important purpose—it destroys bacteria that are present in the food. The stomach also produces mucus, which makes food more slippery and protects the stomach from the strong, digestive solutions. Food moves through your stomach in 2 hours to 4 hours and is changed into a thin, watery liquid called **chyme** (KIME). Little by little, chyme moves out of your stomach and into your small intestine.

Reading Check *Why isn't your stomach digested by hydrochloric acid?*

Figure 15
A band of muscle is at the entrance of the stomach to control the entry of food from the esophagus. Muscles at the end of the stomach control the flow of the partially digested food into the first part of the small intestine.

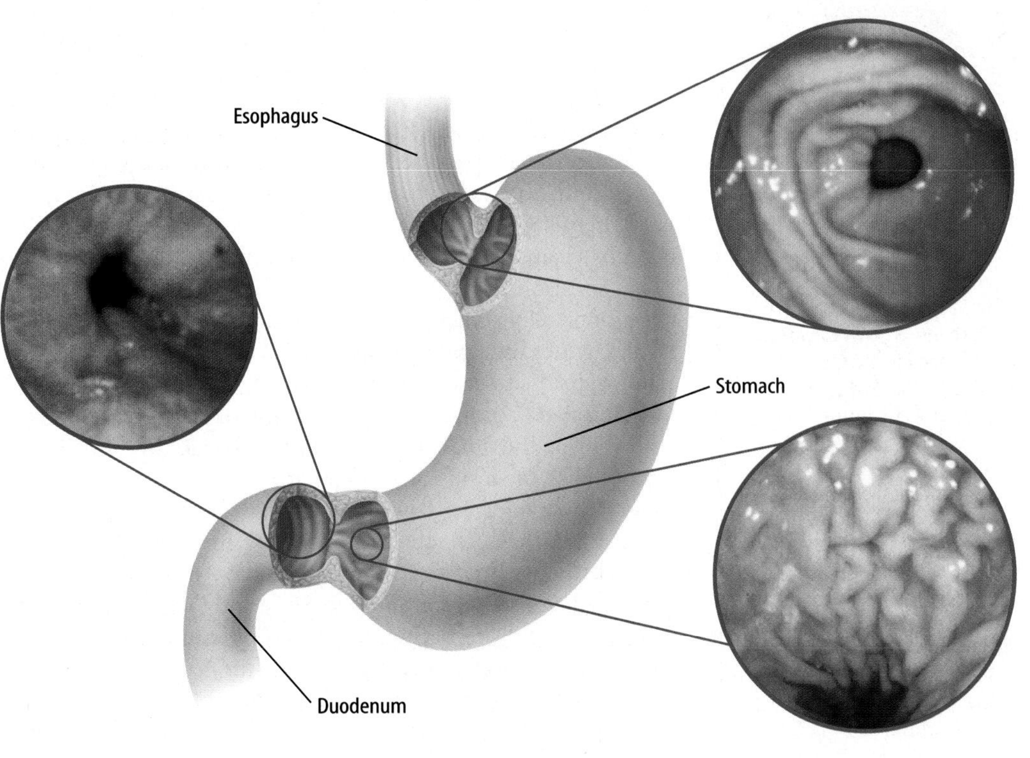

Quick Demo

Place a spoonful of cooking oil in a glass of warm water. Add a quarter-spoonful of dishwashing detergent to the glass. Stir. Have students note how the oil is separated into tiny droplets, giving it a greater surface area. Relate this to the action of bile on fats in the small intestine.

Reading Check

Answer It is protected by a mucous coating.

Visual Learning

Figure 15 Why do you think it is important for the entrance and exit of the stomach to be controlled by strong muscles? Possible answer: The muscles at the entrance to the stomach keep partially digested food and stomach acids from moving back into the esophagus. The muscle at the exit of the stomach allows only chyme to leave the stomach, keeping larger food particles in the stomach for further digestion.

Teacher FYI

It takes between one and six hours for food undergoing digestion to move through the small intestine. The small intestine is subdivided into three parts: the duodenum, jejunum, and ileum. Most of the digestive processes occur in the duodenum and most of the absorption of nutrients takes place in the duodenum and the jejunum. Vitamin B_{12} and bile salts are absorbed in the ileum.

Resource Manager

Chapter Resources Booklet
Lab Activity, pp. 13–15
Science Inquiry Labs, p. 17

Active Reading

Metacognition Journal In this strategy, each student analyzes his or her own thought processes. Have students divide the paper in half. On the left, have them record what they have learned about a topic. On the right, have them record the reason they learned it. Have students write a Metacognition Journal about the digestive system.

Organs of the Digestive System, continued

Caption Answer

Figure 16 The person would lose weight because not as many nutrients could be absorbed by the body; the surface area involved in the process would be reduced.

Purpose Students model how villi increase absorption area. L1 ELL LS **Kinesthetic**

Materials 2 bowls, measuring cup, water, 2 containers, one piece 25 cm x 25 cm smooth cotton cloth, one piece 25 cm x 25 cm cotton terry cloth

Teaching Strategy Cloths should be wrung out completely.

Analysis

1. The terry cloth will absorb more water.
2. The terry cloth's surface of threads is similar to the small intestine's surface of villi.

Assessment

Process Have students compare the absorption of various other cloths and observe differences in their surfaces. Use **Performance Assessment in the Science Classroom,** p. 89.

Figure 16
Hundreds of thousands of densely packed villi give the impression of a velvet cloth surface. If the surface area of your villi could be stretched out, it would cover an area the size of a baseball diamond. *What would happen to a person's weight if the number of villi were drastically reduced? Why?*

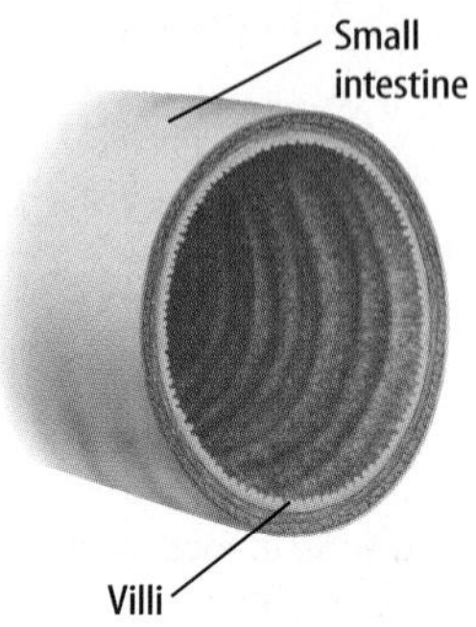

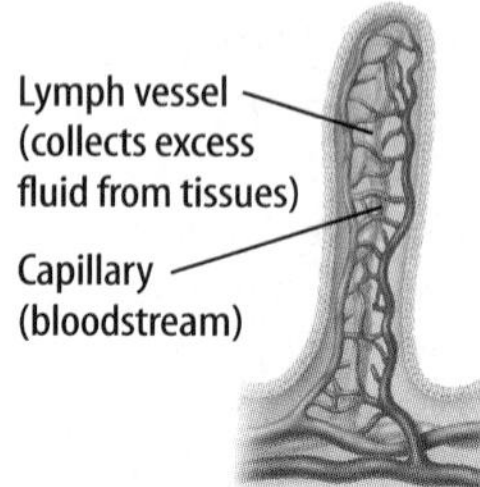

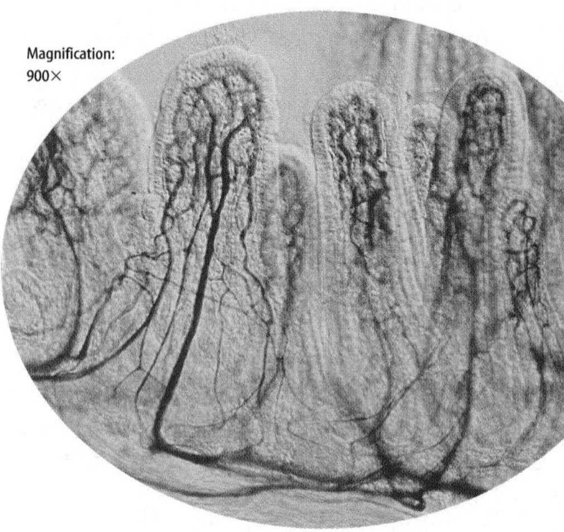

TRY AT HOME Mini LAB

Modeling Absorption in the Small Intestine

Procedure

1. Place one piece of **smooth cotton cloth** (about 25 cm × 25 cm) and a similar-sized piece of **cotton terry cloth** into a **bowl of water.**
2. Soak each for 30 s.
3. Remove the cloths and drain for 1 minute.
4. Wring out each cloth into different containers. Measure the amount of water collected in each.

Analysis

1. Which cloth absorbed the most water?
2. How does the surface of the terry cloth compare to the internal surface of the small intestine?

The Small Intestine Your small intestine is small in diameter, but it measures 4 m to 7 m in length. As chyme leaves your stomach, it enters the first part of your small intestine, called the duodenum (doo AHD un um). Most digestion takes place in your duodenum. Here, a greenish fluid from the liver, called bile, is added. The acid from the stomach makes large fat particles float to the top of the liquid. Bile breaks up the large fat particles, similar to the way detergent breaks up grease.

Chemical digestion of carbohydrates, proteins, and fats occurs when a digestive solution from the pancreas is mixed in. This solution contains bicarbonate ions and enzymes. The bicarbonate ions help neutralize the stomach acid that is mixed with chyme. Your pancreas also makes insulin, a hormone that allows glucose to pass from the bloodstream into your cells.

Absorption of food takes place in the small intestine. Look at the wall of the small intestine in **Figure 16.** The wall is not smooth like the inside of a garden hose but has many ridges and folds. These folds are covered with fingerlike projections called **villi** (VIHL i), which increase the surface area of the small intestine so that nutrients in the chyme have more places to be absorbed. Peristalsis continues to move and mix the chyme. The villi move and are bathed in the soupy liquid. Molecules of nutrients move into blood vessels within the villi. From here, blood transports the nutrients to all cells of your body. Peristalsis continues to force the remaining undigested and unabsorbed materials slowly into the large intestine.

Resource Manager

Chapter Resources Booklet
MiniLAB, p. 4
Reinforcement, p. 28
Home and Community Involvement, p. 41

Inclusion Strategies

Gifted Have students demonstrate the chemical process involved in neutralizing an acid. First, have them use litmus paper to test a vinegar solution (5 mL in 100 mL water) and a baking soda solution (5 mL in 100 mL water). After the two solutions are combined, have students again test to show that the combined solution is no longer acidic or basic. Note: The reaction will produce bubbles of carbon dioxide gas.

The Large Intestine When the chyme enters the large intestine, it is still a thin, watery mixture. The main job of the large intestine is to absorb water from the undigested mass. This keeps large amounts of water in your body and helps maintain homeostasis. Peristalsis usually slows down in the large intestine. The chyme might stay there for as long as three days. After the excess water is absorbed, the remaining undigested materials become more solid. Muscles in the rectum, which is the last section of the large intestine, and the anus control the release of semisolid wastes from the body in the form of feces (FEE seez).

Reading Check *Why does chyme remain in the large intestine for up to three days?*

Bacteria Are Important

Many types of bacteria live in your body. Bacteria live in many of the organs of your digestive tract including your mouth and large intestine. Some of these bacteria live in a relationship that is beneficial to the bacteria and to your body. The bacteria in your large intestine feed on undigested material like cellulose. In turn, bacteria make vitamins you need—vitamin K and two B vitamins. Vitamin K is needed for blood clotting. The two B vitamins, niacin and thiamine, are important for your nervous system and for other body functions. Bacterial action also converts bile pigments into new compounds. The breakdown of intestinal materials by bacteria produces gas.

Environmental Science INTEGRATION

The species of bacteria that live in your large intestine are adapted to their habitat. What do you think would happen to the bacteria if their environment were to change? How would this affect your large intestine? Discuss your ideas with a classmate and write your answers in your Science Journal.

Section 2 Assessment

1. Compare mechanical digestion and chemical digestion.
2. Name, in order, the organs through which food passes as it moves through the digestive tract.
3. How do activities in the large intestine help maintain homeostasis?
4. How do the accessory organs aid digestion?
5. **Think Critically** Crackers contain starch. Explain why a cracker begins to taste sweet after it is in your mouth for five minutes without being chewed.

Skill Builder Activities

6. **Recognizing Cause and Effect** What would happen to some of the nutrients in chyme if the pancreas did not secrete its solution into the small intestine? **For more help, refer to the Science Skill Handbook.**
7. **Communicating** Write a paragraph in your Science Journal explaining what would happen to the mechanical and chemical digestion in a person missing a large portion of his or her stomach. **For more help, refer to the Science Skill Handbook.**

Reading Check

Answer to allow time for water absorption

Bacteria Are Important

Environmental Science INTEGRATION

If the environment changed, the bacteria might die, preventing the decomposition of undigested material and the manufacture of certain vitamins.

3 Assess

Reteach

Have students prepare a two-column chart with these parts of the digestive system in the first column: mouth, stomach, small intestine, and large intestine. In the second column, have them give a brief description of the digestive process associated with each part. L1 LS **Linguistic** P

Challenge

Have students construct a three-dimensional model of an enzyme molecule system and demonstrate how their models work. L3

Assessment

Oral Have students suggest what might happen to digestion and nutrition in people who have lost their teeth. Use **Performance Assessment in the Science Classroom,** p. 93.

Answers to Section Assessment

1. Mechanical digestion involves cutting, grinding, tearing, and crushing by teeth and moving of food by the tongue and peristalsis. Chemical digestion involves the chemical breakdown of food into usable materials.
2. mouth, esophagus, stomach, small intestine, large intestine, rectum, anus
3. Water is removed from wastes and returned to the body in the large intestine.
4. The liver produces digestive juices and bile to break up fat particles. The pancreas also produces digestive juices.
5. Complex carbohydrates in the cracker are broken down into simple sugars by saliva.
6. Food would be acidic in the remainder of the digestive tract, possibly causing ulcers.
7. Journal entries should reflect that both churning action and the digestion of proteins are probably reduced because the stomach is not as large as it was.

Activity

BENCH TESTED

What You'll Investigate

Purpose

Students will observe the relationship between particle size and rate of dissolving. L2 ELL

LS Naturalist

Process Skills

observing and inferring, communicating, recognizing cause and effect, separating and controlling variables, interpreting data, comparing and contrasting

Time Required

50 minutes

Safety Precautions

Remind students not to taste, eat, or drink any materials used in the lab.

Procedure

Teaching Strategies

Troubleshooting Be sure the water temperature and amount of water is the same in each beaker.

Expected Outcome

Most results will show that the ground sugar particles were the quickest to dissolve.

Activity

Particle Size and Absorption

Before food reaches the small intestine, it is digested mechanically in the mouth and the stomach. The food mass is reduced to small particles. You can chew an apple into small pieces, but you would feed applesauce to a small child who didn't have teeth. What is the advantage of reducing the size of the food material?

What You'll Investigate

How does reducing the size of food particles aid the process of digestion?

Materials

beakers or jars (3)
thermometers (3)
sugar granules
mortar and pestle
triple beam balance
stirring rod
sugar cubes
weighing paper
warm water
stopwatch

Safety Precautions

Do not taste, eat, or drink any materials used in the lab.

Goals

- **Compare** the dissolving rates of different sized particles.
- **Predict** the dissolving rate of sugar particles larger than sugar cubes.
- **Predict** the dissolving rate of sugar particles smaller than particles of ground sugar.
- Using the lab results, **infer** why the body must break down and dissolve food particles.

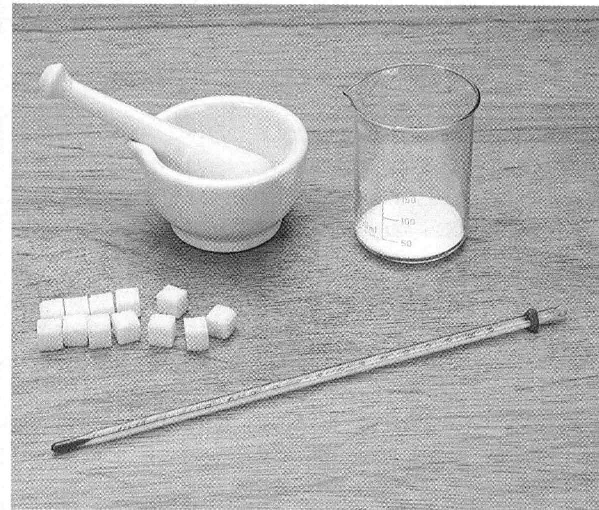

Procedure

1. Copy the data table below into your Science Journal.

Dissolving Time of Sugar Particles

Size of Sugar Particles	Mass	Time Until Dissolved
Sugar cube	Answers	
Sugar granules	will	
Ground sugar particles	vary	

Resource Manager

Chapter Resources Booklet
Activity Worksheet, pp. 7–8

Lab Management and Safety, p. 52

536 CHAPTER 18 Nutrients and Digestion

Procedure

2. Place a sugar cube into your mortar and grind up the cube with the pestle until the sugar becomes powder.
3. Using the triple-beam balance and weighing paper, measure the mass of the powdered sugar from your mortar. Using separate sheets of weighing paper, measure the mass of a sugar cube and the mass of a sample of the granular sugar. The masses of the powdered sugar, sugar cube, and granular sugar should be approximately equal to each other. Record the three masses in your data table.
4. Place warm water into the three beakers. Use the thermometers to be certain the water in each beaker is the same temperature.
5. Place the sugar cube in a beaker, the powdered sugar in a second beaker, and the granular sugar in the third beaker. Place all the sugar samples in the beakers at the same time and start the stopwatch when you put the sugar samples in the beaker.
6. Stir each sample equally.
7. **Measure** the time it takes each sugar sample to dissolve and record the times in your data table.

Conclude and Apply

1. **Identify** the experiment's constants and variables.
2. **Compare** the rate at which the sugar samples dissolved. What type of sugar dissolved most rapidly? Which was the slowest to dissolve?
3. **Predict** how long it would take sugar particles larger than the sugar cubes to dissolve. Predict how long it would take sugar particles smaller than the powdered sugar to dissolve.
4. **Infer and explain** the reason why small particles dissolve more rapidly than large particles.
5. **Infer** why you should thoroughly chew your food.
6. **Explain** how reducing the size of food particles aids the process of digestion.

Communicating Your Data

Write a news column for a health magazine explaining to health-conscious people what they can do to digest their food better.

Conclude and Apply

1. The size of the beakers, mass of the sugar samples, temperature of the water in the beakers, and the amount of time each sample is stirred are the constants. The three particle sizes of the sugar are the variables.
2. The sugar cube should dissolve the slowest. The ground sugar particles should dissolve in the least amount of time.
3. Answers will vary, but larger sugar cubes would require more time to dissolve than the three samples used in the experiment, and smaller ground granules would require less time.
4. Small particles have much more surface area exposed to a dissolving agent than large particles.
5. Smaller particles of food will digest more easily than larger food particles. Chewing food thoroughly speeds up the digestion process.
6. To be used by the body, foods must be broken down into nutrients. Once digested, the blood carries these nutrients to all the cells of the body.

Error Analysis

Have students compare their results and attempt to explain any significant differences.

Assessment

Process Have students investigate and compare the rate of dissolving among table salt, kosher salt, and rock salt. Use **Performance Assessment in the Science Classroom,** p. 97.

Communicating Your Data

Articles should emphasize the idea that smaller particles of food will digest more easily than larger food particles. Chewing food thoroughly speeds up the digestion process. To be used by the body, foods must be broken down into nutrients. Once digested, the blood carries these nutrients to all the cells of the body.

Content Background

Even though scientists are not supposed to be biased or subjective, every scientist comes from a specific culture that has traditions and ways of doing things that are specific to that culture or society. In the case of food scientists and nutritionists, their early studies of food were steeped in the food traditions of the culture from which they came. For instance, food scientists from the West believed a meat-based diet was essential for good health. From 1956–1991, the U.S. government recommended a diet based on four food groups: the meat group, bread and cereal group, vegetable and fruit group, and dairy group. At the top of the list of food recommendations was meat. Americans were supposed to eat a diet high in protein. Culturally, meat was at the center of any meal with grains and vegetables considered only "side dishes."

In 1991, the U.S. Food and Drug Administration introduced a new food pyramid that reflected radical changes in the American diet. The new pyramid emphasizes grains and a carbohydrate-rich diet, rather than a protein-based one. Although the new pyramid has caused nutritionists to reevaluate the American diet, some believe it is still culturally specific to Americans and should not be used to make recommendations in other countries. Thus, some groups have taken the U.S. food pyramid and adapted it so that it reflects the culture and foodways of different regions and countries.

TIME SCIENCE AND Society SCIENCE ISSUES THAT AFFECT YOU!

Does the same diet work for everyone?

R. Rajalakshmi (RAH jah lok shmee) grew up in India in the first half of the twentieth century, seeing many people around her who did not get enough food. Breakfast for a poor child might have been a cup of tea. Lunch might have consisted of a slice of bread. For dinner, a child might have eaten a serving of rice with a small piece of fish. This type of diet, low in calories and nutrients, produced pencil-thin children who were often sick and died young.

Good Diet, Wrong Place

R. Rajalakshmi studied biochemistry and nutrition at universities in India and in Canada. In the 1960s, she was asked to help manage a program to improve nutrition in her country. At that time, most advice on nutrition came from North American and European countries. Nutritionists suggested foods that were common and worked well for people who lived in these nations.

538

Resources for Teachers and Students

American Food Habits in Historical Perspective by Elain N. McIntosh, Ph.D., R.D. Praeger: Westport, Connecticut and London. 1995.

Food and Culture: a Reader. Routledge: London and New York. 1997.

Meat by Nick Fiddes. Routledge, London and New York. 1991.

The Sociology of Food: Eating Diet and Culture by Stephen Mennell, Anne Murcott, and Anneke H. van Otterloo. SAGE Publications/International Sociological Association, London. 1992.

For example, they told poor Indian women to eat more meat and eggs and drink more orange juice. But Rajalakshmi knew this advice was useless in a country such as India. People there didn't eat such foods. They weren't easy to find. And for the poor, such foods were too expensive.

The Proper Diet for India

Rajalakshmi knew that for the program to work, it had to fit Indian culture. So she decided to restructure the nutrition program. She first found out what healthy middle class people in India ate. She took note of the nutrients available in those foods. Then she looked for cheap, easy-to-find foods that would provide the same nutrients.

Rajalakshmi created a balanced diet of locally grown fruits, vegetables, and grains. These foods were cheap and could be cooked with simple equipment. Legumes (plants related to peas and peanuts), vegetables, and an Indian food called dhokla (DOH kluh) were basics. Dhokla is made of grains, legumes, and leafy vegetables. The grains and legumes provided protein, and the vegetables added vitamins and minerals.

Rajalakshmi's ideas were thought unusual in the 1960s. For example, she insisted that a diet without meat could provide all major nutrients. Now we know she was right. But it took persistence to get others to accept her diet about 40 years ago. Because of Rajalakshmi's program, Indian children almost doubled their food intake. And many children who would have been hungry and ill grew healthy and strong.

Thanks to R. Rajalakshmi and other nutritionists, many children in India are eating well and staying healthy.

CONNECTIONS Report **Choose a continent and research what foods are native to that area. Share your findings with your classmates and compile a list of the foods and where they originated. Using the class list, create a world map on a bulletin board that shows the origins of the different foods.**

SCIENCE Online
For more information, visit science.glencoe.com

Discussion

What reasons might there have been for Western nutritionists to suggest that Indian women eat more meat and eggs? Possible answer: The U.S. and European diets were based on consuming animal products and foods high in protein.

Activity

Show students a copy of the U.S. food pyramid. Explain that some groups have developed alternative "healthy eating pyramids" based on dietary traditions that are specific to a region or country. These pyramids take into account the economic, social, cultural, and traditional aspects that play a role in a region or country's diet. Using the food pyramid as a guide, have groups of students make an Indian food pyramid that replaces the meat-based proteins with plant-based ones for the Indian diet. Have students compare the differences between the Indian pyramid and the U.S. one. What differences are notable?

Investigate the Issue

Ask students to think about the foods they eat every day. Explain to students that different cultural, age, ethnic, and even family groups have distinct food traditions. Give students the following examples of food traditions: Asian-American students might consume a largely plant-based diet with rice being served at most meals. Share with the class an example of a food tradition in your own family. Then, ask students to name a food tradition or food item that they believe is unique to their family or ethnic or cultural group.

CONNECTIONS Have students research a specific region, such as a continent, and compile a list of foods that are common there. After students write their lists on the board, direct students to note the differences in diets. **Which cultures have a mostly plant-based diet and which have a mostly meat-based diet? What might be the reasons for the difference?**

SCIENCE Online

Internet Addresses

Explore the Glencoe Science Web site at **science.glencoe.com** to find out more about topics in this feature.

Chapter 18 Study Guide

Reviewing Main Ideas

Preview

Students can answer the questions in their Science Journals. Discuss the answers as you go through the chapter. LS **Linguistic**

Review

Students can write their answers, then compare them with those of other students. LS **Interpersonal**

Reteach

Students can look at the illustrations and describe details that support the main ideas of the chapter. LS **Visual-Spatial**

Answers to Chapter Review

Section 1

3. chicken breasts and beans

Section 2

2. stomach and small intestine

Chapter 18 Study Guide

Reviewing Main Ideas

Section 1 Nutrition

1. Proteins, carbohydrates, fats, vitamins, minerals, and water are the six nutrients found in foods.
2. Carbohydrates provide energy, proteins are needed for growth and repair, and fats store energy and cushion organs. Vitamins and minerals regulate functions. Water makes up about 60 percent of your body's mass and is used for a variety of homeostatic functions.
3. Health is affected by the combination of foods that make up a diet. *In the photograph below, which foods would you choose to get the highest amount of protein in your diet?*

Section 2 The Digestive System

1. Mechanical digestion breaks down food through chewing and churning. Enzymes and other chemicals aid chemical digestion. Both types of digestion are used to break down food into substances that cells can absorb and use. Carbohydrates become simple sugars, proteins become amino acids, and fats are digested into fatty acids and glycerol.

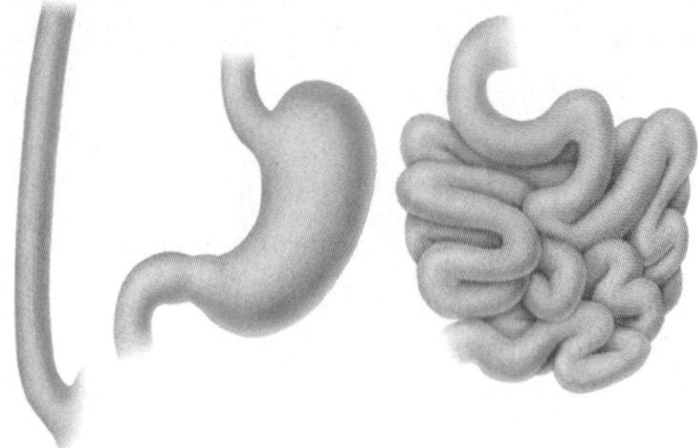

2. Food passes through the mouth, esophagus, stomach, small intestine, and large intestine and then out the anus. Ingestion takes place in the mouth. Digestion occurs in the mouth, stomach, and small intestine, with absorption occurring in the small and large intestines. Wastes are excreted through the anus. *In the illustration of the digestive organs shown above, where does digestion take place?*
3. The accessory digestive organs move and cut up food and supply digestive enzymes and other chemicals, such as bile, needed for digestion.
4. The large intestine absorbs water, which helps the body maintain homeostasis. Homeostasis is the regulation of the body's internal environment.

FOLDABLES Reading & Study Skills — **After You Read**

Use your Classify Study Fold to find an example of a food you eat that supplies four or more of the six nutrients. If there is none, which foods have the most nutrients?

FOLDABLES Reading & Study Skills — **After You Read**

After students have read the chapter and completed the Foldable described in Before You Read, have them do the activity on the student page.

Dinah Zike

Visualizing Main Ideas

Fill in the following table indicating good sources of vitamins and minerals.

Vitamin and Mineral Sources

Food Type	Source of Vitamin	Source of Mineral
Milk	D	calcium
Spinach	A, B, C, K	iron
Meat	B	calcium, potassium
Eggs	E	iron, calcium
Carrots	A	sodium

Vocabulary Review

Vocabulary Words

- **a.** amino acid
- **b.** carbohydrate
- **c.** chemical digestion
- **d.** chyme
- **e.** digestion
- **f.** enzyme
- **g.** fat
- **h.** food group
- **i.** mechanical digestion
- **j.** mineral
- **k.** nutrient
- **l.** peristalsis
- **m.** protein
- **n.** villi
- **o.** vitamin

Using Vocabulary

In each sentence, replace the underlined word with the correct vocabulary word.

1. Digestion is the muscular contractions of the esophagus.
2. The carbohydrates increase the surface area of the small intestine.
3. The building blocks of proteins are enzymes.
4. The liquid product of digestion is called villi.
5. Peristalsis is the breakdown of food.
6. Your body's main source of energy is vitamins.
7. Proteins are inorganic nutrients.
8. Pears and apples belong to the same mineral.
9. Chyme is when food is chewed and mixed.
10. A fat is a nutrient needed in small quantities for growth and for regulating body functions.

Study Tip

Practice reading graphs and charts. Make a table that contains the same information as a graph does. Have a friend make a graph of the information from a table. Exchange items and see if you can interpret each other's tables.

Chapter 18 Study Guide

Visualizing Main Ideas

See student page.

Vocabulary Review

Using Vocabulary

1. Peristalsis
2. villi
3. amino acids
4. chyme
5. Digestion
6. carbohydrates
7. Minerals
8. food group
9. Mechanical digestion
10. vitamin

IDENTIFYING Misconceptions

Assess

Use the assessment as follow-up to page 516F after students have completed the chapter.

Materials test tubes, starch solution, Lugol's solution, saliva

Procedure As a demonstration, take two large test tubes and add to each some of the starch solution and Lugol's solution. Add saliva that has been safely collected to one of the tubes. Explain that saliva contains an enzyme, amylase. (The danger of using body fluids in experiments should be stressed to students.) The blue color in the tube with the saliva should disappear. Ask students what they think happened to the blue color.

Expected Outcome Students should be able to explain that the enzyme helped digest the starch.

Chapter 18 Assessment

Checking Concepts

1. A
2. B
3. D
4. D
5. C
6. C
7. B
8. D
9. A
10. B

Thinking Critically

11. As food passes through the digestive tract it is broken down into smaller pieces, eventually reaching the molecular level. These molecules are absorbed by the blood, transported to body cells, and used as an energy source.
12. The stomach, because acids are produced there. Antacids are used to counteract an excess of acid.
13. Bile breaks down fats into smaller droplets, which have an increased surface area; this allows digestion to occur more quickly and easily.
14. Your body would retain vitamin D. It is fat-soluble and stored in fat deposits.
15. If we eat nutritious food, the body will have good building blocks to use. A poor diet will not supply good building blocks.

Chapter 18 Assessment

Checking Concepts

Choose the word or phrase that best answers the question.

1. Where in humans does most chemical digestion occur?
   A) duodenum **C)** liver
   B) stomach **D)** large intestine
2. Which organ makes bile?
   A) gallbladder **C)** stomach
   B) liver **D)** small intestine
3. In which organ is water absorbed?
   A) liver **C)** small intestine
   B) esophagus **D)** large intestine
4. Which of these organs is an accessory organ?
   A) mouth **C)** small intestine
   B) stomach **D)** liver
5. What beneficial substances are produced by bacteria in the large intestine?
   A) fats **C)** vitamins
   B) minerals **D)** proteins
6. Which vitamin is found most abundantly in citrus fruits?
   A) A **C)** C
   B) B **D)** K
7. Where is hydrochloric acid added to the food mass?
   A) mouth **C)** small intestine
   B) stomach **D)** large intestine
8. From which food group should the largest number of servings in your diet come?
   A) fruit
   B) vegetable
   C) milk, yogurt, and cheese
   D) bread, cereal, rice, and pasta
9. Which food group contains yogurt and cheese?
   A) dairy **C)** meat
   B) grain **D)** fruit
10. Which organ produces enzymes that help in digestion of proteins, fats, and carbohydrates?
    A) mouth **C)** large intestine
    B) pancreas **D)** gallbladder

Thinking Critically

11. Food does not enter your body until it is absorbed into the blood. Explain why.
12. In what part of the digestive system do antacids work? Explain your choice.
13. Bile's action is similar to that of soap. Use this information to explain how bile works on fats.
14. Vitamin C and vitamin D are important for good health. Which of these might your body store? Explain your answer.
15. Based on your knowledge of food groups and nutrients, discuss the meaning of the familiar statement: "You are what you eat."

Developing Skills

16. **Making and Using Tables** In a table, sequence the order of organs in the digestive system through which food passes. Indicate whether ingestion, digestion, absorption, or elimination takes place.
17. **Comparing and Contrasting** Compare and contrast the three types of carbohydrates—sugar, starch, and fiber.
18. **Concept Mapping** Make a sequencing or events chain concept map showing the process of fat digestion.
19. **Classifying** Describe your favorite sandwich, then sort its parts into three of the nutrient categories—carbohydrates, proteins, and fats.

Chapter Assessment Planner

Portfolio Encourage students to place in their portfolios one or two items of what they consider to be their best work. Examples include:

- Activity, p. 526
- Science Journal, p. 532
- Reteach, p. 535

Performance Additional performance assessments, Performance Task Assessment Lists, and rubrics for evaluating these activities can be found in Glencoe's **Performance Assessment in the Science Classroom.**

20. Making and Using Graphs Recommended Dietary Allowances (RDA) are the amounts of nutrients people need to maintain health. A product nutrient label is listed below. Make a bar graph of this information.

Recommended Dietary Allowances

Nutrient	Percent U.S. RDA
Protein	2
Vitamin A	20
Vitamin C	25
Vitamin D	15
Calcium (Ca)	less than 2
Iron (Fe)	25
Zinc (Zn)	15
Total Fat	5
Saturated Fat	3
Cholesterol	0
Sodium	3

Performance Assessment

21. Project Research the ingredients used in antacid medications. Identify the compounds used to neutralize the excess stomach acid. Place an antacid tablet in a glass of vinegar. Using pH paper, check when the acid is neutralized. Record the time it took for the antacid to neutralize the vinegar. Repeat with different antacids.

Technology

Go to the Glencoe Science Web site at **science.glencoe.com** or use the **Glencoe Science CD-ROM** for additional chapter assessment.

Test Practice

Kyle has just eaten a serving of vanilla ice cream after his lunch. The table below lists the nutritional facts of the ice cream.

Nutrition Facts of Vanilla Ice Cream

Item	Amount	DV (Daily Values)
Serving Size	112 g	0
Calories	208	0
Total Fat	19 g	29%
Saturated Fat	11 g	55%
Cholesterol	0.125 g	42%
Sodium	0.90 g	4%
Total Carbohydrates	22 g	7%
Fiber	0 g	0%
Sugars	22 g	n/a
Protein	5 g	n/a
Calcium	0.117 g	15%
Iron	n/a	0%

Study the table and answer the following questions.

1. According to this information, which nutrient has the greatest Daily Value (DV) percentage?
   A) total fat **C)** saturated fat
   B) calcium **D)** cholesterol
2. According to the table, ice cream would NOT be a good source of _____.
   F) fiber **H)** carbohydrates
   G) saturated fat **J)** calcium

Assessment Resources

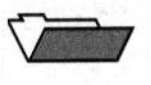

Reproducible Masters

Chapter Resources Booklet
Chapter Review, pp. 35–36
Chapter Tests, pp. 37–40
Assessment Transparency Activity, p. 47

Glencoe Science Web site
Interactive Tutor
Chapter Quizzes

Glencoe Technology
Assessment Transparency
Interactive CD-ROM Chapter Quizzes
ExamView Pro Test Bank
Vocabulary PuzzleMaker Software
MindJogger Videoquiz

Chapter 18 Assessment

Test Practice

The Test-Taking Tip was written by The Princeton Review, the nation's leader in test preparation.

1. C
2. F

Developing Skills

16. mouth: ingestion, mechanical and chemical digestion; esophagus: ingestion; stomach: mechanical and chemical digestion; small intestine: digestion and absorption; large intestine: absorption and elimination
17. Sugar—simple carbohydrate, dissolves in water, tastes sweet; starch and fiber—complex carbohydrates, do not dissolve in water; fiber absorbs water, starch does not.
18. mouth: fat mechanically broken down; esophagus: passes through; stomach: mixes with digestive juices; duodenum: bile breaks it into droplets, digestive juices from the pancreas begin chemical digestion
19. Answers will vary: bread is a carbohydrate; meat and cheese are proteins and fats; margarine is fat; peanut butter is protein and fat; jelly is carbohydrate.
20. Check student graphs to ensure consistency with data provided.

Performance Assessment

21. Common ingredients in antacids include sodium bicarbonate, calcium carbonate, ranitidine hydrochloride, and famotidine. Use **Performance Assessment in the Science Classroom,** p. 115.

Section/Objectives	Standards		Activities/Features
	National	State/Local	
Chapter Opener	See p. 5T for a Key to Standards.		**Explore Activity:** Recognize transportation, p. 545 **Before You Read,** p. 545
Section 1 The Circulatory System 3 sessions 1.5 blocks 1. **Compare and contrast** arteries, veins, and capillaries. 2. **Explain** how blood moves through the heart. 3. **Identify** the functions of the pulmonary and systemic circulation systems.	National Content Standards: UCP1, A1, C1		**MiniLAB:** Inferring How Hard the Heart Works, p. 547 **Physics Integration,** p. 551 **Visualizing Atherosclerosis,** p. 552 **Science Online,** p. 553 **Activity:** The Heart as a Pump, p. 555
Section 2 Blood 2 sessions 1 block 1. **Identify** the parts and functions of blood. 2. **Explain** why blood types are checked before a transfusion. 3. **Give examples** of diseases of blood.	National Content Standards: UCP5, A1, C1, F1		**Science Online,** p. 557 **MiniLAB:** Modeling Scab Formation, p. 558 **Chemistry Integration,** p. 560 **Problem-Solving Activity:** Will there be enough blood donors?, p. 560
Section 3 The Lymphatic System 2 sessions 1 block 1. **Describe** the functions of the lymphatic system. 2. **Identify** where lymph comes from. 3. **Explain** how lymph organs help fight infections.	National Content Standards: UCP5, A1, C1, F1, G3		**Science Online,** p. 563 **Activity:** Blood Type Reactions, pp. 564–565 **Science and History:** Have a Heart, pp. 566–567

NATIONAL GEOGRAPHIC

Teacher's Corner

PRODUCTS AVAILABLE FROM GLENCOE
To order call 1-800-334-7344:
CD-ROM
NGS PictureShow: Human Body 2
Curriculum Kit
GeoKit: Human Body 1
Transparency Set
NGS PicturePack: Human Body 2
Videodisc
STV: Human Body

PRODUCTS AVAILABLE FROM NATIONAL GEOGRAPHIC SOCIETY
To order call 1-800-368-2728:
Videos
Circulatory and Respiratory Systems (The Human Body Series)
Incredible Human Machine

Activity Materials	Reproducible Resources	Section Assessment	Technology
Explore Activity: a city, county, or state map; Science Journal	**Chapter Resources Booklet** Foldables Worksheet, p. 17 Directed Reading Overview, p. 19 Note-taking Worksheets, pp. 33–37	Glencoe's Assessment Advantage	
MiniLAB: bowl of water, stop watch or clock **Activity:** watch or clock with second hand	**Chapter Resources Booklet** Transparency Activity, p. 46 MiniLAB, p. 3 Enrichment, p. 30 Reinforcement, p. 27 Directed Reading, p. 20 Activity Worksheet, pp. 5–6 Lab Activities, pp. 9–12, 13–16 Transparency Activity, pp. 49–50 **Home and Community Involvement,** p. 26	Portfolio Assessment, p. 554 Performance MiniLAB, p. 547 Skill Builder Activities, p. 554 Content Section Assessment, p. 554 Challenge, p. 554	Section Focus Transparency Teaching Transparency Interactive CD-ROM Guided Reading Audio Program
MiniLAB: gauze, aluminum foil, liquid bandage solution, dropp[er]	**Chapter Resources Booklet** Transparency Activity, p. 47 MiniLAB, p. 4 Enrichment, p. 31 Reinforcement, p. 28 Directed Reading, p. 20 **Mathematics Skill Activities,** p. 33 **Cultural Diversity,** p. 18	Portfolio Science Journal, p. 558 Performance MiniLAB, p. 558 Skill Builder Activities, p. 561 Content Section Assessment, p. 561 Challenge, p. 561	Section Focus Transparency Interactive CD-ROM Guided Reading Audio Program
Activity: simulated blood (10 mL low-fat milk and 10 mL water plus red food coloring), lemon juice, water, droppers, small paper cups, marking pen, 10-mL graduated cylinder	**Chapter Resources Booklet** Transparency Activity, p. 48 Enrichment, p. 32 Reinforcement, p. 29 Directed Reading, pp. 21, 22 Activity Worksheet, pp. 7–8 **Lab Management and Safety,** p. 69	Portfolio Reteach, p. 563 Activity, p. 564–565 Performance Skill Builder Activities, p. 563 Content Section Assessment, p. 563 Challenge, p. 563	Section Focus Transparency Interactive CD-ROM Guided Reading Audio Program

Need materials? Contact Science Kit at 1-800-828-7777 or www.sciencekit.com on the Internet.

End of Chapter Assessment

Glencoe's Assessment Advantage

Blackline Masters	Technology	Professional Series
Chapter Resources Booklet Chapter Review, pp. 39–40 Chapter Tests, pp. 41–44 **Standardized Test Practice by The Princeton Review,** pp. 83–86	MindJogger Videoquiz Interactive CD-ROM Vocabulary PuzzleMakers ExamView Pro Test Bank Interactive Lesson Planner Interactive Teacher Edition	Performance Assessment in the Science Classroom (PASC)

Transparencies

Section Focus

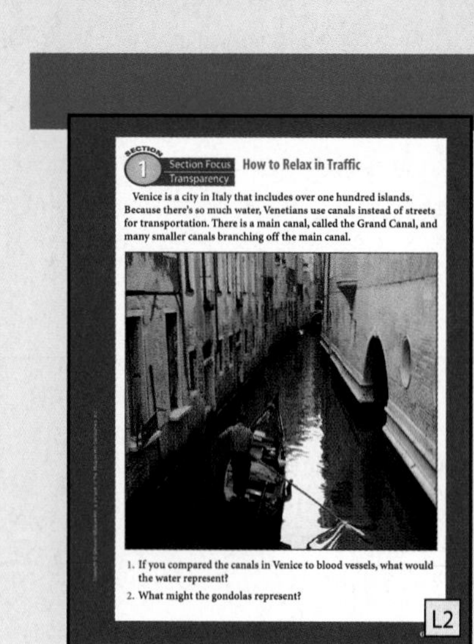

Section 1 Section Focus Transparency **How to Relax in Traffic**

Venice is a city in Italy that includes over one hundred islands. Because there's so much water, Venetians use canals instead of streets for transportation. There is a main canal, called the Grand Canal, and many smaller canals branching off the main canal.

1. If you compared the canals in Venice to blood vessels, what would the water represent?
2. What might the gondolas represent?

L2

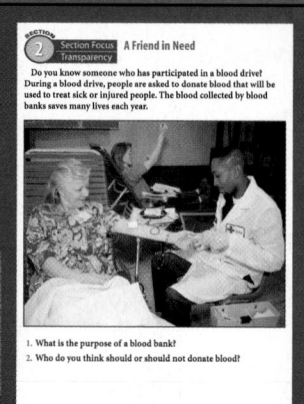

Section 2 Section Focus Transparency **A Friend in Need**

Do you know someone who has participated in a blood drive? During a blood drive, people are asked to donate blood that will be used to treat sick or injured people. The blood collected by blood banks saves many lives each year.

1. What is the purpose of a blood bank?
2. Who do you think should or should not donate blood?

L2

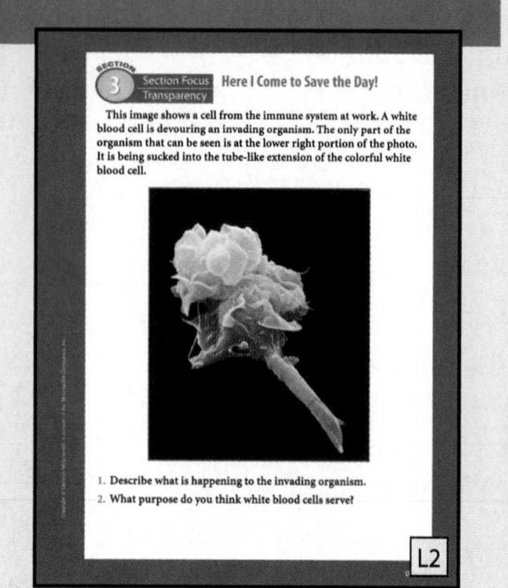

Section 3 Section Focus Transparency **Here I Come to Save the Day!**

This image shows a cell from the immune system at work. A white blood cell is devouring an invading organism. The only part of the organism that can be seen is at the lower right portion of the photo. It is being sucked into the tube-like extension of the colorful white blood cell.

1. Describe what is happening to the invading organism.
2. What purpose do you think white blood cells serve?

L2

This is a representation of key blackline masters available in the Teacher Classroom Resources. See Resource Manager boxes within the chapter for additional information.

Assessment

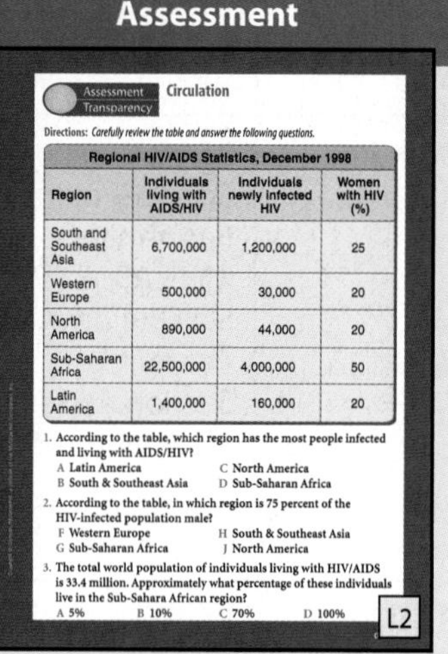

Assessment Transparency **Circulation**

Directions: *Carefully review the table and answer the following questions.*

Regional HIV/AIDS Statistics, December 1998			
Region	Individuals living with AIDS/HIV	Individuals newly infected HIV	Women with HIV (%)
South and Southeast Asia	6,700,000	1,200,000	25
Western Europe	500,000	30,000	20
North America	890,000	44,000	20
Sub-Saharan Africa	22,500,000	4,000,000	50
Latin America	1,400,000	160,000	20

1. According to the table, which region has the most people infected and living with AIDS/HIV?
   A Latin America C North America
   B South & Southeast Asia D Sub-Saharan Africa
2. According to the table, in which region is 75 percent of the HIV-infected population male?
   F Western Europe H South & Southeast Asia
   G Sub-Saharan Africa J North America
3. The total world population of individuals living with HIV/AIDS is 33.4 million. Approximately what percentage of these individuals live in the Sub-Sahara African region?
   A 5% B 10% C 70% D 100%

L2

Teaching

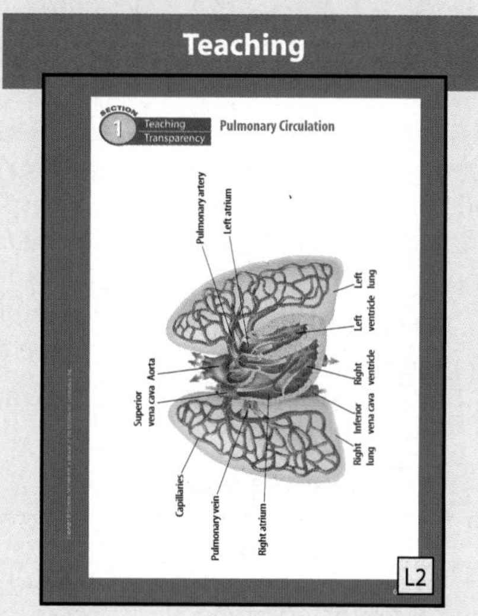

Key to Teaching Strategies

The following designations will help you decide which activities are appropriate for your students.

- L1 Level 1 activities should be appropriate for students with learning difficulties.
- L2 Level 2 activities should be within the ability range of all students.
- L3 Level 3 activities are designed for above-average students.
- ELL ELL activities should be within the ability range of English Language Learners.
- COOP LEARN Cooperative Learning activities are designed for small group work.
- LS Multiple Learning Styles logos, as described on page 22T, are used throughout to indicate strategies that address different learning styles.
- P These strategies represent student products that can be placed into a best-work portfolio.

Hands-on Activities

Activity Worksheets

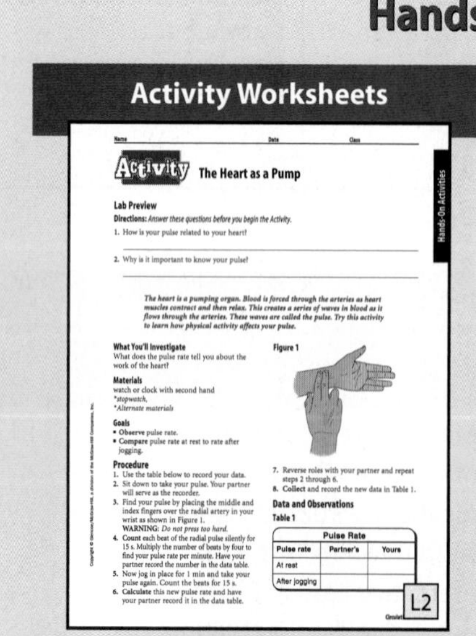

Name Date Class

Activity **The Heart as a Pump**

Hands-On Activities

Lab Preview

Directions: *Answer these questions before you begin the Activity.*

1. How is your pulse related to your heart?
2. Why is it important to know your pulse?

The heart is a pumping organ. Blood is forced through the arteries as heart muscles contract and then relax. This creates a series of waves in blood as it flows through the arteries. These waves are called the pulse. Try this activity to learn how physical activity affects your pulse.

What You'll Investigate
What does the pulse rate tell you about the work of the heart?

Materials
watch or clock with second hand
**stopwatch,*
**Alternate materials*

Goals
- **Observe** pulse rate.
- **Compare** pulse rate at rest to rate after jogging.

Procedure
1. Use the table below to record your data.
2. Sit down to take your pulse. Your partner will serve as the recorder.
3. Find your pulse by placing the middle and index fingers over the radial artery in your wrist as shown in Figure 1. WARNING: *Do not press too hard.*
4. **Count** each beat of the radial pulse silently for 15 s. Multiply the number of beats by four to find your pulse rate per minute. Have your partner record the number in the data table.
5. Now jog in place for 1 min and take your pulse again. Count the beats for 15 s.
6. **Calculate** this new pulse rate and have your partner record it in the data table.
7. Reverse roles with your partner and repeat steps 2 through 6.
8. **Collect** and record the new data in Table 1.

Figure 1

Data and Observations

Table 1

Pulse Rate		
Pulse rate	Partner's	Yours
At rest		
After jogging		

L2

Laboratory Activities

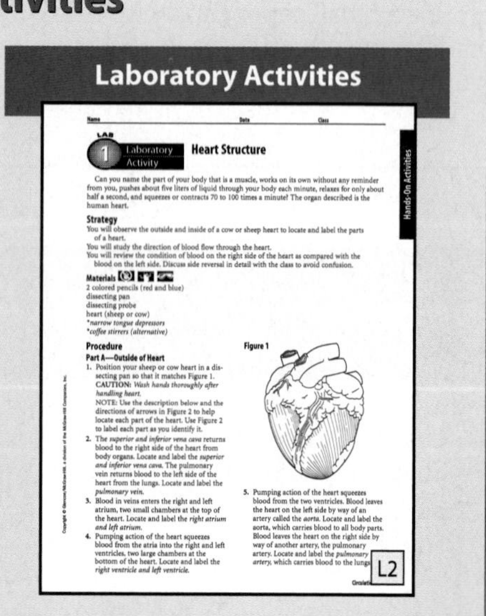

Name Date Class

Lab 1 Laboratory Activity **Heart Structure**

Hands-On Activities

Can you name the part of your body that is a muscle, works on its own without any reminder from you, pushes about five liters of liquid through your body each minute, relaxes for only about half a second, and squeezes or contracts 70 to 100 times a minute? The organ described is the human heart.

Strategy
You will observe the outside and inside of a cow or sheep heart to locate and label the parts of a heart.
You will study the direction of blood flow through the heart.
You will review the condition of blood on the right side of the heart as compared with the blood on the left side. Discuss side reversal in detail with the class to avoid confusion.

Materials
2 colored pencils (red and blue)
dissecting pan
dissecting probe
heart (sheep or cow)
**narrow tongue depressors*
**coffee stirrers (alternative)*

Procedure

Part A—Outside of Heart
1. Position your sheep or cow heart in a dissecting pan so that it matches Figure 1. CAUTION: *Wash hands thoroughly after handling heart.* NOTE: Use the description below and the directions of arrows in Figure 2 to help locate each part of the heart. Use Figure 2 to label each part as you identify it.
2. The *superior and inferior vena cava* returns blood to the right side of the heart from body organs. Locate and label the *superior and inferior vena cava.* The pulmonary vein returns blood to the left side of the heart from the lungs. Locate and label the *pulmonary vein.*
3. Blood in veins enters the right and left atrium, two small chambers at the top of the heart. Locate and label the *right atrium and left atrium.*
4. Pumping action of the heart squeezes blood from the atria into the right and left ventricles, two large chambers at the bottom of the heart. Locate and label the *right ventricle and left ventricle.*
5. Pumping action of the heart squeezes blood from the two ventricles. Blood leaves the heart on the left side by way of an artery called the *aorta.* Locate and label the aorta, which carries blood to all body parts. Blood leaves the heart on the right side by way of another artery, the pulmonary artery. Locate and label the *pulmonary artery,* which carries blood to the lungs.

Figure 1

L2

Meeting Different Ability Levels

Content Outline

Name ______ Date ______ Class ______

Note-taking Worksheet **Circulation**

Section 1 The Circulatory System

A. Your ________________ system includes the blood, heart, and blood vessels. It moves materials to all parts of your body.

1. Movement of materials into and out of your cells occurs by ____________, or movement of materials from an area of high concentration to an area of low concentration.
2. Movement also occurs by ________________, which is the opposite of diffusion.

B. ____________—controls blood flow through all parts of the body

1. Has four chambers
   a. ____________—upper two chambers
   b. ____________—lower two chambers
   c. A one-way ____________ separates each atrium from the ventricle below it.
   d. Blood ____________ only from an atrium to a ventricle.
   e. A wall between the two atriums and the two ventricles prevents oxygen rich and oxygen poor blood from ____________.
2. Circulatory system—divided into ________ sections
   a. ____________ circulation is the flow of blood to and from the tissues of the heart.
   b. In ____________ circulation, blood flows through the heart to the lungs, where carbon dioxide and other waste materials diffuse out, oxygen diffuses in, and the blood goes back to the heart.
   c. ____________ circulation moves oxygen-rich blood to all the organs and body tissues, except the heart and lungs, and returns oxygen-poor blood to the heart.

C. ____________ carry blood to every part of your body.

1. ____________ are blood vessels that move oxygen-rich blood from the heart to the body.
   a. Each ventricle of the heart is connected to an artery.
   b. The right ventricle connects to the ____________ artery.
   c. The left ventricle connects to the ____________.
   d. Every time your heart ____________, blood is moved from your heart into your arte...

Meeting Individual Needs

L2

Reinforcement

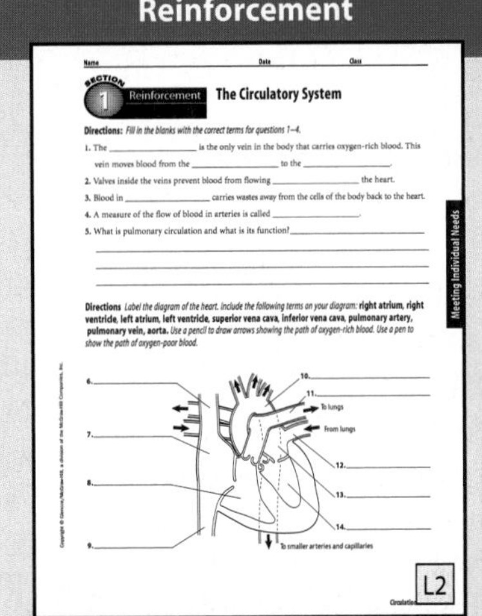

Name ______ Date ______ Class ______

Section 1 Reinforcement **The Circulatory System**

Directions: *Fill in the blanks with the correct terms for questions 1–4.*

1. The ________________ is the only vein in the body that carries oxygen-rich blood. This vein moves blood from the ____________ to the ____________.
2. Valves inside the veins prevent blood from flowing ____________ the heart.
3. Blood in ____________ carries wastes away from the cells of the body back to the heart.
4. A measure of the flow of blood in arteries is called ________________.
5. What is pulmonary circulation and what is its function?

Directions: *Label the diagram of the heart. Include the following terms on your diagram:* **right atrium, right ventricle, left atrium, left ventricle, superior vena cava, inferior vena cava, pulmonary artery, pulmonary vein, aorta.** *Use a pencil to draw arrows showing the path of oxygen-rich blood. Use a pen to show the path of oxygen-poor blood.*

Meeting Individual Needs

L2

Directed Reading

Name ______ Date ______ Class ______

Directed Reading for Content Mastery *Overview* **Circulation**

Directions: *Use the following terms to complete the concept map below.*

heart, capillaries, arteries, vena cava, lungs

Directions: *Complete the following sentences using the correct terms.*

6. Once tissue fluid diffuses into the lymphatic capillaries, it is called ________________.
7. ________________ are lymphatic organs that protect your mouth and nose form harmful microorganisms.

Meeting Individual Needs

L1

Enrichment

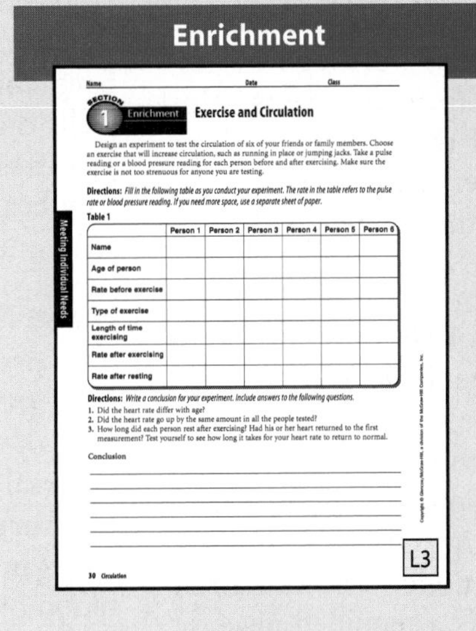

Name ______ Date ______ Class ______

Section 1 Enrichment **Exercise and Circulation**

Design an experiment to test the circulation of six of your friends or family members. Choose an exercise that will increase circulation, such as running in place or jumping jacks. Take a pulse reading or a blood pressure reading for each person before and after exercising. Make sure the exercise is not too strenuous for anyone you are testing.

Directions: *Fill in the following table as you conduct your experiment. The rate in the table refers to the pulse rate or blood pressure reading. If you need more space, use a separate sheet of paper.*

Table 1

	Person 1	Person 2	Person 3	Person 4	Person 5	Person 6
Name						
Age of person						
Rate before exercise						
Type of exercise						
Length of time exercising						
Rate after exercising						
Rate after resting						

Directions: *Write a conclusion for your experiment. Include answers to the following questions.*

1. Did the heart rate differ with age?
2. Did the heart rate go up by the same amount in all the people tested?
3. How long did each person rest after exercising? Had his or her heart returned to the first measurement? Test yourself to see how long it takes for your heart rate to return to normal.

Conclusion

Meeting Individual Needs

L3

Spanish Directed Reading

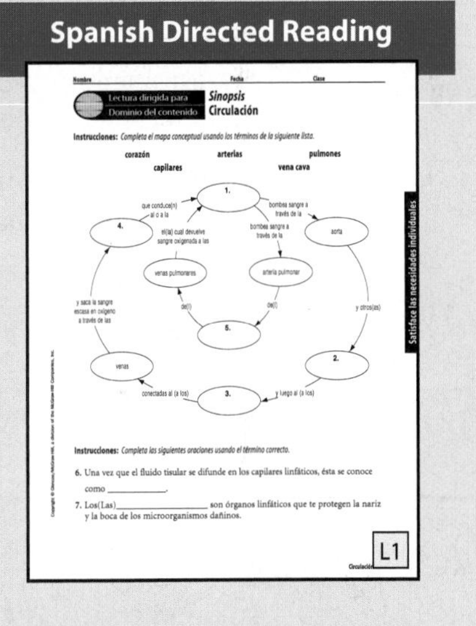

Nombre ______ Fecha ______ Clase ______

Lectura dirigida para Dominio del contenido *Sinopsis* **Circulación**

Instrucciones: *Completa el mapa conceptual usando los términos de la siguiente lista.*

corazón, capilares, arterias, vena cava, pulmones

Instrucciones: *Completa las siguientes oraciones usando el término correcto.*

6. Una vez que el fluido tisular se difunde en los capilares linfáticos, ésta se conoce como ____________.
7. Los(Las) ________________ son órganos linfáticos que te protegen la nariz y la boca de los microorganismos dañinos.

Satisface las necesidades individuales

L1

Assessment

Chapter Tests

Name ______ Date ______ Class ______

Chapter Test **Circulation**

I. Testing Concepts

Directions: *Match the description in the first column with the term in the second column by writing the correct letter in the space provided. Some items in the second column may not be used.*

_____ 1. the two upper chambers of the heart
_____ 2. the two lower chambers of the heart
_____ 3. blood vessels that move blood away from the heart
_____ 4. blood vessels that move blood toward the heart
_____ 5. microscopic blood vessels connecting larger vessels
_____ 6. moves blood to all tissues except lungs and heart
_____ 7. collects fluid from body tissue spaces and returns it to the blood
_____ 8. the liquid part of the blood, consisting mostly of water
_____ 9. a chemical that can carry oxygen and carbon dioxide

a. arteries
b. atria
c. capillaries
d. coronary circulation
e. hemoglobin
f. hypertension
g. lymphatic system
h. plasma
i. pulmonary circulation
j. systemic circulation
k. veins
l. ventricles

Directions: *For each of the following, write the letter of the term or phrase that best completes each sentence.*

_____ 10. Another name for high blood pressure is _____.
a. atherosclerosis b. hypertension c. leukemia d. thrombosis

_____ 11. Blood in veins is _____.
a. high in oxygen b. high in nutrients c. low in wastes d. low in oxygen

_____ 12. In pulmonary circulation, blood flows through two organs, the _____.
a. brain and heart b. heart and kidneys c. heart and liver d. lungs and heart

_____ 13. In systemic circulation, blood returns from your abdomen through the inferior vena cava to the _____.
a. left atrium b. left ventricle c. right atrium d. right ventricle

_____ 14. Coronary circulation is the flow of blood to the tissues of the _____.
a. brain b. heart c. kidneys d. lungs

_____ 15. A stroke can occur if an artery in the _____ is clogged.
a. brain b. heart c. liver d. lungs

_____ 16. When blood moves from an atrium to a ventricle, it must pass through a _____.
a. one-way valve b. murmur c. semilunar valve d. lymph node

_____ 17. _____, the liquid part of blood, is mostly made of water.
a. Hemoglobin b. Lymph c. Plasma d. Platelets

Assessment

L2

Test Practice Workbook

L2

Chapter Review

Name ______ Date ______ Class ______

Chapter Review **Circulation**

Part A. Vocabulary Review

Directions: *Complete the following sentences using the vocabulary words listed below.*

arteries	atria	capillaries
coronary circulation	hemoglobin	lymph
lymph nodes	lymphatic system	lymphocytes
plasma	platelets	veins
pulmonary circulation	ventricles	systemic circulation

1. The ____________ are the upper two chambers of the heart.
2. The two lower chambers of the heart are the ____________.
3. The blood vessels that move blood away from the heart are called ____________.
4. The blood vessels that move blood in the direction of the heart are called ____________.
5. ____________ are microscopic blood vessels that connect arteries and veins.
6. ____________ is the flow of blood through the heart and lungs.
7. ____________ moves blood to all tissues except the lungs and the heart.
8. ____________ is the liquid part of blood and is made mostly of water.
9. Red blood cells contain ____________, a chemical that can carry oxygen and carbon dioxide.
10. ____________ are the odd-shaped cell fragments that help clot blood.
11. ____________ is the flow of blood to the tissues of the heart.
12. The ____________ collects fluid from body tissue spaces and returns it to the blood through lymph capillaries and large lymph vessels.
13. ____________ filter out microorganisms and foreign materials.
14. Tissue fluid found inside lymphatic capillaries is known as ____________.
15. The tissue fluid inside lymphatic capillaries consists mostly of water, dissolved substances, and a type of white blood cell known as ____________.

Assessment

L2

Science Content Background

SECTION 1

The Circulatory System

How Materials Move Through the Body

In 1628, William Harvey published his findings, which indicated that blood in the human body follows "a motion as it were in a circle." Pumped by the heart, the blood moved through arteries into the body and returned to the heart via the veins. However, it was still a mystery how the blood made its way from the arteries, through tissues, and into the veins. Not until the invention of the microscope was it discovered that minute vessels, the capillaries, made the connection.

Fun Fact

It is estimated that it takes about 30 seconds for a particular blood cell to complete one circulation.

The Heart

The heart is a muscular organ that lies in the thoracic cavity between the lungs. It is enclosed by a protective sac of fibrous tissue, the pericardium.

The initiation of the heartbeat originates within the heart muscle. The sinoatrial node is a modified piece of cardiac muscle tissue located near the superior vena cava. An impulse for this node spreads to the atria of the heart, causing them to contract. Another node (atrioventricular) receives the signal and then transmits it to the ventricles, causing them to contract.

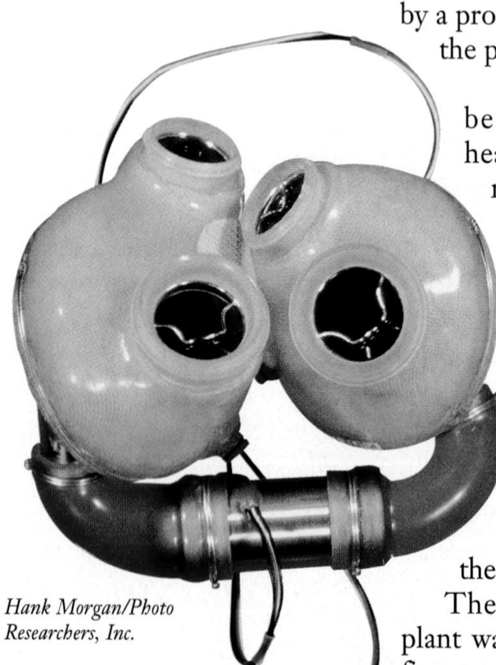

Hank Morgan/Photo Researchers, Inc.

The first human heart transplant was conducted in 1967. The first permanent artificial heart was implanted in 1982, but the patient lived for only three months afterward. In July 2001, a self-contained, battery-powered, titanium and plastic heart was successfully implanted into a man.

Blood Vessels

A cross section of arteries and veins shows that the walls have three layers. The inner lining of the vessels is covered with two types of tissue; one of these is a network of elastic connective tissue. The middle layer is smooth muscle and elastic tissue. The outer layer is collagenous connective tissue. The middle layer in veins is less developed than it is in arteries, and therefore collapses more easily. Capillaries have walls only one cell thick. This allows materials to diffuse through them. So numerous are the capillaries in the body that most cells are less than one fourth of a millimeter from a capillary.

Blood Pressure

The pressure in the blood vessels is the result of a greater amount of blood being pumped into the arteries than can be absorbed by the arterioles and capillaries. Blood pressure is measured in millimeters of mercury with a sphygmomanometer. The person taking the blood pressure is listening for the flow of blood to be cut off and then return to normal while taking note of the respective pressures.

SECTION 2

Blood

A Liquid Tissue

The liquid component of blood, plasma, is a complex solution of organic and inorganic substances dissolved in water. Blood is about 90 percent water and eight percent proteins. The remaining two percent is made up of dissolved substances such as electrolytes, gases, and nutrients. Blood characteristics such as pH and sugar content are precisely controlled by the body. The ph of blood is slightly alkaline, and

Fun Fact

The first known blood transfusion was conducted in the seventeenth century by a French physician. Jean Baptiste Denis infused sheep's blood into the patient.

serious problems can occur if the pH changes only slightly. Because blood supplies for transfusions often are in short supply, synthetic substitutes for blood or blood parts are being developed.

SECTION 3

The Lymphatic System

Understanding Tissue Fluid

The lymphatic system can be thought of as a branch of the circulatory system. Lymph is blood plasma that has diffused and filtered from the blood capillaries into the spaces between cells. Often the lymph in these spaces is referred to as intercellular or interstitial fluid. Like blood plasma, lymph consists mainly of water, some dissolved substances, and white blood cells called lymphocytes.

Lymph from the interstitial spaces passes through lymph capillaries, larger lymph vessels, lymph nodes, and lymph glands before entering a vein. Lymph is not under great pressure; therefore, external forces are needed to cause it to flow. Gravity plays a role in the movement of lymph above the heart. Other forces include the contraction of smooth muscles in the larger lymphatic vessels, the contraction of skeletal muscles, and the movements of breathing muscles. Backflow of lymph is prevented by valves in the large lymph vessels.

For additional content background on this topic, go to the Glencoe Science Web site at science.glencoe.com.

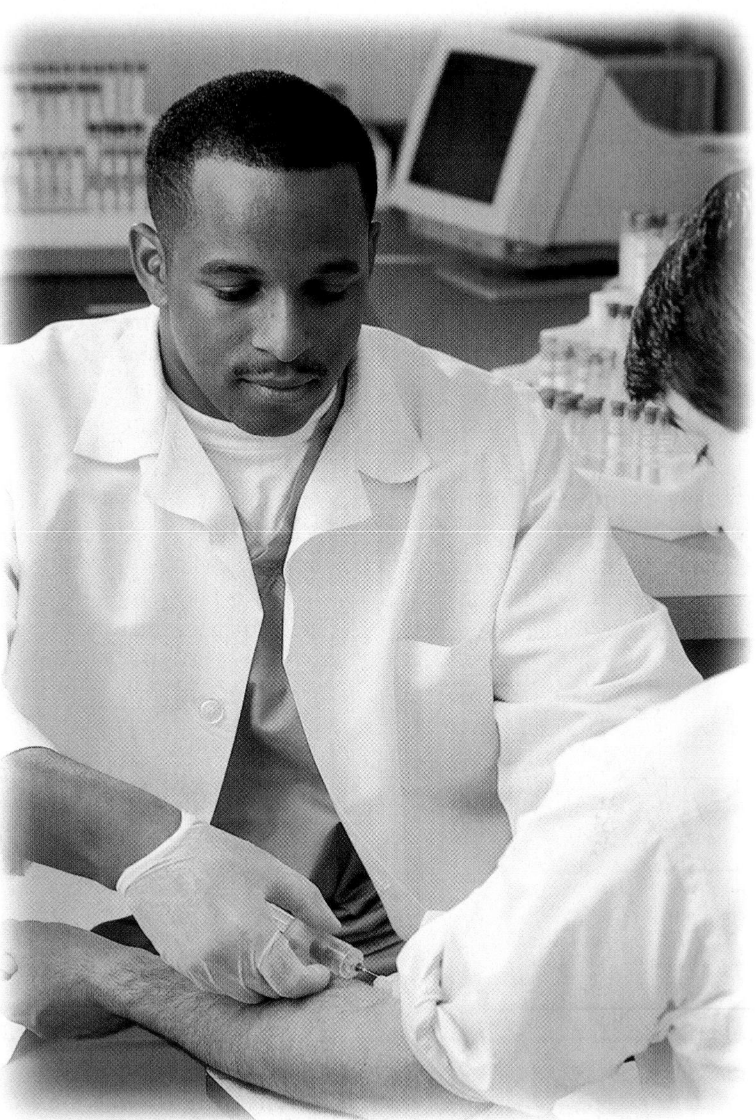

Charles Gupton/The Stock Market

When skin is subjected to continued friction or pressure, a blow, or heat, the blood capillaries dilate. Lymph accumulates in the injured area, and a liquid-filled blister is formed under the skin. If there is poor circulation in a region of the body, lymph may collect and cause a swelling called edema.

Fun Fact

The fluid in the ears is known as endolymph, but it is not true lymph fluid.

CHAPTER 19

Circulation

Chapter Vocabulary

atrium, p. 547
ventricle, p. 547
coronary circulation, p. 547
pulmonary circulation, p. 548
systemic circulation, p. 549
artery, p. 550
vein, p. 550
capillary, p. 551
plasma, p. 556
hemoglobin, p. 557
platelet, p. 557
lymph, p. 562
lymphatic system, p. 562
lymphocyte, p. 562
lymph node, p. 563

What do you think?

Science Journal This is a white blood cell attacking bacteria. White blood cells fight germs and other foreign substances that invade the body.

CHAPTER 19

Circulation

This interchange is simple compared to how blood travels within your body. In this chapter, you will discover how complex your circulatory system is. You'll learn what blood is made of and what it does for your body. You also will read about diseases that affect this body system. And you'll study a body system that helps protect you from disease.

What do you think?

Science Journal Look at the picture below. What do you think is happening? Here's a hint: *A part of your body is trying to protect itself.* Discuss your ideas with a classmate. Then, write your answer or best guess in your Science Journal.

544

Theme Connection

Stability and Change The circulatory system is a good example of a system that functions to maintain stability and respond to changes in human life processes.

If you look at an aerial view of a road system, as shown in the photograph, you see roads leading in many directions. These roads provide a way to carry people and goods from one place to another. Your circulatory system is like a road system. Just as roads are used to transport goods to homes and factories, your blood vessels transport substances throughout your body.

Recognize transportation

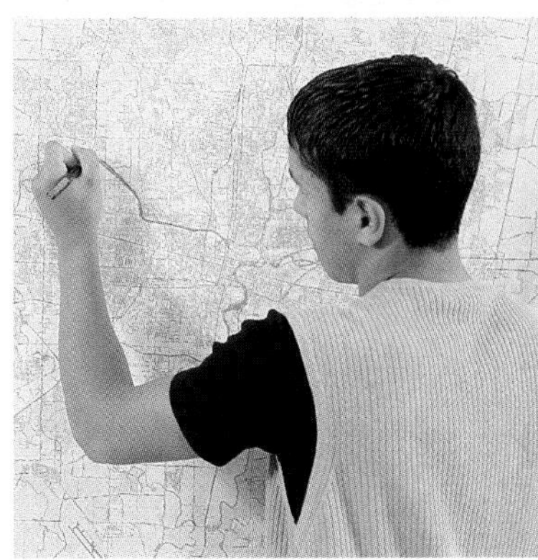

1. Observe a map of your city, county, or state.
2. Identify roads that are interstates, as well as state and county routes, using the map key.
3. Plan a route to a destination that your teacher describes. Then plan a different return trip.
4. Draw a diagram in your Science Journal showing your routes to and from the destination.

Observe

If the destination represents your heart, what do the routes represent? In your Science Journal draw a comparison between a blocked road on your map and a clogged artery in your body.

Before You Read

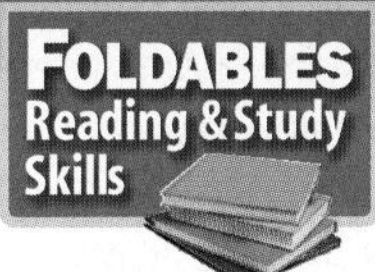

Making a Concept Map Study Fold **Make the following Foldable to help you organize information and diagram ideas about circulation.**

Circulation
Pulmonary
Coronary
Systemic

1. Place a sheet of paper in front of you so the long side is at the top. Fold the bottom of the paper to the top, stopping 4 cm from the top.
2. Fold both sides in to divide the paper into thirds and then unfold. Through the top thickness of paper, cut along each of the fold lines to form three tabs.
3. Draw an oval above the fold. Write *Circulation* inside the oval.
4. Draw three more ovals. Write the terms *Pulmonary*, *Coronary*, and *Systemic* as shown, and draw three arrows from the large oval to the smaller ovals.
5. As you read, write information about each system under its tab.

545

Explore Activity

Purpose Use the Explore Activity to help students model how the circulatory system transports substances throughout the body. L2 LS **Visual-Spatial**

Preparation Obtain enough maps so that each group can plan a route to and from a different destination.

Materials maps of your city, county, or state, Science Journal

Teaching Strategy Help students interpret the map key. Point out that colors as well as symbols can be used to denote different types of roads.

Observe

Possible answer: The routes represent the blood vessels that transport materials to and from the heart.

Assessment

Oral Again refer students to their map's legend. Have them infer why there are different types of roads and how they might be analogous to the circulatory system. Different types of roads carry different amounts of traffic at different speeds. They are analogous to different sizes of blood vessels in the body. Use **Performance Assessment in the Science Classroom,** p. 89.

Before You Read

FOLDABLES Reading & Study Skills

Dinah Zike Study Fold

Purpose Use this activity to determine what students know about the circulatory system before reading the chapter and to provide a Foldable for recording and organizing notes as they read.

For additional help, see Foldables Worksheet, p. 17 in **Chapter Resources Booklet,** or go to the Glencoe Science Web site at **science.glencoe.com.** See After You Read in the Study Guide at the end of this chapter.

SECTION

The Circulatory System

1 Motivate

Bellringer Transparency

Display the Section Focus Transparency for Section 1. Use the accompanying Transparency Activity Master. L2 ELL

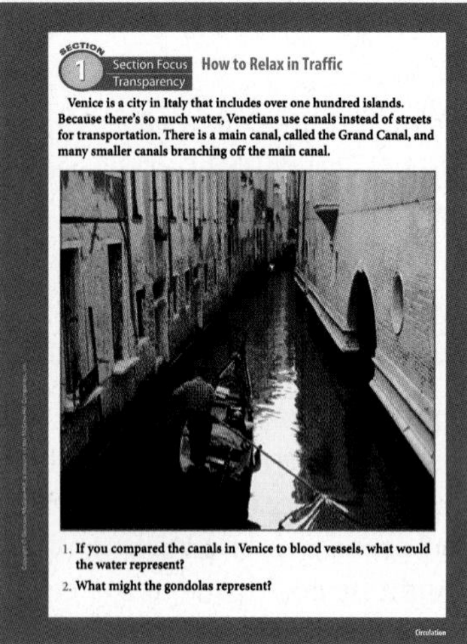

Section 1 Section Focus Transparency How to Relax in Traffic

Venice is a city in Italy that includes over one hundred islands. Because there's so much water, Venetians use canals instead of streets for transportation. There is a main canal, called the Grand Canal, and many smaller canals branching off the main canal.

1. If you compared the canals in Venice to blood vessels, what would the water represent?
2. What might the gondolas represent?

Tie to Prior Knowledge

Have students list the parts of a transportation system. They may suggest roads, trucks and other vehicles, and intersections. Explain that parts similar to these exist in their bodies to carry materials from place to place.

SECTION 1

The Circulatory System

As You Read

What You'll Learn

- **Compare and contrast** arteries, veins, and capillaries.
- **Explain** how blood moves through the heart.
- **Identify** the functions of the pulmonary and systemic circulation systems.

Vocabulary

atrium
ventricle
coronary circulation
pulmonary circulation
systemic circulation
artery
vein
capillary

Why It's Important

Your body's cells depend on the blood vessels to bring nutrients and remove wastes.

How Materials Move Through the Body

It's time to get ready for school, but your younger sister is taking a long time in the shower. "Don't use up all the water," you shout. Water is carried throughout your house in pipes that are part of the plumbing system. The plumbing system supplies water for all your needs and carries away wastes. Just as you expect water to flow when you turn on the faucet, your body needs a continuous supply of oxygen and nutrients and a way to remove wastes. In a similar way materials are moved throughout your body by your cardiovascular (kar dee oh VAS kyuh lur) system. It includes your heart, kilometers of blood vessels, and blood.

Blood vessels carry the blood to every part of your body, as shown in **Figure 1.** Blood moves oxygen and nutrients to cells and carries carbon dioxide and other wastes away from the cells. Sometimes the blood carries substances made in one part of the body to another part of the body where they are needed. Movement of materials into and out of your cells occurs by diffusion (dih FYEW zhun) and active transport. Diffusion occurs when a material moves from an area where there is more of it to an area where there is less of it. Active transport is the opposite of diffusion. Active transport requires energy, but diffusion does not.

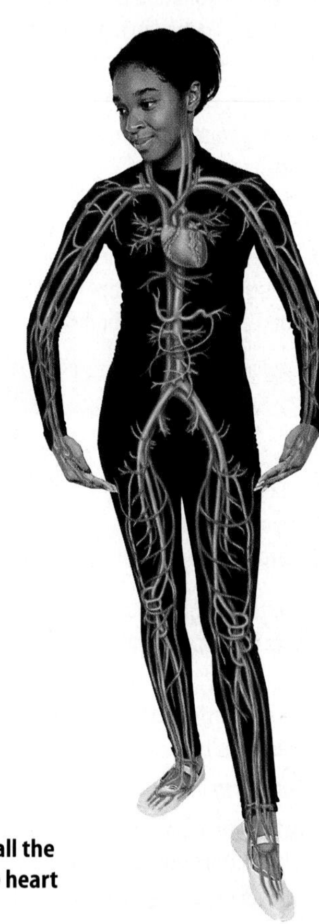

Figure 1
The blood is pumped by the heart to all the cells of the body and then back to the heart through a network of blood vessels.

546 CHAPTER 19 Circulation

Section Assessment Planner

PORTFOLIO
Assessment, p. 554

PERFORMANCE ASSESSMENT
Try at Home MiniLAB, p. 547
Skill Builder Activities, p. 554
See page 570 for more options.

CONTENT ASSESSMENT
Section, p. 554
Challenge, p. 554
Chapter, pp. 570–571

The Heart

Your heart is an organ made of cardiac muscle tissue. It is located behind your breastbone, called the sternum, and between your lungs. Your heart has four compartments called chambers. The two upper chambers are called the right and left **atriums** (AY tree umz). The two lower chambers are called the right and left **ventricles** (VEN trih kulz). During one heartbeat, both atriums contract at the same time. Then, both ventricles contract at the same time. A one-way valve separates each atrium from the ventricle below it. The blood flows only in one direction from an atrium to a ventricle, then from a ventricle into a blood vessel. A wall prevents blood from flowing between the two atriums or the two ventricles. This wall keeps blood rich in oxygen separate from blood low in oxygen. If oxygen-rich blood and oxygen-poor blood were to mix, your body's cells would not get all the oxygen they need.

Scientists have divided the circulatory system into three sections—coronary circulation, pulmonary (PUL muh ner ee) circulation, and systemic circulation. The beating of your heart controls blood flow through each section.

Coronary Circulation Your heart has its own blood vessels that supply it with nutrients and oxygen and remove wastes. **Coronary** (KOR uh ner ee) **circulation,** as shown in **Figure 2,** is the flow of blood to and from the tissues of the heart. When the coronary circulation is blocked, oxygen and nutrients cannot reach all the cells of the heart. This can result in a heart attack.

TRY AT HOME Mini LAB

Inferring How Hard the Heart Works

Procedure

1. Make a fist and observe its size, which is approximately the size of your heart.
2. Place your fist in a **bowl of water.** Then clench and unclench your fist to cause water to squirt out between your thumb and forefinger.
3. Continue the squeezing action for 3 min. Determine the number of squeezes per minute.

Analysis

1. How many times did you squeeze your fist in 1 min? A resting heart beats approximately 70 times per minute.
2. What can you do when the muscles of your hand and arm get tired? Explain why cardiac muscle cannot do the same.

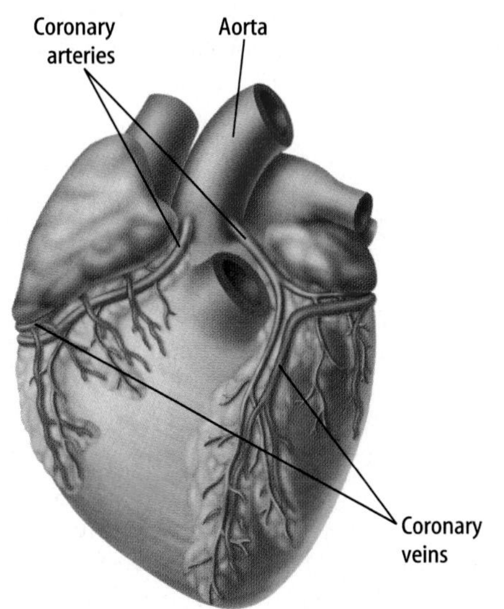

Figure 2
Like the rest of the body, the heart receives the oxygen and nutrients that it needs from the blood. The blood also carries away wastes from the heart's cells. On the diagram, you can see the coronary arteries, which nourish the heart.

2 Teach

The Heart

Quick Demo

To reinforce the actual position and size of the heart, make a closed fist with your right hand and hold it on your chest above your breastbone. Then ask each student to do the same.

Purpose Students explore heart rate. L2 ELL

LS **Logical-Mathematical**

Materials bowl of water, stopwatch or clock

Teaching Strategy Students must squeeze at a steady rate throughout the entire minute.

Troubleshooting Place newspaper around the bowl to absorb spilled water.

Analysis

1. Answers will vary, but most will find it difficult to maintain the 70 clenches per minute rate.
2. Students can stop or change hands when tired. The heart must beat continuously in order to maintain the body's activities.

Process Have students infer the tiring time for cardiac muscles and compare this with the tiring time for skeletal muscles. Use **PASC,** p. 89. P

Resource Manager 

Chapter Resources Booklet

Transparency Activity, p. 46

Directed Reading for Content Mastery, pp. 19, 20

MiniLAB, p. 3

Visual Learning

Figure 3 Direct students to trace the flow of blood through the heart. Then have them explain why this definition of veins is correct or incorrect: "Pulmonary veins are vessels that carry more carbon dioxide than oxygen." The statement is incorrect. In pulmonary circulation the veins carry more oxygen than carbon dioxide.
LS **Visual-Spatial**

Quick Demo

Obtain a beef heart for students to examine. Draw attention to the thick, muscular walls of the ventricles, which are necessary to supply a lifetime of pumping action. L1 LS **Visual-Spatial**

Use Science Words

Word Origins The body's largest artery is the aorta. The name has its origin in the Greek word *aorte,* meaning "to raise or lift." Discuss why this is an appropriate word for this vessel. The aorta rises from the top of the heart.

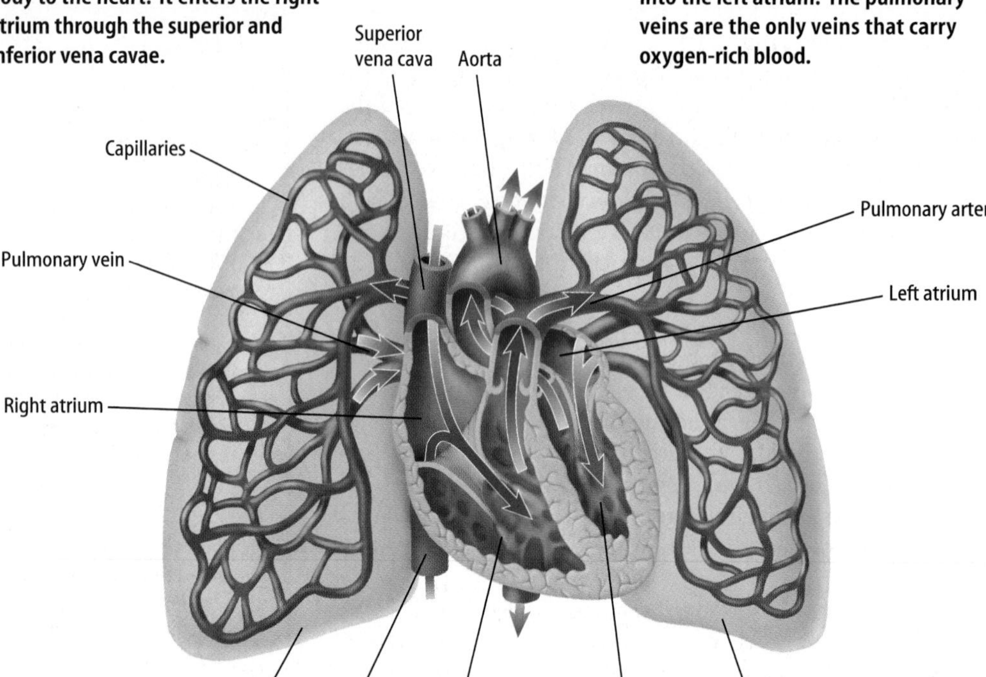

A Blood, high in carbon dioxide and low in oxygen, returns from the body to the heart. It enters the right atrium through the superior and inferior vena cavae.
C Oxygen-rich blood travels from the lungs through the pulmonary vein and into the left atrium. The pulmonary veins are the only veins that carry oxygen-rich blood.
Superior vena cava
Aorta
Capillaries
Pulmonary artery
Pulmonary vein
Left atrium
Right atrium
Right lung
Inferior vena cava
Right ventricle
Left ventricle
Left lung
B The right atrium contracts, forcing the blood into the right ventricle. When the right ventricle contracts, the blood leaves the heart and goes through the pulmonary artery to the lungs. The pulmonary arteries are the only arteries that carry blood that is high in carbon dioxide.
D The left atrium contracts and forces the blood into the left ventricle. The left ventricle contracts, forcing the blood out of the heart and into the aorta.

Figure 3
Pulmonary circulation moves blood between the heart and lungs.

Pulmonary Circulation The flow of blood through the heart to the lungs and back to the heart is **pulmonary circulation.** Use **Figure 3** to trace the path blood takes through this part of the circulatory system. The blood returning from the body through the right side of the heart and to the lungs contains cellular wastes. The wastes include molecules of carbon dioxide and other substances. In the lungs, gaseous wastes diffuse out of the blood, and oxygen diffuses into the blood. Then the blood returns to the left side of the heart. In the final step of pulmonary circulation, the oxygen-rich blood is pumped from the left ventricle into the aorta (ay OR tuh), the largest artery in your body. Next, the oxygen-rich blood flows to all parts of your body.

Active Reading

Double Bubble Map This strategy uses two bubble maps to compare concepts. Each cluster has qualities that are unique to that idea. In the middle, connecting ideas are similar to both cluster ideas. This technique helps students list common qualities before writing or discussing a topic. Have students design a Double Bubble Map about the circulatory system.

Sample map:

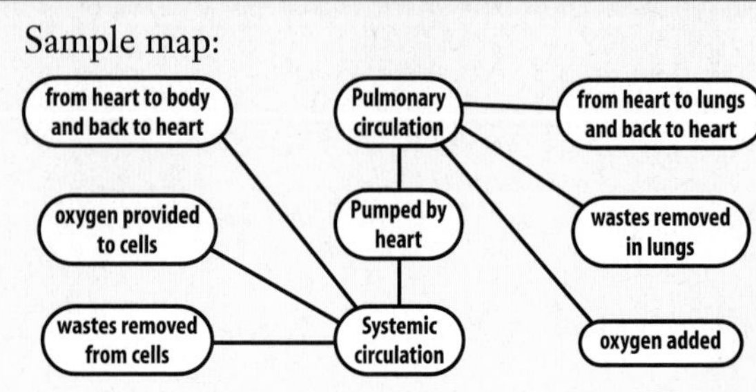

from heart to body and back to heart
Pulmonary circulation
from heart to lungs and back to heart
oxygen provided to cells
Pumped by heart
wastes removed in lungs
wastes removed from cells
Systemic circulation
oxygen added

Systemic Circulation Oxygen-rich blood moves to all of your organs and body tissues, except the heart and lungs, by **systemic circulation,** and oxygen-poor blood returns to the heart. Systemic circulation is the largest of the three sections of your circulatory system. **Figure 4** shows the major arteries (AR tuh reez) and veins (VAYNZ) of the systemic circulation system. Oxygen-rich blood flows from your heart in the arteries of this system. Then nutrients and oxygen are delivered by blood to your body cells and exchanged for carbon dioxide and wastes. Finally, the blood returns to your heart in the veins of the systemic circulation system.

Reading Check ***What are the functions of the systemic circulation system in your body?***

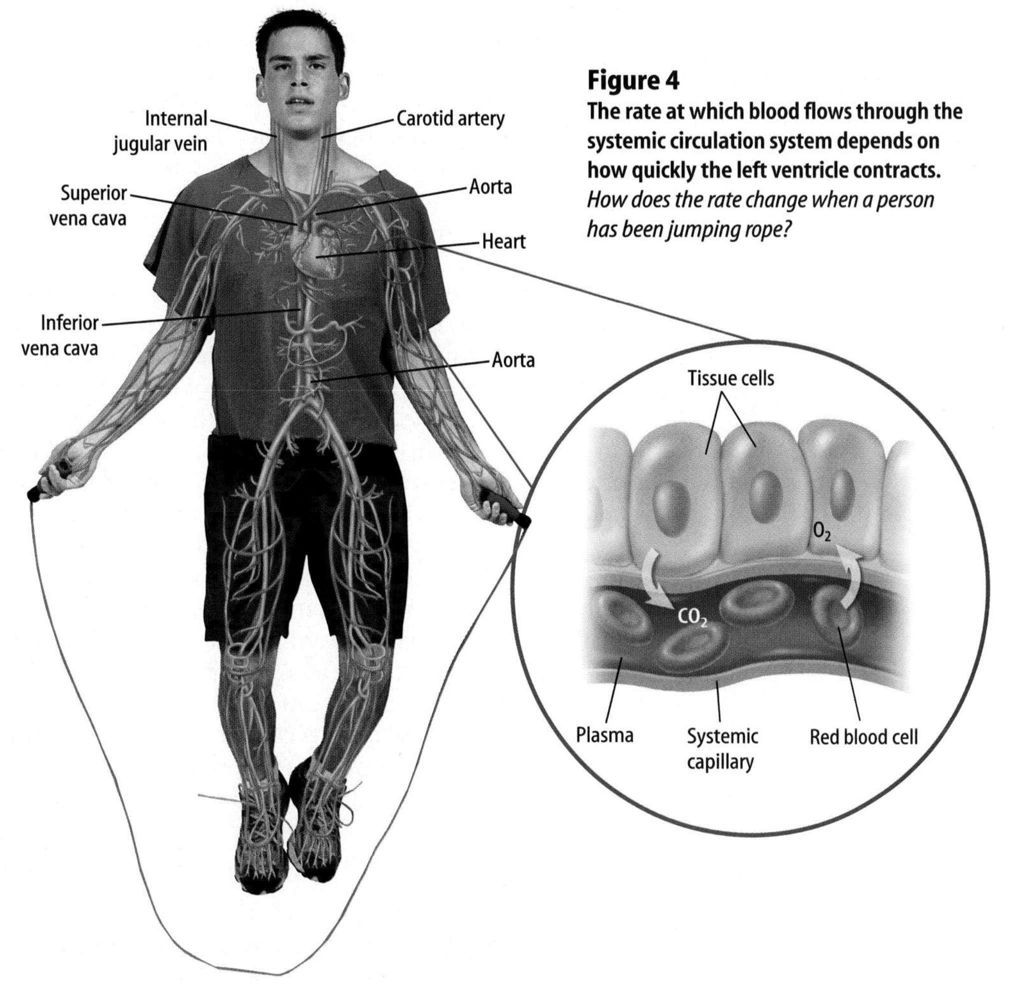

Figure 4
The rate at which blood flows through the systemic circulation system depends on how quickly the left ventricle contracts.
How does the rate change when a person has been jumping rope?

Reading Check

Answer It moves oxygen-rich blood to organs and body tissues, and returns oxygen-poor blood to the heart.

Caption Answer

Figure 4 The rate increases.

Use Science Words

Word Meaning Have students compare the architectural meaning of the word *atrium* with its biological meaning. In architectural use, the word atrium refers to an entrance hall or open court. In biological terms, the atrium is the entrance chamber that receives blood from the body.

Teacher FYI

Cardiac muscles do not directly absorb nutrients and oxygen from the blood that flows through the chambers of the heart. The right and left coronary arteries that branch off the aorta near its origin from the left ventricle supply nutrients and oxygen and remove wastes. In addition, the right coronary artery also supplies the sinoatrial and atrioventricular nodes responsible for coordinating the heartbeat.

Resource Manager

Chapter Resources Booklet
Note-taking Worksheets, pp. 33–37
Home and Community Involvement, p. 26

Inclusion Strategies

Visually Impaired Provide visually impaired students with a three-dimensional model of the heart and lungs. Have students trace with their fingers both pulmonary and coronary circulations. As they trace the flow of blood, have a sighted peer identify major vessels and chambers of the heart. L1 LS **Kinesthetic**

Blood Vessels

Fun Fact

All tissues in the body are nourished by materials from the circulatory system. Every cell is within 0.10 to 0.15 mm from a capillary. Some arteries have such thick walls that they have their own system of capillaries.

Activity

Have students prepare a brief report on how the one-cell thick capillary walls are held together and why a covering would not be practical. A cementing material holds the cells together. A covering would not easily allow materials to pass in and out of the walls. L2 LS **Logical-Mathematical**

Reading Check

Answer Arteries and veins have walls consisting of three layers of tissue. Arteries move blood away from the heart; veins move blood to the heart. Veins have valves that keep blood from flowing backward.

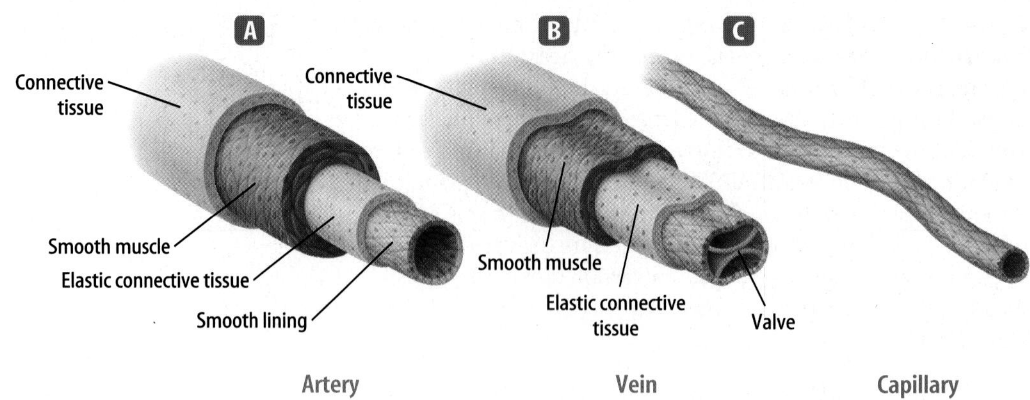

Figure 5
The structures of A arteries, B veins, and C capillaries are different. Valves in veins prevent blood from flowing backward. Capillaries are much smaller. Capillary walls are only one cell thick.

Blood Vessels

In the middle 1600s, scientists proved that blood moves in one direction in a blood vessel, like traffic on a one-way street. They discovered that blood moves by the pumping of the heart and flows from arteries to veins. But, they couldn't explain how blood gets from arteries to veins. Using a new invention of that time, the microscope, scientists discovered capillaries (KAP uh ler eez), the connection between arteries and veins.

Arteries As blood is pumped out of the heart, it travels through arteries, capillaries, and then veins. **Arteries** are blood vessels that carry blood away from the heart. Arteries, shown in **Figure 5A,** have thick, elastic walls made of connective tissue and smooth muscle tissue. Each ventricle of the heart is connected to an artery. The right ventricle is connected to the pulmonary artery, and the left ventricle is attached to the aorta. Every time your heart contracts, blood is moved from your heart into arteries.

Veins The blood vessels that carry blood back to the heart are called **veins,** as shown in **Figure 5B.** Veins have one-way valves that keep blood moving toward the heart. If blood flows backward, the pressure of the blood against the valves causes them to close. The flow of blood in veins also is helped by your skeletal muscles. When skeletal muscles contract, the veins in these muscles are squeezed and help blood move toward the heart. Two major veins return blood from your body to your heart. The superior vena cava returns blood from your head and neck. Blood from your abdomen and lower body returns through the inferior vena cava.

Reading Check *What are the similarities and differences between arteries and veins?*

Science Journal

Have students write brief descriptions in their own words of arteries, veins, and capillaries. Ask them to write a paragraph contrasting these three types of blood vessels. LS **Linguistic**

Capillaries Arteries and veins are connected by microscopic blood vessels called **capillaries,** as shown in **Figure 5C.** The walls of capillaries are only one cell thick. You can see capillaries when you have a bloodshot eye. They are the tiny red lines you see in the white area of your eye. Nutrients and oxygen diffuse into body cells through the thin capillary walls. Waste materials and carbon dioxide diffuse from body cells into the capillaries.

Blood Pressure

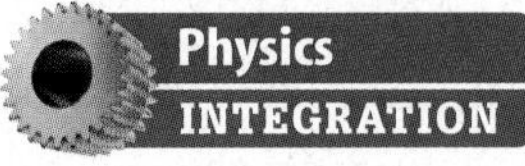

If you fill a balloon with water and then push on it, the pressure moves through the water in all directions, as shown in **Figure 6.** Your circulatory system is like the water balloon. When your heart pumps blood through the circulatory system, the pressure of the push moves through the blood. The force of the blood on the walls of the blood vessels is called blood pressure. This pressure is highest in arteries and lowest in veins. When you take your pulse, you can feel the waves of pressure. This rise and fall of pressure occurs with each heartbeat. Normal resting pulse rates are 60 to 100 heartbeats per minute for adults, and 80 to 100 beats per minute for children.

Measuring Blood Pressure Blood pressure is measured in large arteries and is expressed by two numbers, such as 120 over 80. The first number is a measure of the pressure caused when the ventricles contract and blood is pushed out of the heart. This is called the systolic (sihs TAHL ihk) pressure. Then, blood pressure drops as the ventricles relax. The second number is a measure of the diastolic (di uh STAHL ihk) pressure that occurs as the ventricles fill with blood just before they contract again.

Controlling Blood Pressure Your body tries to keep blood pressure normal. Special nerve cells in the walls of some arteries sense changes in blood pressure. When pressure is higher or lower than normal, messages are sent to your brain by these nerve cells. Then messages are sent by your brain to raise or lower blood pressure—by speeding up or slowing the heart rate for example. This helps keep blood pressure constant within your arteries. When blood pressure is constant, enough blood reaches all organs and tissues in your body and delivers needed nutrients to every cell.

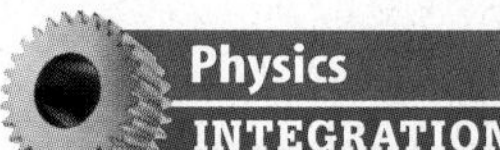

Some molecules of nutrients are forced through capillary walls by the force of blood pressure. What is the cause of the pressure? Discuss your answer with a classmate. Then write your answer in your Science Journal.

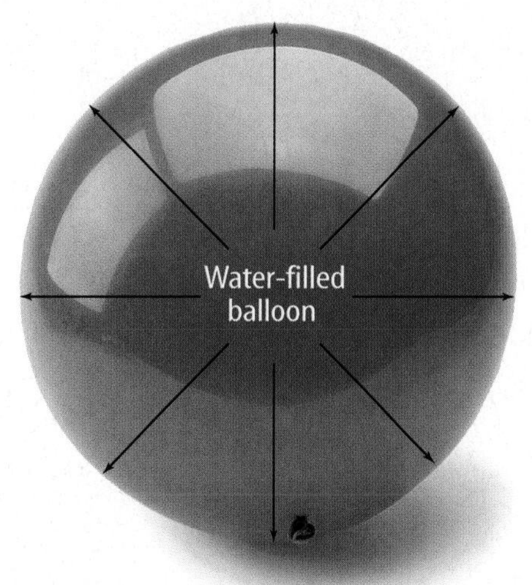

Figure 6
When pressure is exerted on a fluid in a closed container, the pressure is transmitted through the liquid in all directions. Your circulatory system is like a closed container.

Blood Pressure

Blood pressure, a force produced by the pumping action of the heart, is exerted by the blood against the walls of the blood vessels. Blood pressure tends to force fluids into capillaries at their artery end (where blood pressure is higher); osmosis tends to force water out of capillaries at their venous end (where blood pressure is lower).

Fun Fact

Systolic pressure is the peak pressure of blood flow caused by the contraction of the ventricles. Diastolic pressure is the low pressure of blood flow produced when the heart relaxes.

Teacher FYI

The term *pressure* is used in discussions of fluids such as gases and liquids. Pressure is produced when a force is applied to a fluid. The greater the force, the greater the pressure on the fluid, and the smaller the volume it takes up. Usually, the volume of a gas decreases by one-half when the pressure doubles. The volume of liquids changes less dramatically.

Resource Manager

Chapter Resources Booklet
Lab Activity, pp. 9–12

Life Science Critical Thinking/Problem Solving, p. 17

NATIONAL GEOGRAPHIC

Visualizing Atherosclerosis

Have students examine the pictures and read the captions. Then ask the following questions.

How do you think a person with restricted arteries would feel while lifting a heavy object? Possible answers: short of breath, difficulty breathing, dizzy, light-headed, tiring quickly, chest pain.

How do medicines that thin the blood help a person who is suffering from atherosclerosis? Possible answer: The thinner blood will be able to pass more easily through a restricted passage.

Activity

Have students keep a log of all the foods they eat for a few days. Then have them identify foods they have eaten that are high in fat or cholesterol or both. Have them think of low fat substitutes for those foods.

Extension

Have students find statistics on atherosclerosis. This can include percentages in categories such as age, race, gender, countries, or other characteristics that may be associated with the condition.

NATIONAL GEOGRAPHIC **VISUALIZING ATHEROSCLEROSIS**

Figure 7

Healthy blood vessels have smooth, unobstructed interiors like the one at the right. Atherosclerosis is a disease in which fatty substances build up in the walls of arteries, such as the coronary arteries that supply the heart muscle with oxygen-rich blood. As illustrated below, these fatty deposits can gradually restrict—and ultimately block—the life-giving river of blood that flows through an artery.

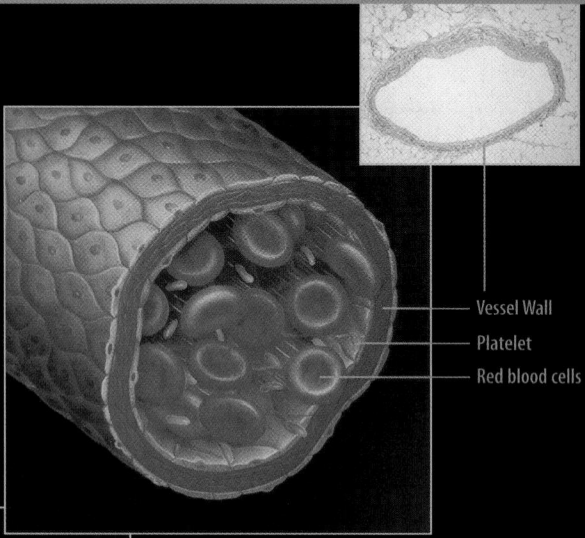

Vessel Wall
Platelet
Red blood cells

▲ HEALTHY ARTERY The illustration and photo above show a normal functioning artery.

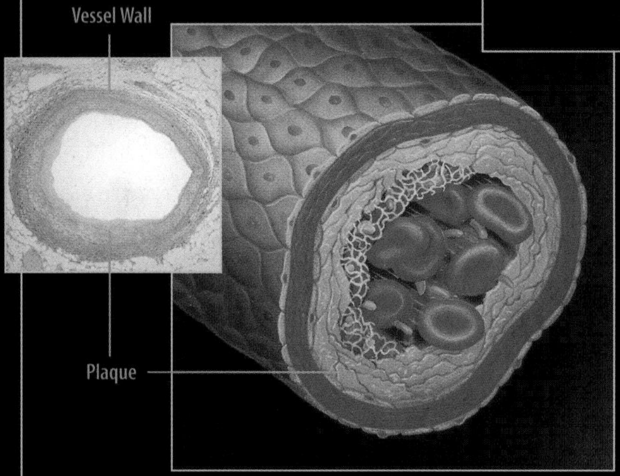

Vessel Wall
Plaque

◀ PARTIALLY CLOGGED ARTERY The illustration and inset photo at left show fatty deposits, called plaques, that have formed along the artery's inner wall. As the diagram illustrates, plaques narrow the pathway through the artery, restricting and slowing blood flow. As blood supply to the heart muscle cells dwindles, they become starved for oxygen and nutrients.

Vessel Wall
Plaque

▶ NEARLY BLOCKED ARTERY In the illustration and photo at right, fatty deposits have continued to build. The pathway through the coronary artery has gradually narrowed until blood flow is very slow and nearly blocked. Under these conditions, the heart muscle cells supplied by the artery are greatly weakened. If blood flow stops entirely, a heart attack will result.

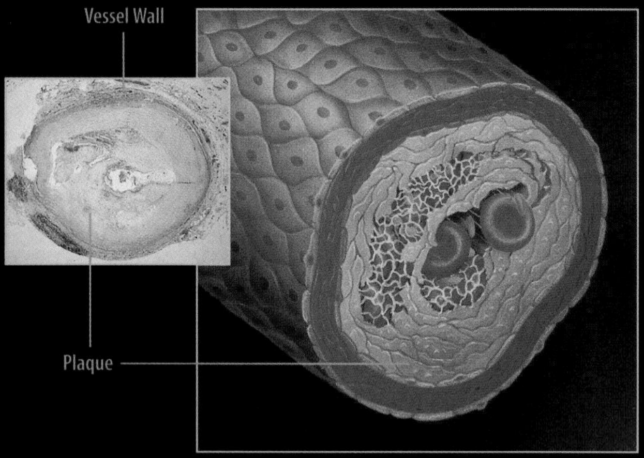

552 CHAPTER 19

Resource Manager

Chapter Resources Booklet

Reinforcement, p. 27

Lab Activity, pp. 13–16

Internet Addresses

Explore the Glencoe Science Web site at **science.glencoe.com** to find out more about topics in this section.

Cardiovascular Disease

Any disease that affects the cardiovascular system—the heart, blood vessels, and blood—can seriously affect the health of your entire body. People often think of cancer and automobile accidents as the leading causes of death in the United States. However, heart disease is the leading cause of death.

Atherosclerosis One leading cause of heart disease is called atherosclerosis (ah thur oh skluh ROH sus). In this condition, shown in **Figure 7,** fatty deposits build up on arterial walls. Eating foods high in cholesterol and saturated fats can cause these deposits to form. Atherosclerosis can occur in any artery in the body, but deposits in coronary arteries are especially serious. If a coronary artery is blocked, a heart attack can occur. Open heart surgery may then be needed to correct the problem.

Hypertension Another condition of the cardiovascular system is called hypertension (HI pur ten chun), or high blood pressure. **Figure 8** shows the instruments used to measure blood pressure. When blood pressure is higher than normal most of the time, extra strain is placed on the heart. The heart must work harder to keep blood flowing. One cause of hypertension is atherosclerosis. A clogged artery can increase pressure within the vessel. The walls become stiff and hard, like a metal pipe. The artery walls no longer contract and dilate easily because they have lost their elasticity.

Heart Failure Heart failure results when the heart cannot pump blood efficiently. It might be caused when heart muscle tissue is weakened by disease or when heart valves do not work properly. When the heart does not pump blood properly, fluids collect in the arms, legs, and lungs. People with heart failure usually are short of breath and tired.

Reading Check *What is heart failure?*

Research Visit the Glencoe Science Web site at **science.glencoe.com** for recent news or magazine articles about cardiovascular disease. Write a paragraph in your Science Journal about steps you can take to lead a healthy lifestyle.

Figure 8
Blood pressure is measured in large arteries using a blood pressure cuff and stethoscope.

Cardiovascular Disease

IDENTIFYING Misconceptions

Cholesterol is a steroid lipid that is the main component of fatty deposits, *atheroma*, in arteries. Some students will assume that any cholesterol is unhealthy. In fact, the liver produces cholesterol. It is a component of nerve cells, and it is involved in the synthesis of certain hormones. Normal levels of cholesterol are essential for good health.

Use an Analogy

The buildup of fatty deposits in the walls of arteries is similar to the buildup of lime deposits in plumbing pipes. In both cases, the pathway is narrowed and the flow is reduced. If possible, show students an old pipe that is full of this type of deposit.

Fun Fact

Not all persons with atherosclerosis suffer discomfort. Sometimes even those with a severe condition do not have any symptoms.

Reading Check

Answer Heart failure occurs when the heart cannot pump blood efficiently.

LAB DEMONSTRATION

Purpose to compare the flow of liquid through an open tube and a partially blocked tube

Materials two 10-cm pieces of plastic tubing, dropper, mineral oil, modeling clay, tweezers

Preparation Be sure there is enough clay to impede but not stop the flow of oil.

Procedure Insert a dropper full of oil into the tubing. Squeeze the oil through the tubing. Observe the amount of oil that comes out. Compare this to the amount of oil that comes out of a clay-clogged tube.

Expected Outcome Students will observe less oil escape from the clogged tube.

Assessment

How does this demonstrate what happens in clogged arteries? The clay represents deposits that may collect on the walls of arteries. Blood flow in these tubes is slower, and blocked tubes can carry less blood than unblocked tubes.

Cardiovascular Disease, continued

Discussion

Why might a food label that proclaims the item has little or no cholesterol be a poor choice for a healthful diet? Foods rated low in cholesterol may be very high in fat and have a negative effect on the cardiovascular system.

3 Assess

Reteach

Show students a piece of flexible garden hose. Have them explain how the walls of the hose are similar to the walls of an artery. Both have structures that provide strength and flexibility. L1 ELL LS **Visual-Spatial**

Challenge

Galen (born in A.D. 129) was a physician and scientist who wrote about the heart and circulation of blood. Have students find out three things that Galen discovered about the circulatory system as he dissected different animals. Galen described heart valves in detail, noted the differences between arteries and veins, and showed that arteries carry blood, not air, as had been thought for 400 years.

Assessment

Content Have students make a concept map describing the flow of the blood through the three types of vessels. Use **Performance Assessment in the Science Classroom,** p. 161. P

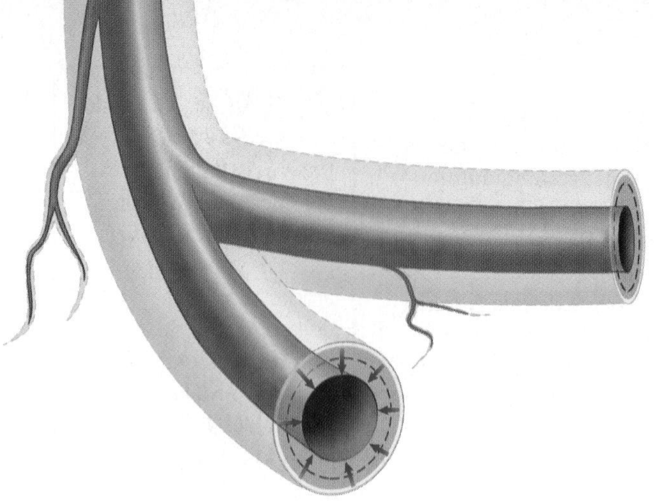

Figure 9
Nicotine, present in tobacco, contracts blood vessels and causes the body to release hormones that raise blood pressure.

Preventing Cardiovascular Disease Having a healthy lifestyle is important for the health of your cardiovascular system. The choices you make to maintain good health may reduce your risk of future serious illness. Regular checkups, a healthful diet, and exercise are part of a heart-healthy lifestyle.

Many diseases, including cardiovascular disease, can be prevented by following a good diet. Choose foods that are low in salt, sugar, cholesterol, and saturated fats. Being overweight is associated with heart disease and high blood pressure. Large amounts of body fat force the heart to pump faster.

Learning to relax and having a regular program of exercise can help prevent tension and relieve stress. Exercise also strengthens the heart and lungs, helps in controlling cholesterol, tones muscles, and helps lower blood pressure.

Another way to prevent cardiovascular disease is to not smoke. Smoking causes blood vessels to contract, as shown in **Figure 9,** and makes the heart beat faster and harder. Smoking also increases carbon monoxide levels in the blood. Not smoking helps prevent heart disease and a number of respiratory system problems, too.

Section 1 Assessment

1. Compare and contrast the structure of the three types of blood vessels.
2. Explain the pathway of blood through the heart.
3. Contrast pulmonary and systemic circulation. Identify which vessels carry oxgen-rich blood.
4. Explain how exercise can help prevent heart disease.
5. **Think Critically** What waste product builds up in blood and cells when the heart is unable to pump blood efficiently?

Skill Builder Activities

6. **Concept Mapping** Make an events chain concept map to show pulmonary circulation beginning at the right atrium and ending at the aorta. **For more help, refer to the** Science Skill Handbook.
7. **Using a Database** Research diseases of the circulatory system. Make a database showing what part of the circulatory system is affected by each disease. Categories should include the organs and vessels of the circulatory system. **For more help, refer to the** Technology Skill Handbook.

Answers to Section Assessment

1. All transport blood. Arteries have thick walls. Veins have valves. Capillary walls are only one cell thick.
2. right atrium, right ventricle, lungs, left atrium, left ventricle
3. Pulmonary circulation transports blood through the heart and to the lungs and back to the heart; veins carry oxygen-rich blood. Systemic circulation transports blood to all parts of the body and back to the heart; arteries carry oxygen-rich blood.
4. It strengthens the heart and lungs, helps control cholesterol, and lowers blood pressure.
5. carbon dioxide
6. Map should show blood moving in this order: right atrium, right ventricle, pulmonary artery, lungs, pulmonary vein, left atrium, left ventricle, aorta.
7. Sample entries: atherosclerosis—arteries; myocardial infarction—heart; leukemia—white blood cells

Activity

The Heart as a Pump

The heart is a pumping organ. Blood is forced through the arteries as heart muscles contract and then relax. This creates a series of waves in blood as it flows through the arteries. These waves are called the pulse. Try this activity to learn how physical activity affects your pulse.

What You'll Investigate

What does the pulse rate tell you about the work of the heart?

Materials

watch or clock with a second hand
*stopwatch
*Alternate materials

Goals

- **Observe** pulse rate.
- **Compare** pulse rate at rest to rate after jogging.

Data Table

Pulse Rate		
Pulse Rate	**Partner's**	**Yours**
At Rest	about 70	about 70
After Jogging	answers will vary	answers will vary

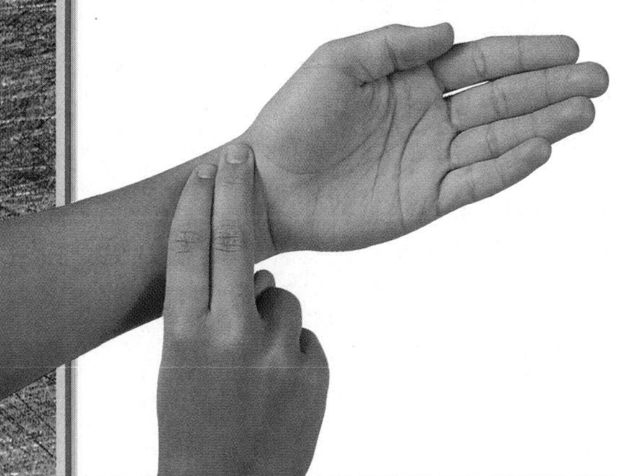

Procedure

1. Make a table like the one shown. Use it to record your data.
2. Sit down to take your pulse. Your partner will serve as the recorder.
3. Find your pulse by placing your middle and index fingers over the radial artery in your wrist as shown in the photo.
   WARNING: *Do not press too hard.*
4. **Count** each beat of the radial pulse silently for 15 s. Multiply the number of beats by four to find your pulse rate per minute. Have your partner record the number in the data table.
5. Now jog in place for 1 min and take your pulse again. Count the beats for 15 s.
6. **Calculate** this new pulse rate and have your partner record it in the data table.
7. Reverse roles with your partner and repeat steps 2 through 6.
8. **Collect** and record the new data.

Conclude and Apply

1. How does the pulse rate change?
2. What causes the pulse rate to change?
3. What can you infer about the heart as a pumping organ?

Communicating Your Data

Record the class average for pulse rate at rest and after jogging. Compare the class averages to your data. **For more help, refer to the Science Skill Handbook.**

Communicating Your Data

Prepare a graph of the class data and include the class average. Compare the data from your classroom with those of another classroom in your school.

Resource Manager

Chapter Resources Booklet
Activity Worksheet, pp. 5–6

Activity

BENCH TESTED

Purpose Students measure radial pulse rate and interpret their data. L2 ELL COOP LEARN
LS **Logical-Mathematical**

Process Skills interpreting data, communicating, making and using graphs, using numbers, inferring

Time Required 30–40 minutes

Safety Precautions Caution students not to press too hard. Students with heart conditions should not jog.

Teaching Strategies

- Encourage all students to perform some activity to increase their heart rate unless medically unadvisable. Suggest that these students be the timekeeper and recorder for a pair of students.
- Students should count their pulses silently and then report results to the recorder.
- Explain the reason for multiplying by four to obtain the pulse rate for one minute (15 s $\times$ 4 = 60 s or one min).

Answers to Questions

1. Pulse rate increases as they jog.
2. Greater muscle activity requires the heart to pump more blood (and thus more oxygen) to the muscles.
3. The heart pumps blood to the body to meet all of its needs—both when at rest and when active.

Assessment

Performance Have students design another activity that will result in an increased pulse rate (i.e., dancing or shooting baskets). Have them do the activity and gather and interpret their data. Use **PASC,** p. 95. P

SECTION 2

Blood

1 Motivate

Bellringer Transparency

Display the Section Focus Transparency for Section 2. Use the accompanying Transparency Activity Master. L2 ELL

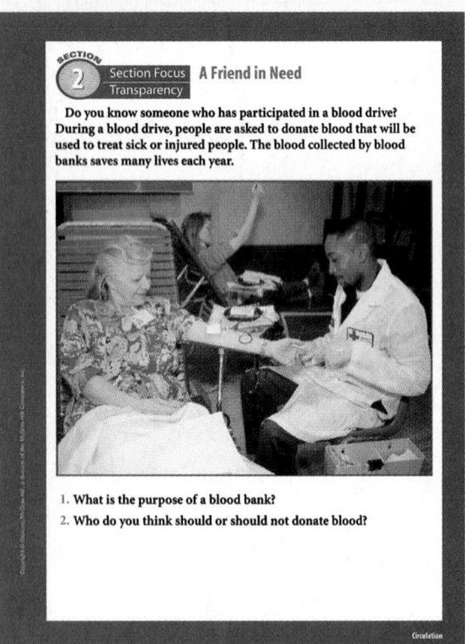

Tie to Prior Knowledge

Fill five 1-L plastic soft drink bottles with red-colored water. Explain to students that this volume of water represents the 5 L of blood in an adult.

Text Question Answer

Blood could be referred to as the tissue of life because it carries oxygen and nutrients to your cells. It also carries waste products to your kidneys to be removed and helps fight infections and heal wounds.

Blood

As You Read

What **You'll Learn**

- **Identify** the parts and functions of blood.
- **Explain** why blood types are checked before a transfusion.
- **Give examples** of diseases of blood.

Vocabulary
plasma
hemoglobin
platelet

Why **It's Important**

Blood plays a part in every major activity of your body.

Functions of Blood

You take a last, deep, calming breath before plunging into a dark, vessel-like tube. Water is everywhere. You take a hard right turn, then left as you streak through a narrow tunnel of twists and turns. The water transports you down the slide much like the way blood carries substances to all parts of your body. Blood has four important functions.

1. Blood carries oxygen from your lungs to all your body cells. Carbon dioxide diffuses from your body cells into your blood. Your blood carries carbon dioxide to your lungs to be exhaled.
2. Blood carries waste products from your cells to your kidneys to be removed.
3. Blood transports nutrients and other substances to your body cells.
4. Cells and molecules in blood fight infections and help heal wounds.

Anything that disrupts or changes these functions affects all the tissues of your body. Can you understand why blood is sometimes called the tissue of life?

Figure 10
The blood in this graduated cylinder has separated into its parts. Each part plays a key role in body functions.

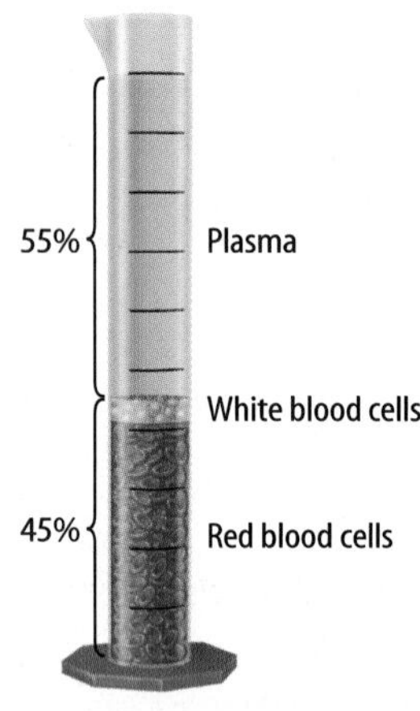

Parts of Blood

A close look at blood tells you that blood is not just a red-colored liquid. Blood is a tissue made of plasma (PLAZ muh), red and white blood cells, and platelets (PLAYT luts), as shown in **Figure 10.** Blood makes up about eight percent of your body's total mass. If you weigh 45 kg, you have about 3.6 kg of blood moving through your body. The amount of blood in an adult would fill five 1-L bottles. If this volume decreases rapidly because of an injury or disease, blood pressure will fall and the body may go into shock.

Plasma The liquid part of blood, which is made mostly of water is called **plasma.** It makes up more than half the volume of blood. Nutrients, minerals, and oxygen are dissolved in plasma so that they can be carried to body cells. Wastes from body cells are also carried in plasma.

Section Assessment Planner

PORTFOLIO
Science Journal, p. 558

PERFORMANCE ASSESSMENT
MiniLAB, p. 558
Skill Builder Activities, p. 561
See page 570 for more options.

CONTENT ASSESSMENT
Section, p. 561
Challenge, p. 561
Chapter, pp. 570–571

556 CHAPTER 19 Circulation

Blood Cells A cubic millimeter of blood has about 5 million red blood cells. These disk-shaped blood cells, shown in **Figure 11,** are different from other cells in your body because they have no nuclei. They contain **hemoglobin** (HEE muh gloh bun), which is a molecule that carries oxygen and carbon dioxide. Hemoglobin carries oxygen from your lungs to your body cells. Then it carries some of the carbon dioxide from your body cells back to your lungs. The rest of the carbon dioxide is carried in the cytoplasm of red blood cells and in plasma. Red blood cells have a life span of about 120 days. They are made at a rate of 2 million to 3 million per second in the center of long bones like the femur in your thigh. Red blood cells wear out and are destroyed at about the same rate.

In contrast to red blood cells, a cubic millimeter of blood has about 5,000 to 10,000 white blood cells. White blood cells fight bacteria, viruses, and other invaders of your body. Your body reacts to invaders by increasing the number of white blood cells. These cells leave the blood through capillary walls and go into the tissues that have been invaded. Here, they destroy bacteria and viruses and absorb dead cells. The life span of white blood cells varies from a few days to many months.

Circulating with the red and white blood cells are platelets. **Platelets** are irregularly shaped cell fragments that help clot blood. A cubic millimeter of blood can contain as many as 400,000 platelets. Platelets have a life span of five to nine days.

SCIENCE Online

Research Visit the Glencoe Science Web site at **science.glencoe.com** for more information about the types of human white blood cells and their functions. Communicate to your class what you learn.

Figure 11
Red blood cells supply your body with oxygen, and white blood cells and platelets have protective roles.

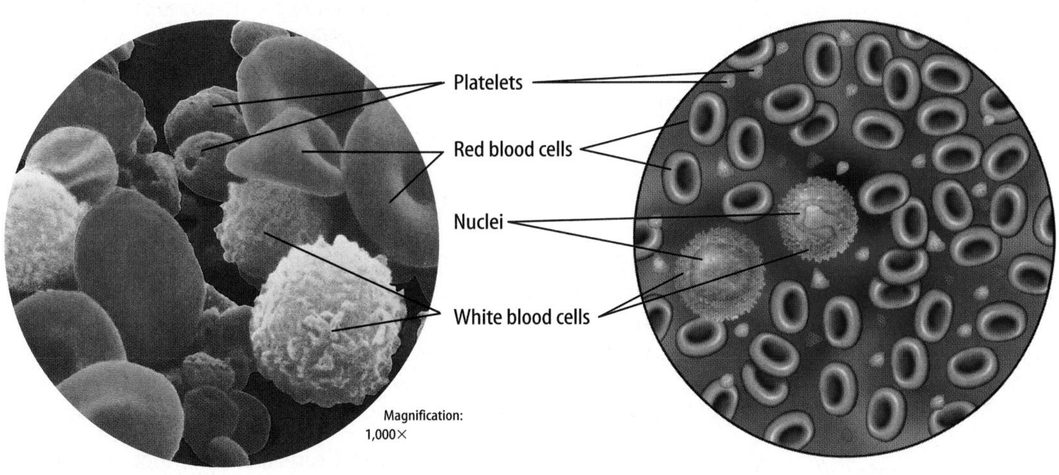

A **Platelets help stop bleeding. Platelets not only plug holes in small vessels, they also release chemicals that help form filaments of fibrin.**

B **Several types, sizes, and shapes of white blood cells exist. These cells destroy bacteria, viruses, and foreign substances.**

2 Teach

Parts of Blood

Make a Model

Have students make models of red and white blood cells from modeling clay. Encourage students to make the models to scale in order to reinforce concepts about the relative sizes, shapes, and colors of the cells. L2 LS **Visual-Spatial**

Use an Analogy

Have students view a film clip of amoeba activity to draw an analogy to white blood cell movement and ingestion.

Discussion

How do blood platelets function in maintaining homeostasis when the skin is cut? Platelets form clots to help prevent further blood loss.

SCIENCE Online

Internet Addresses

Explore the Glencoe Science Web site at **science.glencoe.com** to find out more about topics in this section.

Resource Manager

Chapter Resources Booklet
- Transparency Activity, p. 47
- Directed Reading for Content Mastery, p. 20

Mathematics Skill Activities, p. 33

Science Journal

CPR Have students find out what *CPR* stands for, analyze the parts of the words to determine their meanings, and then describe this technique in their journals. CPR stands for cardiopulmonary resuscitation. Cardio = heart; pulmonary = lungs; resuscitation = to revive. CPR is an emergency procedure that includes clearing air passages, mouth-to-mouth resuscitation, and heart massage. L2

Blood Clotting

Purpose Students use a model to discover how a scab forms. L2 ELL IS **Visual-Spatial**

Materials 5-cm × 5-cm square of gauze, aluminum foil, liquid bandage solution, dropper, water

Teaching Strategy Explain that the gauze represents the fibers formed in the clotting process.

Analysis

1. The water soaks into the untreated gauze but not into the treated area.
2. The treated area is like a scab because it forms a covering that prevents leakage of liquids and protects the area underneath it.

Assessment

Process Have students use cotton cloth and white glue to make another model of scab formation and repeat the water drop test. Use **PASC,** p. 123.

Discussion

Why would relatively minor cuts and bruises be hazardous to a person with hemophilia? Even minor cuts and bruises would cause major bleeding problems that could result in death.

Reading Check

Answer platelets, clotting factors, and fibrin

Figure 12

A When the skin is damaged, a sticky blood clot seals the leaking blood vessel. B Eventually, a scab forms to protect the wound from further damage and allow it to heal.

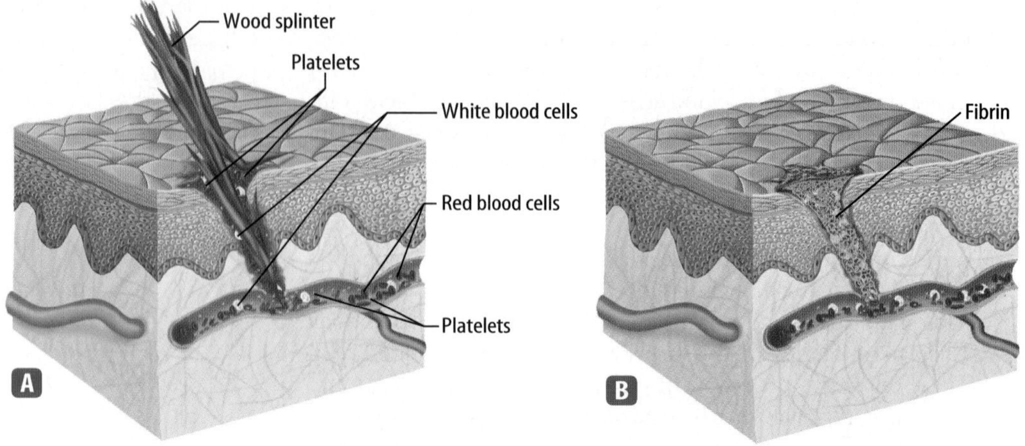

Wood splinter
Platelets
White blood cells
Red blood cells
Platelets
Fibrin
A
B

Mini LAB

Modeling Scab Formation

Procedure

1. Place a 5-cm × 5-cm square of **gauze** on a piece of **aluminum foil.**
2. Place several drops of a **liquid bandage solution** onto the gauze and let it dry. Keep the liquid bandage away from eyes and mouth.
3. Use a **dropper** to place one drop of **water** onto the area of the liquid bandage. Place another drop of water in another area of the gauze.

Analysis

1. Compare the drops of water in both areas.
2. Describe how the treated area of the gauze is like a scab.

Blood Clotting

You're running with your dog in a park, when all of a sudden you trip and fall down. Your knee starts to bleed, but the bleeding stops quickly. Already the wounded area has begun to heal. Bleeding stops because platelets and clotting factors in your blood make a blood clot that plugs the wounded blood vessels. A blood clot also acts somewhat like a bandage. When you cut yourself, platelets stick to the wound and release chemicals. Then substances called clotting factors carry out a series of chemical reactions. These reactions cause threadlike fibers called fibrin (FI brun) to form a sticky net, as shown in **Figure 12.** This net traps escaping blood cells and plasma and forms a clot. The clot helps stop more blood from escaping. After the clot is in place and becomes hard, skin cells begin the repair process under the scab. Eventually, the scab is lifted off. Bacteria that might get into the wound during the healing process are destroyed by white blood cells.

Reading Check *What blood components help form blood clots?*

Most people will not bleed to death from a minor wound, such as a cut or scrape. However, some people have a genetic condition called hemophilia (hee muh FIHL ee uh). Their plasma lacks one of the clotting factors that begins the clotting process. A minor injury can be a life threatening problem for a person with hemophilia.

Science Journal

Blood Clotting Have students find out about the role of vitamin K, prothrombin, calcium ions, thrombin, fibrinogen, and fibrin in the mechanism of blood clotting. Suggest they use this information to draw in their Science Journals a labeled diagram showing the sequence of events and the components involved in this process. L3 IS **Linguistic** P

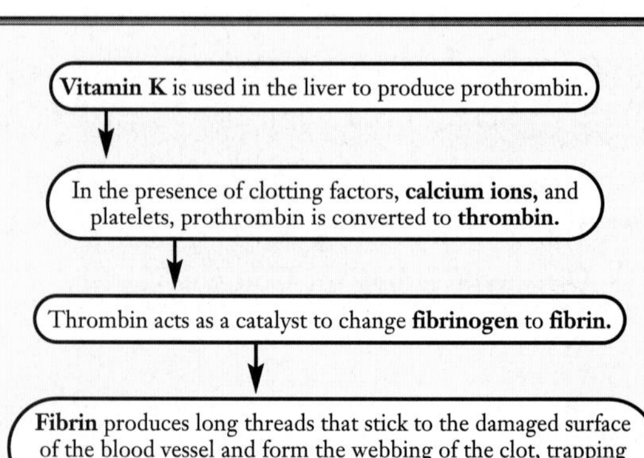

Vitamin K is used in the liver to produce prothrombin.
In the presence of clotting factors, **calcium ions,** and platelets, prothrombin is converted to **thrombin.**
Thrombin acts as a catalyst to change **fibrinogen** to **fibrin.**
Fibrin produces long threads that stick to the damaged surface of the blood vessel and form the webbing of the clot, trapping blood cells and platelets, which strengthen the clot.

558 CHAPTER 19 Circulation

Blood Types

Blood clots stop blood loss quickly in a minor wound, but with a serious wound a person might lose a lot of blood. A blood transfusion might be necessary. During a blood transfusion, a person receives donated blood or parts of blood. The medical provider must be sure that the right type of blood is given. If the wrong type is given, the red blood cells will clump together. Then, clots form in the blood vessels and the person could die.

Table 1 Blood Types

Blood Type	Antigen	Antibody
A	A	Anti-B
B	B	Anti-A
AB	A, B	None
O	None	Anti-A, Anti-B

The ABO Identification System People can inherit one of four types of blood: A, B, AB, or O, as shown in **Table 1.** Types A, B, and AB have chemical identification tags called antigens (AN tih junz) on their red blood cells. Type O red blood cells have no antigens.

Each blood type also has specific antibodies in its plasma. Antibodies are proteins that destroy or neutralize substances that do not belong in or are not part of your body. Because of these antibodies, certain blood types cannot be mixed. This limits blood transfusion possibilities as shown in **Table 2.** If type A blood is mixed with type B blood, the antibodies in type A blood determine that type B blood does not belong there. The antibodies in type A blood cause the type B red blood cells to clump. In the same way, type B blood antibodies cause type A blood to clump. Type AB blood has no antibodies, so people with this blood type can receive blood from A, B, AB, and O types. Type O blood has both A and B antibodies.

Table 2
Blood Transfusion Possibilities

Type	Can Receive	Can Donate To
A	0, A	A, AB
B	0, B	B, AB
AB	all	AB
0	0	all

Reading Check

Why are people with type O blood called universal donors?

Do you know what to do in an emergency? To learn about first aid, see the **Emergencies Field Guide** at the back of the book.

Blood Types

Visual Learning

Table 1 and Table 2 After students have studied the information in these tables, have them explain why people with blood type AB are sometimes called universal recipients. These people can receive all blood types.

Teacher FYI

To determine the blood type of an individual, suspensions of the person's red blood cells are mixed separately with different serums. Each serum has a known, particular antibody. When a serum causes agglutination of blood cells, it indicates that the cells contain the antigen with which that specific antibody agglutinates. This reaction identifies the blood type of the individual.

Extension

Have students research how blood transfusion experiments started in the early 1800s. The first successful blood transfusion was performed in the seventeenth century by a French physician, Jean Baptiste Denis. He used lamb's blood. His second attempt was unsuccessful, and the patient died. L2

Reading Check

Answer People with type 0 blood are able to give blood to people with all other types of blood.

Resource Manager

Chapter Resources Booklet

MiniLAB, p. 4

Enrichment, p. 31

Curriculum Connection

Health Some cultures consider blood to be a necessary part of their diet. Others use it in the preparation of certain foods (blood sausage). Have students find out what nutrients are supplied by the blood. usually sodium and iron L2

Blood Types, continued

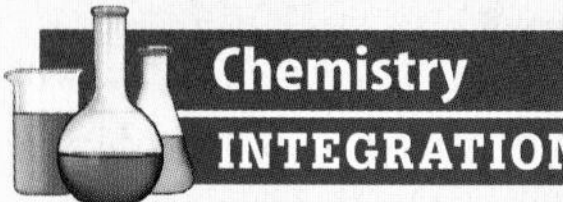

Artificial blood must not cause clumping, or contain certain substances (such as toxins) or organisms (such as bacteria) that cause disease.

Extension

Explain to students that if the blood type of the donor and recipient are the same, it is not always true that a blood transfusion is absolutely safe. Have students research reasons for this. A number of other blood factors can cause harmful reactions. Also, repeated transfusions of even the same blood type may eventually cause agglutination. This is because there are other antigens on red blood cells besides the A and B antigens.

Reading Check

Answer If someone with Rh− blood receives a transfusion from someone with Rh+ blood, the results could be fatal.

Problem-Solving Activity

National Math Standards

Correlation to Mathematics Objectives
1, 5, 6, 8, 9, 10

Answers

1. There would be 54 possible donors. Type B, Rh+ blood can be transfused with Type B, Rh+ (9%); Type B, Rh− (1%); Type O, Rh+ (37%); and Type O, Rh− (7%).
2. Type O, Rh− would be most at risk as this population can only receive Type O, Rh− blood. In an average sample of 100 people, only 7 would match this blood type.

Artificial blood substances have been developed to use in blood transfusions. They can carry oxygen and carbon dioxide. Predict what other properties they must have to be safe. Write your prediction in your Science Journal.

The Rh Factor Another chemical identification tag in blood is the Rh factor. The Rh factor also is inherited. If the Rh factor is on red blood cells, the person has Rh-positive (Rh+) blood. If it is not present, the person's blood is called Rh-negative (Rh−). If an Rh− person receives a blood transfusion from an Rh+ person, he or she will produce antibodies against the Rh factor. These antibodies can cause Rh+ cells to clump. Clots then form in the blood vessels and the person could die.

When an Rh− mother is pregnant with an Rh+ baby, the mother might make antibodies to the child's Rh factor. Close to the time of birth, Rh antibodies from the mother can pass from her blood vessels into the baby's blood vessels. These antibodies can destroy the baby's red blood cells. If this happens, the baby must receive a blood transfusion before or right after birth. At 28 weeks of pregnancy and immediately after the birth, an Rh− mother can receive an injection that blocks the production of antibodies to the Rh+ factor. These injections prevent this life-threatening situation from occurring in future pregnancies. To prevent deadly results, blood groups and Rh factor are checked before transfusions and during pregnancies.

Reading Check *Why is it important to check Rh factor?*

Problem-Solving Activity

Will there be enough blood donors?

Successful human blood transfusions began during World War II. This practice is much safer today due to extensive testing of the donated blood prior to transfusion. Health care professionals have determined that each blood type can receive certain other blood types as illustrated in **Table 2.**

Blood Type Distribution

	Rh+ (%)	Rh− (%)
O	37	7
A	36	6
B	9	1
AB	3	1

Identifying the Problem

The table on the right lists the average distribution of blood types in the United States. The data are recorded as percents, or a sample of 100 people. By examining these data and the data in **Table 2,** can you determine safe donors for each blood type? Recall that people with Rh− blood cannot receive a transfusion from an Rh+ donor.

Solving the Problem

1. If a Type B, Rh+ person needs a blood transfusion, how many possible donors are there?
2. Frequently, the supply of donated blood runs low. Which blood type and Rh factor would be most affected in such a shortage? Explain your answer.

Teacher FYI

The original research regarding the Rh factor was done with blood cells from rhesus monkeys. The antigen found was named using the first two letters of rhesus. Treatment for the Rh problem, *erythroblastosis fetalis,* includes blood transfusions and exposure to fluorescent light.

Resource Manager

Chapter Resources Booklet
Reinforcement, p. 28
Cultural Diversity, p. 18

Diseases of Blood

Because blood circulates to all parts of your body and performs so many important functions, any disease of the blood is a cause for concern. One common disease of the blood is anemia (uh NEE mee uh). In this disease of red blood cells, body tissues can't get enough oxygen and are unable to carry on their usual activities. Anemia has many causes. Sometimes, anemia is caused by the loss of large amounts of blood. A diet lacking iron or certain vitamins also might cause anemia. In addition, anemia can be the result of another disease or a side effect of treatment for a disease. Still other types of anemia are inherited problems related to the structure of the red blood cells. Cells from one such type of anemia, sickle-cell anemia, are shown in **Figure 13.**

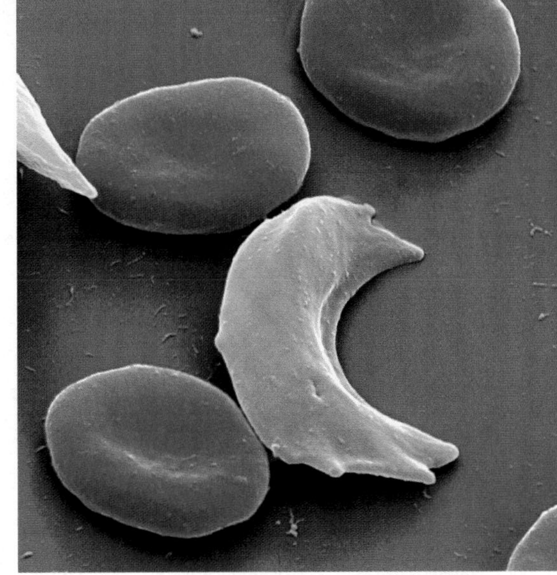

Figure 13
Persons with sickle-cell anemia have misshapened red blood cells. The sickle-shaped cells clog the capillaries of a person with this disease. Oxygen cannot reach tissues served by the capillaries, and wastes cannot be removed. *How does this damage the affected tissues?*

Leukemia (lew KEE mee uh) is a disease in which one or more types of white blood cells are made in excessive numbers. These cells are immature and do not fight infections well. These immature cells fill the bone marrow and crowd out the normal cells. Then not enough red blood cells, normal white blood cells, and platelets can be made. Some types of leukemia affect children. Other kinds are more common in adults. Medicines, blood transfusions, and bone marrow transplants are used to treat this disease. If the treatments are not successful, the person will eventually die from related complications.

Section  Assessment

1. What are the four functions of blood in the body?
2. Compare red blood cells, white blood cells, and platelets.
3. Why are blood type and Rh factor checked before a transfusion?
4. Describe two diseases of blood.
5. **Think Critically** Think about the main job of your red blood cells. If red blood cells couldn't deliver oxygen to your cells, what would be the condition of your body tissues?

Skill Builder Activities

6. **Interpreting Data** Look at the data in **Table 2** about blood group interactions. To which group(s) can blood type AB donate blood? **For more help, refer to the Science Skill Handbook.**
7. **Using Percentages** Find the total number of red blood cells, white blood cells, and platelets in 1 mm^3 of blood. Calculate what percentage of the total each type is. **For more help, refer to the Math Skill Handbook.**

Diseases of Blood

Caption Answer

Figure 13 Built-up wastes are toxic to cells. Without oxygen, cell respiration cannot occur.

3 Assess

Reteach

Divide the class into groups of four. Have each person in each group pick a different blood type. Allow students to decide who can give blood to whom and from whom they can receive blood. L1 IN **Intrapersonal**

Challenge

Survey students to find out whether they know their own blood type. Discuss when it might be important to know this information. If students do not know their blood type, encourage them to ask their parent or guardian.

Assessment

Performance Have students use **Table 1** to determine acceptable donors to those with type AB blood. Individuals with AB blood can receive blood from all the other blood types. Use **Performance Assessment in the Science Classroom,** p. 89.

Answers to Section Assessment

1. carries oxygen to cells and removes carbon dioxide; carries wastes to kidneys; transports nutrients from the digestive system to cells; has materials to fight infections and heal wounds
2. red: transport oxygen and carbon dioxide; white: fight infections; platelets: help in blood clotting
3. to prevent blood cells from clumping
4. Answers will vary. Leukemia is a disease in which large numbers of white blood cells are made. Anemia is a disease in which there are too few red blood cells.
5. Without enough oxygen, cells cannot release from food the energy that is needed for many cellular processes. The tissues made of oxygen-deprived cells could not function properly.
6. only to another person with AB blood type
7. In a cubic millimeter of blood, there are over 5 million red blood cells, 5,000 to 10,000 white blood cells, and 400,000 platelets. Thus blood is approximately 92.5% red blood cells, 0.09–0.18% white blood cells, and 7.4% platelets.

The Lymphatic System

1 Motivate

Bellringer Transparency

Display the Section Focus Transparency for Section 3. Use the accompanying Transparency Activity Master. L2 ELL

Section Focus Transparency — Here I Come to Save the Day!

This image shows a cell from the immune system at work. A white blood cell is devouring an invading organism. The only part of the organism that can be seen is at the lower right portion of the photo. It is being sucked into the tube-like extension of the colorful white blood cell.

1. Describe what is happening to the invading organism.
2. What purpose do you think white blood cells serve?

Tie to Prior Knowledge

Ask students to recall when they may have had an infection and experienced swollen lymph glands in the neck or under the arms. What do you think caused this?

SECTION 3

The Lymphatic System

As You Read

***What* You'll Learn**

- **Describe** functions of the lymphatic system.
- **Identify** where lymph comes from.
- **Explain** how lymph organs help fight infections.

Vocabulary

lymph
lymphatic system
lymphocyte
lymph node

***Why* It's Important**

The lymphatic system helps protect you from infections and diseases.

Functions of the Lymphatic System

You're thirsty after a long walk home in the hot sun. You turn on the water faucet and fill a glass with water. The excess water runs down the drain. In a similiar way, your body's tissue fluid is removed by the lymphatic (lihm FAT ihk) system. The nutrient, water, and oxygen molecules in blood diffuse through capillary walls to nearby cells. Water and other substances become part of the tissue fluid that is found between cells. This fluid is collected and returned to the blood by the lymphatic system.

After tissue fluid diffuses into the lymphatic capillaries it is called **lymph** (LIHMF). Your **lymphatic system,** as shown in **Figure 14,** carries lymph through a network of lymph capillaries and larger lymph vessels. Then, the lymph drains into large veins near the heart. No heartlike structure pumps the lymph through the lymphatic system. The movement of lymph depends on the contraction of smooth muscles in lymph vessels and skeletal muscles. Lymphatic vessels, like veins, have valves that keep lymph from flowing backward.

In addition to water and dissolved substances, lymph also contains **lymphocytes** (LIHM fuh sites), a type of white blood cell. Lymphocytes help your body defend itself against disease-causing organisms. If the lymphatic system is not working properly, severe swelling occurs because the tissue fluid cannot get back to the blood.

Reading Check *What are the differences and similarities between lymph and blood?*

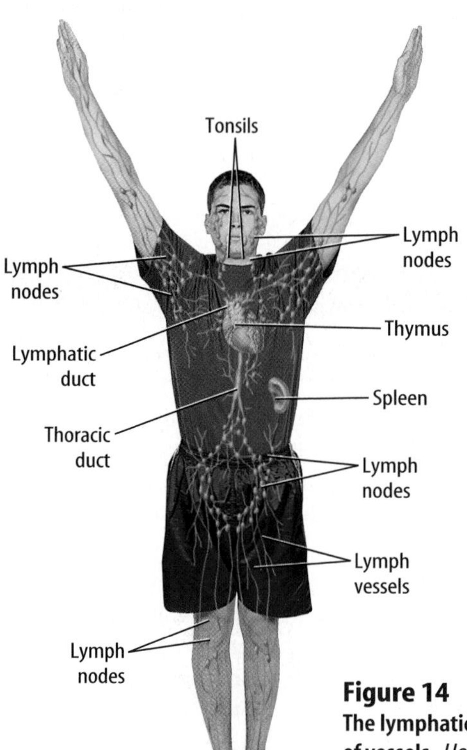

Figure 14
The lymphatic system is connected by a network of vessels. *How do muscles help move lymph?*

Resource Manager

Chapter Resources Booklet
Transparency Activity, p. 48
Directed Reading for Content Mastery, pp. 21, 22
Enrichment, p. 32

Section Assessment Planner

PORTFOLIO ASSESSMENT
Reteach, p. 563
PERFORMANCE ASSESSMENT
Skill Builder Activities, p. 563
See page 570 for more options.

CONTENT ASSESSMENT
Section, p. 563
Challenge, p. 563
Chapter, pp. 570–571

Lymphatic Organs

Before lymph enters the blood, it passes through lymph nodes, which are bean-shaped organs of varying sizes found throughout the body. **Lymph nodes** filter out microorganisms and foreign materials that have been taken up by lymphocytes. When your body fights an infection, lymphocytes fill the lymph nodes. The lymph nodes become warm, reddened, and tender to the touch. After the invaders are destroyed, the redness, warmth, and tenderness in the lymph nodes go away.

Besides lymph nodes, three important lymphatic organs are the tonsils, the thymus, and the spleen. Tonsils are in the back of your throat. They protect your body from harmful microorganisms that enter through your mouth and nose. Your thymus is a soft mass of tissue located behind the sternum. It makes lymphocytes that travel to other lymph organs. The spleen is the largest lymphatic organ. It is located behind the upper-left part of the stomach and filters the blood by removing worn out and damaged red blood cells. Cells in the spleen take up and destroy bacteria and other substances that invade your body.

SCIENCE Online

Data Update For an online update about HIV and AIDS, visit the Glencoe Science Web site at **science.glencoe.com** and select the appropriate chapter.

A Disease of the Lymphatic System

As you probably have heard, HIV is a deadly virus. When HIV enters a person's body, it attacks and destroys a certain kind of lymphocyte called helper T-cells that help make antibodies to fight infections. This affects a person's immunity to certain diseases. Usually, the person dies from these other infections, not from the HIV infection.

Section 3 Assessment

1. List the organs of your lymphatic system and describe their functions.
2. Where does lymph come from and how does it get into the lymphatic capillaries?
3. How do lymphatic organs fight infection?
4. What events occur when HIV enters the body?
5. **Think Critically** When the amount of fluid in the spaces between cells increases, so does the pressure in these spaces. What do you infer will happen?

Skill Builder Activities

6. **Concept Mapping** The circulatory system and the lymphatic system work together in several ways. Make a concept map comparing the two systems. **For more help, refer to the Science Skill Handbook.**
7. **Communicating** An infectious microorganism enters your body. In your Science Journal, describe how the lymphatic system protects the body against the microorganism. **For more help, refer to the Science Skill Handbook.**

2 Teach

Functions of the Lymphatic System

Reading Check

Answer Both contain a lot of water. Blood has red blood cells; lymph does not.

Caption Answer

Figure 14 As skeletal muscles contract, they force lymph to move within the lymph vessels.

3 Assess

Reteach

Have students construct a table to compare the functions of lymph nodes, the thymus, and the spleen. L1 P

Challenge

Explain why lymph nodes are sometimes examined to determine the extent of breast cancer. Nodes along the side of the chest and under the arm filter lymph that drains from the breast. The lymph nodes are examined for cancer cells. If present, further treatments are recommended.

Assessment

Performance Have students research and write about the functions of macrophages. Macrophages engulf foreign materials and probably alter them to initiate the immune response. Use **PASC,** p. 175.

Answers to Section Assessment

1. lymph nodes: filter out microorganisms and foreign particles; tonsils: protect body from harmful microorganisms; thymus: makes lymphocytes; spleen: filters blood and removes damaged red blood cells, destroys bacteria
2. from tissue fluids; by absorption and diffusion
3. Nodes filter out microorganisms and foreign materials; tonsils protect the mouth and throat from germs; thymus makes lymphocytes; spleen removes and recycles old red blood cells and destroys bacteria.
4. It attacks helper T-cells.
5. Diffusion of fluid into the lymphatic capillaries will increase.
6. Cardiovascular: vessels connect heart to body and transport food and gases; Lymphatic: vessels connect lymph nodes to body, transport lymph, return fluid to blood, fight pathogens.
7. Journal entries should reflect the roles of the lymph nodes, lymphocytes, and the spleen in providing protection against microorganisms.

Internet Addresses

Explore the Glencoe Science Web site at **science.glencoe.com** to find out more about topics in this section.

Activity

BENCH TESTED

Recognize the Problem

Purpose

Students determine how different blood types react when mixed. L2 ELL LS Naturalist P

Process Skills

designing an experiment, forming a hypothesis, observing and inferring, communicating, recognizing cause and effect, separating and controlling variables, interpreting data

Time Required

50 minutes

Materials

For simulated blood, mix 10 mL of lowfat milk with 10 mL of water and add 2 or 3 drops of red food coloring. The lemon juice and water are used as antigens. Also needed are droppers, small paper cups, a marking pen, and a graduated cylinder.

Form a Hypothesis

Possible Hypothesis

Most students' hypotheses will reflect that there will be clumping when some blood types are mixed.

Activity Design Your Own Experiment

Blood Type Reactions

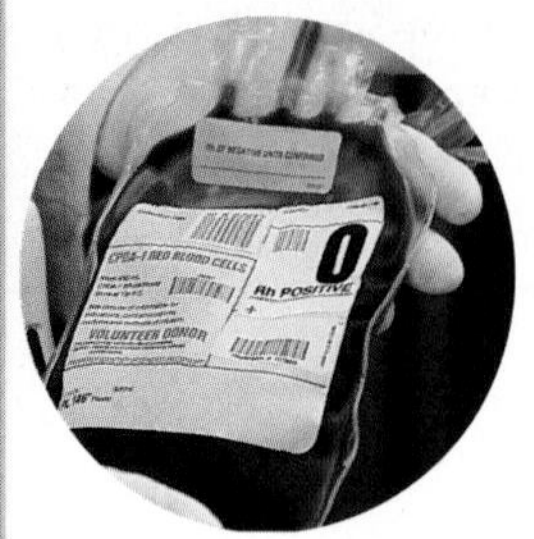

Human blood can be classified into four main blood types—A, B, AB, and O. These types are determined by the presence or absence of antigens on the red blood cells. After blood is collected into a transfusion bag, it is tested to determine the blood type. The type is labeled clearly on the bag. Blood is refrigerated to keep it fresh and available for transfusion.

Recognizing the Problem

What happens when two different blood types are mixed?

Forming a Hypothesis

Based on your reading and observations, state a hypothesis about how different blood types will react to each other.

Safety Precautions

Do not taste, eat, or drink any materials used in the lab.

Possible Materials

simulated blood (10 mL low-fat milk and 10 mL water plus red food coloring)
lemon juice as antigen A (for blood types B and O)
water as antigen A (for blood types A and AB)
droppers
small paper cups
marking pen
10-mL graduated cylinder

Goals

- **Design** an experiment that simulates the reactions between different blood types.
- **Identify** which blood types can donate to which other blood types.

Test Your Hypothesis

Possible Procedures

- Mark four paper cups with blood type names A, B, AB, and O.
- Add 5 mL simulated blood to each cup.
- Use the lemon juice as antigen A for blood types B and O. Add 2 to 3 drops of lemon juice to cups B and O. Clumping occurs.
- Use water as antigen A for blood types A and AB. Add 2 to 3 drops to cups A and AB. No clumping occurs.

Test Your Hypothesis

Plan

1. As a group, agree upon the hypothesis and decide how you will test it. Identify the results that will confirm the hypothesis.
2. **List** the steps you must take and the materials you will need to test your hypothesis. Be specific. Describe exactly what you will do in each step.
3. **Prepare** a data table like the one at the right in your Science Journal to record your observations.
4. Reread the entire experiment to make sure all steps are in logical order.
5. **Identify** constants and variables. Blood type O will be the control.

Blood Type Reactions

Blood Type	Clumping (Yes or No)
A	no
B	yes
AB	no
O	yes

Do

1. Make sure your teacher approves your plan before you start.
2. Carry out the experiment according to the approved plan.
3. While doing the experiment, record your observations and complete the data table in your Science Journal.

Analyze Your Data

1. **Compare** the reactions of each blood type (A, B, AB, and O) when antigen A was added to the blood.
2. **Observe** where clumping took place.
3. **Compare** your results with those of other groups.
4. What was the control factor in this experiment?
5. What were your variables?

Draw Conclusions

1. Did the results support your hypothesis? Explain.
2. **Predict** what might happen to a person if other antigens are not matched properly.
3. What would happen in an investigation with antigen B added to each blood type?

Your Data

Write a brief report on how blood is tested to determine blood type. **Describe** why this is important to know before receiving a blood transfusion. **For more help, refer to the** Science Skill Handbook.

Teaching Strategy

Instruct students to look for curdling of the milk in the simulated blood as it reacts with the acidic lemon juice. This represents the "clumping" of blood cells.

Expected Outcomes

Clumping will occur when the lemon juice antigen is mixed with blood types B and O. No clumping will occur when the water antigen is mixed with blood types A and AB.

Analyze Your Data

1. Blood types B and O clumped when lemon juice antigen A was added. Blood types A and AB did not clump when water antigen A was added.
2. Clumping took place in cups with B and O blood types.
3. Students' results should be similar to those of other groups.
4. The control in this experiment was the blood solution and the amount of each antigen added to the blood.
5. The variable was the type of antigen solution used.

Error Analysis

Have students compare their results with their hypotheses and explain any differences that might have occurred.

Draw Conclusions

1. Answers will be determined by student hypotheses.
2. Clumping of blood cells could result.
3. Clumping would occur with blood types A and O and not with blood types B and AB.

Assessment

Oral Have students explain why persons with blood type O can donate to anyone but can only receive from a person with blood type O. Type O has no A or B antigens and has antibodies A and B. Use **Performance Assessment in the Science Classroom,** p. 143.

Communicating Your Data

Students may search the Glencoe Science Web site to find information on how blood is checked before a transfusion is given. Not knowing the blood type could lead to the formation of blood clots in blood vessels and result in death.

Resource Manager

Chapter Resources Booklet
Reinforcement, p. 29
Activity Worksheet, pp. 7–8

Lab Management and Safety, p. 69

Content Background

Medieval and early Renaissance medicine in Europe was dominated by the theories of Galen, a Roman physician. Galen taught that there were two types of blood and two separate circulatory systems, venous and arterial. It was believed that blood was manufactured in the liver and delivered to veins. The blood received air from the lungs and was carried to the heart by the pulmonary vein, which also took "sooty vapours" back to be expelled by the lungs. Oxygenated blood supposedly seeped from the right to the left side of the heart to become arterial blood that was then consumed by the body.

Renaissance doctors began to question this theory when Arab medical texts became available in the West. The Muslim doctor Ibn Al-Nafis had described pulmonary circulation and the function of the lungs in the 1200s.

A number of sixteenth-century European anatomists made direct observations of pulmonary circulation and one-way valves in the heart and veins. That chain of investigation would culminate in Harvey's correct description of the circulatory system in 1628. Harvey's breakthrough discovery was that the volume of blood exiting the heart could not be replaced by the daily intake of food and water.

TIME SCIENCE AND HISTORY

SCIENCE CAN CHANGE THE COURSE OF HISTORY

Dr. Daniel Hale Williams was a pioneer in open-heart surgery.

Have a Heart

People didn't always know where blood came from or how it moved through the body

"Ouch!" You prick your finger, and when blood starts to flow out of the cut, you put on a bandage. But if you were a scientist living long ago, you might have also asked yourself some questions: How did your blood get to the tip of your finger? And why and how does it flow through (and sometimes out of!) your body?

As early as the 1500s, a Spanish scientist named Miguel Serveto (mee GEL • ser VET oh) asked that question. His studies led him to the theory that blood circulated throughout the human body, but he didn't know how or why.

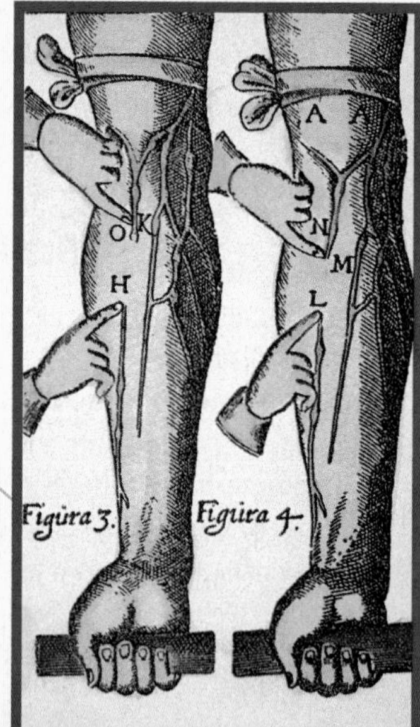

A woodcut from William Harvey's book demonstrates his theory of blood circulation. The book was published in 1628.

566

Resources for Teachers and Students

The Greatest Benefit to Mankind: A Medical History of Humanity by Roy Porter. New York: W. W. Norton, 1998.

Medicine: An Illustrated History by Albert S. Lyons and R. Joseph Petrucelli, II. New York: Harry N. Abrams, Inc., 1978.

"William Harvey" by Frederick G. Kilgour, *Scientific American*, June 1952.

William Harvey (standing) explains his theory of blood circulation to England's King Charles I. The boy is the future King Charles II.

About 100 years later, William Harvey, an English doctor, explored Servet's idea. Harvey studied animals to develop a theory about how the heart and the circulatory system work. Back then, most people thought that food was turned into blood by the liver.

Harvey knew this was untrue from his observations of animals. Blood was pumped from the heart throughout the body, Harvey hypothesized. Then it returned to the heart and recirculated. He published his ideas in 1628 in his famous book, *On the Motion of the Heart and Blood in Animals*. His theories were correct, but many of Harvey's patients left him. They thought his ideas were bloody ridiculous! But over time, Harvey's book became the basis for all modern research on heart and blood vessels.

Medical Pioneer

More than two centuries later, another pioneer would step forward and use Harvey's ideas to change the science frontier again. His name is Dr. Daniel Hale Williams. In 1893, Williams used what he knew about the heart and blood circulation to become a new kind of medical pioneer. He performed the first open-heart surgery by removing a knife from the heart of a stabbing victim. He stitched the wound to the fluid sac surrounding the heart, and the patient lived for several years afterward. In 1970, the U.S. recognized this American medical pioneer by issuing a stamp in his honor.

CONNECTIONS Report **Pioneers in medicine continue to help people lead longer lives. Identify a pioneer in science or medicine who has changed our lives for the better. Find out how this person started in the field, and how they came to make an important discovery. Give a presentation to the class.**

SCIENCE *Online*
For more information, visit science.glencoe.com

Discussion

What did Harvey do to develop his theory of circulation that is still done in medical research today? Possible Answer: He used animals for his early observations and applied his findings to humans.

Historical Significance

Harvey's discovery and theory were based on the observations of his predecessors and measurable phenomenon to construct a result that others could reproduce. He had developed a scientific method. Investigation, as opposed to traditional authority, was a defining aspect of the Renaissance that led to modern scientific practices.

Organize students into teams of two or three and tell them to locate the valves in the veins of their forearms. Allow them to try by their own means before showing them the following method. One student will place a finger firmly over a vein on the inside of the other's forearm. Apply the same pressure with the free thumb, then move it along the vein toward the shoulder. Remove the thumb keeping pressure with the finger and see if the vein fills with blood. Remove the finger and record both results. Repeat the procedure toward the hand and record the result. Try different spots to verify the position of the valves. Students may then compare the results of both methods. Discuss the difference between them. **Which method is scientific? Why?**

CONNECTIONS Students may have difficulty envisioning the results of the last four hundred years of scientific investigation. The following exercise will help to create some perspective. Divide students into teams and assign each an organ of the body, perhaps by drawing out of a hat. Each team will research that organ and prepare a presentation of its functions as they were known before the Renaissance compared with how they are viewed today. The results can be presented as individual team reports or compiled into a pamphlet or bulletin board presentation. A possible variation would be to investigate ancient versus modern treatments for well-known diseases.

Chapter 19 Study Guide

Reviewing Main Ideas

Preview

Students can answer the questions in their Science Journals. Discuss the answers as you go through the chapter. LS **Linguistic**

Review

Students can write their answers, then compare them with those of other students. LS **Interpersonal**

Reteach

Students can look at the illustrations and describe details that support the main ideas of the chapter. LS **Visual-Spatial**

Answers to Chapter Review

Section 1

3. Students should trace the flow through the heart, to the lungs, and back to the heart.

Section 2

3. Anemia may be caused by a lack of iron or certain vitamins in the diet. It may also result as a side effect from another disease.

Section 3

1. Lymph nodes filter out disease organisms and foreign material. The lymphocytes in the nodes attack disease organisms.

Chapter 19 Study Guide

Reviewing Main Ideas

Section 1 The Circulatory System

1. Arteries carry blood away from the heart. Capillaries allow the exchange of nutrients, oxygen, and wastes in cells. Veins return blood to the heart.
2. Blood that is high in carbon dioxide enters the right atrium, moves to the right ventricle, and then goes to the lungs through the pulmonary artery. Oxygen-rich blood returns to the left atrium, moves to the left ventricle, and then leaves through the aorta.
3. Pulmonary circulation is the path of blood between the heart and lungs. Circulation through the rest of the body is called systemic circulation. Coronary circulation is the flow of blood to tissues of the heart. *Trace pulmonary circulation in this image.*

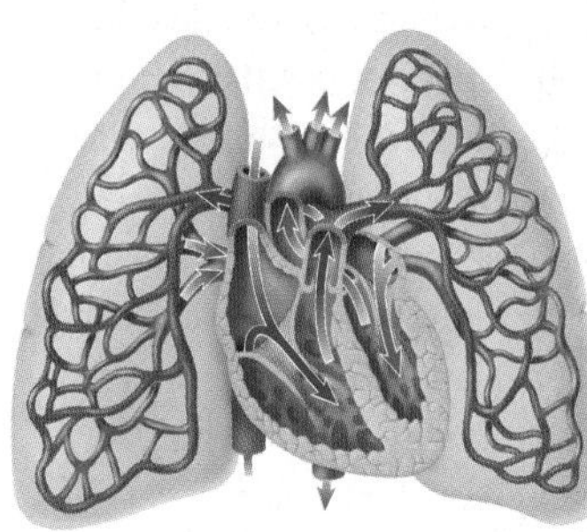

4. A healthy lifestyle is important for the health of your cardiovascular system.

Section 2 Blood

1. Red blood cells carry oxygen and carbon dioxide, platelets form clots, and white blood cells fight infection. Plasma carries nutrients, blood cells, and other substances.
2. A, B, AB, and O blood types are determined by the presence or absence of antigens on red blood cells.
3. Anemia is a disease of red blood cells, shown in the photograph, in which not enough oxygen is carried to the body's cells. *What are some causes of anemia?*

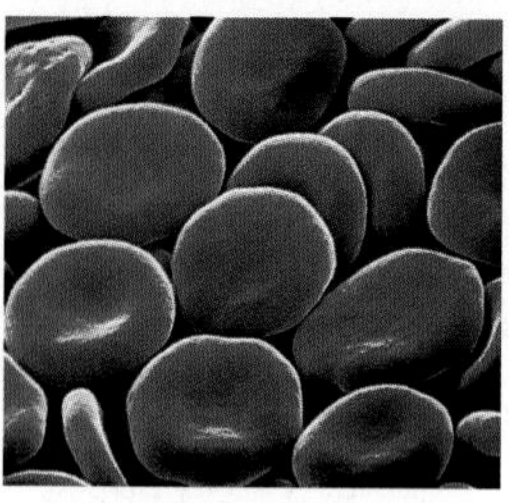

4. Leukemia is a disease of white blood cells in which one or more types of white blood cells are present in excessive numbers. These cells are immature and do not fight infection well.

Section 3 The Lymphatic System

1. Lymph structures filter blood, produce white blood cells that destroy bacteria and viruses, and destroy worn out blood cells. *How does this lymph node help your body fight disease?*

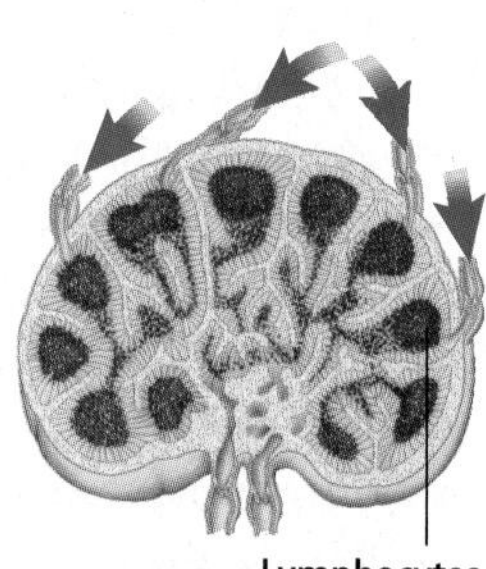

2. HIV attacks helper T-cells, which are a type of lymphocyte. The person is unable to fight infections well.

FOLDABLES Reading & Study Skills — After You Read

Add a labeled arrow and an oval under each of the following and write the major organ of that part of the circulatory system: *Pulmonary*, *Coronary*, and *Systemic*.

FOLDABLES Reading & Study Skills — After You Read

After students have read the chapter and completed the Foldable described in Before You Read, have them do the activity on the student page.

Dinah Zike

Visualizing Main Ideas

Fill in the concept map on the functions of the parts of the blood.

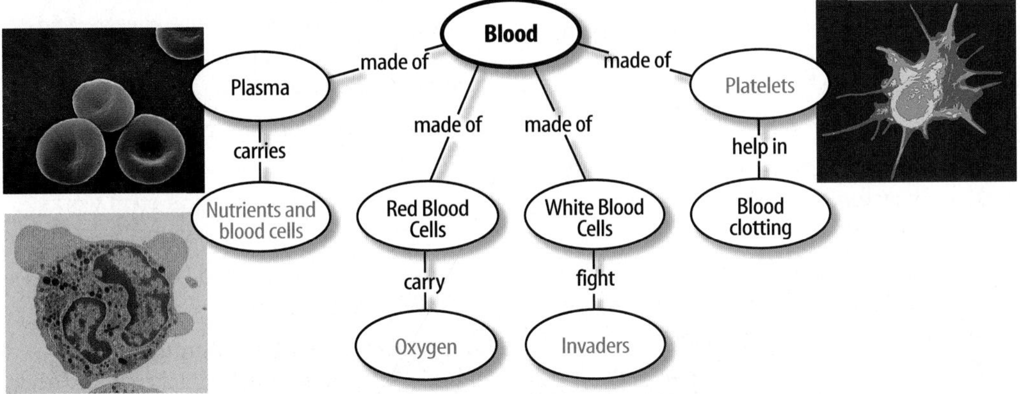

Vocabulary Review

Vocabulary Words

a. artery
b. atrium
c. capillary
d. coronary circulation
e. hemoglobin
f. lymph
g. lymph node
h. lymphatic system
i. lymphocyte
j. plasma
k. platelet
l. pulmonary circulation
m. systemic circulation
n. vein
o. ventricle

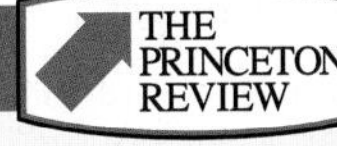

Study Tip

Make a study schedule for yourself. If you have a planner, write down exactly which hours you plan to spend studying and stick to it.

Using Vocabulary

Replace the underlined words with the correct vocabulary words.

1. The plasma carries blood to the heart.
2. The ventricle transports tissue fluid through a network of vessels.
3. Lymph is the chemical in red blood cells.
4. Lymph nodes are cell fragments.
5. The smallest blood vessels are called the lymphatic system.
6. The flow of blood to and from the lungs is called coronary circulation.
7. Hemoglobin helps protect your body against infections.
8. The largest section of the circulatory system is the pulmonary circulation.
9. Lymphocytes are blood vessels that carry blood away from the heart.
10. The two lower chambers of the heart are called the right and left atriums.

Chapter 19 Study Guide

Visualizing Main Ideas

See student page.

Vocabulary Review

Using Vocabulary

1. coronary circulation (or veins)
2. lymphatic system
3. Hemoglobin
4. Platelets
5. capillaries
6. pulmonary circulation
7. Lymphatic system or Lymphocytes
8. systemic circulation
9. Arteries
10. ventricles

CHAPTER STUDY GUIDE 569

Chapter 19 Assessment

Checking Concepts

1. B
2. B
3. C
4. A
5. D
6. C
7. A
8. C
9. D
10. A

Thinking Critically

11. Oxygen-rich blood: aorta, coronary arteries, left atrium, left ventricle; carbon dioxide-filled blood: coronary veins, inferior vena cava, right atrium, right ventricle, superior vena cava
12. All three blood vessels transport blood. Capillaries are only one cell thick; arteries have three layers; veins have valves. Veins carry blood to the heart; arteries carry blood away from the heart; capillaries link veins to arteries.
13. The lymphatic system, much like the cardiovascular system, carries fluid away from body tissues and returns it to your circulatory system through veins. The lymphatic system collects tissue fluid and returns it to the blood.
14. Blood and lymph move throughout the entire body.
15. The arteries there are close to the skin, so the pulse can be easily felt.

Chapter 19 Assessment

Checking Concepts

Choose the word or phrase that best answers the question.

1. Where does the exchange of food, oxygen, and wastes occur?
   A) arteries **C)** veins
   B) capillaries **D)** lymph vessels
2. Where does oxygen-rich blood enter first?
   A) right atrium **C)** left ventricle
   B) left atrium **D)** right ventricle
3. What is circulation to all body organs called?
   A) coronary **C)** systemic
   B) pulmonary **D)** organic
4. Where is blood under greatest pressure?
   A) arteries **C)** veins
   B) capillaries **D)** lymph vessels
5. Which of these is a function of blood?
   A) digest food **C)** dissolve bone
   B) produce CO_2 **D)** carry oxygen
6. Which cells fight off infection?
   A) red blood **C)** white blood
   B) bone **D)** nerve
7. Of the following, which carries oxygen in blood?
   A) red blood cells **C)** white blood cells
   B) platelets **D)** lymph
8. What is required to clot blood?
   A) plasma **C)** platelets
   B) oxygen **D)** carbon dioxide
9. What kind of antigen does type O blood have?
   A) A **C)** A and B
   B) B **D)** no antigen
10. What is the largest filtering lymph organ?
    A) spleen **C)** tonsil
    B) thymus **D)** node

Thinking Critically

11. Identify the following as having oxygen-rich or carbon dioxide-filled blood: *aorta, coronary arteries, coronary veins, inferior vena cava, left atrium, left ventricle, right atrium, right ventricle,* and *superior vena cava.*
12. Compare and contrast the three types of blood vessels.
13. Explain how the lymphatic system works with the cardiovascular system.
14. Why is cancer of the blood cells or lymph nodes hard to control?
15. Arteries are distributed throughout the body, yet a pulse usually is taken at the neck or wrist. Explain why.

Developing Skills

16. **Comparing and Contrasting** Compare the life spans of the red blood cells, white blood cells, and platelets.
17. **Interpreting Data** Interpret the data listed in this table. Find the average heart rate of the three males and the three females and compare the two averages.

Gender and Heart Rate

Sex	Pulse/Minute
Male 1	72
Male 2	64
Male 3	65
Female 1	67
Female 2	84
Female 3	74

18. **Sequencing** Describe the sequence of blood clotting from the wound to forming a scab.
19. **Comparing and Contrasting** Compare and contrast the functions of arteries, veins, and capillaries.

Chapter Assessment Planner

Portfolio Encourage students to place in their portfolios one or two items of what they consider to be their best work. Examples include:
- Assessment, p. 554
- Science Journal, p. 558
- Reteach, p. 563

Performance Additional performance assessments, Performance Task Assessment Lists, and rubrics for evaluating these activities can be found in Glencoe's **Performance Assessment in the Science Classroom.**

20. **Concept Mapping** Complete the events chain concept map showing how lymph moves in your body.

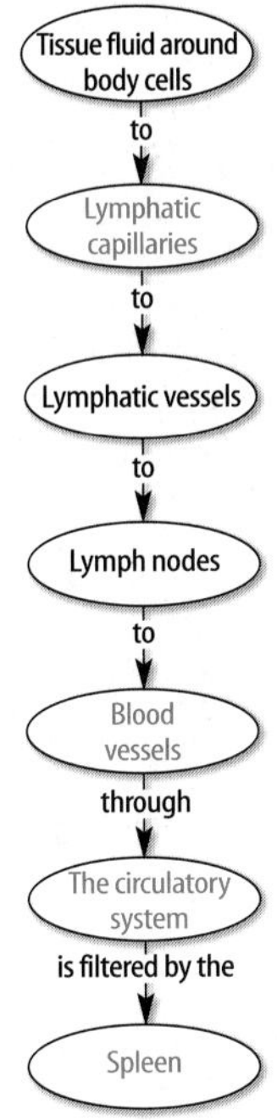

Performance Assessment

21. **Poster** Prepare a poster illustrating heart transplants. Include an explanation of why the patient is given drugs that suppress the immune system and describe the patient's life after the operation.

22. **Scientific Drawing** Prepare a drawing of the human heart and label its parts.

TECHNOLOGY

Go to the Glencoe Science Web site at **science.glencoe.com** or use the **Glencoe Science CD-ROM** for additional chapter assessment.

Test Practice

Ashley has investigated how different activities affect her body. She did five different activities for one minute each. After each activity, she recorded her pulse rate, body temperature, and degree of sweating as shown below.

Results from Ashley's Activities

Activity	Pulse Rate (beats/min)	Body Temperature	Degree of Sweating
1	80	98.6°F	None
2	90	98.8°F	Minimal
3	100	98.9°F	Little
4	120	99.1°F	Moderate
5	150	99.5°F	Considerable

1. According to the information in this table, which activity caused Ashley's pulse to be greater than 120 beats per minute?
   A) Activity 2
   B) Activity 3
   C) Activity 4
   D) Activity 5

2. A reasonable hypothesis based on these data is that during Activity 1, Ashley was probably _____ .
   F) walking quickly
   G) sitting down
   H) jogging
   J) sprinting

Chapter 19 Assessment

THE PRINCETON REVIEW

Test Practice

The Test-Taking Tip was written by The Princeton Review, the nation's leader in test preparation.

1. D
2. G

Developing Skills

16. red blood cells—120 days; white blood cells—a few days to several months; platelets—5 to 9 days
17. males = 67; females = 75; In general, males' heart rates are lower than females'.
18. Student responses should match **Figure 12.**
19. All transport blood. Arteries carry blood away from the heart. Veins carry blood to the heart. Capillaries connect arteries and veins.
20. See student page.

Performance Assessment

21. Drugs are given to prevent the body from rejecting the transplant (an antigen). Patients must avoid conditions that will bring them into contact with germs while their immune systems are suppressed. Use **PASC,** p. 145.
22. Compare student drawings to the illustration of the heart in **Figure 2.** Use **PASC,** p. 127.

Assessment Resources

 **Reproducible Masters**

Chapter Resources Booklet
Chapter Review, pp. 39–40
Chapter Tests, pp. 41–44
Assessment Transparency Activity, p. 51

Glencoe Science Web site
Interactive Tutor
Chapter Quizzes

Glencoe Technology
Assessment Transparency
Interactive CD-ROM Chapter Quizzes
ExamView Pro Test Bank
Vocabulary PuzzleMaker Software
MindJogger Videoquiz

Section/Objectives	Standards		Activities/Features
	National	State/Local	
Chapter Opener	See p. 5T for a Key to Standards.		**Explore Activity:** Measure breathing rate, p. 573 **Before You Read,** p. 573
Section 1 The Respiratory System 2 sessions 1 block 1. **Describe** the functions of the respiratory system. 2. **Explain** how oxygen and carbon dioxide are exchanged in the lungs and in tissues. 3. **Identify** the pathway of air in and out of the lungs. 4. **Explain** the effects of smoking on the respiratory system.	National Content Standards: UCP1, A1, C1, F1		**Earth Science Integration,** p. 575 **Science Online,** p. 577 **MiniLAB:** Comparing Surface Area, p. 578 **Visualizing Abdominal Thrusts,** p. 579 **Science Online,** p. 580
Section 2 The Excretory System 3 sessions 1.5 blocks 1. **Distinguish** between the excretory and urinary systems. 2. **Describe** how the kidneys work. 3. **Explain** what happens when urinary organs don't work.	National Content Standards: UCP1, A1, C1, F1, G3		**MiniLAB:** Modeling Kidney Function, p. 585 **Problem-Solving Activity:** How does your body gain and lose water?, p. 586 **Earth Science Integration,** p. 587 **Activity:** Kidney Structure, p. 589 **Activity:** Simulating the Abdominal Thrust Maneuver, pp. 590–591 **Science and History:** Overcoming the Odds, pp. 592–593

NATIONAL GEOGRAPHIC

Teacher's Corner

PRODUCTS AVAILABLE FROM GLENCOE
To order call 1-800-334-7344:
CD-ROM
NGS PictureShow: Human Body 2
Curriculum Kit
GeoKit: Human Body 1
Transparency Kit
NGS PicturePack: Human Body 2
Videodisc
STV: Human Body

PRODUCTS AVAILABLE FROM NATIONAL GEOGRAPHIC SOCIETY
To order call 1-800-368-2728:
Videos
Circulatory and Respiratory Systems (The Human Body Series)
Incredible Human Machine

Activity Materials	Reproducible Resources	Section Assessment	Technology
Explore Activity: stopwatch or clock with second hand, calculator	**Chapter Resources Booklet** Foldables Worksheet, p. 15 Directed Reading Overview, p. 17 Note-taking Worksheets, pp. 29–31	GLENCOE'S ASSESSMENT ADVANTAGE	
MiniLAB: bathroom-tissue cardboard tube, bowl, marbles, calculator	**Chapter Resources Booklet** Transparency Activity, p. 40 MiniLAB, p. 3 Enrichment, p. 27 Reinforcement, p. 25 Directed Reading, p. 18 Lab Activity, pp. 9–12, 13–14 **Performance Assessment in the Science Classroom,** p. 48 **Reading and Writing Skill Activities,** p. 39 **Life Science Critical Thinking/ Problem Solving,** p. 17	**Portfolio** Extension, p. 577 **Performance** MiniLAB, p. 578 Skill Builder Activities, p. 582 **Content** Section Assessment, p. 582	Section Focus Transparency Interactive CD-ROM Guided Reading Audio Program
MiniLAB: 3 cups, soil, fine gravel, water, funnel, small piece of wire screen, filter paper **Activity:** large animal kidney, scalpel, hand lens, disposable gloves **Activity:** cardboard tube, paper, clay, bicycle pump, sports bottle, scissors *Need materials?* Contact Science Kit at 1-800-828-7777 or www.sciencekit.com on the Internet.	**Chapter Resources Booklet** Transparency Activity, p. 41 MiniLAB, p. 4 Enrichment, p. 28 Reinforcement, p. 26 Directed Reading, pp. 19, 20 Activity Worksheet, pp. 5–6, 7–8 Transparency Activity, pp. 43–44 **Lab Management and Safety,** p. 77 **Mathematics Skill Activities,** p. 1 **Home and Community Involvement,** p. 40	**Portfolio** Assessment, p. 585 **Performance** MiniLAB, p. 585 Problem-Solving Activity, p. 586 Skill Builder Activities, p. 588 **Content** Section Assessment, p. 588	Section Focus Transparency Teaching Transparency Interactive CD-ROM Guided Reading Audio Program

End of Chapter Assessment

GLENCOE'S ASSESSMENT ADVANTAGE

Blackline Masters	Technology	Professional Series
Chapter Resources Booklet Chapter Review, pp. 33–34 Chapter Tests, pp. 35–38 **Standardized Test Practice by The Princeton Review,** pp. 87–90	MindJogger Videoquiz Interactive CD-ROM Vocabulary PuzzleMakers ExamView Pro Test Bank Interactive Lesson Planner Interactive Teacher Edition	Performance Assessment in the Science Classroom (PASC)

Transparencies

Section Focus

Section 1 Section Focus Transparency **Strange Creature from Above**

Scuba diving is an activity that requires special equipment that allows you to breathe while underwater. The word scuba actually stands for self-contained underwater breathing apparatus. This equipment is needed because, unlike fish, people breathe oxygen as a gas in air.

1. What special equipment is required for scuba diving?
2. What do the bubbles in this picture indicate?
3. How do people and fish differ in the way they get oxygen?

L2

Section 2 Section Focus Transparency **Liquid Wastes**

Have you ever thought of your skin as an organ that rids your body of waste? You probably perspire most heavily when you exercise. Perspiration is a liquid waste given off by the body.

1. How is perspiring helpful to the body?
2. Why is it important to drink plenty of fluids before, during, and after periods of intense physical activity?
3. What other body system is involved with the removal of liquid wastes?

L2

This is a representation of key blackline masters available in the Teacher Classroom Resources. See Resource Manager boxes within the chapter for additional information.

Assessment

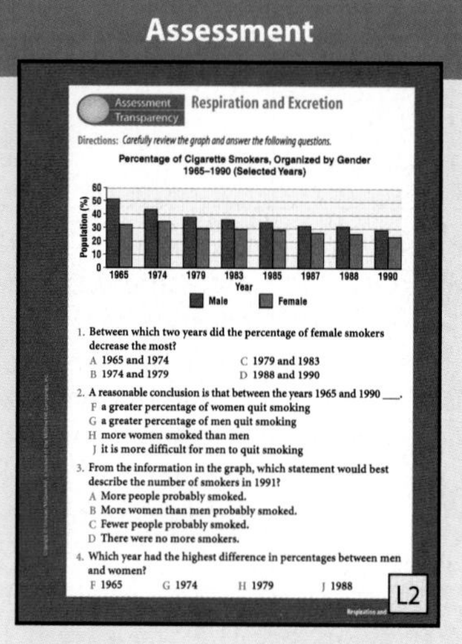
Assessment Transparency **Respiration and Excretion**

Directions: Carefully review the graph and answer the following questions.

1. Between which two years did the percentage of female smokers decrease the most?
   A 1965 and 1974
   B 1974 and 1979
   C 1979 and 1983
   D 1988 and 1990
2. A reasonable conclusion is that between the years 1965 and 1990 ___.
   F a greater percentage of women quit smoking
   G a greater percentage of men quit smoking
   H more women smoked than men
   J it is more difficult for men to quit smoking
3. From the information in the graph, which statement would best describe the number of smokers in 1991?
   A More people probably smoked.
   B More women than men probably smoked.
   C Fewer people probably smoked.
   D There were no more smokers.
4. Which year had the highest difference in percentages between men and women?
   F 1965 G 1974 H 1979 J 1988

L2

Teaching

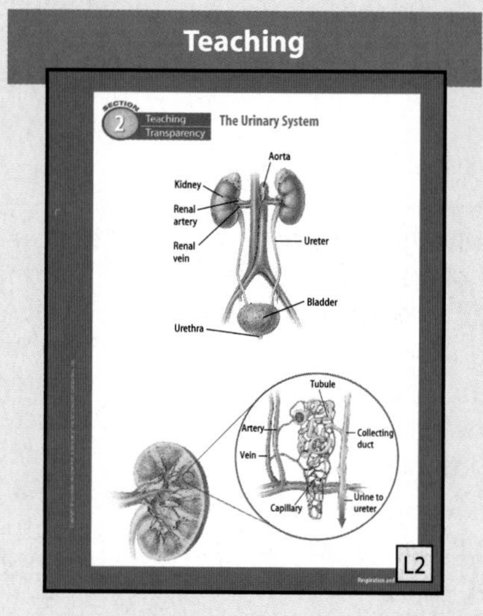
Section 2 Teaching Transparency **The Urinary System**

L2

Key to Teaching Strategies

The following designations will help you decide which activities are appropriate for your students.

- **L1** Level 1 activities should be appropriate for students with learning difficulties.
- **L2** Level 2 activities should be within the ability range of all students.
- **L3** Level 3 activities are designed for above-average students.
- **ELL** ELL activities should be within the ability range of English Language Learners.
- **COOP LEARN** Cooperative Learning activities are designed for small group work.
- **LS** Multiple Learning Styles logos, as described on page 22T, are used throughout to indicate strategies that address different learning styles.
- **P** These strategies represent student products that can be placed into a best-work portfolio.

Hands-on Activities

Activity Worksheets

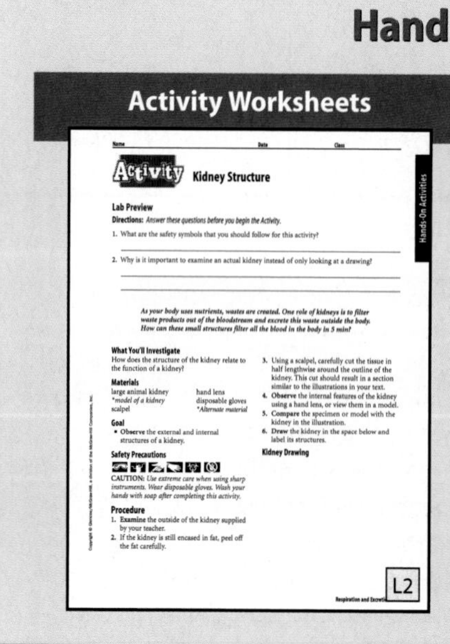
Name Date Class

Activity **Kidney Structure**

Hands-On Activities

Lab Preview

Directions: *Answer these questions before you begin the Activity.*

1. What are the safety symbols that you should follow for this activity?
2. Why is it important to examine an actual kidney instead of only looking at a drawing?

As your body uses nutrients, wastes are created. One role of kidneys is to filter waste products out of the bloodstream and excrete this waste outside the body. How can these small structures filter all the blood in the body in 5 min?

What You'll Investigate

How does the structure of the kidney relate to the function of a kidney?

Materials

large animal kidney
**model of a kidney*
scalpel
hand lens
disposable gloves
**Alternate material*

Goal

- **Observe** the external and internal structures of a kidney.

Safety Precautions

CAUTION: *Use extreme care when using sharp instruments. Wear disposable gloves. Wash your hands with soap after completing this activity.*

Procedure

1. **Examine** the outside of the kidney supplied by your teacher.
2. If the kidney is still encased in fat, peel off the fat carefully.
3. Using a scalpel, carefully cut the tissue in half lengthwise around the outline of the kidney. This cut should result in a section similar to the illustrations in your text.
4. **Observe** the internal features of the kidney using a hand lens, or view them in a model.
5. **Compare** the specimen or model with the kidney in the illustration.
6. **Draw** the kidney in the space below and label its structures.

Kidney Drawing

L2

Laboratory Activities

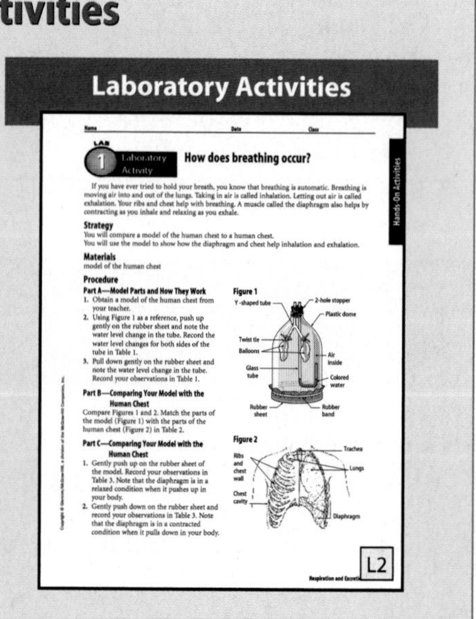
Name Date Class

Lab 1 Laboratory Activity **How does breathing occur?**

Hands-On Activities

If you have ever tried to hold your breath, you know that breathing is automatic. Breathing is moving air into and out of the lungs. Taking in air is called inhalation. Letting out air is called exhalation. Your ribs and chest help with breathing. A muscle called the diaphragm also helps by contracting as you inhale and relaxing as you exhale.

Strategy

You will compare a model of the human chest to a human chest.
You will use the model to show how the diaphragm and chest help inhalation and exhalation.

Materials

model of the human chest

Procedure

Part A—Model Parts and How They Work

1. Obtain a model of the human chest from your teacher.
2. Using Figure 1 as a reference, push up gently on the rubber sheet and note the water level change in the tube. Record the water level changes for both sides of the tube in Table 1.
3. Pull down gently on the rubber sheet and note the water level change in the tube. Record your observations in Table 1.

Part B—Comparing Your Model with the Human Chest

Compare Figures 1 and 2. Match the parts of the model (Figure 1) with the parts of the human chest (Figure 2) in Table 2.

Part C—Comparing Your Model with the Human Chest

1. Gently push up on the rubber sheet of the model. Record your observations in Table 3. Note that the diaphragm is in a relaxed condition when it pushes up in your body.
2. Gently push down on the rubber sheet and record your observations in Table 3. Note that the diaphragm is in a contracted condition when it pulls down in your body.

Figure 1

Figure 2

L2

Meeting Different Ability Levels

Content Outline

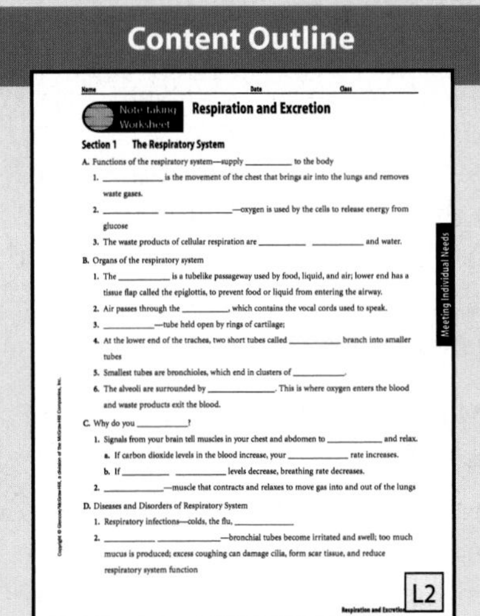

Note-taking Worksheet — Respiration and Excretion

Section 1 The Respiratory System

L2

Reinforcement

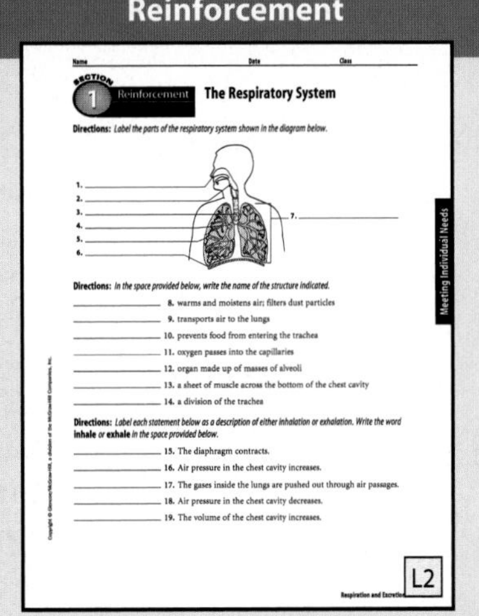

Section 1 Reinforcement — The Respiratory System

L2

Directed Reading

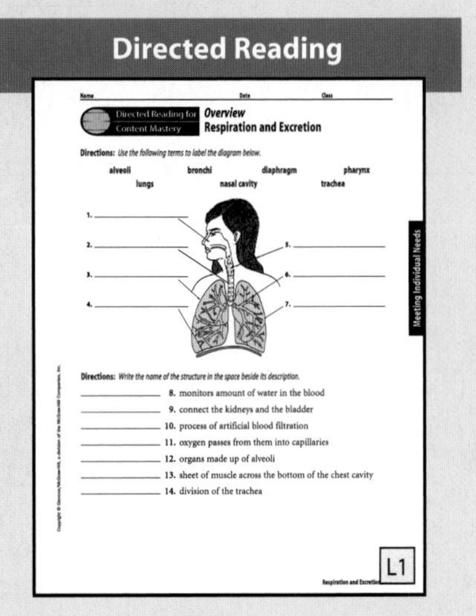

Directed Reading for Content Mastery — Overview: Respiration and Excretion

L1

Enrichment

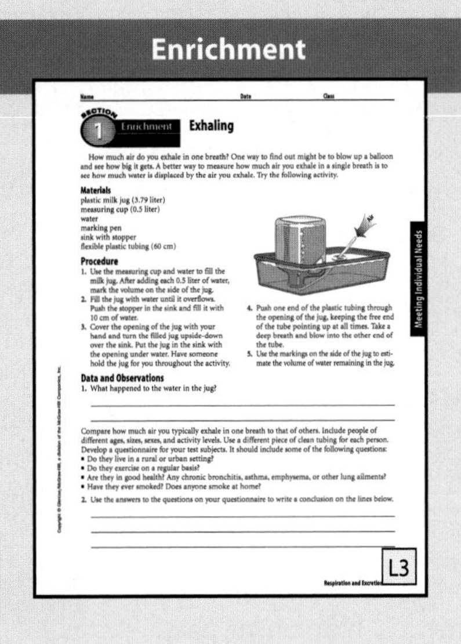

Section 1 Enrichment — Exhaling

L3

Spanish Directed Reading

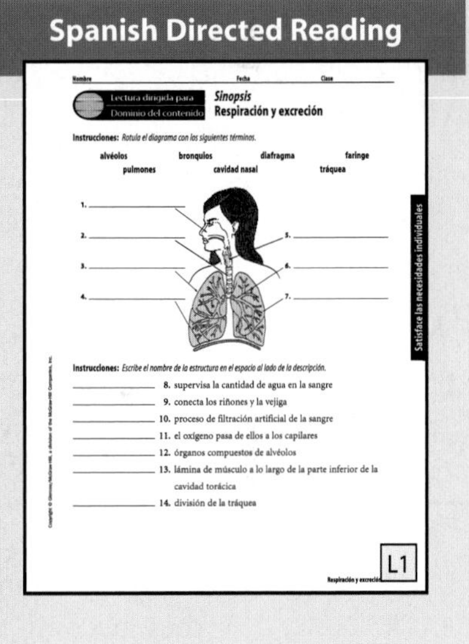

Lectura dirigida para Dominio del contenido — Sinopsis: Respiración y excreción

L1

Assessment

Chapter Tests

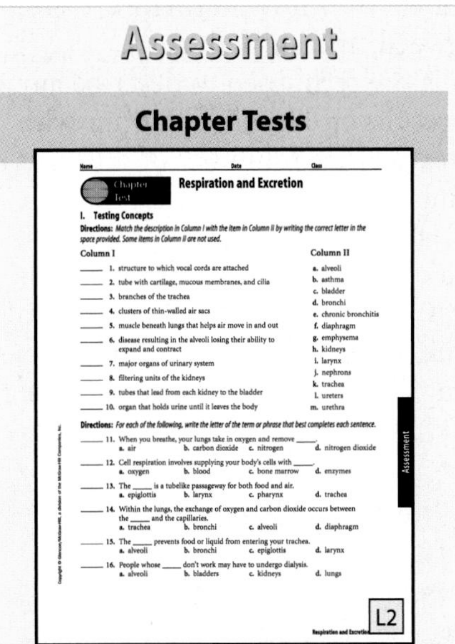

Chapter Test — Respiration and Excretion

L2

Test Practice Workbook

L2

Chapter Review

Chapter Review — Respiration and Excretion

Part A. Vocabulary Review

L2

Science Content Background

SECTION 1

The Respiratory System

Functions of the Respiratory System

In order to function, cells need nutrients, which must be oxidized in order to release energy. The process of obtaining energy from nutrients is called cellular respiration. In respiration the most commonly used carbohydrate is glucose. The oxidation of glucose produces water and carbon dioxide, and releases energy.

$$C_6H_{12}O_6 + 6O_2 \rightarrow 6H_2O + 6CO_2 + \text{energy}$$

Obtaining oxygen and removing carbon dioxide are the major functions of the respiratory system. These processes occur in two successive phases of functioning—breathing and transporting gases. In order to effectively exchange the gases involved in respiration, a large surface area is required. There are 300 million to 400 million alveoli in each lung. The air sacs of both lungs have a total surface area of about 93 m^2, nearly 50 times the total surface area of the skin.

The Lungs

Lungs are pink at birth, but as a person ages, they become gray and mottled from tiny particles breathed in with the air. Usually people who live in cities and industrial areas have darker lungs than those who live in the country.

In the adult human, the left lung is divided into two sections, or lobes—the superior and the inferior. The right lung is somewhat larger than the left lung and is divided into three lobes—the superior, middle, and inferior. The two lungs are separated by an area which contains the heart, trachea, esophagus, and blood vessels.

Fun Fact

Your lungs inhale and exhale about 500 mL of air with an average breath. This may increase to 2,000 mL of air per breath when you do strenuous physical activity.

The movement of air in and out of the lungs is possible due to three factors: the ability of the thoracic cavity to change size, the elasticity of the lung tissue, and the difference in pressure between the lungs and chest.

Diseases and Disorders of the Respiratory System

Many diseases and disorders affect the health of the human respiratory system and interfere with its effectiveness. Allergies affect so many people that pollen counts of the atmosphere are reported in the media. The worst allergens include the pollen of wind-pollinated trees, grasses, and ragweed, and air pollutants.

Pneumonia is the term used to describe any condition that results in alveoli filling up with fluid. It can be caused by a number of different factors, including chemicals, bacteria, viruses, or fungi. Blood infections, chronic alcoholism, inhalation of fluids into the lungs, or even prolonged bed rest can predispose a person to infection of the lungs by microorganisms. Chronic smoking has the potential to promote emphysema and lung cancer.

SECTION 2

The Excretory System

The Urinary System

The metabolic processes of the body produce waste products. The respiratory system rids the body of carbon dioxide and other waste gases. The digestive system eliminates solid wastes. The urinary system removes a variety of dissolved salts and nitrogenous wastes from the blood and lymph systems.

The major organs of the urinary system are a pair of bean-shaped structures called kidneys, each of which is approximately 10 cm long and 5 cm wide. They weigh about 170 g each. The functioning unit of the kidney is the nephron. All of the blood in the body flows through the kidneys about once every five minutes.

Fun Fact

Protozoans are complete organisms (most are one-celled) that ingest food, digest food, expel waste, and breathe without the benefit of separate organs such as those that humans have.

Urine

Urea and uric acid are wastes from the metabolism of proteins. The straw color of fresh urine is due to a pigment called urochrome. The average pH of urine is approximately 6.0, making it slightly acidic.

The urinary system also functions in maintaining the homeostasis of body fluids and electrolytes and keeps the levels of acids and bases in proper balance. All of this provides for the uniform composition of the blood components.

Urinary Disease and Disorders

Urinary tract infections are common, second only to respiratory infections. Normally urine is sterile. An infection occurs when microbes, usually bacteria from the digestive tract, adhere to the opening of the urethra and begin to multiply. Most urinary tract infections can be traced to one type of colon bacteria, *Escherichia coli (E. coli)*. Often the bacteria move from the urethra to the bladder causing a bladder infection. Such infections are usually treated with specific antibacterial drugs.

For additional content background on this topic, go to the Glencoe Science Web site at science.glencoe.com.

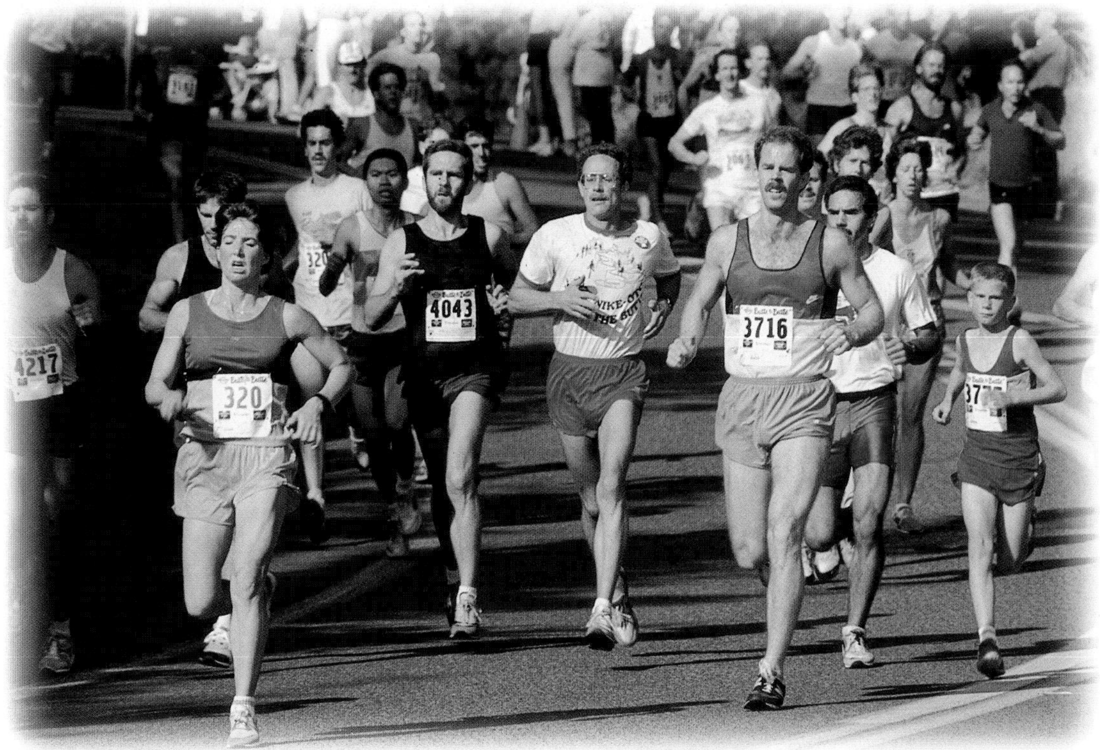

Greg Vaughn/Tom Stack & Associates

CHAPTER 20

Respiration and Excretion

Chapter Vocabulary

pharynx, p. 576
larynx, p. 577
trachea, p. 577
bronchi, p. 577
alveoli, p. 577
diaphragm, p. 578
emphysema, p. 581
asthma, p. 582
urinary system, p. 583
urine, p. 584
kidneys, p. 584
nephron, p. 585
ureter, p. 586
bladder, p. 586
urethra, p. 586

What do you think?

Science Journal The wormlike things are cilia, hairlike structures in the nasal cavity. They help trap foreign material that comes into the nose and move it to the back of the throat.

CHAPTER 20

Respiration and Excretion

How do you feel when you've just finished running a mile, or sliding into home base, or slamming a soccer ball into the goal past your opponent? If you're like most people, you probably breathe hard and perspire. Maybe you have even felt your lungs would burst. You need a constant supply of oxygen to keep your body cells functioning. Your body is adapted to meet that need.

What do you think?

Science Journal Look at the picture below. What do you think these wormlike things are? Here's a hint: *You are glad you have them on a dusty day.* Write your answer or best guess in your Science Journal.

Theme Connection

Energy Energy transformation is a central theme in this text. Human cells require oxygen in order to utilize nutrients and provide energy for cellular activities. Chemical energy is transformed into thermal and mechanical energy.

Your body can store food and water, but it cannot store much oxygen. Breathing brings oxygen into your body. In the following activity, find out about one factor that can change your breathing rate.

Measure breathing rate

1. Put your hand on the side of your rib cage. Take a deep breath. Notice how your rib cage moves out and upward when you inhale.
2. Count the number of breaths you take for 15 s. Multiply this number by four to calculate your normal breathing rate for 1 min.
3. Repeat step 2 two more times, then calculate your average breathing rate.
4. Do a physical activity described by your teacher for 1 min and repeat step 2 to determine your breathing rate now.
5. Time how long it takes for your breathing rate to return to normal.

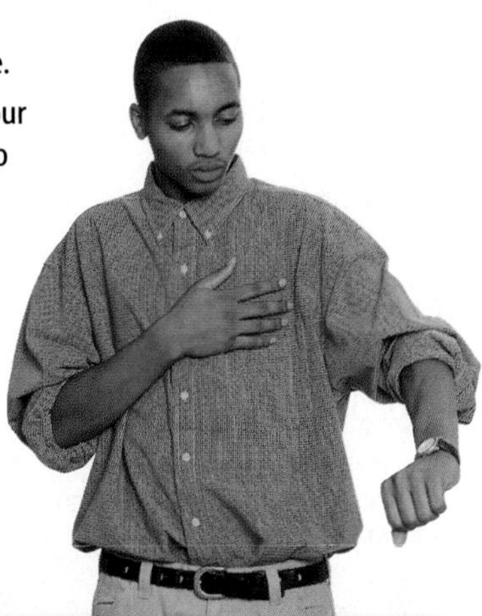

Observe

How does breathing rate appear to be related to physical activity? Write your answer in your Science Journal.

Before You Read

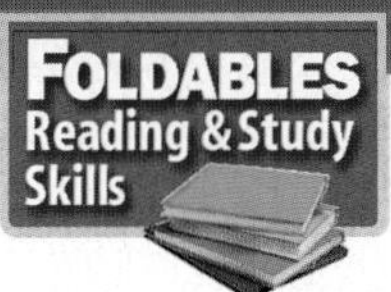

Making a Know-Want-Learn Study Fold Make the following Foldable to help identify what you already know and what you want to know about respiration.

1. Place a sheet of paper in front of you so the long side is at the top. Fold the paper in half from top to bottom.
2. Fold in both sides to divide the paper into thirds. Unfold the paper.
3. Cut through the top thickness of paper along each of the fold lines to the top fold to form three tabs. Label each tab as shown.
4. Before you read the chapter, write *I breathe* under the left tab. Write *Why do I breathe?* under the middle tab.
5. As you read the chapter, write the answer you learn under the right tab.

Explore Activity

Purpose Use the Explore Activity to introduce students to respiration. Students will discover how the respiratory system responds to physical activity. L2 ELL

LS **Kinesthetic**

Preparation Check with the school nurse to determine whether any students should not jog or engage in activities that stress the heart and respiratory system.

Materials watch or clock with second hand, calculator

Teaching Strategies

- Any students not able to participate in the physical part of this activity can be designated as timekeepers or recorders.
- Review the reason for multiplying by four to obtain the pulse rate for one minute.

Observe

Breathing rates increase after physical activity.

Performance Have students design another activity that will result in an increase in breathing rate, do the activity, and gather the data. Use **Performance Assessment in the Science Classroom,** p. 105.

Before You Read

FOLDABLES Reading & Study Skills

Dinah Zike Study Fold

Purpose Use this activity to get students thinking about respiration before they read the chapter by asking them to pose questions to guide their reading. Students record answers to their questions in a Foldable that becomes a study guide.

For additional help, see Foldables Worksheet, p. 15 in **Chapter Resources Booklet,** or go to the Glencoe Science Web site at **science.glencoe.com.** See After You Read in the Study Guide at the end of this chapter.

SECTION

The Respiratory System

1 Motivate

Bellringer Transparency

Display the Section Focus Transparency for Section 1. Use the accompanying Transparency Activity Master. L2

ELL

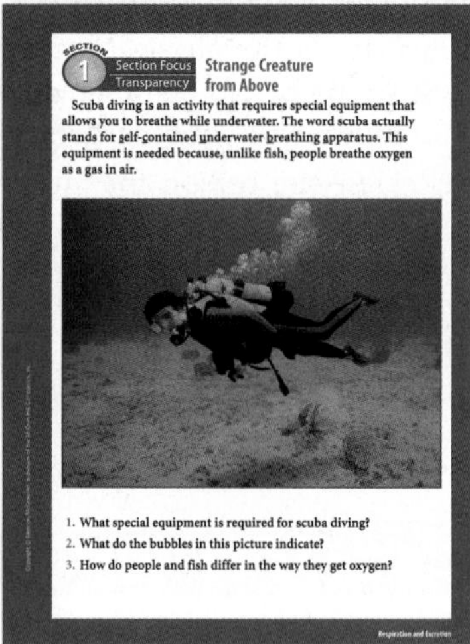

SECTION 1 Section Focus Transparency — Strange Creature from Above

Scuba diving is an activity that requires special equipment that allows you to breathe while underwater. The word scuba actually stands for self-contained underwater breathing apparatus. This equipment is needed because, unlike fish, people breathe oxygen as a gas in air.

1. What special equipment is required for scuba diving?
2. What do the bubbles in this picture indicate?
3. How do people and fish differ in the way they get oxygen?

Respiration and Excretion

Tie to Prior Knowledge

Students are aware that they need oxygen to live. Ask students how they get oxygen into their bodies. Most will say breathing. Point out that oxygen taken in by the respiratory system is transported to the body's cells by the circulatory system.

SECTION 1

The Respiratory System

As You Read

What You'll Learn

- **Describe** the functions of the respiratory system.
- **Explain** how oxygen and carbon dioxide are exchanged in the lungs and in tissues.
- **Identify** the pathway of air in and out of the lungs.
- **Explain** the effects of smoking on the respiratory system.

Vocabulary

pharynx, larynx, trachea, bronchi, alveoli, diaphragm, emphysema, asthma

Why It's Important

Your body's cells depend on your respiratory system to supply oxygen and remove carbon dioxide.

Functions of the Respiratory System

Can you imagine an astronaut walking on the Moon without a space suit or a diver exploring the ocean without scuba gear? Of course not. You couldn't survive in either location under those conditions because you need to breathe air. Earth is surrounded by a layer of gases called the atmosphere (AT muh sfihr). You breathe atmospheric gases that are closest to Earth. As shown in **Figure 1,** oxygen is one of those gases.

For thousands of years people have known that air, food, and water are needed for life. However, the gas in the air that is necessary for life was not identified as oxygen until the late 1700s. At that time, a French scientist experimented and discovered that an animal breathed in oxygen and breathed out carbon dioxide. He measured the amount of oxygen that the animal used and the amount of carbon dioxide produced by its bodily processes. After his work with animals, the French scientist used this knowledge to study the way that humans use oxygen. He measured the amount of oxygen that a person uses when resting and when exercising. These measurements were compared, and he discovered that more oxygen is used by the body during exercise.

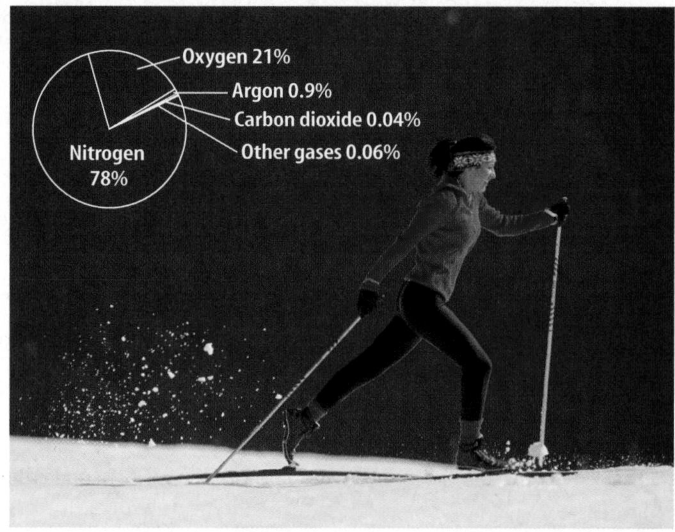

Figure 1
Air, which is needed by most organisms, is only 21 percent oxygen.

Section Assessment Planner

PORTFOLIO
Extension, p. 577

PERFORMANCE ASSESSMENT
Try at Home MiniLAB, p. 578
Skill Builder Activities, p. 582
See page 596 for more options.

CONTENT ASSESSMENT
Section, p. 582
Challenge, p. 582
Chapter, pp. 596–597

574 CHAPTER 20 Respiration and Excretion

Figure 2
Several processes are involved in how the body obtains, transports, and uses oxygen.

$$C_6H_{12}O_6 + 6O_2 \longrightarrow 6CO_2 + 6H_2O + \text{Energy}$$

Glucose + Oxygen → Carbon dioxide + Water + Energy

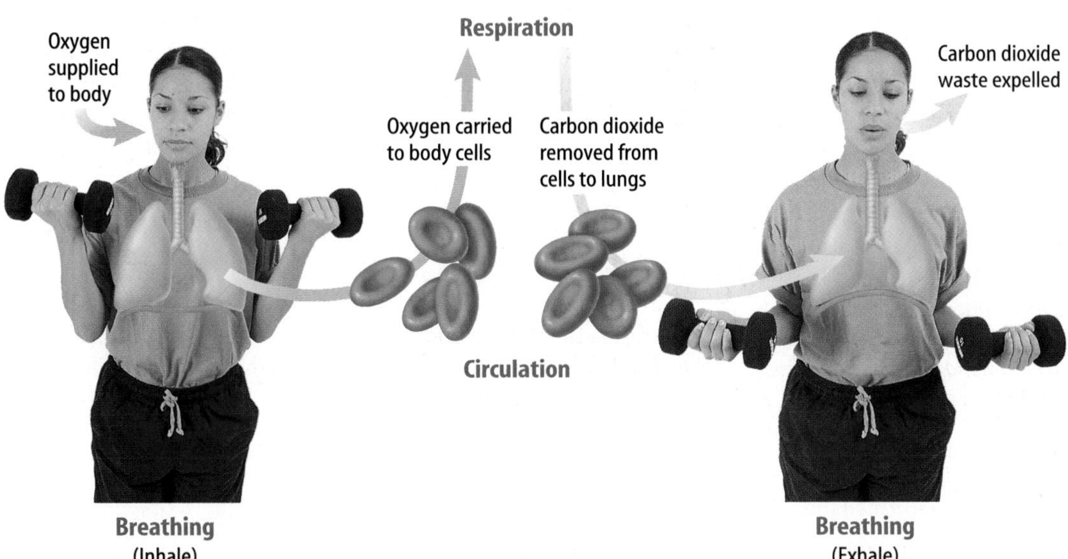

Breathing and Respiration People often confuse the terms *breathing* and *respiration.* Breathing is the movement of the chest that brings air into the lungs and removes waste gases. The air entering the lungs contains oxygen. It passes from the lungs into the circulatory system because there is less oxygen in the blood than in cells of the lungs. Blood carries oxygen to individual cells. At the same time, the digestive system supplies glucose from digested food to the same cells. The oxygen delivered to the cells is used to release energy from glucose. This chemical reaction, shown in the equation in **Figure 2,** is called cellular respiration. Without oxygen, this reaction would not take place. Carbon dioxide and water molecules are waste products of cellular respiration. They are carried back to the lungs in the blood. Exhaling, or breathing out, eliminates waste carbon dioxide and some water molecules.

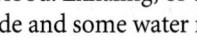

Reading Check *What is respiration?*

Earth Science INTEGRATION

The amount of water vapor in the atmosphere varies from almost none over deserts to nearly four percent in tropical rain forest areas. This means that every 100 molecules that make up air include only four molecules of water. In your Science Journal, infer how breathing dry air can stress your respiratory system.

2 Teach

Functions of the Respiratory System

Earth Science INTEGRATION

Breathing dry air can irritate nasal and throat passages.

Reading Check

Answer A cellular chemical reaction in which glucose and oxygen combine and produce CO_2 and H_2O with the release of energy.

Quick Demo

If possible, obtain pig lungs from a meat-packing house or biological supply company for students to examine. Students are often surprised at the light weight of the organs. Lead a discussion on why lungs aren't heavy. Lungs are composed of alveoli, which are hollow.

Extension

A person can experience oxygen deficiency in carbon monoxide poisoning. Have students research how carbon monoxide impairs the delivery of oxygen to tissues. Prepare a chart to show how to avoid carbon monoxide poisoning in the home. L2

Activity

Have students blow through a straw into a test tube one-fourth full of limewater. Note the change from a clear liquid to a cloudy liquid. This indicates the presence of carbon dioxide. L1
LS **Kinesthetic**

Resource Manager

Chapter Resources Booklet
Transparency Activity, p. 40
Directed Reading for Content Mastery, pp. 17, 18

Inclusion Strategies

Gifted An opera singer's ability to be heard over an orchestra in a large auditorium for an extended period of time is a result of breath control. Breath control enables singers to sustain a long musical phrase, and change volume for dramatic effect. Invite students who have studied voice or a wind instrument to perform for the class and demonstrate their breathing techniques. ELL LS **Auditory-Musical**

Organs of the Respiratory System

Text Question Answer

The food or drink gets into your airway.

Caption Answer

Figure 3 It can be cleaned, warmed, and moistened before moving to the pharynx.

Make a Model

Blow up a balloon and stretch the opening into a narrow slit. Explain to students that the balloon represents a lung and its neck is the trachea. Stretch the slit to make it longer and release a bit to make it shorter, noting the changes in pitch. Correlate the higher-pitched sounds and tighter stretch with the shorter vocal cords of females and the lower-pitched sounds and looser stretch with the longer vocal cords of males.

Teacher FYI

Sinuses are air-filled cavities in the cranial bones that open into the nasal cavity. The cavities act as resonant chambers and affect the sound of our speech.

Use an Analogy

The nasal cavity traps air particles just as a dust mask traps dust and pollen from the air.

Organs of the Respiratory System

The respiratory system, shown in **Figure 3,** is made up of structures and organs that help move oxygen into the body and waste gases out of the body. Air enters your body through two openings in your nose called nostrils or through the mouth. Fine hairs inside the nostrils trap dust from the air. Air then passes through the nasal cavity, where it gets moistened and warmed by the body's heat. Glands that produce sticky mucus line the nasal cavity. The mucus traps dust, pollen, and other materials that were not trapped by nasal hairs. This process helps filter and clean the air you breathe. Tiny, hairlike structures, called cilia (SIHL ee uh), sweep mucus and trapped material to the back of the throat where it can be swallowed.

Pharynx Warmed, moist air then enters the **pharynx** (FER ingks), which is a tubelike passageway used by food, liquid, and air. At the lower end of the pharynx is a flap of tissue called the epiglottis (ep uh GLAHT us). When you swallow, your epiglottis folds down to prevent food or liquid from entering your airway. The food enters your esophagus instead. What do you think has happened if you begin to choke?

Figure 3
Air can enter the body through the nostrils and the mouth. *What is an advantage of having air enter through the nostrils?*

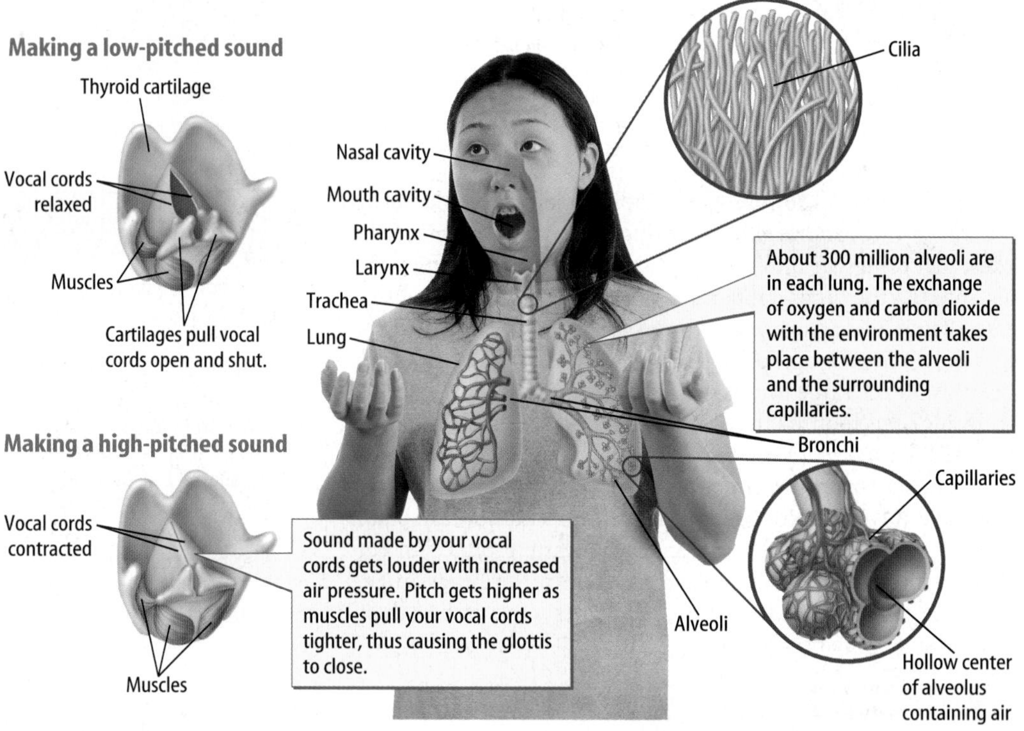

Making a low-pitched sound
Thyroid cartilage
Vocal cords relaxed
Muscles
Cartilages pull vocal cords open and shut.
Making a high-pitched sound
Vocal cords contracted
Muscles
Sound made by your vocal cords gets louder with increased air pressure. Pitch gets higher as muscles pull your vocal cords tighter, thus causing the glottis to close.
Nasal cavity
Mouth cavity
Pharynx
Larynx
Trachea
Lung
Cilia
About 300 million alveoli are in each lung. The exchange of oxygen and carbon dioxide with the environment takes place between the alveoli and the surrounding capillaries.
Bronchi
Capillaries
Alveoli
Hollow center of alveolus containing air

Curriculum Connection

Health The pharynx serves as the passageway of food into the esophagus and air into the trachea. The epiglottis is a small flap of tissue that normally closes over the tracheal opening when food is swallowed. Sometimes food or liquid gets past the epiglottis and goes into the trachea, triggering the choking reflex. Ask students to discuss ways to prevent choking. L2
Logical-Mathematical

Cultural Diversity

Living at High Altitudes People living at high altitudes must deal with a slightly reduced pull of gravity, gas molecules that are spread out in the air, and a reduced pressure gradient. Have students research how the bodies of people native to high altitudes have adapted to these changes. Possible answers: number of red blood cells and amount of hemoglobin increase; increase in the number of small blood vessels. L3

Larynx and Trachea Next, the air moves into your larynx (LER ingks). The **larynx** is the airway to which two pairs of horizontal folds of tissue, called vocal cords, are attached as shown in **Figure 3.** Forcing air between the cords causes them to vibrate and produce sounds. When you speak, muscles tighten or loosen your vocal cords, resulting in different sounds. Your brain coordinates the movement of the muscles in your throat, tongue, cheeks, and lips when you talk, sing, or just make noise. Your teeth also are involved in forming letter sounds and words.

From the larynx, air moves into the **trachea** (TRAY kee uh), which is a tube about 12 cm in length. Strong, C-shaped rings of cartilage prevent the trachea from collapsing. The trachea is lined with mucous membranes and cilia, as shown in **Figure 3,** that trap dust, bacteria, and pollen. Why must the trachea stay open all the time?

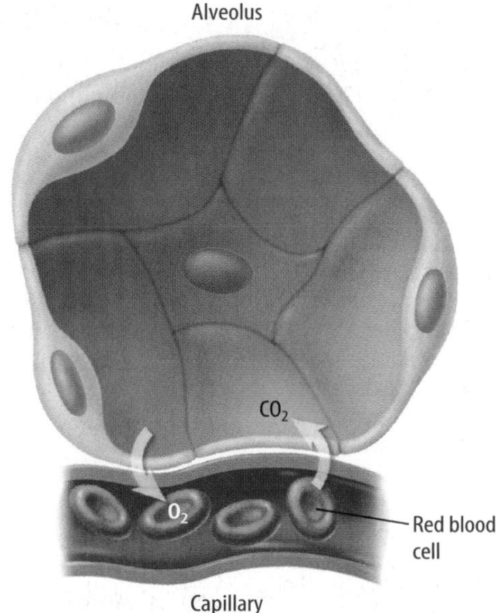

Figure 4
The thin capillary walls allow gases to be exchanged easily between the alveoli and the capillaries.

Bronchi and the Lungs Air is carried into your lungs by two short tubes called **bronchi** (BRAHN ki) (singular, *bronchus)* at the lower end of the trachea. Within the lungs, the bronchi branch into smaller and smaller tubes. The smallest tubes are called bronchioles (BRAHN kee ohlz). At the end of each bronchiole are clusters of tiny, thin-walled sacs called **alveoli** (al VEE uh li). Air passes into the bronchi, then into the bronchioles, and finally into the alveoli. As shown in **Figure 3,** lungs are masses of alveoli arranged in grapelike clusters. The capillaries surround the alveoli like a net.

The exchange of oxygen and carbon dioxide takes place between the alveoli and capillaries. This easily happens because the walls of the alveoli (singular, *alveolus)* and the walls of the capillaries are each only one cell thick, as shown in **Figure 4.** Oxygen moves through the cell membranes of the alveoli and then through the cell membranes of the capillaries into the blood. There the oxygen is picked up by hemoglobin (HEE muh gloh bun), a molecule in red blood cells, and carried to all body cells. At the same time, carbon dioxide and other cellular wastes leave the body cells. The wastes move through the cell membranes of the capillaries. Then they are carried by the blood. In the lungs, waste gases move through the cell membranes of the capillaries and through the cell membranes of the alveoli. Then waste gases leave the body during exhalation.

Research Visit the Glencoe Science Web site at **science.glencoe.com** for more information about how speech sounds are made. Report to your class what you learn.

Activity

Have students place their fingers on the front of their necks, tilt their heads backward, and gently move their fingers up and down. Tell students that the ridges they feel are the rings of cartilage around the trachea. L1 LS **Kinesthetic**

Text Question Answer

If the trachea collapsed, it would be difficult or impossible to breathe.

Use Science Words

Word Origin *Alvearium* is the Latin word for "beehive." Think about the internal structure of the beehive and relate this to the air cells of the lungs, the alveoli.

Extension

Have students research how dry air taken in through the nostrils has about 100% humidity by the time it reaches the alveoli. Have them report on why this is important. L2 P

SCIENCE Online

Internet Addresses

Explore the Glencoe Science Web site at **science.glencoe.com** to find out more about topics in this section.

Fun Fact

During one minute, while the body is at rest, approximately 12.5 mL of oxygen per kg of body weight are used by body cells; an equal amount of carbon dioxide is produced.

Resource Manager

Chapter Resources Booklet
Note-taking Worksheets, pp. 29–31
Reading and Writing Skill Activities, p. 39

Why do you breathe?

Purpose Students observe the increased surface area provided by alveoli. L2 ELL

LS **Logical-Mathematical**

Materials bathroom-tissue cardboard tube, marbles, bowl, calculator

Teaching Strategy Gently shake the tube when half-full of marbles to settle them and avoid gaps.

Analysis

1. Answers will vary depending on stacking techniques, but will usually indicate a more than twofold increase in the surface area when using marbles.
2. The marbles represent the alveoli.
3. More gas can be exchanged because there is greater surface area within the same space.

Assessment

Performance Have students calculate the surface area of a cube that is 10 cm x 5 cm x 2 cm and compare this with the surface area of one hundred 1 cm x 1 cm x 1 cm cubes that have the same volume as the larger cube. Use **PASC**, p. 101.

Reading Check

Answer It helps move gases into and out of the body.

Visual Learning

Figure 5 The position of the diaphragm during the process of inhaling and expanding is shown. Compare this process with the squeezing of the plastic bottle discussed in the text.

Comparing Surface Area

Procedure

1. Stand a **bathroom-tissue cardboard tube** in an **empty bowl.**
2. Drop **marbles** into the tube, filling it to the top.
3. Count the number of marbles used.
4. Repeat steps 2 and 3 two more times. Calculate the average number of marbles needed to fill the tube.
5. The tube's inside surface area is approximately 161.29 cm^2. Each marble has a surface area of approximately 8.06 cm^2. Calculate the surface area of the average number of marbles.

Analysis

1. Compare the inside surface area of the tube with the surface area of the average number of marbles needed to fill the tube.
2. If the tube represents a bronchus, what do the marbles represent?
3. Using this model, explain what makes gas exchange in the lungs efficient.

Why do you breathe?

Signals from your brain tell the muscles in your chest and abdomen to contract and relax. You don't have to think about breathing to breathe, just like your heart beats without you telling it to beat. Your brain can change your breathing rate depending on the amount of carbon dioxide present in your blood. If a lot of carbon dioxide is present, your breathing rate increases. It decreases if less carbon dioxide is in your blood. You do have some control over your breathing—you can hold your breath if you want to. Eventually, though, your brain will respond to the buildup of carbon dioxide in your blood. The brain's response will tell your chest and abdomen muscles to work automatically, and you will breathe whether you want to or not.

Inhaling and Exhaling Breathing is partly the result of changes in air pressure. Under normal conditions, a gas moves from an area of high pressure to an area of low pressure. When you squeeze an empty, soft-plastic bottle, air is pushed out. This happens because air pressure outside the top of the bottle is less than the pressure you create inside the bottle when you squeeze it. As you release your grip on the bottle, the air pressure inside the bottle becomes less than it is outside the bottle. Air rushes back in, and the bottle returns to its original shape.

Your lungs work in a similar way to the squeezed bottle. Your **diaphragm** (DI uh fram) is a muscle beneath your lungs that contracts and relaxes to help move gases into and out of your lungs. **Figure 5** illustrates breathing.

Reading Check *How does your diaphragm help you breathe?*

When a person is choking, a rescuer can use abdominal thrusts, as shown in **Figure 6,** to save the life of the choking victim.

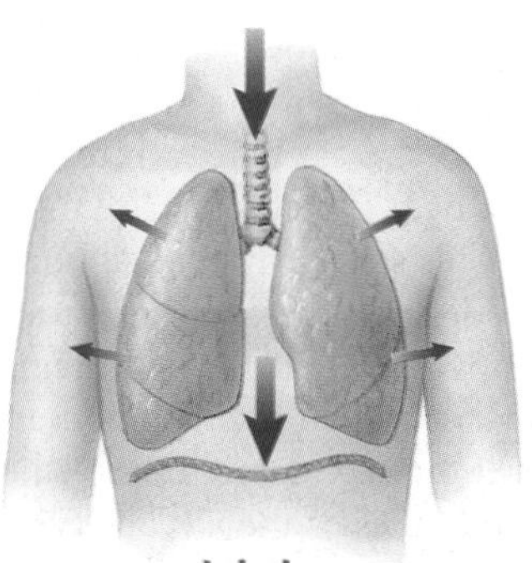

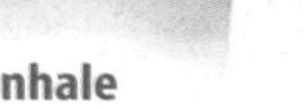

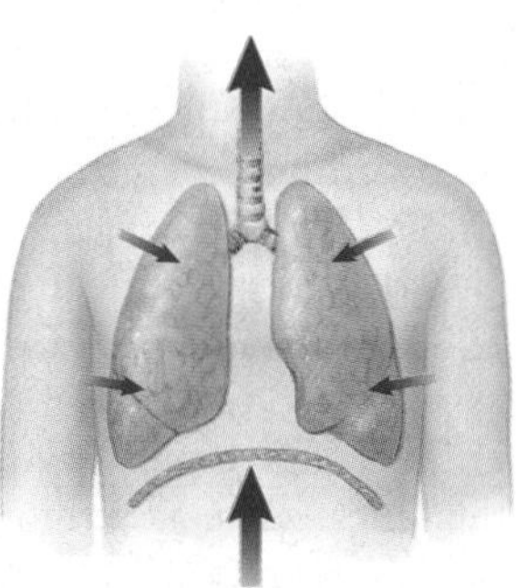

Figure 5
Your lungs inhale and exhale about 500 mL of air with an average breath. This increases to 2,000 mL of air per breath when you do strenuous activity.

Resource Manager

Chapter Resources Booklet
MiniLAB, p. 3
Lab Activity, pp. 9–12

Life Science Critical Thinking/Problem Solving, p. 17

Teacher FYI

Hiccups are caused by spasmodic contractions of the diaphragm. The result is a sudden inhaling of air. Choking could result if a reflex action did not automatically cause the epiglottis to close over the trachea and prevent any food from entering.

NATIONAL GEOGRAPHIC **VISUALIZING ABDOMINAL THRUSTS**

Figure 6

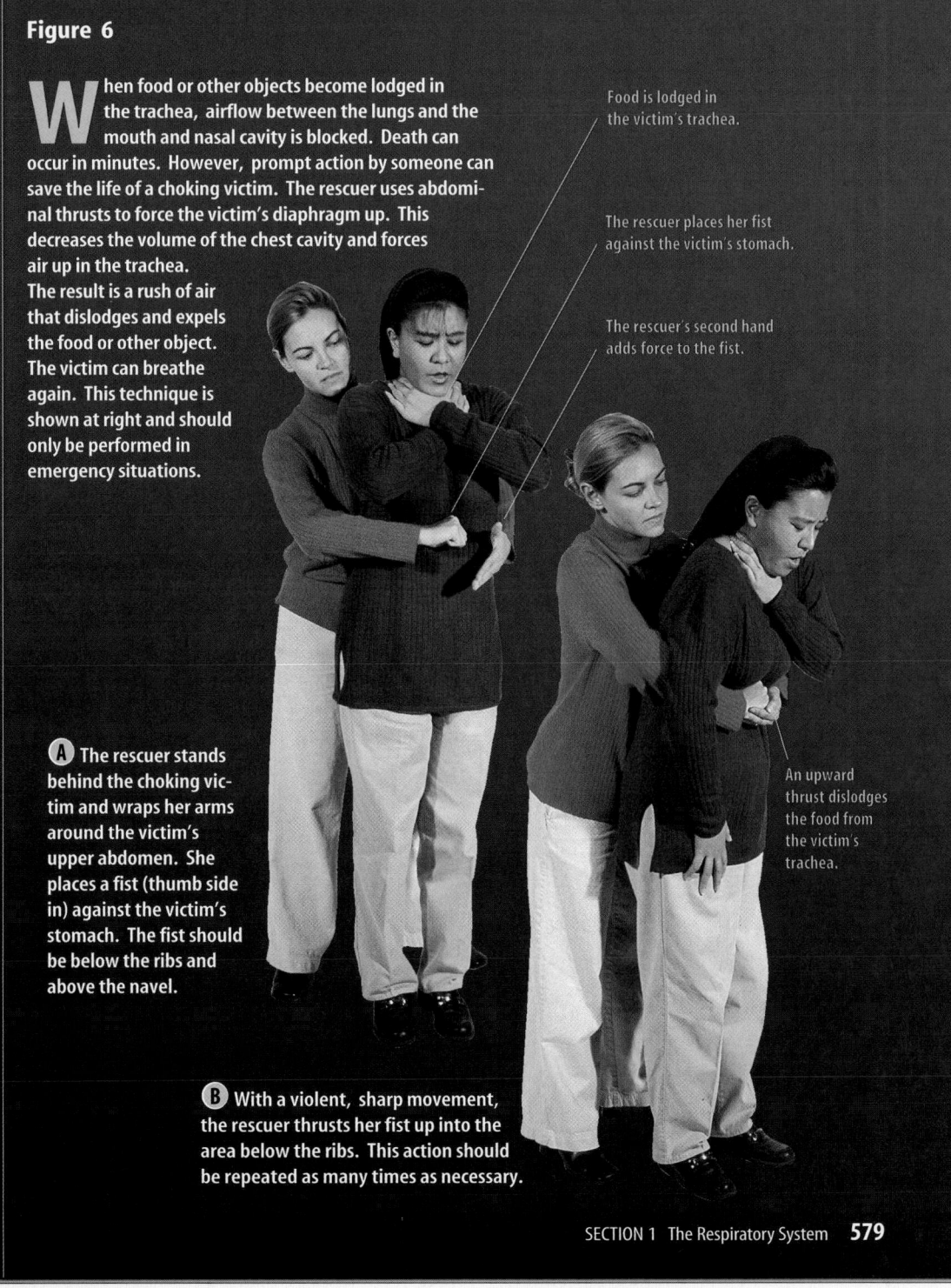

When food or other objects become lodged in the trachea, airflow between the lungs and the mouth and nasal cavity is blocked. Death can occur in minutes. However, prompt action by someone can save the life of a choking victim. The rescuer uses abdominal thrusts to force the victim's diaphragm up. This decreases the volume of the chest cavity and forces air up in the trachea. The result is a rush of air that dislodges and expels the food or other object. The victim can breathe again. This technique is shown at right and should only be performed in emergency situations.

Food is lodged in the victim's trachea.

The rescuer places her fist against the victim's stomach.

The rescuer's second hand adds force to the fist.

An upward thrust dislodges the food from the victim's trachea.

A The rescuer stands behind the choking victim and wraps her arms around the victim's upper abdomen. She places a fist (thumb side in) against the victim's stomach. The fist should be below the ribs and above the navel.

B With a violent, sharp movement, the rescuer thrusts her fist up into the area below the ribs. This action should be repeated as many times as necessary.

SECTION 1 The Respiratory System **579**

Visualizing Abdominal Thrusts

Have students examine the pictures and read the captions. Then ask the following questions.

Why s hould abdominal thrusts only be performed in emergencies, and never performed on other people for practice or for fun? Abdominal thrusts could cause injury if performed on a person who is not choking .

Why is it important that the rescuer's fist be located below the ribs of the choking victim? The fist must be below the diaphragm in order for an upward force to be applied to the diaphragm. A fist located on the rib cage or breastbone could cause injury to the victim.

Activity

Have students work in small groups to develop a mnemonic, or memory device, that will allow them to quickly and accurately remember the steps of proper abdominal thrusts to save a choking victim.

Extension

Have students use the non-emergency number to contact the local rescue squad. Have the students obtain statistics on the number of choking incidents that occur each year in your area, and share the information with the class.

Visual Learning

Figure 6 Review the theory of how abdominal thrusts work. This maneuver is often called the Heimlich maneuver. Abdominal thrusts lift the diaphragm and force enough air from the lungs to create an artificial cough. The cough is intended to move and expel an obstructing foreign body from an airway.

Curriculum Connection

Health Arrange a visit to a Red Cross center or have a health specialist come to school and demonstrate how to use abdominal thrusts and cardiopulmonary resuscitation (CPR) to revive a person who is not breathing. Ask students to find out where CPR training is available in their area. L2

Diseases and Disorders of the Respiratory System

Teacher FYI

The chemical nicotine has been widely used by farmers and gardeners since the seventeenth century in sprays and dusts as an insecticide. Its use is now more carefully regulated to prevent accidental poisonings.

Internet Addresses

Explore the Glencoe Science Web site at **science.glencoe.com** to find out more about topics in this section.

Reading Check

Answer all parts, but usually the upper part, from the nose to the pharynx

Table 1 Smokers' Risk of Death from Disease

Disease	Smokers' Risk Compared to Nonsmokers' Risk
Lung Cancer	23 times higher for males, 11 times higher for females
Chronic Bronchitis and Emphysema	5 times higher
Heart Disease	2 times higher

Diseases and Disorders of the Respiratory System

Environmental Science INTEGRATION

If you were asked to list some of the things that can harm your respiratory system, you probably would put smoking at the top. As you can see in **Table 1,** many serious diseases are related to smoking. The chemical substances in tobacco—nicotine and tars—are poisons and can destroy cells. The high temperatures, smoke, and carbon monoxide produced when tobacco burns also can injure a smoker's cells. Even if you are a nonsmoker, inhaling smoke from tobacco products—called secondhand smoke—is unhealthy and has the potential to harm your respiratory system. Smoking, polluted air, coal dust, and asbestos (as BES tus) have been related to respiratory problems such as bronchitis (brahn KITE us), emphysema (em fuh SEE muh), asthma (AZ muh), and cancer.

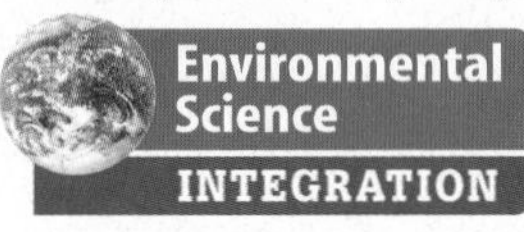

Research Visit the Glencoe Science Web site at **science.glencoe.com** for more information about the health aspects of secondhand smoke. Make a poster explaining what you learn.

Respiratory Infections Bacteria, viruses, and other microorganisms can cause infections that affect any of the organs of the respiratory system. The common cold usually affects the upper part of the respiratory system—from the nose to the pharynx. The cold virus also can cause irritation and swelling in the larynx, trachea, and bronchi. The cilia that line the trachea and bronchi can be damaged. However, cilia usually heal rapidly. A virus that causes influenza, or flu, can affect many of the body's systems. The virus multiplies in the cells lining the alveoli and damages them. Pneumonia is an infection in the alveoli that can be caused by bacteria, viruses, or other microorganisms. Before antibiotics were available to treat these infections, many people died from pneumonia.

Reading Check *What parts of the respiratory system are affected by the cold virus?*

LAB DEMONSTRATION

Purpose to compare cilia functionality in the presence and absence of tar

Materials fine-tooth comb, water, black pepper, molasses, newspaper

Preparation Cover work area with newspaper. The comb teeth represent cilia, pepper represents dust, and the molasses represents tar.

Procedure Put the fine-toothed end of the comb in a cup of water. Remove and sprinkle with pepper. Run a finger over the teeth five times, making them vibrate. Wash the comb and repeat the process using molasses instead of water.

Expected Outcome Students will see how tar prevents cilia from removing dust particles.

Assessment

Why do foreign particles need to be removed from the bronchial tubes? The particles can irritate the tissues, and bacteria can cause infections. **In addition to preventing normal cilia action, why are tars dangerous?** They are poisons that can kill cells.

Chronic Bronchitis When bronchial tubes are irritated and swell and too much mucus is produced, a disease called bronchitis develops. Sometimes, bacterial infections occur in the bronchial tubes because the mucus there provides nearly ideal conditions for bacteria to grow. Antibiotics are effective treatments for this type of bronchitis.

Many cases of bronchitis clear up within a few weeks, but the disease sometimes lasts for a long time. When this happens, it is called chronic (KRAHN ihk) bronchitis. A person who has chronic bronchitis must cough often to try to clear the excess mucus from the airway. However, the more a person coughs, the more the cilia and bronchial tubes can be harmed. When cilia are damaged, they cannot move mucus, bacteria, and dirt particles out of the lungs effectively. Then harmful substances, such as sticky tar from burning tobacco, build up in the airways. Sometimes, scar tissue forms and the respiratory system cannot function properly.

Do you know what to do if someone is having trouble breathing? To find out about such emergencies, see the **Emergencies Field Guide** at the back of the book.

Emphysema A disease in which the alveoli in the lungs enlarge is called **emphysema** (em fuh SEE muh). When cells in the alveoli are reddened and swollen, an enzyme is released that causes the walls of the alveoli to break down. As a result, alveoli can't push air out of the lungs, so less oxygen moves into the bloodstream from the alveoli. When blood becomes low in oxygen and high in carbon dioxide, shortness of breath occurs. Some people with emphysema require extra oxygen as shown in **Figure 7C.** Because the heart works harder to supply oxygen to body cells, people who have emphysema often develop heart problems, as well.

Figure 7
Lung diseases can have major effects on breathing.

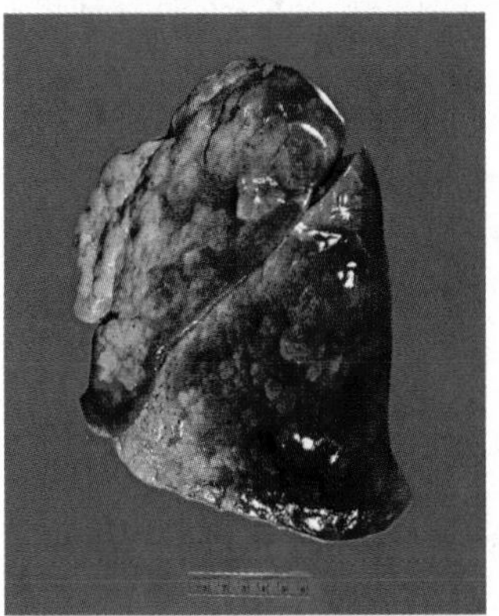

A A normal, healthy lung can exchange oxygen and carbon dioxide effectively.

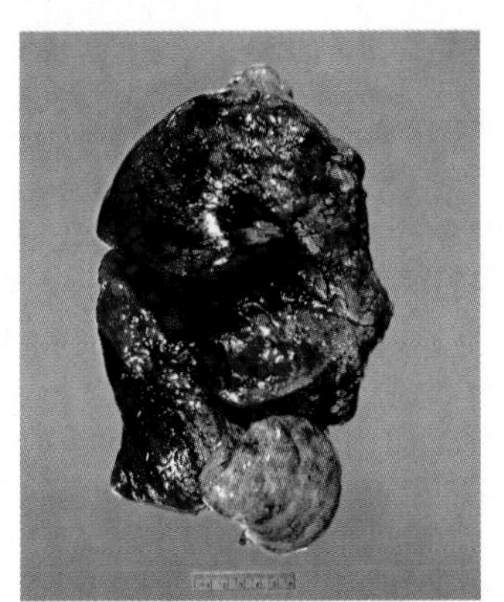

B A diseased lung carries less oxygen to body cells.

C Emphysema may take 20 to 30 years to develop.

IDENTIFYING Misconceptions

Many people believe that being exposed to cold drafts or cold rain will cause a cold. Colds are caused by viruses and not by exposure to cold and wet conditions. People already infected by cold germs who get cold and wet and then develop the full symptoms may thereby associate the two events.

Teacher FYI

Inhaling tobacco smoke or other chemical irritants stimulates an increase in goblet cells and the enlargement of mucous cells in the lining of the bronchial tubes. This is the cause of the increased mucus in the bronchi of bronchitis sufferers.

Use Science Words

Word Origin The word *emphysema* comes from two Greek words: *em-*, meaning "*in*," and *physan*, meaning "*blow*." **How does the origin of the word relate to the symptoms of the disease?** Persons with the disease have difficulty "blowing" air in and out of their lungs.

Use an Analogy

The alveoli of persons with emphysema are like balloons that have been blown up too many times and with too much air. In both cases the walls have been stretched, become thin, and can rupture.

Resource Manager

Chapter Resources Booklet
Enrichment, p. 27
Lab Activity, pp. 13–14
Performance Assessment in the Science Classroom, p. 48

Curriculum Connection

Health To test for healthy lungs, a doctor may thump the back or chest of the patient. If there is a hollow sound, the lungs are filled with air. If there is a dull sound, it is evidence of fluid in the lungs. Have students find out which respiratory infections can cause fluid buildup in the lungs. L2

Diseases and Disorders of the Respiratory System, continued

Reading Check

Answer The air passages will become irritated, and cancer cells may develop and destroy healthy lung tissue.

3 Assess

Reteach

Use a lung demonstration apparatus to illustrate how the downward movement of the diaphragm causes reduced pressure within the chest cavity.

Challenge

Have students write a paragraph describing why air moves into the lungs when the ribs move upward and the diaphragm moves downward. This action reduces air pressure within the chest cavity, and the higher external air pressure causes air to rush into the lungs.

Assessment

Process Have students use a chart of the respiratory system to describe the passage of air into and out of the lungs. Use **Performance Assessment in the Science Classroom,** p. 143.

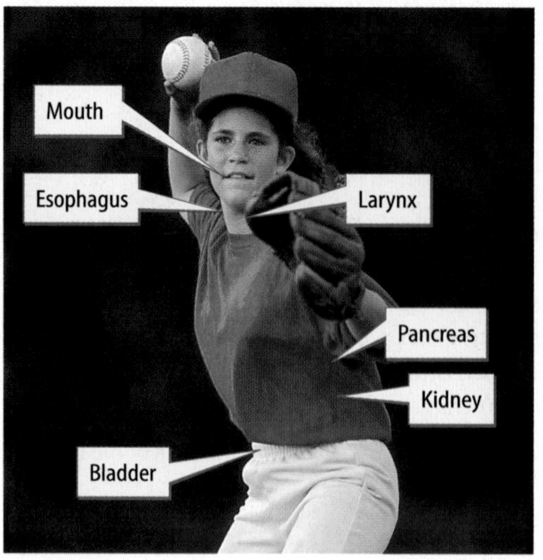

Figure 8
More than 85 percent of all lung cancer is related to smoking. Smoking also can play a part in the development of cancer in other body organs indicated above.

Lung Cancer The third leading cause of death in men and women in the United States is lung cancer. Inhaling the tar in cigarette smoke is the greatest contributing factor to lung cancer. Tar and other ingredients found in smoke act as carcinogens (kar SIHN uh junz) in the body. Carcinogens are substances that can cause an uncontrolled growth of cells. In the lungs, this is called lung cancer. Lung cancer is not easy to detect in its early stages. Smoking also has been linked to the development of cancers of the mouth, esophagus, larynx, pancreas, kidney, and bladder. See **Figure 8.**

Reading Check *What do you think will happen to the lungs of a young person who begins smoking?*

Asthma Shortness of breath, wheezing, or coughing can occur in a lung disorder called **asthma.** When a person has an asthma attack, the bronchial tubes contract quickly. Inhaling medicine that relaxes the bronchial tubes is the usual treatment for an asthma attack. Asthma is often an allergic reaction. An allergic reaction occurs when the body overreacts to a foreign substance. An asthma attack can result from breathing certain substances such as cigarette smoke or certain plant pollen, eating certain foods, or stress in a person's life.

Section 1 Assessment

1. What is the main function of the respiratory system?
2. How are oxygen, carbon dioxide, and other waste gases exchanged in the lungs and body tissues?
3. What causes air to move into and out of a person's lungs?
4. How does smoking affect the respiratory and circulatory systems?
5. **Think Critically** How is the work of the digestive and circulatory systems related to the respiratory system?

Skill Builder Activities

6. **Researching Information** Nicotine in tobacco is a poison. Using library references, find out how nicotine affects the body. **For more help, refer to the** Science Skill Handbook.
7. **Communicating** Use references to find out about lung disease common among coal miners, stonecutters, and sandblasters. Find out what safety measures are required now for these trades. In your Science Journal, write a paragraph about these safety measures. **For more help, refer to the** Science Skill Handbook.

Resource Manager

Chapter Resources Booklet
Reinforcement, p. 25

Physical Science Critical Thinking/Problem Solving, p. 9

Answers to Section Assessment

1. supply oxygen and remove carbon dioxide
2. Oxygen, carbon dioxide, and waste gases are exchanged by diffusion into and out of the blood.
3. movement of the diaphragm and rib cage; differences in pressure
4. Smoking damages the lungs, making breathing labored and causing the heart to work harder.
5. digestive system—provides food for cell respiration; circulatory system—transports oxygen for food break down and carries respiration waste products to the lungs for expulsion
6. Nicotine causes blood vessels to constrict, resulting in increased blood pressure. It also causes nausea, headaches, and gastric upset.
7. Students answers will vary.

SECTION

2 The Excretory System

Functions of the Excretory System

It's your turn to take out the trash. You carry the bag outside and put it in the trash can. The next day, you bring out another bag of trash, but the trash can is full. When trash isn't collected, it piles up. Just as trash needs to be removed from your home to keep it livable, your body must eliminate wastes to remain healthy. Undigested material is eliminated by your large intestine. Waste gases are eliminated through the combined efforts of your circulatory and respiratory systems. Some salts are eliminated when you sweat. These systems function together as parts of your excretory system. If wastes aren't eliminated, toxic substances build up and damage organs. If not corrected, serious illness or death occurs.

As You Read

***What* You'll Learn**

- **Distinguish** between the excretory and urinary systems.
- **Describe** how the kidneys work.
- **Explain** what happens when urinary organs don't work.

Vocabulary

urinary system, urine, kidney, nephron, ureter, bladder, urethra

***Why* It's Important**

The urinary system helps clean your blood of cellular wastes.

The Urinary System

The **urinary system** rids the blood of wastes produced by the cells. **Figure 9** shows how the urinary system functions as a part of the excretory system. The urinary system also controls blood volume by removing excess water produced by body cells during respiration.

Figure 9
The urinary system, along with the digestive and respiratory systems, and the skin make up the excretory system.

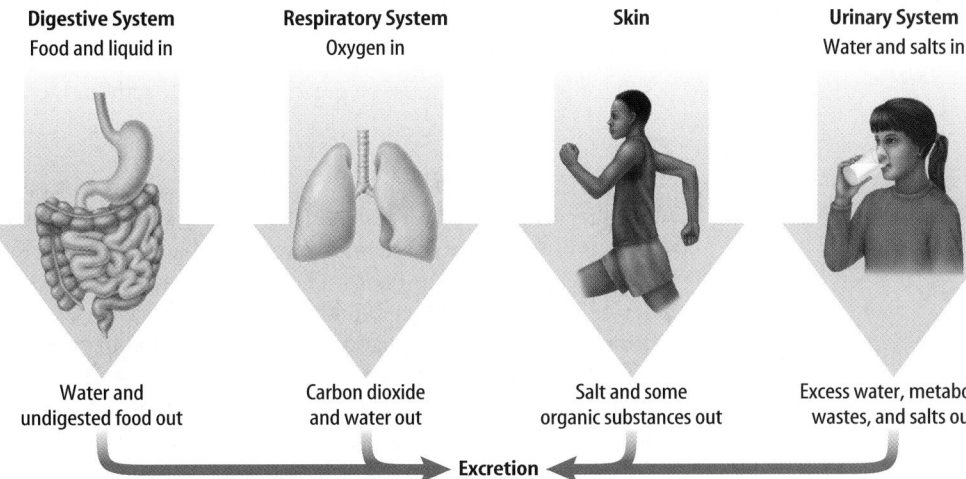

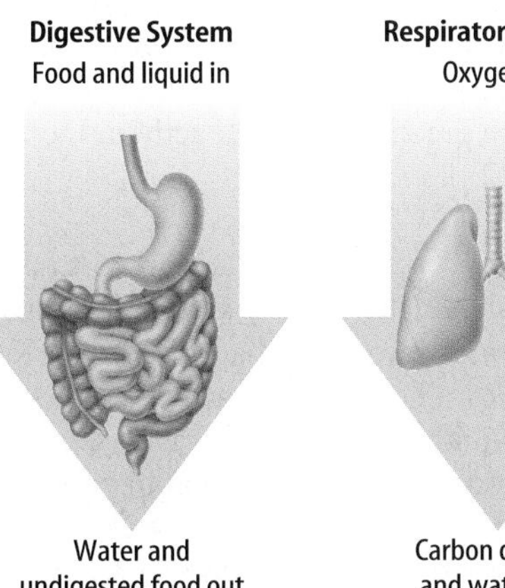

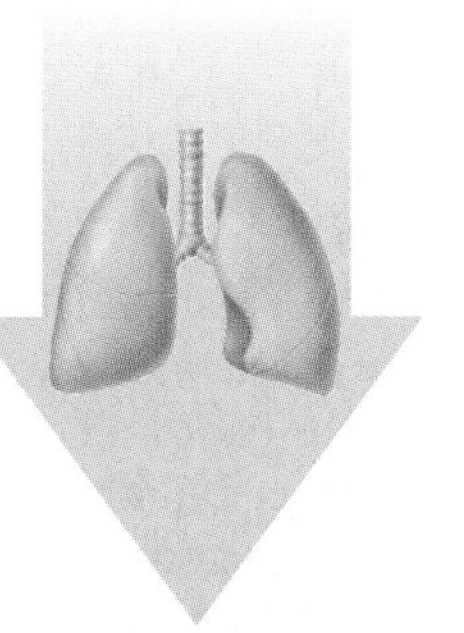

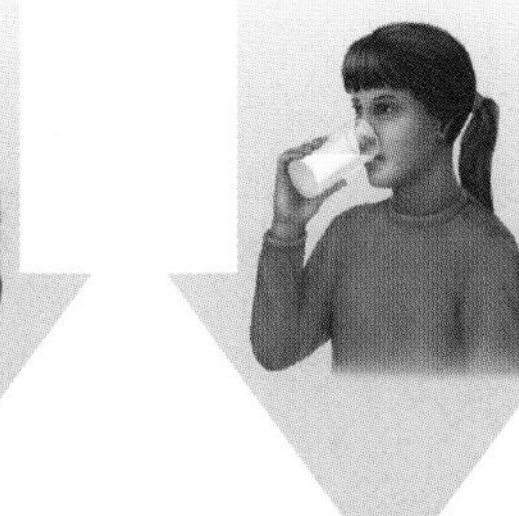

SECTION

The Excretory System

1 Motivate

Bellringer Transparency

Display the Section Focus Transparency for Section 2. Use the accompanying Transparency Activity Master. L2 ELL

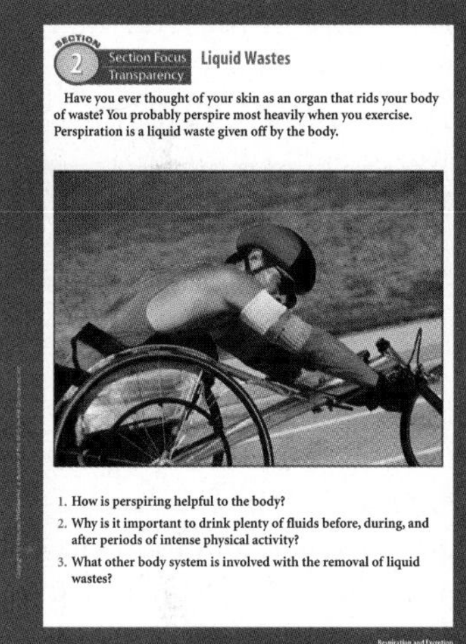

SECTION 2 Section Focus Transparency **Liquid Wastes**

Have you ever thought of your skin as an organ that rids your body of waste? You probably perspire most heavily when you exercise. Perspiration is a liquid waste given off by the body.

1. How is perspiring helpful to the body?
2. Why is it important to drink plenty of fluids before, during, and after periods of intense physical activity?
3. What other body system is involved with the removal of liquid wastes?

Respiration and Excretion

Tie to Prior Knowledge

Remind students of how the filter on a coffeemaker works. Only liquid is allowed to flow through. Explain that, in a similar way, the urinary system acts as a filter.

Section Assessment Planner

PORTFOLIO
Assessment, p. 585

PERFORMANCE ASSESSMENT
MiniLAB, p. 585
Problem-Solving Activity, p. 586
Skill Builder Activities, p. 588
See page 596 for more options.

CONTENT ASSESSMENT
Section, p. 588
Challenge, p. 588
Chapter, pp. 596–597

2 Teach

The Urinary System

Extension

Have students do research and construct a circle graph to illustrate the composition of urine. water = 95%, urea = 2%, sodium chloride = 1%, other substances = 2% L3

LS **Visual-Spatial**

Visual Learning

Figure 10 Have students study this figure and make a sequencing concept map. Student maps should outline each step in the process by which the human body determines how much urine to excrete.

Reading Check

Answer by increasing and decreasing the amount of wastewater excreted

Quick Demo

Set up a diffusion experiment using a cellophane bag with a colored sugar solution placed in a container of water. To demonstrate diffusion in the other direction, place a cellophane bag of colored pure water into a container of sugar solution.

Teacher FYI

Every body cell requires a certain concentration of salt water to function properly. Cell membranes are selectively permeable and regulate the amount of water and salt that go into and out of the cell.

Figure 10
The amount of urine that you eliminate each day is determined by the level of a hormone that is produced by your hypothalamus.

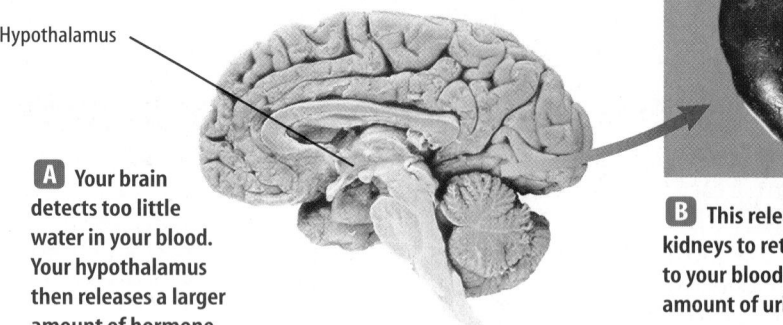

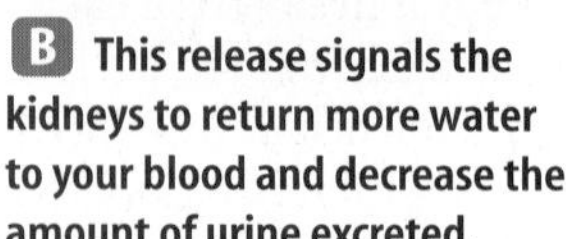

A **Your brain detects too little water in your blood. Your hypothalamus then releases a larger amount of hormone.**

B **This release signals the kidneys to return more water to your blood and decrease the amount of urine excreted.**

Regulating Fluid Levels To stay in good health, the fluid levels within the body must be balanced and normal blood pressure must be maintained. An area in the brain, the hypothalamus (hi poh THAL uh mus), constantly monitors the amount of water in the blood. When the brain detects too much water in the blood, the hypothalamus releases a lesser amount of a specific hormone. This signals the kidneys to return less water to the blood and increase the amount of wastewater, called **urine,** that is excreted. **Figure 10** shows what happens when too little water is in the blood.

Reading Check *How does the urinary system control the volume of water in the blood?*

A specific amount of water in the blood is also important for the movement of gases and excretion of solid wastes from the body. The urinary system also balances the amounts of certain salts and water that must be present for all cell activities to take place.

Organs of the Urinary System Excretory organs is another name for the organs of the urinary system. The main organs of the urinary system are two bean-shaped **kidneys.** Kidneys are located on the back wall of the abdomen at about waist level. The kidneys filter blood that contains wastes collected from cells. In approximately 5 min, all of the blood in your body passes through the kidneys. The red-brown color of the kidneys is due to their enormous blood supply. In **Figure 11A,** you can see that blood enters the kidneys through a large artery and leaves through a large vein.

Curriculum Connection

Math Calculate the ratio of body weight to amount of urine excreted. **If an 11-kg child excretes 600 mL, what would you expect a 45-kg adult to excrete?** 2,453 mL The amount is actually only about 1500 mL. The amount excreted by children is greater in proportion to their weight. L2 LS **Logical-Mathematical**

Teacher FYI

Filtering waste from the circulatory system is essential to maintaining life. The urinary system regulates the concentration and volume of blood by removing and restoring selected amounts of water and chemicals. Any change in the normal functioning of the urinary system represents a health threat.

584 CHAPTER 20 Respiration and Excretion

Filtration in the Kidney The kidney, shown in **Figure 11B,** is a two-stage filtration system. It is made up of about 1 million tiny filtering units called **nephrons** (NEF rahnz), shown in **Figure 11C.** Each nephron has a cuplike structure and a tubelike structure called a duct. Blood moves from a renal artery to capillaries in the cuplike structure. The first filtration occurs when water, sugar, salt, and wastes from the blood pass into the cuplike structure. Left behind in the blood are the red blood cells and proteins. Next, liquid in the cuplike structure is squeezed into a narrow tubule. Capillaries that surround the tubule perform the second filtration. Most of the water, sugar, and salt are reabsorbed and returned to the blood. These collection capillaries merge to form small veins, which merge to form a renal vein in each kidney. Purified blood is returned to the main circulatory system. The liquid left behind flows into collecting tubules in each kidney. This wastewater, or urine, contains excess water, salts, and other wastes that are not reabsorbed by the body. An average-sized person produces about 1 L of urine per day.

Mini LAB

Modeling Kidney Function

Procedure

1. Mix a small amount of **soil** and **fine gravel** with **water** in a **clean cup.**
2. Place the **funnel** into a **second cup.**
3. Place a small piece of **wire screen** in the funnel.
4. Carefully pour the mud-water-gravel mixture into the funnel. Let it drain.
5. Remove the screen and replace it with a piece of **filter paper.**
6. Place the funnel in **another clean cup.**
7. Repeat step 4.

Analysis

1. What part of the blood does the gravel represent?
2. How does this experiment model the function of a person's kidneys?

Figure 11
The urinary system removes wastes from the blood.

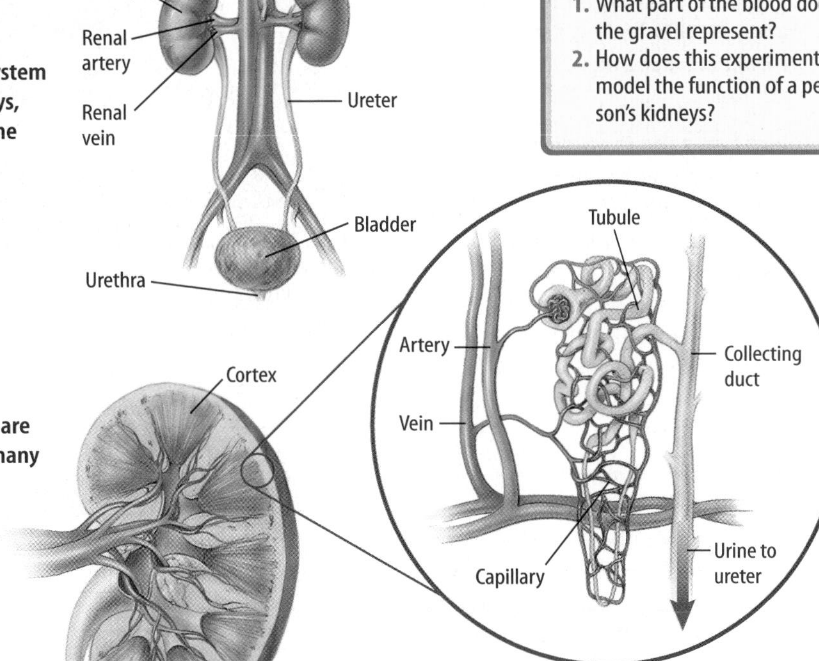

A The urinary system includes the kidneys, the bladder, and the connecting tubes.

B Kidneys are made up of many nephrons.

C A single nephron is shown in detail.
What is the main function of the nephron?

Mini LAB

Purpose Students model and observe the function of a kidney. L2 LS **Kinesthetic**

Materials soil (2 T), fine gravel (1 T), 8-ounce plastic cups (3), funnel, wire screen, filter paper, tap water

Teaching Strategy Students may work in pairs to cut down on the amount of materials needed.

Troubleshooting Moisten the filter paper before filtering the dirty water so that the paper adheres to the funnel.

Analysis

1. the blood cells and proteins
2. This experiment modeled the two-stage filtration process of the kidneys. The filter removes dirt and particles, like a nephron, which filters wastes from the blood.

Assessment

Portfolio Have students make a labeled drawing of the urinary system. Have them place arrows on the diagrams to show the flow of fluids through the nephrons to the bladder and then out of the body. Use **Performance Assessment in the Science Classroom,** p. 127. P

Caption Answer

Figure 11C to filter blood

Active Reading

Synthesis Journal In this strategy, students reflect on a project, a paper, or a performance in light of their own experiences and plan for personal application. Have each student divide a piece of paper into three sections. Have them record "What I did," "What I learned," and "How I can use it." Have students write a Synthesis Journal entry for the MiniLAB.

Resource Manager

Chapter Resources Booklet
Transparency Activity, p. 41
Directed Reading for Content Mastery, pp. 19, 20
MiniLAB, p. 4

The Urinary System, continued

Use an Analogy

In the filtering model constructed in the MiniLAB, have students infer what each part (muddy water, gravel, filter, clear water) represents within the human body. gravel—blood cells; filter—kidney; muddy water—blood containing waste; clear water—filtered blood with wastes removed

Problem-Solving Activity

National Math Standards

Correlation to Mathematics Objectives

1, 4, 5, 6, 8, 9

Answers

1. ingested liquids
2. More water would be lost than taken in; the skin.

Extension

Adult kidneys weigh only about 170 g each. The kidneys of an average adult process about 1,600 L of liquid per day, most of which is recycled. Have students calculate how many liters an adult's kidneys process in a year, in a decade, and in 75 years. 584,000 L; 5,840,000 L; 43,800,000 L [L2]

LS **Logical-Mathematical**

Urine Collection and Release The urine in each collecting tubule drains into a funnel-shaped area of each kidney that leads to the ureter (YER ut ur). **Ureters** are tubes that lead from each kidney to the bladder. The **bladder** is an elastic, muscular organ that holds urine until it leaves the body. The elastic walls of the bladder can stretch to hold up to 0.5 L of urine. When empty, the bladder looks wrinkled and the cells lining the bladder are thick. When full, the bladder looks like an inflated balloon and the cells lining the bladder are stretched and thin. A tube called the **urethra** (yoo REE thruh) carries urine from the bladder to the outside of the body.

Problem-Solving Activity

How does your body gain and lose water?

Your body depends on water. Without water, your cells could not carry out their activities and body systems could not function. Water is so important to your body that your brain and other body systems are involved in balancing water gain and water loss.

Identifying the Problem

Table A shows the major sources by which your body gains water. Oxidation of nutrients occurs when energy is released from nutrients by your body's cells. Water is a waste product of these reactions. **Table B** lists the major sources by which your body loses water. The data show you how daily gain and loss of water are related.

Table A

Major Sources by Which Body Water Is Gained		
Source	**Amount (mL)**	**Percent**
Oxidation of Nutrients	250	10
Foods	750	30
Liquids	1,500	60
Total	**2,500**	**100**

Table B

Major Sources by Which Body Water Is Lost		
Source	**Amount (mL)**	**Percent**
Urine	1,500	60
Skin	500	20
Lungs	350	14
Feces	150	6
Total	**2,500**	**100**

Solving the Problem

1. What is the greatest source of water gained by your body?
2. How would the percentages of water gained and lost change in a person who was working in extremely warm temperatures? In this case, what organ of the body would be the greatest contributor to water loss?

Science Journal

Making an Analogy Ask students to write an essay in which they compare a kidney to a recycling center. Have them consider substances that can and cannot be recycled. Kidney—water, salt, and sugar can be recycled, waste cannot; recycling center—paper, glass, and plastic can be recycled, some synthetic materials cannot. [L2] LS **Linguistic**

Curriculum Connection

Health Small stones made up of precipitated minerals such as uric acid or calcium salts may form in the kidneys. These kidney stones may move into the ureter and can cause severe pain. Drinking large quantities of water can help prevent the formation of the stones. Ask students to investigate what foods may contribute to the formation of kidney stones. [L2]

Other Organs of Excretion

Large amounts of liquid wastes are lost every day by your body in other ways, as shown in **Figure 12.** The liver also filters the blood to remove wastes. Certain wastes are converted to other substances. For example, excess amino acids are changed to urea (yoo REE uh), which is a chemical that ends up in urine. Hemoglobin from broken-down red blood cells becomes part of bile, which is the digestive fluid from the liver.

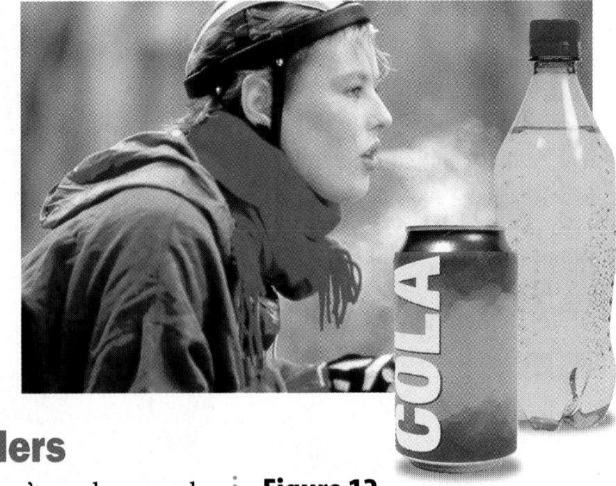

Figure 12
On average, the volume of water lost daily by exhaling is a little more than the volume of a soft-drink can. The volume of water lost by your skin each day is about the volume of a 20-ounce soft-drink bottle.

Urinary Diseases and Disorders

What happens when someone's kidneys don't work properly or stop working? Waste products that are not removed build up and act as poisons in body cells. Water that normally is removed from body tissues accumulates and causes swelling of the ankles and feet. Sometimes these fluids also build up around the heart, and it has to work harder to move blood to the lungs.

Without excretion, an imbalance of salts occurs. The body responds by trying to restore this balance. If the balance isn't restored, the kidneys and other organs can be damaged. Kidney failure occurs when the kidneys don't work as they should. This is always a serious problem because the kidneys' job is so important to the rest of the body.

Infections caused by microorganisms can affect the urinary system. Usually, the infection begins in the bladder. However, it can spread and involve the kidneys. Most of the time, these infections can be cured with antibiotics.

Because the ureters and urethra are narrow tubes, they can be blocked easily in some disorders. A blockage of one of these tubes can cause serious problems because urine cannot flow out of the body properly. If the blockage is not corrected, the kidneys can be damaged.

Reading Check ***Why is a blocked ureter or urethra a serious problem?***

Detecting Urinary Diseases Urine can be tested for any signs of a urinary tract disease. A change in the urine's color can suggest kidney or liver problems. High levels of glucose can be a sign of diabetes. Increased amounts of a protein called albumin (al BYEW mun) indicate kidney disease or heart failure. When the kidneys are damaged, albumin can get into the urine, just as a leaky water pipe allows water to drip.

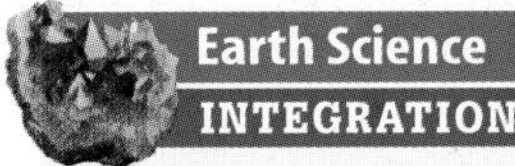

Earth Science INTEGRATION

Nearly 80 percent of Earth's surface is covered by water. Ninety-seven percent of this water is salt water. Humans cannot drink salt water, so they depend on the less than one percent of freshwater that is available for use. In your Science Journal, infer how your kidneys would need to be different for you to be able to drink salt water.

Other Organs of Excretion

Discussion

What organ of the body is most likely to filter out drugs? The liver is able to filter out a number of chemicals, including drugs. **What prevents the liver from being destroyed by the chemicals it filters?** The liver can detoxify most chemicals and render them harmless.

Urinary Diseases and Disorders

Earth Science INTEGRATION

In order to be able to drink seawater, the kidneys would have to be able to filter out more salt and remove it from the body, in order to keep a balance of salt and water within the body.

Reading Check

Answer It can lead to kidney damage.

Resource Manager

Chapter Resources Booklet
Enrichment, p. 28
Transparency Activity, pp. 43–44
Mathematics Skill Activities, p. 1

Curriculum Connection

History Physician-scientists of ancient times noted that there was no blood in the arteries of dissected corpses, but that veins, which entered and left the liver, were full of blood. They concluded that it was the liver that made blood and pumped it to the body, and the heart that gave blood a "vital spirit" as it passed by. Have students write a paragraph explaining the relationship of the liver to the heart. L2 IS **Linguistic**

Other Organs of Excretion, continued

Use Science Words

Word Origin *Urina* is the Latin word for urine. It is the root for many words associated with the urinary system. Ask students to find words with this root and explain their meaning. Possible answers: uric acid—a chemical found in urine; urinal—a toilet

Extension

Have students research advances made in dialysis machines and procedures, and find out what activity restrictions may result from the need for dialysis. They should find out what changes might occur in a person's lifestyle if he or she needed to undergo dialysis. L3

3 Assess

Reteach

Have students prepare a basic diagram of the sequence involved in the processing of liquid wastes in the body. L2

LS **Visual-Spatial**

Challenge

What happens to the dissolved nutrients in the blood that passes through the kidneys? They are filtered out, but later returned to the blood.

✔Assessment

Portfolio Provide students with a diagram of the circulatory, respiratory, and excretory systems. Have them construct concept maps from these diagrams. Use **Performance Assessment in the Science Classroom,** p. 161.

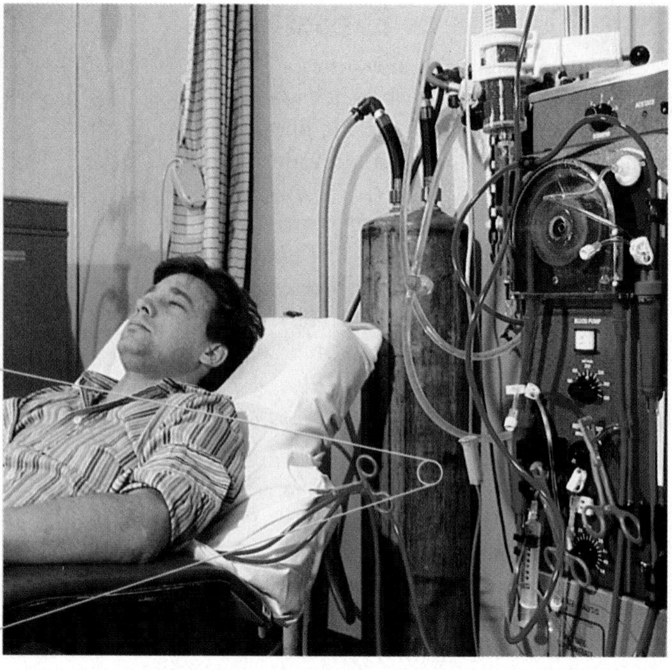

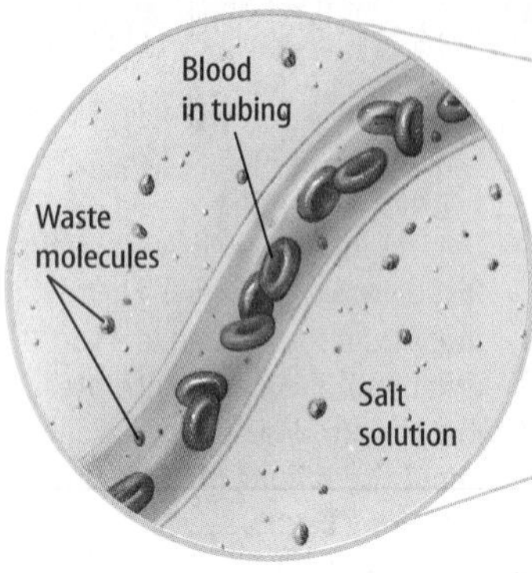

Figure 13
A dialysis machine can replace or help with some of the activities of the kidneys in a person with kidney failure. Like the kidney, the dialysis machine removes wastes from the blood.

Dialysis A person who has only one kidney still can live normally. The remaining kidney increases in size and works harder to make up for the loss of the other kidney. However, if both kidneys fail, the person will need to have his or her blood filtered by an artificial kidney machine in a process called dialysis (di AL uh sus), as shown in **Figure 13.**

Section  Assessment

1. Describe the functions of a person's urinary system.
2. Explain how the kidneys remove wastes and keep fluids and salts in balance.
3. Describe what happens when the urinary system does not function properly.
4. Compare the excretory system and urinary system.
5. **Think Critically** Explain why reabsorption of certain materials in the kidneys is important to your health.

Skill Builder Activities

6. **Concept Mapping** Using a network tree concept map, compare the excretory functions of the kidneys and the lungs. **For more help, refer to the Science Skill Handbook.**
7. **Solving One-Step Equations** In approximately 5 min, all 5 L of blood in the body pass through the kidneys. Calculate the average rate of flow through the kidneys in liters per minute. **For more help, refer to the Math Skill Handbook.**

Answers to Section Assessment

1. rids the body of wastes, controls blood volume, balances salts and water
2. Kidneys filter the blood to remove wastes, sugar, water, and salt. Necessary amounts of water, sugar, and salt are returned to the blood.
3. Waste products not removed cause the destruction of cells. Fluids not removed from body tissues cause swellings in the extremities and buildup of fluids around the heart. Salts are in imbalance in body fluids, which can lead to organ damage.
4. excretory system—includes all systems that rid the body of wastes; urinary system—consists of organs that produce urine as waste
5. Many of the substances are needed by the body to maintain homeostasis.
6. Wastes in blood are carried to the lungs, which remove water and carbon dioxide, and to the kidneys, which remove water and excess salts, and other wastes.
7. 5 liters per 5 minutes = 1 liter per minute rate of flow

Activity

Kidney Structure

As your body uses nutrients, wastes are created. One role of the kidneys is to filter waste products out of the bloodstream and excrete this waste outside the body. How can these small structures filter all the blood in the body in 5 min?

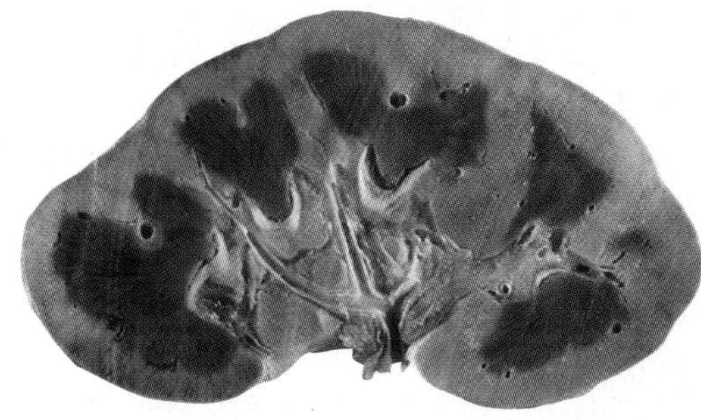

What You'll Investigate

How does the structure of the kidney relate to the function of a kidney?

Materials

dissecting tray
large animal kidney
**model of a kidney*
scalpel
hand lens
disposable gloves
**Alternate material*

Goal

- **Observe** the external and internal structures of a kidney.

Safety Precautions

WARNING: *Use extreme care when using sharp instruments. Wear disposable gloves. Wash your hands with soap after completing this activity.*

Procedure

1. **Examine** the outside of the kidney supplied by your teacher.
2. If the kidney still is encased in fat, peel off the fat carefully.
3. Using a scalpel, carefully cut the tissue in half lengthwise around the outline of the kidney. This cut should result in a section similar to the illustration on this page.
4. **Observe** the internal features of the kidney using a hand lens, or view these features in a model.
5. **Compare** the specimen or model with the kidney in the illustration.
6. **Draw** the kidney in your Science Journal and label its structures.

Conclude and Apply

1. What part makes up the cortex of the kidney? Why is this part red?
2. What is the main function of nephrons?
3. The medulla of the kidney is made up of a network of tubules that come together to form the ureter. What is the function of this network of tubules?
4. How can the kidney be compared to a portable water-purifying system?

Communicating Your Data

Compare your conclusions with those of other students in your class. **For more help, refer to the Science Skill Handbook.**

Activity

BENCH TESTED

Purpose Students examine the structures in a kidney and relate each structure to its function. L2 IS **Kinesthetic**

Process Skills observing and inferring; interpreting scientific illustrations; comparing and contrasting

Time Required 50 minutes

Safety Precautions

Caution students about using sharp objects.

Teaching Strategies

- You may wish to have some kidneys remain intact.
- Other kidneys may be already sliced longitudinally.
- Kidneys can be reused.

Troubleshooting Demonstrate proper techniques for scalpel usage.

Answers to Questions

1. Nephrons; the color is caused by the blood in the nephrons.
2. to filter blood within the kidneys
3. The network of tubules moves the fluid from the kidney to the bladder so it can be excreted.
4. Both are filtering mechanisms.

Assessment

Oral Have students describe the evidence that two kidneys are more than enough to take care of excretory functions. Possible answer: people who have only one kidney are still able to function normally. Use **PASC,** p. 143.

Communicating Your Data

Students should discuss why their conclusions did or did not agree. They can prepare a listing of references that support their findings.

Resource Manager

Chapter Resources Booklet
Activity Worksheet, pp. 5–6
Reinforcement, p. 26

Home and Community Involvement, p. 40

Activity

BENCH TESTED

Recognize the Problem

Purpose

Students model a blocked trachea and demonstrate how the abdominal thrust maneuver is used to remove the blockage. L2

LS **Kinesthetic**

Process Skills

recording observations, making models, analyzing results, recognizing cause and effect, drawing conclusions

Time Required

40 minutes

Thinking Critically

Discussion Tell students that the trachea is a tube that carries air from the mouth to the lungs. This passageway is the only normal path for air to flow into the lungs. **What might happen if this passage were blocked?** The oxygen supply would be cut off, and the person would die within a few minutes. Explain that the abdominal thrust maneuver is a simple method of removing a blockage from this passageway.

Possible Materials

paper towel roll tube or other tube, paper, clay, bellows, bicycle pump, sports bottle, scissors

Safety Precautions

Caution students to use care with scissors.

Activity Model and Invent

Simulating the Abdominal Thrust Maneuver

Have you ever taken a class in CPR or learned about how to help a choking victim? Using the abdominal thrust maneuver, or Heimlich maneuver, is one way to remove food or another object that is blocking someone's airway. What happens internally when the maneuver is used? How can you simulate the internal effects of the abdominal thrust maneuver?

Recognize the Problem

How can you simulate the removal of an object from the trachea when the abdominal thrust maneuver is used?

Thinking Critically

What can you use to make a model of the trachea? How can you simulate what happens during an abdominal thrust maneuver using your model?

Goals

- **Construct** a model of the trachea with a piece of food stuck in it.
- **Demonstrate** what happens when the abdominal thrust maneuver is performed on someone.
- **Predict** another way that air could get into the lungs if the food could not be dislodged with an abdominal thrust maneuver.

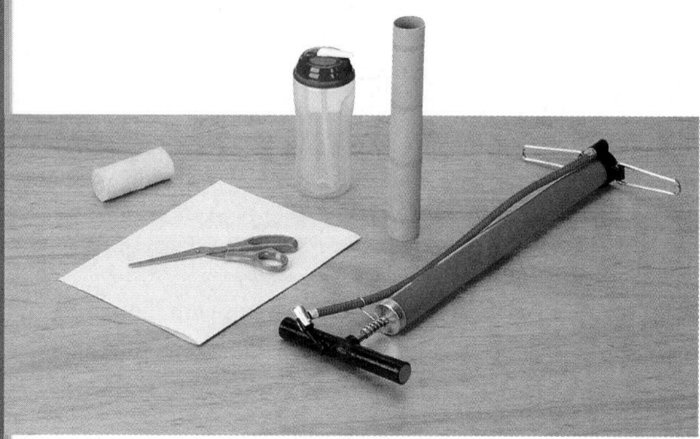

Possible Materials

paper towel roll or other tube
paper (wadded into a ball)
clay
bicycle pump
sports bottle
scissors

Safety Precautions

Always be careful when you use scissors.

Internet Addresses

Explore the Glencoe Science Web site at **science.glencoe.com** to find out more about topics in this activity.

Resource Manager

Chapter Resources Booklet
Activity Worksheet, pp. 7–8
Lab Management and Safety, p. 77

590 CHAPTER 20 Respiration and Excretion

Planning the Model

1. **List** the materials that you will need to construct your model. What will represent the trachea and a piece of food or other object blocking the airway?
2. How can you use your model to simulate the effects of an abdominal thrust maneuver?
3. Suggest a way to get air into the lungs if the food could not be dislodged. How would you simulate this method in your model?

Check the Model Plans

1. **Compare** your plans for the model and the abdominal thrust maneuver simulation with those of other students in your class. Discuss why each of you chose the plans and materials that you did.
2. Make sure your teacher approves your plan and materials for your model before you start.

Making the Model

1. **Construct** your model of a trachea with an object stuck in it. Make sure that air cannot get through the trachea if you try blowing softly through it.
2. Simulate what happens when an abdominal thrust maneuver is used. Record your observations. Was the object dislodged? How hard was it to dislodge the object?
3. Replace the object in the trachea. Use your model to simulate how you could get air into the lungs if an abdominal thrust maneuver did not remove the object. Is it easy to blow air through your model now?
4. Model a crushed trachea. Is it easy to blow air through the trachea in this case?

Analyzing and Applying Results

1. **Describe** how easy it was to get air through the trachea in each step in the Making the Model section above. Include any other observations that you made as you worked with your model.
2. Think about what you did to get air into the trachea when the object could not be dislodged with an abdominal thrust maneuver. How could this be done to a person? Do you know what this procedure is called?
3. **Explain** why the trachea has cartilage around it to protect it. What might happen if it did not?

Explain to your family or friends what you have learned about how the abdominal thrust maneuver can help choking victims.

Planning the Model

Teaching Strategies

- A model or anatomy wall chart showing the mouth, trachea, and lungs will help students conceptualize the problems caused by a blocked trachea.
- Encourage students to make a checklist of items they need to include in their models.

Making the Model

Expected Outcome

Students will build a model that simulates a trachea. They will simulate food blockage and the abdominal thrust maneuver and brainstorm ways to get oxygen to the lungs if the blockage cannot be dislodged.

Analyzing and Applying Results

1. Students should find that the abdominal thrust maneuver successfully dislodges most obstructions.
2. Students will likely suggest that a small incision could be cut below the blockage to allow air into the lungs. This procedure is called tracheostomy or tracheotomy.
3. Cartilage protects the trachea from being punctured and keeps it from collapsing.

Oral Ask students if they can think of other instances where the trachea might become blocked and a tracheostomy or tracheotomy would need to be performed. Possible answers: an accident that causes severe damage to the mouth or neck, cancerous or tumorous growths that block the trachea Use **Performance Assessment in the Science Classroom,** p. 89.

Communicating Your Data

Encourage students to use drawings showing that the trachea is the only pathway to the lungs. Then they can better describe the importance of the abdominal thrust maneuver.

Content Background

It is important to know the function of the kidney and to relay this information to students. The kidney washes the blood as a filtering system, ridding it of toxins and balancing the body's water levels by producing urine to get rid of this waste. In fact, your blood goes through your kidney about 288 times a day.

Before making discoveries with regard to kidney transplants, Samuel Kountz had to overcome many odds, indeed. He was born in extreme poverty in an all-black town in Arkansas in 1930. His grandmother was born a slave. She was his encouragement and inspiration while trying to get into college. He became the first African-American to be accepted to the University of Arkansas Medical School.

While interning at Stanford, Kountz started to research the rejection process for kidney transplants. He discovered that large amounts of the steroid methylprednisolone given to the patient after the transplant operation helped to reverse the rejection of the new organ. Kountz was a man of many achievements. He received several awards during his career including an Outstanding Investigator Award from the American College of Cardiology in 1964. At the University of California in San Francisco he built one of the largest kidney transplant training and research centers in the nation.

TIME SCIENCE AND HISTORY

SCIENCE CAN CHANGE THE COURSE OF HISTORY!

Overcoming the Odds

Guts and determination helped one pioneering doctor to save the lives of thousands

Overcoming the odds—especially when the odds seem stacked against you—is a challenge that many people face. Dr. Samuel Lee Kountz, Jr. (photo, right) had the odds stacked against him. Thanks to his determination he beat them.

Samuel Kountz decided at age eight to become a doctor. He faced his first challenge when he failed the entrance exam to his local Arkansas college. That didn't stop him, though. He asked the college president to give him another chance, and the president did. Kountz got into school and earned As and Bs. Kountz went on to get a graduate degree in biochemistry and was admitted to the University of Arkansas's medical school. For many, these achievements would be more than enough. But for Dr. Kountz, it was just the beginning of his quest to improve medicine—and to change history.

592

Resources for Teachers and Students

"The Black Surgeon in the Twentieth Century: A Tribute to Samuel L. Kountz," by Claude Organ. *Journal of the National Medical Association*, (September 1978).

Understanding Kidney Transplantation by Edith T. Oberley and Neal R. Glass. Thomas; Springfield, Ill. 1987.

Dr. Kountz was especially interested in a process that was still brand new in the 1950s—the kidney transplant. For many patients, a kidney transplant added months or a year to one's life. But then a patient's body would reject the kidney, and the patient would die. Dr. Kountz was determined to see that kidney transplants saved lives and kept patients healthy for years.

Fixing the Problem

Kountz discovered the root of the problem—why and how a patient's body rejected the transplanted kidney. He discovered that the patient's cells attacked and destroyed the small blood vessels of the transplanted kidney. So the new kidney would die from lack of blood-supplied oxygen. He and others at Stanford University developed a way for doctors to watch the flow of the kidney's blood supply following surgery. Then doctors can give patients the right kinds of drugs at the right time, so that their bodies can overcome the rejection process.

In 1959, Kountz performed the first successful kidney transplant. He went on to develop a procedure to keep body organs healthy for up to 60 hours after being taken from a donor. He also set up a system of organ donor cards through the National Kidney Foundation. And in his career, Dr. Kountz transplanted more than 1,000 kidneys himself—and paved the way for thousands more.

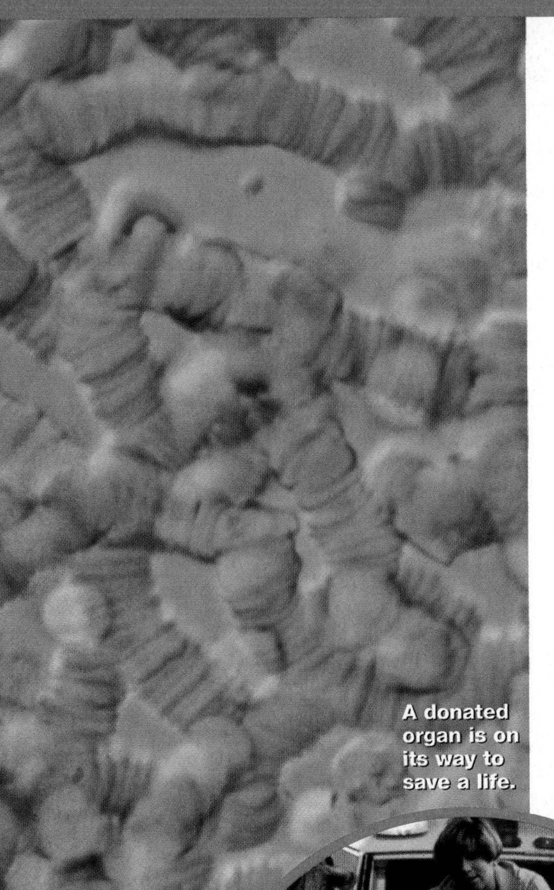

A donated organ is on its way to save a life.

CONNECTIONS Research **What kinds of medical breakthroughs has the last century brought? Locate an article that explains either a recent advance in medicine or the work that doctors and medical researchers are doing. Share your findings with your class.**

SCIENCE Online For more information, visit science.glencoe.com

Discussion

What did Kountz discover was the reason kidneys were being rejected after transplant surgeries? Possible answer: The patient's cells attacked and destroyed the small blood vessels of the transplanted kidney, thus, the kidney would die from lack of blood-supplied oxygen.

Historical Significance

The significance of Kountz's work for people who suffer from kidney disease is obvious. Point out to students that Kountz's work also had a significant impact on other transplant surgeries. Because other transplant procedures encountered similar rejection problems, similar immunosuppressive drug treatments have been developed for heart, liver, and lung transplant recipients.

The first successful kidney transplant without the use of immunosuppressive drugs was performed in 1954. The transplant was successful because the donor was the recipient's twin. In this case, organ rejection was lessened because the donor and recipient had identical genes. Further evidence shows that rejection problems can be lessened when the donor is a sibling or other family member.

As a prelude to the Connections Research activity, have students create a time line of transplant history starting from the early 1900s. This should give them some historical perspective on kidney transplant history, as well as provide information about other medical discoveries. Have students use poster board and ask them to include photographs and illustrations that illustrate transplant history. L2 LS **Visual-Spatial**

CONNECTIONS First, ask students to focus on one part of medicine or one specialization in medicine that interests them. If a student is interested in the brain, suggest a search for an article about neurological advancements in medicine. Perhaps a student is interested in premature babies and advancements in obstetrics. Suggest avenues that are available for your students to successfully fulfill research in whatever interests they present for this project.

SCIENCE Online

Internet Addresses

Explore the Glencoe Science Web site at **science.glencoe.com** to find out more about topics in this feature.

Chapter 20 Study Guide

Reviewing Main Ideas

Preview

Students can answer the questions in their Science Journals. Discuss the answers as you go through the chapter. **LS Linguistic**

Review

Students can write their answers, then compare them with those of other students. **LS Interpersonal**

Reteach

Students can look at the illustrations and describe details that support the main ideas of the chapter. **LS Visual-Spatial**

Answers to Chapter Review

Section 1

2. The cartilage rings reinforce the structure of the trachea. If the trachea collapsed, the organism would be unable to breathe. Movement of gases in the trachea is not dependent upon muscular action. The movement of substances in the esophagus relies on peristalsis and cartilage rings would inhibit this action
5. the circulatory system

Section 2

1. The kidneys help maintain a balance of fluids in the body and filter wastes.

Chapter 20 Study Guide

Reviewing Main Ideas

Section 1 The Respiratory System

1. The respiratory system brings oxygen into the body and removes carbon dioxide.
2. Inhaled air passes through the nasal cavity, pharynx, larynx, trachea, bronchi, and into the alveoli of the lungs. *Why does the trachea, shown in the illustration, have cartilage but the esophagus does not?*

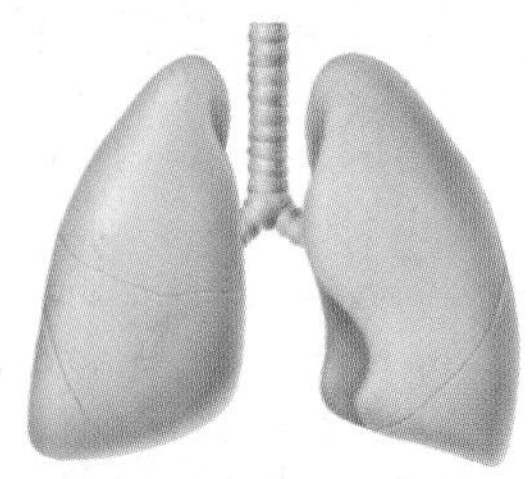

3. Breathing is the movement of the chest that brings air into the lungs and removes waste gases. The chemical reaction in the cells that needs oxygen to release energy from glucose is called cellular respiration.
4. The exchange of oxygen and carbon dioxide happens between capillaries and alveoli or body cells. In the lungs, oxygen moves into the capillaries from the alveoli. Carbon dioxide moves from the capillaries into the alveoli. In the body tissues, oxygen moves from the capillaries into the cells. Carbon dioxide moves from the cells into the capillaries.
5. Smoking causes many problems throughout the respiratory system, including chronic bronchitis, emphysema, and lung cancer. *What other body system is affected severely by smoking?*

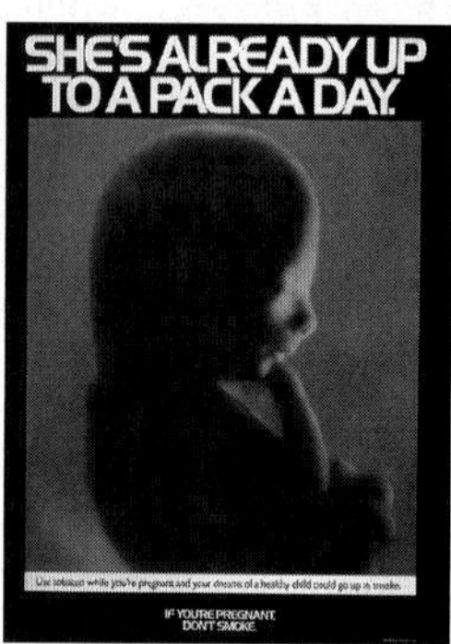

SHE'S ALREADY UP TO A PACK A DAY.
IF YOU'RE PREGNANT DON'T SMOKE.

Section 2 The Excretory System

1. The kidneys are the major organs of the urinary system. They filter wastes from all of the blood in the body. *How do the kidneys, like the one in the photo, regulate fluid levels in the body?*

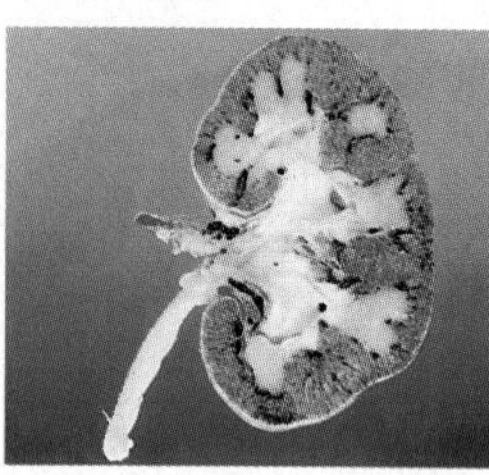

2. The kidney is a two-stage filtration system. The first filtration occurs when water, sugar, salt, and wastes from the blood pass into the cuplike part of the nephron. The capillaries surrounding the tubule part of the nephron perform the second filtration. In this filtration, most of the water, sugar, and salt are reabsorbed and returned to the blood.
3. The urinary system is part of the excretory system. The skin, lungs, liver, and large intestine are also excretory organs.
4. Urine can be tested for signs of urinary tract disease and other diseases.
5. A person who has only one kidney still can live normally. When kidneys fail to work, an artificial kidney can be used to filter the blood in a process called dialysis.

FOLDABLES Reading & Study Skills

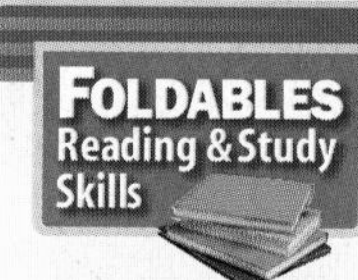

After You Read

Now that you've read the chapter, write the answer to the *Want* question under the *Learned* tab of your Foldable.

FOLDABLES Reading & Study Skills

After You Read

After students have read the chapter and completed the Foldable described in Before You Read, have them do the activity on the student page.

Dinah Zike

594 CHAPTER STUDY GUIDE

Chapter 20 Study Guide

Visualizing Main Ideas

Complete the following table on the respiratory and excretory systems.

Human Body Systems	Respiratory System	Excretory System
Major Organs	lungs	kidneys, lungs, large intestine, skin, liver
Wastes Eliminated	carbon dioxide, water vapor	water, salts, toxins
Disorders	chronic bronchitis, emphysema, lung cancer, asthma	buildup of wastes, infections

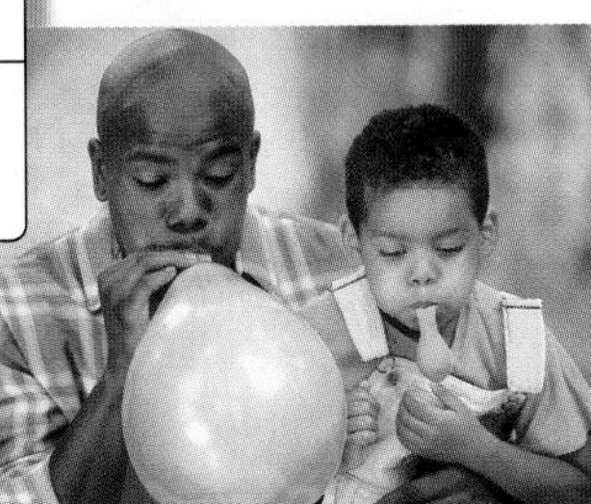

Vocabulary Review

Vocabulary Words

a. alveoli
b. asthma
c. bladder
d. bronchi
e. diaphragm
f. emphysema
g. kidney
h. larynx
i. nephron
j. pharynx
k. trachea
l. ureter
m. urethra
n. urinary system
o. urine

THE PRINCETON REVIEW Study Tip

Listening is a learning tool, too. Try recording a reading of your notes on tape and replaying it for yourself a few times a week.

Using Vocabulary

For each set of vocabulary words below, explain the relationship that exists.

1. alveoli, bronchi
2. bladder, urine
3. larynx, pharynx
4. ureter, urethra
5. alveoli, emphysema
6. nephron, kidney
7. urethra, bladder
8. asthma, bronchi
9. kidney, urine
10. diaphragm, alveoli

Chapter 20 Study Guide

Visualizing Main Ideas

See student page.

Vocabulary Review

Using Vocabulary

1. Both are structures of the respiratory system.
2. Urine is stored in the bladder until it can be eliminated from the body.
3. Both are structures in the passageway leading to the esophagus.
4. The ureter carries urine to the bladder, and the urethra carries urine away from the bladder.
5. Alveoli are structures in the lungs that are damaged by the disease emphysema.
6. A nephron is the filtering unit of the kidney.
7. The urethra is a tube that carries urine away from the bladder.
8. Asthma is a disorder that causes the bronchi to contract.
9. The kidney filters blood and discharges liquid wastes, called urine.
10. Both are structures of the respiratory system.

CHAPTER STUDY GUIDE 595

Chapter 20 Assessment

Checking Concepts

1. B
2. C
3. A
4. A
5. B
6. D
7. B
8. A
9. C
10. C

Thinking Critically

11. Small objects can be sucked into and block their small windpipes, causing the child to choke.
12. Having many air sacs increases the surface area for gas exchange.
13. Tars coat cilia, making them less flexible and unable to move particles out of the lungs; alveoli lose elasticity, decreasing the total surface area of the lungs available for gas exchange; carcinogens cause the growth of cancerous cells in lung tissue.
14. If the kidneys stopped working, blood would accumulate waste products from the body's organs. These wastes would act as poisons, and the person would need immediate medical care.
15. Kidney stones in the ureter extend and block the tube and cause severe pain. Infections may also occur.

Chapter 20 Assessment

Checking Concepts

Choose the word or phrase that best answers the question.

1. When you inhale, which of the following contracts and moves down?
   A) bronchioles **C)** nephrons
   B) diaphragm **D)** kidneys
2. Air is moistened, filtered, and warmed in which of the following structures?
   A) larynx **C)** nasal cavity
   B) pharynx **D)** trachea
3. Exchange of gases occurs between capillaries and which of the following structures?
   A) alveoli **C)** bronchioles
   B) bronchi **D)** trachea
4. Which of the following is a lung disorder that can occur as an allergic reaction?
   A) asthma **C)** emphysema
   B) atherosclerosis **D)** cancer
5. When you exhale, which way does the rib cage move?
   A) up **C)** out
   B) down **D)** stays the same
6. Which of the following conditions does smoking worsen?
   A) arthritis **C)** excretion
   B) respiration **D)** emphysema
7. Urine is held temporarily in which of the following structures?
   A) kidneys **C)** ureter
   B) bladder **D)** urethra
8. What are the filtering units of the kidneys?
   A) nephrons **C)** neurons
   B) ureters **D)** alveoli
9. Approximately 1 L of water is lost per day through which of the following?
   A) sweat **C)** urine
   B) lungs **D)** large intestine
10. Which of the following substances is not reabsorbed by blood after it passes through the kidneys?
    A) salt **C)** wastes
    B) sugar **D)** water

Thinking Critically

11. Explain why certain foods, such as peanuts, can cause choking in small children.
12. Why is it an advantage to have lungs with many smaller air sacs instead of having just two large sacs, like balloons?
13. Explain the damage to cilia, alveoli, and lungs from smoking.
14. What happens to the blood if the kidneys stop working?
15. Small, solid particles called kidney stones can form in the kidneys. Explain why it is often painful when a kidney stone passes into the ureter.

Developing Skills

16. **Interpreting Data** Study the data below. How much of each substance is reabsorbed into the blood in the kidneys? What substance is excreted completely in the urine?

Materials Filtered by the Kidneys

Substance Filtered in Urine	Amount Moving Through Kidney	Amount Excreted
Water	125 L	1 L
Salt	350 g	10 g
Urea	1 g	1 g
Glucose	50 g	0 g

17. **Recognizing Cause and Effect** Discuss how lack of oxygen is related to lack of energy.

Chapter Assessment Planner

Portfolio Encourage students to place in their portfolios one or two items of what they consider to be their best work. Examples include:
- Extension, p. 577
- Assessment, p. 585
- Science Journal, p. 586

Performance Additional performance assessments, Performance Task Assessment Lists, and rubrics for evaluating these activities can be found in Glencoe's **Performance Assessment in the Science Classroom.**

18. **Making and Using Graphs** Make a circle graph of total lung capacity using the following data:
- volume of air in a normal inhalation or exhalation = 500 mL
- volume of additional air that can be inhaled forcefully after a normal inhalation = 3,000 mL
- volume of additional air that can be exhaled forcefully after a normal expiration = 1,100 mL
- volume of air still left in the lungs after all the air that can be exhaled has been forcefully exhaled = 1,200 mL

19. **Forming Hypotheses** Make a hypothesis about the number of breaths a person might take per minute in each of these situations: asleep, exercising, and on top of Mount Everest. Give a reason for each hypothesis.

20. **Concept Mapping** Make an events chain concept map showing how urine forms in the kidneys. Begin with, "In the nephron …"

Performance Assessment

21. **Questionnaire and Interview** Prepare a questionnaire that can be used to interview a health specialist who works with lung cancer patients. Include questions on reasons for choosing the career, new methods of treatment, and the most encouraging or discouraging part of the job.

Technology

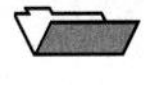

Go to the Glencoe Science Web site at **science.glencoe.com** or use the **Glencoe Science CD-ROM** for additional chapter assessment.

THE PRINCETON REVIEW Test Practice

For one week, research scientists collected and accurately measured the amount of body water lost and gained per day for four different patients. They placed their results in the following table.

Body Water Gained (+) and Lost (–)

Person	Day 1 (L)	Day 2 (L)	Day 3 (L)	Day 4 (L)
Mr. Stoler	+0.05	+0.15	–0.35	+0.12
Mr. Jemma	–0.01	0.00	–0.20	–0.01
Mr. Lowe	0.00	+0.10	–0.28	+0.01
Mr. Cheng	–0.50	–0.50	–0.55	–0.32

Study the table and answer the following questions.

1. According to this information, which patient may be suffering from dehydration or an excessive amount of body water loss?
   A) Mr. Stoler
   B) Ms. Jemma
   C) Mr. Lowe
   D) Mr. Cheng

2. According to the table, it was probably very hot in each patient's hospital room during _____.
   F) day one
   G) day two
   H) day three
   J) day four

Assessment Resources

Reproducible Masters

Chapter Resources Booklet
Chapter Review, pp. 33–34
Chapter Tests, pp. 35–38
Assessment Transparency Activity, p. 45

Glencoe Science Web site
Interactive Tutor
Chapter Quizzes

Glencoe Technology
- Assessment Transparency
- Interactive CD-ROM Chapter Quizzes
- ExamView Pro Test Bank
- Vocabulary PuzzleMaker Software
- MindJogger Videoquiz

Chapter 20 Assessment

THE PRINCETON REVIEW Test Practice

The Test-Taking Tip was written by The Princeton Review, the nation's leader in test preparation.

1. D
2. H

Developing Skills

16. Water: 124 L; salt: 340 g; glucose: 50 g; all urea is excreted.
17. Cells need oxygen to break down food and release energy.
18. Check student graphs for accuracy: 500 mL = 9% of circle (32°); 3,000 mL = 52% (187°); 1,100 mL = 19% (68°); 1,200 mL = 21% (76°).
19. Possible answers: Sleeping—breathing rate is low because less respiration is occurring; exercising—breathing rate would increase to get oxygen to the muscles; on Mount Everest—breathing rate would increase because less oxygen is present.
20. In the nephron, wastes, water, salt, and sugar are removed from blood; water, sugar, and salt are reabsorbed; urine is produced and removed from the kidneys through the ureter.

Performance Assessment

21. Students should prepare questionnaires and conduct interviews. Use **PASC**, p. 91.

Section/Objectives	Standards		Activities/Features
	National	State/Local	
Chapter Opener	See p. 5T for a Key to Standards.		**Explore Activity:** Observe a response, p. 599 **Before You Read,** p. 599
Section 1 The Nervous System 2 sessions 1 block 1. **Describe** the basic structure of a neuron and how an impulse moves across a synapse. 2. **Compare** the central and peripheral nervous systems. 3. **Explain** how drugs affect the body.	National Content Standards: UCP1, A1, C1, C3		**Visualizing Nerve Impulse Pathways,** p. 602 **Chemistry Integration,** p. 604 **Science Online,** p. 605 **Science Online,** p. 607 **Activity:** Improving Reaction Time, p. 609
Section 2 The Senses 3 sessions 1.5 blocks 1. **List** the sensory receptors in each sense organ. 2. **Explain** what type of stimulus each sense organ responds to and how. 3. **Explain** why healthy senses are needed.	National Content Standards: UCP1, A1, C1, C3, G1		**Astronomy Integration,** p. 612 **MiniLAB:** Observing Balance Control, p. 614 **Science Online,** p. 615 **Math Skills Activity:** Calculating Distance Using the Speed of Sound, p. 615 **Science Online,** p. 541 **MiniLAB:** Comparing Sense of Smell, p. 616 **Activity:** Skin Sensitivity, pp. 618–619 **Science and Language Arts:** Sula, pp. 620–621

NATIONAL GEOGRAPHIC

Teacher's Corner

Products Available from Glencoe
To order call 1-800-334-7344:
CD-ROM
NGS PictureShow: Human Body 1
Curriculum Kit
Geokit: Human Body 2
Transparency Set
NGS PicturePack: Human Body 1
Videodisc
STV: Human Body

Products Available from National Geographic Society
To order call 1-800-368-2728:
Videos
Nervous System (The Human Body Series)
Incredible Human Machine

Activity Materials	Reproducible Resources	Section Assessment	Technology
Explore Activity: safety goggles, chair, sheet of discarded paper	**Chapter Resources Booklet** Foldables Worksheet, p. 17 Directed Reading Overview, p. 19 Note-taking Worksheets, pp. 31–33	GLENCOE'S ASSESSMENT ADVANTAGE	
Activity: metric ruler	**Chapter Resources Booklet** Transparency Activity, p. 42 Activity Worksheet, pp. 5–6 Enrichment, p. 29 Reinforcement, p. 27 Directed Reading, p. 20 Transparency Activity, pp. 45–46 Lab Activity, pp. 9–12 **Reading and Writing Skill Activities,** p. 17 **Life Science Critical Thinking/ Problem Solving,** pp. 2, 18 **Mathematics Skill Activities,** p. 9	Portfolio Science Journal, p. 601 Assessment, p. 608 Performance Skill Builder Activities, p. 608 Content Section Assessment, p. 608	Section Focus Transparency Teaching Transparency Interactive CD-ROM Guided Reading Audio Program
MiniLAB: 2 narrow strips of paper, tape **MiniLAB:** samples of different foods, colognes, or household products, cotton balls, blindfold **Activity:** 3 × 5-in. index card, toothpicks, tape, metric ruler	**Chapter Resources Booklet** Activity Worksheet, pp. 7–8 Enrichment, p. 30 Reinforcement, p. 28 Directed Reading, pp. 21, 22 Transparency Activity, p. 43 Lab Activity, pp. 13–16 MiniLAB, pp. 3, 4 **Earth Science Critical Thinking/ Problem Solving,** p. 22 **Home and Community Involvement,** p. 28 **Performance Assessment in the Science Classroom,** p. 66 **Lab Management and Safety,** p. 65	Portfolio Reteach, p. 617 Performance MiniLAB, p. 614 MiniLAB, p. 616 Skill Builder Activities, p. 617 Content Section Assessment, p. 617	Section Focus Transparency Interactive CD-ROM Guided Reading Audio Program

Need materials? Contact Science Kit at 1-800-828-7777 or www.sciencekit.com on the Internet.

End of Chapter Assessment

GLENCOE'S ASSESSMENT ADVANTAGE

Blackline Masters	Technology	Professional Series
Chapter Resources Booklet Chapter Review, pp. 35–36 Chapter Tests, pp. 37–40 **Standardized Test Practice by The Princeton Review,** pp. 91–94	MindJogger Videoquiz Interactive CD-ROM Vocabulary PuzzleMakers ExamView Pro Test Bank Interactive Lesson Planner Interactive Teacher Edition	Performance Assessment in the Science Classroom (PASC)

Transparencies

Section Focus

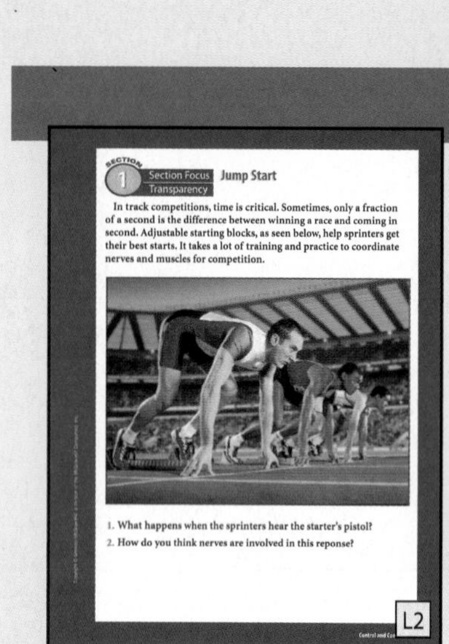

This is a representation of key blackline masters available in the Teacher Classroom Resources. See Resource Manager boxes within the chapter for additional information.

Assessment

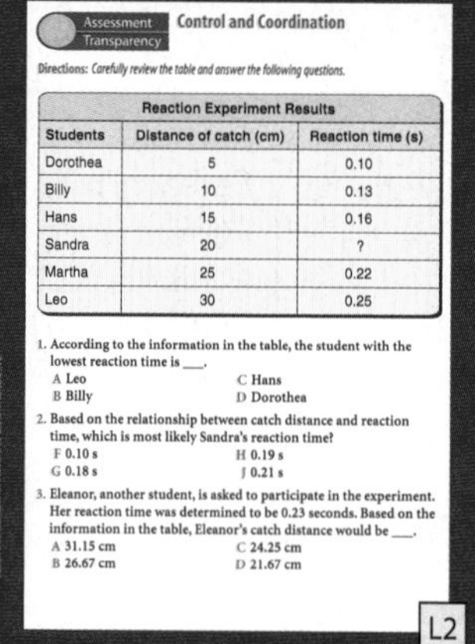

Teaching

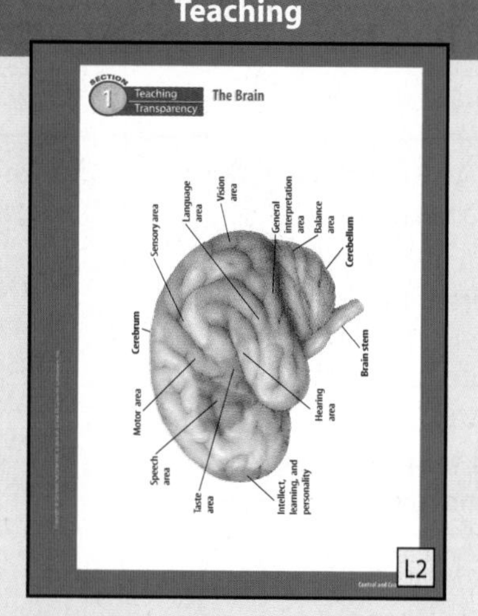

Key to Teaching Strategies

The following designations will help you decide which activities are appropriate for your students.

L1 Level 1 activities should be appropriate for students with learning difficulties.

L2 Level 2 activities should be within the ability range of all students.

L3 Level 3 activities are designed for above-average students.

ELL ELL activities should be within the ability range of English Language Learners.

COOP LEARN Cooperative Learning activities are designed for small group work.

LS Multiple Learning Styles logos, as described on page 22T, are used throughout to indicate strategies that address different learning styles.

P These strategies represent student products that can be placed into a best-work portfolio.

Hands-on Activities

Activity Worksheets

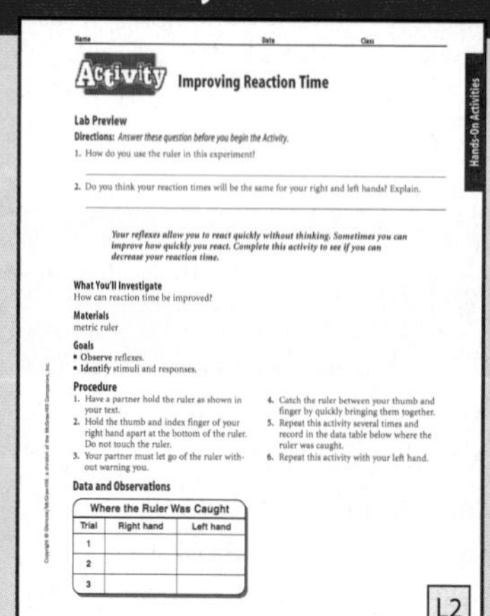

Laboratory Activities

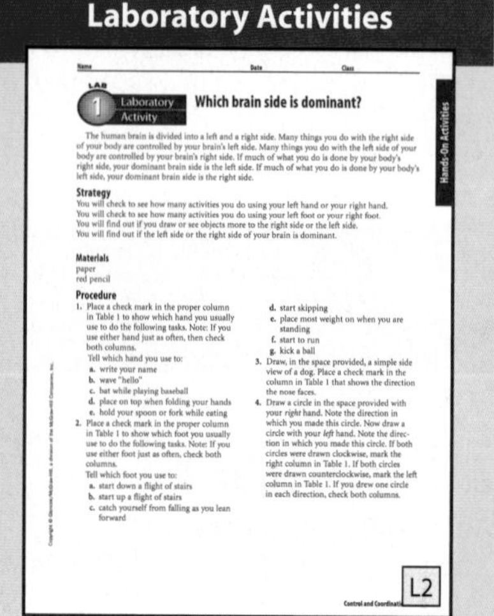

Meeting Different Ability Levels

Content Outline

Note-taking Worksheet — Control and Coordination — L2

Reinforcement

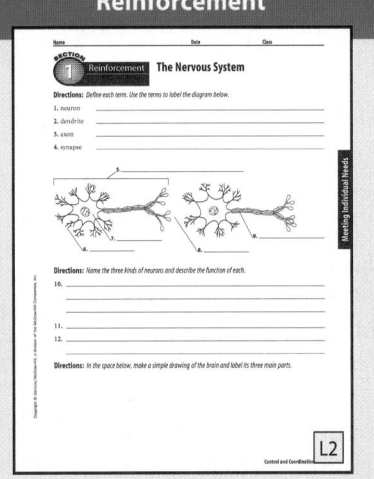

Reinforcement — The Nervous System — L2

Directed Reading

Directed Reading for Content Mastery — Overview — Control and Coordination — L1

Enrichment

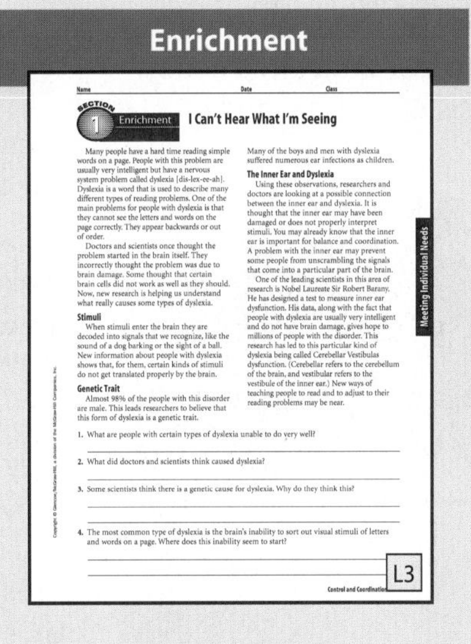

Name / Date / Class

SECTION 1 Enrichment — I Can't Hear What I'm Seeing

Many people have a hard time reading simple words on a page. People with this problem are usually very intelligent but have a nervous system problem called dyslexia (dis-lex-ee-ah). Dyslexia is a word that is used to describe many different types of reading problems. One of the main problems for people with dyslexia is that they cannot see the letters and words on the page correctly. They appear backwards or out of order.

Doctors and scientists once thought the problem started in the brain itself. They incorrectly thought the problem was due to brain damage. Some thought that certain brain cells did not work as well as they should. Now, new research is helping us understand what really causes some types of dyslexia.

Stimuli

When stimuli enter the brain they are decoded into signals that we recognize, like the sound of a dog barking or the sight of a ball. New information about people with dyslexia shows that, for them, certain kinds of stimuli do not get translated properly by the brain.

Genetic Trait

Almost 98% of the people with this disorder are male. This leads researchers to believe that this form of dyslexia is a genetic trait.

Many of the boys and men with dyslexia suffered numerous ear infections as children.

The Inner Ear and Dyslexia

Using these observations, researchers and doctors are looking at a possible connection between the inner ear and dyslexia. It is thought that the inner ear may have been damaged or does not properly interpret stimuli. You may already know that the inner ear is important for balance and coordination. A problem with the inner ear may prevent some people from unscrambling the signals that come into a particular part of the brain.

One of the leading scientists in this area of research is Nobel Laureate Sir Robert Barany. He has designed a test to measure inner ear dysfunction. His data, along with the fact that people with dyslexia are usually very intelligent and do not have brain damage, gives hope to millions of people with the disorder. This research has led to this particular kind of dyslexia being called Cerebellar Vestibular dysfunction. (Cerebellar refers to the cerebellum of the brain, and vestibular refers to the vestibule of the inner ear.) New ways of teaching people to read and to adjust to their reading problems may be near.

1. What are people with certain types of dyslexia unable to do very well?
2. What did doctors and scientists think caused dyslexia?
3. Some scientists think there is a genetic cause for dyslexia. Why do they think this?
4. The most common type of dyslexia is the brain's inability to sort out visual stimuli of letters and words on a page. Where does this inability seem to start?

L3

Spanish Directed Reading

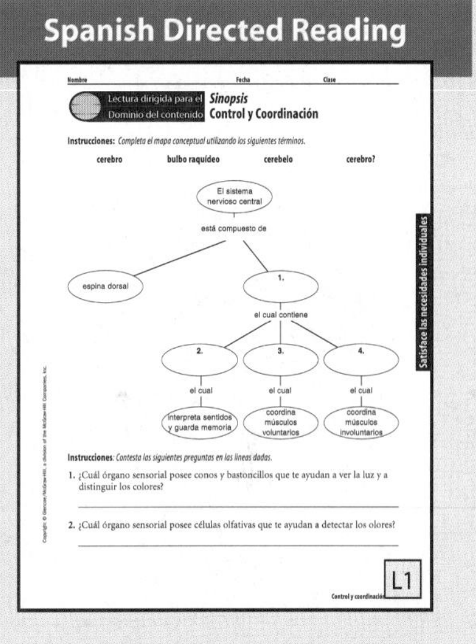

Nombre / Fecha / Clase

Lectura dirigida para el Dominio del contenido — Sinopsis — Control y Coordinación

Instrucciones: Completa el mapa conceptual utilizando las siguientes términos.

cerebro — bulbo raquídeo — cerebelo — cerebro?

Instrucciones: Contesta las siguientes preguntas en las líneas dadas.

1. ¿Cuál órgano sensorial posee conos y bastoncillos que te ayudan a ver la luz y a distinguir los colores?
2. ¿Cuál órgano sensorial posee células olfativas que te ayudan a detectar los olores?

L1

Assessment

Chapter Tests

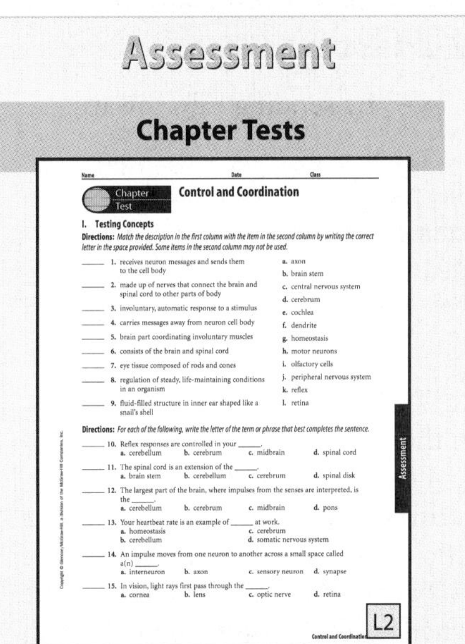

Name / Date / Class

Chapter Test — Control and Coordination

I. Testing Concepts

Directions: Match the description in the first column with the item in the second column by writing the correct letter in the space provided. Some items in the second column may not be used.

1. receives neuron messages and sends them to the cell body
2. made up of nerves that connect the brain and spinal cord to other parts of body
3. involuntary, automatic response to a stimulus
4. carries messages away from neuron cell body
5. brain part coordinating involuntary muscles
6. consists of the brain and spinal cord
7. eye tissue composed of rods and cones
8. regulation of steady, life-maintaining conditions in an organism
9. fluid-filled structure in inner ear shaped like a snail's shell

a. axon
b. brain stem
c. central nervous system
d. cerebrum
e. cochlea
f. dendrite
g. homeostasis
h. motor neurons
i. olfactory cells
j. peripheral nervous system
k. reflex
l. retina

Directions: For each of the following, write the letter of the term or phrase that best completes the sentence.

10. Reflex responses are controlled in your ____. a. cerebellum b. cerebrum c. midbrain d. spinal cord
11. The spinal cord is an extension of the ____. a. brain stem b. cerebellum c. cerebrum d. spinal disk
12. The largest part of the brain, where impulses from the senses are interpreted, is the ____. a. cerebellum b. cerebrum c. midbrain d. pons
13. Your heartbeat rate is an example of ____ at work. a. homeostasis b. cerebellum c. cerebrum d. somatic nervous system
14. An impulse moves from one neuron to another across a small space called a(n) ____. a. interneuron b. axon c. sensory neuron d. synapse
15. In vision, light rays first pass through the ____. a. cornea b. lens c. optic nerve d. retina

L2

Test Practice Workbook

L2

Chapter Review

Chapter Review — Control and Coordination — L2

Science Content Background

SECTION 1 The Nervous System

Nerve Cells

Specialized receptor cells respond to specific stimuli from various parts of the body. These stimuli produce a self-propagating wave of negative charges that is transmitted to the central nervous system via peripheral nerves. The nerve impulse travels at a rate of approximately 120 m/s. The brain and spinal cord of the central nervous system interpret the stimuli information. Appropriate responses are sent via nerves to the various body parts, which react to the stimulus. The response is a coordinated, integrated action that maintains homeostasis within the body.

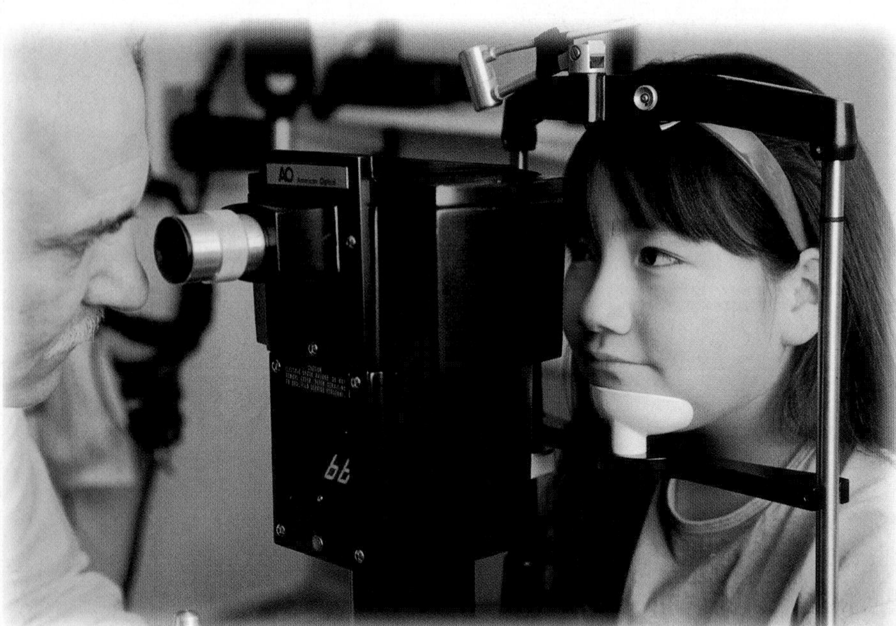

Michel Newman/PhotoEdit

SECTION 2 The Senses

Hearing and Taste

The sensory receptors for the senses of hearing, equilibrium, and taste are specialized. Each type is found in only one place, or pair of places, in the body. Vibrations in the air with frequencies between about 16,000 and 20,000 cycles per second can be detected as a sound by your ears. Hair cells within the inner ear are found in the organ of Corti. The hair cells' responses to the vibrations are converted to electrical signals. Sensory hair cells help maintain balance by responding to movements of liquids and of the tiny bits of calcium carbonate called otoliths in the labyrinth canals. Taste buds, located on small projections called papillae on the tongue, the soft palate, and the walls of the pharynx, are sensitive to substances dissolved in liquids. Specialized taste cells within the taste buds function as receptors.

Student Misconception

Human eyes "see" by sending rays toward an object.

Refer to the facing page for teaching strategies to address this misconception. Refer to pages 610–612 for content related to this topic.

Understanding the Eye

At the back of the human eye is a layer called the retina that contains photosensitive cells. These cells contain pigments that, when exposed to sufficient light, change their shape and break into two parts. This stimulates the nerve cell attached to the photoreceptor, which sends a signal down the optic nerve and into the back of the brain. For humans to see an object, therefore, light must strike the object and be reflected toward the eye. The light energy must have a wavelength between 380 nm and 760 nm in order to stimulate the photoreceptive pigments in the retina.

For additional content background on this topic, go to the Glencoe Science Web site at science.glencoe.com.

IDENTIFYING Misconceptions

Find Out What Students Think

Students may think that . . .

- **Human eyes "see" by sending rays toward an object.**

Students seldom understand the link between light and sight. Light is often viewed as a substance that fills a space, as in "the room was filled with light." Students' everyday experiences with light do not reveal the nature of light as wave energy. Student models of how vision works range from no connection between the eye and the object it sees to believing that the eyes themselves send out beams of light or some other energy to illuminate the object and allow sight. Some students may even conclude that it is possible to see in total darkness if they think that the eye provides its own source of illumination. The experience of seeing animal eyes "glow" at night may support this. Very few students have experienced total darkness, so they are confident in their abilities to see in the dark. They know their eyes "get used" to, or adapt to, semidarkness, allowing limited vision. Even if students are exposed to total darkness, the conclusion they draw may be that they will be able to see once their eyes "get used" to the dark.

Activity

After identifying the parts of the eye, sketch a diagram of an eye on one end of the board and an object at the other end. Ask students to draw a diagram that explains how the eye is able to "see" the object. Students should label all parts of their diagram to make their explanations clear.

Promote Understanding

Demonstration

Materials shoe box, sharp knife, cardboard tube (about 5 cm. long), black electrician's tape, flashlight, black spray paint, small object

Preparation Cut a hole in the box top. Tape a flashlight over the hole. Seal the edges with tape. Cut a peephole in one box end. Tape the cardboard tube over the hole. Paint the inside of the box black. Place an object inside and replace the lid.

Procedure

- Have students look in the box with the light off and describe what they can see. They should see nothing. Have students turn the flashlight on and look in the box again. The object is now visible.
- On the board, sketch a picture of the box with the object inside. Show how light comes from the flashlight and illuminates the object. Light reflected from the object reaches the eye and stimulates the retina, allowing the viewer to see the object.

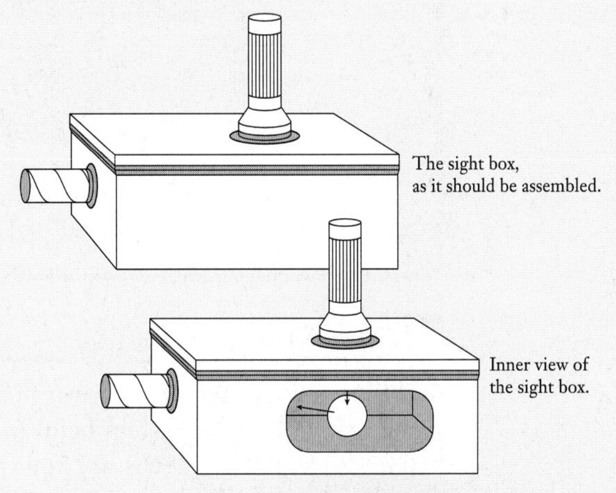

The sight box,
as it should be assembled.
Inner view of
the sight box.

Assess

After completing the chapter, see *Identifying Misconceptions* in the Study Guide.

CHAPTER 21

Control and Coordination

Chapter Vocabulary

homeostasis, p. 601
neuron, p. 601
dendrite, p. 601
axon, p. 601
synapse, p. 603
central nervous system, p. 603
peripheral nervous system, p. 603
cerebrum, p. 604
cerebellum, p. 604
brain stem, p. 604
reflex, p. 607
retina, p. 611
cochlea, p. 614
olfactory cell, p. 615
taste bud, p. 616

What do you think?

Science Journal These are papillae, tiny protuberances on the surface of the tongue. The taste buds found in their walls enable us to tell one taste from another.

CHAPTER 21 Control and Coordination

One second, the puck is halfway across the ice. In the next second you're trying to stop it from making a goal. For a hockey goalie, keen eyesight is not enough. He needs to be able to respond quickly, without even thinking about it. In this chapter, you will learn how your body senses and responds to the world around you.

What do you think?

Science Journal Look at the picture below with a classmate. Discuss what you think this must be. Here's a hint: *It can separate the bitter from the sweet.* Write your answer or best guess in your Science Journal.

598

Theme Connection

Stability and Change The stimulus-response action of the nervous system helps maintain the stable environment necessary for the healthy functioning of the body.

If the weather is cool, you might put on a jacket. If you see friends, you might call out to them. You also might pick up a crying baby. Every second of the day you react to different sights, sounds, and smells in your environment. You control some of these reactions, but others take place in your body without thought. Some reactions protect you from harm. Do the activity below to see how one response can keep your body safe.

Observe a response

1. Wearing safety goggles, sit on a chair 1 m away from a partner.
2. Ask your partner to toss a wadded-up piece of paper at your face without warning you.
3. Switch positions and repeat the activity.

Observe

Describe in your Science Journal how you reacted to the ball of paper being thrown at you. Explain how your anticipation of being hit altered your body's response.

Before You Read

FOLDABLES Reading & Study Skills

Making a Main Ideas Study Fold **A main idea consists of the major concepts or topics talked about in a chapter. Before you read the chapter, make the following Foldable to help you identify the main idea(s) of this chapter.**

1. Stack three sheets of paper in front of you so the short side of all sheets is at the top.
2. Slide the top sheet up so that about 4 cm of the middle sheet show. Slide the bottom sheet down so that about 4 cm of it shows below the middle sheet.
3. Fold the sheets top to bottom to form six tabs and staple along the top fold, as shown.
4. Label the flaps *Five Senses*, *Vision*, *Hearing*, *Smell*, *Taste*, and *Touch*, as shown. Before you read the chapter, write what you know about the five senses under the tabs.
5. As you read the chapter, add to or change the information you wrote under the tabs.

599

Explore Activity

Purpose Use the Explore Activity to introduce students to an aspect of the nervous system—reactions to stimuli. L2 ELL COOP LEARN

LS **Kinesthetic**

Preparation Place chairs about one meter apart.

Materials two chairs, wadded pieces of paper, safety goggles

Teaching Strategy Inform students that they will be learning more about the nervous system in this chapter.

Observe

Possible answers: moved head or body to avoid being hit, closed eyes, or placed hands in front of eyes; anticipation made the body respond more quickly.

Oral Have students discuss the value of avoidance reactions such as the one they observed in this activity. Use **Performance Assessment in the Science Classroom,** p. 169.

Before You Read

FOLDABLES Reading & Study Skills

Dinah Zike Study Fold

Purpose Students will demonstrate what they know about control and coordination before reading the chapter. They will make a Foldable for recording and organizing notes on vision, hearing, smell, taste, and touch as they read.

For additional help, see Foldables Worksheet, p. 17 in **Chapter Resources Booklet,** or go to the Glencoe Science Web site at **science.glencoe.com.** See After You Read in the Study Guide at the end of this chapter.

SECTION

The Nervous System

1 Motivate

Bellringer Transparency

Display the Section Focus Transparency for Section 1. Use the accompanying Transparency Activity Master. L2 ELL

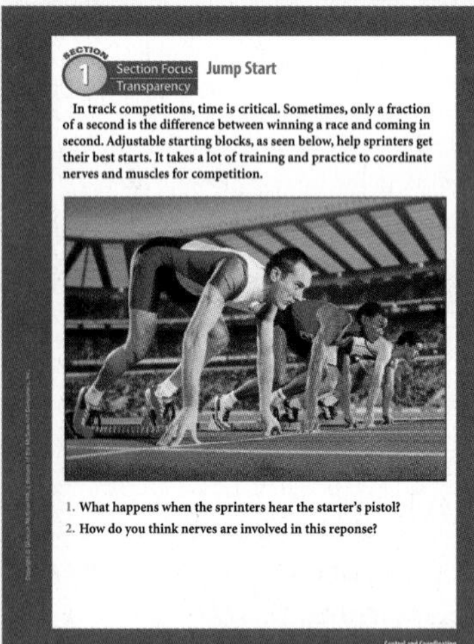

Section Focus Transparency 1 — Jump Start

In track competitions, time is critical. Sometimes, only a fraction of a second is the difference between winning a race and coming in second. Adjustable starting blocks, as seen below, help sprinters get their best starts. It takes a lot of training and practice to coordinate nerves and muscles for competition.

1. What happens when the sprinters hear the starter's pistol?
2. How do you think nerves are involved in this reponse?

Control and Coordination

Tie to Prior Knowledge

Have students brainstorm a list of muscle actions that are out of their conscious control. Lists might include blinking or heartbeat. Explain that these actions occur as the body responds to stimuli.

Caption Answer

Figure 1 Sights, sounds, odors, tastes; accept reasonable answers.

SECTION 1

The Nervous System

As You Read

***What* You'll Learn**

- **Describe** the basic structure of a neuron and how an impulse moves across a synapse.
- **Compare** the central and peripheral nervous systems.
- **Explain** how drugs affect the body.

Vocabulary

homeostasis
neuron
dendrite
axon
synapse
central nervous system
peripheral nervous system
cerebrum
cerebellum
brain stem
reflex

***Why* It's Important**

Your body reacts to your environment because of your nervous system.

How the Nervous System Works

After doing the dishes and finishing your homework, you settle down in your favorite chair and pick up that mystery novel you've been trying to finish. Only three pages to go . . . Who did it? Why did she do it? Crash! You scream. What made that unearthly noise? You turn around to find that your dog's wagging tail has just swept the lamp off the table. Suddenly, you're aware that your heart is racing and your hands are shaking. After a few minutes though, your breathing returns to normal and your heartbeat is back to its regular rate. What's going on?

Responding to Stimuli The scene described above is an example of how your body responds to changes in its environment. Any internal or external change that brings about a response is called a stimulus (STIHM yuh lus). Each day, you're bombarded by thousands of stimuli, as shown in **Figure 1.** Noise, light, the smell of food, and the temperature of the air are all stimuli from outside your body. Chemical substances such as hormones are examples of stimuli from inside your body. Your body adjusts to changing stimuli with the help of your nervous system.

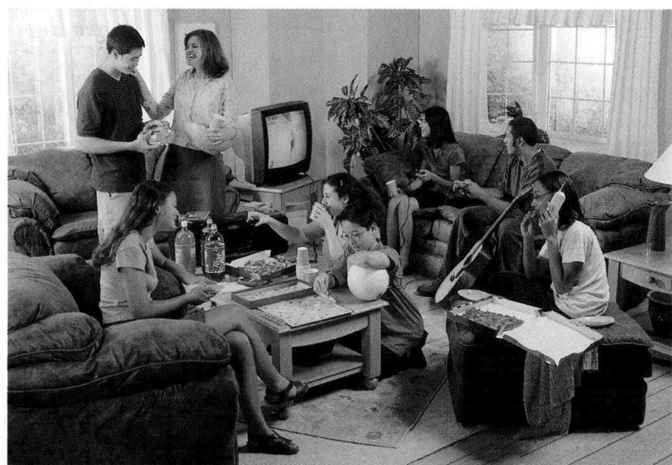

Figure 1
Stimuli are found everywhere and all the time, even when you're enjoying being with your friends. *What types of stimuli are present at this party?*

Section Assessment Planner

PORTFOLIO
Science Journal, p. 606
Assessment, p. 608

PERFORMANCE ASSESSMENT
Skill Builder Activities, p. 608
See page 624 for more options.

CONTENT ASSESSMENT
Section, p. 608
Challenge, p. 608
Chapter, pp. 624–625

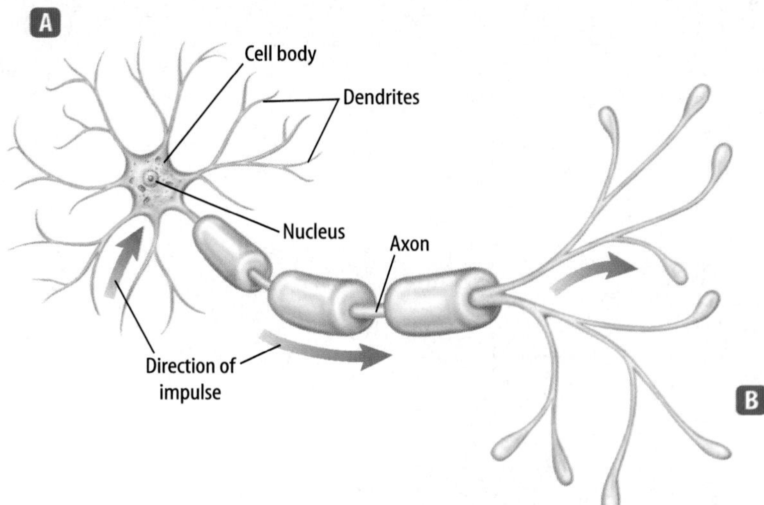

Figure 2
A A neuron is made up of a cell body, dendrites, and an axon. *How does the branching of the dendrites allow for more impulses to be picked up by the neuron?*
B In this photograph of brain neurons, can you find the cell parts named in A?

B
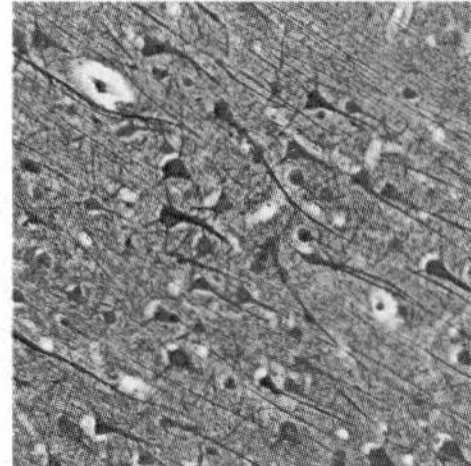

Homeostasis It's amazing how your body handles all these stimuli. Control systems maintain steady internal conditions. The regulation of steady, life-maintaining conditions inside an organism, despite changes in its environment, is called **homeostasis.** Examples of homeostasis are the regulation of your breathing, heartbeat, and digestion. Your nervous system is one of several control systems used by your body to maintain homeostasis.

Nerve Cells

The basic functioning units of the nervous system are nerve cells, or **neurons** (NOO rahnz). As shown in **Figure 2,** a neuron is made up of a cell body and branches called dendrites and axons. **Dendrites** receive messages from other neurons and send them to the cell body. **Axons** (AK sahns) carry messages away from the cell body. Any message carried by a neuron is called an impulse. Notice the branching at the end of the axon. This allows the impulses to move to many other muscles, neurons, or glands.

Types of Nerve Cells Your body has sensory receptors that produce electrical impulses and respond to stimuli, such as changes in temperature, sound, pressure, and taste. Three types of neurons—sensory neurons, motor neurons, and interneurons—transport impulses. Sensory neurons receive information and send impulses to the brain or spinal cord, where interneurons relay these impulses to motor neurons. Motor neurons then conduct impulses from the brain or spinal cord to muscles or glands throughout your body.

Would you know what to do if you saw someone unconscious? To find out what to do in a situation such as this, see the **Emergencies Field Guide** at the back of the book.

2 Teach

Nerve Cells

Caption Answer

Figure 2A Each neuron can receive impulses from several different sensory receptors because of the branched dendrites.

Quick Demo

In a school yard or athletic field, position two students 100 meters apart. Use this visual representation to illustrate the distance that some nerve impulses travel in one second.

Discussion

What would happen if all your sensory neurons stopped working? Your brain would stop receiving stimuli from inside and outside your body, making it impossible to maintain homeostasis.

Fun Fact

The structure of an axon of a neuron can change when used. More and better connections with other neurons result from learning. Schoolwork helps neurons make connections.

Resource Manager

Chapter Resources Booklet
Note-taking Worksheets, pp. 31–33
Transparency Activity, p. 42

Science Journal

Nerve Analogy Have students write a paragraph in their Science Journals that explains how a nerve is similar to a wire going from a controlling switch (stimulus) to a light bulb (response). Possible response: The switch receives a stimulus, which travels along the wire. The bulb responds to the stimulus by lighting up. L2 LS **Linguistic** P

Visualizing Nerve Impulse Pathways

Have students examine the pictures and read the captions. Then ask the following questions.

What would happen if an interneuron could not perform its function? Possible answer: There would be no connection between the sensory neuron and the motor neuron. The nerve impulse may not be passed on.

What are the differences between a sensory neuron and a motor neuron? Possible answer: Sensory neurons detect internal or external stimuli and transfer impulses to the spinal cord or brain. Motor neurons respond to stimuli from the spinal cord or brain and carry impulses back out to muscles.

Activity

Have students make a model of a neuron. Students can use yarn and markers on construction paper to model and label the different parts of a neuron including the dendrites, the cell body, and the axon. Students can also show the direction of impulse transmission. Dendrites receive an impulse from another neuron and pass it on to the cell body. The axon carries the impulse to the next neuron.

Extension

Have students research the differences between myelinated neurons and unmyelinated neurons. Students should determine which type of nerve impulse conduction each has. They can present their results on a poster.

Figure 3

Millions of nerve impulses are moving throughout your body as you read this page. In response to stimuli, many impulses follow a specific pathway—from sensory neuron to interneuron to motor neuron—to bring about a response. Like a relay team, these three types of neurons work together. The illustration on this page shows how the sound of a breaking window might startle you and cause you to drop a glass of water.

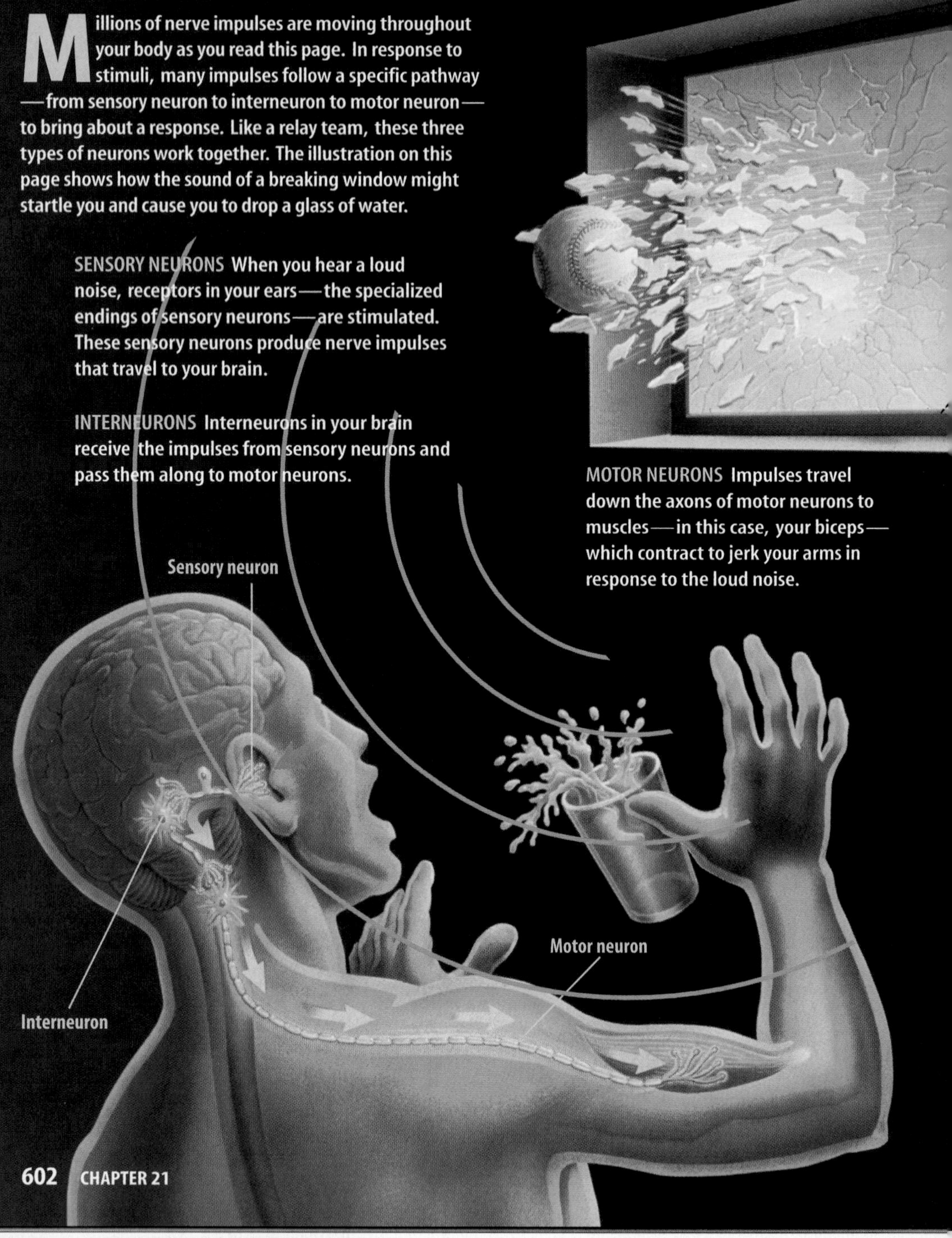

SENSORY NEURONS When you hear a loud noise, receptors in your ears—the specialized endings of sensory neurons—are stimulated. These sensory neurons produce nerve impulses that travel to your brain.

INTERNEURONS Interneurons in your brain receive the impulses from sensory neurons and pass them along to motor neurons.

MOTOR NEURONS Impulses travel down the axons of motor neurons to muscles—in this case, your biceps—which contract to jerk your arms in response to the loud noise.

Sensory neuron

Motor neuron

Interneuron

Resource Manager 

Chapter Resources Booklet
- Activity Worksheet, pp. 5–6
- Transparency Activity, pp. 45–46

Reading and Writing Skill Activities, p. 17

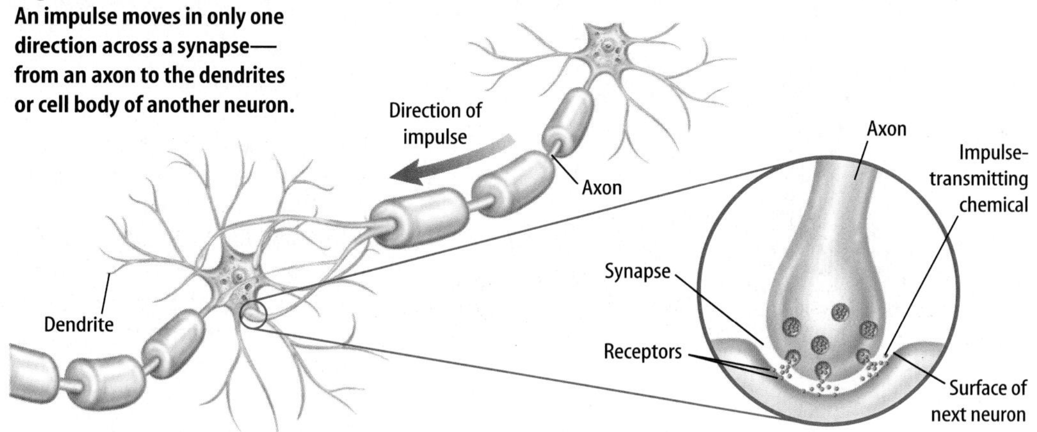

Figure 4
An impulse moves in only one direction across a synapse—from an axon to the dendrites or cell body of another neuron.

Synapses In a relay race, the first runner sprints down the track with a baton in his or her hand. As the runner rounds the track, he or she hands the baton off to the next runner. The two runners never physically touch each other. The transfer of the baton signals the second runner to continue the race.

As shown in **Figure 3,** your nervous system works in a similar way. Like the runners in a relay race, neurons don't touch each other. How does an impulse move from one neuron to another? To move from one neuron to the next, an impulse crosses a small space called a **synapse** (SIH naps). In **Figure 4,** note that when an impulse reaches the end of an axon, the axon releases a chemical. This chemical flows across the synapse and stimulates the impulse in the dendrite of the next neuron. An impulse moves from neuron to neuron just like a baton moves from runner to runner in a relay race. The baton represents the chemical at the synapse.

Figure 5
The brain and spinal cord (yellow) form the central nervous system (CNS). All other nerves (green) are part of the peripheral nervous system (PNS).

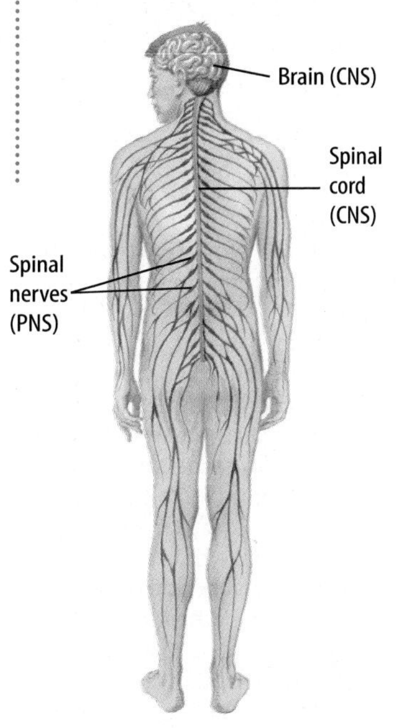

The Central Nervous System

Figure 5 shows how organs of the nervous system are grouped into two major divisions—the central nervous system (CNS) and the peripheral (puh RIH fuh rul) nervous system (PNS). The **central nervous system** is made up of the brain and spinal cord. The **peripheral nervous system** is made up of all the nerves outside the CNS. These include the nerves in your head, called cranial nerves, and spinal nerves, which are nerves that come from your spinal cord. The peripheral nervous system connects the brain and spinal cord to other body parts. Your neurons are adapted in such a way that impulses move in only one direction. Sensory neurons send impulses to the brain or spinal cord.

The Central Nervous System

Activity

Have three students stand side by side. Their arms and fingers should be outstretched at their sides. Starting at one end of the line, have the students pass a ruler from person to person. Students' fingers should not touch. Use this to show how an impulse travels from a sensory neuron through an interneuron to a motor neuron. Have students identify the axon and dendrites of each "nerve cell." L2 ELL COOP LEARN
LS **Kinesthetic**

Use Science Words

Word Origin Have students look up *synapse* in the dictionary. Students will find that it comes from the Greek roots *syn* ("together") and *haptein* ("unite"). Ask students to think about how the roots of the word reflect its meaning. At a synapse, neurons are close together, allowing an impulse to move from one to another. L2
LS **Linguistic**

Curriculum Connection

Health Have interested students research and report on concussions. They should find out how they occur, what happens to the brain, symptoms of concussion, and treatment. Preventive measures such as wearing seat belts and safety helmets should also be included. L2
LS **Linguistic**

The Central Nervous System, continued

Reading Check

Answer Thinking takes place in the cerebrum, as well as interpretation of impulses from senses, storage of memory, and control of movement.

Chemistry INTEGRATION

If acetylcholine did not break down, there would be a continual carrying of the impulse across the synapse.

Make a Model

Have students make a model of the vertebral column and spinal cord by stringing 33 thread spools on a thin rope. Use circular pieces of foam rubber for the disks between the vertebrae. Have students note how the cord (rope) is protected. The spools (vertebrae) protect the rope (spinal cord); vertebrae are cushioned by the foam rubber.

Use Science Words

Word Origin Have students compare the use of the word *cortex* as used by botanists and physiologists. To botanists, the cortex is the plant tissue between the epidermis and the vascular tissue. To physiologists, it is the outer part of an organ, especially the outer layer of gray matter of the cerebrum and cerebellum.

Fun Fact

The adult human brain weighs about 1.4 kg (approximately 3 lb) and has a volume of approximately 1,500 cm^3. It contains over 100 billion neurons.

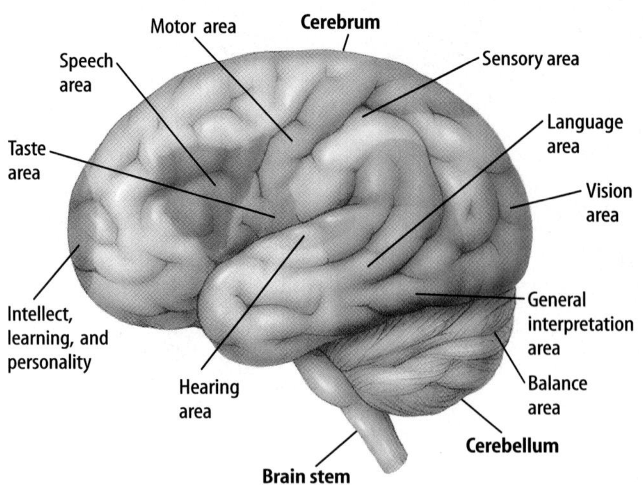

Figure 6
Different areas of the brain control specific body activities.

The Brain The brain coordinates all of your body activities. If someone tickles your feet, why does your whole body seem to react? The brain is made up of approximately 100 billion neurons, which is nearly ten percent of all the neurons in the human body. Surrounding and protecting the brain are a bony skull, three membranes, and a layer of fluid. As shown in **Figure 6,** the brain is divided into three major parts—the cerebrum (suh REE brum), the cerebellum (ser uh BEL um), and the brain stem.

Cerebrum Thinking takes place in the cerebrum. The **cerebrum** is the largest part of the brain. This is where impulses from the senses are interpreted, memory is stored, and movements are controlled. The outer layer of the cerebrum, called the cortex, is marked by many ridges and grooves. These structures increase the surface area of the cortex, allowing more complex thoughts to be processed. **Figure 6** shows some of the motor and sensory tasks that the cortex controls.

Reading Check ***What major activity takes place within the cerebrum?***

Cerebellum Stimuli from the eyes and ears and from muscles and tendons, which are the tissues that connect muscles to bones, are interpreted in the **cerebellum.** With this information, the cerebellum is able to coordinate voluntary muscle movements, maintain muscle tone, and help maintain balance. A complex activity, such as riding a bike, requires a lot of coordination and control of your muscles. The cerebellum coordinates your muscle movements so that you maintain your balance.

Brain Stem At the base of the brain is the **brain stem.** It extends from the cerebrum and connects the brain to the spinal cord. The brain stem is made up of the midbrain, the pons, and the medulla (muh DUH luh). The midbrain and pons act as pathways connecting various parts of the brain with each other. The medulla controls involuntary actions such as heartbeat, breathing, and blood pressure. The medulla also is involved in such actions as coughing, sneezing, swallowing, and vomiting.

Chemistry INTEGRATION

Acetylcholine (uh see tul KOH leen) is a chemical produced by neurons, which carries an impulse across a synapse to the next neuron. After the impulse is started, the acetylcholine breaks down rapidly. In your Science Journal, hypothesize why the breakdown of acetylcholine is important.

Visual Learning

Figure 6 Have students describe how the brain is protected. Hair, skin, skull bones, membranes, and fluids protect the brain.

Inclusion Strategies

Gifted, Visually Impaired, and Learning Disabled Have gifted students make a model of the brain from papier-mâché or craft foam. Have them paint each part a different color and label the areas of activity. These models can then be used by visually impaired and learning disabled students for study. LS **Kinesthetic**

604 CHAPTER 21 Control and Coordination

The Spinal Cord Your spinal cord, illustrated in **Figure 7,** is an extension of the brain stem. It is made up of bundles of neurons that carry impulses from all parts of the body to the brain and from the brain to all parts of your body. The adult spinal cord is about the width of an adult thumb and is about 43 cm long.

Research Visit the Glencoe Science Web site at **science.glencoe.com** for more information about the nervous system. Make a brochure outlining recent medical advances.

The Peripheral Nervous System

Your brain and spinal cord are connected to the rest of your body by the peripheral nervous system. The PNS is made up of 12 pairs of nerves from your brain called cranial nerves, and 31 pairs from your spinal cord called spinal nerves. Spinal nerves are made up of bundles of sensory and motor neurons bound together by connective tissue. For this reason, a single spinal nerve can have impulses going to and from the brain at the same time. Some nerves contain only sensory neurons, and some contain only motor neurons, but most nerves contain both types of neurons.

Somatic and Autonomic Systems The peripheral nervous system has two major divisions. The somatic system controls voluntary actions. It is made up of the cranial and spinal nerves that go from the central nervous system to your skeletal muscles. The autonomic system controls involuntary actions—those not under conscious control—such as your heart rate, breathing, digestion, and glandular functions. These two divisions, along with the central nervous system, make up your body's nervous system.

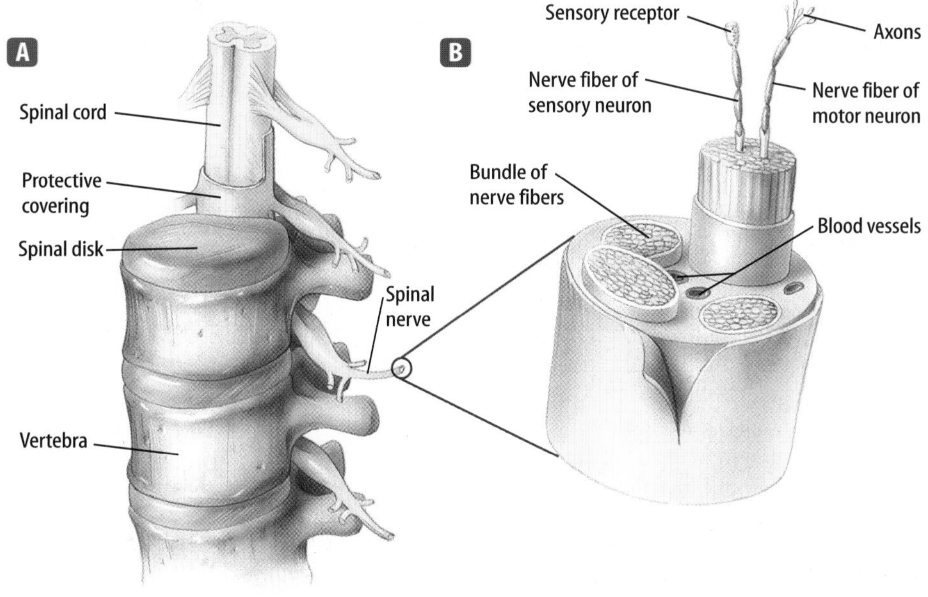

Figure 7
A A column of vertebrae, or bones, protects the spinal cord.
B The spinal cord is made up of bundles of neurons that carry impulses to and from all parts of the body, similar to a telephone cable.

IDENTIFYING Misconceptions

Alcohol is often perceived as a stimulant because it initially makes a person feel more energetic. However, alcohol actually slows down the actions of the central nervous system.

The Peripheral Nervous System

SCIENCE Online
Internet Addresses
Explore the Glencoe Science Web site at science.glencoe.com to find out more about topics in this section.

Extension

Have an interested student interview a pediatrician to find out which motor reflexes a child is born with. A partial list includes gag reflex, blink reflex, pain avoidance reflex, shivering in response to cold, sucking reflex, and swallowing reflex. L3

Resource Manager 

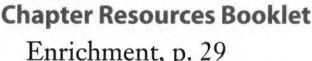

Chapter Resources Booklet
Enrichment, p. 29

Life Science Critical Thinking/Problem Solving, p. 2

Curriculum Connection

History In the latter part of the eighteenth century, scientists investigated animals that were able to produce an electric shock such as the electric eel. These investigations led to research on the effects of electricity on nerves and the muscular contractions that could be produced. Have students research the results of such investigations and share their findings. L3

Safety and the Nervous System

Discussion

Have students discuss other types of reflex responses to stimuli that prevent injury to the body. Examples include holding hands over the ear when there are loud noises and rapid upward foot movement when stepping on a sharp object.

Discussion

What kinds of accidents at home might cause head injuries? Possible answers: slipping in the bathtub or falling off a ladder

Use Science Words

Word Origin When the brain is damaged, paralysis can result. Quadriplegics are individuals whose arms and legs are paralyzed. The word *quadriplegic* has its roots in the Latin word *quadra*, meaning "four," and the Greek word *plege*, meaning "stroke." **How is this combination of words appropriate for its definition?** A stroke can cause paralysis of all four limbs. Have students research the word origin of hemiplegia. Hemiplegia is total or partial paralysis of one side of the body (hemi = half).

Safety and the Nervous System

Every mental process and physical action of the body is associated with the structures of the central and peripheral nervous systems. Therefore, any injury to the brain or the spinal cord can be serious. A severe blow to the head can bruise the brain and cause temporary or permanent loss of mental and physical abilities. For example, the back of the brain controls vision. An injury in this region could result in the loss of vision.

Although the spinal cord is surrounded by the bones in your spine called vertebrae, spinal cord injuries do occur. They can be just as dangerous as a brain injury. Injury to the spine can bring about damage to nerve pathways and result in paralysis (puh RAH luh suhs), which is the loss of muscle movement. As shown in **Figure 8,** a neck injury that damages certain nerves could prevent a person from breathing. Major causes of head and spinal injuries include automobile, motorcycle, and bicycle accidents, as well as sports injuries. Just like wearing seat belts in automobiles, it is important to wear the appropriate safety gear while playing sports and riding on bicycles and skateboards.

Figure 8
Head and spinal cord damage can result in paralysis depending on where the injury occurs.

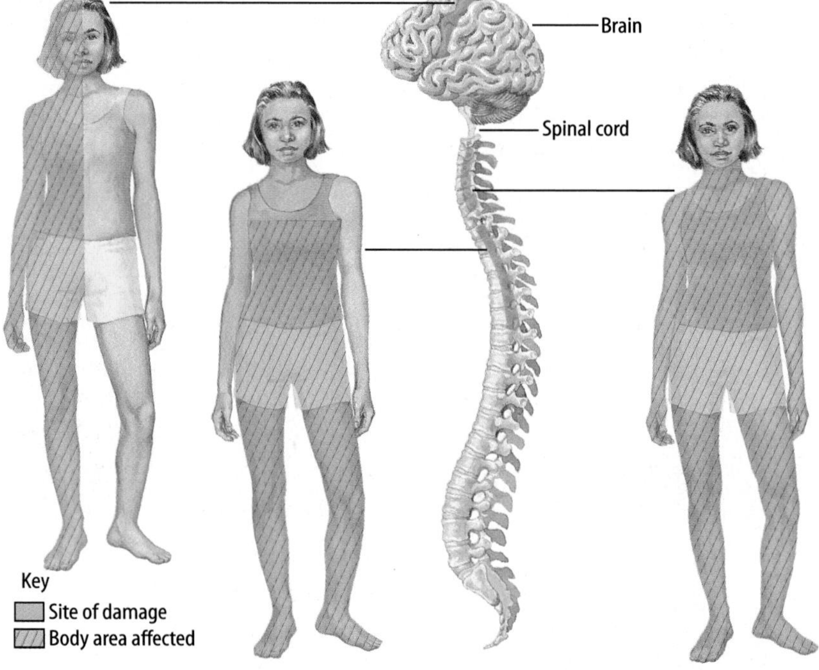

A Damage to one side of the brain can result in the paralysis of the opposite side of the body.

B Damage to the middle or lower spinal cord can result in the legs and possibly part of the body being paralyzed.

C Damage to the spinal cord in the lower neck area can cause the body to be paralyzed from the neck down.

Science Journal

Recovering from Injury Christopher Reeve, the actor who portrayed Superman in the movies, suffered severe injuries while horseback riding. Ask students to describe in their Science Journals his progress in adapting to and dealing with his paralysis. L2 LS **Linguistic**

Teacher FYI

A closed head injury does not involve any breaks in the skull. Loss of consciousness and diminished brain function may result. In an open head injury, the skull bones are penetrated. There is then the added risk of infection. Immediate surgery is necessary to clean and repair the wound.

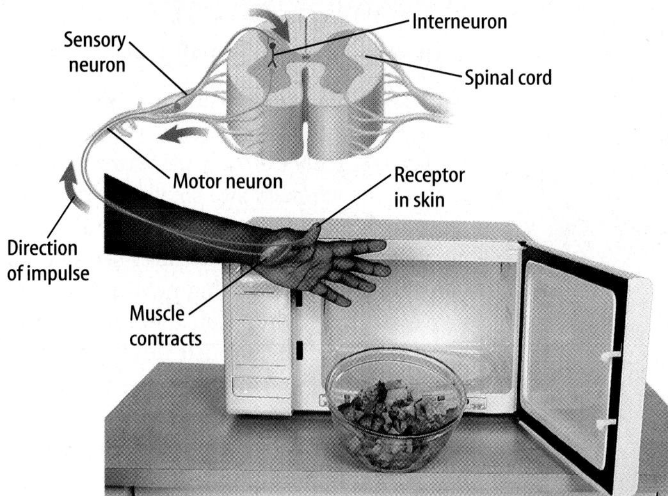

Figure 9
Your response in a reflex is controlled in your spinal cord, not your brain.

Reflexes You experience a reflex if you accidentally touch something sharp, something extremely hot or cold, or when you cough or vomit. A **reflex** is an involuntary, automatic response to a stimulus. You can't control reflexes because they occur before you know what has happened. A reflex involves a simple nerve pathway called a reflex arc, as illustrated in **Figure 9.**

While walking on a sandy beach, a pain suddenly shoots through your foot as you step on the sharp edge of a broken shell. Sensory receptors in your foot respond to this sharp object, and an impulse is sent to the spinal cord. As you just learned, the impulse passes to an interneuron in the spinal cord that immediately relays the impulse to motor neurons. Motor neurons transmit the impulse to muscles in your leg. Instantly, without thinking, you lift up your leg in response to the sharp-edged shell. This is a withdrawal reflex.

A reflex allows the body to respond without having to think about what action to take. Reflex responses are controlled in your spinal cord, not in your brain. Your brain acts after the reflex to help you figure out what to do to make the pain stop.

Reading Check *Why are reflexes important?*

Do you remember reading at the beginning of this chapter about being frightened after a lamp was broken? What would have happened if your breathing and heart rate didn't calm down within a few minutes? Your body systems can't be kept in a state of continual excitement. The organs of your nervous system control and coordinate body responses. This helps maintain homeostasis within your body.

SCIENCE Online

Research Visit the Glencoe Science Web site at **science.glencoe.com** for more information about reflexes and paralysis. Make a small poster illustrating what you learn.

Teacher FYI

Alzheimer's disease is the result of brain neurons slowly dying. This results in less production of the chemical needed for neurons to communicate with each other.

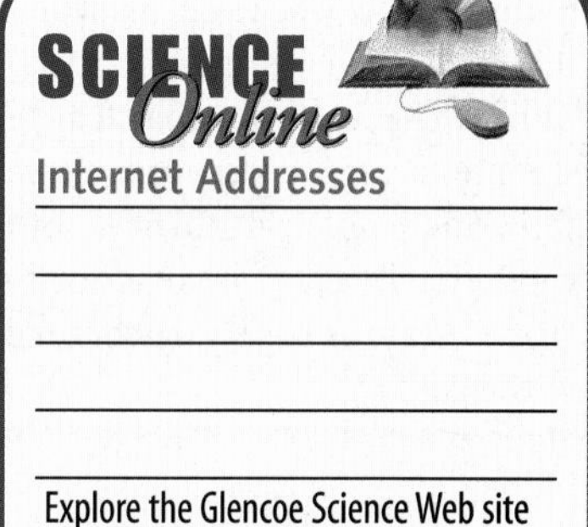

Explore the Glencoe Science Web site at **science.glencoe.com** to find out more about topics in this section.

Reading Check

Answer They allow quick reactions to dangerous situations without having to think about what to do.

Text Question Answer

If your breathing and heart rate hadn't calmed down, you might have lost consciousness; your body systems would not have been able to keep up with your high rate of respiration and heartbeat.

Resource Manager

Chapter Resources Booklet

Directed Reading for Content Mastery, pp. 19, 20

Life Science Critical Thinking/Problem Solving, p. 18

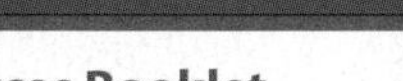

How Drugs Affect the Nervous System

IDENTIFYING Misconceptions

Some students may think that drinking a lot of coffee in order to keep awake to study for exams is a good idea. While the caffeine may cause sleeplessness, it also can cause nervousness, irritability, and hyperactivity. These conditions may actually interfere with studying.

3 Assess

Reteach

Have students make flash cards of the names of the major parts of the nervous system. Have them write a brief description of the function of each part on the back of its card. Students can use the cards to quiz each other to review section content. L2

Challenge

Why might a hard blow to the back of the head cause a vision disorder? The primary visual area of the brain is located at the lower rear side of the cerebrum.

Assessment

Portfolio Have students make models of two neurons. Have them clearly label the synapse, axons, dendrites, cell bodies, and neurotransmitters. Use **Performance Assessment in the Science Classroom**, p. 123. P

Figure 10
Caffeine, a substance found in colas, coffee, chocolate, and some teas, can cause excitability and sleeplessness.

How Drugs Affect the Nervous System

Many drugs, such as alcohol and caffeine, directly affect your nervous system. When swallowed, alcohol directly passes through the walls of the stomach and small intestine into the circulatory system. After it is inside the circulatory system, it can travel throughout your body. Upon reaching neurons, alcohol moves through their cell membranes and disrupts their normal cell functions. As a result, this drug slows the activities of the central nervous system and is classified as a depressant. Muscle control, judgment, reasoning, memory, and concentration also are impaired. Heavy alcohol use destroys brain and liver cells.

A stimulant is a drug that speeds up the activity of the central nervous system. Caffeine is a stimulant found in coffee, tea, cocoa, and many soft drinks, as shown in **Figure 10.** Too much caffeine can increase heart rate and aggravates restlessness, tremors, and insomnia in some people. It also can stimulate the kidneys to produce more urine.

Think again about a scare from a loud noise. The organs of your nervous system control and coordinate responses to maintain homeostasis within your body. This task might be more difficult when your body must cope with the effects of drugs.

Section 1 Assessment

1. Draw and label the parts of a neuron.
2. Compare the central and peripheral nervous systems.
3. During a cold, winter evening, you have several cups of hot cocoa. Explain why you have trouble falling asleep that night.
4. Explain the advantage of having reflexes controlled by the spinal cord.
5. **Think Critically** Explain why many medications caution the consumer not to operate heavy machinery.

Skill Builder Activities

6. **Concept Mapping** Prepare an events-chain concept map of the different kinds of neurons that pass an impulse from a stimulus to a response. **For more help, refer to the Science Skill Handbook.**
7. **Using a Word Processor** Create a flowchart showing the reflex pathway of a nerve impulse when you step on a sharp object. Label the body parts involved in each step. **For more help, refer to the Technology Skill Handbook.**

Answers to Section Assessment

1. Drawings should resemble Figure 2.
2. The central nervous system is made up of the brain and spinal cord. The peripheral nervous system is made up of cranial and spinal nerves.
3. Cocoa contains caffeine, which is a stimulant that can cause sleeplessness.
4. The response time to stimuli is shorter.
5. Many drugs contain components which slow your central nervous system, affecting muscle control, judgment, reasoning, memory, and concentration; this could be dangerous if operating heavy machinery.
6. The concept map should contain the following: stimulus–sensory neurons–interneurons–motor neurons–response.
7. Flowcharts should show an impulse moving from receptor to sensory neuron to interneuron in the spinal cord to motor neuron to muscles in the foot.

Activity

Improving Reaction Time

Your reflexes allow you to react quickly without thinking. Sometimes you can improve how quickly you react. Complete this activity to see if you can decrease your reaction time.

What You'll Investigate

How can reaction time be improved?

Materials

metric ruler

Goals

- **Observe** reflexes.
- **Identify** stimuli and responses.

Procedure

1. Make a data table in your Science Journal to record where the ruler is caught during this activity. Possible column heads are Trial, Right Hand, and Left Hand.
2. Have a partner hold the ruler as shown.
3. Hold the thumb and index finger of your right hand apart at the bottom of the ruler. Do not touch the ruler.
4. Your partner must let go of the ruler without warning you.
5. Catch the ruler between your thumb and finger by quickly bringing them together.
6. Repeat this activity several times and record in a data table where the ruler was caught.
7. Repeat this activity with your left hand.

Conclude and Apply

1. **Identify** the stimulus, response, and variable in this activity.
2. Use the table on the right to determine your reaction time.
3. What was the average reaction time for your right hand? For your left hand?
4. **Compare** the response of your writing hand and your other hand for this activity.
5. Draw a conclusion about how practice relates to stimulus-response time.

Reaction Time

Where Caught (cm)	Reaction Time (s)
5	0.10
10	0.14
15	0.17
20	0.20
25	0.23
30	0.25

Communicating Your Data

Compare your conclusions with those of other students in your class. **For more help, refer to the** Science Skill Handbook.

Activity

BENCH TESTED

Purpose Students observe reaction time. L2 COOP LEARN
LS **Kinesthetic**

Process Skills observing, communicating, using numbers, recognizing and using spatial relationships, measuring in SI, interpreting data

Time Required 30 minutes

Teaching Strategy Students should keep their eyes on the ruler as their partners release it.

Answers to Questions

1. stimulus: the ruler falling; response: catching the ruler; variable: which hand is used
2. Answers will vary.
3. To find the average, students should add all reaction times for each hand separately and divide by the number of trials.
4. Answers will vary. Generally, the writing hand reacts faster.
5. With practice, stimulus-response time usually improves.

✓Assessment

Performance To further assess students' abilities to measure and improve reaction time, have them repeat the experiment with slight variations. Have students blindfolded, and instruct their partner to tell them when they drop the ruler. See how quickly they can react to verbal stimuli. Use **PASC,** p. 97.

Resource Manager

Chapter Resources Booklet
Lab Activity, pp. 9–12
Reinforcement, p. 27
Mathematics Skill Activities, p. 9

Communicating Your Data

Students should discuss why their reaction times were or were not the same.

SECTION

The Senses

1 Motivate

Bellringer Transparency

Display the Section Focus Transparency for Section 2. Use the accompanying Transparency Activity Master. L2 ELL

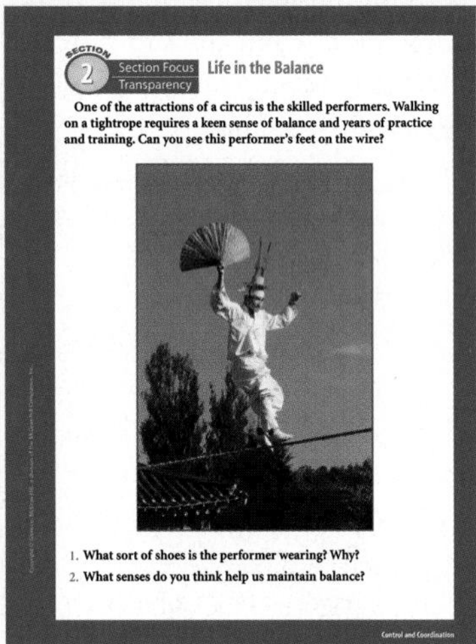

SECTION 2
Section Focus Transparency
Life in the Balance
One of the attractions of a circus is the skilled performers. Walking on a tightrope requires a keen sense of balance and years of practice and training. Can you see this performer's feet on the wire?
1. What sort of shoes is the performer wearing? Why?
2. What senses do you think help us maintain balance?
Control and Coordination

Tie to Prior Knowledge

Have students compare the sensory system of information processing with that of a telephone system. Have them brainstorm similarities and differences.

SECTION 2

The Senses

As You Read

***What* You'll Learn**

- **List** the sensory receptors in each sense organ.
- **Explain** what type of stimulus each sense organ responds to and how.
- **Explain** why healthy senses are needed.

Vocabulary

retina
cochlea
olfactory cell
taste bud

***Why* It's Important**

Your senses make you aware of your environment, enable you to enjoy your world, and help keep you safe.

The Body's Alert System

"Danger . . . danger . . . code red alert! An unidentified vessel has entered the spaceship's energy force field. All crew members are to be on alert!" Like spaceships in science fiction movies, your body has an alert system, too—your sense organs. You might see a bird, hear a dog bark, or smell popcorn. You can enjoy the taste of salt on a pretzel, the touch of a fuzzy peach, or feel heat from a warm, cozy fire. Light rays, sound waves, heat, chemicals, or pressure that comes into your personal territory will stimulate your sense organs. Sense organs are adapted for intercepting these different stimuli. They are then converted into impulses by the nervous system.

Vision

The eye, shown in **Figure 11,** is a sense organ. Think about the different kinds of objects you might look at every day. It's amazing that at one glance you might see the words on this page, the color illustrations, and your classmate sitting next to you. Your eyes have unique adaptations that usually enable you to see shapes of objects, shadows, and color.

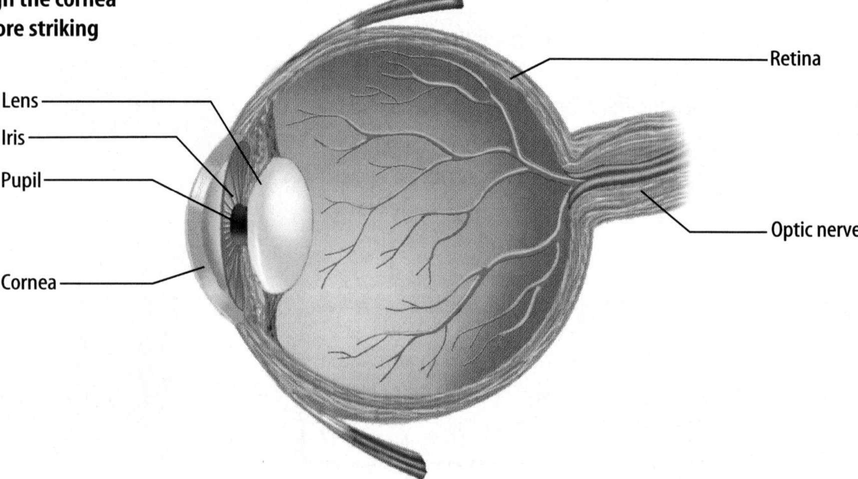

Figure 11
Light moves through the cornea and the lens—before striking the retina.

Resource Manager

Chapter Resources Booklet
Transparency Activity, p. 43
Enrichment, p. 30

Section Assessment Planner

Portfolio
Reteach, p. 617

Performance Assessment
Try at Home MiniLAB, p. 614
Math Skills Activity, p. 615
MiniLAB, p. 616
Skill Builder Activities, p. 617

See page 624 for more options.

Content Assessment
Section, p. 617
Challenge, p. 617
Chapter, pp. 624–625

How do you see? Light travels in a straight line unless something causes it to refract or change direction. Your eyes are equipped with structures that refract light. Two of these structures are the cornea and the lens. As light enters the eye, it passes through the cornea—the transparent section at the front of the eye—and is refracted. Then light passes through a lens and is refracted again. The lens directs the light onto the retina (RET nuh). The **retina** is a tissue at the back of the eye that is sensitive to light energy. Two types of cells called rods and cones are found in the retina. Cones respond to bright light and color. Rods respond to dim light. They are used to help you detect shape and movement. Light energy stimulates impulses in these cells.

The impulses pass to the optic nerve. This nerve carries the impulses to the vision area of the cortex, located on your brain's cerebrum. The image transmitted from the retina to the brain is upside down and reversed. The brain interprets the image correctly, and you see what you are looking at. The brain also interprets the images received by both eyes. It blends them into one image that gives you a sense of distance. This allows you to tell how close or how far away something is.

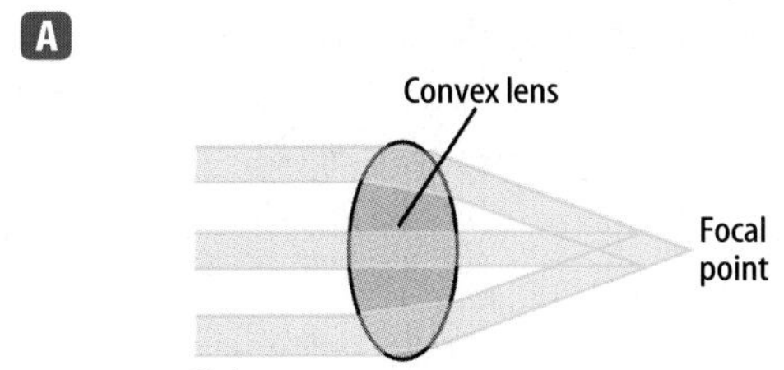

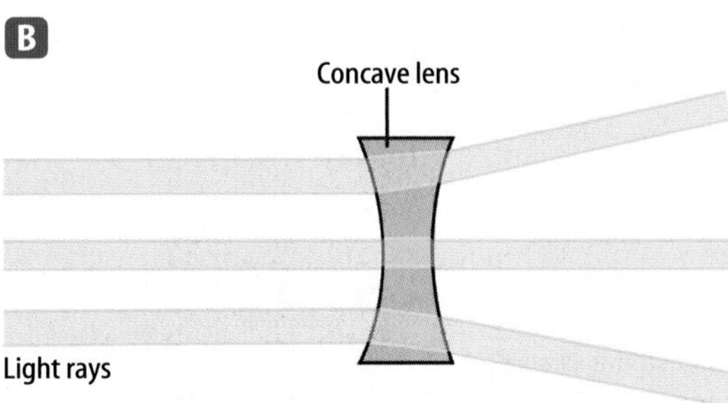

Figure 12
A Light passing through a convex lens is refracted toward the center and passes through a focal point. B Light that passes through a concave lens is refracted outward.

Reading Check *What difficulties would a person who had vision only in one eye encounter?*

Lenses

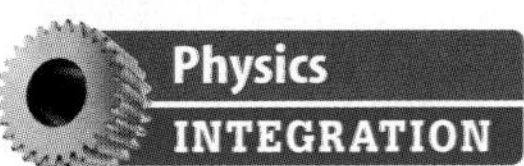

Light is refracted when it passes through a lens. The way it refracts depends on the type of lens it passes through. A lens that is thicker in the middle and thinner on the edges is called a convex lens. As shown in **Figure 12A,** the lens in your eye refracts light so that it passes through a point, called a focal point. Convex lenses can be used to magnify objects. The light passes through a convex lens and enters the eye in such a way that your brain interprets the image as enlarged.

A lens that is thicker at its edges than in its middle is called a concave lens. Follow the light rays in **Figure 12B** as they pass through a concave lens. You'll see that this kind of lens causes the parallel light to spread out.

2 Teach

Vision

Reading Check

Answer It would be difficult to perceive depth.

Lenses

Quick Demo

Obtain a double convex lens. Use it to illustrate the refraction and focusing of light rays similar to that which occurs in the eye.

Extension

Have students research the phenomenon of afterimage, where an image is still perceived after its external cause is gone. Afterimage may be positive, corresponding in color or brightness to the original image, or negative, being less bright or of colors complementary to the original. A common afterimage is the spot of light seen after a camera flash has been fired. L2

IDENTIFYING Misconceptions

Students may think that human eyes "see" by sending rays toward an object. Refer to page 598F for teaching strategies that address this misconception.

Teacher FYI

The term *fatigue* is sometimes used to describe a decreased sensitivity of a receptor, such as the eye, to stimuli. A red surface seems to become gray when it is stared at for a long period of time. The retina is said to be fatigued by long exposure to the color red. The same is true of hearing. Continuous noise eventually seems less intense due to fatigue of the processes of the inner ear.

Curriculum Connection

History Have students find out how Helen Keller was able to communicate even though she was deprived of sight and hearing at an early age. Her teacher, Anne Sullivan, taught Helen to feel objects and associate them with words spelled out by finger signals on her palm, to read sentences by feeling raised words on cardboard, and to make her own sentences by arranging words in a frame. L2

Lenses, continued

Activity

Have students who wear corrective eyeglasses examine the lenses to determine whether they are concave or convex. L1

Use an Analogy

Have students open up a camera to view the internal components and compare them to the human eye. **What part of the eye is like the diaphragm of the camera?** the iris **What part of the camera is like the retina?** the film

Quick Demo

Place a 5-cm × 5-cm sheet of thin, clear plastic (like that used to cover food) over a newspaper. Place one drop of water on the waxed paper. Have students note how the curved surface of the water drop acts as a lens and magnifies the print.

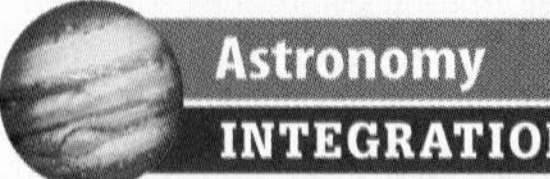

A third lens is needed to make the inverted image right-side up for normal viewing.

Use Science Words

Word Origin Cataracts are a disorder of the eye in which the lens becomes cloudy and vision is not clear. The word *cataract* can also mean "a great waterfall" or "a downpour of water." **How are these meanings related?** With cataracts on the lens of the eye, vision is like looking through a wall of water.

Figure 13
Glasses and contact lenses sharpen your vision.

A **A nearsighted person cannot see distant objects because the image is focused in front of the retina.**

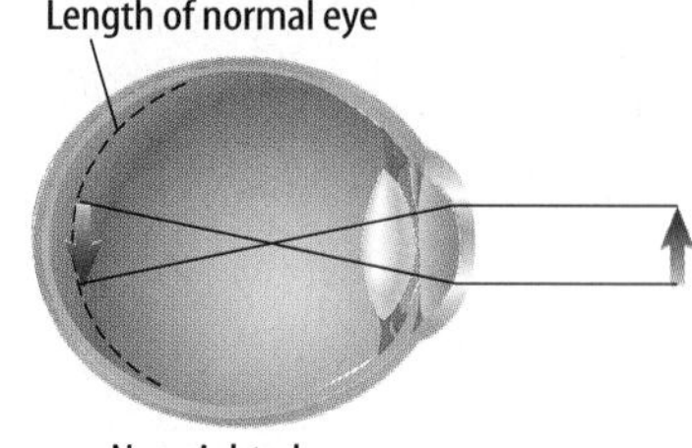

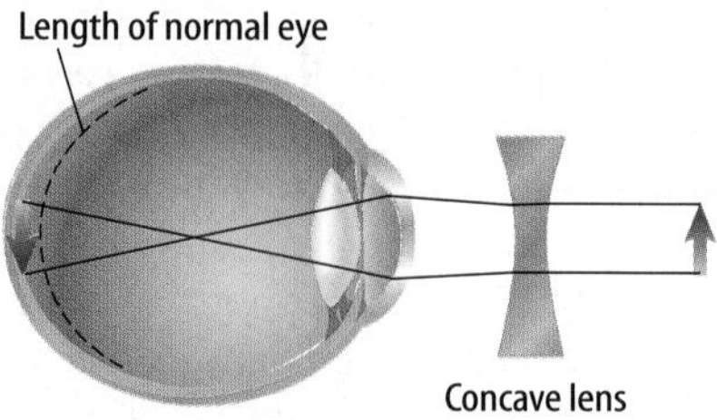

A concave lens corrects nearsightedness.

B **A farsighted person cannot see close objects because the image is focused behind the retina.**

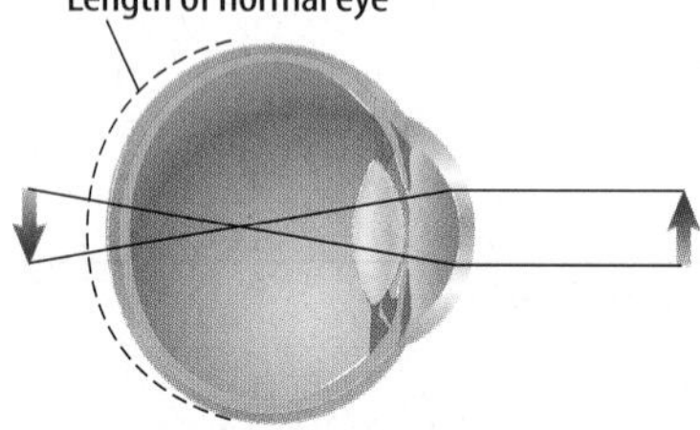

Length of normal eye

Convex lens

A convex lens corrects farsightedness.

Astronomy INTEGRATION

Refracting telescopes have two convex lenses for viewing objects in space. The larger lens collects light and forms an inverted, or upside-down, image of the object. The second lens magnifies the inverted image. In your Science Journal, hypothesize why telescopes used to view things on Earth have three lenses, not two.

Correcting Vision Problems Do you wear contact lenses or eyeglasses to correct your vision? Are you nearsighted or farsighted? In an eye with normal vision, light rays are focused onto the retina by the coordinated actions of the eye muscles, the cornea, and the lens. The image formed on the retina is interpreted by the brain as being sharp and clear. However, if the eyeball is too long from front to back, as illustrated in **Figure 13A,** light from objects is focused in front of the retina. This happens because the shape of the eyeball and lens cannot be changed enough by the eye muscles to focus a sharp image onto the retina. The image that reaches the retina is blurred. This condition is called nearsightedness—near objects are seen more clearly than distant objects. To correct nearsightedness, concave lenses are used to help focus images sharply on the retina.

Similarly, vision correction is needed when the eyeball is too short from front to back. In this case, light from objects is focused behind the retina despite the coordinated actions of the eye muscles, cornea, and lens. This condition is called farsightedness, as illustrated in **Figure 13B,** because distant objects are clearer than near objects. Convex lenses correct farsightedness.

LAB DEMONSTRATION

Purpose to find the area of insensitivity to light on the retina, called the blind spot

Materials 3 × 5 card, black marking pen

Preparation Draw a black dot 0.5 cm in diameter near the left edge of the horizontally-held card. Draw an *X* 5 cm to the right of the dot.

Procedure Hold the card at arm's length. Close the right eye and look only at the *X*. Slowly move the card toward the face. Measure the distance of the card from the face when the dot is no longer visible.

Expected Outcome Students observe that the dot disappears when the card is 15 to 20 cm from the face.

Assessment

Why do you not have a blind spot whenever you are looking at things? The brain interprets the images from your eyes as a complete picture.

Hearing

Whether it's the roar of a rocket launch, the cheers at a football game, or the distant song of a robin in a tree, sound waves are necessary for hearing sound. Sound energy is to hearing as light energy is to vision. When an object vibrates, sound waves are produced. These waves can travel through solids, liquids, and gases as illustrated in **Figure 14.** When the waves reach your ear, they usually stimulate nerve cells deep within your ear. Impulses are sent to the brain. When the sound impulse reaches the hearing area of the cortex, it responds and you hear a sound.

Figure 14
Objects produce sound waves that are heard by your ears.

The Outer Ear and Middle Ear **Figure 15** shows that your ear is divided into three sections—the outer ear, middle ear, and inner ear. Your outer ear intercepts sound waves and funnels them down the ear canal to the middle ear. The sound waves cause the eardrum to vibrate much like the membrane on a musical drum vibrates when you tap it. These vibrations then move through three tiny bones called the hammer, anvil, and stirrup. The stirrup bone rests against a second membrane on an opening to the inner ear.

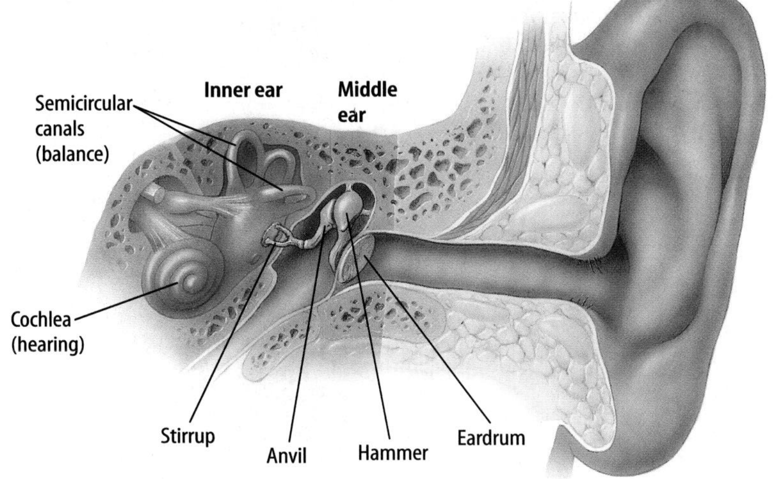

Figure 15
Your ear responds to sound waves and to changes in the position of your head.

Hearing

Activity

Have students line up and practice making a "human wave" as seen at sports events. Once they have perfected the wave, they can try making waves of different speeds to simulate the different speeds at which sound waves move through different types of matter. L2 ELL COOP LEARN LS **Kinesthetic**

Discussion

Grip one end of a plastic ruler and wave it back and forth as fast as you can. Discuss why it is not producing sound even though it is vibrating. Help students understand that not all vibrations produce sound that we can hear. **What kinds of vibrations might produce sounds we can sense?** Those that have frequencies in the proper range to be detected by our ears.

Visual Learning

Figure 15 When a friend shouts your name, how do you get the message? Sound waves reach the eardrum–eardrum vibrates–causes hammer, anvil, and stirrup to vibrate–fluid in cochlea vibrates–receptor hairs in cochlea vibrate, sending message to brain–brain analyzes and interprets message–you "hear" your name.

Active Reading

Problem/Solution Journal Have students divide a piece of paper in half and label the left side Problems and the right side Consequences of Failing to Resolve the Problem. Through writing, the student identifies a problem, brainstorms possible alternatives, chooses a probable solution, anticipates stumbling blocks, and proposes arguments. Have students apply this strategy to a problem such as damage to hearing caused by loud music.

Resource Manager

Chapter Resources Booklet
Directed Reading for Content Mastery, p. 21, 22

Earth Science Critical Thinking/Problem Solving, p. 22

Purpose to observe and make inferences concerning the factors that affect students' ability to maintain balance L2 ELL

Materials two narrow strips of paper, masking tape

Teaching Strategies

- Partners should take turns standing and observing.
- Record whether the person standing tends to lean more to one side or the other.

Safety Precautions Some people may become disoriented. Alert students to be prepared to help someone who looks as if he or she might fall.

Analysis

1. When the eyes were closed; when the eyes are open, a person can focus on a point to help the body remain balanced.
2. Answers could include such conditions as an inner ear infection or loud, continuous noise.

Assessment

Performance To further assess students' understanding of balance, have them repeat the activity with feet apart or arms extended sideways. Use **Performance Assessment in the Science Classroom,** p. 97.

Observing Balance Control

Procedure

1. Place **two narrow strips of paper** on the wall to form two parallel vertical lines 20–25 cm apart. Have a person stand between them for 3 min, without leaning on the wall.
2. Observe how well balance is maintained.
3. Have the person close his or her eyes, then stand within the lines for 3 min.

Analysis

1. When was balance more difficult to maintain? Why?
2. What other factors might cause a person to lose his or her sense of balance?

The Inner Ear The **cochlea** (KOH klee uh) is a fluid-filled structure shaped like a snail's shell. When the stirrup vibrates, fluids in the cochlea begin to vibrate. These vibrations bend hair cells in the cochlea, which causes electrical impulses to be sent to the brain by a nerve. High-pitched sounds make the endings move differently than lower sounds do. Depending on how the nerve endings are stimulated, you hear a different type of sound.

Balance Structures in your inner ear also control your body's balance. Structures called the cristae ampullaris (KRIHS tee • am pyew LEER ihs) and the maculae (MA kyah lee), illustrated in **Figure 16,** sense different types of body movement.

Both structures contain tiny hair cells. As your body moves, gel-like fluid surrounding the hair cells moves and stimulates the nerve cells at the base of the hair cells. This produces nerve impulses that are sent to the brain, which interprets the body movements. The brain, in turn, sends impulses to skeletal muscles, resulting in body movements that maintain balance.

The cristae ampullaris react to rotating body movements. Fluid in the semicircular canals swirls when the body rotates. This causes the gel-like fluid around the hair cells to move and a stimulus is sent to the brain. In a similar way, when the head tips, the gel-like fluid surrounding the hair cells in the maculae is pulled down by gravity. The hair cells are then stimulated and the brain interprets that the head has tilted.

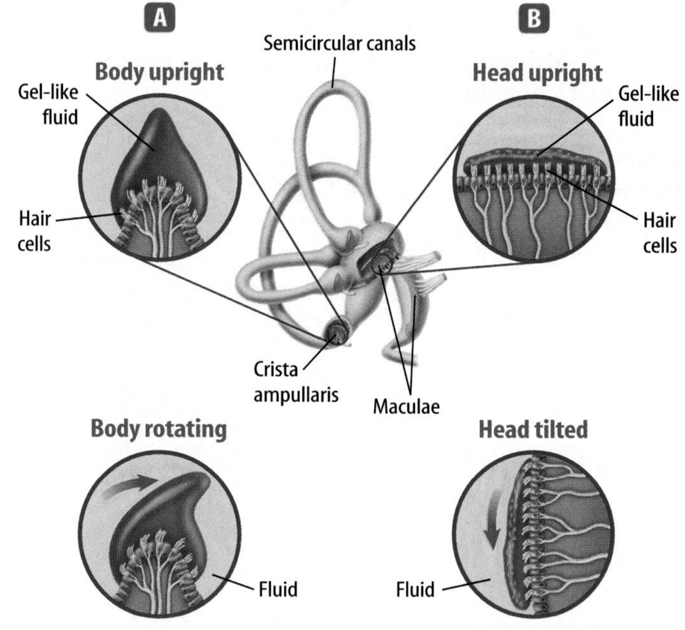

Figure 16
Two structures in your inner ear are responsible for maintaining your sense of balance. A The cristae ampullaris react to rotating movements of your body. B The maculae check the position of your head with respect to the ground. *Why does spinning around make you dizzy?*

Caption Answer

Figure 16B Spinning makes the fluids in the inner ear send impulses to the brain that conflict with the actual position of the head. Dizziness results.

Cultural Diversity

Drums Drums are used by cultures worldwide. Drums made in various shapes and sizes and from various materials have different pitches. Have students research how drums are made in different areas of the world and infer what all drums have in common. If possible, have them compare the sounds of different drums. L2

Senses on the Job Ask students to clip advertisements from the "help wanted" section of a newspaper about jobs that require keenness of certain senses. They should put these ads in their Science Journals, along with brief descriptions of how and why specific senses such as hearing, vision, balance and coordination, or smell would be involved. L2

Smell

Some sharks can sense as few as ten drops of tuna liquid in an average-sized swimming pool. Even though your ability to detect odors is not as good as a shark's, your sense of smell is still important. Smell can determine which foods you eat. Strong memories or feelings also can be responses to something you smell.

You smell food because it gives off molecules into the air. These molecules stimulate sensitive nerve cells, called **olfactory** (ohl FAK tree) **cells,** in your nasal passages. Olfactory cells are kept moist by mucus. When molecules in the air dissolve in this moisture, the cells become stimulated. If enough molecules are present, an impulse starts in these cells, then travels to the brain where the stimulus is interpreted. If the stimulus is recognized from a previous experience, you may identify the odor. If you don't recognize a particular odor, it is remembered and may be identified the next time you encounter it.

Research Visit the Glencoe Science Web site at **science.glencoe.com** for more information about the sense of smell in humans compared with other mammals. Make a chart in your Science Journal summarizing your research.

Math Skills Activity

Calculating Distance Using the Speed of Sound

Example Problem

You see the flash of fireworks and then four seconds later, you hear the boom because light waves travel faster than sound waves. Light travels so fast that you see it almost instantaneously. Sound, on the other hand, travels at 340 m/s. How far away are you from the source of the fireworks?

Solution

1. *This is what you know:* time: $t = 4$ s; speed of sound: $v = 340$ m/s
2. *This is what you need to find:* distance: d
3. *This is the equation you need to use:* $d = vt$
4. *Substitute the known values* $d = (340 \text{ m/s})(4 \text{ s})$; $d = 1360$ m

Check your answer by dividing your answer by time. Do you calculate the same speed that was given?

Practice Problem

A hiker standing at one end of a lake hears his echo 2.5 s after he shouts. It was reflected by a cliff at the end of the lake. How long is the lake?

For more help, refer to the Math Skill Handbook.

Smell

Teacher FYI

The sense of smell can become desensitized to a specific odor if it is exposed to it for a period of time. If you walk into a movie theater, you are instantly aware of the odor of popcorn. After a while, however, the odor is hardly noticeable because your chemoreceptors have become desensitized.

Fun Fact

The sense of smell is much more sensitive than the sense of taste. It is estimated that the human nose can detect more than 10,000 different odors but identification of odors is limited.

Math Skills Activity

National Math Standards

Correlation to Mathematics Objectives

1, 2, 4, 6, 9

Teaching Strategy

Remind students that the distance traveled by the sound is twice the length of the lake—the distance to the cliff and back again.

Answer to Practice Problem

$t = 2.5$ s
$v = 340$ m/s
$2d = (340 \text{ m/s})(2.5 \text{ s})$
$2d = 850$ m
$d = 425$ m

Resource Manager

Chapter Resources Booklet

Reinforcement, p. 28

Cultural Diversity, p. 15

Home and Community Involvement, p. 28

SCIENCE Online

Internet Addresses

Explore the Glencoe Science Web site at **science.glencoe.com** to find out more about topics in this section.

Taste

Mini LAB

Purpose Students observe the difference in the sense of smell between males and females. L2 LS **Kinesthetic**

Materials small samples of food, colognes, or household products; cotton balls; blindfold

Teaching Strategy Place a small amount of the odorous substance on a cotton ball for each sniff test. Do not use a cotton ball for more than one person.

Safety Precautions Students should not use any substances with strong, noxious odors (e.g., ammonia). Survey students before class to determine whether any of them have allergies or asthma that might be affected by the odors.

Analysis

1. Answers may vary, but more females should correctly identify specific odors.
2. Generally, females are more acutely aware of odors than are males.

Performance Have students conduct a test of identifying odors while blindfolded. Use **PASC,** p. 97.

Reading Check

Answer It has to be dissolved in water.

Mini LAB

Comparing Sense of Smell

Procedure

1. To test your classmates' abilities to recognize different odors, blindfold them one at a time, then pass near their noses small **samples of different foods, colognes, or household products. WARNING:** *Do not eat or drink anything in the lab. Do not use any products that give off noxious fumes.*
2. Ask each student to identify the different samples.
3. Record each student's response in a data table according to his or her gender.

Analysis

1. Compare the numbers of correctly identified odors for males and females.
2. What can you conclude about the differences between males and females in their abilities to recognize odors?

Taste

Sometimes you taste a new food with the tip of your tongue and find that it tastes sweet. Then when you chew it, you are surprised to find that it tastes bitter. **Taste buds** on your tongue are the major sensory receptors for taste. About 10,000 taste buds are found all over your tongue, enabling you to tell one taste from another.

Tasting Food Taste buds, shown in **Figure 17,** respond to chemical stimuli. When you think of hot french fries, your mouth begins to water. This response is helpful because in order to taste something, it has to be dissolved in water. Saliva begins this process. This solution of saliva and food washes over the taste buds, and impulses are sent to your brain. The brain interprets the impulses, and you identify the tastes. Most taste buds respond to several taste sensations. However, certain areas of the tongue are more receptive to one taste than another. The five taste sensations are sweet, salty, sour, bitter, and the taste of MSG (monosodium glutamate).

Reading Check *What needs to happen to food before you are able to taste it?*

Smell and Taste Smell and taste are related. The sense of smell is needed to identify some foods such as chocolate. When saliva in your mouth mixes with the chocolate, odors travel up the nasal passage in the back of your throat. The olfactory cells are stimulated, and the taste and smell of chocolate are sensed. So when you have a stuffy nose and some foods seem tasteless, it may be because the food's molecules are blocked from contacting the olfactory cells in your nasal passages.

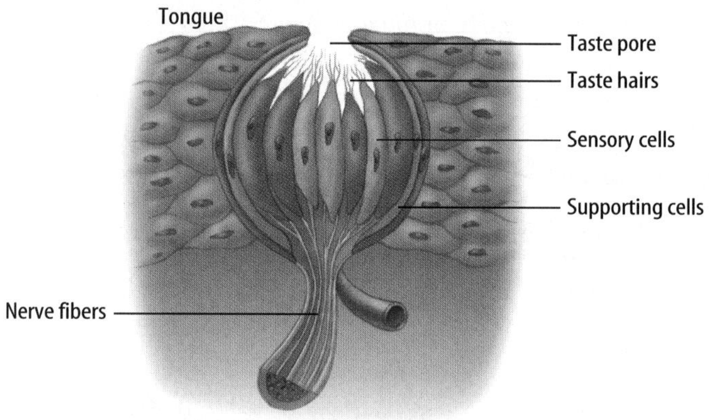

Tongue
Taste pore
Taste hairs
Sensory cells
Supporting cells
Nerve fibers

Figure 17
Taste buds are made up of a group of sensory cells with tiny taste hairs projecting from them. When food is taken into the mouth, it is dissolved in saliva. This mixture then stimulates receptor sites on the taste hairs, and an impulse is sent to the brain.

Chapter Resources Booklet
MiniLAB, pp. 3, 4

Science Inquiry Labs, p. 59

Cultural Diversity, p. 61

Cultural Diversity

Flavor Enhancement In many cultures, certain herbs and spices are used to enhance the flavors of foods. Asian foods often contain such spices as coriander, cumin, curry, fenugreek, ginger, star anise, turmeric, or Szechuan pepper. Have students find and share with the class a recipe that uses one of these spices.

616 CHAPTER 21 Control and Coordination

Other Sensory Receptors in the Body

As you are reading at school, you suddenly experience a bad pain in your lower right abdomen. The pain is not going away and you yell for help. Several hours later, you are resting in a hospital bed. The doctor has removed the source of your problem—your appendix. If not removed, a burst appendix can spread poison throughout your body.

Your internal organs have several kinds of sensory receptors. These receptors respond to touch, pressure, pain, and temperature. They pick up changes in touch, pressure, and temperature and transmit impulses to the brain or spinal cord. In turn, your body responds to this new information.

Sensory receptors also are located throughout your skin. As shown in **Figure 18,** your fingertips have many different types of receptors for touch. As a result, you can tell whether an object is rough or smooth, hot or cold, and hard or soft. Your lips are sensitive to heat and prevent you from drinking something so hot that it would burn you. Pressure-sensitive skin cells warn you of danger and enable you to move to avoid injury.

The body responds to protect itself from harm. All of your body's senses work together to maintain homeostasis. Your senses help you enjoy or avoid things around you. You constantly react to your environment because of information received by your senses.

Figure 18
Many of the sensations picked up by receptors in the skin are stimulated by mechanical energy. Pressure, motion, and touch are examples.

Section 2 Assessment

1. What type of stimulus do your ears respond to?
2. What are the sensory receptors for the eyes and nose?
3. Why is it important to have sensory receptors for pain and pressure in your internal organs?
4. What is the role of saliva in tasting?
5. **Think Critically** Unlike many other organs, the brain is insensitive to pain. What is the advantage of this?

Skill Builder Activities

6. **Making and Using Tables** Organize the information on senses in a table that names the sense organs and which stimuli they respond to. **For more help, refer to the** Science Skill Handbook.
7. **Communicating** Write a paragraph in your Science Journal that describes what each of the following objects would feel like: ice cube, snake, silk blouse, sandpaper, jelly, and smooth rock. **For more help, refer to the** Science Skill Handbook.

3 Assess

Reteach

Have students make concept maps of the sensory organs described in this section. L2
LS **Visual-Spatial** P

Challenge

What design elements would be necessary for a robot to handle an egg? The robot would have to sense that the egg is a fragile object and then be able to manipulate it without applying too much pressure.

Assessment

Process Provide students with illustrations of people engaged in various activities and have them describe the sense organs involved and the different types of energy that stimulate the sensory receptors. Use **Performance Assessment in the Science Classroom,** p. 89.

Answers to Section Assessment

1. sound waves
2. eyes: rods and cones; nose: olfactory cells
3. Internal sensory receptors alert the brain when something is wrong. This allows the body to respond and protect itself and to maintain homeostasis.
4. Saliva dissolves food, enabling the food to wash over the taste buds.
5. The brain can continue to function when injured, allowing the body to carry out activities for survival.
6. eyes—light; tongue—taste; ears—sound; skin and other organs—touch, pressure, pain, temperature; nose—odors
7. Possible answers: ice cube—cold, smooth, hard; snake—rough; silk blouse—soft, smooth; sandpaper—rough, scratchy; jelly—sticky, squishy; smooth rock—hard, smooth

Activity

BENCH TESTED

Recognize the Problem

Purpose

Students design and carry out an experiment to determine skin sensitivity on various parts of the body by testing for the location of receptors in the skin. L2 ELL COOP LEARN LS **Kinesthetic**

Process Skills

observing and inferring, forming a hypothesis, designing an experiment, interpreting data, making and using tables, comparing and contrasting

Time Required

two class periods

Materials

Obtain materials for cooperative groups. To save time, prepare the test cards the day before the activity to allow the glue to dry.

Safety Precautions

Caution students not to apply heavy pressure when using any contact-point device.

Form a Hypothesis

Possible Hypothesis

The fingertips are the most sensitive areas of the skin.

Test Your Hypothesis

Possible Procedures

Predict which skin areas are most sensitive to touch. Rank the areas from most (5) to least (1) sensitive in a data table. Glue toothpicks onto a card so that side one has a pair 1 mm apart, and side two has a pair 3 mm apart. Another card should have pairs 5 mm and 10 mm apart. With partner's eyes closed, use the side with a pair 1 mm apart and carefully touch the skin. If partner feels two points, record a plus (+). If partner cannot feel both points, record a minus (−). Repeat using the other sides of the card.

Activity **Design Your Own Experiment**

Skin Sensitivity

Your body responds to touch, pressure, temperature, and other stimuli. Not all parts of your body are equally sensitive to stimuli. Some areas are more sensitive than others are. For example, your lips are sensitive to heat. This protects you from burning your mouth and tongue. Now think about touch. How sensitive is the skin on various parts of your body to touch? Which areas can distinguish the smallest amount of distance between stimuli?

Recognize the Problem

What areas of the body are most sensitive to touch?

Form a Hypothesis

Based on your experiences, state a hypothesis about which of the following five areas of the body—fingertip, forearm, back of the neck, palm, and back of the hand—you believe to be most sensitive. Rank the areas from 5 (the most sensitive) to 1 (the least sensitive).

Goals

- **Observe** the sensitivity to touch on specific areas of the body.
- **Design** an experiment that tests the effects of a variable, such as how close the contact points are, to determine which body areas can distinguish which stimuli are closest to one another.

Possible Materials

3 × 5-inch index card
toothpicks
tape
**glue*
metric ruler
**Alternate materials*

Safety Precautions

Do not apply heavy pressure when touching the toothpicks to the skin of your classmates.

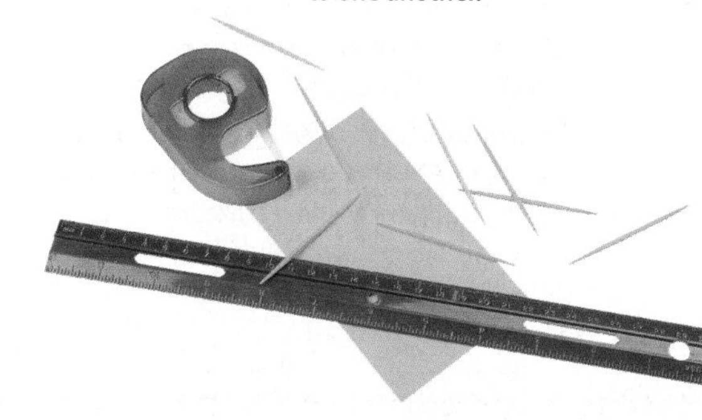

Resource Manager 

Chapter Resources Booklet
Lab Activity, pp. 13–16
Activity Worksheet, pp. 7–8
Lab Management and Safety, p. 65

Using Scientific Methods

Test Your Hypothesis

Plan

1. As a group, agree upon and write the hypothesis statement.
2. As a group, list the steps you need to test your hypothesis. Describe exactly what you will do at each step. Consider the following as you list the steps. How will you know that sight is not a factor? How will you use the card shown on the right to determine sensitivity to touch? How will you determine that one or both points are sensed?
3. **Design** a data table in your Science Journal to record your observations.
4. Reread your entire experiment to make sure that all steps are in the correct order.
5. **Identify** constants, variables, and controls of the experiment.

Do

1. Make sure your teacher approves your plan before you start.
2. Carry out the experiment as planned.
3. While the experiment is going on, write down any observations that you make and complete the data table in your Science Journal.

Analyze Your Data

1. **Identify** which part of the body is least sensitive and which part is most sensitive.
2. **Identify** which part of the body tested can distinguish between the closest stimuli.
3. **Compare** your results with those of other groups.
4. Rank body parts tested from most to least sensitive. Did your results from this investigation support your hypothesis? Explain.

Draw Conclusions

1. Based on the results of your investigation, what can you infer about the distribution of touch receptors on the skin?
2. What other parts of your body would you predict to be less sensitive? Explain your predictions.

Communicating Your Data

Write a report to share with your class about body parts of animals that are sensitive to touch. **For more help, refer to the** Science Skill Handbook.

Teaching Strategy
Have students vary the order of toothpick pairs they use.

Expected Outcome
The more sensitive areas are the fingertips, palms, and cheeks. Less sensitive are the backs of the hands, forearms, and back of the neck.

Analyze Your Data

1. least: backs of the hands, forearms, back of neck; most: fingertips, palms, cheeks
2. fingertips and usually the palms
3. Results should be consistent.
4. Answers will vary.

Error Analysis
Have students compare their results and their hypotheses and explain any differences that occurred.

Draw Conclusions

1. Touch receptors are closer together in the fingertips and farther apart on the backs of the hands and forearms. Receptors in the palms and back of the neck vary.
2. Answers may include the back and the legs because they are unlikely to be used to gather new information about an object.

Performance To further assess students' understanding of skin sensitivity, have them repeat this activity on the lower part of the leg and on the foot. Use **PASC,** p. 97.

Sample Data Table:

Body Part Tested	predictions	Felt two points (mm)			
		1	3	5	10
fingertip	5	–	+	+	+
palm	4	–	–	+	+
back of hand	3	–	–	–	+
forearm	1	–	–	–	–
back of neck	2	–	–	–	–

Communicating Your Data

Students can use the Internet or texts from the school library to gather data on animals with special sense organs on their legs, ears, noses, and mouth parts.

Science and Language Arts

Pre-Reading Activity

Divide the class into groups of five students each. Ask students to think silently to themselves about their favorite month of the year. Have each student in the group describe to other group members the month they are thinking about without saying the name of the month. Other members of the group can guess the month about which the student is thinking. Tell students that they must use images associated with the month to describe it. Discourage students from saying proper names of holidays or other well-known events that would distinguish the month from others.

Respond to the Reading

Connect Connect the description of the scene to how the characters feel. **How does Nel feel about Sula? How do you know?**

Visualize Try to visualize the scene that Nel sees. Imagine objects with sheen or that glimmer during the month of May. **What shining objects could you add to the author's description?**

Answers to Questions

1. Nel seems happy about the return of Sula.
2. The phrases that describe Nel doing " a little dance" and being "moved to smile" help the reader understand Nel's feelings.

Science and Language Arts

Sula

by Toni Morrison

Respond to the Reading

1. Describe, in your own words, how Nel feels about the return of her friend Sula.
2. What parts of the passage help you determine Nel's feelings?

In the following passage from Sula, *a novel by Toni Morrison, the author describes Nel's response to the arrival of her old friend Sula.*

Nel alone noticed the peculiar quality of the May that followed the leaving of the birds. It had a sheen, a glimmering as of green, rain-soaked Saturday nights (lit by the excitement of newly installed street lights); of lemon-yellow afternoons bright with iced drinks and splashes of daffodils. It showed in the damp faces of her children and the river-smoothness of their voices. Even her own body was not immune to the magic. She would sit on the floor to sew as she had done as a girl, fold her legs up under her or do a little dance that fitted some tune in her head. There were easy sun-washed days and purple dusks . . . .

Although it was she alone who saw this magic, she did not wonder at it. She knew it was all due to Sula's return to the Bottom.

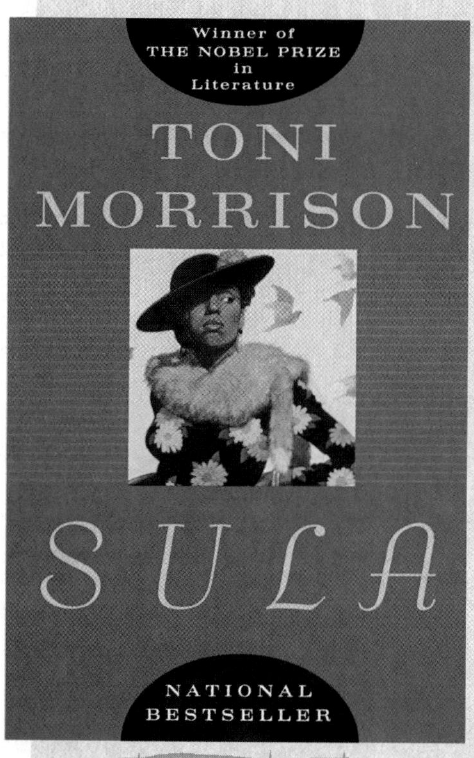

Reading Further

Other works by this author include:

"Beloved", *Plume*, reprint edition, September 1998.

The Bluest Eye, Penguin USA, 2000.

"Song of Solomon", *Plume* reissue edition, September 1987.

Other sources on this topic include:

"A Symphony in the Brain: The Evolution of the New Brain Wave Biofeedback", by Jim Robbins, *Atlantic Monthly Press*, May 2000.

The Man Who Mistook His Wife for a Hat, by Oliver Sacks, Touchstone Books, April 1998.

Understanding Literature

Diction and Tone An author's choice of words, or diction, can help convey a certain tone in the writing. In the passage, Toni Morrison begins by describing a day in May. Her choice of words—like *sheen, glimmering, lemon-yellow afternoons,* and *splashes of daffodils*—conveys a happy or pleasant tone. These word choices help the reader understand that the character Nel is enjoying the month of May. Many other examples found in the passage show how the author's diction helps convey a happy or pleasant tone. Find two more examples in which diction conveys a pleasant tone.

Science Connection In this chapter, you learned how the body and its nervous system react to stimuli in the environment. In the passage you just read, Nel has a physical reaction to her environment. She is moved to "do a little dance" in response to the sights and sounds of May. This action is an example of a voluntary response to stimuli from outside the body. Movement of the body is a coordinated effort of the skeletal, muscular, and nervous system. Nel can dance because motor neurons conduct impulses from the brain to her muscles.

Linking Science and Writing

Choosing Words to Convey a Tone Write a paragraph describing the month of January that clearly shows a person's dislike for the month. Think about the month of January and the physical reactions people have to their surroundings during this time of the year. Convey your character's dislike through the description of his or her nervous system's response to stimuli from the January environment. For example, you might say that your character shivers in the harsh wind. The trick is to do this without directly saying that your character does not like January.

Career Connection

Anthropologist

Katherine Mary Dunham has transferred her knowledge and experience with control and coordination into two careers. She is a dance choreographer as well as an anthropologist, which is someone who studies the origins of the physical, social, and cultural development of human beings. She received a master's degree in science from the University of Chicago and a doctoral degree from Northwestern University. Her research in these two fields led her to the development of an African-based theory of movement. She has created a training center in St. Louis, Missouri where she teaches inner-city youths African culture and dance.

SCIENCE*Online* To learn more about careers in anthropology, visit the Glencoe Science Web site at **science.glencoe.com.**

Understanding Literature

Answers to Questions

Other examples of diction conveying a pleasant tone in the passage are excitement of newly installed light, bright with iced drinks, easy sun-washed days and purple dusks.

Science Connection

Nel's dance is a complex neurological process. However, it is a response to other sensory systems that are also neurological processes, such as the process of seeing. The eye's retina contains receptors that respond to light. The retina is the back part of the eye that contains cells called photoreceptors. Photoreceptors respond to light by generating electrical impulses that travel out of the eye through the optic nerve. Nel is able to see the sheen and glimmer of May because of this neurological process.

Linking Science and Writing

Writing Strategies

Ask students to write in their Science Journals about how their bodies feel while they're outside during inclement weather. Have them describe the reaction of their skin, nose, top of head and extremities.

Career Connection

The field of anthropology has grown enormously in the last 30 years and is no longer strictly the province of social scientists who study other cultures. Anthropology has become a multidisciplinary field. Today, an anthropologist can specialize in dance, theater, paleontology, ethnography (writings of a culture), folklore or archaeology.

Internet Addresses

Explore the Glencoe Science Web site at **science.glencoe.com** to find out more about topics in this feature.

Chapter 21 Study Guide

Reviewing Main Ideas

Preview

Students can answer the questions in their Science Journals. Discuss the answers as you go through the chapter. **LS Linguistic**

Review

Students can write their answers, then compare them with those of other students. **LS Interpersonal**

Reteach

Students can look at the illustrations and describe details that support the main ideas of the chapter. **LS Visual-Spatial**

Answers to Chapter Review

Section 1

3. heartbeat, breathing, and hormone levels in the blood
6. Caffeine can cause an increase in heartbeat and urine production, restlessness, tremors, and insomnia.

Section 2

4. sight, smell, touch, and taste

Chapter 21 Study Guide

Reviewing Main Ideas

Section 1 The Nervous System

1. Your body constantly is receiving a variety of stimuli from inside and outside the body. The nervous system responds to these stimuli to maintain homeostasis.
2. A neuron is the basic unit of structure and function of the nervous system.
3. A stimulus is detected by sensory neurons. Electrical impulses are carried to the interneurons and transmitted to the motor neurons. The result is the movement of a body part. *What are some body functions that are being checked and regulated constantly?*

4. A response that is made automatically is a reflex.
5. The central nervous system contains the brain and spinal cord. The peripheral nervous system is made up of cranial and spinal nerves.
6. Many drugs, such as alcohol and caffeine, have a direct effect on your nervous system. *What are some effects of caffeine found in foods such as chocolate?*

Section 2 The Senses

1. Your senses respond to stimuli. The eyes respond to light energy, and the ears respond to sound waves.
2. Olfactory cells of the nose and taste buds of the tongue are stimulated by chemicals.
3. Sensory receptors in your internal organs and skin respond to touch, pressure, pain, and temperature.
4. Your senses enable you to enjoy or avoid things around you. You are able to react to the changing conditions of your environment. *What senses are involved when you pick up and eat a freshly baked piece of pita bread filled with delicious ingredients?*

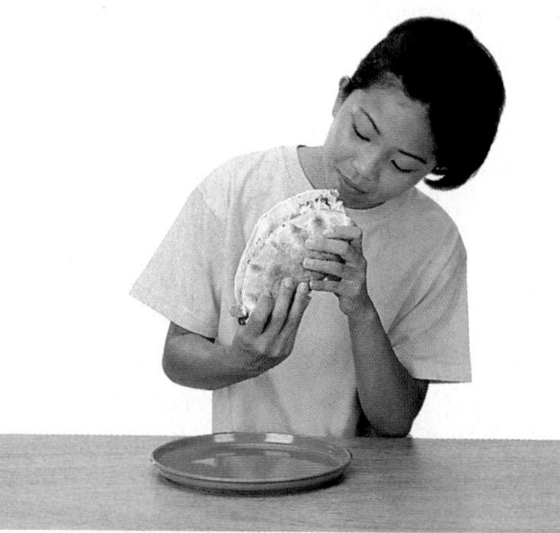

FOLDABLES Reading & Study Skills — After You Read

Use the information you collected in your Foldable to help explain how some senses are interdependent.

FOLDABLES Reading & Study Skills — After You Read

After students have read the chapter and completed the Foldable described in Before You Read, have them do the activity on the student page.

Dinah Zike

Visualizing Main Ideas

Examine the following concept map of the nervous system and fill in the missing terms.

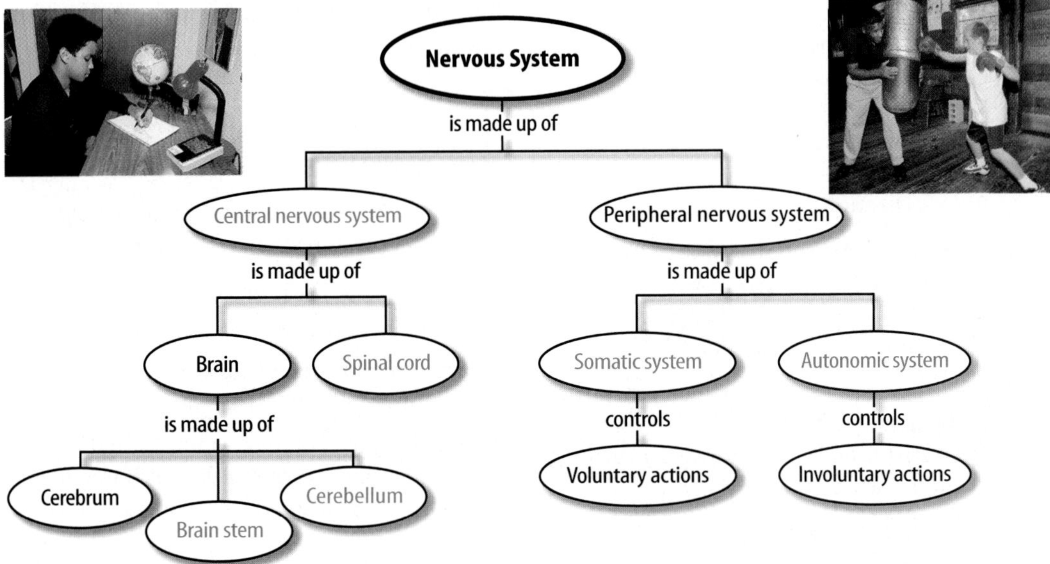

Vocabulary Review

Vocabulary Words

- **a.** axon
- **b.** brain stem
- **c.** central nervous system
- **d.** cerebellum
- **e.** cerebrum
- **f.** cochlea
- **g.** dendrite
- **h.** homeostasis
- **i.** neuron
- **j.** olfactory cell
- **k.** peripheral nervous system
- **l.** reflex
- **m.** retina
- **n.** synapse
- **o.** taste bud

THE PRINCETON REVIEW Study Tip

Use word webs. Write the main idea of the chapter on a piece of paper and circle it. Connect other related facts to it with lines and arrows.

Using Vocabulary

Explain the difference between the vocabulary words in each of the following sets.

1. axon, dendrite
2. central nervous system, peripheral nervous system
3. cerebellum, cerebrum
4. reflex, synapse
5. brain stem, neuron
6. olfactory cell, taste bud
7. dendrite, synapse
8. cerebrum, central nervous system
9. retina, cochlea
10. synapse, neuron

Chapter 21 Study Guide

Visualizing Main Ideas

See student page.

Vocabulary Review

Using Vocabulary

1. Axons carry messages away from the cell body. Dendrites receive and carry messages to the cell body.
2. central nervous system—brain and spinal cord; peripheral nervous system—all the nerves outside the central nervous system
3. The cerebellum coordinates voluntary muscle movement. The cerebrum is where impulses are interpreted, memory is stored, and movements are controlled.
4. A reflex is an involuntary, automatic response to a stimulus. A synapse is the small space between an axon and a dendrite.
5. The brain stem is part of the brain. A neuron is a nerve cell.
6. An olfactory cell detects odors; a taste bud detects tastes.
7. A dendrite is part of a neuron. A synapse is the small space between an axon and a dendrite.
8. The cerebrum is a part of the brain. The central nervous system consists of the brain and the spinal cord.
9. The retina is a tissue of the eye. The cochlea is a structure in the inner ear.
10. A synapse is a small space between an axon and a dendrite. A neuron is a nerve cell.

IDENTIFYING Misconceptions

Assess

Use the assessment as follow-up to page 598F after students have completed the chapter.

Procedure Draw on the board the correct model of how light reflects off an object and toward the eye to cause vision. Draw several other models, such as the misconception that light comes from the eye to cause vision. Have students individually assess the models and decide what is correct and incorrect about each diagram. Ask students to identify which diagram is most correct.

Expected Outcome After completing the Sight Box activity, students should be able to recognize a model which shows light from a light source reflecting off of an object and toward the eye as the most correct model.

Chapter 21 Assessment

Checking Concepts

1. D
2. B
3. C
4. D
5. A
6. C
7. A
8. B
9. C
10. D

Thinking Critically

11. Possible responses: so messages do not get mixed; so that responses can be coordinated
12. Reflexes are automatic acts that occur without our thinking about them. Therefore, they happen quickly and can shield our bodies from danger, such as sharp or hot objects.
13. When food is put into the mouth and made moist, both the taste buds and olfactory cells are stimulated, and the food item is sensed by both.
14. Alcohol affects muscle control, judgment, reasoning, memory, and concentration. All of these influence driving.
15. The sense of touch is more pronounced on the face than on the back. One could check this by using something lightweight, such as a feather or small paintbrush, to test the sensitivity of the face and back.

Chapter 21 Assessment

Checking Concepts

Choose the word or phrase that best answers the question.

1. How do impulses cross synapses between neurons?
   A) by osmosis
   B) through interneurons
   C) through a cell body
   D) by a chemical

2. What are the neuron structures that carry impulses to the cell body called?
   A) axons **C)** synapses
   B) dendrites **D)** nuclei

3. What are neurons called that detect stimuli in the skin and eyes?
   A) interneurons **C)** sensory neurons
   B) motor neurons **D)** synapses

4. Which of the following does the skin not sense?
   A) pain **C)** temperature
   B) pressure **D)** taste

5. What part of the brain controls voluntary muscles?
   A) cerebellum **C)** cerebrum
   B) brain stem **D)** pons

6. What part of the brain has an outer layer called the cortex?
   A) pons **C)** cerebrum
   B) brain stem **D)** spinal cord

7. What does the somatic system of the PNS control?
   A) skeletal muscles **C)** glands
   B) heart **D)** salivary glands

8. What part of the eye is light finally focused on?
   A) lens **C)** pupil
   B) retina **D)** cornea

9. What is the largest part of the brain?
   A) cerebellum **C)** cerebrum
   B) brain stem **D)** pons

10. Which of the following is in the inner ear?
   A) anvil **C)** eardrum
   B) hammer **D)** cochlea

Thinking Critically

11. Why is it helpful to have impulses move only in one direction in a neuron?
12. How are reflexes protective?
13. Describe how smell and taste are related.
14. How does the use of alcohol influence a person's ability to drive a car?
15. If a fly were to land on your face and another one on your back, which might you feel first? How could you test your choice?

Developing Skills

16. **Concept Mapping** Fill in this events-chain concept map that shows the correct sequence of the structures through which light passes in the eye.

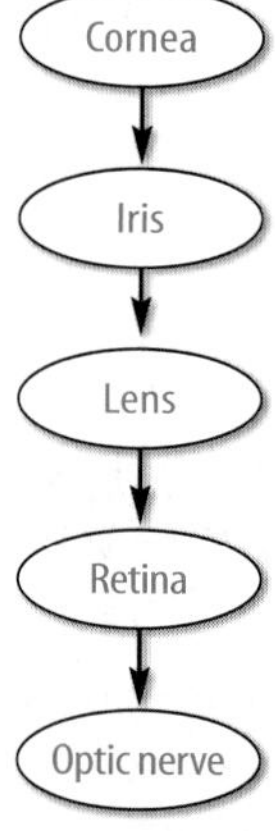

Chapter Assessment Planner

Portfolio Encourage students to place in their portfolios one or two items of what they consider to be their best work. Examples include:
- Science Journal, p. 601
- Assessment, p. 608
- Reteach, p. 617

Performance Additional performance assessments, Performance Task Assessment Lists, and rubrics for evaluating these activities can be found in Glencoe's **Performance Assessment in the Science Classroom.**

17. **Classifying** Group the types of neurons as to their location and direction of impulse.

18. **Comparing and Contrasting** Compare and contrast the structures and functions of the cerebrum, cerebellum, and brain stem. Include in your discussion the following functions: balance, involuntary muscle movements, muscle tone, memory, voluntary muscles, thinking, and senses.

19. **Drawing Conclusions** If an impulse traveled down one neuron but failed to move on to the next neuron, what might you conclude about the first neuron?

20. **Interpreting Scientific Illustrations** Using the following diagram, explain how an impulse crosses a synapse.

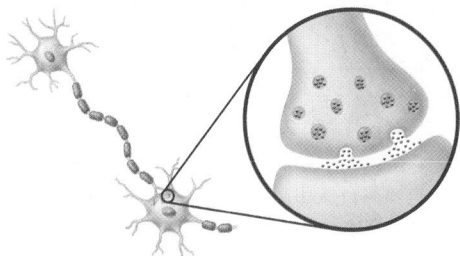

Performance Assessment

21. **Illustrate** In an emergency room, the doctor notices that a patient has uncoordinated body movements and has difficulty maintaining his balance. Draw and label which part of the brain may be injured.

Technology

Go to the Glencoe Science Web site at **science.glencoe.com** or use the **Glencoe Science CD-ROM** for additional chapter assessment.

THE PRINCETON REVIEW Test Practice

A police officer brought the following table into a school to educate students about the dangers of drinking and driving.

Approximate Blood Alcohol Percentage for Men

Drinks	Body Weight in Kilograms							
	45.4	54.4	63.5	72.6	81.6	90.7	99.8	108.9
1	0.04	0.03	0.03	0.02	0.02	0.02	0.02	0.02
2	0.08	0.06	0.05	0.05	0.04	0.04	0.03	0.03
3	0.11	0.09	0.08	0.07	0.06	0.06	0.05	0.05
4	0.15	0.12	0.11	0.09	0.08	0.08	0.07	0.06
5	0.19	0.16	0.13	0.12	0.11	0.09	0.09	0.08

Subtract 0.01% for each 40 minutes of drinking. One drink is 40 mL of 80 proof liquor, 355 mL of beer, or 148 mL of table wine.

Study the table and answer the questions.

1. In some states, the legal blood alcohol percentage limit for driving while under the influence of alcohol is 0.08 percent. According to this information, how many drinks would it take for a 99-kg man to exceed this limit?
   A) three
   B) four
   C) five
   D) six

2. A 72-kg man has been tested for blood alcohol content. His blood alcohol percentage is 0.07. Based upon the information in the table, about how much has he had to drink?
   F) 628 mL of 80-proof liquor
   G) 1,064 mL of beer
   H) 295 mL of table wine
   J) four drinks

Assessment Resources

 **Reproducible Masters**

Chapter Resources Booklet
Chapter Review, pp. 35–36
Chapter Tests, pp. 37–40
Assessment Transparency Activity, p. 47

Glencoe Science Web site
Interactive Tutor
Chapter Quizzes

Glencoe Technology
Assessment Transparency
Interactive CD-ROM Chapter Quizzes
ExamView Pro Test Bank
Vocabulary PuzzleMaker Software
MindJogger Videoquiz

Chapter 21 Assessment

THE PRINCETON REVIEW Test Practice

The Test-Taking Tip was written by The Princeton Review, the nation's leader in test preparation.

1. C
2. G

Developing Skills

16. See student page.
17. Sensory neurons are located in the sense organs and spinal cord; they carry impulses to the brain. Interneurons are located in the central nervous system; they carry impulses from the central nervous system to motor neurons. Motor neurons are in muscles and glands; they carry impulses from the brain to muscles and glands.
18. cerebrum—voluntary muscles, memory, senses, thinking; cerebellum—balance, muscle tone; brain stem—coordinates involuntary muscle movements, controls heartbeat, breathing, and blood pressure
19. It may be lacking the nerve-transmitting chemical released by axons.
20. A nerve-transmitting chemical is released from the axon of one neuron, diffuses across the synapse, and starts an impulse in the next neuron.

Performance Assessment

21. Drawings should indicate that the cerebellum is injured. Use **Performance Assessment in the Science Classroom**, p. 127.

<table>
<tr><th rowspan="2">Section/Objectives</th><th colspan="2">Standards</th><th rowspan="2">Activities/Features</th></tr>
<tr><th>National</th><th>State/Local</th></tr>
<tr><td>Chapter Opener</td><td>See p. 5T for a Key to Standards.</td><td></td><td>Explore Activity: Model a chemical message, p. 627
Before You Read, p. 627</td></tr>
<tr><td>Section 1 The Endocrine System
2 sessions
1 block
1. Define how hormones function.
2. Identify different endocrine glands and the effects of the hormones they produce.
3. Describe how a feedback system works in your body.</td><td>National Content Standards: UCP1, UCP5, C1, C3</td><td></td><td>Earth Science Integration, p. 629
Math Skills Activity: Calculating Blood Sugar Percentage, p. 629
Visualizing the Endocrine System, p. 630</td></tr>
<tr><td>Section 2 The Reproductive System
2 sessions
1 block
1. Identify the function of the reproductive system.
2. Compare and contrast the major structures of the male and female reproductive systems.
3. Sequence the stages of the menstrual cycle.</td><td>National Content Standards: UCP1, UCP3, A1, C1, C2, C3, F1</td><td></td><td>Science Online, p. 635
MiniLAB: Graphing Hormone Levels, p. 636
Activity: Interpreting Diagrams, p. 638</td></tr>
<tr><td>Section 3 Human Life Stages
3 sessions
1.5 blocks
1. Describe the fertilization of a human egg.
2. List the major events in the development of an embryo and fetus.
3. Describe the developmental stages of infancy, childhood, adolescence, and adulthood.</td><td>National Content Standards: UCP5, A1, C1, C2, C3, F1</td><td></td><td>MiniLAB: Interpreting Fetal Development, p. 642
Science Online, p. 643
Physics Integration, p. 646
Activity: Changing Body Proportions, p. 648
Science Stats: Facts About Infants, p. 650</td></tr>
</table>

NATIONAL GEOGRAPHIC **Teacher's Corner**

PRODUCTS AVAILABLE FROM GLENCOE
To order call 1-800-334-7344:
CD-ROM
NGS PictureShow: Human Body 3
Curriculum Kit
GeoKit: Human Body 2
Transparency Set
NGS PicturePack: Human Body 3
Videodisk
STV: Human Body

PRODUCTS AVAILABLE FROM NATIONAL GEOGRAPHIC SOCIETY
To order call 1-800-368-2728:
Videos
Reproductive System (The Human Body Series)
Incredible Human Machine

Activity Materials	Reproducible Resources	Section Assessment	Technology
Explore Activity: filter paper; metric ruler; plastic, ceramic, or glass plate; baking soda; salt; dropper; vinegar	**Chapter Resources Booklet** Foldables Worksheet, p. 15 Directed Reading Overview, p. 17 Note-taking Worksheets, pp. 31–33	GLENCOE'S ASSESSMENT ADVANTAGE	
Need materials? Contact Science Kit at 1-800-828-7777 or www.sciencekit.com on the Internet.	**Chapter Resources Booklet** Transparency Activity, p. 42 Enrichment, p. 28 Reinforcement, p. 25 Directed Reading, p. 18 Lab Activity, pp. 9–11 Transparency Activity, pp. 45–46	Portfolio Visual Learning, p. 631 Performance Math Skills Activity, p. 629 Skill Builder Activities, p. 632 Content Section Assessment, p. 632	Section Focus Transparency Teaching Transparency Interactive CD-ROM Guided Reading Audio Program
MiniLAB: graph paper **Activity:** paper, pencil	**Chapter Resources Booklet** Transparency Activity, p. 43 MiniLAB, p. 3 Enrichment, p. 29 Reinforcement, p. 26 Directed Reading, p. 18 Activity Worksheet, pp. 5–6	Portfolio Science Journal, p. 635 Performance MiniLAB, p. 636 Skill Builder Activities, p. 637 Content Section Assessment, p. 637	Section Focus Transparency Interactive CD-ROM Guided Reading Audio Program
MiniLAB: graph paper **Activity:** tape measure, erasable pencil, graph paper	**Chapter Resources Booklet** Transparency Activity, p. 44 MiniLAB, p. 4 Enrichment, p. 30 Reinforcement, p. 27 Directed Reading, pp. 19, 20 Activity Worksheet, pp. 7–8 Lab Activity, pp. 13–14 **Lab Management and Safety,** p. 70 **Home and Community Involvement,** p. 43 **Reading and Writing Skill Activities,** p.39 **Life Science Critical Thinking/ Problem Solving,** p. 19	Portfolio Make a Model, p. 640 Performance MiniLAB, p. 642 Skill Builder Activities, p. 647 Content Section Assessment, p. 647	Section Focus Transparency Interactive CD-ROM Guided Reading Audio Program

End of Chapter Assessment

GLENCOE'S ASSESSMENT ADVANTAGE

Blackline Masters	Technology	Professional Series
Chapter Resources Booklet Chapter Review, pp. 35–36 Chapter Tests, pp. 37–40 **Standardized Test Practice by The Princeton Review,** pp. 95–98	MindJogger Videoquiz Interactive CD-ROM Vocabulary PuzzleMakers ExamView Pro Test Bank Interactive Lesson Planner Interactive Teacher Edition	Performance Assessment in the Science Classroom (PASC)

Transparencies

Section Focus

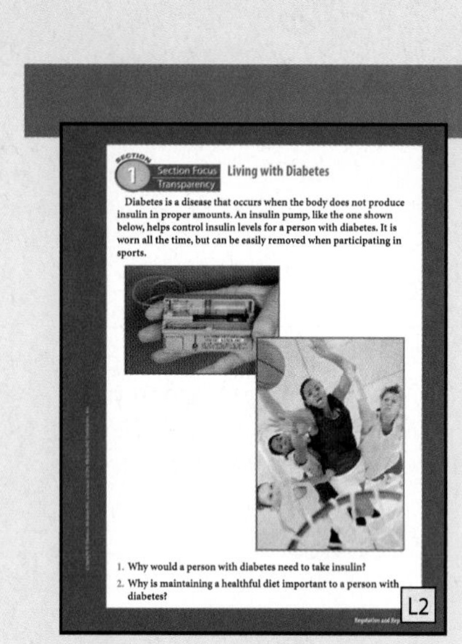
Section 1 Section Focus Transparency **Living with Diabetes**

Diabetes is a disease that occurs when the body does not produce insulin in proper amounts. An insulin pump, like the one shown below, helps control insulin levels for a person with diabetes. It is worn all the time, but can be easily removed when participating in sports.

1. Why would a person with diabetes need to take insulin?
2. Why is maintaining a healthful diet important to a person with diabetes?

L2

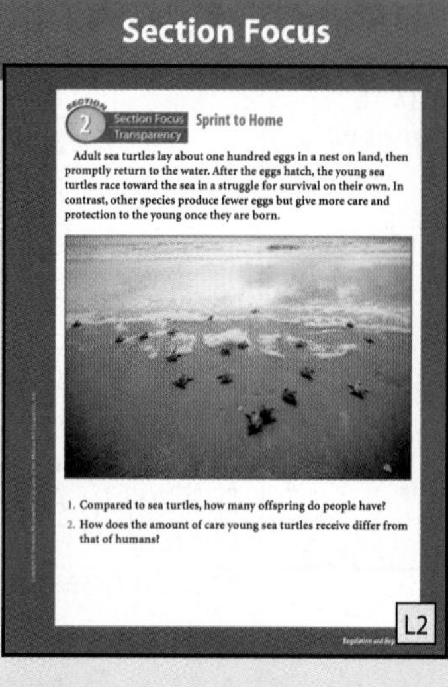
Section 2 Section Focus Transparency **Sprint to Home**

Adult sea turtles lay about one hundred eggs in a nest on land, then promptly return to the water. After the eggs hatch, the young sea turtles race toward the sea in a struggle for survival on their own. In contrast, other species produce fewer eggs but give more care and protection to the young once they are born.

1. Compared to sea turtles, how many offspring do people have?
2. How does the amount of care young sea turtles receive differ from that of humans?

L2

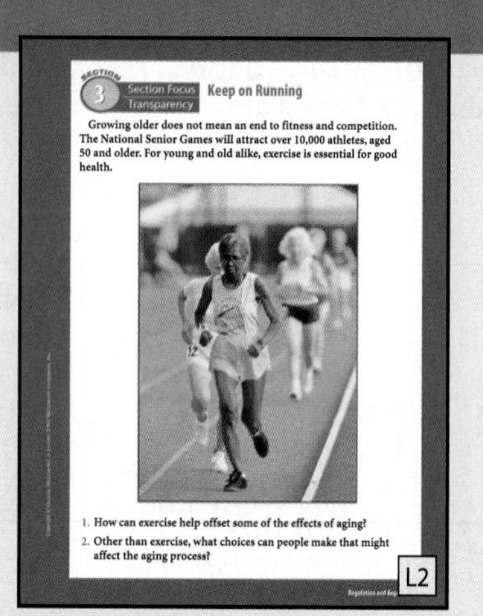
Section 3 Section Focus Transparency **Keep on Running**

Growing older does not mean an end to fitness and competition. The National Senior Games will attract over 10,000 athletes, aged 50 and older. For young and old alike, exercise is essential for good health.

1. How can exercise help offset some of the effects of aging?
2. Other than exercise, what choices can people make that might affect the aging process?

L2

This is a representation of key blackline masters available in the Teacher Classroom Resources. See Resource Manager boxes within the chapter for additional information.

Assessment

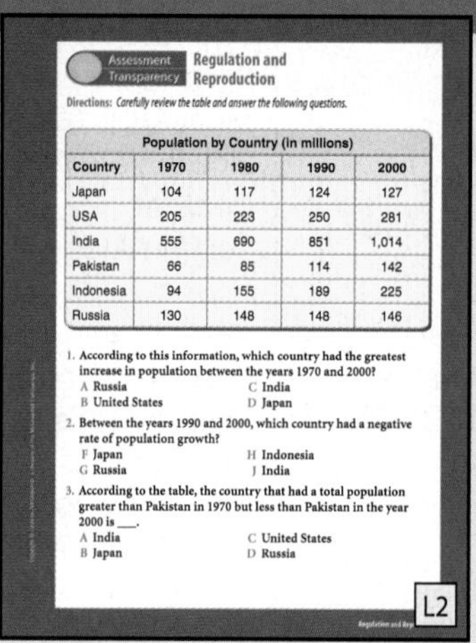
Assessment Transparency **Regulation and Reproduction**

Directions: Carefully review the table and answer the following questions.

Population by Country (in millions)				
Country	1970	1980	1990	2000
Japan	104	117	124	127
USA	205	223	250	281
India	555	690	851	1,014
Pakistan	66	85	114	142
Indonesia	94	155	189	225
Russia	130	148	148	146

1. According to this information, which country had the greatest increase in population between the years 1970 and 2000?
   A Russia C India
   B United States D Japan
2. Between the years 1990 and 2000, which country had a negative rate of population growth?
   F Japan H Indonesia
   G Russia J India
3. According to the table, the country that had a total population greater than Pakistan in 1970 but less than Pakistan in the year 2000 is ___.
   A India C United States
   B Japan D Russia

L2

Teaching

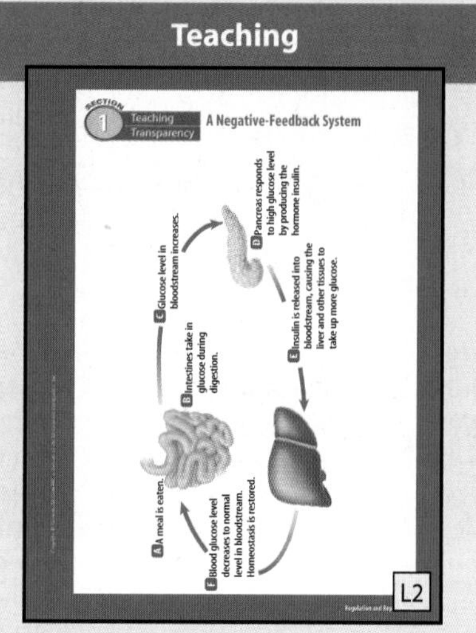
Section 1 Teaching Transparency **A Negative-Feedback System**

A meal is eaten.
Intestines take in glucose during digestion.
Glucose level in bloodstream increases.
Pancreas responds to high glucose level by producing the hormone insulin.
Insulin is released into bloodstream, causing the liver and other tissues to take up more glucose.
Blood glucose level decreases to normal level in bloodstream. Homeostasis is restored.

L2

Key to Teaching Strategies

The following designations will help you decide which activities are appropriate for your students.

- **L1** Level 1 activities should be appropriate for students with learning difficulties.
- **L2** Level 2 activities should be within the ability range of all students.
- **L3** Level 3 activities are designed for above-average students.
- **ELL** ELL activities should be within the ability range of English Language Learners.
- **COOP LEARN** Cooperative Learning activities are designed for small group work.
- **LS** Multiple Learning Styles logos, as described on page 22T, are used throughout to indicate strategies that address different learning styles.
- **P** These strategies represent student products that can be placed into a best-work portfolio.

Hands-on Activities

Activity Worksheets

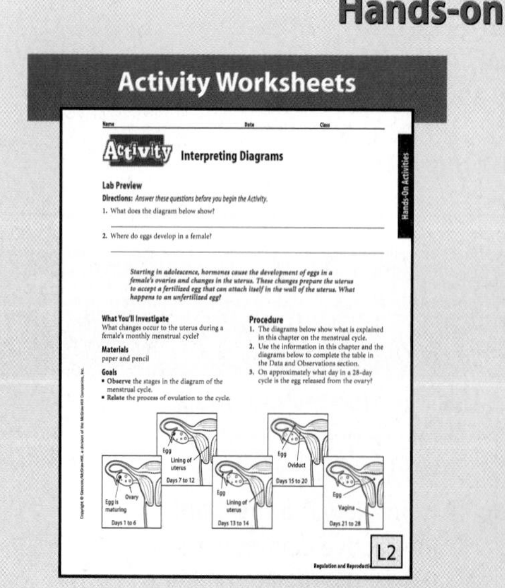
Activity **Interpreting Diagrams**

Lab Preview

Directions: Answer these questions before you begin the Activity.

1. What does the diagram below show?
2. Where do eggs develop in a female?

Starting in adolescence, hormones cause the development of eggs in a female's ovaries and changes in the uterus. These changes prepare the uterus to accept a fertilized egg that can attach itself in the wall of the uterus. What happens to an unfertilized egg?

What You'll Investigate
What changes occur to the uterus during a female's monthly menstrual cycle?

Materials
paper and pencil

Goals
- Observe the stages in the diagram of the menstrual cycle.
- Relate the process of ovulation to the cycle.

Procedure
1. The diagrams below show what is explained in this chapter on the menstrual cycle.
2. Use the information in this chapter and the diagrams below to complete the table in the Data and Observations section.
3. On approximately what day in a 28-day cycle is the egg released from the ovary?

Egg is maturing
Ovary
Days 1 to 6
Egg
Lining of uterus
Days 7 to 12
Egg
Lining of uterus
Days 13 to 14
Egg
Oviduct
Days 15 to 20
Egg
Vagina
Days 21 to 28

L2

Laboratory Activities

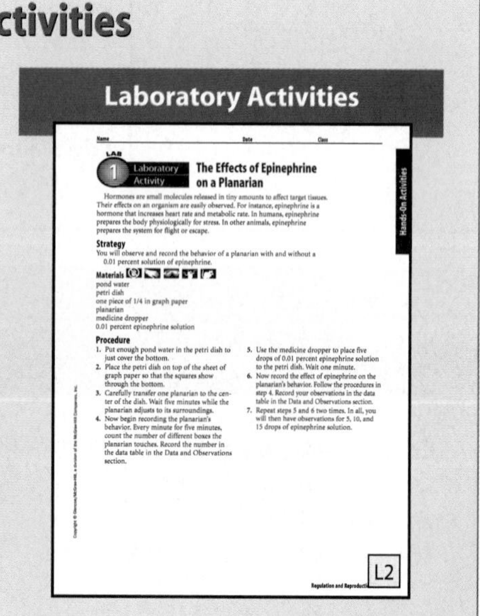
Lab 1 Laboratory Activity **The Effects of Epinephrine on a Planarian**

Hormones are small molecules released in tiny amounts to affect target tissues. Their effects on an organism are easily observed. For instance, epinephrine is a hormone that increases heart rate and metabolic rate. In humans, epinephrine prepares the body physiologically for stress. In other animals, epinephrine prepares the system for flight or escape.

Strategy
You will observe and record the behavior of a planarian with and without a 0.01 percent solution of epinephrine.

Materials
pond water
petri dish
one piece of 1/4 in graph paper
planarian
medicine dropper
0.01 percent epinephrine solution

Procedure
1. Put enough pond water in the petri dish to just cover the bottom.
2. Place the petri dish on top of the sheet of graph paper so that the squares show through the bottom.
3. Carefully transfer one planarian to the center of the dish. Wait five minutes while the planarian adjusts to its surroundings.
4. Now begin recording the planarian's behavior. Every minute for five minutes, count the number of different boxes the planarian touches. Record the number in the data table in the Data and Observations section.
5. Use the medicine dropper to place five drops of 0.01 percent epinephrine solution to the petri dish. Wait one minute.
6. Now record the effect of epinephrine on the planarian's behavior. Follow the procedures in step 4. Record your observations in the data table in the Data and Observations section.
7. Repeat steps 5 and 6 two times. In all, you will then have observations for 5, 10, and 15 drops of epinephrine solution.

L2

Meeting Different Ability Levels

Content Outline

Note-taking Worksheet — Regulation and Reproduction

Section 1 The Endocrine System

Section 2 The Reproductive System

L2

Reinforcement

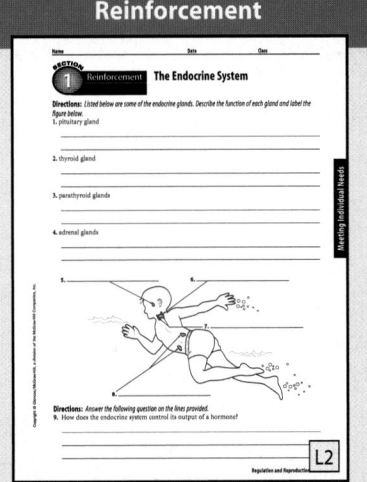

Section 1 Reinforcement — The Endocrine System

L2

Directed Reading

Directed Reading for Content Mastery — Overview: Regulation and Reproduction

L1

Enrichment

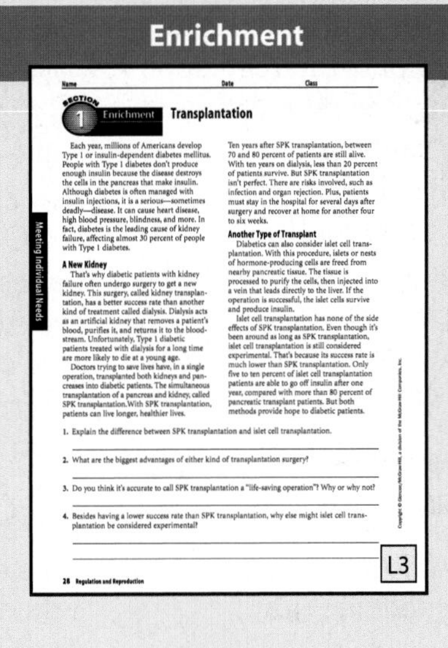

Section 1 Enrichment — Transplantation

L3

Spanish Directed Reading

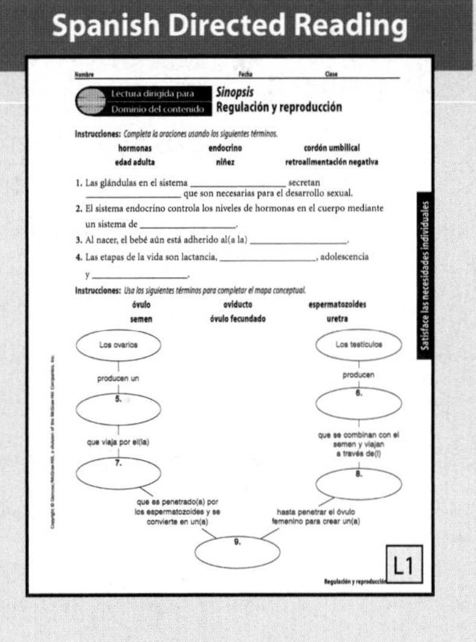

Lectura dirigida para Dominio del contenido — Sinopsis: Regulación y reproducción

L1

Assessment

Chapter Tests

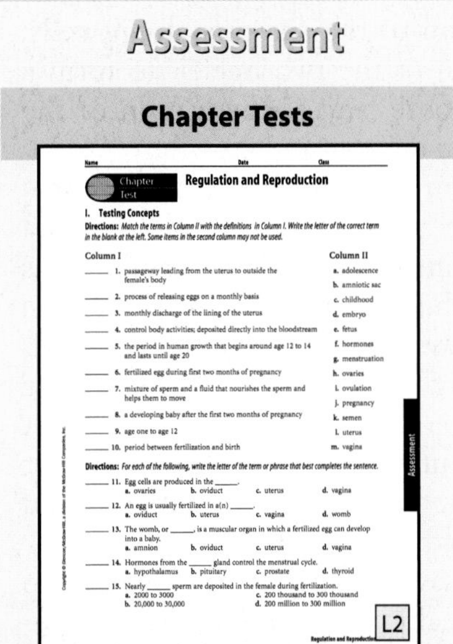

Chapter Test — Regulation and Reproduction

L2

Test Practice Workbook

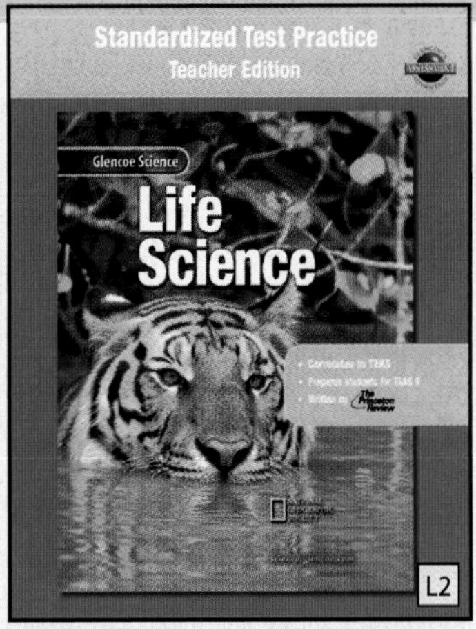

L2

Chapter Review

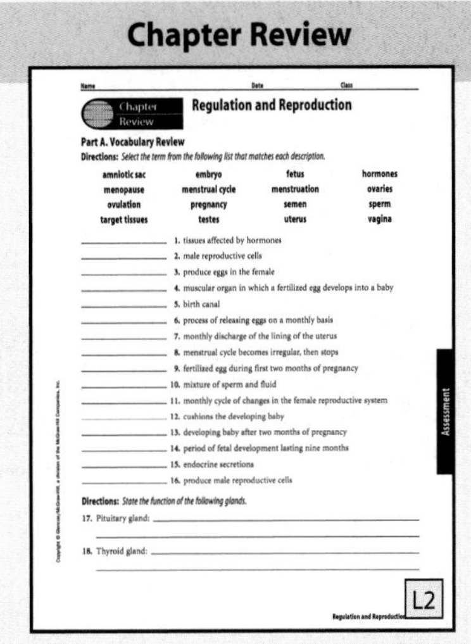

Chapter Review — Regulation and Reproduction

L2

Science Content Background

SECTION 1 The Endocrine System

Regulation

The endocrine system backs up the regulatory functions of the nervous system. The endocrine system uses hormones to control body functions such as defense, hunger, growth and reproduction. All organs of the endocrine system are glands that produce and empty hormones into the circulatory system.

The anterior lobe of the pituitary gland produces hormones that cause the stimulation of growth, the production of milk, the regulation of thyroid gland secretions, the regulation of adrenal cortex secretions, the stimulation of egg and sperm production, and egg release.

The posterior lobe of the pituitary gland aids in the regulation of water secretion by the kidneys, muscle contractions during labor, and the contraction of milk- producing glands.

The pituitary's intermediate lobe controls melanin production, which determines skin color.

Student Misconception

Fertilization and embryonic development are mysterious processes that are not understandable.

Refer to the facing page for teaching strategies to address this misconception. Refer to pages 639–642 for content related to this topic.

SECTION 2 The Reproductive System

Hormones

Hormones produced by the endocrine system control sexual development, maturation, and functioning of the reproductive system. Hormones stimulate the production and release of sperm and semen in the male reproductive system. In the female reproductive system, hormones stimulate the production and release of ova, or eggs. A mature ovum is about 0.10 mm in diameter. Hormones also play a role during labor and birth. In later years, menopause is brought on when the body stops producing certain hormones.

SECTION 3 Human Life Stages

Embryonic Development

Fertilization is the union of a sperm cell from a male with an egg from a female. Fertilization results in two events: (1) fusion of the sperm and egg cells, including fusion of the two nuclei, to form a cell called a zygote, and (2) activation of the new cell to begin division and growth.

Once a sperm fertilizes an egg, the egg produces an outer protective layer. Next, the zygote divides into thousands of smaller cells that cling together like a ball of soap bubbles. After several days and until about two weeks later, the ball of cells begins to differentiate into three parts: an outer layer of cells that attaches to the uterus of the mother, an inner mass of cells that develops into the embryo, and a fluid-filled sac that surrounds the embryo.

The next phase, which occurs between two and eight weeks after fertilization, involves specialization of cells into primary organ systems. This set of events marks the end of the embryo stage and the beginning of the fetal stage.

SCIENCE Online

For additional content background on this topic, go to the Glencoe Science Web site at science.glencoe.com.

IDENTIFYING Misconceptions

Find Out What Students Think

Students may think that . . .

- **Fertilization and embryonic development are mysterious processes that are not understandable.**

Many students may find the concepts of fertilization and embryonic development very abstract. Using concrete demonstrations and activities will help these students understand the processes and sequences of events that occur.

Demonstration

- Using two different colors of clay, form a large ball from one color, representing an egg cell, and many smaller balls from the second color, representing sperm cells. Fertilization can be modeled by molding the "egg" and "sperm" into one ball. Explain that this fertilized cell is called a zygote. No other sperm cells can fuse with the egg cell at this point because the zygote produces a protective barrier blocking other sperm cells. Emphasize that the molding together of the sperm and egg cells is a simulation of the combining of genetic material from both.
- Next, model the phase of rapid cell division by dividing the ball into many smaller, connected balls. Explain that these cells cling together like a ball of soap bubbles. Continue by drawing the "soap bubble" stage on the board and labeling it as time from fertilization to a few days.
- Next, draw the three-part stage and the specialization. Label these drawings as "a few days to 2 weeks" and "2 weeks to 8 weeks," respectively.

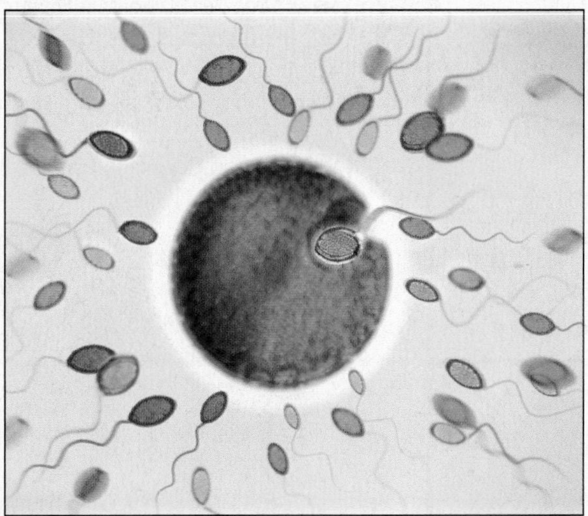

VCG/FPG International

Promote Understanding

Activity

After discussion, have students draw diagrams of the events that occur from fertilization through the stages of early development to the early fetal stage. Have students work in small groups to explain to one another their diagrams and the events that take place during each stage.

Assess

After completing the chapter, see *Identifying Misconceptions* in the Study Guide.

Regulation and Reproduction

Chapter Vocabulary

hormone, p. 628
testes, p. 634
sperm, p. 634
semen, p. 634
ovary, p. 635
ovulation, p. 635
uterus, p. 635
vagina, p. 635
menstrual cycle, p. 636
menstruation, p. 636
pregnancy, p. 640
embryo, p. 641
amniotic sac, p. 641
fetus, p. 642
fetal stress, p. 644

What do you think?

Science Journal This bumpy-looking cluster of cells is the morula stage of human development. A morula is a ball of cells that forms by cell division following fertilization. The name morula comes from the Latin word for mulberry.

Regulation and Reproduction

The control room blinks with monitors and panels of dials and buttons. Not much is going to get past this complex monitoring system. Your body also is designed with a system that monitors and controls the actions of many of your body's functions. In this chapter, you'll learn about this system—the endocrine system. You'll also study the human reproductive system and the stages of growth.

What do you think?

Science Journal Look at the picture below with a classmate. Discuss what this might be. Here's a hint: *This object could be considered a small beginning.* Write your answer or best guess in your Science Journal.

626

Theme Connection

Stability and Change and **Energy** The endocrine system maintains stable body functions and responds to changes. The unique functioning of the reproductive system is dependent on energy for cell division and differentiation of cells.

Your body has systems that work together to control your body's activities. One of these systems sends chemical messages through your blood to certain tissues, which, in turn, respond. You may feel the results of this system's action, but you cannot see them. Do the activity below to see how a chemical signal can be sent.

Model a chemical message

1. Cut a 10-cm-tall Y shape from filter paper and place it on a plastic, ceramic, or glass plate.
2. Sprinkle baking soda on one arm of the Y and salt on the other arm.
3. Using a dropper, place five or six drops of vinegar halfway up the leg of the Y.

Observe

Describe in your Science Journal how the chemical moves along the paper and the reaction(s) it causes.

Before You Read

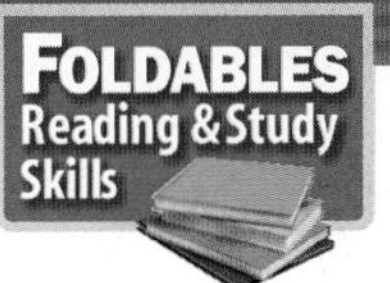

Making a Sequence Study Fold

Make the following Foldable to help you predict what might occur next in the sequence of life.

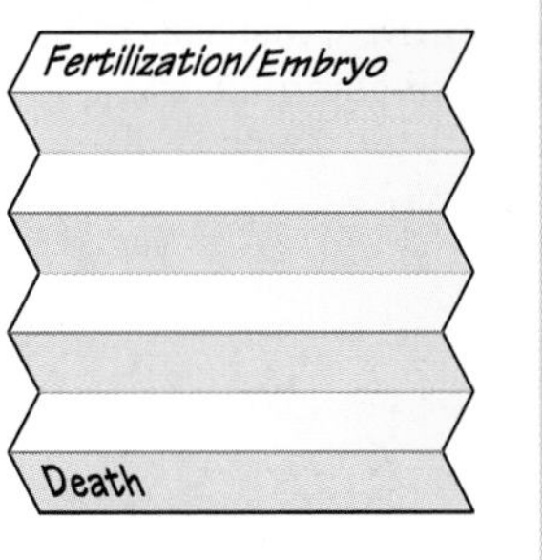

1. Place a sheet of paper in front of you so the short side is at the top. Fold the paper in half from top to bottom. Then fold it in half again top to bottom two more times. Unfold all the folds.
2. Using the fold lines as a guide, refold the paper into a fan. Unfold all the folds again.
3. Before you read the chapter list as many stages of life as you can on your foldable, beginning with *Fertilization/Embryo* and ending with *Death*. As you read the chapter add to your list.

627

Explore Activity

Purpose Use the Explore activity to introduce students to the endocrine system. L2

LS **Visual-Spatial**

Preparation Cut Y-shaped pieces of filter paper before class.

Materials filter paper or coffee filters; baking soda; salt; vinegar; plastic, ceramic, or glass plate; dropper

Teaching Strategy Have students observe the bubbles that form when the vinegar and baking soda react.

Observe

Students should observe the vinegar moving along the leg of the Y and then into the arms of the Y. The vinegar reacts with the baking soda and bubbles are produced.

Assessment

Performance Have students repeat this activity using baking powder in place of baking soda and water instead of vinegar and observe the reaction. Use **Performance Assessment in the Science Classroom,** p. 97.

Before You Read

FOLDABLES Reading & Study Skills

Dinah Zike Study Fold

Purpose Students make and use a Foldable to determine what they know about the endocrine system and the cause and effect relationship between endocrine glands and hormones.

For additional help, see Foldables Worksheet, p. 15 in **Chapter Resources Booklet,** or go to the Glencoe Science Web site at **science.glencoe.com.** See After You Read in the Study Guide at the end of this chapter.

The Endocrine System

1 Motivate

Bellringer Transparency

Display the Section Focus Transparency for Section 1. Use the accompanying Transparency Activity Master. L2 ELL

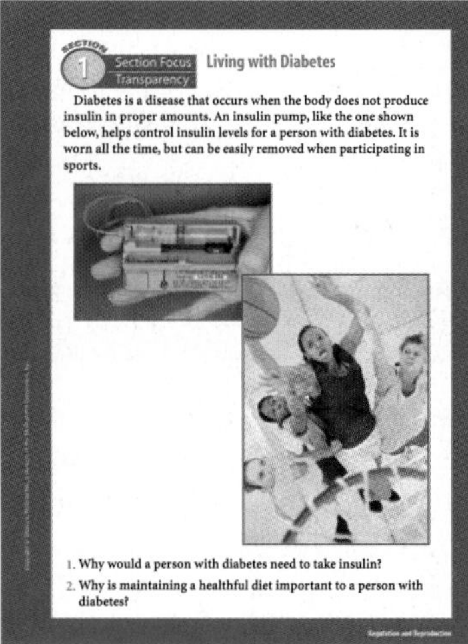
Section Focus Transparency 1 Living with Diabetes

Diabetes is a disease that occurs when the body does not produce insulin in proper amounts. An insulin pump, like the one shown below, helps control insulin levels for a person with diabetes. It is worn all the time, but can be easily removed when participating in sports.

1. Why would a person with diabetes need to take insulin?
2. Why is maintaining a healthful diet important to a person with diabetes?

Tie to Prior Knowledge

Have students recall how their bodies react to stimuli such as the touching of a hot object or how they respond to a loud noise.

The Endocrine System

As You Read

What You'll Learn

- **Define** how hormones function.
- **Identify** different endocrine glands and the effects of the hormones they produce.
- **Describe** how a feedback system works in your body.

Vocabulary
hormone

Why It's Important
The endocrine system uses chemicals to control many systems in your body.

Functions of the Endocrine System

You go through the dark hallways of a haunted house. You can't see a thing. Your heart is pounding. Suddenly, a monster steps out in front of you. You scream and jump backwards. Your body is prepared to defend itself or get away. Preparing the body for fight or flight in times of emergency, as shown in **Figure 1,** is one of the functions of the body's control systems.

Chemical Messengers Your body is made up of systems that are controlled, or regulated, to work together. The nervous system and the endocrine (EN duh krun) system are the control systems of your body. The nervous system sends messages to and from the brain throughout the body. The endocrine system uses **hormones** (HOR mohnz)—chemicals that are made in tissues called glands found throughout your body. Hormones from endocrine glands are released directly into your bloodstream. They affect specific tissues called target tissues, usually located in the body far from the hormone-producing gland. The body doesn't react as quickly to messages from the endocrine system as it does to those of the nervous system.

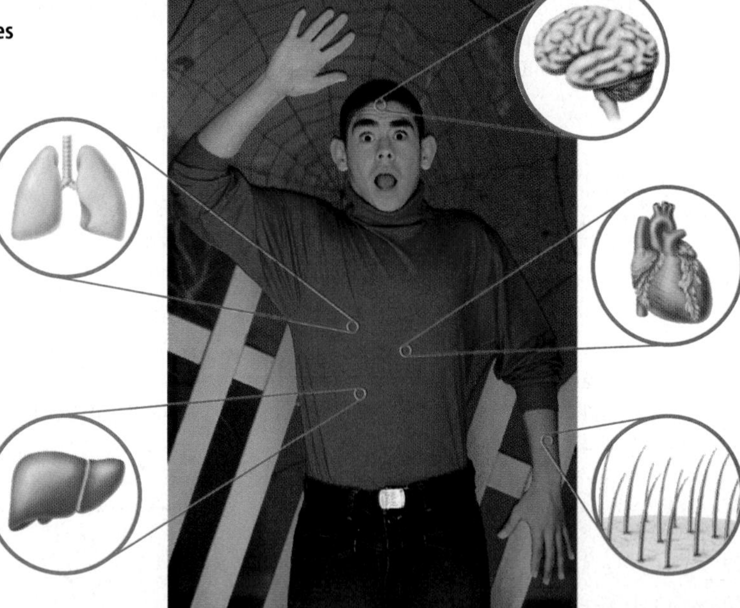

Figure 1
Your endocrine system enables many parts of your body to respond with an immediate reaction to a fearful situation.

628

Section Assessment Planner

Portfolio
Visual Learning, p. 631

Performance Assessment
Math Skills Activity, p. 629
Skill Builder Activities, p. 632
See page 654 for more options.

Content Assessment
Section, p. 632
Challenge, p. 632
Chapter, pp. 654–655

Endocrine Glands

Unlike some glands, such as your mouth's saliva glands, that release their products through small tubes called ducts, endocrine glands are ductless. Hormones from endocrine glands pour directly into the blood to reach target tissues. Hormones regulate certain cellular activities. **Figure 2** on the next page describes some of your major endocrine glands and how they function to regulate your body.

What is the function of hormones?

Without the element iodine, the thyroid gland cannot function properly. Iodine is found in seawater, soil, and rocks. How does your body take in iodine? Write your answer in your Science Journal.

Math Skills Activity

Calculating Blood Sugar Percentage

Example Problem

Calculate how much higher the blood sugar (glucose) level of a diabetic is before breakfast when compared to a nondiabetic before breakfast. Express this number as a percentage of the nondiabetic sugar level before breakfast.

Blood sugar (g sugar/L blood)
3.0
2.5
2.0
1.5
1.0
0.5
0
1 2 3 4 5 6
Hours after breakfast
Key
Diabetic
Nondiabetic

Solution

1. *This is what you know:*
   blood sugar of a nondiabetic person at 0 h = 0.85 g sugar/L blood
   blood sugar of a diabetic person at 0 h = 1.8 g sugar/L blood
2. *This is what you must do first:*
   Find the difference between the two values. 1.8 g/L − 0.85 g/L = 0.95 g/L
3. *This is the equation you need to use:*
   $$\frac{\text{difference between values}}{\text{nondiabetic value}} \times 100\% = \text{percent difference}$$
4. *Substitute in the known values:*
   $$\frac{0.95}{0.85} \times 100\% = 111\%$$
   At 0 h before breakfast, a diabetic's blood sugar is 111 percent higher than that of a nondiabetic.

Practice Problem

Express as a percentage how much higher the blood sugar value is for a diabetic person compared to a nondiabetic person 1 h, 3 h, and 6 h after breakfast.

For more help, refer to the Math Skill Handbook.

2 Teach

Functions of the Endocrine System

Extension

Have students research the function of the chemical messengers called prostaglandins. Though not true hormones, they act like hormones. In reality, they are fatty-acid derivatives. L2

Endocrine Glands

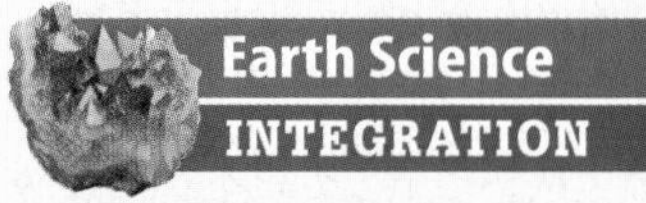

The human body absorbs iodine from food.

Reading Check

Answer to speed up and slow down certain cellular activities

Math Skills Activity

National Math Standards

Correlation to Mathematics Objectives

1, 2, 4, 5, 6, 8, 9

Answer to Practice Problem

Hour one = 130 / 110 × 100 = 118 %

Hour three = 95 / 85 × 100 = 111 %

Hour six = 110 / 70 × 100 = 157 %

Note: student answers may vary slightly due to the values read from the graph. Accept answers that are reasonably close.

Teacher FYI

In addition to hormones produced by endocrine glands, other organs also produce hormones. Endocrine cells in the stomach produce a hormone that regulates the release of its digestive enzymes. The kidneys release a hormone that controls the rate of production of red blood cells. The heart makes a hormone that regulates blood pressure and volume.

Resource Manager 

Chapter Resources Booklet

Transparency Activity, p. 42

Directed Reading for Content Mastery, pp. 17, 18

Note-taking Worksheets, pp. 31–33

Visualizing the Endocrine System

Have students examine the pictures and read the captions. Then ask the following questions.

How do hormones from the thyroid gland and the parathyroid gland work together? Possible answers: Both glands release hormones that work together to regulate the levels of calcium in the blood.

What could be the result if a person's thymus gland was not functioning properly? Possible answer: The thymus gland produces hormones that stimulate the production of cells involved in immune reactions. Without these cells the body has difficulty fighting infection.

Activity

Have students write and act out a skit that demonstrates the negative feedback cycle of hormone regulation. Students can break into groups of 6 or 7 and produce the skits. The instructor would need to provide a different sequence of events for each student group. Each student can play the role of the brain, a hormone or an endocrine gland, and one student can be the messenger between the body and the brain.

Extension

Have students research disorders of the endocrine system such as Graves' disease, Cushing's Syndrome, Addison's disease, diabetes, gigantism and acromegaly.

NATIONAL GEOGRAPHIC **VISUALIZING THE ENDOCRINE SYSTEM**

Figure 2

Your endocrine system is involved in regulating and coordinating many body functions, from growth and development to reproduction. This complex system consists of many diverse glands and organs, including the nine shown here. Endocrine glands produce chemical messenger molecules, called hormones, that circulate in the bloodstream. Hormones exert their influence only on the specific target cells to which they bind.

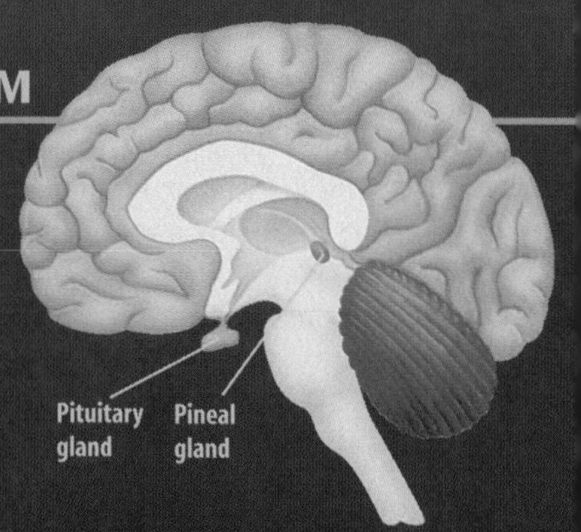

PINEAL GLAND Shaped like a tiny pine cone, the pineal gland lies deep in the brain. It produces melatonin, a hormone that may function as a sort of body clock by regulating wake/sleep patterns.

PITUITARY GLAND A pea-size structure attached to the hypothalamus of the brain, the pituitary gland produces hormones that affect a wide range of body activities, from growth to reproduction.

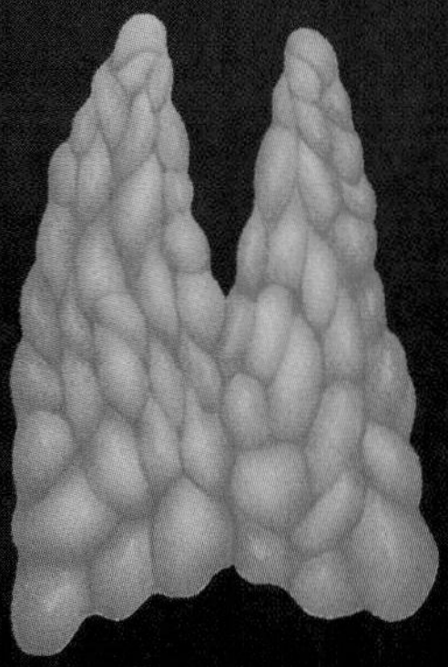

THYMUS The thymus is located in the upper chest, just behind the sternum. Hormones produced by this organ stimulate the production of certain infection-fighting cells.

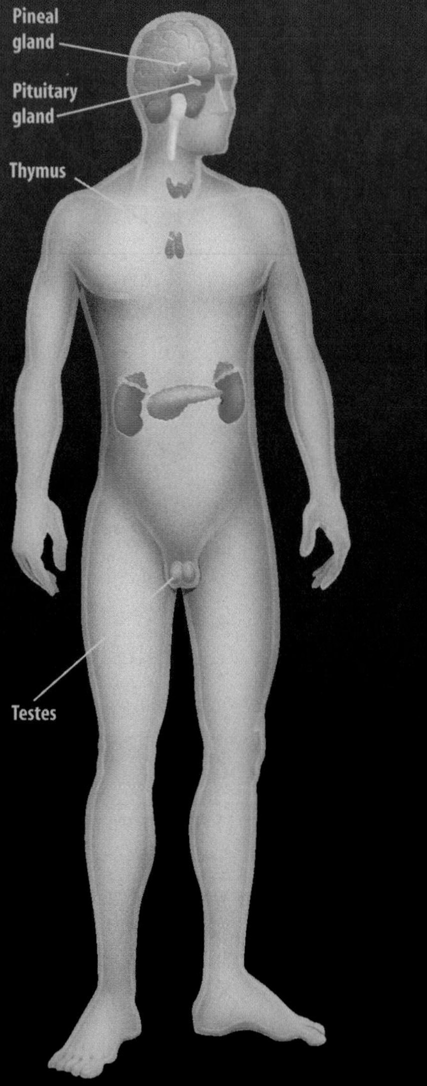

TESTES These paired male reproductive organs primarily produce testosterone, a hormone that controls the development and maintenance of male sexual traits. Testosterone also plays an important role in the production of sperm.

Pituitary gland
Pineal gland
Pineal gland
Pituitary gland
Thymus
Testes

Curriculum Connection

Language Arts The word *adrenal* is derived from two Latin words: *ad-* meaning "to," and *renalis*, meaning "kidneys." **How is this word related to the location of the adrenal glands?** The adrenal glands are located on top of the kidneys.

Visualizing the Endocrine System

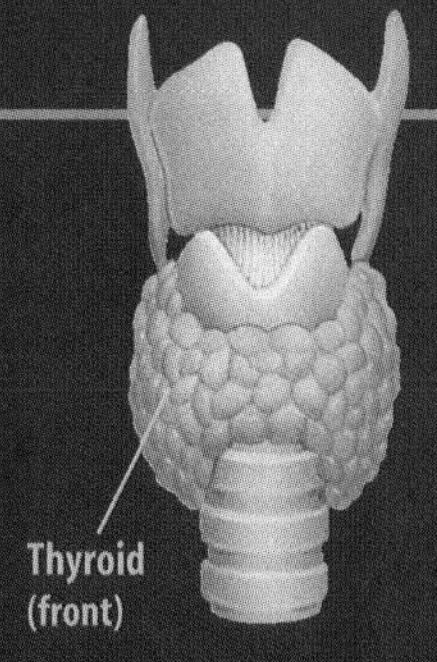

THYROID GLAND Located below the larynx, the bilobed thyroid gland is richly supplied with blood vessels. It produces hormones that regulate metabolic rate, control the uptake of calcium by bones, and promote normal nervous system development.

PARATHYROID GLANDS Attached to the back surface of the thyroid are tiny parathyroids, which help regulate calcium levels in the body. Calcium is important for bone growth and maintenance, as well as for muscle contraction and nerve impulse transmission.

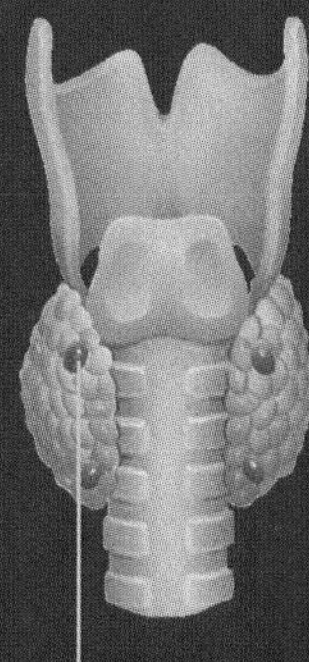

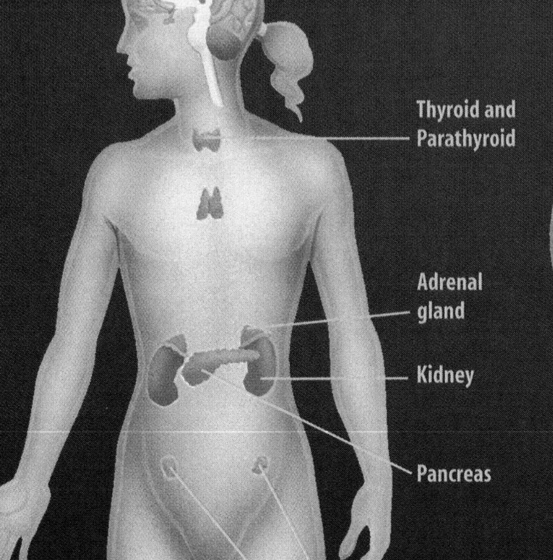

ADRENAL GLANDS On top of each of your kidneys is an adrenal gland. This complex endocrine gland produces a variety of hormones. Some play a critical role in helping your body adapt to physical and emotional stress. Others help stabilize blood sugar levels.

PANCREAS Scattered throughout the pancreas are millions of tiny clusters of endocrine tissue called the islets of Langerhans. Cells that make up the islets produce hormones that help control sugar levels in the bloodstream.

OVARIES Found deep in the pelvic cavity, ovaries produce female sex hormones known as estrogen and progesterone. These hormones regulate the female reproductive cycle and are responsible for producing and maintaining female sex characteristics.

Visual Learning

Figure 2 Have students make a network tree concept map depicting the major endocrine glands in the human body and the function of each. L2
LS **Visual-Spatial** P

Teacher FYI

An overproduction of melatonin by the pineal gland is hypothesized by scientists to be one cause of Seasonal Affective Disorder (SAD). SAD is a type of depression that some people suffer when there are fewer hours of daylight during winter months. The treatment of SAD includes exposing sufferers to artificial bright light for several hours at a time.

Science Words

Word Meanings Have students research the meaning of the roots of the word *endocrine*. Students should record their findings in their Science Journal. The prefix *endo-* means "within." The Greek root word *Krinein* means "to separate." The substance is separated from the gland when it moves into the blood.

Resource Manager

Chapter Resources Booklet
- Enrichment, p. 28
- Lab Activity, pp. 9–11
- Transparency Activity, pp. 45–46
- Reinforcement, p. 25

A Negative-Feedback System

Discussion

Infer the probable results of too much growth hormone in the blood of a young person. The person would grow at an accelerated rate and become abnormally tall. **What if there were too little of the hormone produced?** Shortness might result.

3 Assess

Reteach

Using a chart of the circulatory system, have students trace the pathway of a hormone to its target tissue. L2 LS **Kinesthetic**

Challenge

Why do you think the pituitary is often referred to as the "master gland?" The hormones from the pituitary control a number of body activities such as blood pressure, metabolism, growth, secretion of sex hormones, and the growth and development of the sex cells.

Assessment

Content Make a table describing the characteristics and components of the endocrine system. Use **Performance Assessment in the Science Classroom,** p. 109.

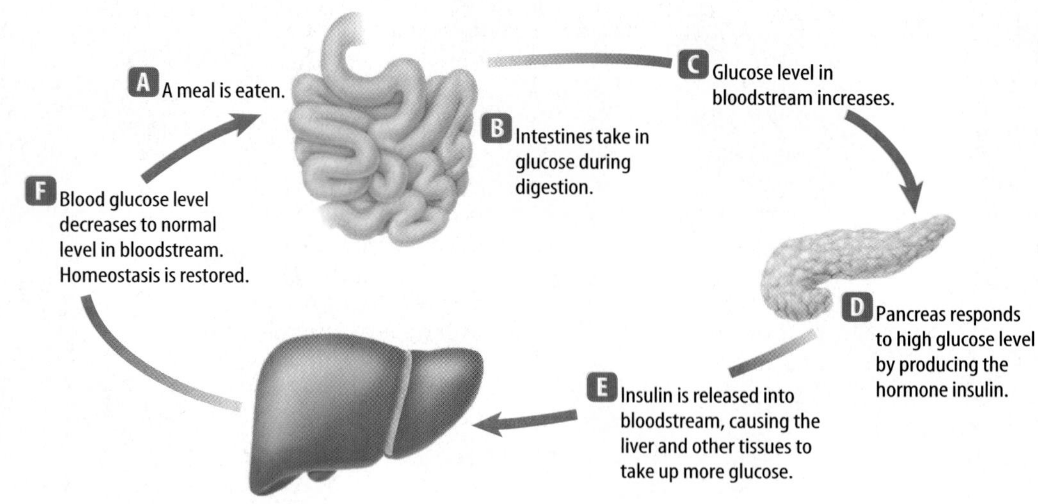

Figure 3
Many internal body conditions, such as hormone level, blood sugar level, and body temperature, are controlled by negative-feedback systems. Using a negative-feedback system, the pancreas controls the level of glucose in your bloodstream.

A Negative-Feedback System

To control the amount of hormones that are in your body, the endocrine system sends chemical messages back and forth within itself. This is called a negative-feedback system. It works much the way a thermostat works. When the temperature in a room drops below a set level, the thermostat signals the furnace to turn on. Once the furnace has raised the temperature in the room to the set level, the thermostat signals the furnace to shut off. It will continue to stay off until the thermostat signals that the temperature has dropped again. **Figure 3** shows how a negative-feedback system controls the level of glucose in your bloodstream.

Section  Assessment

1. Compare and contrast the human body's two control systems.
2. What is the function of hormones?
3. Choose one endocrine gland and explain how it works.
4. What is a negative-feedback system?
5. **Think Critically** Glucose is required for cellular respiration, the process that releases energy within cells. How would lack of insulin affect this process?

Skill Builder Activities

6. **Predicting** Predict why the circulatory system is a good mechanism for delivering hormones throughout the body. **For more help, refer to the** Science Skill Handbook.
7. **Researching Information** Research recent treatments for growth disorders involving the pituitary gland. Write a brief paragraph of your results in your Science Journal. **For more help, refer to the** Science Skill Handbook.

Answers to Section Assessment

1. The nervous system sends messages to and from the brain throughout the body. The endocrine system uses hormones to affect specific tissues in the body.
2. Hormones regulate certain cellular activities.
3. Pancreas—secretes insulin to regulate glucose levels; refer to **Figure 2** for other possible answers.
4. a system that uses blood hormone levels to signal when a gland should and should not secrete the hormone
5. Insulin causes tissues to take up more glucose, without which cells can't carry on respiration.
6. The circulatory system reaches every cell of the body.
7. Answers will vary. Possible topic: the use of hormone therapy to stimulate growth in young children.

SECTION 2

The Reproductive System

Reproduction and the Endocrine System

Reproduction is the process that continues life on Earth. Most human body systems, such as the digestive system and the nervous system, are the same in males and females, but this is not true for the reproductive system. Males and females each have structures specialized for their roles in reproduction. Although structurally different, both the male and female reproductive systems are adapted to allow for a series of events that can lead to the birth of a baby.

Hormones are the key to how the human reproductive system functions, as shown in **Figure 4.** Sex hormones are necessary for the development of sexual characteristics, such as breast development in females and facial hair growth in males. Hormones from the pituitary gland also begin the production of eggs in females and sperm in males. Eggs and sperm transfer hereditary information from one generation to the next.

As You Read

What You'll Learn

- **Identify** the function of the reproductive system.
- **Compare and contrast** the major structures of the male and female reproductive systems.
- **Sequence** the stages of the menstrual cycle.

Vocabulary

testes, sperm, semen, ovary, ovulation, uterus, vagina, menstrual cycle, menstruation

Why It's Important

The reproductive system helps ensure that life continues on Earth.

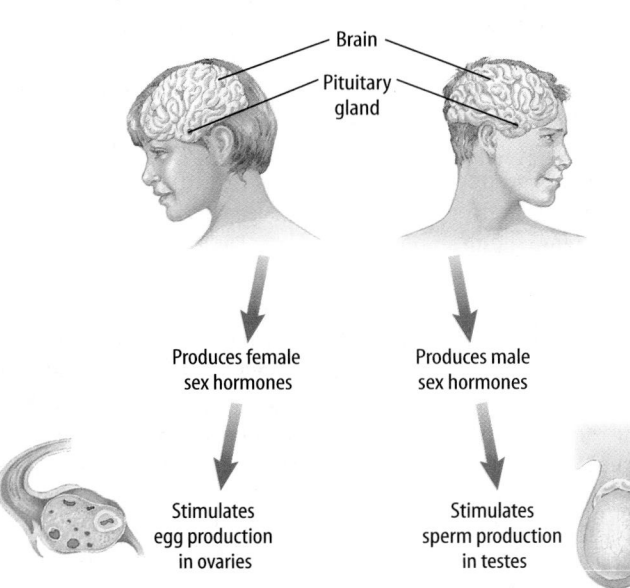

Brain
Pituitary gland
Produces female sex hormones
Produces male sex hormones
Stimulates egg production in ovaries
Stimulates sperm production in testes

Figure 4
The pituitary gland produces hormones that control the male and female reproductive systems.

SECTION

The Reproductive System

1 Motivate

Bellringer Transparency

Display the Section Focus Transparency for Section 2. Use the accompanying Transparency Activity Master. L2 ELL

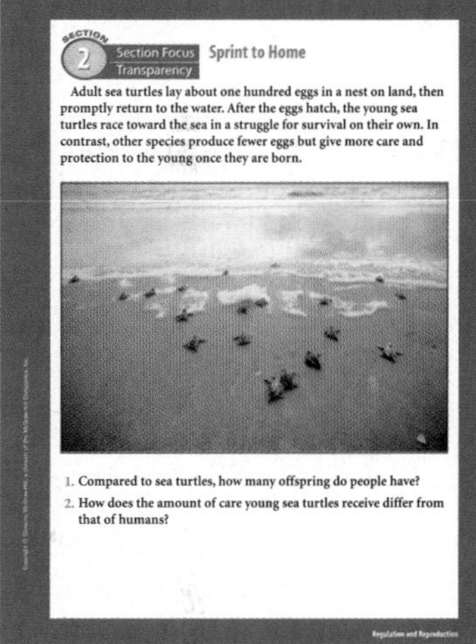

Section Focus Transparency — Sprint to Home

Adult sea turtles lay about one hundred eggs in a nest on land, then promptly return to the water. After the eggs hatch, the young sea turtles race toward the sea in a struggle for survival on their own. In contrast, other species produce fewer eggs but give more care and protection to the young once they are born.

1. Compared to sea turtles, how many offspring do people have?
2. How does the amount of care young sea turtles receive differ from that of humans?

Tie to Prior Knowledge

Ask students to think of common animals that begin life by the union of an egg and sperm. Examples may include humans, cats, dogs, horses, toads, and so on.

Section Assessment Planner

Portfolio
Science Journal, p. 635

Performance Assessment
MiniLAB, p. 636
Skill Builder Activities, p. 637
See page 654 for more options.

Content Assessment
Section, p. 637
Challenge, p. 637
Chapter, pp. 654–655

Resource Manager

Chapter Resources Booklet
Transparency Activity, p. 43
Directed Reading for Content Mastery, p. 18

2 Teach

The Male Reproductive System

Teacher FYI

Sperm production is a continuous process from puberty throughout the life of a male. Egg production in females begins before birth. There is no production after birth. Each ovary may have nearly a million primary oocytes—cells from which eggs form.

Discussion

Infer why sperm have a streamlined head and an active tail. The streamlined head of a sperm reduces friction as it moves through liquids. The active tail propels the sperm in a direction that can be against gravity.

Use an Analogy

The movement of sperm is not unlike the movement of flagellate protozoans. Wavelike movements of the tail propel the organism forward. LS **Visual-Spatial**

Discussion

What other functions does semen have in addition to carrying the sperm? Chemical substances in semen provide energy for sperm movement. Explain that because semen is slightly alkaline, it protects sperm from acidic conditions, such as those found in the female reproductive system.

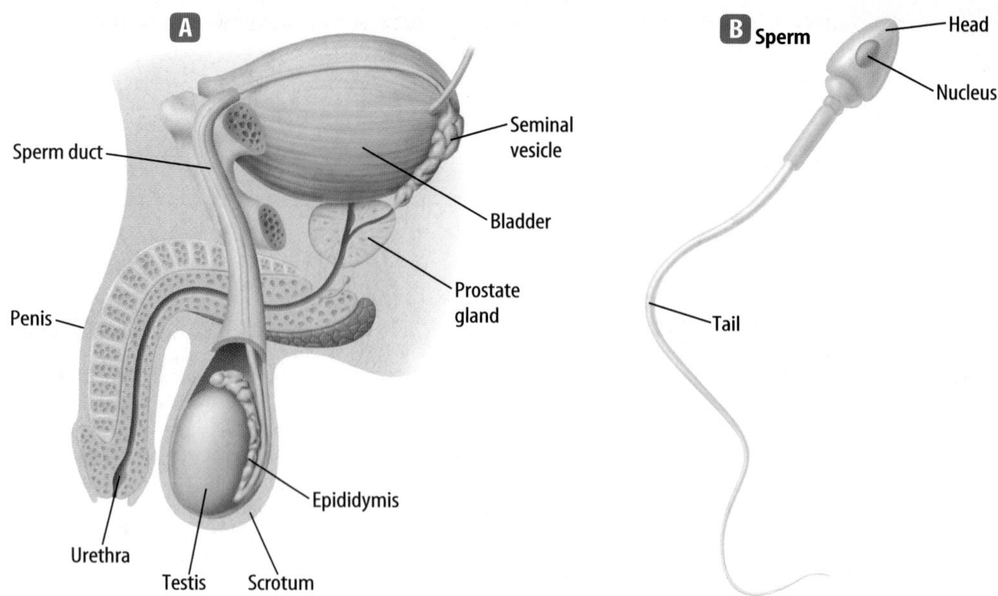

Figure 5
The structures of A the male reproductive system are shown with B a close-up of the sperm, which is produced in the testis. Sperm are produced throughout the life of a male.

The Male Reproductive System

The male reproductive system is made up of external and internal organs. The external organs of the male reproductive system are the penis and scrotum, shown in **Figure 5.** The scrotum contains two organs called testes (TES teez). As males mature sexually, the **testes** begin to produce testosterone, the male hormone, and **sperm,** which are male reproductive cells.

Sperm Each sperm cell has a head and tail. The head contains hereditary information, and the tail moves the sperm. Because the scrotum is located outside the body cavity, the testes, where sperm are produced, are kept at a lower temperature than the rest of the body. Sperm are produced in greater numbers at lower temperatures.

Many organs help in the production, transportation, and storage of sperm. After sperm are produced, they travel from the testes through sperm ducts that circle the bladder. Behind the bladder, a gland called the seminal vesicle provides sperm with a fluid. This fluid supplies the sperm with an energy source and helps them move. This mixture of sperm and fluid is called **semen** (SEE mun). Semen leaves the body through the urethra, which is the same tube that carries urine from the body. However, semen and urine never mix. A muscle at the back of the bladder contracts to prevent urine from entering the urethra as sperm leave the body.

Curriculum Connection

Language Arts Have students look up the words *sperm* and *ovary* and find out why the Latin roots are appropriate to their meanings. The Late Latin term *sperma* means seed; the Latin term *ovum* means egg. L1 LS **Linguistic**

Resource Manager

Chapter Resources Booklet
Enrichment, p. 29

The Female Reproductive System

Unlike male reproductive organs, most of the reproductive organs of the female are inside the body. The **ovaries**—the female sex organs—are located in the lower part of the body cavity. Each of the two ovaries is about the size and shape of an almond. **Figure 6** shows the different organs of the female reproductive system.

The Egg When a female is born, she already has all of the cells in her ovaries that eventually will develop into eggs—the female reproductive cells. At puberty, eggs start to develop in her ovaries because of specific sex hormones.

About once a month, an egg is released from an ovary in a hormone-controlled process called **ovulation** (ahv yuh LAY shun). The two ovaries release eggs on alternating months. One month, an egg is released from an ovary. The next month, the other ovary releases an egg and so on. After the egg is released, it enters the oviduct. Sometimes a sperm fertilizes the egg. If fertilization takes place, it usually happens in an oviduct. Short, hairlike structures called cilia help sweep the egg through the oviduct toward the uterus (YEWT uh rus).

Reading Check *When are eggs released by the ovaries?*

The **uterus** is a hollow, pear-shaped, muscular organ with thick walls in which a fertilized egg develops. The lower end of the uterus, the cervix, narrows and is connected to the outside of the body by a muscular tube called the **vagina** (vuh JI nuh). The vagina also is called the birth canal because during birth, a baby travels through this tube from the uterus to the outside of the mother's body.

Research Visit the Glencoe Science Web site at **science.glencoe.com** for information about ovarian cysts. Make a small pamphlet explaining what cysts are and how they can be treated.

Figure 6
The structures of the female reproductive system are shown from the A side of the body and from the B front. *Where in the female reproductive system do the eggs develop?*

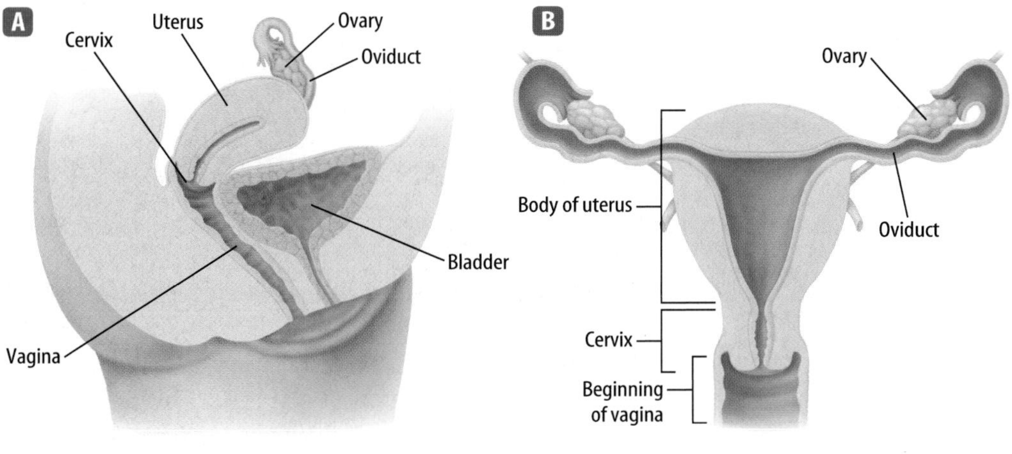

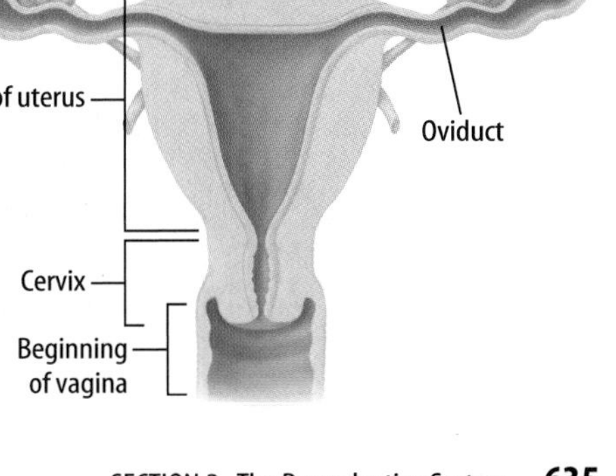

The Female Reproductive System

IDENTIFYING Misconceptions

Ovaries produce the hormone estrogen, which controls the development of female secondary sex characteristics. Many people think males do not produce this hormone. However, small amounts of estrogen are produced by adrenal and certain testicular cells in males.

Explore the Glencoe Science Web site at **science.glencoe.com** to find out more about topics in this section.

Reading Check

Answer about once a month

Visual Learning

Figure 6 Have students trace the movement of an egg after ovulation.

Caption Answer

Figure 6 in the ovaries

Teacher FYI

Rarely, an egg from the ovary does not enter the opening of the oviduct but enters the abdominal cavity and becomes fertilized. Abdominal pregnancies rarely are carried to term. If so, the baby is delivered by a C-section. Usually, the fetus does not survive and must be surgically removed.

Science Journal

Conception Have students investigate and write a short paragraph about the chances of conception. Fertilization can occur only during a two- to three-day time period, when the cervical mucus forms small channels that allow sperm to enter the uterus. Once in the mucus, the sperm can live up to 48 hours. A sexually-active 30-year-old female has a 20% chance each month of conceiving. L2 LS **Logical-Mathematical** P

The Menstrual Cycle

Use Science Words

Word Origin The Greek word for egg is *oion*. It is the root for many words related to eggs or the shape of an egg. Have students look up words with this root and explain their meanings. Possible answers: oocyte—an egg before maturation, oology—the study of bird eggs, oogenesis—the formation and maturation of an egg L2 LS **Linguistic**

Answer the monthly cycle of changes in the female reproductive system

Purpose Students observe and interpret data illustrating changes in hormone levels during the menstrual cycle. L2 LS **Logical-Mathematical**

Materials graph paper

Teaching Strategy Have students note the range of the data figures before constructing their graphs.

Analysis

1. day 13
2. ovulation

Assessment

Process Have students correlate the data in the MiniLAB chart with the events shown in **Figure 7**. Use **Performance Assessment in the Science Classroom**, p. 99.

Graphing Hormone Levels

Procedure

Make a line graph of this table.

Hormone Changes

Day	Level of Hormone
1	12
5	14
9	15
13	70
17	13
21	12
25	8

Analysis

1. On what day is the highest level of hormone present?
2. What event takes place around the time of the highest hormone level?

The Menstrual Cycle

How is the female body prepared for having a baby? The **menstrual cycle** is the monthly cycle of changes in the female reproductive system. Before and after an egg is released from an ovary, the uterus undergoes changes. The menstrual cycle of a human female averages 28 days. However, the cycle can vary in some individuals from 20 to 40 days. Changes include the maturing of an egg, the production of female sex hormones, and the preparation of the uterus to receive a fertilized egg.

Reading Check *What is the menstrual cycle?*

Endocrine Control Hormones control the entire menstrual cycle. The pituitary gland responds to chemical messages from the hypothalamus by releasing several hormones. These hormones start the development of eggs in the ovary. They also start the production of other hormones in the ovary, including estrogen (ES truh jun) and progesterone (proh JES tuh rohn). The interaction of all these hormones results in the physical processes of the menstrual cycle.

Phase One As shown in **Figure 7,** the first day of phase 1 starts when menstrual flow begins. Menstrual flow consists of blood and tissue cells released from the thickened lining of the uterus. This flow usually continues for four to six days and is called **menstruation** (men STRAY shun).

Figure 7
The three phases of the menstrual cycle make up the monthly changes in the female reproductive system.

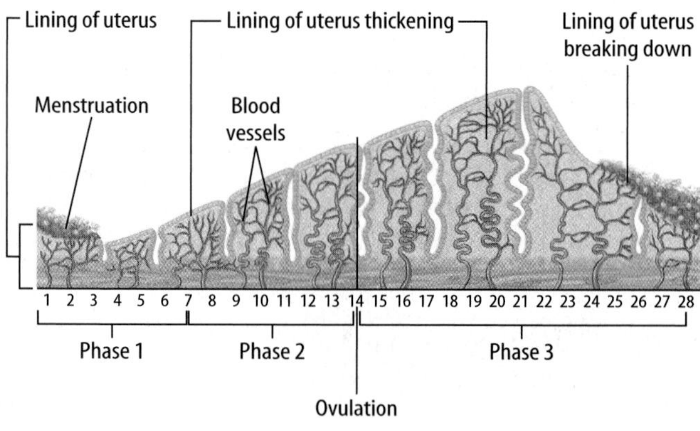

Resource Manager

Chapter Resources Booklet

Reinforcement, p. 26
MiniLAB, p. 3

Teacher FYI

The length of the menstrual period can vary. During the week before menstruation, a woman may experience premenstrual syndrome (PMS). Symptoms include depression, fatigue, headache, irritability, nervousness, and lack of concentration. Diet, exercise, aspirin, or other medicines are used to lessen the discomfort.

Phase Two Hormones cause the lining of the uterus to thicken in phase 2. Hormones also control the development of an egg in the ovary. Ovulation occurs about 14 days before menstruation begins. Once the egg is released, it must be fertilized within 24 h or it usually begins to break down. Because sperm can survive in a female's body for up to three days, fertilization can occur soon after ovulation.

Phase Three Hormones produced by the ovaries continue to cause an increase in the thickness of the uterine lining during phase 3. If a fertilized egg does arrive, the uterus is ready to support and nourish the developing embryo. If the egg is not fertilized, the lining of the uterus breaks down as the hormone levels decrease. Menstruation begins and the cycle repeats itself.

Menopause For most females the first menstrual period happens between ages nine years and 13 years and continues until 45 years of age to 60 years of age. Then, a gradual reduction of menstruation takes place as hormone production by the ovaries begins to shut down. Menopause occurs when both ovulation and menstrual periods end. It can take several years for the completion of menopause. As **Figure 8** indicates, menopause does not inhibit a woman's ability to enjoy an active life.

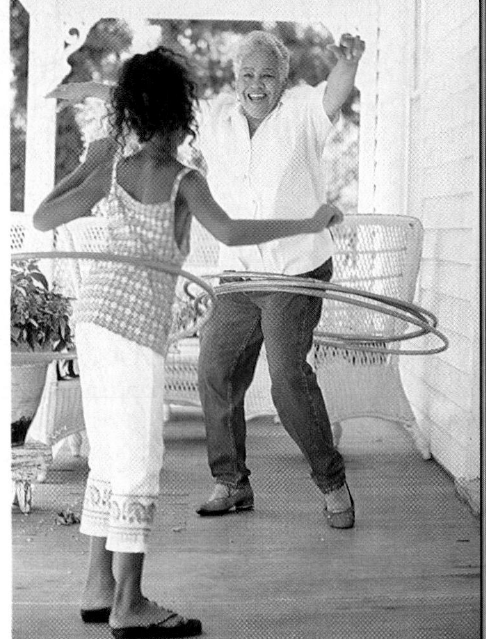

Figure 8
This older woman enjoys exercising with her granddaughter.

Section  Assessment

1. What is the major function of male and female reproductive systems in humans?
2. Explain the movement of sperm through the male reproductive system.
3. Compare and contrast the major organs and structures of the male and female reproductive systems.
4. Using diagrams and captions, sequence the stages of the menstrual cycle in a human female.
5. **Think Critically** Adolescent females often require additional amounts of iron in their diet. Explain.

Skill Builder Activities

6. **Concept Mapping** Make an events chain concept map to sequence the movement of an egg through the female reproductive system. **For more help, refer to the** Science Skill Handbook.
7. **Solving One-Step Equations** Usually, one egg is released each month during a female's reproductive years. If menstruation begins at 12 years of age and ends at 50 years of age, calculate the possible number of eggs her body can release during her reproductive years. **For more help, refer to the** Math Skill Handbook.

Quick Demo

With a sharp-tipped pencil, make a tiny dot on a piece of paper. This dot is about 0.5 mm in diameter. The human egg is about 5 times smaller in size. After demonstrating this, have students do it so they can get an idea of the size of a human egg.

3 Assess

Reteach

Have students diagram the pathway an egg follows as it moves from the ovary to the uterus. L1 **Visual-Spatial**

Challenge

Why might women going through menopause experience some of the same symptoms as women beginning their menstrual cycles? Both are experiencing changing levels of hormones.

Assessment

Performance Further assess students' abilities by having them sequence the thickness of the uterus during the menstrual cycle using **Figure 7.** Use **Performance Assessment in the Science Classroom,** p. 163.

Answers to Section Assessment

1. to allow for a series of events that can lead to the birth of a baby
2. testes→tubes that encircle the bladder→seminal vesical→urethra
3. Sex cell production: female—ovaries within the body; male—testes in scrotum outside of body; movement of sex cells: female—eggs released from ovary and swept into oviduct and uterus; male—sperm swim from testes through sperm duct and into the urethra.
4. Phase one: menstrual flow begins; phase two: wall of uterus thickens, ovulation occurs; phase three: wall of uterus continues to thicken; if a fertilized egg arrives, it burrows into the wall; if a fertilized egg does not arrive, the lining deteriorates.
5. The body may have a temporary iron deficiency resulting from loss of blood.
6. ovary→oviduct→uterus→vagina.
7. 50 years − 12 years = 38 years; 38 years × 1 egg/month × 12 month/year = 456 eggs released

Activity BENCH TESTED

Purpose Students examine and interpret diagrams of the menstrual cycle. L2 LS **Visual-Spatial**

Process Skills observing, interpreting data

Time Required 40 minutes

Teaching Strategy Stress to students the importance of examining labels and captions when interpreting diagrams.

Answers to Questions

1. 28 days
2. days 7 to 28
3. If fertilization does not occur, menstruation takes place, another egg is released, and the process is repeated.
4. about 14

Assessment

Content Have students use the diagrams to write a summary of the process of menstruation. The lining of the uterus is shed and then builds up. The egg matures, is released, and travels to the uterus. If it is fertilized, pregnancy results. If it is not, the cycle repeats. Use **Performance Assessment in the Science Classroom,** p. 159.

Activity

Interpreting Diagrams

Starting in adolescence, hormones cause the development of eggs in the ovary and changes in the uterus. These changes prepare the uterus to accept a fertilized egg that can attach itself in the wall of the uterus. What happens to an unfertilized egg?

What You'll Investigate

What changes occur to the uterus during a female's monthly menstrual cycle?

Materials

paper and pencil

Goals

- **Observe** the stages of the menstrual cycle in the diagram.
- **Relate** the process of ovulation to the cycle.

Procedure

1. The diagrams below show what is explained in this chapter on the menstrual cycle.
2. Use the information in this chapter and the diagrams below to complete a data table.
3. On approximately what day in a 28-day cycle is the egg released from the ovary?

Menstruation Cycle

Days	Condition of Uterus	What Happens
1–6	breakdown of lining	menstruation
7–12	lining begins to thicken	egg matures in ovary
13–14	lining is thicker	ovulation
15–18	lining thickens	egg moves to uterus

Conclude and Apply

1. How many days does the average menstrual cycle last?
2. On what days does the lining of the uterus build up?
3. **Infer** why this process is called a cycle.
4. **Calculate** how many days before menstruation ovulation usually occurs.

Compare your data table with those of other students in your class. **For more help, refer to the** Science Skill Handbook.

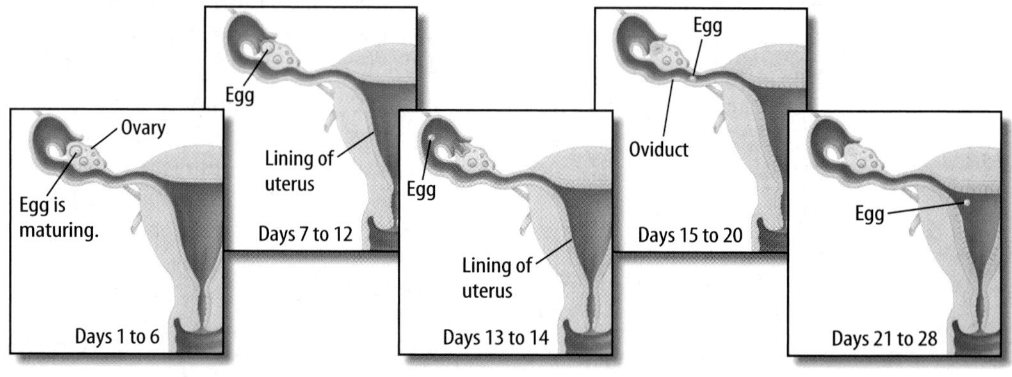

Communicating Your Data

Students should discuss why their interpretations of the diagram did or did not agree. They can cite references to support their arguments.

Resource Manager 

Chapter Resources Booklet

Activity Worksheet, pp. 5–6

SECTION 3

Human Life Stages

The Function of the Reproductive System

Before the invention of powerful microscopes, some people imagined an egg or a sperm to be a tiny person that grew inside a female. In the latter part of the 1700s, experiments using amphibians showed that contact between an egg and sperm is necessary for the development of life. With the development of the cell theory in the 1800s, scientists recognized that a human develops from an egg that has been fertilized by a sperm. The uniting of a sperm and an egg is known as fertilization. Fertilization, as shown in **Figure 9,** usually takes place in the oviduct.

Fertilization

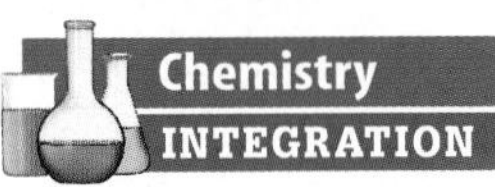

Although 200 millon to 300 million sperm can be deposited in the vagina, only several thousand reach an egg in the oviduct. As they enter the female, the sperm come into contact with chemical secretions in the vagina. It appears that this contact causes a change in the membrane of the sperm. The sperm then become capable of fertilizing the egg. The one sperm that makes successful contact with the egg releases an enzyme from the saclike structure on its head. Enzymes help speed up chemical reactions that have a direct effect on the protective membranes on the egg's surface. The structure of the egg's membrane is disrupted, and the sperm head can enter the egg.

Zygote Formation Once a sperm has entered the egg, changes in the electric charge of the egg's membrane prevent other sperm from entering the egg. At this point, the nucleus of the successful sperm joins with the nucleus of the egg. This joining of nuclei creates a fertilized cell called the zygote. It begins to undergo many cell divisions.

As You Read

***What* You'll Learn**

- **Describe** the fertilization of a human egg.
- **List** the major events in the development of an embryo and fetus.
- **Describe** the developmental stages of infancy, childhood, adolescence, and adulthood.

Vocabulary

pregnancy
embryo
amniotic sac
fetus
fetal stress

***Why* It's Important**

Fertilization begins the entire process of human growth and development.

Figure 9
After the sperm releases enzymes that disrupt the egg's membrane, it penetrates the egg.

Magnification: 425×

Section Assessment Planner

PORTFOLIO
Make a Model, p. 640

PERFORMANCE ASSESSMENT
Try at Home MiniLAB, p. 642
Skill Builder Activities, p. 647
See page 654 for more options.

CONTENT ASSESSMENT
Section, p. 647
Challenge, p. 647
Chapter, pp. 654–655

SECTION

Human Life Stages

1 Motivate

Bellringer Transparency

Display the Section Focus Transparency for Section 3. Use the accompanying Transparency Activity Master. L2 ELL

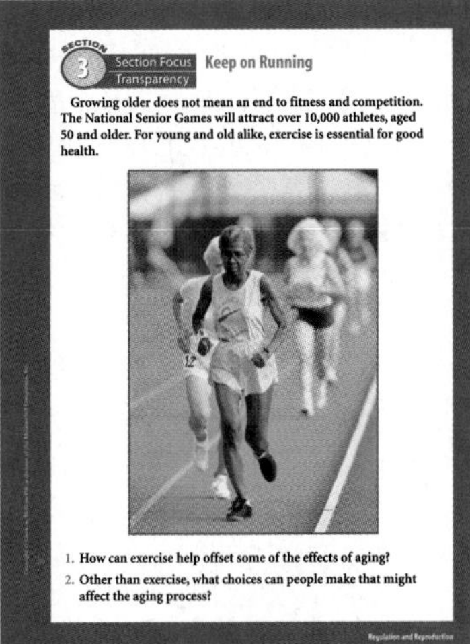

Tie to Prior Knowledge

Display photographs of people in different life stages, e.g., an infant, a small child, an adolescent, a young adult, and an older adult. Explain that these represent life stages and ask how many students can identify. Ask what stage they are in.

2 Teach

Fertilization

Use Science Words

Word Usage Have students compare the biological use of the word *fertilization* to the agronomic use of the word. Biologists use fertilization to refer to the process by which two sex cells join to produce offspring. Agronomists use fertilization to refer to the application of manure or chemicals to make soil more fertile. L2 IS **Linguistic**

Multiple Births

Visual Learning

Figure 10 **What are the differences between the development of fraternal and identical twins?** Fraternal twins develop from two separate eggs that have been fertilized by two different sperm. Identical twins result when one egg is fertilized by one sperm and the resulting zygote splits.

Development Before Birth

Extension

Have students research the unusual breeding processes of such animals as the sea horse and midwife toad. In both, the fertilized eggs are carried by the male until the young are ready to be born. L2

Make a Model

Have students use polystyrene foam balls to construct four- and eight-cell models to illustrate the earliest stages of zygote growth. L2 IS **Kinesthetic** P

Figure 10
The development of fraternal and identical twins is different.

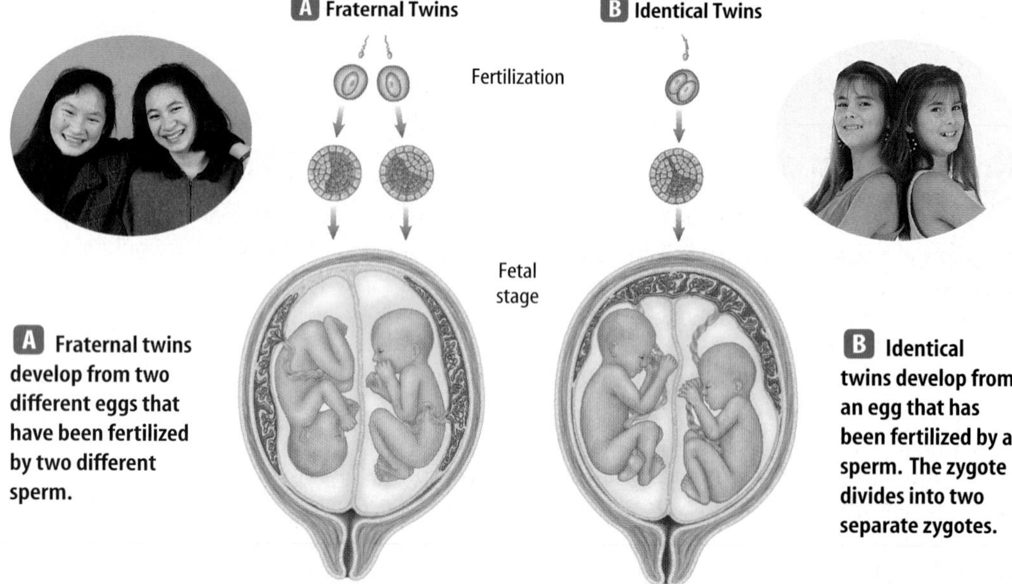

A Fraternal twins develop from two different eggs that have been fertilized by two different sperm.

B Identical twins develop from an egg that has been fertilized by a sperm. The zygote divides into two separate zygotes.

Multiple Births

Sometimes two eggs leave the ovary at the same time. If both eggs are fertilized and both develop, fraternal twins are born. Fraternal twins, as shown in **Figure 10A,** can be two girls, two boys, or a boy and a girl. Because fraternal twins come from two eggs, they only resemble each other.

Because identical twin zygotes develop from the same egg and sperm, as explained in **Figure 10B,** they have the same hereditary information. These identical zygotes develop into identical twins, which are either two girls or two boys. Multiple births also can occur when three or more eggs are produced at one time or when the zygote separates into three or more parts.

Development Before Birth

After fertilization, the zygote moves along the oviduct to the uterus. During this time, the zygote is dividing and forming into a ball of cells. After about seven days, the zygote attaches to the wall of the uterus, which has been thickening in preparation to receive a zygote, as shown in **Figure 11.** If attached to the wall of the uterus, the zygote will develop into a baby in about nine months. This period of development from fertilized egg to birth is known as **pregnancy.**

Curriculum Connection

Health Have students research ectopic pregnancies. **How frequently do they occur?** 1 in every 250–300 pregnancies **How does the female know there is a problem?** She experiences pain and bleeding. **What is the treatment?** Ectopic pregnancies often end in a miscarriage; if not miscarried, surgical removal of the fetus is sometimes necessary; abdominal pregnancies can be carried to term and the baby delivered by C-section. L2

Active Reading

Speculation About Effects/Prediction Journal This strategy allows students to examine events and speculate about their possible long-term effects. Have students divide their papers in half. On the left side record "What happened." On the right side, write "What might/should happen as a result of this." Have students write a Speculation About Effects/Prediction Journal about an aspect of human life stages.

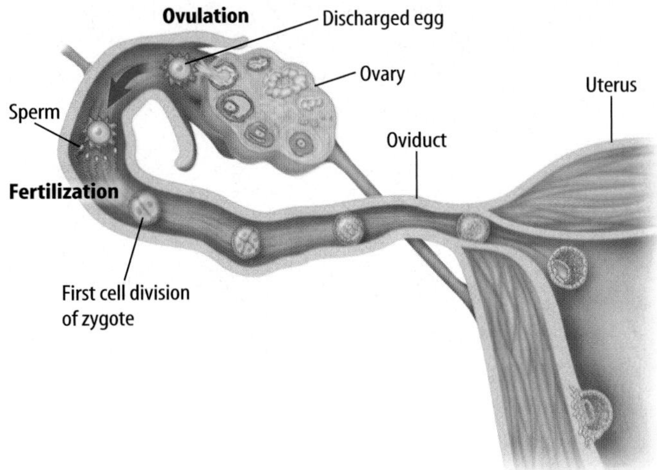

Figure 11
After a few days of rapid cell division, the zygote, now a ball of cells, reaches the lining of the uterus, where it attaches itself to the lining for development.

The Embryo After the zygote attaches to the wall of the uterus, it is known as an **embryo,** illustrated in **Figure 12.** It receives nutrients from fluids in the uterus until the placenta (pluh SENT uh) develops from tissues of the uterus and the embryo. An umbilical cord develops that connects the embryo to the placenta. In the placenta, materials diffuse between the mother's blood and the embryo's blood, but their bloods do not mix. Blood vessels in the umbilical cord carry nutrients and oxygen from the mother's blood through the placenta to the embryo. Other substances in the mother's blood can move into the embryo, including drugs, toxins, and disease organisms. Wastes from the embryo are carried in other blood vessels in the umbilical cord through the placenta to the mother's blood.

Reading Check *Why must a pregnant woman avoid alcohol, tobacco, and harmful drugs?*

Pregnancy in humans lasts about 38 to 39 weeks. During the third week, a thin membrane called the **amniotic** (am nee AH tihk) **sac** begins to form around the embryo. The amniotic sac is filled with a clear liquid called amniotic fluid, which acts as a cushion for the embryo and stores nutrients and wastes.

During the first two months of development, the embryo's major organs form and the heart structure begins to beat. At five weeks, the embryo has a head with eyes, nose, and mouth features. During the sixth and seventh weeks, fingers and toes develop.

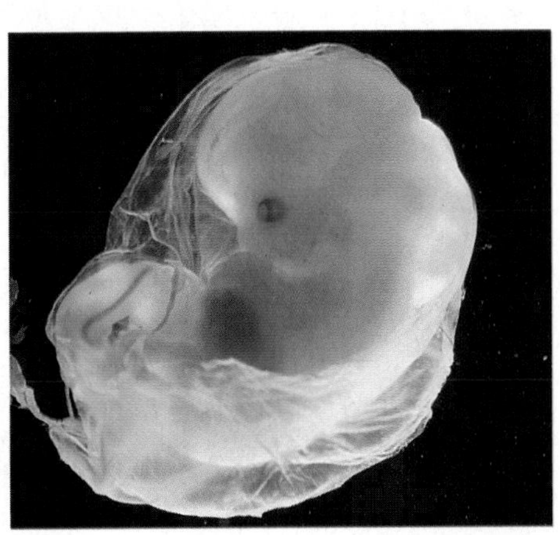

Figure 12
By two months, the developing embryo is about 2.5 cm long and is beginning to develop recognizable features.

Reading Check

Answer Any substances taken in by the mother and carried in her blood can pass to the embryo through the umbilical cord and cause the embryo damage.

Teacher FYI

In the interior of the blastocyst, a specialized mass of cells differentiates and forms the embryo. The outer layer of cells attach to the uterus and form the placenta.

IDENTIFYING Misconceptions

Students may think that fertilization and embryonic development are mysterious processes that are not understandable. Refer to page 626F for teaching strategies that address this misconception.

Resource Manager

Chapter Resources Booklet
- Transparency Activity, p. 44
- Directed Reading for Content Mastery, pp. 19, 20

Development Before Birth, continued

Purpose Students observe data on the growth rate of a fetus. L2 LS **Logical-Mathematical**

Materials graph paper

Teaching Strategy Have students note the range of the data before constructing their graphs.

Analysis
1. during the ninth month
2. about 5.7 cm per month

Performance To further assess students' understanding of fetus size, have them find and measure common household items that correspond to the various fetus sizes. Set up a display of these items. Use **PASC**, p. 97.

Activity

Have students prepare a series of actual-size cutouts of the fetus from three months to birth to have a visual demonstration of its size while developing. L2 ELL LS **Visual-Spatial**

Figure 13
A fetus at about 16 weeks is approximately 15 cm long and weighs 140 g.

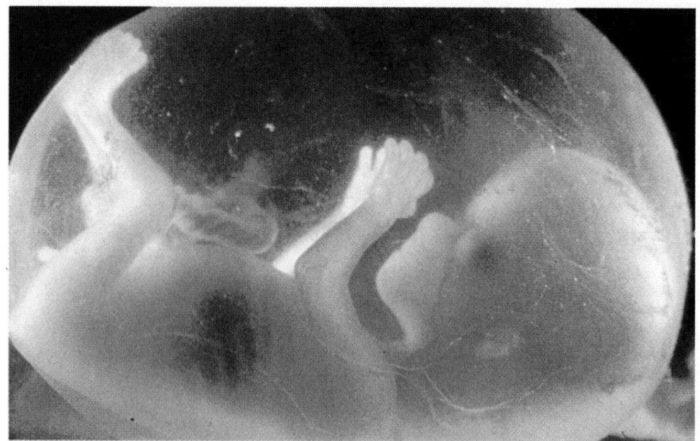

TRY AT HOME Mini LAB

Interpreting Fetal Development

Procedure
Make a bar graph of the following data.

Fetal Development

End of Month	Length (cm)
3	8
4	15
5	25
6	30
7	35
8	40
9	51

Analysis
1. During which month does the greatest increase in length occur?
2. On average, how many centimeters does the baby grow per month?

The Fetus After the first two months of pregnancy, the developing embryo is called a **fetus,** shown in **Figure 13.** At this time, body organs are present. Around the third month, the fetus is 8 cm to 9 cm long. The mother may feel the fetus move. The fetus can even suck its thumb. By the fourth month, an ultrasound test can determine the sex of the fetus. The fetus is 30 cm to 38 cm in length by the end of the seventh month of pregnancy. Fatty tissue builds up under the skin, and the fetus looks less wrinkled. By the ninth month, the fetus usually has shifted to a head-down position within the uterus, a position beneficial for delivery. The head usually is in contact with the opening of the uterus to the vagina. The fetus is about 50 cm in length and weighs from 2.5 kg to 3.5 kg.

The Birthing Process

The process of childbirth, as shown in **Figure 14,** begins with labor, the muscular contractions of the uterus. As the contractions increase in strength and number, the amniotic sac usually breaks and releases its fluid. Over a period of hours, the contractions cause the opening of the uterus to widen. More powerful and more frequent contractions push the baby out through the vagina into its new environment.

Delivery Often a mother is given assistance by a doctor during the delivery of the baby. As the baby emerges from the birth canal, a check is made to determine if the umbilical cord is wrapped around the baby's neck or any body part. When the head is free, any fluid in the baby's nose and mouth is removed by suction. After the head and shoulders appear, contractions force the baby out completely. Up to an hour after delivery, contractions occur that push the placenta out of the mother's body.

LAB DEMONSTRATION

Purpose to observe the proportions of girls and boys born in the population

Materials pennies

Preparation Collect small foam trays to deaden the sound and catch the tossed pennies.

Procedure Have students toss a penny one hundred times and record the order and number of times it lands on heads or tails.

Expected Outcome About a 50:50 ratio; there may be sequences of one side landing faceup repeatedly. Relate this to families of several boys or several girls.

Assessment

Infer the chances of a family with five girls or a family with five boys having a girl if there were a sixth child born. The chance of a girl being born into either family as the next child is 50:50.

Cesarean Section Sometimes a baby must be delivered before labor begins or before it is completed. At other times, a baby cannot be delivered through the birth canal because the mother's pelvis might be too small or the baby might be in the wrong birthing position. In cases like these, surgery called a cesarean (suh SEER ee uhn) section is performed. An incision is made through the mother's abdominal wall, then through the wall of the uterus. The baby is delivered through this opening.

Reading Check *What is a cesarean section?*

Research Visit the Glencoe Science Web site at **science.glencoe.com** for more information about cesarean section delivery. Communicate what you learn to your class.

After Birth When the baby is born, it is attached to the umbilical cord. The person assisting with the birth clamps the cord in two places and cuts it between the clamps. The baby does not feel any pain from this procedure. The baby might cry, which is the result of air being forced into its lungs. The scar that forms where the cord was attached is called the navel.

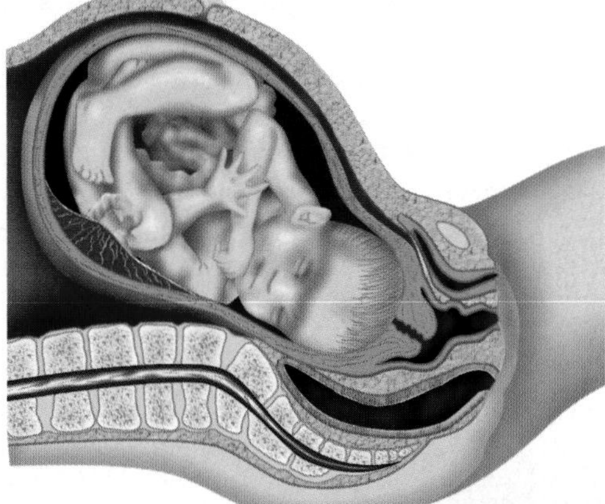

A **The fetus moves into the opening of the birth canal, and the uterus begins to widen.**

Figure 14
Childbirth begins with labor. The opening to the uterus widens, and the baby passes through.

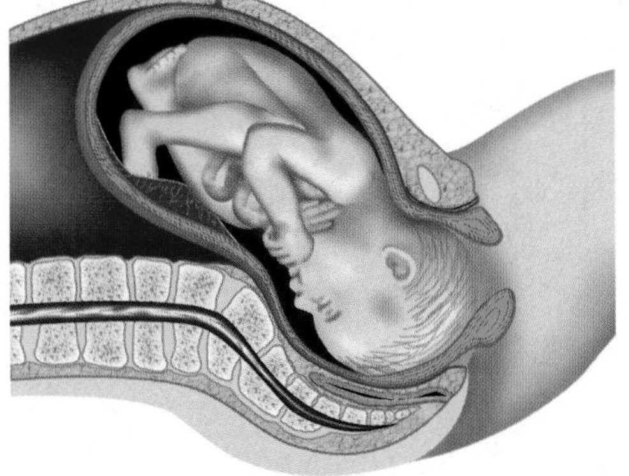

B **The base of the uterus is completely dilated.**

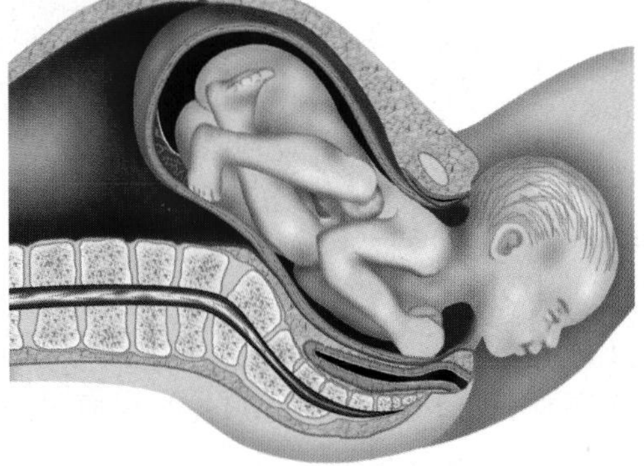

C **The fetus is pushed out through the birth canal.**

The Birthing Process

Internet Addresses

Explore the Glencoe Science Web site at **science.glencoe.com** to find out more about topics in this section.

Reading Check

Answer a surgical procedure in which an incision in the mother's abdomen and uterus is made and the baby removed

Use Science Words

Word Meaning Have students find out why the surgical removal of a baby from the mother is called a "cesarean section." It was named after Julius Caesar, who was supposedly delivered in this manner. L2 LS **Linguistic**

Visual Learning

Figure 14 Have students list the stages involved in childbirth. Fetus moves to opening of birth canal, base of uterus dilates, muscle contractions push fetus through the birth canal. L2 LS **Visual-Spatial**

Resource Manager

Chapter Resources Booklet
MiniLAB, p. 4

Home and Community Involvement, p. 43

Life Science Critical Thinking/Problem Solving, p. 19

Curriculum Connection

Health Arrange a visit to an X-ray lab to view X rays of bones of infants or young children and compare them with X rays of adults to show the differences in cartilage and bone. If a visit is impractical, arrange to view X-ray photos in class. L2 LS **Visual-Spatial**

Stages After Birth

Use Science Words

Neonatal means "newborn," and refers to a child younger than one month. *Neo-* is from the Greek and means "new" or "recent." Ask students to find words with this root and explain their meanings. Neophyte is a beginner, neolithic is the new stone age, neogenic refers to newly formed rocks and minerals. L2 LS **Linguistic**

Discussion

How might a newborn react to loud sounds or bright lights? Possible answer: he or she might be startled by loud sounds and bright lights.

Teacher FYI

Certain animals are ready to care for themselves immediately after birth. Precocial birds such as ducks are able to immediately move around and take care of themselves. Other self-sufficient animals are deer, hares, bison, and many types of insects, fish, amphibians, and reptiles. However, many of these animals, though mobile, still depend upon their mothers for milk.

Fun Fact

The major constituents of human milk are water, proteins, fats, and lactose, a carbohydrate. In addition, there are small amounts of vitamins and electrolytes.

Stages After Birth

Defined stages of development occur after birth, based on the major developments that take place during those specific years. Infancy lasts from birth to around 18 months of age. Childhood extends from the end of infancy to sexual maturity, or puberty. The years of adolescence vary, but they usually are considered to be the teen years. Adulthood covers the years of age from the early 20s until life ends, with older adulthood considered to be over 60. The age spans of these different stages are not set, and scientists differ in their opinions regarding them.

Infancy What type of environment must the infant adjust to after birth? The experiences the fetus goes through during birth cause **fetal stress.** The fetus has emerged from an environment that was dark, watery, a constant temperature, and nearly soundless. In addition, the fetus might have been forced through the constricted birth canal. However, in a short period of time, the infant's body becomes adapted to its new world.

The first four weeks after birth are known as the neonatal(nee oh NAY tul) period. The term *neonatal* means "newborn." During this time, the baby's body begins to function normally. Unlike the newborn of some other animals, human babies, shown in **Figure 15A,** depend on other humans for their survival. In contrast, many other animals, such as horses like those shown in **Figure 15B,** begin walking a few hours after they are born.

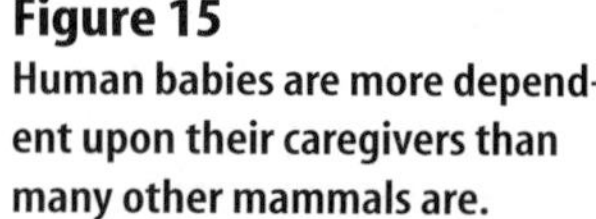

Figure 15
Human babies are more dependent upon their caregivers than many other mammals are.

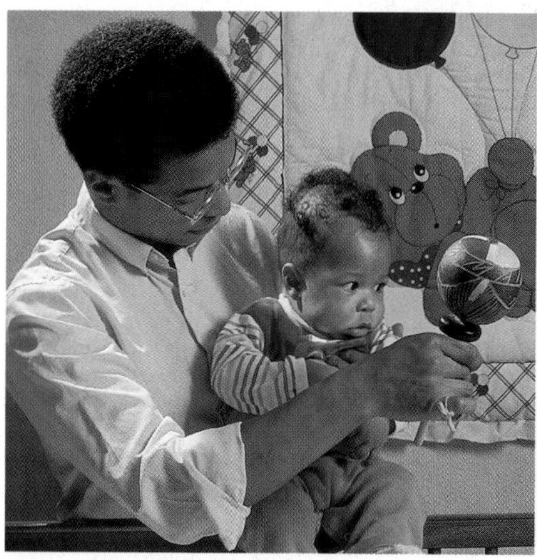

A Infants and toddlers are completely dependent upon caregivers for all their needs.

B Other young mammals are more self-sufficient. This colt is able to stand within an hour after birth.

Inclusion Strategies

Behaviorally Disordered Have students bring photos of themselves at various stages and describe favorite activities they remember from these stages. L1

Science Journal

Immunizations Babies and young children need certain vaccines to prevent disease. Have students find out what vaccinations are recommended between birth and age 6. Between birth and 6 yrs. old, the following vaccines are recommended: Polio; Hepatitis B; Diphtheria, Tetanus, Pertussis; Varicella or Chicken Pox; Haemophilus Influenza B; Measles, Mumps, Rubella.

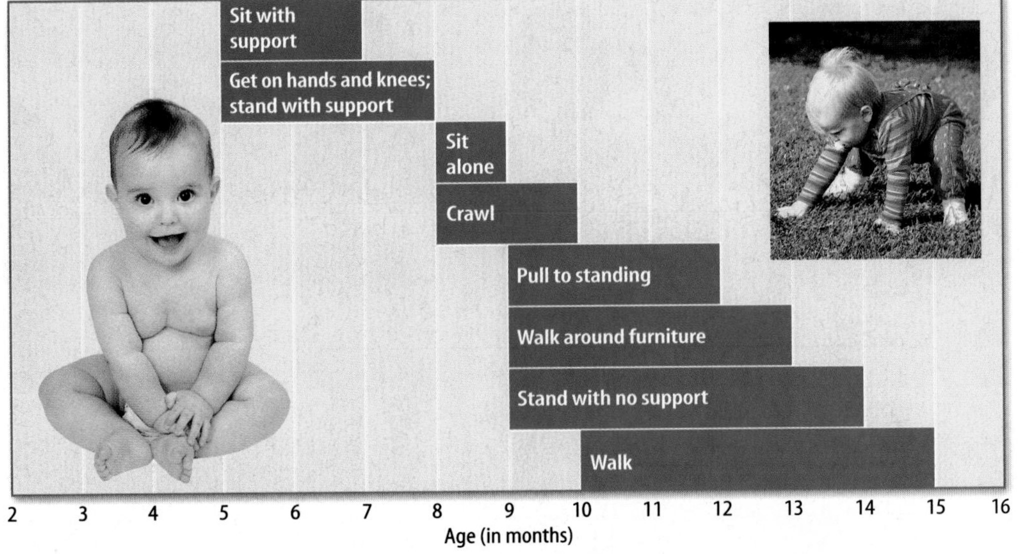

Figure 16
Infants show rapid development in their nervous and muscular systems through 18 months of age.

During these first 18 months, infants show increased physical coordination, mental development, and rapid growth. Many infants will triple their weight in the first year. **Figure 16** shows the extremely rapid development of the nervous and muscular systems during this stage, which enables infants to start interacting with the world around them.

Childhood After infancy is childhood, which lasts until about puberty, or sexual maturity. Sexual maturity occurs around 12 years of age. Overall, growth during early childhood is rather rapid, although the physical growth rate for height and weight is not as rapid as it is in infancy. Between two and three years of age, the child learns to control his or her bladder and bowels. At age two to three, most children can speak in simple sentences. Around age four, the child is able to get dressed and undressed with some help. By age five, many children can read a limited number of words. By age six, children usually have lost their chubby baby appearance, as seen in **Figure 17.** However, muscular coordination and mental abilities continue to develop. Throughout this stage, children develop their abilities to speak, read, write, and reason. These ages of development are only guidelines because each child develops at a different rate.

Figure 17
Children grow and develop at different rates, like these kindergartners.

Activity

Have students conduct a survey of parents with young children. Have them ask questions such as: What changes did you notice at different ages? What stage seemed to have the most changes? L2 LS **Interpersonal**

Make a Model

Have students make a timeline of the stages from infancy to adulthood using long pieces of paper. Identify various milestones such as the start of walking, puberty, and menopause. L2 LS **Kinesthetic**

Discussion

Have students think about how they learned to talk. **How might hearing problems in young children cause speech problems?** Children learn speech by listening to others. If they have a hearing problem, they cannot properly hear the sounds of speech. They are unable to reproduce sounds that other people can understand.

Resource Manager

Chapter Resources Booklet
Enrichment, p. 30
Reading and Writing Skill Activities, p. 39

Inclusion Strategies

Gifted Have students observe a lower elementary or preschool classroom. What adaptations would they have to make to teach this chapter to the class they observed? Have them make a sample presentation to your class, pretending they are preschoolers. Have a class discussion on how they modified the chapter and why. L3

Stages After Birth, continued

Caption Answer

Figure 18 A baby's head is almost one-fourth its total body length. This reduces as the child grows into an adult. In adulthood, the head is approximately one-eighth of the body's length.

Teacher FYI

The onset of puberty varies greatly in the growth patterns of adolescents. The variations are caused by a number of factors. Heredity is a key factor in determining the development of the body. Other factors are diet and illnesses. Poor diet and sickness can delay the onset of puberty. Often adolescents are disturbed that they are developing earlier or later than their peers. By age 17–18, the differences have usually disappeared.

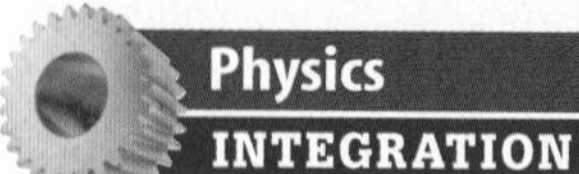

Physics INTEGRATION

Since the body may be off balance, it is difficult to be coordinated and to do some of the maneuvers required in sports activities.

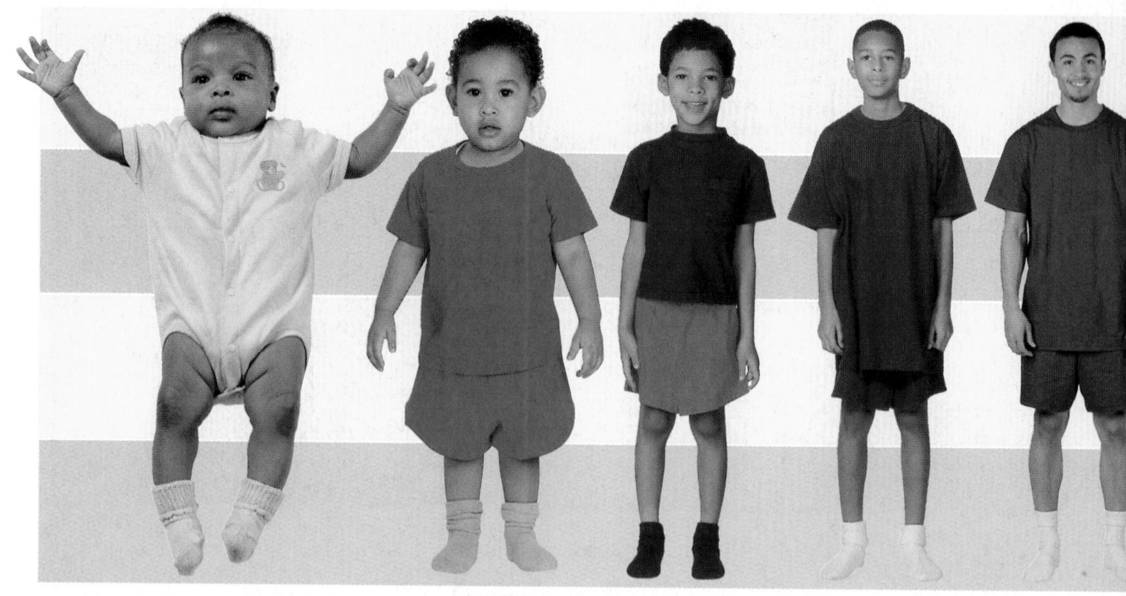

Figure 18
The proportions of body parts change over time as the body develops. *Describe how the head changes proportion.*

Adolescence Adolescence usually begins around age 12 or 13. A part of adolescence is puberty—the time of development when a person becomes physically able to reproduce. For girls, puberty occurs between ages nine and 13. For boys, puberty occurs between ages 13 and 16. During puberty, hormones produced by the pituitary gland cause changes in the body. These hormones produce reproductive cells and sex hormones. Secondary sex characteristics also develop. In females, the breasts develop, pubic and underarm hair appears, and fatty tissue is added to the buttocks and thighs. In males, the hormones cause a deepened voice, an increase in muscle size, and the growth of facial, pubic, and underarm hair.

Adolescence usually is when the final growth spurt occurs. Because the time when hormones begin working varies among individuals and between males and females, growth rates differ. Girls often begin their final growth phase at about age 11 and end around age 16. Boys usually start their growth spurt at age 13 and end around 18 years of age.

Physics INTEGRATION

During adolescence, the body parts do not all grow at the same rate. The legs grow longer before the upper body lengthens. This changes the body's center of gravity, the point at which the body maintains its balance. This is one cause of teenager clumsiness. In your Science Journal, write a paragraph about how this might affect playing sports.

Adulthood The final stage of development, adulthood, begins with the end of adolescence and continues through old age. This is when the growth of the muscular and skeletal system stops. **Figure 18** shows how body proportions change as you age.

People from age 45 to age 60 are sometimes considered middle-aged adults. During these years, physical strength begins to decline. Blood circulation and respiration become less efficient. Bones become more brittle, and the skin becomes wrinkled.

Cultural Diversity

Rites of Passage Have students research and write a report on ceremonies in other societies, past or present, that mark the transition of young people to adults. These ceremonies are often referred to as "rites of passage." L2 LS **Linguistic**

Resource Manager

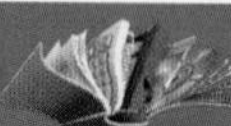

Chapter Resources Booklet
Reinforcement, p. 27
Lab Activity, pp. 13–14

Older Adulthood People over the age of 60 may experience an overall decline in their physical body systems. The cells that make up these systems no longer function as well as they did at a younger age. Connective tissues lose their elasticity, causing muscles and joints to be less flexible. Bones become thinner and more brittle. Hearing and vision are less sensitive. The lungs and heart work less efficiently. However, exercise and eating well over a lifetime can help extend the health of one's body systems. Many healthy older adults enjoy full lives and embrace challenges, as shown in **Figure 19.**

Figure 19
Astronaut and Senator John Glenn traveled into space twice. In 1962, at age 40, he was the first U.S. citizen to orbit Earth. He was part of the space shuttle crew in 1998 at age 77. Senator Glenn has helped change people's views of what many older adults are capable of doing.

 **Reading Check** *What physical changes occur during late adulthood?*

Human Life Spans Seventy-five years is the average life span—from birth to death—of humans, although an increasing number of people live much longer. However, body systems break down with age, resulting in eventual death. Death can occur earlier than old age for many reasons, including diseases, accidents, and bad health choices.

Section 3 Assessment

1. What happens when an egg is fertilized in a female?
2. What happens to an embryo during the first two months of pregnancy?
3. Describe the major events that occur during childbirth.
4. What stage of development are you in? What physical changes have occurred or will occur during this stage of human development?
5. **Think Critically** Why is it hard to compare the growth and development of different adolescents?

Skill Builder Activities

6. **Making Models** Use references to construct a time line that highlights the major events in the various stages of development from the embryo to adulthood. **For more help, refer to the** Science Skill Handbook.
7. **Using an Electronic Spreadsheet** Using your text and other resources, make a spreadsheet for the stages of human development from a zygote to a fetus. Title one column *Zygote,* another *Embryo,* and a third *Fetus.* Complete the spreadsheet. **For more help, refer to the** Technology Skill Handbook.

Reading Check

Answer Connective tissue loses elasticity, bones become brittle, hearing and vision are less sensitive, and the lungs and heart work less efficiently.

3 Assess

Reteach

Divide the class into groups and have each group write descriptions of a particular life stage—one per index card. Mix up the cards, divide the class into teams, and read the descriptions. Students take turns stating the life stage. The team with the greatest number of correct answers wins. L2 ELL
LS **Visual-Spatial**

Challenge

What features of a pregnant woman protect the developing child? The woman's body has a thickened uterine wall; the placenta develops to transport food and wastes through the umbilical cord; amniotic fluid cushions the embryo.

Assessment

Performance To further assess students' understanding of neonatal development, have them construct a time line to correspond with the stages of neonatal development. Use **Performance Assessment in the Science Classroom,** p. 163.

Answers to Section Assessment

1. Sperm and egg nuclei combine, producing a zygote; egg membrane changes; cell division begins
2. Amniotic sac and placenta develop, major organs form, and the heart structure begins to beat.
3. Events include contraction, rupture of the amniotic sac, and widening of the uterus's opening to allow the baby to pass through the cervix and the birth canal.
4. Adolescence; sex hormones are produced, secondary sex characteristics develop, last growth spurt occurs.
5. Each person has his or her own rate of development.
6. Time line should reflect all information presented in this section.
7. Zygote undergoes cell divisions, forms a ball of cells, and attaches to the uterine wall; see information in "Development Before Birth".

Activity

BENCH TESTED

What You'll Investigate

Purpose

Students measure the body proportions of adolescents and infer how body proportions differ between males and females. L2

LS **Logical-Mathematical**

Process Skills

calculating, comparing, graphing, inferring

Time Required

40 minutes

Materials

Students may use metersticks instead of a tape measure. Masking tape can be used to mark heights on the wall instead of pencil marks.

Procedure

Teaching Strategy

- Encourage students to measure each dimension twice to improve accuracy.

Activity

Changing Body Proportions

The ancient Greeks believed the perfect body was completely balanced. Arms and legs should not be too long or short. A person's head should not be too large or small. The extra large muscles of a body builder would have been ugly to the Greeks. How do you think they viewed the bodies of infants and children? Infants and young children have much different body proportions than adults, and teenagers often go through growth spurts that quickly change their body proportions. How do body proportions differ among people?

What You'll Investigate

How do the body proportions differ between adolescent males and females?

Materials

tape measure
erasable pencil
graph paper

Goals

- **Measure** specific body proportions of adolescents.
- **Infer** how body proportions differ between adolescent males and females.

648

Resource Manager

Chapter Resources Booklet
Activity Worksheet, pp. 7–8

Lab Management and Safety, p. 70

Procedure

1. Copy the data table in your Science Journal and record the gender of each person that you measure.
2. Measure each person's head circumference by starting in the middle of the forehead and wrapping the tape measure around the head. Record these measurements.
3. Measure each person's arm length from the top of the shoulder to the tip of the middle finger while the arm is held straight out to the side of the body. Record these measurements.
4. Ask each person to remove his or her shoes and stand next to a wall. Mark their height with an erasable pencil and measure their height from the floor to the mark. Record these measurements in the data table.
5. **Combine** your data with that of your classmates. Find the averages of head circumference, arm length, and height. Then, find these averages for males and females.
6. Make a bar graph of your calculations in step 5. Plot the measurements on the y-axis and plot all of the averages along the x-axis.
7. **Calculate** the proportion of average head circumference to average height for everyone in your class by dividing the average head circumference by the average height. Repeat this calculation for males and females.
8. **Calculate** the proportion of average arm length to average height for everyone in your class by dividing the average arm length by the average height. Repeat this calculation for males and females.

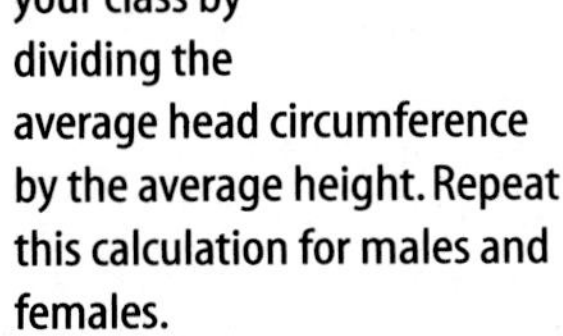

Age and Body Measurements

Gender of Person	Head Circumference (cm)	Arm Length (cm)	Height (cm)

Conclude and Apply

1. Do adolescent males or females have larger head circumferences or longer arms? Which group has the larger proportion of head circumference or arm length to height?
2. Does this activity support the information in this chapter about the differences between growth rates of adolescent males and females? Explain.

Communicating Your Data

On poster board, **construct** data tables showing your results and those of your classmates. Discuss with your classmates why these results might be different.

Communicating Your Data

Encourage students to use a spreadsheet program to construct their data tables.

Expected Outcome

Because adolescent girls generally undergo growth sooner than adolescent males, their body parts will be in different proportions than those of adolescent males.

Conclude and Apply

1. Answers will vary depending on students' measurements.
2. Answers will vary but data should support chapter information about differences in growth rates between adolescent males and females.

Error Analysis

Form students into groups of four or five and have each student compare his or her data with that of other group members. If data disagree, have each group list reasons for discrepancies.

Assessment

Portfolio Ask students to draw what they envision as the Greek ideal of a perfectly proportioned body. Use **Performance Assessment in the Science Classroom,** p. 127.

Science Stats

Content Background

Mammals can be divided into three groups based on their development. Humans are placentals; a mammal whose young develop in the female parent's uterus. The offspring of placental mammals are usually comparatively well developed. Marsupials, like the kangaroo shown in this feature, give birth to less-developed young, which usually develop in a pouch, or attached to the mother's body. Throughout the world, there are more than 250 species of marsupials. Monotremes are mammals that lay eggs. All monotremes are found in Australia, New Guinea and Tasmania. All female mammals produce milk to feed their infants. Female marsupials and placentals have mammary glands with nipples for infants to suck on, but monotreme mammary glands simply release milk through pores in the mother's skin.

Discussion

Why might a baby kangaroo need to spend such a long period of time in its mother's pouch after it is born? Possible answer: Kangaroo babies are not developed enough to survive outside of the pouch when they are born, they need a period of protected growth and development.

Activity

Assign small groups of students an animal to research. Have the students find the age at which the young become independent from their parents. Have the students compare their findings on a bar graph.

Internet Addresses

Explore the Glencoe Science Web site at **science.glencoe.com** to find out more about topics in this feature.

Science Stats

Facts About Infants

Did you know...

...Humans and chimpanzees share about 99 percent of their genes. Although humans look different than chimps, reproduction is similar and gestation is the same—about nine months. Youngsters of both species lose their baby teeth at about six years of age.

Female kangaroo and joey

...Unlike humans and most other mammals, the newborn kangaroo develops in its mother's pouch longer than in her uterus. About one month after fertilization, the kangaroo is born and moves from its mother's uterus into her pouch. It spends seven to ten months in the pouch, drinking milk and growing.

...The blue whale calf is the biggest newborn in the world. At birth, it measures about 7 m and weighs about 2,700 kg. The average human newborn measures about 50 cm and weighs about 3.3 kg. In its first year of life, a blue whale calf gains about 90 kg every day. Compare that to an average human baby who gains about 10 kg during his or her entire first year.

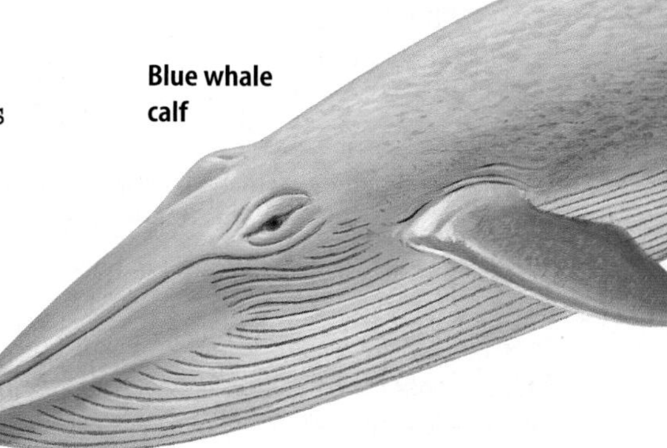

Blue whale calf

Connecting To Math

Mammal Facts

Mammal	Average Gestation	Average Birth Weight	Average Adult Weight	Average Life Span (years)
African Elephant	22 months	136 kg	4,989.5 kg	35
Blue Whale	12 months	1,800 kg	135,000 kg	60
Human	**9 months**	**3.3 kg**	**59–76 kg**	**76***
Brown Bear	7 months	0.23–0.5 kg	350 kg	22.5
Cat	2 months	99 g	2.7–7 kg	13.5
Kangaroo	1 month	0.75–1.0 g	45 kg	5
Golden Hamster	2.5 weeks	0.3 g	112 g	2

* In the United States

1-day-old to 7-day-old mice

...Of about 4,000 species of mammals, only three lay eggs. These species are the platypus, the short-beaked echidna (ih KIHD nuh), and the long-beaked echidna. No other mammals lay eggs.

Echidna

... House mice can have up to ten litters per year, each one containing up to seven mice. Mice have this many offspring because so few of them survive.

Do the Math

1. Look at the data table above. Make a generalization about a mammal's birth weight and the length of its gestation period.
2. Make a bar graph that compares the length of the human gestation period to that of two other mammals.
3. Assume that a female of each mammal listed in the table above is pregnant once during her life. Which mammal is pregnant for the greatest proportion of her life?

Go Further

Do research to find out which species of vertebrate animals has the longest life span and which has the shortest. Present your findings in a table that also shows the life span of humans.

Connecting To Math

Do the Math

Teaching Strategies

- Remind the students that they need to convert all of the numbers to the same units before they can be compared.
- Discuss the appropriate labels for both axis of the bar graph, and remind students that the graph needs a descriptive title.
- Review proportions, and remind students that the numbers being compared in a proportion must have the same units. In this case the gestation period must be converted to years, or the life span to months or weeks.

Answers

1. The larger the mammal is at birth, the longer its gestation period is—the smaller the mammal is, the shorter its gestation period is.
2. Check student's graphs.
3. elephant, about 5%

Go Further

Students can use reference material to explore the life spans of different animals. Explain that the life span of humans varies greatly between countries, so the statistic that different students use for this number may vary.

Visual Learning

Mammal Facts Ask students to compare the birth weights of humans and whales as a percent of adult weight. They will find that whales are born at about 1.5% of the weight they will be as adults, while humans are born at 4.5% to 5.5 % of their adult weight. Proportionately, newborn humans are larger than newborn whales. Have students determine which animals listed in the chart are born at the smallest (brown bear) and the largest (human) proportion of their adult weight.

Chapter 22 Study Guide

Reviewing Main Ideas

Preview

Students can answer the questions in their Science Journals. Discuss the answers as you go through the chapter. LS **Linguistic**

Review

Students can write their answers, then compare them with those of other students. LS **Interpersonal**

Reteach

Students can look at the illustrations and describe details that support the main ideas of the chapter. LS **Visual-Spatial**

Answers to Chapter Review

Section 1

2. The gland releases a hormone into the bloodstream, which carries it to its target tissue.

Section 2

3. The sphere-shaped egg allows for a large volume-to-surface-area ratio. Sperm have heads that contain hereditary information and tails that enable them to swim.

Section 3

2. Labor is physical or mental exertion and corresponds to the activities of childbirth.

Chapter 22 Study Guide

Reviewing Main Ideas

Section 1 The Endocrine System

1. Endocrine glands secrete hormones directly into the bloodstream.
2. Hormones affect specific tissues throughout the body. *How can a gland near your head control chemical activities in other parts of your body?*

3. A change in the body causes an endocrine gland to function. When homeostasis is reached, the endocrine gland receives a signal to slow or stop its production.

Section 2 The Reproductive System

1. The reproductive system allows new organisms to be formed.
2. The testes produce sperm that leave the male through the penis.
3. The female ovary produces an egg. If fertilized, it becomes a zygote and later develops into a fetus within the uterus. *How are the structures of the egg and sperm suited for their functions?*

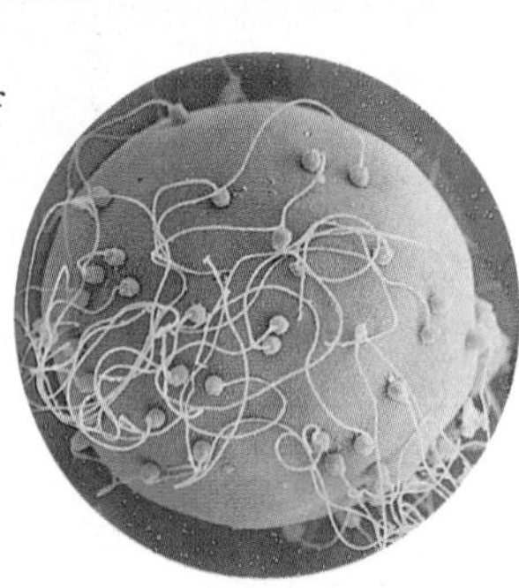

4. When an egg is not fertilized, the built-up lining of the uterus is shed in a process called menstruation. This process begins 14 days after ovulation.

Section 3 Human Life Stages

1. After fertilization, the zygote undergoes developmental changes to become an embryo, then a fetus. Twins occur when two eggs are fertilized or when a zygote divides after fertilization.
2. Birth begins with labor—muscular contractions of the uterus. The amniotic sac breaks. Then, usually after several hours, the contractions force the baby out of the mother's body. *Why is the first stage in the birthing process called labor?*

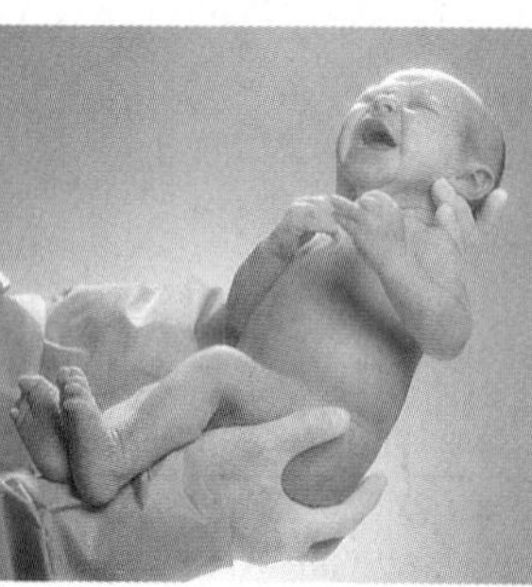

3. Infancy is the stage of development from birth to 18 months of age. It is a period of rapid growth of mental and physical skills. Childhood, which lasts until age 12, is marked by development of muscular coordination and mental abilities.
4. Adolescence is the stage of development when a person becomes physically able to reproduce. The final stage of development is adulthood. Physical development is complete and body systems become less efficient. Death occurs at the end of life.

FOLDABLES Reading & Study Skills — After You Read

Using the information on your Foldable as an outline, explain each stage of human life.

FOLDABLES Reading & Study Skills — After You Read

After students have read the chapter and completed the Foldable described in Before You Read, have them do the activity on the student page.

Dinah Zike

Visualizing Main Ideas

Complete the following table on life stages.

Human Development		
Stages of Life	**Age Range**	**Physical Development**
Infant	birth–18 months	sits, stands, words spoken
Childhood	18 months–12 years	walks, speaks, writes, reads
Adolescent	12–18 years	physically able to reproduce, sexual characteristics develop, final growth spurt
Adulthood	18 years–death	end of muscular and skeletal growth

Vocabulary Review

Vocabulary Words

a. amniotic sac
b. embryo
c. fetal stress
d. fetus
e. hormone
f. menstrual cycle
g. menstruation
h. ovary
i. ovulation
j. pregnancy
k. semen
l. sperm
m. testes
n. uterus
o. vagina

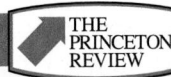

THE PRINCETON REVIEW Study Tip

Use lists to help you memorize facts. For example, when trying to memorize the stages of human development, write them down several times on a piece of paper until you know them.

Using Vocabulary

Replace the underlined words with the correct vocabulary word(s).

1. Testes is a mixture of sperm and fluid.
2. The time of the development until the birth of a baby is known as menstruation.
3. During the first two months of pregnancy, the unborn child is known as fetal stress.
4. The vagina is a hollow, pear-shaped muscular organ.
5. The ovary is the membrane that protects the unborn child.
6. After two months of pregnancy, the unborn child is known as a(n) embryo.
7. The testes is the organ that produces eggs.

Chapter 22 Study Guide

Visualizing Main Ideas

See student page.

Vocabulary Review

Using Vocabulary

1. Semen
2. pregnancy
3. an embryo
4. uterus
5. amniotic sac
6. fetus
7. ovary

IDENTIFYING Misconceptions

Assess

Use the assessment as follow-up to page 626F after students have completed the chapter.

Activity Ask students to describe the events that take place during fertilization and what the new fused cell is called. Give students a handout or write on the board the stages of development (0 to a few days, a few days to 2 weeks, and 2 weeks to 8 weeks). Have students fill in the stages with diagrams and/or verbal descriptions of the stages of development.

Expected Outcome Students should know that during fertilization the sperm and egg cells fuse, their nuclei fuse, and the fused cell is called a zygote. No other sperm can fuse with the newly formed zygote. They should draw or describe the "soap bubble" stage, the three-part state, and the differentiation stage.

Chapter 22 Assessment

Checking Concepts

1. C
2. D
3. C
4. B
5. A
6. A
7. C
8. B
9. B
10. B

Thinking Critically

11. Adrenal hormones cause your heart to beat faster, increasing blood flow to major organs and giving a sense of increased strength.
12. Both are paired organs that produce sex cells.
13. ovulation—ovary; fertilization—oviduct; implantation—uterus
14. According to the level of hormone in the blood, the target tissue sends a chemical message back to the gland to stop or start hormone secretion. Likewise, the thermostat in a house signals the heating or air conditioning unit to start or stop according to the temperature in the house. Both are negative-feedback systems.
15. Either; zygote splits into four parts—identical quadruplets; four eggs fertilized by four different sperm—fraternal quadruplets.

Chapter 22 Assessment

Checking Concepts

Choose the word or phrase that best answers the question.

1. What are the chemicals produced by the endocrine system?
   A) enzymes **C)** hormones
   B) target tissues **D)** saliva
2. Which gland produces melatonin?
   A) adrenal **C)** pancreas
   B) thyroid **D)** pineal
3. Where does the embryo develop?
   A) oviduct **C)** uterus
   B) ovary **D)** vagina
4. What is the monthly process that releases an egg called?
   A) fertilization **C)** menstruation
   B) ovulation **D)** puberty
5. What is the union of an egg and a sperm?
   A) fertilization **C)** menstruation
   B) ovulation **D)** puberty
6. Where is the egg usually fertilized?
   A) oviduct **C)** vagina
   B) uterus **D)** ovary
7. When does puberty occur?
   A) childhood **C)** adolescence
   B) adulthood **D)** infancy
8. Which sex characteristics are common to males and females?
   A) breasts **C)** increased fat
   B) pubic hair **D)** increased muscles
9. During which period does growth stop?
   A) childhood **C)** adolescence
   B) adulthood **D)** infancy
10. During what stage of development does the amniotic sac form?
    A) zygote **C)** fetus
    B) embryo **D)** newborn

Thinking Critically

11. List the effects that adrenal gland hormones can have on your body as you prepare to run a race.
12. Explain the similar functions of the ovaries and testes.
13. Identify the structure in the following diagram in which each process occurs: ovulation, fertilization, and implantation.

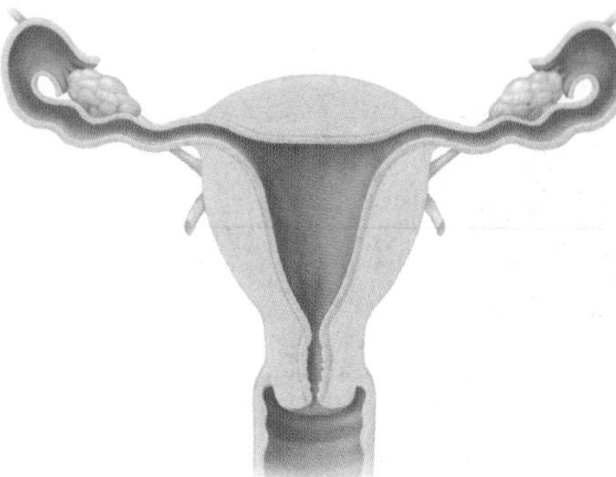

14. How is your endocrine system like the thermostat in your house?
15. Are quadruplets always identical or always fraternal, or can they be either? Explain.

Developing Skills

16. **Predicting** During the ninth month of pregnancy, the fetus develops a white, greasy coating. Predict what the function of this coating might be.
17. **Forming Hypotheses** Make a hypothesis about the effect of raising identical twins apart from each other.
18. **Classifying** Classify each of the following structures as female or male and internal or external: ovary, penis, scrotum, testes, uterus, and vagina.

Chapter Assessment Planner

Portfolio Encourage students to place in their portfolios one or two items of what they consider to be their best work. Examples include:

- Visual Learning, p. 631
- Science Journal, p. 635
- Make a Model, p. 640

Performance Additional performance assessments, Performance Task Assessment Lists, and rubrics for evaluating these activities can be found in Glencoe's **Performance Assessment in the Science Classroom.**

19. Concept Mapping Complete the following concept map of egg release and implantation using the appropriate scientific words.

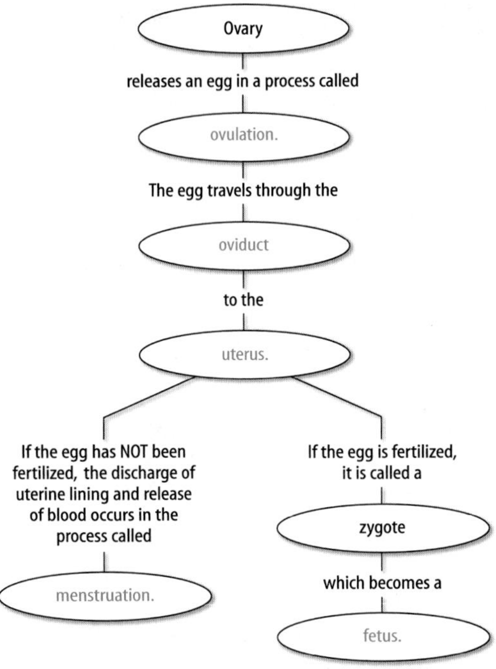
Ovary
releases an egg in a process called
ovulation.
The egg travels through the
oviduct
to the
uterus.
If the egg has NOT been fertilized, the discharge of uterine lining and release of blood occurs in the process called
menstruation.
If the egg is fertilized, it is called a
zygote
which becomes a
fetus.

Performance Assessment

20. Letter Find newspaper or magazine articles on the effects of smoking on the health of the developing embryo and newborn. Write a letter to the editor about why a mother's smoking is damaging her unborn baby's health.

Technology

Go to the Glencoe Science Web site at **science.glencoe.com** or use the **Glencoe Science CD-ROM** for additional chapter assessment.

THE PRINCETON REVIEW Test Practice

In health class, Angela decided to do a report about the cases of syphilis in the United States. She brought the following graph to accompany her report, which shows syphilis rates by year between 1970 and 1997.

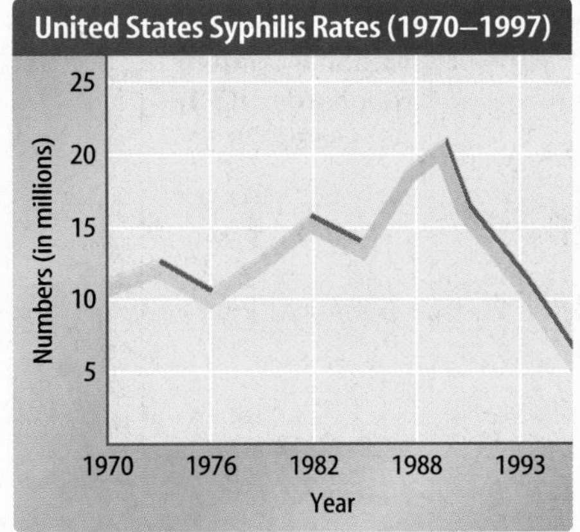
United States Syphilis Rates (1970–1997)
25
20
15
10
5
Numbers (in millions)
1970
1976
1982
1988
1993
Year

Study the graph and answer the following questions.

1. According to the information in the graph, when did an epidemic of syphilis occur in the United States?
   A) 1970–1972
   B) 1982–1984
   C) 1988–1990
   D) 1992–1994

2. A reasonable hypothesis for the information in the graph is that the number of people infected with syphilis _____.
   F) is increasing
   G) is decreasing
   H) has remained the same
   J) is related to gender

Chapter 22 Assessment

THE PRINCETON REVIEW Test Practice

The Test-Taking Tip was written by The Princeton Review, the nation's leader in test preparation.

1. C
2. G

Developing Skills

16. This coating aids in the movement of the baby through the birth canal.
17. Students might hypothesize that they will be the same because of their genes or that the environment will have an effect, making them different.
18. female internal: ovary, uterus, vagina; male external: penis, scrotum, testes
19. See student page.

Performance Assessment

20. Information in the letter might include how smoking reduces the oxygen supply to the fetus, increases the heart rate and blood pressure, and interferes with body chemistry. Use **PASC**, p. 139.

Assessment Resources

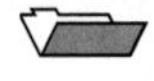

Reproducible Masters

Chapter Resources Booklet
Chapter Review, pp. 35–36
Chapter Tests, pp. 37–40
Assessment Transparency Activity, p. 47

Glencoe Science Web site
Interactive Tutor
Chapter Quizzes

Glencoe Technology
Assessment Transparency
Interactive CD-ROM Chapter Quizzes
ExamView Pro Test Bank
Vocabulary PuzzleMaker Software
MindJogger Videoquiz

Section/Objectives	Standards		Activities/Features
	National	State/Local	
Chapter Opener	See p. 5T for a Key to Standards.		**Explore Activity:** Model the spread of disease-causing organisms, p. 657 **Before You Read,** p. 657
Section 1 The Immune System 2 sessions 1 block 1. **Describe** the natural defenses your body has against disease. 2. **Explain** the difference between an antigen and an antibody. 3. **Compare and contrast** active and passive immunity.	National Content Standards: UCP1, A1, C1, C3, C5, F1		**Science Online,** p. 660 **MiniLAB:** Determining Reproduction Rates, p. 661
Section 2 Infectious Diseases 2 sessions 1 block 1. **Describe** the work of Pasteur, Koch, and Lister in the discovery and prevention of disease. 2. **Identify** diseases caused by viruses and bacteria. 3. **List** sexually transmitted diseases, their causes, and treatments. 4. **Explain** how HIV affects the immune system.	National Content Standards: UCP2, A1, C1, C3, C5, F1, G3		**Earth Science Integration,** p. 664 **Visualizing Koch's Rules,** p. 665 **MiniLAB:** Observing Antiseptic Action, p. 666 **Problem-Solving Activity:** Has the annual percentage of deaths from major diseases changed?, p. 667 **Science Online,** p. 669 **Activity:** Microorganisms and Disease, p. 671
Section 3 Noninfectious Diseases 3 sessions 1.5 blocks 1. **Define** noninfectious diseases and list causes of them. 2. **Describe** the basic characteristics of cancer. 3. **Explain** what happens during an allergic reaction.	National Content Standards: UCP4, A1, C1, C3, C5, E1, E2, F1, F4, G1		**Environmental Science Integration,** p. 675 **Activity:** Defensive Saliva, pp. 678–679 **Science Stats:** Battling Bacteria, pp. 680–681

NATIONAL GEOGRAPHIC

Teacher's Corner

Products Available from Glencoe
To order call 1-800-334-7344:
CD-ROM
NGS PictureShow; Human Body 3
Curriculum Kit
GeoKit: Human Body 1
Transparency Set
NGS PicturePack: Human Body 3
Videodisc
STV: Human Body

Products Available from National Geographic Society
To order call 1-800-368-2728:
Videos
Incredible Human Machine
Our Immune System

Activity Materials	Reproducible Resources	Section Assessment	Technology
Explore Activity: cotton ball, peppermint food flavoring	**Chapter Resources Booklet** Foldables Worksheet, p. 15 Directed Reading Overview, p. 17 Note-taking Worksheets, pp. 31–33	GLENCOE'S ASSESSMENT ADVANTAGE	
MiniLAB: 31 pennies, calculator *Need materials?* Contact Science Kit at 1-800-828-7777 or www.sciencekit.com on the Internet.	**Chapter Resources Booklet** Transparency Activity, p. 42 MiniLAB, p. 3 Lab Activity, pp. 9–12 Enrichment, p. 28 Reinforcement, p. 25 Directed Reading, p. 18 Transparency Activity, pp. 45–46	**Portfolio** Extension, p. 660 **Performance** MiniLAB, p. 661 Skill Builder Activities, p. 662 **Content** Section Assessment, p. 662	Section Focus Transparency Teaching Transparency Interactive CD-ROM Guided Reading Audio Program
MiniLAB: glass plate, dried yeast, hydrogen peroxide, dropper **Activity:** 6 fresh apples, rotting apple, rubbing alcohol, 6 self-sealing plastic bags, labels, latex gloves, paper towels, sandpaper, cotton ball, soap and water, newspaper	**Chapter Resources Booklet** Transparency Activity, p. 43 MiniLAB, p. 4 Enrichment, p. 29 Reinforcement, p. 26 Directed Reading, p. 19 Activity Worksheet, pp. 5–6 **Cultural Diversity,** p. 17 **Mathematics Skill Activities,** p. 1 **Reading and Writing Skill Activities,** pp. 25, 31	**Portfolio** Science Journal, p. 666 **Performance** MiniLAB, p. 661 Problem-Solving Activity, p. 667 Skill Builder Activities, p. 670 **Content** Section Assessment, p. 670	Section Focus Transparency Interactive CD-ROM Guided Reading Audio Program
Activity: head of red cabbage, cooking pot, coffee filter, drinking glasses, clear ammonia, bicarbonate of soda, water, spoon, white vinegar, lemon juice, orange juice, baking soda	**Chapter Resources Booklet** Transparency Activity, p. 44 Lab Activity, pp. 13–14 Enrichment, p. 30 Reinforcement, p. 27 Directed Reading, pp. 19, 20 Activity Worksheet, pp. 7–8 **Lab Management and Safety,** p. 70	**Portfolio** Extension, p. 674 **Performance** Skill Builder Activities, p. 677 **Content** Section Assessment, p. 677	Section Focus Transparency Interactive CD-ROM Guided Reading Audio Program

End of Chapter Assessment

GLENCOE'S ASSESSMENT ADVANTAGE

Blackline Masters	Technology	Professional Series
Chapter Resources Booklet Chapter Review, pp. 35–36 Chapter Tests, pp. 37–40 **Standardized Test Practice by The Princeton Review,** pp. 99–102	MindJogger Videoquiz Interactive CD-ROM Vocabulary PuzzleMakers ExamView Pro Test Bank Interactive Lesson Planner Interactive Teacher Edition	Performance Assessment in the Science Classroom (PASC)

Transparencies

Section Focus

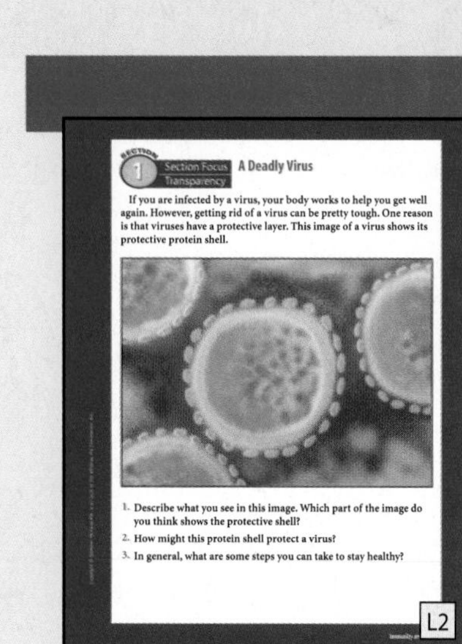
Section 1 Section Focus Transparency **A Deadly Virus**

If you are infected by a virus, your body works to help you get well again. However, getting rid of a virus can be pretty tough. One reason is that viruses have a protective layer. This image of a virus shows its protective protein shell.

1. Describe what you see in this image. Which part of the image do you think shows the protective shell?
2. How might this protein shell protect a virus?
3. In general, what are some steps you can take to stay healthy?

L2

Section 2 Section Focus Transparency **The Invisible World**

The first person to see many microorganisms, including bacteria, was Antonie van Leeuwenhoek (1632–1723). Leeuwenhoek wasn't a scientist by training, and he didn't invent the microscope. But he did learn to grind lenses very skillfully, and his small but powerful microscopes allowed him to see what no one else ever had.

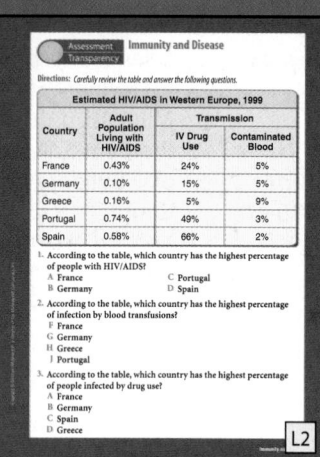

1. What advantages do microscopes give researchers?
2. How would a more powerful microscope help Leeuwenhoek see what other people could not?
3. One of Leeuwenhoek's microscopes is shown on the right. Where do you think he placed the sample he wished to magnify?

L2

Section 3 Section Focus Transparency **Ah-Chooo! (Gesundheit)**

Organisms are not the only things that can make you sick. Matter present in the environment, such as toxic chemicals, particles, and certain types of fibers, also can cause disease. The spiny spheres you see below are responsible for a certain type of allergic reaction that afflicts many people. Can you guess what they are?

1. How do allergies affect people?
2. What kind of help is there for allergy sufferers?
3. If people work around materials such as asbestos, burning tar, or smoke, what kinds of safety equipment should they use?

L2

This is a representation of key blackline masters available in the Teacher Classroom Resources. See Resource Manager boxes within the chapter for additional information.

Assessment

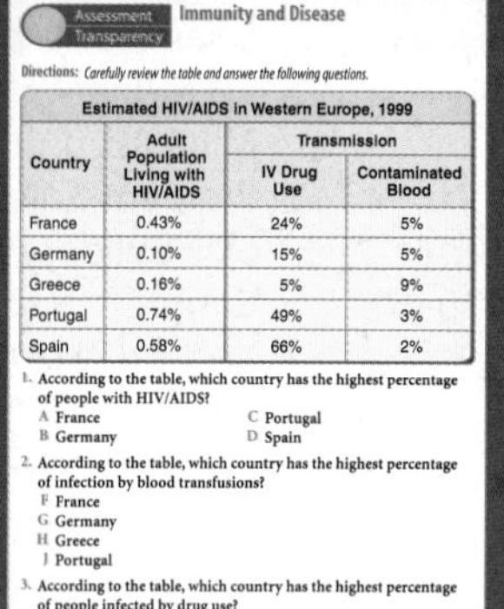
Assessment Transparency **Immunity and Disease**

Directions: *Carefully review the table and answer the following questions.*

Estimated HIV/AIDS in Western Europe, 1999			
Country	Adult Population Living with HIV/AIDS	Transmission: IV Drug Use	Transmission: Contaminated Blood
France	0.43%	24%	5%
Germany	0.10%	15%	5%
Greece	0.16%	5%	9%
Portugal	0.74%	49%	3%
Spain	0.58%	66%	2%

1. According to the table, which country has the highest percentage of people with HIV/AIDS?
   A France
   B Germany
   C Portugal
   D Spain
2. According to the table, which country has the highest percentage of infection by blood transfusions?
   F France
   G Germany
   H Greece
   J Portugal
3. According to the table, which country has the highest percentage of people infected by drug use?
   A France
   B Germany
   C Spain
   D Greece

L2

Teaching

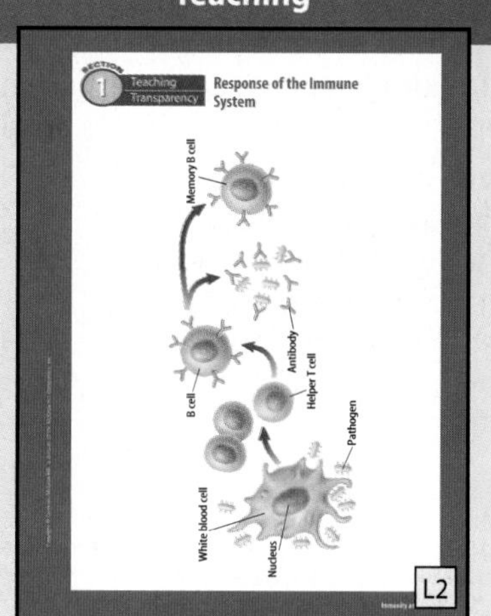
Section 1 Teaching Transparency **Response of the Immune System**

L2

Key to Teaching Strategies

The following designations will help you decide which activities are appropriate for your students.

- L1 Level 1 activities should be appropriate for students with learning difficulties.
- L2 Level 2 activities should be within the ability range of all students.
- L3 Level 3 activities are designed for above-average students.
- ELL ELL activities should be within the ability range of English Language Learners.
- COOP LEARN Cooperative Learning activities are designed for small group work.
- LS Multiple Learning Styles logos, as described on page 22T, are used throughout to indicate strategies that address different learning styles.
- P These strategies represent student products that can be placed into a best-work portfolio.

Hands-on Activities

Activity Worksheets

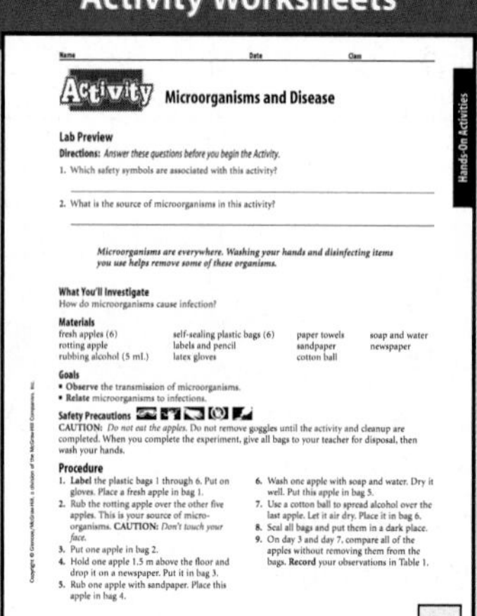
Name Date Class

Activity **Microorganisms and Disease**

Hands-On Activities

Lab Preview

Directions: *Answer these questions before you begin the Activity.*

1. Which safety symbols are associated with this activity?
2. What is the source of microorganisms in this activity?

Microorganisms are everywhere. Washing your hands and disinfecting items you use helps remove some of these organisms.

What You'll Investigate

How do microorganisms cause infection?

Materials

fresh apples (6), rotting apple, rubbing alcohol (5 mL), self-sealing plastic bags (6), labels and pencil, latex gloves, paper towels, sandpaper, cotton ball, soap and water, newspaper

Goals

- **Observe** the transmission of microorganisms.
- **Relate** microorganisms to infections.

Safety Precautions

CAUTION: *Do not eat the apples.* Do not remove goggles until the activity and cleanup are completed. When you complete the experiment, give all bags to your teacher for disposal, then wash your hands.

Procedure

1. **Label** the plastic bags 1 through 6. Put on gloves. Place a fresh apple in bag 1.
2. Rub the rotting apple over the other five apples. This is your source of microorganisms. **CAUTION:** *Don't touch your face.*
3. Put one apple in bag 2.
4. Hold one apple 1.5 m above the floor and drop it on a newspaper. Put it in bag 3.
5. Rub one apple with sandpaper. Place this apple in bag 4.
6. Wash one apple with soap and water. Dry it well. Put this apple in bag 5.
7. Use a cotton ball to spread alcohol over the last apple. Let it air dry. Place it in bag 6.
8. Seal all bags and put them in a dark place.
9. On day 3 and day 7, compare all of the apples without removing them from the bags. **Record** your observations in Table 1.

L2

Laboratory Activities

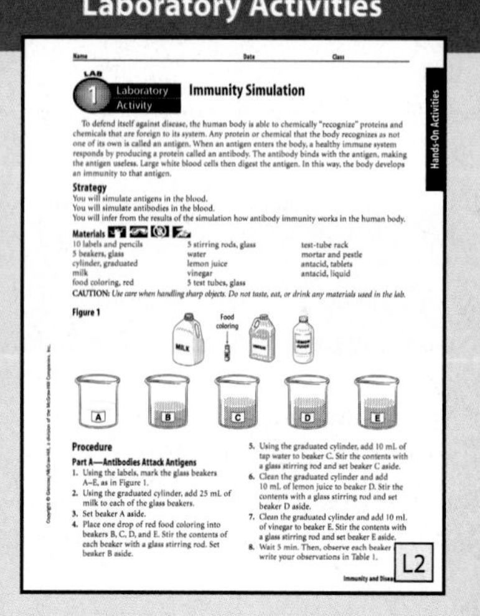
Name Date Class

LAB 1 Laboratory Activity **Immunity Simulation**

Hands-On Activities

To defend itself against disease, the human body is able to chemically "recognize" proteins and chemicals that are foreign to its system. Any protein or chemical that the body recognizes as not one of its own is called an antigen. When an antigen enters the body, a healthy immune system responds by producing a protein called an antibody. The antibody binds with the antigen, making the antigen useless. Large white blood cells then digest the antigen. In this way, the body develops an immunity to that antigen.

Strategy

You will simulate antigens in the blood.
You will simulate antibodies in the blood.
You will infer from the results of the simulation how antibody immunity works in the human body.

Materials

10 labels and pencils, 5 beakers, glass, cylinder, graduated, milk, food coloring, red, 5 stirring rods, glass, water, lemon juice, vinegar, 5 test tubes, glass, test-tube rack, mortar and pestle, antacid, tablets, antacid, liquid

CAUTION: *Use care when handling sharp objects. Do not taste, eat, or drink any materials used in the lab.*

Figure 1

Procedure

Part A—Antibodies Attack Antigens

1. Using the labels, mark the glass beakers A–E, as in Figure 1.
2. Using the graduated cylinder, add 25 mL of milk to each of the glass beakers.
3. Set beaker A aside.
4. Place one drop of red food coloring into beakers B, C, D, and E. Stir the contents of each beaker with a glass stirring rod. Set beaker B aside.
5. Using the graduated cylinder, add 10 mL of tap water to beaker C. Stir the contents with a glass stirring rod and set beaker C aside.
6. Clean the graduated cylinder and add 10 mL of lemon juice to beaker D. Stir the contents with a glass stirring rod and set beaker D aside.
7. Clean the graduated cylinder and add 10 mL of vinegar to beaker E. Stir the contents with a glass stirring rod and set beaker E aside.
8. Wait 5 min. Then, observe each beaker write your observations in Table 1.

L2

Meeting Different Ability Levels

Content Outline

Name Date Class

Note-taking Worksheet **Immunity and Disease**

Section 1 The Immune System

A. ________—complex set of defenses to protect the body from pathogens

B. ________—resist pathogens

1. Unbroken ________ is a barrier that prevents many pathogens from entering the body.
2. The ________ traps pathogens with cilia and mucus.
3. The ________ uses saliva, enzymes, hydrochloric acid, and mucus to kill bacteria.
4. The ________ contains white blood cells that patrol the body and destroy pathogens.
5. Damaged or diseased tissue becomes ________, attracting certain white blood cells to fight bacteria.

C. Specific immunity—the immune system works against a ________ **antigen** by producing an **antibody**.

1. In ________ **immunity** the body makes its own antibodies in response to an antigen.
   a. Some ________ remain in the bloodstream to fight later infections of the same pathogen.
   b. ________ provides a form of an antigen to provide active immunity.
2. ________ **immunity**—results when antibodies produced in another animal are introduced into the body
   a. Passive immunity does not ________ as active immunity.
   b. Many vaccines or boosters must be taken more than ________ to maintain immunity.

Meeting Individual Needs

L2

Immunity and Disease

Reinforcement

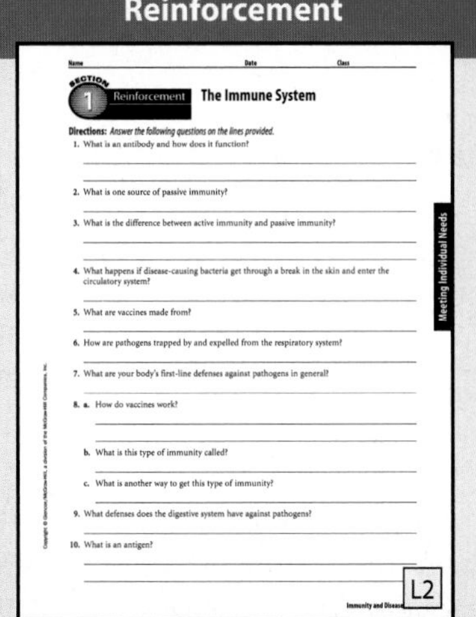

Name Date Class

Section 1 Reinforcement **The Immune System**

Directions: Answer the following questions on the lines provided.

1. What is an antibody and how does it function?
2. What is one source of passive immunity?
3. What is the difference between active immunity and passive immunity?
4. What happens if disease-causing bacteria get through a break in the skin and enter the circulatory system?
5. What are vaccines made from?
6. How are pathogens trapped by and expelled from the respiratory system?
7. What are your body's first-line defenses against pathogens in general?
8. a. How do vaccines work?
   b. What is this type of immunity called?
   c. What is another way to get this type of immunity?
9. What defenses does the digestive system have against pathogens?
10. What is an antigen?

Meeting Individual Needs

L2

Immunity and Disease

Directed Reading

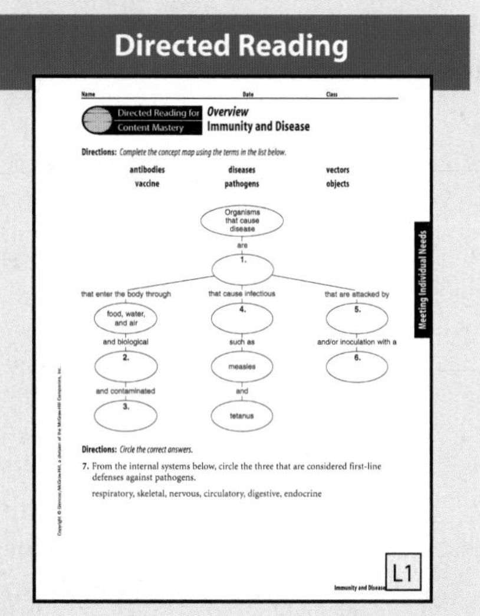

Name Date Class

Directed Reading for Content Mastery *Overview* **Immunity and Disease**

Directions: Complete the concept map using the terms in the list below.

antibodies	diseases	vectors
vaccine	pathogens	objects

Directions: Circle the correct answers.

7. From the internal systems below, circle the three that are considered first-line defenses against pathogens.
respiratory, skeletal, nervous, circulatory, digestive, endocrine

Meeting Individual Needs

L1

Immunity and Disease

Assessment

Chapter Tests

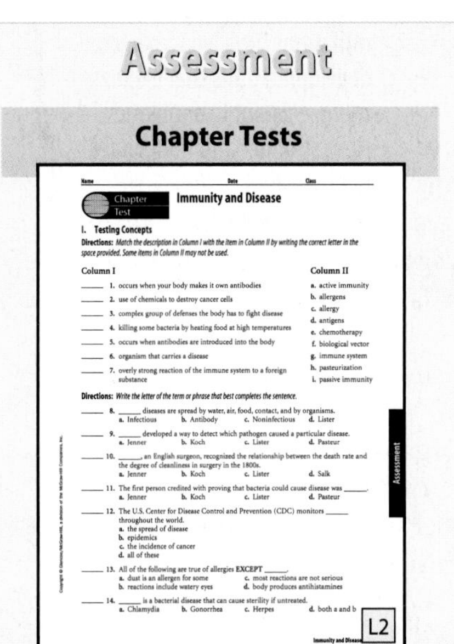

Name Date Class

Chapter Test **Immunity and Disease**

I. Testing Concepts

Directions: Match the description in Column I with the item in Column II by writing the correct letter in the space provided. Some items in Column II may not be used.

Column I	Column II
____ 1. occurs when your body makes it own antibodies	a. active immunity
____ 2. use of chemicals to destroy cancer cells	b. allergens
____ 3. complex group of defenses the body has to fight disease	c. allergy
____ 4. killing some bacteria by heating food at high temperatures	d. antigens
____ 5. occurs when antibodies are introduced into the body	e. chemotherapy
____ 6. organism that carries a disease	f. biological vector
____ 7. overly strong reaction of the immune system to a foreign substance	g. immune system
	h. pasteurization
	i. passive immunity

Directions: Write the letter of the term or phrase that best completes the sentence.

____ 8. ____ diseases are spread by water, air, food, contact, and by organisms.
a. Infectious b. Antibody c. Noninfectious d. Lister

____ 9. ____ developed a way to detect which pathogen caused a particular disease.
a. Jenner b. Koch c. Lister d. Pasteur

____ 10. ____, an English surgeon, recognized the relationship between the death rate and the degree of cleanliness in surgery in the 1800s.
a. Jenner b. Koch c. Lister d. Salk

____ 11. The first person credited with proving that bacteria could cause disease was ____.
a. Jenner b. Koch c. Lister d. Pasteur

____ 12. The U.S. Center for Disease Control and Prevention (CDC) monitors ____ throughout the world.
a. the spread of disease
b. epidemics
c. the incidence of cancer
d. all of these

____ 13. All of the following are true of allergies EXCEPT ____.
a. dust is an allergen for some c. most reactions are not serious
b. reactions include watery eyes d. body produces antihistamines

____ 14. ____ is a bacterial disease that can cause sterility if untreated.
a. Chlamydia b. Gonorrhea c. Herpes d. both a and b

Assessment

L2

Immunity and Disease

Enrichment

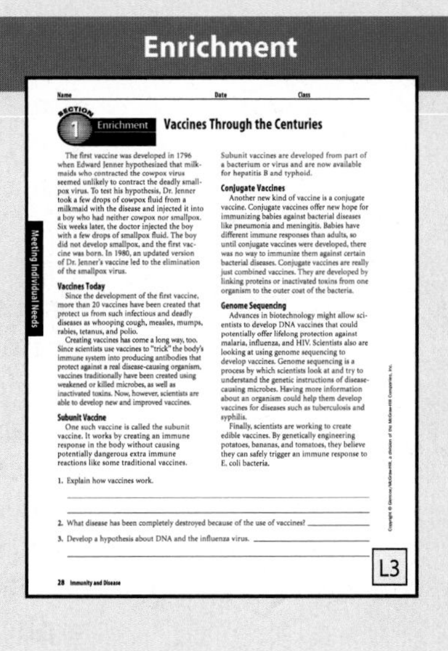

Name Date Class

Section 1 Enrichment **Vaccines Through the Centuries**

The first vaccine was developed in 1796 when Edward Jenner hypothesized that milkmaids who contracted the cowpox virus seemed unlikely to contract the deadly smallpox virus. To test his hypothesis, Dr. Jenner took a few drops of cowpox fluid from a milkmaid with the disease and injected it into a boy who had neither cowpox nor smallpox. Six weeks later, the doctor injected the boy with a few drops of smallpox fluid. The boy did not develop smallpox, and the first vaccine was born. In 1980, an updated version of Dr. Jenner's vaccine led to the elimination of the smallpox virus.

Vaccines Today

Since the development of the first vaccine, more than 20 vaccines have been created that protect us from such infectious and deadly diseases as whooping cough, measles, mumps, rabies, tetanus, and polio.

Creating vaccines has come a long way, too. Since scientists use vaccines to "trick" the body's immune system into producing antibodies that protect against a real disease-causing organism, vaccines traditionally have been created using weakened or killed microbes, as well as inactivated toxins. Now, however, scientists are able to develop new and improved vaccines.

Subunit Vaccine

One such vaccine is called the subunit vaccine. It works by creating an immune response in the body without causing potentially dangerous extra immune reactions like some traditional vaccines. Subunit vaccines are developed from part of a bacterium or virus and are now available for hepatitis B and typhoid.

Conjugate Vaccines

Another new kind of vaccine is a conjugate vaccine. Conjugate vaccines offer new hope for immunizing babies against bacterial diseases like pneumonia and meningitis. Babies have different immune responses than adults, so until conjugate vaccines were developed, there was no way to immunize them against certain bacterial diseases. Conjugate vaccines are really just combined vaccines. They are developed by linking proteins or inactivated toxins from one organism to the outer coat of the bacteria.

Genome Sequencing

Advances in biotechnology might allow scientists to develop DNA vaccines that could potentially offer lifelong protection against malaria, influenza, and HIV. Scientists also are looking at using genome sequencing to develop vaccines. Genome sequencing is a process by which scientists look at and try to understand the genetic instructions of disease-causing microbes. Having more information about an organism could help them develop vaccines for diseases such as tuberculosis and syphilis.

Finally, scientists are working to create edible vaccines. By genetically engineering potatoes, bananas, and tomatoes, they believe they can safely trigger an immune response to E. coli bacteria.

1. Explain how vaccines work.
2. What disease has been completely destroyed because of the use of vaccines?
3. Develop a hypothesis about DNA and the influenza virus.

Meeting Individual Needs

L3

28 Immunity and Disease

Spanish Directed Reading

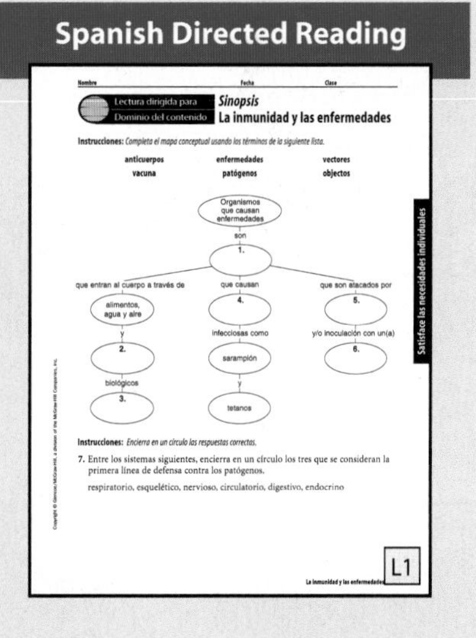

Nombre Fecha Clase

Lectura dirigida para Dominio del contenido *Sinopsis* **La inmunidad y las enfermedades**

Instrucciones: Completa el mapa conceptual usando los términos de la siguiente lista.

anticuerpos	enfermedades	vectores
vacuna	patógenos	objectos

Instrucciones: Encierra en un círculo las respuestas correctas.

7. Entre los sistemas siguientes, encierra en un círculo los tres que se consideran la primera línea de defensa contra los patógenos.
respiratorio, esquelético, nervioso, circulatorio, digestivo, endocrino

Satisface las necesidades individuales

L1

La inmunidad y las enfermedades

Test Practice Workbook

L2

Chapter Review

Name Date Class

Chapter Review **Immunity and Disease**

Part A. Vocabulary Review

Directions: Write the correct term in the space beside each definition.

________ 1. disease caused by uncontrolled cell growth
________ 2. immunity that occurs when a body makes its own antibodies
________ 3. protein made in response to foreign invaders
________ 4. immunity that occurs when antibodies come from another source
________ 5. method of using heat to kill some pathogens in food
________ 6. abbreviation for a sexually transmitted disease
________ 7. a tiny piece of genetic material that infects and multiplies in host cells, killing the host cells
________ 8. diseases that are long-lasting and non-infectious
________ 9. use of chemicals to destroy cancer cells
________ 10. strong reaction of the immune system to a foreign substance
________ 11. substances foreign to the body
________ 12. the process of giving by mouth or injection a weakened virus that allows one to develop immunity against a disease
________ 13. substance that causes an allergic reaction
________ 14. diseases not spread by people
________ 15. diseases that are spread by water, air, food, contact, and vectors
________ 16. system of defenses the body has to fight disease

Part B. Concept Review

Directions: Answer the following questions on the lines provided.

1. List three diseases caused by viruses.
2. List three diseases caused by bacteria.

Assessment

L2

Immunity and Disease

Science Content Background

SECTION 1 The Immune System

Immunity

The lymphatic system produces various white blood cells, each of which fights a specific type of antigen. This type of defense is called specific immunity.

Active Immunity

Active immunity can be natural or induced. A natural active immunity is developed after a person contracts and recovers from diseases such as measles or mumps. Defensive proteins, called antibodies, produced in the body counteract the invading microorganism's proteins called antigens. The interaction between antigens and antibodies stimulates the release of histamine and complement compounds.

Artificial active immunity is an induced immunity. A person is given an injection or an oral dose of a noninfectious disease antigen. The body forms antibodies against the antigen providing immunity. The noninfectious antigens come from three sources:

1) microorganism secretions that have been detoxified,
2) dead microorganisms, and
3) living microorganisms.

Booster shots may be required to keep the artificial immunity active.

Fun Fact

Antibiotics frequently are viewed as a sure cure for whatever ails us and may be requested when they aren't necessary. Antibiotics kill bacteria but not viruses. Since the 1950's mutations have led to bacteria developing traits that make them resistant to antibiotics. New, stronger antibiotics have to be made.

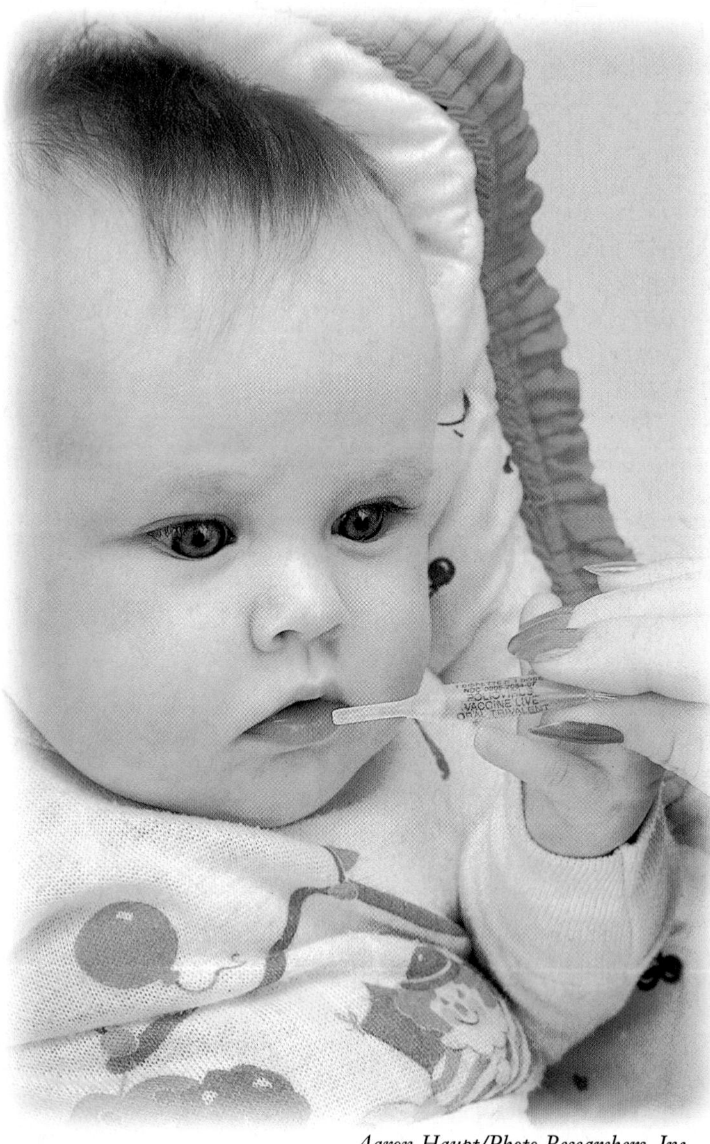

Aaron Haupt/Photo Researchers, Inc.

Passive Immunity

Passive immunity can be either natural or induced. Passive artificial immunity is acquired when antibodies produced in another animal are injected into the body. The serum containing the antibodies is often obtained from horses that were inoculated with disease antigens and then produced antibodies within their own body systems.

Passive natural immunity is that which an infant receives from the mother via the placenta. Because this protection only lasts for a few months, the child must be given inoculations to establish his or her own immunity to diseases.

SECTION 2

Infectious Diseases

Germ Theory

In early history, the causes of diseases were associated with the anger of the gods, sorcerers, evil vapors, or imbalances of body fluids. By the early and mid 1800s, researchers, such as French chemist Louis Pasteur, developed a germ theory that indicated microorganisms might be responsible for disease. It is now known that pathogenic organisms such as viruses, bacteria, yeasts, protozoans, flatworms, roundworms, and hookworms cause disease by secreting toxins, by destroying red blood cells, or by ingesting tissues. Infections or communicable diseases can be transmitted from one organism to another by food, through the air, by insects, by parasites, or by sexual contact or exchange of body fluids. Bacteria and viruses cause sexually transmitted diseases.

Preventing Food Spoilage

Before the causes of diseases were discovered, various methods were used to prevent foods from spoiling. Foods were dried, smoked, pickled, or salted to prevent the growth of microorganisms. Establishment of the germ theory led to the use of chemicals and Pasteur's idea of the use of heat to destroy pathogens. Additional modern methods of safeguarding food include the use of extreme cold, steam, and radiation.

Germs in the Body

Some organisms are able to gain entrance to the body through the thin membranes of the eyes, nose, and mouth. Good hygiene habits of washing with soap and water remove many potentially troublesome organisms from the surface of the skin. After germs enter the body, some are unable to function because body temperature is either too warm or too cool, the pH of body fluids is unsuitable, or the available nutrients are inappropriate for their metabolism.

SECTION 3

Noninfectious Diseases

Causes and Cures

Some diseases and disorders are noninfectious. Although they are not contracted from other people or from objects, these conditions are usually unavoidable. Some noncommunicable diseases are the result of poor nutrition. People who are unable to ingest a proper diet or people who do not choose a balanced diet are prone to such diseases. Other noncommunicable diseases and disorders are the result of inheriting certain genes. Included in such genetic disorders are cystic fibrosis, hemophilia, Huntington's chorea, muscular dystrophy, sickle-cell anemia, and Tay-Sachs disease.

Toxins, or chemicals, introduced into the body through breathing, touching, drinking or eating, can cause non-infectious diseases such as allergies, emphysema, and cancer. Prevention is the first line of defense for these diseases. Early detection of some diseases, such as cancer, paired with appropriate drug treatment and/or surgery is a second line of defense.

For additional content background on this topic, go to the Glencoe Science Web site at science.glencoe.com.

CHAPTER 23

Immunity and Disease

Chapter Vocabulary

immune system, p. 658
antigen, p. 660
antibody, p. 660
active immunity, p. 661
passive immunity, p. 661
vaccination, p. 661
pasteurization, p. 663
virus, p. 664
infectious disease, p. 667
biological vector, p. 667
sexually transmitted disease (STD), p. 668
noninfectious diseases, p. 672
allergy, p. 672
allergen, p. 673
chemotherapy, p. 676

What do you think?

Science Journal This is a microphotograph of tetanus bacteria. Shots for tetanus were given to you as a child, but booster shots are necessary every 10 years.

CHAPTER

Immunity and Disease

It never makes newspaper headlines, but there's a war being fought in your body. Every second of your life your body is fighting harmful attacks. You usually don't know it's occurring. But sometimes your body cannot fight a battle without bringing in help from the laboratory—vaccines or medicines. In this chapter, you'll learn about disease and how your body is equipped to survive.

What do you think?

Science Journal Look at the picture below with a classmate. Discuss what this might be. Here's a hint: *You can receive a booster shot so you don't get this disease from dirty cuts.* Write your answer in your Science Journal.

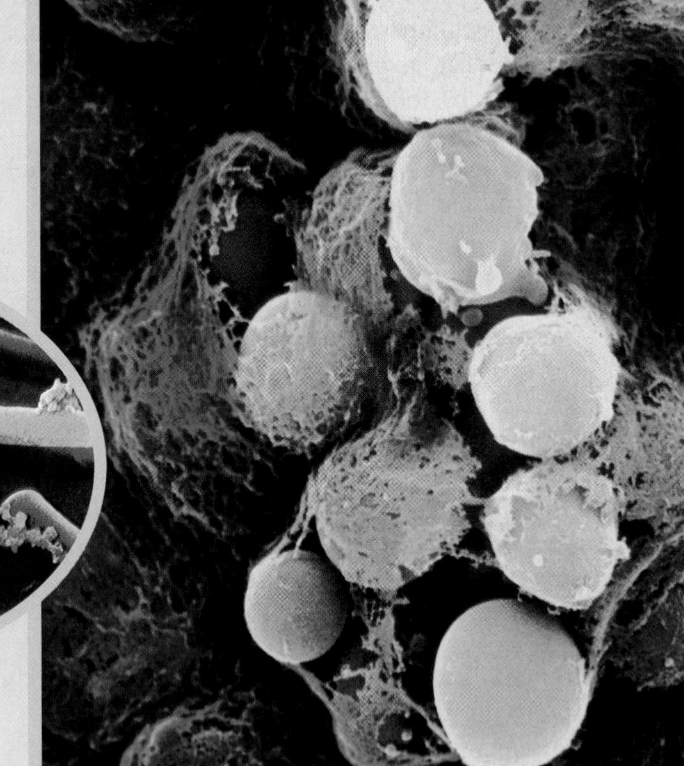

656

Theme Connection

Systems and Interactions One major theme of science is interaction among systems. This chapter focuses on interactions within the body. Natural defenses in the body aid in preventing disease. Vaccines also provide active immunity to body systems.

It is a fact that disease-causing organisms are in the air you breathe and on the objects you touch. Knowing how diseases are spread will help you understand how your body fights disease. You can discover one way diseases are spread by doing the following activity.

Model the spread of disease-causing organisms

1. Wash your hands before and after this activity. Don't touch your face until the activity is completed and your hands are washed.
2. Work with a partner. Place a drop of peppermint food flavoring on a cotton ball. Pretend that the flavoring is a mass of cold viruses.
3. Use the cotton ball to rub an X over the palm of your right hand. Let it dry.
4. Shake hands with your partner.
5. Have your partner shake hands with another student. Then each student should smell their hands

Observe

Observe how many persons your "virus" infected. Describe in your Science Journal some ways diseases are spread. How could some of these diseases be stopped?

Before You Read

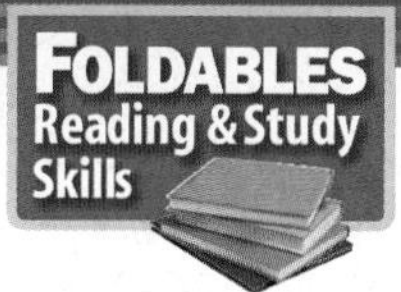

Making a Classify Study Fold Make the following Foldable to help organize objects or events into their groups based on their common features.

1. Place a sheet of paper in front of you so the long side is at the top. Fold the paper in half from the left side to the right side. Then unfold.
2. Label the left side of the paper *Infectious Diseases* and the right side of the paper *Noninfectious Diseases* as shown.
3. Before you read the chapter, classify diseases you are familiar with as infectious or noninfectious by listing them on the proper fold.
4. As you read the chapter, change and add to your lists.

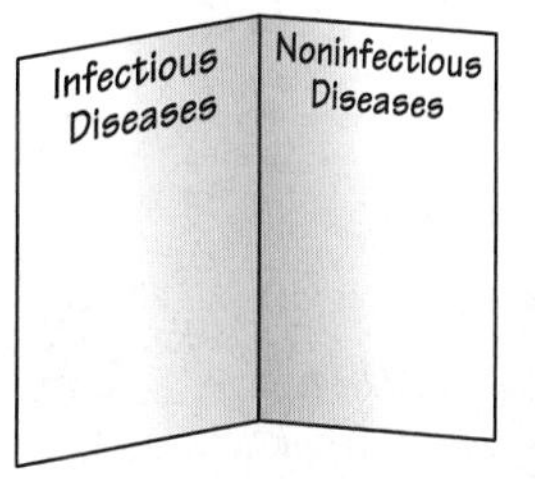

657

Explore Activity

Purpose Use this Explore Activity to introduce students to how disease can spread. L1 ELL LS **Kinesthetic**

Preparation Before beginning this activity, obtain food flavoring and cotton balls.

Materials peppermint food flavoring, one cotton ball for each pair

Alternate Materials Orange, almond, or banana flavors can be used.

Teaching Strategies

- Have students discuss how the mass of cold virus could have gotten on the hands in the first place.
- Have students infer whether the infection could be passed around on drinking glasses and handkerchiefs.

Safety Precautions Following the activity, have students wash their hands thoroughly.

Observe

Possible answer: Many diseases are spread through physical contact. The spread of some diseases can be stopped by carefully washing eating utensils and hands with warm water and soap.

Assessment

Performance Determine whether any flavoring remains on their hands after washing them. Discuss how washing hands affects the spread of disease. Use **Performance Assessment in the Science Classroom,** p. 89.

Before You Read

Foldables Reading & Study Skills

Dinah Zike Study Fold

Purpose Students make and use a Foldable to classify diseases as infectious or noninfectious. Students use this information to explain the cause-and-effect relationships of common diseases.

For additional help, see Foldables Worksheet, p. 15 in **Chapter Resources Booklet,** or go to the Glencoe Science Web site at **science.glencoe.com.** See After You Read in the Study Guide at the end of this chapter.

SECTION

The Immune System

1 Motivate

Bellringer Transparency

Display the Section Focus Transparency for Section 1. Use the accompanying Transparency Activity Master. L2 ELL

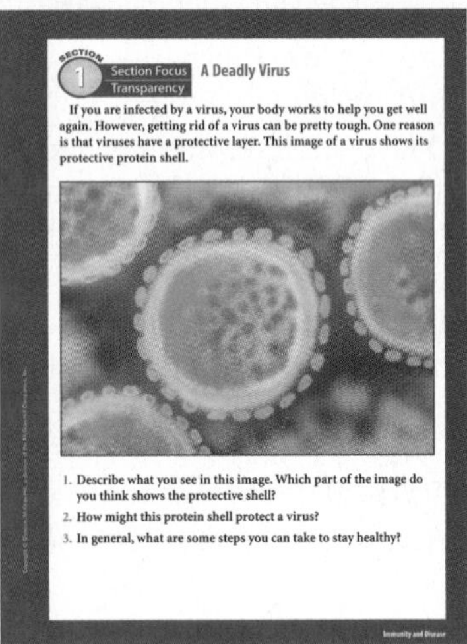

SECTION 1 Section Focus Transparency A Deadly Virus

If you are infected by a virus, your body works to help you get well again. However, getting rid of a virus can be pretty tough. One reason is that viruses have a protective layer. This image of a virus shows its protective protein shell.

1. Describe what you see in this image. Which part of the image do you think shows the protective shell?
2. How might this protein shell protect a virus?
3. In general, what are some steps you can take to stay healthy?

Tie to Prior Knowledge

Have students recall the shots they received before entering school. Ask them to describe any immunizations they have been given in recent years.

Answer first-line (general) and second-line (specific) defenses

SECTION

The Immune System

As You Read

What You'll Learn

- **Describe** the natural defenses your body has against disease.
- **Explain** the difference between an antigen and an antibody.
- **Compare and contrast** active and passive immunity.

Vocabulary

immune system	active immunity
antigen	passive immunity
antibody	vaccination

Why It's Important

Your body's defenses fight the pathogens that you are exposed to every day.

Lines of Defense

The Sun has just begun to peek over the horizon, casting an orange glow on the land. A skunk ambles down a dirt path. Behind the skunk, you and your dog come over a hill for your morning exercise. Suddenly, the skunk stops and raises its tail high in the air. Your dog creeps forward. "No!" you shout. The dog ignores your command. Without further warning, the skunk sprays your dog. Yelping pitifully and carrying an awful stench, your dog takes off. The skunk used its scent to protect itself. Its first-line defense was to warn your dog with its posture. Its second-line defense was its spray. Just as the skunk protects itself from predators, your body also protects itself from harm.

Your body has many ways to defend itself. Its first-line defenses work against harmful substances and all types of disease-causing organisms, called pathogens (PA thuh junz). Your second-line defenses are specific and work against specific pathogens. This complex group of defenses is called your **immune system.** Tonsils, shown in **Figure 1,** are one of the immune system organs that protect your body.

Reading Check *What types of defenses does your body have?*

First-Line Defenses Your skin and respiratory, digestive, and circulatory systems are first-line defenses against pathogens. Skin is a barrier that prevents many pathogens from entering your body. Although most pathogens can't get through unbroken skin, as shown in **Figure 2,** they can get into your body easily through a cut or through your mouth and the membranes in your nose and eyes. The conditions on the skin can affect pathogens. Perspiration contains substances that can slow the growth of some pathogens. At times, secretions from the skin's oil glands and perspiration are acidic. Some pathogens cannot grow in this acidic environment.

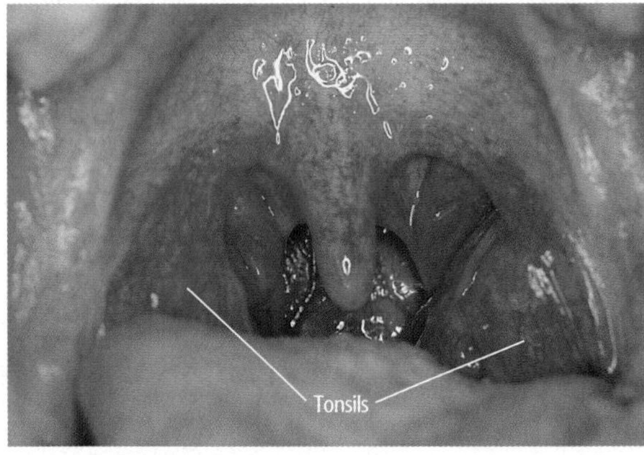

Figure 1
Tonsils help prevent infection in your respiratory and digestive tract.

Section Assessment Planner

Portfolio
Extension, p. 660

Performance Assessment
Try at Home MiniLAB, p. 661
Skill Builder Activities, p. 662
See page 684 for more options.

Content Assessment
Section, p. 662
Challenge, p. 662
Chapter, pp. 684–685

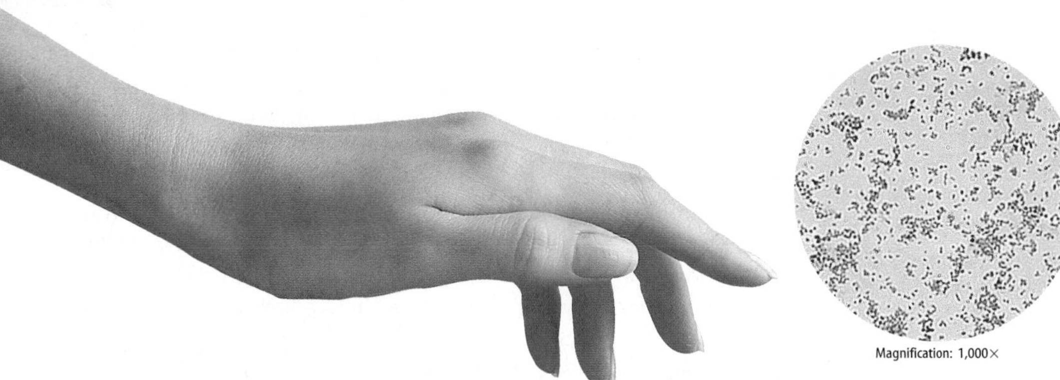

Figure 2
Most pathogens, like the staphylococci bacteria shown here, cannot get through unbroken skin.

Internal First-Line Defenses Your respiratory system traps pathogens with hairlike structures, called cilia (SIH lee uh), and mucus. Mucus contains an enzyme that weakens the cell walls of some pathogens. When you cough or sneeze, you get rid of some of these trapped pathogens.

Your digestive system has several defenses against pathogens—saliva, enzymes, hydrochloric acid, and mucus. Saliva in your mouth contains substances that kill bacteria. Also, enzymes (EN zimez) in your stomach, pancreas, and liver help destroy pathogens. Hydrochloric acid in your stomach helps digest your food. It also kills some bacteria and stops the activity of some viruses that enter your body on the food that you eat. The mucus found on the walls of your digestive tract contains a chemical that coats bacteria and prevents them from binding to the inner lining of your digestive organs.

Your circulatory system contains white blood cells, like the one in **Figure 3,** that surround and digest foreign organisms and chemicals. These white blood cells constantly patrol your body, sweeping up and digesting bacteria that invade. They slip between cells of tiny blood vessels called capillaries. If the white blood cells cannot destroy the bacteria fast enough, you might develop a fever. Many pathogens are sensitive to temperature. A slight increase in body temperature slows their growth and activity but speeds up your body's defenses.

Figure 3
A white blood cell leaves a capillary. It will search out and destroy harmful microorganisms in your body tissues.

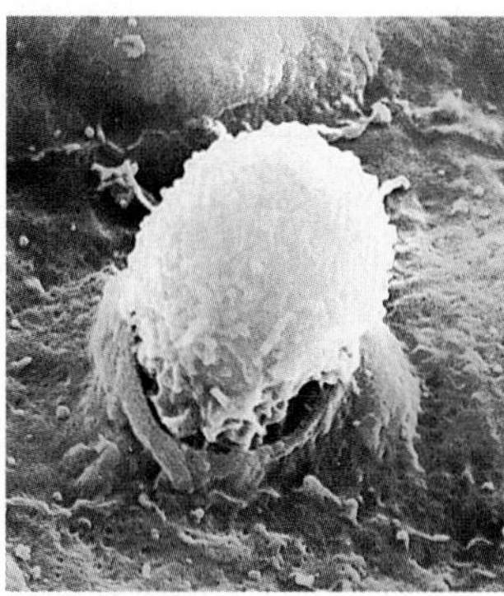

Inflammation When tissue is damaged by injury or infected by pathogens, it becomes inflamed. Signs of inflammation include redness, temperature increase, swelling, and pain. Chemical substances released by damaged cells cause capillary walls to expand, allowing more blood to flow into the area. Other chemicals released by damaged tissue attract certain white blood cells that surround and take in pathogenic bacteria. If pathogens get past these first-line defenses, your body uses another line of defense called specific immunity.

2 Teach

Lines of Defense

Activity

Have students test the acidity of their sweat using pH indicator paper. Sweat may range from pH 3.0 to slightly alkaline. L2 LS **Kinesthetic**

Fun Fact

The saliva of cats and dogs contains various substances that can kill bacteria. The licking of wounds aids in the healing process.

Discussion

Why should a fever not be ignored? Fevers are an indication of infection, a sign that the body is fighting a pathogen. Temperatures over 104°F are potentially dangerous and medical help should be sought immediately.

IDENTIFYING Misconceptions

There is an old adage that "sweating out a fever" will rid the body of it. Extra blankets and keeping a room extra warm will only cause the patient's temperature to rise. Drinking lots of fluids and taking medicines recommended by a physician are better remedies.

Resource Manager

Chapter Resources Booklet
- Transparency Activity, p. 42
- Directed Reading for Content Mastery, p. 18
- Note-Taking Worksheets, pp. 31–33
- Lab Activity, pp. 9–12

Visual Learning

Figure 2 Have students discuss how the surface of the skin may be broken. Possible answers: Falls and accidents may cause cuts, punctures, and scrapes of the skin that can allow the entrance of bacteria.

Lines of Defense, continued

SCIENCE Online

Internet Addresses

Explore the Glencoe Science Web site at science.glencoe.com to find out more about topics in this section.

Reading Check

Answer a protein made by the body in response to a specific antigen

Teacher FYI

Antibiotics are medicines used to destroy or neutralize pathogens in the body. Antibiotics have been developed to combat bacterial infections. They do not destroy viruses. Some medicines have been developed to relieve symptoms of colds and influenza, but there are no antibiotics for viral infections.

Caption Answer

Figure 4 to produce antibodies

Extension

Have students research the discovery of chemicals that are used to destroy or neutralize viruses. Have them write two or three paragraphs on what they have found. L2 ELL LS **Linguistic** P

SCIENCE Online

Research Visit the Glencoe Science Web site at **science.glencoe.com** for more information on the various types of T cells and their functions. Communicate to your class what you learn.

Specific Immunity When your body fights disease, it is battling complex molecules that don't belong there. Molecules that are foreign to your body are called **antigens** (AN tih junz). Antigens can be separate molecules or they can be found on the surface of a pathogen. For example, the protein in the cell membrane of a bacterium can be an antigen. When your immune system recognizes molecules as being foreign to your body, as in **Figure 4,** special lymphocytes called T cells respond. Lymphocytes are a type of white blood cell. One type of T cells, called killer T cells, releases enzymes that help destroy invading foreign matter. Another type of T cells, called helper T cells, turns on the immune system. They stimulate other lymphocytes, known as B cells, to form antibodies.

An **antibody** is a protein made in response to a specific antigen. The antibody attaches to the antigen and makes it useless. This can happen in several ways. The pathogen might not be able to stay attached to a cell. It might be changed in such a way that a killer T cell can capture it more easily or the pathogen can be destroyed.

Reading Check *What is an antibody?*

Another type of lymphocyte, called memory B cells, also has antibodies for the specific pathogen. Memory B cells remain in the blood ready to defend against an invasion by that same pathogen another time.

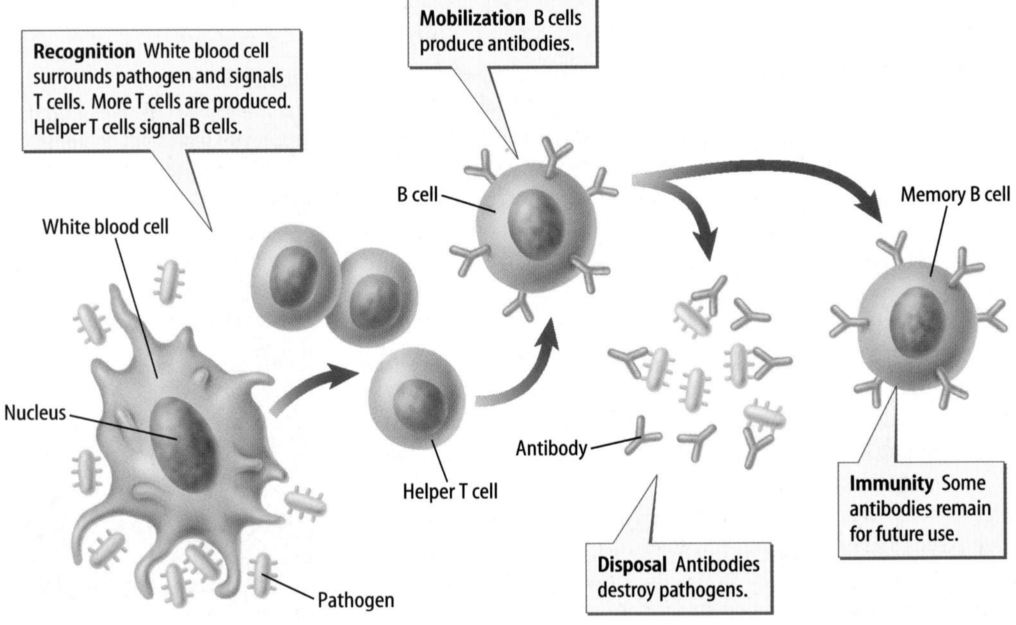
Recognition White blood cell surrounds pathogen and signals T cells. More T cells are produced. Helper T cells signal B cells.
Mobilization B cells produce antibodies.
White blood cell
B cell
Memory B cell
Nucleus
Antibody
Helper T cell
Pathogen
Disposal Antibodies destroy pathogens.
Immunity Some antibodies remain for future use.

Figure 4
The response of your immune system to disease-causing organisms can be divided into four steps—recognition, mobilization, disposal, and immunity.
What is the function of B cells?

Teacher FYI

When a virus enters the body, the protein interferon is synthesized. The chemical can leave the cell and enter the circulatory system. Molecules of interferon bind to cell membranes and stimulate their production of antiviral proteins to inhibit virus reproduction.

Active Reading

Write-Draw-Discuss This strategy encourages students to actively participate in reading and lectures, assimilating content creatively. Have students write about an idea, clarify it, then make an illustration or drawing. Ask students to share responses with the class and display several examples. Have students Write-Draw-Discuss about a concept concerning the immune system.

Active Immunity Antibodies help your body build defenses in two ways—actively and passively. In **active immunity** your body makes its own antibodies in response to an antigen. **Passive immunity** results when antibodies that have been produced in another animal are introduced into your body.

When a pathogen invades your body, the pathogen quickly multiplies and you get sick. Your body immediately starts to make antibodies to attack the pathogen. After enough antibodies form, you usually get better. Some antibodies stay on duty in your blood, and more are produced rapidly if the pathogen enters your body again. Because of this defense system you usually don't get certain diseases such as chicken pox more than once.

Vaccination Another way to develop active immunity to a disease is to be inoculated with a vaccine. The process of giving a vaccine by injection or by mouth is called **vaccination.** A vaccine is a form of the antigen that gives you active immunity against a disease. For example, suppose a measles vaccine is injected into your body. Your body forms antibodies against the measles antigen. If you later encounter the same measles virus, antibodies that are needed to fight and destroy the measles virus already are in your bloodstream. Vaccines have helped reduce cases of childhood diseases, as shown in **Table 1.**

Antibodies that immunize you against one virus may not guard against a different virus. For example, flu shots are given annually because each year a different flu virus causes the disease. A vaccine can prevent a disease, but it is not a cure. As you grow older, you will be exposed to many more types of pathogens and will build a separate immunity to each one.

TRY AT HOME Mini LAB

Determining Reproduction Rates

Procedure

1. Place one penny on a table. Imagine that the penny is a bacterium that can divide every 10 min.
2. Place **two pennies** below (but not under) the first penny to indicate the two bacteria present after the first bacterium divides.
3. Repeat three more divisions, placing two pennies under each penny in the row above.
4. Stop using pennies, wash your hands, and calculate how many bacteria you would have after 5 h of reproduction. Graph your data.

Analysis

1. How many bacteria are present after 5 h?
2. Why is it important to take antibiotics promptly if you have an infection?

Table 1 Cases of Disease Before and After Vaccine Availability in the U.S.

Disease	Average Number of Cases per Year Before Vaccine Available	Cases in 1998 After Vaccine Available
Measles	503,282	89
Diptheria	175,885	1
Tetanus	1,314	34
Mumps	152,209	606
Rubella	47,745	345
Pertussis (whooping cough)	147,271	6,279

Data from the National Immunization Program, CDC

TRY AT HOME Mini LAB

Purpose to model bacterial reproduction

Materials pennies, paper, pencil, calculator

Teaching Strategies

- Make sure students understand that bacteria reproduce exponentially, allowing their populations to grow very quickly.
- Students should label the vertical axis of the graph *Bacteria* (thousands) and the horizontal axis *Time* (hours).

Analysis

1. At the five-hour point, there will be 1,073,741,824 bacteria.
2. Taking antibiotics promptly will inhibit the reproduction of bacteria. It is also important to take all of the antibiotic prescribed. Failing to do so will leave a few bacteria that can reinfect the body.

Assessment

Performance To further assess students' understanding of bacterial infections, have them research a variety of bacteria that cause common infections. Possible topics: staphylococci, streptococci, *Mycobacterium tuberculosis, Treponema pallidum* Use **Performance Assessment in the Science Classroom,** p. 97.

Resource Manager

Chapter Resources Booklet

MiniLAB, p. 3
Enrichment, p. 28
Reinforcement, p. 25
Transparency Activity, pp. 45–46

Curriculum Connection

History In 1796, Edward Jenner pioneered the use of vaccines by inoculating a young boy with cowpox material to keep him from contracting the deadly disease smallpox. Editorial cartoons in the newspaper ridiculed the treatment and showed illustrations of people growing cow parts on their bodies as a result of being vaccinated. Have students find out more about Jenner's work. L2

Lines of Defense, continued

Discussion

Why might a person who is allergic to horse serum have an allergic reaction to a tetanus vaccine? The tetanus vaccine is often obtained from horse serum that contains the needed antibodies.

3 Assess

Reteach

Use an anatomy chart or model to illustrate the various body systems involved in defense against microbes. L2
LS **Visual-Spatial**

Challenge

Have students contrast the healing processes for cuts that were adequately cleaned and those that were not. Possible answers: Uncleaned cuts would most likely become infected, causing a sore to form, and taking longer to heal.

✓Assessment

Portfolio To assess students' understanding of active and passive immunity, have them draw a concept map comparing and contrasting the two. Use **PASC,** p. 161.

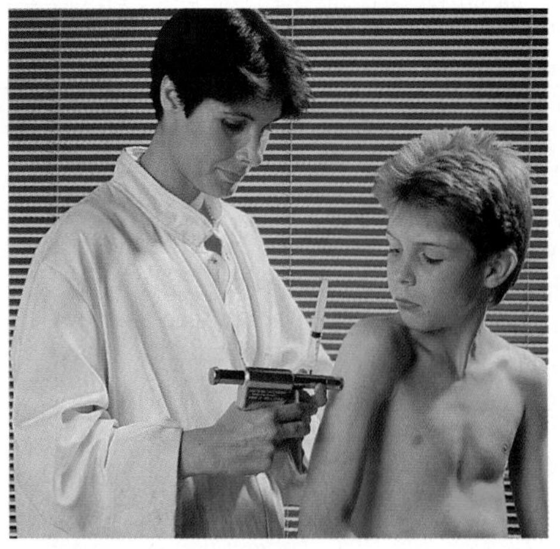

Figure 5
Between ages 14 and 16, immunization against diptheria and tetanus (DT) called booster shots are given.

Passive Immunity Passive immunity does not last as long as active immunity does. For example, you were born with all the antibodies that your mother had in her blood. However, these antibodies stayed with you for only a few months. Because newborn babies lose their passive immunity in a few months, they need to be vaccinated to develop their own immunity.

Tetanus Tetanus is a disease caused by a common soil bacterium. The bacterium produces a chemical that paralyzes muscles. Puncture wounds, deep cuts, and other wounds can be infected by this bacterium. Several times in early childhood you received active vaccines that stimulated antibody production to tetanus toxin. As shown in **Figure 5,** you should continue to get vaccines or boosters every ten years to maintain protection. Booster shots for diphtheria, which is a dangerous infectious respiratory disease, are given in the same vaccine with tetanus.

Suppose a person who hasn't been vaccinated against tetanus toxin gets a puncture wound. The person would be given passive immunity—antibodies to the toxin. These antibodies usually are from humans but can be from horses or cattle if human antibodies are not available. This passive immunity against tetanus lasts long enough to prevent the person from getting the disease. But he or she still needs to receive active vaccine to develop antibodies against tetanus and to maintain protection.

Section  Assessment

1. Describe how harmful bacteria cause infections in your body.
2. List natural defenses that your body has against disease.
3. How does an active vaccine work in the human body?
4. How does your immune system react when it detects an antigen?
5. **Think Critically** Several diseases have symptoms similar to those of measles. Why doesn't the measles vaccine protect you from all of these diseases?

Skill Builder Activities

6. **Making Models** Create models of the different types of T cells, antigens, and B cells from clay, construction paper, or other art materials. Use them to explain how T cells function in the immune system. **For more help, refer to the** **Science Skill Handbook.**
7. **Using a Word Processor** Using the information in this section, create a flowchart that compares active immunity and passive immunity. **For more help, refer to the** **Technology Skill Handbook.**

Answers to Section Assessment

1. Harmful bacteria enter your body and rapidly reproduce, causing you to get sick.
2. white blood cells, cilia, mucus, coughing, enzymes in the digestive system, hydrochloric acid, active immunity, sneezing, saliva, skin, perspiration, fever
3. It causes the immune system to produce antibodies against a specific antigen.
4. The body starts to make antibodies against the antigen to destroy it. After the antigen is destroyed, some antibodies remain in the bloodstream to combat the return of the antigen.
5. Antibodies formed to fight a specific antigen will protect only against that antigen.
6. Models should show the role of T cells in the response of the immune system to antigens.
7. Both confer immunity; active immunity—the body makes its own antibodies, long-term immunity; passive immunity—antibodies are introduced, short-term immunity.

662 CHAPTER 23 Immunity and Disease

SECTION 2 Infectious Diseases

Disease in History

For thousands of years, people have feared outbreaks of disease. The plague, smallpox, and influenza have killed millions of people worldwide. It is estimated that during the 1918 influenza outbreak, 20 million to 40 million people died, as **Table 2** shows. Today, the causes of these diseases are known, and treatments can prevent or cure them. But even today, there are diseases such as the Ebola virus in Africa that cannot be cured.

Discovering Disease Organisms With the invention of the microscope in the latter part of the seventeenth century, bacteria, yeast, and mold spores were seen for the first time. However, it took almost 200 years more to discover the relationship between some of them and disease. Scientists gradually learned that microorganisms were responsible for fermentation and decay. If decay-causing microorganisms could cause changes in other organisms, it was hypothesized that microorganisms could cause diseases and carry them from one person to another. Scientists did not make a connection between viruses and disease transmission until the late 1800s and early 1900s.

The French chemist Louis Pasteur learned that microorganisms might cause disease in humans. Many scientists of his time did not believe that microorganisms could harm larger organisms, such as humans. However, Pasteur discovered that microorganisms could spoil wine and milk. He then realized that microorganisms could attack the human body in the same way. Pasteur invented **pasteurization** (pas chuh ruh ZAY shun), which is the process of heating a liquid to a specific temperature that kills most bacteria.

As You Read

What **You'll Learn**

- **Describe** the work of Pasteur, Koch, and Lister in the discovery and prevention of disease.
- **Identify** diseases caused by viruses and bacteria.
- **List** sexually transmitted diseases, their causes, and treatments.
- **Explain** how HIV affects the immune system.

Vocabulary

pasteurization
virus
infectious disease
biological vector
sexually transmitted disease (STD)

Why **It's Important**

You can help prevent certain illnesses if you know what causes disease and how disease spreads.

Table 2 Deaths from the 1918 Influenza Epidemic

Country or Region	Estimated Number of Deaths
United States	550,000
United Kingdom	228,000
India	12,500,000
Africa	8,450,000
Australia and Samoa	2,988,000
Total Worldwide	20,000,000 to 40,000,000

SECTION 2

Infectious Diseases

1 Motivate

Bellringer Transparency

Display the Section Focus Transparency for Section 2. Use the accompanying Transparency Activity Master. L2 ELL

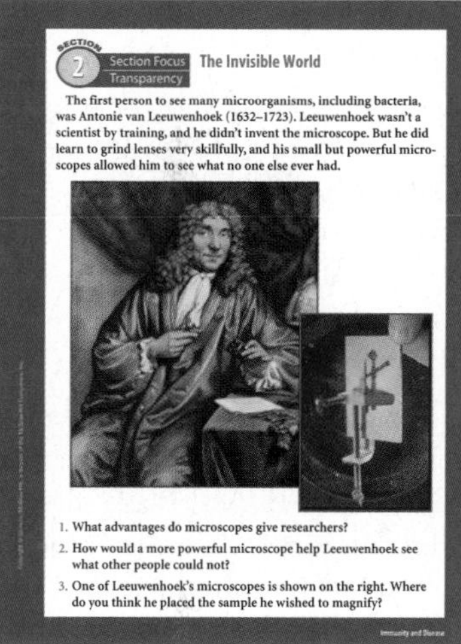

SECTION 2 Section Focus Transparency The Invisible World

The first person to see many microorganisms, including bacteria, was Antonie van Leeuwenhoek (1632–1723). Leeuwenhoek wasn't a scientist by training, and he didn't invent the microscope. But he did learn to grind lenses very skillfully, and his small but powerful microscopes allowed him to see what no one else ever had.

1. What advantages do microscopes give researchers?
2. How would a more powerful microscope help Leeuwenhoek see what other people could not?
3. One of Leeuwenhoek's microscopes is shown on the right. Where do you think he placed the sample he wished to magnify?

Tie to Prior Knowledge

Have students compare the population figures of their town with the 550,000 people who died in the United States in the 1918 flu epidemic. This is a graphic way of illustrating the effect disease has on history.

Section Assessment Planner

PORTFOLIO

Science Journal, p. 666

PERFORMANCE ASSESSMENT

MiniLAB, p. 666
Problem-Solving Activity, p. 667
Skill Builder Activities, p. 670
See page 684 for more options.

CONTENT ASSESSMENT

Section, p. 670
Challenge, p. 670
Chapter, pp. 684–685

Resource Manager

Chapter Resources Booklet

Transparency Activity, p. 43
Directed Reading for Content Mastery, p. 19

2 Teach

Disease in History

Quick Demo

Obtain prepared microscope slides of various stained bacteria to give students an idea of their sizes and shapes.

Reading Check

Answer The virus invades the host cell and multiples within it; the host cell dies when the viruses break out of it.

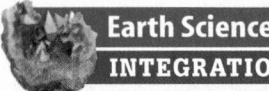

Earth Science INTEGRATION

The drug streptomycin comes from the mold *Streptomyces griseus,* and was discovered in 1943 after many years of research on soil microorganisms.

Make a Model

Have students prepare a display of Koch's Rules. Use agar or gelatin petri dishes. Place several bright-colored cake decorations (nonpareils) on the surface of the medium. The color will diffuse onto the surface to give the appearance of bacterial colonies.

L2 LS **Kinesthetic and Visual-Spatial**

Table 3 Human Diseases and Their Agents

Agent	Diseases
Bacteria	Tetanus, tuberculosis, typhoid fever, strep throat, bacterial pneumonia, plague
Protists	Malaria, sleeping sickness
Fungi	Athlete's foot, ringworm
Viruses	Colds, influenza, AIDS, measles, mumps, polio, smallpox

Disease Organisms Today, it is known that many diseases are caused by bacteria, certain viruses, protists (PROH tihsts), or fungi. **Table 3** lists some of the diseases caused by various groups of pathogens. Many harmful bacteria that infect your body can reproduce rapidly. The conditions in your body, such as temperature and available nutrients, help the bacteria grow and multiply. Bacteria can slow down the normal growth and metabolic activities of body cells and tissues. Some bacteria even produce toxins that kill cells on contact.

A **virus** is a minute piece of genetic material surrounded by a protein coating that infects and multiplies in host cells. The host cells die when the viruses break out of them. These new viruses infect other cells, leading to the destruction of tissues or the interruption of vital body activities.

Earth Science INTEGRATION

Soil contains many microorganisms—some that are harmful, such as tetanus bacteria, and some that are helpful. Some infections are treated with antibiotics made from bacteria and molds found in the soil. One such antibiotic is streptomycin. In your Science Journal, write a brief report about the drug streptomycin.

Reading Check *What is the relationship between a virus and a host cell?*

Pathogenic protists, such as the organisms that cause malaria, can destroy tissues and blood cells or interfere with normal body functions. In a similar manner, fungus infections can cause athlete's foot, nonhealing wounds, chronic lung disease, or inflammation of the membranes of the brain.

Koch's Rules Many diseases caused by pathogens can be treated with medicines. In many cases, these organisms need to be identified before specific treatment can begin. Today, a method developed in the nineteenth century still is used to identify organisms.

Pasteur may have shown that bacteria cause disease, but he didn't know how to tell which specific organism causes which disease. It was a young German doctor, Robert Koch, who first developed a way to isolate and grow one type of bacterium at a time, as shown in **Figure 6.**

LAB DEMONSTRATION

Purpose to observe microorganism growth

Materials sterile agar or gelatin plates, masking tape

Preparation Make or obtain prepared sterile agar petri plates. Have students wash their hands.

Procedure Have students lightly press their fingertips onto the surface of a sterile agar plate. Tape plates shut and place them in a dark place. Observe daily for several days. Don't open dishes. Carefully dispose of plates when done.

Expected Outcome small bacterial colonies and mold growth should be observed

Assessment

Why was there microbial growth even after hands were washed? Not all microorganisms were washed off the hands; some may have been in the air. **How could more microorganisms have been removed from the hands?** by washing them with antiseptic

Figure 6

In the 1880s, German doctor Robert Koch developed a series of methods for identifying which organism was the cause of a particular disease. Koch's Rules are still in use today. Developed mainly for determining the cause of particular diseases in humans and other animals, these rules have been used for identifying diseases in plants as well.

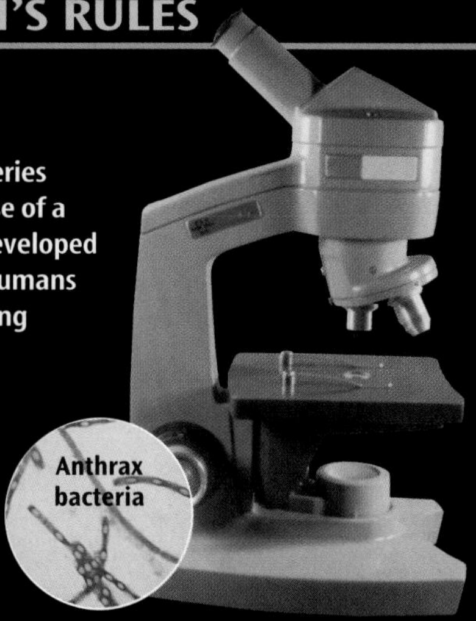

A In every case of a particular disease, the organism thought to cause the disease—the pathogen—must be present.

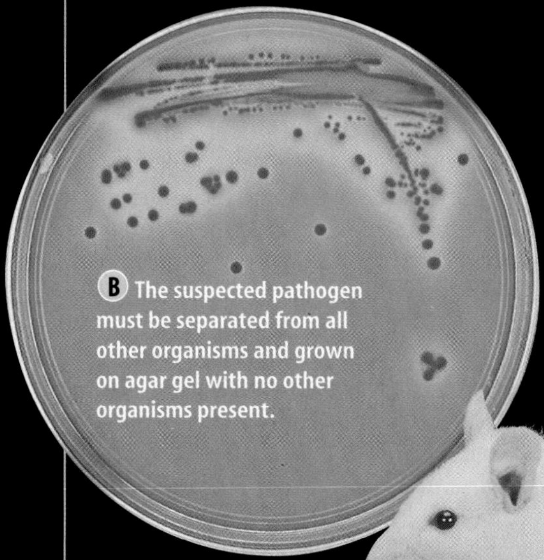

B The suspected pathogen must be separated from all other organisms and grown on agar gel with no other organisms present.

C When inoculated with the suspected pathogen, a healthy host must come down with the original illness.

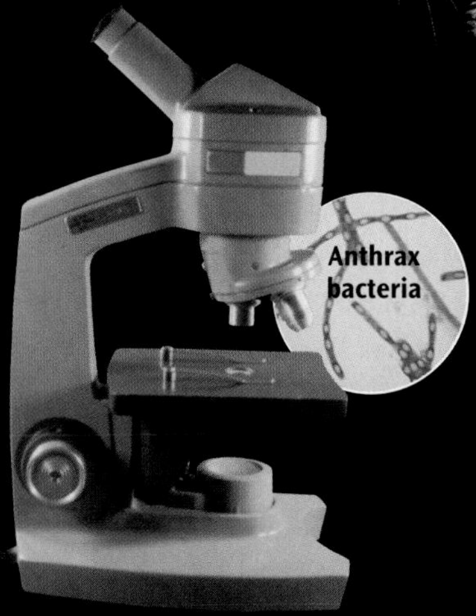

D Finally, when the suspected pathogen is removed from the host and grown on agar gel again, it must be compared with the original organism. Only when they match can that organism be identified as the pathogen that causes the disease.

Visualizing Koch's Rules

Have students examine the pictures and read the captions. Then ask the following questions.

Why does the suspected pathogen need to be grown on agar with no other organisms present? A suspected organism needs to be isolated (grown in a pure culture) to make sure that the suspected pathogen and only the suspected pathogen is inoculated into the healthy host. If not, there would be no way to know which organism caused the disease.

Why is it important to prove that a particular pathogen causes a particular disease? Possible answer: Knowing which pathogen causes a disease can help scientists develop treatments and preventative measures.

Activity

Have students write and perform a skit demonstrating Koch's rules. Possible characters include Robert Koch, and person or animal with a disease. Props: mouse, microscope, and petri dishes. IS **Interpersonal**

Extension

Challenge students to find out more about anthrax, a disease that Koch studied. Possible topics to investigate include which animals are affected, symptoms of the disease, how the disease is detected, and treatment. Have students make posters to explain what they found out.

Resource Manager 

Cultural Diversity, p. 17

Reading and Writing Skill Activities, p. 25

Disease in History, continued

Caption Answer

Figure 7 Hands, mouth, hair, and the patient's body are covered in the modern scene.

Purpose to observe the action of an antiseptic

L2 IS **Kinesthetic**

Materials dried yeast, glass plate or saucer, dropper, 3% hydrogen peroxide solution

Teaching Strategy If time is short, do this MiniLAB as a demonstration. Then have students answer the questions on their own.

Analysis

1. The bubbling action moves dirt and other substances out of the wound.
2. The oxygen that is released destroys bacteria in the wound and cleanses the tissue.

Assessment

Process Have students observe the action of hydrogen peroxide on a piece of raw meat and relate this to its antiseptic action. Use **Performance Assessment in the Science Classroom,** p. 89.

Reading Check

Possible answers use of antiseptics, filtering of air, sterilization techniques

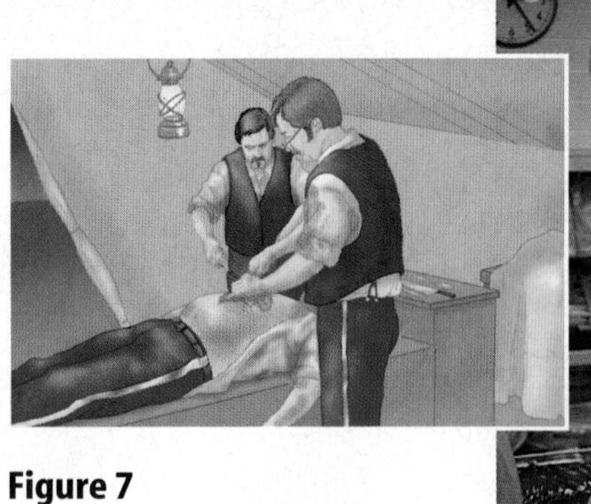

Figure 7
Antiseptics and strictly followed rules of cleanliness have made surgical procedures safer than they once were. *What differences do you see in the two operating scenes shown?*

Observing Antiseptic Action

Procedure

1. Place a few grains of **dried yeast** onto a **glass plate** or a saucer.
2. Add two drops of **hydrogen peroxide** to the yeast. Observe.
3. Clean up and wash hands before removing goggles.

Analysis

1. How does the action of hydrogen peroxide mechanically clean a wound?
2. Explain why hydrogen peroxide is classified as an antiseptic.

Keeping Clean Washing your hands before or after certain activities should be part of your daily routine. Restaurant employees are required to wash their hands immediately after using the rest room. Medical professionals wash their hands before examining each patient. However, hand washing was not always a routine, even for doctors. Into the late 1800s, doctors such as those in **Figure 7** regularly operated in their street clothes and with bare, unwashed hands. A bloody apron and well-used tools were considered signs of prestige for a surgeon. More patients died from the infections that they contracted during or after the surgery than from the surgery itself.

Joseph Lister, an English surgeon, recognized the relationship between the infection rate and cleanliness. Lister dramatically reduced the number of deaths among his patients by washing their skin and his hands with carbolic (kar BAH lihk) acid, which is a liquid that kills pathogens. Lister also used carbolic acid to clean his instruments and soak bandages, and he even sprayed the air with it. The odor was strong and it irritated the skin, but more and more people began to survive surgical procedures.

Modern Operating Procedures Today antiseptics and antiseptic soaps are used to kill pathogens on skin. Every person on the surgical team washes his or her hands thoroughly and wears sterile gloves and a covering gown. The patient's skin is cleaned around the area of the body to be operated on and then covered with sterile cloths. Tools that are used to operate on the patient and all operating room equipment also are sterilized. Even the air is filtered.

Reading Check *What are three ways that pathogens are reduced in today's operating room?*

Visual Learning

Figure 7 Note the contrast in concern for cleanliness in these illustrations. Have students explain why cleanliness is especially important in the emergency room of a hospital. Because so many people are treated there, rules of cleanliness are strictly observed to prevent the spread of pathogens.

Joseph Lister Have students research Lister's use of a carbolic spray in the operating room to reduce infection. They should infer how this might affect the surgeon's work and write a brief report. L2 IS **Linguistic** P

How Diseases Are Spread

You walk into your kitchen before school. Your younger sister sits at the table eating a bowl of cereal. She has a fever, a runny nose, and a cough. She coughs loudly. "Hey, cover your mouth! I don't want to catch your cold," you tell her. A disease that is caused by a virus, bacterium, protist, or fungus and is spread from an infected organism or the environment to another organism is called an **infectious disease.** Infectious diseases are spread by direct contact with the infected organism, through water and air, on food, by contact with contaminated objects, and by disease-carrying organisms called **biological vectors.** Examples of vectors that have been sources of disease are rats, birds, cats, dogs, mosquitoes, fleas, and flies, as shown in **Figure 8.**

People also can be carriers of disease. When you have influenza and sneeze, you expel thousands of virus particles into the air. Colds and many other diseases are spread through contact. Each time you turn a doorknob, press the button on a water fountain, or use a telephone, your skin comes in contact with bacteria and viruses, which is why regular handwashing is recommended. The Centers for Disease Control and Prevention (CDC) in Atlanta, Georgia, monitors the spread of diseases throughout the United States. The CDC also tracks worldwide epidemics and watches for diseases brought into the United States.

Figure 8
When flies land on food, they can transport pathogens from one person to another.

Problem-Solving Activity

Has the annual percentage of deaths from major diseases changed?

Each year, many people die from diseases. Medical science has found numerous ways to treat and cure disease. Have new medicines, improved surgery techniques, and healthier lifestyles helped decrease the number of deaths from disease? By using your ability to interpret data tables, you can find out.

Identifying the Problem

The table to the right shows the percentage of total deaths due to six major diseases for a 45-year time period. Study the data for each disease. Can you see any trends in the percentage of deaths?

Solving the Problem

1. Has the percentage increased for any disease that is listed?
2. What factors could have contributed to this increase?

Percentage of Deaths Due to Major Diseases

Disease	Year			
	1950	1980	1990	1995
Heart	37.1	38.3	33.5	32.0
Cancer	14.6	20.9	23.5	23.3
Stroke	10.8	8.6	6.7	6.8
Diabetes	1.7	1.8	2.2	2.6
Pneumonia and Flu	3.3	2.7	3.7	3.6
Tuberculosis	2.3	0.1	0.08	0.06

How Diseases Are Spread

Use an Analogy

When a fly walks across the table and onto food, you may not be able to see its tracks, but it is analogous to a dog walking across the floor with muddy paws. Both leave a trail of debris that can contain bacteria.

Teacher FYI

Several terms are used to describe patterns of disease occurrence. *Endemic* refers to diseases that are constantly present at a certain level in a given geographic area. *Epidemic* refers to cases of disease that occur above the normal expectancy in a community or region. For example, two cases of a very rare disease in a city many constitute an epidemic. *Pandemic* diseases are epidemics that occur worldwide.

Use Science Words

Word Usage Have students use the word *vector* in a sentence. Possible answer: Certain mosquitoes are vectors of malaria. L2 LS **Linguistic**

Problem-Solving Activity

National Math Standards

Correlation to Mathematics Objectives
1,5,6,8,9,10

Answers

1. yes; cancer, diabetes and pneumonia and flu
2. Possible answers: changes in lifestyles, increase in pollution, and better medical disease identification

Resource Manager

Chapter Resources Booklet
MiniLAB, p. 4
Enrichment, p. 29

Curriculum Connection

History Have students research the effects of malaria and yellow fever on the construction of the Panama Canal. L2 ELL LS **Linguistic**

Sexually Transmitted Diseases

Extension

Have students research the relationship between the herpes simplex virus type 2 and the herpes simplex virus type 1 that causes cold sores. L2 LS **Linguistic**

IDENTIFYING Misconceptions

There is a belief that sexually transmitted diseases can be contracted through casual contact, such as touching a person with the disease or handling an object touched by such a person. STDs are not transmitted through casual contact. There must be direct contact with bodily fluids such as blood, semen, or vaginal secretions.

Teacher FYI

In the development of untreated syphilis, there is a period when victims may believe they have healed. Lesions heal and outward symptoms disappear. However, the bacteria have already migrated to many parts of the body such as the spleen, liver, and various sites in the circulatory and nervous systems. After a few months the bacteria again manifest themselves through skin and mouth rashes and the loss of hair and teeth. These outward symptoms also may disappear and once again give false hope of healing. If untreated for long enough, syphilis can attack the brain and cause mental illness.

Sexually Transmitted Diseases

Infectious diseases that are passed from person to person during sexual contact are called **sexually transmitted diseases (STDs).** STDs are caused by bacteria or viruses.

Bacterial STDs Gonorrhea (gah nuh REE uh), and chlamydia (kluh MIH dee uh) are STDs caused by bacteria. The bacteria that cause gonorrhea are shown in **Figure 9A.** A person may have one of these diseases for some time before symptoms appear. When symptoms do appear, they can include painful urination, genital discharge, and genital sores. Antibiotics are used to treat these diseases. Some of the bacteria that cause gonorrhea may be resistant to the antibiotics usually used to treat the infection. However, the disease usually can be treated with other antibiotics. If they are untreated, gonorrhea and chlamydia can leave a person sterile because the reproductive organs can be damaged permanently.

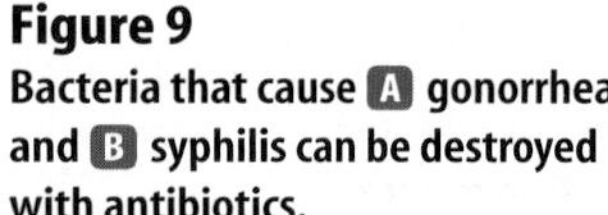

Figure 9
Bacteria that cause A gonorrhea and B syphilis can be destroyed with antibiotics.

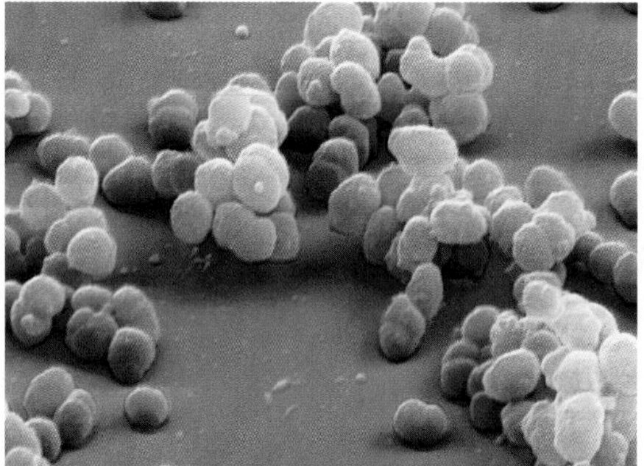
Magnification: 1,200×

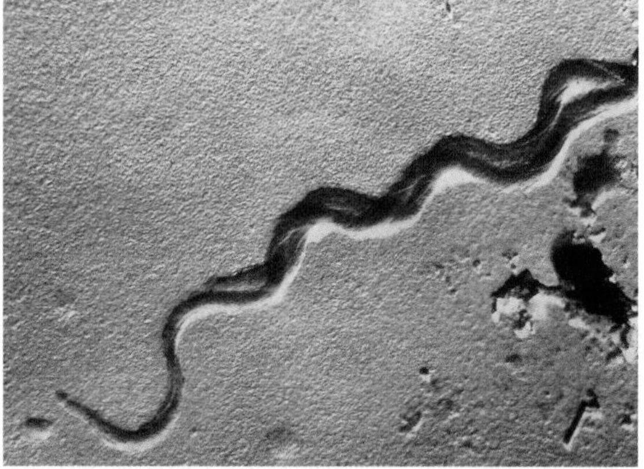
Magnification: 19,000×

The spiral-shaped bacterium that causes syphilis (SIH fuh lus) is seen in **Figure 9B.** Syphilis has three stages. In stage 1, a sore that lasts 10 to 14 days appears on the mouth or genitals. Stage 2 may involve a rash, fever, and swollen lymph glands. Within weeks to a year, these symptoms usually disappear. The person with syphilis often believes that the disease has gone away, but it hasn't. If he or she does not seek treatment, the disease advances to stage 3, when syphilis may infect the cardiovascular and nervous systems. In all stages, syphilis is treatable with antibiotics. However, the damage to body organs in stage 3 cannot be reversed and death can result.

Viral STDs Genital herpes, a lifelong viral disease, causes painful blisters on the sex organs. This type of herpes can be transmitted during sexual contact or from an infected mother to her child during birth. The herpes virus hides in the body for long periods of time and then reappears suddenly. Herpes has no cure, and no vaccine can prevent it. However, the symptoms of herpes can be treated with antiviral medicines.

Curriculum Connection

Health The previous indiscriminate use of antibiotics in the treatment of STDs has resulted in the development of drug-resistant strains of bacteria. Modern methods of treatment use more potent forms of antibiotics and combinations of drugs. Ask students to write a paragraph about the problems that drug-resistant bacteria pose for individuals and society. L2 ELL LS **Linguistic**

Resource Manager

Mathematics Skill Activities, p. 1

Reading and Writing Skill Activities, p. 31

HIV and Your Immune System

Human immunodeficiency virus (HIV) can exist in blood and body fluids. This virus can hide in body cells, sometimes for years. You can become infected with HIV by having sex with an HIV-infected person or by reusing an HIV-contaminated hypodermic needle for an injection. However, a freshly unwrapped sterile needle cannot transmit infection. The risk of getting HIV through blood transfusion is small because all donated blood is tested for the presence of HIV. A pregnant female with HIV can infect her child when the virus passes through the placenta. The child also may become infected from contacts with blood during the birth process or when nursing after birth.

Reading Check ***What are ways that a person can become infected with HIV?***

HIV cannot multiply outside the body, and it does not survive long in the environment. The virus cannot be transmitted by touching an infected person, by handling objects used by the person unless they are contaminated with body fluids, or from contact with a toilet seat.

AIDS An HIV infection can lead to Acquired Immune Deficiency Syndrome (AIDS), which is a disease that attacks the body's immune system. HIV, as shown in **Figure 10,** is different from other viruses. It attacks the helper T cells in the immune system. The virus enters the T cell and multiplies. When the infected cell bursts open, it releases more HIV. These infect other T cells. Soon, so many T cells are destroyed that not enough B cells are stimulated to produce antibodies. The body no longer has an effective way to fight invading antigens. The immune system then is unable to fight HIV or any other pathogen. For this reason, when people with AIDS die it is from other diseases such as tuberculosis (too bur kyuh LOH sus), pneumonia, or cancer.

From 1981 to 1999, more than 724,000 cases of AIDS were documented in the United States. At this time the disease has no known cure. However, several medications help treat AIDS in some patients. One group of medicines, such as AZT, interferes with the way that the virus multiplies in the host cell and is effective if it is used in the early stages of the disease. Another group of medicines that is being tested blocks the entrance of HIV into the host cell. These medicines prevent the pathogen from binding to the cell's surface.

Data Update Visit the Glencoe Science Web site at **science.glencoe.com** for recent data about the the number of AIDS cases worldwide. Communicate to your class what you learn.

Figure 10
A person can be infected with HIV and not show any symptoms of the infection for several years.
Why does this characteristic make the spread of AIDS more likely?

Magnification: 130,000×

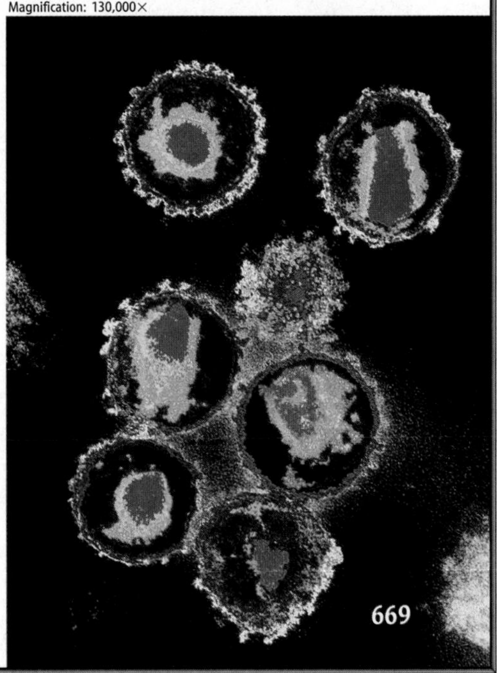

669

HIV and Your Immune System

Reading Check

Answer By having sex with an HIV-infected person, or using a hypodermic needle contaminated with fluids from an infected person; a baby can get it from its mother; there is a small chance of getting it from a blood transfusion.

Teacher FYI

The first case of AIDS was reported in the United States in 1981. It was not until 1984 that research teams in France and the United States identified the virus responsible for the disease. There is evidence that the disease was transmitted from African green monkeys to humans, possibly from the bite of a monkey.

Discussion

How can a person determine if he or she is infected with HIV? A blood sample is taken and analyzed for the antibodies against the virus. The presence of the antibodies confirms the person has HIV.

Caption Answer

Figure 10 A person may not take the necessary health precautions to avoid spreading the virus if he or she is unaware that the disease was contracted.

Internet Addresses

Explore the Glencoe Science Web site at **science.glencoe.com** to find out more about topics in this section.

Cultural Diversity

Native American Herbs Explorers and pioneers in the Americas learned a great deal from Native Americans about the healing power of certain herbs. Have students find out about the use of herbs by Native Americans in the treatment of disease symptoms. Possible topics: ipecac, cinchona, witch hazel, and cascara sagrada L2

LS **Linguistic**

Fighting Disease

Discussion

What are other good health habits that can help the body fight disease? Possible answer: Getting sufficient sleep allows the body to repair itself and restore energy resources. Drinking lots of water each day helps maintain body fluids necessary for bodily functions.

3 Assess

Reteach

Review the concept of microorganisms as causes of infections and the need to keep clean. L1

Challenge

Why do you think having a garbage collection system helps prevent disease? Possible answer: Garbage can be a breeding place for many kinds of disease-carrying organisms.

Assessment

Portfolio Assess students' abilities to recognize cause and effect by having them describe in writing the effect of sneezing on the spread of microorganisms. Use **Performance Assessment in the Science Classroom,** p. 159.

Figure 11
Proper hand washing includes using warm water and soap. The soapy lather must be rubbed over the hands, wrists, fingers, and thumbs for 15-20 s. Thoroughly rinse and dry with a clean towel.

Fighting Disease

Washing a small wound with soap and water is the first step in preventing an infection. Cleaning the wound with an antiseptic and covering it with a bandage are other steps. Is it necessary to wash your body to help prevent diseases? Yes! In addition to reducing body odor, washing your body removes and destroys some surface microorganisms. In medical facilities, hand washing as shown in **Figure 11,** is important to reduce the spread of pathogens. It is also important for everyone to wash his or her hands to reduce the spread of disease.

In your mouth, microorganisms are responsible for mouth odor and tooth decay. Using dental floss and routine tooth brushing keep these organisms under control.

Exercise and good nutrition help the circulatory and respiratory systems work more effectively. Good health habits, including getting enough rest and eating well-balanced meals, can make you less susceptible to the actions of disease organisms such as those that cause colds and flu. Keeping up with recommended immunizations and having annual health checkups also can help you stay healthy.

Section 2 Assessment

1. How did the discoveries of Pasteur, Koch, and Lister help in the battle against the spread of disease?
2. List an infectious disease caused by each of the following: *a virus, a bacterium, a protist,* and *a fungus.*
3. How is the way HIV affects the immune system different from other viruses?
4. What are STDs? How are they contracted and treated?
5. **Think Critically** In what ways does Koch's procedure demonstrate the use of scientific methods?

Skill Builder Activities

6. **Recognizing Cause and Effect** How is poor cleanliness related to the spread of disease? Write your answer in your Science Journal. **For more help, refer to the** Science Skill Handbook.
7. **Making and Using Graphs** Make a bar graph using the following data about the number of deaths from AIDS-related diseases for children younger than 13 years old: *1995, 536; 1996, 420; 1997, 209; 1998, 115; and 1999, 76.* **For more help, refer to the** Science Skill Handbook.

Answers to Section Assessment

1. Pasteur: discovered bacteria could cause disease; Koch: developed methods to isolate bacteria; Lister: related infection to lack of cleanliness.
2. Possible answers: virus–genital herpes; bacterium–syphilis; protist–malaria; fungus–athlete's foot
3. It attacks the helper T cells in the immune system.
4. sexually transmitted diseases; contracted through sexual activity with an infected person; those caused by bacteria are treated with antibiotics; symptoms of viral STDs can often be alleviated with antiviral medicines
5. Possible answer: Koch used strict isolation techniques and retested suspected pathogens.
6. Poor cleanliness can allow disease organisms on the body to be transmitted to other people through physical contact or contact with a common object.
7. Check bar graph to ensure it matches data given.

Activity

Microorganisms and Disease

Microorganisms are everywhere. Washing your hands and disinfecting items you use helps remove some of these organisms.

What You'll Investigate

How do microorganisms cause infection?

Materials

fresh apples (6)
rotting apple
rubbing alcohol (5 mL)
self-sealing plastic bags (6)
labels and pencil
latex gloves
paper towels
sandpaper
cotton ball
soap and water
newspaper

Goals

- **Observe** the transmission of microorganisms.
- **Relate** microorganisms to infections.

Safety Precautions

WARNING: *Do not eat the apples. Do not remove goggles until the activity and cleanup are completed.* When you complete the experiment, give all bags to your teacher for disposal, then wash your hands.

Procedure

1. **Label** the plastic bags 1 through 6. Put on gloves. Place a fresh apple in bag 1.
2. Rub the rotting apple over the other five apples. This is your source of microorganisms. **WARNING:** *Don't touch your face.*
3. Put one apple in bag 2.
4. Hold one apple 1.5 m above the floor and drop it on a newspaper. Put it in bag 3.
5. Rub one apple with sandpaper. Place this apple in bag 4.
6. Wash one apple with soap and water. Dry it well. Put this apple in bag 5.
7. Use a cotton ball to spread alcohol over the last apple. Let it air dry. Place it in bag 6.
8. Seal all bags and put them in a dark place.
9. On day 3 and day 7, compare all of the apples without removing them from the bags. **Record** your observations in a data table.

Apple Observations

Condition	Day 3	Day 7
1. Fresh	no change	no change
2. Untreated	no change	some decay
3. Dropped	brown spots	some decay
4. Rubbed with sandpaper	some brown at soft areas	decay at soft areas
5. Washed with soap and water	no change	little or no change
6. Covered with alcohol	no change	no change

Conclude and Apply

1. How does this experiment relate to infections on your skin?
2. Why is it important to clean a wound?

Communicating Your Data

Prepare a poster illustrating the advantages of washing hands to avoid the spread of disease. Get permission to put the poster near a school rest room. **For more help, refer to the** Science Skill Handbook.

Activity

Purpose to predict and explain how microbes spread L2
LS **Visual-Spatial**

Process Skills observing and inferring, predicting, interpreting data, comparing and contrasting, recognizing cause and effect, separating and controlling variables

Time Required 30 minutes for initial setup; 15 minutes of observation time on days 3 and 7

Safety Precautions Have students wash their hands after handling microorganisms. Provide for safe disposal of the rotting apples.

Teaching Strategy Point out that bruises may be caused by bacteria.

Answers to Questions

1. Pathogens can cause infections by entering damaged or cut surfaces on an organism's skin.
2. Cleaning a wound removes pathogens and prevents infection.

Assessment

Performance To further assess students' understanding of microorganisms and disease, repeat the activity using 3% hydrogen peroxide to clean an infected apple. Determine whether it stops bacterial growth. Use **PASC,** p. 97.

Resource Manager

Chapter Resources Booklet
Reinforcement, p. 26
Activity Worksheet, pp. 5–6

Communicating Your Data

Students may want to include other good health habits that will help them fight disease. Posters dealing with good nutrition might be posted near the school cafeteria.

SECTION

Noninfectious Diseases

1 Motivate

Bellringer Transparency

Display the Section Focus Transparency for Section 3. Use the accompanying Transparency Activity Master. L2 ELL

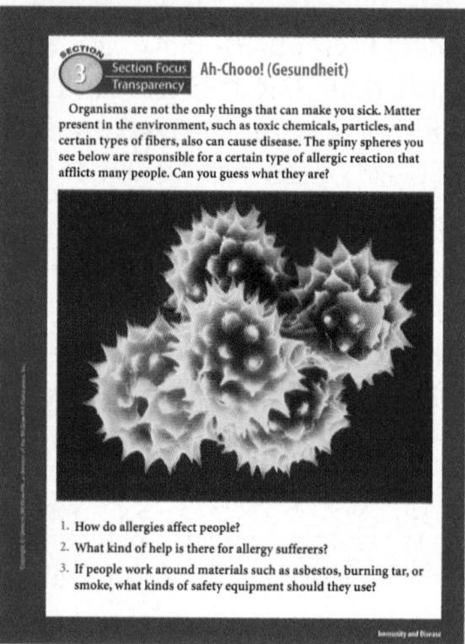

Section Focus Transparency 3 Ah-Chooo! (Gesundheit)

Organisms are not the only things that can make you sick. Matter present in the environment, such as toxic chemicals, particles, and certain types of fibers, also can cause disease. The spiny spheres you see below are responsible for a certain type of allergic reaction that afflicts many people. Can you guess what they are?

1. How do allergies affect people?
2. What kind of help is there for allergy sufferers?
3. If people work around materials such as asbestos, burning tar, or smoke, what kinds of safety equipment should they use?

Tie to Prior Knowledge

Have students recall that some diseases are not "catching." They are not transmitted by pathogens. Have students list as many of these diseases as they can. Possible answers: cancer, heart disease, leukemia, diabetes

SECTION

Noninfectious Diseases

As You Read

***What* You'll Learn**

- **Define** noninfectious diseases and list causes of them.
- **Describe** the basic characteristics of cancer.
- **Explain** what happens during an allergic reaction.

Vocabulary

noninfectious disease
allergy
allergen
chemotherapy

***Why* It's Important**

Knowing the causes of noninfectious diseases can help you understand their prevention and treatment.

Chronic Disease

It's a beautiful, late-summer day. Flowers are blooming everywhere. You and your cousin hurry to get to the ballpark before the first pitch of the game. "Achoo!" Your cousin sneezes. Her eyes are watery and red. "Oh no! I sure don't want to catch that cold," you mutter. "I don't have a cold," she responds, "it's my allergies." Not all diseases are caused by pathogens. Diseases and disorders such as diabetes, allergies, asthma, cancer, and heart disease are **noninfectious diseases.** They are not spread from one person to another. Many are chronic (KRAH nihk). This means that they can last for a long time. Although some chronic diseases can be cured, others cannot.

Some infectious diseases can be chronic too. For example, deer ticks carry a bacterium that causes Lyme disease. This bacterium can affect the nervous system, heart, and joints for weeks to years. It can become chronic if not treated. Antibiotics will kill the bacteria, but some damage cannot be reversed.

Allergies

If you've had an itchy rash after eating a certain food, you probably have an allergy to that food. An **allergy** is an overly strong reaction of the immune system to a foreign substance. Many people have allergic reactions to cosmetics, shellfish, strawberries, peanuts, and insect stings. Most allergic reactions are minor, as shown in **Figure 12.** However, severe allergic reactions can occur, causing shock and even death if they aren't treated promptly.

A

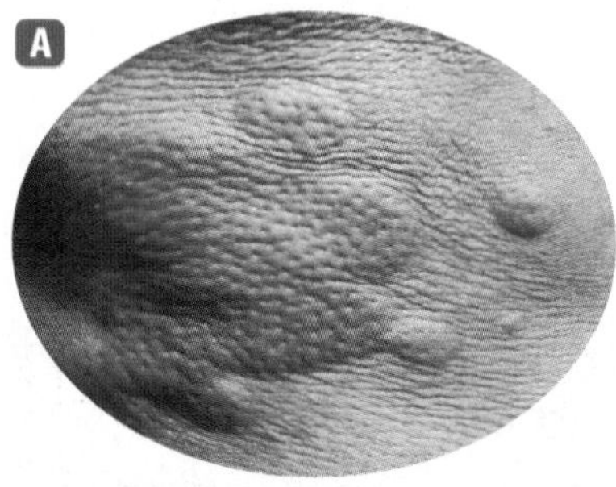

B

Figure 12
Allergic reactions are caused by many things. A Hives are one kind of allergic reaction. B Some common substances stimulate allergic responses in people.

Section Assessment Planner

PORTFOLIO
Extension, p. 674

PERFORMANCE ASSESSMENT
Skill Builder Activities, p. 677
See page 684 for more options.

CONTENT ASSESSMENT
Section, p. 677
Challenge, p. 677
Chapter, pp. 684–685

672 CHAPTER 23 Immunity and Disease

Allergens Substances that cause an allergic response are called **allergens.** Some chemicals, certain foods, pollen, molds, some antibiotics, and dust are allergens for some people. Some foods cause hives or stomach cramps and diarrhea. Pollen can cause a stuffy nose, breathing difficulties, watery eyes, and a tired feeling in some people. Dust can contain cat and dog dander and dust mites, as shown in **Figure 13.** Asthma (AZ muh) is a lung disorder that is associated with reactions to allergens. A person with asthma can have shortness of breath, wheezing, and coughing when he or she comes into contact with something they are allergic to.

When you come in contact with an allergen, your immune system usually forms antibodies. Your body reacts by releasing chemicals called histamines (HIHS tuh meenz) that promote red, swollen tissues. Antihistamines are medications that can be used to treat allergic reactions and asthma. Some severe allergies are treated with repeated injections of small doses of the allergen. This allows your body to become less sensitive to the allergen.

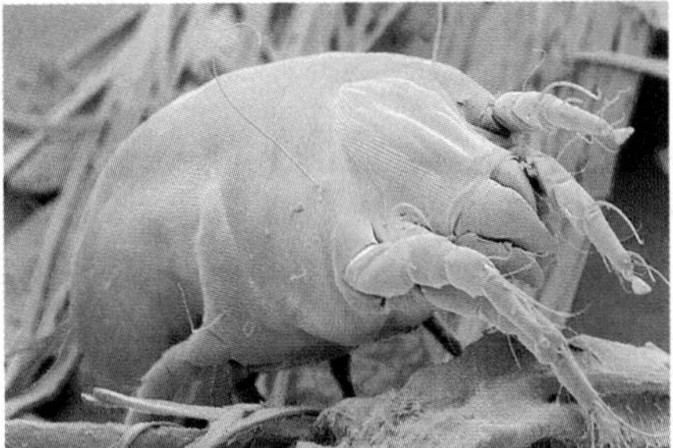

Figure 13
Dust mites are smaller than a period at the end of a sentence. They can live in pillows, mattresses, carpets, furniture, and other places.

 *What does your body release in response to an allergen?*

Diabetes

A chronic disease associated with the levels of insulin produced by the pancreas is diabetes. Insulin is a hormone that enables glucose to pass from the bloodstream into your cells. Doctors recognize two types of diabetes—Type 1 and Type 2. Type 1 diabetes is the result of too little or no insulin production. In Type 2 diabetes, your body cannot properly process the insulin. Symptoms of diabetes include fatigue, excessive thirst, frequent urination, and tingling sensations in the hands and feet.

If glucose levels in the blood remain high for a long time, health problems can develop. These problems can include blurred vision, kidney failure, heart attack, stroke, loss of feeling in the feet, and the loss of consciousness (diabetic coma). Patients with Type 1 diabetes, as shown in **Figure 14,** must monitor their intake of sugars and usually require daily injections of insulin to control their glucose levels. Careful monitoring of diet and weight usually are enough to control Type 2 diabetes. Since 1980, there has been an increase in the number of people with diabetes. Although the cause of diabetes is unknown, scientists have discovered that Type 2 diabetes is more common in people who are overweight and that it might be inherited.

Figure 14
Type 1 diabetes requires daily monitoring by either checking the amount of glucose in blood or the amount excreted in urine.

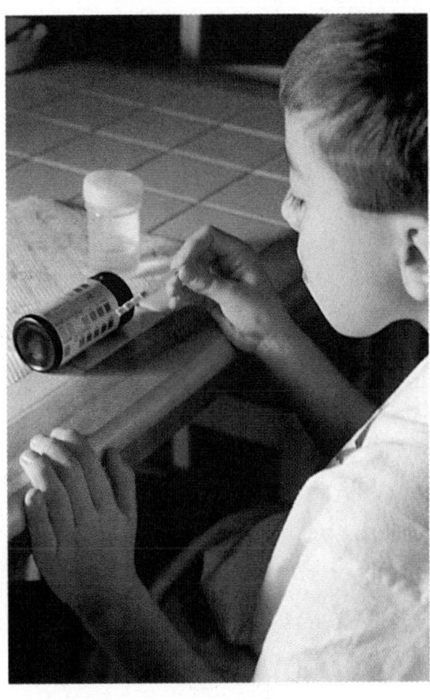

2 Teach

Allergies

Teacher FYI

Sometimes the body may experience an intense reaction to an allergen, causing blood vessels to dilate and bronchiole tubes to constrict. This condition is known as anaphylactic shock and can lead to death if not treated. A single bee sting to a hypersensitive person can trigger anaphylactic shock.

Reading Check

Answer histamines

Use an Analogy

The neutralizing action of antihistamines to the histamines produced in allergic reactions can be compared to acids neutralizing bases in chemical reactions.

Diabetes

Teacher FYI

An estimated 15 million people in the United States have diabetes, but only two-thirds of them are aware of it. Only about 10 percent of people with diabetes have Type 1; about 90 percent have Type 2.

Resource Manager

Chapter Resources Booklet
Transparency Activity, p. 44
Directed Reading for Content Mastery, pp. 19, 20
Cultural Diversity, pp. 15–23

Inclusion Strategies

Gifted Have a team of students prepare a joint report and a poster on first aid procedures for individuals who are experiencing a severe allergic reaction. Have them present their material to the class. L3 ELL COOP LEARN  **Interpersonal**

Chemicals and Disease

Teacher FYI

Many people are exposed to chemicals and other pollutants that adversely affect the environment. Chemicals released into the air can damage the ozone layer and produce smog and acid precipitation. Agricultural chemicals build up in our waterways. Research to understand the cause-and-effect relationship between pollutants and some chronic diseases is underway.

Discussion

People often think only about air, water, and soil pollution. Pollution is also found in our homes. **What are some sources of pollutants in homes?** Possible answer: Carpets, curtains, furniture, and insulation may contain chemicals that can cause illness.

Activity

Have students compare the chemicals in bottled spring water with those found in their tap water at home. L2 ELL LS **Visual-Spatial**

Extension

When air pollution reaches a level considered unsafe, the EPA issues an alert. Have students research what activities must be curtailed during these alerts to prevent a further decrease in air quality. Have them make a list of activities and write a paragraph about what they have found. Possible answers: decrease in use of gas powered lawn and garden equipment; use of household, workshop, and garden chemicals L2 LS **Linguistic** P

Chemicals and Disease

Chemistry INTEGRATION Chemicals are everywhere—in your body, the foods you eat, cosmetics, cleaning products, pesticides, fertilizers, and building materials. Of the thousands of chemical substances used by consumers, less than two percent are harmful. Those chemicals that are harmful to living things are called toxins, as shown in **Figure 15.** Toxins can cause birth defects, cell mutations, cancers, tissue damage, chronic diseases, and death.

The Effects The amount of a chemical that is taken into your body and how long your body is in contact with it determine how it affects you. For example, low levels of a toxin might cause cardiac or respiratory problems. However, higher levels of the same toxin might cause death. Some chemicals, such as the asbestos shown in **Figure 15C,** can be inhaled over a long period of time. Eventually, the asbestos can cause chronic diseases of the lungs. Lead-based paints, if ingested, can accumulate in your body and eventually cause damage to the central nervous system. Another toxin, ethyl (EH thul) alcohol, is found in beer, wine, and liquor. It can cause birth defects in the children of mothers who drink alcohol during pregnancy.

Manufacturing, mining, transportation, and farming produce chemical wastes. These chemical substances interfere with the ability of soil, water, and air to support life. Pollution, caused by harmful chemicals, sometimes produces chronic diseases in humans. For example, long-term exposure to carbon monoxide, sulfur oxides, and nitrogen oxides in the air might cause a number of diseases, including bronchitis, emphysema (em fuh ZEE muh), and lung cancer.

Figure 15
Toxins can be in the environment.

A Chemical spills can be dangerous and might end up in groundwater.

B These scientists are testing the contents of barrels found in a dump.

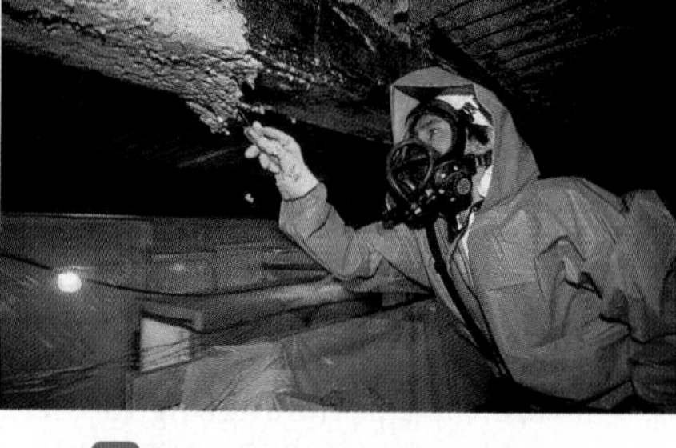

C Asbestos, if inhaled into the lungs over a long period of time, can cause chronic diseases of the lungs. Protective clothing must be worn when removing asbestos.

674

Curriculum Connection

Health Have an employee of the Environmental Protection Agency explain how various pollutants are monitored in the local community and discuss any health problems associated with the pollutants. Ask students to have questions prepared. L1 LS **Linguistic**

Visual Learning

Figure 15 These figures show harmful chemicals that have been found and are being properly disposed of. **What are some examples of chemicals that may be improperly disposed of and will not be found?** Possible answer: Homeowners may dispose of hazardous chemicals such as batteries, paints, and pesticides with their regular trash.

Table 4 Characteristics of Cancer Cells
Cell growth is uncontrolled.
These cells do not function as part of your body.
The cells take up space and interfere with normal bodily functions.
The cells travel throughout your body.
The cells produce tumors and abnormal growths anywhere in your body.

Cancer

Cancer has been a disease of humans since ancient times. Egyptian mummies show evidence of bone cancer. Ancient Greek scientists described several different kinds of cancers. Even medieval manuscripts report details about the disease.

Cancer is the name given to a group of closely related diseases that result from uncontrolled cell growth. It is a complicated disease, and no one fully understands how cancers form. Characteristics of cancer cells are shown in **Table 4.** Certain regulatory molecules in the body control the beginning and ending of cell division. If this control is lost, a mass of cells called a tumor (TEW mur) results from this abnormal growth. Tumors can occur anywhere in your body. Cancerous cells can leave a tumor, spread throughout the body via blood and lymph vessels, and then invade other tissues.

Reading Check *How do cancers spread?*

Environmental Science INTEGRATION

Dioxin is a dangerous chemical found in small amounts in certain herbicides. It can cause miscarriages, cancers, and liver disorders. Research to find out about the dioxin contamination in Times Beach, Missouri. Write a brief report in your Science Journal.

Types of Cancers Cancers can develop in any body tissue or organ. Leukemia (lew KEE mee uh) is a cancer of white blood cells. The cancerous white blood cells are immature and are no longer effective in fighting disease. The cancer cells multiply in the bone marrow and crowd out red blood cells, normal white blood cells, and platelets. Cancer of the lungs often starts in the bronchi and then spreads into the lungs. The surface area for air exchange in the lungs is reduced and breathing becomes difficult. Colorectal cancer, or cancer of the large intestine, is one of the leading causes of death among men and women. Changes in bowel movements and blood in the feces may be indications of the disease. In breast cancer, tumors grow in the breast. The second most common cancer in males is cancer of the prostate gland, which is an organ that surrounds the urethra.

Cancer

Activity

Have students research the top ten causes of death in the United States and identify which are infectious and which are noninfectious. L2 **LS Logical-Mathematical**

Environmental Science INTEGRATION

Dioxin was found as a contaminant in the oil that was spread on the roads in Times Beach. The entire town was abandoned in 1983 and much of the surface soil was incinerated.

Reading Check

Answer Cancer cells may leave a tumor and move throughout the body via the blood and lymph vessels.

People are often heard to say, "Everything causes cancer, so why bother to do anything?". The fact is that there are a number of specific actions a person can take to reduce the risk of cancer. Students should take these seriously.

Resource Manager

Home and Community Involvement, p. 45

Life Science Critical Thinking/Problem Solving, pp. 4, 17

Science Inquiry Labs, p. 39

Inclusion Strategies

Hearing Impaired Have students request pamphlets from health organizations such as the American Heart Association, the American Cancer Society, the American Diabetes Association, and the Arthritis Foundation, to learn about new treatment methods for some chronic diseases and arrange a bulletin board display for the classroom. L1 **LS Linguistic**

Cancer, continued

Use Science Words

Word Origin The Latin word for the crab, a crustacean, is *cancer*. Ask students to relate the activities of this animal to the spread of cancer cells. Possible answer: Crabs are known for their tenacious hold on prey with their claws. Cancer cells are tenacious in their invasion of tissues.

Discussion

Have students research the relationship between being fair-skinned and having a greater risk for skin cancer. Have them discuss their findings. Fair-skinned people have less of the pigment melanin which protects skin cells from UV rays. With less of this pigment, cells and even genes may be damaged and these cells may develop into skin cancers. **How can the use of a sunscreen help?** Sunscreens block UV rays.

Teacher FYI

Cancer is often thought of as a disease of industrial times. However, examination of bones from Neolithic people, Egyptian mummies, and pre-Columbian Native Americans has revealed tumors. Ancient writings from Egypt, Babylon, and India give descriptions of malignant tumors. Hippocrates, a Greek physician of the third century B.C., described the differences between benign and malignant tumors.

Figure 16
Tobacco products have been linked directly to lung cancer. Some chemicals around the home are carcinogenic.

Causes In the latter part of the eighteenth century, a British physician recognized the association of soot to cancer in chimney sweeps. Since that time, scientists have learned more about causes of cancer. Research done in the 1940s and 1950s related genes to cancer.

Although not all the causes of cancer are known, many causes have been identified. Smoking has been linked to lung cancer. Lung cancer is the leading cause of cancer deaths for males in the United States. Exposure to certain chemicals also can increase your chances of developing cancer. These substances, called carcinogens, (kar SIH nuh junz) include asbestos, various solvents, heavy metals, alcohol, and home and garden chemicals, as shown in **Figure 16.**

Exposure to X rays, nuclear radiation, and ultraviolet radiation of the Sun also increases your risk of getting cancer. Exposure to ultraviolet radiation might lead to skin cancer. Certain foods that are cured, or smoked, including barbecued meats, can give rise to cancers. Some food additives and certain viruses are suspected of causing cancers. Some people have a genetic predisposition for cancer, meaning that they have genes that make them more susceptible to the disease. This does not mean that they definitely will have cancer, but if it is triggered by certain factors they have a greater chance of developing cancer.

Treatment Surgery to remove cancerous tissue, radiation with X rays to kill cancer cells, and chemotherapy are some treatments for cancer. **Chemotherapy** (kee moh THUR uh pee) is the use of chemicals to destroy cancer cells. However, early detection of cancer is the key to any successful treatment.

Research in the science of immune processes, called immunology, has led to some new approaches for treating cancer. For example, specialized antibodies produced in the laboratory are being tested as anticancer agents. These antibodies are used as carriers to deliver medicines and radioactive substances directly to cancer cells. In another test, killer T cells are removed from a cancer patient and treated with chemicals that stimulate T cell production. The treated cells are then reinjected into the patient. Trial tests have shown some success in destroying certain types of cancer cells with this technique.

Curriculum Connection

Health People who smoke pipes or cigars generally do not inhale. This reduces their chances for lung cancer and emphysema. However, since the burning tobacco is in close contact with the mouth and these products have a higher content of nicotine and tars, the smoker has a high risk of developing cancers of the lips and mouth. Have students make a poster to illustrate these facts. L2 LS **Kinesthetic**

Resource Manager

Chapter Resources Booklet
Enrichment, p. 30
Reinforcement, p. 27
Lab Activity, pp. 13–14

Prevention Knowing some causes of cancer might help you prevent it. The first step is to know the early warning signs, shown in **Table 5.** Medical attention and treatments such as chemotherapy or surgery in the early stages of some cancers can cure or keep them inactive.

A second step in cancer prevention concerns lifestyle choices. Choosing not to use tobacco and alcohol products can help prevent mouth and lung cancers and the other associated respiratory and circulatory system diseases. Selecting a healthy diet without many foods that are high in fats, salt, and sugar also might reduce your chances of developing cancer. Using sunscreen lotions and limiting the amount of time that you expose your skin to direct sunlight are good preventive measures against skin cancer. Careful handling of harmful home and garden chemicals will help you avoid the dangers connected with these substances. Carefully read the entire label before you use any product.

Inhaling certain air pollutants such as carbon monoxide, sulfur dioxide, nitric oxide, and asbestos fibers is dangerous to your health. To keep the air you breathe cleaner, the U.S. Government has regulations such as the Clean Air Act. These laws are intended to reduce the amount of these substances that are released into the air.

Table 5 Early Warning Signs of Cancer (from the National Cancer Institute)

Early Warning Signs of Cancer
Changes in bowel or bladder habits
A sore that does not heal
Unusual bleeding or discharge
Thickening or lump in the breast or elsewhere
Indigestion or difficulty swallowing
Obvious change in a wart or mole
Nagging cough or hoarseness

Section  Assessment

1. Explain why diabetes is classified as a noninfectious disease.
2. Describe two ways cancer cells affect body organ functions.
3. Relate two causes of cancer to two methods to prevent cancer.
4. What are some ways your body can respond to allergens?
5. **Think Critically** Joel has an ear infection. The doctor prescribes an antibiotic. After taking the antibiotic, Joel breaks out in a rash. What is happening to him?

Skill Builder Activities

6. **Making and Using Tables** Make a table that relates several causes of cancer and their effects on your body. **For more help, refer to the** Science Skill Handbook.
7. **Using a Database** Use references to find information on different allergens. Group the allergens into the following categories: *chemical, food, mold, pollen,* and *antibiotic.* Use a computer to make a database. Which group has the most allergens? **For more help, refer to the** Technology Skill Handbook.

IDENTIFYING Misconceptions

There is a false assumption that using smokeless tobacco products, such as snuff and chewing tobacco, prevents cancer and other diseases. While there is no inhaling of smoke, there is contact with nicotine and other carcinogens, leading to greater risks of oral and throat cancers. Have students find statistics for diseases associated with smokeless tobacco products. L2

3 Assess

Reteach

Have students name all the different ways they have learned to reduce the risk of developing cancer. L1

Challenge

What are "environmentally friendly" products? Possible answer: Products that do not pollute the soil, water, or air by use or disposal.

Assessment

Performance Use Skill Builder question 6 to assess students' abilities to make and use tables by having them relate causes of other diseases and their effects on the body. Use **Performance Assessment in the Science Classroom,** p. 109.

Answers to Section Assessment

1. Diabetes is not caused by a pathogen.
2. crowd out blood cells in bone marrow; reduce surface area for gas exchange in lungs
3. cause: smoking tobacco, prevention: stop using tobacco products; cause: ultraviolet light exposure, prevention: limit exposure to sunlight and use sunscreens
4. your immune system forms antibodies; your body reacts by releasing chemicals called histamines
5. Joel's immune system formed antibodies and he seems to be having an allergic reaction to the antibiotic.
6. cause: smoking, effect: impaired lung functioning; cause: ultraviolet light, effect: abnormal skin growths; cause: asbestos, effect: impaired lung functioning
7. Possible examples: chemical—nickel metal; food—strawberries; mold—mold on bird droppings; pollen—ragweed; antibiotic—penicillin

Activity BENCH TESTED

Recognize the Problem

Purpose

Students determine how bicarbonates in saliva protect their mouths from bacteria and chemical substances. L2 COOP LEARN

LS **Kinesthetic**

Process Skills

preparing data table, observing, comparing, identifying and manipulating controls and variables, explaining, predicting.

Time Required

two 45 minute periods

Materials

- The red cabbage juice should be prepared by chopping the cabbage into small pieces and boiling the pieces for 20 to 30 minutes. The juice must be filtered before it is used as an indicator.
- Dilute HCl can be used in place of vinegar or lemon juice. Prepare dilute acid by dissolving 80 mL of concentrated Wheal in 1 L of water.

Safety Precautions

Students should wear safety goggles. Caution students not to eat or drink anything in science class.

Form a Hypothesis

Possible Hypothesis

Many students will hypothesize that bicarbonates will neutralize acids to some degree.

Activity Design Your Own Experiment

Defensive Saliva

What happens when you think about a juicy cheeseburger or smell freshly baked bread? Your mouth starts making saliva. Saliva is the first line of defense for fighting harmful bacteria, acids, and bases entering your body. Saliva contains salts and chemicals known as bicarbonates. An example of a bicarbonate found in your kitchen is baking soda. Bicarbonates help to maintain normal pH levels in your mouth. When surfaces in your mouth have normal pH levels, the growth of bacteria is slowed and the effects of acids and bases are reduced. In this activity, you will design your own experiment to show the importance of saliva bicarbonates.

Recognize the Problem

How do the bicarbonates in saliva work to protect your mouth from harmful bacteria, acids, and bases?

Form a Hypothesis

Based on your reading in the text, form a hypothesis about how the bicabonates in saliva react to acids and bases.

Goals

- **Design** an experiment to test the reaction of a bicarbonate to acids and bases.
- **Test** the reaction of a bicarbonate to acids and bases.

Possible Materials

head of red cabbage
cooking pot
coffee filter
drinking glasses
clear household ammonia
bicarbonate of soda
water
spoon
white vinegar
lemon juice
orange juice

Safety Precautions

WARNING: *Never eat or drink anything used in an investigation.*

678

Test Your Hypothesis

Possible Procedure

Add 4 parts acid or base to one part red cabbage juice indicator. Add a spoonful of bicarbonate a little at a time until a color change is observed. Proportions of the ingredients may have to be adjusted depending on their strength.

Resource Manager

Chapter Resources Booklet
Activity Worksheet, pp. 7–8

Performance Assessment in the Science Classroom, p. 48

Lab Management and Safety, p. 70

Test Your Hypothesis

Plan

1. **List** the materials you will need for your experiment. Red cabbage juice can be used as an indicator to test for acids and bases. Vinegar and citrus juices are acids, ammonia is a base, and baking soda (bicarbonate of soda) is a bicarbonate.
2. **Describe** how you will prepare the red cabbage juice and how you will use it to test for the presence of acids and bases.
3. **Describe** how you will test the effect of bicarbonate on acids and bases.
4. **List** the steps you will take to set up and complete your experiment. Describe exactly what you will do in each step.
5. Prepare a data table in your Science Journal to record your observations.
6. Examine the steps of your experiment to make certain they are in logical order.

Do

1. Ask your teacher to examine the steps of your experiment and data table before you start.
2. Conduct your experiment according to the approved plan.
3. **Record** your observations in your data table.

Analyze Your Data

1. **Compare** the color change of the acids and bases in the cabbage juice.
2. **Describe** how well the bicarbonate neutralized the acids and bases.
3. **Identify** any problems you had while setting up and conducting your experiment.

Draw Conclusions

1. Did your results support your hypothesis?
2. Based on your experiment, explain why your saliva contains a bicarbonate.
3. **Predict** how quickly bacteria would grow in your glass containing acid compared to another glass containing acid and the bicarbonate.
4. **Explain** how saliva protects your mouth from bacteria.
5. **Predict** what would happen if your saliva were made of only water.

Communicating Your Data

Using what you learned in this experiment, create a poster about the importance of good dental hygiene. Invite a dental hygienist to speak to your class.

Teaching Strategies

Most students will be familiar with the terms acid and base and understand that a base is the opposite of an acid.

Expected Outcomes The bicarbonate should successfully neutralize both acids and bases as indicated by the appropriate color change.

Analyze Your Data

1. Acids turn pink; bases turn green.
2. All the solutions will turn blue signifying both acids and bases are neutralized.
3. Common problems include the preparation of cabbage juice and determining the proportions of the substances.

Error Analysis Have students compare the color changes that occurred during their experiments and explain why differences were observed.

Draw Conclusions

1. Answers will vary.
2. Bicarbonates in saliva neutralize harmful acids and bases.
3. Bacteria would grow more rapidly in acid without bicarbonate added.
4. Bicarbonates maintain neutral pH levels to slow bacterial growth.
5. Acids and bases from foods would easily damage tooth enamel . Harmful bacteria also would grow unchecked increasing tooth decay, illness, and disease.

Assessment

Oral Have students explain how the strength of acids, bases, and neutral substances are compared. A pH value of 1 to 6 indicate acids with 1 being the strongest. Ph values of 8 to 14 are bases with 14 being the strongest base. Neutral substances have a value of 7. Use **Performance Assessment in the Science Classroom,** p. 89.

Communicating Your Data

Encourage students to illustrate their posters with drawings. They may wish to make the poster a cartoon in which the main character is a tooth that explains the steps in good oral hygiene.

Science Stats

Content Background

The development of antibiotics has truly changed medicine. Injuries and illnesses that were once fatal are now easily treated. How do antibiotics kill bacteria without harming the cells of the person being treated? The key is the differences between bacterial cells and animal cells. For example, some antibiotics work by inhibiting cell wall formation. Because human cells do not have a cell wall, the drug does not affect them. Other antibiotics are less specific to bacterial characteristics, and therefore more toxic to humans.

Discussion

Why is there always a need for newly developed or discovered antibiotics? Bacteria develop resistance to antibiotics over time. A newly developed or discovered antibiotic may allow treatment of bacteria that have developed resistance to other drugs.

Activity

Have student pairs interview their grandparents or older family friends. Have students ask about treatments for disease and infection that were used in the past. If interview subjects are not available, have students use reference materials to find their information. Students should present their findings to the class. LS **Interpersonal**

Science Stats

Battling Bacteria

Did you know...

...The term *antibiotic* was first coined by an American microbiologist. The scientist received a Nobel prize in 1952 for the discovery of streptomycin (strep toh MY suhn), an antibiotic used against tuberculosis.

United States Death Rates from Tuberculosis

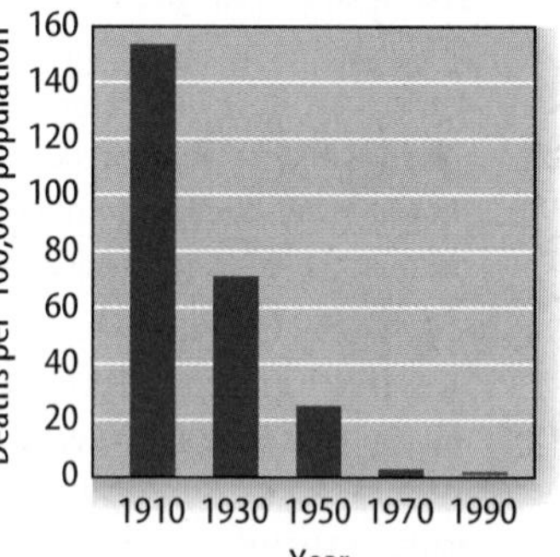

State of North Dakota
PRESCRIPTION BLANK

Mary Jackson, M.D.
General Medicine
265 Main Street
Greenville, ND

Patient *Julia Ramion* DOB *12/04/65*
Addr. *62 North St. Greenville* Date *11/06/01*
Rx *Amoxicillin 250mg tabs*
Sig: † tab po q8h

Substitution permissible ✓ Do Not Substitute ___
Do Not Refill ✓
Refill ___ Signature *Mary Jackson*
Times ___

...One of the frequently prescribed drugs is the antibiotic amoxicillin (uh mahk see SI luhn), a chemical variation of penicillin. It is prescribed for a variety of infections. In 1998 alone, amoxicillin was prescribed 16.7 million times, comprising 1.4 percent of the total prescriptions written that year.

...Not all bacteria are harmful. Our bodies contain millions of helpful bacteria that promote digestion, produce B vitamins, and crowd out bacteria that cause disease. Bacterial cells outnumber human cells in your body.

...People have long used natural remedies to treat infections. These remedies include garlic, *Echinacea* (purple coneflower), and an antibiotic called squalamine, found in sharks' stomachs.

Internet Addresses

Explore the Glencoe Science Web site at **science.glencoe.com** to find out more about topics in this feature.

Connecting To Math

...Pharmaceutical companies in the United States produce nearly 23 million kg of antibiotics each year. That's equivalent to the weight of about 50 space shuttles. In 1954, these companies produced only about 90,000 kg of antibiotics.

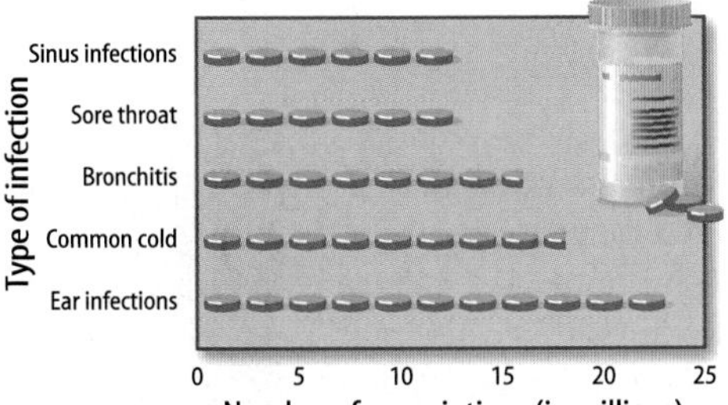

...In recent decades many bacteria have become resistant to antibiotics. For example, one group of bacteria that cause illnesses of the stomach and intestines—*Shigella* (shih GEL uh)—became harder to control. In 1985, less than one third of *Shigella* were resistant to the antibiotic ampicillin (am puh SI luhn). By 1991, however, more than two thirds of *Shigella* could continue to grow in the presence of the drug.

Do the Math

1. Calculate the percentage by which antibiotic production in the United States has increased from 1954 to today.
2. An estimated 100 million doses of antibiotics are prescribed each year. With 273 million people living in the United States, what is the average number of doses per person?
3. It is believed that 30 percent of the antibiotics prescribed for ear infections are unnecessary. Using the graph, calculate the number of unnecessary prescriptions.

Go Further

Go to **science.glencoe.com** to research the production of four antibiotics. Create a graph comparing the number of kilograms of each antibiotic produced in one year.

Visual Learning

Pharmaceutical Companies in the United States Have students use the data in the paragraph to determine the approximate mass of a space shuttle. 23,000,000 kg/50 = 460,000 kg

Connecting To Math

Do the Math

Teaching Strategies

- The formula for determining the percentage increase between two numbers is: Percentage increase = [(larger–smaller) × 100]/smaller.
- Point out the difference between the phrases *percentage increase* and *how many times more*. Use easily manipulated numbers, such as 5 and 10, to show that 2 times as much is the same as a 100% increase.
- Remind students to divide the number of doses by the number of people to determine the doses per person.
- Students should determine that about 24 million prescriptions for ear infections were written. They can then divide to find the number of unnecessary prescriptions.

Answers

1. 25,455 percent increase
2. 0.366 doses per person
3. about 7.2 million

Go Further

Have interested students research ethnobotany, the scientific study of plants used by particular cultural groups. Researchers in this field have explored many substances used as medicine in different areas of the world. Students should report their findings to the class. L2 LS **Linguistic**

Chapter 23 Study Guide

Reviewing Main Ideas

Preview

Students can answer the questions in their Science Journals. Discuss the answers as you go through the chapter. LS **Linguistic**

Review

Students can write their answers, then compare them with those of other students. LS **Interpersonal**

Reteach

Students can look at the illustrations and describe details that support the main ideas of the chapter. LS **Visual-Spatial**

Answers to Chapter Review

Section 1

2. by observing good health habits in personal hygiene and the handling of foods; using disinfectants and antiseptics

Section 2

2. Infected mosquitoes transfer disease organisms when they bite people.

Section 3

2. allergens

Chapter 23 Study Guide

Reviewing Main Ideas

Section 1 The Immune System

1. Your body is protected against most pathogens by the immune system, which includes skin, cilia and mucus in the respiratory system, white blood cells in the circulatory system, and enzymes and hydrochloric acid in the digestive system. The purpose of the immune system is to fight disease.

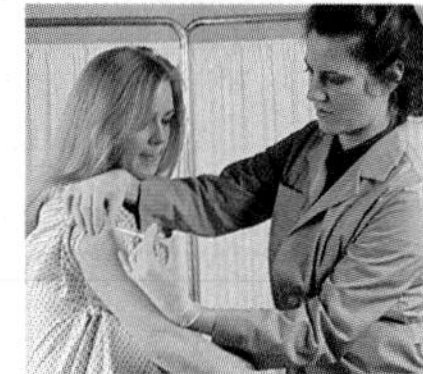

2. Active immunity is long lasting, but passive immunity is not. *What are other ways to prevent the spread of disease?*
3. Antigens are complex molecules that identify foreign molecules in your body. Your body makes an antibody that attaches to a specific antigen, making it harmless.

Section 2 Infectious Diseases

1. Pasteur and Koch discovered that microorganisms cause diseases. Lister learned that cleanliness helps control microorganisms.

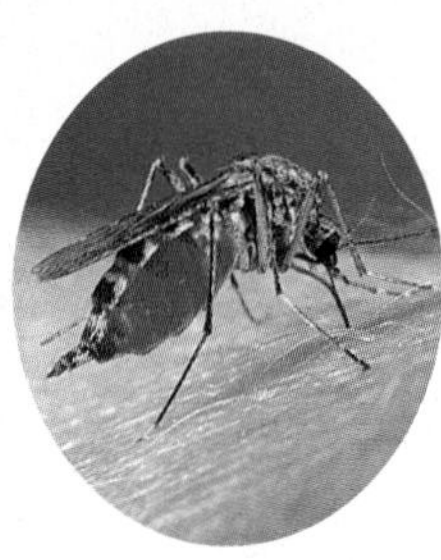

2. Air, water, food, and animal contact can pass a pathogen from one person to another. Bacteria, viruses, fungi, and protists can cause infectious diseases. *How could this mosquito pass on disease?*
3. Sexually transmitted diseases (STDs) can be passed between persons during sexual contact. They include genital herpes, gonorrhea, syphilis, and AIDS.
4. HIV can be transmitted by sexual contact, by using a disease-contaminated needle, by transfusion with contaminated blood, and to a fetus from its mother. AIDS damages your body's immune system so that it cannot fight infections.

Section 3 Noninfectious Diseases

1. Causes of noninfectious diseases include genetics, chemicals, poor diet, and uncontrolled cell growth. Chronic noninfectious diseases include diabetes, cancer, heart disease, and allergies.

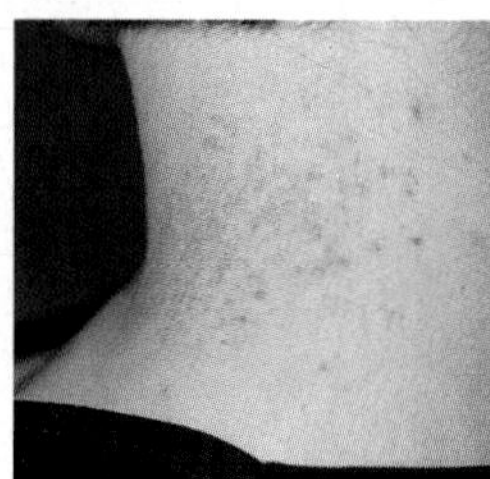

2. An allergy is a reaction of the immune system to a foreign substance. Your body releases histamines that cause red, swollen tissues. *What are substances that can cause rashes called?*
3. Cancer results from uncontrolled cell growth. When this control is lost, the cells multiply, spread through the blood and lymph vessels, and invade normal tissues.
4. Some cancers can be cured or kept in remission by medical intervention if they are detected early. Cancer is treated with surgery, chemotherapy, and radiation. Lifestyle choices can help prevent cancer.

FOLDABLES Reading & Study Skills **After You Read**

Based on information in this chapter, circle the diseases on your Foldable that are the greatest threat to people on Earth.

FOLDABLES Reading & Study Skills **After You Read**

After students have read the chapter and completed the Foldable described in Before You Read, have them do the activity on the student page.

Dinah Zike

Chapter 23 Study Guide

Visualizing Main Ideas

Complete the following concept map on infectious diseases.

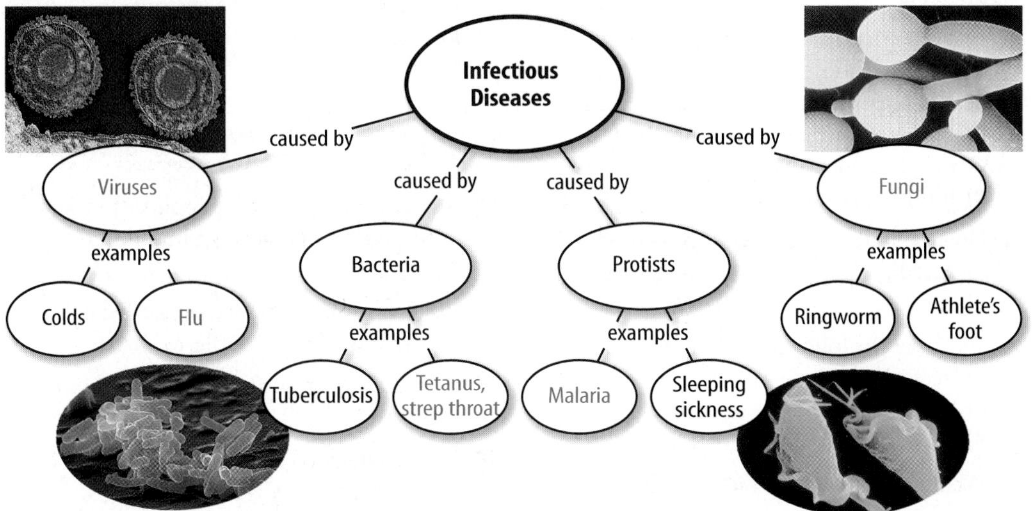

Vocabulary Review

Vocabulary Words

a. active immunity
b. allergen
c. allergy
d. antibody
e. antigen
f. biological vector
g. chemotherapy
h. immune system
i. infectious disease
j. noninfectious disease
k. passive immunity
l. pasteurization
m. sexually transmitted disease (STD)
n. vaccination
o. virus

Study Tip

Keep all your homework assignments, and read them from time to time. Make sure you understand any questions that you may have answered incorrectly.

Using Vocabulary

Replace each underlined word with the correct vocabulary word.

1. An allergen can cause infectious diseases.
2. A disease-carrying organism is called a noninfectious disease.
3. Measles is an example of pastueurization.
4. Injection of weakened viruses is called biological vector.
5. Passive immunity occurs when your body makes its own antibodies.
6. An antigen stimulates histamine release.
7. Heating a liquid to kill harmful bacteria is called chemotherapy.
8. Diabetes is an example of a sexually transmitted disease.

Chapter 23 Study Guide

Visualizing Main Ideas

See student page.

Vocabulary Review

Using Vocabulary

1. antigen
2. biological vector
3. infectious disease
4. vaccination
5. Active immunity
6. allergen
7. pasteurization
8. noninfectious disease

Chapter 23 Assessment

Checking Concepts

1. A
2. D
3. A
4. D
5. A
6. C
7. A
8. C
9. A
10. A

Thinking Critically

11. In many cases, it is better to vaccinate, as the antigens introduced by vaccinations are usually weakened or killed, and will therefore not cause the person to get the disease.
12. Breast-fed babies receive passive immunity from antibodies in their mother's milk.
13. Your skin prevents pathogens from entering the body, white blood cells destroy pathogens, cilia and mucus trap pathogens, and digestive juices kill pathogens that enter the stomach.
14. Helper T cells activate the immune system. B cells form antibodies and remain in the blood to defend against future attacks by the same antigen.
15. Antigens—foreign proteins and chemicals that invade your body; antibodies—formed by your immune system to destroy antigens; antibiotics—medicines that destroy or neutralize pathogens in the body

Chapter 23 Assessment

Checking Concepts

Choose the word or phrase that best answers the question.

1. How do scientists know that a pathogen causes a specific disease?
A) It is present in all cases of the disease.
B) It does not infect other animals.
C) It causes other diseases.
D) It is treated with heat.

2. How can infectious diseases be caused?
A) heredity **C)** chemicals
B) allergies **D)** organisms

3. Which of the following might be a biological vector?
A) bird **C)** water
B) rock **D)** soil

4. What is formed in the blood to fight invading antigens?
A) hormones **C)** pathogens
B) allergens **D)** antibodies

5. Which of the following is one of your body's general defenses against some pathogens?
A) stomach enzymes **C)** some vaccines
B) HIV **D)** hormones

6. Which of the following is known as an infectious disease?
A) allergies **C)** syphilis
B) asthma **D)** diabetes

7. Which disease is caused by a virus that attacks white blood cells?
A) AIDS **C)** flu
B) measles **D)** polio

8. Which of the following is a characteristic of cancer cells?
A) controlled cell growth
B) help your body stay healthy
C) interfere with normal body functions
D) do not multiply or spread

9. Which of the following is caused by a virus?
A) AIDS **C)** ringworm
B) gonorrhea **D)** syphilis

10. How can cancer cells be destroyed?
A) chemotherapy **C)** vaccines
B) antigens **D)** viruses

Thinking Critically

11. Is it better to vaccinate people or to wait until they build their own immunity? Explain.

12. What advantage might a breast-fed baby have compared to a bottle-fed baby?

13. How does your body protect itself from antigens?

14. How do helper T cells and B cells work to eliminate antigens?

15. Describe the differences among antibodies, antigens, and antibiotics.

Developing Skills

16. Making and Using Tables Complete this table.

Comparing Diseases

Disease	Cause	Prevention
Cancer	See Section 3	
Tetanus	See Section 2	
Measles	See Section 2	

17. Recognizing Cause and Effect Use library references to identify the cause—bacteria, virus, fungus, or protist—of each of these diseases: athlete's foot, AIDS, cold, dysentery, flu, pinkeye, acne, and strep throat.

Chapter Assessment Planner

Portfolio Encourage students to place in their portfolios one or two items of what they consider to be their best work. Examples include:
- Extension, p. 660
- Science Journal, p. 666
- Extension, p. 674

Performance Additional performance assessments, Performance Task Assessment Lists, and rubrics for evaluating these activities can be found in Glencoe's **Performance Assessment in the Science Classroom.**

18. **Classifying** Using word processing software, make a table to classify the following diseases as infectious or noninfectious: diabetes, gonorrhea, herpes, strep throat, syphilis, cancer, and flu.

19. **Interpreting Data** Using the graph below, explain the rate of polio cases between 1952 and 1965. What conclusions can you draw about the effectiveness of the polio vaccines?

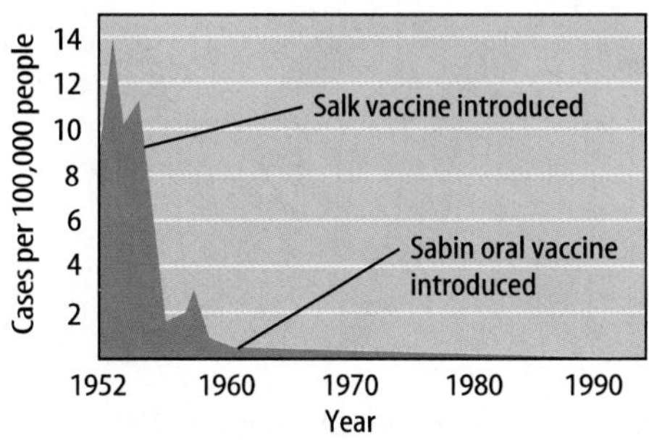

20. **Concept Mapping** Make a network tree concept map that compares the various defenses your body has against diseases. Compare general defenses, active immunity, and passive immunity.

Performance Assessment

21. **Poster** Design and construct a poster to illustrate how a person with the flu could spread the disease to family members, classmates, and others.

TECHNOLOGY

Go to the Glencoe Science Web site at **science.glencoe.com** or use the **Glencoe Science CD-ROM** for additional chapter assessment.

THE PRINCETON REVIEW Test Practice

Mrs. Henson showed her class a graph about life expectancy between the years 1970 and 1997.

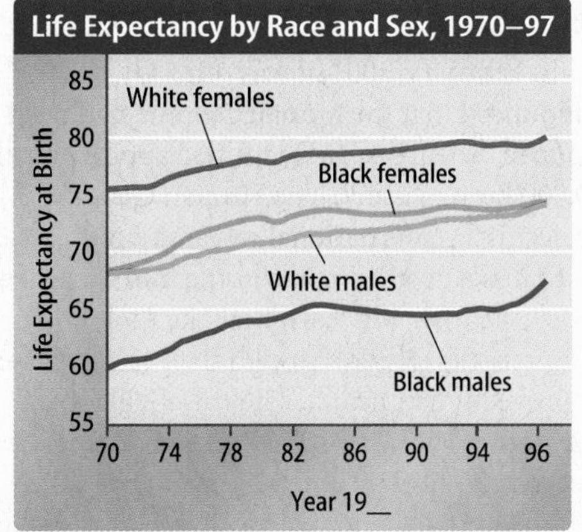

Study the graph and answer the following questions.

1. According to the information in the graph, which group had the highest life expectancy in both 1975 and 1994?
   A) white males
   B) black females
   C) white females
   D) black males

2. A reasonable hypothesis based on the information in the graph is that _____ .
   F) life expectancy has decreased in the period between 1970 and 1994
   G) life expectancy of white females is the lowest because they suffer the most disease
   H) females usually live shorter lives than males
   J) life expectancy has slowly increased in the period between 1970 and 1994

Chapter 23 Assessment

THE PRINCETON REVIEW Test Practice

The Test-Taking Tip was written by the Princeton Review, the nation's leader in test preparation.

1. C
2. J

Developing Skills

16. See student page.
17. bacteria: strep throat, pinkeye, acne; virus: AIDS, cold, flu, pinkeye; fungus: ringworm, athlete's foot; protist: dysentery
18. infectious: gonorrhea, herpes, strep throat, syphilis, flu; noninfectious: diabetes, cancer
19. rate dropped after the vaccine was introduced; the dramatic decline was a result of the vaccine
20. General—fever, white blood cells; active immunity—production of antibodies, long-term; passive immunity—antibodies given to body, short-term

Performance Assessment

21. Poster could show a person sneezing without covering the mouth and nose, coughing over food, and handling objects without washing hands. Use **PASC**, p. 145.

Assessment Resources

Reproducible Masters

Chapter Resources Booklet
Chapter Review, pp. 35–36
Chapter Tests, pp. 37–40
Assessment Transparency Activity, p. 47

Glencoe Science Web site
Interactive Tutor
Chapter Quizzes

Glencoe Technology
Assessment Transparency
Interactive CD-ROM Chapter Quizzes
ExamView Pro Test Bank
Vocabulary PuzzleMaker Software
MindJogger Videoquiz

Standardized Test Practice

Reading Comprehension

Question 1: C

Students can use context clues, such as *hereditary*, to identify the correct meaning of *inherited* as choice C, *inborn*. Choices A, B, and D are not supported by the passage.

Question 2: G

Students must identify the answer choice that expresses the main idea of the passage.

- **Choice F** No; this is a detail from the passage.
- **Choice G** Yes; this is the main idea of the passage.
- **Choice H** No; this is a detail from the passage.
- **Choice J** No; this is a detail from the passage.

Teaching Tip

Encourage students to underline all the important information in a passage.

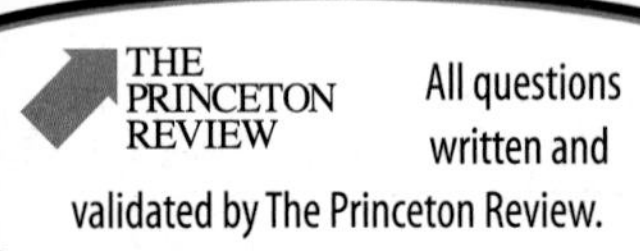

All questions written and validated by The Princeton Review.

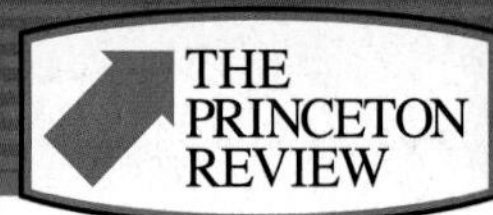

Standardized Test Practice

Reading Comprehension

Read the passage carefully. Then read the questions that follow the passage. Decide which is the best answer to each question.

The Human Genome Project

In February, 2001, it was officially announced that the human genome had been mapped. Scientists had identified approximately 30,000 human genes. The Human Genome Project is an international research program set up to make detailed maps of the human genetic code. Scientists will learn how the tools and resources developed through their research can improve human health. They also will look at the ethical, legal, and social concerns their research brings up.

The human genome is comprised of all the DNA that exists in human beings. This includes all of your genes. The DNA in your genes carries information on how to manufacture the proteins that are required for human life. These proteins determine many of your characteristics, such as how you look, how well you fight off infections, how you digest food, and the color of your hair. Your genes are located on 23 pairs of chromosomes in the nucleus of each of your cells. Many diseases such as cystic fibrosis, sickle-cell anemia, and Parkinson's disease are passed on from generation to generation through the information in genes.

The completion of the Human Genome Project might help scientists develop medicines that could cure hereditary diseases. The information gathered by the Human Genome Project also might help doctors identify and alert patients who are at risk of certain <u>inherited</u> diseases. With knowledge and awareness, doctors and patients might be able to take steps to prevent such diseases from developing.

Scientists hope that the Human Genome Project will advance medical science into a new era of diagnosing, preventing, treating, and curing diseases.

Test-Taking Tip When you read a passage, make a list of vocabulary words that you do not understand.

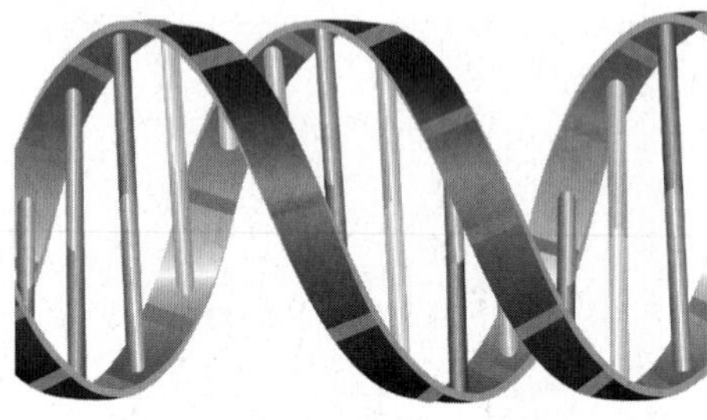

Watson and Crick's double-helix model of DNA

1. The term <u>inherited</u> in this passage best means _____.
   A) averted
   B) acquired
   C) inborn
   D) lost

2. One of the main ideas of the passage is that _____.
   F) human genes are located on the 23 pairs of chromosomes
   G) the Human Genome Project might help doctors diagnose, prevent, and cure diseases
   H) the Human Genome Project is a historic scientific achievement
   J) genes are responsible for many diseases, such as cystic fibrosis, sickle-cell anemia, and Parkinson's disease

Reasoning and Skills

Read each question and choose the best answer.

NEURONS DENDRITES AXON

1. Which of the following belongs with the group above?
A) arteries
B) synapses
C) tendons
D) lymph nodes

Test-Taking Tip Think about which human body system the words in the box relate to.

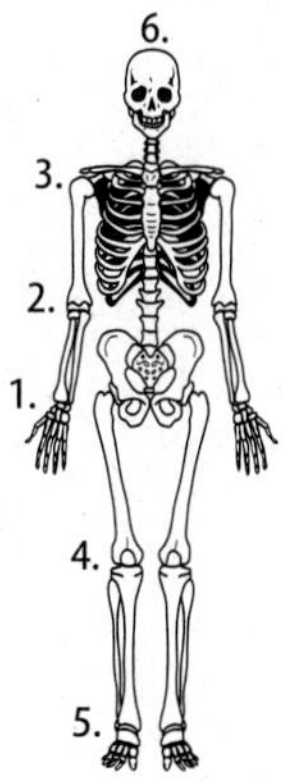

2. The place where two or more bones come together is called a joint. Joints can be movable or immovable. Which joint is an example of an immovable joint?
F) 2
G) 3
H) 5
J) 6

Test-Taking Tip Think about which joints move when you move.

3. Laticia has just jogged for two miles. When she stops, her heart rate and her breathing rate are higher than normal and have increased to 150 beats per minute and 40 breaths per minute. The reason why her heart rate and her breathing rate are high is because _____.
A) her body is fighting off an infection
B) her muscles and cells need more oxygen and nutrients
C) her nervous system is reacting to a lot of stimuli
D) she is not in good physical shape

Test-Taking Tip Consider the responsibilities of the human circulatory and respiratory systems.

Consider this question carefully before writing your answer on a separate sheet of paper.

4. Doctors recommend that you eat a well-balanced diet that contains food from each category of the food pyramid and that you consume an appropriate number of Calories per day. What are some reasons why it is important for you to eat a well-balanced diet?

Test-Taking Tip Think about the effects that eating healthy and unhealthy food has on the human body.

Teaching Tip

Encourage students to include factual details, where appropriate, to support their answers.

Standardized Test Practice

Reasoning and Skills

Question 1: B

Students must understand that all the words in the box belong to the nervous system. Only choice B, *synapses*, also belongs to the nervous system. Choices A, C, and D all belong to other human body systems.

Question 2: J

Students can use the information in the question and their own knowledge of joints to identify which joint in the picture is immovable. Students will need to recognize that the skull has immovable joints. Choices F, G, and H are all examples of movable joints.

Question 3: C

Students must understand human body systems to identify the correct cause of the changes in Laticia's heart rate and breathing rate.

- **Choice A** No; there is no information to support this.
- **Choice B** No; even though exercise increases breathing and heart rates, these are involuntary responses, not voluntary.
- **Choice C** Yes; heart rate and breathing are controlled by the nervous system. They are responses to multiple stimuli from the body.
- **Choice D** No; there is no information to support this.

Question 4: Answers will vary.

Students should use their knowledge of the food guide pyramid and human body systems to write a thorough response.

UNIT 5

Unit Contents

Pre-Reading Activity

Have students compare and contrast the living and nonliving resources shown in the illustrations in this unit.

UNIT 5 Ecology

How Are Oatmeal & Carpets Connected?

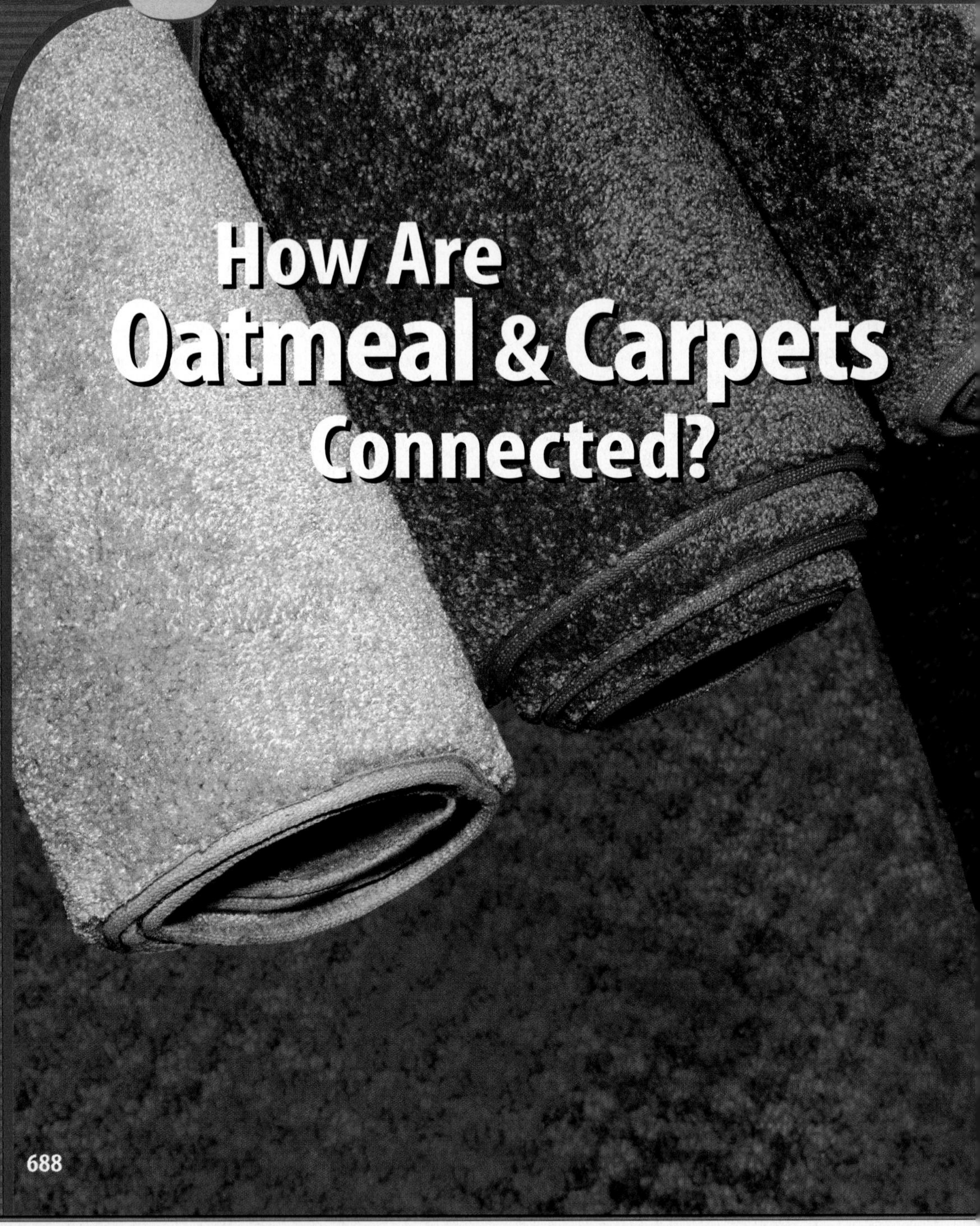

688

Teacher to Teacher

"To evaluate student understanding of abiotic and biotic factors of the environment, I take them outside and have them make two lists of the factors and how they are interrelated to one another. I also have the students make food chains from their observations."

Steve Manns, Teacher
Derry Area Middle School
Derry, PA

Introducing the Unit

How Are Oatmeal & Carpets Connected?

Furfural can be produced by treating carbohydrates, which are long chains of simple sugars. Commercially, furfural is often used as an industrial solvent. It is also used in the production of certain resins. When furfural is reduced chemically, it produces furfural alcohol. This alcohol is then polymerized to produce resins that are heat- and alkali-resistant.

In the 1850s, the first oatmeal mill began operation in the United States. Over the next few decades, hot, creamy oatmeal became a popular breakfast cereal across the country. By the early 1900s, oatmeal was getting some stiff competition from newly invented cold breakfast cereals such as cornflakes. Hot or cold, cereal had become a breakfast staple. But the processing of oats and corn for cereal leaves behind waste products—oat hulls and corncobs. In 1922, a cereal company discovered it could do something useful with these waste products. The company used oat hulls to make a substance called furfural. Today, furfural also is made from corncobs and other cereal waste products. Manufacturers use furfural in the production of synthetic rubber, plastic, and nylon—including the nylon that goes into carpets.

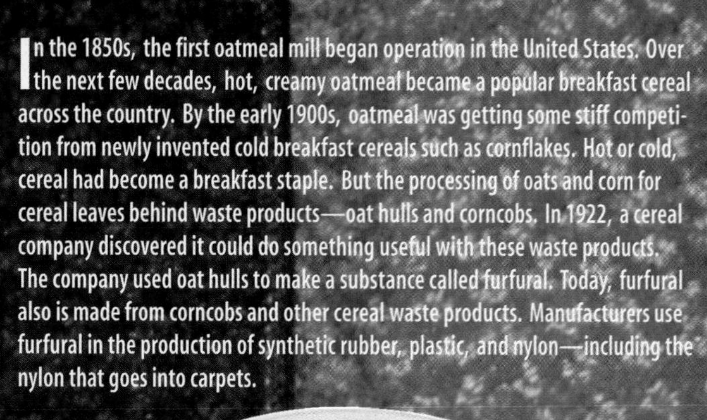

SCIENCE CONNECTION

Activity

Ask students to identify the sources of many of the items they use. What other materials can be used to achieve the same purpose? Possible answer: Wood used in homes and furniture comes from many species of trees. Trees from rain forests are irreplaceable. Using wood products from tree farms may slow the destruction of the world's rain forests.

SCIENCE CONNECTION

RECYCLED PRODUCTS Furfural manufacturers make use of materials that might otherwise go to waste. Recycling programs operate in a similar way. What types of items do you and your family collect for recycling? Do you know what happens to them once they leave your home? Conduct research to learn what happens when plastics, metals, glass, and paper are recycled. Working with classmates, create a tabletop display of products that are made from recycled materials.

Internet Addresses

Explore the Glencoe Science Web site at **science.glencoe.com** to find out more about topics in this unit.

Section/Objectives	Standards		Activities/Features
	National	State/Local	
Chapter Opener	See p. 5T for a Key to Standards.		**Explore Activity:** Examine sod from a lawn, p. 691 **Before You Read,** p. 691
Section 1 Living Earth 2 sessions 1 block 1. **Identify** places where life is found on Earth. 2. **Define** ecology. 3. **Observe** how the environment influences life.	National Content Standards: UCP1, A1, C1, C4		**Science Online,** p. 694
Section 2 Populations 2 sessions 1 block 1. **Identify** methods for estimating population sizes. 2. **Explain** how competition limits population growth. 3. **List** factors that influence changes in population size.	National Content Standards: UCP1, A1, C1, C4		**MiniLAB:** Observing Seedling Competition, p. 697 **Problem Solving Activity:** Do you have too many crickets?, p. 699 **Science Online,** p. 700 **MiniLAB:** Comparing Biotic Potential, p. 701 **Visualizing Population Growth,** p. 702
Section 3 Interactions Within Communities 3 sessions 1.5 blocks 1. **Describe** how organisms obtain energy for life. 2. **Explain** how organisms interact. 3. **Recognize** that every organism occupies a niche.	National Content Standards: UCP1, A1, C1, C4, F5, G1, G3		**Chemistry Integration,** p. 705 **Health Integration,** p. 707 **Activity:** Feeding Habits of Planaria, p. 709 **Activity:** Population Growth in Fruit Flies, pp. 710–711 **Science and History:** You Can Count On It, pp. 712–713

NATIONAL GEOGRAPHIC — Teacher's Corner

PRODUCTS AVAILABLE FROM GLENCOE
To order call 1-800-334-7344:
CD-ROMs
NGS Picture Show: Looking at Ecosystems
NGS Picture Show: Looking at Living Things

Videodisc
STV: Habitats
STV: Water

PRODUCTS AVAILABLE FROM NATIONAL GEOGRAPHIC SOCIETY
To order call 1-800-368-2728:

Videos
Ecosystem: A Struggle For Survival
Pond-Life: Food Web
Web of Life

Activity Materials	Reproducible Resources	Section Assessment	Technology
Explore Activity: a section of sod, hand lens	**Chapter Resources Booklet** Foldables Worksheet, p. 17 Directed Reading Overview, p. 19 Note-taking Worksheets, pp. 33–35	GLENCOE'S ASSESSMENT ADVANTAGE	
Need materials? Contact Science Kit at 1-800-828-7777 or www.sciencekit.com on the Internet.	**Chapter Resources Booklet** Transparency Activity, p. 44 Enrichment, p. 30 Reinforcement, p. 27 Directed Reading, p. 20 **Science Inquiry Labs,** p. 7	**Portfolio** Activity, p. 694 **Performance** Skill Builder Activities, p. 695 **Content** Section Assessment, p. 695 Challenge, p. 695	Section Focus Transparency Interactive CD-ROM Guided Reading Audio Program
MiniLAB: 2 pots of plants, moist potting soil, radish seeds, watering can, basin, metric ruler **MiniLAB:** whole fruit, plastic knife, paper towels	**Chapter Resources Booklet** Transparency Activity, p. 45 MiniLAB, pp. 3, 4 Enrichment, p. 31 Reinforcement, p. 28 Directed Reading, p. 20 Transparency Activity, pp. 47–48 **Mathematics Skill Activities,** p. 5	**Portfolio** Curriculum Connection, p. 699 **Performance** MiniLAB, p. 697 MiniLAB, p. 701 Skill Builder Activities, p. 703 **Content** Section Assessment, p. 703 Challenge, p. 703	Section Focus Transparency Teaching Transparency Interactive CD-ROM Guided Reading Audio Program
Activity: small bowl, several planarians, lettuce leaf, raw liver or meat, several guppies, pond or stream water, hand lens **Activity:** fruit flies; fruit fly culture kit; food items (banana, orange peel, or other fruit); water; culture containers; cloth, plastic, or other tops for containers; hand lens; heating or cooling source	**Chapter Resources Booklet** Transparency Activity, p. 46 Activity Worksheets, pp. 5–6, 7–8 Enrichment, p. 32 Reinforcement, p. 29 Directed Reading, pp. 21, 22 Lab Activities, pp. 9–11, 13–16 **Home and Community Involvement,** p. 47 **Lab Management and Safety,** p. 71	**Portfolio** Science Journal, p. 707 **Performance** Skill Builder Activities, p. 708 **Content** Section Assessment, p. 708 Challenge, p. 708	Section Focus Transparency Interactive CD-ROM Guided Reading Audio Program

End of Chapter Assessment

GLENCOE'S ASSESSMENT ADVANTAGE

Blackline Masters	Technology	Professional Series
Chapter Resources Booklet Chapter Review, pp. 37–38 Chapter Tests, pp. 39–42 **Standardized Test Practice by The Princeton Review,** pp. 103–106	MindJogger Videoquiz Interactive CD-ROM Vocabulary PuzzleMakers ExamView Pro Test Bank Interactive Lesson Planner Interactive Teacher Edition	Performance Assessment in the Science Classroom (PASC)

Transparencies

Section Focus

Section 1 Section Focus Transparency — Hot Enough for Ya?

At one time it was thought that no organisms could survive below the soil layer. Over the last twenty years, however, scientists have discovered microorganisms that like hot, high-pressure, and even radioactive conditions! These scientists are working deep in an abandoned gold mine. They are investigating bacteria that thrive in similar harsh conditions.

1. What do you find most surprising about microorganisms living in extreme conditions?
2. Name some other places where living things thrive, but humans cannot.

L2

Section 2 Section Focus Transparency — That's a Lot of Penguins

Every living thing on Earth has a particular environment that it calls home. These penguins like cold, icy Antarctica. This environment provides the penguins with all of the things they need for survival.

1. Name some factors that might affect penguin population.
2. How might you estimate the number of penguins in this picture?

L2

Section 3 Section Focus Transparency — Frolics with Sharks

Remoras are several different species of related fishes that attach themselves to sharks and other ocean organisms. Both the shark and the remora benefit from this relationship.

1. Why doesn't the shark eat the remora?
2. How do the shark and remora help each other?

L2

This is a representation of key blackline masters available in the Teacher Classroom Resources. See Resource Manager boxes within the chapter for additional information.

Assessment

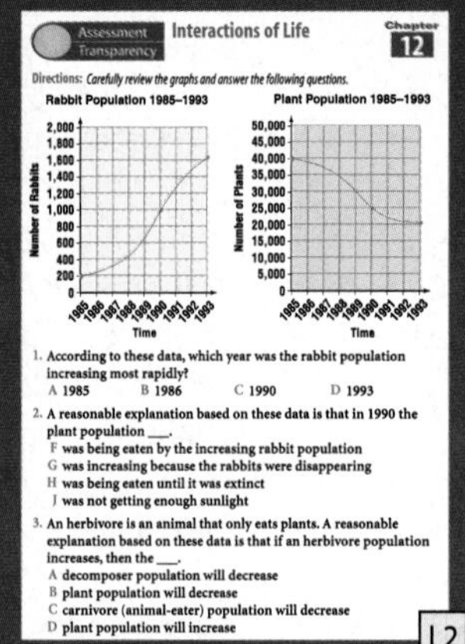
Assessment Transparency — Interactions of Life — Chapter 12

Directions: *Carefully review the graphs and answer the following questions.*

1. According to these data, which year was the rabbit population increasing most rapidly?
A 1985 B 1986 C 1990 D 1993
2. A reasonable explanation based on these data is that in 1990 the plant population ___.
F was being eaten by the increasing rabbit population
G was increasing because the rabbits were disappearing
H was being eaten until it was extinct
J was not getting enough sunlight
3. An herbivore is an animal that only eats plants. A reasonable explanation based on these data is that if an herbivore population increases, then the ___.
A decomposer population will decrease
B plant population will decrease
C carnivore (animal-eater) population will decrease
D plant population will increase

L2

Teaching

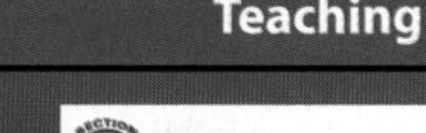

Section 2 Teaching Transparency — Population Density

L2

Key to Teaching Strategies

The following designations will help you decide which activities are appropriate for your students.

- L1 Level 1 activities should be appropriate for students with learning difficulties.
- L2 Level 2 activities should be within the ability range of all students.
- L3 Level 3 activities are designed for above-average students.
- ELL ELL activities should be within the ability range of English Language Learners.
- COOP LEARN Cooperative Learning activities are designed for small group work.
- LS Multiple Learning Styles logos, as described on page 22T, are used throughout to indicate strategies that address different learning styles.
- P These strategies represent student products that can be placed into a best-work portfolio.

Hands-on Activities

Activity Worksheets

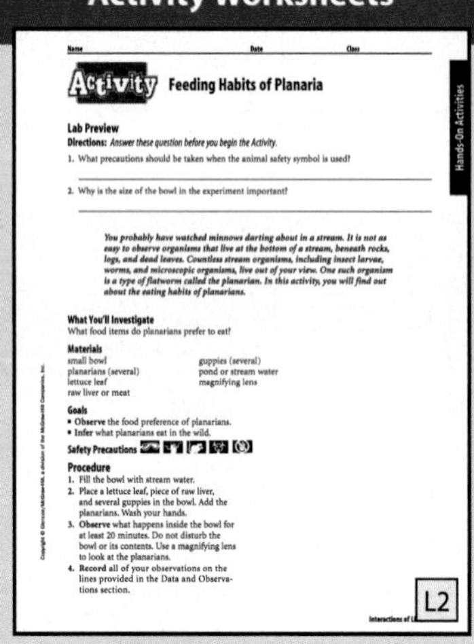
Activity — Feeding Habits of Planaria

Lab Preview

Directions: *Answer these questions before you begin the Activity.*

1. What precautions should be taken when the animal safety symbol is used?
2. Why is the size of the bowl in the experiment important?

You probably have watched minnows darting about in a stream. It is not as easy to observe organisms that live at the bottom of a stream, beneath rocks, logs, and dead leaves. Countless stream organisms, including insect larvae, worms, and microscopic organisms, live out of your view. One such organism is a type of flatworm called the planarian. In this activity, you will find out about the eating habits of planarians.

What You'll Investigate

What food items do planarians prefer to eat?

Materials: small bowl, planarians (several), lettuce leaf, raw liver or meat, guppies (several), pond or stream water, magnifying lens

Goals
- Observe the food preference of planarians.
- Infer what planarians eat in the wild.

Safety Precautions

Procedure
1. Fill the bowl with stream water.
2. Place a lettuce leaf, piece of raw liver, and several guppies in the bowl. Add the planarians. Wash your hands.
3. Observe what happens inside the bowl for at least 20 minutes. Do not disturb the bowl or its contents. Use a magnifying lens to look at the planarians.
4. Record all of your observations on the lines provided in the Data and Observations section.

L2

Laboratory Activities

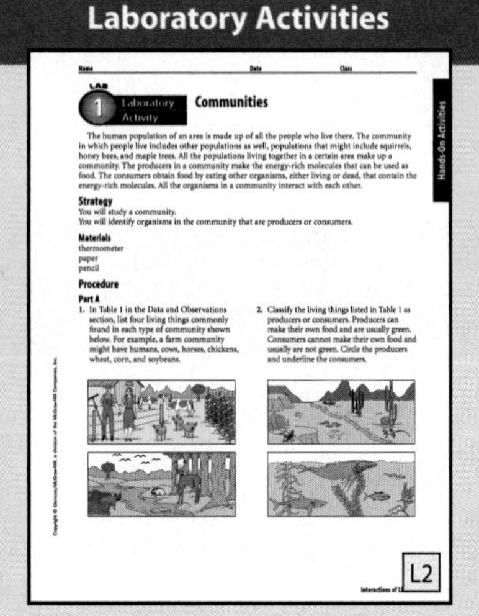
Lab 1 Laboratory Activity — Communities

The human population of an area is made up of all the people who live there. The community in which people live includes other populations as well, populations that might include squirrels, honey bees, and maple trees. All the populations living together in a certain area make up a community. The producers in a community make the energy-rich molecules that can be used as food. The consumers obtain food by eating other organisms, either living or dead, that contain the energy-rich molecules. All the organisms in a community interact with each other.

Strategy

You will study a community.
You will identify organisms in the community that are producers or consumers.

Materials: thermometer, paper, pencil

Procedure

Part A
1. In Table 1 in the Data and Observations section, list four living things commonly found in each type of community shown below. For example, a farm community might have humans, cows, horses, chickens, wheat, corn, and soybeans.
2. Classify the living things listed in Table 1 as producers or consumers. Producers can make their own food and are usually green. Consumers cannot make their own food and usually are not green. Circle the producers and underline the consumers.

L2

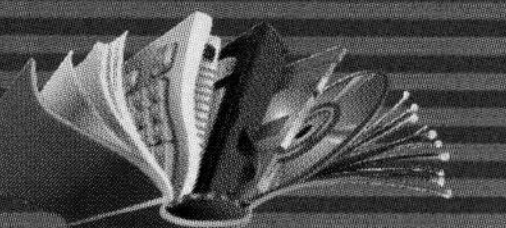

Meeting Different Ability Levels

Content Outline

Note-taking Worksheet — Interactions of Life

Section 1 Living Earth

A. Biosphere—the part of Earth that supports ______

1. The ______ portion of Earth's crust, all the waters on Earth's surface, and the surrounding ______
2. Made up of different ______ that are home to different kinds of organisms

B. Ecosystem—all the organisms living in an area and the ______ features of their environment

1. ______ is the study of interactions that occur among organisms and their environment.
2. A population is made up of all the organisms in an ecosystem that belong to the same ______.
3. A community is all the ______ in an ecosystem.

C. ______—the place in which an organism lives

1. Must provide the kinds of food, shelter, temperature, and ______ the organism needs to survive
2. Example: ______ are the woodpecker's habitat

Section 2 Populations

A. Competition—two or more organisms seek the same ______ at the same time

1. Competition for food, living space, or other resources can ______ the population.
2. Competition is usually most intense between members of ______ species.

B. Population ______—indicates whether a population is healthy and growing

1. Population ______—the size of a population that occupies a specific area
2. Two ways to measure the ______ of a wildlife population
 a. ______ method
 b. ______ method
3. Elements that affect population size
 a. ______—any living or nonliving feature that restricts the number of individuals in a population
 b. Carrying capacity—the ______ number of individuals of one species that an ecosystem can support

L2

Reinforcement

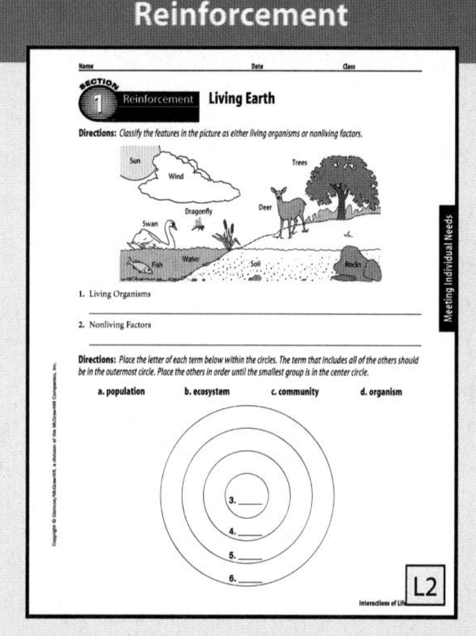

Section 1 Reinforcement — Living Earth

Directions: Classify the features in the picture as either living organisms or nonliving factors.

1. Living Organisms
2. Nonliving Factors

Directions: Place the letter of each term below within the circles. The term that includes all of the others should be in the outermost circle. Place the others in order until the smallest group is in the center circle.

a. population b. ecosystem c. community d. organism

L2

Directed Reading

Directed Reading for Content Mastery — Overview: Interactions of Life

Directions: Complete the two concept maps using the words listed below.

population, consumers, decomposers, biosphere, herbivores, producers, community, carnivores, omnivores, ecosystem

The 4. ______ includes the top portion of Earth's crust, all the waters that cover Earth's surface, and the surrounding environment.
An 3. ______ consists of all the communities that live in an area and the nonliving features of their environment.
A 2. ______ consists of all the populations that live in an area.
A 1. ______ consists of all the organisms of one species that live in an area.

All living organisms on Earth are either producers or consumers.

Green plants and other 5. ______ use an outside energy source to make energy-rich compounds.

There are four categories of 6. ______, none of which can make their own energy-rich compounds.
7. ______ eat producers.
8. ______ eat consumers.
9. ______ eat producers and consumers.
10. ______ consume dead organisms.

L1

Assessment

Chapter Tests

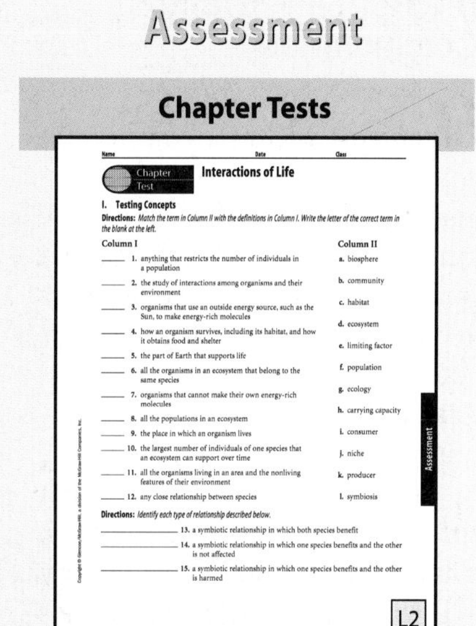

Chapter Test — Interactions of Life

I. Testing Concepts

Directions: Match the term in Column II with the definitions in Column I. Write the letter of the correct term in the blank at the left.

Column I	Column II
1. anything that restricts the number of individuals in a population	a. biosphere
2. the study of interactions among organisms and their environment	b. community
3. organisms that use an outside energy source, such as the Sun, to make energy-rich molecules	c. habitat
4. how an organism survives, including its habitat, and how it obtains food and shelter	d. ecosystem
5. the part of Earth that supports life	e. limiting factor
6. all the organisms in an ecosystem that belong to the same species	f. population
7. organisms that cannot make their own energy-rich molecules	g. ecology
8. all the populations in an ecosystem	h. carrying capacity
9. the place in which an organism lives	i. consumer
10. the largest number of individuals of one species that an ecosystem can support over time	j. niche
11. all the organisms living in an area and the nonliving features of their environment	k. producer
12. any close relationship between species	l. symbiosis

Directions: Identify each type of relationship described below.

13. a symbiotic relationship in which both species benefit
14. a symbiotic relationship in which one species benefits and the other is not affected
15. a symbiotic relationship in which one species benefits and the other is harmed

L2

Enrichment

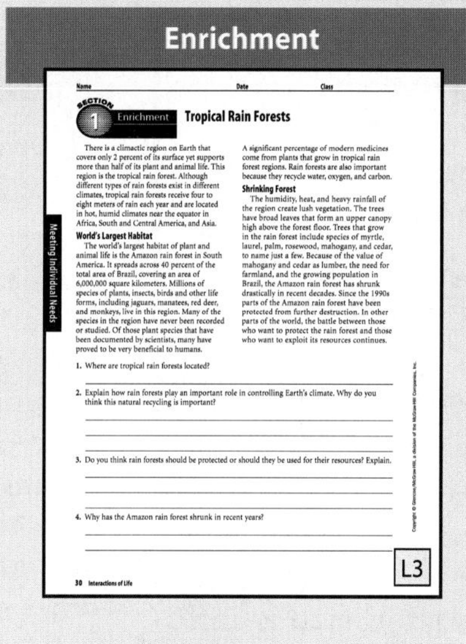

Section 1 Enrichment — Tropical Rain Forests

There is a climactic region on Earth that covers only 2 percent of its surface yet supports more than half of its plant and animal life. This region is the tropical rain forest. Although different types of rain forests exist in different climates, tropical rain forests receive four to eight meters of rain each year and are located in hot, humid climates near the equator in Africa, South and Central America, and Asia.

World's Largest Habitat

The world's largest habitat of plant and animal life is the Amazon rain forest in South America. It spreads across 40 percent of the total area of Brazil, covering an area of 6,000,000 square kilometers. Millions of species of plants, insects, birds and other life forms, including jaguars, manatees, red deer, and monkeys, live in this region. Many of the species in the region have never been recorded or studied. Of those plant species that have been documented by scientists, many have proved to be very beneficial to humans.

A significant percentage of modern medicines come from plants that grow in tropical rain forest regions. Rain forests are also important because they recycle water, oxygen, and carbon.

Shrinking Forest

The humidity, heat, and heavy rainfall of the region create lush vegetation. The trees have broad leaves that form an upper canopy high above the forest floor. Trees that grow in the rain forest include species of myrtle, laurel, palm, rosewood, mahogany, and cedar, to name just a few. Because of the value of mahogany and cedar as lumber, the need for farmland, and the growing population in Brazil, the Amazon rain forest has shrunk drastically in recent decades. Since the 1990s parts of the Amazon rain forest have been protected from further destruction. In other parts of the world, the battle between those who want to protect the rain forest and those who want to exploit its resources continues.

1. Where are tropical rain forests located?
2. Explain how rain forests play an important role in controlling Earth's climate. Why do you think this natural recycling is important?
3. Do you think rain forests should be protected or should they be used for their resources? Explain.
4. Why has the Amazon rain forest shrunk in recent years?

L3

Spanish Directed Reading

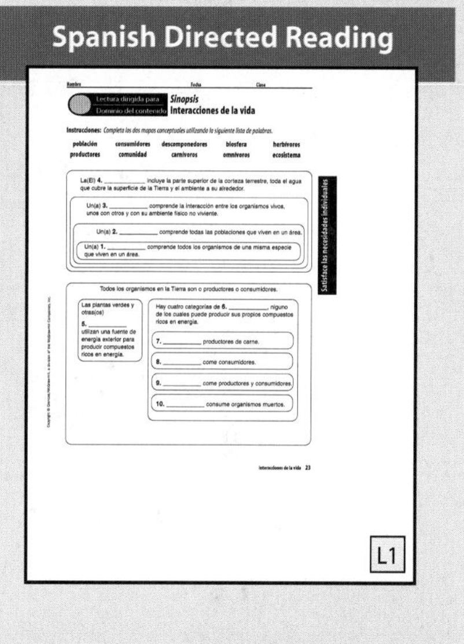

Lectura dirigida para Dominio del contenido — Sinopsis: Interacciones de la vida

Instrucciones: Completa los dos mapas conceptuales utilizando la siguiente lista de palabras.

población, consumidores, descomponedores, biosfera, herbívoros, productores, comunidad, carnívoros, omnívoros, ecosistema

La(El) 4. ______ incluye la parte superior de la corteza terrestre, toda el agua que cubre la superficie de la Tierra y el ambiente a su alrededor.
Un(a) 3. ______ comprende la interacción entre los organismos vivos, unos con otros y con su ambiente físico no viviente.
Un(a) 2. ______ comprende todas las poblaciones que viven en un área.
Un(a) 1. ______ comprende todos los organismos de una misma especie que viven en un área.

Todos los organismos en la Tierra son o productores o consumidores.

Las plantas verdes y otros(as) 5. ______ utilizan una fuente de energía exterior para producir compuestos ricos en energía.

Hay cuatro categorías de 6. ______, ninguno de los cuales puede producir sus propios compuestos ricos en energía.
7. ______ productores de carne.
8. ______ come consumidores.
9. ______ come productores y consumidores.
10. ______ consume organismos muertos.

L1

Test Practice Workbook

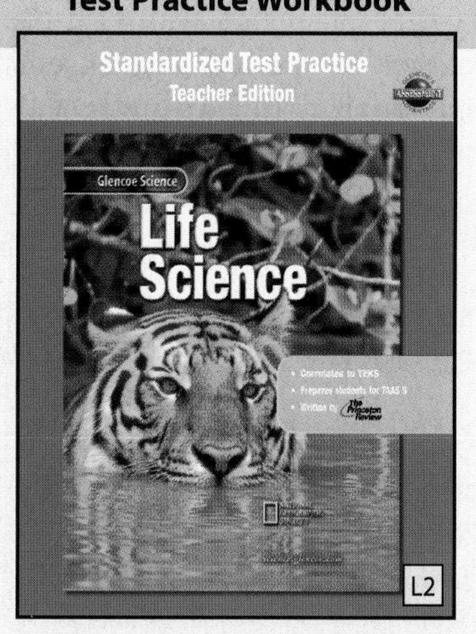

L2

Chapter Review

Chapter Review — Interactions of Life

Part A. Vocabulary Review

Directions: Unscramble the letters to form the correct term for each definition.

1. iglimeti cotraf — anything that restricts the number of individuals in a population
2. chein — the ways an organism meets its survival needs
3. drouscerp — organisms that use any outside energy source, such as the sun, to produce energy-rich molecules
4. omyntcium — all the populations in an ecosystem
5. cloogey — the study of interactions that occur among organisms and their environment
6. smurcores — organisms that cannot make their own energy-rich molecules
7. rhibosepe — the part of Earth that supports life
8. loonpuapti — all the organisms in an ecosystem that belong to the same species
9. grycairn acyacipt — the largest number of individuals of one species that an ecosystem can support over time
10. emyescost — all the organisms living in an area and the nonliving features of their environment
11. ibatath — the place in which an organism lives

Directions: Complete the following sentences using the terms listed below. Some terms will not be used.

symbiosis, mutualism, commensalism, parasitism, ecosystem, competition

12. ______ refers to any close relationship between species.
13. When one organism benefits and the other organism is not affected, the symbiotic relationship is called ______.
14. ______ is a symbiotic relationship in which one organism benefits but the other is harmed.
15. A symbiotic relationship in which both organisms benefit is called ______.

L2

Science Content Background

SECTION 1

Living Earth

Understanding Ecosystems

The biosphere is the total part of Earth where life can exist and includes a great variety of conditions. An ecosystem is a smaller area consisting of the organisms and nonliving features that interact in the system. Sir Arthur George Tansley, a British plant ecologist, coined the word *ecosystem* in 1935.

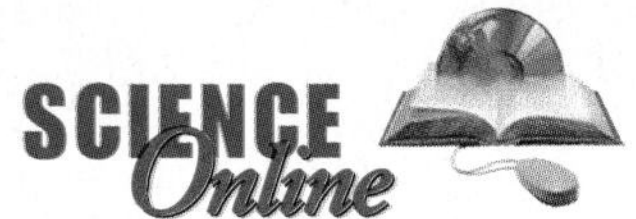

For additional content background on this topic, go to the Glencoe Science Web site at science.glencoe.com.

SECTION 2

Populations

Population Size

Population size is an important characteristic, but it can be difficult to measure. Animal population size is influenced by the amount of food and space available. Natural populations cannot increase forever. Population density measures how crowded a population is. It is always expressed as the number of individuals per unit area or volume.

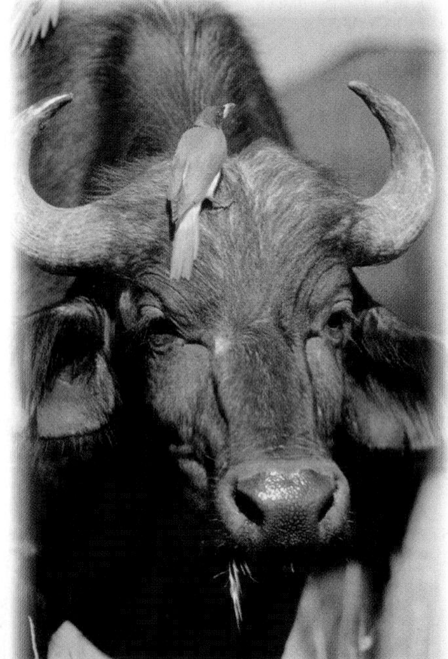

Manoj Shah/DRK Photo

Carrying Capacity

When a population's size is no longer increasing, it has reached the carrying capacity of its ecosystem. The carrying capacity is the greatest number of individuals in a certain population that a given environment is capable of supporting under a given set of conditions. If a population is at carrying capacity, the number of organisms born in a given period of time is balanced by the number of organisms that die during that same time. Carrying capacity can vary with changing seasonal conditions. For example, cold winter weather may cause a reduction in the food supply and a resulting decrease in carrying capacity. In summer, when temperatures are favorable and food supplies increase, carrying capacity also increases.

SECTION 3

Interactions Within Communities

Types of Interactions

Organisms within a community interact in many ways. Plants and other photosynthetic organisms produce sugars that they use as food. Animals, fungi, and other nonphotosynthetic organisms must consume other organisms for food. In addition to predator/prey or producer/consumer relationships, organisms may participate in symbiotic relationships, such as mutualism, commensalism, and parasitism, or they may compete with other species with similar needs for resources. A single species interacts directly or indirectly with nearly all the other species in its community. For example, a squirrel in a forest interacts not only with the plants it eats or with the predators that eat it but also with the plants it uses for cover or shelter, with insects that share its nest, with other animals that use its abandoned nest for shelter, with the bacteria that live on its skin, and so on.

Student Misconception

Plants do not depend on other organisms.

Refer to the facing page for teaching strategies to address this misconception. Refer to pages 704–705 for content related to this topic.

IDENTIFYING Misconceptions

Find Out What Students Think

Students may think that . . .

- **Plants do not depend on other organisms.**
- **Organisms do not depend on one another.**
- **Interdependence is primarily predator/prey relationships.**

While most students can draw a picture of a natural community that includes producers, herbivores, and predators, few can explain their selections in terms of ecological relationships. Many students understand that the organisms they have depicted belong in the environment, but they don't understand how the organisms interact with one another and with the nonliving environment. While students may be able to identify predator/prey relationships, or plant/herbivore relationships, they seldom understand other types of relationships, nor do they see how interconnected one organism may be with many other organisms in its environment.

Activity

Have students draw a terrestrial community, using the local environment as a model. Their drawings should include several different types of organisms. Ask students to indicate as many interactions between organisms as they can. Then have them describe, aloud or in essay form, how each organism in the picture interacts with other organisms. Note the types and complexity of interactions that students describe.

Promote Understanding

Activity

After students read Section 3, organize the class into teams of three or four students. Assign each team a color. Have each team make ten or so flags from paper corresponding to their team's color and toothpicks.

- Take the class outside to a grassy or weedy area of the school grounds.
- Have teams hunt for examples of organisms interacting in various ways, including consumption, competition, and symbiosis, and mark each area where an interaction is occurring with a flag. On each flag, team members should identify the type of interaction and write a short description in their Science Journals of what they found. Encourage students to include drawings along with their verbal descriptions.
- After the allotted time, give students time to examine the findings of other teams before gathering up the flags and returning to the classroom.
- Give each team time to summarize their findings. Then have representatives from each team report their findings to the class. Encourage teams to include their drawings of the interactions they observed.

When all teams have reported, discuss the relationships discovered by the class. Focus the discussion on a few organisms identified by most teams. Challenge students to brainstorm a list of ways in which those organisms interact with other organisms.

Assess

After completing the chapter, see *Identifying Misconceptions* in the Study Guide.

Interactions of Life

Chapter Vocabulary

biosphere, p. 692
ecosystem, p. 693
ecology, p. 693
population, p. 694
community, p. 694
habitat, p. 695
limiting factor, p. 698
carrying capacity, p. 699
producer, p. 704
consumer, p. 705
symbiosis, p. 706
mutualism, p. 706
commensalism, p. 706
parasitism, p. 706
niche, p. 707

What do you think?

Science Journal These are the little mud tunnels that termites build across a non-wood surface to provide protection as they travel back and forth between their nest and their food source.

CHAPTER 24

Interactions of Life

Why would a powerful rhinoceros allow birds to perch on its back? Why aren't these birds safely perched in a tree? How do they find food? You don't have to go to Africa to see birds on the back of a rhino. You can see these animals at zoos or wildlife parks, like the one near New Braunfels, Texas. In this chapter, you will learn how living organisms interact with each other and their surroundings. You also will learn about the roles each organism plays in the flow of energy through the environment.

What do you think?

Science Journal Look at the picture below with a classmate. Discuss what you think this might be or what is happening. Here's a hint: *It's a city within a city.* Write your answer or best guess in your Science Journal.

690

Theme Connection

Systems and Interactions A discussion of ecosystems, habitats, and communities shows how organisms interact. These interactions within the system affect population sizes and organisms' abilities to survive in their environments.

In your lifetime, you probably have taken thousands of footsteps on grassy lawns or playing fields. If you take a close look at the grass, you'll see that each blade is attached to roots in the soil. How do the grass plants obtain everything they need to live and grow? What other kinds of organisms live in the grass? The following activity will give you a chance to take a closer look at the life in a lawn.

Examine sod from a lawn

1. Examine a section of sod from a lawn.
2. How do the roots of the grass plants hold the soil?
3. Do you see signs of other living things besides grass?

Observe

In your Science Journal, answer the above questions and describe any organisms that are present in your section of sod. Explain how these organisms might affect the growth of grass plants. Draw a picture of your section of sod.

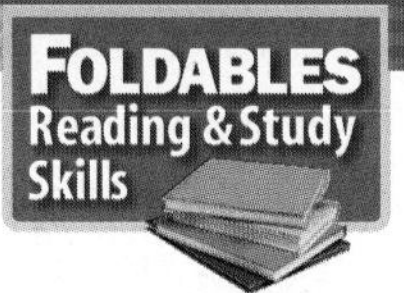

Before You Read

Making a Concept Map Study Fold **The following Foldable will help you organize information by diagramming ideas about your favorite wild animal.**

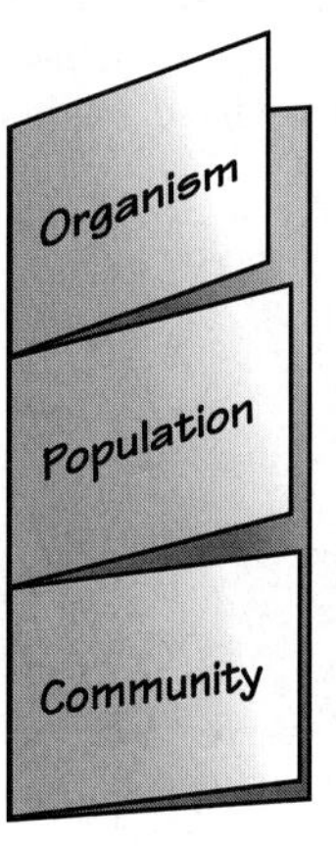

1. Place a sheet of paper in front of you with the short side at the top. Fold the paper in half from the left side to the right side.
2. Fold from top to bottom to divide the paper into thirds, then open up the three folds.
3. Through the top thickness of paper, cut along each of the fold lines to the side fold, forming three tabs.
4. Label *Organism, Population,* and *Community* across the front of the paper, as shown. Write the name of your favorite wild animal under the *Organism* tab.
5. Before you read the chapter, write what you know about your favorite animal under the top tab. As you read the chapter, write how this animal is part of a population and a community under the middle and bottom tabs.

FOLDABLES Reading & Study Skills

Before You Read

Dinah Zike Study Fold

Purpose Students develop and use a Foldable concept map to describe a specific animal as part of a population and a community.

For additional help, see Foldables Worksheet, p. 17 in **Chapter Resources Booklet,** or go to the Glencoe Science Web site at **science.glencoe.com.** See After You Read in the Study Guide at the end of this chapter.

Purpose Use the Explore Activity to introduce students to characteristics of ecosystems and communities. Explain that they will be learning about interactions among organisms of the same or different species. L1 ELL LS **Kinesthetic**

Preparation Purchase sod from a garden center, or dig up a square of sod, including the soil that surrounds the roots. Temporarily fill the area with soil so you don't leave a divot. Replace the sod when you are finished. Keep the sod in a cool, moist area so that it stays fresh and retains small animal life.

Materials small piece of sod for each group, hand lens (optional)

Teaching Strategy After a few minutes of examination, instruct students to tear the sod in half. This may reveal animals that have moved to the interior of the sod.

Observe

Organisms may include one or more grasses, clover, ants, grasshopper nymphs, earthworms, fungi, or bacteria. The effects of the organisms will vary. A grasshopper might slow the growth of grass, but an earthworm might accelerate it.

Process Have students show each other an organism that they observed. Then have them infer the effect of the organism on the grass. Use **Performance Assessment in the Science Classroom,** p. 89.

SECTION

Living Earth

1 Motivate

Bellringer Transparency

Display the Section Focus Transparency for Section 1. Use the accompanying Transparency Activity Master. L2 ELL

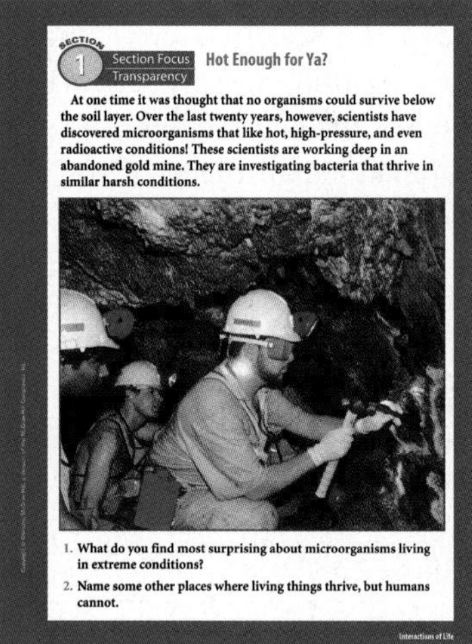

SECTION 1 Section Focus Transparency **Hot Enough for Ya?**

At one time it was thought that no organisms could survive below the soil layer. Over the last twenty years, however, scientists have discovered microorganisms that like hot, high-pressure, and even radioactive conditions! These scientists are working deep in an abandoned gold mine. They are investigating bacteria that thrive in similar harsh conditions.

1. What do you find most surprising about microorganisms living in extreme conditions?
2. Name some other places where living things thrive, but humans cannot.

Interactions of Life

Tie to Prior Knowledge

Ask students to identify several habitats—the places where plants and animals live. Have them describe living and nonliving things in those habitats.

SECTION 1

Living Earth

As You Read

***What* You'll Learn**

- **Identify** places where life is found on Earth.
- **Define** ecology.
- **Observe** how the environment influences life.

Vocabulary

biosphere	population
ecosystem	community
ecology	habitat

***Why* It's Important**

All living things on Earth depend on each other for survival.

The Biosphere

What makes Earth different from other planets in the solar system? One difference is Earth's abundance of living organisms. The part of Earth that supports life is the **biosphere** (BI uh sfihr). The biosphere includes the top portion of Earth's crust, all the waters that cover Earth's surface, and the atmosphere that surrounds Earth.

Reading Check *What three things make up the biosphere?*

As **Figure 1** shows, the biosphere is made up of different environments that are home to different kinds of organisms. For example, desert environments receive little rain. Cactus plants, coyotes, and lizards are included in the life of the desert. Tropical rain forest environments receive plenty of rain and warm weather. Parrots, monkeys, and tens of thousands of other organisms live in the rain forest. Coral reefs form in warm, shallow ocean waters. Arctic regions near the north pole are covered with ice and snow. Polar bears, seals, and walruses live in the arctic.

Figure 1
Earth's biosphere consists of many environments, including ocean waters, polar regions, and deserts.

Desert

Arctic

Coral reef

Section Assessment Planner

Portfolio	**Content Assessment**
Activity, p. 694	Section, p. 695
Performance Assessment	Challenge, p. 695
Skill Builder Activities, p. 695	Chapter, pp. 716–717
See page 716 for more options.	

Life on Earth In our solar system, Earth is the third planet from the Sun. The amount of energy that reaches Earth from the Sun helps make the temperature just right for life. Mercury, the planet closest to the Sun, is too hot during the day and too cold at night to make life possible there. Venus, the second planet from the Sun, has a thick, carbon dioxide atmosphere and high temperatures. It is unlikely that life could survive there. Mars, the fourth planet, is much colder than Earth because it is farther from the Sun and has a thinner atmosphere. It might support microscopic life, but none has been found. The planets beyond Mars probably do not receive enough heat and light from the Sun to have the right conditions for life.

Ecosystems

On a visit to Yellowstone National Park in Wyoming, you might see a prairie scene like the one shown in **Figure 2.** Bison graze on prairie grass. Cowbirds follow the bison, catching grasshoppers that jump away from the bisons' hooves. This scene is part of an ecosystem. An **ecosystem** consists of all the organisms living in an area and the nonliving features of their environment. Bison, grass, birds, and insects are living organisms of this prairie ecosystem. Water, temperature, sunlight, soil, and air are nonliving features of this prairie ecosystem. **Ecology** is the study of interactions that occur among organisms and their environment. Ecologists are scientists who study these interactions.

Reading Check *What is an ecosystem?*

Figure 2
Ecosystems are made up of living organisms and the nonliving features of their environment. In this prairie ecosystem, cowbirds eat insects and bison graze on grass. *What other kinds of organisms might live in this ecosystem?*

The Biosphere

Reading Check

Answer the top portion of the crust, surface water, and Earth's atmosphere

Ecosystems

Caption Answer

Figure 2 Possible answers: rabbits, prairie dogs, antelope, small shrubs, hawks

Reading Check

Answer all living organisms and nonliving features of an area

Teacher FYI

Ecosystems are the basic unit of study of ecology. They contain living (biotic) and nonliving (abiotic) components. The terms biotic and abiotic are introduced later in this unit.

Resource Manager

Chapter Resources Booklet
- Transparency Activity, p. 44
- Directed Reading for Content Mastery, pp. 19, 20
- Note-taking Worksheets, pp. 33–35

Cultural Diversity

Varieties of Ecosystems Have students who are originally from different cities, states, or countries describe to the class ecosystems from where they used to live. Encourage these students to explain why the ecosystem is important to the people in that area. Show the locations of these areas on a map after students describe them.

Populations

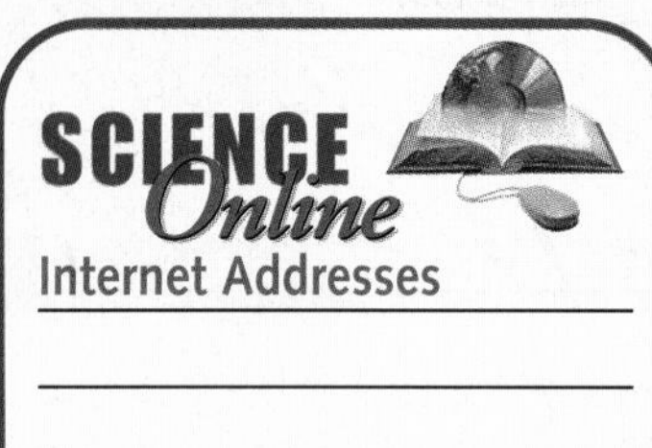

Internet Addresses

Explore the Glencoe Science Web site at science.glencoe.com to find out more about topics in this section.

Identifying Misconceptions

Uses of the term *population* may lead to confusion. When discussing human population size it is common to simply say population. For example, "What is the population of San Diego?" In ecology, a population refers to all the organisms of a species in an area. A population has many characteristics, only one of which is size.

Activity

Have students observe a natural setting and draw or photograph a habitat that contains visible plant and animal life. Ask students to place their drawings or photographs, along with a list of the populations observed, in their Science Journals. L2 ELL LS Naturalist P

Populations

Suppose you meet an ecologist who studies how a herd of bison moves from place to place and how the female bison in the herd care for their young. This ecologist is studying the members of a population. A **population** is made up of all the organisms in an ecosystem that belong to the same species. For example, all the bison in a prairie ecosystem are one population. All the cowbirds in this ecosystem make up a different population. The grasshoppers make up yet another population.

Ecologists often study how populations interact. For example, an ecologist might try to answer questions about several prairie species. How does grazing by bison affect the growth of prairie grass? How does grazing influence the insects that live in the grass and the birds that eat those insects? This ecologist is studying a community. A **community** refers to all the populations in an ecosystem. The prairie community is made of populations of bison, grasshoppers, cowbirds, and all other species in the prairie ecosystem. An arctic community might include populations of fish, seals that eat fish, and polar bears that hunt and eat seals. **Figure 3** shows how organisms, populations, communities, and ecosystems are related.

Research Visit the Glencoe Science Web site at **science.glencoe.com** and find out the estimated human population size for the world today. In your Science Journal, create a graph that shows the population change between the year 2000 and this year.

Figure 3
The living world is arranged in several levels of organization.

Inclusion Strategies

Learning Disabled Give student pairs a one-inch column of newspaper text. Ask them to find, circle, and count different populations. For example, have them find the population of the letter *P* by circling each *P* and counting to determine population size. Explain that one letter is an organism, each type of letter is a population, and all the types of letters are a community. L1

Resource Manager

Chapter Resources Booklet
Reinforcement, p. 27
Enrichment, p. 30

Science Inquiry Labs, p. 7

Figure 4
The trees of the forest provide a habitat for woodpeckers and other birds. This salamander's habitat is the moist forest floor.

Habitats

Each organism in an ecosystem needs a place to live. The place in which an organism lives is called its **habitat.** The animals shown in **Figure 4** live in a forest ecosystem. Trees are the woodpecker's habitat. These birds use their strong beaks to pry insects from tree bark or break open acorns and nuts. Woodpeckers usually nest in holes in dead trees. The salamander's habitat is the forest floor, beneath fallen leaves and twigs. Salamanders avoid sunlight and seek damp, dark places. This animal eats small worms, insects, and slugs. An organism's habitat provides the kinds of food and shelter, the temperature, and the amount of moisture the organism needs to survive.

Section  Assessment

1. What is the biosphere?
2. What is ecology?
3. How are the terms *habitat* and *biosphere* related to each other?
4. What is the major difference between a community and a population? Give one example of each.
5. **Think Critically** Does the amount of rain that falls in an area determine which kinds of organisms can live there? Why or why not?

Skill Builder Activities

6. **Forming Hypotheses** Make a hypothesis about how one nonliving feature of an ecosystem would affect the growth of dandelions in that ecosystem. **For more help, refer to the** **Science Skill Handbook.**
7. **Communicating** Pretend you are a nonhuman organism in the wild. Describe what you are and list living and nonliving features of the environment that affect you. **For more help, refer to the** **Science Skill Handbook.**

Habitats

Discussion

Point out that a habitat may describe a very small location, such as a nest in a tree, or a much larger area, such as a freshwater lake. **What is your habitat?** house or apartment **What is the habitat of a humpback whale?** the ocean

3 Assess

Reteach

Have students write a paragraph in their Science Journals explaining the relationships among a population, a community, and an ecosystem. They should include that populations interact to form a community and that communities and nonliving things together make up the ecosystem. L2 LS **Linguistic**

Challenge

Have students research the natural habitat of an organism and then tell the class five interesting things about this habitat. L3 LS **Naturalist**

Assessment

Content Provide students with photographs from discarded magazines. Have them identify living and nonliving things in each photograph and explain how the nonliving things might affect living things. Use **Performance Assessment in the Science Classroom,** p. 89.

Answers to Section Assessment

1. the part of Earth that supports life
2. the study of the interactions between organisms and between organisms and their environment
3. Habitat—place where organisms live; the biosphere includes all Earth's habitats.
4. A population is a single species living in an area. Example: all the maple trees of the Catskill Mountains. A community is all the populations that live in an area. Example: all the species of the Catskill Mountains.
5. Yes; organisms that need a lot of water cannot exist in areas with little rainfall.
6. Hypotheses should indicate that a nonliving factor, such as light, moisture, chemical fertilizers, or pH can have a positive or negative affect on the growth of dandelions.
7. Answers will vary but should include interactions with both the living and nonliving components of the environment.

SECTION 2

Populations

1 Motivate

Bellringer Transparency

Display the Section Focus Transparency for Section 2. Use the accompanying Transparency Activity Master. L2 ELL

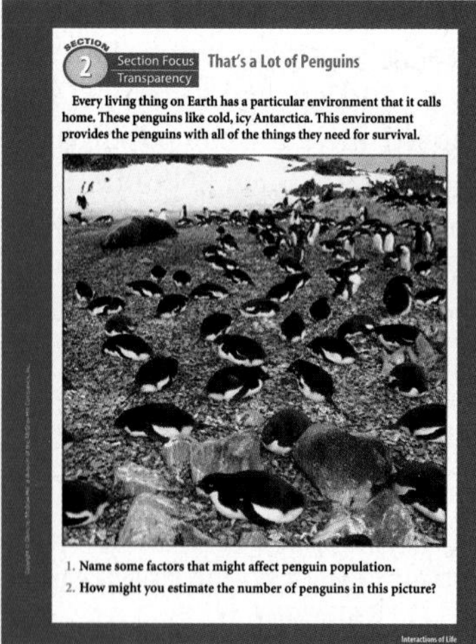

Tie to Prior Knowledge

Have students recall the needs of living things. Knowing what living things need to grow and reproduce will be helpful in understanding limiting factors.

SECTION 2

Populations

As You Read

***What* You'll Learn**

- **Identify** methods for estimating population sizes.
- **Explain** how competition limits population growth.
- **List** factors that influence changes in population size.

Vocabulary
limiting factor
carrying capacity

***Why* It's Important**
Competition caused by population growth affects many organisms, including humans.

Competition

Some pet shops sell lizards, snakes, and other reptiles. Crickets are raised as a food supply for pet reptiles. In the wild, crickets come out at night and feed on plant material. During the day, they hide in dark areas, beneath leaves or under buildings. Pet shop workers who raise crickets make sure that the insects have plenty of food, water, and hiding places. As the cricket population grows, the workers increase the crickets' food supply and the number of hiding places. To avoid crowding, some of the crickets could be moved into larger containers.

Food and Space Organisms living in the wild do not always have enough food or living space. The Gila woodpecker, shown in **Figure 5,** lives in the Sonoran Desert of Arizona and Mexico. This bird makes its nest in a hole that it drills in a saguaro (suh GWAR oh) cactus. If an area has too many Gila woodpeckers or too few saguaros, the woodpeckers must compete with each other for nesting spots. Competition occurs when two or more organisms seek the same resource at the same time.

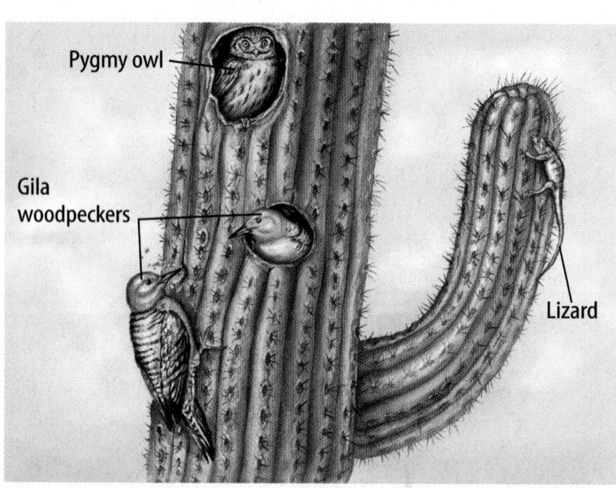

Figure 5
Gila woodpeckers make nesting holes in the saguaro cactus. Many animals compete for the shelter these holes provide.

Growth Limits Competition limits population size. If the amount of available nesting space is limited, some woodpeckers will not be able to raise young. Gila woodpeckers eat cactus fruit, berries, and insects. If food becomes scarce, some woodpeckers might not survive to reproduce. Competition for food, living space, or other resources can prevent population growth.

In nature, the most intense competition is usually among individuals of the same species, because they need the same kinds of food and shelter. Competition also takes place among individuals of different species. For example, after a Gila woodpecker has abandoned its nesting hole, owls, flycatchers, snakes, and lizards compete for the shelter of the empty hole.

Section Assessment Planner

PORTFOLIO
Curriculum Connection, p. 699

PERFORMANCE ASSESSMENT
Try at Home MiniLAB, p. 697
MiniLAB, p. 701
Skill Builder Activities, p. 703
See page 716 for more options.

CONTENT ASSESSMENT
Section, p. 703
Challenge, p. 703
Chapter, pp. 716–717

Population Size

Ecologists often need to measure the size of a population. This information can indicate whether or not a population is healthy and growing. Population counts can help identify populations that could be in danger of disappearing.

Some populations are easy to measure. If you were raising crickets, you could measure the size of your cricket population simply by counting all the crickets in the container. What if you wanted to compare the cricket populations in two different containers? You would calculate the number of crickets per square meter (m^2) of your container. The size of a population that occupies a specific area is called population density. **Figure 6** shows human population density in different places in the world.

Reading Check *What is population density?*

Measuring Populations Counting crickets can be tricky. They look alike, move a lot, and hide. The same cricket could be counted more than once, and others could be completely missed. Ecologists have similar problems when measuring wildlife populations. One of the methods they use is called trap-mark-release. Suppose you want to count wild rabbits. Rabbits live underground and come out at dawn and dusk to eat. Ecologists set traps that capture rabbits without injuring them. Each captured rabbit is marked and released. Later, another sample of rabbits is captured. Some of these rabbits will have marks, but many will not. By comparing the number of marked and unmarked rabbits in the second sample, ecologists can estimate the population size.

TRY AT HOME Mini LAB

Observing Seedling Competition

Procedure

1. Fill **two plant pots** with **moist potting soil.**
2. Plant **radish seeds** in one pot, following the spacing instructions on the seed packet. Label this pot "Recommended Spacing."
3. Plant radish seeds in the second pot, spaced half the recommended distance apart. Label this pot "Densely Populated." Wash your hands.
4. Keep the soil moist. When the seeds sprout, move them to a well-lit area.
5. Measure the height of the seedlings every two days for two weeks. Record the data in your **Science Journal.**

Analysis

1. Which plants grew faster?
2. Which plants looked healthiest after two weeks?
3. How did competition influence the plants?

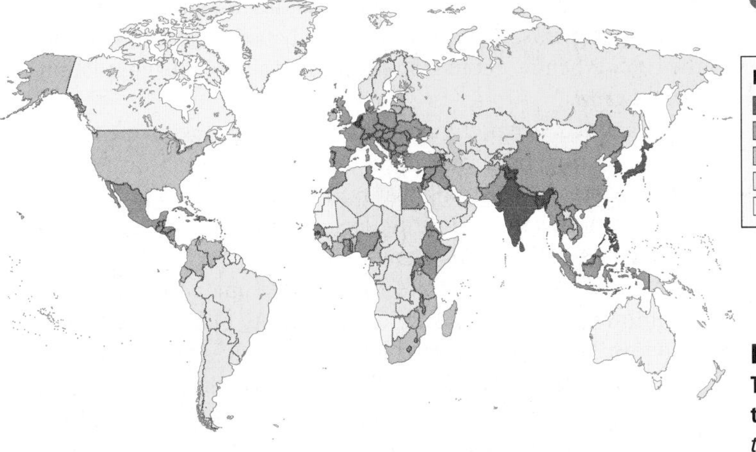

Figure 6
This map shows human population density. *Which countries have the highest population density?*

2 Teach

Population Size

Purpose Students determine if population density affects the growth of certain plants. L2 **IS Logical-Mathematical**

Materials 2 plant pots, potting soil, radish seeds, watering can, large basin, metric ruler

Teaching Strategies

- Avoid putting plants in hot areas.
- Have students premeasure water before adding.

Troubleshooting Follow seed packets instructions as to the number of seeds to plant per hole. Thin plants so that the density of seedlings in one pot is twice the density in the other pot.

Analysis

1. In many cases the densely planted seedlings grew faster.
2. The plants with more space will usually look healthier. They may not be as tall, but they look greener, fuller, and more robust.
3. Competition probably caused the less densely planted seedlings to grow better because they were able to get more light.

Reading Check

Answer the size of a population that occupies a specific area

Caption Answer

Figure 6 India, Japan, the Philippines, and South Korea

Resource Manager 

Chapter Resources Booklet
Transparency Activity, p. 45
MiniLAB, p. 3
Reading and Writing Skill Activities, p. 1

Assessment

Oral Have students explain why the more densely planted seedlings might have grown faster. Have them predict which plants would be healthier if the experiment was continued for another four weeks. Use **Performance Assessment in the Science Classroom,** p. 99.

Population Size, continued

Discussion

Why would people want to know the population size of organisms such as deer? Ecologists may want the data for research. Game and Fish Departments may want the information to decide how many hunting permits to issue.

Caption Answer

Figure 7 Answers will vary. Students may suggest that they can count the number of wildebeests in the enlarged square, and then multiply by 25, the number of squares in the entire photograph.

Extension

Crabgrass is an annual plant. Assume one crabgrass plant produces 100 seeds every season, and each of those sprouts into a plant next season that will also produce 100 seeds. **If you start with one grass plant, how many will you have after three years?**
year 1-1 plant
year 2-100 plants
year 3-10,000 plants

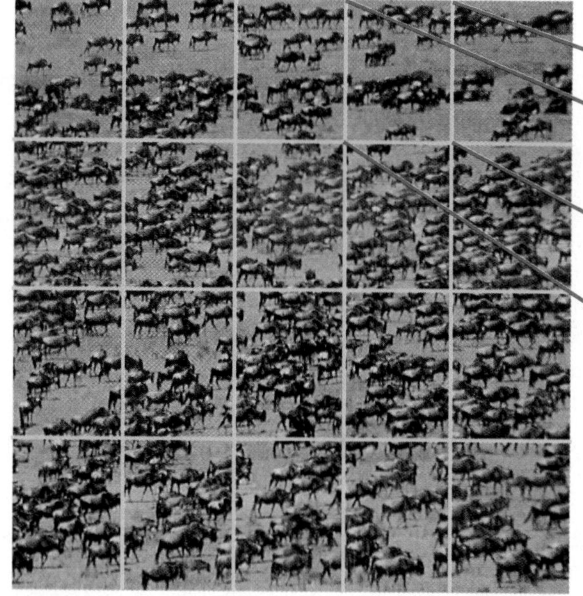

Figure 7
Ecologists can estimate population size by making a sample count. Wildebeests graze on the grassy plains of Africa. *How could you use the enlarged square to estimate the number of wildebeests in the entire photograph?*

Sample Counts What if you wanted to count rabbits over a large area? Ecologists use sample counts to estimate the sizes of large populations. To estimate the number of rabbits in a 100-acre area, for example, you could count the rabbits in one acre and multiply by 100 to estimate the population size. **Figure 7** shows another approach to sample counting.

Limiting Factors One grass plant can produce hundreds of seeds. Imagine those seeds drifting onto a vacant field. Many of the seeds sprout and grow into grass plants that produce hundreds more seeds. Soon the field is covered with grass. Can this grass population keep growing forever? Suppose the seeds of wildflowers or trees drift onto the field. If those seeds sprout, trees and flowers would compete with grasses for sunlight, soil, and water. Even if the grasses did not have to compete with other plants, they might eventually use up all the space in the field. When no more living space is available, the population cannot grow.

In any ecosystem, the availability of food, water, living space, mates, nesting sites, and other resources is often limited. A **limiting factor** is anything that restricts the number of individuals in a population. Limiting factors include living and nonliving features of the ecosystem.

A limiting factor can affect more than one population in a community. Suppose a lack of rain limits plant growth in a meadow. Fewer plants produce fewer seeds. For seed-eating mice, this reduction in the food supply could become a limiting factor. A smaller mouse population could, in turn, become a limiting factor for the hawks and owls that feed on mice.

LAB DEMONSTRATION

Purpose to estimate population size

Materials overhead projector (OHP), 4 sheets of paper, transparency, marker, ruler, cardboard to screen the OHP surface, hole punch

Preparation Punch 100 discs. Draw a grid on the transparency consisting of 25 1.25″ x 1.25″ squares.

Procedure Display the grid. Erect the screen. Evenly sprinkle 25 discs. Position papers to reveal one square. Turn on the OHP; count the discs. Repeat twice. Estimate and then count population size. Repeat for 50 and 100 discs.

Expected Outcome Estimates will approximate actual population size.

Assessment

How could a better estimate be made? Collect data from a greater number of cells. **When would an ecologist use this technique?** when it is difficult or expensive to count all the organisms in an area

Carrying Capacity A population of robins lives in a grove of trees in a park. Over several years, the number of robins increases and nesting space becomes scarce. Nesting space is a limiting factor that prevents the robin population from getting any larger. This ecosystem has reached its carrying capacity for robins. **Carrying capacity** is the largest number of individuals of one species that an ecosystem can support over time. If a population begins to exceed the environment's carrying capacity, some individuals will not have enough resources. They could die or be forced to move elsewhere, like the deer shown in **Figure 8.**

Figure 8
These deer might have moved into a residential area because a nearby forest's carrying capacity for deer has been reached.

 ***How are limiting factors related to carrying capacity?***

Problem-Solving Activity

Do you have too many crickets?

You've decided to raise crickets to sell to pet stores. A friend says you should not allow the cricket population density to go over 210 crickets/m^2. Use what you've learned in this section to measure the population density in your cricket tanks.

Identifying the Problem

The table on the right lists the areas and populations of your three cricket tanks. How can you determine if too many crickets are in one tank? If a tank contains too many crickets, what could you do? Explain why too many crickets in a tank might be a problem.

Cricket Population

Tank	Area (m^2)	Number of Crickets
1	0.80	200
2	0.80	150
3	1.5	315

Solving the Problem

1. Do any of the tanks contain too many crickets? Could you make the population density of the three tanks equal by moving crickets from one tank to another? If so, which tank would you move crickets into?
2. The population density of wild crickets living in a field is 2.4 crickets/m^2. If the field has an area of 250 m^2, what is the approximate size of the cricket population? Why would the population density of crickets in a field be lower than the population density of crickets in a tank?

Activity

Have the classroom represent an ecosystem. Set the carrying capacity of the room at 80 percent of the number of students present. Have the remaining 20 percent of the students stand to the side. Have these "extra" individuals enter the ecosystem through birth or immigration and have others leave through death or emigration so that the size of the population remains steady. IS **Kinesthetic**

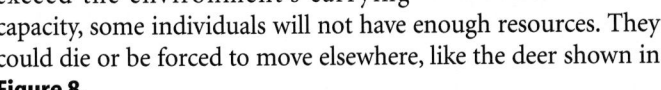

Reading Check

Answer Carrying capacity exists because of limiting factors. A shortage of one or more things limits population size.

Problem-Solving Activity

National Math Standards

Correlation to Mathematics Objectives
1, 2, 4, 5, 6, 8, 9

Answers

1. The population densities of the three tanks are 1: 250 crickets/m^2 2: 187.5 crickets/m^2 3: 210 crickets/m^2. Tank 1 has too many crickets. You might try putting some of the extra crickets into tank 2, because it has a lower population density. Tank 3 has the maximum population density allowed.
2. To find this answer, multiply the population density by the area: 250 $m^2 \times 2.4$ crickets/$m^2 = 600$ crickets. The population density in the field would be much lower than the tank because the crickets have more space to spread out. They are also free from competition.

Resource Manager

Chapter Resources Booklet
Enrichment, p. 31

Mathematics Skill Activities, p. 5

Life Science Critical Thinking/Problem Solving, p. 12

Curriculum Connection

Art Have students research populations that live in areas in which limiting factors severely restrict the kinds of organisms that can live there. Have them make a collage that shows several different populations and environments, such as penguins in Antarctica and cacti in a hot, dry desert. P

Changes in Populations

Visual Learning

Table 1 **Which country has the fastest population growth?** Zimbabwe **Which country has the slowest growth?** Germany **What does a negative growth rate mean?** Death rate is greater than birthrate.

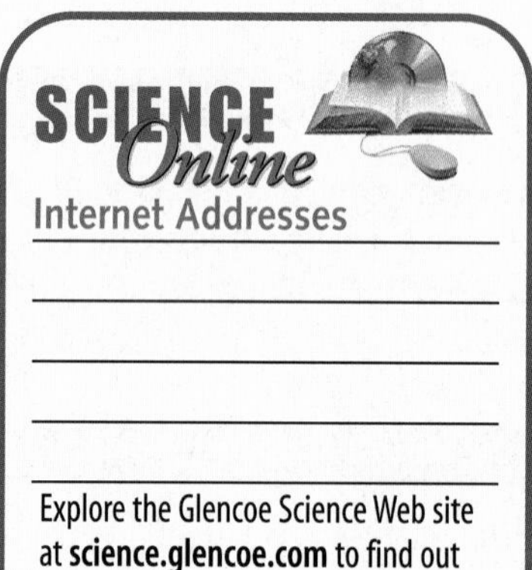

Explore the Glencoe Science Web site at **science.glencoe.com** to find out more about topics in this section.

Teacher FYI

Some organisms produce few offspring and some produce many. Fewer offspring benefit because they can be supplied with more of the parents' resources. Having many offspring increases the odds that one or more will survive to reproduce.

Quick Demo

Bring in seeds that travel, such as those from dandelions and maple trees. Blow the dandelion seeds and drop the maple seeds to show how they travel. You might also show burrs and explain how they travel by sticking to animals.

Data Update For an online update of recent data on human birthrates and death rates around the world, visit the Glencoe Science Web site at **science.glencoe.com** and select the appropriate chapter.

Biotic Potential What would happen if no limiting factors restricted the growth of a population? Think about a population that has an unlimited supply of food, water, and living space. The climate is favorable. Population growth is not limited by diseases, predators, or competition with other species. Under ideal conditions like these, the population would continue to grow.

The highest rate of reproduction under ideal conditions is a population's biotic potential. The larger the number of offspring that are produced by parent organisms, the higher the biotic potential of the species will be. Compare an avocado tree to a tangerine tree. Assume that each tree produces the same number of fruits. Each avocado fruit contains one large seed. Each tangerine fruit contains a dozen seeds or more. Because the tangerine tree produces more seeds per fruit, it has a higher biotic potential than the avocado tree.

Changes in Populations

Birthrates and death rates also influence the size of a population and its rate of growth. A population gets larger when the number of individuals born is greater than the number of individuals that die. When the number of deaths is greater than the number of births, populations get smaller. Take the squirrels living in New York City's Central Park as an example. In one year, if 900 squirrels are born and 800 die, the population increases by 100. If 400 squirrels are born and 500 die, the population decreases by 100.

The same is true for human populations. **Table 1** shows birthrates, death rates, and population changes for several countries around the world. In countries with faster population growth, birthrates are much higher than death rates. In countries with slower population growth, birthrates are only slightly higher than death rates. In Germany, where the population is getting smaller, the birthrate is lower than the death rate.

Table 1 Population Growth

	Birthrate*	Death Rate*	Population Increase (percent)
Rapid-Growth Countries			
Jordan	38.8	5.5	3.3
Uganda	50.8	21.8	2.9
Zimbabwe	34.3	9.4	5.2
Slow-Growth Countries			
Germany	9.4	10.8	–1.5
Sweden	10.8	10.6	0.1
United States	14.8	8.8	0.6

*Number per 1,000 people

Inclusion Strategies

Hearing Impaired Have students use index cards to make flipbooks showing variations in population growth. On the first cards, have them show a few organisms followed by exponential growth. Next, have them show how competition for resources affects the population. Finally, have them show a constant population size. Suggest they include a line graph that indicates change in population size in each scene.

Resource Manager

Chapter Resources Booklet

Directed Reading for Content Mastery, p. 20

MiniLAB, p. 4

Science Inquiry Labs, p. 37

Figure 9
The mangrove seeds sprout while they are still attached to the parent tree. Some sprouted seeds drop into the mud below the parent tree and continue to grow. Others drop into the water and can be carried away by tides and ocean currents. When they wash ashore, they might start a new population of mangroves or add to an existing mangrove population.

Moving Around Most animals can move easily from place to place, and these movements can affect population size. For example, a male mountain sheep might wander many miles in search of a mate. After he finds a mate, their offspring might establish a completely new population of mountain sheep far from the male's original population.

Many bird species move from one place to another during their annual migrations. During the summer, populations of Baltimore orioles are found throughout eastern North America. During the winter, these populations disappear because the birds migrate to Central America. They spend the winter there, where the climate is mild and food supplies are plentiful. When summer approaches, the orioles migrate back to North America.

Even plants and microscopic organisms can move from place to place, carried by wind, water, or animals. The tiny spores of mushrooms, mosses, and ferns float through the air. The seeds of dandelions, maple trees, and other plants have feathery or winglike growths that allow them to be carried by wind. Spine-covered seeds hitch rides by clinging to animal fur or people's clothing. Many kinds of seeds can be transported by river and ocean currents. Mangrove trees growing along Florida's Gulf Coast, shown in **Figure 9,** provide an example of how water moves seeds.

Mini LAB

Comparing Biotic Potential

Procedure
1. Remove all the seeds from a **whole fruit.** Do not put fruit or seeds in your mouth.
2. Count the total number of seeds in the fruit. Wash your hands, then record these data in your Science Journal.
3. Compare your seed totals with those of classmates who examined other types of fruit.

Analysis
1. Which type of fruit had the most seeds? Which had the fewest seeds?
2. What is an advantage of producing many seeds? Can you think of a possible disadvantage?
3. To estimate the total number of seeds produced by a tomato plant, what would you need to know?

Mini LAB

Purpose Students observe and compare the number of seeds in different types of fruit. L2 ELL LS **Logical-Mathematical**

Materials plastic knives, paper towels, assorted fruits

Teaching Strategies
- Arrange for students to bring in fruits from home.
- Explain that many of our vegetables are actually fruits, including tomatoes, eggplants, and squashes.

Safety Precautions Instruct students on the proper way to handle and use the plastic knives.

Analysis
1. Tomatoes and strawberries have many seeds; avocados and peaches have one seed.
2. Advantage: There is a greater chance that a seed will find an optimal place to grow. Disadvantage: The seeds are small and carry few nutrients.
3. How many tomatoes the plant produces and about how many seeds are produced by each tomato

Assessment

Oral Based on the number of seeds contained in each fruit, which has a greater biotic potential—a nectarine or a watermelon? Explain. A watermelon—it contains many seeds, while a nectarine contains only one. Use **PASC,** p. 89.

Active Reading

Four-Corner Discussion This strategy encourages the class to debate a complex issue. Make four signs: Strongly Agree, Agree, Disagree, Strongly Disagree. Place one sign in each corner of the room. Write on the chalkboard a statement that will elicit reactions from students. Have students respond on paper to the statement. After several minutes, direct them to move to the corner with the sign that most closely reflects their opinions. In the corners, students share responses. Each group then selects a spokesperson to report the opinions of the group. After all groups have reported, open the floor for debate. Allow students who have changed their opinions to change corners. Have students conduct a Four-Corner Discussion about the causes of changes in populations.

NATIONAL GEOGRAPHIC

Visualizing Population Growth

Have students examine the pictures and read the captions. Then ask the following question.

What happens when a population exceeds carrying capacity? Possible answer: There may not be enough resources to support all members of the population. It is likely that members will begin to die from lack of resources such as food and water.

Extension

Have students graph the following data on predator-prey cycles between lynx and snowshoe hares.

Years	# of lynx	# of hares
1845	30,000	18,000
1850	10,000	40,000
1855	30,000	78,000
1860	8,000	21,000
1865	67,000	71,000
1870	7,000	12,000
1875	40,000	99,000
1880	12,000	9,000

What is the pattern between the population numbers of the lynx and the hares? As the number of hares increases, the number of lynx increases. As the larger lynx population feeds on hares, the number of hares decreases, followed by a decrease in the number of lynx.

NATIONAL GEOGRAPHIC **VISUALIZING POPULATION GROWTH**

Figure 10

When a species enters an ecosystem that has abundant food, water, and other resources, its population can flourish. Beginning with a few organisms, the population increases until the number of organisms and available resources are in balance. At that point, population growth slows or stops. A graph of these changes over time produces an S-curve, as shown here for coyotes.

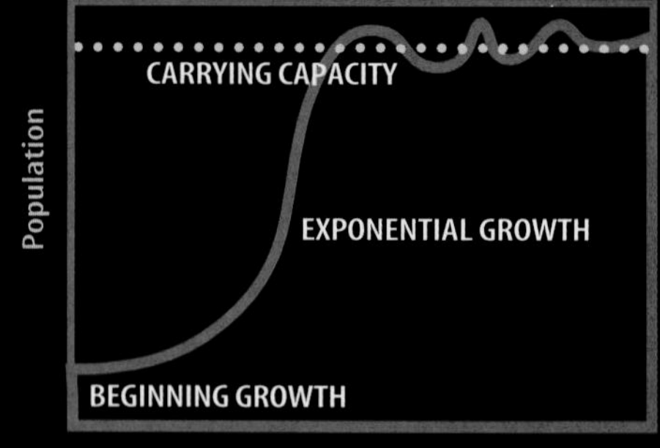

BEGINNING GROWTH During the first few years, population growth is slow, because there are few adults to produce young. As the population grows, so does the number of breeding adults.

EXPONENTIAL GROWTH As the number of adults in the population grows, so does the number of births. The coyote population undergoes exponential growth, quickly increasing in size.

CARRYING CAPACITY As resources become less plentiful, the birthrate declines and the death rate may rise. Population growth slows. The coyote population has reached the environmental carrying capacity—the maximum number of coyotes that the environment can sustain.

702

Resource Manager

Chapter Resources Booklet
- Transparency Activity, pp. 47–48
- Reinforcement, p. 28

Life Science Critical Thinking/Problem Solving, p. 13

Curriculum Connection

Math The bacterium *E. coli* can double in population size every twenty minutes under suitable conditions. Starting with a single bacterium, have students calculate the length of time it would take for the population to reach 1 million. The population would reach 1 million in only 6 hours and 40 minutes. L2 LS **Logical-Mathematical**

Exponential Growth

Imagine what might happen if a pair of coyotes moves into a valley where no other coyotes live. Food and water are abundant, and there are plenty of areas where female coyotes can build dens for their young. This population grows quickly in a pattern called exponential growth. Exponential growth means that the larger a population becomes, the faster it grows.

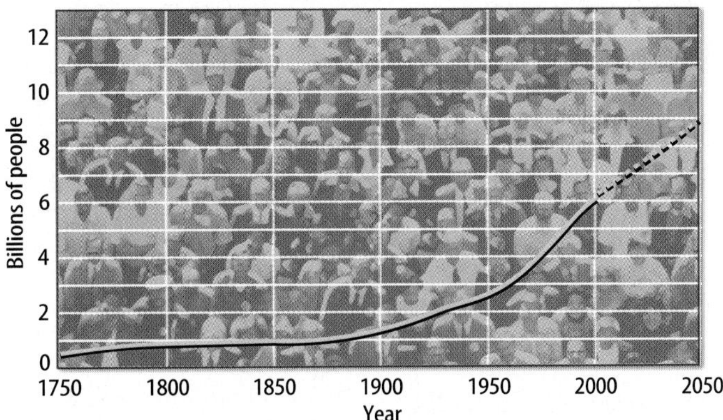

After several years, the population becomes so large that the coyotes begin to compete for food and den sites. Population growth slows, and the number of coyotes remains fairly constant and reaches equilibrium. This ecosystem has reached its carrying capacity for coyotes. A graph that describes each stage in this pattern of population growth is shown in **Figure 10.** As you can see in **Figure 11,** Earth's human population shows exponential growth. In the year 2000, Earth's human population exceeded 6 billion. By the year 2050, it is estimated that Earth's human population could reach 10 billion.

Figure 11
The size of the human population is increasing by about 1.6 percent per year. *What factors affect human population growth?*

Section  Assessment

1. How can an ecologist predict the size of a population without counting every organism in the population?
2. Why does competition between individuals of the same species tend to be greater than competition between individuals of different species?
3. How do birthrates and death rates influence the size of a population?
4. How does carrying capacity influence the number of organisms in an ecosystem?
5. **Think Critically** Why does the supply of food and water in an ecosystem usually affect population size more than other limiting factors?

Skill Builder Activities

6. **Making and Using Tables** Construct a table using the following data on changes in the size of a deer population in Arizona. In 1910 there were 6 deer; in 1915, 36 deer; in 1920, 143 deer; in 1925, 86 deer; and in 1935, 26 deer. Propose a hypothesis to explain what might have caused these changes. **For more help, refer to the** Science Skill Handbook.
7. **Solving One-Step Equations** A vacant lot that measures 12 m × 12 m contains 46 dandelion plants, 212 grass plants, and 14 bindweed plants. What is the population density, per square meter, of each species? **For more help, refer to the** Math Skill Handbook.

Answers to Section Assessment

1. Count the organisms in a portion of an area, and then multiply that number by the number of portions needed to make a whole.
2. Organisms of the same species have similar needs.
3. If birthrate exceeds death rate, population size increases. If death rate exceeds birthrate, population size decreases. If they are equal, population size is maintained.
4. The number of organisms cannot permanently exceed the carrying capacity of the environment.
5. Food and water are critical for survival. Things such as oxygen also are critical, but they usually are not in short supply.
6. Possible answer: The population grew when predators were eliminated. When the deer exceeded the carrying capacity of their environment, their numbers were again reduced.
7. dandelion: 46/144 = 0.3; grass: 212/144 = 1.5; bindweed: 14/144 = 0.1

Caption Answer

Figure 11 Accept all reasonable answers. Sample responses: availability of resources (e.g., food, water, and space), birthrate, death rate.

3 Assess

Reteach

Ask students to work in groups to (a) guess the size of your school's seventh-grade population, (b) devise a way to more accurately estimate that population size, and (c) give reasons for seventh-grade immigration and emigration. L1 COOP LEARN

Challenge

The number of a certain bacteria doubles every hour. If you start at time zero with one bacterium, how many bacteria will you have after 10 hours? Make a graph showing the number you have every hour. Graphs should show the following data:

Time (hours)	Number of Bacteria	Time (hours)	Number of Bacteria
0	1	6	64
1	2	7	128
2	4	8	256
3	8	9	512
4	16	10	1024
5	32		

Assessment

Performance Have students research the population trends of an endangered species. Ask students to graph the data, showing numbers of individuals on the vertical axis and year on the horizontal axis. Have students describe the growth curve. Use **PASC,** p. 111.

SECTION

Interactions Within Communities

1 Motivate

Bellringer Transparency

Display the Section Focus Transparency for Section 3. Use the accompanying Transparency Activity Master. L2 ELL

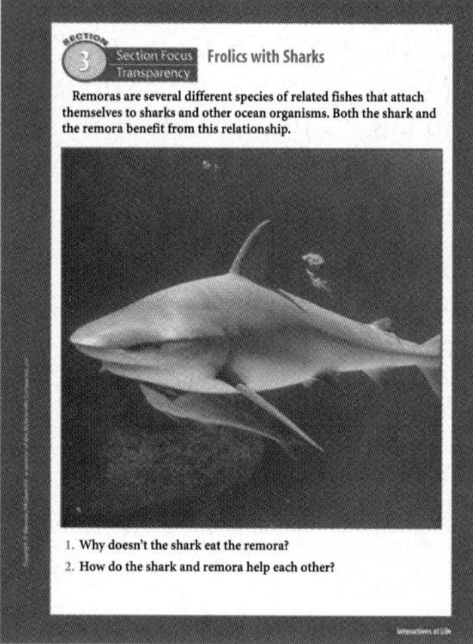

Section Focus Transparency — Frolics with Sharks

Remoras are several different species of related fishes that attach themselves to sharks and other ocean organisms. Both the shark and the remora benefit from this relationship.

1. Why doesn't the shark eat the remora?
2. How do the shark and remora help each other?

Tie to Prior Knowledge

Have students consider a familiar ecosystem. Ask them to name organisms that make up the community and describe interactions among these organisms.

SECTION

Interactions Within Communities

As You Read

***What* You'll Learn**

- **Describe** how organisms obtain energy for life.
- **Explain** how organisms interact.
- **Recognize** that every organism occupies a niche.

Vocabulary

producer, consumer, symbiosis, mutualism, commensalism, parasitism, niche

***Why* It's Important**

How organisms obtain food and meet other needs is critical for their survival.

Obtaining Energy

Just as a car engine needs a constant supply of gasoline, living organisms need a constant supply of energy. The energy that fuels most life on Earth comes from the Sun. Some organisms use the Sun's energy to create energy-rich molecules through the process of photosynthesis. The energy-rich molecules, usually sugars, serve as food. They are made up of different combinations of carbon, hydrogen, and oxygen atoms. Energy is stored in the chemical bonds that hold the atoms of these molecules together. When the molecules break apart—for example, during digestion—the energy in the chemical bonds is released to fuel life processes.

Producers Organisms that use an outside energy source like the Sun to make energy-rich molecules are called **producers.** Most producers contain chlorophyll (KLOR uh fihl), a chemical that is required for photosynthesis. As shown in **Figure 12,** green plants are producers. Some producers do not contain chlorophyll and do not use energy from the Sun. Instead, they make energy-rich molecules through a process called chemosynthesis (kee moh SIHN thuh sus). These organisms can be found near volcanic vents on the ocean floor. Inorganic molecules in the water provide the energy source for chemosynthesis.

Figure 12
Green plants, including the grasses that surround this pond, are producers. The pond also contains many other producers, including microscopic organisms like A *Euglena* and B simple plantlike organisms called algae.

704 CHAPTER 24 Interactions of Life

Section Assessment Planner

PORTFOLIO
Science Journal, p. 707

PERFORMANCE ASSESSMENT
Skill Builder Activities, p. 708
See page 716 for more options.

CONTENT ASSESSMENT
Section, p. 708
Challenge, p. 708
Chapter, pp. 716–717

Consumers

Herbivores

Carnivores

Omnivores

Decomposers

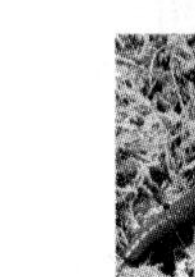

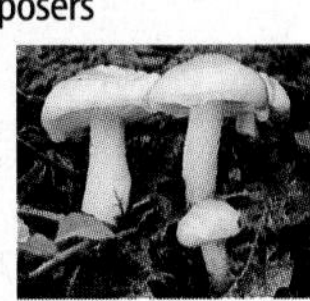

Figure 13
Four categories of consumers are shown. ***What kind of consumer is a bear? A mushroom?***

Consumers Organisms that cannot make their own energy-rich molecules are called **consumers.** Consumers obtain energy by eating other organisms. **Figure 13** shows the four general categories of consumers. Herbivores are the vegetarians of the world. They include rabbits, deer, and other plant eaters. Carnivores are animals that eat other animals. Frogs and spiders are carnivores that eat insects. Omnivores, including pigs and humans, eat mostly plants and animals. Decomposers, including fungi, bacteria, and earthworms, consume wastes and dead organisms. Decomposers help recycle once-living matter by breaking it down into simple, energy-rich substances. These substances might serve as food for decomposers, be absorbed by plant roots, or be consumed by other organisms.

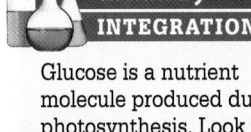

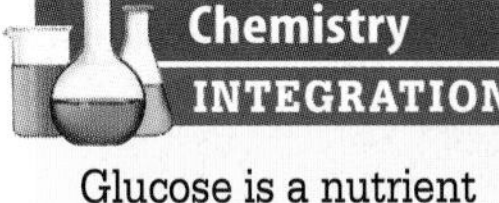

Chemistry INTEGRATION

Glucose is a nutrient molecule produced during photosynthesis. Look up the chemical structure of glucose and draw it in your Science Journal.

Reading Check *How are producers different from consumers?*

Food Chains Ecology includes the study of how organisms depend on each other for food. A food chain is a simple model of the feeding relationships in an ecosystem. For example, shrubs are food for deer, and deer are food for mountain lions, as illustrated in **Figure 14.** What food chain would include you?

Figure 14
Food chains illustrate how consumers obtain energy from other organisms in an ecosystem.

2 Teach

Obtaining Energy

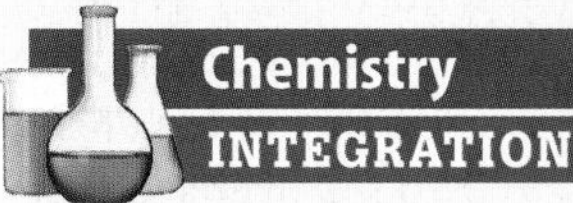

Chemistry INTEGRATION

Energy for life is stored in the bonds of organic molecules such as glucose. A molecule of glucose is made of 6 carbons, 12 hydrogens, and 6 oxygens atoms ($C_6H_{12}O_6$). The structure is as follows.

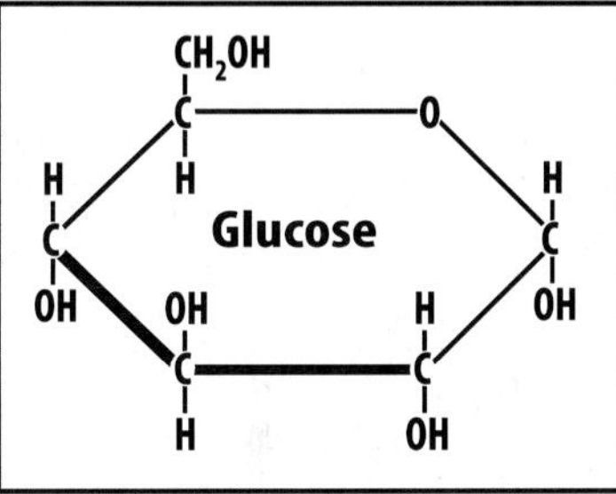

Reading Check

Answer A producer can make its own energy-rich molecules; a consumer must obtain energy-rich molecules from other organisms.

Use Science Words

Word Origin Types of consumers are described by words derived from Latin. *Vorare* means "to devour," *herba* means "grass," *caro* means "flesh," and *omnis* means "all." Present this information to students and have them use it to explain the terms *herbivore*, *carnivore*, and *omnivore.*

Discussion

Most humans are omnivores. Are humans suited for this type of diet? Possible responses: Humans have canine teeth, which carnivores have, as well as molars, which herbivores have. Herbivores have long digestive tracts; carnivores have shorter tracts. Humans have digestive tracts of intermediate length.

Resource Manager

Chapter Resources Booklet

Transparency Activity, p. 46
Enrichment, p. 32
Directed Reading for Content Mastery, pp. 21, 22

Text Question Answer

Accept any answer that shows a human eating food derived from a plant or animal. For example, in Figure 14, humans might replace the mountain lion, because humans eat venison.

Caption Answer

Figure 13 A bear is an omnivore; a mushroom is a decomposer.

Symbiotic Relationships

Activity

Bring in stones or pieces of tree bark with lichens growing on them. Have students look at the lichens using hand lenses. Then have them prepare wet-mount slides of lichen pieces and observe them using microscopes. **How do the algae and fungus benefit each other?** Algae make food for the fungus, and the fungus provides a habitat and moisture for the algae. L2 IN **Visual-Spatial**

Use an Analogy

Challenge students to describe a human interaction that is analogous to commensalism. Possible example: A person may go through another's trash and find something useful. This is analogous to commensalism because one person benefits, while the other is neither helped nor harmed.

Fun Fact

Some people might say that animals are solar powered. Going back in the food chain, all energy can be traced back to producers, which make carbohydrates using the Sun's energy.

Figure 15
Many examples of symbiotic relationships exist in nature.

A Lichens are a result of mutualism.

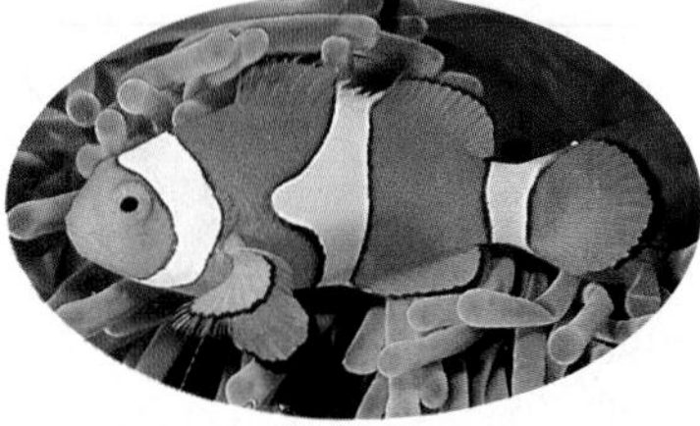

B Clown fish and sea anemones have a commensal relationship.

Magnification: 128×

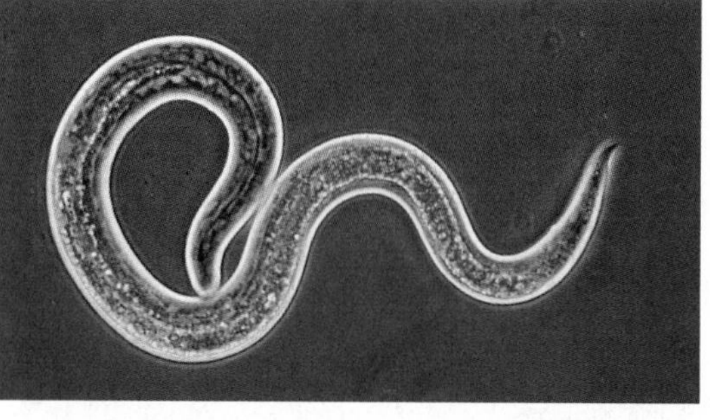

C Some roundworms are parasites that rob nutrients from their hosts.

Symbiotic Relationships

Not all relationships among organisms involve food. Many organisms live together and share resources in other ways. Any close relationship between species is called **symbiosis.**

Mutualism You may have noticed crusty lichens growing on fences, trees, or rocks. Lichens, like those shown in **Figure 15A,** are made up of an alga or a cyanobacterium that lives within the tissues of a fungus. Through photosynthesis, the cyanobacterium or alga supplies energy to itself and the fungus. The fungus provides a protected space in which the cyanobacterium or alga can live. Both organisms benefit from this association. A symbiotic relationship in which both species benefit is called **mutualism** (MYEW chuh wuh lih zum).

Commensalism If you've ever visited a marine aquarium, you might have seen the ocean organisms shown in **Figure 15B.** The creature with gently waving, tubelike tentacles is a sea anemone. The tentacles contain a mild poison. Anemones use their tentacles to capture shrimp, fish, and other small animals to eat. The striped clown fish can swim among the tentacles without being harmed. The anemone's tentacles protect the clown fish from predators. In this relationship, the clown fish benefits but the sea anemone is not helped or hurt. A symbiotic relationship in which one organism benefits and the other is not affected is called **commensalism** (kuh MEN suh lih zum).

Parasitism Pet cats or dogs sometimes have to be treated for worms. Roundworms, like the one shown in **Figure 15C,** are common in puppies. This roundworm attaches itself to the inside of the puppy's intestine and feeds on nutrients in the puppy's blood. The puppy may have abdominal pain, bloating, and diarrhea. If the infection is severe, the puppy might die. A symbiotic relationship in which one organism benefits but the other is harmed is called **parasitism** (PER uh suh tih zum).

Inclusion Strategies

Learning Disabled Help make the differences between the types of symbiotic relationships more clear by asking students to categorize these examples: a bee gets nectar from a flower and pollinates the flower *(mutualism)*; an orchid, which gets it moisture and nutrients from the air, grows on a tall tree *(commensalism)*; a tick attaches to a deer and sucks its blood *(parasitism)*.

Niches

One habitat might contain hundreds or even thousands of species. Look at the rotting log habitat shown in **Figure 16.** A rotting log in a forest can be home to many species of insects, including termites that eat decaying wood and ants that feed on the termites. Other species that live on or under the rotting log include millipedes, centipedes, spiders, and worms. You might think that competition for resources would make it impossible for so many species to live in the same habitat. However, each species has different requirements for its survival. As a result, each species has its own niche (NIHCH). A **niche** refers to how an organism survives, how it obtains food and shelter, how it finds a mate and cares for its young, and how it avoids danger.

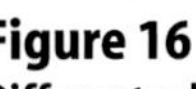

Reading Check *Why does each species have its own niche?*

Special adaptations that improve survival are often part of an organism's niche. Milkweed plants contain a poison that prevents many insects from feeding on them. Monarch butterfly caterpillars have an adaptation that allows them to eat milkweed. Monarchs can take advantage of a food resource that other species cannot use. Milkweed poison also helps protect monarchs from predators. When the caterpillars eat milkweed, they become slightly poisonous. Birds avoid eating monarchs because they learn that the caterpillars and adult butterflies have an awful taste and can make them sick.

Health INTEGRATION

The poison in milkweed is similar to the drug digitalis. Small amounts of digitalis are used to treat heart ailments in humans, but it is poisonous in large doses. Look up digitalis and explain in your Science Journal how it affects the human body.

Figure 16
Different adaptations enable each species living in this rotting log to have its own niche. A Termites eat wood. They make tunnels inside the log. B Millipedes feed on plant matter and find shelter beneath the log. C Wolf spiders capture insects living in and around the log.

Niches

Discussion

The term *niche* is sometimes described as an activity that one person is good at, but others find difficult. **How is this similar to the biological definition?** Organisms with a particular niche often have adaptations that give them an advantage in their environment.

Health INTEGRATION

Digitalis and similar drugs control heart rate. They tend to increase the force but decrease the frequency of heartbeats. Very small doses are used in medicine because larger amounts can cause death.

Reading Check

Answer Each species has different requirements for its survival.

IDENTIFYING Misconceptions

Students may think that plants do not depend on other organisms. Refer to page 690F for teaching strategies that address this misconception.

Resource Manager

Chapter Resources Booklet
Reinforcement, p. 29
Reading and Writing Skill Activities, p. 49
Cultural Diversity, p. 13

Science Journal

Local Niches Have students identify organisms in local habitats that have different niches. Encourage them to research one organism and to write descriptive paragraphs in their science journals about how the organism survives, obtains food and shelter, finds a mate, cares for young, and avoids danger. P

3 Assess

Reteach

What might happen if all insects were eliminated? Possible responses: Other animals that eat insects for food would be in danger of dying if they could not substitute another food source; insects would no longer decompose wastes or once-living materials, allowing wastes to accumulate. Bees and other insects would not pollinate plants, so they wouldn't form fruits and seeds. This would result in less food for people and other animals. L2

LS Naturalist

Challenge

Find the name of a bird or other animal that lives in the area around your school or home. Ask students to research the niche of the animal and suggest reasons that the animal is able to survive there. L3

LS Naturalist

✓Assessment

Process Have students classify the following organisms based on how each obtains nutrition: spider (carnivore); pig (omnivore); goat (herbivore); fungus (decomposer); frog (carnivore). Use **Performance Assessment in the Science Classroom,** p. 121.

Figure 17
The alligator is a predator. The turtle is its prey.

Predator and Prey When you think of survival in the wild, you might imagine an antelope running away from a lion. An organism's niche includes how it avoids being eaten and how it finds or captures its food. Predators, like the one shown in **Figure 17,** are consumers that capture and eat other consumers. The prey is the organism that is captured by the predator. The presence of predators usually increases the number of different species that can live in an ecosystem. Predators limit the size of prey populations. As a result, food and other resources are less likely to become scarce, and competition between species is reduced.

Cooperation Individual organisms often cooperate in ways that improve survival. For example, a white-tailed deer that detects the presence of wolves or coyotes will alert the other deer in the herd. Many insects, such as ants and honeybees, live in social groups. Different individuals perform different tasks required for the survival of the entire nest. Soldier ants protect workers that go out of the nest to gather food. Worker ants feed and care for ant larvae that hatch from eggs laid by the queen. These cooperative actions improve survival and are a part of the species' niche.

Section 3 Assessment

1. Explain why all consumers ultimately depend on producers for food.
2. Draw a food chain that models the feeding relationships of three species in a community. Choose a food chain other than the one shown in **Figure 14.**
3. Make up two imaginary organisms that have a mutualistic relationship. Give them names and explain how they benefit from the association.
4. What is the difference between a habitat and a niche?
5. **Think Critically** A parasite can obtain food only from a host organism. Most parasites weaken but do not kill their hosts. Why?

Skill Builder Activities

6. **Manipulating Variables and Controls** You are sure that Animal A benefits from a relationship with Plant B, but you are not sure if Plant B benefits, is harmed, or is unaffected by the relationship. Design an experiment to compare how well Plant B grows on its own and when Animal A is present. **For more help, refer to the Science Skill Handbook.**
7. **Using Graphics Software** Use graphics software to make three different food chains. Represent each organism with a shape that resembles it. For example, you could use a leaf shape to represent a plant. Label each shape. **For more help, refer to the Technology Skill Handbook.**

Answers to Section Assessment

1. Producers can make their own carbohydrates from nonliving materials; other types of organisms cannot do this and must feed on producers, either directly or indirectly.
2. Answers will vary but must begin with a producer; for example, desert broom—hare—coyote.
3. Answers will vary, but both species should benefit from the relationship.
4. The place an organism lives is its habitat. How an organism survives is its niche.
5. If a parasite kills its host, the parasite will also die.
6. Answers will vary but should include a sample of Animal A grown with Plant B. This will be compared to a sample of Plant B grown alone.
7. Answers will vary, but each food chain must begin with a producer.

Activity

Feeding Habits of Planaria

You probably have watched minnows darting about in a stream. It is not as easy to observe organisms that live at the bottom of a stream, beneath rocks, logs, and dead leaves. Countless stream organisms, including insect larvae, worms, and microscopic organisms, live out of your view. One such organism is a type of flatworm called a planarian. In this activity, you will find out about the eating habits of planarians.

What You'll Investigate

What food items do planarians prefer to eat?

Materials

small bowl
planarians (several)
lettuce leaf
raw liver or meat
guppies (several)
pond or stream water
magnifying lens

Goals

- **Observe** the food preference of planarians.
- **Infer** what planarians eat in the wild.

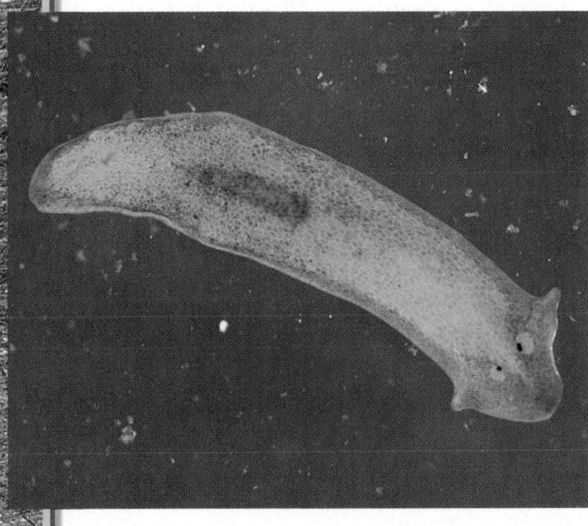

Safety Precautions

Procedure

1. Fill the bowl with stream water.
2. Place a lettuce leaf, piece of raw liver, and several guppies in the bowl. Add the planarians. Wash your hands.
3. **Observe** what happens inside the bowl for at least 20 minutes. Do not disturb the bowl or its contents. Use a magnifying lens to look at the planarians.
4. **Record** all of your observations in your Science Journal.

Conclude and Apply

1. Which food did the planarians prefer?
2. **Infer** what planarians might eat when in their natural environment.
3. Based on your observations during this activity, what is a planarian's niche in a stream ecosystem?
4. **Predict** where in a stream you might find planarians. Use references to find out whether your prediction is correct.

Communicating Your Data

Share your results with other students in your class. Plan an adult-supervised trip with several classmates to a local stream to search for planarians in their native habitat. **For more help, refer to the Science Skill Handbook.**

Resource Manager

Chapter Resources Booklet
Activity Worksheets, pp. 5–6, 7–8
Lab Activities, pp. 9–11, 13–16
Home and Community Involvement, p. 47
Lab Management and Safety, p. 71

Communicating Your Data

Have students write a paragraph describing their results. They can exchange papers with a classmate to see their results.

Activity

BENCH TESTED

Purpose Students observe the eating habits of planarians and infer what wild planarians eat. L2 LS **Visual-Spatial**

Process Skills observing, predicting, inferring

Time Required 30 minutes

Safety Precautions Instruct students to handle planarians with care and to wash their hands after the lab.

Teaching Strategies To house the planarians for an extended period of time, change the water of their bowls every other day and keep a small piece of liver in the bowl.

Troubleshooting

- Set up a bowl of planarians to serve as a reference.
- The piece of liver should be about the size of a quarter.
- Tell students to cover their dishes for a few minutes; planaria do not like light.

Answers to Questions

1. liver
2. Most planaria are carnivorous night feeders. They eat protozoans, tiny snails, worms, and dead animals.
3. Although planarians prey on slow-moving animals, they primarily scavenge dead organisms from the bottom of streams.
4. Planarians live in slow-moving or still portions of a stream where dead organisms settle to the stream bottom. They are found beneath rotting leaves or rocks.

Assessment

Performance Ask students to infer how their results might have differed had they used tap water instead of stream water. Tap water contains chemicals toxic to soft bodied animals and could kill the planarians. Use **PASC,** p. 89.

Activity BENCH TESTED

Recognize the Problem

Purpose

Students will test the effect of a change in one environmental factor on the rate of growth of a fruit fly population.

Process Skills

identifying a question, forming hypotheses, testing a hypothesis, identifying and manipulating variables, collecting data, making and using tables, recording data, recording observations, analyzing results, forming operational definitions, evaluating other's data and conclusions, communicating, making and using graphs

Time

two 45–minute periods and once weekly observations for one to two months

Materials

Standard fruit fly culture kits are available from biological supply houses. Possible culture containers include mayonnaise jars or other empty, sanitized food jars.

Safety Precautions

- Students should take care not to release their fruit flies within the school building.
- Used fruit fly culture containers can contain bacteria and mold, and should not be reused for other purposes.

Activity **Design Your Own Experiment**

Population Growth in Fruit Flies

Populations can grow at an exponential rate only if the environment provides the right amount of food, shelter, air, moisture, heat, living space, and other factors. You probably have seen fruit flies hovering near ripe bananas or other fruit. Fruit flies are fast-growing organisms often raised in science laboratories. The flies are kept in culture tubes and fed a diet of specially prepared food flakes. Can you improve on this standard growing method to achieve faster population growth?

Recognize the Problem

Will a change in one environmental factor affect the growth of a fruit fly population?

Form a Hypothesis

Based on your reading about fruit flies, state a hypothesis about how changing one environmental factor will affect the rate of growth of a fruit fly population.

Goals

- **Identify** the environmental factors needed by a population of fruit flies.
- **Design** an experiment to investigate how a change in one environmental factor affects in any way the size of a fruit fly population.
- **Observe** and **measure** changes in population size.

Possible Materials

fruit flies
standard fruit fly culture kit
food items (banana, orange peel, or other fruit)
water
heating or cooling source
culture containers
cloth, plastic, or other tops for culture containers
hand lens

Safety Precautions

Data Table:

Fruit Fly Population				
Culture number	Number of Flies			
	Date	Date	Date	Date
1				
2				
3				

Form a Hypothesis

Students' hypotheses should reflect a change in one environmental factor, such as type of food, amount of water, or size of container, and its possible effect on the rate of growth of the fruit fly population. For example: A larger living space will result in a faster-growing fruit fly population.

710 CHAPTER 24 Interactions of Life

Test Your Hypothesis

Plan

1. As a group, decide on one environmental factor to investigate. Agree on a hypothesis about how a change in this factor will affect population growth. Decide how you will test your hypothesis, and identify the experimental results that would support your hypothesis.
2. **List** the steps you will need to take to test your hypothesis. Describe exactly what you will do. List your materials.
3. **Determine** the method you will use to measure changes in the size of your fruit fly populations.
4. Prepare a data table in your Science Journal to record weekly measurements of your fruit fly populations.
5. Read the entire experiment and make sure all of the steps are in a logical order.
6. **Research** the standard method used to raise fruit flies in the laboratory. Use this method as the control in your experiment.
7. **Identify** all constants, variables, and controls in your experiment.

Do

1. Make sure your teacher approves your plan before you start.
2. Carry out your experiment.
3. **Measure** the growth of your fruit fly populations weekly and record the data in your data table.

Analyze Your Data

1. What were the constants in your experiment? The variables?
2. **Compare** changes in the size of your control population with changes in your experimental population. Which population grew faster?
3. Using the information in your data table, make a line graph that shows how the sizes of your two fruit fly populations changed over time. Use a different colored pencil for each population's line on the graph.

Draw Conclusions

1. Did the results support your hypothesis? Explain.
2. **Compare** the growth of your control and experimental populations. Did either population reach exponential growth? How do you know?

Communicating Your Data

Compare the results of your experiment with those of other students in your class. **For more help, refer to the** Science Skill Handbook.

Test Your Hypothesis

Possible Procedures

Provide two equal-sized populations of fruit flies with the same amount of food and moisture and the same temperature, but two different sized containers to test the effect of living area on fruit fly population growth. Make observations of the fly populations over the next one to two months. The life cycle of a fruit fly takes approximately two weeks, so students should see rapid changes in population size.

Teaching Strategy

Most students are familiar with fruit flies "appearing" near ripe fruit. Have students consider the source of these flies. Sometimes the eggs were already present on the fruit; other times flies have used their great sense of smell to locate the ripe fruit.

Expected Outcome

Most results will show that any extreme change from the standard method of maintaining fruit flies will result in a decreased rate of population growth.

Analyze Your Data

1. Answers will vary.
2. Answers will vary.
3. Student graphs will vary. Check students' work.

Error Analysis

Have students compare their results and their hypotheses and explain why differences occurred.

Draw Conclusions

1. Answers will be determined by student's hypotheses.
2. A population shows exponential growth if it increases at a fixed percentage per time period. Student answers will depend on results.

Assessment

Oral Have students explain the relationship between environmental conditions and population growth in fruit flies. Flies achieve the fastest rate of growth when all the conditions in their environment are at optimal levels. Any change in these conditions will result in a decrease in population growth rates. Use **Performance Assessment in the Science Classroom,** p. 89.

Communicating Your Data

Students can make an electronic spreadsheet that allows comparison of data about different environmental factors that affect the rate of growth of the fruit fly population.

TIME SCIENCE AND HISTORY

Content Background

The election year 2000 raised a number of questions concerning electors in the Electoral College. For perhaps the first time in recent U.S. history, a large number of people began to wonder how electors are chosen and how many are apportioned for each state.

The answer to these questions lies in the process of census taking. The census affects not only the number and distribution of congressional candidates, but also the number of electors to the Electoral College. Each state has as many electors as it has members of Congress, and every state must have at least one representative and two senators. Every 10 years the census results are used to determine the number of congressional seats of each state. The number of U.S. Representatives gained or lost in the year 1990 as a result of the census affected 21 states. For example, California gained seven seats to the 103rd Congress and New York lost three. Regionally, the South and the West gained 15 seats between 1980 and 1990 and the Northeast and the Midwest lost 15. In the year 2000, the Sun belt won 12 seats at the expense of the Rust belt.

Even though the number of Representatives remains at 435, reapportionment of seats to Congress can have significant impact.

Reapportionment of seats within states necessitates redistricting within those states so that the Representatives stand for equal numbers of people in that state.

TIME SCIENCE AND HISTORY

SCIENCE CAN CHANGE THE COURSE OF HISTORY!

YOU CAN COUNT

The Census gives a snapshot of the people of the United States

The doorbell rings and you hear someone at the door say to your mom, "I'm working for the U.S. Census Bureau, doing follow-up interviews. Do you have a few minutes to answer some questions?" What does this person—and the U.S. government—want to know about your family?

Counting people is important to the United States and to many other countries around the world. It helps governments determine the distribution of people in the various regions of a nation. To obtain this information, the government takes a census—a count of how many people are living in their country on a particular day at a particular time, and in a particular place. A census is a snapshot of a country's population. The time at which the count occurs is called the "census moment." Some countries close their borders for a day or two so everyone will "sit still" for the census camera at the census moment, as was done in Nigeria in 1991.

Counting on the Count

When the United States government was formed, its founders set up the House of Representatives based on population. Areas with more people had more government representatives, and areas with fewer people had fewer representatives. In 1787, the requirement for a census became part of the Constitution. A census must be taken every ten years so the proper number of representatives for each state can be calculated.

Over the years, the U.S. Census Bureau has added questions to obtain more information than just a population count. In 1810, questions about manufacturing were added. In 1850, as more immigrants began coming to the United States, a new question about where people were born was added. In 1880, census takers asked people whether or not they were married. And in 1950, the first electronic computers were used to add up the census results.

Next, read on to find out more about the census.

712

Resources for Teachers and Students

The American Census: A Social History by Margo J. Anderson. Yale University Press, New Haven, CT. 1988.

"The History of Census Tabulation" by Keith S. Reid-Green. *Scientific American* 260 (February 1989): 98-103.

Understanding the Census by Michael R. Lavin. Epic Books, New York. 1996.

Who Counts? The Politics of Census-Taking in Contemporary America by Margo J. Anderson and Stephen E. Fienberg. Russell Sage Foundation, New York. 1999.

Growing by the Numbers

Chances are you just blinked your eyes. While you did it, three people were added to the world's population. There, you blinked again—that's another three people! It may seem impossible, but that's how quickly the world's population is growing. It adds up to 184 people every minute, 11,040 every hour, 264,960 every day, and 97 million every year! On October 12, 1999, the official number of people on the planet reached a record 6 billion.

ON IT

The Short Form

Before 1970, United States census data was collected by field workers. They went door to door to count the number of people living in each household. Since then, the census has been done mostly by mail. People are sent a form they must fill out. The form asks for the number of people living at an address and their names, races, ages, and relationships. Answers to these and other questions are confidential. Census workers visit some homes to check on the accuracy of the information. The census helps the government to figure out how the population is aging. Census data are also important in deciding how to distribute government services and funding.

The 2000 Snapshot

One of the findings of the 2000 Census is that the U.S. population is becoming more equally spread out across age groups. By analyzing the data from the census, officials estimate that by 2020 the population of children, middle-aged people, and senior citizens will be about equal. It's predicted also that there will be more people who are over 100 years old than ever before.

Martha F. Riche researches population changes in the United States. She was also a director of the Census Bureau. Riche thinks that the more equal distribution in age will lead to challenges for the nation. How will we meet the demands of more people who are living longer? Will we need to build more hospitals to care for them? Will more children mean a need to build more schools? Federal, state, and local governments will be using the results of the 2000 Census for years to come as they plan our future.

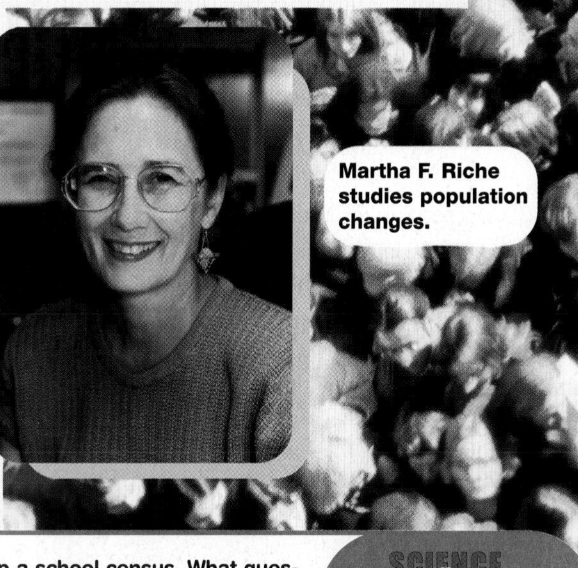

Martha F. Riche studies population changes.

CONNECTIONS Class Census **Develop a school census. What questions will you ask? (Don't ask questions that are too personal.) Who will ask them? How will you make sure you counted everyone? Using the results, can you make any predictions about your school's future or its current students?**

SCIENCE *Online*

For more information, visit science.glencoe.com

CONNECTIONS Today, the entire census is taken using a mail-in form. Have students develop a short mail-in form to take a school census. Have groups write questions to include on the forms. Challenge students to design the form so that it is understandable. After the census is taken, have students discuss challenges they encountered.

SCIENCE *Online*

Internet Addresses

Explore the Glencoe Science Web site at **science.glencoe.com** to find out more about topics in this feature.

Discussion

What do you think accounts for the U.S. population becoming more spread out across age groups? Remind students that from the 1940s through the 1960s there was a sharp increase in the number of babies being born. This created what is popularly known as a "baby boom," which has accounted for the disproportionate number of people in a certain age bracket. Possible answer: The population is becoming more equal in number across age groups because the population in general is declining. People are having smaller families. Seniors are living longer, so their numbers are rising to meet the numbers of middle-aged people.

Historical Significance

Explain to students that census data can have a direct affect on electing our President and Congressmen and Congresswomen. Explain to students that the Electoral College is made up of selected representatives in each state that cast their vote for the President. Tell students that the number of Electoral College votes, not popular votes, elects the President. States with large populations have more electors than do states with small populations. Explain that the number of electors gained or lost in a given state is a direct result of the U.S. Census. Tell students that in the 1990 census, the South and the West gained 15 electors and the Northeast and the Midwest lost 15. Ask students what they think accounts for the shift. Do they think that this shift had an affect on the 2000 election?

Chapter 24 Study Guide

Reviewing Main Ideas

Preview

Students can answer the questions in their Science Journals. Discuss the answers as you go through the chapter. LS **Linguistic**

Review

Students can write their answers, then compare them with those of other students. LS **Interpersonal**

Reteach

Students can look at the illustrations and describe details that support the main ideas of the chapter. LS **Visual-Spatial**

Answers to Chapter Review

Section 1

1. Yes, because it is part of the upper layer of crust and supports life.

Section 2

2. Answers may include the availability of food, water, and choice nesting places. Predators can also be a limiting factor.

Section 3

4. The monarch caterpillar has an adaptation that allows it to feed on the poisonous milkweed plants. This causes the adult monarch to be poisonous to its predators.

Chapter 24 Study Guide

Reviewing Main Ideas

Section 1 Living Earth

1. Ecology is the study of interactions that take place in the biosphere. *Is ice-covered Antarctica a part of Earth's biosphere? Why or why not?*

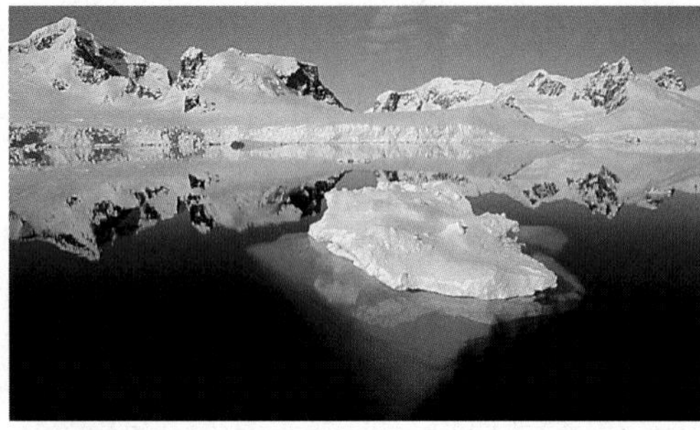

2. Populations are made up of all organisms of the same species living in an area.
3. Communities are made up of all the populations of different species of organisms living in one ecosystem.
4. Living and nonliving factors affect an organism's ability to survive in its habitat.

Section 2 Populations

1. Population size can be estimated by counting a sample of a total population.
2. Competition for limiting factors can restrict the size of a population. *What limiting factors might influence the size of a rabbit population?*

3. Population growth is affected by birthrate, death rate, and the movement of individuals into or out of a community.
4. Exponential population growth can occur in environments that provide a species with plenty of food, shelter, and other resources.

Section 3 Interactions Within Communities

1. All life requires energy.
2. Most producers use the Sun's energy to make food in the form of energy-rich molecules. Consumers obtain their food by eating other organisms.
3. Mutualism, commensalism, and parasitism are the three kinds of symbiosis.
4. Every species has its own niche, which includes adaptations for survival. *What adaptations are involved in the relationship between the milkweed plant and the caterpillar of the monarch butterfly?*

FOLDABLES Reading & Study Skills — **After You Read**

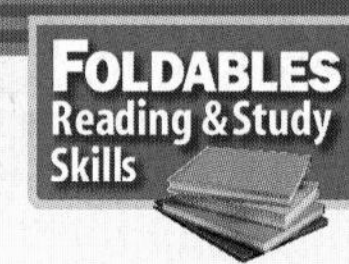

Under the population tab of your Concept Map Study Fold, write what would happen if there were an increase in the population of your animal.

FOLDABLES Reading & Study Skills — **After You Read**

After students have read the chapter and completed the Foldable described in Before You Read, have them do the activity on the student page.

Dinah Zike

Visualizing Main Ideas

Complete the following concept map on communities.

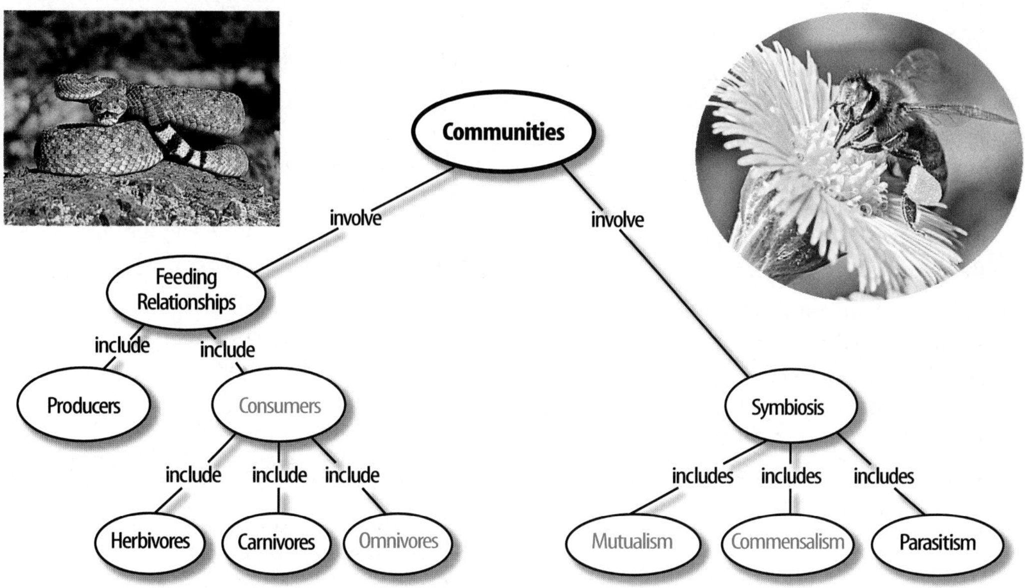

Vocabulary Review

Vocabulary Words

- a. biosphere
- b. carrying capacity
- c. commensalism
- d. community
- e. consumer
- f. ecology
- g. ecosystem
- h. habitat
- i. limiting factor
- j. mutualism
- k. niche
- l. parasitism
- m. population
- n. producer
- o. symbiosis

Study Tip

Get together with a friend to study. Quiz each other about specific topics from your textbook and class material to prepare for a test.

Using Vocabulary

Explain the difference between the vocabulary words in each of the following sets.

1. niche, habitat
2. mutualism, commensalism
3. limiting factor, carrying capacity
4. biosphere, ecosystem
5. producer, consumer
6. population, ecosystem
7. community, population
8. parasitism, symbiosis
9. ecosystem, ecology
10. parasitism, commensalism

IDENTIFYING Misconceptions

Assess

Use the assessment as follow-up to page 690F after students have completed the chapter.

Activity After completing the activity in which students find and label interactions outdoors, have students again draw a picture of a natural community. Have students describe the interactions in the picture.

Expected Outcome In this second drawing, students should be able to identify more relationships between organisms than they did in the first drawing. The interactions they depict should include not only predation, but also various types of symbiosis. Students should also recognize that each organism interacts with many other organisms, not just a single predator or prey species.

Visualizing Main Ideas

See student page.

Vocabulary Review

Using Vocabulary

1. Habitat is the place an organism lives. Niche refers to adaptations that help an organism survive.
2. Both describe symbiotic relationships. In mutualism both organisms benefit. In commensalism, one organism benefits, and the other neither benefits nor is harmed.
3. Carrying capacity is the largest number of individuals of one species that an ecosystem can support. Limiting factors restrict carrying capacity.
4. An ecosystem is all the living and nonliving components of an area. The biosphere is the part of Earth that supports life. It is made up of many ecosystems.
5. Producers make their own nutrients. Consumers eat producers or other consumers for nutrients.
6. An ecosystem is all the living and nonliving components of an area. A population is all the individuals of one species living in an area.
7. A community is all the different species in an area. A population refers to one species in an area.
8. Symbiosis describes a close relationship between species. Parasitism is a type of symbiosis in which one species benefits and the other species is harmed.
9. An ecosystem is all the living and nonliving components of an area. Ecology is the study of interactions between these components.
10. Both are types of symbiosis. In parasitism, one species benefits, and the other is harmed. In commensalism, one organism benefits, and the other neither benefits nor is harmed.

Chapter 24 Study Guide

Checking Concepts

1. A
2. C
3. D
4. D
5. B
6. A
7. C
8. C
9. D
10. A

Thinking Critically

11. It may absorb nutrients from the organism, as does a tapeworm living inside a human's intestine, or it may slowly feed on the tissue of an organism, as does a tick feeding on the blood of a deer.
12. Possible answers: food, water, shelter, space, birthrates and death rates, immigration, emigration
13. Description of habitat should include where the student lives. Description of niche should include adaptations and behaviors that enhance the student's survival.
14. commensalism
15. Organisms are adapted to feed on different foods, hunt at different times, and nest in different places. Therefore many niches can exist in the same habitat.

Chapter 24 Assessment

Checking Concepts

Choose the word or phrase that best answers the question.

1. Which of the following is a living factor in the environment?
   A) animals **C)** sunlight
   B) air **D)** soil
2. What is made up of all the populations in an area?
   A) niches **C)** community
   B) habitats **D)** ecosystem
3. What does the number of individuals in a population that occupies an area of a specific size describe?
   A) clumping **C)** spacing
   B) size **D)** density
4. Which of the following animals is an example of an herbivore?
   A) wolf **C)** tree
   B) moss **D)** rabbit
5. What term best describes a symbiotic relationship in which one species is helped and the other is harmed?
   A) mutualism **C)** commensalism
   B) parasitism **D)** consumerism
6. Which of the following conditions tends to increase the size of a population?
   A) births exceed deaths
   B) population size exceeds the carrying capacity
   C) movements out of an area exceed movements into the area
   D) severe drought
7. Which of the following is most likely to be a limiting factor in a population of fish living in the shallow water of a large lake?
   A) sunlight **C)** food
   B) water **D)** soil
8. An ecologist wants to know the size of a population of wild daisy plants growing in a meadow. The meadow measures 1,000 m^2. The ecologist counts 30 daisy plants in a sample area that is 100 m^2. What is the estimated population of daisies in the entire meadow?
   A) 3 **C)** 300
   B) 30 **D)** 3,000
9. Which of these organisms is a producer?
   A) mole **C)** whale
   B) owl **D)** oak tree
10. Which pair of words is incorrect?
   A) black bear—carnivore
   B) grasshopper—herbivore
   C) pig—omnivore
   D) lion—carnivore

Thinking Critically

11. Why does a parasite have a harmful effect on the organism it infects?
12. What factors affect carrying capacity?
13. Describe your own habitat and niche.
14. The female cowbird lays eggs in the nest of another bird. The other birds care for and feed the cowbird chicks when they hatch. Which type of symbiosis is this?

15. Explain how several different niches can exist in the same habitat.

Developing Skills

16. **Making Models** Place the following organisms in the correct sequence to model a food chain: grass, snake, mouse, and hawk.

Chapter Assessment Planner

Portfolio Encourage students to place in their portfolios one or two items of what they consider to be their best work. Examples include:

- Activity, p. 694
- Curriculum Connection, p. 699
- Science Journal, p. 707

Performance Additional performance assessments, Performance Task Assessment Lists, and rubrics for evaluating these activities can be found in Glencoe's **Performance Assessment in the Science Classroom.**

716 CHAPTER ASSESSMENT

17. **Predicting** Dandelion seeds can float great distances on the wind with the help of white, featherlike attachments. Predict how a dandelion seed's ability to be carried on the wind helps reduce competition among dandelion plants.

18. **Classifying** Classify the following relationships as parasitism, commensalism, or mutualism: a shark and a remora fish that cleans and eats parasites from the shark's gills; head lice and a human; a spiny sea urchin and a tiny fish that hides from predators by floating among the sea urchin's spines.

19. **Comparing and Contrasting** Compare and contrast the diets of omnivores and herbivores. Give examples of each.

20. **Making and Using Tables** Complete the following table.

Types of Symbiosis		
Organism A	**Organism B**	**Relationship**
Gains	Doesn't gain or lose	Commensalism
Gains	Gains	Mutualism
Gains	Loses	Parasitism

Performance Assessment

21. **Poster** Use photographs from old magazines to create a poster that shows at least three different food chains. Display your poster for your classmates.

TECHNOLOGY

Go to the Glencoe Science Web site at **science.glencoe.com** or use the **Glencoe Science CD-ROM** for additional chapter assessment.

Test Practice

A food web shows how organisms in a particular ecosystem depend on each other for food. The food web below shows how the plants and animals in a grassland ecosystem obtain energy from each other.

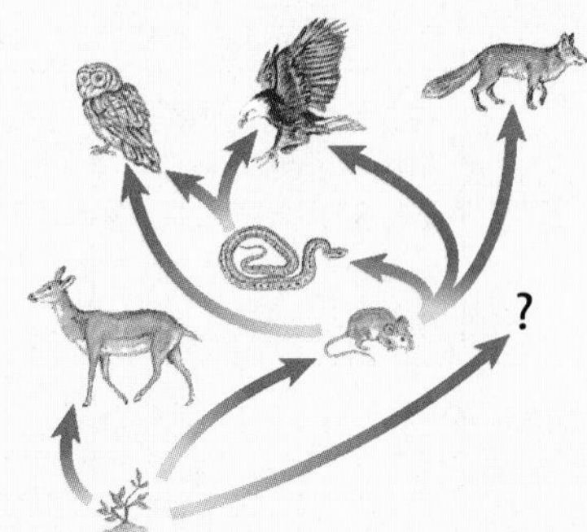

Study the picture and answer the following questions.

1. Other organisms also live in this habitat. Which of the following organisms could fill in the blank space in this food web?
   A) tree
   B) bison
   C) alligator
   D) hawk

2. Suppose all the snakes were removed from this ecosystem. Which of the following statements represents the most reasonable prediction of what could happen in this ecosystem?
   F) The plants would die.
   G) The owls would start eating foxes.
   H) There would be no more predators to eat the mice.
   J) The eagles would start eating more mice.

Test Practice

The Test-Taking Tip was written by The Princeton Review, the nation's leader in test preparation.

1. B
2. J

Developing Skills

16. grass, mouse, snake, hawk
17. Individual seeds are able to float far from the parent plant, which helps reduce population density.
18. mutualism; parasitism; commensalism
19. Both eat plants. Omnivores, such as pigs and humans, eat both plants and animals. Herbivores, such as goats, eat only plants.
20. See student page.

Performance Assessment

21. Posters should show photographs in the correct order of energy flow. All food chains should start with a producer and then move to consumers. Use **Performance Assessment in the Science Classroom**, p. 145.

Assessment Resources

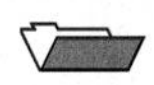

Reproducible Masters

Chapter Resources Booklet
Chapter Review, pp. 37–38
Chapter Tests, pp. 39–42
Assessment Transparency Activity, p. 49

Glencoe Science Web site
Interactive Tutor
Chapter Quizzes

Glencoe Technology
Assessment Transparency
Interactive CD-ROM Chapter Quizzes
ExamView Pro Test Bank
Vocabulary PuzzleMaker Software
MindJogger Videoquiz

Section/Objectives	Standards		Activities/Features
	National	State/Local	
Chapter Opener	See p. 5T for a Key to Standards.		**Explore Activity:** Compare climate differences, p. 719 **Before You Read,** p. 719
Section 1 **Abiotic Factors** 2 sessions 1 block 1. **Identify** common abiotic factors in most ecosystems. 2. **List** the components of air that are needed for life. 3. **Explain** how climate influences life in an ecosystem.	National Content Standards: UPC1, A1, C1, C4, D1, F2		**MiniLAB:** Determining Soil Makeup, p. 722 **Math Skills Activity:** Graphing Temperature Versus Elevation, p. 724 **Physics Integration,** p. 725 **Science Online,** p. 725 **Activity:** Humus Farm, p. 727
Section 2 **Cycles of Nature** 2 sessions 1 block 1. **Explain** the importance of Earth's water cycle. 2. **Diagram** the carbon cycle. 3. **Recognize** the role of nitrogen in life on Earth.	National Content Standards: UPC1, A1, B1, C1, C4, D1, F2		**MiniLAB:** Comparing Fertilizers, p. 731 **Visualizing the Carbon Cycle,** p. 732 **Science Online,** p. 733
Section 3 **Energy Flow** 3 sessions 1.5 blocks 1. **Explain** how organisms produce energy-rich compounds. 2. **Describe** how energy flows through ecosystems. 3. **Recognize** how much energy is available at different levels in a food chain.	National Content Standards: UPC1, A1, B1, B3, C1, C4, D1, F2		**Earth Science Integration,** p. 735 **Activity:** Where does the mass of a plant come from?, pp. 738–739 **Science Stats:** Extreme Climates, pp. 740–741

Activity Materials	Reproducible Resources	Section Assessment	Technology
Explore Activity: globe or world map, weather references	**Chapter Resources Booklet** Foldables Worksheet, p. 17 Directed Reading Overview, p. 19 Note-taking Worksheets, pp. 33–34	GLENCOE'S ASSESSMENT ADVANTAGE	
MiniLAB: soil (2 cups), quart jar with lid, water, dishwashing liquid (1 teaspoon), watch or clock, metric ruler **Activity:** widemouth jar, soil, grass clippings or green leaves, water, marker, metric ruler, graduated cylinder	**Chapter Resources Booklet** Transparency Activity, p. 44 MiniLAB, p. 3 Enrichment, p. 30 Reinforcement, p. 27 Directed Reading, p. 20 Lab Activity, pp. 9–12 Activity Worksheet, pp. 5–6 **Cultural Diversity,** p. 33 **Reading and Writing Skill Activities,** p. 3 **Science Inquiry Labs,** p. 7	**Portfolio** Assessment, p. 726 **Performance** MiniLAB, p. 722 Math Skills Activity, p. 724 Skill Builder Activities, p. 726 **Content** Section Assessment, p. 726	Section Focus Transparency Interactive CD-ROM Guided Reading Audio Program
MiniLAB: labels (and prices) of 3 brands of houseplant fertilizer *Need materials?* Contact Science Kit at 1-800-828-7777 or www.sciencekit.com on the Internet.	**Chapter Resources Booklet** Transparency Activity, p. 45 MiniLAB, p. 4 Enrichment, p. 31 Reinforcement, p. 28 Directed Reading, p. 21 Lab Activity, pp. 13–16 **Science Inquiry Labs,** pp. 29, 39	**Portfolio** Activity, p. 732 **Performance** MiniLAB, p. 731 Skill Builder Activities, p. 733 **Content** Section Assessment, p. 733	Section Focus Transparency Interactive CD-ROM Guided Reading Audio Program
Activity: 8 oz. plastic or paper cup, potting soil to fill cup, scale or balance, 4 radish seeds, water, paper towels	**Chapter Resources Booklet** Transparency Activity, p. 46 Enrichment, p. 32 Reinforcement, p. 29 Directed Reading, pp. 21, 22 Transparency Activity, pp. 47–48 Activity Worksheet, pp. 7–8 **Lab Management and Safety,** p. 38	**Portfolio** Visual Learning, p. 735 **Performance** Skill Builder Activities, p. 737 **Content** Section Assessment, p. 737	Section Focus Transparency Teaching Transparency Interactive CD-ROM Guided Reading Audio Program

End of Chapter Assessment

GLENCOE'S ASSESSMENT ADVANTAGE

Blackline Masters	Technology	Professional Series
Chapter Resources Booklet Chapter Review, pp. 37–38 Chapter Tests, pp. 39–42 **Standardized Test Practice by The Princeton Review,** pp. 107–110	MindJogger Videoquiz Interactive CD-ROM Vocabulary PuzzleMakers ExamView Pro Test Bank Interactive Lesson Planner Interactive Teacher Edition	Performance Assessment in the Science Classroom (PASC)

Transparencies

Section Focus

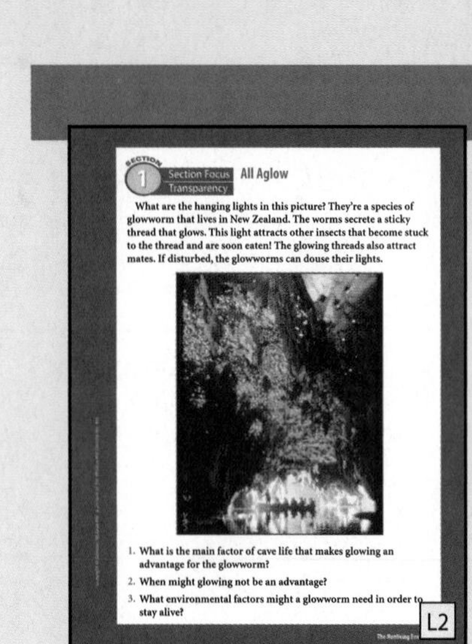
SECTION 1 Section Focus Transparency **All Aglow**

What are the hanging lights in this picture? They're a species of glowworm that lives in New Zealand. The worms secrete a sticky thread that glows. This light attracts other insects that become stuck to the thread and are soon eaten! The glowing threads also attract mates. If disturbed, the glowworms can douse their lights.

1. What is the main factor of cave life that makes glowing an advantage for the glowworm?
2. When might glowing not be an advantage?
3. What environmental factors might a glowworm need in order to stay alive?

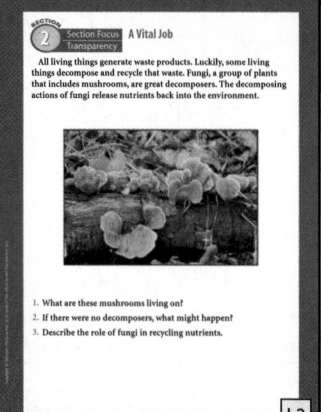

L2

SECTION 2 Section Focus Transparency **A Vital Job**

All living things generate waste products. Luckily, some living things decompose and recycle that waste. Fungi, a group of plants that includes mushrooms, are great decomposers. The decomposing actions of fungi release nutrients back into the environment.

1. What are these mushrooms living on?
2. If there were no decomposers, what might happen?
3. Describe the role of fungi in recycling nutrients.

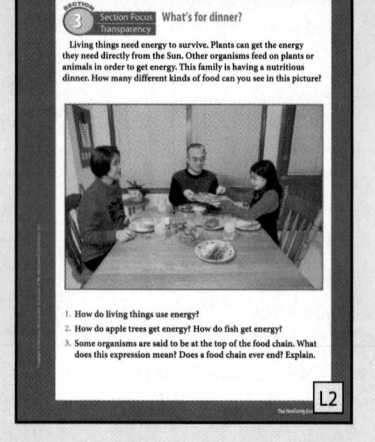

L2

SECTION 3 Section Focus Transparency **What's for dinner?**

Living things need energy to survive. Plants can get the energy they need directly from the Sun. Other organisms feed on plants or animals in order to get energy. This family is having a nutritious dinner. How many different kinds of food can you see in this picture?

1. How do living things use energy?
2. How do apple trees get energy? How do fish get energy?
3. Some organisms are said to be at the top of the food chain. What does this expression mean? Does a food chain ever end? Explain.

L2

This is a representation of key blackline masters available in the Teacher Classroom Resources. See Resource Manager boxes within the chapter for additional information.

Assessment

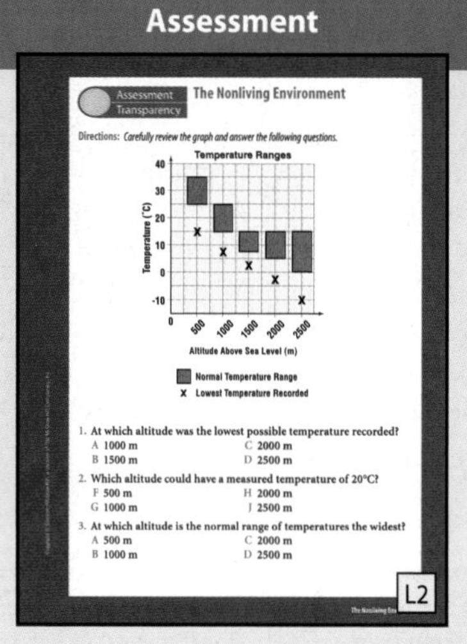
Assessment Transparency **The Nonliving Environment**

Directions: *Carefully review the graph and answer the following questions.*

1. At which altitude was the lowest possible temperature recorded?
   A 1000 m C 2000 m
   B 1500 m D 2500 m
2. Which altitude could have a measured temperature of 20°C?
   F 500 m H 2000 m
   G 1000 m J 2500 m
3. At which altitude is the normal range of temperatures the widest?
   A 500 m C 2000 m
   B 1000 m D 2500 m

L2

Teaching

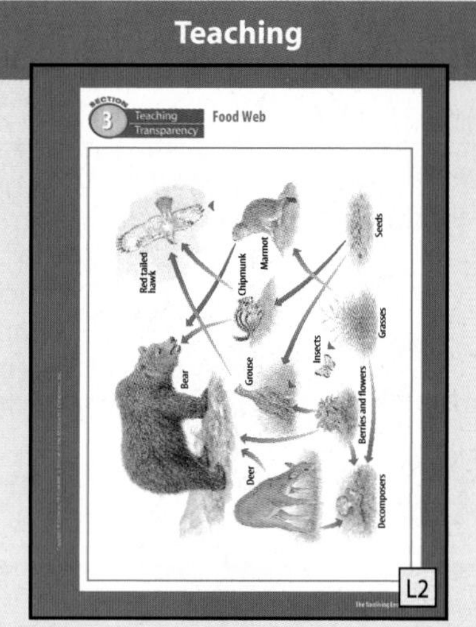
SECTION 3 Teaching Transparency **Food Web**

L2

Key to Teaching Strategies

The following designations will help you decide which activities are appropriate for your students.

L1 Level 1 activities should be appropriate for students with learning difficulties.

L2 Level 2 activities should be within the ability range of all students.

L3 Level 3 activities are designed for above-average students.

ELL ELL activities should be within the ability range of English Language Learners.

COOP LEARN Cooperative Learning activities are designed for small group work.

LS Multiple Learning Styles logos, as described on page 22T, are used throughout to indicate strategies that address different learning styles.

P These strategies represent student products that can be placed into a best-work portfolio.

Hands-on Activities

Activity Worksheets

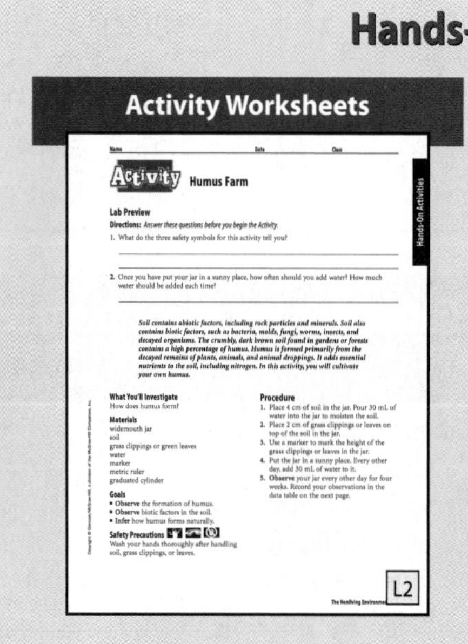
Name Date Class

Activity **Humus Farm**

Lab Preview

Directions: *Answer these questions before you begin the Activity.*

1. What do the three safety symbols for this activity tell you?
2. Once you have put your jar in a sunny place, how often should you add water? How much water should be added each time?

Soil contains abiotic factors, including rock particles and minerals. Soil also contains biotic factors, such as bacteria, molds, fungi, worms, insects, and decayed organisms. The crumbly, dark brown soil found in gardens or forests contains a high percentage of humus. Humus is formed primarily from the decayed remains of plants, animals, and animal droppings. It adds essential nutrients to the soil, including nitrogen. In this activity, you will cultivate your own humus.

What You'll Investigate
How does humus form?

Materials
widemouth jar
soil
grass clippings or green leaves
water
marker
metric ruler
graduated cylinder

Goals
- **Observe** the formation of humus.
- **Observe** biotic factors in the soil.
- **Infer** how humus forms naturally.

Safety Precautions
Wash your hands thoroughly after handling soil, grass clippings, or leaves.

Procedure
1. Place 4 cm of soil in the jar. Pour 30 mL of water into the jar to moisten the soil.
2. Place 2 cm of grass clippings or leaves on top of the soil in the jar.
3. Use a marker to mark the height of the grass clippings or leaves in the jar.
4. Put the jar in a sunny place. Every other day, add 30 mL of water to it.
5. **Observe** your jar every other day for four weeks. Record your observations in the data table on the next page.

Hands-On Activities

L2

Laboratory Activities

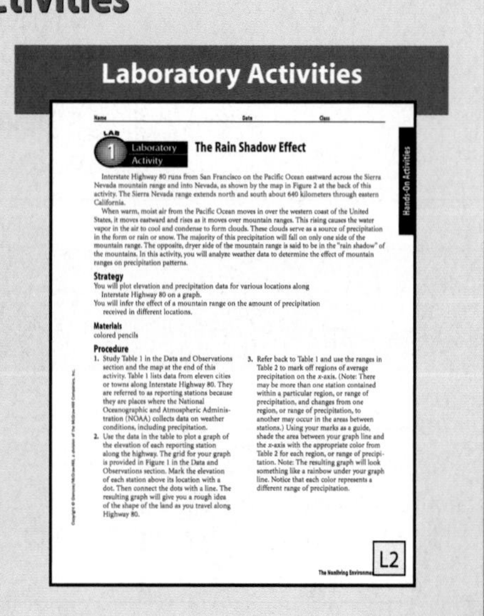
Name Date Class

LAB 1 Laboratory Activity **The Rain Shadow Effect**

Interstate Highway 80 runs from San Francisco on the Pacific Ocean eastward across the Sierra Nevada mountain range and into Nevada, as shown by the map in Figure 2 at the back of this activity. The Sierra Nevada range extends north and south about 640 kilometers through eastern California.

When warm, moist air from the Pacific Ocean moves in over the western coast of the United States, it moves eastward and rises as it moves over mountain ranges. This rising causes the water vapor in the air to cool and condense to form clouds. These clouds serve as a source of precipitation in the form or rain or snow. The majority of this precipitation will fall on only one side of the mountain range. The opposite, dryer side of the mountain range is said to be in the "rain shadow" of the mountains. In this activity, you will analyze weather data to determine the effect of mountain ranges on precipitation patterns.

Strategy
You will plot elevation and precipitation data for various locations along Interstate Highway 80 on a graph.
You will infer the effect of a mountain range on the amount of precipitation received in different locations.

Materials
colored pencils

Procedure
1. Study Table 1 in the Data and Observations section and the map at the end of this activity. Table 1 lists data from eleven cities or towns along Interstate Highway 80. They are referred to as reporting stations because they are places where the National Oceanographic and Atmospheric Administration (NOAA) collects data on weather conditions, including precipitation.
2. Use the data in the table to plot a graph of the elevation of each reporting station along the highway. The grid for your graph is provided in Figure 1 in the Data and Observations section. Mark the elevation of each station above its location with a dot. Then connect the dots with a line. The resulting graph will give you a rough idea of the shape of the land as you travel along Highway 80.
3. Refer back to Table 1 and use the ranges in Table 2 to mark off regions of average precipitation on the x-axis. (Note: There may be more than one station contained within a particular region, or range of precipitation, and changes from one region, or range of precipitation, to another may occur in the areas between stations.) Using your marks as a guide, shade the area between your graph line and the x-axis with the appropriate color from Table 2 for each region, or range of precipitation. Note: The resulting graph will look something like a rainbow under your graph line. Notice that each color represents a different range of precipitation.

Hands-On Activities

L2

Meeting Different Ability Levels

Content Outline

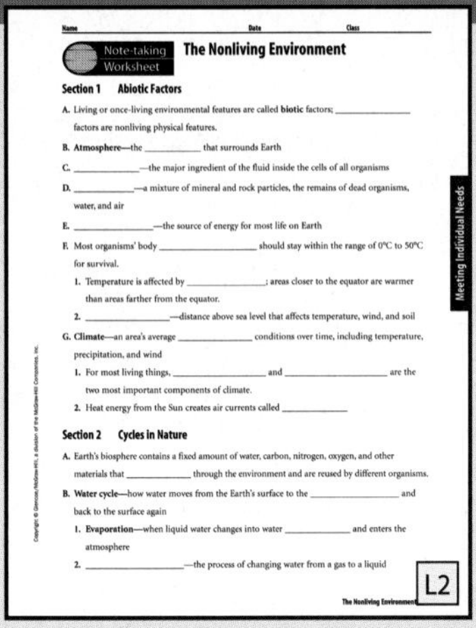
Note-taking Worksheet
The Nonliving Environment
L2

Reinforcement

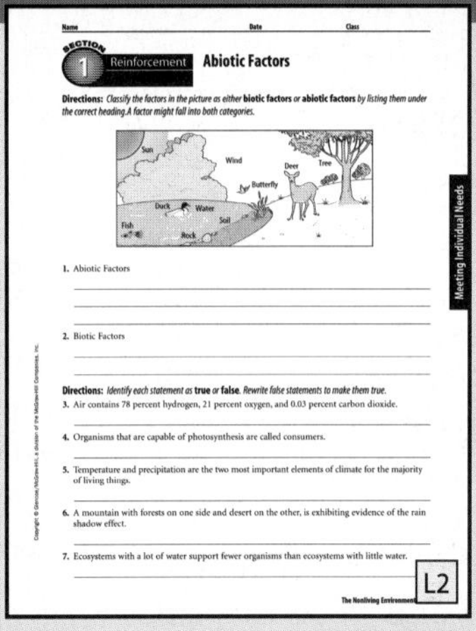
Reinforcement
Abiotic Factors
L2

Directed Reading

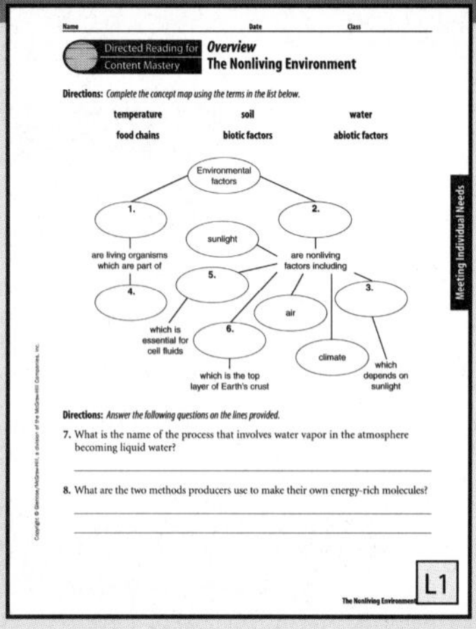
Directed Reading for Content Mastery
Overview
The Nonliving Environment
L1

Enrichment

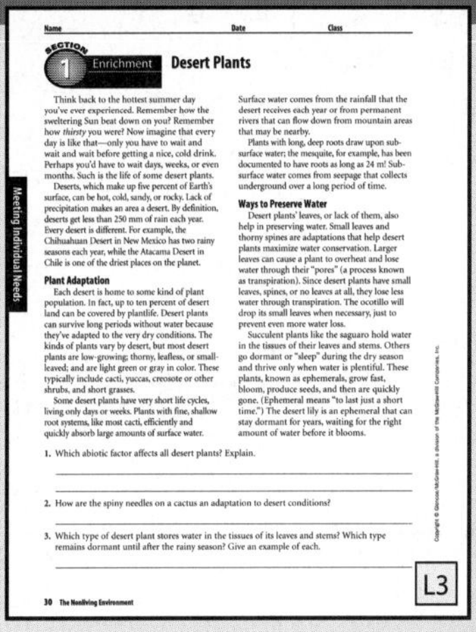
Enrichment
Desert Plants
L3

Spanish Directed Reading

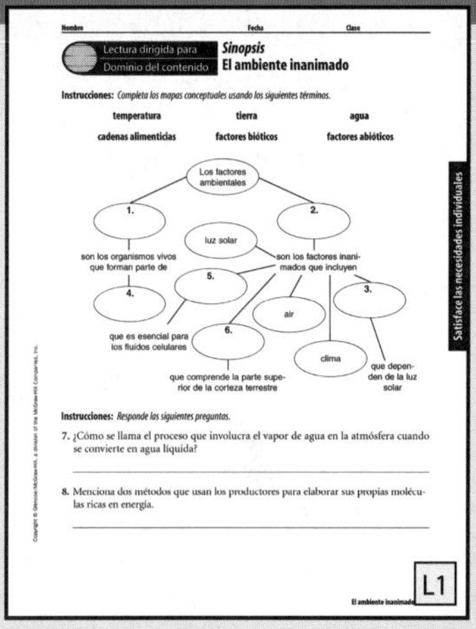
Lectura dirigida para Dominio del contenido
Sinopsis
El ambiente inanimado
L1

Assessment

Chapter Tests

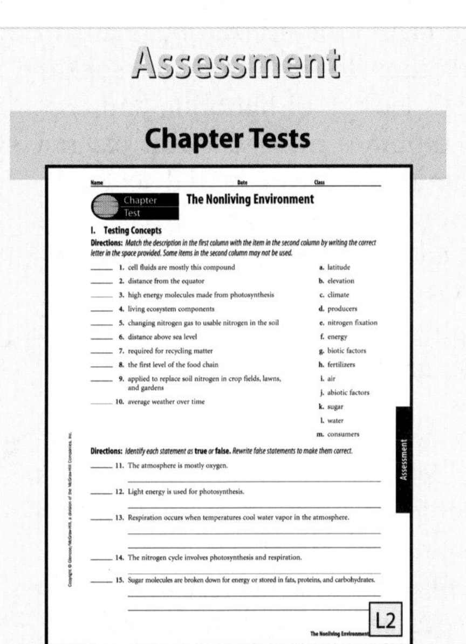

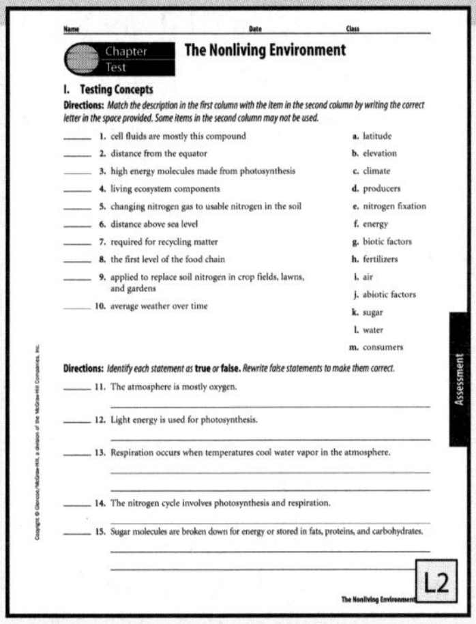
Chapter Test
The Nonliving Environment
L2

Test Practice Workbook

Standardized Test Practice
Teacher Edition
Glencoe Science
Life Science
L2

Chapter Review

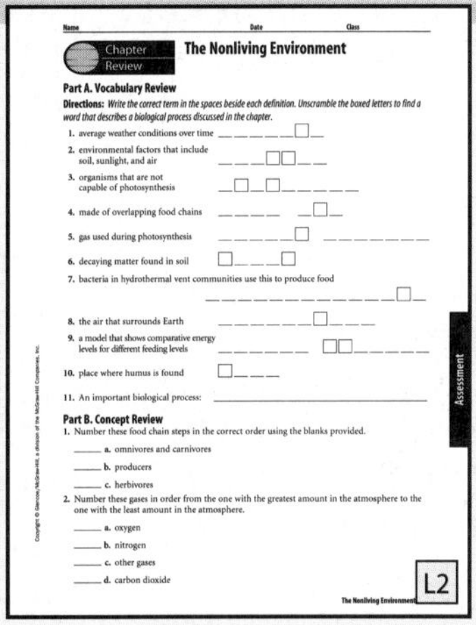
Chapter Review
The Nonliving Environment
L2

Science Content Background

SECTION 1

Abiotic Factors

Importance to Life

Important abiotic factors include air, water, soil, sunlight, temperature, and climate. These factors are interrelated and can vary from environment to environment and over time. Consider temperature, which changes from hour to hour, day to day, season to season, and year to year. Abiotic and biotic factors are not independent. Lack of rainfall can cause a drought in a grassland. The animals that depend on plants for food would find it hard to survive. Many of the factors are predictable and cyclic, but may have extreme variations. Some can be influenced by other factors such as pollution in air, water, and soil.

Fun Fact

According to the *Guinness Book of Records,* the greatest temperature variation in one day in the United States was 100°F. This occurred in Browning, Montana on January 23–24, 1916, when the temperature dropped from 44°F to –56°F.

SECTION 2

Cycles of Nature

Natural Recycling

Matter, in the form of nutrients, moves through the organisms at each trophic level in an ecosystem. But matter cannot be replenished like the energy from sunlight. The atoms of carbon, nitrogen, and other elements that make up the bodies of organisms alive today are the same atoms that have been on Earth since life began. Matter is constantly being recycled.

Water Cycle

The amount of water on Earth remains fairly constant. While some of the water on Earth cycles, much of it is held in oceans or as ice and does not enter the cycle. At a given time, the atmosphere holds about 12,000 cubic kilometers of water, while all the freshwater rivers and lakes hold 120,000 cubic kilometers. Every day about 1,200 cubic kilometers of water evaporates from the ground or transpires from plants and about the same amount falls back to the surface as rain.

Fun Fact

If evaporation did not replenish the water in the atmosphere, it would dry out in ten days.

Nitrogen Cycle

Nitrogen gas makes up about 79 percent of the atmosphere, but cannot be utilized by plants in this form. In addition to fixation in the soil by bacteria, the high energy of lightning and cosmic radiation combines nitrogen with oxygen into usable nitrates that are carried to Earth with precipitation. The nitrogen in fertilizers is artificially fixed in processing plants. Nitrogen, which is taken up directly by plants and incorporated into plant tissue, enters the food web when plants are consumed.

Carbon Cycle

In 1994, it was reported that the total amount of carbon available on Earth was about 47,000 gigatons (1 gigaton=1 billion metric tons). About 83 percent of the available carbon was in the oceans, 22 percent in fossil fuels, and four percent in dead organic matter, living organisism, and soils. Only two percent was in the atmosphere. Many scientist believe the accelerated greenhouse effect is caused by an increased amount of carbon dioxide in the atmosphere, due largely to the burning of fossil fuels.

SCIENCE Online

For additional content background on this topic, go to the Glencoe Science Web site at science.glencoe.com.

SECTION 3

Energy Flow

Food Chains

The law of conservation of energy states that energy cannot be created or destroyed, but can change from one form to another. The energy in an ecosystem is passed from one organism to another through a series of interactions called a food chain. Food chains, food webs and ecological pyramids show how energy moves in only one direction through the trophic levels of an ecosystem and how energy is lost at each transition, from one trophic level to the next. The energy is lost to the environment in the form of heat generated by the body processes of organisms. Although the heat is ultimately lost to the environment, it also serves the purpose of maintaining the body temperature of the organism. Sunlight is the source of most energy, so energy is constantly being replaced.

Fun Fact

Animal muscle yields only about one calorie of work for every four given up as heat.

Food Webs

Some food webs are terrestrial, some are aquatic, and some are combinations. Two types of food webs are grazing and detrital. Detritivores are organisms such as crabs and earthworms that consume dead or decomposing organic matter. The largest amount of energy passes through detrital food webs.

Fritz Polking/Peter Arnold, Inc.

CHAPTER 25

The Nonliving Environment

Chapter Vocabulary

biotic, p. 720
abiotic, p. 720
atmosphere, p. 721
soil, p. 722
climate, p. 725
evaporation, p. 728
condensation, p. 729
water cycle, p. 729
nitrogen fixation, p. 730
nitrogen cycle, p. 730
carbon cycle, p. 733
chemosynthesis, p. 735
food web, p. 736
energy pyramid, p. 737

What do you think?

Science Journal The photograph shows a chloroplast. Chlorophyll within chloroplasts traps light energy and converts it to carbohydrates. Almost all living things on Earth depend on this process to provide the energy they need to live.

CHAPTER 25

The Nonliving Environment

Could you write a story about what would happen if the Sun stopped shining? Most life on Earth depends on the Sun's energy. In this chapter, you'll learn about how organisms called producers use energy to make food and how other organisms called consumers take in that food. You'll also read about cycles in nature such as the water, carbon, and nitrogen cycles, and many other nonliving factors that affect your life.

What do you think?

Science Journal Look at the picture below with a classmate. Discuss what this might be. Here's a hint: *It's a factory that relies on sunlight for its energy supply.* Write your answer or best guess in your Science Journal.

Theme Connection

Systems and Interactions The ingredients for life are a part of the nonliving environment. Organisms can't exist without interaction with nonliving systems.

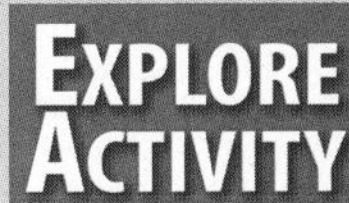

Do you live in a dry, sandy region covered with cactus plants or desert scrub? Is your home in the mountains? Does snow fall during the winter? Perhaps you live near the coast, where flowers bloom year-round. Earth has many ecosystems. In this chapter, you'll learn why the nonliving factors in each ecosystem are different. The following activity will get you started.

Compare climate differences

1. Locate your city or town on a globe or world map. Find your latitude. Latitude shows your distance from the equator and is expressed in degrees, minutes, and seconds.
2. Locate another city with the same latitude as your city but on a different continent.
3. Locate a third city with latitude close to the equator.
4. Using references, compare average annual precipitation and average high and low temperatures for all three cities.

Observe

In your Science Journal, hypothesize how latitude affects average temperatures and rainfall.

Before You Read

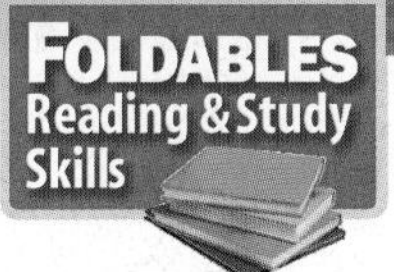

Making a Cause and Effect Study Fold Make the following Foldable to help you understand the cause and effect relationship of the nonliving environment.

1. Place a sheet of paper in front of you so the long side is at the top. Fold the left and right sides in to divide the paper into thirds. Then fold it in half from left to right. Unfold all the folds.
2. Using the fold lines as a guide, refold the paper into a fan. Unfold all the folds again.
3. Before you read the chapter, draw a picture of a familiar ecosystem on one side of the paper. On the other side, label the folds *Nonliving, Water, Soil, Wind, Temperature,* and *Elevation* as shown.
4. As you read the chapter, write on the folds how each nonliving factor affects the environment you drew.

Explore Activity

Purpose Use the Explore Activity to show students how latitude affects climate. L2 **Visual-Spatial**

Preparation Obtain reference information that provides climate data for various cities.

Materials world maps or globes, climate reference information

Teaching Strategy Have students compare their findings with other students' findings. Discuss differences and similarities.

Observe

In general, the lower the latitude, the higher the temperature. Rainfall is influenced by many variables, so there was probably no consistent relationship found between latitude and rainfall.

✔Assessment

Performance Give students a map of the United States and ask them to put Phoenix, San Francisco, and Los Angeles in order from lowest average temperature to highest. Use **Performance Assessment in the Science Classroom,** p. 89.

Before You Read

FOLDABLES Reading & Study Skills

Dinah Zike Study Fold

Purpose Students make and use a Foldable to understand the cause and effect relationship of the nonliving environment. They examine five nonliving aspects of an ecosystem and the effects of these aspects on the environment as a whole.

For additional help, see Foldables Worksheet, p. 17 in **Chapter Resources Booklet,** or go to the Glencoe Science Web site at **science.glencoe.com.** See After You Read in the Study Guide at the end of this chapter.

SECTION

Abiotic Factors

1 Motivate

Bellringer Transparency

Display the Section Focus Transparency for Section 1. Use the accompanying Transparency Activity Master. L2 ELL

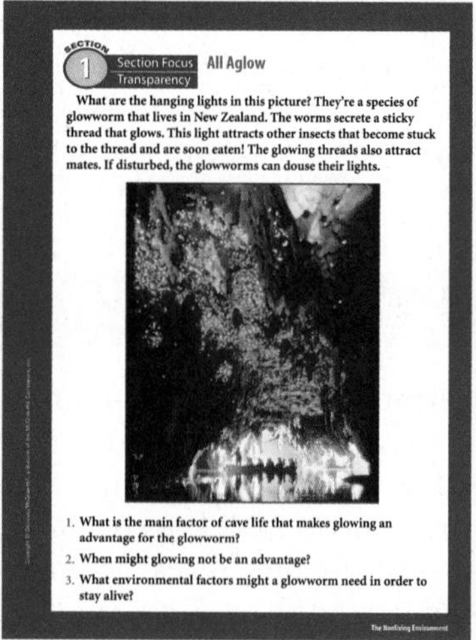

SECTION 1 Section Focus Transparency **All Aglow**

What are the hanging lights in this picture? They're a species of glowworm that lives in New Zealand. The worms secrete a sticky thread that glows. This light attracts other insects that become stuck to the thread and are soon eaten! The glowing threads also attract mates. If disturbed, the glowworms can douse their lights.

1. **What is the main factor of cave life that makes glowing an advantage for the glowworm?**
2. **When might glowing not be an advantage?**
3. **What environmental factors might a glowworm need in order to stay alive?**

The Nonliving Environment

Tie to Prior Knowledge

Have students examine a fish tank or a scene from nature. Ask them to identify nonliving things that are important for living things to survive.

SECTION

Abiotic Factors

As You Read

***What* You'll Learn**

- **Identify** common abiotic factors in most ecosystems.
- **List** the components of air that are needed for life.
- **Explain** how climate influences life in an ecosystem.

Vocabulary

biotic, abiotic, atmosphere, soil, climate

***Why* It's Important**

Knowing how organisms depend on the nonliving world can help humans maintain a healthy environment.

Environmental Factors

Living organisms depend on one another for food and shelter. The leaves of plants provide food and a home for grasshoppers, caterpillars, and other insects. Many birds depend on insects for food. Dead plants and animals decay and become part of the soil. The features of the environment that are alive, or were once alive, are called **biotic** (bi AH tihk) factors. The term *biotic* means "living."

Biotic factors are not the only things in an environment that are important to life. Most plants cannot grow without sunlight, air, water, and soil. Animals cannot survive without air, water, or the warmth that sunlight provides. The nonliving, physical features of the environment are called **abiotic** (ay bi AH tihk) factors. The prefix *a* means "not." The term *abiotic* means "not living." Abiotic factors include air, water, soil, sunlight, temperature, and climate. The abiotic factors in an environment often determine which kinds of organisms can live there. For example, water is an important abiotic factor in the environment, as shown in **Figure 1.**

Figure 1
Abiotic factors—air, water, soil, sunlight, temperature, and climate—influence all life on Earth.

Section Assessment Planner

PORTFOLIO
Assessment, p. 726

PERFORMANCE ASSESSMENT
Try at Home MiniLAB, p. 722
Math Skills Activity, p. 724
Skill Builder Activities, p. 726
See page 744 for more options.

CONTENT ASSESSMENT
Section, p. 726
Challenge, p. 726
Chapter, pp. 744–745

Air

Air is invisible and plentiful, so it is easily overlooked as an abiotic factor of the environment. The air that surrounds Earth is called the **atmosphere.** Air contains 78 percent nitrogen, 21 percent oxygen, 0.94 percent argon, 0.03 percent carbon dioxide, and trace amounts of other gases. Some of these gases provide substances that support life.

Carbon dioxide (CO_2) is required for photosynthesis. Photosynthesis—a series of chemical reactions—uses CO_2, water, and energy from sunlight to produce sugar molecules. Organisms like plants that can use photosynthesis are called producers because they produce their own food. During photosynthesis, oxygen is released into the atmosphere.

When a candle burns, oxygen from the air chemically combines with the molecules of candle wax. Chemical energy stored in the wax is converted and released as heat and light energy. In a similar way, cells use oxygen to release the chemical energy stored in sugar molecules. This process is called respiration. Through respiration, cells obtain the energy needed for all life processes. Air-breathing animals aren't the only organisms that need oxygen. Plants, some bacteria, algae, fish, and most other organisms also need oxygen for respiration.

Figure 2
Water is an important abiotic factor in deserts and rain forests.

A Life in deserts is limited to species that can survive for long periods without water.

B Thousands of species can live in lush rain forests where rain falls almost every day.

Water

Water is essential to life on Earth. It is a major ingredient of the fluid inside the cells of all organisms. In fact, most organisms are 50 percent to 95 percent water. Respiration, digestion, photosynthesis, and many other important life processes can take place only in the presence of water. As **Figure 2** shows, environments that have plenty of water usually support a greater diversity of and a larger number of organisms than environments that have little water.

2 Teach

Environmental Factors

Use Science Words

Word Origin Write the words *biotic* and *abiotic* on the board. Ask students to find the meanings of *bio-*, *sphere*, and *a-*. *bio:* life; *sphere:* area; *a:* without, or not

Activity

Have students make a list of the biotic and abiotic factors that would affect the population growth of frogs near a pond. L2 IS **Naturalist**

Air

Quick Demo

Light a candle and explain that oxygen helps release heat and light energy from the wax. In a similar way, oxygen in living things helps release the energy from food. Put a bell jar over the candle and direct students to observe. As the flame goes out, explain that without oxygen, energy cannot be released. IS **Visual-Spatial**

Water

Extension

Refer to a world map of biomes. Have students compare areas of similar latitude that have different biomes. Varying amounts of precipitation is most likely the primary difference between these areas. L2 IS **Visual-Spatial**

Resource Manager

Chapter Resources Booklet

- Transparency Activity, p. 44
- Directed Reading for Content Mastery, pp. 19, 20
- Note-taking Worksheets, pp. 33–34

Inclusion Strategies

Learning Disabled Ask students to comment on this question: **We can't see air, so how do we know it exists?** A variety of evidence can be discussed. We can feel the air when we move our hands very fast. We can see the effect of air when we blow it into a balloon. L1 IS **Naturalist**

Soil

Fun Fact

One gram of soil may contain hundreds of millions of organisms.

Purpose Students investigate the components that make up soil. L2 LS **Kinesthetic**

Materials two cups soil, large jar with lid, water, alum or dishwashing liquid, spoon, metric ruler

Teaching Strategy Review the components of soil before students carry out the activity.

Analysis

1. Clay is likely suspended in the water.
2. Answers will vary. It is likely that silt will form the greatest component.

Assessment

Oral **Why did you examine the sample at different times?** Different-sized particles settle at different rates. Use **Performance Assessment in the Science Classroom,** p. 89.

Determining Soil Makeup

Procedure

1. Collect 2 cups of **soil.** Remove large pieces of debris and break up clods.
2. Put the soil in a **quart jar or similar container that has a lid.**
3. Fill the container with **water** and add 1 teaspoon of **dishwashing liquid.**
4. Put the lid on tightly and shake the container.
5. After 1 min, measure and record the depth of sand that settled on the bottom.
6. After 2 h, measure and record the depth of silt that settles on top of the sand.
7. After 24 h, measure and record the depth of the layer between the silt and the floating organic matter.

Analysis

1. Clay particles are so small that they can remain suspended in water. Where is the clay in your sample?
2. Is sand, silt, or clay the greatest part of your soil sample?

Soil

Soil is a mixture of mineral and rock particles, the remains of dead organisms, water, and air. It is the topmost layer of Earth's crust, and it supports plant growth. Soil is formed, in part, of rock that has been broken down into tiny particles.

Soil is considered an abiotic factor because most of it is made up of nonliving rock and mineral particles. However, soil also contains living organisms and the decaying remains of dead organisms. Soil life includes bacteria, fungi, insects, and worms. The decaying matter found in soil is called humus. Soils contain different combinations of sand, clay, and humus. The type of soil present in a region has an important influence on the kinds of plant life that grow there.

Sunlight

All life requires energy, and sunlight is the energy source for almost all life on Earth. During photosynthesis, producers convert light energy into chemical energy that is stored in sugar molecules. Consumers are organisms that cannot make their own food. Energy is passed to consumers when they eat producers or other consumers. As shown in **Figure 3,** photosynthesis cannot take place if light is never available.

A

B

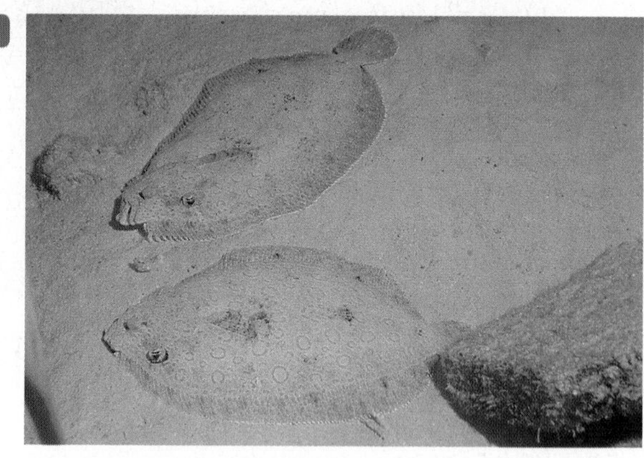

Figure 3
Photosynthesis requires light. A Little sunlight reaches the shady forest floor, so plant growth beneath trees is limited. B Sunlight does not reach into deep lake or ocean waters. Photosynthesis can take place only in shallow water or near the water's surface. *How do fish that live at the bottom of the deep ocean obtain energy?*

LAB DEMONSTRATION

Purpose to determine the amount of humus in soil

Materials Bunsen burner, crucible, topsoil rich in humus, goggles, scale

Preparation Obtain and dry topsoil before class. Explain to students that humus can burn, but the rest of soil cannot.

Procedure Fill a crucible with soil, pour it out, and weigh it. Return soil to the crucible and heat on high for 10 min. Allow to cool. Pour out the soil and reweigh it. Determine the mass of the humus, and its percentage of the original soil.

Expected Outcome Topsoils are 2–15% humus.

Assessment

Give students the following measurements and have them calculate the mass and percentage of humus in soil.

initial mass = 10 grams

final mass = 9 grams

mass of humus = 1 gram; 10% of original soil

722 CHAPTER 25 The Nonliving Environment

Figure 4
Temperature is an abiotic factor that can affect an organism's survival.

A The penguin has a thick layer of fat to hold in heat and keep the bird from freezing. These emperor penguins huddle together for added warmth.

B The Arabian camel stores fat only in its hump. This way, the camel loses heat from other parts of its body, which helps it stay cool in the hot desert.

Temperature

Sunlight supplies life on Earth with light energy for photosynthesis and heat energy for warmth. Most organisms can survive only if their body temperatures stay within the range of 0°C to 50°C. Water freezes at 0°C. The penguins in **Figure 4** are adapted for survival in the freezing Antarctic. Camels can survive the hot temperatures of the Arabian Desert because their bodies are adapted for staying cool. The temperature of a region depends in part on the amount of sunlight it receives. The amount of sunlight depends on the land's latitude and elevation.

What does sunlight provide for life on Earth?

Latitude In this chapter's Explore Activity, you discovered that temperature is affected by latitude. You found that cities located at latitudes farther from the equator tend to have colder temperatures than cities at latitudes nearer to the equator. As **Figure 5** shows, polar regions receive less of the Sun's energy than equatorial regions. Near the equator, sunlight strikes Earth directly. Near the poles, sunlight strikes Earth at an angle, which spreads the energy over a larger area.

Figure 5
Because Earth is curved, latitudes farther from the equator are colder than latitudes near the equator.

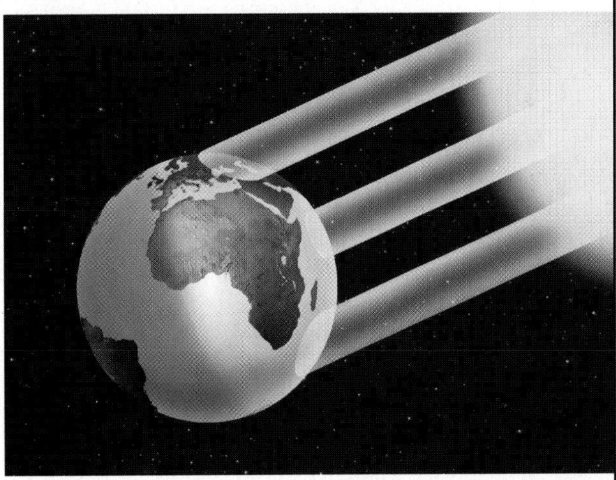

Sunlight

Caption Answer

Figure 3B These fish often depend on biotic materials that fall from above.

Temperature

Visual Learning

Figure 4B Have students identify other adaptations camels have to their native desert environment. Possible answers: Their feet are widespread to enable them to walk easily on sand; to protect them from blowing sand, they have a double row of eyelashes, haired ear openings, and the ability to close their nostrils; they also have keen senses of sight and smell.

Reading Check

Answer Sunlight provides light and heat. Students may also say that, through the process of photosynthesis, sunlight provides energy for life processes.

Resource Manager

Chapter Resources Booklet
MiniLAB, p. 3
Lab Activity, pp. 9–12
Science Inquiry Labs, p. 7
Cultural Diversity, p. 33

Curriculum Connection

Health Children in orphanages and hospitals often used to get rickets. Eventually, scientists discovered that sunlight prevented rickets, because it enables the skin to produce vitamin D. Ingesting vitamin D will also prevent rickets. Have students research which foods are good sources of vitamin D. Foods rich in vitamin D include milk, eggs, fortified breakfast cereals, sardines, salmon, beef, and margarine. L2

Teacher FYI

Altitude sickness is a condition resulting from the lack of oxygen at elevations above 2,400 meters (8,000 ft). Mountain climbers might be affected if climbing without supplemental oxygen. Symptoms may include shortness of breath, headaches, decreased coordination, impaired sight and hearing, nosebleeds, decreased mental clarity, dizziness, and hallucinations. If untreated, the condition can be fatal. In most cases, returning to a lower altitude and receiving oxygen quickly reverses the symptoms.

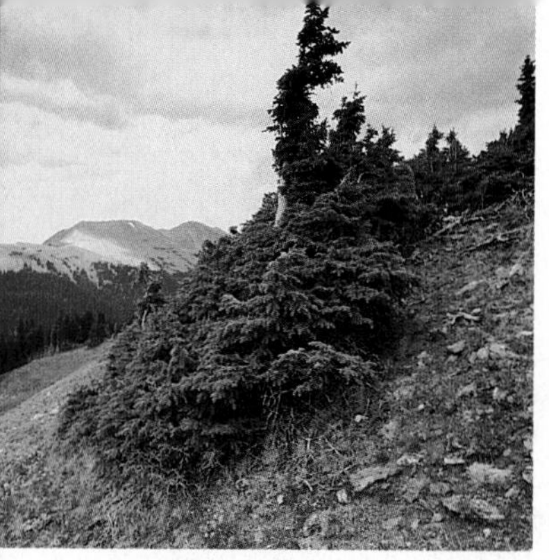

Figure 6
The stunted growth of these trees is a result of abiotic factors.

Elevation If you have climbed or driven up a mountain, you probably noticed that the temperature got cooler as you went higher. A region's elevation, or distance above sea level, affects its temperature. Earth's atmosphere acts as insulation that traps the Sun's heat. At higher elevations, the atmosphere is thinner than it is at lower elevations. Air becomes warmer when sunlight heats the air molecules. Because there are fewer air molecules at higher elevations, air temperatures there tend to be cooler.

Figure 6 shows how elevation affects other abiotic conditions, including soil and wind. At higher elevations, trees are shorter and the ground is rocky. Above the timberline—the elevation beyond which trees do not grow—plant life is limited to low-growing plants. The tops of some mountains are so cold that no plants can survive. Some mountain peaks are covered with snow year-round.

Math Skills Activity

Graphing Temperature Versus Elevation

Example Problem

You climb a mountain and record the temperature every 1,000 m of elevation. The temperature is 30°C at 304.8 m, 25°C at 609.6 m, 20°C at 914.4 m, 15°C at 1,219.2 m, and 5°C at 1,828.8 m. Make a graph of the data. Use your graph to predict the temperature at an altitude of 2,133.6 m.

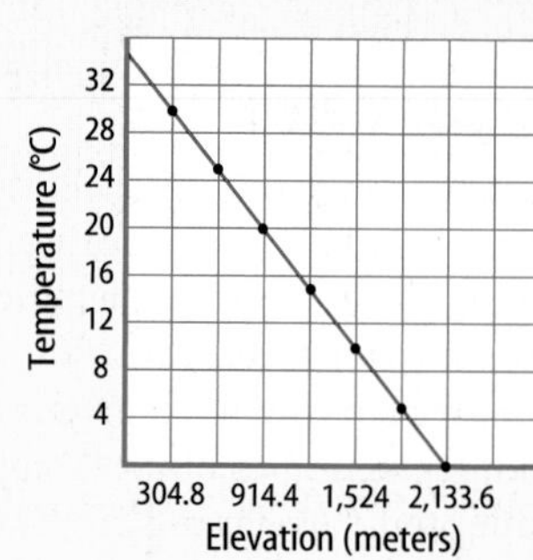

Solution

1. *This is what you know:*
   The data can be written as ordered pairs (elevation, temperature). The ordered pairs for these data are (304.8, 30), (609.6, 25), (914.4, 20), (1,219.2, 15), (1,828.8, 5).
2. *This is what you want to find:*
   Predict the temperature at an elevation of 2,133.6 m.
3. *This is what you need to do:*
   Graph the data by plotting elevation on the x-axis and temperature on the y-axis. Draw a line to connect the data points on your graph.
4. *Predict the temperature at 2,133.6 m:*
   Extend the graph line to predict the temperature at 2,133.6 m.

Practice Problem

Temperatures on another mountain are 33°C at sea level, 31°C at 125 m, 29°C at 250 m, and 26°C at 425 m. Graph the data and predict the temperature at 550 m.

For more help, refer to the Math Skill Handbook.

724 CHAPTER 25 The Nonliving Environment

Math Skills Activity

National Math Standards

Correlation to Mathematics Objectives
1, 2, 4, 5, 6, 9, 10

Answer to Practice Problem

Students should predict temperatures of around 23°C.

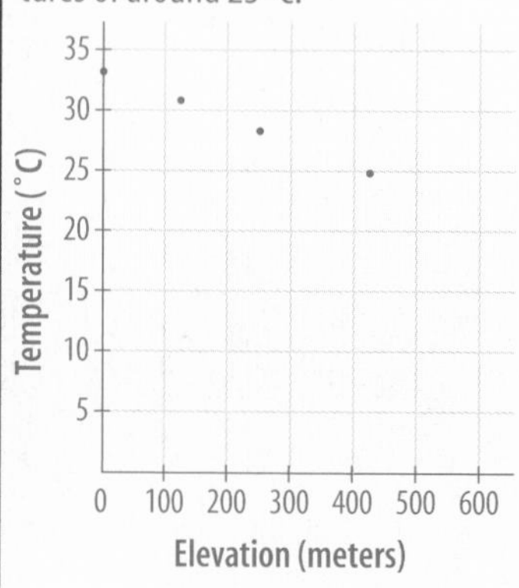

Cultural Diversity

Kenyan Runners Many great long distance runners are from the Kalenjin tribe in a high-altitude area of Kenya. **Why might great runners come from this area?** Possible answers: Because of lower oxygen levels at high altitudes, these Kenyans may have adaptations for increased cardiovascular efficiency; their high-altitude training may help them produce more red blood cells; there may also be social reasons.

Active Reading

Quickwrites This strategy, sometimes called freewrites, lets students use spontaneous writing to discover what they already know. Have students write a list of ideas about a topic, then share these ideas with the class. Next, have students write their ideas without worrying about punctuation, spelling, and grammar. Have students use a Quickwrite to share ideas about abiotic factors.

Climate

In Fairbanks, Alaska, winter temperatures may be as low as −52°C, and more than a meter of snow might fall in one month. In Key West, Florida, snow never falls and winter temperatures rarely dip below 5°C. These two cities have different climates. **Climate** refers to an area's average weather conditions over time, including temperature, rainfall or other precipitation, and wind.

For the majority of living things, temperature and precipitation are the two most important components of climate. The average temperature and rainfall in an area influence the type of life found there. Suppose a region has an average temperature of 25°C and receives an average of less than 25 cm of rain every year. It is likely to be the home of cactus plants and other desert life. A region with similar temperatures that receives more than 300 cm of rain every year is probably a tropical rain forest.

Wind Heat energy from the Sun not only determines temperature, but also is responsible for the wind. The air is made up of molecules of gas. As the temperature increases, the molecules spread farther apart. As a result, warm air is lighter than cold air. Colder air sinks below warmer air and pushes it upward, as shown in **Figure 7.** These motions create air currents that are called wind.

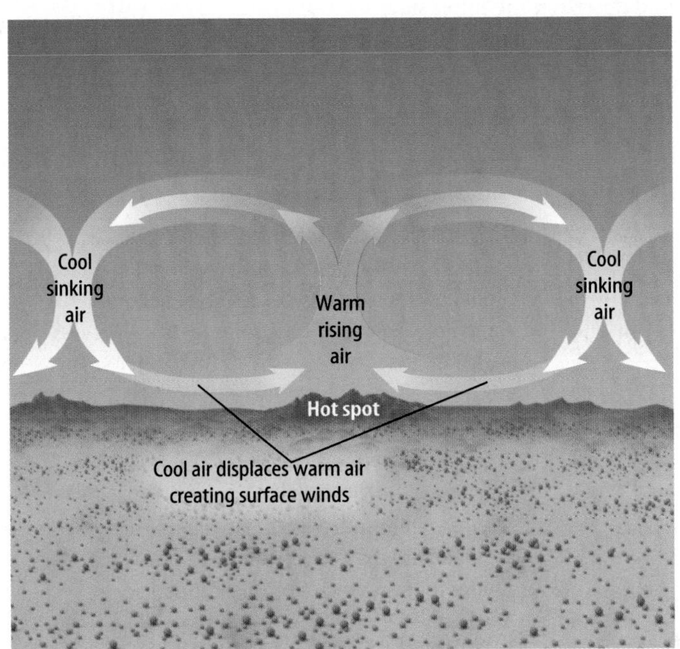

Figure 7
Winds are created when sunlight heats some portions of Earth's surface more than others. In areas that receive more heat, the air becomes warmer. Cold air sinks beneath the warm air, forcing the warm air upward.

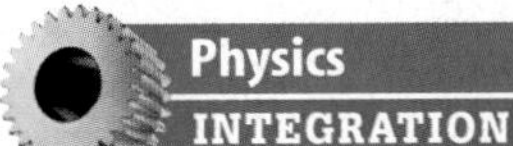

Physics INTEGRATION

Gravity pulls the gases of the atmosphere toward Earth's surface. Also, the weight of the air at the top of the atmosphere presses down on the air below it. In your Science Journal, explain why air at sea level is thicker than air at the top of a mountain.

SCIENCE Online

Data Update Visit the Glencoe Science Web site at **science.glencoe.com** to look up recent weather data for your area. In your Science Journal, describe how these weather conditions affect plants or animals that live in your area.

Climate

Teacher FYI

Weather refers to the day-to-day atmospheric conditions in an area. Climate takes a long-term view and describes the general weather conditions associated with an area.

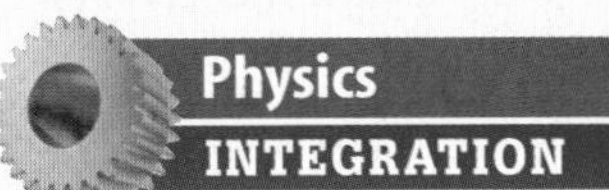

Physics INTEGRATION

Imagine the air as columns in the atmosphere. A column reaching a mountaintop would be shorter than one reaching land at sea level. The taller column of air presses down, making the air at the bottom of the column at sea level denser.

Quick Demo

Show the rain shadow effect by moving a damp sponge over an imaginary mountain. As it rises up, explain that the air cools and water condenses into rain. Squeeze the sponge to show rain. As air decends on the other side of the moutain, it warms. Any remaining water in the air changes back to water vapor. L2 ELL IS **Visual-Spatial**

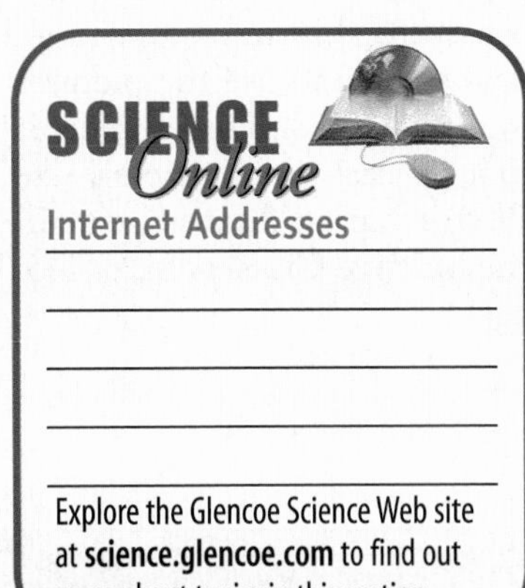

SCIENCE Online

Internet Addresses

Explore the Glencoe Science Web site at **science.glencoe.com** to find out more about topics in this section.

Resource Manager

Chapter Resources Booklet
- Enrichment, p. 30
- Reinforcement, p. 27

Reading and Writing Skill Activities, p. 3

Earth Science Critical Thinking/Problem Solving, pp. 6, 22

Inclusion Strategies

Learning Disabled Show a globe and explain that since areas near the equator receive more direct sunshine, they are much warmer than areas toward the poles. As hot air is pushed aloft near the equator, cooler air rushes in to take its place. This causes wind, which is responsible for precipitation patterns. L1 IS **Visual-Spatial**

Teacher FYI

The Cascade Mountains, part of the Pacific mountain system, extend from California to Canada. The tallest peak in this range is Mt. Ranier, which reaches 4,392 m (14,410 ft). Most of the peaks are extinct volcanoes, although some have erupted in the recent past. Mount St. Helens is one of these, with eruptions in 1980 and 1981.

3 Assess

Reteach

Have students explain how water, air, and temperature can affect life. L1 LS **Naturalist**

Challenge

Have students investigate how professional greenhouses increase the levels of carbon dioxide and the temperature to achieve an optimal plant growing environment.

Assessment

Portfolio Have students cut out pictures from magazines that illustrate abiotic factors in an ecosystem and use the pictures to make posters. Direct students to label each abiotic factor. Use **Performance Assessment in the Science Classroom,** p. 145. P

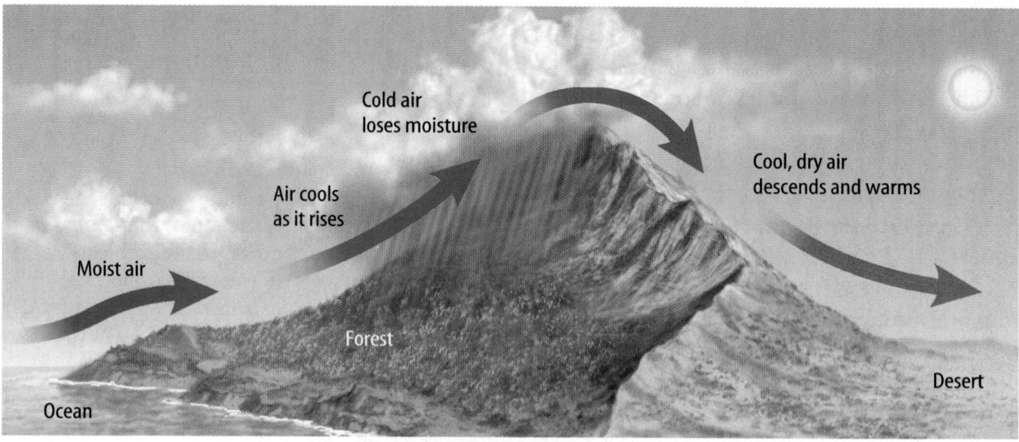

Figure 8
In Washington State, the western side of the Cascade Mountains receives an average of 101 cm of rain each year. The eastern side of the Cascades is in a rain shadow that receives only about 25 cm of rain per year.

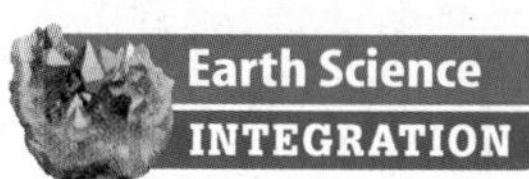
Earth Science INTEGRATION

The Rain Shadow Effect The presence of mountains can affect rainfall patterns. As **Figure 8** shows, wind blowing toward one side of a mountain is forced upward by the mountain's shape. As the air nears the top of the mountain, it cools. When air cools, the moisture it contains falls as rain or snow. By the time the cool air crosses over the top of the mountain, it has lost most of its moisture. The other side of the mountain range receives much less precipitation. It is not uncommon to find lush forests on one side of a mountain range and desert on the other side.

Section 1 Assessment

1. What is the difference between biotic and abiotic factors?
2. What substances in the air are required for life on Earth?
3. Why is soil considered an abiotic factor and a biotic factor?
4. Why is climate an important abiotic factor?
5. **Think Critically** On day 1 of a hiking trip, you walk in shade under tall trees. On day 2, the trees are shorter and farther apart. On day 3, you see small plants but no trees. On day 4, you see snow. What abiotic factors might contribute to these changes?

Skill Builder Activities

6. **Identifying and Manipulating Variables and Controls** Describe an experiment to find out how much water different types of dry soil can hold. **For more help, refer to the** Science Skill Handbook.
7. **Using an Electronic Spreadsheet** Obtain two months of temperature and precipitation data for two cities in your state. Enter the data in a spreadsheet and calculate average daily temperature and rainfall. Use your calculations to compare the two climates. **For more help, refer to the** Technology Skill Handbook.

Answers to Section Assessment

1. Biotic factors are, or once were, living. Abiotic factors are nonliving.
2. carbon dioxide, nitrogen, oxygen
3. While it is mostly nonliving material, there are many things living in soil, as well as decaying organic matter called humus.
4. Climate refers to an area's temperature, amount of precipitation, and wind. These are physical features of the environment that affect the life found there.
5. Changes in elevation, which influence temperature, are probably responsible. This could occur on a mountain, as you reach and surpass the timberline.
6. Answers will vary. Possible answer: Put soil into a funnel. Then, pour measured amounts of water into the funnel until water flows through the soil and comes out the funnel.
7. Spreadsheets should result in average temperature and rainfall for two different cities.

Activity

Humus Farm

Soil contains abiotic factors, including rock particles and minerals. Soil also contains biotic factors, such as bacteria, molds, fungi, worms, insects, and decayed organisms. The crumbly, dark brown soil found in gardens or forests contains a high percentage of humus. Humus is formed primarily from the decayed remains of plants, animals, and animal droppings. It adds essential nutrients to the soil, including nitrogen. In this activity, you will cultivate your own humus.

What You'll Investigate

How does humus form?

Materials

widemouth jar	water
soil	marker
grass clippings or green leaves	metric ruler
	graduated cylinder

Goals

- **Observe** the formation of humus.
- **Observe** biotic factors in the soil.
- **Infer** how humus forms naturally.

Safety Precautions

Wash your hands thoroughly after handling soil, grass clippings, or leaves.

Humus Formation	
Date	**Observations**
	Answers will vary

Procedure

1. Copy the data table below into your Science Journal.
2. Place 4 cm of soil in the jar. Pour 30 mL of water into the jar to moisten the soil.
3. Place 2 cm of grass clippings or green leaves on top of the soil in the jar.
4. Use a marker to mark the height of the grass clippings or green leaves in the jar.
5. Put the jar in a sunny place. Every other day, add 30 mL of water to it. In your Science Journal, write a prediction of what you think will happen in your jar.
6. **Observe** your jar every other day for four weeks. Record your observations in your data table.

Conclude and Apply

1. **Describe** what happened during your investigation.
2. **Infer** how molds and bacteria help the process of humus formation.
3. **Infer** how humus forms on forest floors or in grasslands.

Communicating Your Data

Compare your humus farm with those of your classmates. With several classmates, write a recipe for creating the richest humus. Ask your teacher to post your recipe in the classroom. **For more help, refer to the** **Science Skill Handbook.**

Activity

BENCH TESTED

Purpose Students observe humus formation over several weeks. **IS Visual-Spatial**

Process Skills observing, describing, inferring

Time Required 25 minutes for set-up; 5 minute observation periods every other day for four weeks

Alternate Materials If green leaves are used instead of grass clippings, the leaves must be chopped in order for the activity to work.

Safety Precautions Instruct students to wash their hands when finished.

Teaching Strategy Encourage students to bring in leaf litter to be used in the activity.

Troubleshooting To be certain the humus farms get enough water, assign a person from each group to water the jars every other day. Keep grass clippings moist but not water logged. Do not seal jars.

Answers to Questions

1. Students should first observe the growth of mold in their jar. As the mold and decomposing bacteria break down the clippings or litter, large particles of organic matter will form. As the organic materials decompose, their height will decrease. These particles are the beginning of humus.
2. Molds and bacteria decompose materials into organic particles.
3. Organic materials such as leaves, twigs, or grasses fall to the ground and are decomposed into organic particles.

Assessment

Process Ask students to discuss how forest ecosystems would be affected if leaf litter if did not become humus. Use **PASC**, p. 93.

Resource Manager

Chapter Resources Booklet
Activity Worksheet, pp. 5–6

Performance Assessment in the Science Classroom, p. 48

Communicating Your Data

Students may want to consult cookbooks to see how the ingredients for recipes are written and arranged.

SECTION 2

Cycles in Nature

1 Motivate

Bellringer Transparency

Display the Section Focus Transparency for Section 2. Use the accompanying Transparency Activity Master. L2 ELL

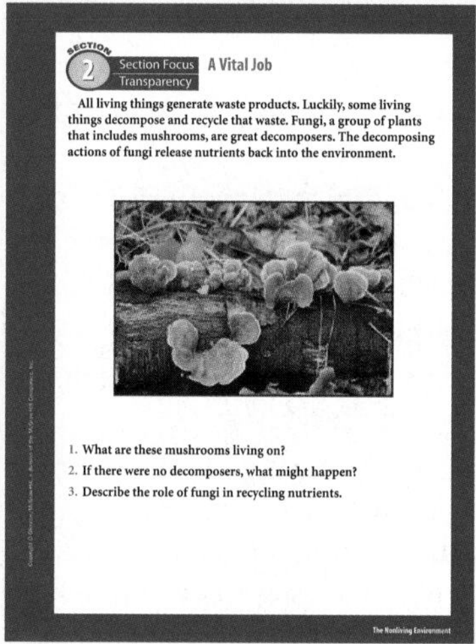
SECTION 2 Section Focus Transparency **A Vital Job**

All living things generate waste products. Luckily, some living things decompose and recycle that waste. Fungi, a group of plants that includes mushrooms, are great decomposers. The decomposing actions of fungi release nutrients back into the environment.

1. What are these mushrooms living on?
2. If there were no decomposers, what might happen?
3. Describe the role of fungi in recycling nutrients.

The Nonliving Environment

Tie to Prior Knowledge

Most students will have some familiarity with the water cycle. Ask students to explain how water cycles through the environment. Ask them to think of other materials that also cycle.

Teacher FYI

This section deals with how matter changes its form as it cycles through the environment. Matter cycles, but energy does not.

SECTION

Cycles in Nature

As You Read

What **You'll Learn**

- **Explain** the importance of Earth's water cycle.
- **Diagram** the carbon cycle.
- **Recognize** the role of nitrogen in life on Earth.

Vocabulary

evaporation	nitrogen fixation
condensation	nitrogen cycle
water cycle	carbon cycle

Why **It's Important**

The recycling of matter on Earth demonstrates natural processes.

The Cycles of Matter

Imagine an aquarium tank containing water, fish, snails, plants, algae, and bacteria. The tank is sealed so that only light can enter. Food, water, and air cannot be added. Will the organisms in this environment survive? Through photosynthesis, plants and algae produce their own food. They also supply oxygen to the tank. Fish and snails take in oxygen and eat plants and algae. Wastes from fish and snails fertilize plants and algae. Organisms that die are decomposed by the bacteria. The organisms in this closed environment can survive because the materials are recycled. A constant supply of light energy is the only requirement. Earth's biosphere also contains a fixed amount of water, carbon, nitrogen, oxygen, and other materials required for life. These materials cycle through the environment and are reused by different organisms.

Water Cycle

If you leave a glass of water on a sunny windowsill, the water will disappear. It evaporates. **Evaporation** takes place when liquid water changes into water vapor, which is a gas, and enters the atmosphere, as shown in **Figure 9.** Water evaporates from the surfaces of lakes, streams, puddles, and oceans. Water vapor enters the atmosphere from plant leaves in a process known as transpiration (trans puh RAY shun). Animals release water vapor into the air when they exhale. Water also returns to the environment from animal wastes.

Figure 9
Water vapor is a gas that is present in the atmosphere.

A **Water evaporates after a summer rain.**

B **Water also evaporates from the ocean.**

Section Assessment Planner

PORTFOLIO
Activity, p. 732

PERFORMANCE ASSESSMENT
MiniLAB, p. 731
Skill Builder Activities, p. 733
See page 744 for more options.

CONTENT ASSESSMENT
Section, p. 733
Challenge, p. 733
Chapter, pp. 744–745

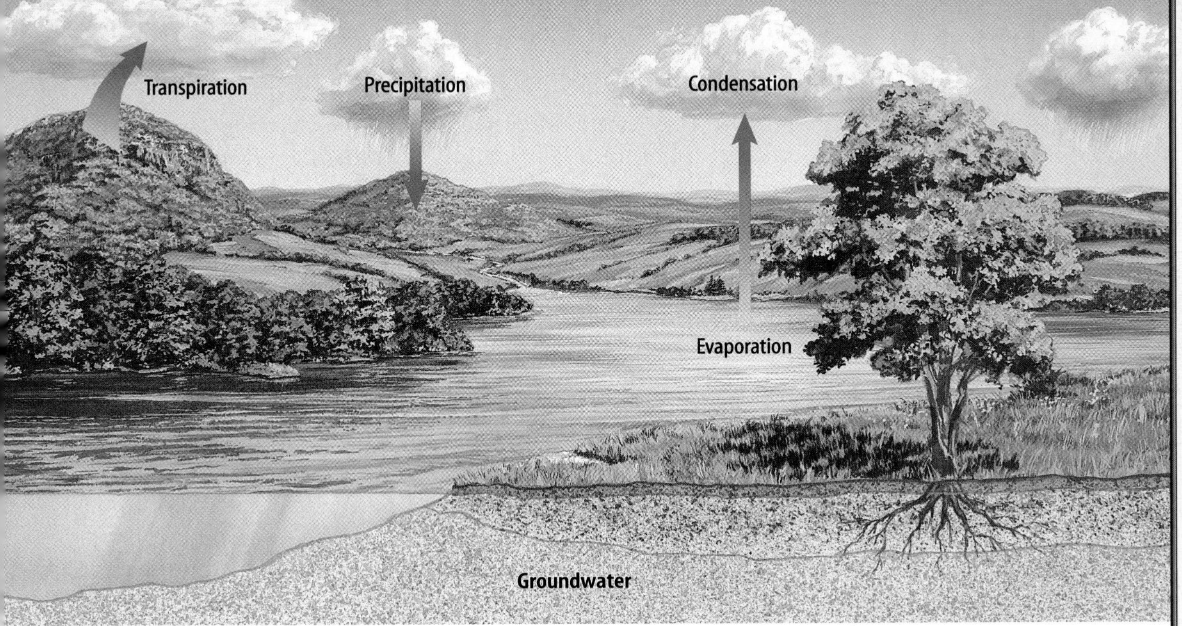

Condensation Water vapor that has been released into the atmosphere eventually comes into contact with colder air. The temperature of the water vapor drops. Over time, the water vapor cools enough to change back into liquid water. The process of changing from a gas to a liquid is called **condensation.** Water vapor condenses on particles of dust in the air, forming tiny droplets. At first, the droplets clump together to form clouds. When they become large and heavy enough, they fall to the ground as rain or other precipitation. As the diagram in **Figure 10** shows, the **water cycle** is a model that describes how water moves from the surface of Earth to the atmosphere and back to the surface again.

Figure 10
The water cycle involves evaporation, condensation, and precipitation. Water molecules can follow several pathways through the water cycle. *How many water cycle pathways can you identify from this diagram?*

Water Use **Table 1** gives data on the amount of water people take from reservoirs, rivers, and lakes for use in households, businesses, agriculture, and power production. These actions can reduce the amount of water that evaporates into the atmosphere. They also can influence how much water returns to the atmosphere by limiting the amount of water available to plants and animals.

Table 1 U.S. Estimated Water Use in 1990

Water Use	Millions of Gallons per Day	Percent of Total
Homes and Businesses	39,100	11.5
Industry and Mining	27,800	8.2
Farms and Ranches	141,000	41.5
Electricity Production	131,800	38.6

2 Teach

The Cycles of Matter

Teacher FYI

Although it is possible to achieve a closed aquarium system, it is not easy. The system must be perfectly balanced between producer and consumer, and this balance must remain constant over time.

Water Cycle

IDENTIFYING Misconceptions

Students may think that the same water falls in a given area again and again. Emphasize that water vapor moves great distances in the air all over Earth; that water in lakes, rivers, and streams is always moving; that currents in the ocean are constantly moving; and that groundwater may move great distances.

Caption Answer

Figure 10 Pathways include precipitation, evaporation, transpiration, seeping into groundwater, and runoff from the ground into other bodies of water.

Visual Learning

Table 1 Which type of water use consumes the most water? farms and ranches **Suggest a reason why.** Possible answers: irrigation of crops or grasses, watering of livestock

Resource Manager

Chapter Resources Booklet
Transparency Activity, p. 45
Directed Reading for Content Mastery, p. 21
Reading and Writing Skill Activities, p. 29

Science Journal

Water Stories Have students imagine they are molecules of water. They should each make up a story as to how they travel and what they encounter as they go through one complete cycle of the water cycle. L2 IN **Linguistic**

Nitrogen Cycle

Extension

Ask students to use the internet to find photographs of plants with a nitrogen deficiency. Have them describe some symptoms. Possible answers: yellow leaves, stunted growth L2

LS **Visual-Spatial**

Use an Analogy

What would happen to a student who ate only candy? They would ingest a lot of sugar but not enough protein. Sugar provides energy but no protein to build or repair tissues. In a similar way, if a plant did not have enough nitrogen it could make sugars, but its growth and functioning would be impaired because it could not make enough proteins.

LS **Logical-Mathematical**

Reading Check

Answer the changing of atmospheric nitrogen into nitrogen compounds that plants can use

Visual Learning

Figure 11 Ask students to use the diagram as a basis for suggesting to farmers one thing they can do to increase the nitrogen in their soil. Add decaying organic matter (compost).

Nitrogen Cycle

The element nitrogen is important to all living things. Nitrogen is a necessary ingredient of proteins. Proteins are required for the life processes that take place in the cells of all organisms. Nitrogen is also an essential part of the DNA of all organisms. Although nitrogen is the most plentiful gas in the atmosphere, most organisms cannot use nitrogen directly from the air. Plants need nitrogen that has been combined with other elements to form nitrogen compounds. Through a process called **nitrogen fixation,** some types of soil bacteria can form the nitrogen compounds that plants need. Plants absorb these nitrogen compounds through their roots. Animals obtain the nitrogen they need by eating plants or other animals. When dead organisms decay, the nitrogen in their bodies returns to the soil or to the atmosphere. This transfer of nitrogen from the atmosphere to the soil, to living organisms, and back to the atmosphere is called the **nitrogen cycle,** shown in **Figure 11.**

Reading Check *What is nitrogen fixation?*

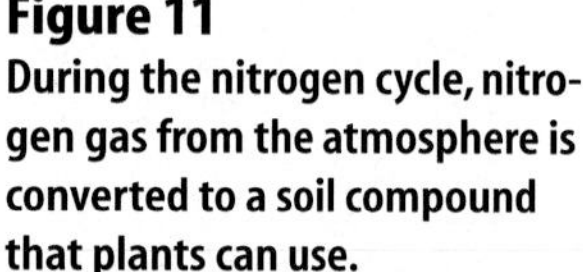

Figure 11
During the nitrogen cycle, nitrogen gas from the atmosphere is converted to a soil compound that plants can use.

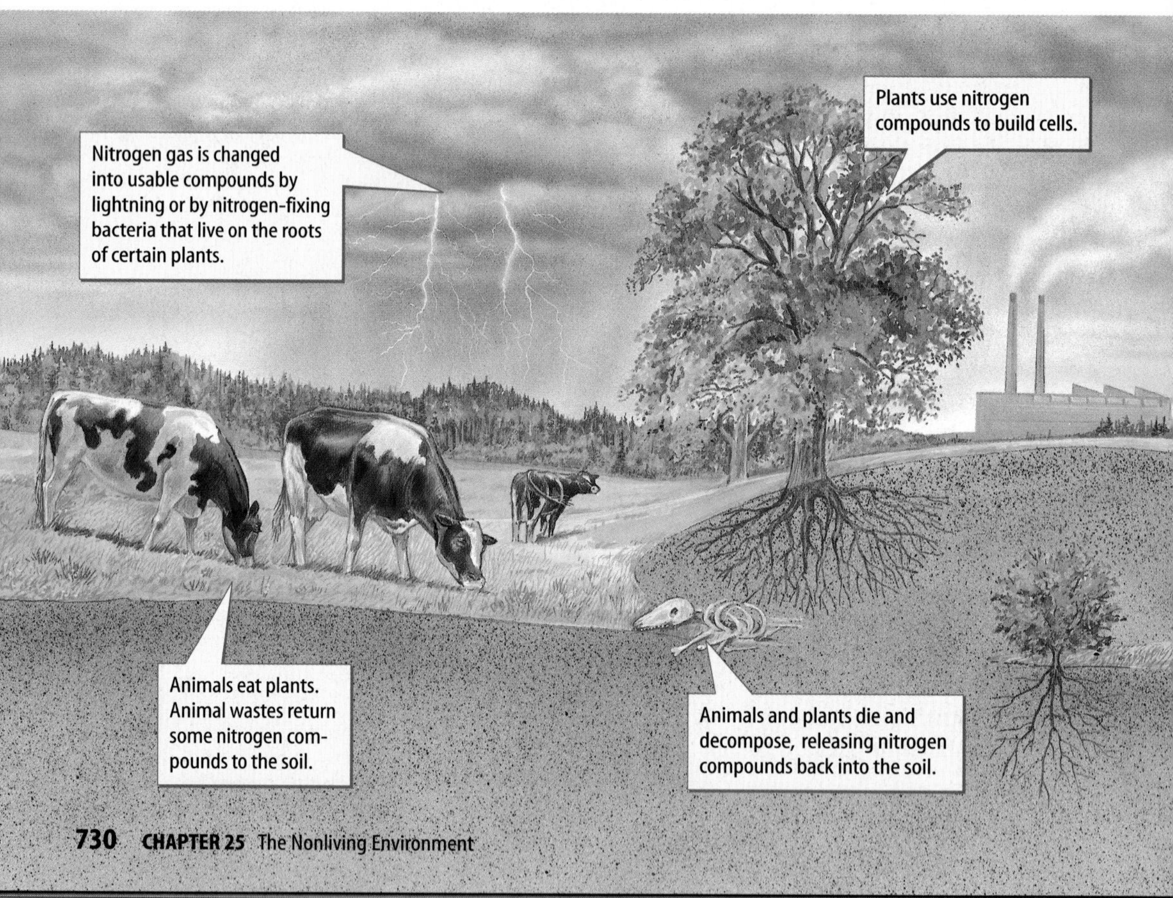
Nitrogen gas is changed into usable compounds by lightning or by nitrogen-fixing bacteria that live on the roots of certain plants.
Plants use nitrogen compounds to build cells.
Animals eat plants. Animal wastes return some nitrogen compounds to the soil.
Animals and plants die and decompose, releasing nitrogen compounds back into the soil.
730 CHAPTER 25 The Nonliving Environment

Inclusion Strategies

Gifted Have students research how ammonia wastes are converted to less toxic forms by bacteria in aquariums. Ammonia is oxidized by bacteria to form nitrates and nitrites. L3 LS **Naturalist**

Learning Disabled Help students realize that as plants grow, they use minerals from the soil. As plants die or drop leaves, these minerals are restored. In farming, however, the nutrients are taken away from the soil. If this is ongoing, the soil will become less fertile. In organic farming, humus and animal wastes are added to the soil to restore fertility. Other farmers also use chemical fertilizers. L1 LS **Naturalist**

Figure 12
Nitrogen fixation is important to plant growth.

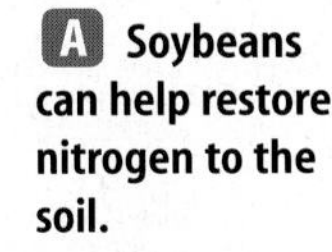

A **Soybeans can help restore nitrogen to the soil.**

B **The swollen nodules on the roots of the soybean plants contain colonies of nitrogen-fixing bacteria.**

C **The bacteria depend on the plant for food. The plant depends on the bacteria to form the nitrogen compounds the plant needs.**

Magnification: 1,000×

Soil Nitrogen Human activities can affect the part of the nitrogen cycle that takes place in the soil. If a farmer grows a crop, such as corn or wheat, most of the plant material is taken away when the crop is harvested. The plants are not left in the field to decay and return their nitrogen compounds to the soil. If these nitrogen compounds are not replaced, the soil could become infertile. You might have noticed that adding fertilizer to soil can make plants grow greener, bushier, or taller. Most fertilizers contain the kinds of nitrogen compounds that plants need for growth. Fertilizers can be used to replace soil nitrogen in crop fields, lawns, and gardens. Compost and animal manure also contain nitrogen compounds that plants can use. They also can be added to soil to improve fertility.

Another method farmers use to replace soil nitrogen is to grow nitrogen-fixing crops. Most nitrogen-fixing bacteria live on or in the roots of certain plants. Some plants, such as peas, clover, and beans including the soybeans shown in **Figure 12,** have roots with swollen nodules that contain nitrogen-fixing bacteria. These bacteria supply nitrogen compounds to the soybean plants and add nitrogen compounds to the soil.

Mini LAB

Comparing Fertilizers

Procedure

1. Examine the three numbers (e.g., 5-10-5) on the **labels of three brands of houseplant fertilizer.** The numbers indicate the percentages of nitrogen, phosphorus, and potassium, respectively, that the product contains.
2. Compare the prices of the three brands of fertilizer.
3. Compare the amount of each brand needed to fertilize a typical houseplant.

Analysis

1. Which brand has the highest percentage of nitrogen?
2. Which brand is the most expensive source of nitrogen? The least expensive?

Mini LAB

Purpose Students compare the nutrient amounts in different fertilizer brands. L2
LS **Kinesthetic**

Materials labels and pricing information for three different brands of fertilizer

Teaching Strategy Have students ask their parents if they can bring from home fertilizers that have price tags on them.

Analysis

1. Answers will vary; the nitrogen percentage is listed first on the label.
2. Answers will vary depending on brands examined.

Assessment

Performance Give students the following information. Brand Q is 5-2-6 and Brand R is 10-4-1. **Which would be the better fertilizer for soil that has adequate amounts of nitrogen and phosphorous but that is low in potassium?** Brand Q Use **Performance Assessment in the Science Classroom,** p. 99.

Resource Manager

Chapter Resources Booklet
MiniLAB, p. 4
Lab Activity, pp. 13–16

Science Inquiry Labs, pp. 29, 39

Physical Science Critical Thinking/Problem Solving, pp. 12, 17

Cultural Diversity

Beans Nitrogen-fixing legumes are so important in traditional agriculture that the food they produce has become part of many cultures. Ask students to recall dishes they eat at home that are made from beans. L2

NATIONAL GEOGRAPHIC

Visualizing the Carbon Cycle

Have students examine the pictures and read the captions. Then ask the following questions.

What activities release carbon dioxide into the atmosphere? The burning of fossil fuels, the decomposition of carbon-containing molecules by decomposers, and the break down of sugar molecules in plants and by other organisms releases carbon dioxide into the atmosphere.

Why is this process called a cycle? Possible answer: Plants use carbon dioxide from the atmosphere to make sugars. The plants then are consumed by other organisms and the carbon dioxide is released back into the atmosphere as a waste product.

Activity

Have students make their own diagram of the carbon cycle, without looking at this page, and label each part. **LS Visual-Spatial**

Extension

Have students review or research photosynthesis and how plants use carbon dioxide to make food. Then have them write a report on how photosynthesis ties into the carbon cycle. **LS Naturalist**

NATIONAL GEOGRAPHIC **VISUALIZING THE CARBON CYCLE**

Figure 13

Carbon—in the form of different kinds of carbon-containing molecules—moves through an endless cycle. The diagram below shows several stages of the carbon cycle. It begins when plants and algae remove carbon from the environment during photosynthesis. This carbon returns to the atmosphere via several carbon-cycle pathways.

Ⓐ Air contains carbon in the form of carbon dioxide gas. Plants and algae use carbon dioxide to make sugars, which are energy-rich, carbon-containing compounds.

Ⓑ Organisms break down sugar molecules made by plants and algae to obtain energy for life and growth. Carbon dioxide is released as a waste.

Ⓒ Burning fossil fuels and wood releases carbon dioxide into the atmosphere.

Ⓓ When organisms die, their carbon-containing molecules become part of the soil. The molecules are broken down by fungi, bacteria, and other decomposers. During this decay process, carbon dioxide is released into the air.

Ⓔ Under certain conditions, the remains of some dead organisms may gradually be changed into fossil fuels such as coal, gas, and oil. These carbon compounds are energy rich.

Resource Manager

Chapter Resources Booklet
Enrichment, p. 31
Reinforcement, p. 28

Life Science Critical Thinking/Problem Solving, pp. 12, 22

Inclusion Strategies

Learning Disabled Have students work in groups to prepare a concept map that describes the carbon cycle. Include terms such as *consumers*, *photosynthesis*, *respiration*, and *producers*. L2 ELL COOP LEARN **LS Visual-Spatial**

The Carbon Cycle

Carbon atoms are found in the molecules that make up living organisms. Carbon is an important part of soil humus, which is formed when dead organisms decay, and it is found in the atmosphere as carbon dioxide gas (CO_2). The **carbon cycle** describes how carbon molecules move between the living and nonliving world, as shown in **Figure 13.**

The carbon cycle begins when producers remove CO_2 from the air during photosynthesis. They use CO_2, water, and sunlight to produce energy-rich sugar molecules. Energy is released from these molecules during respiration—the chemical process that provides energy for cells. Respiration uses oxygen and releases CO_2. Photosynthesis uses CO_2 and releases oxygen. These two processes help recycle carbon on Earth.

Reading Check *How does carbon dioxide enter the atmosphere?*

Human activities also release CO_2 into the atmosphere. Fossil fuels such as gasoline, coal, and heating oil are the remains of organisms that lived millions of years ago. These fuels are made of energy-rich, carbon-based molecules. When people burn these fuels, CO_2 is released into the atmosphere as a waste product. People also use wood for building and for fuel. Trees that are harvested for these purposes no longer remove CO_2 from the atmosphere during photosynthesis. The amount of CO_2 in the atmosphere is increasing. Extra CO_2 could trap more heat from the Sun and cause average temperatures on Earth to rise.

SCIENCE Online

Research Visit the Glencoe Science Web site at **science.glencoe.com** for the chemical equations that describe photosynthesis and respiration. In your Science Journal, write these equations and use them to explain how respiration is the reverse of photosynthesis.

Section 2 Assessment

1. Describe the water cycle.
2. Explain how respiration can be considered the reverse of photosynthesis.
3. How might burning fossil fuels affect the composition of gases in the atmosphere?
4. Why do plants, animals, and other organisms need nitrogen?
5. **Think Critically** Most chemical fertilizers contain nitrogen, phosphorus, and potassium. Why don't they contain carbon? How do plants obtain carbon?

Skill Builder Activities

6. **Identifying and Manipulating Variables and Controls** Describe an experiment that would determine whether extra carbon dioxide enhances the growth of tomato plants. **For more help, refer to the** Science Skill Handbook.
7. **Communicating** Pretend you are a carbon molecule. Write a fictional account of your travels from the atmosphere, through at least two organisms, and back to the atmosphere. **For more help, refer to the** Science Skill Handbook.

The Carbon Cycle

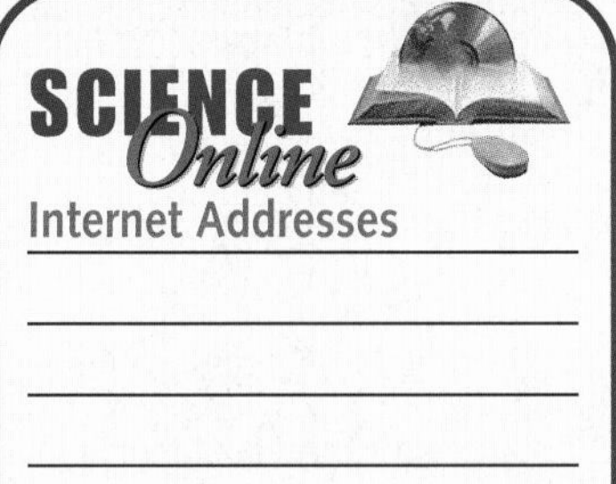

SCIENCE Online

Internet Addresses

Explore the Glencoe Science Web site at **science.glencoe.com** to find out more about topics in this section.

Reading Check

Answer as a by product of cellular respiration

3 Assess

Reteach

Ask students to explain the different paths water vapor, carbon, and nitrogen in the air would follow before they could enter a plant. L2 IS **Naturalist**

Challenge

Suppose you covered all the bodies of water on Earth with oil. **How would this affect the water cycle?** Possible answers: water could not evaporate; the water cycle would be disrupted; a drought may result.

Assessment

Portfolio Have students draw a diagram of the nitrogen cycle. Use **Performance Assessment in the Science Classroom,** p. 127.

Answers to Section Assessment

1. Cycles should include evaporation, condensation, and precipitation.
2. Respiration usually requires oxygen to break down substances and to obtain energy. The process releases CO_2 and water vapor. Photosynthesis requires CO_2, water, and light energy to make sugars. The process gives off oxygen as a waste.
3. It could result in an increase in the concentration of carbon dioxide.
4. to make amino acids for proteins and nucleic acids
5. Plants can get carbon from the atmosphere.
6. Answers will vary, but should include one group with normal CO_2 and one with extra CO_2. An operational definition of the growth of the tomato plants should be given, along with plans for taking measurements.
7. Answers will vary, but the first step should be photosynthesis.

SECTION 3

Energy Flow

1 Motivate

Bellringer Transparency

Display the Section Focus Transparency for Section 3. Use the accompanying Transparency Activity Master. L2 ELL

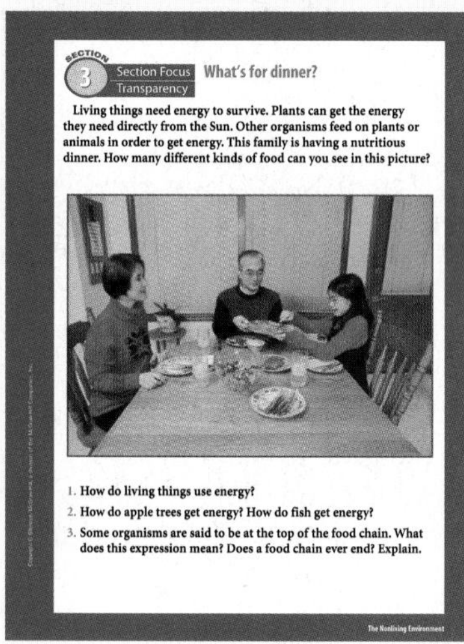

SECTION 3 Section Focus Transparency **What's for dinner?**

Living things need energy to survive. Plants can get the energy they need directly from the Sun. Other organisms feed on plants or animals in order to get energy. This family is having a nutritious dinner. How many different kinds of food can you see in this picture?

1. How do living things use energy?
2. How do apple trees get energy? How do fish get energy?
3. Some organisms are said to be at the top of the food chain. What does this expression mean? Does a food chain ever end? Explain.

The Nonliving Environment

Tie to Prior Knowledge

Students may have seen athletes "hit the wall." Ask why this happens, and if they have ever "run out of energy." Explain that energy is necessary to fuel life.

SECTION 3

Energy Flow

As You Read

What You'll Learn

- **Explain** how organisms produce energy-rich compounds.
- **Describe** how energy flows through ecosystems.
- **Recognize** how much energy is available at different levels in a food chain.

Vocabulary

chemosynthesis energy pyramid food web

Why It's Important

All living things, including people, need a constant supply of energy.

Converting Energy

All living things are made of matter, and all living things need energy. Matter and energy move through the natural world in different ways. Matter can be recycled over and over again. The recycling of matter requires energy. Energy is not recycled, but it is converted from one form to another. The conversion of energy is important to all life on Earth.

Photosynthesis During photosynthesis, producers convert light energy into the chemical energy in sugar molecules. Some of these sugar molecules are broken down as energy is needed. Others are used to build complex carbohydrate molecules that become part of the producer's body. Fats and proteins also contain stored energy.

Chemosynthesis Not all producers rely on light for energy. During the 1970s, scientists exploring the ocean floor were amazed to find communities teeming with life. These communities were at a depth of almost 3.2 km and living in total darkness. They were found near powerful hydrothermal vents like the one shown in **Figure 14.**

Figure 14
A Chemicals in the water that flows from hydrothermal vents provide bacteria with a source of energy. **B** The bacterial producers use this energy to make nutrients through the process of chemosynthesis. Consumers, such as tubeworms, feed on the bacteria.

Section Assessment Planner

Portfolio
Activity, p. 735

Performance Assessment
Skill Builder Activities, p. 737
See page 744 for more options.

Content Assessment
Section, p. 737
Challenge, p. 737
Chapter, pp. 744–745

Hydrothermal Vents A hydrothermal vent is a deep crack in the ocean floor through which the heat of molten magma can escape. The water from hydrothermal vents is extremely hot from contact with molten rock that lies deep in Earth's crust.

Because no sunlight reaches these deep ocean regions, plants or algae cannot grow there. How do the organisms living in this community obtain energy? Scientists learned that the hot water contains nutrients such as sulfur molecules that bacteria use to produce their own food. The production of energy-rich nutrient molecules from chemicals is called **chemosynthesis** (kee moh SIN thuh sus). Consumers living in the hydrothermal vent communities rely on chemosynthetic bacteria for nutrients and energy. Chemosynthesis and photosynthesis allow producers to make their own energy-rich molecules.

Earth Science INTEGRATION

The first hydrothermal vent community discovered was found along the Galápagos rift zone. A rift zone forms where two plates of Earth's crust are spreading apart. In your Science Journal, describe the energy source that heats the water in the hydrothermal vents of the Galápagos rift zone.

Reading Check *What is chemosynthesis?*

Energy Transfer

Energy can be converted from one form to another. It also can be transferred from one organism to another. Consumers cannot make their own food. Instead, they obtain energy by eating producers or other consumers. This way, energy stored in the molecules of one organism is transferred to another organism. At the same time, the matter that makes up those molecules is transferred from one organism to another. Throughout nature, energy and matter move from organism to organism when one organism becomes food for another organism.

Food Chains A food chain is a way of showing how matter and energy pass from one organism to another. Producers—plants, algae, and other organisms that are capable of photosynthesis or chemosynthesis—are always the first step in a food chain. Animals that consume producers such as herbivores are the second step. Carnivores and omnivores—animals that eat other consumers—are the third and higher steps of food chains. One example of a food chain is shown in **Figure 15.**

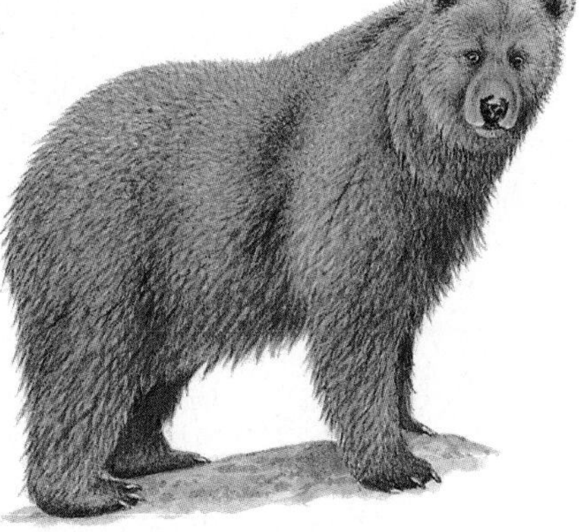

Figure 15
In this food chain, grasses are producers, marmots are herbivores that eat the grasses, and grizzly bears are consumers that eat marmots. The arrows show the direction in which matter and energy flow.

2 Teach

Converting Energy

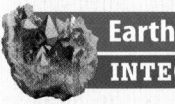

Earth Science INTEGRATION

The source of heat in vents is geothermal energy. The hot magna heats the water to 400°C but it does not boil because of the pressure at these depths. The water quickly cools to about 2°C.

Reading Check

Answer Chemosynthesis is the production of energy-rich food molecules from chemical energy.

Energy Transfer

Discussion

What do the arrows in food chains represent? the flow of matter and energy from one organism to another Ask students to generate other food chains. Answers will vary.

Activity

Have students make a food chain for a deep sea community. Food chains should be similar to that of a simple aquatic system, except that chemosynthetic bacteria will replace aquatic plants as producers. L2

LS **Visual-Spatial** P

Resource Manager

Chapter Resources Booklet

- Transparency Activity, p. 46
- Directed Reading for Content Mastery, pp. 21, 22
- Transparency Activity, pp. 47–48

Mathematics Skill Activities, p. 9

Inclusion Strategies

Learning Disabled Have students who understand the concepts of producer and consumer work with students who are having difficulty. Have partners group the terms *producer, photosynthesis, plants, consumer,* and *animal.* L1
COOP LEARN LS **Interpersonal**

Energy Transfer, continued

Visual Learning

Figure 16 Have students draw three different food chains based on the food web. Then have students assess the impact on other organisms if one organism from the food web were removed. The impact varies, depending upon many factors, such as how much one organism relies only on another organism for its food. If species X feeds only on species Y, when species Y dies out, so will species X. However, if species X feeds on many species, the loss of one will not cause species X to die out.

Energy Pyramids

Make a Model

Find a grasshopper or cricket and weigh it. Then have students collect ten times the weight of the insect in grass. For example, if the insect weighs 1 g, they should gather 10 g of grass. Place the insect on top of the pile of grass to make a model of a biomass pyramid. L1 IS **Logical-Mathematical**

Use an Analogy

Help students understand why so much energy is lost from one level to another. If they raised a cat from a kitten, ask them to imagine how much food the cat has eaten in its life. It is far more than the weight of the cat. Most of the food was used for energy. If a coyote ate their cat, it would not get all the food the cat ate, just the caloric value of

Food Webs A forest community includes many feeding relationships. These relationships can be too complex to show with a food chain. For example, grizzly bears eat many different organisms, including berries, insects, chipmunks, and fish. Berries are eaten by bears, birds, insects, and other animals. A bear carcass might be eaten by wolves, birds, or insects. A **food web** is a model that shows all the possible feeding relationships among the organisms in a community. A food web is made up of many different food chains, as shown in **Figure 16.**

Energy Pyramids

Food chains usually have at least three links, but rarely more than five. This limit exists because the amount of available energy is reduced as you move from one level to the next in a food chain. Imagine a grass plant that absorbs energy from the Sun. The plant uses some of this energy to grow and produce seeds. Some of the energy is stored in the seeds.

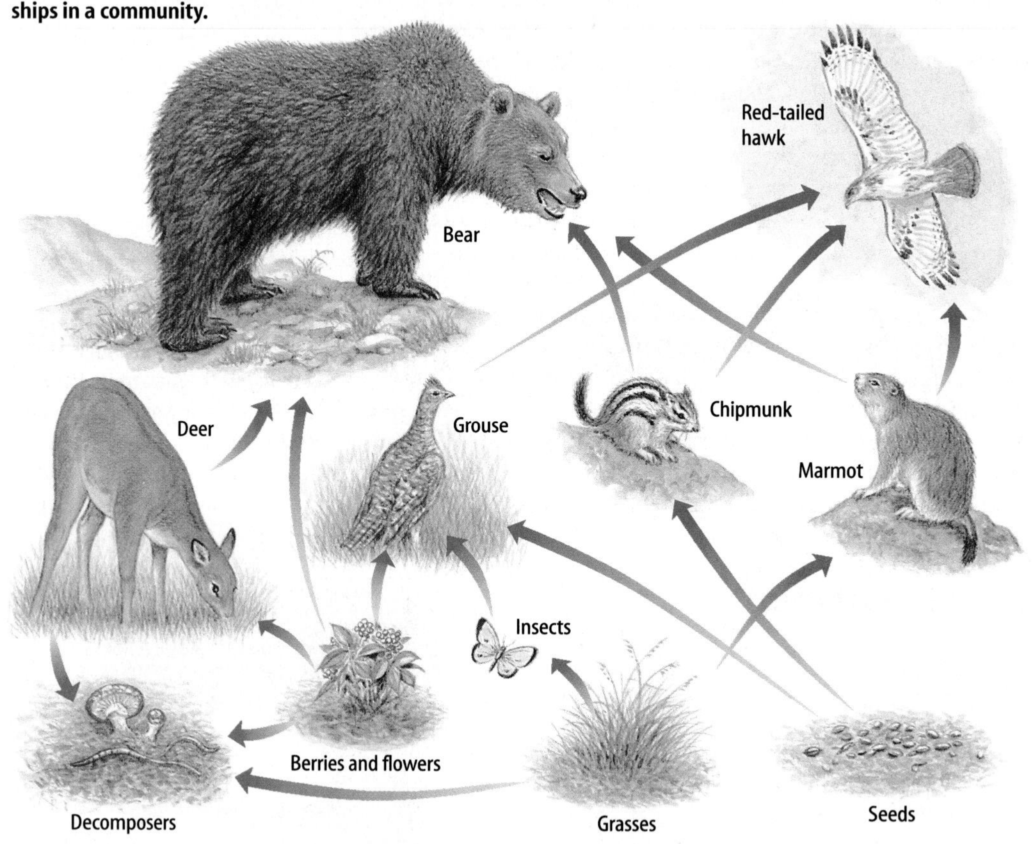

Figure 16
Compared to a food chain, a food web provides a more complete model of the feeding relationships in a community.

Resource Manager

Chapter Resources Booklet
Enrichment, p. 32
Reinforcement, p. 29

Teacher FYI

The law of conservation of energy states that energy is not created or destroyed, but only converted into other forms of energy. In most ecosystems the energy starts as light energy, which is converted through photosynthesis into chemical energy.

Inclusion Strategies

Visually Impaired Obtain or make a pyramid-shaped object. Allow students to handle the model to identify its shape. Explain that the model depicts the relative amount of energy available as one moves up feeding levels in a food web.
IS **Kinesthetic**

Available Energy When a mouse eats grass seeds, energy stored in the seeds is transferred to the mouse. However, most of the energy the plant absorbed from the Sun was used for the plant's growth. Much less energy is stored in the seeds eaten by the mouse. The mouse uses much of the energy remaining in the seeds for its own life processes, including respiration, digestion, and growth. A hawk that eats the mouse obtains even less energy.

The same thing happens at every feeding level of a food chain. The amount of available energy is reduced from one feeding level to another. An **energy pyramid,** like the one in **Figure 17,** shows the amount of energy available at each feeding level in an ecosystem. The bottom layer of the pyramid, which represents all of the producers, is the first feeding level. It is the largest level because it contains the most energy and the largest number of organisms. As you move up the pyramid, each level becomes smaller. Only about ten percent of the energy available at each feeding level of an energy pyramid is transferred to the next higher level.

Figure 17
This energy pyramid shows that each feeding level contains less energy than the level below it.
What would happen if the hawks and snakes outnumbered the rabbits and mice in this ecosystem?

Reading Check ***Why does the first feeding level of an energy pyramid contain the most energy?***

Section  Assessment

1. Compare and contrast photosynthesis and chemosynthesis.
2. Explain how your three favorite foods provide you with energy from the Sun.
3. What is the difference between a food web and an energy pyramid?
4. Why is there a limit to the number of links in a food chain?
5. **Think Critically** Use your knowledge of food chains and the energy pyramid to explain why the number of mice in a grassland ecosystem is greater than the number of hawks.

Skill Builder Activities

6. **Classifying** Classify each species as photosynthetic or chemosynthetic: *Red hattus* uses red light to make its food; *Selen dion* makes food if the element selenium is present. **For more help, refer to the** Science Skill Handbook.
7. **Solving One-Step Equations** A forest has 24,055,000 kilocalories (kcals) of producers, 2,515,000 kcals of herbivores, and 235,000 kcals of carnivores. How much energy is lost between producers and herbivores? Between herbivores and carnivores? **For more help, refer to the** Math Skill Handbook.

Caption Answer

Figure 17 Less energy would be available to hawks and snakes. Eventually they would begin to die off until a balance was achieved or move out of the ecosystem.

Reading Check

Answer because little energy has been lost in maintaining body systems

3 Assess

Reteach

Write the word *humans* on the board. Have students write the names of all the animals we eat below this word. Below this write all the plants that we eat or that are eaten by the animals we eat. Connect lines to make food chains. Then draw more lines to show a food web. L1
LS **Visual-Spatial**

Challenge

Ask students to research the following organisms and design a food web that shows their relationships: *corn, rabbit, hawk, grass, wheat, rat, fox, human,* and *cow.*

Assessment

Performance Use the overhead projector to project a scene from nature. Help students identify the organisms in the picture. Then have them design food chains based on the picture and their knowledge of the organisms. Use **Performance Assessment in the Science Classroom,** p. 127.

Answers to Section Assessment

1. Both involve nutrient production; photosynthesis uses energy from the Sun to produce nutrients, while chemosynthesis uses energy from chemicals.
2. All of the foods we eat provide us with energy from the Sun, either directly (producers) or indirectly (consumers).
3. A food web shows the path of energy and matter in an ecosystem. An energy pyramid shows the amount of energy available at each level.
4. because a significant amount of energy is lost at each level
5. Hawks eat mice. For the mice to support the hawk population, there must be far more energy at the mouse level than at the hawk level. Since mice are smaller than hawks, this means that there must be many more mice than hawks.
6. *Red hattus* is photosynthetic; *Selen dion* is chemosynthetic.
7. producers and herbivores: 21,540,000 kcal; herbivores and carnivores: 2,280,000 kcal

Activity

BENCH TESTED

What You'll Investigate

Purpose

Students perform a variation of Johannes Baptista Van Helmont's famous experiment to determine if plants get their mass from the soil. L2 IS **Logical-Mathematical**

Process Skills

observing, measuring, predicting, interpreting data, using numbers

Time Required

45 minutes to set up; three weeks for the plants to grow; 1 hour for the final measurements, calculations, and cleanup

Safety Precautions

Caution students to wash their hands after handling plants and soil.

Activity

Where does the mass of a plant come from?

An enormous oak tree starts out as a tiny acorn. The acorn sprouts in dark, moist soil. Roots grow down through the soil. Its stem and leaves grow up toward the light and air. Year after year, the tree grows taller, its trunk grows thicker, and its roots grow deeper. It becomes a towering oak that produces thousands of acorns of its own. An oak tree has much more mass than an acorn. Where does this mass come from? The soil? The air? In this activity, you'll find out by conducting an experiment with radish plants.

What You'll Investigate

Does all of the matter in a radish plant come from the soil?

Goals

- **Measure** the mass of soil before and after radish plants have been grown in it.
- **Measure** the mass of radish plants grown in the soil.
- **Analyze** the data to determine whether the mass gained by the plants equals the mass lost by the soil.

Materials

8-oz plastic or paper cup
potting soil to fill cup
scale or balance
radish seeds (4)
water
paper towels

Safety Precautions 

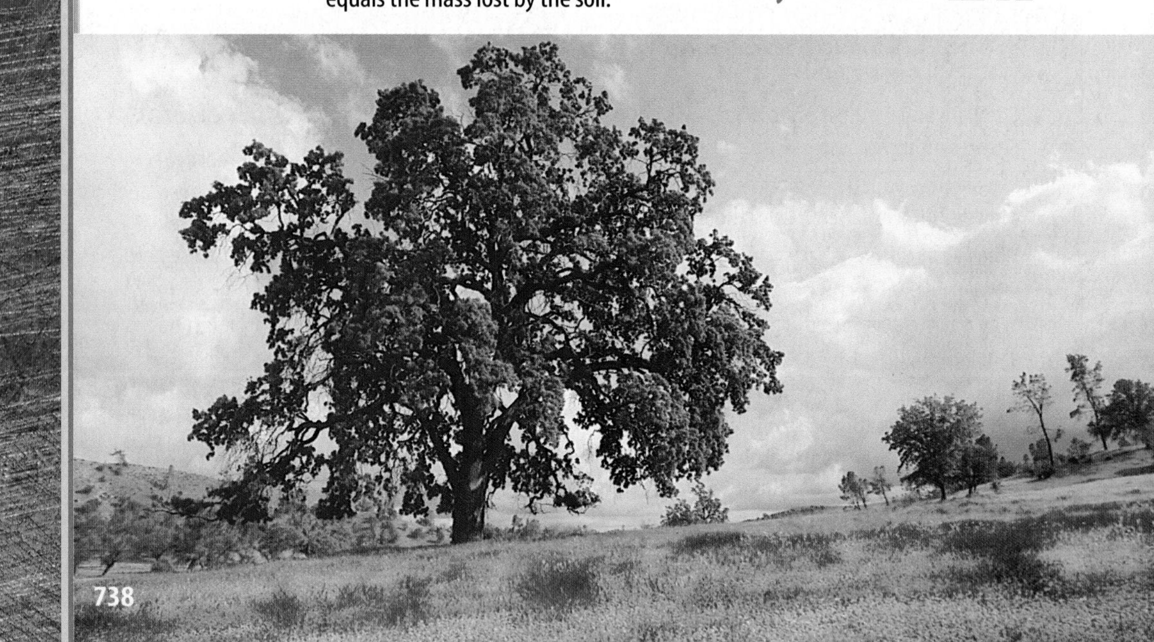

738

Inclusion Strategies

Learning Disabled Help students understand the purpose of the investigation. Hand students a piece of two-by-four lumber so they can feel how heavy it is. Ask them where the weight of the tree came from. The weight came from the food the tree produced and utilized to build its body.

Resource Manager 

Chapter Resources Booklet
Activity Worksheet, pp. 7–8

Lab Management and Safety, p. 38

Procedure

1. Copy the data table into your Science Journal.
2. Fill the cup with dry soil.
3. Find the mass of the cup of soil and record this value in your data table.
4. Moisten the soil in the cup. Plant four radish seeds 2 cm deep in the soil. Space the seeds an equal distance apart. Wash your hands.
5. Add water to keep the soil barely moist as the seeds sprout and grow.
6. When the plants have developed four to six true leaves, usually after two to three weeks, carefully remove the plants from the soil. Gently brush the soil off the roots. Make sure all the soil remains in the cup.
7. Spread the plants out on a paper towel. Place the plants and the cup of soil in a warm area to dry out.
8. When the plants are dry, measure their mass and record this value in your data table. Write this number with a plus sign in the Gain or Loss column.
9. When the soil is dry, find the mass of the cup of soil. Record this value in your data table. Subtract the End mass from the Start mass and record this number with a minus sign in the Gain or Loss column.

Sample Data

Mass of Soil and Radish Plants

	Start	End	Gain (+) or Loss (−)
Mass of dry soil and cup	75.8 g	75.7 g	0.1 g −
Mass of dried radish plants	0 g	2.1 g	2.1 g +

Conclude and Apply

1. In the early 1600s, a Belgian scientist named J. B. van Helmont conducted this experiment with a willow tree. What is the advantage of using radishes instead of a tree?
2. How much mass was gained or lost by the soil? By the radish plants?
3. Did the mass of the plants come completely from the soil? How do you know?
4. If all of the mass gained by the plants did not come from the soil, where could it have come from?

Communicating Your Data

Compare your conclusions with those of other students in your class. **For more help, refer to the** Science Skill Handbook.

Procedure

Teaching Strategy

This experiment helps uncover and correct the misconception that the material for a mass increase in a plant comes from the soil. Prior to getting results, ask students if most of the mass gained by the radish plants will come from the soil. If they don't think it will come from the soil, ask where they think it will come from.

Expected Outcome

The radish plants' mass gain will be more than the soil's mass loss.

Conclude and Apply

1. Radishes grow faster and use less space. You can get a quantitative amount of mass gained and lost.
2. Answers will vary, but the soil will have a very small mass loss and the plants will have a much larger mass gain.
3. No, because the mass loss of the soil is smaller than the mass gain of the plants.
4. Answers will vary, but should include carbon dioxide from the air and water from the soil.

Error Analysis

Some errors may occur because the plants and soil are not completely dry. However, this usually does not affect the conclusion.

✓Assessment

Content Pretend that you grew a willow tree for five years like Van Helmont. Write down how much mass the tree might have gained and how much mass the soil might have lost. Use **Performance Assessment in the Science Classroom,** p. 89.

Communicating Your Data

Have students post their data tables on a bulletin board for other students to see.

Science Stats

Content Background

The term *climate* refers to the average weather of a region over a period of time. Earth has a huge variety of climates and the climate of any region can change over time. The following list explains the main influences on the climate of a region.

1. Wind, which distributes moisture and heat
2. Distance of the region from the equator, which determines how much solar radiation reaches the area
3. Presence of large bodies of water, which decrease temperature variation in the surrounding regions
4. Altitude, which affects the temperature
5. Presence of mountains and other surface features, which influence cloud formation and precipitation

Discussion

What type of weather would you expect the south pole to have while it is pointed away from the Sun? Students should infer that the South Pole would have low temperatures and cold weather during the time it is pointed away from the Sun.

Activity

Have students work as a class to record and graph daily high and low temperatures each day for a month.
LS Logical-Mathematical

Science Stats

Extreme Climates

Did you know...

... The greatest snowfall in one year occurred at Mount Baker in Washington State. Approximately 2,896 cm of snow fell on Mount Baker during the 1998-99, 12-month snowfall season. That's enough snow to bury an eight-story building.

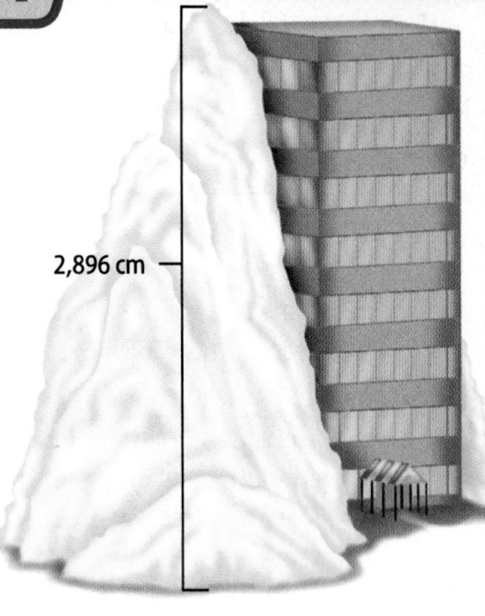

... The hottest climate in the United States is found in Death Valley, California. In July 1913, Death Valley reached approximately 57°C. This is the hottest officially recognized temperature on Earth. As a comparison, a comfortable room temperature is about 20°C.

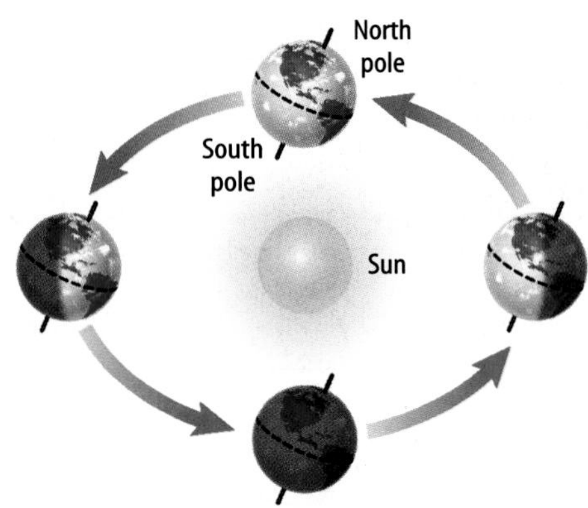

... The record for the lowest temperature was set in Antarctica in 1983. The temperature was a frigid −89°C. As a comparison, the temperature of your freezer at home is about −15°C.

... The south pole receives sunshine for less than 50 percent of the days in a year. Because Earth is tilted, the south pole is pointed away from the Sun for about half the year and receives very little during that time.

Internet Addresses

Explore the Glencoe Science Web site at **science.glencoe.com** to find out more about topics in this feature.

Connecting To Math

... The fastest tornado winds have been measured at a speed of about 512 km/h. That's faster than the blades of some helicopters, which can rotate at about 450 km/h.

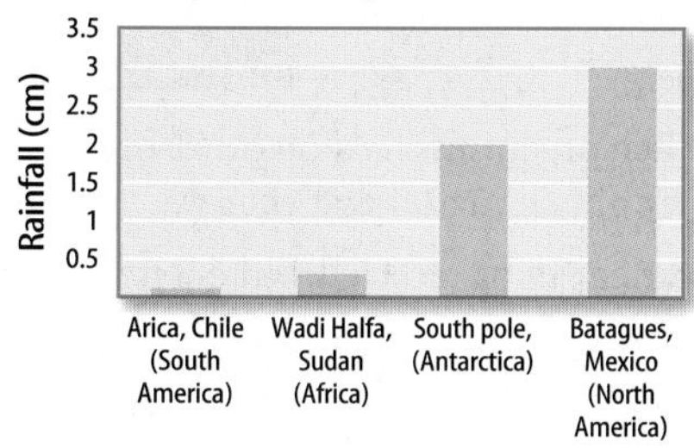

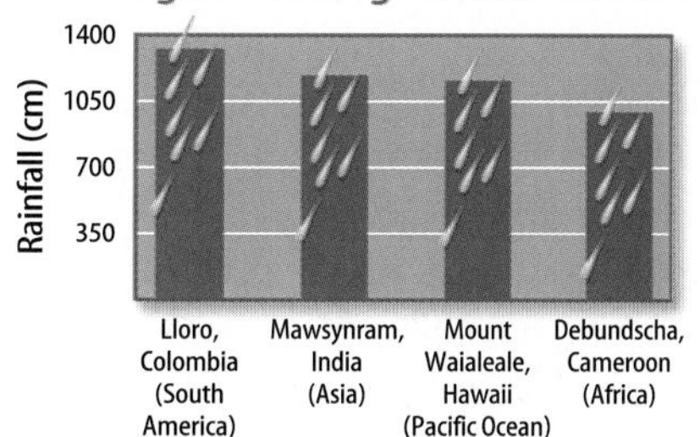

Do the Math

1. Look at the graph above. How many years of average south pole precipitation would it take to equal a single year of average precipitation in Lloro, Colombia?
2. What is the difference in degrees Celsius between the world record low temperature and the world record high temperature?
3. What was the average monthly snowfall at Mount Baker during the 1998-99 snowfall season?

Go Further

Go to **science.glencoe.com** and find out the average monthly rainfall in a tropical rain forest. Make a line graph to show how the amount of precipitation changes during the 12 months of the year.

Connecting To Math

Do the Math

Teaching Strategies

- Remind students to use the label on each graph to determine the value represented by each bar. Also remind students to include the unit (years) with their answer.
- Use a number line to demonstrate the relative position of −89°C and +57°C. Remind students that the difference between these two values will be larger than either of the numbers.
- Inform students that the snowfall season on Mount Baker is 12 months long. The average monthly snowfall can be calculated by dividing the total snowfall by 12.

Answers

1. approximately 650 years
2. 146°C
3. 241.3 cm

Go Further

Have students add lines to their graphs to represent the average monthly rainfall in your area. Compare the amount of precipitation received in your location to that received in a tropical rain forest. Ask students to predict how the local environment would change if the amount of precipitation increased.

Visual Learning

Lowest Average Annual Rainfall, Highest Average Annual Rainfall Have each student choose one location represented on each graph and use the annual rainfall number to calculate an average monthly rainfall number for each location. Then, have students cut a strip of paper the same height as the average amount of monthly rainfall in each of the locations they have chosen. Use the paper strips for comparison. **LS Visual-Spatial**

Chapter 25 Study Guide

Reviewing Main Ideas

Preview

Students can answer the questions in their Science Journals. Discuss the answers as you go through the chapter. **LS Linguistic**

Review

Students can write their answers, then compare them with those of other students. **LS Interpersonal**

Reteach

Students can look at the illustrations and describe details that support the main ideas of the chapter. **LS Visual-Spatial**

Answers to Chapter Review

Section 1

1. Possible answers: proper temperatures, sufficient water and oxygen, sunlight and soil minerals for trees to make nuts

Section 2

1. They produce oxygen as a waste product of photosynthesis.

Section 3

1. through photosynthesis
5. Most of the apple's energy is converted into energy for your life functions.

Chapter 25 Study Guide

Reviewing Main Ideas

Section 1 Abiotic Factors

1. Abiotic factors include air, water, soil, sunlight, temperature, and climate. *What abiotic factors are required for this squirrel's survival? Explain.*
2. The availability of water and light influences where life exists on Earth.
3. Soil and climate have an important influence on the types of organisms that can survive in different environments.
4. High latitudes and elevations generally have lower average temperatures.

Section 2 Cycles in Nature

1. Matter is limited on Earth and is recycled through the environment. *How do green plants help recycle oxygen?*

2. The water cycle involves evaporation, condensation, and precipitation.
3. The carbon cycle involves photosynthesis and respiration.
4. Nitrogen in the form of soil compounds enters plants, which are then consumed by other organisms.

Section 3 Energy Flow

1. Producers make energy-rich molecules through photosynthesis or chemosynthesis. *How do seaweeds in shallow water obtain energy?*

2. When organisms feed on other organisms, they obtain matter and energy.
3. Matter can be recycled, but energy cannot.
4. Food webs are models of the complex feeding relationships in communities.
5. Available energy decreases as you go to higher feeding levels in an energy pyramid. *What happens to most of the energy in an apple that you eat?*

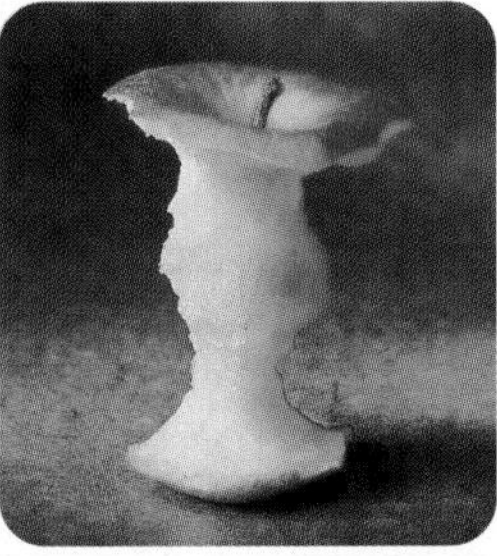

FOLDABLES Reading & Study Skills — After You Read

Find a student who drew a different ecosystem on his or her Cause and Effect Study Fold. Then, compare and contrast the information on your two Foldables.

FOLDABLES Reading & Study Skills — After You Read

After students have read the chapter and completed the Foldable described in Before You Read, have them do the activity on the student page.

Dinah Zike

Visualizing Main Ideas

This diagram shows photosynthesis in a leaf. Fill in the blank lines with the terms light, carbon dioxide, *and* oxygen.

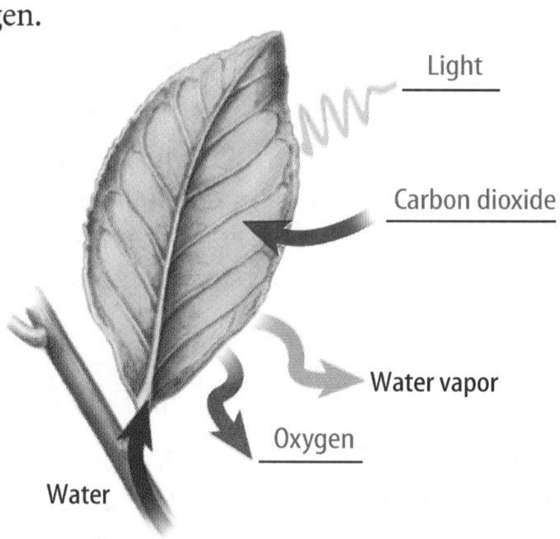

Vocabulary Review

Vocabulary Words

a. abiotic
b. atmosphere
c. biotic
d. carbon cycle
e. chemosynthesis
f. climate
g. condensation
h. energy pyramid
i. evaporation
j. food web
k. nitrogen cycle
l. nitrogen fixation
m. soil
n. water cycle

Study Tip

Write out the full questions and answers to end-of-chapter quizzes, not just the answers. This will help you form complete responses to important questions.

Using Vocabulary

Which vocabulary word best corresponds to each of the following events?

1. A liquid changes to a gas.
2. Some types of bacteria form nitrogen compounds in the soil.
3. Decaying plants add nitrogen to the soil.
4. Chemical energy is used to make energy-rich molecules.
5. Decaying plants add carbon to the soil.
6. A gas changes to a liquid.
7. Water flows downhill into a stream. The stream flows into a lake, and water evaporates from the lake.
8. Burning coal and exhaust from automobiles release carbon into the air.

Chapter 25 Study Guide

Visualizing Main Ideas

See student page.

Vocabulary Review

Using Vocabulary

1. evaporation
2. nitrogen fixation
3. nitrogen cycle
4. chemosynthesis
5. carbon cycle
6. condensation
7. water cycle
8. carbon cycle

Chapter 25 Assessment

Checking Concepts

1. B
2. B
3. A
4. D
5. A
6. A
7. B
8. B
9. A
10. C

Thinking Critically

11. The country should grow corn and other vegetables for the people to eat. If they grow corn to feed cattle, most of the energy of the corn will be lost.
12. Webs show complex interactions rather than the simple interactions of a chain.
13. Yes; nitrogen is an important component of DNA and proteins.
14. In the mature forest, the tall trees block most of the sunlight from reaching the floor. There is therefore little plant growth, making it easy to walk.
15. As the air blows over the mountains from the ocean on the west side, it cools and loses moisture. Thus there is a forest on one side, but a desert on the other.

Chapter 25 Assessment

Checking Concepts

Choose the word or phrase that best answers the question.

1. Which of the following is an abiotic factor?
   A) penguins **C)** soil bacteria
   B) rain **D)** redwood trees
2. Which group makes up the largest level of an energy pyramid?
   A) herbivores **C)** decomposers
   B) producers **D)** carnivores
3. You climb up the western slope of the Cascade Mountains and down the eastern side. Which of the following weather changes do you observe?
   A) Warm and wet changes to cold and wet, then cold and dry, then warm and dry.
   B) Cold and wet changes to warm and wet, then warm and dry, then cold and dry.
   C) Warm and wet changes to cold and wet, then cold and dry, then warm and wet.
   D) Warm and dry changes to cold and dry, then warm and dry, then cold and dry.
4. Which of the following applies to latitudes farther from the equator?
   A) higher elevations
   B) higher temperatures
   C) higher precipitation levels
   D) lower temperatures
5. Water vapor forming droplets that form clouds directly involves which process?
   A) condensation **C)** evaporation
   B) respiration **D)** transpiration
6. Which one of the following components of air is least necessary for life on Earth?
   A) argon **C)** carbon dioxide
   B) nitrogen **D)** oxygen
7. What do plants make that requires nitrogen?
   A) sugars **C)** fats
   B) proteins **D)** carbohydrates
8. Which of the following processes removes carbon dioxide from the air?
   A) condensation **C)** burning
   B) photosynthesis **D)** respiration
9. Earth receives a constant supply of which of the following items?
   A) light energy **C)** nitrogen
   B) carbon **D)** water
10. Which of these is an energy source for chemosynthesis?
    A) sunlight **C)** sulfur molecules
    B) moonlight **D)** carnivores

Thinking Critically

11. A country has many starving people. Should they grow vegetables and corn to eat, or should they grow corn to feed cattle so they can eat beef? Explain.
12. Why is a food web a better model than a food chain?
13. Do bacteria need nitrogen? Why or why not?
14. It is often easier to walk through an old, mature forest of tall trees than through a young forest that is full of small trees. Why?
15. The Inyo Mountains are located in central California. Explain why giant sequoia trees grow on the west side of the mountains and Death Valley, a desert, is on the east side.

Developing Skills

16. **Classifying** Classify each of the following environmental concerns according to the cycle it affects—carbon, nitrogen, or water.
    a. algal blooms caused by excess fertilizer
    b. acid rain damage to pine trees
    c. the unnatural warming of Earth

Chapter Assessment Planner

Portfolio Encourage students to place in their portfolios one or two items of what they consider to be their best work. Examples include:

- Assessment, p. 726
- Activity, p. 732
- Activity, p. 735

Performance Additional performance assessments, Performance Task Assessment Lists, and rubrics for evaluating these activities can be found in Glencoe's **Performance Assessment in the Science Classroom.**

17. Recognizing Cause and Effect A lake in Kenya has been taken over by a floating weed. What could you do to determine if nitrogen fertilizer runoff from farms is causing the problem?

18. Making and Using Graphs Abiotic factors, such as climate, cause populations to move from place to place. Make a bar graph of the following migration distances.

Mighty Migrators

Species	Distance (km)
Desert locust	4,800
Caribou	800
Green turtle	1,900
Arctic tern	35,000
Gray whale	19,000

19. Forming Hypotheses For each hectare of land, ecologists found 10,000 kcals of producers, 10,000 kcals of herbivores, and 2,000 kcals of carnivores. Suggest a reason why producer and herbivore levels are equal.

20. Concept Mapping Draw a food web of these organisms: *caterpillars and rabbits eat grasses, raccoons eat rabbits and mice, mice eat grass seeds,* and *birds eat caterpillars.*

Performance Assessment

21. Poster Use magazine photographs to make a visual representation of the water cycle.

Technology

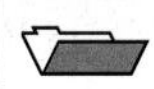

Go to the Glencoe Science Web site at **science.glencoe.com** or use the **Glencoe Science CD-ROM** for additional chapter assessment.

THE PRINCETON REVIEW Test Practice

Food chains model how energy is transferred from one organism to another organism in the environment. The diagram below shows a food chain that includes aquatic plants and animals and a land animal.

Study the diagram and answer the following questions.

1. Which of the following statements is true based on the order of the food chain shown above?
   A) Algae eat plankton.
   B) Plankton eat salmon.
   C) Herring eat plankton.
   D) Salmon eat algae.

2. If the supply of salmon were suddenly depleted, the numbers of which of the following might also be depleted?
   F) algae
   G) plankton
   H) herring
   J) eagles

Chapter 25 Assessment

THE PRINCETON REVIEW Test Practice

The Test-Taking Tip was written by The Princeton Review, the nation's leader in test preparation.

1. C
2. J

Developing Skills

16. a. nitrogen cycle
b. water cycle
c. carbon cycle

17. Possible answer: Ask farmers to restrict their use of nitrogen fertilizer and see if this clears up the lake.

18. From highest bar to lowest: Arctic tern, gray whale, desert locust, green turtle, caribou

19. Reasons may include a poor growth year for plants or a very good year for herbivore reproduction.

20. Check student food webs to ensure correct relationships are in place.

Performance Assessment

21. Posters will vary, but should show how the cycle continues. Use **PASC**, p. 145.

Assessment Resources

Reproducible Masters

Chapter Resources Booklet
Chapter Review, pp. 37–38
Chapter Tests, pp. 39–42
Assessment Transparency Activity, p. 49

Glencoe Science Web site
Interactive Tutor
Chapter Quizzes

Glencoe Technology
Assessment Transparency
Interactive CD-ROM Chapter Quizzes
ExamView Pro Test Bank
Vocabulary PuzzleMaker Software
MindJogger Videoquiz

Section/Objectives	Standards		Activities/Features
	National	State/Local	
Chapter Opener	See p. 5T for a Key to Standards.		**Explore Activity:** Infer the origin of houseplants, p. 747 **Before You Read,** p. 747
Section 1 How Ecosystems Change 2 sessions 1 block 1. **Explain** how ecosystems change over time. 2. **Describe** how new communities begin in areas without life. 3. **Compare** pioneer communities and climax communities.	National Content Standards: UCP1, UCP3, C4, F2		**Science Online,** p. 749 **Visualizing Secondary Succession,** p. 750
Section 2 Biomes 2 sessions 1 block 1. **Explain** how climate influences land environments. 2. **Identify** seven biomes of Earth. 3. **Describe** the adaptations of organisms found in each biome.	National Content Standards: UCP1, A1, C4, C5		**MiniLAB:** Modeling Rain Forest Leaves, p. 756 **Earth Science Integration,** p. 758 **Activity:** Studying a Land Ecosystem, p. 760
Section 3 Aquatic Ecosystems 3 sessions 1.5 blocks 1. **Compare** flowing freshwater and standing freshwater ecosystems. 2. **Identify** and describe important saltwater ecosystems. 3. **Identify** problems that affect aquatic ecosystems.	National Content Standards: UCP1, A1, C4, C5, F2, G1		**MiniLAB:** Modeling Freshwater Environments, p. 762 **Chemistry Integration,** p. 763 **Math Skills Activity: Calculating Temperatures,** p. 764 **Science Online,** p. 765 **Activity:** Exploring Wetlands, pp. 768–769 **Science and Society:** Helping Nature Help Itself, pp. 770–771

NATIONAL GEOGRAPHIC

Teacher's Corner

PRODUCTS AVAILABLE FROM GLENCOE
To order call 1-800-334-7344:
CD-ROM
NGS PictureShow: Looking at Ecosystems
Poster
Water

Transparency Set
NGS PicturePack: Looking at Ecosystems
Videodiscs
STV: Habitats; STV: Water

PRODUCTS AVAILABLE FROM NATIONAL GEOGRAPHIC SOCIETY
To order call 1-800-368-2728:
Videos
The Living Ocean; Water: A Celebration; Water: A Precious Resource

Activity Materials	Reproducible Resources	Section Assessment	Technology
Explore Activity: houseplant	**Chapter Resources Booklet** Foldables Worksheet, p. 15 Directed Reading Overview, p. 17 Note-taking Worksheets, pp. 31–33	GLENCOE'S ASSESSMENT ADVANTAGE	
Need materials? Contact Science Kit at 1-800-828-7777 or www.sciencekit.com on the Internet.	**Chapter Resources Booklet** Transparency Activity, p. 42 Enrichment, p. 28 Reinforcement, p. 25 Directed Reading, p. 18 Lab Activity, pp. 9–10	Portfolio Visual Learning, p. 750 Performance Skill Builder Activities, p. 751 Content Section Assessment, p. 751	Section Focus Transparency Interactive CD-ROM Guided Reading Audio Program
MiniLAB: poster board, metric ruler, scissors, sink, water, spray bottle **Activity:** graph paper, thermometer, hand lens, notebook, binoculars, field guides, compass	**Chapter Resources Booklet** MiniLAB, p. 3 Transparency Activity, p. 43 Enrichment, p. 29 Reinforcement, p. 26 Directed Reading, p. 19 Activity Worksheet, pp. 5–6 **Reading and Writing Skill Activities,** p. 1	Portfolio Assessment, p. 759 Performance MiniLAB, p. 756 Skill Builder Activities, p. 759 Content Section Assessment, p. 759	Section Focus Transparency Interactive CD-ROM Guided Reading Audio Program
MiniLAB: pond sediment or debris; pond plants, pond water, and organisms; clear-plastic container with lid; net; hand lens **Activity:** Internet sites or reference sources on wetlands	**Chapter Resources Booklet** MiniLAB, p. 4 Transparency Activity, p. 44 Enrichment, p. 30 Reinforcement, p. 27 Directed Reading, pp. 19, 20 Activity Worksheet, pp. 7–8 Lab Activity, pp. 11–14 Transparency Activity, pp. 45–46 **Lab Management and Safety,** p. 37	Portfolio Science Journal, p. 764 Performance MiniLAB, p. 762 Math Skills Activity, p. 764 Skill Builder Activities, p. 767 Content Section Assessment, p. 767	Section Focus Transparency Teaching Transparency Interactive CD-ROM Guided Reading Audio Program

End of Chapter Assessment

GLENCOE'S ASSESSMENT ADVANTAGE

Blackline Masters	Technology	Professional Series
Chapter Resources Booklet Chapter Review, pp. 35–36 Chapter Tests, pp. 37–40 **Standardized Test Practice by The Princeton Review,** pp. 111–114	MindJogger Videoquiz Interactive CD-ROM Vocabulary PuzzleMakers ExamView Pro Test Bank Interactive Lesson Planner Interactive Teacher Edition	Performance Assessment in the Science Classroom (PASC)

Transparencies

Section Focus

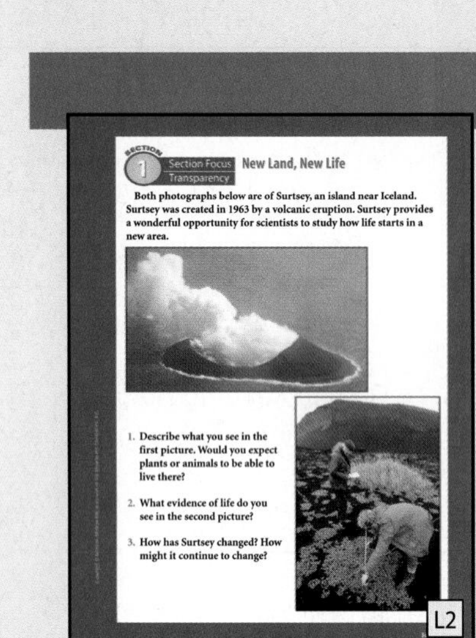
Section 1 Section Focus Transparency — New Land, New Life

Both photographs below are of Surtsey, an island near Iceland. Surtsey was created in 1963 by a volcanic eruption. Surtsey provides a wonderful opportunity for scientists to study how life starts in a new area.

1. Describe what you see in the first picture. Would you expect plants or animals to be able to live there?
2. What evidence of life do you see in the second picture?
3. How has Surtsey changed? How might it continue to change?

L2

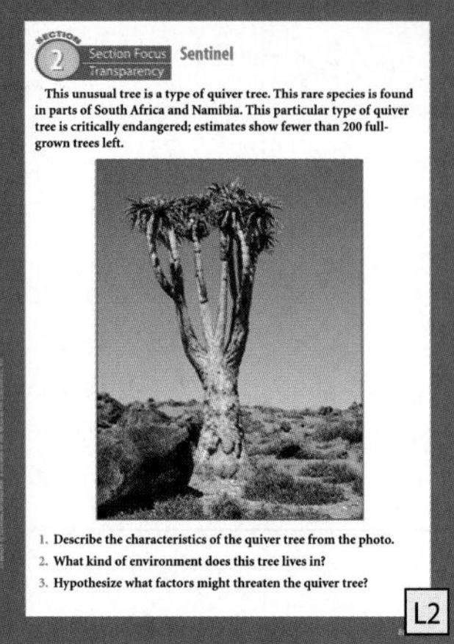
Section 2 Section Focus Transparency — Sentinel

This unusual tree is a type of quiver tree. This rare species is found in parts of South Africa and Namibia. This particular type of quiver tree is critically endangered; estimates show fewer than 200 full-grown trees left.

1. Describe the characteristics of the quiver tree from the photo.
2. What kind of environment does this tree lives in?
3. Hypothesize what factors might threaten the quiver tree?

L2

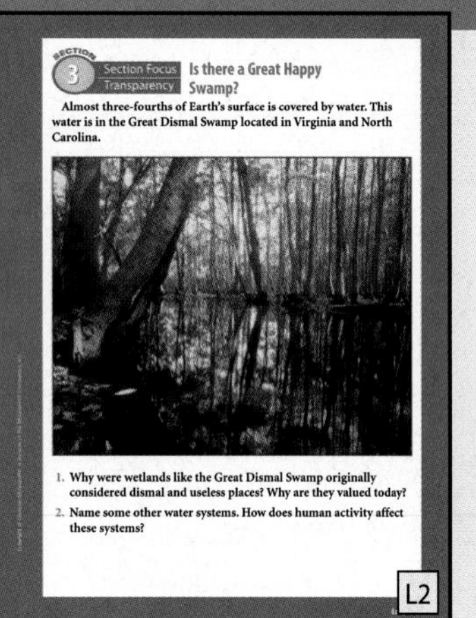
Section 3 Section Focus Transparency — Is there a Great Happy Swamp?

Almost three-fourths of Earth's surface is covered by water. This water is in the Great Dismal Swamp located in Virginia and North Carolina.

1. Why were wetlands like the Great Dismal Swamp originally considered dismal and useless places? Why are they valued today?
2. Name some other water systems. How does human activity affect these systems?

L2

This is a representation of key blackline masters available in the Teacher Classroom Resources. See Resource Manager boxes within the chapter for additional information.

Assessment

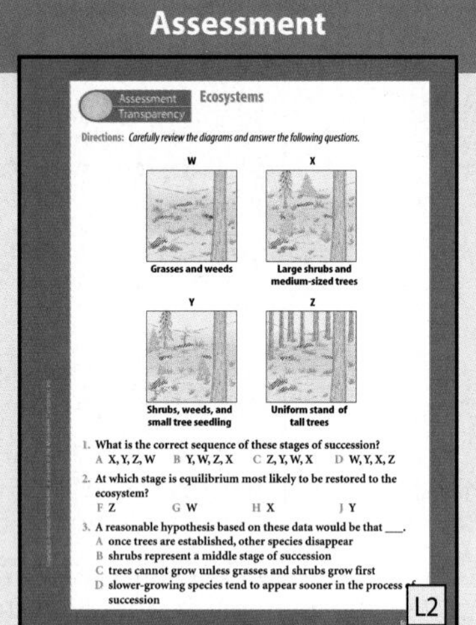
Assessment Transparency — Ecosystems

Directions: *Carefully review the diagrams and answer the following questions.*

1. What is the correct sequence of these stages of succession?
   A X, Y, Z, W B Y, W, Z, X C Z, Y, W, X D W, Y, X, Z
2. At which stage is equilibrium most likely to be restored to the ecosystem?
   F Z G W H X J Y
3. A reasonable hypothesis based on these data would be that ___.
   A once trees are established, other species disappear
   B shrubs represent a middle stage of succession
   C trees cannot grow unless grasses and shrubs grow first
   D slower-growing species tend to appear sooner in the process of succession

L2

Teaching

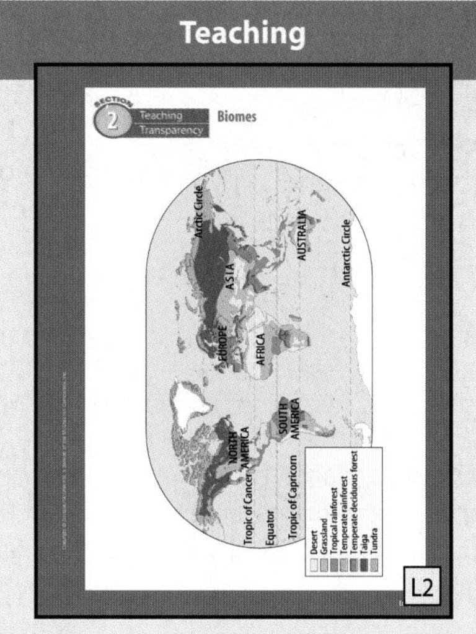
Section 2 Teaching Transparency — Biomes

L2

Key to Teaching Strategies

The following designations will help you decide which activities are appropriate for your students.

- L1 Level 1 activities should be appropriate for students with learning difficulties.
- L2 Level 2 activities should be within the ability range of all students.
- L3 Level 3 activities are designed for above-average students.
- ELL ELL activities should be within the ability range of English Language Learners.
- COOP LEARN Cooperative Learning activities are designed for small group work.
- LS Multiple Learning Styles logos, as described on page 22T, are used throughout to indicate strategies that address different learning styles.
- P These strategies represent student products that can be placed into a best-work portfolio.

Hands-on Activities

Activity Worksheets

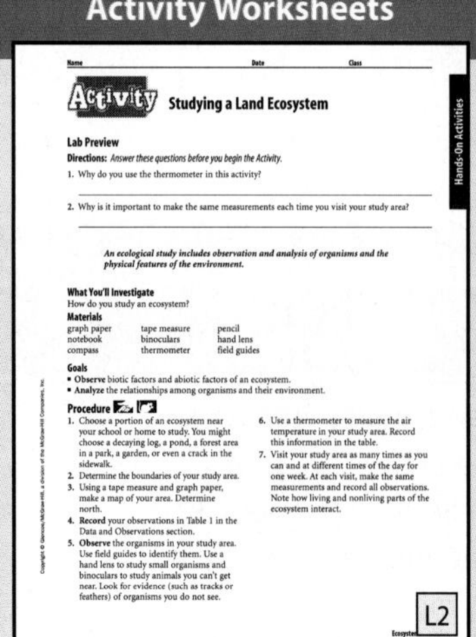
Name Date Class

Activity — Studying a Land Ecosystem

Lab Preview

Directions: *Answer these questions before you begin the Activity.*

1. Why do you use the thermometer in this activity?
2. Why is it important to make the same measurements each time you visit your study area?

An ecological study includes observation and analysis of organisms and the physical features of the environment.

What You'll Investigate

How do you study an ecosystem?

Materials

graph paper, notebook, compass, tape measure, binoculars, thermometer, pencil, hand lens, field guides

Goals

- Observe biotic factors and abiotic factors of an ecosystem.
- Analyze the relationships among organisms and their environment.

Procedure

1. Choose a portion of an ecosystem near your school or home to study. You might choose a decaying log, a pond, a forest area in a park, a garden, or even a crack in the sidewalk.
2. Determine the boundaries of your study area.
3. Using a tape measure and graph paper, make a map of your area. Determine north.
4. Record your observations in Table 1 in the Data and Observations section.
5. Observe the organisms in your study area. Use field guides to identify them. Use a hand lens to study small organisms and binoculars to study animals you can't get near. Look for evidence (such as tracks or feathers) of organisms you do not see.
6. Use a thermometer to measure the air temperature in your study area. Record this information in the table.
7. Visit your study area as many times as you can and at different times of the day for one week. At each visit, make the same measurements and record all observations. Note how living and nonliving parts of the ecosystem interact.

Hands-On Activities

L2

Laboratory Activities

Name Date Class

Lab 1 Laboratory Activity — Succession Communities and Grasses

Once lichens and other pioneer species die and organic matter is added to the soil, other plants are able to grow. Grasses are a characteristic species of primary and secondary succession. They are tough and adaptable, grow quickly and readily, and further enrich the soil when they die.

Strategy

You will observe the effect of sunlight and water on the growth of grass.
You will identify differences between the characteristics of a succession community and the characteristics of a climax community.

Materials

four small plastic pots filled with soil and planted with grass seed, permanent marker, small box open only at one end, water

Procedure

1. Label the pots 1, 2, 3, and 4.
2. Place pot 1 in a location that will receive a lot of indirect sunlight.
3. Cover pot 2 with the box. Place it next to pot 1.
4. Water pots 1 and 2 with the same amount of water twice a week. Keep the soil moist but not wet.
5. Place pots 3 and 4 in the same location as plants 1 and 2.
6. Water pot 3 daily. Keep the soil wet.
7. Do not water pot 4.
8. In the Data and Observations table, write a hypothesis describing how you think the amount of light will affect pots 1 and 2. Write another hypothesis describing how you think the amount of water will affect pots 1, 3, and 4.
9. Care for the plants daily for three weeks. Record observations at the end of each week.

Data and Observations

Hypothesis	
Plants 1 and 2 (light)	
Plants 1, 3 and 4 (water)	

Observations			
Plant	Week 1	Week 2	Week 3
1			
2			
3			
4			

Hands-On Activities

L2

Meeting Different Ability Levels

Content Outline

Name / Date / Class

Note-taking Worksheet — Ecosystems

Section 1 How Ecosystems Change

A. Ecological ____________—normal, gradual changes that occur in the types of species that live in an area

1. Primary succession begins in a place without ______

a. Starts with ____________ such as ____________, that can grow on rock

b. New ____________ forms as weather and erosion break down rock.

c. Decaying plants add ____________ to new soil.

2. ____________ begins in a place that has soil and once had living organisms

a. Examples: after a ____________ or removal of buildings

b. Occurs faster and has different pioneer species than primary succession

B. ____________—stable stage of ecological diversity and balance

Section 2 Biomes

A. Factors that affect biomes climate

1. temperature

2. ______

B. Major ____________—large areas with similar climates and ecosystems

1. ____________—cold, dry, treeless region

a. Permanently frozen soil called ____________

b. Average temperature: ____________

c. Average precipitation is ____________ per year.

d. Plants: ____________, grasses, small shrubs, lichens

e. Animals: insects, ducks, geese, other birds, mice, arctic ____________, reindeer

2. ____________— cold forest of mostly evergreen trees

a. Soil ____________ in the short summer.

b. Precipitation: mostly snow, ____________ per year

Meeting Individual Needs

L2

Reinforcement

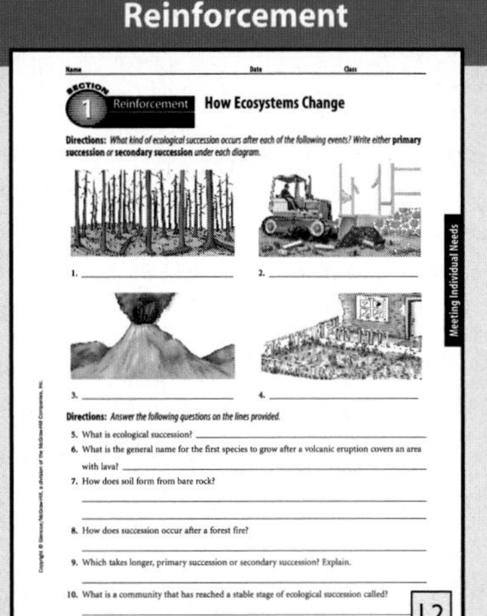

Name / Date / Class

Section 1 Reinforcement — How Ecosystems Change

Directions: What kind of ecological succession occurs after each of the following events? Write either primary succession or secondary succession under each diagram.

1. ______ 2. ______ 3. ______ 4. ______

Directions: Answer the following questions on the lines provided.

5. What is ecological succession?

6. What is the general name for the first species to grow after a volcanic eruption covers an area with lava?

7. How does soil form from bare rock?

8. How does succession occur after a forest fire?

9. Which takes longer, primary succession or secondary succession? Explain.

10. What is a community that has reached a stable stage of ecological succession called?

Meeting Individual Needs

L2

Directed Reading

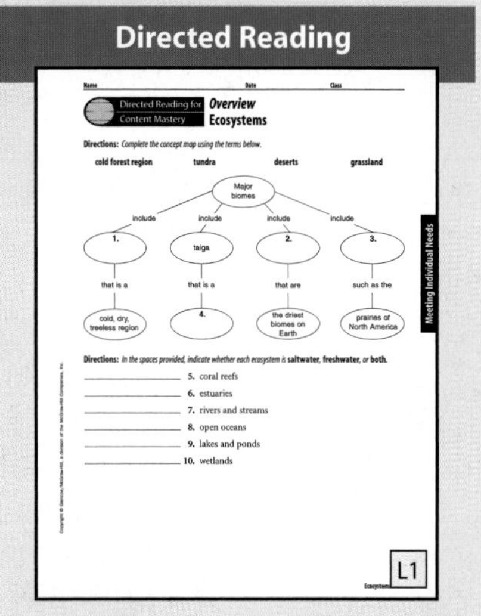

Name / Date / Class

Directed Reading for Content Mastery — Overview — Ecosystems

Directions: Complete the concept map using the terms below.

cold forest region — tundra — deserts — grassland

Directions: In the spaces provided, indicate whether each ecosystem is saltwater, freshwater, or both.

5. coral reefs

6. estuaries

7. rivers and streams

8. open oceans

9. lakes and ponds

10. wetlands

Meeting Individual Needs

L1

Enrichment

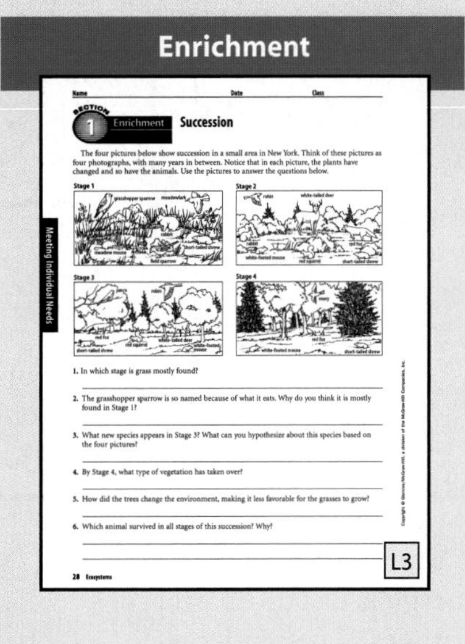

Name / Date / Class

Section 1 Enrichment — Succession

The four pictures below show succession in a small area in New York. Think of these pictures as four photographs, with many years in between. Notice that in each picture, the plants have changed and so have the animals. Use the pictures to answer the questions below.

1. In which stage is grass mostly found?

2. The grasshopper sparrow is so named because of what it eats. Why do you think it is mostly found in Stage 1?

3. What new species appears in Stage 3? What can you hypothesize about this species based on the four pictures?

4. By Stage 4, what type of vegetation has taken over?

5. How did the trees change the environment, making it less favorable for the grasses to grow?

6. Which animal survived in all stages of this succession? Why?

28 Ecosystems

Meeting Individual Needs

L3

Spanish Directed Reading

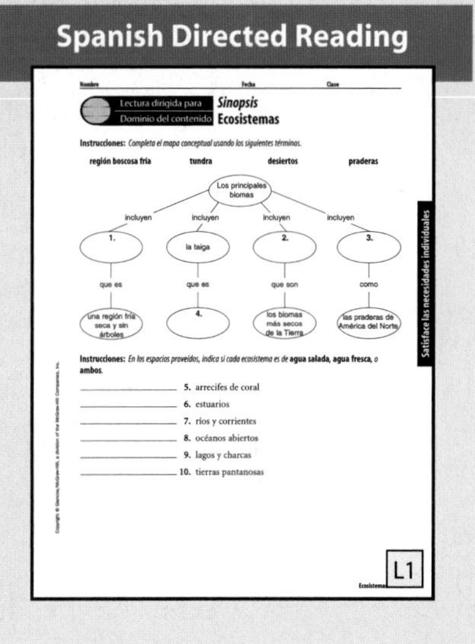

Nombre / Fecha / Clase

Lectura dirigida para Dominio del contenido — Sinopsis — Ecosistemas

Instrucciones: Completa el mapa conceptual usando los siguientes términos.

región boscosa fría — tundra — desiertos — praderas

Instrucciones: En los espacios provistos, indica si cada ecosistema es de agua salada, agua fresca, o ambos.

5. arrecifes de coral

6. estuarios

7. ríos y corrientes

8. océanos abiertos

9. lagos y charcas

10. tierras pantanosas

Satisface las necesidades individuales

L1

Assessment

Chapter Tests

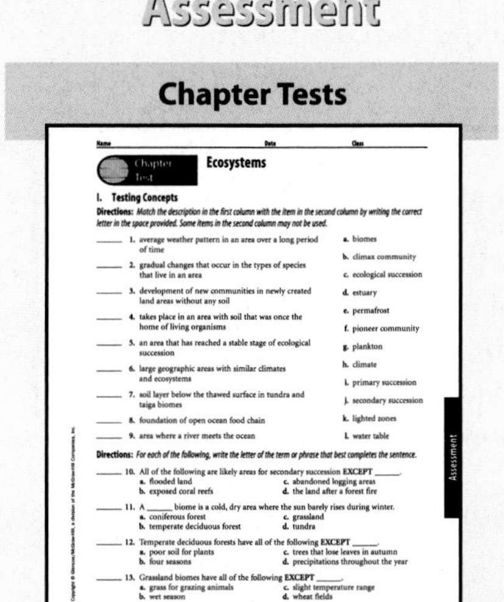

Name / Date / Class

Chapter Test — Ecosystems

I. Testing Concepts

Directions: Match the description in the first column with the item in the second column by writing the correct letter in the space provided. Some items in the second column may not be used.

1. average weather pattern in an area over a long period of time — a. biomes

2. gradual changes that occur in the types of species that live in an area — b. climax community

3. development of new communities in newly created land areas without any soil — c. ecological succession

4. takes place in an area with soil that was once the home of living organisms — d. estuary

5. an area that has reached a stable stage of ecological succession — e. permafrost

6. large geographic areas with similar climates and ecosystems — f. pioneer community

7. soil layer below the thawed surface in tundra and taiga biomes — g. plankton

8. foundation of open ocean food chain — h. climate

9. area where a river meets the ocean — i. primary succession; j. secondary succession; k. lighted zones; l. water table

Directions: For each of the following, write the letter of the term or phrase that best completes the sentence.

10. All of the following are likely areas for secondary succession EXCEPT ______. a. flooded land b. exposed coral reefs c. abandoned logging areas d. the land after a forest fire

11. A ______ biome is a cold, dry area where the sun barely rises during winter. a. coniferous forest b. temperate deciduous forest c. grassland d. tundra

12. Temperate deciduous forests have all of the following EXCEPT ______. a. poor soil for plants b. four seasons c. trees that lose leaves in autumn d. precipitations throughout the year

13. Grassland biomes have all of the following EXCEPT ______. a. grass for grazing animals b. wet season c. slight temperature range d. wheat fields

14. Deserts have all of the following EXCEPT ______. a. little rainfall b. little wind c. soil with little organic matter d. few large animals

Assessment

L2

Test Practice Workbook

L2

Chapter Review

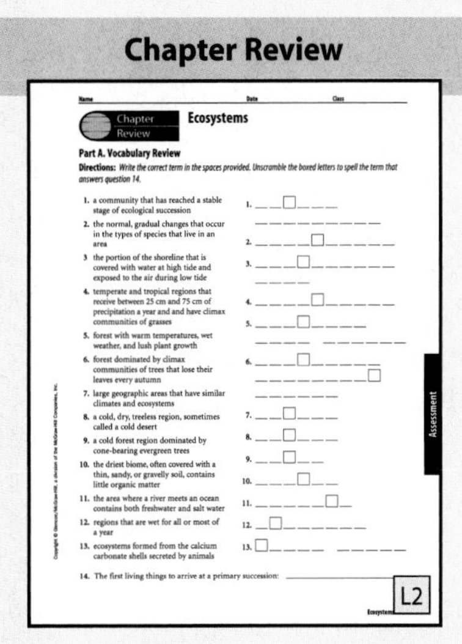

Name / Date / Class

Chapter Review — Ecosystems

Part A. Vocabulary Review

Directions: Write the correct term in the spaces provided. Unscramble the boxed letters to spell the term that answers question 14.

1. a community that has reached a stable stage of ecological succession

2. the normal, gradual changes that occur in the types of species that live in an area

3. the portion of the shoreline that is covered with water at high tide and exposed to the air during low tide

4. temperate and tropical regions that receive between 25 cm and 75 cm of precipitation a year and have climax communities of grasses

5. forest with warm temperatures, wet weather, and lush plant growth

6. forest dominated by climax communities of trees that lose their leaves every autumn

7. large geographic areas that have similar climates and ecosystems

8. a cold, dry, treeless region, sometimes called a cold desert

9. a cold forest region dominated by cone-bearing evergreen trees

10. the driest biome, often covered with a thin, sandy, or gravelly soil, contains little organic matter

11. the area where a river meets an ocean contains both freshwater and salt water

12. regions that are wet for all or most of a year

13. ecosystems formed from the calcium carbonate shells secreted by animals

14. The first living things to arrive at a primary succession:

Assessment

L2

Science Content Background

SECTION 1 How Ecosystems Change

Defining Ecosystems

A system is a group of parts that work together to form a functioning whole. Some common examples of systems include cars, watches, and digestive systems. An ecosystem is groups of organisms interacting with each other and their environment through a flow of energy and cycling of matter. It is the interdependence of all the parts that makes the whole a system.

Student Misconception

Ecosystems consist of only a few interactions among living things in an area.

Refer to the facing page for teaching strategies to address this misconception. Refer to pages 748–751 for content related to this topic.

SECTION 2 Biomes

Tundra

The tundra receives less energy from the Sun than does any other biome. The Sun's energy is dispersed over a greater area at higher latitudes. The Sun's rays lose much of their energy because they travel a greater distance through the atmosphere.

Desert

Desert covers less than 5% of North America. The North American deserts are the Mojave, Sonoran, Great Basin, and Chihuahuan. Temperatures in the desert undergo drastic changes over a 24-hour period. Daytime temperatures can be 30°C higher than nighttime readings. These fluctuations occur because of the lack of heat-retaining moisture in the desert air.

SECTION 3 Aquatic Ecosystems

Nutrients in Aquatic Ecosystems

In aquatic ecosystems, nutrients tend to sink below the light zone where many organisms cannot use them. In the ocean, the process that moves the bottom water with its valuable nutrients up to the surface is called an upwelling. In an upwelling, winds and currents work together near the continental shelf. The winds carry water away from land. Bottom water with its nutrients is pulled up into the photic zone to replace water that has moved out to sea. Upwellings occur in only a few places, such as along the coast of Peru.

For additional content background on this topic, go to the Glencoe Science Web site at science.glencoe.com.

Kevin & Cat Sweeney/DRK Photo

IDENTIFYING Misconceptions

Find Out What Students Think

Students may think that . . .

- **Systems only exist as parts of an organism or process.**
- **Ecosystems consist of only a few interactions among living things in an area.**

Students often do not understand the nature of systems in general, and they understand even less about the specific aspects of an ecosystem. Students may have learned that some things are called systems or ecosystems, but they may not be aware that ecosystems consist of parts, subsystems, and many interactions between biotic and abiotic factors.

Discussion

Show a photo of a bicycle, or bring in a bicycle for students to examine. Have students describe what they see. It is likely that students will respond that they see a bike. Point out that although there is one bicycle functioning as a whole unit, the bicycle consists of many components such as wheels, seat, chain, pedals, and so on. If any one of these components is removed, the bicycle will not function properly. The individual parts work together to do what a bicycle is supposed to do. In addition, in order for the bike to function, it needs an input of energy from a rider. Like a bicycle, an ecosystem is made up of many components, both abiotic (nonliving) and biotic (living), and it receives energy in the form of light and heat from the Sun.

Promote Understanding

Activity

Have students make a terrarium or display a completed terrarium.

- Discuss the biotic (living) and abiotic (nonliving) factors included in the terrarium, such as plants, insects, light, water, soil, and air.
- Have students diagram connections between the components. Then relate these connections to the flow of energy and cycling of materials. **What do you think would happen if one of the components of the terrarium were removed?** Explain that if a component such as light were removed, the plants would not be able to photosynthesize. Have students discuss the long-term effects of this event. The plants would die, the insects that eat the plants would not have food, and so on.
- Emphasize that the removal of light would cause the ecosystem to function improperly. Underscore this idea, using a diagram of the flow of energy and cycling of materials in the terrarium.

As an extension, have students choose another component of the terrarium and discuss how its removal would affect all other components of the terrarium.

Assess

After completing the chapter, see *Identifying Misconceptions* in the Study Guide.

CHAPTER 26

Ecosystems

Chapter Vocabulary

succession, p. 748
pioneer species, p. 748
climax community, p. 751
biome, p. 752
tundra, p. 753
taiga, p. 754
temperate deciduous forest, p. 755
temperate rain forest, p. 755
tropical rain forest, p. 756
desert, p. 758
grassland, p. 759
wetland, p. 763
coral reef, p. 765
intertidal zone, p. 766
estuary, p. 766

What do you think?

Science Journal Lava covers the soil on land, forming a rock layer. Lichens grow on the rock, helping to break it down gradually and starting the process of primary succession.

CHAPTER 26

Ecosystems

During the summer of 2000, wildfires burned out of control in Montana and other western states. Can this Montana hillside recover from the forest fire? Can the animals that lived here before the fire adapt to the changed environment? How is the forest in this picture different from a rain forest in South America? In this chapter, you will learn about the different ecosystems that exist on Earth. You also will learn how ecosystems change and how plants and animals adapt to those changes.

What do you think?

Science Journal Look at the picture below with a classmate. Discuss what this might be or what is happening. Here's a hint: *It is the first step in creating land.* Write your answer or best guess in your Science Journal.

746

Theme Connection

Stability and Change Ecosystems change in ways that can be predicted. In the process of succession, each community affects the environment, often producing conditions that result in the community's replacement.

The plants growing in your classroom or home may not look like the same types of plants that you find growing outside. Where do indoor plants come from? Many indoor plants don't grow well outside in most North American climates. Do the activity below to determine what type of climate most houseplants thrive in.

Infer the origin of houseplants

1. Examine a healthy houseplant in your classroom or home.
2. Describe the environmental conditions found in your classroom or home. For example, is the air humid or dry? Are temperatures warm and nearly constant?
3. Using observations from step 1 and descriptions from step 2, hypothesize about the natural environment of the plants in your classroom or home.

Observe

In your Science Journal, record the observations that led to your hypothesis. How would you design an experiment to test your hypothesis?

Before You Read

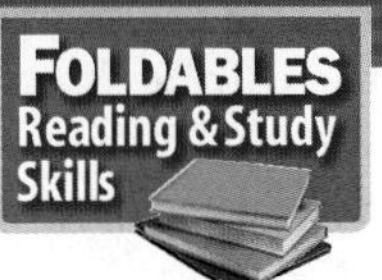

Making a Main Ideas Study Fold **A main idea consists of the major concepts or topics talked about in a chapter. Before you read the chapter, make the following Foldable to help you understand succession, or the gradual change in the types of species that live in an area.**

Primary Succession → Climax Communities
Secondary Succession → Climax Communities

1. Place a sheet of paper in front of you so the long side is at the top. Fold the paper in half from the left side to the right side. Fold top to bottom but do not crease and unfold.
2. Turn the paper so the fold is at the top and label *Primary Succession* and *Secondary Succession* across the front of the paper, as shown. Draw an arrow down from each and then label *Climax Communities,* as shown. Circle all four labels.
3. Through the top thickness of paper, cut along the middle fold line to form two tabs as shown.
4. As you read the chapter, define terms and collect information under the tabs.

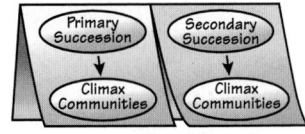

Explore Activity

Purpose Students observe common houseplants and make hypotheses about the climate of the area they originally inhabited. L2 IS **Naturalist**

Preparation Establish successfully growing houseplants in your classroom several weeks before the start of this chapter.

Materials houseplants; optional thermometers and humidity meter

Teaching Strategies

- Help students describe the amount of light, heat, and moisture the plants receive.
- Have students compare their observations and hypotheses with other students. Discuss differences and similarities.

Observe

Houseplants generally grow best when they have moist soil, moderate temperatures, and medium to low light. These plants are typically found in the understories of tropical rain forests. Students might suggest placing different specimens of the same type of plant in bright and low light, or giving them varying amounts of water.

Process Have students explain how the local climate would affect houseplants if they were planted outside the school for one year. Use **Performance Assessment in the Science Classroom,** p. 89.

Before You Read

FOLDABLES Reading & Study Skills

Dinah Zike Study Fold

Purpose Students make and use a Foldable to define terms and collect information on primary and secondary succession, and then use what they have learned to compare and contrast the two.

For additional help, see Foldables Worksheet, p. 15 in **Chapter Resources Booklet,** or go to the Glencoe Science Web site at **science.glencoe.com.** See After You Read in the Study Guide at the end of this chapter.

SECTION 1

How Ecosystems Change

1 Motivate

Bellringer Transparency

Display the Section Focus Transparency for Section 1. Use the accompanying Transparency Activity Master. L2 ELL

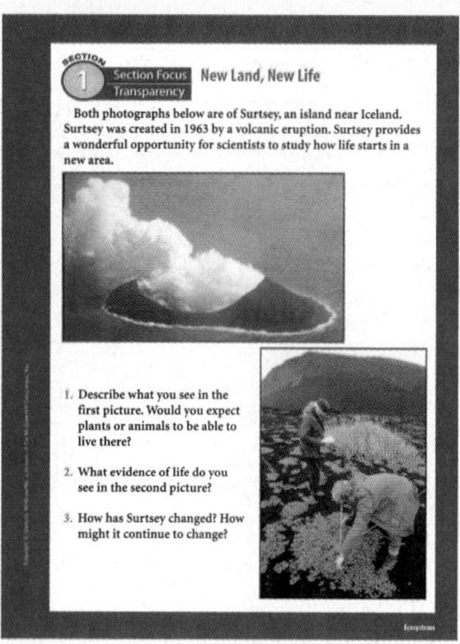
SECTION 1 Section Focus Transparency **New Land, New Life**

Both photographs below are of Surtsey, an island near Iceland. Surtsey was created in 1963 by a volcanic eruption. Surtsey provides a wonderful opportunity for scientists to study how life starts in a new area.

1. Describe what you see in the first picture. Would you expect plants or animals to be able to live there?
2. What evidence of life do you see in the second picture?
3. How has Surtsey changed? How might it continue to change?

Ecosystems

Tie to Prior Knowledge

Relate the idea of succession to examples found in the local environment. For example, there may be abandoned lots or farm fields showing succession. Many communities are allowing roadside grass areas to revert back to their natural states.

SECTION 1

How Ecosystems Change

As You Read

What You'll Learn

- **Explain** how ecosystems change over time.
- **Describe** how new communities begin in areas without life.
- **Compare** pioneer species and climax communities.

Vocabulary

succession
pioneer species
climax community

Why It's Important

Understanding how ecosystems change can help you predict what can happen to the land around you in the years to come.

Ecological Succession

What would happen if the lawn at your home were never cut? The grass would get longer, as in **Figure 1,** and soon it would look like a meadow. Later, larger plants would grow from seeds brought to the area by animals or wind. Then, trees might sprout. In fact, in 20 years or less you wouldn't be able to tell that the land was once a mowed lawn. An ecologist can tell you what type of ecosystem your lawn would become. If it would become a forest, they can tell you how long it would take and predict the type of trees that would grow there. **Succession** refers to the normal, gradual changes that occur in the types of species that live in an area. Succession occurs differently in different places around the world.

Primary Succession As lava flows from the mouth of a volcano, it is so hot that it destroys everything in its path. When it cools, lava forms new land composed of rock. It is hard to imagine that this land eventually could become a forest or grassland someday.

The process of succession that begins in a place without any soil is called primary succession. It starts with the arrival of living things such as lichens (LI kunz). These living things, called **pioneer species,** do not need soil to survive. They survive drought, extreme heat and cold, and other harsh conditions and start the soil-building process.

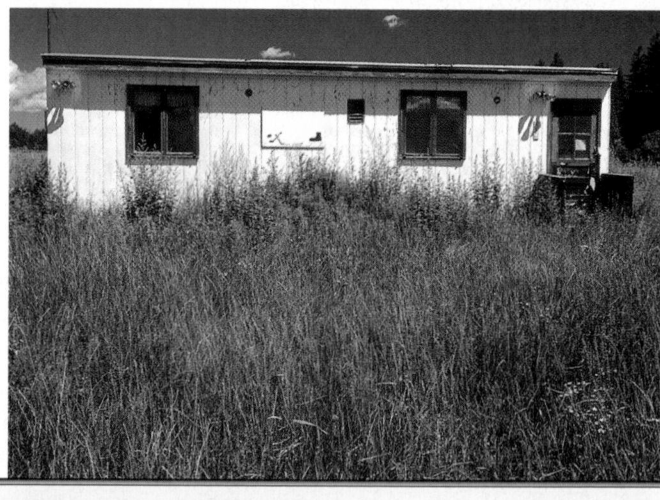

Figure 1
Open areas that are not maintained will become overgrown with grasses and shrubs as succession begins.

Section Assessment Planner

PORTFOLIO ASSESSMENT
Visual Learning, p. 750

PERFORMANCE ASSESSMENT
Skill Builder Activities, p. 751
See page 774 for more options.

CONTENT ASSESSMENT
Section, p. 751
Challenge, p. 751
Chapter, pp. 774–775

748 CHAPTER 26 Ecosystems

Figure 2
Lichens, like these in Colorado, are fragile and take many years to grow. They often cling to bare rock where many other organisms can't survive. *How do lichens form soil?*

New Soil During primary succession, shown in **Figure 2,** soil begins to form as lichens and the forces of weather and erosion help break down rocks into smaller pieces. When lichens die, they decay, adding small amounts of organic matter to the rock. Plants such as mosses and ferns can grow in this new soil. Eventually, these plants die, adding more organic material. The soil layer thickens, and grasses, wildflowers, and other plants begin to take over. When these plants die, they add more nutrients to the soil. This buildup is enough to support the growth of shrubs and trees. All the while, insects, small birds, and mammals have begun to move in. What was once bare rock now supports a variety of life.

Secondary Succession What happens when a fire, such as the one in **Figure 3,** destroys a forest or when a building is torn down in a city? After a forest fire, not much is left except dead trees and ash-covered soil. After the rubble of a building is removed, all that remains is bare soil. However, these places do not remain lifeless for long. The soil already contains the seeds of weeds, grasses, and trees. More seeds are carried to the area by wind and birds. Other wildlife may move in. Succession that begins in a place that already has soil and was once the home of living organisms is called secondary succession. Because soil already is present, secondary succession occurs faster and has different pioneer species than primary succession does.

Reading Check *Which type of succession starts without soil?*

SCIENCE Online
Data Update Visit the Glencoe Science Web site at **science.glencoe.com** to learn how forests in the western United States are recovering from the wildfires of 2000. Communicate to your class what you learn.

2 Teach

Ecological Succession

Caption Answer

Figure 2 Lichens help to break down rocks into smaller pieces. When lichens die, they decay, adding small amounts of organic material to the soil.

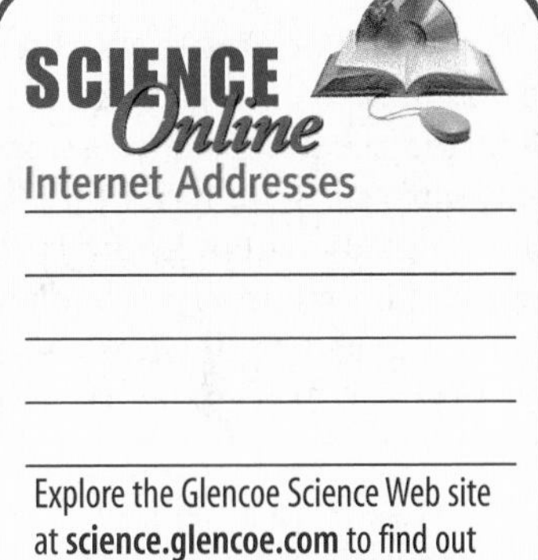

Teacher FYI

The small size of lichens and mosses makes them successful in the harsh environments typical of primary succession. Fast reproduction is a characteristic of secondary pioneers. These plants, which often pop up in gardens, are usually called weeds.

SCIENCE Online
Internet Addresses

Explore the Glencoe Science Web site at **science.glencoe.com** to find out more about topics in this section.

Reading Check

Answer primary succession

Resource Manager 

Chapter Resources Booklet
- Transparency Activity, p. 42
- Note-taking Worksheets, pp. 31–33
- Directed Reading for Content Mastery, pp. 17, 18

Curriculum Connection

History As the eastern United States was settled by Europeans, large tracts of forest were converted into farmland. With increasing industrialization, many of the farms were abandoned and the land reverted back into forests. Ask students to determine the past extent of the eastern forests and draw a map of this region.

Visualizing Secondary Succession

Have students examine the pictures and read the captions. Then ask the following questions.

What characteristics would make a seed likely to survive a fire? A seed that is surrounded by a thick seed coat is more likely to survive a fire than one with a thin seed coat.

As succession proceeds, what changes will occur in the population of plants found on the forest floor? At first, plants that need lots of sunlight can live on the forest floor, because there are no tall trees to block the sunlight. As trees grow and mature there will be less sunlight penetrating to the forest floor, so species that require less light will be found.

Activity

Have the students work in teams to write song lyrics that describe secondary succession. Students can write lyrics that fit any melody they know and enjoy. The steps of secondary succession should be clearly and accurately described in the lyrics.

Extension

Have students research in detail the current state of the areas of Yellowstone Park that burned in 1988. Students should share their findings with the class.

NATIONAL GEOGRAPHIC **VISUALIZING SECONDARY SUCCESSION**

Figure 3

In the summer of 1988, wind-driven flames like those shown in the background photo swept through Yellowstone National Park, scorching nearly a million acres. The Yellowstone fire was one of the worst forest fires in United States history. The images on this page show secondary succession—the process of ecological regeneration—triggered by the fire.

▶ After the fire, burned timber and blackened soil seemed to be all that remained. However, the fire didn't destroy the seeds that were protected under the soil.

◀ Within weeks, grasses and other plants were beginning to grow in the burned areas. Ecological succession was underway.

▶ Many burned areas in the park opened new plots for stands of trees. This picture shows young lodgepole pines in August 1999. The forest habitat of America's oldest national park is being restored gradually through secondary succession.

750 CHAPTER 26

Visual Learning

Figure 3 Have students make an outline of the stages in secondary succession that are shown. Then, have them go back and fill in any stages that aren't shown. P

Resource Manager

Chapter Resources Booklet
- Enrichment, p. 28
- Reinforcement, p. 25
- Lab Activity, pp. 9–10

Figure 4
This beech-maple forest is an example of a climax community.

Climax Communities A community that has reached a stable stage of ecological succession is called a **climax community.** It is a combination of plants and animals that use the available resources most efficiently. The beech-maple forest shown in **Figure 4** is an example of a community that has reached the end of succession. Diversity and balance are maintained in a climax community because as trees die, they provide nutrients for new communities of organisms. Some physical disturbances also are important in maintaining equilibrium in a climax community.

Primary succession begins in areas with no life at all. It can take hundreds or even thousands of years to develop into a climax community. Secondary succession is usually a shorter process, but it still can take a century or more.

Section 1 Assessment

1. What is ecological succession?
2. Explain the difference between primary and secondary succession.
3. What is the difference between pioneer species and climax communities?
4. What kind of succession will take place on an abandoned, unpaved country road?
5. **Think Critically** After a climax community is established in an area, explain how long it can survive there.

Skill Builder Activities

6. **Concept Mapping** Show the sequence of events in primary succession. Include the term *climax community.* **For more help, refer to the** Science Skill Handbook.
7. **Solving One-Step Equations** A tombstone etched with 1802 as the date of death has a lichen on it that is 6 cm in diameter. Assuming that the lichen started to grow in1802, calculate the average yearly growth of the lichen. **For more help, refer to the** Math Skill Handbook.

IDENTIFYING Misconceptions

Students may think that ecosystems consist of only a few interactions among living things in an area. Refer to page 746F for teaching strategies that address this misconception.

3 Assess

Reteach

Arrange the stages of succession for a forest community out of sequence in a diagram. Photocopy the diagram and have students use numbers to put the pictures in the proper sequence. L2 LS **Logical-Mathematical**

Challenge

Managers of some protected wildlife areas do not put out natural fires; sometimes they even do controlled burns. **Why is this done?** Controlled burns promote succession so that there are a variety of plants and animals in the ecosystem. In addition, these burns minimize tinder build-up so that naturally-occurring fires do not get out of control.

Assessment

Content Have students write a paragraph identifying how each of the following is undergoing succession: a cornfield after a flood, the area around a volcanic eruption, and a newly formed sandbar in a river. Use **Performance Assessment in the Science Classroom,** p. 159.

Answers to Section Assessment

1. the gradual change of the types of species that live in an area
2. Primary succession begins on rocky surfaces. Secondary succession begins on soil.
3. Pioneer species first settle in an area. Climax communities are stable and are composed of species that use available resources efficiently.
4. Secondary succession
5. indefinitely, unless damaged
6. Sequences will vary but should begin with lichens and mosses, progress to grasses, then bushes, and finally progress to a climax community of trees.
7. Growth per year = 6 cm / (current year − 1802). For example, if the year is 2002 then 6 cm / (2002 − 1802) = 0.03 cm per yr.

SECTION

Biomes

1 Motivate

Bellringer Transparency

Display the Section Focus Transparency for Section 2. Use the accompanying Transparency Activity Master. L2 ELL

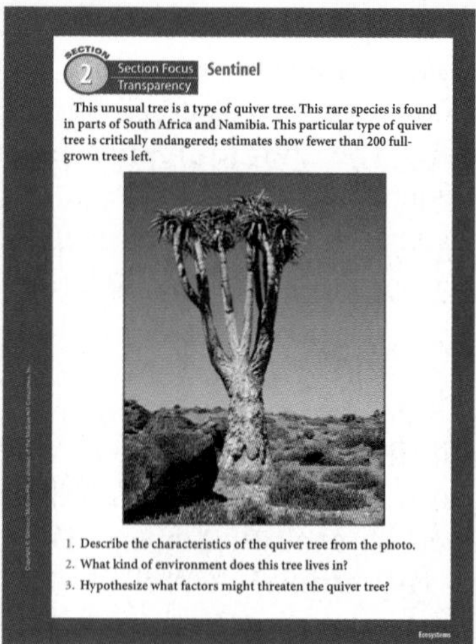

Tie to Prior Knowledge

Choose a biome that students are likely to have some knowledge about, such as a desert or a tropical rain forest. Have students make a list of organisms that live in that biome and the biome in which they live. Then have students hypothesize why different plants and animals live in these different biomes.

SECTION 2

Biomes

As You Read

***What* You'll Learn**

- **Explain** how climate influences land environments.
- **Identify** seven biomes of Earth.
- **Describe** the adaptations of organisms found in each biome.

Vocabulary

biome · temperate deciduous forest · tundra · temperate rain forest · taiga · tropical rain forest · desert · grassland

***Why* It's Important**

Resources that you need to survive are found in a variety of biomes.

Factors That Affect Biomes

Does a desert in Arizona have anything in common with a desert in Africa? Both have heat, little rain, poor soil, water-conserving plants with thorns, and lizards. Even widely separated regions of the world can have similar biomes because they have similar climates. Climate is the average weather pattern in an area over a long period of time. The two most important climatic factors that affect life in an area are temperature and precipitation.

Major Biomes

Large geographic areas that have similar climates and ecosystems are called **biomes** (BI ohmz). Seven common types of biomes are mapped in **Figure 5.** Areas with similar climates produce similar climax communities. Tropical rain forests are climax communities found near the equator, where temperatures are warm and rainfall is plentiful. Coniferous forests grow where winter temperatures are cold and rainfall is moderate.

Figure 5
The land portion of Earth can be divided into seven biomes.

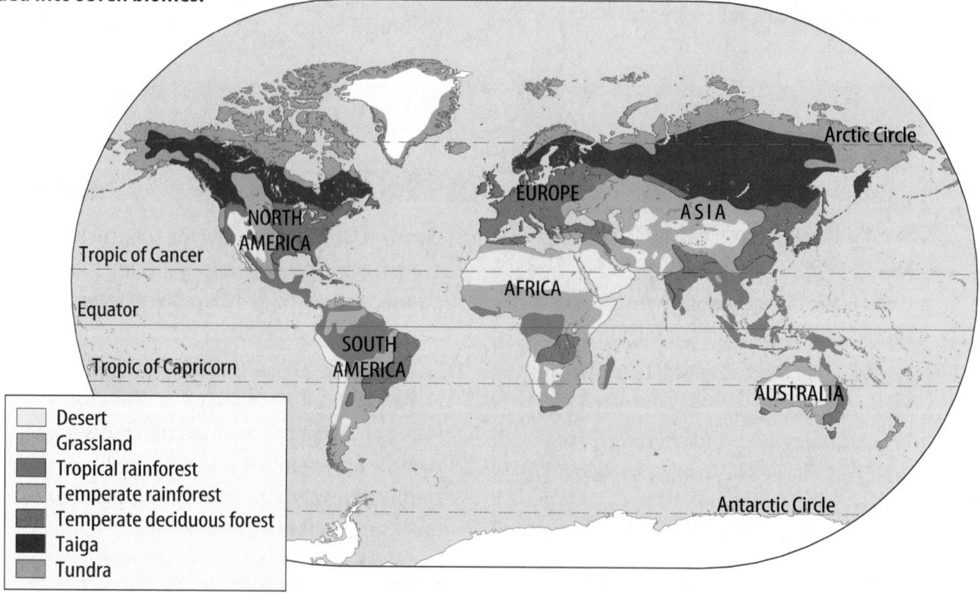

Section Assessment Planner

PORTFOLIO
Assessment, p. 759

PERFORMANCE ASSESSMENT
Try at Home MiniLAB, p. 756
Skill Builder Activities, p. 759
See page 774 for more options.

CONTENT ASSESSMENT
Section, p. 759
Challenge, p. 759
Chapter, pp. 774–775

752 CHAPTER 26 Ecosystems

Tundra At latitudes just south of the north pole lies a biome that receives little precipitation but is covered with ice most of the year. The **tundra** is a cold, dry, treeless region, sometimes called a cold desert. Precipitation averages less than 25 cm per year. Winters can be six to nine months long. For some of these months, when the Sun never appears above the horizon, the land is dark 24 hours a day. The average temperature of the tundra is about –12°C. For a few days during the short, cold summer, the Sun is always visible. Only the top portion of soil thaws in the summer. Below the thawed surface is a layer of permanently frozen soil called permafrost, shown in **Figure 6.** Tundra soil has few nutrients because the cold temperatures slow the process of decomposition.

Figure 6
This permafrost in Alaska is covered by soil that freezes in the winter and thaws in the summer. *What types of problems might this cause for people living in this area?*

Tundra Life Tundra plants are adapted to drought and cold. They include mosses, grasses, and small shrubs, as seen in **Figure 7.** Many lichens grow on the tundra. During the summer, mosquitoes, blackflies, and other biting insects fill the air. Migratory birds such as ducks, geese, shorebirds, and songbirds nest on the tundra during the summer. Other inhabitants include hawks, snowy owls, and willow grouse. Mice, voles, lemmings, arctic hares, caribou, reindeer, and musk oxen also are found there.

People are concerned about overgrazing by animals on the tundra. Fences, roads, and pipelines have disrupted the migratory routes of some animals and forced them to stay in a limited area. Because the growing season is so short, plants and other vegetation can take decades to recover from damage.

A

B

Figure 7
A Lichens, mosses, grasses, and small shrubs thrive on the tundra. B Ptarmigan live on the tundra. In winter, their feathers turn white. Extra feathers on their feet keep them warm and prevent them from sinking into the snow.

2 Teach

Factors That Affect Biomes

Quick Demo

Use a globe and flashlight to show why some winter days in the tundra have 24 hours of darkness and some summer days have 24 hours of light.

Major Biomes

Caption Answer

Figure 6 Permafrost makes it impossible to farm the land.

Discussion

Would you prefer to live in a house with ten acres of land in the tundra or in a small apartment in New York City? Have students defend their responses.

Teacher FYI

Limited light and heat, and a short growing season are factors that limit producer growth in the tundra. Lichen species here grow extremely slowly—only 1/6 cm per year. It can take 40 years for lichens to recover from damage caused by a passing herd of caribou.

Fun Fact

The nose botfly has unique adaptations for surviving the cold winter. It lays its eggs in the nose of a caribou. The maggots emerge and travel to the caribou's throat where they are kept warm. In the spring, caribou cough the maggots up. The maggots pupate and then become flies.

Resource Manager

Chapter Resources Booklet
Transparency Activity, p. 43
Enrichment, p. 29
Reading and Writing Skill Activities, p. 1

Cultural Diversity

Inuit Life Have students research the Inuit who live in the Arctic tundra and report on how they have adapted to the harsh climate. L2 LS **Linguistic**

Major Biomes, continued

Use Science Words

Word Origin "Taiga" comes from the Russian word *taiga*, which means "swampy forest." Ask students why this is a good description of the taiga biome. The taiga is a cold forest region that is warmer and wetter than the tundra.

IDENTIFYING Misconceptions

Students may think that the location of a particular biome on Earth is permanent. They may not realize that changes in climate have affected the locations of biomes and probably will continue to do so in the future.

Quick Demo

Cut strips of paper of appropriate length to represent the amount of precipitation in centimeters for each biome. Tape these to the board as you discuss the biomes. Start with a strip of paper that represents the amount of rainfall in your area.

Figure 8
A The taiga is dominated by cone-bearing evergreen trees.
B The lynx has broad, heavily furred feet that act like snowshoes to prevent it from sinking in the snow.

Taiga South of the tundra—between latitudes 50°N and 60°N and stretching across Canada, northern Europe, and Asia—is the world's largest biome. The **taiga** (TI guh), shown in **Figure 8,** is a cold, forest region dominated by cone-bearing evergreen trees. Although the winter is long and cold, the taiga is warmer and wetter than the tundra. Precipitation is mostly snow and averages 35 cm to 100 cm each year.

Most soils of the taiga thaw completely during the summer, making it possible for trees to grow. However, permafrost is present in the extreme northern regions of the taiga. The forests of the taiga might be so dense that little sunlight penetrates the trees to reach the forest floor. However, some lichens and mosses do grow on the forest floor. Moose, lynx, shrews, bears, and foxes are some of the animals that live in the taiga.

Temperate Deciduous Forest Temperate regions usually have four distinct seasons each year. Annual precipitation ranges from about 75 cm to 150 cm and is distributed throughout the year. Temperatures range from below freezing during the winter to 30°C or more during the warmest days of summer.

Figure 9
A The leaves on trees in deciduous forests change color in autumn.
B White-tailed deer are found in deciduous forests. They feed on a variety of plants and nuts.

Science Journal

Metric Measurements Students should become familiar with metric measurements, such as those used in this section for temperature. Have them convert the following Celsius temperatures to Fahrenheit:

10°C (50°F); 0°C (32°F); 20°C (68°F); 30°C (86°F)

Inclusion Strategies

Learning Disabled A concept map of "The Forests of the World" may help students visualize the relationship between taiga, temperate deciduous forest, temperate rain forest, and tropical rain forest. L1 LS **Visual-Spatial**

Temperate Forest Life Many evergreen trees grow in the temperate regions of the world. However, most of the temperate forests in Europe and North America are dominated by climax communities of deciduous trees, which lose their leaves every autumn. These forests, like the one in **Figure 9,** are called **temperate deciduous forests.** In the United States, most of them are located east of the Mississippi River.

When European settlers first came to America, they cut trees to create farmland and to supply wood. As forests were cut, organisms lost their habitats. When agriculture shifted from the eastern to the midwestern and western states, secondary succession began, and trees eventually returned to some areas. Now, nearly as many trees grow in the New England states as did before the American Revolutionary War. Many trees are located in smaller patches. Yet, the recovery of large forests such as those in the Adirondack Mountains in New York State shows that succession is possible.

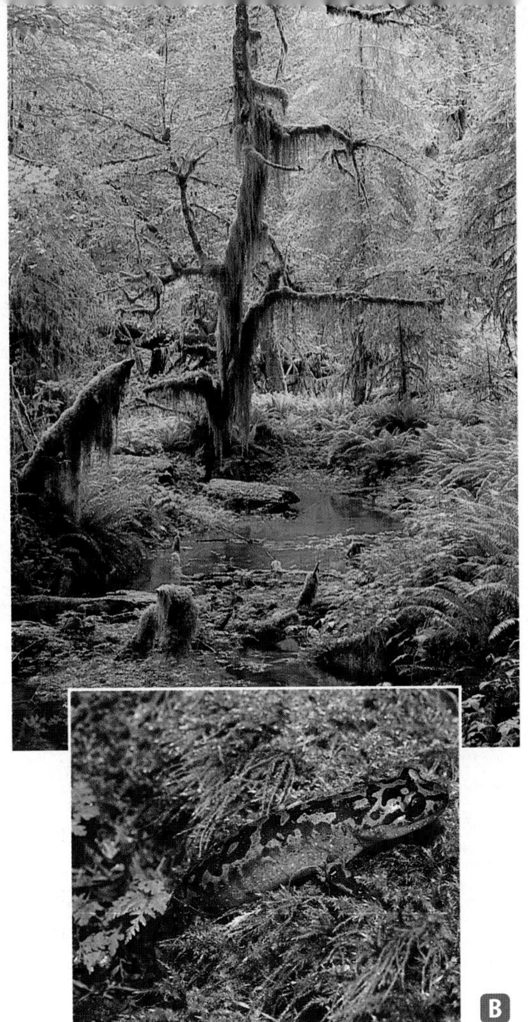

Figure 10
A In the Olympic rain forest in Washington State, mosses and lichens blanket the ground and hang from the trees. B Wet areas are perfect habitats for amphibians like this Pacific giant salamander.

Temperate Rain Forest New Zealand, southern Chile, and the Pacific Northwest of the United States are some of the places where **temperate rain forests,** shown in **Figure 10,** are found. The average temperature of a temperate rain forest ranges from 9°C to 12°C. Precipitation ranges from 200 cm to 400 cm per year.

Trees with needlelike leaves dominate these forests, including the Douglas fir, western red cedar, and spruce. Many grow to great heights. Animals of the temperate rain forest include the black bear, cougar, bobcat, endangered northern spotted owl, and threatened marbled murrelet. Many species of amphibians also inhabit the temperate rain forest, including salamanders.

The logging industry in the Northwest provides jobs for many people. However, it also removes large parts of the temperate rain forest and destroys the habitat of many organisms. Many logging companies now are required to replant trees to replace the ones they cut down. Also, some rain forest areas are protected as national parks and forests.

Make a Model

Have students:
(a) use long wooden dowels representing trees to show how the land in the Northeastern United States looked before European settlers,
(b) remove the dowels and put up short dowel fences and black paper roads to represent how the land looked when it was made into farms,
(c) return many of the long dowels but keep the fences and roads to show the return of trees. Make the point that although trees are present, many animals are restricted in their movement.

Teacher FYI

The spotted owl is an endangered species that lives in old-growth temperate rain forests. These forests are over 100 years old. Clear-cutting the forest and planting new trees destroys the necessary habitat of these birds.

Resource Manager

Chapter Resources Booklet
Directed Reading for Content Mastery, p. 19

Earth Science Critical Thinking/Problem Solving, p. 6

Inclusion Strategies

Gifted Six common land biomes are presented in this chapter. Students may be assigned other biomes to research, such as tidal wetlands, extreme deserts, bogs, chapparal, continental slope, temperate oceans, tropic savannahs, or coastal arctic tundra. Have them present their findings to the class as posters or other visuals.
L3 LS **Visual-Spatial**

Major Biomes, continued

Purpose Students observe rain forest leaves, analyze their structures, and relate leaf structure to leaf function. L2
LS **Kinesthetic**

Materials poster board, pencil, scissors, sink, water, spray bottle

Teaching Strategy Show students philodendron or ficus leaves so they can see real drip tips.

Analysis

1. the leaf with the drip tip
2. Removing water from the leaf's surface prohibits growth of mosses, fungi, or other moisture-loving organisms.

Assessment

Process Ask students how they could perform a similar experiment but obtain quantitative results. Answers should involve the measurement of the amount of water falling off the leaves using a graduated cylinder. Use **PASC**, p. 105.

Reading Check

Answer forest floor, understory, canopy, emergents

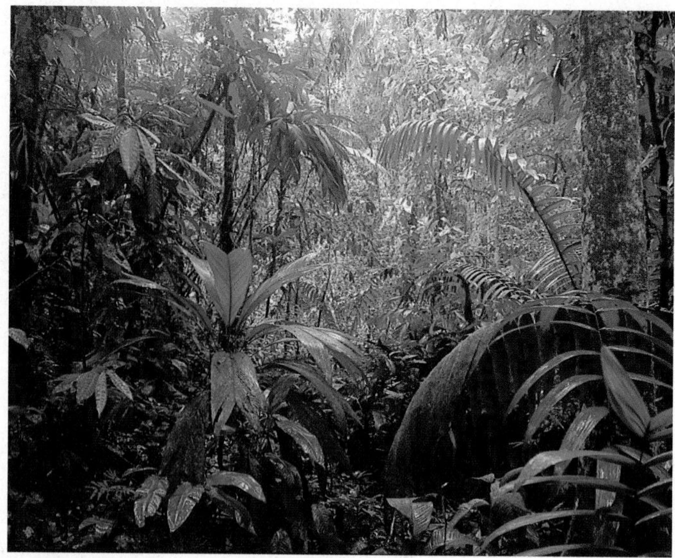

Figure 11
Tropical rain forests are lush environments that contain such a large variety of species that many have not been discovered.

TRY AT HOME Mini LAB

Modeling Rain Forest Leaves

Procedure

1. Draw an oval leaf about 10 cm long on a piece of **poster board.** Cut it out.
2. Draw a second leaf the same size but make the end pointed. This is called a drip tip. Cut this leaf out.
3. Lay a leaf on each of your hands over a **sink.** Point the drip tip away from you. Tilt your hands down but do not allow the leaves to fall off.
4. Have someone gently spray **water** on the leaves and observe what happens.

Analysis

1. From which leaf does water drain faster?
2. Infer why it is an advantage for a leaf to get rid of water quickly in a rain forest.

Tropical Rain Forest Warm temperatures, wet weather, and lush plant growth are found in **tropical rain forests.** These forests are warm because they are near the equator. The average temperature, about 25°C, doesn't vary much between night and day. Most tropical rain forests receive at least 200 cm of rain annually. Some receive as much as 600 cm of rain each year.

Tropical rain forests, like the one in **Figure 11,** are home to an astonishing variety of organisms. They are the most biologically diverse places in the world. For example, one tree in a South American rain forest might contain more species of ants than exist in all of the British Isles.

Tropical Rain Forest Life Different animals and plants live in different parts of the rain forest. Scientists divide the rain forest into zones based on the types of plants and animals that live there, just as a library separates books about different topics onto separate shelves. The zones are as follows: forest floor, understory, canopy, and emergents, as shown in **Figure 12.** These zones often blend together, but their existence allows many organisms to live in the tropical rain forest.

Reading Check *What are the four zones of a tropical rain forest?*

Although tropical rain forests support a huge variety of organisms, the soil of the rain forest contains few nutrients. The soil is poor because of the high number of organisms that live in the soil and because of erosion by water. Any dead leaves or vegetation are consumed quickly.

LAB DEMONSTRATION

Purpose to show the stabilizing effect of buttress roots on rain forest trees

Materials paper towel tubes, scissors, tape, trough with thin layer of sand

Preparation Cut out four buttresses (which resemble rocket fins) from two paper towel tubes, and tape them to one tube.

Procedure Nutrients are near the surface in rain forest soils, so tree roots don't go very deep. When trees grow to reach light, stability problems often occur. Put two paper towel tubes (one with buttresses, one without) 1 cm into the sand. Blow on the tubes to see which falls first.

Expected Outcome The tube without buttresses will fall first.

Assessment

Why do buttresses make trees more stable? They give the trees a wider base. **Why would a rain forest tree be more likely to have buttresses than a temperate forest tree?** Rain forest tree roots do not penetrate the soil as deeply.

Human Impact Farmers that live in tropical areas clear the land to farm and to sell the valuable wood. After a few years, the crops use up the nutrients in the soil, and the farmers must clear more land. As a result, tropical rain forest habitats are being destroyed. Through education, people are realizing the value and potential value of preserving the species of the rain forest. In some areas, logging is prohibited. In other areas, farmers are taught new methods of farming so they do not have to clear rain forest lands continually.

Is where you live like a tropical rain forest or some other biome? To find out more about biomes, see the Biome Field Guide at the back of the book.

Figure 12
Emergents These giant trees are much higher than the average canopy tree. Birds such as the macaw and insects are found here.

Canopy The canopy includes the upper parts of the trees. It's full of life—insects, birds, reptiles, and mammals.

Understory This dark, cool environment is under the canopy leaves but above the ground. Many insects, reptiles, and amphibians live in the understory.

Forest Floor The forest floor is full of life. Many insects and the largest mammals in the rain forest generally live here.

757

Use an Analogy

The layers of a rain forest are comparable to the shelves of a library. Just as the shelves provide more space for books, the layers of the rain forest provide more niches for supporting life. This is one of the reasons rain forests are biologically diverse.

Activity

Have students make charts of the main features of the three major zones of the tropical rain forest: the canopy, understory, and forest floor. L2 IS **Naturalist**

Extension

Certain human diseases, such as malaria and yellow fever, are common among human populations living in tropical areas. Have students research tropical diseases and identify misconceptions of the cause of each disease. L3

Resource Manager

Chapter Resources Booklet
MiniLAB, p. 3

Science Inquiry Labs, p. 7

Life Science Critical Thinking/Problem Solving, p. 5

Visual Learning

Figure 12 Ask students to explain how conditions above the canopy differ from conditions below the canopy. much more sunlight and wind above the canopy, darker and more humid below the canopy

Major Biomes, continued

Earth Science INTEGRATION

Areas with heavy agriculture in the Southwest are the most likely to be affected by desertification in the United States. Changes in climate and human activities also contribute to desertification, which is the loss of productivity of land in arid or semi-arid areas.

Reading Check

Answer because of lack of water

IDENTIFYING Misconceptions

A common idea about deserts is that they are hot, dry places. While this is true of the majority of deserts, there are some cold deserts such as Patagonia in Argentina. Cold deserts are usually caused by their remoteness from the coast, or by mountains that block moist coastal winds. The largest cold desert is in central Asia.

Fun Fact

At one time, the grassland biome covered nearly half of the land on Earth. Today, most of the grassland is used by humans for growing crops, raising animals, and housing.

Earth Science INTEGRATION

When vegetation is removed from soil in areas that receive little rain, the dry, unprotected surface can be blown away. If the soil remains bare, a desert might form. This process is called desertification. Look on a biome map and hypothesize about which areas of the United States are most likely to become deserts.

Desert The driest biome on Earth is the **desert.** Deserts receive less than 25 cm of rain each year and support little plant life. Some desert areas receive no rain for years. When rain does come, it quickly drains away. Any water that remains on the ground evaporates rapidly.

Most deserts, like the one in **Figure 13,** are covered with a thin, sandy, or gravelly soil that contains little organic matter. Due to the lack of water, desert plants are spaced far apart and much of the ground is bare. Barren, windblown sand dunes are characteristics of the driest deserts.

Reading Check *Why is much of a desert bare ground?*

Desert Life Desert plants are adapted for survival in the extreme dryness and hot and cold temperatures of this biome. Cactus plants are probably the most familiar desert plants of the western hemisphere. Desert animals also have adaptations that help them survive the extreme conditions. Some, like the kangaroo rat, never need to drink water. They get all the moisture they need from the breakdown of food during digestion. Most animals are active only during the night, late afternoon, or early morning when temperatures are less extreme. Few large animals are found in the desert.

In order to provide water for desert cities, rivers and streams have been diverted. When this happens, wildlife tends to move closer to cities in their search for food and water. Education about desert environments has led to an awareness of the impact of human activities. As a result, large areas of desert have been set aside as national parks and wilderness areas to protect desert habitats.

Figure 13
A Desert plants, like these in the Sonoran Desert, are adapted for survival in the extreme conditions of the desert biome. **B** The giant hairy scorpion found in some deserts has a venomous sting.

Cultural Diversity

Biomes and Dress Discuss how the dress of people in different areas is influenced by the biome in which they live. For example, Arabic people may wear long robes to shield themselves from the desert heat. Inuits may dress in animal skins to insulate themselves from the cold. Encourage interested students to present a show of "Biome Fashions Around the World." COOP LEARN

Resource Manager

Chapter Resources Booklet
Reinforcement, p. 26
Activity Worksheet, pp. 5–6

Grasslands Temperate and tropical regions that receive between 25 cm and 75 cm of precipitation each year and are dominated by climax communities of grasses are called **grasslands.** Most grasslands have a dry season, when little or no rain falls. This lack of moisture prevents the development of forests. Grasslands are found in many places around the world, and they have a variety of names. The prairies and plains of North America, the steppes of Asia, the savannas of Africa shown in **Figure 14,** and the pampas of South America are types of grasslands.

Figure 14
Animals such as zebras and wildebeests feed on the grasses of the savannas in Africa.

Grasslands Life The most noticeable animals in grassland biomes are usually mammals that graze on the stems, leaves, and seeds of grass plants. Kangaroos graze in the grasslands of Australia. In Africa, communities of animals such as wildebeests, impalas, and zebras thrive in the savannas.

Grasslands are perfect for growing many crops such as wheat, rye, oats, barley, and corn. Grasslands also are used to raise cattle and sheep. However, overgrazing can result in the death of grasses and the loss of valuable topsoil from erosion. Most farmers and ranchers take precautions to prevent the loss of valuable habitats and soil.

Section  Assessment

1. Which two biomes are the driest?
2. Compare and contrast tundra organisms and desert organisms.
3. What is the biggest climatic difference between a temperate rain forest and a tropical rain forest?
4. Why does the soil of tropical rain forests make poor farmland?
5. **Think Critically** If you climb a mountain in Arizona, you might reach an area where the trees resemble the taiga trees in northern Canada. Why would a taiga forest exist in Arizona?

Skill Builder Activities

6. **Recording Observations** Animals have adaptations that help them survive in their environments. Make a list of animals that live in your area, and record the physical or behavioral adaptations that help them survive. **For more help, refer to the** **Science Skill Handbook.**
7. **Using a Database** Create a database of information about Earth's biomes. Include data about *temperature range, annual precipitation, limiting factors,* and *descriptions of climax communities.* **For more help, refer to the** **Technology Skill Handbook.**

3 Assess

Reteach

Make a table showing precipitation, temperature, common plants, and common animals for each biome. Have students identify the name of each biome described. L2 ELL IS **Naturalist**

Challenge

Have students draw a four-organism food chain for any five of the six biomes presented in this section. L3 IS **Logical-Mathematical**

Assessment

Portfolio Have each student write a story with one of the biomes in this section as the setting. The plot should revolve around an organism that lives in the biome they chose and its interactions with other organisms and the environment. Students can take turns reading their stories to the class. Use **Performance Assessment in the Science Classroom,** p. 155. P

Answers to Section Assessment

1. desert and tundra
2. Tundra organisms are adapted to survive cold and drought. Desert organisms are adapted to survive extreme dryness and hot and cold temperatures.
3. Tropical rain forests are warmer (have a higher average temperature) than temperate rain forests, and tend to have more precipitation.
4. The majority of available nutrients in the rainforest are in the biomass of the plants and trees, not in the soil. When trees are cut down, nutrients go with them leaving behind very nutrient-poor soil that is easily eroded in the next big rain.
5. Temperatures cool with increased elevation, so places with higher altitude in warm areas can resemble the taiga.
6. Answers will vary but should include adaptations to survive conditions including cold or heat, humidity or dryness, and land or aquatic environments.
7. Databases should include information on the taiga, tundra, desert, temperate deciduous forest, temperate rain forest, tropical rain forest and grassland biomes.

Activity

BENCH TESTED

Purpose Students conduct a study of an ecosystem and determine how the living things interact with each other and the environment. L2 LS **Intrapersonal**

Process Skills observing, classifying, communicating, defining operationally, recognizing cause and effect, predicting

Time Required 50 minutes for setup, four weeks to make observations

Teaching Strategies

- Arrange for students to check out binoculars, field guides, and other useful materials from the science classroom and library.
- Approve the ecosystems chosen by the students before they begin their observations.
- Offer students a set time each day to discuss any problems they may have concerning their method of study.

Answers to Questions

1. Populations would be affected by changes in temperature, water, or other abiotic factors. The entire ecosystem could be disrupted.
2. Other populations could be affected.
3. Possible hypotheses: competition for available resources could make one population extinct or forced away; students may hypothesize about results from favorable or unfavorable interactions among the populations in response to the introduction of a new population.

Activity

Studying a Land Ecosystem

An ecological study includes observation and analysis of organisms and the physical features of the environment.

What You'll Investigate

How do you study an ecosystem?

Materials

- graph paper
- thermometer
- hand lens
- notebook
- binoculars
- pencil
- field guides
- compass

Goals

- **Observe** biotic factors and abiotic factors of an ecosystem.
- **Analyze** the relationships among organisms and their environment.

Safety Precautions

Procedure

1. Choose a portion of an ecosystem near your school or home to study. You might choose a decaying log, a pond, a forest area in a park, a garden, or even a crack in the sidewalk.
2. Determine the boundaries of your study area.
3. Using a tape measure and graph paper, make a map of your area. Determine north.
4. **Record** your observations in a table similar to the one shown on this page.
5. **Observe** the organisms in your study area. Use field guides to identify them. Use a hand lens to study small organisms and binoculars to study animals you can't get near. Look for evidence (such as tracks or feathers) of organisms you do not see.

Environmental Observations		
Date		
Time of Day		
Temperature	Answers	will vary.
Organisms Observed		
Comments		

6. Use a thermometer to measure the air temperature in your study area. Record this information in the table.
7. Visit your study area as many times as you can and at different times of the day for one week. At each visit, make the same measurements and record all observations. Note how the living and nonliving parts of the ecosystem interact.

Conclude and Apply

1. **Predict** what might happen if one or more abiotic factors were changed suddenly.
2. What might happen if one or more populations of plants or animals were removed from the area?
3. Form a hypothesis about the effect that a new population of organisms might have on your ecosystem.

Communicating Your Data

Make a poster of your data. Then compare your data with those of other students in your class. **For more help, refer to the Science Skill Handbook.**

Assessment

Performance Have students alter the ecosystem in a way that is not harmful. Have them observe how foreign materials affect the behavior of living things in the ecosystem. Use **PASC,** p. 97.

You may choose to display the best student posters along one wall. Allow volunteers to present their poster and data to the class in a short presentation.

760 CHAPTER 26 Ecosystems

SECTION

3 Aquatic Ecosystems

Freshwater Ecosystems

In a land environment, temperature and precipitation are the most important factors that determine which species can survive. In aquatic environments, water temperature, the amount of sunlight present, and the amounts of dissolved oxygen and salt in the water are important. Earth's freshwater ecosystems include flowing water such as rivers and streams and standing water such as lakes, ponds, and wetlands.

Rivers and Streams Flowing freshwater environments vary from small, gurgling brooks to large, slow-moving rivers. Currents can quickly wash loose particles downstream, leaving a rocky or gravelly bottom. As the water tumbles and splashes, as shown in **Figure 15,** air from the atmosphere mixes in. Naturally fast-flowing streams usually have clearer water and higher oxygen content than slow-flowing streams.

Most nutrients that support life in flowing-water ecosystems are washed into the water from land. In areas where the water movement slows, such as in the pools of streams or in large rivers, debris settles to the bottom. These environments tend to have higher nutrient levels and more plant growth. They contain organisms that are not as well adapted to swiftly flowing water, such as freshwater mussels, minnows, and leeches.

As You Read

What **You'll Learn**

- **Compare** flowing freshwater and standing freshwater ecosystems.
- **Identify** and describe important saltwater ecosystems.
- **Identify** problems that affect aquatic ecosystems.

Vocabulary

wetland, coral reef, intertidal zone, estuary

Why **It's Important**

All of the life processes in your body depend on water.

Figure 15
Streams like this one are high in oxygen because of the swift, tumbling water. *Where do most nutrients in streams come from?*

Section Assessment Planner

PORTFOLIO
Science Journal, p. 764

PERFORMANCE ASSESSMENT
MiniLAB, p. 762
Math Skills Activity, p. 764
Skill Builder Activities, p. 767
See page 774 for more options.

CONTENT ASSESSMENT
Section, p. 767
Challenge, p. 767
Chapter, pp. 774–775

SECTION

Aquatic Ecosystems

1 Motivate

Bellringer Transparency

Display the Section Focus Transparency for Section 3. Use the accompanying Transparency Activity Master. L2

ELL

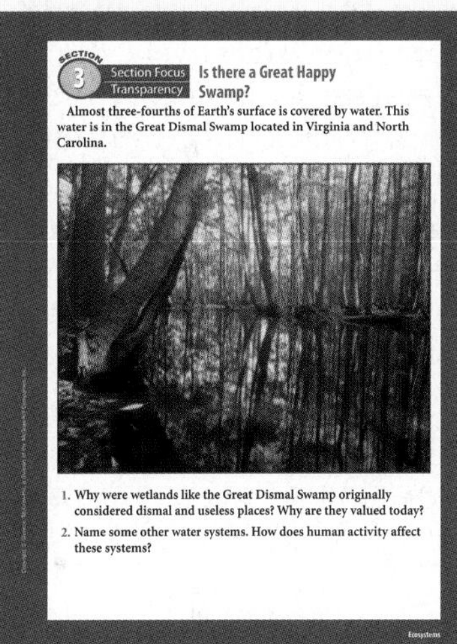

Section Focus Transparency Is there a Great Happy Swamp?

Almost three-fourths of Earth's surface is covered by water. This water is in the Great Dismal Swamp located in Virginia and North Carolina.

1. Why were wetlands like the Great Dismal Swamp originally considered dismal and useless places? Why are they valued today?
2. Name some other water systems. How does human activity affect these systems?

Tie to Prior Knowledge

Most students have some experience with water environments. Have them explain what body of water they observed and which organisms live there.

Caption Answer

Figure 15 They are washed into the stream from the land.

Resource Manager

Chapter Resources Booklet
Transparency Activity, p. 44

Mathematics Skill Activities, p. 9

2 Teach

Freshwater Ecosystems

Mini LAB

Purpose Students observe a freshwater ecosystem. L2

LS **Naturalist**

Materials clear plastic container, material from the bottom of a pond, pond organisms, net, pond water, hand lens

Teaching Strategy Make sure students don't disturb the container excessively while observing, as sediment stirred up will make observations difficult.

Safety Precaution Make sure to get permission from the land owner or appropriate authorities before collecting samples from the pond.

Analysis

Students' paragraphs will vary depending on organisms obtained.

Assessment

Oral Have students use their observations from the MiniLAB to identify adaptations of the organisms. Use **PASC**, p. 89.

Mini LAB

Modeling Freshwater Environments

Procedure

1. Obtain a sample of **pond sediment or debris, plants, water, and organisms** from your teacher.
2. Cover the bottom of a **clear, plastic container** with about 2 cm of the debris.
3. Add one or two plants to the container.
4. Carefully pour pond water into the container until it is about two-thirds full.
5. Use a **net** to add several organisms to the water. Seal the container.
6. Using a **hand lens,** observe as many organisms as possible. Record your observations. Return your sample to its original habitat.

Analysis

Write a short paragraph describing the organisms in your sample. How did the organisms interact with each other?

Human Impact People use rivers and streams for many activities. Once regarded as a free place to dump sewage and other pollutants, many people now recognize the damage this causes. Treating sewage and restricting pollutants have led to an improvement in the water quality in some rivers.

Lakes and Ponds When a low place in the land fills with rainwater, snowmelt, or water from an overflowing stream, a lake or pond might form. Pond or lake water hardly moves. It contains more plant growth than flowing-water environments contain.

Lakes, such as the one in **Figure 16A,** are larger and deeper than ponds. They have more open water because most plant growth is limited to shallow areas along the shoreline. In fact, organisms found in the warm, sunlit waters of the shorelines often are similar to those found in ponds. If you were to dive to the bottom, you would discover few, if any, plants or algae growing. Colder temperatures and lower light levels limit the types of organisms that can live in deep lake waters. Floating in the warm, sunlit waters near the surface of freshwater lakes and ponds are microscopic algae, plants, and other organisms known as plankton.

A pond, shown in **Figure 16B,** is a small, shallow body of water. Because ponds are shallow, they are filled with animal and plant life. Sunlight usually penetrates to the bottom. The warm, sunlit water promotes the growth of plants and algae. In fact, many ponds are filled almost completely with plant material, so the only clear, open water is at the center. Because of the lush growth in pond environments, they tend to be high in nutrients.

Figure 16
A The population of organisms in the shallow water of lakes is high. Fewer types of organisms live in the deeper water.
B Ponds contain more vegetation than lakes contain.

Inclusion Strategies

Physically Challenged If students have difficulty with manual dexterity in the MiniLAB, mount the magnifying glass on a ring stand. Have them look through the magnifying glass and slowly move the plastic container.

Resource Manager

Chapter Resources Booklet
Enrichment, p. 30
MiniLAB, p. 4
Home and Community Involvement, p. 45

Figure 17
Life in the Florida Everglades was threatened due to pollution, drought, and draining of the water. Conservation efforts are being made in an attempt to preserve this ecosystem.

Water Pollution Human activities can harm freshwater environments. Fertilizer-filled runoff from farms and lawns, as well as sewage dumped into the water, can lead to excessive growth of algae and plants in lakes and ponds. The growth and decay of these organisms reduces the oxygen level in the water, which makes it difficult for some organisms to survive. To prevent problems, sewage is treated before it is released. People also are being educated about problems associated with polluting lakes and ponds. Fines and penalties are issued to people caught polluting waterways. These controls have led to the recovery of many freshwater ecosystems.

Wetlands As the name suggests, **wetlands,** shown in **Figure 17,** are regions that are wet for all or most of a year. They are found in regions that lie between land masses and water. Other names for wetlands include swamps, bogs, and fens. Some people refer to wetlands as biological supermarkets. They are fertile ecosystems, but only plants that are adapted to waterlogged soil survive there. Wetland animals include beavers, muskrats, alligators, and the endangered bog turtle. Many migratory bird populations use wetlands as breeding grounds.

Reading Check ***Where are wetlands found?***

Wetlands once were considered to be useless, disease-ridden places. Many were drained and destroyed to make roads, farmland, shopping centers, and housing developments. Only recently have people begun to understand the importance of wetlands. Products that come from wetlands, including fish, shellfish, cranberries, and plants, are valuable resources. Now many developers are restoring wetlands, and in most states access to land through wetlands is prohibited.

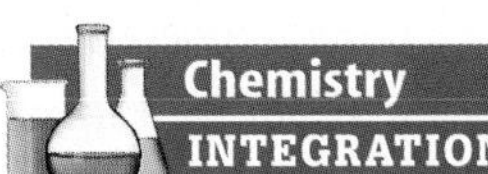

Chemistry INTEGRATION

Osmosis is the movement of water molecules through a membrane from an area where there are more of them compared to other molecules present to an area where there are fewer of them compared to other molecules present. The blood of a freshwater fish is saltier than the lake water is. Explain in your Science Journal whether fish in a lake tend to absorb water or lose water through osmosis.

IDENTIFYING Misconceptions

Freshwater is not water without salts; it is water that has fewer salts than ocean or estuary water. Distilled water has no salts or other impurities. Obtain a liter of freshwater and put it into a glass beaker. Allow it to evaporate so students can see the ample amount of salts and other materials left behind.

Chemistry INTEGRATION

Because the fish has saltier blood than the surrounding water, water tends to move into the fish by osmosis. Freshwater fish are covered with scales and a mucous secretion that slows the movement of water into their tissues. The kidneys of these fish are adapted to filter out excess water, and they excrete large amounts of dilute urine.

Teacher FYI

Slow-moving rivers and standing lakes and ponds are easily polluted. There is less dissolved oxygen in the water, which is needed by organisms that break down the pollutants, and no currents wash pollutants away.

Reading Check

Answer in regions that lie between solid land and water

Curriculum Connection

History Have students research the Seminole people of Florida and how they survived attacks by the United States Army by hiding in the Everglades. L2

Inclusion Strategies

Visually Impaired Have a small shallow container represent a pond and a larger container represent a lake. Form a "V" with a plastic sheet. Incline the V at a steep angle, and pour water down it to represent a stream. Hold the V at a slighter angle, and pour a greater volume of water down it. This represents a river. Have students put their hands into the four conditions to feel the differences.

Saltwater Ecosystems

Quick Demo

Float identical corks in freshwater and salt water. Students should observe that the cork in salt water floats higher than the one in freshwater. Explain that this occurs because salt water is denser than freshwater.

Make a Model

Ask students to use clay, colored water, or other materials to show the mixing of freshwater and salt water when a river and ocean combine to form an estuary.

Activity

From a science supply company, purchase kits that measure the dissolved oxygen in water. Compare different bodies of water such as lakes, streams, and oceans. L3 IN **Naturalist**

Math Skills Activity

National Math Standards

Correlation to Mathematics Objectives

1,2,4,6,9

Answers to Practice Problems

1. $(78°F - 32) / 1.8 = 25.6°C$
2. $(12°C \times 1.8) + 32 = 53.6°F$
   $(23°C \times 1.8) + 32 = 73.4°F$
   $73.4°F - 53.6°F = 19.8°F$

Saltwater Ecosystems

About 95 percent of the water on the surface of Earth contains high concentrations of various salts. The amount of dissolved salts in water is called salinity. Saltwater ecosystems include oceans, seas, a few inland lakes such as the Great Salt Lake in Utah, coastal inlets, and estuaries.

Math Skills Activity

Calculating Temperatures

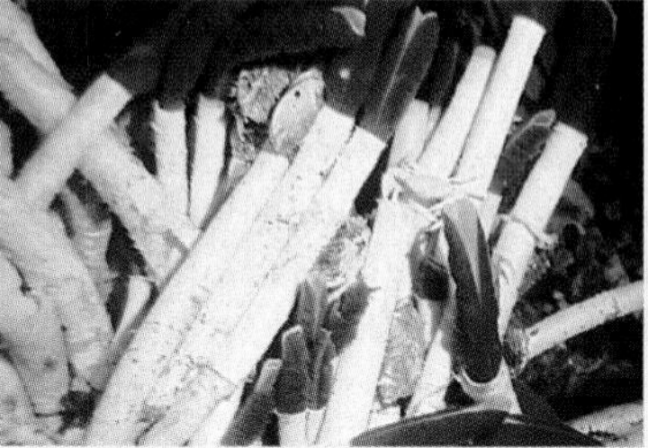

Organisms that live around hydrothermal vents in the ocean deal with temperatures that range from 1.7°C to 371°C. You have probably seen temperatures measured in degrees Celsius (°C) and degrees Fahrenheit (°F). Which one are you familiar with? If you know the temperature in one system, you can convert it to the other.

Example Problem

You have a Fahrenheit thermometer and measure the water temperature of a pond at 59°F. What is that temperature in degrees Celsius?

Solution

1. *This is what you know:*
   water temperature in degrees Fahrenheit = 59°F
2. *This is what you want to find:*
   water temperature in degrees Celsius
3. *This is the equation you need to use:*
   $(°C \times 1.8) + 32 = °F$
4. *Solve the equation for degrees Celsius and then substitute the known value:*
   $°C = (°F - 32)/1.8$
   $°C = (59°F - 32)/1.8 = 15°C$

Check your answer by substituting the Celsius temperature back into the original equation. Do you calculate the Fahrenheit temperature that was given?

Practice Problems

1. The thermometer outside your classroom reads 78°F. What is the temperature in degrees Celsius?
2. If lake water was 12°C in October and 23°C in May, what is the difference in degrees Fahrenheit?

For more help, refer to the Math Skill Handbook.

Science Journal

Marine Biomes Have students compare estuaries and oceans. As part of this comparison, ask students to focus on living and nonliving factors associated with each ecosystem. Have them write a paragraph about each biome in their Science Journals. P

Resource Manager 

Chapter Resources Booklet

Directed Reading for Content Mastery, pp. 19, 20

Transparency Activity, pp. 45–46

Science Inquiry Labs, p. 37

Open Oceans Life abounds in the open ocean. Scientists divide the ocean into different life zones, based on the depth to which sunlight penetrates the water. The lighted zone of the ocean is the upper 200 m or so. It is the home of the plankton that make up the foundation of the food chain in the open ocean. Below about 200 m is the dark zone of the ocean. Animals living in this region feed on material that floats down from the lighted zone, or they feed on each other. A few organisms are able to produce their own food.

Coral Reefs One of the most diverse ecosystems in the world is the **coral reef.** Coral reefs are formed over long periods of time from the calcium carbonate shells secreted by animals called corals. When corals die, their shells remain. Over time, the shell deposits form reefs such as the Great Barrier Reef off the coast of Australia, shown in **Figure 18.**

Reefs do not adapt well to long-term stress. Runoff from fields, sewage, and increased sedimentation from cleared land harm reef ecosystems. Organizations like the Environmental Protection Agency have developed management plans to protect the diversity of coral reefs. These plans treat a coral reef as a system that includes all the areas that surround the reef. Keeping the areas around reefs healthy will result in a healthy environment for the coral reef ecosystem.

Research Visit the Glencoe Science Web site at **science.glencoe.com** for more information about coral reefs. Communicate to your class what you learn.

A

B

Figure 18
A The lighter areas around this island are part of the Great Barrier Reef. It comprises about 3,000 reefs and about 900 islands. B Reefs contain colorful fish and a large variety of other organisms.

SCIENCE Online

Internet Addresses

Explore the Glencoe Science Web site at **science.glencoe.com** to find out more about topics in this section.

Misconceptions

Students may think that sea anemones and the coral in coral reefs are plants rather than animals. Help them realize that they are animals that feed on small organisms in the water.

Quick Demo

Bring in a piece of coral such as those used in saltwater aquariums. Explain that this is the calcium carbonate skeleton left behind by the once-living coral.

Active Reading

Jigsaw In this collaborative learning technique, individuals become experts on a portion of a text and share their expertise with a small group, called their home group. Everyone shares responsibility for learning the assigned reading. Assign each person in each home group an expert number (1 through 5, for example). Have students gather into the expert groups that correspond to the number they were assigned. Have them read, discuss, and master chapter concepts, and determine how best to teach them to their home groups. Have students return to their home groups and share the content they learned in their expert groups. Have students use the Jigsaw strategy with the text on aquatic ecosystems.

Saltwater Ecosystems, continued

Fun Fact

The largest tides occur when the Earth, Sun, and Moon are in line. This is when the combined gravities of the Sun and Moon have their greatest effect on Earth's waters.

Visual Learning

Figure 19 Explain that sea stars have special adaptions that enable them to inhabit the intertidal zone. One of these adaptations is the presence of numerous small tube feet under each arm, which allow the sea star to resist being swept away by the tide.

Figure 19
As the tide recedes, small pools of seawater are left behind. These pools contain a variety of organisms such as sea stars and periwinkles.

Seashores All of Earth's landmasses are bordered by ocean water. The shallow waters along the world's coastlines contain a variety of saltwater ecosystems, all of which are influenced by the tides and by the action of waves. The gravitational pull of the Sun and Moon on Earth causes the tides to rise and fall each day. The height of the tides varies according to the phases of the Moon, the season, and the slope of the shoreline. The **intertidal zone** is the portion of the shoreline that is covered with water at high tide and exposed to the air during low tide. Organisms that live in the intertidal zone, such as those in **Figure 19,** must be adapted to dramatic changes in temperature, moisture, and salinity and must be able to withstand the force of wave action.

Estuaries Almost every river on Earth eventually flows into an ocean. The area where a river meets an ocean and contains a mixture of freshwater and salt water is called an **estuary** (ES chuh wer ee). Other names for estuaries include bays, lagoons, harbors, inlets, and sounds. They are located near coastlines and border the land. Salinity in estuaries changes with the amount of freshwater brought in by rivers and streams, and with the amount of salt water pushed inland by the ocean tides.

Estuaries, shown in **Figure 20,** are extremely fertile, productive environments because freshwater streams bring in tons of nutrients washed from inland soils. Therefore, nutrient levels in estuaries are higher than in freshwater ecosystems or other saltwater ecosystems.

Curriculum Connection

Geography Have students locate Australia on a globe and then identify the location of the Great Barrier Reef. L1 LS **Visual-Spatial**

Resource Manager 

Chapter Resources Booklet
Reinforcement, p. 27

Cultural Diversity, p. 7

Earth Science Critical Thinking/Problem Solving, p. 1

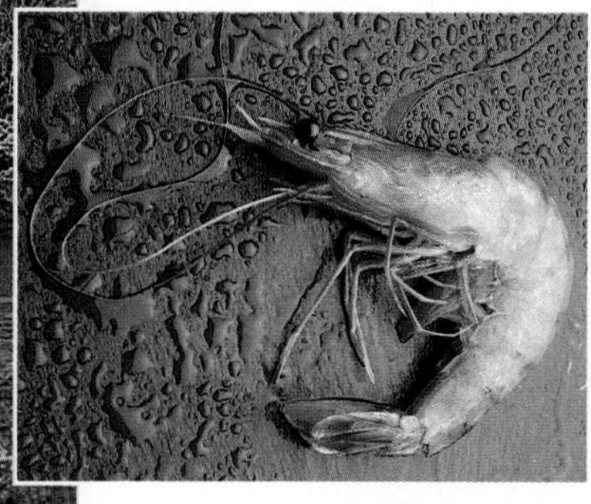

Figure 20
The Chesapeake Bay is an estuary rich in resources. Fish and shrimp are harvested by commercial fishing boats. *What other resources can be found in estuaries?*

Estuary Life Organisms found in estuaries include many species of algae, salt-tolerant grasses, shrimp, crabs, clams, oysters, snails, worms, and fish. Estuaries also serve as important nurseries for many species of ocean fish. They provide much of the seafood consumed by humans.

 **Reading Check** ***What types of organisms live in estuaries?***

Section 3 Assessment

1. What are the similarities and differences between a lake and a stream?
2. Compare and contrast the dark zone of the ocean with the forest floor of a tropical rain forest. What living or nonliving factors affect these areas?
3. Why do you find few plants at the bottom of deep lakes?
4. What adaptations are necessary for organisms that live in the intertidal zone?
5. **Think Critically** Why do few plants grow in a swift-flowing mountain stream?

Skill Builder Activities

6. **Concept Mapping** Make an events chain concept map of these ecosystems from least salty to most salty: *lake, open ocean, estuary,* and *stream.* **For more help, refer to the Science Skill Handbook.**
7. **Communicating** Wetlands trap and slowly release rain, snow, and groundwater. Describe in your Science Journal what might happen to a town located on a floodplain if nearby wetlands are destroyed. **For more help, refer to the Science Skill Handbook.**

Caption Answer

Figure 20 crabs, clams, oysters

Reading Check

Answer algae, grasses, shrimp, crabs, clams, oysters, snails, worms, fish

3 Assess

Reteach

Write on the chalkboard or on an overhead transparency a description of the three major ocean ecosystems. Have students identify each one. L2
IS Naturalist

Challenge

Ask students to make up a story about a molecule of water in a cloud falling to Earth as a raindrop. Direct students to have it pass through three aquatic ecosystems before it evaporates and begins the process again. L3

Assessment

Process Assess students' abilities to compare and contrast by having them compare the salinity of rivers, estuaries, and the open ocean. Responses can be written in their Science Journal. Rivers have lower salinity than oceans. The amount of salt in an estuary varies, but they contain more salt than rivers, and less than oceans. Use **Performance Assessment in the Science Classroom,** p. 175.

Answers to Section Assessment

1. Both contain freshwater. A lake has standing water, low oxygen levels, and rich plant growth in shallow water. A stream has swift-moving water, high oxygen levels, and a rocky bottom with little plant life.
2. Both contain scavengers and decomposers; both are affected by temperature and lack of light. The dark zone is a cold envrionment, and the rain forest is warm.
3. Cold temperatures and low light levels limit the types of organisms that can grow there.
4. Such organisms must be able to adapt to drastic changes in temperature, moisture, and salinity; they must be able to withstand wave motion.
5. Possible answer: The water washes away the soil. Plants would be uprooted and washed downstream.
6. stream, lake, estuary, open ocean
7. The town would flood much more often.

Activity

BENCH TESTED

Recognize the Problem

Internet

Students will use Internet sites that can be accessed through the Glencoe Science Web site at **science.glencoe.com**. They will investigate wetlands regions and their unique role in our environment.

Non-Internet Sources

Collect pamphlets from a variety of wetlands conservancy groups.

Time Required

three days to five days

Preparation

Internet Access the Glencoe Science Web site at **science.glencoe.com** to run through the steps that the students will follow.

Non-Internet Organize printed materials by wetlands regions.

Form a Hypothesis

Possible Hypothesis

Students will identify a specific wetlands region and describe the plants and animals native to that environment. For example, a specific wetlands area may be the only regional location for a particular species of endangered animal.

Activity Use the Internet

Exploring Wetlands

Wetlands, such as the one shown below, are an important part of the environment. These fertile ecosystems support unique plants and animals that can survive only in wetland conditions. The more you understand the importance of wetlands, the more you can do to preserve and protect them.

Recognize the Problem

Why are wetlands an important part of the ecosystem?

Form a Hypothesis

Why do wetlands need to be protected? What laws are in place to protect wetlands? Form a hypothesis about why wetlands should be protected.

Goals

- **Identify** wetland regions in Texas and other parts of the United States.
- **Describe** the significance of the wetland ecosystem.
- **Identify** plant and animal species native to a wetland region.
- **Identify** strategies for supporting the preservation of wetlands.

Data Source

SCIENCE*Online* Visit the Glencoe Science Web site at **science.glencoe.com** to get more information about wetland environments and for data collected by other students.

Resource Manager

Chapter Resources Booklet

Activity Worksheet, pp. 7–8

Lab Activity, pp. 11–14

Lab Management and Safety, p. 37

Internet Addresses

Explore the Glencoe Science Web site at **science.glencoe.com** to find out more about topics in this activity.

768 CHAPTER 26 Ecosystems

Test Your Hypothesis

Plan

1. Determine where some major wetlands are located in the United States.
2. Select one wetland area to study in depth. Where is it located? Is it classified as a marsh, bog, or something else?
3. What role does this ecosystem play in the overall ecology of the area?
4. Find out about the plants and animals that live in the wetland environment you are researching.
5. In most cases, there are federal laws to protect the environment. Additional state and local laws are specific to the area. Investigate what laws protect the wetland you are studying.

Do

1. Make sure your teacher approves your plan before you start.
2. Perform the investigation.
3. Go to the Glencoe Science Web site at **science.glencoe.com** to post your data.

Analyze Your Data

1. **Describe** the wetland area you have researched. What region of the United States is it located in? What other ecological factors are found in that region?
2. What laws protect the wetland you are investigating? How long have the laws been in place?
3. What plants and animals are native to the wetland area you are researching? Are those plants and animals found in other parts of the region or the United States? What adaptations do the plants and animals have that help them survive in a wetland environment?

Draw Conclusions

1. Are all wetlands the same?
2. What is the ecological significance of the wetland area that you studied for that region of the country?
3. Why should wetland environments be protected?
4. What can people do to support the continued preservation of wetland environments in the United States?

Communicating Your Data

SCIENCE Online Find this *Use the Internet* activity on the Glencoe Science Web site at **science. glencoe.com** and **post** your data in the table provided. **Review** other students' data to learn about other wetland environments in the United States.

Test Your Hypothesis

Teaching Strategies Remind students to investigate how the amount of wetlands areas has decreased over the last 25 years, and how that has made an impact on native plants and animals.

Analyze Your Data

Answers will be based on the students' individual research.

Draw Conclusions

1. Wetlands regions are not all the same. Depending on where they are located, one area may have different species of plants than another.
2. Answers will vary. Remind students to think about the plants and animals that live in that wetlands region and if those species are found elsewhere.
3. Answers will vary. Students should investigate the amount of open space in that region.
4. Answers will vary. Have students find out about conservancy groups and their work to preserve wetlands regions.

Assessment

Portfolio Have students make a wetlands field guide for the area they investigated. Include maps and pictures. Have them describe how to support wetlands preservation. Use **Performance Assessment in the Science Classroom,** p. 129.

Communicating Your Data

Have students organize their field guides with section names. Suggest Native Animals and Maps to help them arrange their information.

TIME SCIENCE AND Society

Content Background

The idea of using wetlands to process municipal wastewater was first conceived in the 1970s. Wetlands are flat, low-lying areas where water collects and saturates the soil. The conditions provide habitats for various plants like cattails and bulrushes. The low flow rates prolong contact between the water and plants, enabling the roots and trapped microorganisms to remove pollutants and organic matter.

Since natural wetlands provide wildlife habitats and help control river flooding, many are being restored. A constructed wetland mimics the action of a natural marsh. The primary difference is the separation of the natural subsoil from the wetland soil by a concrete trough or layer of heavy clay. This substructure prevents polluted inflow from leaching into the soil before the wetland has processed it. The troughs are filled with sand and soil and then planted with appropriate wetland vegetation. Inflow volume, local climate, and degree of pre-processing of the wastewater determine the size and nature of a constructed wetland.

In arid and water-intensive agricultural areas, the aim of wetlands water treatment is to enable the direct reuse of the outflow. Most constructed wetlands in the U.S. are in the South and West where the warm climate ensures year-round plant growth, but there are experimental wetland projects in the northern U.S. and southern Canada.

TIME SCIENCE AND Society — SCIENCE ISSUES THAT AFFECT YOU!

Helping Nature

1

Pebbles were added to the Corrales wetlands to help with drainage.

2

When you wash your hands or flush the toilet, you probably don't think much about where the wastewater goes. In most places, it eventually ends up being processed in a traditional sewage-treatment facility. But a handful of places are experimenting with a new method that processes wastewater by creating wetlands. Wetlands, such as swamps or marshes, are home to filtering plants, such as cattails, and sewage-eating bacteria.

In 1996, school officials at the Corrales Elementary School in the city of Albuquerque, New Mexico, faced a big problem. The old wastewater-treatment system had failed. Replacing it was going to cost a lot of money. The school officials came up with an alternative plan. Instead of constructing a new sewage-treatment plant, they decided to create a natural wetlands system. The wetlands system could do the job less expensively, while protecting the environment. Today, this wetlands efficiently converts polluted water into cleaner water that's good for the environment. U.S. government officials are closely watching this alternative sewage-treatment system to see how successful it is. So far, so good! And if it continues to work well, other communities may start creating wetlands to filter their sewage.

770

Resources for Teachers and Students

Constructed Wetlands in the Sustainable Landscape by Craig S. Campbell and Michael H. Ogden. New York, NY: John Wiley & Sons, 1999.

"Nothing Goes to Waste in Arcata's Teeming Marshes." D. Stewart. *Smithsonian*, Vol. 21. 1990.

University of South Alabama,
Department of Civil Engineering
Mobile, Alabama 36688-0002

U.S. Department of Agriculture
National Agricultural Library
Water Quality Information Center
10301 Baltimore Avenue, Beltsville, MD 20705

Creating Wetlands to Purify Wastewater

Help Itself

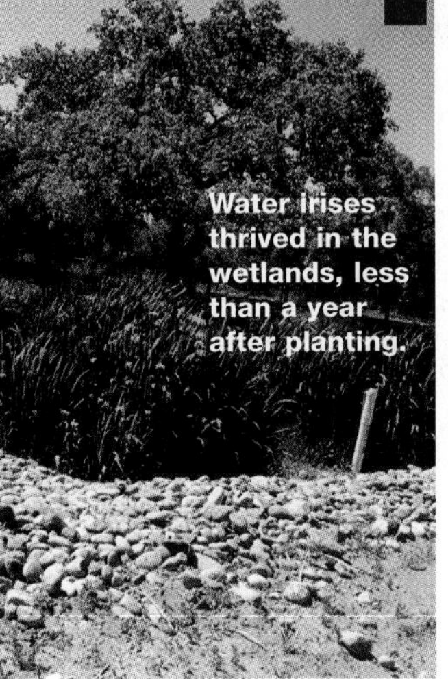
Water irises thrived in the wetlands, less than a year after planting.

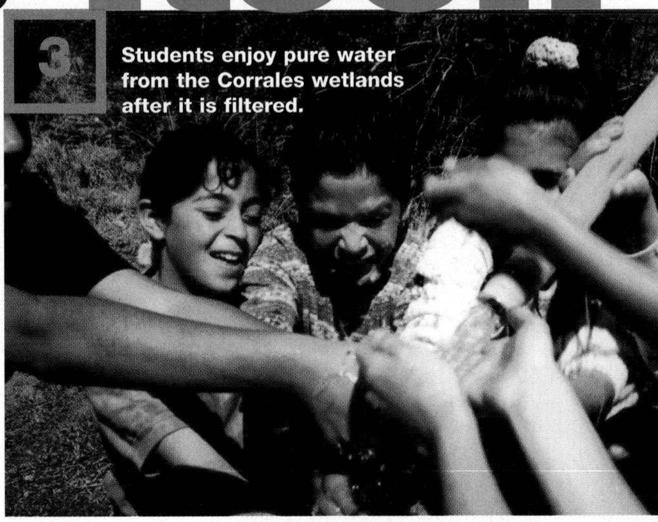
3 Students enjoy pure water from the Corrales wetlands after it is filtered.

How Wetlands Work

Wetlands filter water through the actions of the plants and microorganisms that live there. When plants absorb water into their roots, some, such as cattails, also take up pollutants. The plants convert the pollutants to forms that are not dangerous. At the same time, bacteria and other microorganisms are filtering water as they feed. Water does not move quickly through wetlands, so the organisms have plenty of time to do their work. The wetlands built at Corrales Elementary is called a "constructed" wetlands. That is a wetlands built by people to filter small amounts of pollutants. In many places, constructed wetlands are better at cleaning wastewater than sewers or septic systems.

From Sewage to Flowers

Nancy Griego, a wetlands plant expert, planted a variety of colorful plants that bloom at different times of the year. A local official said, "School classes are taking field trips to the wetlands to learn what plants do as part of the environment. It's become a real educational asset."

CONNECTIONS Visit and Observe **Visit a wetlands. Create a field journal of your observations. Sketch pictures of the plants and animals you see. BONUS: Use a field guide to help identify the wildlife you see. If you don't live near a wetlands, use resources to research wetlands environments.**

SCIENCE *Online*

For more information, visit science.glencoe.com

Discussion

Have students research wastewater treatment, both municipal and individual septic systems. **Under what circumstances might wetlands be a better option?** Possible answer: In arid regions where groundwater is depleted by well drilling and irrigation and low-lying areas where high water tables compromise standard leach fields. **Are there any instances of natural wetlands being used for wastewater treatment?** Possible answer: Arcata, California

Activity

Research or visit your local sewage treatment plant to find out how wastewater is handled in your community. Help students conduct a survey to determine how much wastewater their school produces. Based on the results of their research, discuss the appropriateness of wetlands treatment for the school and the community.

Investigate the Issue

Wastewater is only one product of sewage treatment. Wetlands, both natural and constructed, can effectively process only second- or third-stage water. The solid waste is removed in the primary stage or a septic tank. Students can research methods of dealing with "sludge." Have them present the findings in a graph format and discuss the implications of their data.

CONNECTIONS Lead a discussion on how a constructed wetland benefits wildlife. In coastal areas, the discussion may include the importance of marshes to the ocean food chain. Near river systems, the effect on wildlife can be discussed in light of the flood control function of wetlands. Discuss how the decline in total wetland acreage can affect the food chain in general.

SCIENCE *Online*

Internet Addresses

____

____

Explore the Glencoe Science Web site at **science.glencoe.com** to find out more about topics in this feature.

Chapter 26 Study Guide

Reviewing Main Ideas

Preview

Students can answer the questions in their Science Journals. Discuss the answers as you go through the chapter. LS **Linguistic**

Review

Students can write their answers, then compare them with those of other students. LS **Interpersonal**

Reteach

Students can look at the illustrations and describe details that support the main ideas of the chapter. LS **Visual-Spatial**

Answers to Chapter Review

Section 1

3. secondary succession

Section 2

2. taiga

Section 3

3. The shell deposits of coral provide shelter for a wide range of organisms on and around a coral reef.

Chapter 26 Study Guide

Reviewing Main Ideas

Section 1 How Ecosystems Change

1. Ecological succession is the gradual change from one community to another.
2. Primary succession begins in a place where no soil exists. It begins with organisms that are called pioneer species.
3. Secondary succession begins in a place that has soil and was once the home of living organisms. *What type of succession is occurring here?*

4. A community that has reached a stable stage of ecological succession is called a climax community.

Section 2 Biomes

1. Temperature and precipitation help determine the climate of a region.
2. Large geographic areas with similar climax communities are called biomes. *What type of biome is shown in the photo to the right?*

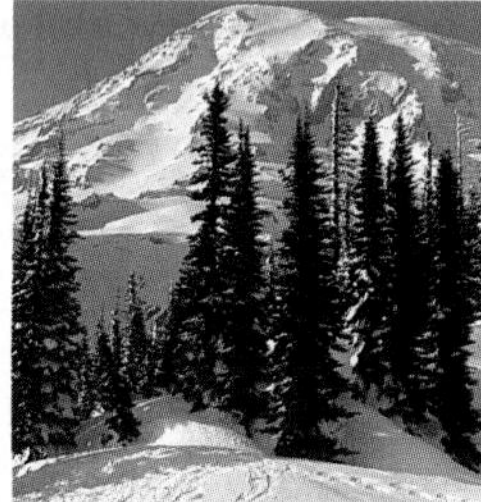

3. Earth's land biomes include tundra, taiga, temperate deciduous forest, temperate rain forest, tropical rain forest, grassland, and desert.

Section 3 Aquatic Ecosystems

1. Freshwater ecosystems include flowing water, such as streams and rivers, and standing water such as lakes, ponds, and wetlands.
2. Wetlands are land areas that are covered with water most of the year. They are found in regions that lie between land masses and water.
3. Saltwater ecosystems include estuaries, seashores, coral reefs, a few inland lakes, and the deep ocean. *Why are coral reefs, like this one, rich in biodiversity?*

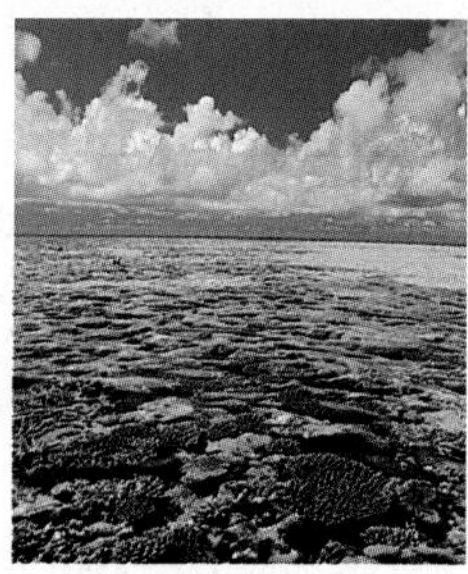

4. Estuaries are important transitional zones between freshwater and saltwater environments. They are extremely fertile, and provide much of the seafood consumed by humans.

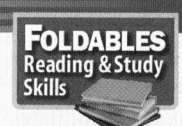

FOLDABLES Reading & Study Skills — After You Read

To help review succession, use the Main Ideas Study Fold that you made at the beginning of this chapter. Which type of succession starts with bare rock?

FOLDABLES Reading & Study Skills — After You Read

After students have read the chapter and completed the Foldable described in Before You Read, have them do the activity on the student page.

Dinah Zike

Chapter 26 Study Guide

Visualizing Main Ideas

Fill in the circles of the concept map showing land biomes.

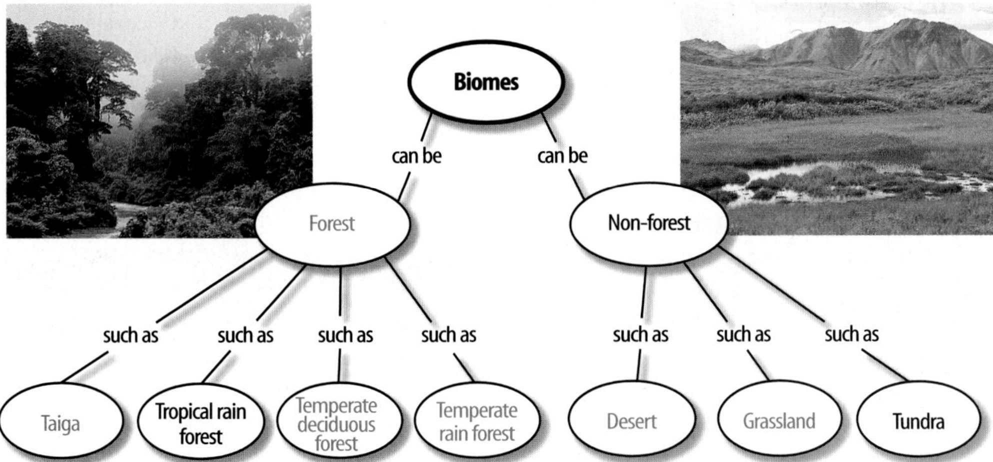

Vocabulary Review

Vocabulary Words

a. biome
b. climax community
c. coral reef
d. desert
e. estuary
f. grassland
g. intertidal zone
h. pioneer species
i. succession
j. taiga
k. temperate deciduous forest
l. temperate rain forest
m. tropical rain forest
n. tundra
o. wetland

Study Tip

Pay attention to the chapter's illustrations. Try to figure out exactly what main point the picture is trying to stress.

Using Vocabulary

Each of the following sentences is false. Make the sentence true by replacing the underlined word with the correct vocabulary word.

1. Biome refers to the normal changes in the types of species that live in communities.
2. A pioneer species is a group of organisms found in a stable stage of succession.
3. Deciduous trees are dominant in the temperate rain forest.
4. The average temperature in tropical rain forests is between 9°C and 12°C.
5. Taigas are the most biologically diverse biomes in the world.
6. An intertidal zone is an area where freshwater meets the ocean.

IDENTIFYING Misconceptions

Assess

Use the assessment as follow-up to page 746F after students have completed the chapter.

Discussion Ask students to think of components that go into a particular ecosystem, such as a marine or forest ecosystem. Have them draw connections between the components. Have the students pick a few components to remove. Ask students to explain what happens to the flow of energy and/or cycling of materials if these components are removed. While removing some components, depending on what they are, may not cause the system to collapse, it may not be able to function optimally without them.

Chapter 26 Study Guide

Visualizing Main Ideas

See student page.

Vocabulary Review

Using Vocabulary

1. Succession
2. climax community
3. temperate deciduous forests
4. temperate rain forests
5. Tropical rain forests
6. estuary

Chapter 26 Assessment

Checking Concepts

1. B
2. A
3. B
4. C
5. C
6. B
7. A
8. B
9. B
10. B

Thinking Critically

11. The temperate deciduous forest contains more nutrients in its soil because there is less rainfall to wash away the nutrients.
12. These plants grow under the canopy so they do not need a lot of light. They thrive in moderate temperatures, and they are perennials.
13. After a fire burns away the existing plant life, these seeds are ready to germinate in an environment without much competition.
14. It is likely that the grassy meadow is experiencing succession toward an oak-maple forest. The presence of the forest suggests that this climate and land is appropriate for the growth of forests.
15. The tundra soil is thin above the permafrost. Roots cannot penetrate deeply, so plants are small. The growing season is also short.

Chapter 26 Assessment

Checking Concepts

Choose the word or phrase that best answers the question.

1. What are tundra and desert examples of?
A) ecosystems **C)** habitats
B) biomes **D)** communities

2. What is a hot, dry biome called?
A) desert **C)** coral reef
B) tundra **D)** grassland

3. Where would organisms that are adapted to live in freshwater and salt water be found?
A) lake **C)** open ocean
B) estuary **D)** intertidal zone

4. Which biome contains the largest number of species?
A) taiga
B) temperate deciduous forest
C) tropical rain forest
D) grassland

5. Which biome contains mostly frozen soil called permafrost?
A) taiga
B) temperate rain forest
C) tundra
D) temperate deciduous forest

6. A new island is formed from a volcanic eruption. Which species probably would be the first to grow and survive?
A) oak trees **C)** grasses
B) lichens **D)** ferns

7. What would the changes in communities that take place on a recently formed volcanic island best be described as?
A) primary succession
B) secondary succession
C) tertiary succession
D) magma

8. What is the stable stage of succession?
A) pioneer species **C)** limiting factor
B) climax community **D)** permafrost

9. Which of the following aquatic ecosystems would have the lowest salinity?
A) estuaries **C)** coral reefs
B) rivers **D)** open oceans

10. Which ecosystem would experience the most drastic changes in a 24-hour period?
A) open ocean **C)** lake
B) intertidal zone **D)** coral reef

Thinking Critically

11. In most cases, would a soil sample from a temperate deciduous forest be more or less nutrient-rich than a soil sample from a tropical rain forest? Explain.

12. Why do many tropical rain forest plants make good houseplants?

13. Some plant seeds need fire in order to germinate. Explain how this gives these plants an advantage in secondary succession.

14. A grassy meadow borders a beech-maple forest. Is one of these ecosystems undergoing succession? Why?

15. Why are tundra plants usually small?

Developing Skills

16. Concept Mapping Make a network-tree concept map for water environments. Include these terms: *saltwater ecosystems, freshwater ecosystems, intertidal zone, lighted zone, dark zone, lake, pond, coral reef, river, stream, flowing water,* and *standing water.*

17. Comparing and Contrasting Compare and contrast the adaptations of organisms living in the tundra with those living in the taiga.

Chapter Assessment Planner

Portfolio Encourage students to place in their portfolios one or two items of what they consider to be their best work. Examples include:
- Visual Learning, p. 750
- Assessment, p. 759
- Science Journal, p. 764

Performance Additional performance assessments, Performance Task Assessment Lists, and rubrics for evaluating these activities can be found in Glencoe's **Performance Assessment in the Science Classroom.**

18. **Forming Hypotheses** Make a hypothesis about what would happen to succession in a pond if the pond owner removed all the cattails and reeds from around the pond edges every summer.

19. **Recognizing Cause and Effect** Devastating fires, like the one in Yellowstone National Park in 1988, cause many changes to the land. Determine the effect of a fire on an area that has reached its climax community.

20. **Making and Using Graphs** Make a graph of the amount of rainfall per year in each biome. Which type of graph is best suited to display the data?

Rainfall Amounts

Biome	Rainfall/Year (cm)
Tundra	25
Taiga	50
Temperate rain forest	200
Tropical rain forest	400
Grassland	35
Temperate deciduous forest	150
Desert	25

Performance Assessment

21. **Oral Presentation** Research a biome that was not covered in this chapter. Find out about the climate, where it is located, and which organisms live there. Present this information to your class.

Technology

Go to the Glencoe Science Web site at **science.glencoe.com** or use the **Glencoe Science CD-ROM** for additional chapter assessment.

THE PRINCETON REVIEW Test Practice

Each biome around the world contains many different groups of organisms that are unique to that biome. Plants and animals from two different biomes have been drawn in separate boxes below.

A

B

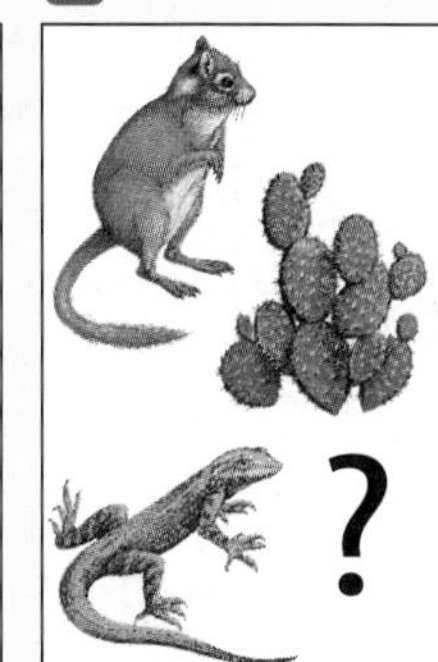

Study the pictures above and answer the following questions.

1. The animals in Box B are different from the animals in Box A because the animals in Box B have adaptations that _____.
   - **A)** allow them to survive during heavy rainfall
   - **B)** allow them to reproduce asexually and sexually
   - **C)** allow them to conserve water
   - **D)** allow them to maintain a constant internal temperature

2. Which of the following organisms would be most likely to complete the group shown in Box B?
   - **F)** palm tree
   - **G)** salamander
   - **H)** fish
   - **J)** snake

Chapter 26 Assessment

THE PRINCETON REVIEW Test Practice

The Test-Taking Tip was written by The Princeton Review, the nation's leader in test preparation.

1. C
2. J

Developing Skills

16. Students should separate water ecosystems into salt water and freshwater. Salt water ecosystems: intertidal zone, lighted zone, dark zone, coral reefs; freshwater ecosystems: lakes and ponds (which contain standing water), rivers and streams (which contain flowing water).
17. Tundra plants are short, unlike the plants of the taiga. Tundra animals need thick fur and other adaptations for extreme cold.
18. Possible answers: (a) succession will slow, (b) succession will stop, or (c) the natural spreading of cattails and reeds toward the center of the pond will be prevented.
19. The area will begin the process of secondary succession with annual plants and grasses.
20. Students should make a bar graph with the biomes across the bottom and amounts of rainfall indicated on the side.

Performance Assessment

21. Answers will vary but should contain a description and example of other biomes, such as tallgrass prairies. Use **Performance Assessment in the Science Classroom,** p. 143.

Assessment Resources

Reproducible Masters

Chapter Resources Booklet
- Chapter Review, pp. 35–36
- Chapter Tests, pp. 37–40
- Assessment Transparency Activity, p. 47

Glencoe Science Web site
- Interactive Tutor
- Chapter Quizzes

Glencoe Technology
- Assessment Transparency
- Interactive CD-ROM Chapter Quizzes
- ExamView Pro Test Bank
- Vocabulary PuzzleMaker Software
- MindJogger Videoquiz

CHAPTER 27 CONSERVING RESOURCES

Section/Objectives	Standards		Activities/Features
	National	State/Local	
Chapter Opener	See p. 5T for a Key to Standards.		**Explore Activity:** Model topsoil loss, p. 777 **Before You Read,** p. 777
Section 1 Resources 2 sessions 1 block 1. **Compare** renewable and nonrenewable resources. 2. **List** uses of fossil fuels. 3. **Identify** alternatives to fossil fuel use.	National Content Standards: UCP2, A1, F2, F4, F5		**MiniLAB:** Observing Mineral Mining Effects, p. 780 **Physics Integration,** p. 781 **Visualizing Solar Energy,** p. 785
Section 2 Pollution 2 sessions 1 block 1. **Describe** types of air pollution. 2. **Identify** causes of water pollution. 3. **Explain** methods that can be used to prevent erosion.	National Content Standards: UCP2, A1, E2, F1, F2, F4, F5		**MiniLAB:** Measuring Acid Rain, p. 787 **Science Online,** p. 788 **Health Integration,** p. 790 **Activity:** The Greenhouse Effect, p. 795
Section 3 The Three Rs of Conservation 3 sessions 1.5 blocks 1. **Recognize** ways you can reduce your use of natural resources. 2. **Explain** how you can reuse resources to promote conservation. 3. **Describe** how many materials can be recycled.	National Content Standards: UCP2, A1, E2, F2, F4, F5, G1		**Science Online,** p. 798 **Problem-Solving Activity:** What items are you recycling at home?, p. 798 **Activity:** Solar Cooking, pp. 800–801 **Science and Language Arts:** Beauty Plagiarized, pp. 802–803

NATIONAL GEOGRAPHIC

Teacher's Corner

PRODUCTS AVAILABLE FROM GLENCOE
To order call 1-800-334-7344:
Posters: *Energy, Ozone, Pollution, Vanishing Wildlife*

...DUCTS AVAILABLE FROM ...AL GEOGRAPHIC SOCIETY
...r call 1-800-368-2728:
Books: *National Geographic Book of Mammals; The Company We Keep: America's Endangered Species; There's Still Time: The Success of the Endangered Species Act*
Videos: *America's Endangered Species: Don't Say Goodbye; Endangered Animals: Suvivors on the Brink; Energy:The Fuels and Man; Energy: The Problems and the Future; Investigating Global Warming; Ozone: Protecting the Invisible Shield; Pollution: World at Risk; Power of Water; Recycling: The Endless Cycle*

Activity Materials	Reproducible Resources	Section Assessment	Technology
Explore Activity: moist sand, potting soil, plastic basin or aluminum-foil baking pan, moss, water, spray bottle, beaker	**Chapter Resources Booklet** Foldables Worksheet, p. 17 Directed Reading Overview, p. 19 Note-taking Worksheets, pp. 33–35	Glencoe's Assessment Advantage	
MiniLAB: chocolate chip cookie, paper plate, toothpick *Need materials?* Contact Science Kit at 1-800-828-7777 or www.sciencekit.com on the Internet.	**Chapter Resources Booklet** Transparency Activity, p. 44 MiniLAB, p. 3 Enrichment, p. 30 Reinforcement, p. 27 Directed Reading, p. 20 **Cultural Diversity,** p. 41 **Mathematics Skill Activities,** p. 9	Portfolio Physics Integration, p. 781 Performance MiniLAB, p. 780 Skill Builder Activities, p. 784 Content Section Assessment, p. 784	Section Focus Transparency Interactive CD-ROM Guided Reading Audio Program
MiniLAB: cup, rainwater, pH indicator paper, tap water, distilled water **Activity:** 1-L clear plastic soft-drink bottle with top cut off and label removed (2), 2 thermometers, potting soil, masking tape, plastic wrap, rubber band, lamp with 100-W lightbulb, watch or clock with second hand	**Chapter Resources Booklet** Transparency Activity, p. 45 MiniLAB, p. 4 Enrichment, p. 31 Reinforcement, p. 28 Directed Reading, p. 21 Activity Worksheet, pp. 5–6 Lab Activity, pp. 9–12 Transparency Activity, pp. 47–48	Portfolio Assessment, p. 794 Performance MiniLAB, p. 787 Skill Builder Activities, p. 794 Content Section Assessment, p. 794	Section Focus Transparency Teaching Transparency Interactive CD-ROM Guided Reading Audio Program
Activity: poster board, cardboard boxes, aluminum foil, string, wire coat hangers, clear plastic sheets, black cookware, thermometer, stopwatch, glue, tape, scissors	**Chapter Resources Booklet** Transparency Activity, p. 46 Enrichment, p. 32 Reinforcement, p. 29 Directed Reading, pp. 21, 22 Activity Worksheet, pp. 7–8 Lab Activity, pp. 13–16 **Lab Management and Safety,** p. 37	Portfolio Challenge, p. 799 Performance Problem-Solving Activity, p. 798 Skill Builder Activities, p. 799 Content Section Assessment, p. 799	Section Focus Transparency Interactive CD-ROM Guided Reading Audio Program

End of Chapter Assessment

Glencoe's Assessment Advantage

Blackline Masters	Technology	Professional Series
Chapter Resources Booklet Chapter Review, pp. 37–38 Chapter Tests, pp. 39–42 **Standardized Test Practice by The Princeton Review,** pp. 115–118	MindJogger Videoquiz Interactive CD-ROM Vocabulary PuzzleMakers ExamView Pro Test Bank Interactive Lesson Planner Interactive Teacher Edition	Performance Assessment in the Science Classroom (PASC)

Transparencies

Section Focus

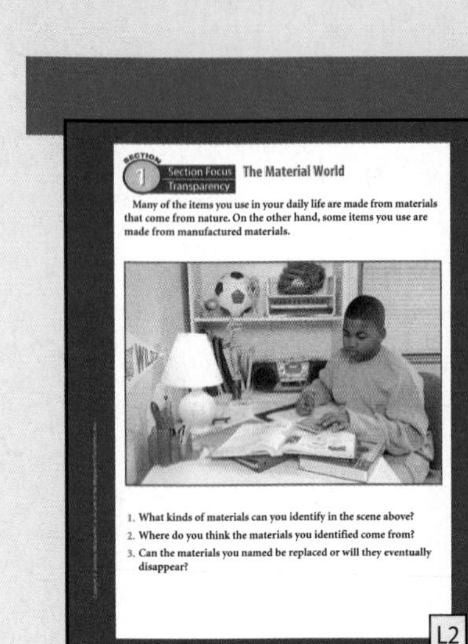
Section 1 Section Focus Transparency — The Material World

Many of the items you use in your daily life are made from materials that come from nature. On the other hand, some items you use are made from manufactured materials.

1. What kinds of materials can you identify in the scene above?
2. Where do you think the materials you identified come from?
3. Can the materials you named be replaced or will they eventually disappear?

L2

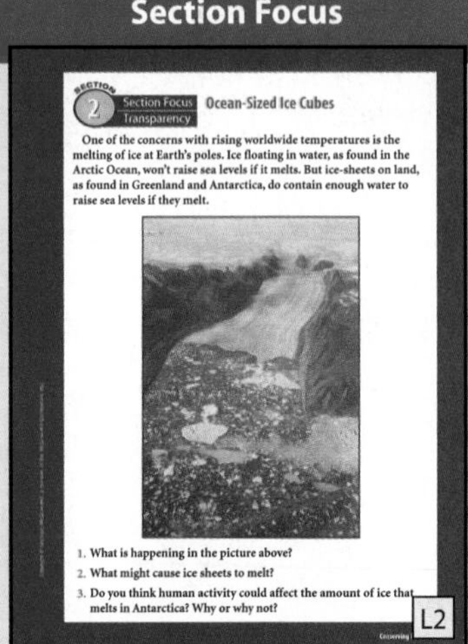
Section 2 Section Focus Transparency — Ocean-Sized Ice Cubes

One of the concerns with rising worldwide temperatures is the melting of ice at Earth's poles. Ice floating in water, as found in the Arctic Ocean, won't raise sea levels if it melts. But ice-sheets on land, as found in Greenland and Antarctica, do contain enough water to raise sea levels if they melt.

1. What is happening in the picture above?
2. What might cause ice sheets to melt?
3. Do you think human activity could affect the amount of ice that melts in Antarctica? Why or why not?

L2

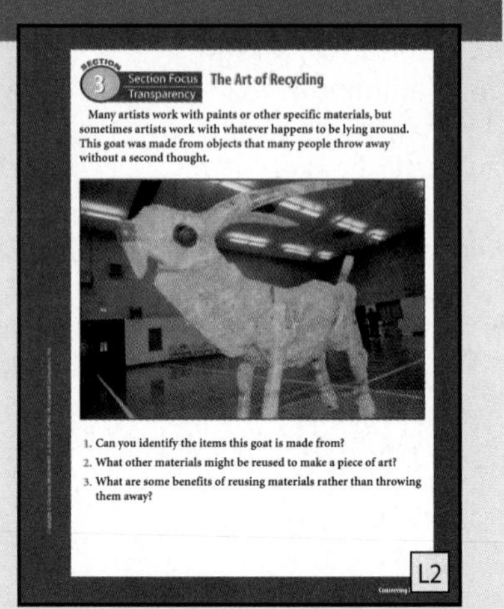
Section 3 Section Focus Transparency — The Art of Recycling

Many artists work with paints or other specific materials, but sometimes artists work with whatever happens to be lying around. This goat was made from objects that many people throw away without a second thought.

1. Can you identify the items this goat is made from?
2. What other materials might be reused to make a piece of art?
3. What are some benefits of reusing materials rather than throwing them away?

L2

This is a representation of key blackline masters available in the Teacher Classroom Resources. See Resource Manager boxes within the chapter for additional information.

Assessment

Assessment Transparency — Conserving Resources

Directions: Carefully review the table and answer the following questions.

Alternatives to Fossil Fuels		
Type	**How it works**	**Environmental impacts**
Hydroelectric power	Energy of moving water is converted into electrical energy.	Habitats destroyed by dams
Wind power	Energy of moving air is converted into electrical energy.	No significant problem
Nuclear power	Energy of nuclear fission heats water, which is used to generate electricity.	Produces hazardous waste and has risk of accidents
Solar power	Energy from the Sun is absorbed and converted into heat and electrical energy.	No significant problem

1. According to the table, a windmill would be an example of ___.
   A hydroelectric power C nuclear power
   B wind power D solar power
2. Which of these could be added to the table?
   F Coal power H Gasoline power
   G Oil power J Geothermal power
3. According to the table, which fuel is most likely to affect human health?
   A Hydroelectric power C Nuclear power
   B Wind power D Solar power

L2

Teaching

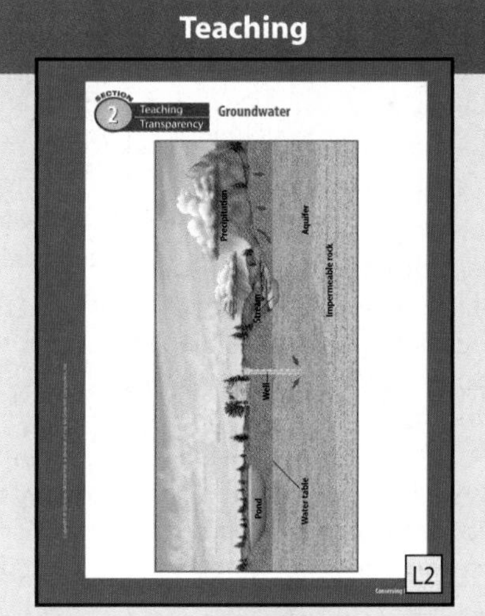

Key to Teaching Strategies

The following designations will help you decide which activities are appropriate for your students.

- L1 Level 1 activities should be appropriate for students with learning difficulties.
- L2 Level 2 activities should be within the ability range of all students.
- L3 Level 3 activities are designed for above-average students.
- ELL ELL activities should be within the ability range of English Language Learners.
- COOP LEARN Cooperative Learning activities are designed for small group work.
- LS Multiple Learning Styles logos, as described on page 22T, are used throughout to indicate strategies that address different learning styles.
- P These strategies represent student products that can be placed into a best-work portfolio.

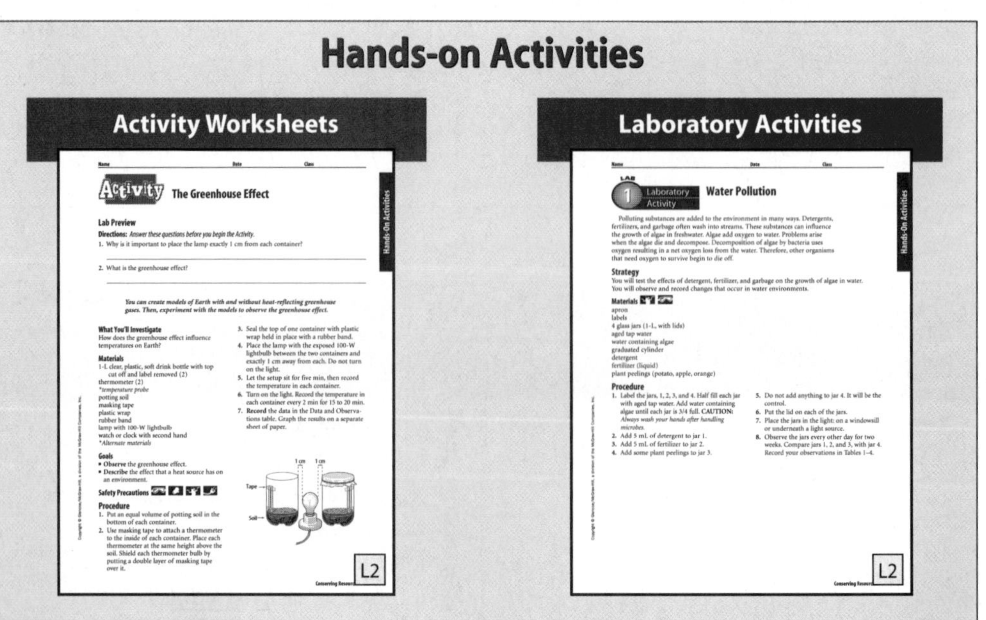

Hands-on Activities

Activity Worksheets

Name Date Class

Activity — The Greenhouse Effect

Lab Preview

Directions: *Answer these questions before you begin the Activity.*

1. Why is it important to place the lamp exactly 1 cm from each container?
2. What is the greenhouse effect?

You can create models of Earth with and without heat-reflecting greenhouse gases. Then, experiment with the models to observe the greenhouse effect.

What You'll Investigate
How does the greenhouse effect influence temperatures on Earth?

Materials
1-L clear, plastic, soft drink bottle with top cut off and label removed (2)
thermometer (2)
**temperature probe*
potting soil
masking tape
plastic wrap
rubber band
lamp with 100-W lightbulb
watch or clock with second hand
**Alternate materials*

Goals
- **Observe** the greenhouse effect.
- **Describe** the effect that a heat source has on an environment.

Safety Precautions

Procedure
1. Put an equal volume of potting soil in the bottom of each container.
2. Use masking tape to attach a thermometer to the inside of each container. Place each thermometer at the same height above the soil. Shield each thermometer bulb by putting a double layer of masking tape over it.
3. Seal the top of one container with plastic wrap held in place with a rubber band.
4. Place the lamp with the exposed 100-W lightbulb between the two containers and exactly 1 cm away from each. Do not turn on the light.
5. Let the setup sit for five min, then record the temperature in each container.
6. Turn on the light. Record the temperature in each container every 2 min for 15 to 20 min.
7. **Record** the data in the Data and Observations table. Graph the results on a separate sheet of paper.

L2

Laboratory Activities

Name Date Class

Lab 1 Laboratory Activity — Water Pollution

Polluting substances are added to the environment in many ways. Detergents, fertilizers, and garbage often wash into streams. These substances can influence the growth of algae in freshwater. Algae add oxygen to water. Problems arise when the algae die and decompose. Decomposition of algae by bacteria uses oxygen resulting in a net oxygen loss from the water. Therefore, other organisms that need oxygen to survive begin to die off.

Strategy
You will test the effects of detergent, fertilizer, and garbage on the growth of algae in water. You will observe and record changes that occur in water environments.

Materials
apron
labels
4 glass jars (1-L, with lids)
aged tap water
water containing algae
graduated cylinder
detergent
fertilizer (liquid)
plant peelings (potato, apple, orange)

Procedure
1. Label the jars, 1, 2, 3, and 4. Half fill each jar with aged tap water. Add water containing algae until each jar is 3/4 full. **CAUTION:** *Always wash your hands after handling microbes.*
2. Add 5 mL of detergent to jar 1.
3. Add 5 mL of fertilizer to jar 2.
4. Add some plant peelings to jar 3.
5. Do not add anything to jar 4. It will be the control.
6. Put the lid on each of the jars.
7. Place the jars in the light: on a windowsill or underneath a light source.
8. Observe the jars every other day for two weeks. Compare jars 1, 2, and 3, with jar 4. Record your observations in Tables 1–4.

L2

Meeting Different Ability Levels

Content Outline

Note-taking Worksheet — Conserving Resources

L2

Reinforcement

Section 1 Reinforcement — Resources

L2

Directed Reading

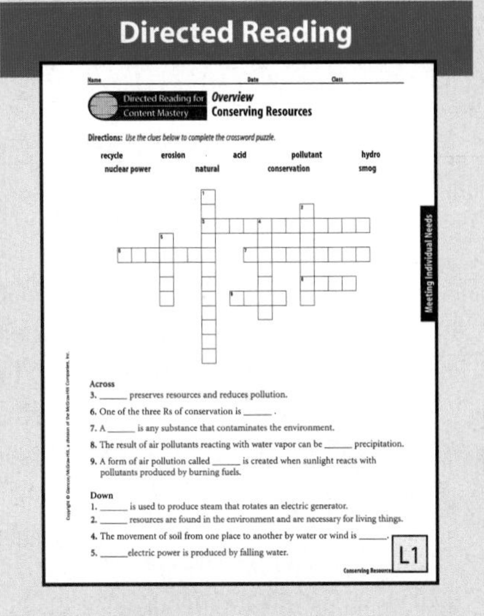

Directed Reading for Content Mastery — Overview: Conserving Resources

L1

Enrichment

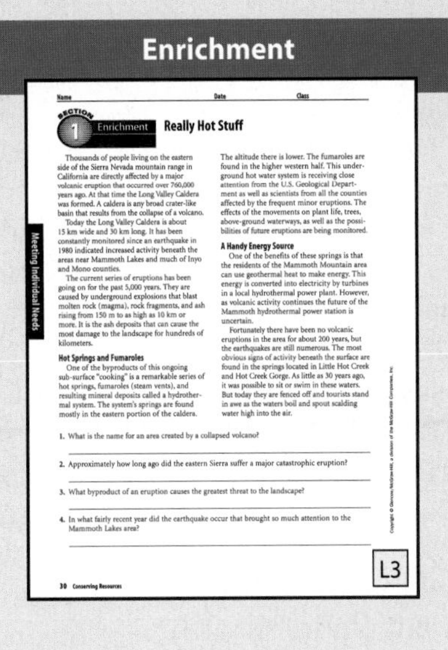

Section 1 Enrichment — Really Hot Stuff

L3

Spanish Directed Reading

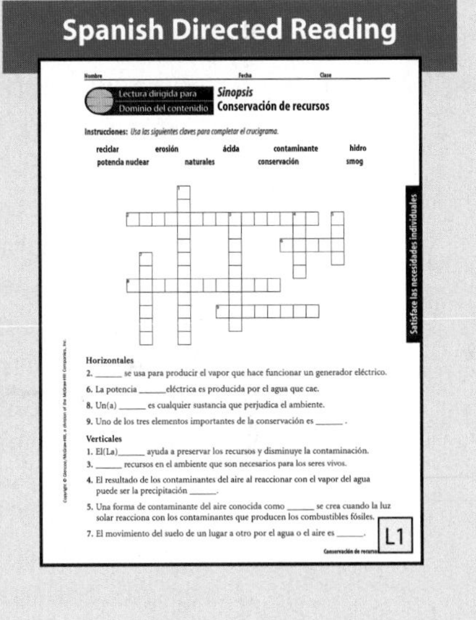

Lectura dirigida para Dominio del contenido — Sinopsis: Conservación de recursos

L1

Assessment

Chapter Tests

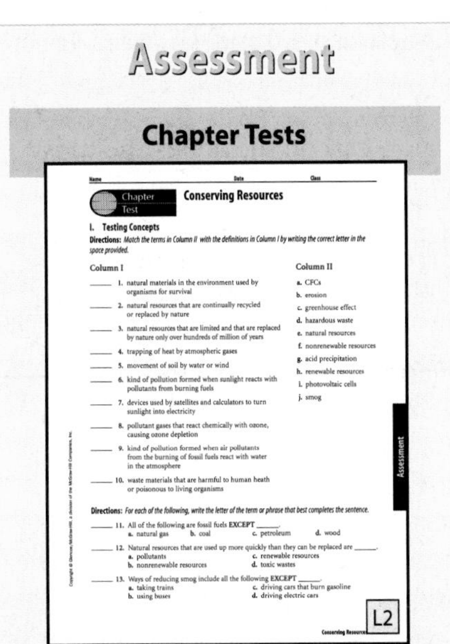

Chapter Test — Conserving Resources

L2

Test Practice Workbook

L2

Chapter Review

Chapter Review — Conserving Resources

L2

Science Content Background

SECTION 1

Resources

Renewable Resources

Renewable resources include trees in forests; fish in lakes, rivers, and oceans; fertile agricultural soil; and freshwater in lakes and rivers. Nature replaces these resources, and they can be used forever as long as they are not overexploited in the short term. Some resources, like agricultural soil, can be considered renewable or nonrenewable. Soil is constantly replaced but at a very slow rate.

Fun Fact

Simple windmills may have been used in Persia as early as the seventh century A.D.

Nonrenewable Resources

Nonrenewable resources, which include minerals and fossil fuels, are present in limited supplies and are depleted by use. They are not replenished by natural processes within a reasonable amount of time. Fossil fuels, for example, take millions of years to form. Recycling nonrenewable resources can help sustain the supply of certain substances. In the future, most products will contain some recycled material.

Nuclear Power

In 1942 Enrico Fermi established the first successful controlled nuclear chain reaction. Nuclear fission reactions release a great deal of energy, several million times the energy of a typical chemical reaction. Nuclear reactors use uranium-235 for the production of power. Once started, the reactions are self-sustaining: the neutrons released by each splitting in turn split other atoms, causing a chain reaction. There is no danger of nuclear chain reactions starting in nature since uranium-235 makes up only 0.71% of the naturally occurring uranium. Most of the remainder is uranium-238, which is not fissible.

SECTION 2

Pollution

Acid Precipitation

Acid precipitation is a worldwide problem. Reports of highly acidic precipitation have come from Canada, England, Germany, France, Scandinavia, and the United States. Precipitation is normally slightly acidic, with a pH between 5.6 and 5.7 that is caused by atmospheric carbonic acid. But acid precipitation sometimes has a concentration of acid 1,000 times higher than normal. The average precipitation in much of the northeastern part of the United States and adjoining parts of Ontario has a pH between 4.0 and 4.5.

Greenhouse Effect

Next to water vapor, carbon dioxide is the most abundant greenhouse gas. It occurs as a natural consequence of respiration. However, carbon dioxide is emitted into the atmosphere as a by-product of energy production. Coal, oil, natural gas, and biomass are burned to provide heat and electricity for industrial processes, home heating, and cooking. These sources are increasing the amount of carbon dioxide in the atmosphere. Some evidence suggests that increased levels of carbon dioxide in the atmosphere may cause Earth's average temperature to increase.

Jeff Greenberg/Visuals Unlimited

Telegraph Colour Library/FPG International

Ozone Depletion

Ozone, a molecule made up of three oxygen atoms, traps excess ultraviolet radiation and prevents it from reaching Earth. In 1985, it was discovered that a significant thinning of the ozone layer over the Antarctic occurred during the southern hemisphere's spring. Some regions of the ozone layer showed 95 percent depletion. Ozone depletion is also occurring farther north. Measurements in arctic regions suggest a thinning of the ozone layer there. These findings have caused countries to stop producing ozone-destroying chemicals.

Soil Loss

Erosion is a natural process that has occurred since Earth was formed. Humans have little control over the erosion caused by glaciers, rivers, and oceans. A number of human activities, mainly farming and logging, have increased erosion. Scientists estimate that between 2 and 3 billion metric tons of soil are lost from farmlands in the United States each year.

Soil Pollution—Solid Wastes

About 90 percent of our solid wastes are disposed of on land, mostly in landfills. Several methods of producing energy from solid waste are used on a small scale and further research is being done in this area. One example is a combustion chamber lined with water lines in which selected wastes are burned and the heat is used to produce steam to power a generator.

SECTION 3 The Three Rs of Conservation

Recycle

In 1997, the overall recycling rate in the U.S. was 28 percent, with the composting of yard waste accounting for 2/5 of this. The overall recycling rate of plastic was only 5.2 percent, 24.3 percent for glass and, 38.4 percent for steel. Paper and paper products are the most voluminous waste products, and they make up about 41.7 percent of the solid waste produced in the United States.

Fun Fact

Recycling is an ancient practice. In prehistoric times, metal tools and weapons were melted down to make new ones.

For additional content background on this topic, go to the Glencoe Science Web site at science.glencoe.com.

Conserving Resources

Chapter Vocabulary

What do you think?

Science Journal This photo is of compost. Compost, which consists mostly of decayed organic matter, can be used instead of fertilizer to enrich soil.

CHAPTER 27

Conserving Resources

It's sweltering and you haven't felt a breeze in hours. You lift the hose over your head and turn the faucet handle. Instead of clear, cool water, greenish-yellow sludge flows out. Yuck! Clean water isn't the only resource that is commonly taken for granted. In this chapter, you'll learn the difference between renewable and nonrenewable resources. You'll also read about the various energy sources available on Earth and how pollution can affect your life.

What do you think?

Science Journal Look at the picture below with a classmate. Discuss what this might be. Here's a hint: *It's enriching.* Write your answer or best guess in your Science Journal.

776

Theme Connection

Energy Even though the total amount of energy on Earth remains constant, the sources of usable energy are limited. Energy is often transformed from one form to another, such as fossil fuel energy into electricity and then into light energy.

Land, earth, dirt, soil—the ground beneath your feet is called by many names. You walk on it. People build roads and buildings on it. Plants grow in the top, nutrient-rich layer, called topsoil. Plants help keep topsoil in place by protecting it from wind and rain. What happens when topsoil is left unprotected?

Model topsoil loss

1. Use a mixture of moist sand and potting soil to create a miniature landscape in a plastic basin or aluminum-foil baking pan. Form hills and valleys in your landscape.
2. Use clumps of moss to cover areas of your landscape. Leave some sloping portions without plant cover.
3. Simulate a rainstorm over your landscape by spraying water on it from a spray bottle or by pouring a slow stream of water on it from a beaker.

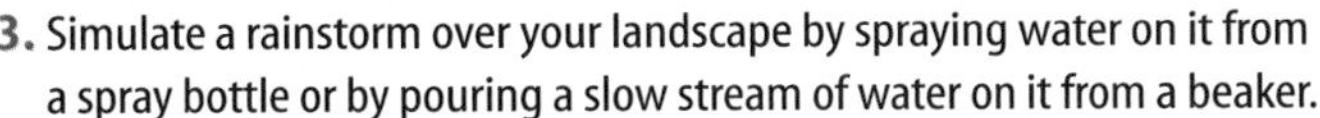

Observe

In your Science Journal record your observations and describe what happened to the land that was not protected by plant cover.

Before You Read

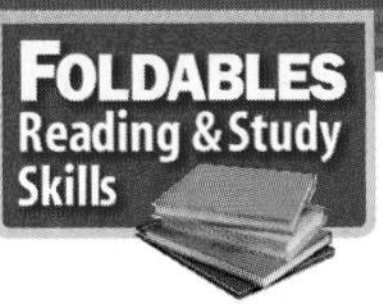

Making a Concept Map Study Fold Make the following Foldable to help you organize information and diagram ideas about renewable and nonrenewable resources.

1. Place a sheet of paper in front of you so the short side is at the top. Fold the bottom of the paper to the top, stopping about four centimeters from the top.
2. Draw an oval above the fold. Write *Natural Resources* inside the oval.
3. Fold the paper in half from the left side to the right side and then unfold. Through the top thickness of the paper, cut along the fold line to form two tabs.
4. Label the tabs *Renewable* and *Nonrenewable* and draw an oval around each word. Draw arrows from the large oval to the smaller ovals.
5. Before you read the chapter, list examples of each type of natural resource you already know on the front of the tabs. As you read the chapter, add to your lists.

777

Explore Activity

Purpose Use the Explore Activity to show students how plant cover protects topsoil. L2 ELL LS **Kinesthetic**

Preparation Mix one part sand and two parts topsoil.

Materials sand and topsoil mixture, containers, clumps of moss or grass, spray bottles, beaker.

Teaching Strategies

- Have students vary the strength of the spray to simulate both light and heavy rainfall and compare the results.
- Point out that water flowing downhill is called "runoff." Have students note the formation of small streams and observe what happens to the land under and around these streams. Students should infer that this is how streams and rivers are formed.

Observe

Water washes the uncovered soil down slopes, forming gullies.

Assessment

Performance Have students reuse the materials to demonstrate the effects of terracing. Remove the plants and form two hills, one with a steady incline and one with a series of ridges (terraces) cut into the incline. Observe what happens as rain falls. Soil does not wash away on the incline with ridges. Use **PASC**, p. 89.

Before You Read

FOLDABLES Reading & Study Skills

Dinah Zike Study Fold

Purpose Students make a Foldable concept map to determine what they know about renewable and nonrenewable natural resources.

For additional help, see Foldables Worksheet, p. 17 in **Chapter Resources Booklet,** or go to the Glencoe Science Web site at **science.glencoe.com.** See After You Read in the Study Guide at the end of this chapter.

SECTION

Resources

1 Motivate

Bellringer Transparency

Display the Section Focus Transparency for Section 1. Use the accompanying Transparency Activity Master. L2 ELL

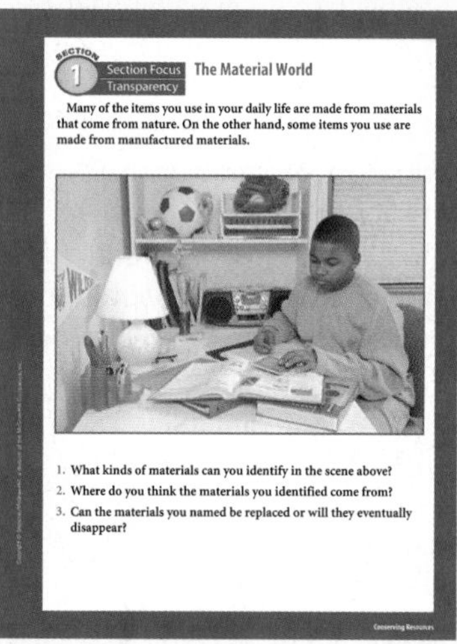

Section Focus Transparency 1 — The Material World

Many of the items you use in your daily life are made from materials that come from nature. On the other hand, some items you use are made from manufactured materials.

1. What kinds of materials can you identify in the scene above?
2. Where do you think the materials you identified come from?
3. Can the materials you named be replaced or will they eventually disappear?

Tie to Prior Knowledge

Hold up a bottle of corn oil and a quart of motor oil. Ask students to explain how they are similar and different? Both are oil and come from living things. Corn is a renewable resource that grew in one summer. The motor oil is a nonrenewable resource that took millions of years to form from the remains of organisms.

SECTION

Resources

As You Read

What You'll Learn

- **Compare** renewable and nonrenewable resources.
- **List** uses of fossil fuels.
- **Identify** alternatives to fossil fuel use.

Vocabulary

natural resource
renewable resource
nonrenewable resource
petroleum
fossil fuel
hydroelectric power
nuclear energy
geothermal energy

Why It's Important

Wise use of natural resources is important for the health of all life on Earth.

Natural Resources

An earthworm burrowing in moist soil eats decaying plant material. A robin catches the worm and flies to a tree. The leaves of the tree use sunlight during photosynthesis. Leaves fall to the ground, decay, and perhaps become an earthworm's meal. What do these living things have in common? They rely on Earth's **natural resources**—the parts of the environment that are useful or necessary for the survival of living organisms.

What kinds of natural resources do you use? Like other organisms, you need food, air, and water. You also use resources that are needed to make everything from clothes to cars. Natural resources supply energy for automobiles and power plants. Although some natural resources are plentiful, others are not.

Renewable Resources The Sun, an inexhaustible resource, provides a constant supply of heat and light. Rain fills lakes and streams with water. When plants carry out photosynthesis, they add oxygen to the air. Sunlight, water, air, and the crops shown in **Figure 1** are examples of renewable resources. A **renewable resource** is any natural resource that is recycled or replaced constantly by nature.

Figure 1
Cotton and wood are renewable resources. A Cotton cloth is used for rugs, curtains, and clothing. A new crop of cotton can be grown every year. B Wood is used for furniture, building materials, and paper. It will take 20 years for these young trees to grow large enough to harvest.

Section Assessment Planner

Portfolio
Physics Integration, p. 781

Performance Assessment
Try at Home MiniLAB, p. 780
Skill Builder Activities, p. 784
See page 806 for more options.

Content Assessment
Section, p. 784
Challenge, p. 784
Chapter, pp. 806–807

Supply and Demand Even though renewable resources are recycled or replaced, they are sometimes in short supply. Rain and melted snow replace the water in streams, lakes, and reservoirs. Sometimes, there may not be enough rain or snowmelt to meet all the needs of people, plants, and animals. In some parts of the world, especially desert regions, water and other resources usually are scarce. Other resources can be used instead, as shown in **Figure 2.**

Nonrenewable Resources Natural resources that are used up more quickly than they can be replaced by natural processes are **nonrenewable resources.** Earth's supply of nonrenewable resources is limited. You use nonrenewable resources when you take home groceries in a plastic bag, paint a wall, or travel by car. Plastics, paints, and gasoline are made from an important nonrenewable resource called petroleum, or oil. **Petroleum** is formed mostly from the remains of microscopic marine organisms buried in Earth's crust. It is nonrenewable because it takes hundreds of millions of years for it to form.

Reading Check *What are nonrenewable resources?*

Minerals and metals found in Earth's crust are nonrenewable resources. Petroleum is a mineral. So are diamonds and the graphite in pencil lead. The aluminum used to make soft-drink cans is a metal. Iron, copper, tin, gold, silver, tungsten, and uranium also are metals. Many manufactured items, like the car shown in **Figure 3,** are made from nonrenewable resources.

Figure 2
In parts of Africa, firewood has become scarce. People in this village now use solar energy instead of wood for cooking.

Figure 3
Iron, a nonrenewable resource, is the main ingredient in steel. Steel is used to make cars, trucks, appliances, buildings, bridges, and even tires. *What other nonrenewable resources are used to build a car?*

2 Teach

Natural Resources

Use an Analogy

Compare nonrenewable resources to a noninterest bearing savings account to which nothing is added. The depletion of the savings account depends on how fast withdrawals are made and how large they are.

Activity

Have pairs work together to make a list of the things they used or relied upon today. Have them circle the items as Food, Transportation, Clothing, or Household Items. Finally, have them make check marks by the items they think are renewable. Have groups compare and discuss their answers. L2 COOP LEARN

IS **Interpersonal**

Reading Check

Answer resources that are used up more quickly than they can be replaced

IDENTIFYING Misconceptions

Some students may not realize that fossil fuels and other mineral resources are nonrenewable. Point out that much of the coal used today was formed during the Carboniferous Period. Have students research how long ago that was. about 345–280 million years ago

Resource Manager 

Chapter Resources Booklet

Transparency Activity, p. 44

Directed Reading for Content Mastery, pp. 19, 20

Reading and Writing Skill Activities, p. 9

Active Reading

News Summary Assign students the job of being television reporters. Allow different students to summarize the information on renewable and nonrenewable resources. Then have students present their summaries to the "television" audience.

Caption Answer

Figure 3 Most of the materials are nonrenewable and include chrome, plastic, and synthetic rubber.

Fossil Fuels

Purpose to "mine" a model mineral deposit and attempt to restore the site to its original condition L1 LS **Kinesthetic**

Materials chocolate-chip, or oatmeal-raisin cookie, or nut filled brownie; paper plate; toothpick

Teaching Strategy Suggest students use drops of water to soften the surface if they have trouble removing the "minerals."

Analysis

1. Students will experience difficulty in the restoration process.
2. The minerals closer to the surface are easier to remove than those found deeper within Earth's crust.
3. An ecosystem could be permanently damaged by mining.

Assessment

Oral Which do you think is more expensive: mining at the surface or deep within Earth's crust? Explain. In general, surface mining is less expensive. It doesn't require as much machinery or time. Use **PASC,** p. 89.

Observing Mineral Mining Effects

Procedure

1. Place a **chocolate chip cookie** on a **paper plate.** Pretend the chips are mineral deposits and the rest of the cookie is Earth's crust.
2. Use a **toothpick** to locate and dig up the mineral deposits. Try to disturb the land as little as possible.
3. When mining is completed, try to restore the land to its original condition.

Analysis

1. How well were you able to restore the land?
2. Compare the difficulty of digging for mineral deposits found close to the surface with digging for those found deep in Earth's crust.
3. Describe environmental changes that might result from a mining operation.

Fossil Fuels

Coal, oil, and natural gas are nonrenewable resources that supply energy. Most of the energy you use comes from these fossil fuels, as the graph in **Figure 4** shows. **Fossil fuels** are fuels formed in Earth's crust over hundreds of millions of years. Cars, buses, trains, and airplanes are powered by gasoline, diesel fuel, and jet fuel, which are made from oil. Coal is used in many power plants to produce electricity. Natural gas is used in manufacturing, for heating and cooking, and sometimes as a vehicle fuel.

Fossil Fuel Conservation Billions of people all over the world use fossil fuels every day. Because fossil fuels are nonrenewable, Earth's supply of them is limited. In the future, they may become more expensive and difficult to obtain. Also, the use of fossil fuels can lead to environmental problems. For example, mining coal can require stripping away thick layers of soil and rock, as shown in **Figure 4,** which destroys ecosystems. Another problem is that fossil fuels must be burned to release the energy stored in them. The burning of fossil fuels produces waste gases that cause air pollution, including smog and acid rain. For these reasons, many people suggest reducing the use of fossil fuels and finding other sources of energy.

You can use simple conservation measures to help reduce fossil fuel use. Switch off the light when you leave a room and turn off the television when you're not watching it. These actions reduce your use of electricity, which often is produced in power plants that burn fossil fuels. Hundreds of millions of automobiles are in use in the United States. Riding in a car pool or taking public transportation uses fewer liters of gasoline than driving alone in a car. Walking or riding a bicycle uses even less fossil fuel. Reducing fossil fuel use has an added benefit—the less you use, the more money you save.

Figure 4
Coal is a fossil fuel. It often is obtained by strip mining, which removes all the soil above the coal deposit. The soil is replaced, but it takes many years for the ecosystem to recover. The graph shows that 84 percent of the energy used in the United States in 1999 came from fossil fuels.

Curriculum Connection

Social Studies Have students investigate ways petroleum was used in ancient cultures. Egyptians used petroleum to help preserve mummies. The Chinese used petroleum to heat and light their homes and to cook. Tar pits supplied crude oil that was used for fuel, cooking, and lighting in Latin America. At the same time, petroleum was used in Europe for lubricating wagon wheels and to make ointments. L3 LS **Naturalist**

Resource Manager

Chapter Resources Booklet
- Note-taking Worksheets, pp. 33–35
- MiniLAB, p. 3
- Enrichment, p. 30

Cultural Diversity, p. 41

Figure 5
Most power plants use turbine generators to produce electricity. In fossil fuel plants, burning fuel boils water and produces steam that turns the turbine.

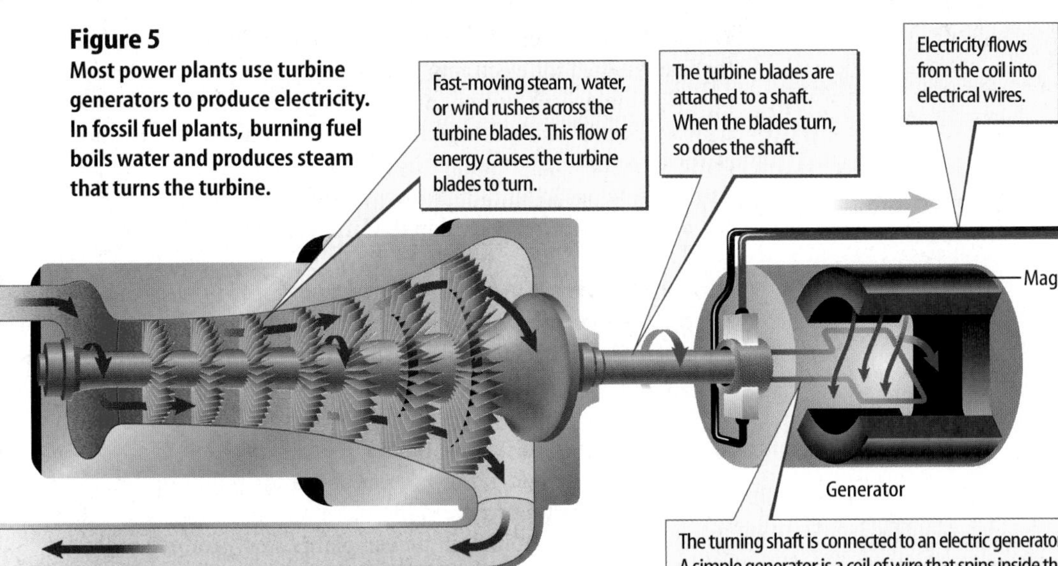

Fast-moving steam, water, or wind rushes across the turbine blades. This flow of energy causes the turbine blades to turn.
The turbine blades are attached to a shaft. When the blades turn, so does the shaft.
Electricity flows from the coil into electrical wires.
Magnet
Generator
The turning shaft is connected to an electric generator. A simple generator is a coil of wire that spins inside the field of a magnet. The turbine shaft spins the coil. The spinning coil generates electricity.
Turbine

Alternatives to Fossil Fuels

Another approach to reducing fossil fuel use is to develop other sources of energy. Much of the electricity used today comes from power plants that burn fossil fuels. As **Figure 5** shows, electricity is generated when a rotating turbine turns a coil of wires in the magnetic field of an electric generator. Fossil-fuel power plants boil water to produce steam that turns the turbine. Alternative energy sources, including water, wind, and atomic energy can be used instead of fossil fuels to turn turbines. Also, solar cells can produce electricity using only sunlight, with no turbines at all. Some of these alternative energy sources—particularly wind and solar energy—are so plentiful they could be considered inexhaustible resources.

Water Power Water is a renewable energy source that can be used to generate electricity. **Hydroelectric power** is electricity that is produced when the energy of falling water is used to turn the turbines of an electric generator. Hydroelectric power does not contribute to air pollution because no fuel is burned. However, it does present environmental concerns. Building a hydroelectric plant usually involves constructing a dam across a river. The dam raises the water level high enough to produce the energy required for electricity generation. Many acres behind the dam are flooded, destroying land habitats and changing part of the river into a lake.

Physics INTEGRATION

Potential energy is stored energy. Kinetic energy is energy in motion, like a car moving along a street. In your Science Journal, explain why water stored behind a dam has potential energy. Describe how this potential energy becomes kinetic energy.

Alternatives to Fossil Fuels

Visual Learning

Figure 5 Have students trace the process of producing electricity using a turbine generator. Then have students identify at which point of the process different energy sources can be used to generate the energy. at the first stage of the process, where the turbine blades are turned

Fun Fact

The movement of coils of wire within a magnetic field is how electricity is produced. This electricity is called alternating current (AC) as opposed to electricity from batteries or photovoltaic cells, which is called direct current (DC).

Discussion

Hydroelectricity is a clean way to produce electricity, but should dams that flood thousands of acres be built? Have students discuss the advantages and disadvantages of this type of electricity production. Advantages: clean, doesn't use nonrenewable resources, provides inexpensive electricity; disadvantages: loss of natural habitats or human communities

Physics INTEGRATION

The water will have potential energy because of its height. As the water falls, it loses height and therefore potential energy. At the same time, the water gains speed, or kinetic energy. Thus potential energy is converted into kinetic energy. P

Inclusion Strategies

Visually Impaired Natural waterfalls are not numerous enough or high enough, so dams are often built to raise the water level. Height is an important determinant of the amount of hydroelectric power produced. Have students feel the effects of water dropped from a cup held one, two, and four feet above their hands. L1
LS **Kinesthetic**

Teacher FYI

Students may wonder why they don't see the water actually turning turbines at waterfalls such as Niagara Falls. The reason is that water diverted before it actually gets to the falls is what goes through the turbines. During the night at Niagara Falls, more water is diverted than in the day in order to keep the daytime visitors happy.

Alternatives to Fossil Fuels, continued

Make a Model

Use a pinwheel and a fan to show how wind can be used to turn a turbine. Give some pinwheels to students and ask them to find the spot on the school grounds that would be best for generating electricity using the wind. L1 ELL
LS **Naturalist**

Some students may think that nuclear radiation makes a person glow or turn green. Combat this misconception by asking students if they turn green when they receive dental X rays, which are a form of radiation.

Discussion

Ask students to compare modern windmills with old-style windmills found in Holland, Spain, or the United States. They both have blades that are turned by the force of the wind. Modern windmills are more streamlined and generate electricity. Older ones were used to grind grain or pump water from underground.

Extension

Have students explain why hydroelectric and wind energy can both be considered forms of solar energy. Solar energy drives the water cycle, which is necessary for hydroelectric energy. The Sun warms areas of Earth's surface, which results in the formation of wind. L2 **Linguistic**

Wind Power Wind power is another renewable energy source that can be used for electricity production. Wind turns the blades of a turbine, which powers an electric generator. When winds blow at least 32 km/h, energy is produced. Wind power does not cause air pollution, but electricity can be produced only when the wind is blowing. So far, wind power accounts for only a small percentage of the electricity used in the United States and Europe.

Nuclear Power Another alternative to fossil fuels makes use of the huge amounts of energy in the nuclei of atoms, as shown in **Figure 6. Nuclear energy** is released when billions of atomic nuclei from uranium, a radioactive element, are split apart in a nuclear fission reaction. This energy is used to produce steam that rotates the turbine blades of an electric generator.

Nuclear power does not contribute to air pollution. However, uranium is a nonrenewable resource, and mining it can disrupt ecosystems. Nuclear power plants also produce radioactive wastes that can seriously harm living organisms. Some of these wastes remain radioactive for thousands of years, and their safe disposal is a problem that has not yet been solved. Accidents are also a danger.

Figure 6
Nuclear power plants are designed to withstand the high energy produced by nuclear reactions.

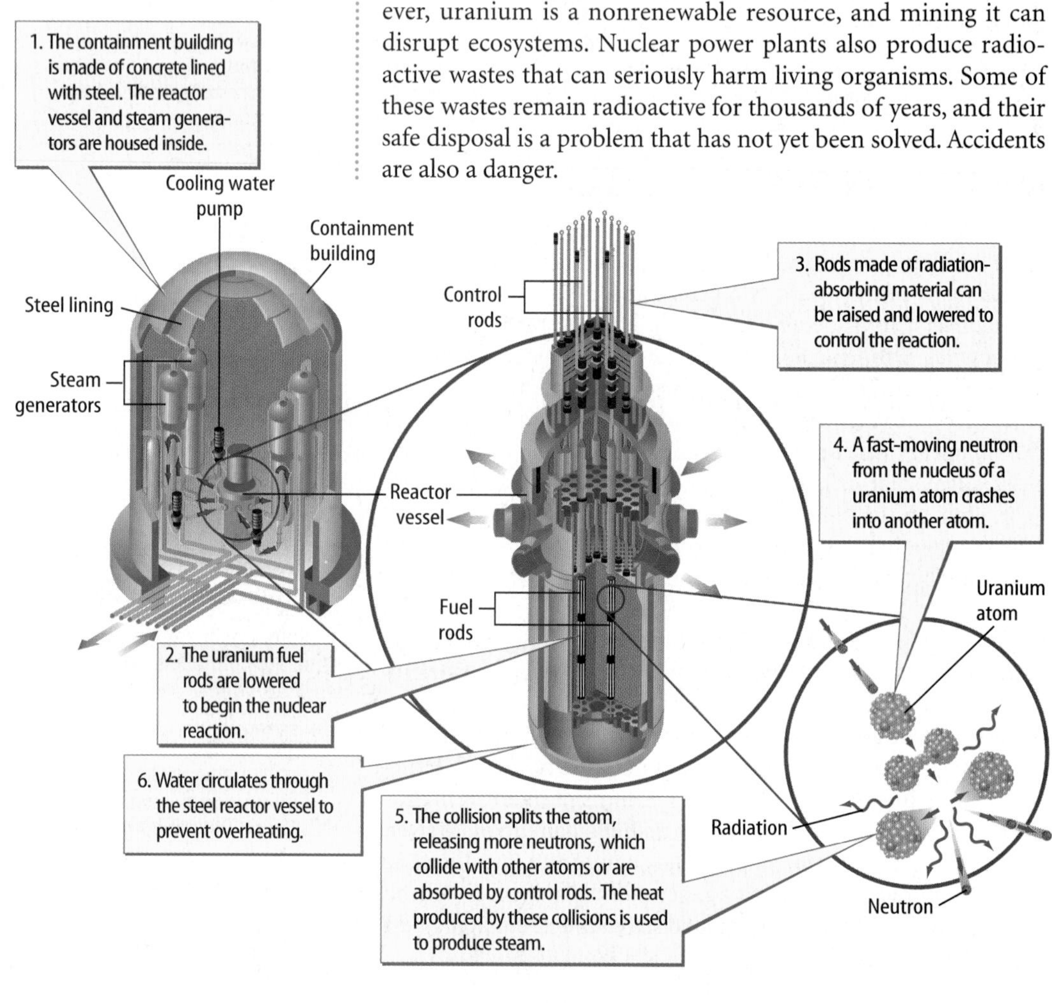

1. The containment building is made of concrete lined with steel. The reactor vessel and steam generators are housed inside.
Cooling water pump
Containment building
Steel lining
Steam generators
Control rods
3. Rods made of radiation-absorbing material can be raised and lowered to control the reaction.
4. A fast-moving neutron from the nucleus of a uranium atom crashes into another atom.
Reactor vessel
Uranium atom
Fuel rods
2. The uranium fuel rods are lowered to begin the nuclear reaction.
6. Water circulates through the steel reactor vessel to prevent overheating.
5. The collision splits the atom, releasing more neutrons, which collide with other atoms or are absorbed by control rods. The heat produced by these collisions is used to produce steam.
Radiation
Neutron

Science Journal

Nuclear Power Plant Sometimes people think something is a good idea but they don't want it in their own backyards. Have students describe in their journals how they might feel and what they might do if they learned of plans to build a nuclear power plant near their neighborhood. L2 LS **Intrapersonal**

Geothermal Energy The hot, molten rock that lies deep beneath Earth's surface is also a source of energy. You see the effects of this energy when lava and hot gases escape from an erupting volcano or when hot water spews from a geyser. The heat energy contained in Earth's crust is called **geothermal energy.** Most geothermal power plants use this energy to produce steam to generate electricity.

Geothermal power plants can be constructed only where there are underground reservoirs of geothermal energy. A geothermal power plant in California uses steam produced by geysers. The island nation of Iceland was formed by volcanoes, and geothermal energy is plentiful there. Geothermal power plants supply heat and electricity to about 90 percent of the homes in Iceland. Outdoor swimming areas also are heated with geothermal energy, as shown in **Figure 7.**

Figure 7
In Iceland, a geothermal power plant pumps hot water out of the ground to heat buildings and generate electricity. Leftover hot water goes into this lake, making it warm enough for swimming even when the ground is covered with snow.

Solar Energy The most inexhaustible source of energy for all life on Earth is the Sun. Solar energy is an alternative to fossil fuels. One use of solar energy is in solar-heated buildings. During winter in the northern hemisphere, the parts of a building that face south receive the most sunlight. Large windows placed on the south side of a building help heat it by allowing warm sunshine into the building during the day. Floors and walls of most solar-heated buildings are made of materials that absorb heat during the day. During the night, the stored heat is released slowly, keeping the building warm. **Figure 8** shows how solar energy can be used.

Figure 8
The Zion National Park Visitor Center in Utah is a solar-heated building designed to save energy. The roof holds solar panels that are used to generate electricity. High windows can be opened to circulate air and help cool the building on hot days. The overhanging roof shades the windows during summer.

Use Science Words

Word Meaning Have students think about the parts of the word *geothermal. Geo* refers to Earth, and *thermal* refers to heat. Have students list other words that have either of these word parts in them. Possible answers: geology, geography, geomagnetic; thermometer, thermostat, homeotherm

Quick Demo

Demonstrate how a radiometer works. First show students the device. Then place it in an area where light will shine on the vanes. Have students speculate what causes the vanes to turn. Block the light, and have them observe the vanes slowing and eventually stopping. Explain that radiant energy is reflected from the polished sides of the vanes and is absorbed by the dark sides of the vanes. This raises the temperature of the dark surfaces. The air near the dark surfaces also is heated and exerts pressure on the dark surfaces, causing the rotor to turn.

Teacher FYI

Nongovernmental organizations in the United States are working to promote the use of solar cooking in regions where firewood has become scarce. In African refugee villages, as well as in many other areas, women and men are trained in making and using simple solar cookers in exchange for spreading this knowledge to their families and friends. Cooker designs are modified to make use of materials that are inexpensive and easy to obtain locally.

Inclusion Strategies

Gifted Have interested students research tidal energy, nuclear fusion, or biomass fuels as alternative energy sources and present their findings in a poster. After students have examined all the posters, have them discuss which energy source they think has the most potential. L3

Resource Manager

Earth Science Critical Thinking/Problem Solving, p. 17

Physical Science Critical Thinking/Problem Solving, p. 17

3 Assess

Reteach

Have students list reasons why renewable resources should be used wisely and nonrenewable resources should be conserved. L1

Challenge

Have students sort the following terms into renewable and nonrenewable resources: sisal, palladium, paprika, topaz, papaya, vinegar, diamond. Suggest they use a dictionary or the Internet to look up unfamiliar words. renewable: sisal, paprika, papaya, vinegar; nonrenewable: topaz, palladium, diamond

Assessment

Oral Have students explain which energy alternative to fossil fuels they think has the most promise to decrease fossil fuel use. Have them justify their answers. Use **Performance Assessment in the Science Classroom,** p. 89.

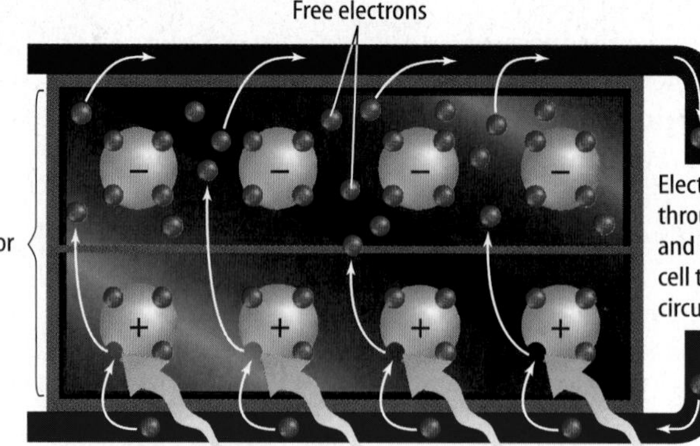

Figure 9
Light energy from the Sun travels in tiny packets of energy called photons. Photons crash into the atoms of PV cells, knocking electrons loose. These electrons create an electric current.

Solar Cells Do you know how a solar-powered calculator works? How do spacecraft use sunlight to generate electricity? These devices use photovoltaic (foht oh vohl TAY ihk) cells to turn sunlight into electric current, as shown in **Figure 9.** Photovoltaic (PV) cells are small and easy to use. However, they produce electricity only in sunlight, so batteries are needed to store electricity for use at night or on cloudy days. Also, PV cells presently are too expensive to use for generating large amounts of electricity. Improvements in this technology continue to be made, and prices probably will go down in the future. As **Figure 10** shows, solar buildings and PV cells are just two of the many ways solar energy can be used to replace fossil fuels.

Section 1 Assessment

1. What are natural resources?
2. Compare and contrast renewable and nonrenewable resources. Give five examples of each.
3. Name five energy sources that provide alternatives to fossil fuels.
4. Describe two ways solar energy can be used to reduce fossil fuel use.
5. **Think Critically** Explain why the water that is used to cool the reactor vessel of a nuclear power plant is kept separate from the water that is heated to produce steam for the turbine generators.

Skill Builder Activities

6. **Concept Mapping** Draw a concept map showing how the following terms are related: *renewable resources, nonrenewable resources, fossil fuels, natural gas, coal, oil, solar energy, PV cells, solar cookers, nuclear energy,* and *geothermal energy.* **For more help, refer to the Science Skill Handbook.**
7. **Solving One-Step Equations** Most cars in the U.S. are driven about 10,000 miles each year. If a car can travel 30 miles on one gallon of gasoline, how many gallons will it use in a year? **For more help, refer to the Math Skill Handbook.**

Answers to Section Assessment

1. the raw materials that organisms use for survival or to enhance life
2. Renewable: can be replaced quickly by nature, include water, plants, animals, sunlight, air; nonrenewable: cannot be replaced quickly by nature, include petroleum, diamonds, metals, phosphorous, topsoil.
3. nuclear, solar, geothermal, wind, and water power
4. Passively, to heat homes (and water) and thus reduce use of fuels for this purpose; directly, to make electricity directly so that fossil fuels don't have to be burned.
5. to prevent possible radioactive contamination
6. Fossil fuels and nuclear energy branch from nonrenewable; fossil fuels is divided into natural gas, coal, and oil. Solar and geothermal energy branch from renewable; solar is divided into PV cells and solar cookers.
7. $10{,}000/30 = 333.33$ gallons per year

NATIONAL GEOGRAPHIC VISUALIZING SOLAR ENERGY

Figure 10

Sunlight is a renewable energy source that provides an alternative to fossil fuels. Solar technologies use the Sun's energy in many ways—from heating to electricity generation.

▲ POWER PLANTS In the Mojave Desert, an experimental solar power plant used hundreds of mirrors to focus sunlight on a water-filled tower. The steam produced by this system could have generated enough electricity to power 2,400 homes.

▼ ELECTRICITY Photovoltaic (PV) cells turn sunlight into electric current. They are commonly used to power small devices, such as calculators. Panels that combine many PV cells provide enough electricity for a home—or an orbiting satellite, such as the International Space Station, below.

▼ COOKING In hot, sunny weather, a solar oven or panel cooker can be used to cook a pot of rice or heat water. The powerful solar cooker shown below reaches even higher temperatures. It is being used to fry food.

▼ INDOOR HEATING South-facing windows and heat-absorbing construction materials turn a room into a solar collector that can help heat an entire building, such as this Connecticut home.

▲ WATER HEATING Water is heated as it flows through small pipes in this roof-mounted solar heat collector. The hot water then flows into an insulated tank for storage.

785

NATIONAL GEOGRAPHIC

Visualizing Solar Energy

Have students examine the pictures and read the captions. Then ask the following questions.

How are photovoltic cells similar to chloroplasts? How are they different? Possible answer: Both chloroplasts and photovoltic cells capture sunlight and turn it into another form of energy. Chloroplasts convert solar energy to chemical energy, and photovoltic cells convert solar energy into electric energy.

What are some potential disadvantages of using solar energy as the only source of energy for your home? How could you overcome these disadvantages? Possible answer: Solar energy might not be consistent or reliable, a cloudy day could result in no heat or electricity. However, a method of storing solar energy for future use would overcome this problem.

Activity

Have students work in pairs to make posters that diagram an innovative way to capture or use the Sun's energy. Encourage creative and different thinking. Have students explain their diagrams to the class.

Extension

Have students research the percentage of energy used in the United States that was supplied by solar energy in the past year. Have the students compare this percentage to the percentage in 1950.

Resource Manager

Chapter Resources Booklet
Reinforcement, p. 27

Mathematics Skill Activities, p. 9

Life Science Critical Thinking/Problem Solving, p. 23

SECTION

Pollution

1 Motivate

Bellringer Transparency

Display the Section Focus Transparency for Section 2. Use the accompanying Transparency Activity Master. L2 ELL

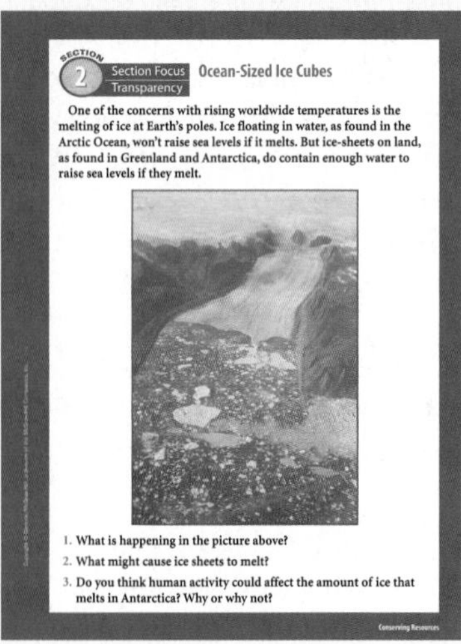

SECTION 2 Section Focus Transparency **Ocean-Sized Ice Cubes**

One of the concerns with rising worldwide temperatures is the melting of ice at Earth's poles. Ice floating in water, as found in the Arctic Ocean, won't raise sea levels if it melts. But ice-sheets on land, as found in Greenland and Antarctica, do contain enough water to raise sea levels if they melt.

1. What is happening in the picture above?
2. What might cause ice sheets to melt?
3. Do you think human activity could affect the amount of ice that melts in Antarctica? Why or why not?

Conserving Resources

Tie to Prior Knowledge

Most students will be familiar with some forms of pollution. Ask for examples. For each example, have students list what people can do to reduce that form of pollution.

SECTION 2

Pollution

As You Read

***What* You'll Learn**

- **Describe** types of air pollution.
- **Identify** causes of water pollution.
- **Explain** methods that can be used to prevent erosion.

Vocabulary

pollutant
acid precipitation
greenhouse effect
ozone depletion
erosion
hazardous waste

***Why* It's Important**

By understanding the causes of pollution, you can help solve pollution problems.

Keeping the Environment Healthy

More than six billion people live on Earth. This large human population puts a strain on the environment, but each person can make a difference. You can help safeguard the environment by paying attention to how your use of natural resources affects air, land, and water.

Air Pollution

On a still, sunny day in almost any large city, you might see a dark haze in the air, like that in **Figure 11.** The haze comes from pollutants that form when wood or fuels are burned. A **pollutant** is a substance that contaminates the environment. Air pollutants include soot, smoke, ash, and gases such as carbon dioxide, carbon monoxide, nitrogen oxides, and sulfur oxides. Wherever cars, trucks, airplanes, factories, homes, or power plants are found, air pollution is likely. Air pollution also can be caused by volcanic eruptions, wind-blown dust and sand, forest fires, and the evaporation of paints and other chemicals.

Smog is a form of air pollution created when sunlight reacts with pollutants produced by burning fuels. It can irritate the eyes and make breathing difficult for people with asthma or other lung diseases. Smog can be reduced if people take buses or trains instead of driving or if they use vehicles, such as electric cars, that produce fewer pollutants than gasoline-powered vehicles.

Figure 11
The term *smog* was used for the first time in the early 1900s to describe the mixture of smoke and fog that often covers large cities in the industrial world.

Section Assessment Planner

Portfolio
Assessment, p. 794

Performance Assessment
MiniLAB, p. 787
Skill Builder Activities, p. 794
See page 806 for more options.

Content Assessment
Section, p. 794
Challenge, p. 794
Chapter, pp. 806–807

Figure 12

A **Compare these two photographs of the same statue. The photo on the left was taken before acid rain became a problem. The photo on the right shows acid rain damage.**
B **The pH scale indicates whether a solution is acidic or basic.**

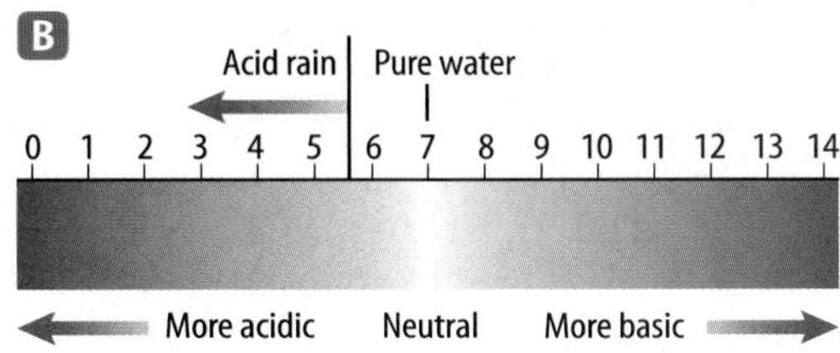

Acid Precipitation

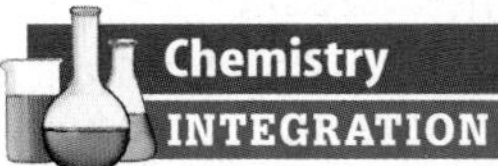

Water vapor condenses on dust particles in the air to form droplets that combine to create clouds. Eventually, the droplets become large enough to fall to the ground as precipitation—mist, rain, snow, sleet, or hail. Air pollutants from the burning of fossil fuels can react with water in the atmosphere to form strong acids. Acidity is measured by a value called pH, as shown in **Figure 12. Acid precipitation** has a pH below 5.6.

Effects of Acid Rain Acid precipitation washes nutrients from the soil, which can lead to the death of trees and other plants. Runoff from acid rain that flows into a lake or pond can lower the pH of the water. If algae and microscopic organisms cannot survive in the acidic water, fish and other organisms that depend on them for food also die.

Preventing Acid Rain Sulfur from burning coal and nitrogen oxides from vehicle exhaust are the pollutants primarily responsible for acid rain. Using low-sulfur fuels, such as natural gas or low-sulfur coal, can help reduce acid precipitation. However, these fuels are less plentiful and more expensive than high-sulfur coal. Smokestacks that remove sulfur dioxide before it enters the atmosphere also help. Reducing automobile use and keeping car engines properly tuned can reduce acid rain caused by nitrogen oxide pollution. The use of electric cars, or hybrid-fuel cars that can run on electricity as well as gasoline, also could help.

Mini LAB

Measuring Acid Rain

Procedure

1. Collect **rainwater** by placing a clean **cup** outdoors. Do not collect rainwater that has been in contact with any object or organism.
2. Dip a piece of **pH indicator paper** into the sample.
3. Compare the color of the paper to the pH chart provided. Record the pH of the rainwater.
4. Use separate pieces of pH paper to test the pH of **tap water** and **distilled water.** Record these results.

Analysis

1. Is the rainwater acidic, basic, or neutral?
2. How does the pH of the rainwater compare with the pH of tap water? With the pH of distilled water?

2 Teach

Acid Precipitation

Discussion

Guide students to predict the effects of increased automobile usage on renewable resources such as trees and crops. Have them draw conclusions about the effects of other human activities on Earth's renewable resources.

Mini LAB

Purpose Students collect samples and determine the pH of rainwater. L2 COOP LEARN

IS **Kinesthetic**

Materials cups, pH probe or pH paper, rain gauge (optional), rainwater, tap water

Teaching Strategies

- If your school has a rain gauge, this is a convenient place to obtain rainwater. Otherwise, cups can be placed outside to catch rain.
- Have students test the pH of rain on different days throughout the school year to detect variations.

Analysis

1. pH of most rainwater is acidic and averages 5.6. Student results may range from a pH of 4 to 7.
2. Tap water pH varies, but in most of the U.S. it is about 6; distilled water always has a pH of 7.

Assessment

Performance Set up several liquids of unknown pH. Have students use pH paper to test each and determine whether it is an acid or base. Then have them make a chart showing the pH of each unknown liquid and comparing the liquids with substances of known pH. Use **PASC,** p. 109.

Resource Manager

Chapter Resources Booklet

Transparency Activity, p. 45
Directed Reading for Content Mastery, p. 21
MiniLAB, p. 4

Curriculum Connection

Social Studies Vinegar is a mild acid that has been used for hundreds of years to preserve foods. Pickles and sauerkraut are examples of foods still eaten today that were developed to take advantage of vinegar's acidic properties, which kill many microorganisms. Have students research other foods that are prepared in pickling solution. Fish, fruits and vegetables, and pig's feet are pickled, to name a few. L2

Greenhouse Effect

Use an Analogy

Compare the greenhouse effect to getting into a car with the windows rolled up on a summer day. It is much hotter inside the car than outside.

Teacher FYI

The greenhouse effect has given Earth a sufficiently warm climate for life to flourish. Venus, however, has such a thick layer of CO_2 that its atmosphere is as hot as an oven. Some scientists predict that if people continue to add CO_2 to our atmosphere, Earth's atmospheric temperatures will increase. Other scientists think that if we produce more CO_2, plants will be able to use it to grow faster.

Visual Learning

Figure 13 Ask students what the glass in the greenhouse is analogous to in the atmosphere. carbon dioxide

Internet Addresses

Explore the Glencoe Science Web site at **science.glencoe.com** to find out more about topics in this section.

SCIENCE Online

Research Visit the Glencoe Science Web site at **science.glencoe.com** for information about the hypothesis that rising levels of carbon dioxide in the atmosphere cause global warming. In your Science Journal, write one fact that supports the hypothesis and one fact that does not.

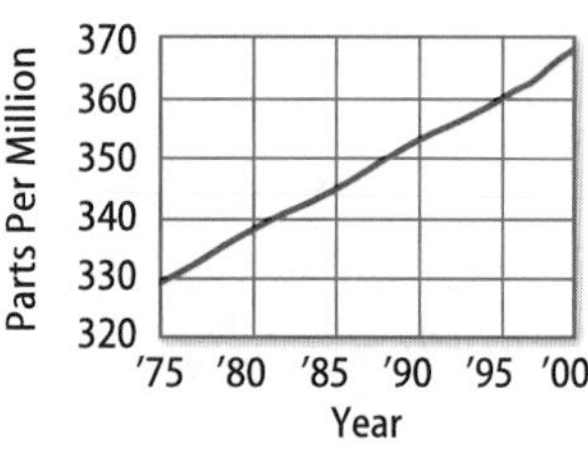

Figure 13
The moment you step inside a greenhouse, you feel the results of the greenhouse effect. Heat is trapped by the glass walls. In a similar way, atmospheric greenhouse gases trap heat close to Earth's surface.

Greenhouse Effect

Energy from the Sun travels through the atmosphere to Earth's surface. Some of this energy normally is re-emitted back into space. The rest is trapped by certain atmospheric gases, as shown in **Figure 13.** This heat-trapping feature of the atmosphere is the **greenhouse effect.** Without it, temperatures on Earth probably would be too cold to support life.

Atmospheric gases that trap heat are called greenhouse gases. One of the most important greenhouse gases is carbon dioxide (CO_2). CO_2 is a normal part of the atmosphere. It is also a by-product that forms when fossil fuels are burned. Over the past century, more fossil fuels have been burned than ever before, which is increasing the percentage of CO_2 in the atmosphere. The atmosphere might be trapping more of the Sun's heat, making Earth warmer. A rise in Earth's average temperature, possibly caused by an increase in greenhouse gases, is known as global warming.

Global Warming Temperature data collected from 1900 through 2000 indicate that Earth's temperature increased by about 0.6°C over that 100-year period. Most of this temperature increase occurred between the years 1910 and 1945 and between the years 1976 to 2000. No one is certain whether this increase in temperature was caused by human activities or is a natural part of Earth's weather cycle. For example, the output of energy from the Sun varies by small amounts. These variations in solar output might cause climate to change. Volcanic eruptions also can affect global temperatures, although they usually cause temperatures to decrease for several years after the eruption. Global warming might cause rainfall patterns to change and could affect the rate of plant growth.

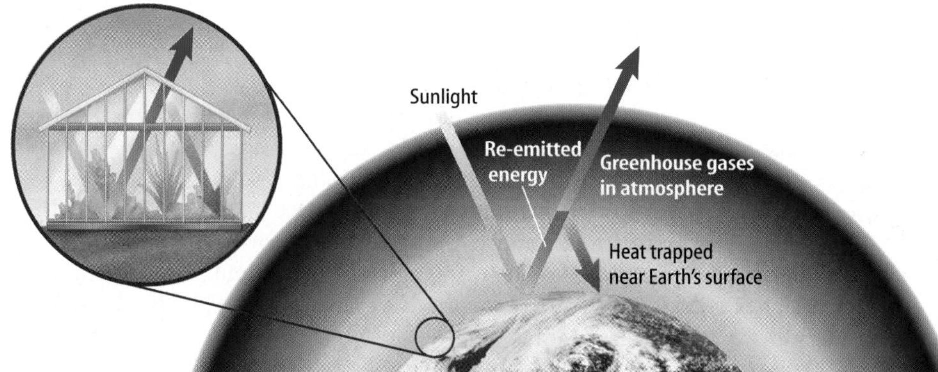

LAB DEMONSTRATION

Purpose to use changes in color to determine relative pH

Materials purple cabbage, hot plate, pot, water, strainer, 4 test tubes, stand, goggles, test materials: club soda, vinegar, ammonia, baking soda water

Preparation Boil the cabbage, cool, and strain. Retain the liquid.

Procedure Explain that purple cabbage juice can be used as a pH indicator. Add 1″ juice to each tube. Add a small amount of one test material to each tube. Observe.

Expected Outcome Acids turn cabbage juice purple, bases turn it blue. The darker the color, the stronger the acid or base.

Assessment

Have students sort the test materials into acids vinegar, club soda and bases ammonia, baking soda. Set up another tube. Add lemon juice until the color changes. Have students identify lemon juice as an acid or base. acid

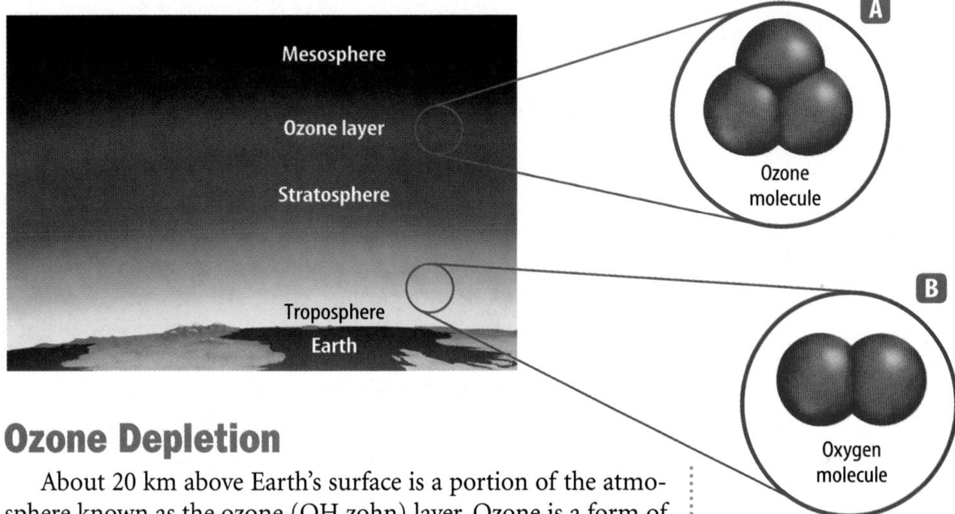

Ozone Depletion

About 20 km above Earth's surface is a portion of the atmosphere known as the ozone (OH zohn) layer. Ozone is a form of oxygen, as shown in **Figure 14.** The ozone layer absorbs some of the Sun's harmful ultraviolet (UV) radiation. UV radiation can damage living cells.

Every year, the ozone layer temporarily becomes thinner over each polar region during its spring season. The thinning of the ozone layer is called **ozone depletion.** This problem is caused by certain pollutant gases, especially chlorofluorocarbons (klor oh FLOR oh kar bunz) (CFCs). CFCs are used in the cooling systems of refrigerators, freezers, and air conditioners. When CFCs leak into the air, they slowly rise into the atmosphere until they arrive at the ozone layer. CFCs react chemically with ozone, breaking apart the ozone molecules.

UV Radiation Because of ozone depletion, the amount of UV radiation that reaches Earth's surface could be increasing. UV radiation could be causing a rise in the number of skin cancer cases in humans. It also might be harming other organisms. The ozone layer is so important to the survival of life on Earth that world governments and industries have agreed to stop making and using CFCs.

Ozone that is high in the upper atmosphere protects life on Earth. Near Earth's surface though, it can be harmful. Ozone is produced when fossil fuels are burned. This ozone stays in the lower atmosphere, where it pollutes the air. Ozone damages the lungs and other sensitive tissues of animals and plants. For example, it can cause the needles of a Ponderosa pine to drop, harming growth.

Reading Check ***What is the difference between ozone in the upper atmosphere and ozone in the lower atmosphere?***

Figure 14
The atmosphere's ozone layer absorbs large amounts of UV radiation, preventing it from reaching Earth's surface.
A Ozone molecules are made of three oxygen atoms. They are formed in a chemical reaction between sunlight and oxygen.
B The oxygen you breathe has two oxygen atoms in each molecule.

Ozone Depletion

Teacher FYI

Although the production of CFC has halted, there is a reserve supply available for air conditioning and refrigeration units. In many cases, HFCs are being used as coolants to replace CFCs, as they do not lead to ozone depletion.

Quick Demo

Have two students join hands to represent the normal state of oxygen (O_2) and three students join hands to represent ozone (O_3).

Reading Check

Answer Ozone in the upper atmosphere is helpful to life; ozone in the lower atmosphere can be harmful to life as it pollutes the air.

IDENTIFYING Misconceptions

Students sometimes confuse common environmental problems. For example, they may think that not littering will help with the problem of acid rain. Make sure that for each problem, students understand the related causes and effects and what can be done to reduce the problem.

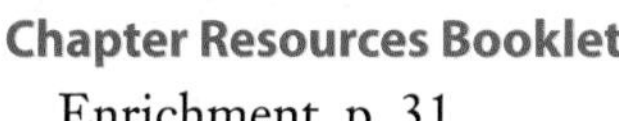

Resource Manager

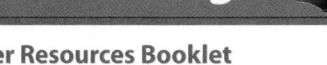

Chapter Resources Booklet
Enrichment, p. 31

Reading and Writing Skill Activities, p. 19

Performance Assessment in the Science Classroom, p. 48

Cultural Diversity

Sun Exposure Australia leads the world in skin cancer because of the many fair-skinned people, the ozone hole over the country, and changes in culture. In the past, wealthy Australians avoided the Sun. After WWI, Australians embraced a tanned look. As a result, skin cancer rates rapidly increased. It has now become a culturally accepted practice to have children wear hats when they go outside.

Indoor Air Pollution

Discussion

Why might better-insulated buildings make indoor air pollution more of a problem? Less air enters and leaves a building. **Why do radon levels tend to be higher in wintertime?** People are more likely to keep windows tightly closed. Have students discuss the pros and cons of insulating buildings to this extent.

Health INTEGRATION

Carbon monoxide has an affinity for hemoglobin in red blood cells, so when it attaches, it doesn't let go. This prevents red blood cells from functioning properly. Because of this, appliances designed for outdoor use should only be used outdoors, as they often are not equipped with ventilation devices for indoor use.

Teacher FYI

Radon is the second leading cause of lung cancer in the United States. Cigarette smoking is the leading cause.

IDENTIFYING Misconceptions

Some students may think that people are responsible for all pollutants. Although many pollutants can be traced to people, radon is a naturally occurring substance. It is formed from the radioactive decay of uranium present in soil.

Health INTEGRATION

Carbon monoxide enters the body through the lungs. It attaches to red blood cells, preventing the cells from absorbing oxygen. In your Science Journal, explain why heaters and barbecues designed for outdoor use never should be used indoors.

Indoor Air Pollution

Air pollution can occur indoors. Today's buildings are better insulated to conserve energy. However, better insulation reduces the flow of air into and out of a building, so air pollutants can build up indoors. For example, burning cigarettes release hazardous particles and gases into the air. Even nonsmokers can suffer ill effects from secondhand cigarette smoke. As a result, smoking no longer is allowed in many public and private buildings. Paints, carpets, glues and adhesives, printers, and photocopy machines also give off dangerous gases, including formaldehyde. Like cigarette smoke, formaldehyde is a carcinogen, which means it can cause cancer.

Carbon Monoxide Carbon monoxide (CO) is a colorless, odorless, poisonous gas that is produced whenever charcoal, natural gas, kerosene, or other fuels are burned. CO is difficult to detect and CO poisoning can cause serious illness or death. Fuel-burning cooking or heating equipment must be vented to the outside to prevent CO from building up indoors. Alarms are available that warn of dangerous CO buildup.

Radon Radon is a naturally occurring, radioactive gas that is given off by some types of rock and soil, as shown in **Figure 15.** Radon has no color or odor. It can seep into basements and the lower floors of buildings. Radon exposure is the second leading cause of lung cancer in this country. A radon detector sounds an alarm when levels of the gas in indoor air become too high. If radon is present, increasing a building's ventilation can eliminate any damaging effects.

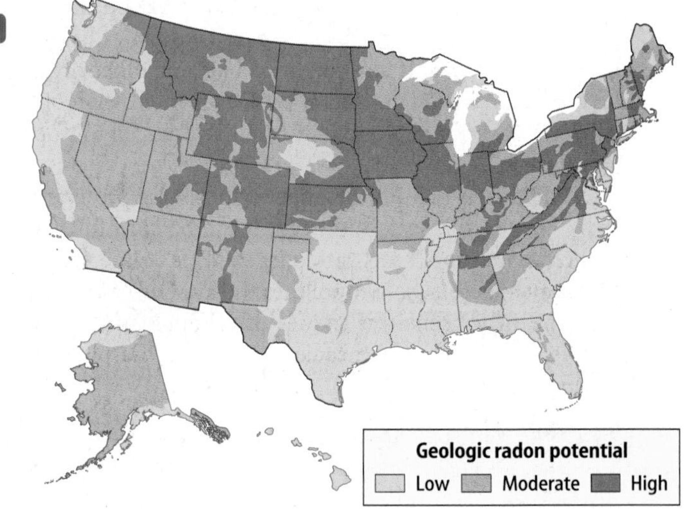

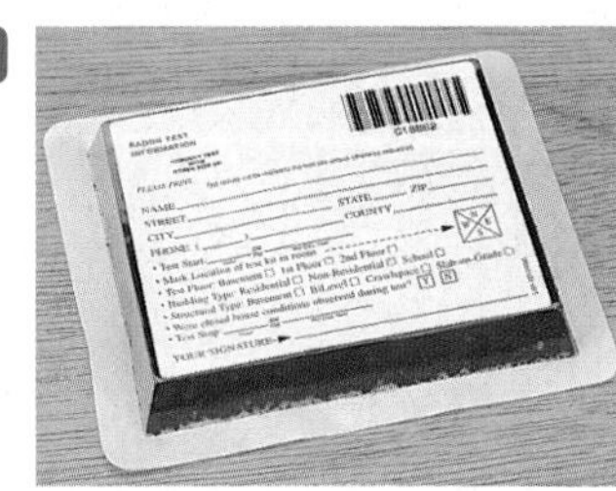

Figure 15
A The map shows the potential for radon exposure in different parts of the United States. Soils of the northern and northeastern portions of the country produce more radon gas than in most other areas. B A radon detection kit can tell the user if a dangerous level of radon is present.

Teacher FYI

If combustion were complete, only carbon dioxide and water would be produced. Complete combustion is hard to achieve, especially in a barbecue. This is why barbecues should not be used indoors.

Curriculum Connection

Health Have students research sources of indoor air pollution. Suggest different students study the effects of asbestos, formaldehyde, radon, cigarette smoke, and other substances found in homes. Have students combine their findings and present them as an informative bulletin board. L2 COOP LEARN

A When rain falls on roads and parking lots, it can wash oil and grease onto the soil and into nearby streams.

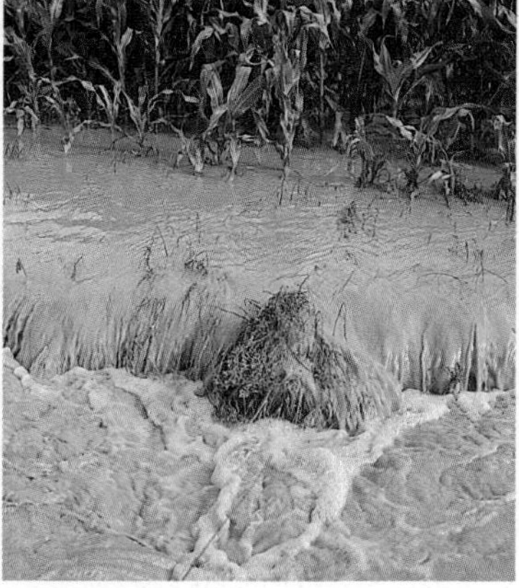

B Rain can wash agricultural pesticides and fertilizers into lakes, streams, or oceans.

C Industrial wastes are sometimes released directly into surface waters.

Figure 16
Pollution of surface waters can occur in several ways.

Water Pollution

Pollutants enter water, too. Air pollutants can drift into water or be washed out of the sky by rain. Rain can wash land pollutants into waterways, as shown in **Figure 16.** Wastewater from factories and sewage-treatment plants often is released into waterways. In the United States and many other countries, laws require that wastewater be treated to remove pollutants before it is released. But, in many parts of the world, wastewater treatment is not always possible. Pollution also enters water when people dump litter or waste materials into rivers, lakes, and oceans.

Surface Water Some water pollutants poison fish and other wildlife, and can be harmful to people who swim in or drink the water. For example, chemical pesticides sprayed on farmland can wash into lakes and streams. These chemicals can harm the insects that fish, turtles, or frogs rely on for food. Shortages of food can lead to deaths among water-dwelling animals. Some pollutants, especially those containing mercury and other metals, can build up in the tissues of fish. Eating contaminated fish and shellfish can transfer these metals to people, birds, and other animals. In some areas, people are advised not to eat fish or shellfish taken from polluted waterways.

Algal blooms are another water pollution problem. Raw sewage and excess fertilizer contain large amounts of nitrogen. If they are washed into a lake or pond, they can cause the rapid growth of algae. When the algae die, they are decomposed by huge numbers of bacteria that use up much of the oxygen in the water. Fish and other organisms can die from a lack of oxygen in the water.

Water Pollution

Quick Demo

Drop food coloring into a glass jar or beaker full of water. Have students observe how the color spreads out and occupies the entire area. Explain that dumping a little waste into a lake might not be bad, but as more is added, the concentration increases. Add more drops of food coloring to illustrate this concept. LS **Visual-Spatial**

Activity

Obtain some aquarium water that has algae growing in it. Have students add varying amounts of commercial fertilizer to test tubes of the water. Place the tubes in sunlight, and add fresh water as the old water evaporates. In a few days, students should observe an algal bloom in one or more of the tubes. Continue the activity so that students can observe the effect of algal decay on the quality of the water. L2
LS **Kinesthetic**

Resource Manager

Chapter Resources Booklet

Lab Activity, pp. 9–12
Transparency Activity, pp. 47–48

Cultural Diversity

Significance of Water Water is so important for civilization that it has becomes part of human culture. Water and waterscapes have been described in words, drawings, songs, and other art forms by all cultures on Earth. Water also plays an important part in religion. From Japanese Shintoism to Christianity, water symbolizes cleansing in spiritual ceremonies.

Water Pollution, continued

Activity

Float some corn oil on the surface of water in a beaker. Ask students to try and clean up the oil with balls of cotton. They will observe that it is possible, but not very easy. L1 ELL

Visual Learning

Figure 18 Have students study the illustration. Emphasize that groundwater is an important source of water for many people. Then prepare a beaker with sand or soil on top and gravel on the bottom. Pour a little water on the soil's surface and show students how the water percolates through the layers to the bottom of the beaker. Have students relate this to the movement of groundwater shown in the illustration. LS **Visual-Spatial**

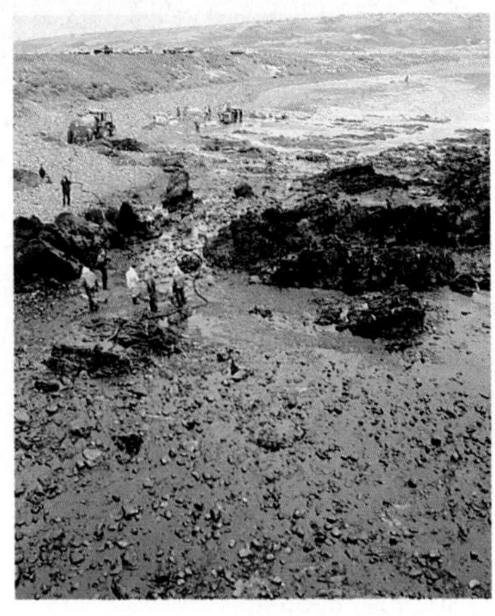

Figure 17
In 1996, the oil tanker *Sea Empress* spilled more than 72 million kg of oil into the sea along the coast of Wales. More than $40 million was spent on the cleanup effort, but thousands of ocean organisms were destroyed, including birds, fish, and shellfish.

Ocean Water Rivers and streams eventually flow into oceans, bringing their pollutants along. Also, polluted water can enter the ocean in coastal areas where factories, sewage-treatment plants, or shipping activities are located. Oil spills are a well-known ocean pollution problem. About 4 billion kg of oil are spilled into ocean waters every year. Much of that oil comes from ships that use ocean water to wash out their fuel tanks. Oil also can come from oil tanker wrecks, as shown in **Figure 17.**

Groundwater Pollution can affect water that seeps underground, as shown in **Figure 18.** Groundwater is water that collects between particles of soil and rock. It comes from precipitation and runoff that soaks into the soil. This water can flow slowly through permeable layers of rock called aquifers. If this water comes into contact with pollutants as it moves through the soil and into an aquifer, the aquifer could become polluted. Polluted groundwater is difficult—and sometimes impossible—to clean. In some parts of the country, chemicals leaking from underground storage tanks have created groundwater pollution problems.

Figure 18
Water from rainfall slowly filters through sand or soil until it is trapped in underground aquifers. Pollutants picked up by the water as it filters through the soil can contaminate water wells.

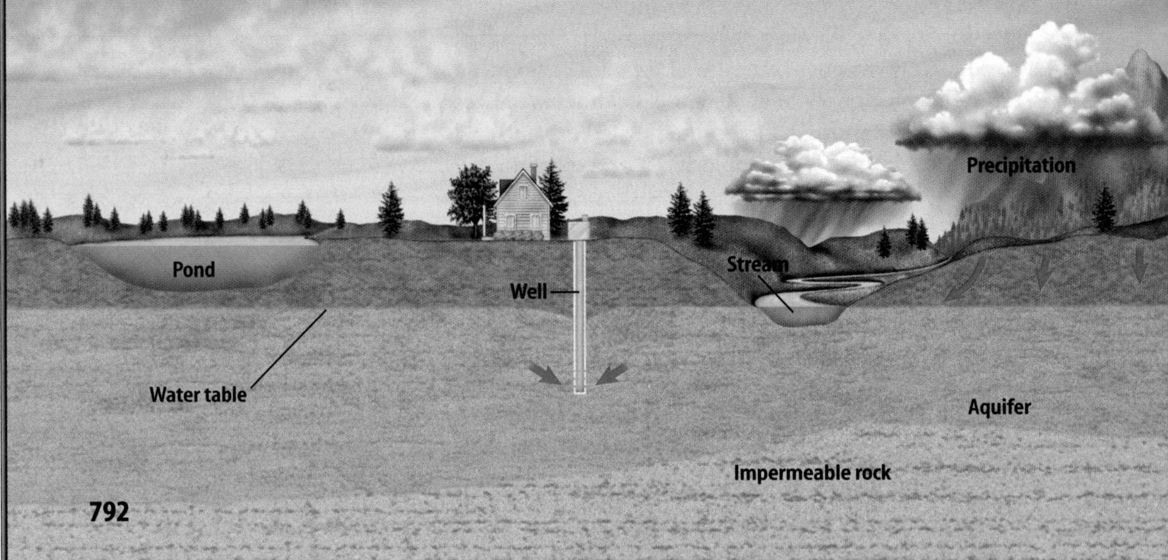

Science Journal

Well Water Have students imagine that they depend on a well as their source of water. They find out that pesticides that can injure their health have seeped into the groundwater the well draws from. Have students write in their Science Journals the changes they will make in their use of the well's water. L2 LS **Intrapersonal**

Inclusion Strategies

Hearing Impaired Fill a funnel with soil and place in a beaker. Add a teaspoon of food coloring to the top of the soil. Slowly pour water through the funnel. At first, water flowing out of the funnel is probably clear, but eventually colored water exits. Explain that soil may act as a filter for a time, but eventually pollutants will work their way through the soil. L1 ELL

A **Contour plowing reduces the downhill flow of water.**

Soil Loss

Fertile topsoil is important to plant growth. New topsoil takes hundreds or thousands of years to form. The Explore Activity at the beginning of this chapter shows that rain washes away loose topsoil. Wind also blows it away. The movement of soil from one place to another is called **erosion** (ih ROH zhun). Eroded soil that washes into a river or stream can block sunlight and slow photosynthesis. It also can harm fish, clams, and other organisms. Erosion is a natural process, but human activities increase it. When a farmer plows a field or a forest is cut down, soil is left bare. Bare soil is more easily carried away by rain and wind. **Figure 19** shows some methods farmers use to reduce soil erosion.

Soil Pollution

Soil can become polluted when air pollutants drift to the ground or when water leaves pollutants behind as it flows through the soil. Soil also can be polluted when people toss litter on the ground or dispose of trash in landfills.

Solid Wastes What happens to the trash you throw out every week? What do people do with old refrigerators, TVs, and toys? Most of this solid waste is dumped in landfills. Most landfills are designed to seal out air and water. This helps prevent pollutants from seeping into surrounding soil, but it slows normal decay processes. Even food scraps and paper, which usually break down quickly, can last for decades in a landfill. In populated areas, landfills fill up quickly. Reducing the amount of trash people generate can reduce the need for new landfills.

Figure 19
The farming methods shown here help prevent soil erosion. *Why is soil erosion a concern for farmers?*

B **On steep hillsides, flat areas called terraces reduce downhill flow.**

C **In strip cropping, cover crops are planted between rows to reduce wind erosion.**

D **In no-till farming, soil is never left bare.**

Soil Loss

Caption Answer

Figure 19 Erosion carries away nutrient-rich topsoil that farmers need to grow crops.

Soil Pollution

Quick Demo

Bring a container of trash to class. Include a glass bottle, an aluminum can, plastic wrappers, a coffee filter with grounds, vegetable peelings, eggshells, and other household items. While wearing rubber gloves, remove each item and have students discuss whether the item is biodegradable. Explain that the biodegradable wastes may decay, but the nonbiodegradable wastes will not.
LS **Logical-Mathematical**

Extension

Ask students to contact their town officials or trash collection agency to find out what happens to trash after it leaves their homes. Ask students to present their findings to the class. L2

Activity

Many household cleaners contain toxic chemicals. Numerous new products are available that are just as effective, but do not contain harmful chemicals. Have students obtain an adult's permission to investigate cleaning products in their homes to see what kinds of ingredients they contain. Caution students to take care when handling cleaning products or other chemicals. L2

Resource Manager

Earth Science Critical Thinking/Problem Solving, p. 7

Reading and Writing Skill Activities, p. 29

Teacher FYI

Pollution refers to the degradation of the environment. Erosion fits into this definition because as valuable topsoil is lost, land becomes less fertile. The erosion of land in arid areas may make these places resemble deserts, a process called desertification.

Soil Pollution, continued

Reading Check

Answer Hazardous wastes are waste materials that are harmful to human health or poisonous to other living things.

3 Assess

Reteach

Have students make a chart summarizing the causes and effects of air pollution, soil pollution, and water pollution. L1

Challenge

Challenge students to calculate the following: **If your family produces an average of 1.8 kg of solid waste per person per day, how much waste will your entire family generate in the month of October?** Answers will vary depending on the number of family members (f). Students should use the following equation to solve this problem: $(f \times 1.8) \times 31 =$ amount of waste produced by the family.

Assessment

Content Have student pairs work together to write a song or poem about the dangers of environmental pollution. Use **PASC,** p. 151. P

Figure 20
Leftover paints, batteries, pesticides, drain cleaners, and medicines are hazardous wastes that should not be discarded in the trash. They should never be poured down a drain, onto the ground, or into a storm sewer. Most communities have collection facilities where people can dispose of hazardous materials like these.

Hazardous Wastes Waste materials that are harmful to human health or poisonous to living organisms are **hazardous wastes.** They include dangerous chemicals, such as pesticides, oil, and petroleum-based solvents used in industry. They also include radioactive wastes from nuclear power plants, from hospitals that use radioactive materials to treat disease, and from nuclear weapons production. Many household items also are considered hazardous like those shown in **Figure 20.** If these materials are dumped into landfills, they could seep into the soil, surface water, or groundwater over time. Hazardous wastes usually are handled separately from other types of trash. They are sealed in steel drums or treated in other ways to prevent them from polluting the environment.

Reading Check *What are hazardous wastes?*

Section 2 Assessment

1. List four ways in which air pollution affects the environment.
2. In what ways can an algal bloom affect pond life?
3. What methods can farmers use to prevent erosion?
4. Describe the possible causes and effects of ozone depletion.
5. **Think Critically** How could hazardous chemicals deposited in landfills eventually affect groundwater?

Skill Builder Activities

6. **Comparing and Contrasting** Compare and contrast the causes and effects of air and water pollution. **For more help, refer to the Science Skill Handbook.**
7. **Solving One-Step Equations** A pH of 4 is ten times more acidic than a pH of 5. A pH of 5 is ten times more acidic than a pH of 6. How many times more acidic is a solution with pH 4 than one with pH 6? **For more help, refer to the Math Skill Handbook.**

Answers to Section Assessment

1. smog, acid rain, enhanced greenhouse effect, ozone depletion
2. Algal blooms grow and eventually die. Their decay uses up oxygen, making it difficult for other organisms to survive.
3. contour farming, terracing, strip cropping, no-till farming
4. CFCs that escape into the air can cause ozone depletion; as ozone is depleted, more UV radiation reached Earth, resulting in more cases of skin cancer.
5. They can leach into the soil and be picked up by groundwater, making the water hazardous for people to drink.
6. The burning of fossil fuels causes most air pollution. Water pollution occurs when runoff carries pollutants from dumps and landfills into waterways. It also may occur from direct dumping of wastes into water. Air pollution causes smog, acid rain, enhanced greenhouse effect, and ozone depletion. Water pollution may cause algal blooms, the death of aquatic organisms, and contamination of drinking supplies.
7. A solution with a pH of 4 is 100 times more acidic than a solution with a pH of 6.

Activity

The Greenhouse Effect

You can create models of Earth with and without heat-reflecting greenhouse gases. Then, experiment with the models to observe the greenhouse effect.

What You'll Investigate

How does the greenhouse effect influence temperatures on Earth?

Materials

1-L clear, plastic, soft-drink bottle with top cut off and label removed (2)
thermometer (2)
*temperature probe
potting soil
masking tape
plastic wrap
rubber band
lamp with 100-W lightbulb
watch or clock with second hand
*Alternate materials

Goals

- **Observe** the greenhouse effect.
- **Describe** the effect that a heat source has on an environment.

Safety Precautions

Procedure

1. Copy the data table and use it to record your temperature measurements.
2. Put an equal volume of potting soil in the bottom of each container.
3. Use masking tape to attach a thermometer to the inside of each container. Place each thermometer at the same height above the soil. Shield each thermometer bulb by putting a double layer of masking tape over it.
4. Seal the top of one container with plastic wrap held in place with a rubber band.
5. Place the lamp with the exposed 100-W lightbulb between the two containers and exactly 1 cm away from each. Do not turn on the light.
6. Let the setup sit for 5 min, then record the temperature in each container.
7. Turn on the light. Record the temperature in each container every 2 min for 15 min to 20 min. Graph the results.

Changes in Temperature

Time (min)	Open Container Temperature (°C)	Closed Container Temperature (°C)
0		
2		
4		
6		

Conclude and Apply

1. **Compare and contrast** temperatures in each container at the end of the experiment.
2. What does the lightbulb represent in this experimental model? What does the plastic wrap represent?

Communicating Your Data

Average the data obtained in the experiments conducted by all the groups in your class. Prepare a line graph of these data. **For more help, refer to the** Science Skill Handbook.

Activity

BENCH TESTED

Purpose Students make models of the atmosphere and determine what happens when light shines on the model. L2 COOP LEARN

IS **Interpersonal**

Process Skills modeling, observing and inferring, interpreting data, communicating, comparing and contrasting, recognizing cause and effect, measuring in SI, making and using tables, making and using graphs

Time Required 50 minutes

Safety Precautions Caution students to use care in working with thermometers and 100-W light bulbs. Use only alcohol thermometers.

Teaching Strategies

- Drafts can affect results.
- Make sure the thermometers face outward to make it easier for students to read them.

Troubleshooting If the two thermometers did not read the same temperature when the experiment began, adjust readings so both data sets can be plotted on the same graph.

Answers to Questions

1. The temperatures of both containers has increased. The container covered with plastic wrap had a greater increase.
2. The light bulb represents the Sun; the plastic wrap represents carbon dioxide in the atmosphere.

Resource Manager

Chapter Resources Booklet
Reinforcement, p. 28
Activity Worksheet, pp. 5–6

Physical Science Critical Thinking/Problem Solving, p. 12

Communicating Your Data

Have students write the final temperatures for the two conditions on the board. Students should compare data and see if the results were the same for everyone. Discuss how differences may have occurred.

Assessment

Oral Have students summarize the information in their graphs in writing. Make sure summaries are clear and concise. Use **Performance Assessment in the Science Classroom,** p. 159.

SECTION

The Three Rs of Conservation

1 Motivate

Bellringer Transparency

Display the Section Focus Transparency for Section 3. Use the accompanying Transparency Activity Master. L2 ELL

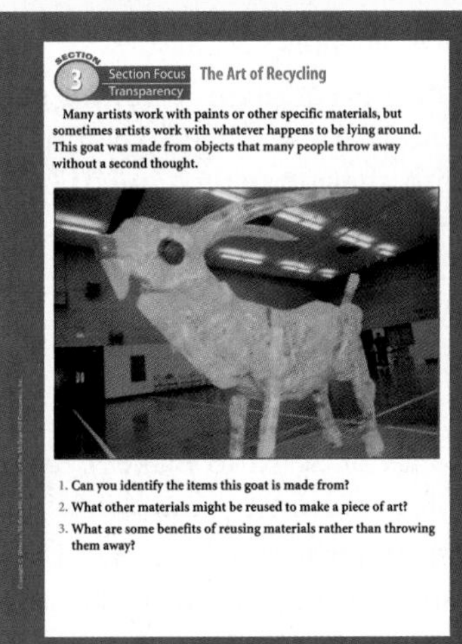

SECTION 3 Section Focus Transparency **The Art of Recycling**

Many artists work with paints or other specific materials, but sometimes artists work with whatever happens to be lying around. This goat was made from objects that many people throw away without a second thought.

1. **Can you identify the items this goat is made from?**
2. **What other materials might be reused to make a piece of art?**
3. **What are some benefits of reusing materials rather than throwing them away?**

Conserving Resources

Tie to Prior Knowledge

Most students will be familiar with the idea of recycling. Ask the class to describe some things that are commonly recycled. Ask for reasons why we recycle.

SECTION 3

The Three Rs of Conservation

As You Read

What **You'll Learn**

- **Recognize** ways you can reduce your use of natural resources.
- **Explain** how you can reuse resources to promote conservation.
- **Describe** how many materials can be recycled.

Vocabulary
recycling

Why **It's Important**

Conservation preserves resources and reduces pollution.

Conservation

A teacher travels to school in a car pool. In the school cafeteria, students place glass bottles and cans in separate containers from the rest of the garbage. Conservation efforts like these can help prevent shortages of natural resources, slow growth of landfills, reduce pollution levels, and save people money. Every time a new landfill is created, an ecosystem is disturbed. Reducing the need for landfills is a major benefit of conservation. The three Rs of conservation are reduce, reuse, and recycle.

Reduce

You contribute to conservation whenever you reduce your use of natural resources. You use less fossil fuel when you walk or ride a bicycle instead of taking the bus or riding in a car. If you buy a carton of milk, reduce your use of petroleum by telling the clerk you don't need a plastic bag to carry it in.

You also can avoid buying things you don't need. For example, most of the paper, plastic, and cardboard used to package items for display on store shelves is thrown away as soon as the product is brought home. You can look for products with less packaging or with packaging made from recycled materials. What are some other ways you can reduce your use of natural resources?

Reuse

Another way to help conserve natural resources is to use items more than once. Reusing an item means using it again without changing it or reprocessing it, as shown in **Figure 21.** Bring reusable canvas bags to the grocery store to carry home your purchases. Donate clothes you've outgrown to charity so that others can reuse them. Take reusable plates and utensils on picnics instead of disposable paper items.

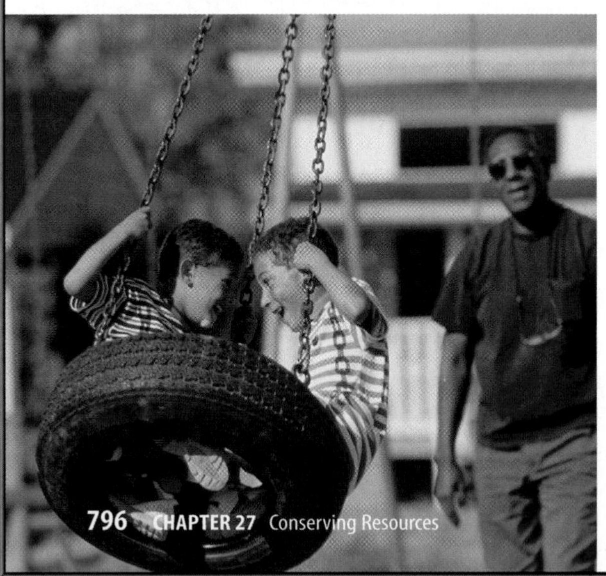

Figure 21
Automobile tires are almost indestructible. They usually are disposed of but can have other useful purposes.

Section Assessment Planner

PORTFOLIO
Challenge, p. 799

PERFORMANCE ASSESSMENT
Problem-Solving Activity, p. 798
Skill Builder Activities, p. 799
See page 806 for more options.

CONTENT ASSESSMENT
Section, p. 799
Challenge, p. 799
Chapter, pp. 806–807

Recycle

If you can't avoid using an item, and if you can't reuse it, the next best thing is to recycle it. **Recycling** is a form of reuse that requires changing or reprocessing an item or natural resource. If your city or town has a curbside recycling program, you already separate recyclables from the rest of your garbage. Materials that can be recycled include glass, metals, paper, plastics, and yard and kitchen waste.

Reading Check *How is recycling different from reusing?*

Plastics Plastic is more difficult to recycle than other materials, mainly because several types of plastic are in use. A recycle code marked on every plastic container indicates the type of plastic it is made of. Plastic soft-drink bottles, like the one shown in **Figure 22,** are made of type 1 plastic and are the easiest to recycle. Most plastic bags are made of type 2 or type 4 plastic; they can be reused as well as recycled. Types 6 and 7 can't be recycled at all because they are made of a mixture of different plastics. Each type of plastic must be separated carefully before it is recycled because a single piece of a different type of plastic can ruin an entire batch.

Figure 22
Many soft-drink bottles are made of PETE, which is the most common type of recyclable plastic. It can be melted down and spun into fibers to make carpets, paintbrushes, rope, and clothing.

2 Teach

Reduce

Text Question Answer

Possible answer: Turn off lights in vacant rooms.

Discussion

Bring in a product that is clearly over-packaged. Have students suggest ways to reduce the amount of material used in the packaging of this item.

Reduse

Activity

Find an item that is commonly thrown out, such as a plastic soft-drink bottle. Have students brainstorm a list of possible ways to reuse the bottle. L2 ELL IN **Interpersonal**

Recycle

Reading Check

Answer Reusing does not require reprocessing; recycling does.

Extension

Reinforce the differences among reduce, reuse, and recycle. Give students the example of a soft-drink bottle and ask them to come up with a plan to reduce, reuse, and recycle the bottle. Reduce: Buy one big bottle instead of many smaller bottles. Reuse: Wash bottle and use it to store drinking water. Recycle: Separate the bottles from trash so that they can be melted down and the plastic reused. L2

Resource Manager

Chapter Resources Booklet

Transparency Activity, p. 46

Directed Reading for Content Mastery, pp. 21, 22

Activity Worksheet, pp. 7–8

Visual Learning

Figure 22 The objects in these photographs are made from the same type 1 plastic (PET). Ask students to bring in materials with this symbol on them. When the objects are collected, discuss why recycling is a good idea. Possible answer: It reduces the amount of nonbiodegradable materials going into landfills.

Recycle, continued

IDENTIFYING Misconceptions

Many people think that recycled paper is paper that has been used by consumers. Most of it, however, comes from wood or paper scrap in logging or paper manufacturing. Some companies indicate how much recycled paper comes directly from consumers by labeling the percent that is post-consumer content.

Teacher FYI

Composting is considered recycling because the form of the materials is changed (through decay) so they can be used again.

Problem-Solving Activity

National Math Standards

Correlation to Mathematics Objectives

1, 2, 5, 6, 8–10

Answer

Students' lists should include some of each type of item. Possible exceptions would be yard wastes, depending on the season, and newspapers. The percentages will depend on student data. Tin cans are steel cans coated with tin. They should be included.

SCIENCE Online

Research Visit the Glencoe Science Web site at **science.glencoe.com** and find out how to make your own recycled paper. In your Science Journal, describe how you might use the paper you make.

Metals The manufacturing industry has been recycling all kinds of metals, especially steel, for decades. At least 25 percent of the steel in cans, appliances, and automobiles is recycled steel. Up to 100 percent of the steel in plates and beams used to build skyscrapers is made from reprocessed steel. About one metric ton of recycled steel saves about 1.1 metric tons of iron ore and 0.5 metric ton of coal. Using recycled steel to make new steel products reduces energy use by 75 percent. Other metals, including iron, copper, aluminum, and lead also can be recycled.

You can conserve metals by recycling food cans, which are mostly steel, and aluminum cans. It takes less energy to make a can from recycled aluminum than from raw materials. Also, remember that recycled cans do not take up space in landfills.

Glass Glass bottles and jars can be sterilized and reused. They also can be melted and re-formed into new bottles, especially those made of clear glass. Most glass bottles already contain at least 25 percent recycled glass. Glass can be recycled again and again. It never needs to be thrown away. Recycling about one metric ton of glass saves more than one metric ton of mineral resources and cuts the energy used to make new glass by 25 percent or more.

Problem-Solving Activity

What items are you recycling at home?

Many people participate in community recycling programs. Recyclable items such as plastic, glass, newspapers, and metals may be picked up at the curbside or the resident may hire a licensed recycling handler to pick them up. What do you recycle in your home?

Identifying the Problem

The following bar graph shows the recycling rates in the U. S. of six types of household items for the years 1992, 1994, and 1995. How do your and your classmates' recycling rates compare with the recycling rates shown on the chart?

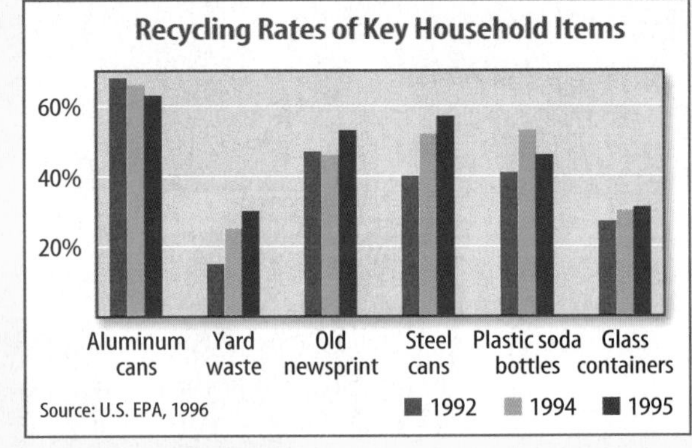

Solving the Problem

1. For one week, list each glass, plastic, and aluminum item you use. Note which items you throw away and which ones you recycle. Calculate the percentage of glass, plastic, and aluminum you recycled. How do your percentages compare with those on the graph?

SCIENCE Online

Internet Addresses

Explore the Glencoe Science Web site at **science.glencoe.com** to find out more about topics in this section.

Resource Manager

Chapter Resources Booklet
- Enrichment, p. 32
- Lab Activity, pp. 13–16
- Reinforcement, p. 29

Lab Management and Safety, p. 37

Paper Used paper is recycled into paper towels, insulation, newsprint, cardboard, and stationery. Ranchers and dairy farmers sometimes use shredded paper instead of straw for bedding in barns and stables. Used paper can be made into compost. Recycling about one metric ton of paper saves 17 trees, more than 26,000 L of water, close to 1,900 L of oil, and more than 4,000 kw of electric energy. You can do your part by recycling newspapers, notebook and printer paper, cardboard, and junk mail.

Figure 23
Composting is a way of turning plant material you would otherwise throw away into rich garden soil. Dry leaves and weeds, grass clippings, vegetable trimmings, and nonmeat food scraps can be composted.

✔ Reading Check ***What nonrenewable resource(s) do you conserve by recycling paper?***

Compost Grass clippings, leaves, and fruit and vegetable scraps that are discarded in a landfill can remain there for decades without breaking down. The same items can be turned into soil-enriching compost in just a few weeks, as shown in **Figure 23.** Many communities distribute compost bins to encourage residents to recycle fruit and vegetable scraps and yard waste.

Buy Recycled People have become so good at recycling that recyclable materials are piling up, just waiting to be put to use. You can help by reading labels when you shop and choosing products that contain recycled materials. What other ways of recycling natural resources can you think of?

Section 3 Assessment

1. What is meant by the term *reuse*? How does it differ from recycling?
2. List three materials that can be recycled. Describe one product that can be made from each recycled material you listed.
3. Describe at least three actions you could take to reduce your use of natural resources.
4. Describe how you could reuse three items people usually throw away.
5. **Think Critically** Why is reusing something better than recycling it?

Skill Builder Activities

6. **Making and Using Tables** Make a table of data on the number of aluminum cans thrown away in the United States: *22.7 billion in 1982; 35.0 billion in 1986; 33.0 billion in 1990; 38.8 billion in 1994; 44.6 billion in 1998.* **For more help, refer to the** Science Skill Handbook.
7. **Communicating** Write a letter to a local newspaper suggesting ways to reuse or recycle an item or items that most people in your community currently throw away. **For more help, refer to the** Science Skill Handbook.

✔ Reading Check

Answer oil

Text Question Answer
Answers will vary.

3 Assess

Reteach

Ask students to give their opinions about whether a soft-drink company should reuse glass bottles by washing them out or recycle the bottles by melting them and making new. L1
 **Linguistic**

Challenge

Have students investigate the trash generated by your school's cafeteria. Challenge them to devise a plan to reduce the amount of trash that is thrown away. Have them write a report on their investigation and plan. P

✔Assessment

Performance Hold up a newspaper and ask students to write specific examples of how a community can reduce its use of newspapers, reuse newspapers, and recycle newspapers. Use **Performance Assessment in the Science Classroom,** p. 89.

Answers to Section Assessment

1. Reuse means to use an object over again for its original task or to use it for another task. Unlike recycling, reuse does not involve making a big change to the object.
2. Possible answers: aluminum, iron, certain plastics, biodegradable materials into compost, paper
3. Possible answers: turn off lights in vacant rooms, buy materials with less packaging, carpool, buy items made from recycled materials
4. Possible answers: store water in plastic soft-drink bottles, use plastic grocery bags as trash can liners, use margarine tubs to store left-over food.
5. There is less energy used in reusing than in recycling.
6. Check tables for accuracy.
7. Answers will vary. Look for creativity in the use of commonly discarded objects.

Activity

BENCH TESTED

Recognize the Problem

Purpose

Students will design and build a solar cooker.

Process Skills

designing and making a model, researching, comparing

Time Required

one class period

Thinking Critically

Discussion

Discuss with students the problems some people in the world face just trying to cook a meal. Explain to students that in some places where fuel is scarce, people use solar cookers to prepare food. **Why do people cook most food?** Possible answers: To improve taste; to kill harmful bacteria **Why does cooking food require energy?** Energy is needed to raise the temperature of the food.

Alternate Materials

Oven bags are available at most supermarkets. Kitchen timers are available at most hardware stores.

Safety Precautions

Remind students to use insulated gloves or tongs when handling hot objects.

Activity **Model and Invent**

Solar Cooking

The disappearance of forests in some places on Earth has made firewood extremely difficult and expensive to obtain. People living in these regions often have to travel long distances or sell some of their food to get firewood. This can be a serious problem for people who may not have much food to begin with. Is there a way they could cook food without using firewood?

Recognize the Problem

Can you design a solar cooker that cooks food without burning fuel?

Thinking Critically

How would you build a cooking device that uses the Sun's energy?

Possible Materials

poster board
cardboard boxes
aluminum foil
string
wire coat hangers
clear plastic sheets
*oven bags
black cookware
thermometer
stopwatch
*timer
glue
tape
scissors
Alternate materials

Safety Precautions

Be careful when cutting your materials. Your solar cooker will get hot. When handling hot liquids or objects, use insulated gloves or tongs.

Goals

- **Research** designs for solar panel cookers or box cookers.
- **Design** a solar cooker that can be used to cook food.
- **Plan** an experiment to measure the effectiveness of your solar cooker.

Data Source

SCIENCE*Online* Visit the Glencoe Science Web site at **science.glencoe.com** for more information about solar cooker designs.

Internet Addresses

Explore the Glencoe Science Web site at **science.glencoe.com** to find out more about topics in this activity.

Inclusion Strategies

Learning Disabled Assign these students the task of gathering the materials their group decides they want to use.

Planning the Model

1. **Design** a solar cooker. In your Science Journal, explain why you chose this design and draw a picture of it.
2. **Write** a summary explaining how you will measure the effectiveness of your solar cooker. What will you measure? How will you collect and organize your data? How will you present your results?

Check the Model Plans

1. **Compare** your solar cooker design to those of other students.
2. Share your experimental plan with students in your class. Discuss the reasoning behind your plan. Be specific about what you intend to test and how you are going to test it.
3. Make sure your teacher approves your plan before you start working on your model.

Making the Model

1. Using all of the information you have gathered, construct a solar cooker that follows your design.
2. **Test** your design to determine how well it works. Try out a classmate's design. How do the two compare?

Analyzing and Applying Results

1. Combine the results for your entire class and decide which type of solar cooker was most effective. How could you design a more effective solar cooker, based on what you learned from this activity?
2. Do you think your results might have been different if you tested your solar cooker on a different day? Explain. Why might a solar cooker be more useful in some regions of the world than in others?
3. Based on what you've read and the results obtained by you and your classmates, do you think that your solar cooker could boil water? Explain.
4. **Compare** the amount of time needed to cook food with a solar cooker and with more traditional cooking methods. Assuming plenty of sunlight is available, would you prefer to use a solar cooker or a traditional oven? Explain.

Communicating Your Data

Prepare a demonstration showing how to use a solar cooker. **Present** your demonstration to another class of students or to a group of friends or relatives. **For more help, refer to the** Science Skill Handbook.

Planning the Model

Teaching Strategies

- Comparisons of solar cookers will be difficult if students do not use the same method of testing them.
- You might want to have a cook-off with the two best solar ovens to see which one could cook a small red potato in the shortest time. Be sure both potatoes are the same size.

Trouble Shooting Students can move the cookers during the testing to keep them in the sun.

Making the Model

Expected Outcome

Solar cookers should be able to raise the temperature of a cup of water to at least 75°C. A well-designed cooker might reach temperatures approaching 150°C.

Analyzing and Applying Results

1. Answers will depend on the designs of the solar cookers that are compared.
2. Results would vary in different weather conditions. Solar cookers function best on clear, sunny days. Solar cookers are more useful in areas that have many clear, sunny days.
3. Answers will depend on the success of the design. Some well-designed cookers could boil water.
4. Solar cookers generally take two to three times as long to cook a meal as a traditional oven. However, the energy for a solar cooker is free and the energy for a traditional oven is not.

Assessment

Process Have students use a foam cup of water with a thermometer in it to test whether their solar ovens can boil water. Be sure that each group uses the same amount of water for the test and that students record the time it takes to boil the water. Based on the results, have students rank the solar cooker designs from best to worst. Use **PASC**, p. 89.

Communicating Your Data

Students should prepare a poster that shows the construction of their solar cooker and an explanation of how it works.

Science and Language Arts

Pre-Reading Activity

Have students think about the renewable and nonrenewable resources they use daily. Have students list in their Science Journals all the renewable and nonrenewable resources they can see on the school grounds and in the classroom.

Respond to the Reading

Active Reading Strategies

Visualize Try to visualize the scenes described by the poet as you read. **Do the settings remind you of places you know? Do the descriptions of the seasons differ from the seasons you experience in your community? How?**

Respond Be aware of the mood of the poem as you read. Although the poem does not talk about conserving resources, there is an implied understanding about the importance of conserving resources and reducing pollution. **Do you think the beauty of your neighborhood has been plagiarized? What things can you do to preserve the beauty of nature?**

Answers to Questions

1. The four verses correspond to the four seasons.
2. pollution from the use of nonrenewable resources such as fossil fuels; clear-cutting trees for buildings
3. Civilization has plagiarized beauty.

Science and Language Arts

Beauty Plagiarized

by Amitabha Mukerjee

Respond to the Reading

1. What do the four verses in the poem correspond to?
2. What has destroyed nature's beauty?
3. To plagiarize is to copy without giving credit to the source. In this poem, who or what has plagiarized beauty?

I wandered lonely as a cloud –
Except for a motorboat,
Nary a soul in sight.
Beside the lake beneath the trees,
Next to the barbed wire fence,
There was a picnic table
And beer bottle caps from many years.
A boat ramp to the left,
And the chimney from a power station on the other side,
A summer haze hung in the air,
And the lazy drone of traffic far away.

Crimson autumn of mists and mellow fruitfulness
Blue plastic covers the swimming pools
The leaves fall so I can see
Dark glass reflections in the building
That came up
where the pine cones crunched underfoot . . .

And then it is snow
White lining on trees and rooftops . . .
And through my windshield wipers
The snow is piled dark and grey . . .
Next to my driveway where I check my mail
Little footprints on fresh snow —
A visiting rabbit.

I knew a bank where the wild thyme blew
Over-canopied with luscious woodbine
It is now a landfill —
Fermentation of civilization
Flowers on TV
Hyacinth rose tulip chrysanthemum
Acres of colour
Wind up wrapped in decorous plastic,
In this landfill where oxlips grew. . .

Reading Further

A Walk in the Woods: Rediscovering America on the Appalachian Trail, by Bill Bryson, Broadway Books, 1999.

The Best American Science & Nature Writing 2000, ed. Burkhard Bilger, Houghton Mifflin Co., 2000.

Lost Woods: The Discovered Writing of Rachel Carson, by Rachel Carson, ed. Linda Lear, Beacon Press, 1999.

gration compound dichotomous greenhou
skeleton permafrost magma isotopes plat

Cause and Effect

Understanding Literature

Cause and Effect Recognizing cause-and-effect relationships can help you make sense out of what you read. One event causes another event. The second event is the effect of the first event. In the poem, the author describes the causes and effects of pollution and waste. For example, the summer haze is the effect of the "chimney from a power station" as well as the "traffic far away." What other effects do pollution and the use of nonrenewable resources have on nature in the poem?

The poet also makes a connection between the four seasons of the year and the pollution and waste products created by civilization. For example, in the spring, a landfill for dumping garbage replaces a field of wildflowers. Describing four seasons instead of one reinforces the poet's message that the beauty of nature has been stolen, or plagiarized.

Science Connection The poet describes renewable and nonrenewable resources. For example, the lake and tree described in the first verse are renewable resources. The beer bottle caps in the same verse are nonrenewable. Can you identify all the nonrenewable resources in the poem? How does the narrator contribute to the use of fossil fuels and nonrenewable resources?

Linking Science and Writing

Write a Poem Copy the poem you just read in pencil. Change the poem by erasing the lines that describe nonrenewable resources. Add lines to the poem that show how recycling, reusing, and other conservation measures could restore the beauty of the four seasons.

Career Connection

Ecologist

Vandana Shiva is the director of the Research Foundation for Science, Technology, and Natural Resource Policy in Dehradun, India. Shiva had an early appreciation for global natural resources as a daughter of a forester growing up in the Himalayan forest. As an adult she has become involved in the efforts of the Chipko Indian women's movement to save trees in the Himalaya. Her involvement in this movement led to the banning of logging in the Himalayan area above 1,000 meters.

SCIENCE*Online* To learn more about careers in ecology, visit the Glencoe Science Web site at **science.glencoe.com.**

Understanding Literature

Answer to Question

Answers will vary but might include that bottle caps litter the picnic area and that exhaust fumes from cars make the snow banks dark and gray.

Science Connection

Review what nonrenewable and renewable resources are. It should be stressed that even renewable resources can be rendered nonrenewable. This happens when renewable resources are removed at a rate that prevents their renewal, or if the environment that supports them deteriorates faster than renewal can take place. For example, although forests are considered a renewable resource, if they are not carefully managed they can disappear as a result of excessive logging or clear-cutting. Also, although Earth's supply of air is inexhaustible, the quality of Earth's air can be affected by human activity, and air quality directly affects other renewable resources.

Linking Science and Writing

Teaching Strategies

Use a quickwrite exercise to help students prepare for rewriting lines in the poem. Working in groups, have students list ways of recycling, reusing, and reducing solid waste. Also, have students brainstorm on ways to reduce the use of fossil fuels. Encourage students to be creative. They can then use these ideas to help them complete the lines in the poem.

Career Connection

The field of ecology encompasses many different careers and areas of expertise, from air quality management and hazardous waste management to forestry and conservation, agricultural sciences and biological sciences. Students interested in pursuing such careers should focus on mathematics, biology, chemistry, physics, and computer science.

Internet Addresses

Explore the Glencoe Science Web site at **science.glencoe.com** to find out more about topics in this feature.

Chapter 27 Study Guide

Reviewing Main Ideas

Preview

Students can answer the questions in their Science Journals. Discuss the answers as you go through the chapter. LS **Linguistic**

Review

Students can write their answers, then compare them with those of other students. LS **Interpersonal**

Reteach

Students can look at the illustrations and describe details that support the main ideas of the chapter. LS **Visual-Spatial**

Answers to Chapter Review

Section 1

3. Renewable: the cotton clothes and air; nonrenewable: the gasoline and metals in the car

Section 2

3. leaching of fertilizer into the water

Section 3

3. Recycling reduces the need to alter environments to gather raw materials and it decreases energy use.

Chapter 27 Study Guide

Reviewing Main Ideas

Section 1 Resources

1. Natural resources are the parts of the environment that supply materials needed for the survival of living organisms.
2. Renewable resources are being replaced continually by natural processes.
3. Nonrenewable resources cannot be replaced or are replaced very slowly. *What renewable and nonrenewable resources appear in this photograph?*

4. Energy sources include fossil fuels, wind, solar energy, geothermal energy, hydroelectric power, and nuclear power.

Section 2 Pollution

1. Most air pollution is made up of waste products from the burning of fossil fuels.
2. The greenhouse effect is the warming of Earth by a blanket of heat-reflecting gases in the atmosphere.
3. Water can be polluted by acid rain and by the spilling of oil or other wastes into waterways. *What could have caused this algal bloom?*

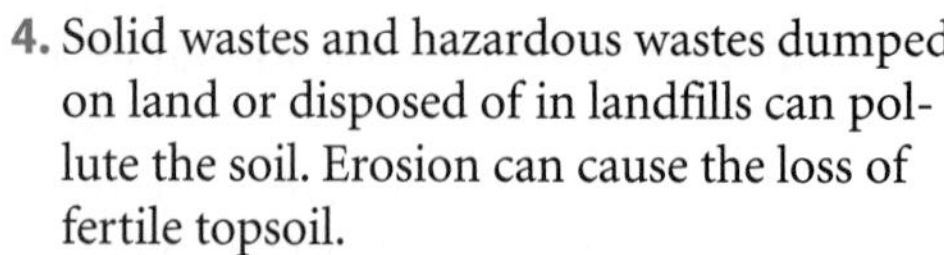

4. Solid wastes and hazardous wastes dumped on land or disposed of in landfills can pollute the soil. Erosion can cause the loss of fertile topsoil.

Section 3 The Three Rs of Conservation

1. You can reduce your use of natural resources in many ways.
2. Reusing items is an excellent way to practice conservation.
3. In recycling, materials are changed in some way so that they can be used again. *How does recycling benefit the environment?*

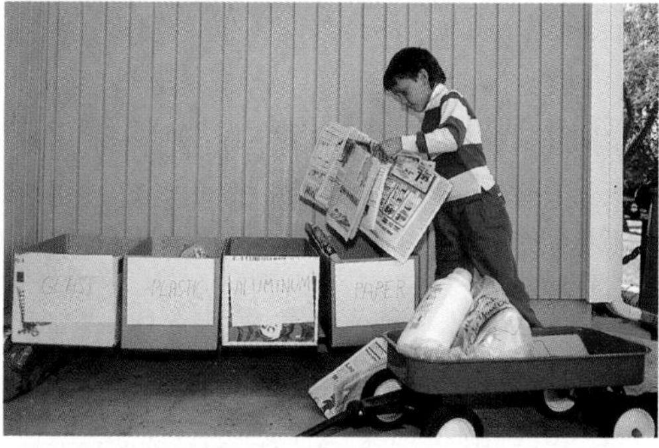

4. Materials that can be recycled include paper, metals, glass, plastics, yard waste, and nonmeat kitchen scraps.

FOLDABLES Reading & Study Skills — After You Read

Use the Foldable you made at the beginning of the chapter to list ways your community conserves resources under the tabs.

FOLDABLES Reading & Study Skills — After You Read

After students have read the chapter and completed the Foldable described in Before You Read, have them do the activity on the student page.

Dinah Zike

Visualizing Main Ideas

Complete the following concept map on air pollution. Use the terms smog, acid precipitation, *and* ozone depletion.

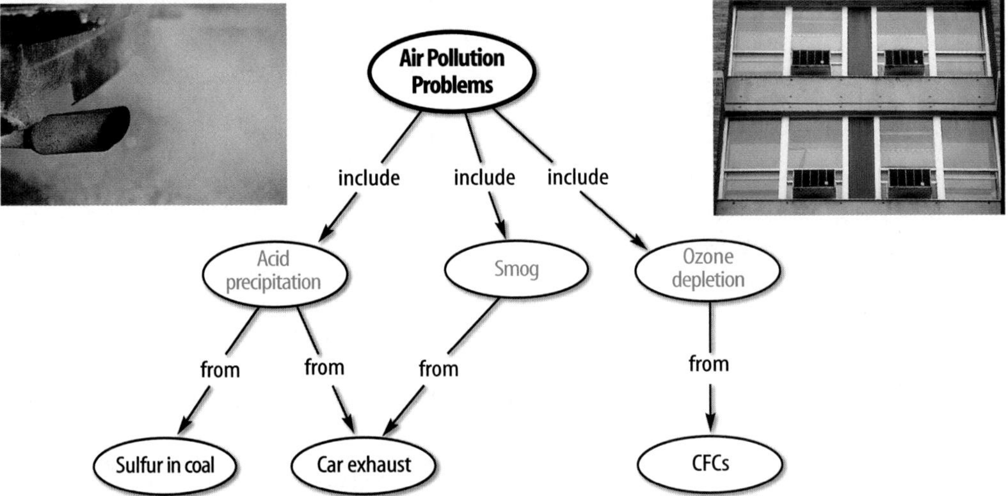

Vocabulary Review

Vocabulary Words

- a. acid precipitation
- b. erosion
- c. fossil fuel
- d. geothermal energy
- e. greenhouse effect
- f. hazardous waste
- g. hydroelectric power
- h. natural resource
- i. nonrenewable resource
- j. nuclear energy
- k. ozone depletion
- l. petroleum
- m. pollutant
- n. recycling
- o. renewable resource

Study Tip

THE PRINCETON REVIEW

When you read a chapter, make a list of things you find confusing or do not completely understand. Then ask your teacher to explain them.

Using Vocabulary

Explain the differences in the vocabulary words given below. Then explain how the words are related. Use complete sentences in your answers.

1. fossil fuel, petroleum
2. erosion, pollutant
3. ozone depletion, acid precipitation
4. greenhouse effect, fossil fuels
5. hazardous wastes, nuclear energy
6. hydroelectric power, fossil fuels
7. acid precipitation, fossil fuels
8. ozone depletion, pollutant
9. recycle, nonrenewable resources
10. geothermal energy, fossil fuels

Chapter 27 Study Guide

Visualizing Main Ideas

See student page.

Vocabulary Review

Using Vocabulary

1. Petroleum is a type of fossil fuel.
2. Erosion produces pollutants and degrades the environment.
3. These are both types of air pollution, but one does not cause the other.
4. The burning of fossil fuels and the release of excess carbon dioxide may enhance the greenhouse effect.
5. The use of nuclear energy generates radioactive materials, which are hazardous wastes.
6. The use of hydroelectric power can decrease the use of fossil fuels.
7. Coal is a fossil fuel. The burning of coal that contains sulfur causes acid precipitation.
8. The pollutant called CFC causes ozone depletion.
9. Recycling is a good way of conserving nonrenewable resources.
10. The use of geothermal energy can decrease the use of fossil fuels.

Chapter 27 Assessment

Checking Concepts

1. B
2. C
3. B
4. B
5. C
6. C
7. B
8. B
9. A
10. C

Thinking Critically

11. Fossil fuels were formed from plants and animals. Wood is from a plant.
12. Desert region; sunshine is more constant there than at the poles.
13. to prevent erosion of topsoil
14. Yes; it is constantly replaced and has many uses.
15. Solar, wind, geothermal, and water energy are renewable resources. Nuclear energy is not a renewable resource, but no severe shortages are expected.

Chapter 27 Assessment

Checking Concepts

Choose the word or phrase that best answers the question.

1. Which of the following is a fossil fuel?
A) wood
B) oil
C) nuclear power
D) photovoltaic cell

2. Of the following, which is considered a renewable resource?
A) coal
B) oil
C) sunlight
D) aluminum

3. Which energy resource uses heat from below Earth's crust?
A) solar energy
B) geothermal energy
C) hydroelectric energy
D) photovoltaic energy

4. An architect wants to design a solar house in the northern hemisphere. For maximum warmth, which side of the house should have the most windows?
A) north
B) south
C) east
D) west

5. Which of the following contributes to ozone depletion?
A) carbon dioxide
B) radon
C) CFCs
D) carbon monoxide

6. What is a substance that contaminates the environment called?
A) acid rain
B) pollution
C) pollutant
D) ozone

7. If there were no greenhouse effect in Earth's atmosphere, which of the following statements would be true?
A) Earth would be much hotter.
B) Earth would be much colder.
C) The temperature of Earth would be the same.
D) The polar ice caps would melt.

8. What is the process in which glass bottles are crushed, melted, and shaped into new bottles?
A) reuse
B) recycling
C) reduction
D) coal

9. Which of the following can change solar energy into electricity?
A) photovoltaic cells
B) smog
C) nuclear power plants
D) geothermal power plants

10. What is a radioactive gas that can cause indoor air pollution?
A) ozone
B) carbon dioxide
C) radon
D) chlorofluorocarbons (CFCs)

Thinking Critically

11. Why do burning wood and burning fossil fuels produce similar pollutants?

12. Which would make a better location for a solar power plant—a polar region (left) or a desert region(right)? Why?

13. Why is it beneficial to grow a different crop on soil after the major crop has been harvested?

14. Is garbage a renewable resource? Why or why not?

15. Solar, nuclear, wind, water, and geothermal energy are alternatives to fossil fuels. Are they all renewable? Why or why not?

Chapter Assessment Planner

Portfolio Encourage students to place in their portfolios one or two items of what they consider to be their best work. Examples include:
- Physics Integration, p. 781
- Assessment, p. 794
- Challenge, p. 799

Performance Additional performance assessments, Performance Task Assessment Lists, and rubrics for evaluating these activities can be found in Glencoe's **Performance Assessment in the Science Classroom.**

Chapter 27 Assessment

Developing Skills

16. Drawing Conclusions Would you save more energy by recycling or reusing a plastic bag?

17. Recognizing Cause and Effect Forests use large amounts of carbon dioxide during photosynthesis. How might cutting down a large percentage of Earth's forests affect the greenhouse effect?

18. Making and Using Graphs Make a bar graph of the following data.

Estimated Recycling Rates

Item	Percent Recycled
Aluminum cans	60
Glass beverage bottles	31
Plastic soft-drink containers	37
Newsprint	56
Magazines	23

19. Forming Hypotheses Form a hypothesis about why Americans throw away more aluminum cans each year.

20. Comparing and Contrasting Compare and contrast contour farming, terracing, strip cropping, and no-till farming.

Performance Assessment

21. Poster Create a poster to illustrate and describe three things students at your school can do to conserve natural resources.

Technology

Go to the Glencoe Science Web site at **science.glencoe.com** or use the **Glencoe Science CD-ROM** for additional chapter assessment.

Test Practice

Some of Earth's important natural resources are pictured in the two boxes below.

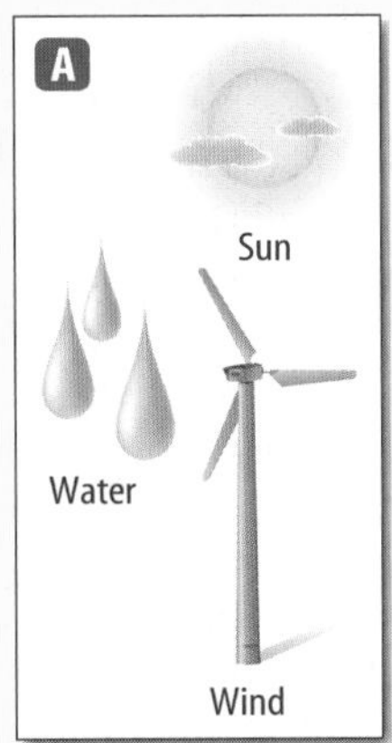

Review the pictures and answer the following questions.

1. Which of the following is a major characteristic of all of the natural resources shown in Box B?
   A) They are made and used by humans on a regular basis.
   B) They are substances made out of metal.
   C) They are materials that occur naturally in a solid form not a liquid form.
   D) They are used up by humans faster than nature can replace them.

2. The resources in Box A are different from the resources in Box B because only the resources in Box A are _____
   F) easily and quickly replaced by nature.
   G) easily and quickly created by humans.
   H) never made by nature.
   J) never used by humans.

Assessment Resources

Reproducible Masters

Chapter Resources Booklet
Chapter Review, pp. 37–38
Chapter Tests, pp. 39–42
Assessment Transparency Activity, p. 49

Glencoe Science Web site
Interactive Tutor
Chapter Quizzes

Glencoe Technology
Assessment Transparency
Interactive CD-ROM Chapter Quizzes
ExamView Pro Test Bank
Vocabulary PuzzleMaker Software
MindJogger Videoquiz

Chapter 27 Assessment

Test Practice

The Test-Taking Tip was written by The Princeton Review, the nation's leader in test preparation.

1. D
2. F

Developing Skills

16. Reusing the bag would save energy because it wouldn't need to be changed back into its raw form and then a new bag made.
17. Cutting large forests could result in more carbon dioxide in the atmosphere, possibly resulting in an enhanced greenhouse effect and accelerated global warming.
18. Bars (highest to lowest): aluminum cans, newsprint, plastic soft drink containers, glass beverage bottles, magazines
19. Answers will vary. Students should support their answers.
20. Contour farming and terracing are similar in that they are farming methods for hillsides that reduce soil erosion. Strip cropping compares to no-till farming in that they are both methods of reducing soil erosion by leaving soil covered by vegetation. The first two methods contrast to the last two in that they are used on hillsides, while the last two are used on level ground.

Performance Assessment

21. Posters should involve reducing, reusing, or recycling. Use **PASC**, p. 145.

Standardized Test Practice

Reading Comprehension

QUESTION 1: B

Students must use information from the passage to identify the best supported answer choice.

- **Choice A** No; this is the reverse order of the food chain described in the passage.
- **Choice B** Yes; this is the food chain described in the passage.
- **Choice C** No; this is not the food chain described in the passage.
- **Choice D** No; this is not the food chain described in the passage.

QUESTION 2: J

Students must use information from the passage to identify the best-supported answer choice.

- **Choice F** No; this is a producer.
- **Choice G** No; this is an herbivore.
- **Choice H** No; this is a source of energy.
- **Choice J** Yes; this is a predator.

All questions written and validated by The Princeton Review.

Standardized Test Practice

Reading Comprehension

Read the passage. Then read each question that follows the passage. Decide which is the best answer to each question.

Interactions in Ecosystems

Fearing for their safety and the safety of their livestock, early settlers of northern Wisconsin killed the native timber wolves. Timber wolves are a natural predator of white-tailed deer. Over time the deer population increased in size. The available vegetation could not support the deer population. Even though emergency feeding stations were set up, thousands of deer died of starvation. The deer population now is kept down by controlled hunting seasons. In some areas wolves have been reintroduced.

An ecosystem consists of organisms from many different species living together and connected by the flow of energy, nutrients, and matter. Organisms in an ecosystem can be classified as either producers or consumers. Most producers use the Sun's radiant energy and convert it into chemical energy through photosynthesis. Consumers take in and use this chemical energy. Herbivores eat producers, carnivores eat other consumers, and omnivores eat producers and consumers. As organisms die, decomposers take in and use the energy in the dead organisms. In doing so, they release nutrients into the soil and carbon dioxide into the air that are used by producers again.

The loss of one species from an ecosystem may lead to the overpopulation or extinction of other species. This loss degrades the ecosystem upon which humans and other organisms depend for clean air, water, and food.

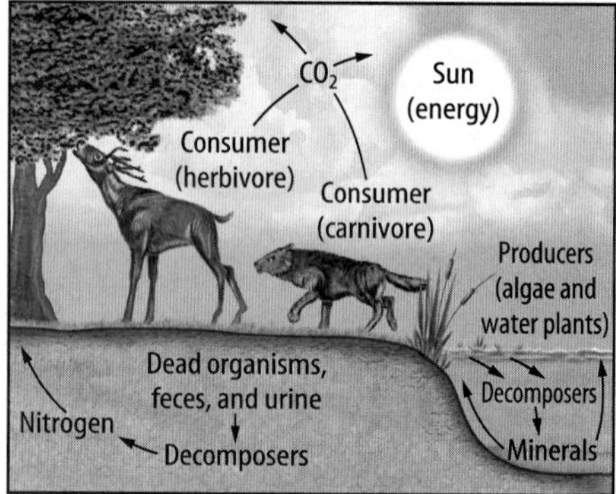

The major components of an ecosystem

Test-Taking Tip Use the figure to help you visualize the ecosystem that is being described in the passage.

1. Food chains are a way of showing how energy, nutrients, and matter flow through an ecosystem. Which of the following is a food chain of the ecosystem described in the passage?
   A) carnivore, producer, herbivore
   B) producer, herbivore, carnivore
   C) carnivore, producer, decomposer
   D) decomposer, carnivore, herbivore

2. Predators are consumers that capture and eat other consumers. The presence of a predator limits the size of the prey population. This means that food and other resources are less likely to become scarce. What is the predator in this passage?
   F) vegetation
   G) deer
   H) Sun
   J) timberwolf

Standardized Test Practice

Reasoning and Skills

Read each question and choose the best answer.

1. Within an ecosystem there are many populations as well as abiotic factors. Groups of populations that interact within a specific area of an ecosystem are referred to as which of the following?

A) a habitat
B) a community
C) a food web
D) an atmosphere

Test-Taking Tip Think about the levels of an ecosystem and how they relate to each other.

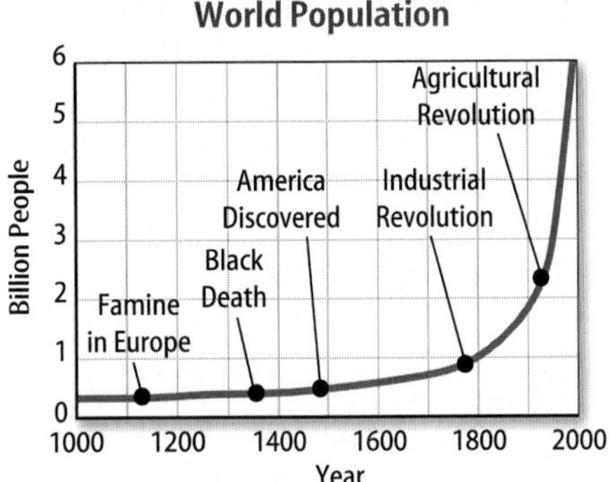

2. Refer to the World Population graph. In which of the following years were the birth rate and the death rate nearly equal?

F) 1800
G) 2000
H) 1200
J) 1600

Test-Taking Tip Consider what you know about the effects of birth and death rates on population size.

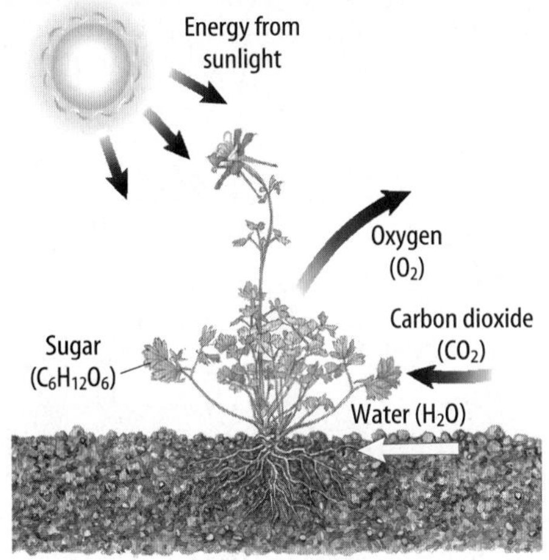

3. The conversion of energy is important to all life on Earth. Some producers use sunlight as an energy source, converting it into chemical energy through photosynthesis. Other producers that live where sunlight does not reach them, can use which of the following as an energy source?

A) water
B) air
C) soil
D) chemicals

Test-Taking Tip Read about converting energy before answering the question.

Consider this question carefully before writing your answer on a separate sheet of paper.

4. Ecologists are encouraging people to take buses and trains rather than drive their own cars. They say this will help reduce air pollution. How will having more people take public transportation reduce air pollution?

Test-Taking Tip Imagine how 100 people on a train instead of 100 cars on the highway would affect air pollution.

Standardized Test Practice

Reasoning and Skills

QUESTION 1: B

Students must understand populations and ecosystems. Only B, *a community*, is correct.

QUESTION 2: H

Students must understand that if the birth rate and the death rate are equal, then there is no growth in the population. Only H, *1200*, indicates a year on the graph in which the growth rate does not change.

QUESTION 3: D

Students must understand producers and energy conversion in order to identify D, *chemicals*, as the correct answer choice. Choices A, B, and C are used whether or not the producer receives sunlight.

QUESTION 4: Answers will vary.

Students should understand that transporting many people in one large vehicle or other mode of transportation consumes less energy and produces less pollution than transporting each person individually.

Teaching Tip

Suggest that students brainstorm a list of ideas and then organize these ideas before writing a response.

Student Resources

CONTENTS

Field Guides 812

Skill Handbooks 832

Reference Handbook 857

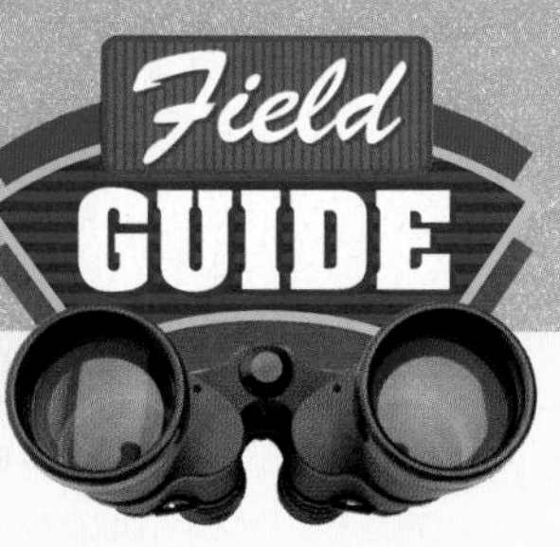

About the Field Guide

- This field guide contains representative photos of some breeds of cats and descriptions of the traits characteristic of each breed.
- In using a field guide, students will apply steps of a scientific method as they observe, investigate, analyze data and draw conclusions.
- Encourage students to use this field guide outside the classroom.

Tie to Prior Knowledge

Most students will be familiar with cats as house pets. Have students name traits that are present in the cats with which they are familiar. List their responses on the board. **What traits are common to all cats, and which are present only in a particular cat or breed of cats?** Students should conclude that there are certain traits common to all cats, other traits are present only in some cats.

Field Activity

Student responses to the questions in this activity will vary. Encourage students to use specific and detailed notes when recording the traits present in each cat. Have each student make a Venn diagram that shows the traits of two or three of the cats on their list.
LS Logical-Mathematical

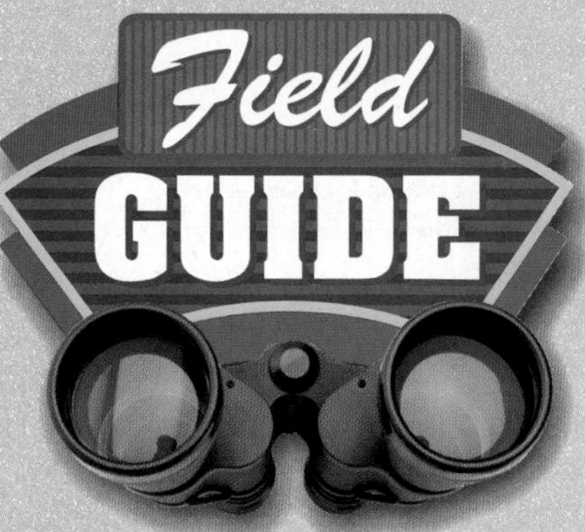

For centuries, humans have lived with cats. They have kept cats in their homes and on their properties. Cats hunt mice and other rodents that eat stored grains and other human foods. Cats also are companions and family pets. Today, the cat is the most popular pet in the United States.

When animals mate, they pass their genetic traits to their offspring. Occasionally, a natural mutation results in a new breed. Sometimes animal scientists try to create new breeds through selective breeding. They study the pedigree, or family history, of several animals of the same species to see what genetic traits they carry. Then they mate the animals that are most likely to pass the desired traits to their offspring. Over time, a new breed can be developed.

The Cat Fancier's Association recognizes 37 breeds of cats. This field guide describes the traits of 14 of these recognized breeds. None of these breeds has come about by recent selective breeding. Some of these breeds have ancient histories, and others have resulted from natural mutations.

Most cats that people adopt today have a mixed ancestry of several breeds. Read about different breeds on the next few pages. Do you know a cat that has one or more of the described traits?

Feline Traits

Feline Breeds

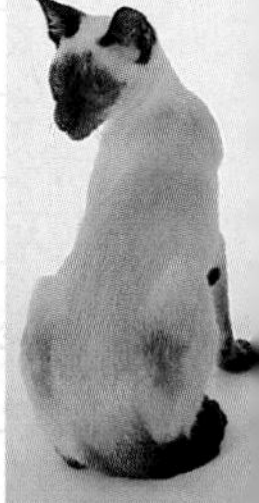
Siamese

Siamese

This is an ancient breed from Siam, which is now called Thailand. Siamese have long bodies and tails, and their fur is short. They are easy to recognize because they have light-colored bodies and dark ears, masks, tails, and legs. Their eyes are blue.

Devon Rex

Devon Rex

This breed is a natural mutation that first appeared in Devonshire, England, in 1960. Their eyes and batlike ears look huge against their tiny faces. When you stroke a Devon Rex's coat, its fur ripples.

Field Activity

For a week, use this field guide to observe the cats in your neighborhood. What traits do they have? What breeds might be part of their pedigree? Go to the Glencoe Science Web site at **science.glencoe.com** to find more photographs of felines. In your Science Journal, record each cat's name, the traits you noticed, and the breeds that have those traits.

Resources for Teachers and Students

ASPCA Complete Guide to Cats, by James R. Richards, Chronicle Books, 1999.

Cat Breeds of the World, by Paddy Cutts, Lorenz, 1999.

Cats!, by Kate Zentall, BowTie Press, 1998.

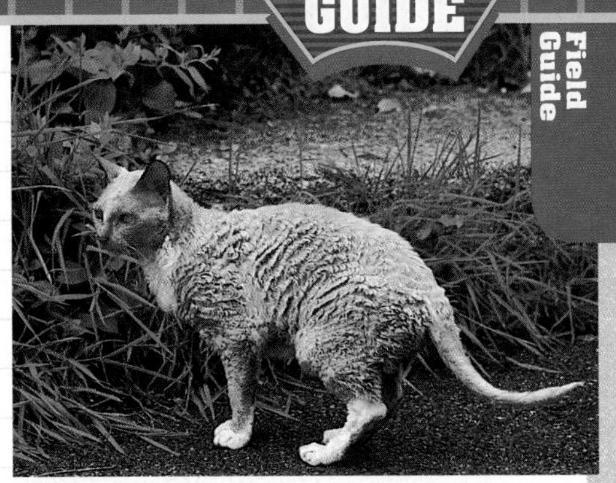
Cornish Rex

Cornish Rex

This natural mutation first appeared in Cornwall, England, in about 1950. Cornish Rex cats remind some people of a skinny breed of dog called a whippet. They have arched backs, small waists, and long legs. Their ears are large, and they have small, egg-shaped heads. Their short, curly fur is soft.

Chartreux

Chartreux [shahr-TROOZ]

This breed dates back at least to the sixteenth century. Their name comes from a type of Spanish wool, but they are considered French cats. Chartreux cats are large and powerful, but they tend to be gentle. They are known for their woolly, bluish coats.

British Shorthair

This breed descends from ancient Roman house cats. They are large, powerful animals with broad chests and round faces. They have short legs and short, thick fur. You might have seen these calm, intelligent cats in TV commercials.

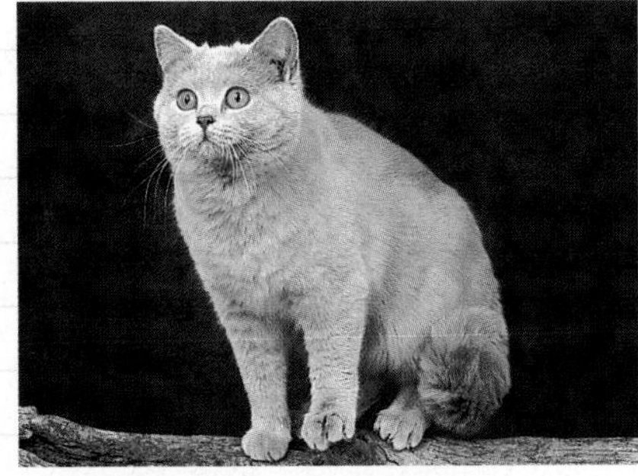
British Shorthair

American Wirehair

American Wirehair

This breed is a natural mutation that first appeared in New York in 1966. The feature that makes them special is their unusual coat. Each hair is stiff and crimped, which makes the coat hard. Their whiskers also are wiry.

Use Science Words

Word Usage Remind students that the term *feline* refers to all members of the cat family, not only the domesticated cats shown in this field guide. See how many types of felines students can list. Then have students research library sources for information on types of wild or extinct felines.

Teacher FYI

Purebred cats sometimes are shown competitively. Cats entered in shows sponsored by the Cat Fancier's Association are judged against a list of traits considered desirable for each breed. These traits are determined by a breed council, and are developed to promote healthy and beautiful cats. The Household Pet class is the only group not compared with a set of written standards.

Fun Fact

Siamese kittens are completely white when they are born. The markings that are distinctive to their breed develop during the first year of life.

Internet Addresses

Explore the Glencoe Science Web site at **science.glencoe.com** to find out more about topics in this field guide.

Extension

Have interested students do additional research on one of the breeds shown in this field guide. Instruct them to pay particular attention to the traits that define the breed. Encourage students to contact a cat breeder or association to obtain information. Have students present their findings to the class. L2

Discussion

Hair color and texture is one of the most variable traits among individual cats and between breeds. Why might this be so? Possible answer: Hair color and texture are traits that can show wide variability without affecting the survival and reproduction of an individual cat or breed of cat.

Quick Demo

At some time during the discussion, dim the room lights. Point out that cat eyes function in dim light six times better than do human eyes. This is because a layer of cells in a cat's eyes reflects incoming light toward the retina much like a mirror. Remind students that cats are naturally nocturnal, and then discuss the advantage to cats of being able to see in reduced light. LS **Visual-Spatial**

Field GUIDE

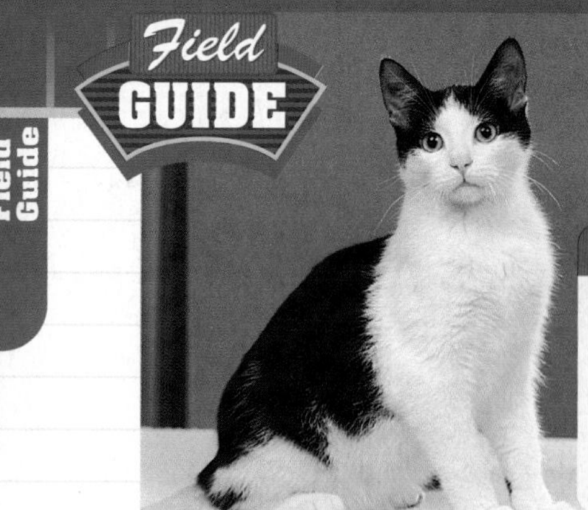

American Shorthair

American Shorthair

This breed came to America with the English Puritans in the 1600s. As the name suggests, they have short fur. They come in many colors, but most are silver with black bands.

Abyssinian (a buh SIH nee un)

In the mid-1800s, this breed was brought to England from Ethiopia, which was then called Abyssinia. However, some scientists believe these cats might have originated in Asia. Abyssinians have arched necks, muscular bodies, large ears, and almond-shaped eyes. Their coats can be ruddy, fawn, auburn, or bluish, and they are marked with several dark bands.

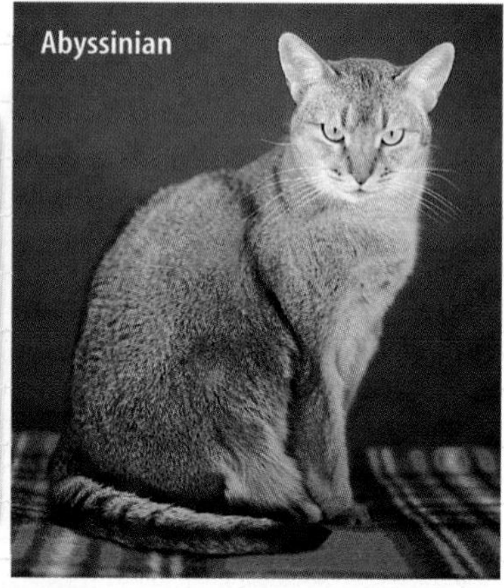

Abyssinian

Sphynx

Sphynx

The Sphynx is a natural mutation. It first appeared in Canada in 1966. At first glance, these cats appear to be totally bald. In fact, their bodies are covered with a soft, fuzzy, downlike hair. They have short whiskers or none at all, and their skin is often wrinkled.

Selkirk Rex

This breed first appeared as a natural mutation in Wyoming. Selkirk Rexs are large and powerful like the British Shorthair, and they have curly hair and whiskers. Unlike Devon Rex and Cornish Rex, their hair can be long or short. They come in many colors.

Selkirk Rex

Curriculum Connection

Art Throughout history, cats have been depicted in sculptures and paintings. Have students research cats shown in the artwork of various cultures and time periods. Students can report their findings to the class, and should provide visuals of their findings whenever possible.
LS **Visual-Spatial**

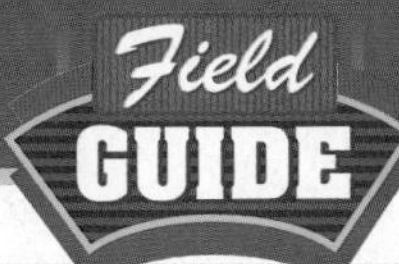

Norwegian Forest Cat

These green-eyed cats came to North America with the Viking explorers. In the winter, their hair is thick and a plush mane grows around their necks and chests. The long hair of their inner ears stays with them all year. They come in many colors.

Norwegian Forest Cat

Manx

Manx

This breed first appeared on the Isle of Man. Manx cats are best known as the cats without tails, but some have stubby tails called rises. They have arched backs, round heads, and round bodies. Their hair can be long or short.

Maine Coon

This breed developed in North America and was first recognized in Maine. Maine Coons are large, sturdy cats. Long hair and the tufts of hair in their ears help them tolerate extreme cold. Their coats are shaggy, but they feel silky.

Maine Coon cats

Egyptian Mau

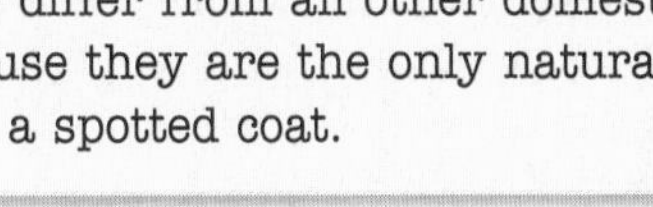

Egyptian Mau

The ancient Egyptians loved to draw this breed, which descends from the African wildcat. Egyptian Maus have green eyes, and their fur can be silver, bronze, black, bluish, or smoke colored. They differ from all other domestic cats because they are the only natural breed with a spotted coat.

Visual Learning

Manx The breeding of purebred cats can magnify their undesirable traits as well as their desirable ones. The Manx is an example of a breed that is sometimes subject to health problems due to its unique characteristics. The back legs of this breed are long in proportion to its body, causing these cats to walk with an unusual gait, more like a hobble than a walk. This breed can also have trouble with incontinence. Stillbirths in litters are common as well. LS **Visual-Spatial**

Make a Model

Have students make models of fictional cat breeds that incorporate traits they find appealing. Students should use the information in this field guide and additional reference sources for ideas. Depending on the materials that are available, the models can be two-dimensional, three dimensional, or computer generated. L2 LS **Kinesthetic**

Discussion

How does the environment in which a cat breed originated affect its traits? Possible answer: Cat breeds that originated in cold climates often have long, thick hair, while those that originated in warmer climates often have shorter hair.

Inclusion Strategies

Gifted Have especially able students research the "personalities" that are characteristic to selected breeds of cat. Instruct students to research whether there is a genetic component contributing to each breed's unique personality. Have students present their findings to the class. L3 LS **Linguistic**

FIELD GUIDE 815

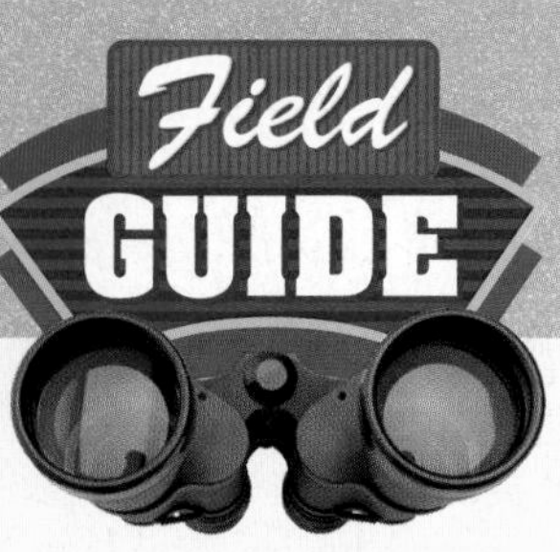

About the Field Guide

- This field guide contains representative descriptions and photos of the cones of twelve types of conifers that enable the user to classify some cones.
- In using a field guide, students will apply steps of a scientific method as they observe, investigate, and draw conclusions.
- This field guide applies nationally; local and regional field guides are usually available. Remind students that plants vary and cones may not match exactly.
- Encourage students to use the field guide outside the classroom.

Tie to Prior Knowledge

Students may have seen cones on different needled trees and referred to all of them as pinecones. After using this field guide, they will be aware of the different needled plants and the uniqueness of their cones.

Field Activity

Student responses to this activity will vary. If students use cones from craft items, they may need help in identifying the species from which they came. Be sure they research each cone's plant in order to include a description of it. Student sketches of cones should reflect one of the shapes shown in the field guide.

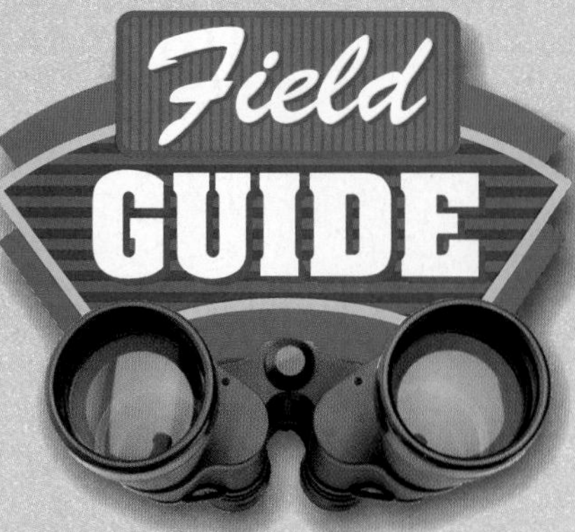

When you hear the word *cone,* you might think of a tasty, edible holder for your favorite ice cream. Maybe you think of the orange cones used on highways and in public places to direct vehicular or pedestrian traffic. However, there's another type of cone in the environment that plays an important role for some plants. These cones are the reproductive organs of a large plant group called the conifers, or cone bearers. The seeds of pines, firs, spruces, redwoods, and other conifers are formed in cones.

Types of Cones

Conifers have two types of cones, male and female. The male cones produce pollen grains and break apart soon after they release pollen. Depending on the species of conifer, the female cones can stay on plants for up to three years. Female cones can be woody or berrylike. Woody cones consist of scales growing from a central stalk and vary in shape and size. Berrylike cones are round and either hard or soft. Each genus of conifers has a different type of female cone. They are so different from one another that you can use them to identify a conifer's genus.

816 STUDENT RESOURCES

Cones

Cone Characteristics

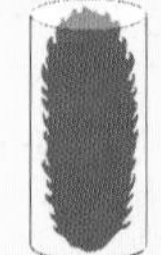

Cylindrical
This cone is shaped like a cylinder and is nearly uniform in size from the base to the tip.

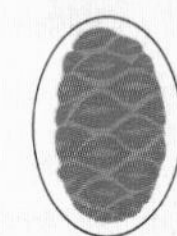

Ovoid
Although this cone is shaped like a cylinder, it is smaller at the ends than in the middle.

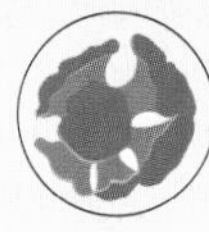

Globose
This cone is rounded like a globe.

Conic
Shaped like a cone, it decreases in diameter from the base to the tip.

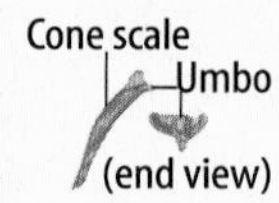

Umbo
A raised, triangular area at the tip of a cone scale varies in size and thickness.

Field Activity

Find three different cones in your neighborhood, a park, around your school, or as part of a craft item. Using this guide, identify the genus of each cone. Go to the Glencoe Science Web site at **science.glencoe.com** if you don't have cones in your neighborhood. Here you can link to different sites about cones. In your Science Journal, sketch each cone and write a description of the plant it came from.

Resources for Teachers and Students

Trees: An Explore your World Handbook, by Jon Arno, Discovery Books, 2000.

Conifers: The Illustrated Encyclopedia, by D.M. van Gelderen, Timber Press, 1996.

Cone Identification

This field guide contains some of the conifers. Plant features might differ in appearance because of environmental conditions.

Douglas Fir—*Psuedotsuga*

These ovoid cones on short stalks have a three-pointed, papery structure that extends from below each cone scale. The cones range from 5 cm to 10 cm in length.

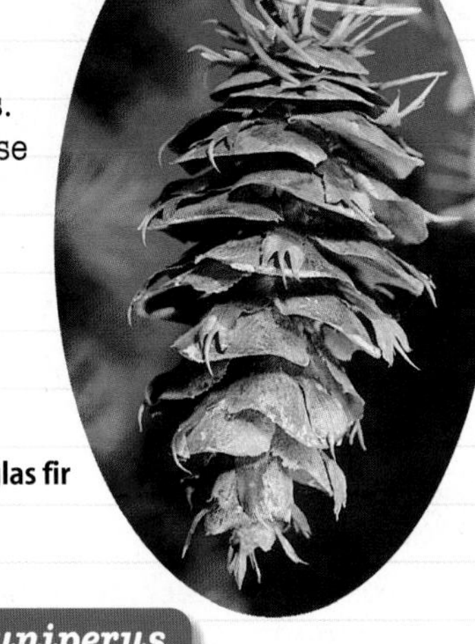

Douglas fir cone

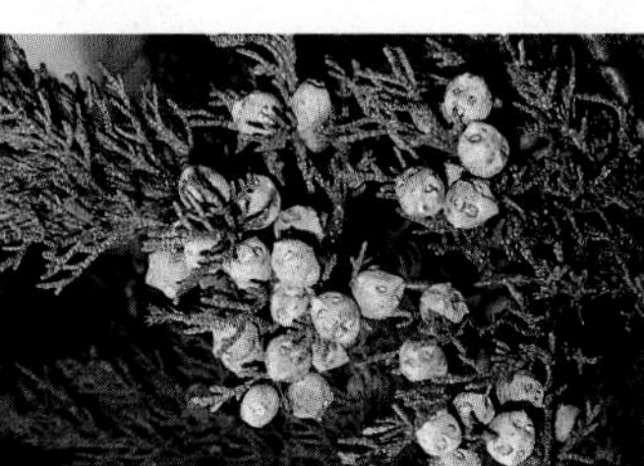

Juniper berries

Juniper—*Juniperus*

These cones are hard, berrylike structures that stay on the tree or shrub for two to three years. They measure about 1.3 cm in diameter. They are bluish, pale green, reddish, or brown and covered with a white, waxy coating called a bloom.

Spruce—*Picea*

These cones are cylindrical and brown with thin cone scales and tips that usually are pointed. They can be 6 cm to 15 cm long. They stay on the plant for two years and hang from branches on the upper third of the tree. As they mature, they become brittle.

Spruce cones

Redwood—*Sequoia*

Ovoid and reddish brown, these cones hang from the tips of needled twigs. They develop in one year and are small in comparison to the size of the tree—only 1.2 cm to 3 cm. The cone scales are flattened on their ends.

Redwood cones

Discussion

What are some of the characteristics of cones that scientists could use to classify a newly discovered species of tree? Possible answers: size, shape, color, and texture of the cone; its location on the tree; the length of time it stays on the tree

Quick Demo

Bring in branches from several different pines. Show students that pines have their needles in groups of two or three to five. Use enlarged pictures if pines are not available in your area. LS **Visual-Spatial**

Visual Learning

Junipers The female cones of the juniper plant are often referred to as "juniper berries." These cones have fleshy scales that are fused together, giving a berrylike appearance. The "berries" of some species of juniper are used to flavor food and beverages.

Fun Fact

The Giant Sequoias are the largest of the conifers. The largest Giant Sequoia tree is about 80 meters high and weighs about 2,500 metric tons.

Curriculum Connection

Geography Have students choose a type of conifer and research where it grows. Have students plot on a large world map the locations of the conifers they have researched. Discuss these locations, and have students draw conclusions based on their knowledge of climates in various locations around the world.
L2 LS **Logical-Mathematical**

Internet Addresses

Explore the Glencoe Science Web site at **science.glencoe.com** to find out more about topics in this field guide.

Content Background

In 1994 a park ranger in an Australian National Park discovered a species of coniferous tree thought to have been extinct for thousands of years. The trees were growing in a deep cavern about 150 km outside Sidney, Australia. Fossil evidence shows that this ancient form of conifer was plentiful during the Jurassic and Cretaceous periods. There currently are fewer than 100 trees of this species known to exist. Botanists and conservationists are working to ensure the species' survival.

Fun Fact

The seeds of nearly all pines are edible. They contain mostly oils, but the protein content ranges from 15 percent to 30 percent.

Activity

Have each student bring in an item or a picture of an item made from the wood of a conifer. Make a list of all of the uses of conifer wood represented by the items.

Extension

Have interested students research amber, the fossilized resin of pines. Amber sometimes contains fossilized insects and provides valuable information to paleontologists and other scientists. Have students report their findings to the class. LS **Linguistic**

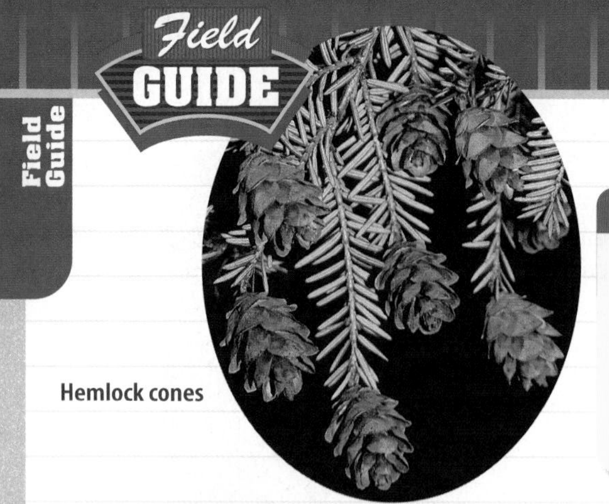

Hemlock cones

Hemlock—*Tsuga*

These cones hang from twigs and are small, ovoid to cylindrical, and 2 cm to 7 cm long. The few cone scales have rounded tips. Although they develop in one year, they usually stay on the tree for more than one year.

Pine—*Pinus*

Each cone has a thick, woody scale tipped with an umbo. The umbo can have a small spine, or prickle. Most pine cones are cylindrical or conic and grow on a small stalk. They vary in length from about 4 cm (scrub pine) to 45 cm (sugar pine) and remain on the tree or shrub for two to three years.

Pine cone

Arborvitae cones

Arborvitae—*Thuja*

These egg-shaped cones are 1.2 cm to 1.5 cm long. They have paired cone scales, usually from six to 12, that are straplike and end in a sharp point. The cones remain attached to the shrub after opening and releasing their seeds.

Cypress—*Cupressus*

These globose cones, which are usually 2 cm to 2.5 cm in diameter, have only six to eight scales. The cone scales have a raised point in the center. They develop in about 18 months and stay closed and attached to the tree.

Cypress cones

Inclusion Strategies

Visually Impaired Help visually impaired students develop a key for several cones using sensory characteristics such as texture, size, and smell. LS **Kinesthetic**

SCIENCE Online

Internet Addresses

Explore the Glencoe Science Web site at **science.glencoe.com** to find out more about topics in this field guide.

Field GUIDE

Field Guide

False Cypress—*Chamaecyparis*

These small globose cones are only 0.5 cm to 4 cm in diameter with four to ten cone scales. Unlike the cones of the *Cupressus* trees, they open after they are fully developed.

False cypress cones

Swamp cypress cones

Swamp or Bald Cypress—*Taxodium*

This globose cone is about 2.5 cm across and develops in one year. The tips of the cone scales are four sided, forming an irregular pattern on the surface of the cone. Trees in this genus are recognized by the projections, called knees, that grow upward from around the base of the tree trunk.

Fir—*Abies*

Fir cones grow upright on branches and range from 5 cm to 20 cm in length. They are seldom used for identification because the scales drop off when they are developed, leaving only the bare central stalk.

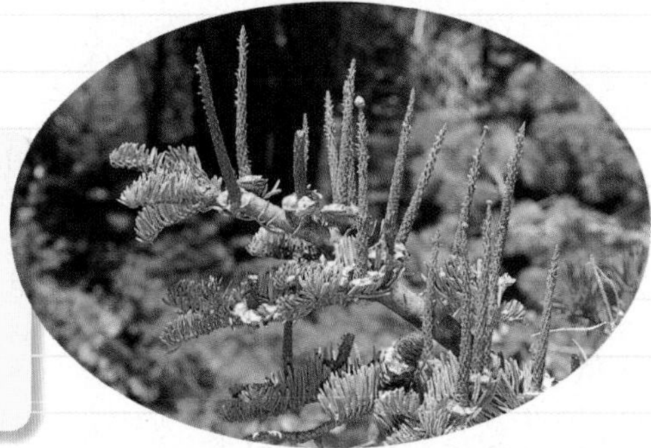

Fir cones

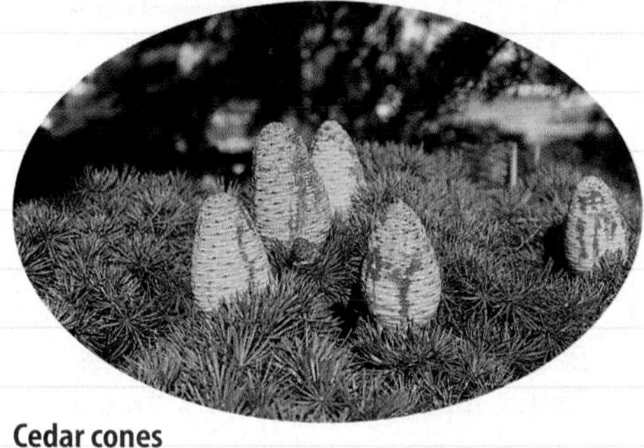

Cedar cones

Cedar—*Cedrus*

These barrel-shaped cones with flattened tips grow upright on branches. They are 5 cm to 10 cm in length and nearly half as wide. After two years, the scales drop off. Cedar trees do not produce these cones until they are 40 to 50 years old.

Field Guides

Discussion

How might your life be different if all species of conifer trees were extinct? Possible answers: Some students may mention that if there were no conifers, they would have to use something different for a Christmas tree. Other students may mention that much of their furniture would not exist without conifers. Students may also point out the value of conifers as a beautiful part of nature that couldn't be enjoyed if they were extinct.

Make a Model

Have students use available materials to make a model of one of the types of cones discussed in this field guide. Students should label their model to indicate the shape and characteristics of the cone, as well as the type of tree on which it is found. Students should share their model with the class.
L1 LS **Kinesthetic**

Visual Learning

Bald Cypress Show students additional pictures of bald cypress trees. Point out the knees that form around the base of the trunk. Some scientists think the knees provide stability in loose soil.

Science Journal

More on Cones Provide students with pictures of cones of genera not described in this guide. Have them use other field guides to identify the cones. Encourage students to write descriptions of these cones and their genera in their Science Journals. They should also explain the steps they used to identify the cones.
LS **Logical-Mathematical**

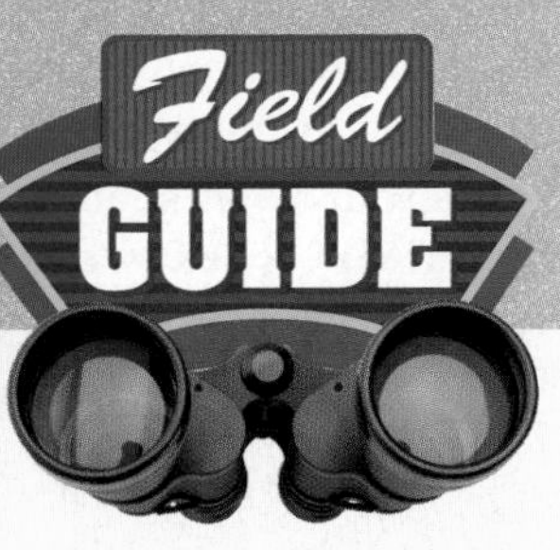

About the Field Guide

- This field guide contains representative descriptions and photos of ten insect orders that enable the user to classify some insects.
- In using a field guide, students will apply steps of a scientific method as they observe, investigate, and draw conclusions.
- This field guide applies nationally; local and regional field guides are usually available for more specific local use.
- Encourage students to use this field guide outside the classroom.

Tie to Prior Knowledge

List responses on the board as students name insects they have seen or with which they are familiar. **Are some of these insects related? Explain.** Students may mention that some are anatomically similar. Other students may recognize that some similar insects have common ancestors.

Field Activity

Have students work in small groups to classify the insects on the list into orders. Then have students work as a class to draw or find pictures of each insect and group them into their respective orders on a bulletin-board display.  **Logical-Mathematical and Visual-Spatial**

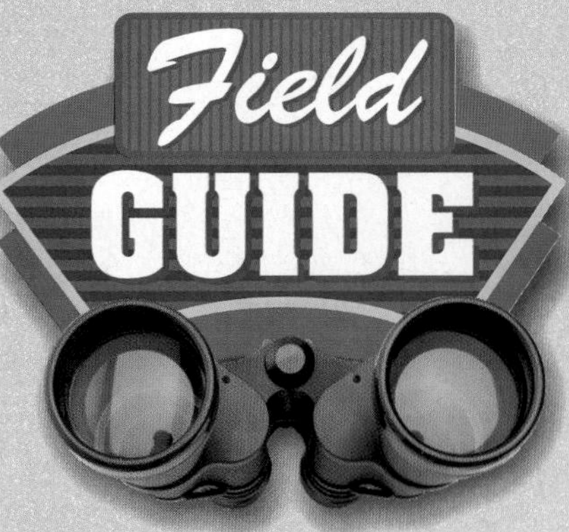

It's brown and creepy, and it has wings and six legs. If you call it a bug, you might be correct, but if you call it an insect, you are definitely correct. Insects belong to a large group of animals called arthropods. They are related to shrimp, spiders, lobsters, and centipedes. More insect species exist than all other animal species on Earth. Insects are found from the tropics to the tundra. Some live in water all or part of their lives, and some insects even live inside other animals. Insects play important roles in the environment. Many are helpful, but others are destructive.

How Insects Are Classified

An insect's body is divided into three parts—head, thorax, and abdomen. The head has a pair of antennae and eyes and paired mouthparts. Three pairs of jointed legs and, sometimes, wings are attached to the thorax. The abdomen has neither wings nor legs. Insects have a hard covering over their entire body. They shed this covering, then replace it as they grow. Insects are classified into smaller groups called orders. By observing an insect and recognizing certain features, you can identify the order it belongs to. This field guide presents ten insect orders.

Insects

Insect Orders

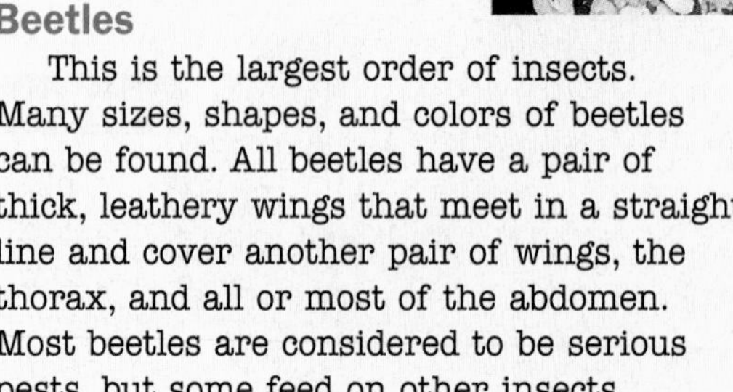
Convergent ladybug beetle

Coleoptera

Beetles

This is the largest order of insects. Many sizes, shapes, and colors of beetles can be found. All beetles have a pair of thick, leathery wings that meet in a straight line and cover another pair of wings, the thorax, and all or most of the abdomen. Most beetles are considered to be serious pests, but some feed on other insects and others eat dead and decaying organisms. Not all beetles are called beetles. For example, fireflies, June bugs, and weevils are types of beetles.

Male stag beetle

Field Activity

For a week, use this field guide to help identify insect orders. Look for insects in different places and at different times. Visit the Glencoe Science Web site at **science.glencoe.com** to view other insects that might not be found in your city. In your Science Journal, record the order of insect found, along with the date, time, and place.

Resources for Teachers and Students

The Audubon Society Field Guide to North American Insects and Spiders, by Lorus Johnson Milne and Margery Milne, Alfred A. Knopf, 1980.

Insects: The Little Things That Run the World, Smithsonian Institution, Unipix Consumer Products, 1995. (Video)

Bugs: Insects, Spiders, Centipedes, Millipedes and Other Closely Related Arthropods, by Frank W. Lowenstein and Sheryl Lechner, Black Dog and Levanthal, 1999.

Dermaptera

Earwigs

The feature that quickly identifies this brown, beetlelike insect is the pair of pincerlike structures that extend from the end of the abdomen. Earwigs usually are active at night and hide under litter or in any dark, protected place during the day. They can damage plants.

Earwig

Diptera

Flies and Mosquitoes

These are small insects with large eyes. They have two pair of wings but only one pair can be seen when the insect is at rest and the wings are folded. Their mouths are adapted for piercing and sucking, or scraping and lapping. Many of these insects are food for larger animals. Some spread diseases, others are pests, and some eat dead and decaying organisms. They are found in many different environments.

Common housefly

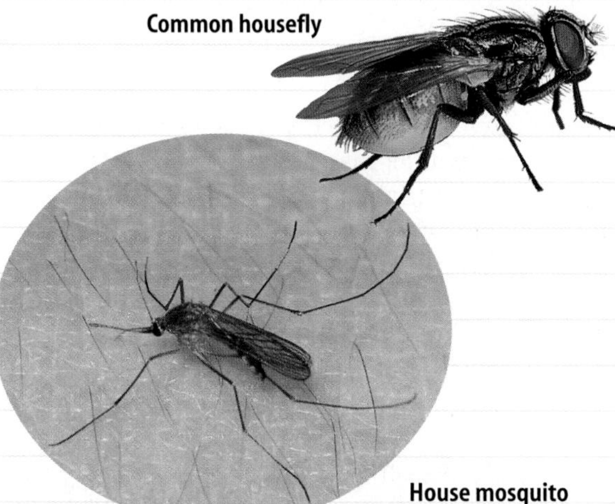

House mosquito

Odonata

Dragonflies and Damselflies

These insects have two pairs of transparent, multi-veined wings that are nearly equal in size and are never folded against the insect's body. The head has a pair of large eyes on it, and the abdomen is long and thin. These insects are usually seen near bodies of water. All members of this group hunt during flight and catch small insects, such as mosquitoes.

Dragonfly

Visual Learning

Explain to students that the photographs included with the description of each order illustrate the major characteristics of the order. Insects they observe may have characteristics slightly different from those shown in the photos. **LS Visual-Spatial**

Teacher FYI

Nearly 100,000 of the estimated 1.5 million species of insects live in North America. Many insects provide valuable commercial products; others serve as the primary pollinators of flowers. Some insects harm plants or animals or damage their products.

Extension

Some students may wish to make an insect collection. Instruct them to use reference materials to find information about proper preservation and display. Have these students share their collections with the class. **LS Kinesthetic**

Activity

Have students work in small groups to write a poem describing the insects in a particular order. Encourage groups to share their poems with the class. **LS Interpersonal and Auditory-Musical**

Curriculum Connection

Math Have each student make a bar graph of the number of insects they find for each of the ten orders. Remind students to label both axes and provide a descriptive title for their graphs. **LS Logical-Mathematical**

SCIENCE Online

Internet Addresses

Explore the Glencoe Science Web site at **science.glencoe.com** to find out more about topics in this field guide.

Quick Demo

Bring in several examples of ants and termites along with a hand lens, or enlarged pictures of ants and termites. Show students the small differences between the structure of the thorax and abdomen of an ant and the thorax and abdomen of a termite. LS **Visual-Spatial**

Fun Fact

When taken all together, the termites on Earth are estimated to weigh more than the humans on Earth.

Make A Model

Divide the class into small groups. Direct each group to create a fictitious insect belonging to one of the ten orders. Depending on available resources, the fictitious insects may be drawings, construction paper, three-dimensional models, or computer designed. Each model should show the characteristics of the order it represents. These characteristics should be clearly labeled.
COOP LEARN LS **Kinesthetic**

Field Guide

Isoptera

Termites

Adult termites are small, dark brown or black, and can have wings. Immature forms of this insect are small, soft bodied, pale yellow or white, and wingless. The adults are sometimes confused with ants. The thorax and abdomen of a termite look like one body part, but a thin waist separates the thorax and abdomen of an ant. Termites live in colonies in the ground or in wood.

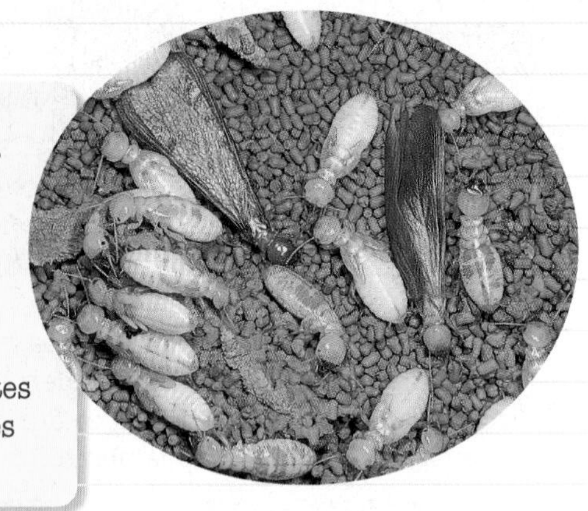
Pacific coast termites

American cockroach

Dictyoptera

Cockroaches and Mantises

These insects have long, thin antennae on the head. The front wings are smaller than the back wings. The back wings are thin and fanlike when they are opened. In the mantis, the front legs are adapted for grasping. The other two pairs of legs are similar to those of a cockroach. Praying mantises are beneficial because they eat other, often harmful, insects. Cockroaches are pests.

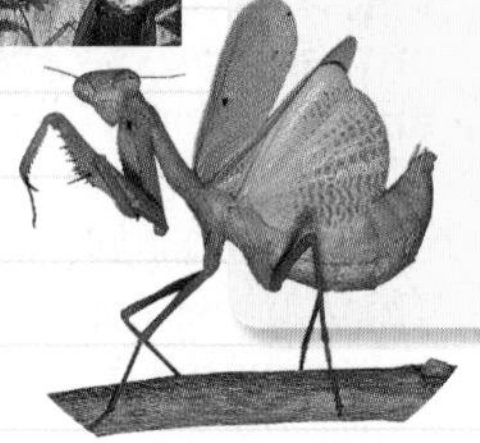
Carolina praying mantis

Paper wasp

American bumblebee

Hymenoptera

Ants, Bees, and Wasps

Members of this order can be so small that they're visible only with a magnifier. Others may be nearly 35 mm long. These insects have two pairs of transparent wings, if present. They are found in many different environments, either in colonies or alone. They are important because they pollinate flowers, and some prey on harmful insects. Honeybees make honey and wax.

Black carpenter ant

Internet Addresses

Explore the Glencoe Science Web site at **science.glencoe.com** to find out more about topics in this field guide.

Lepidoptera

Butterflies and Moths

Butterflies and moths have two pairs of wings with colorful patterns created by thousands of tiny scales. A moth's antennae are feathery. A butterfly's antennae are thin, and each has a small knob on the tip. Adult's mouthparts are adapted as a long, coiled tube for drinking nectar. Moths are active at night, and butterflies are active on warm, sunny days.

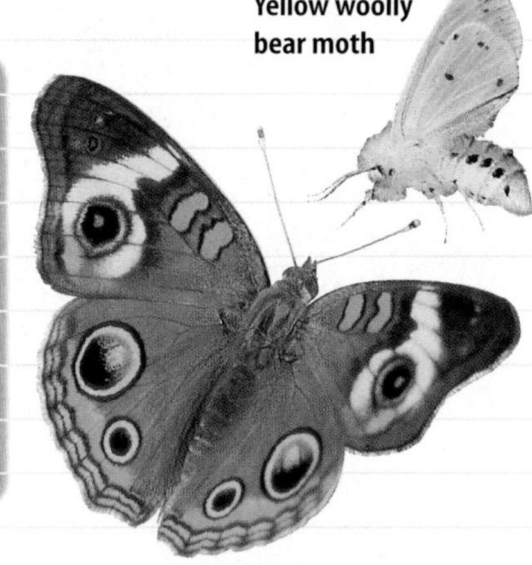

Yellow woolly bear moth

Buckeye butterfly

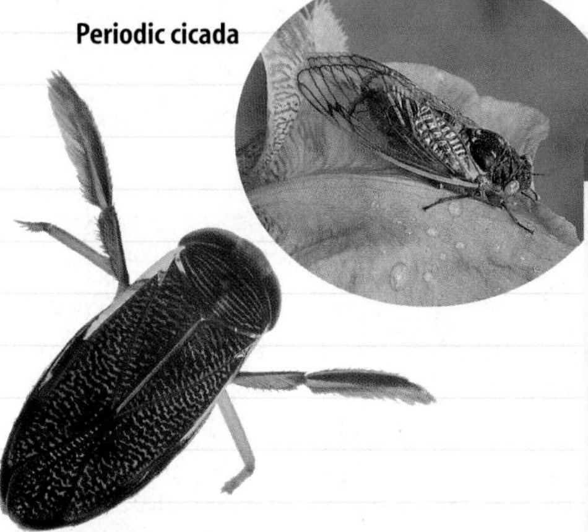

Periodic cicada

Water boatman

Hemiptera

Bugs

The prefix of this order, *"Hemi-"*, means "half" and describes the front pair of wings. Near the insect's head, the front wings are thick and leathery, and are thin at the tip. Wing tips usually overlap when they are folded over the insect's back and cover a smaller pair of thin wings. Some bugs live on land and others are aquatic.

Orthoptera

Grasshoppers, Crickets, and Katydids

These insects have large hind legs adapted for leaping. They usually have two pairs of wings. The outer pair is hard and covers a transparent pair. Many of these insects make singing noises by rubbing one body part against another. Males generally make these sounds. These insects are considered pests because swarms of them can destroy a farmer's crops in a few days.

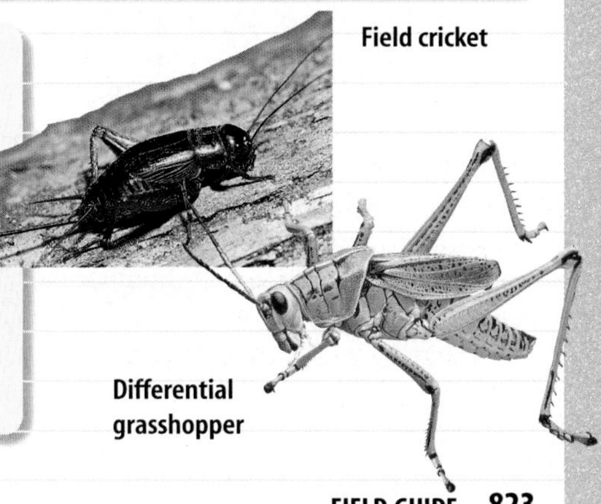

Field cricket

Differential grasshopper

Discussion

Why are some insects active only during daylight hours, and others are active only at night? Possible answer: By being active at different times, there is less competition for resources. This is also a way for some insects to avoid predators.

Extension

Have interested students interview an entomologist from a university, a specialist from a pest control business, a speaker from a natural history museum, or a consultant for an agricultural extension service. Students can write down the questions and answers in an interview format and share the interview with the class. LS **Interpersonal**

Teacher FYI

The classification of insects is an evolving process. As scientists learn more about the DNA of insects, new orders are suggested and insects are moved from one order to another. Not all scientists agree on a single classification system.

Curriculum Connection

Language Arts The names of orders that include winged insects all end with *-ptera* except for the order Odonata. Wingless insect orders have different endings. Have students find the roots for one of the ten orders in the field guide and report their findings to the class. LS **Linguistic**

Inclusion Strategies

Visually Impaired Many insects make distinctive sounds. Suggest that students research these sounds and make an audio presentation to the class. LS **Auditory-Musical**

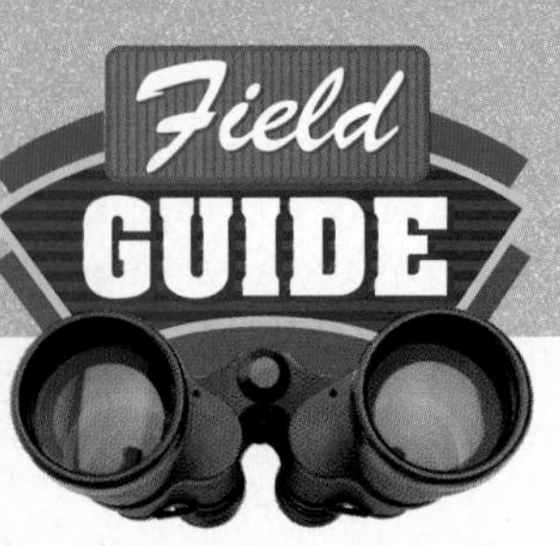

About the Field Guide

- This field guide describes the basic steps required to respond to an emergency situation.
- Encourage students to study this field guide so that they are properly prepared if an emergency arises.
- Remind students that there are many types of emergencies, and they should always use good judgment before offering assistance.

Tie to Prior Knowledge

All students are familiar with the concept of first aid. Have students recall situations in which they observed or participated in an emergency situation that required first aid or the use of emergency phone numbers.

Field Activity

Students can contact the local Red Cross office by looking up the telephone number and address in your local telephone directory. Remind students that their posters should clearly display the steps involved in dealing with the emergencies. Discuss with them that posters are most effective with clear illustrations and a minimum of text. Encourage students to develop memory devices that will allow others to easily remember how to react in an emergency. Have them use the memory devices as a part of their posters.

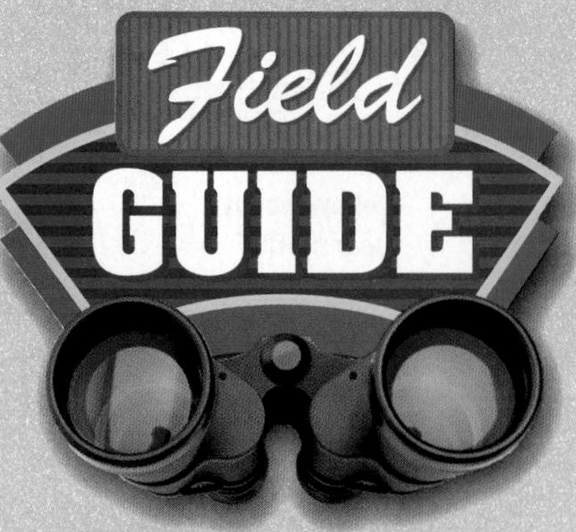

Emergencies

When you hear a scream or see smoke, do you wonder if you are witnessing an emergency? Emergencies can be difficult to identify. The scream you hear could be a hungry baby, and the smoke could be coming from a neighbor's grill, but sometimes the emergency is real. You might be the only one around to help. Knowing ahead of time how to identify an emergency will help you decide what to do when you are in an emergency situation.

Recognizing an Emergency

Emergencies can happen anytime and anyplace. A teammate might slip and twist her ankle during soccer practice. How can you tell whether the situation is a true emergency?

It can be hard to know whether the situation is an emergency. If you decide that it is, then you must determine the best way to help. Taking action is the first step to helping in an emergency. This can be difficult because you might be afraid of becoming involved. Calling the local emergency telephone number for help is important. If there isn't a telephone nearby, you can help by getting an adult.

Use your senses and look for these signs.

Noises

You know there could be an emergency when you hear screaming, calls for help, breaking glass, sudden or loud noises made by things or people, or screeching tires.

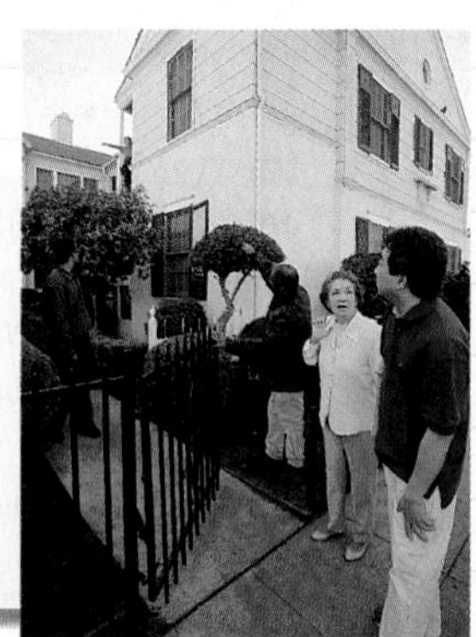

Sights

If you see a stalled vehicle or a vehicle off the road, smoke or fire, or a person lying unconscious on the floor or on the ground, you know there's an emergency.

Field Activity

Visit the Glencoe Science Web site at **science.glencoe.com** to connect to the National Red Cross site where you can get further information on emergencies. Record this information in your Science Journal. Set up posters at school showing how to recognize each of them.

Resources for Teachers and Students

The Complete Idiot's Guide to First Aid Basics, by Stephen J. Rosenberg and Karla Dougherty, Alpha Books, 1996.

Focus on Safety: Recreation Can Be Risky, by Bill Gutman, Twenty-First Century Books, 1996.

Focus on Safety: Hazards at Home, by Bill Gutman, Twenty-First Century Books, 1996.

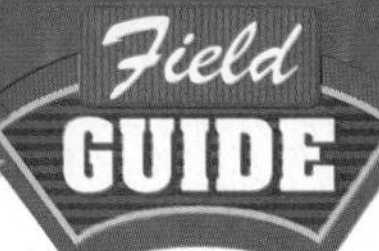

Odors

If you detect different or strange odors or familiar odors that are stronger than usual, it might be a signal that there's a problem. Leave the area immediately if you notice these unusual or very strong odors. They might be poisonous and extremely dangerous.

Behavior or Appearance of Another Person

If someone you know or someone you see shows any of the following signs, treat the situation as an emergency: unconsciousness, severe bleeding, vomiting or passing blood, difficulty breathing, grabbing his or her own throat, unexplained confusion or drowsiness, sudden change in skin color, complaining of chest pains or pressure, seizure, severe headache, or slurred speech.

Signs and symptoms vary from person to person, so you still might be unsure if it's a true emergency. In this case, pay attention to your instincts. Do you feel that getting involved might be dangerous for you? If so, stay away and try to get help. Do you feel that someone's safety depends on you and that you can help safely? If so, it's time to respond. **WARNING:** *If you become injured, you can't help.*

Content Background

Remind students that they must always be prepared for emergency situations. They should keep the telephone numbers of emergency services near the telephone. They should also have the necessary first aid material on hand. It is especially helpful for students to take a course in first aid and cardiopulmonary resuscitation (CPR). The American Red Cross and the American Heart Association, in addition to many local community organizations, offer these courses.

Activity

Have groups of students interview the school nurse or health teacher. Each team should pick a specific topic to learn more about. Have the groups present their findings to the class or videotape their interviews and present the videos to the class.

LS Interpersonal

SCIENCE Online

Internet Addresses

Explore the Glencoe Science Web site at **science.glencoe.com** to find out more about topics in this field guide.

Science Journal

Survey Have students survey a group of people to assess their awareness of the steps to follow in an emergency. People that students might survey include their friends, families, neighbors, and social groups. Survey questions may address issues such as recognizing an emergency, emergency phone numbers, and general first aid knowledge. Have students write a paragraph that summarizes their results.

Quick Demo

Use a disconnected telephone as a prop for demonstrating how to make an emergency phone call. Explain the questions the emergency operator will ask, as well as the importance of following exactly the instructions provided by the emergency operator, including staying on the line or hanging up as instructed. Remind students who baby sit to always write down the address of the home in which they are sitting in case they need to summon emergency help to the home. LS **Visual-Spatial**

Extension

Have interested students interview an emergency operator about his or her career. Instruct students NOT to call 911 to contact the operator. Have students find out about the training required and the operator's favorite and least favorite parts of the job. Have students summarize their findings in a paragraph they can share with the class.
LS **Interpersonal**

Discussion

What are some situations in which it is best to call for help instead of directly assisting victims? Accept answers that indicate that students understand that avoiding personal injury is important when helping others. Possible answers: downed power lines, fire, a person fallen through ice

Responding to an Emergency

After you decide that the situation is an emergency, you should follow three basic steps: **check, call,** and **care.**

CHECK

When you call for help, you will need to be able to pass on as much information as possible about the situation to the emergency operator. Your first priority is to identify the people who are hurt or in trouble. Sometimes, a quiet victim can be overlooked if another is screaming. Get help from others. Bystanders might tell you exactly what happened or the location of the nearest phone. They also might help comfort victims or apply first aid if they are qualified. Be conscious of signs that tell you what might have caused the emergency, such as broken glass, heavy objects, or odors.

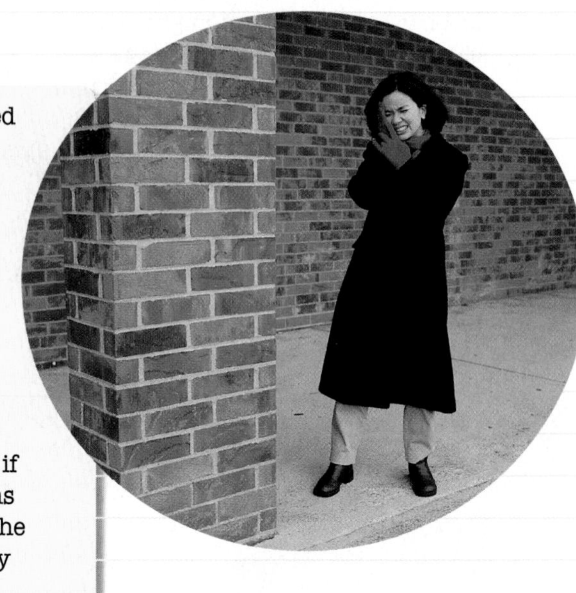

CALL

The most important first-aid tool at your disposal is the telephone. In most but not all areas, the emergency number is 911. Research your local emergency number and memorize it. **Never hesitate to call for help when you are in an emergency.**

When speaking with an emergency operator, remain calm and answer each question as clearly as possible. Stay on the line until the operator tells you to hang up.

Curriculum Connection

Art Have students research different styles of jewelry, including bracelets, necklaces, and charms, that identify the wearer as having specific medical conditions such as diabetes, epilepsy, and allergies to medication. Have students design a unique piece of jewelry to indicate a medical condition of their choice.
LS **Visual-Spatial**

CARE

If you are trained in first aid, follow standard procedures. Otherwise, do not perform any procedures on victims. Your job is to stay with the victims until help arrives. Here are some pointers. Respond to victims with life-threatening injuries or illnesses first. **WARNING:** *Do not move victims unless they are in danger* from an explosion, fire, or poisonous gas. Before helping a victim, get his or her permission and explain what you are going to do. If the person declines your help, do not insist. Keep victims comfortable, talk to them, and reassure them. Prevent victims from becoming chilled or overheated.

If you remember the 3 Cs—**check, call,** and **care**—someone who is injured or ill might have a better chance of surviving or recovering more quickly. What can you do right now to prepare for the emergency that might occur tomorrow, next week, or next year?

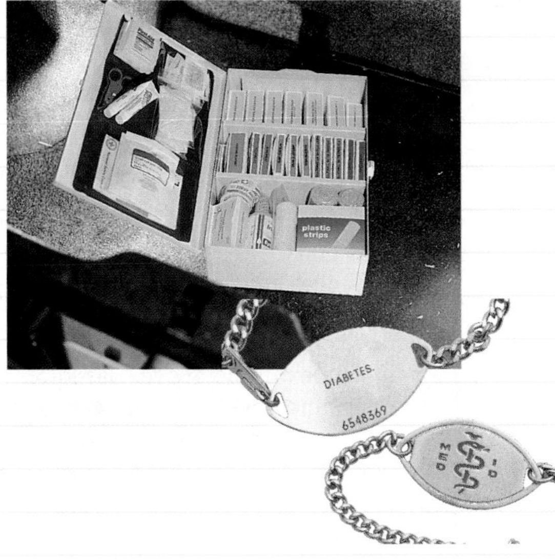

Emergency Checklist

Place first-aid kits in your home, car, and garage. Post emergency numbers near all phones and tape them to the first-aid kits. Teach children how to call for help. Find out whether your town has a 911 system. Put easy-to-read street numbers on your home or apartment. If you have special medical needs, wear a medical alert tag. Learn first-aid techniques including when and how to use CPR (cardiopulmonary resuscitation) and the abdominal thrust for choking victims.

Use Science Words

Word Meaning The term *cardiopulmonary resuscitation* (or CPR) was first used in 1972. The word *cardiopulmonary* comes from the Greek words *kardia*, meaning "heart action or location" and *pleumon*, meaning "lung." CPR is a procedure designed to restore normal breathing after cardiac arrest. Have students list other words that use these roots, and explain their meanings. Possible answers: cardiology: the study of the heart, cardiopathy: any disease of the heart; pulmonate: having lungs

Visual Learning

First Aid Kit Explain to students that the following items are vital for a first aid kit: sterile gauze, adhesive tape and bandages, antiseptic wipes, elastic bandages, soap, antibiotic cream, acetaminophen, tweezers, scissors, cold packs, syrup of ipecac, thermometer, vinyl or latex gloves, flashlight, emergency phone numbers. Have students discuss the possible uses for each item and suggest other items they feel should be included.

Inclusion Strategies

Behaviorally Disordered Have students examine the illustrations in this field guide that include people. For each person illustrated, have the students identify two emotions or feelings they think the person is experiencing. LS **Visual-Spatial**

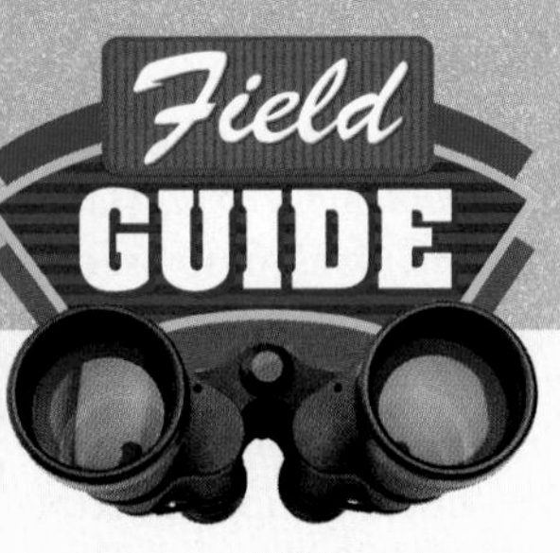

About the Field Guide

- This field guide contains a key that enables the user to classify or identify some biomes.
- This field guide applies globally; local and regional resources are available for more specific local use. Several sources of information are listed below.
- In using a field guide, students will apply steps of a scientific method as they observe, investigate, and draw conclusions.
- Encourage students to use this field guide outside the classroom.

Tie to Prior Knowledge

Students will probably be familiar with your local biome. However, they may not be aware of the diversity of organisms present. Have students list as many plants and animals as they can think of that they have seen in your local biome.

Field Activity

Student answers should be based on information obtained from a local weather station or newspaper. Student graphs will not be identical to the graphs in the field guide but should resemble one closely enough to draw conclusions. The types of organisms found will vary depending on the biome in which you live.

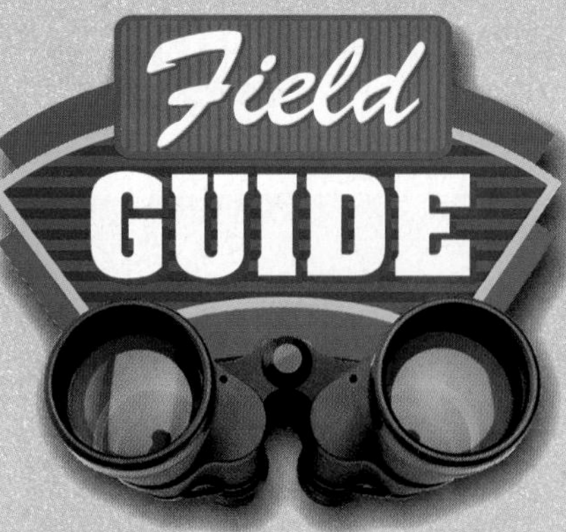

Why don't you find polar bears in Florida or palm trees in Alaska? Organisms are limited to certain areas where they can live and survive due to factors such as temperature, amount of rainfall, and type of soil that is found in a region. A biome's boundaries are determined by climate more than anything else. Climate is a way of categorizing temperature extremes and yearly precipitation patterns. Use this field guide to identify some of the world's biomes and to determine which biome you live in.

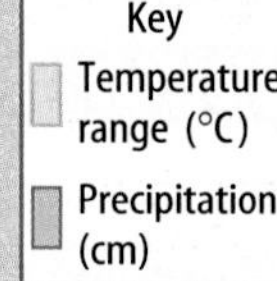

Interpreting Land Biome Climates

The following graphs represent typical climates in seven different biomes. To read each biome graph, use the following information in the key above. Note how each graph displays temperature range, precipitation levels, and the variation between months.

Biomes

Tundra

Winters in the tundra are long and harsh, and summers are short. There is little precipitation. In the tundra, you find mosses, lichens, grasses, and sedges. The tundra supports weasels, arctic foxes, arctic hares, snowy owls, and hawks.

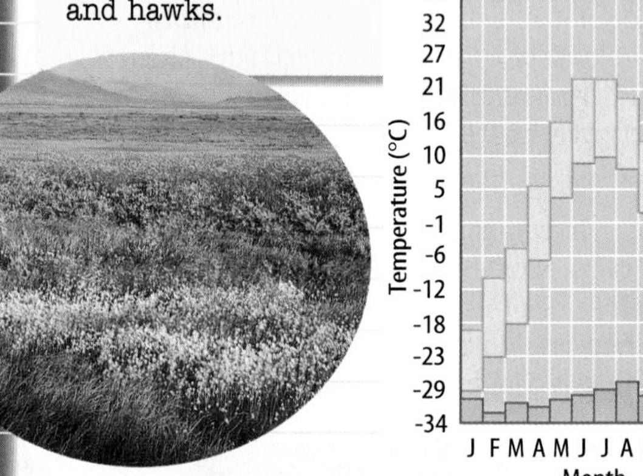

Field Activity

Research to find last year's monthly averages for rainfall, high temperature, and low temperature for your area or a nearby city. For further help on last year's averages, visit the Glencoe Science Web site at **science.glencoe.com.** Prepare a graph of data using the example above. Based on your findings, which biome graph most closely matches your data? What biome do you live in? What type of plant and animal life do you expect to find in your biome?

Resources for Teachers and Students

Biomes of the World, Volumes 1–9, by Michael Allaby, Grolier Educational, 1999.

The Natural History of North America, by Edward Ricciuti, Random House, Cresent, 1995.

Internet Addresses

Explore the Glencoe Science Web site at **science.glencoe.com** to find out more about topics in this field guide.

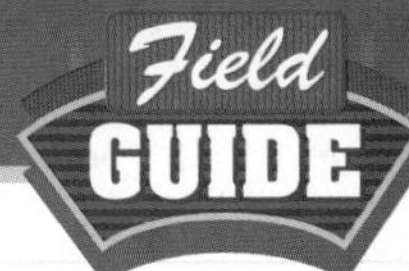

Taiga

Winters in the taiga are cold and severe with much snow. Growing seasons are short. Conifers such as spruces, firs, and larches are common. In the taiga, you find caribou, wolves, moose, bear, ducks, loons, owls and other birds.

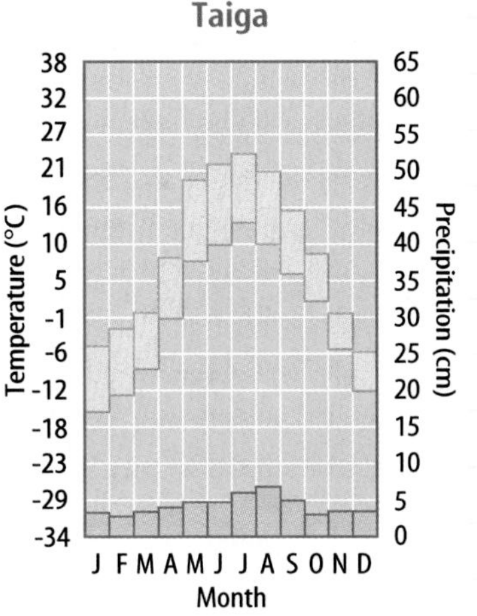

Temperate Deciduous Forest

The temperate deciduous forest has cold winters, hot summers, and moderate precipitation. In a temperate deciduous forest, you can see trees such as oak, hickory, and beech, which lose their leaves every autumn. Wolves, deer, bears, small mammals, and many species of birds are common in a temperate deciduous forest.

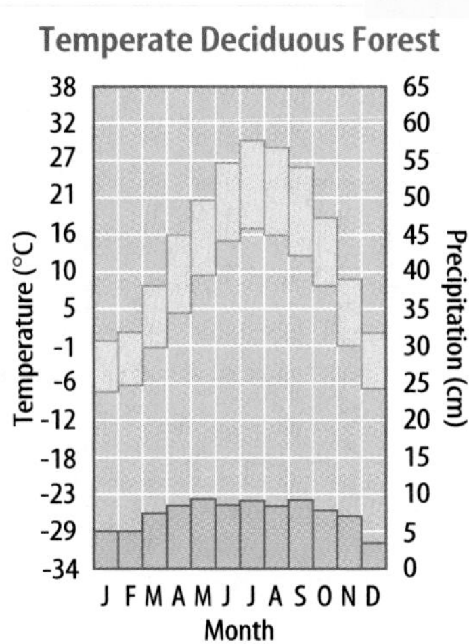

Discussion

Lead students in a discussion about plants and animals of the biome in which you live. **Why might you not be able to observe the expected types of plants and animals in your biome?** Many plants and animals live only in certain areas of a given biome. For example, pink ladies slipper orchids are found in temperate forests, but only in certain soils. Therefore, you could live in a temperate region and never see a pink ladies slipper.

Teacher FYI

The taiga is forest that lies south of the tundra. Most trees that grow in the taiga are conifers. Usually these areas are too cold and have soil that is too poor to support the growth of tall trees. The taiga is home to many species of birds, including several species of woodpeckers and owls. Mammals that live in the taiga biome include elk, lynx and snowshoe hares.

Using Science Words

Word Meaning Have students investigate the meaning of the word *deciduous*, which is derived from Latin. The word *deciduous* means "to fall off" and describes the seasonal shedding of leaves by trees. Trees that shed their leaves each year are called deciduous trees.

Curriculum Connection

Geography The Grand Canyon has starkly different climate zones that are arranged vertically instead of horizontally. The floor of the canyon has a hot, dry climate and vegetation similar to that of the Sonoran Desert. The rim of the canyon has piñon pines, which are typical of mid-altitude mountain slopes. Explain to students that the rim of the canyon is far above its floor, accounting for its major climatic differences. Have students locate the Grand Canyon on a map of the United States and determine in which biome it is located. LS **Visual-Spatial**

Quick Demo

Obtain a map of the United States. Use the information in the field guide to show students how the United States is divided into biomes.
LS **Visual-Spatial**

Extension

Explain to students that biomes are not static, permanent divisions. The biome of a particular area can change over time. Have students research an area that has been classified into different biomes in different time periods throughout history. Have them report their findings to the class.
LS **Logical-Mathematical**

Discussion

What are some adaptations that grasslands organisms might have? Explain. Possible answers: These organisms must be adapted to living without much water in the summer and winter. The organisms must also be able to withstand hot summers and cold winters, or be able to migrate.

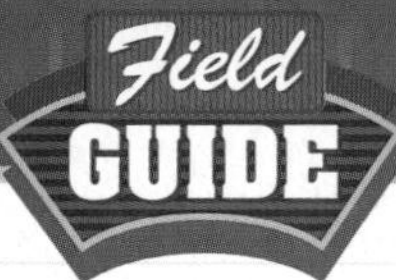

Temperate Rain Forest

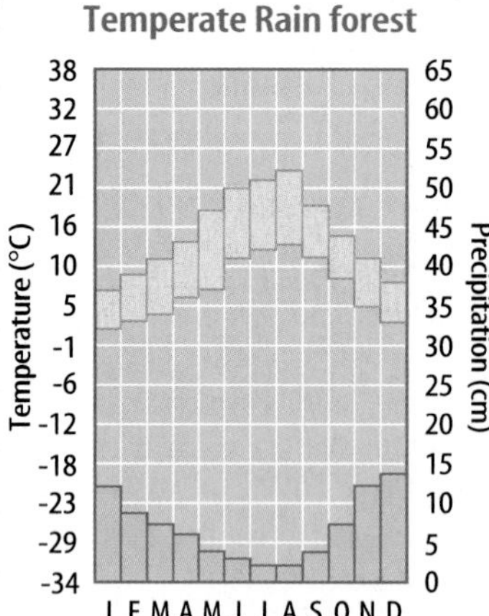

The summers and the winters in the temperate rain forest are mild. Temperatures rarely fall below freezing. The temperate rain forest has heavy precipitation and high humidity. Trees with needlelike leaves, mosses, and ferns are common. Many organisms including salamanders, frogs, black bears, cougars, pileated woodpeckers, and owls make their homes in the temperate rain forest.

Grassland

There is little precipitation during the grassland's cold winters and hot summers. The plants in the grassland are predominantly grasses although there are also a few trees. The grassland supports grazing animals, wolves, prairies dogs, foxes, ferrets, snakes, lizards, and insects.

Grassland

Temperature (°C): 38 32 27 21 16 10 5 -1 -6 -12 -18 -23 -29 -34

Precipitation (cm): 65 60 55 50 45 40 35 30 25 20 15 10 5 0

J F M A M J J A S O N D

Month

SCIENCE Online

Internet Addresses

Explore the Glencoe Science Web site at **science.glencoe.com** to find out more about topics in this field guide.

Science Journal

Transitional Biome The grasslands are a transitional biome. This means that if amounts of average precipitation change, the area will become a different biome. Have students write a paragraph in their Science Journals that describes what they think would happen if a grassland biome received either more or less precipitation. LS **Linguistic**

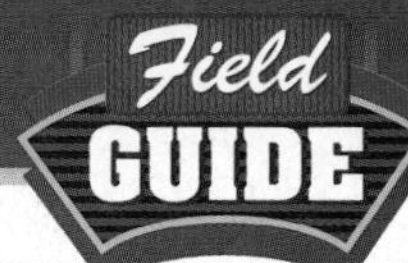

Field Guide

Desert

Deserts are warm to hot in the daytime and cool in the evening. They receive sparse precipitation throughout the year. Cacti, yuccas, Joshua trees, and bunchgrasses grow in the desert. Small rodents, jackrabbits, birds of prey, and snakes make their homes in the desert.

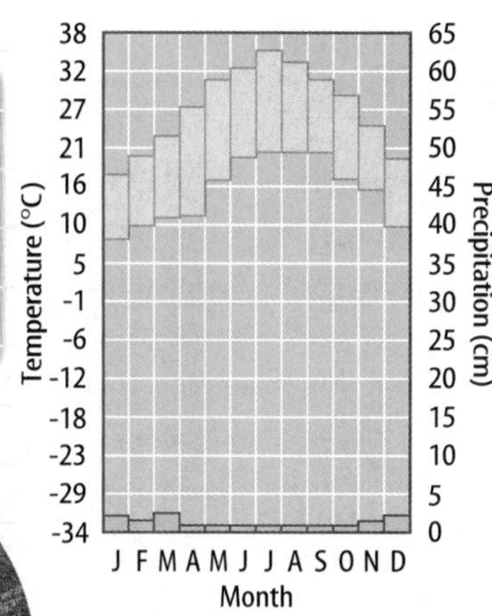

Tropical Rain Forest

Temperature (°C)

38 32 27 21 16 10 5 -1 -6 -12 -18 -23 -29 -34

Precipitation (cm)

65 60 55 50 45 40 35 30 25 20 15 10 5 0

J F M A M J J A S O N D

Month

Tropical Rain Forest

The tropical rain forest is hot all year with precipitation almost every day. A great diversity of plant species grow in the tropical rain forest. It provides homes for birds, reptiles, insects, monkeys, and sloths.

Content Background

Deserts are known for venomous species of spiders and scorpions. However, only a few of the many species of spiders and scorpions are venomous enough to endanger humans. For example, the tarantula and giant hairy scorpion look fierce, but they are not deadly to humans.

Field Guides

Fun Fact

Many students think deserts are large expanses of sand that have little or no life. In fact, most deserts contain a large variety of plants and animals that are specially adapted to living in desert environments.

Visual Learning

Tropical Rain Forest As students study the illustration, have them note the canopy, or heavy layer of growth at the top level of the forest. In many parts of the rain forest, this canopy allows little light to penetrate to the forest floor. Many plants have adaptations that allow them to grow close to the top of the canopy in order to receive light. **What can you infer light levels are like in the understory, which is below the canopy?** Light levels are low here, and plants grow in the shade.

Inclusion Strategies

Learning Disabled Have students make "biome boxes" using shoe boxes. Direct them to label their boxes with a particular biome name. They should then cut out or draw pictures that represent the plant and animal life found in that biome and arrange them in the biome box.

Organizing Information

As you study science, you will make many observations and conduct investigations and experiments. You will also research information that is available from many sources. These activities will involve organizing and recording data. The quality of the data you collect and the way you organize it will determine how well others can understand and use it. In **Figure 1,** the student is obtaining and recording information using a microscope.

Putting your observations in writing is an important way of communicating to others the information you have found and the results of your investigations and experiments.

Figure 1
Making an observation is one way to gather information directly.

Researching Information

Scientists work to build on and add to human knowledge of the world. Before moving in a new direction, it is important to gather the information that already is known about a subject. You will look for such information in various reference sources. Follow these steps to research information on a scientific subject:

Step 1 Determine exactly what you need to know about the subject. For instance, you might want to find out what happened to local plant life when Mount St. Helens erupted in 1980.

Step 2 Make a list of questions, such as: When did the eruption begin? How long did it last? How large was the area in which plant life was affected?

Step 3 Use multiple sources such as textbooks, encyclopedias, government documents, professional journals, science magazines, and the Internet.

Step 4 List where you found the sources. Make sure the sources you use are reliable and the most current available.

Evaluating Print and Nonprint Sources

Not all sources of information are reliable. Evaluate the sources you use for information, and use only those you know to be dependable. For example, suppose you want information about the digestion of fats and proteins. You might find two Websites on digestion. One Web site contains "Fat Zapping Tips" written by a company that sells expensive, high-protein supplements to help your body eliminate excess fat. The other is a Web page on "Digestion and Metabolism" written by a well-respected medical school. You would choose the second Web site as the more reliable source of information.

In science, information can change rapidly. Always consult the most current sources. A 1985 source about the human genome would not reflect the most recent research and findings.

Interpreting Scientific Illustrations

As you research a science topic, you will see drawings, diagrams, and photographs. Illustrations help you understand what you read. Some illustrations are included to help you understand an idea that you can't see easily by yourself. For instance, you can't see the bones of a blue whale, but you can look at a diagram of a whale skeleton as labeled in **Figure 2** that helps you understand them. Visualizing a drawing helps many people remember details more easily. Illustrations also provide examples that clarify difficult concepts or give additional information about the topic you are studying.

Most illustrations have a label or a caption. A label or caption identifies the illustration or provides additional information to better explain it. Can you find the caption or labels in **Figure 2?**

Figure 2
A labeled diagram of the skeletal structure of a blue whale

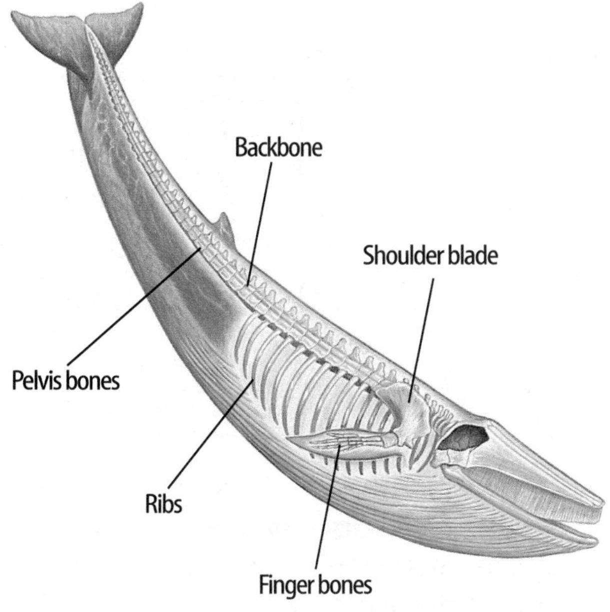

Venn Diagram

Although it is not a concept map, a Venn diagram illustrates how two subjects compare and contrast. In other words, you can see the characteristics that the subjects have in common and those that they do not.

The Venn diagram in **Figure 3** shows the relationship between two categories of organisms, plants and animals. Both share some basic characteristics as living organisms. However, there are differences in the ways they carry out various life processes, such as obtaining nourishment, that distinguish one from the other.

Concept Mapping

If you were taking a car trip, you might take some sort of road map. By using a map, you begin to learn where you are in relation to other places on the map.

A concept map is similar to a road map, but a concept map shows relationships among ideas (or concepts) rather than places. It is a diagram that visually shows how concepts are related. Because a concept map shows relationships among ideas, it can make the meanings of ideas and terms clear and help you understand what you are studying.

Overall, concept maps are useful for breaking large concepts down into smaller parts, making learning easier.

Figure 3
A Venn diagram shows how objects or concepts are alike and how they are different.

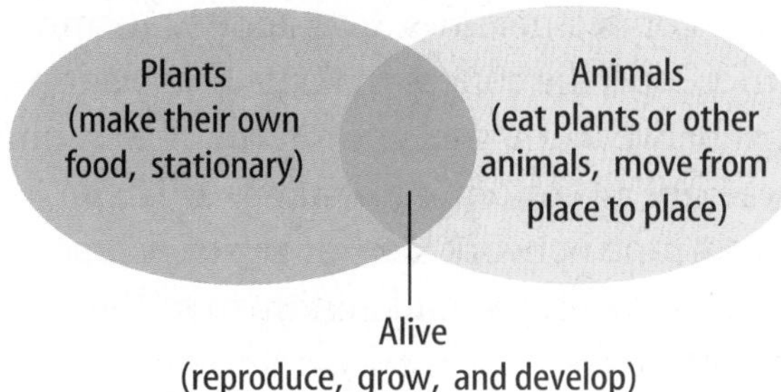

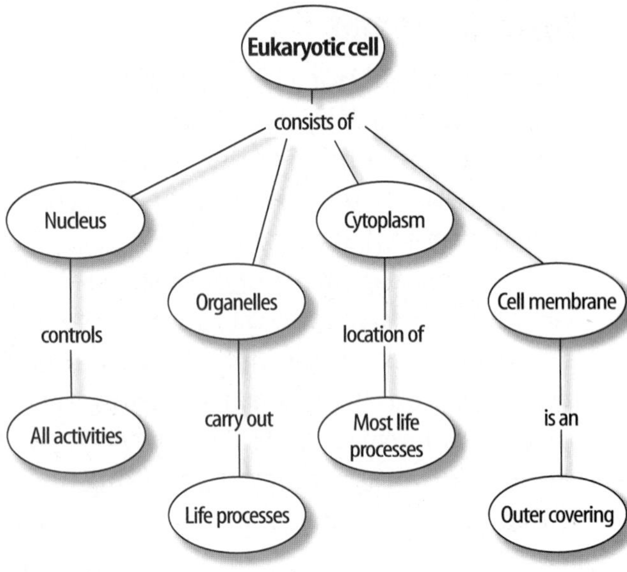

Figure 4
A network tree shows how concepts or objects are related.

Network Tree Look at the network tree in **Figure 4,** that shows details about a eukaryotic cell. A network tree is a type of concept map. Notice how some words are in ovals while others are written across connecting lines. The words inside the ovals are science terms or concepts. The words written on the connecting lines describe the relationships between the concepts.

When constructing a network tree, write the topic on a note card or piece of paper. Write the major concepts related to that topic on separate note cards or pieces of paper. Then arrange them in order from general to specific. Branch the related concepts from the major concept and describe the relationships on the connecting lines. Continue branching to more specific concepts. Write the relationships between the concepts on the connecting lines until all concepts are mapped. Then examine the network tree for relationships that cross branches, and add them to the network tree.

Events Chain An events chain is another type of concept map. It models the order of items or their sequence. In science, an events chain can be used to describe a sequence of events, the steps in a procedure, or the stages of a process.

When making an events chain, first find the one event that starts the chain. This event is called the *initiating event.* Then, find the next event in the chain and continue until you reach an outcome. Suppose you are asked to describe the main stages in the growth of a plant from a seed. You might draw an events chain such as the one in **Figure 5.** Notice that connecting words are not necessary in an events chain.

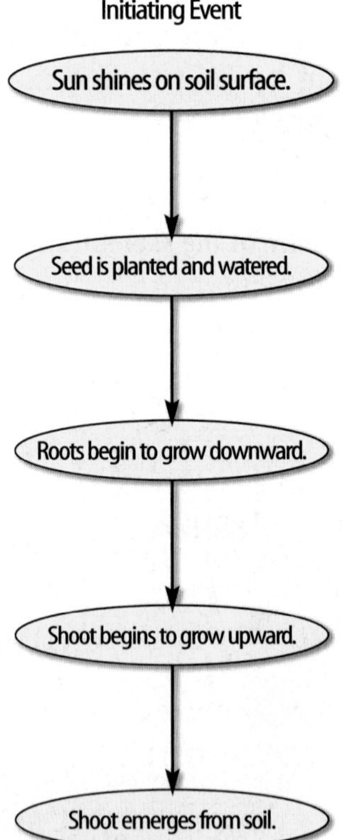

Figure 5
Events chains show the order of steps in a process or event.

Cycle Map A cycle concept map is a specific type of events chain map. In a cycle concept map, the series of events does not produce a final outcome. Instead, the last event in the chain relates back to the beginning event.

You first decide what event will be used as the beginning event. Once that is decided, you list events in order that occur after it. Words are written between events that describe what happens from one event to the next. The last event in a cycle concept map relates back to the beginning event. The number of events in a cycle concept varies but is usually three or more. Look at the cycle map in **Figure 6.**

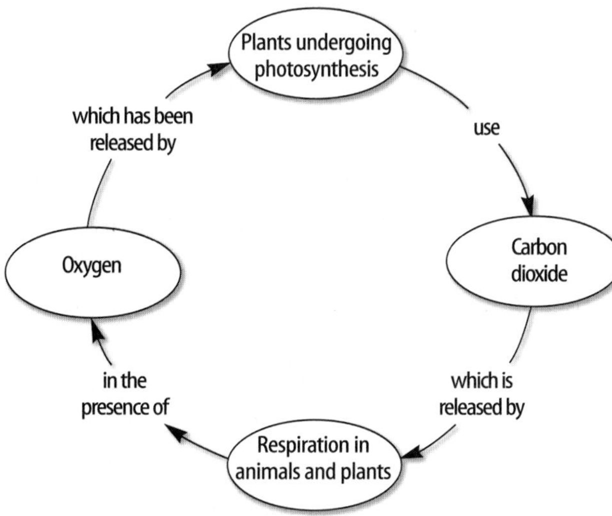

Figure 6
A cycle map shows events that occur in a cycle.

Spider Map A type of concept map that you can use for brainstorming is the spider map. When you have a central idea, you might find you have a jumble of ideas that relate to it but might not clearly relate to each other. The circulatory system spider map in **Figure 7** shows that if you write these ideas outside the main concept, then you can begin to separate and group unrelated terms so they become more useful.

Figure 7
A spider map allows you to list ideas that relate to a central topic but not necessarily to one another.

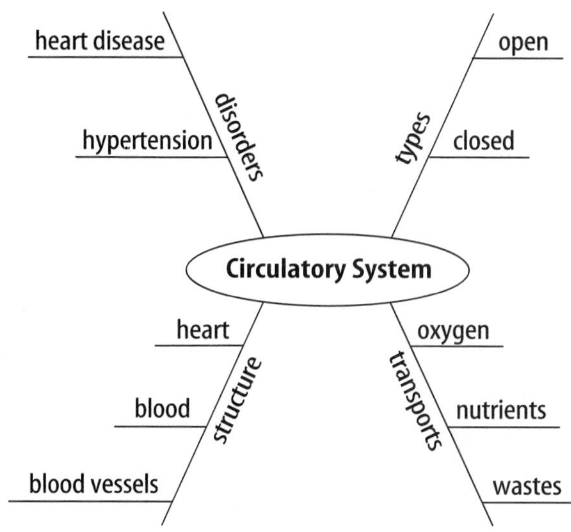

Writing a Paper

You will write papers often when researching science topics or reporting the results of investigations or experiments. Scientists frequently write papers to share their data and conclusions with other scientists and the public. When writing a paper, use these steps.

Step 1 Assemble your data by using graphs, tables, or a concept map. Create an outline.

Step 2 Start with an introduction that contains a clear statement of purpose and what you intend to discuss or prove.

Step 3 Organize the body into paragraphs. Each paragraph should start with a topic sentence, and the remaining sentences in that paragraph should support your point.

Step 4 Position data to help support your points.

Step 5 Summarize the main points and finish with a conclusion statement.

Step 6 Use tables, graphs, charts, and illustrations whenever possible.

Investigating and Experimenting

You might say the work of a scientist is to solve problems. When you decide to find out why one corner of your yard is always soggy, you are problem solving, too. You might observe that the corner is lower than the surrounding area and has less vegetation growing in it. You might decide to see if planting some grass will keep the corner drier.

Scientists use orderly approaches to solve problems. The methods scientists use include identifying a question, making observations, forming a hypothesis, testing a hypothesis, analyzing results, and drawing conclusions.

Scientific investigations involve careful observation under controlled conditions. Such observation of an object or a process can suggest new and interesting questions about it. These questions sometimes lead to the formation of a hypothesis. Scientific investigations are designed to test a hypothesis.

Identifying a Question

The first step in a scientific investigation or experiment is to identify a question to be answered or a problem to be solved. You might be interested in knowing why an animal like the one in **Figure 8** looks the way it does.

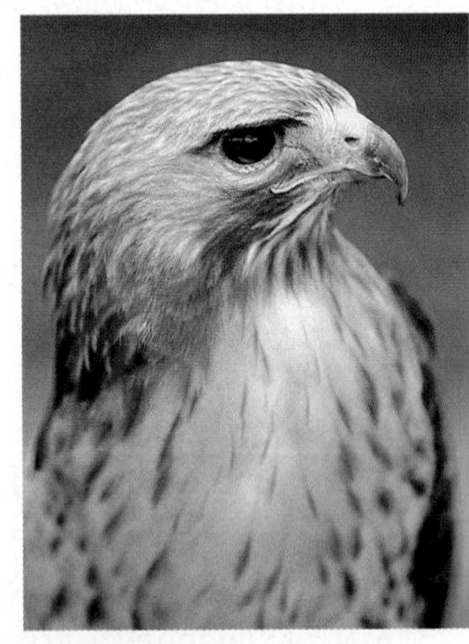

Figure 8
When you see a bird, you might ask yourself, "How does the shape of this bird's beak help it feed?"

Forming Hypotheses

Hypotheses are based on observations that have been made. A hypothesis is a possible explanation based on previous knowledge and observations.

Perhaps a scientist has observed that bean plants grow larger if they are fertilized than if they are not. Based on these observations, the scientist can make a statement that he or she can test. The statement is a hypothesis. The hypothesis could be: *Fertilizer makes bean plants grow larger.* A hypothesis has to be something you can test by using an investigation. A testable hypothesis is a valid hypothesis.

Predicting

When you apply a hypothesis to a specific situation, you predict something about that situation. First, you must identify which hypothesis fits the situation you are considering. People use predictions to make everyday decisions. Based on previous observations and experiences, you might form a prediction that if fertilizer makes bean plants grow larger, then fertilized plants will yield more beans than plants not fertilized. Someone could use this prediction to plan to grow fewer plants.

Testing a Hypothesis

To test a hypothesis, you need a procedure. A procedure is the plan you follow in your experiment. A procedure tells you what materials to use, as well as how and in what order to use them. When you follow a procedure, data are generated that support or do not support the original hypothesis statement.

For example, suppose you notice that your guppies don't seem as active as usual when your aquarium heater is not working. You wonder how water temperature affects guppy activity level. You decide to test the hypothesis, "If water temperature increases, then guppy activity should increase." Then you write the procedure shown in **Figure 9** for your experiment and generate the data presented in the table below.

Procedure

1. Fill five identical glass containers with equal amounts of aquarium water.
2. Measure and record the temperature of the water in the first container.
3. Heat and cool the other containers so that two have higher and two have lower water temperatures.
4. Place a guppy in each container; count and record the number of movements each guppy makes in 5 minutes.

Figure 9
A procedure tells you what to do step by step.

Number of Guppy Movements		
Container	**Temperature (°C)**	**Movements**
1	38	56
2	40	61
3	42	70
4	36	46
5	34	42

Are all investigations alike? Keep in mind as you perform investigations in science that a hypothesis can be tested in many ways. Not every investigation makes use of all the ways that are described on these pages, and not all hypotheses are tested by investigations. Scientists encounter many variations in the methods that are used when they perform experiments. The skills in this handbook are here for you to use and practice.

Identifying and Manipulating Variables and Controls

In any experiment, it is important to keep everything the same except for the item you are testing. The one factor you change is called the independent variable. The factor that changes as a result of the independent variable is called the dependent variable. Always make sure you have only one independent variable. If you allow more than one, you will not know what causes the changes you observe in the dependent variable. Many experiments also have controls—individual instances or experimental subjects for which the independent variable is not changed. You can then compare the test results to the control results.

For example, in the guppy experiment, you made everything the same except the temperature of the water. The glass containers were identical. The volume of aquarium water in each container and beginning water temperature were the same. Each guppy was like the others, as much as possible. In this way, you could be sure that any difference in the number of guppy movements was caused by the temperature change—the independent variable. The activity level of the guppy was measured as the number of guppy movements—the dependent variable. The guppy in the container in which the water temperature was not changed was the control.

Collecting Data

Whether you are carrying out an investigation or a short observational experiment, you will collect data, or information. Scientists collect data accurately as numbers and descriptions and organize it in specific ways.

Observing Scientists observe items and events, then record what they see. When they use only words to describe an observation, it is called qualitative data. For example, a scientist might describe the color of a bird or the shape of a bird's beak as seen through binoculars. Scientists' observations also can describe how much there is of something. These observations use numbers, as well as words, in the description and are called quantitative data. For example, if a particular dog is described as being "furry, yellow, and short-haired," the data are clearly qualitative. Quantitative data for this dog might include "a mass of 14 kg, a height of 46 cm, and an age of 150 days." Quantitative data often are organized into tables. Then, from information in the table, a graph can be drawn. Graphs can reveal relationships that exist in experimental data.

When you make observations in science, you should examine the entire object or situation first, then look carefully for details. If you're looking at a plant, for instance, check general characteristics such as size and overall structure before using a hand lens to examine the leaves and other smaller structures such as flowers or fruits. Remember to record accurately everything you see.

Scientists try to make careful and accurate observations. When possible, they use instruments such as microscopes, metric rulers, graduated cylinders, thermometers, and balances. Measurements provide numerical data that can be repeated and checked.

Sampling When working with large numbers of objects or a large population, scientists usually cannot observe or study every one of them. Instead, they use a sample or a portion of the total number. To *sample* is to take a small, representative portion of the objects or organisms of a population for research. By making careful observations or manipulating variables within a portion of a group, information is discovered and conclusions are drawn that might apply to the whole population.

Estimating Scientific work also involves estimating. To *estimate* is to make a judgment about the size or the number of something without measuring or counting every object or member of a population. Scientists first count the number of objects in a small sample. Looking through a microscope lens, for example, a scientist can count the number of bacterial colonies in the 1-cm^2 frame shown in **Figure 10.** Then the scientist can multiply that number by the number of cm^2 in the petri dish to get an estimate of the total number of bacterial colonies present.

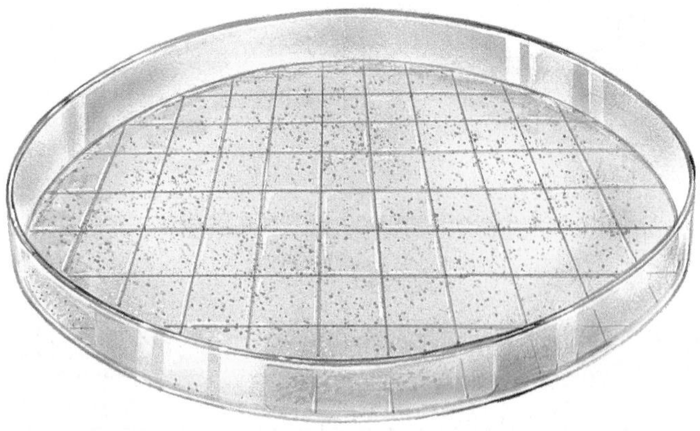

Figure 10
To estimate the total number of bacterial colonies that are present on a petri dish, count the number of bacterial colonies within a 1-cm^2 frame and multiply that number by the number of frames on the dish.

Measuring in SI

The metric system of measurement was developed in 1795. A modern form of the metric system, called the International System, or SI, was adopted in 1960. SI provides standard measurements that all scientists around the world can understand.

The metric system is convenient because unit sizes vary by multiples of 10. When changing from smaller units to larger units, divide by a multiple of 10. When changing from larger units to smaller, multiply by a multiple of 10. To convert millimeters to centimeters, divide the millimeters by 10. To convert 30 mm to centimeters, divide 30 by 10 (30 mm equal 3 cm).

Prefixes are used to name units. Look at the table below for some common metric prefixes and their meanings. Do you see how the prefix *kilo-* attached to the unit *gram* is *kilogram*, or 1,000 g?

Metric Prefixes

Prefix	Symbol	Meaning	
kilo-	k	1,000	thousand
hecto-	h	100	hundred
deka-	da	10	ten
deci-	d	0.1	tenth
centi-	c	0.01	hundredth
milli-	m	0.001	thousandth

Now look at the metric ruler shown in **Figure 11.** The centimeter lines are the long, numbered lines, and the shorter lines are millimeter lines.

When using a metric ruler, line up the 0-cm mark with the end of the object being measured, and read the number of the unit where the object ends. In this instance it would be 4.5 cm.

Figure 11
This metric ruler shows centimeter and millimeter divisions.

Liquid Volume In some science activities, you will measure liquids. The unit that is used to measure liquids is the liter. A liter has the volume of 1,000 cm^3. The prefix *milli-* means "thousandth (0.001)." A milliliter is one thousandth of 1 L and 1 L has the volume of 1,000 mL. One milliliter of liquid completely fills a cube measuring 1 cm on each side. Therefore, 1 mL equals 1 cm^3.

You will use beakers and graduated cylinders to measure liquid volume. A graduated cylinder, as illustrated in **Figure 12,** is marked from bottom to top in milliliters. This graduated cylinder contains 79 mL of a liquid.

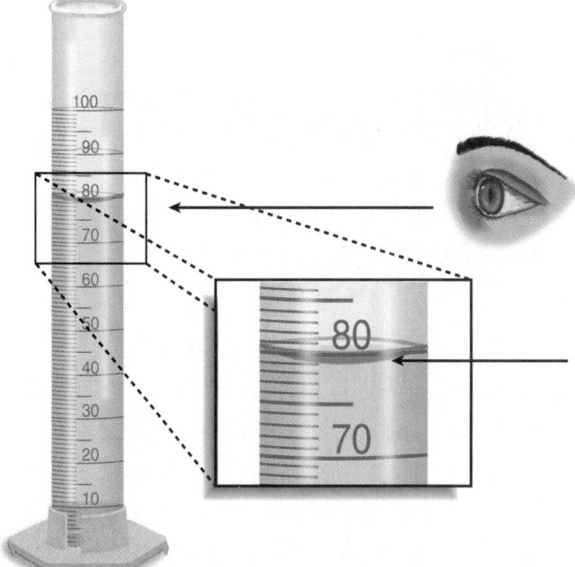

Figure 12
Graduated cylinders measure liquid volume.

Mass Scientists measure mass in grams. You might use a beam balance similar to the one shown in **Figure 13.** The balance has a pan on one side and a set of beams on the other side. Each beam has a rider that slides on the beam.

Before you find the mass of an object, slide all the riders back to the zero point. Check the pointer on the right to make sure it swings an equal distance above and below the zero point. If the swing is unequal, find and turn the adjusting screw until you have an equal swing.

Place an object on the pan. Slide the largest rider along its beam until the pointer drops below zero. Then move it back one notch. Repeat the process on each beam until the pointer swings an equal distance above and below the zero point. Sum the masses on each beam to find the mass of the object. Move all riders back to zero when finished.

Figure 13
A triple beam balance is used to determine the mass of an object.

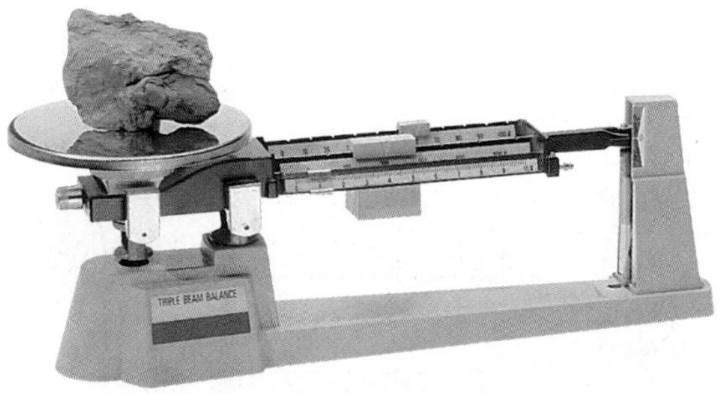

You should never place a hot object on the pan or pour chemicals directly onto the pan. Instead, find the mass of a clean container. Remove the container from the pan, then place the chemicals in the container. Find the mass of the container with the chemicals in it. To find the mass of the chemicals, subtract the mass of the empty container from the mass of the filled container.

Making and Using Tables

Browse through your textbook and you will see tables in the text and in the activities. In a table, data, or information, are arranged so that they are easier to understand. Activity tables help organize the data you collect during an activity so results can be interpreted.

Making Tables To make a table, list the items to be compared in the first column and the characteristics to be compared in the first row. The title should clearly indicate the content of the table, and the column or row heads should tell the reader what information is found in there. The table below lists materials collected for recycling on three weekly pick-up days. The inclusion of kilograms in parentheses also identifies for the reader that the figures are mass units.

Recyclable Materials Collected During Week

Day of Week	Paper (kg)	Aluminum (kg)	Glass (kg)
Monday	5.0	4.0	12.0
Wednesday	4.0	1.0	10.0
Friday	2.5	2.0	10.0

Using Tables How much paper, in kilograms, is being recycled on Wednesday? Locate the column labeled "Paper (kg)" and the row "Wednesday." The information in the box where the column and row intersect is the answer. Did you answer "4.0"? How much aluminum, in kilograms, is being recycled on Friday? If you answered "2.0," you understand how to read the table. How much glass is collected for recycling each week? Locate the column labeled "Glass (kg)" and add the figures for all three rows. If you answered "32.0," then you know how to locate and use the data provided in the table.

Recording Data

To be useful, the data you collect must be recorded carefully. Accuracy is key. A well-thought-out experiment includes a way to record procedures, observations, and results accurately. Data tables are one way to organize and record results. Set up the tables you will need ahead of time so you can record the data right away.

Record information properly and neatly. Never put unidentified data on scraps of paper. Instead, data should be written in a notebook like the one in **Figure 14.** Write in pencil so information isn't lost if your data gets wet. At each point in the experiment, record your data and label it. That way, your information will be accurate and you will not have to determine what the figures mean when you look at your notes later.

Figure 14
Record data neatly and clearly so it is easy to understand.

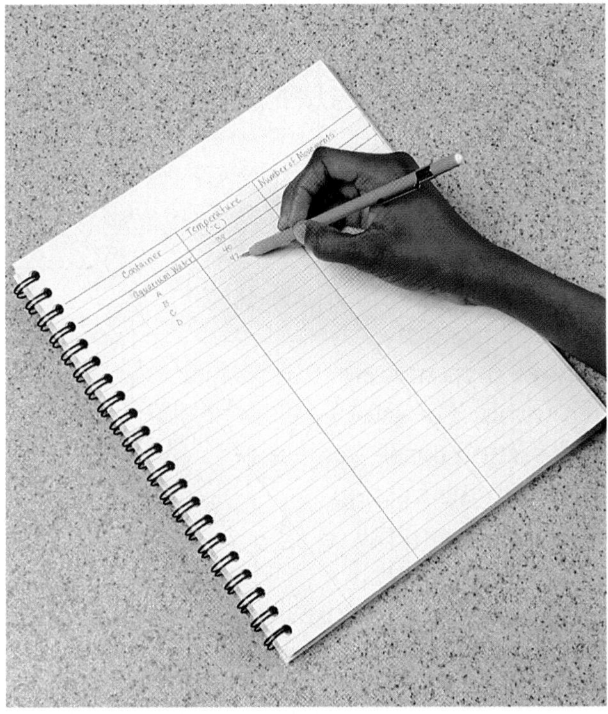

Recording Observations

It is important to record observations accurately and completely. That is why you always should record observations in your notes immediately as you make them. It is easy to miss details or make mistakes when recording results from memory. Do not include your personal thoughts when you record your data. Record only what you observe to eliminate bias. For example, when you record that a plant grew 12 cm in one day, you would note that this was the largest daily growth for the week. However, you would not refer to the data as "the best growth spurt of the week."

Making Models

You can organize the observations and other data you collect and record in many ways. Making models is one way to help you better understand the parts of a structure you have been observing or the way a process for which you have been taking various measurements works.

Models often show things that are very large or small or otherwise would be difficult to see and understand. You can study blood vessels and know that they are hollow tubes. The size and proportional differences among arteries, veins, and capillaries can be explained in words. However, you can better visualize the relative sizes and proportions of blood vessels by making models of them. Gluing different kinds of pasta to thick paper so the openings can be seen can help you see how the differences in size, wall thickness, and shape among types of blood vessels affect their functions.

Other models can be devised on a computer. Some models, such as disease control models used by doctors to predict the spread of the flu, are mathematical and are represented by equations.

Making and Using Graphs

After scientists organize data in tables, they might display the data in a graph that shows the relationship of one variable to another. A graph makes interpretation and analysis of data easier. Three types of graphs are the line graph, the bar graph, and the circle graph.

Line Graphs A line graph like in **Figure 15** is used to show the relationship between two variables. The variables being compared go on two axes of the graph. For data from an experiment, the independent variable always goes on the horizontal axis, called the *x*-axis. The dependent variable always goes on the vertical axis, called the *y*-axis. After drawing your axes, label each with a scale. Next, plot the data points.

A data point is the intersection of the recorded value of the dependent variable for each tested value of the independent variable. After all the points are plotted, connect them.

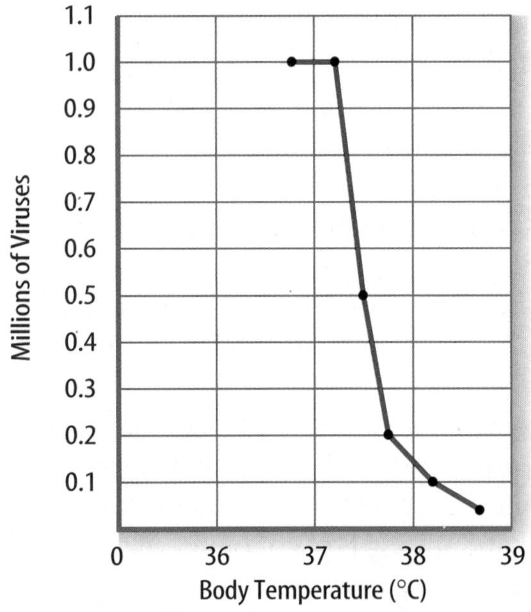

Figure 15
This line graph shows the relationship between body temperature and the millions of infecting viruses present in a human body.

Bar Graphs Bar graphs compare data that do not change continuously. Vertical bars show the relationships among data.

To make a bar graph, set up the *y*-axis as you did for the line graph. Draw vertical bars of equal size from the *x*-axis up to the point on the *y*-axis that represents the value of *x*.

Figure 16
The number of wing vibrations per second for different insects can be shown as a bar graph or circle graph.

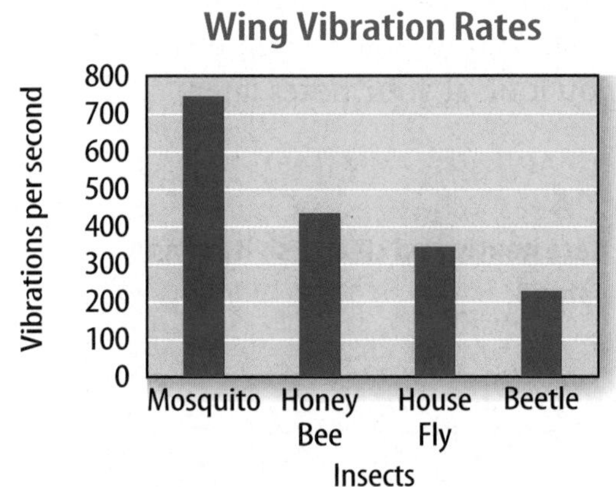

Circle Graphs A circle graph uses a circle divided into sections to display data as parts (fractions or percentages) of a whole. The size of each section corresponds to the fraction or percentage of the data that the section represents. So, the entire circle represents 100 percent, one-half represents 50 percent, one-fifth represents 20 percent, and so on.

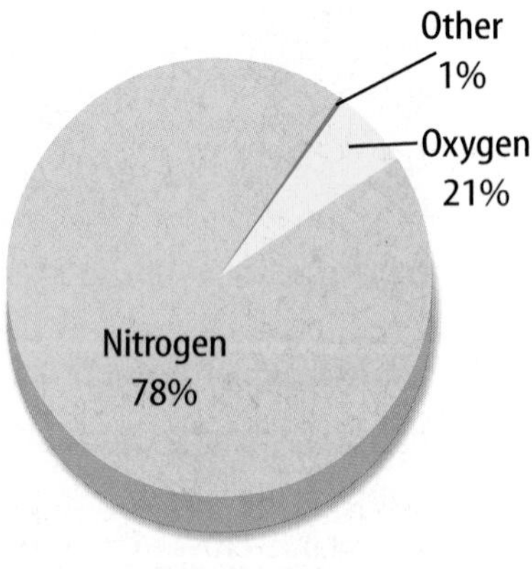

Analyzing and Applying Results

Analyzing Results

To determine the meaning of your observations and investigation results, you will need to look for patterns in the data. You can organize your information in several of the ways that are discussed in this handbook. Then you must think critically to determine what the data mean. Scientists use several approaches when they analyze the data they have collected and recorded. Each approach is useful for identifying specific patterns in the data.

Forming Operational Definitions

An operational definition defines an object by showing how it functions, works, or behaves. Such definitions are written in terms of how an object works or how it can be used; that is, they describe its job or purpose.

For example, a ruler can be defined as a tool that measures the length of an object (how it can be used). A ruler also can be defined as something that contains a series of marks that can be used as a standard when measuring (how it works).

Classifying

Classifying is the process of sorting objects or events into groups based on common features. When classifying, first observe the objects or events to be classified. Then select one feature that is shared by some members in the group but not by all. Place those members that share that feature into a subgroup. You can classify members into smaller and smaller subgroups based on characteristics.

How might you classify a group of animals? You might first classify them by putting all of the dogs, cats, lizards, snakes, and birds into separate groups. Within each group, you could then look for another common feature by which to further classify members of the group, such as size or color.

Remember that when you classify, you are grouping objects or events for a purpose. For example, classifying animals can be the first step in identifying them. You might know that a cardinal is a red bird. To find it in a large group of animals, you might start with the classification scheme mentioned here. You'll locate a cardinal within the red grouping of the birds that you separate from the rest of the animals. A male ruby-throated hummingbird could be located within the birds by its tiny size and the bright red color of its throat. Keep your purpose in mind as you select the features to form groups and subgroups.

Figure 17
Color is one of many characteristics that are used to classify animals.

Comparing and Contrasting

Observations can be analyzed by noting the similarities and differences between two or more objects or events that you observe. When you look at objects or events to see how they are similar, you are comparing them. Contrasting is looking for differences in objects or events. The table below compares and contrasts the nutritional value of two cereals.

Nutritional Values		
	Cereal A	Cereal B
Calories	220	160
Fat	10 g	10 g
Protein	2.5 g	2.6 g
Carbohydrate	30 g	15 g

Recognizing Cause and Effect

Have you ever gotten a cold and then suggested that you probably caught it from a classmate who had one recently? If so, you have observed an effect and inferred a cause. The event is the effect, and the reason for the event is the cause.

When scientists are unsure of the cause of a certain event, they design controlled experiments to determine what caused it.

Interpreting Data

The word *interpret* means "to explain the meaning of something." Look at the problem originally being explored in an experiment and figure out what the data show. Identify the control group and the test group so you can see whether or not changes in the independent variable have had an effect. Look for differences in the dependent variable between the control and test groups.

These differences you observe can be qualitative or quantitative. You would be able to describe a qualitative difference using only words, whereas you would measure a quantitative difference and describe it using numbers. If there are qualitative or quantitative differences, the independent variable that is being tested could have had an effect. If no qualitative or quantitative differences are found between the control and test groups, the variable that is being tested apparently had no effect.

For example, suppose that three pepper plants are placed in a garden and two of the plants are fertilized, but the third is left to grow without fertilizer. Suppose you are then asked to describe any differences in the plants after two weeks. A qualitative difference might be the appearance of brighter green leaves on fertilized plants but not on the unfertilized plant. A quantitative difference might be a difference in the height of the plants or the number of flowers on them.

Inferring Scientists often make inferences based on their observations. An inference is an attempt to explain, or interpret, observations or to indicate what caused what you observed. An inference is a type of conclusion.

When making an inference, be certain to use accurate data and accurately described observations. Analyze all of the data that you've collected. Then, based on everything you know, explain or interpret what you've observed.

Drawing Conclusions

When scientists have analyzed the data they collected, they proceed to draw conclusions about what the data mean. These conclusions are sometimes stated using words similar to those found in the hypothesis formed earlier in the process.

Conclusions To analyze your data, you must review all of the observations and measurements that you made and recorded. Recheck all data for accuracy. After your data are rechecked and organized, you are almost ready to draw a conclusion such as "Plants need sunlight in order to grow."

Before you can draw a conclusion, however, you must determine whether the data allow you to come to a conclusion that supports a hypothesis. Sometimes that will be the case; other times it will not.

If your data do not support a hypothesis, it does not mean that the hypothesis is wrong. It means only that the results of the investigation did not support the hypothesis. Maybe the experiment needs to be redesigned, but very likely, some of the initial observations on which the hypothesis was based were incomplete or biased. Perhaps more observation or research is needed to refine the hypothesis.

Avoiding Bias Sometimes drawing a conclusion involves making judgments. When you make a judgment, you form an opinion about what your data mean. It is important to be honest and to avoid reaching a conclusion if no supporting evidence for it exists or if it is based on a small sample. It also is important not to allow any expectations of results to bias your judgments. If possible, it is a good idea to collect additional data. Scientists do this all the time.

For example, animal behaviorist Katharine Payne made an important observation about elephant communication. While visiting a zoo, Payne felt the air vibrating around her. At the same time, she also noticed that the skin on an elephant's forehead was fluttering. She suspected that the elephants were generating the vibrations and that they might be using the low-frequency sounds to communicate.

Payne conducted an experiment to record these sounds and simultaneously observe the behavior of the elephants in the zoo. She later conducted a similar experiment in Namibia in southwest Africa, where elephant herds roam. The additional data she collected supported the judgment Payne had made, which was that these low-frequency sounds were a form of communication between elephants.

Evaluating Others' Data and Conclusions

Sometimes scientists have to use data that they did not collect themselves, or they have to rely on observations and conclusions drawn by other researchers. In cases such as these, the data must be evaluated carefully.

How were the data obtained? How was the investigation done? Has it been duplicated by other researchers? Did they come up with the same results? Look at the conclusion, as well. Would you reach the same conclusion from these results? Only when you have confidence in the data of others can you believe it is true and feel comfortable using it.

Communicating

The communication of ideas is an important part of the work of scientists. A discovery that is not reported will not advance the scientific community's understanding or knowledge. Communication among scientists also is important as a way of improving their investigations.

Scientists communicate in many ways, from writing articles in journals and magazines that explain their investigations and experiments, to announcing important discoveries on television and radio, to sharing ideas with colleagues on the Internet or presenting them as lectures.

People who study science rely on computers to record and store data and to analyze results from investigations. Whether you work in a laboratory or just need to write a lab report with tables, good computer skills are a necessity.

Using a Word Processor

Suppose your teacher has assigned a written report. After you've completed your research and decided how you want to write the information, you need to put all that information on paper. The easiest way to do this is with a word processing application on a computer.

A computer application that allows you to type your information, change it as many times as you need to, and then print it out so that it looks neat and clean is called a word processing application. You also can use this type of application to create tables and columns, add bullets or cartoon art to your page, include page numbers, and even check your spelling.

Helpful Hints

- If you aren't sure how to do something using your word processing program, look in the help menu. You will find a list of topics there to click on for help. After you locate the help topic you need, just follow the step-by-step instructions you see on your screen.
- Just because you've spell checked your report doesn't mean that the spelling is perfect. The spell check feature can't catch misspelled words that look like other words. If you've accidentally typed *wind* instead of *wing*, the spell checker won't know the difference. Always reread your report to make sure you didn't miss any mistakes.

Figure 18
You can use computer programs to make graphs and tables.

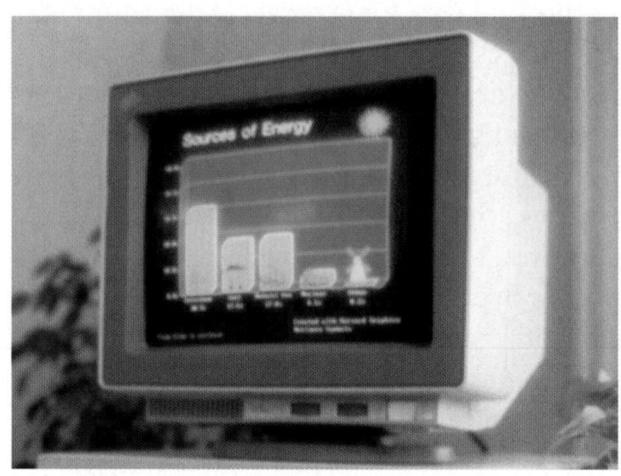

Using a Database

Imagine you're in the middle of a research project busily gathering facts and information. You soon realize that it's becoming more difficult to organize and keep track of all the information. The tool to use to solve information overload is a database. Just as a file cabinet organizes paper records, a database organizes computer records. However, a database is more powerful than a simple file cabinet because at the click of a mouse, the contents can be reshuffled and reorganized. At computer-quick speeds, databases can sort information by any characteristics and filter data into multiple categories.

Helpful Hints

- Before setting up a database, take some time to learn the features of your database software by practicing with established database software.
- Periodically save your database as you enter data. That way, if something happens such as your computer malfunctions or the power goes off, you won't lose all of your work.

Doing a Database Search

When searching for information in a database, use the following search strategies to get the best results. These are the same search methods used for searching Internet databases.

- Place the word *and* between two words in your search if you want the database to look for any entries that have both words. For example, "fox *and* mink" would give you information that mentions both fox and mink.
- Place the word *or* between two words if you want the database to show entries that have at least one of the words. For example "fox *or* mink" would show you information that mentions either fox or mink.
- Place the word *not* between two words if you want the database to look for entries that have the first word but do not have the second word. For example, "canine *not* fox" would show you information that mentions the term *canine* but does not mention the fox.

In summary, databases can be used to store large amounts of information about a particular subject. Databases allow biologists, Earth scientists, and physical scientists to search for information quickly and accurately.

Using an Electronic Spreadsheet

Your science fair experiment has produced lots of numbers. How do you keep track of all the data, and how can you easily work out all the calculations needed? You can use a computer program called a spreadsheet to record data that involve numbers. A spreadsheet is an electronic mathematical worksheet.

Type in your data in rows and columns, just as in a data table on a sheet of paper. A spreadsheet uses simple math to do data calculations. For example, you could add, subtract, divide, or multiply any of the values in the spreadsheet by another number. You also could set up a series of math steps you want to apply to the data. If you want to add 12 to all the numbers and then multiply all the numbers by 10, the computer does all the calculations for you in the spreadsheet. Below is an example of a spreadsheet that records data from an experiment with mice in a maze.

Helpful Hints

- Before you set up the spreadsheet, identify how you want to organize the data. Include any formulas you will need to use.
- Make sure you have entered the correct data into the correct rows and columns.
- You also can display your results in a graph. Pick the style of graph that best represents the data with which you are working.

Figure 19
A spreadsheet allows you to display large amounts of data and do calculations automatically.

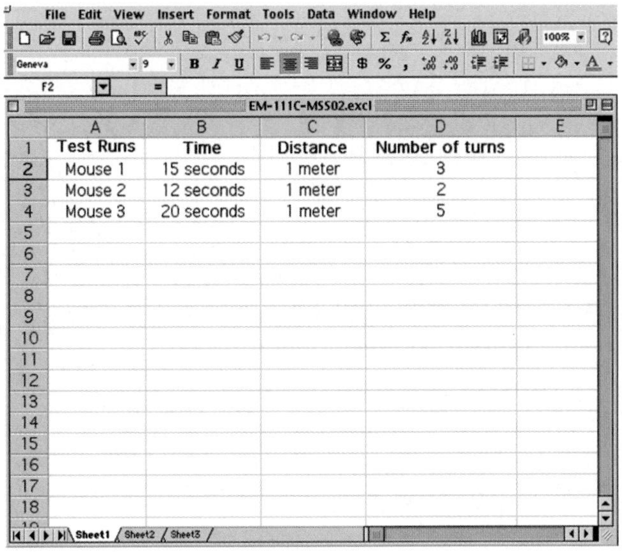

File Edit View Insert Format Tools Data Window Help

EM-111C-MSS02.excl

	A	B	C	D	E
1	Test Runs	Time	Distance	Number of turns	
2	Mouse 1	15 seconds	1 meter	3	
3	Mouse 2	12 seconds	1 meter	2	
4	Mouse 3	20 seconds	1 meter	5	
5					
6					
7					
8					
9					
10					
11					
12					
13					
14					
15					
16					
17					
18					

Sheet1 / Sheet2 / Sheet3

Using a Computerized Card Catalog

When you have a report or paper to research, you probably go to the library. To find the information you need in the library, you might have to use a computerized card catalog. This type of card catalog allows you to search for information by subject, by title, or by author. The computer then will display all the holdings the library has on the subject, title, or author requested.

A library's holdings can include books, magazines, databases, videos, and audio materials. When you have chosen something from this list, the computer will show whether an item is available and where in the library to find it.

Helpful Hints

- Remember that you can use the computer to search by subject, author, or title. If you know a book's author but not the title, you can search for all the books the library has by that author.
- When searching by subject, it's often most helpful to narrow your search by using specific search terms, such as *and*, *or*, and *not*. If you don't find enough sources, you can broaden your search.
- Pay attention to the type of materials found in your search. If you need a book, you can eliminate any videos or other resources that come up in your search.
- Knowing how your library is arranged can save you a lot of time. The librarian will show you where certain types of materials are kept and how to find specific holdings.

Using Graphics Software

Are you having trouble finding that exact piece of art you're looking for? Do you have a picture in your mind of what you want but can't seem to find the right graphic to represent your ideas? To solve these problems, you can use graphics software. Graphics software allows you to create and change images and diagrams in almost unlimited ways. Typical uses for graphics software include arranging clip art, changing scanned images, and constructing pictures from scratch. Most graphics software applications work in similar ways. They use the same basic tools and functions. Once you master one graphics application, you can use any other graphics application relatively easily.

Figure 20
Graphics software can use your data to draw bar graphs.

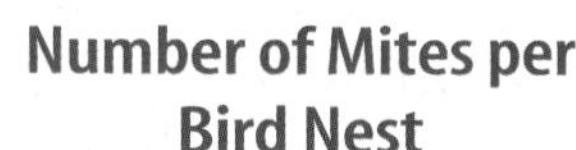

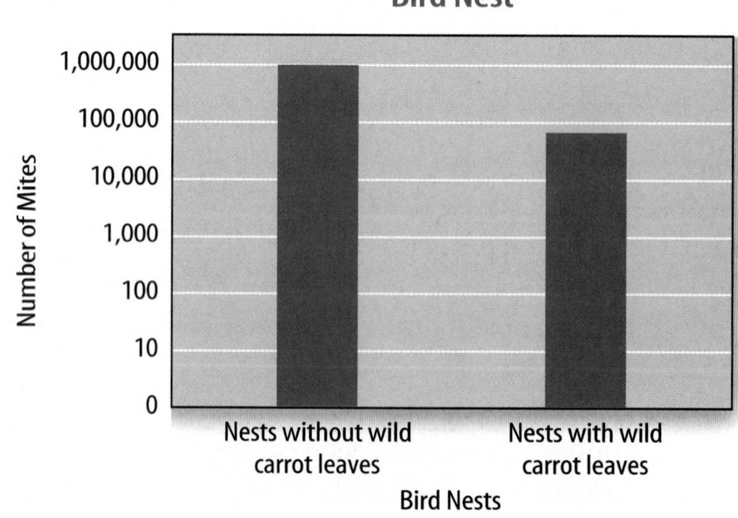

Figure 21
Graphics software can use your data to draw circle graphs.

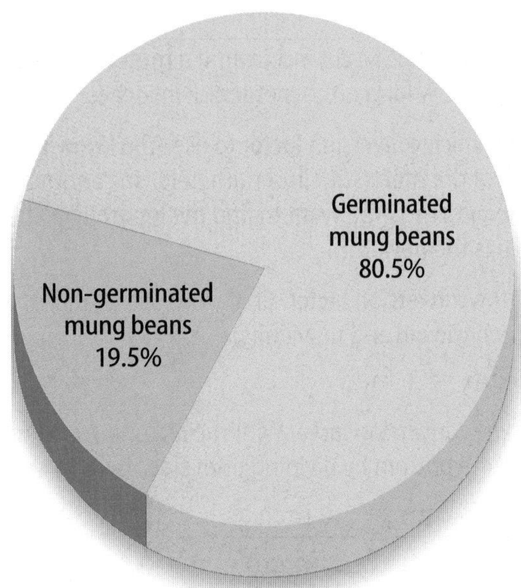

Helpful Hints

- As with any method of drawing, the more you practice using the graphics software, the better your results will be.
- Start by using the software to manipulate existing drawings. Once you master this, making your own illustrations will be easier.
- Clip art is available on CD-ROMs and the Internet. With these resources, finding a piece of clip art to suit your purposes is simple.
- As you work on a drawing, save it often.

Developing Multimedia Presentations

It's your turn—you have to present your science report to the entire class. How do you do it? You can use many different sources of information to get the class excited about your presentation. Posters, videos, photographs, sound, computers, and the Internet can help show your ideas.

First, determine what important points you want to make in your presentation. Then, write an outline of what materials and types of media would best illustrate those points. Maybe you could start with an outline on an overhead projector, then show a video, followed by something from the Internet or a slide show accompanied by music or recorded voices. You might choose to use a presentation builder computer application that can combine all these elements into one presentation. Make sure the presentation is well constructed to make the most impact on the audience.

Figure 22
Multimedia presentations use many types of print and electronic materials.

Helpful Hints

- Carefully consider what media will best communicate the point you are trying to make.
- Make sure you know how to use any equipment you will be using in your presentation.
- Practice the presentation several times.
- If possible, set up all of the equipment ahead of time. Make sure everything is working correctly.

Math Skill Handbook

Use this Math Skill Handbook to help solve problems you are given in this text. You might find it useful to review topics in this Math Skill Handbook first.

Converting Units

In science, quantities such as length, mass, and time sometimes are measured using different units. Suppose you want to know how many miles are in 12.7 km.

Conversion factors are used to change from one unit of measure to another. A conversion factor is a ratio that is equal to one. For example, there are 1,000 mL in 1 L, so 1,000 mL equals 1 L, or:

$$1{,}000 \text{ mL} = 1 \text{ L}$$

If both sides are divided by 1 L, this equation becomes:

$$\frac{1{,}000 \text{ mL}}{1 \text{ L}} = 1$$

The **ratio** on the left side of this equation is equal to 1 and is a conversion factor. You can make another conversion factor by dividing both sides of the top equation by 1,000 mL:

$$1 = \frac{1 \text{ L}}{1{,}000 \text{ mL}}$$

To **convert units,** you multiply by the appropriate conversion factor. For example, how many milliliters are in 1.255 L? To convert 1.255 L to milliliters, multiply 1.255 L by a conversion factor.

Use the **conversion factor** with new units (mL) in the numerator and the old units (L) in the denominator.

$$1.255 \cancel{\text{L}} \times \frac{1{,}000 \text{ mL}}{1 \cancel{\text{L}}} = 1{,}255 \text{ mL}$$

The unit L divides in this equation, just as if it were a number.

Example 1 There are 2.54 cm in 1 inch. If a meterstick has a length of 100 cm, how long is the meterstick in inches?

Step 1 Decide which conversion factor to use. You know the length of the meterstick in centimeters, so centimeters are the old units. You want to find the length in inches, so inch is the new unit.

Step 2 Form the conversion factor. Start with the relationship between the old and new units.

$$2.54 \text{ cm} = 1 \text{ inch}$$

Step 3 Form the conversion factor with the old unit (centimeter) on the bottom by dividing both sides by 2.54 cm.

$$1 = \frac{2.54 \text{ cm}}{2.54 \text{ cm}} = \frac{1 \text{ inch}}{2.54 \text{ cm}}$$

Step 4 Multiply the old measurement by the conversion factor.

$$100 \cancel{\text{cm}} \times \frac{1 \text{ inch}}{2.54 \cancel{\text{cm}}} = 39.37 \text{ inches}$$

The meterstick is 39.37 inches long.

Example 2 There are 365 days in one year. If a person is 14 years old, what is his or her age in days? (Ignore leap years)

Step 1 Decide which conversion factor to use. You want to convert years to days.

Step 2 Form the conversion factor. Start with the relation between the old and new units.

$$1 \text{ year} = 365 \text{ days}$$

Step 3 Form the conversion factor with the old unit (year) on the bottom by dividing both sides by 1 year.

$$1 = \frac{1 \text{ year}}{1 \text{ year}} = \frac{365 \text{ days}}{1 \text{ year}}$$

Step 4 Multiply the old measurement by the conversion factor:

$$14 \cancel{\text{years}} \times \frac{365 \text{ days}}{1 \cancel{\text{year}}} = 5{,}110 \text{ days}$$

The person's age is 5,110 days.

Practice Problem A cat has a mass of 2.31 kg. If there are 1,000 g in 1 kg, what is the mass of the cat in grams? 2310 g

Using Fractions

A **fraction** is a number that compares a part to the whole. For example, in the fraction $\frac{2}{3}$, the 2 represents the part and the 3 represents the whole. In the fraction $\frac{2}{3}$, the top number, 2, is called the numerator. The bottom number, 3, is called the denominator.

Sometimes fractions are not written in their simplest form. To determine a fraction's **simplest form,** you must find the greatest common factor (GCF) of the numerator and denominator. The greatest common factor is the largest common factor of all the factors the two numbers have in common.

For example, because the number 3 divides into 12 and 30 evenly, it is a common factor of 12 and 30. However, because the number 6 is the largest number that evenly divides into 12 and 30, it is the **greatest common factor.**

After you find the greatest common factor, you can write a fraction in its simplest form. Divide both the numerator and the denominator by the greatest common factor. The number that results is the fraction in its **simplest form.**

Example Twelve of the 20 corn plants in a field are more than 1.5 m tall. What fraction of the corn plants in the field is 1.5 m tall?

Step 1 Write the fraction.

$$\frac{\text{part}}{\text{whole}} = \frac{12}{20}$$

Step 2 To find the GCF of the numerator and denominator, list all of the factors of each number.

Factors of 12: 1, 2, 3, 4, 6, 12 (the numbers that divide evenly into 12)

Factors of 20: 1, 2, 4, 5, 10, 20 (the numbers that divide evenly into 20)

Step 3 List the common factors.

1, 2, 4.

Step 4 Choose the greatest factor in the list of common factors.

The GCF of 12 and 20 is 4.

Step 5 Divide the numerator and denominator by the GCF.

$$\frac{12 \div 4}{20 \div 4} = \frac{3}{5}$$

In the field, $\frac{3}{5}$ of the corn plants are more than 1.5 m tall.

Practice Problem There are 90 duck eggs in a population. Of those eggs, 66 hatch over a one-week period. What fraction of the eggs hatch over a one-week period? Write the fraction in simplest form. $\frac{11}{15}$

Skill Handbooks

Calculating Ratios

A **ratio** is a comparison of two numbers by division.

Ratios can be written 3 to 5 or 3:5. Ratios also can be written as fractions, such as $\frac{3}{5}$. Ratios, like fractions, can be written in simplest form. Recall that a fraction is in **simplest form** when the greatest common factor (GCF) of the numerator and denominator is 1.

Example From a package of sunflower seeds, 40 seeds germinated and 64 did not. What is the ratio of germinated to not germinated seeds as a fraction in simplest form?

Step 1 Write the ratio as a fraction.

$$\frac{\text{germinated}}{\text{not germinated}} = \frac{40}{64}$$

Step 2 Express the fraction in simplest form. The GCF of 40 and 64 is 8.

$$\frac{40}{64} = \frac{40 \div 8}{64 \div 8} = \frac{5}{8}$$

The ratio of germinated to not germinated seeds is $\frac{5}{8}$.

Practice Problem Two children measure 100 cm and 144 cm in height. What is the ratio of their heights in simplest fraction form? $\frac{25}{36}$

Using Decimals

A **decimal** is a fraction with a denominator of 10, 100, 1,000, or another power of 10. For example, 0.854 is the same as the fraction $\frac{854}{1{,}000}$.

In a decimal, the decimal point separates the ones place and the tenths place. For example, 0.27 means twenty-seven hundredths, or $\frac{27}{100}$, where 27 is the **number of units** out of 100 units. Any fraction can be written as a decimal using division.

Example Write $\frac{5}{8}$ as a decimal.

Step 1 Write a division problem with the numerator, 5, as the dividend and the denominator, 8, as the divisor. Write 5 as 5.000.

Step 2 Solve the problem.

$$\begin{array}{r} 0.625 \\ 8\overline{)5.000} \\ \underline{48} \\ 20 \\ \underline{16} \\ 40 \\ \underline{40} \\ 0 \end{array}$$

Therefore, $\frac{5}{8} = 0.625$.

Practice Problem Write $\frac{19}{25}$ as a decimal. 0.76

Using Percentages

The word *percent* means "out of one hundred." A **percent** is a ratio that compares a number to 100. Suppose you read that 77 percent of all fish on Earth live in the Pacific Ocean. That is the same as reading that the ratio of Earth's fish that live in the Pacific Ocean is $\frac{77}{100}$. To express a fraction as a percent, first find an equivalent decimal for the fraction. Then, multiply the decimal by 100 and add the percent symbol. For example, $\frac{1}{2} = 1 \div 2 = 0.5$. Then $0.5 \cdot 100 = 50 = 50\%$.

Example Express $\frac{13}{20}$ as a percent.

Step 1 Find the equivalent decimal for the fraction.

$$\begin{array}{r} 0.65 \\ 20\overline{)13.00} \\ \underline{12\,0} \\ 100 \\ \underline{100} \\ 0 \end{array}$$

Step 2 Rewrite the fraction $\frac{13}{20}$ as 0.65.

Step 3 Multiply 0.65 by 100 and add the % sign.

$$0.65 \cdot 100 = 65 = 65\%$$

So, $\frac{13}{20} = 65\%$.

Practice Problem In an experimental population of 365 sheep, 73 were brown. What percent of the sheep were brown? 20%

Using Precision and Significant Digits

When you make a **measurement,** the value you record depends on the precision of the measuring instrument. When adding or subtracting numbers with different precision, the answer is rounded to the smallest number of decimal places of any number in the sum or difference. When multiplying or dividing, the answer is rounded to the smallest number of significant figures of any number being multiplied or divided. When counting the number of **significant figures,** all digits are counted except zeros at the end of a number with no decimal such as 2,500, and zeros at the beginning of a decimal such as 0.03020.

Example The lengths 5.28 and 5.2 are measured in meters. Find the sum of these lengths and report the sum using the least precise measurement.

Step 1 Find the sum.

$$\begin{array}{rl} 5.28 \text{ m} & \text{2 digits after the decimal} \\ +\ 5.2\ \ \text{m} & \text{1 digit after the decimal} \\ \hline 10.48 \text{ m} & \end{array}$$

Step 2 Round to one digit after the decimal because the least number of digits after the decimal of the numbers being added is 1.

The sum is 10.5 m.

Practice Problem Multiply the numbers in the example using the rule for multiplying and dividing. Report the answer with the correct number of significant figures. $27 m^2$

Solving One-Step Equations

An **equation** is a statement that two things are equal. For example, $A = B$ is an equation that states that A is equal to B.

Sometimes one side of the equation will contain a **variable** whose value is not known. In the equation $3x = 12$, the variable is x.

The equation is solved when the variable is replaced with a value that makes both sides of the equation equal to each other. For example, the solution of the equation $3x = 12$ is $x = 4$. If the x is replaced with 4, then the equation becomes $3 \cdot 4 = 12$, or $12 = 12$.

To solve an equation such as $8x = 40$, divide both sides of the equation by the number that multiplies the variable.

$$8x = 40$$
$$\frac{8x}{8} = \frac{40}{8}$$
$$x = 5$$

You can check your answer by replacing the variable with your solution and seeing if both sides of the equation are the same.

$$8x = 8 \cdot 5 = 40$$

The left and right sides of the equation are the same, so $x = 5$ is the solution.

Sometimes an equation is written in this way: $a = bc$. This also is called a **formula.** The letters can be replaced by numbers, but the numbers must still make both sides of the equation the same.

Example 1 Solve the equation $10x = 35$.

Step 1 Find the solution by dividing each side of the equation by 10.

$$10x = 35 \qquad \frac{10x}{10} = \frac{35}{10} \qquad x = 3.5$$

Step 2 Check the solution.

$$10x = 35 \qquad 10 \times 3.5 = 35 \qquad 35 = 35$$

Both sides of the equation are equal, so $x = 3.5$ is the solution to the equation.

Example 2 In the formula $a = bc$, find the value of c if $a = 20$ and $b = 2$.

Step 1 Rearrange the formula so the unknown value is by itself on one side of the equation by dividing both sides by b.

$$a = bc$$
$$\frac{a}{b} = \frac{bc}{b}$$
$$\frac{a}{b} = c$$

Step 2 Replace the variables a and b with the values that are given.

$$\frac{a}{b} = c$$
$$\frac{20}{2} = c$$
$$10 = c$$

Step 3 Check the solution.

$$a = bc$$
$$20 = 2 \times 10$$
$$20 = 20$$

Both sides of the equation are equal, so $c = 10$ is the solution when $a = 20$ and $b = 2$.

Practice Problem In the formula $h = gd$, find the value of d if $g = 12.3$ and $h = 17.4$. 1.41

Using Proportions

A **proportion** is an equation that shows that two ratios are equivalent. The ratios $\frac{2}{4}$ and $\frac{5}{10}$ are equivalent, so they can be written as $\frac{2}{4} = \frac{5}{10}$. This equation is an example of a proportion.

When two ratios form a proportion, the **cross products** are equal. To find the cross products in the proportion $\frac{2}{4} = \frac{5}{10}$, multiply the 2 and the 10, and the 4 and the 5. Therefore **$2 \cdot 10 = 4 \cdot 5$, or $20 = 20$.**

Because you know that both proportions are equal, you can use cross products to find a missing term in a proportion. This is known as **solving the proportion.** Solving a proportion is similar to solving an equation.

Example The heights of a tree and a pole are proportional to the lengths of their shadows. The tree casts a shadow of 24 m at the same time that a 6-m pole casts a shadow of 4 m. What is the height of the tree?

Step 1 Write a proportion.

$$\frac{\text{height of tree}}{\text{height of pole}} = \frac{\text{length of tree's shadow}}{\text{length of pole's shadow}}$$

Step 2 Substitute the known values into the proportion. Let *h* represent the unknown value, the height of the tree.

$$\frac{h}{6} = \frac{24}{4}$$

Step 3 Find the cross products.

$$h \cdot 4 = 6 \cdot 24$$

Step 4 Simplify the equation.

$$4h = 144$$

Step 5 Divide each side by 4.

$$\frac{4h}{4} = \frac{144}{4}$$

$$h = 36$$

The height of the tree is 36 m.

Practice Problem The proportions of bluefish are stable by the time they reach a length of 30 cm. The distance from the tip of the mouth to the back edge of the gill cover in a 35-cm bluefish is 15 cm. What is the distance from the tip of the mouth to the back edge of the gill cover in a 59-cm bluefish? 25 cm

Using Statistics

Statistics is the branch of mathematics that deals with collecting, analyzing, and presenting data. In statistics, there are three common ways to summarize the data with a single number—the mean, the median, and the mode.

The **mean** of a set of data is the arithmetic average. It is found by adding the numbers in the data set and dividing by the number of items in the set.

The **median** is the middle number in a set of data when the data are arranged in numerical order. If there were an even number of data points, the median would be the mean of the two middle numbers.

The **mode** of a set of data is the number or item that appears most often.

Another number that often is used to describe a set of data is the range. The **range** is the difference between the largest number and the smallest number in a set of data.

A **frequency table** shows how many times each piece of data occurs, usually in a survey. The frequency table below shows the results of a student survey on favorite color.

Color	Tally	Frequency
red	||||	4
blue	~~||||~~	5
black	||	2
green	|||	3
purple	~~||||~~ ||	7
yellow	~~||||~~ |	6

Based on the frequency table data, which color is the favorite?

Example The high temperatures (in °C) on five consecutive days in a desert habitat under study are 39°, 37°, 44°, 36°, and 44°. Find the mean, median, mode, and range of this set.

To find the mean:

Step 1 Find the sum of the numbers.

$$39 + 37 + 44 + 36 + 44 = 200$$

Step 2 Divide the sum by the number of items, which is 5.

$$200 \div 5 = 40$$

The mean high temperature is 40°C.

To find the median:

Step 1 Arrange the temperatures from least to greatest.

36, 37, <u>39</u>, 44, 44

Step 2 Determine the middle temperature.

The median high temperature is 39°C.

To find the mode:

Step 1 Group the numbers that are the same together.

44, 44, 36, 37, 39

Step 2 Determine the number that occurs most in the set.

<u>44, 44</u>, 36, 37, 39

The mode measure is 44°C.

To find the range:

Step 1 Arrange the temperatures from largest to smallest.

44, 44, 39, 37, 36

Step 2 Determine the largest and smallest temperature in the set.

<u>44</u>, 44, 39, 37, <u>36</u>

Step 3 Find the difference between the largest and smallest temperatures.

$$44 - 36 = 8$$

The range is 8°C.

Practice Problem Find the mean, median, mode, and range for the data set 8, 4, 12, 8, 11, 14, 16.

mean, 10; median, 11; mode, 8; range, 12

Reference Handbook A

Reference Handbook

SI—Metric/English, English/Metric Conversions

	When you want to convert:	To:	Multiply by:
Length	inches	centimeters	2.54
	centimeters	inches	0.39
	yards	meters	0.91
	meters	yards	1.09
	miles	kilometers	1.61
	kilometers	miles	0.62
Mass and Weight*	ounces	grams	28.35
	grams	ounces	0.04
	pounds	kilograms	0.45
	kilograms	pounds	2.2
	tons (short)	tonnes (metric tons)	0.91
	tonnes (metric tons)	tons (short)	1.10
	pounds	newtons	4.45
	newtons	pounds	0.22
Volume	cubic inches	cubic centimeters	16.39
	cubic centimeters	cubic inches	0.06
	liters	quarts	1.06
	quarts	liters	0.95
	gallons	liters	3.78
Area	square inches	square centimeters	6.45
	square centimeters	square inches	0.16
	square yards	square meters	0.83
	square meters	square yards	1.19
	square miles	square kilometers	2.59
	square kilometers	square miles	0.39
	hectares	acres	2.47
	acres	hectares	0.40
Temperature	To convert °Celsius to °Fahrenheit		°C × 9/5 + 32
	To convert °Fahrenheit to °Celsius		5/9 (°F − 32)

*Weight is measured in standard Earth gravity.

Safety in the Science Classroom

1. Always obtain your teacher's permission to begin an investigation.

2. Study the procedure. If you have questions, ask your teacher. Be sure you understand any safety symbols shown on the page.

3. Use the safety equipment provided for you. Goggles and a safety apron should be worn during most investigations.

4. Always slant test tubes away from yourself and others when heating them or adding substances to them.

5. Never eat or drink in the lab, and never use lab glassware as food or drink containers. Never inhale chemicals. Do not taste any substances or draw any material into a tube with your mouth.

6. Report any spill, accident, or injury, no matter how small, immediately to your teacher, then follow his or her instructions.

7. Know the location and proper use of the fire extinguisher, safety shower, fire blanket, first aid kit, and fire alarm.

8. Keep all materials away from open flames. Tie back long hair and tie down loose clothing.

9. If your clothing should catch fire, smother it with the fire blanket, or get under a safety shower. NEVER RUN.

10. If a fire should occur, turn off the gas then leave the room according to established procedures.

Follow these procedures as you clean up your work area

1. Turn off the water and gas. Disconnect electrical devices.

2. Clean all pieces of equipment and return all materials to their proper places.

3. Dispose of chemicals and other materials as directed by your teacher. Place broken glass and solid substances in the proper containers. Make sure never to discard materials in the sink.

4. Clean your work area. Wash your hands thoroughly after working in the laboratory.

First Aid

Injury	Safe Response ALWAYS NOTIFY YOUR TEACHER IMMEDIATELY
Burns	Apply cold water.
Cuts and Bruises	Stop any bleeding by applying direct pressure. Cover cuts with a clean dressing. Apply ice packs or cold compresses to bruises.
Fainting	Leave the person lying down. Loosen any tight clothing and keep crowds away.
Foreign Matter in Eye	Flush with plenty of water. Use eyewash bottle or fountain.
Poisoning	Note the suspected poisoning agent.
Any Spills on Skin	Flush with large amounts of water or use safety shower.

Care and Use of a Microscope

Eyepiece Contains magnifying lenses you look through.

Arm Supports the body tube.

Low-power objective Contains the lens with the lowest power magnification.

Stage clips Hold the microscope slide in place.

Fine adjustment Sharpens the image under high magnification.

Coarse adjustment Focuses the image under low power.

Body tube Connects the eyepiece to the revolving nosepiece.

Revolving nosepiece Holds and turns the objectives into viewing position.

High-power objective Contains the lens with the highest magnification.

Stage Supports the microscope slide.

Light source Provides light that passes upward through the diaphragm, the specimen, and the lenses.

Base Provides support for the microscope.

Caring for a Microscope

1. Always carry the microscope holding the arm with one hand and supporting the base with the other hand.
2. Don't touch the lenses with your fingers.
3. The coarse adjustment knob is used only when looking through the lowest-power objective lens. The fine adjustment knob is used when the high-power objective is in place.
4. Cover the microscope when you store it.

Using a Microscope

1. Place the microscope on a flat surface that is clear of objects. The arm should be toward you.
2. Look through the eyepiece. Adjust the diaphragm so light comes through the opening in the stage.
3. Place a slide on the stage so the specimen is in the field of view. Hold it firmly in place by using the stage clips.
4. Always focus with the coarse adjustment and the low-power objective lens first. After the object is in focus on low power, turn the nosepiece until the high-power objective is in place. Use ONLY the fine adjustment to focus with the high-power objective lens.

Making a Wet-Mount Slide

1. Carefully place the item you want to look at in the center of a clean, glass slide. Make sure the sample is thin enough for light to pass through.
2. Use a dropper to place one or two drops of water on the sample.
3. Hold a clean coverslip by the edges and place it at one edge of the water. Slowly lower the coverslip onto the water until it lies flat.
4. If you have too much water or a lot of air bubbles, touch the edge of a paper towel to the edge of the coverslip to draw off extra water and draw out unwanted air.

Reference Handbook D

Diversity of Life: Classification of Living Organisms

A six-kingdom system of classification of organisms is used today. Two kingdoms—Kingdom Archaebacteria and Kingdom Eubacteria—contain organisms that do not have a nucleus and that lack membrane-bound structures in the cytoplasm of their cells. The members of the other four kingdoms have a cell or cells that contain a nucleus and structures in the cytoplasm, some of which are surrounded by membranes. These kingdoms are Kingdom Protista, Kingdom Fungi, Kingdom Plantae, and Kingdom Animalia.

Kingdom Archaebacteria

one-celled; some absorb food from their surroundings; some are photosynthetic; some are chemosynthetic; many are found in extremely harsh environments including salt ponds, hot springs, swamps, and deep-sea hydrothermal vents

Kingdom Eubacteria

one-celled; most absorb food from their surroundings; some are photosynthetic; some are chemosynthetic; many are parasites; many are round, spiral, or rod-shaped; some form colonies

Kingdom Protista

Phylum Euglenophyta one-celled; photosynthetic or take in food; most have one flagellum; euglenoids

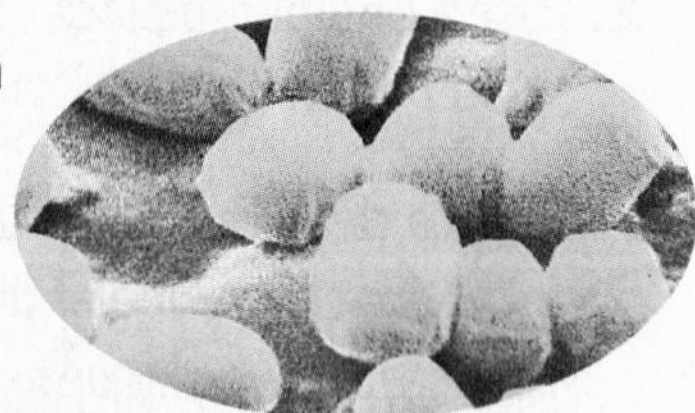

Kingdom Eubacteria
Bacillus anthracis

Phylum Chlorophyta
Desmids

Phylum Bacillariophyta one-celled; photosynthetic; have unique double shells made of silica; diatoms

Phylum Dinoflagellata one-celled; photosynthetic; contain red pigments; have two flagella; dinoflagellates

Phylum Chlorophyta one-celled, many-celled, or colonies; photosynthetic; contain chlorophyll; live on land, in freshwater, or salt water; green algae

Phylum Rhodophyta most are many-celled; photosynthetic; contain red pigments; most live in deep, saltwater environments; red algae

Phylum Phaeophyta most are many-celled; photosynthetic; contain brown pigments; most live in saltwater environments; brown algae

Phylum Rhizopoda one-celled; take in food; are free-living or parasitic; move by means of pseudopods; amoebas

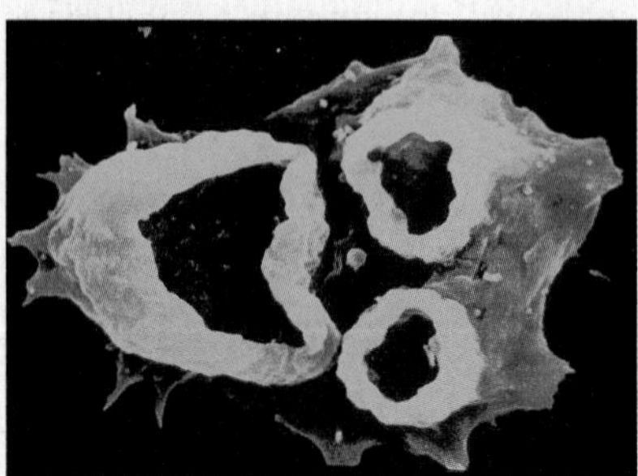

Amoeba

Phylum Zoomastigina one-celled; take in food; free-living or parasitic; have one or more flagella; zoomastigotes

Phylum Ciliophora one-celled; take in food; have large numbers of cilia; ciliates

Phylum Sporozoa one-celled; take in food; have no means of movement; are parasites in animals; sporozoans

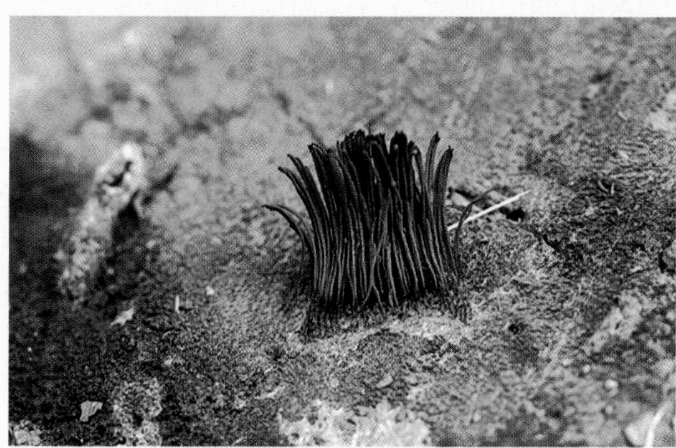

Phylum Myxomycota
Slime mold

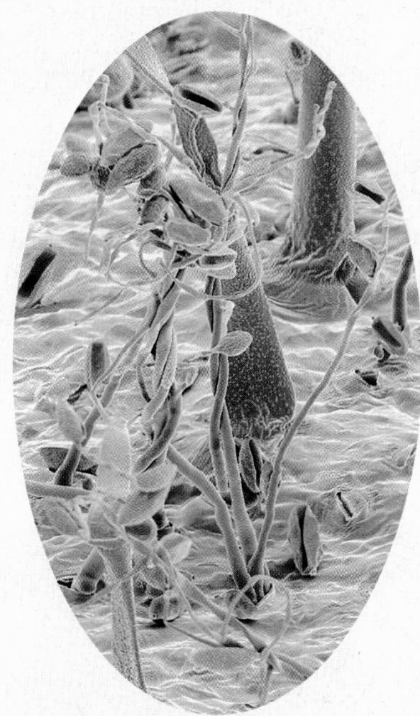

Phylum Oomycota
Phytophthora infestans

Phyla Myxomycota and Acrasiomycota one- or many-celled; absorb food; change form during life cycle; cellular and plasmodial slime molds

Phylum Oomycota many-celled; are either parasites or decomposers; live in freshwater or salt water; water molds, rusts and downy mildews

Kingdom Fungi

Phylum Zygomycota many-celled; absorb food; spores are produced in sporangia; zygote fungi; bread mold

Phylum Ascomycota one- and many-celled; absorb food; spores produced in asci; sac fungi; yeast

Phylum Basidiomycota many-celled; absorb food; spores produced in basidia; club fungi; mushrooms

Phylum Deuteromycota members with unknown reproductive structures; imperfect fungi; *Penicillium*

Mycophycota organisms formed by symbiotic relationship between an ascomycote or a basidiomycote and green alga or cyanobacterium; lichens

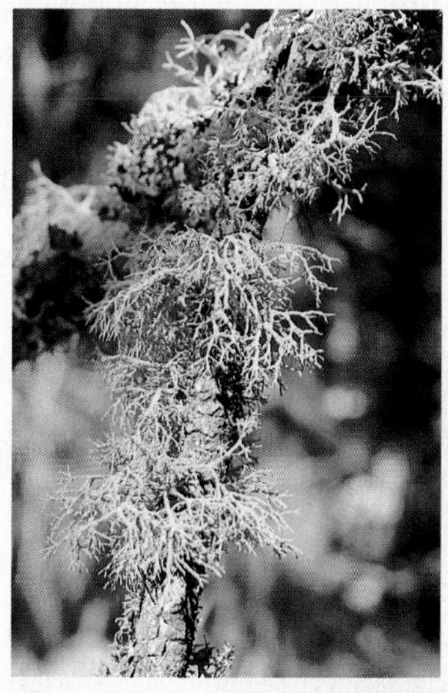

Lichens

Kingdom Plantae

Divisions Bryophyta (mosses), **Anthocerophyta** (hornworts), **Hepatophytal** (liverworts), **Psilophytal** (whisk ferns) many-celled nonvascular plants; reproduce by spores produced in capsules; green; grow in moist, land environments

Division Lycophyta many-celled vascular plants; spores are produced in conelike structures; live on land; are photosynthetic; club mosses

Division Sphenophyta vascular plants; ribbed and jointed stems; scalelike leaves; spores produced in conelike structures; horsetails

Division Pterophyta vascular plants; leaves called fronds; spores produced in clusters of sporangia called sori; live on land or in water; ferns

Division Ginkgophyta deciduous trees; only one living species; have fan-shaped leaves with branching veins and fleshy cones with seeds; ginkgoes

Division Cycadophyta palmlike plants; have large, featherlike leaves; produces seeds in cones; cycads

Division Coniferophyta deciduous or evergreen; trees or shrubs; have needlelike or scalelike leaves; seeds produced in cones; conifers

Division Gnetophyta shrubs or woody vines; seeds are produced in cones; division contains only three genera; gnetum

Division Anthophyta dominant group of plants; flowering plants; have fruits with seeds

Kingdom Animalia

Phylum Porifera aquatic organisms that lack true tissues and organs; are asymmetrical and sessile; sponges

Phylum Cnidaria radially symmetrical organisms; have a digestive cavity with one opening; most have tentacles armed with stinging cells; live in aquatic environments singly or in colonies; includes jellyfish, corals, hydra, and sea anemones

Phylum Platyhelminthes bilaterally symmetrical worms; have flattened bodies; digestive system has one opening; parasitic and free-living species; flatworms

Division Anthophyta
Tomato plant

Division Bryophyta
Liverwort

Phylum Platyhelminthes
Flatworm

Phylum Chordata

Phylum Nematoda round, bilaterally symmetrical body; have digestive system with two openings; free-living forms and parasitic forms; roundworms

Phylum Mollusca soft-bodied animals, many with a hard shell and soft foot or footlike appendage; a mantle covers the soft body; aquatic and terrestrial species; includes clams, snails, squid, and octopuses

Phylum Annelida bilaterally symmetrical worms; have round, segmented bodies; terrestrial and aquatic species; includes earthworms, leeches, and marine polychaetes

Phylum Arthropoda largest animal group; have hard exoskeletons, segmented bodies, and pairs of jointed appendages; land and aquatic species; includes insects, crustaceans, and spiders

Phylum Echinodermata marine organisms; have spiny or leathery skin and a water-vascular system with tube feet; are radially symmetrical; includes sea stars, sand dollars, and sea urchins

Phylum Chordata organisms with internal skeletons and specialized body systems; most have paired appendages; all at some time have a notochord, nerve cord, gill slits, and a postanal tail; include fish, amphibians, reptiles, birds, and mammals

Reference Handbook E

Reference Handbook

PERIODIC TABLE OF THE ELEMENTS

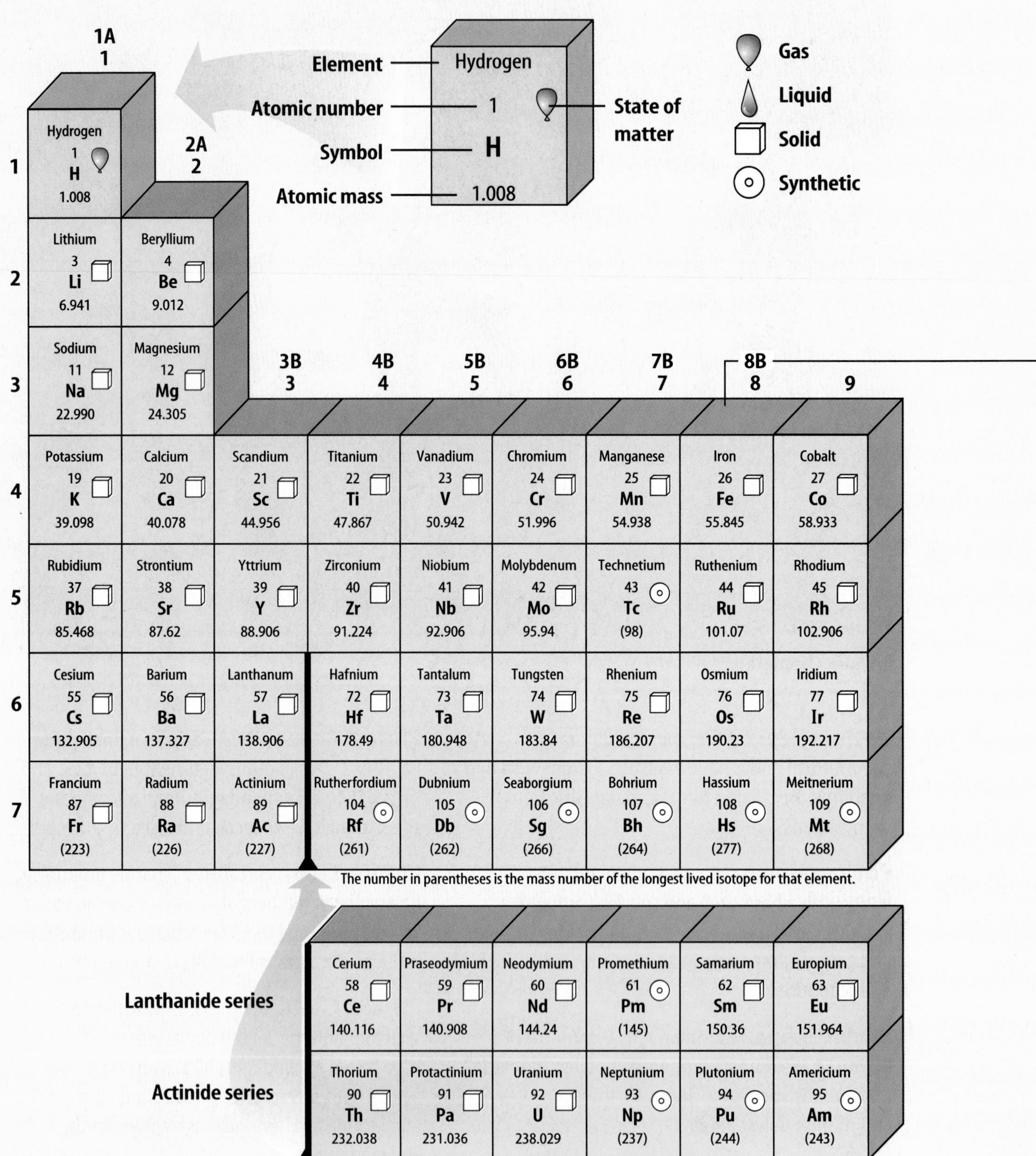

Period	1A 1	2A 2	3B 3	4B 4	5B 5	6B 6	7B 7	8B 8	9
1	Hydrogen 1 H 1.008								
2	Lithium 3 Li 6.941	Beryllium 4 Be 9.012							
3	Sodium 11 Na 22.990	Magnesium 12 Mg 24.305							
4	Potassium 19 K 39.098	Calcium 20 Ca 40.078	Scandium 21 Sc 44.956	Titanium 22 Ti 47.867	Vanadium 23 V 50.942	Chromium 24 Cr 51.996	Manganese 25 Mn 54.938	Iron 26 Fe 55.845	Cobalt 27 Co 58.933
5	Rubidium 37 Rb 85.468	Strontium 38 Sr 87.62	Yttrium 39 Y 88.906	Zirconium 40 Zr 91.224	Niobium 41 Nb 92.906	Molybdenum 42 Mo 95.94	Technetium 43 Tc (98)	Ruthenium 44 Ru 101.07	Rhodium 45 Rh 102.906
6	Cesium 55 Cs 132.905	Barium 56 Ba 137.327	Lanthanum 57 La 138.906	Hafnium 72 Hf 178.49	Tantalum 73 Ta 180.948	Tungsten 74 W 183.84	Rhenium 75 Re 186.207	Osmium 76 Os 190.23	Iridium 77 Ir 192.217
7	Francium 87 Fr (223)	Radium 88 Ra (226)	Actinium 89 Ac (227)	Rutherfordium 104 Rf (261)	Dubnium 105 Db (262)	Seaborgium 106 Sg (266)	Bohrium 107 Bh (264)	Hassium 108 Hs (277)	Meitnerium 109 Mt (268)

The number in parentheses is the mass number of the longest lived isotope for that element.

Lanthanide series	Cerium 58 Ce 140.116	Praseodymium 59 Pr 140.908	Neodymium 60 Nd 144.24	Promethium 61 Pm (145)	Samarium 62 Sm 150.36	Europium 63 Eu 151.964
Actinide series	Thorium 90 Th 232.038	Protactinium 91 Pa 231.036	Uranium 92 U 238.029	Neptunium 93 Np (237)	Plutonium 94 Pu (244)	Americium 95 Am (243)

Reference Handbook E

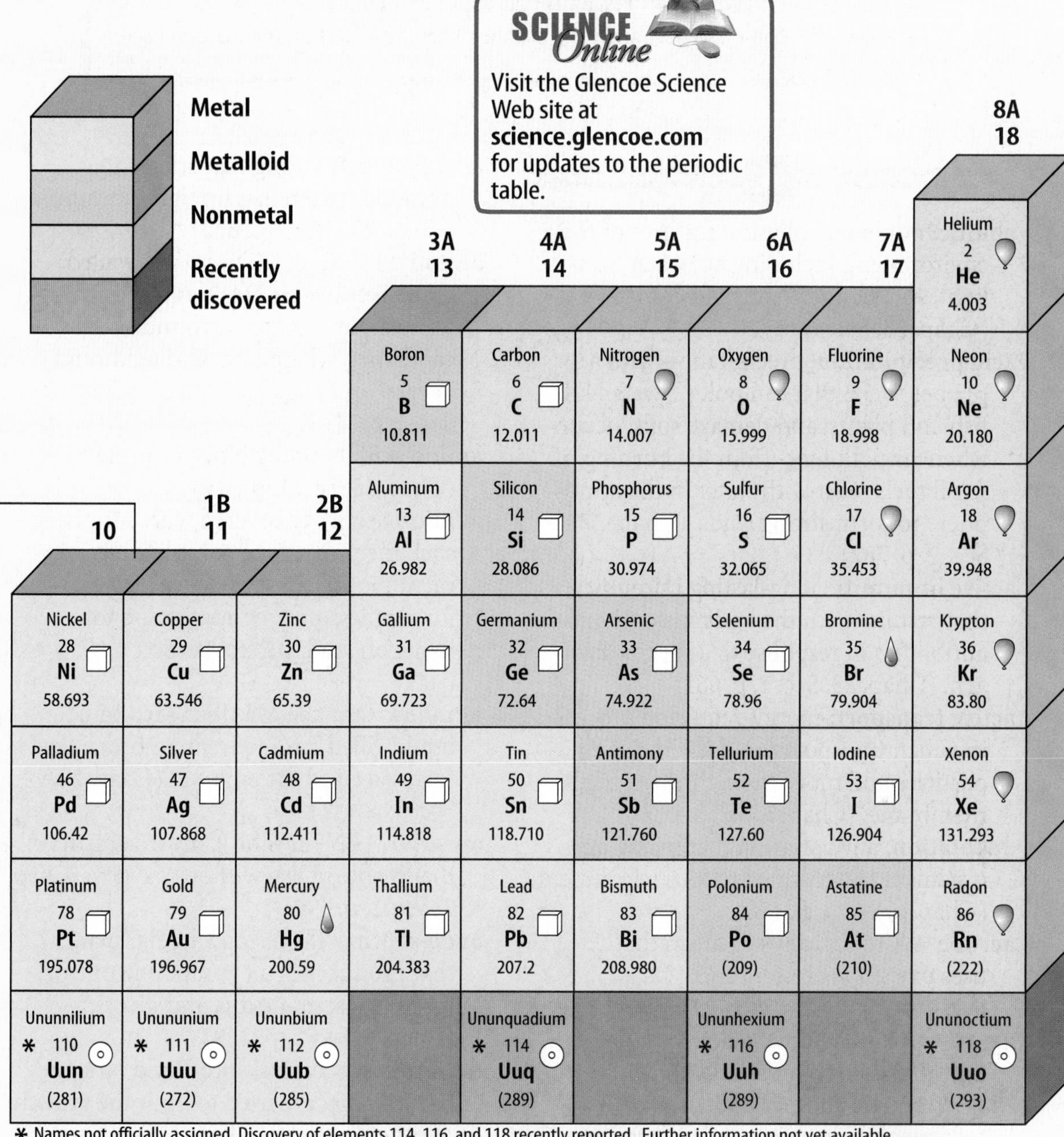

Legend
Metal
Metalloid
Nonmetal
Recently discovered

SCIENCE Online

Visit the Glencoe Science Web site at **science.glencoe.com** for updates to the periodic table.

10	1B 11	2B 12	3A 13	4A 14	5A 15	6A 16	7A 17	8A 18
								Helium 2 **He** 4.003
			Boron 5 **B** 10.811	Carbon 6 **C** 12.011	Nitrogen 7 **N** 14.007	Oxygen 8 **O** 15.999	Fluorine 9 **F** 18.998	Neon 10 **Ne** 20.180
			Aluminum 13 **Al** 26.982	Silicon 14 **Si** 28.086	Phosphorus 15 **P** 30.974	Sulfur 16 **S** 32.065	Chlorine 17 **Cl** 35.453	Argon 18 **Ar** 39.948
Nickel 28 **Ni** 58.693	Copper 29 **Cu** 63.546	Zinc 30 **Zn** 65.39	Gallium 31 **Ga** 69.723	Germanium 32 **Ge** 72.64	Arsenic 33 **As** 74.922	Selenium 34 **Se** 78.96	Bromine 35 **Br** 79.904	Krypton 36 **Kr** 83.80
Palladium 46 **Pd** 106.42	Silver 47 **Ag** 107.868	Cadmium 48 **Cd** 112.411	Indium 49 **In** 114.818	Tin 50 **Sn** 118.710	Antimony 51 **Sb** 121.760	Tellurium 52 **Te** 127.60	Iodine 53 **I** 126.904	Xenon 54 **Xe** 131.293
Platinum 78 **Pt** 195.078	Gold 79 **Au** 196.967	Mercury 80 **Hg** 200.59	Thallium 81 **Tl** 204.383	Lead 82 **Pb** 207.2	Bismuth 83 **Bi** 208.980	Polonium 84 **Po** (209)	Astatine 85 **At** (210)	Radon 86 **Rn** (222)
Ununnilium * 110 **Uun** (281)	Unununium * 111 **Uuu** (272)	Ununbium * 112 **Uub** (285)		Ununquadium * 114 **Uuq** (289)		Ununhexium * 116 **Uuh** (289)		Ununoctium * 118 **Uuo** (293)

* Names not officially assigned. Discovery of elements 114, 116, and 118 recently reported. Further information not yet available.

Gadolinium 64 **Gd** 157.25	Terbium 65 **Tb** 158.925	Dysprosium 66 **Dy** 162.50	Holmium 67 **Ho** 164.930	Erbium 68 **Er** 167.259	Thulium 69 **Tm** 168.934	Ytterbium 70 **Yb** 173.04	Lutetium 71 **Lu** 174.967
Curium 96 **Cm** (247)	Berkelium 97 **Bk** (247)	Californium 98 **Cf** (251)	Einsteinium 99 **Es** (252)	Fermium 100 **Fm** (257)	Mendelevium 101 **Md** (258)	Nobelium 102 **No** (259)	Lawrencium 103 **Lr** (262)

English Glossary

This glossary defines each key term that appears in bold type in the text. It also shows the chapter, section, and page number where you can find the word(s) used.

A

abiotic: nonliving, physical features of the environment, including air, water, sunlight, soil, temperature, and climate. (Chap. 25, Sec. 1, p. 720)

acid precipitation: precipitation with a pH below 5.6 that can pollute water, kill fish and plants, and damage soils; occurs when air pollutants from the burning of fossil fuels react with water in the atmosphere to form strong acids. (Chap. 27, Sec. 2, p. 787)

active immunity: long-lasting immunity that results when the body makes its own antibodies in response to a specific antigen. (Chap. 23, Sec. 1, p. 661)

active transport: energy-requiring process in which transport proteins bind with particles and move them through a cell membrane. (Chap. 3, Sec. 2, p. 77)

adaptation: any variation that makes an organism better suited to its environment. (Chap. 6, Sec. 1, p. 158)

aerobe (AY rohb): any organism that uses oxygen for respiration. (Chap. 7, Sec. 1, p. 190)

aggression: forceful behavior, such as fighting, used by an animal to control or dominate another animal in order to protect their young, defend territory, or get food. (Chap. 16, Sec. 2, p. 468)

algae (AL jee): chlorophyll-containing, plantlike protists that produce oxygen as a result of photosynthesis. (Chap. 8, Sec. 1, p. 213)

allele (uh LEEL): an alternate form that a gene may have for a single trait; can be dominant or recessive. (Chap. 5, Sec. 1, p. 126)

allergen: substance that causes an allergic reaction. (Chap. 23, Sec. 3, p. 673)

allergy: overly strong reaction of the immune system to a foreign substance. (Chap. 23, Sec. 3, p. 672)

alveoli (al VEE uh li): tiny, thin-walled, grapelike clusters at the end of each bronchiole that are surrounded by capillaries, where carbon dioxide and oxygen exchange takes place. (Chap. 20, Sec. 1, p. 577)

amino acid: building block of protein. (Chap. 18, Sec. 1, p. 519)

amniotic egg: egg covered with a leathery shell that provides a complete environment for the embryo's development; for reptiles, a major adaptation for living on land. (Chap. 14, Sec. 4, p. 417)

amniotic (am nee AH tihk) **sac:** thin, liquid-filled, protective membrane that forms around the embryo. (Chap. 22, Sec. 3, p. 641)

anaerobe (AN uh rohb): any organism that is able to live without oxygen. (Chap. 7, Sec. 1, p. 190)

angiosperms: flowering vascular plants that produce a fruit containing one or more seeds; monocots and dicots. (Chap. 9, Sec. 3, p. 259)

antibiotics: chemicals produced by some bacteria that are used to limit the growth of other bacteria. (Chap. 7, Sec. 2, p. 195)

antibody: a protein made in response to a specific antigen that can attach to the antigen and cause it to be useless. (Chap. 23, Sec. 1, p. 660)

antigen (AN tih jun): complex molecule that is foreign to your body. (Chap. 23, Sec. 1, p. 660)

anus: opening at the end of the digestive tract through which wastes leave the body. (Chap. 12, Sec. 3, p. 351)

appendages: jointed structures of arthropods, such as legs, wings, or antennae. (Chap. 13, Sec. 3, p. 374)

artery: blood vessel that carries blood away from the heart and has thick, elastic walls made of connective tissue and smooth muscle tissue. (Chap. 19, Sec. 1, p. 550)

ascus (AS kus): saclike, spore-producing structure of sac fungi. (Chap. 8, Sec. 2, p. 226)

asexual reproduction: a type of reproduction—fission, budding, and regeneration—in which a new organism is produced from one parent and has DNA identical to the parent organism. (Chap. 4, Sec. 1, p. 101)

asthma: lung disorder in which the bronchial tubes contract quickly and cause shortness of breath, wheezing, or coughing; may occur as an allergic reaction. (Chap. 20, Sec. 1, p. 582)

atmosphere: air surrounding Earth; is made up of gases, including 78 percent nitrogen, 21 percent oxygen, and 0.03 percent carbon dioxide. (Chap. 25, Sec. 1, p. 721)

atriums (AY tree umz): two upper chambers of the heart that contract at the same time during a heartbeat. (Chap. 19, Sec. 1, p. 547)

auxin (AWK sun): plant hormone that causes plant leaves and stems to exhibit positive phototropisms. (Chap. 11, Sec. 2, p. 316)

axon (AK sahn): neuron structure that carries messages away from the cell body. (Chap. 21, Sec. 1, p. 601)

B

basidium (buh SIHD ee uhm): club-shaped, reproductive structure in which club fungi produce spores. (Chap. 8, Sec. 2, p. 226)

behavior: the way in which an organism interacts with other organisms and its environment; can be innate or learned. (Chap. 16, Sec. 1, p. 460)

bilateral symmetry: body parts arranged in a similar way on both sides of the body, with each half being a mirror image of the other half. (Chap. 12, Sec. 1, p. 339)

binomial nomenclature (bi NOH mee ul • NOH mun klay chur): two-word naming system for organisms; first word is the genus and second word is the species. (Chap. 1, Sec. 4, p. 20)

biogenesis (bi oh JEN us suhs): theory that living things can come only from other living things. (Chap. 1, Sec. 3, p. 19)

biological vector: disease-carrying organism, such as a rat, mosquito, or fly, that spreads infectious disease. (Chap. 23, Sec. 2, p. 667)

biomes (BI ohmz): large geographic areas with similar climates and ecosystems; includes tundra, taiga, desert, temperate deciduous forest, temperate rain forest, tropical rain forest, and grassland. (Chap. 26, Sec. 2, p. 752)

biosphere: part of Earth that supports life, including the top portion of Earth's crust, the atmosphere, and all the water on Earth's surface. (Chap. 24, Sec. 1, p. 692)

biotic (bi AHT ik): features of the environment that are alive or were once alive. (Chap. 25, Sec. 1, p. 720)

bladder: elastic, muscular organ that holds urine until it leaves the body through the urethra. (Chap. 20, Sec. 2, p. 586)

brain stem: connects the brain to the spinal cord and is made up of the midbrain, the pons, and the medulla. (Chap. 21, Sec. 1, p. 604)

bronchi (BRAHN ki): two short tubes that branch off the lower end of the trachea and carry air into the lungs. (Chap. 20, Sec. 1, p. 577)

budding: form of asexual reproduction in which a new, genetically identical organism forms on the side of its parent. (Chap. 8, Sec. 2, p. 226)

C

cambium (KAM bee um): vascular tissue that produces xylem and phloem cells as a plant grows. (Chap. 9, Sec. 3, p. 257)

capillary: microscopic blood vessel that connects arteries and veins; has walls one cell thick, through which nutrients and oxygen diffuse into body cells and waste materials and carbon dioxide diffuse out. (Chap. 19, Sec. 1, p. 551)

carbohydrate (kar boh HI drayt): nutrient that usually is the body's main source of energy. (Chap. 18, Sec. 1, p. 520)

carbon cycle: model describing how carbon molecules move between the living and nonliving world. (Chap. 25, Sec. 2, p. 733)

cardiac muscle: striated, involuntary muscle found only in the heart. (Chap. 17, Sec. 2, p. 499)

carnivore: animal that eats only other animals or the remains of other animals. (Chap. 12, Sec. 1, p. 335) (Chap. 15, Sec. 2, p. 441)

carrying capacity: largest number of individuals of a particular species that an ecosystem can support over time. (Chap. 24, Sec. 2, p. 699)

cartilage: tough, flexible tissue that joins vertebrae and makes up all or part of the vertebrate endoskeleton. (Chap. 14, Sec. 1, p. 399) (Chap. 17, Sec. 1, p. 492)

cell: smallest unit of a living thing that can perform the functions of life; has an orderly structure and contains hereditary material. (Chap. 1, Sec. 2, p. 10)

cell membrane: protective outer covering of all cells that is made up of a double layer of fatlike molecules and regulates the interaction between the cell and the environment. (Chap. 2, Sec. 1, p. 38)

cell theory: states that all organisms are made up of one or more cells, the cell is the basic unit of life, and all cells come from other cells. (Chap. 2, Sec. 2, p. 51)

cellulose (SEL yuh lohs): chemical compound made out of sugar; forms tangled fibers in the cell walls of many plants and provides structure and support. (Chap. 9, Sec. 1, p. 244)

cell wall: rigid structure that encloses, supports, and protects the cells of plants, algae, fungi, and most bacteria. (Chap. 2, Sec. 1, p. 39)

central nervous system: division of the nervous system, made up of the brain and spinal cord. (Chap. 21, Sec. 1, p. 603)

cerebellum (sur uh BEL um): part of the brain that controls voluntary muscle movements, maintains muscle tone, and helps maintain balance. (Chap. 21, Sec. 1, p. 604)

cerebrum (suh REE brum): largest part of the brain, where memory is stored, movements are controlled, and impulses from the senses are interpreted. (Chap. 21, Sec. 1, p. 604)

chemical digestion: occurs when enzymes and other chemicals break down large food molecules into smaller ones. (Chap. 18, Sec. 2, p. 529)

chemosynthesis (kee moh SIN thuh sus): process in which producers make energy-rich nutrient molecules from chemicals. (Chap. 25, Sec. 3, p. 735)

chemotherapy (kee moh THAYR uh pee): use of chemicals to destroy cancer cells. (Chap. 23, Sec. 3, p. 676)

chlorophyll (KLOR uh fihl): green, light-trapping pigment in plant chloroplasts that is important in photosynthesis. (Chap. 11, Sec. 1, p. 306)

chloroplast: green, chlorophyll-containing, plant-cell organelle that converts sunlight, carbon dioxide, and water into sugar. (Chap. 2, Sec. 1, p. 42)

chordate: animal that has a notochord, a nerve cord, gill slits, and a postanal tail present at some stage in its development. (Chap. 14, Sec. 1, p. 398)

chromosome: structure in a cell's nucleus that contains genetic material. (Chap. 4, Sec. 1, p. 98)

chyme (KIME): liquid product of digestion. (Chap. 18, Sec. 2, p. 533)

cilia (SIHL ee uh): short, threadlike structures that extend from the cell membrane of a ciliate and allow the organism to move quickly. (Chap. 8, Sec. 1, p. 217)

climate: average weather conditions of an area over time, including wind, temperature, and rainfall or other types of precipitation such as snow or sleet. (Chap. 25, Sec. 1, p. 725)

climax community: stable, end stage of ecological succession in which the plants and animals of a community use resources efficiently and balance is maintained by disturbances such as fire. (Chap. 26, Sec. 1, p. 751)

closed circulatory system: blood circulation system in which blood moves through the body in closed vessels. (Chap. 13, Sec. 1, p. 366)

cochlea (KOH klee uh): fluid-filled structure in the inner ear in which sound vibrations are converted into nerve impulses that are sent to the brain. (Chap. 21, Sec. 2, p. 614)

commensalism: a type of symbiotic relationship in which one organism benefits and the other organism is not affected. (Chap. 24, Sec. 3, p. 706)

community: all the populations of different species that live in an ecosystem. (Chap. 24, Sec. 1, p. 694)

condensation: process that takes place when a gas changes to a liquid. (Chap. 25, Sec. 2, p. 729)

conditioning: occurs when the response to a stimulus becomes associated with another stimulus. (Chap. 16, Sec. 1, p. 464)

consumer: organism that cannot create energy-rich molecules but obtains its food by eating other organisms. (Chap. 24, Sec. 3, p. 705)

contour feathers: strong, lightweight feathers that give birds their coloring and shape and that are used for flight. (Chap. 15, Sec. 1, p. 434)

control: in an experiment, the standard to which the outcome of the test will be compared. (Chap. 1, Sec. 1, p. 9)

coral reef: diverse ecosystem formed from the calcium carbonate shells secreted by corals. (Chap. 26, Sec. 3, p. 765)

coronary (KOR uh ner ee) **circulation:** flow of blood to and from the tissues of the heart. (Chap. 19, Sec. 1, p. 547)

courtship behavior: behavior that allows males and females of the same species to recognize each other and prepare to mate. (Chap. 16, Sec. 2, p. 469)

crop: digestive system sac in which earthworms store ingested soil. (Chap. 13, Sec. 2, p. 370)

cuticle (KYEWT ih kul): waxy, protective layer that covers the stems, leaves, and flowers of many plants and helps prevent water loss. (Chap. 9, Sec. 1, p. 244)

cyclic behavior: behavior that occurs in repeated patterns. (Chap. 16, Sec. 2, p. 472)

cytoplasm: constantly moving gel-like mixture inside the cell membrane that contains heredity material and is the location of most of a cell's life processes. (Chap. 2, Sec. 1, p. 38)

D

day-neutral plant: plant that doesn't require a specific photoperiod and can begin the flowering process over a range of night lengths. (Chap. 11, Sec. 2, p. 318)

dendrite: neuron structure that receives messages and sends them to the cell body. (Chap. 21, Sec. 1, p. 601)

dermis: skin layer below the epidermis that contains blood vessels, nerves, oil and sweat glands, and other structures. (Chap. 17, Sec. 3, p. 503)

desert: driest biome on Earth with less than 25 cm of rain each year; has dunes or thin soil with little organic matter and plants and animals specially adapted to survive extreme conditions. (Chap. 26, Sec. 2, p. 758)

diaphragm (DI uh fram): muscle beneath the lungs that contracts and relaxes to move gases in and out of the body. (Chap. 20, Sec. 1, p. 578)

dicot: angiosperm with two cotyledons inside its seed, flower parts in multiples of four or five, and vascular bundles in rings. (Chap. 9, Sec. 3, p. 260)

diffusion: a type of passive transport in cells in which molecules move from areas where there are more of them to areas where there are fewer of them. (Chap. 3, Sec. 2, p. 75)

digestion: mechanical and chemical breakdown of food into small molecules that cells can absorb and use. (Chap. 18, Sec. 2, p. 529)

diploid (DIH ployd): cell whose chromosomes occur in pairs. (Chap. 4, Sec. 2, p. 104)

DNA: deoxyribonucleic acid; the genetic material of all organisms; made up of two twisted strands of sugar-phosphate molecules and nitrogen bases. (Chap. 4, Sec. 3, p. 110)

dominant (DAHM uh nunt): describes a trait that covers over, or dominates, another form of that trait. (Chap. 5, Sec. 1, p. 128)

down feathers: soft, fluffy feathers that provide an insulating layer next to the skin of adult birds and that cover the bodies of young birds. (Chap. 15, Sec. 1, p. 434)

E

ecology: study of the interactions that take place among organisms and their environment. (Chap. 24, Sec. 1, p. 693)

ecosystem: all the living organisms that live in an area and the nonliving features of their environment. (Chap. 24, Sec. 1, p. 693)

ectotherm: vertebrate animal whose internal temperature changes when the temperature of its environment changes. (Chap. 14, Sec. 1, p. 401)

egg: haploid sex cell formed in the female reproductive organs. (Chap. 4, Sec. 2, p. 104)

embryo: fertilized egg that has attached to the wall of the uterus. (Chap. 22, Sec. 3, p. 641)

embryology (em bree AHL uh jee): study of embryos and their development. (Chap. 6, Sec. 2, p. 167)

emphysema (em fuh SEE muh): lung disease in which the alveoli enlarge. (Chap. 20, Sec. 1, p. 581)

endocytosis (en duh si TOH sus): process by which a cell takes in a substance by surrounding it with the cell membrane. (Chap. 3, Sec. 2, p. 78)

endoplasmic reticulum (ER): cytoplasmic organelle that moves materials around in a cell and is made up of a complex series of folded membranes; can be rough (with attached ribosomes) or smooth (without attached ribosomes). (Chap. 2, Sec. 1, p. 43)

endoskeleton: supportive framework of bone and/or cartilage that provides an internal place for muscle attachment and protects a vertebrate's internal organs. (Chap. 14, Sec. 1, p. 399)

endospore: thick-walled, protective structure produced by a pathogen when conditions are unfavorable for survival. (Chap. 7, Sec. 2, p. 199)

endotherm: vertebrate animal with a constant internal temperature. (Chap. 14, Sec. 1, p. 401)

energy pyramid: model that shows the amount of energy available at each feeding level in an ecosystem. (Chap. 25, Sec. 3, p. 737)

enzyme: a type of protein that regulates nearly all chemical reactions in cells. (Chap. 3, Sec. 1, p. 71) (Chap. 18, Sec. 2, p. 530)

epidermis: outer, thinnest skin layer that constantly produces new cells to replace the dead cells rubbed off its surface. (Chap. 17, Sec. 3, p. 502)

equilibrium: occurs when molecules of one substance are spread evenly throughout another substance. (Chap. 3, Sec. 2, p. 75)

erosion: movement of soil from one place to another. (Chap. 27, Sec. 2, p. 793)

estivation: inactivity in hot, dry months during which amphibians hide in cooler ground. (Chap. 14, Sec. 3, p. 411)

estuary: extremely fertile area where a river meets an ocean; contains a mixture of freshwater and salt water and serves as a nursery for many species of fish. (Chap. 26, Sec. 3, p. 766)

evaporation: process that takes place when a liquid changes to a gas. (Chap. 25, Sec. 2, p. 728)

evolution: change in inherited characteristics over time. (Chap. 6, Sec. 1, p. 154)

exocytosis (ek soh si TOH sus): process by which vesicles release their contents outside the cell. (Chap. 3, Sec. 2, p. 78)

exoskeleton: thick, hard, outer covering that protects and supports arthropod bodies and provides places for muscles to attach. (Chap. 13, Sec. 3, p. 374)

F

fat: nutrient that stores energy, cushions organs, and helps the body absorb vitamins. (Chap. 18, Sec. 1, p. 521)

fermentation: process by which oxygen-lacking cells and some one-celled organisms release small amounts of energy from glucose molecules and produce wastes such as alcohol, carbon dioxide, and lactic acid. (Chap. 3, Sec. 3, p. 84)

fertilization: in sexual reproduction, the joining of a sperm and egg. (Chap. 4, Sec. 2, p. 104)

fetal stress: can occur during the birth process or after birth as an infant adjusts from a watery, dark, constant-temperature environment to its new environment. (Chap. 22, Sec. 3, p. 644)

fetus: a developing baby after the first two months of pregnancy until birth. (Chap. 22, Sec. 3, p. 642)

fin: fanlike structure used by fish for steering, balancing, and movement. (Chap. 14, Sec. 2, p. 403)

fission: simplest form of asexual reproduction in which two new cells are produced with genetic material identical to each other and identical to the previous cell. (Chap. 7, Sec. 1, p. 190)

flagellum: long, thin, whiplike structure of some protists that helps them move through moist or wet surroundings. (Chap. 7, Sec. 1, p. 189) (Chap. 8, Sec. 1, p. 214)

food group: group of foods—such as bread, cereal, rice, and pasta—containing the same type of nutrients. (Chap. 18, Sec. 1, p. 526)

food web: model that shows the complex feeding relationships among organisms in a community. (Chap. 25, Sec. 3, p. 736)

fossil fuels: nonrenewable energy resources—coal, oil, and natural gas—that formed in Earth's crust over hundreds of millions of years. (Chap. 27, Sec. 1, p. 780)

free-living organism: organism that does not depend on another organism for food or a place to live. (Chap. 12, Sec. 3, p. 348)

frond: leaf of a fern that grows from the rhizome. (Chap. 10, Sec. 2, p. 280)

G

gametophyte (guh MEE tuh fite) **stage:** plant life cycle stage that begins when cells in reproductive organs undergo meiosis and produce haploid cells (spores). (Chap. 10, Sec. 1, p. 277)

gene: section of DNA on a chromosome that contains instructions for making specific proteins. (Chap. 4, Sec. 3, p. 112)

genetic engineering: biological and chemical methods to change the arrangement of a gene's DNA to improve crop production, produce large volumes of medicine, and change how cells perform their normal functions. (Chap. 5, Sec. 3, p. 141)

genetics (juh NET ihks): the study of how traits are inherited through the actions of alleles. (Chap. 5, Sec. 1, p. 126)

genotype (JEE nuh tipe): an organism's genetic makeup. (Chap. 5, Sec. 1, p. 130)

genus: a group of similar species. (Chap. 1, Sec. 4, p. 24)

geothermal energy: heat energy within Earth's crust; available only where natural geysers or volcanoes are located. (Chap. 27, Sec. 1, p. 783)

germination: series of events that results in the growth of a plant from a seed. (Chap. 10, Sec. 3, p. 292)

gestation period: period during which an embryo develops in the uterus; the length of time varies among species. (Chap. 15, Sec. 2, p. 445)

gills: organs that exchange carbon dioxide for oxygen in water. (Chap. 13, Sec. 1, p. 364)

gill slits: in developing chordates, the paired openings found in the area between the mouth and digestive tube. (Chap. 14, Sec. 1, p. 399)

gizzard: muscular digestive system structure in which earthworms grind soil and organic matter. (Chap. 13, Sec. 2, p. 370)

Golgi bodies: organelles that package cellular materials and transport them within the cell or out of the cell. (Chap. 2, Sec. 1, p. 43)

gradualism: model describing evolution as a slow process by which one species changes into a new species through a continuing series of mutations and variations over time. (Chap. 6, Sec. 1, p. 160)

grasslands: temperate and tropical regions with 25 cm to 75 cm of precipitation each year that are dominated by climax communities of grasses; ideal for growing crops and raising cattle and sheep. (Chap. 26, Sec. 2, p. 759)

greenhouse effect: heat-trapping feature of the atmosphere that keeps Earth warm enough to support life. (Chap. 27, Sec. 2, p. 788)

guard cells: pairs of cells that surround stomata and control their opening and closing. (Chap. 9, Sec. 3, p. 255)

gymnosperms: vascular plants that do not flower, generally have needlelike or scale-like leaves, and produce seeds that are not protected by fruit; conifers, cycads, ginkgoes, and gnetophytes. (Chap. 9, Sec. 3, p. 258)

H

habitat: place where an organism lives and that provides the types of food, shelter, moisture, and temperature needed for survival. (Chap. 24, Sec. 1, p. 695)

haploid (HA ployd): cell that has only one of each type of chromosome. (Chap. 4, Sec. 2, p. 105)

hazardous wastes: waste materials, such as pesticides and leftover paints, that are harmful to human health or poisonous to living organisms. (Chap. 27, Sec. 2, p. 794)

hemoglobin (HEE muh gloh bun): chemical in red blood cells that carries oxygen from the lungs to body cells and carries some carbon dioxide from body cells back to the lungs. (Chap. 19, Sec. 2, p. 557)

herbivore: animal that eats only plants or parts of plants. (Chap. 12, Sec. 1, p. 335) (Chap. 15, Sec. 2, p. 441)

heredity (huh RED ut ee): the passing of traits from parent to offspring. (Chap. 5, Sec. 1, p. 126)

hermaphrodite (hur MA fruh dite): animal that produces sperm and eggs in the same body, but its sperm cannot fertilize its own eggs. (Chap. 12, Sec. 2, p. 342)

heterozygous (het uh roh ZI gus): describes an organism with two different alleles for a trait. (Chap. 5, Sec. 1, p. 130)

hibernation: cyclic response of inactivity and slowed metabolism that occurs during periods of cold temperatures and limited food supplies. (Chap. 14, Sec. 3, p. 411) (Chap. 16, Sec. 2, p. 473)

homeostasis: regulation of an organism's internal, life-maintaining conditions despite changes in its environment. (Chap. 1, Sec. 2, p. 15) (Chap. 21, Sec. 1, p. 601)

hominid: humanlike primate that appeared about 4 million to 6 million years ago, ate both plants and meat, and walked upright on two legs. (Chap. 6, Sec. 3, p. 171)

homologous (huh MAHL uh gus): body parts that are similar in structure and origin and can be similar in function. (Chap. 6, Sec. 2, p. 168)

Homo sapiens: early humans that likely evolved from Cro-Magnons. (Chap. 6, Sec. 3, p. 173)

homozygous (hoh muh ZI gus): describes an organism with two alleles that are the same for a trait. (Chap. 5, Sec. 1, p. 130)

hormone (HOR mohn): chemical produced by the endocrine system; released directly into the bloodstream by ductless glands; affects specific target tissues, and can speed up or slow down cellular activities. (Chap. 22, Sec. 1, p. 628)

host cell: living cell in which a virus can actively reproduce or in which a virus can hide until activated by environmental stimuli. (Chap. 2, Sec. 3, p. 52)

hybrid (HI brud): an offspring that was given different genetic information for a trait from each parent. (Chap. 5, Sec. 1, p. 128)

hydroelectric power: electricity produced when the energy of falling water turns the blades of a generator turbine. (Chap. 27, Sec. 1, p. 781)

hyphae (HI fee): mass of many-celled, threadlike tubes forming the body of a fungus. (Chap. 8, Sec. 2, p. 224)

hypothesis: a prediction that can be tested. (Chap. 1, Sec. 1, p. 8)

I

immune system: complex group of defenses that protects the body against pathogens—includes the skin and respiratory, digestive, and circulatory systems. (Chap. 23, Sec. 1, p. 658)

imprinting: occurs when an animal forms a social attachment to another organism during a specific period following birth or hatching. (Chap. 16, Sec. 1, p. 463)

incomplete dominance: production of a phenotype that is intermediate between the two homozygous parents. (Chap. 5, Sec. 2, p. 134)

infectious disease: disease caused by a virus, bacterium, fungus, or protist that is spread from an infected organism or the environment to another organism. (Chap. 23, Sec. 2, p. 667)

innate behavior: behavior that an organism is born with and does not have to be learned, such as a reflex or instinct. (Chap. 16, Sec. 1, p. 461)

inorganic compound: compound, such as H_2O, that is made from elements other than carbon and whose atoms usually can be arranged only in one structure. (Chap. 3, Sec. 1, p. 71)

insight: form of reasoning that allows animals to use past experiences to solve new problems. (Chap. 16, Sec. 1, p. 465)

instinct: complex pattern of innate behavior, such as spinning a web, that can take weeks to complete. (Chap. 16, Sec. 1, p. 462)

intertidal zone: part of the shoreline that is underwater at high tide and exposed to the air at low tide. (Chap. 26, Sec. 3, p. 766)

invertebrate: animal without a backbone. (Chap. 12, Sec. 1, p. 338)

involuntary muscle: muscle, such as heart muscle, that cannot be controlled consciously. (Chap. 17, Sec. 2, p. 497)

J

joint: any place where two or more bones come together; can be movable or immovable. (Chap. 17, Sec. 1, p. 493)

K

kidney: bean-shaped urinary system organ that is made up of about 1 million nephrons and filters blood, producing urine. (Chap. 20, Sec. 2, p. 584)

kingdom: first and largest category in the scientific classification system of organisms; can be divided into smaller groups: phylum, class, order, family, genus, and species. (Chap. 1, Sec. 4, p. 23)

L

larynx: airway to which the vocal cords are attached. (Chap. 20, Sec. 1, p. 577)

law: a scientific statement about how things happen in nature and that seems to be true at all times. (Chap. 1, Sec. 1, p. 10)

lichen (LI kun): organism made up of a fungus and a green alga or a cyanobacterium. (Chap. 8, Sec. 2, p. 228)

ligament: tough band of tissue that holds bones together at joints. (Chap. 17, Sec. 1, p. 493)

limiting factor: anything that can restrict the size of a population, including living and nonliving features of an ecosystem, such as predators or drought. (Chap. 24, Sec. 2, p. 698)

long-day plant: plant that generally requires short nights—less than ten to 12 hours of darkness—to begin the flowering process. (Chap. 11, Sec. 2, p. 318)

lymph (LIHMF): tissue fluid that has diffused into the capillaries. (Chap. 19, Sec. 3, p. 562)

lymphatic system: carries lymph though a network of lymph capillaries and vessels and drains it into large veins near the heart; helps fight infections and diseases. (Chap. 19, Sec. 3, p. 562)

lymph node: bean-shaped organ found throughout the body that filters out microorganisms and foreign materials taken up by the lymphocytes. (Chap. 19, Sec. 3, p. 563)

lymphocyte (LIHM fuh site): a type of white blood cell that fights infection. (Chap. 19, Sec. 3, p. 562)

M

mammals: endothermic vertebrates that have hair, teeth specialized for eating certain foods, and whose females have mammary glands that produce milk for feeding their young. (Chap. 15, Sec. 2, p. 440)

mammary glands: milk-producing glands of female mammals used to feed their young. (Chap. 15, Sec. 2, p. 440)

mantle: thin layer of tissue that covers a mollusk's body organs; secretes the shell or protects the body of mollusks without shells. (Chap. 13, Sec. 1, p. 364)

marsupial: a mammal with an external pouch for the development of its immature young. (Chap. 15, Sec. 2, p. 444)

mechanical digestion: breakdown of food through chewing, mixing, and churning. (Chap. 18, Sec. 2, p. 529)

medusa (mih DEW suh): cnidarian body type that is bell-shaped and free-swimming. (Chap. 12, Sec. 2, p. 343)

meiosis (mi OH sus): reproductive process that produces four haploid sex cells from one diploid cell and ensures offspring will have the same number of chromosomes as the parent organisms. (Chap. 4, Sec. 2, p. 105)

melanin: pigment produced by the epidermis that protects skin from Sun damage and gives skin and eyes their color. (Chap. 17, Sec. 3, p. 503)

menstrual cycle: hormone-controlled monthly cycle of changes in the female reproductive system that includes the maturation of an egg and preparation of the uterus for possible pregnancy. (Chap. 22, Sec. 2, p. 636)

menstruation (men STRAY shun): monthly flow of blood and tissue cells that occurs when the lining of the uterus breaks down and is shed. (Chap. 22, Sec. 2, p. 636)

metabolism: the total of all chemical reactions in an organism. (Chap. 3, Sec. 3, p. 81)

metamorphosis: process in which many insect species change their body form to become adults; can be complete (egg, larva, pupa, adult) or incomplete (egg, nymph, adult). (Chap. 13, Sec. 3, p. 376)

migration: instinctive seasonal movement of animals to find food or to reproduce in better conditions. (Chap. 16, Sec. 2, p. 474)

mineral: inorganic nutrient that regulates many chemical reactions in the body. (Chap. 18, Sec. 1, p. 524)

mitochondrion: cell organelle that breaks down lipids and carbohydrates and releases energy. (Chap. 2, Sec. 1, p. 42)

mitosis (mi TOH sus): cell process in which the nucleus divides to form two nuclei identical to each other, and identical to the original nucleus, in a series of steps (prophase, metaphase, anaphase, and telophase). (Chap. 4, Sec. 1, p. 98)

mixture: a combination of substances in which the individual substances do not change or combine chemically but instead retain their own individual properties; can be gases, solids, liquids, or any combination of them. (Chap. 3, Sec. 1, p. 69)

molting: shedding and replacing of an arthropod's exoskeleton. (Chap. 13, Sec. 3, p. 374)

monocot: angiosperm with one cotyledon inside its seed, flower parts arranged in multiples of three, and vascular tissues in bundles scattered throughout the stem. (Chap. 9, Sec. 3, p. 260)

muscle: organ that can relax, contract, and provide the force to move bones and body parts. (Chap. 17, Sec. 2, p. 496)

mutation: any permanent change in a gene or chromosome of a cell; may be beneficial, harmful, or have little effect on an organism. (Chap. 4, Sec. 3, p. 114)

mutualism: a type of symbiotic relationship in which both organisms benefit. (Chap. 24, Sec. 3, p. 706)

mycorrhizae (mi kuh RI zee): network of hyphae and plant roots that helps plants absorb water and minerals from soil. (Chap. 8, Sec. 2, p. 228)

N

natural resources: parts of Earth's environment that supply materials useful or necessary for the survival of living organisms. (Chap. 27, Sec. 1, p. 778)

natural selection: organisms with traits best suited to their environment are more likely to survive and reproduce; includes concepts of variation, overproduction, and competition. (Chap. 6, Sec. 1, p. 157)

nephron (NEF rahn): tiny filtering unit of the kidney. (Chap. 20, Sec. 2, p. 585)

nerve cord: tubelike structure above the notochord that in most chordates develops into the brain and spinal cord. (Chap. 14, Sec. 1, p. 399)

neuron (NOO rahn): basic functioning unit of the nervous system; made up of a cell body, dendrites, and axons. (Chap. 21, Sec. 1, p. 601)

niche: in an ecosystem, refers to the unique ways an organism survives, obtains food and shelter, and avoids danger. (Chap. 24, Sec. 3, p. 707)

nitrogen cycle: model describing how nitrogen moves from the atmosphere to the soil, to living organisms, and then back to the atmosphere. (Chap. 25, Sec. 2, p. 730)

nitrogen fixation: process in which some types of bacteria in the soil change nitrogen gas into a form of nitrogen that plants can use. (Chap. 25, Sec. 2, p. 730)

nitrogen-fixing bacteria: bacteria that convert nitrogen in the air into forms that can be used by plants and animals. (Chap. 7, Sec. 2, p. 196)

noninfectious disease: disease, such as cancer, diabetes, or asthma, that is not spread from one person to another. (Chap. 23, Sec. 3, p. 672)

nonrenewable resources: natural resources, such as petroleum, minerals, and metals, that are used more quickly than they can be replaced by natural processes. (Chap. 27, Sec. 1, p. 779)

nonvascular plant: plant that absorbs water and other substances directly through its cell walls instead of through tubelike structures. (Chap. 9, Sec. 1, p. 247)

notochord: firm but flexible structure that extends along the upper part of a chordate's body. (Chap. 14, Sec. 1, p. 398)

nuclear energy: energy produced from the splitting apart of billions of uranium nuclei by a nuclear fission reaction. (Chap. 27, Sec. 1, p. 782)

nucleus: organelle that controls all the activities of a cell and contains hereditary material made of proteins and DNA. (Chap. 2, Sec. 1, p. 40)

nutrients (NEW tree unts): substances in foods—proteins, carbohydrates, fats, vitamins, minerals, and water—that provide energy and materials for cell development, growth, and repair. (Chap. 18, Sec. 1, p. 518)

O

olfactory (ohl FAK tree) **cell:** nasal nerve cell that becomes stimulated by molecules in the air and sends impulses to the brain for interpretation of odors. (Chap. 21, Sec. 2, p. 615)

omnivore: animal that eats plants and animals or animal flesh. (Chap. 12, Sec. 1, p. 335) (Chap. 15, Sec. 2, p. 441)

open circulatory system: blood circulation system in which blood moves through vessels and into open spaces around the body organs. (Chap. 13, Sec. 1, p. 364)

organ: structure, such as the heart, made up of different types of tissues that work together. (Chap. 2, Sec. 1, p. 45)

organelle: structure in the cytoplasm of a eukaryotic cell that can act as a storage site, process energy, move materials, or manufacture substances. (Chap. 2, Sec. 1, p. 40)

organic compounds: compounds that always contain hydrogen and carbon; carbohydrates, lipids, proteins, and nucleic acids are organic compounds found in living things. (Chap. 3, Sec. 1, p. 70)

organism: any living thing; uses energy, is made of cells, reproduces, responds, grows, and develops. (Chap. 1, Sec. 2, p. 14)

osmosis: a type of passive transport that occurs when water diffuses through a cell membrane. (Chap. 3, Sec. 2, p. 76)

ovary: female reproductive organ that produces eggs and is located in the lower part of the body. (Chap. 10, Sec. 3, p. 287) (Chap. 22, Sec. 2, p. 635)

ovulation (ahv yuh LAY shun): monthly process in which an egg is released from an ovary and enters the oviduct, where it can become fertilized by sperm. (Chap. 22, Sec. 2, p. 635)

ovule: in gymnosperms, the female reproductive part that produces eggs and food-storage tissues. (Chap. 10, Sec. 3, p. 285)

ozone depletion: thinning of Earth's ozone layer caused by chlorofluorocarbons (CFCs) leaking into the air and reacting chemically with ozone, breaking the ozone molecules apart. (Chap. 27, Sec. 2, p. 789)

P

parasitism: a type of symbiotic relationship in which one organism benefits and the other organism is harmed. (Chap. 24, Sec. 3, p. 706)

passive immunity: immunity that results when antibodies produced in one animal are introduced into another's body; does not last as long as active immunity. (Chap. 23, Sec. 1, p. 661)

passive transport: movement of substances through a cell membrane without the use of cellular energy; includes diffusion, osmosis, and facilitated diffusion. (Chap. 3, Sec. 2, p. 74)

pasteurization (pas chur ruh ZAY shun): process in which a liquid is heated to a temperature that kills most bacteria. (Chap. 23, Sec. 2, p. 663)

pathogen: disease-producing organism. (Chap. 7, Sec. 2, p. 199)

periosteum (pur ee AHS tee um): tough, tight-fitting membrane that covers a bone's surface and contains blood vessels that transport nutrients into the bone. (Chap. 17, Sec. 1, p. 491)

peripheral nervous system: division of the nervous system; made up of all the nerves outside the CNS; connects the brain and spinal cord to other body parts. (Chap. 21, Sec. 1, p. 603)

peristalsis (per uh STAHL sus): waves of muscular contractions that move food through the digestive tract. (Chap. 18, Sec. 2, p. 532)

petroleum: nonrenewable resource formed over hundreds of millions of years, mostly from the remains of microscopic marine organisms buried in Earth's crust. (Chap. 27, Sec. 1, p. 779)

pharynx (FER ingks): tubelike passageway for food, liquid, and air. (Chap. 20, Sec. 1, p. 576)

phenotype (FEE nuh tipe): outward physical appearance and behavior of an organism. (Chap. 5, Sec. 1, p. 130)

pheromone (FER uh mohn): powerful chemical produced by an animal to influence the behavior of another animal of the same species. (Chap. 16, Sec. 2, p. 469)

phloem (FLOH em): vascular tissue that forms tubes that transport dissolved sugar throughout a plant. (Chap. 9, Sec. 3, p. 257)

photoperiodism: a plant's response to the lengths of daylight and darkness each day. (Chap. 11, Sec. 2, p. 318)

photosynthesis (foh toh SIHN thuh suhs): food-making process by which plants and many other producers use light energy to produce glucose and oxygen from carbon dioxide and water. (Chap. 3, Sec. 3, p. 82)(Chap. 11, Sec. 1, p. 307)

phylogeny (fi LAH juh nee): evolutionary history of an organism; used by scientists to group organisms into kingdoms. (Chap. 1, Sec. 4, p. 23)

pioneer species: first organisms to grow in new or disturbed areas; break down rock and build soil. (Chap. 9, Sec. 2, p. 249) (Chap. 26, Sec. 1, p. 748)

pistil: female reproductive organ inside the flower of an angiosperm; consists of an ovary and a sticky stigma, where pollen grains land. (Chap. 10, Sec. 3, p. 287)

placenta: a saclike organ in which a placental embryo develops; absorbs oxygen and food from the mother's blood. (Chap. 15, Sec. 2, p. 445)

placental: a mammal whose offspring develop inside a placenta in the female's uterus. (Chap. 15, Sec. 2, p. 445)

plasma: liquid part of blood, made mostly of water, in which oxygen, nutrients, and minerals are dissolved. (Chap. 19, Sec. 2, p. 556)

platelet: irregularly shaped cell fragment that helps clot blood and releases chemicals that help form fibrin. (Chap. 19, Sec. 2, p. 557)

pollen grain: small structure produced by the male reproductive organs of a seed plant; has a water-resistant coat, can develop from a spore, and contains gametophyte parts that will produce sperm. (Chap. 10, Sec. 3, p. 283)

pollination: transfer of pollen grains to the female part of a seed plant by agents such as gravity, water, wind, and animals. (Chap. 10, Sec. 3, p. 283)

pollutant: substance that contaminates any part of the environment. (Chap. 27, Sec. 2, p. 786)

polygenic (pahl ih JEHN ihk) **inheritance:** occurs when a group of gene pairs acts together and produces a specific trait, such as human eye color, skin color, or height. (Chap. 5, Sec. 2, p. 136)

polyp (PAH lup): cnidarian body type that is vase-shaped and is usually sessile. (Chap. 12, Sec. 2, p. 343)

population: all the organisms that belong to the same species living in a community. (Chap. 24, Sec. 1, p. 694)

postanal tail: muscular structure at the end of a developing chordate. (Chap. 14, Sec. 1, p. 398)

preening: process in which a bird rubs oil from an oil gland over its feathers to condition them and make them water repellent. (Chap. 15, Sec. 1, p. 434)

pregnancy: period of development—usually about 38 or 39 weeks in humans—from fertilized egg until birth. (Chap. 22, Sec. 3, p. 640)

primates: group of mammals including humans, monkeys, and apes that share characteristics such as opposable thumbs, binocular vision, and flexible shoulders. (Chap. 6, Sec. 3, p. 170)

producer: organism, such as a green plant or alga, that uses an outside source of energy like the Sun to create energy-rich food molecules. (Chap. 24, Sec. 3, p. 704)

protein: nutrient made up of amino acids that is used by the body for growth and for replacement and repair of body cells. (Chap. 18, Sec. 1, p. 519)

prothallus (proh THA lus): small, green, heart-shaped gametophyte plant form of a fern that can make its own food and absorb water and nutrients from the soil. (Chap. 10, Sec. 2, p. 280)

protist: one- or many-celled eukaryotic organism that can be plantlike, animal-like, or funguslike. (Chap. 8, Sec. 1, p. 212)

protozoan: one-celled, animal-like protist that can live in water, soil, and living and dead organisms. (Chap. 8, Sec. 1, p. 217)

pseudopods (SEWD uh pahdz): temporary cytoplasmic extensions used by some protists to move about and trap food. (Chap. 8, Sec. 1, p. 218)

pulmonary circulation: flow of blood through the heart to the lungs and back to the heart. (Chap. 19, Sec. 1, p. 548)

punctuated equilibrium: model describing the rapid evolution that occurs when mutation of a few genes results in a species suddenly changing into a new species. (Chap. 6, Sec. 1, p. 160)

Punnett (PUN ut) **square:** a tool to predict the probability of certain traits in offspring that shows the different ways alleles can combine. (Chap. 5, Sec. 1, p. 130)

R

radial symmetry: body parts arranged in a circle around a central point. (Chap. 12, Sec. 1, p. 339)

radioactive element: element that gives off a steady amount of radiation as it slowly changes to a nonradioactive element. (Chap. 6, Sec. 2, p. 165)

radula (RA juh luh): in gastropods, the tonguelike organ with rows of teeth used to scrape and tear food. (Chap. 13, Sec. 1, p. 365)

recessive (rih SES ihv): describes a trait that is covered over, or dominated, by another form of that trait and seems to disappear. (Chap. 5, Sec. 1, p. 129)

recycling: conservation method that is a form of reuse and requires changing or reprocessing an item or natural resource. (Chap. 27, Sec. 3, p. 797)

reflex: simple innate behavior, such as yawning or blinking, that is an automatic response and does not involve a message to the brain. (Chap. 16, Sec. 1, p. 461) (Chap. 21, Sec. 1, p. 607)

renewable resources: natural resources, such as water, sunlight, and crops, that are constantly being recycled or replaced by nature. (Chap. 27, Sec. 1, p. 778)

respiration: series of chemical reactions used to release energy stored in food molecules. (Chap. 3, Sec. 3, p. 83) (Chap. 11, Sec. 1, p. 309)

retina: light-sensitive tissue at the back of the eye; contains rods and cones. (Chap. 21, Sec. 2, p. 611)

rhizoids (RI zoydz): threadlike structures that anchor nonvascular plants to the ground. (Chap. 9, Sec. 2, p. 248)

rhizome: underground stem of a fern. (Chap. 10, Sec. 2, p. 280)

ribosome: small structure on which cells make their own proteins. (Chap. 2, Sec. 1, p. 42)

RNA: ribonucleic acid, which carries codes for making proteins from the nucleus to the ribosomes. (Chap. 4, Sec. 3, p. 112)

S

saprophyte: organism that feeds on dead or decaying tissues of other organisms. (Chap. 7, Sec. 2, p. 196) (Chap. 8, Sec. 2, p. 224)

scales: thin, hard plates that cover a fish's skin and protect its body. (Chap. 14, Sec. 2, p. 403)

scientific method: problem-solving techniques used to investigate observations that can be made about living and nonliving things; may include stating a problem, gathering information, forming and testing a hypothesis, analyzing data, and drawing conclusions. (Chap 1, Sec. 1, p. 7)

sedimentary rock: a type of rock, such as limestone, that is most likely to contain fossils and is formed when layers of sand, silt, clay, or mud are cemented and compacted together or when minerals are deposited from a solution. (Chap. 6, Sec. 2, p. 164)

semen (SEE mun): mixture of sperm and a fluid that helps sperm move and supplies them with an energy source. (Chap. 22, Sec. 2, p. 634)

sessile (SE sile): describes an organism that remains attached to one place during its lifetime. (Chap. 12, Sec. 2, p. 341)

setae (SEE tee): bristlelike structures on the outside of each body segment that helps segmented worms move. (Chap. 13, Sec. 2, p. 369)

sex-linked gene: an allele inherited on a sex chromosome; can cause human genetic disorders such as color blindness and hemophilia. (Chap. 5, Sec. 2, p. 139)

sexual reproduction: a type of reproduction in which two sex cells, usually an egg and a sperm, join to form a zygote, which will develop into a new organism with a unique identity. (Chap. 4, Sec. 2, p. 104)

sexually transmitted disease (STD): infectious disease, such as chlamydia, AIDS, or genital herpes, that is passed from one person to another during sexual contact. (Chap. 23, Sec. 2, p. 668)

short-day plant: plant that generally requires long nights—12 or more hours of darkness—to begin the flowering process. (Chap. 11, Sec. 2, p. 318)

skeletal muscle: voluntary, striated muscle that moves bones, works in pairs, and is attached to bones by tendons. (Chap. 17, Sec. 2, p. 499)

skeletal system: all the bones in the body; forms an internal, living framework that provides shape and support, protects internal organs, moves bones, forms blood cells, and stores calcium and phosphorus compounds for later use. (Chap. 17, Sec. 1, p. 490)

smooth muscle: involuntary, nonstriated muscle that controls movement of internal organs. (Chap. 17, Sec. 2, p. 499)

social behavior: interactions among members of the same species, including courtship and mating, getting food, caring for young, and protecting each other. (Chap. 16, Sec. 2, p. 466)

society: a group of animals of the same species that live and work together in an organized way, with each member doing a specific job. (Chap. 16, Sec. 2, p. 467)

soil: mixture of mineral and rock particles, the remains of dead organisms, air, and water that forms the topmost layer of Earth's crust and supports plant growth. (Chap. 25, Sec. 1, p. 722)

sori: fern structures in which spores are produced. (Chap. 10, Sec. 2, p. 280)

species: group of organisms that share similar characteristics and can reproduce among themselves. (Chap. 6, Sec. 1, p. 154)

sperm: haploid sex cells formed in the male reproductive organs. (Chap. 4, Sec. 2, p. 104) (Chap. 22, Sec. 2, p. 634)

spiracles (SPIHR ih kulz): openings in the abdomen and thorax of insects through which air enters and waste gases leave. (Chap. 13, Sec. 3, p. 375)

spontaneous generation: theory that living things can come from nonliving things. (Chap. 1, Sec. 3, p. 19)

sporangium (spuh RAN jee uhm): round spore case of a zygote fungus. (Chap. 8, Sec. 2, p. 227)

spore: waterproof reproductive cell of a fungus. (Chap. 8, Sec. 2, p. 225)

spores: haploid cells produced in the gametophyte stage of a plant that can divide by mitosis and form structures or an entire new plant or can develop into sex cells. (Chap. 10, Sec. 1, p. 277)

sporophyte (SPOR uh fite) **stage:** plant life cycle stage that begins when an egg is fertilized by a sperm. (Chap. 10, Sec. 1, p. 277)

stamen: male reproductive organ inside the flower of an angiosperm; consists of an anther, where pollen grains form, and a filament. (Chap. 10, Sec. 3, p. 287)

stinging cells: capsules with coiled triggerlike structures that help cnidarians capture food. (Chap. 12, Sec. 2, p. 344)

stomata (STOH muh tuh): small openings in the surface of most plant leaves that allow carbon dioxide, water, and oxygen to enter and exit. (Chap. 9, Sec. 3, p. 255) (Chap. 11, Sec, 1, p. 305)

succession: natural, gradual changes in the types of species that live in an area; can be primary or secondary. (Chap. 26, Sec. 1, p. 748)

symbiosis: any close relationship between species, including mutualism, commensalism, and parasitism. (Chap. 24, Sec. 3, p. 706)

synapse (SIHN aps): small space across which an impulse moves from an axon to the dendrites or cell body of another neuron. (Chap. 21, Sec. 1, p. 603)

systemic circulation: largest part of the circulatory system in which oxygen-rich blood flows to all the organs and body tissues, except the heart and lungs, and oxygen-poor blood is returned to the heart. (Chap. 19, Sec. 1, p. 549)

T

taiga (TI guh): world's largest biome, located south of the tundra between 50° N and 60° N latitude; has long, cold winters, precipitation between 35 cm and 100 cm each year, cone-bearing evergreen trees, and dense forests. (Chap. 26, Sec. 2, p. 754)

taste bud: major sensory receptor on the tongue; contains taste hairs that send impulses to the brain for interpretation of tastes. (Chap. 21, Sec. 2, p. 616)

temperate deciduous forest: biome usually having four distinct seasons, annual precipitation between 75 cm and 150 cm, and climax communities of deciduous trees. (Chap. 26, Sec. 2, p. 755)

temperate rain forest: biome with 200 cm to 400 cm of precipitation each year, average temperatures between 9°C and 12°C, and forests dominated by trees with needlelike leaves. (Chap. 26, Sec. 2, p. 755)

tendon: thick band of tissue that attaches bones to muscles. (Chap. 17, Sec. 2, p. 499)

tentacles (TEN tih kulz): armlike structures that have stinging cells and surround the mouths of most cnidarians. (Chap. 12, Sec. 2, p. 344)

testis: male organ that produces sperm and testosterone. (Chap. 22, Sec. 2, p. 634)

theory: an explanation of events or things based on scientific knowledge resulting from repeated observations and tests. (Chap. 1, Sec. 1, p. 10)

tissue: group of similar cells that work together to do one job. (Chap. 2, Sec. 1, p. 45)

toxin: poisonous substance produced by some pathogens. (Chap. 7, Sec. 2, p. 199)

trachea (TRAY kee uh): air-conducting tube that connects the larynx with the bronchi, is lined with mucous membranes and cilia, and contains strong cartilage rings. (Chap. 20, Sec. 1, p. 577)

tropical rain forest: most biologically diverse biome; has an average temperature of 25°C and receives between 200 cm and 600 cm of precipitation each year. (Chap. 26, Sec. 2, p. 756)

tropism: positive or negative plant response to an external stimulus such as touch, light, or gravity. (Chap. 11, Sec. 2, p. 314)

tube feet: hydraulic, hollow, thin-walled tubes that end in suction cups and enable echinoderms to move. (Chap. 13, Sec. 4, p. 384)

tundra: cold, dry, treeless biome with less than 25 cm of precipitation each year, a short growing season, permafrost, and winters that can be six to nine months long. (Chap. 26, Sec. 2, p. 753)

U

umbilical cord: connects the embryo to the placenta; moves food and oxygen from the placenta to the embryo and removes the embryo's waste products. (Chap. 15, Sec. 2, p. 445)

ureter: tube that carries urine from each kidney to the bladder. (Chap. 20, Sec. 2, p. 586)

urethra (yoo REE thruh): tube that carries urine from the bladder to the outside of the body. (Chap. 20, Sec. 2, p. 586)

urinary system: system of excretory organs that rids the blood of wastes, controls blood volume by removing excess water, and balances concentrations of salts and water. (Chap. 20, Sec. 2, p. 583)

urine: wastewater that contains excess water, salts, and other wastes that are not reabsorbed by the body. (Chap. 20, Sec. 2, p. 584)

uterus: hollow, muscular, pear-shaped organ where a fertilized egg develops into a baby. (Chap. 22, Sec. 2, p. 635)

V

vaccination: process of giving a vaccine by mouth or by injection to provide active immunity against a disease. (Chap. 23, Sec. 1, p. 661)

vaccine: preparation made from killed bacteria or damaged particles from bacterial cell walls that can prevent some bacterial diseases. (Chap. 7, Sec. 2, p. 201)

vagina (vuh JI nuh): muscular tube that connects the lower end of the uterus to the outside of the body; the birth canal through which a baby travels when being born. (Chap. 22, Sec. 2, p. 635)

variable: in an experiment, the one thing that can change. (Chap. 1, Sec. 1, p. 9)

variation: inherited trait that makes an individual different from other members of the same species and results from a mutation in the organism's genes. (Chap. 6, Sec. 1, p. 158)

vascular plant: plant with tubelike structures that move minerals, water, and other substances throughout the plant. (Chap. 9, Sec. 1, p. 247)

vein: blood vessel that carries blood back to the heart and has one-way valves that keep blood moving toward the heart. (Chap. 19, Sec. 1, p. 550)

ventricles (VEN trih kulz): two lower chambers of the heart that contract at the same time during a heartbeat. (Chap. 19, Sec. 1, p. 547)

vertebrae: backbones that are joined by flexible cartilage and protect a vertebrate's spinal nerve cord. (Chap. 14, Sec. 1, p. 399)

vertebrate: animal with a backbone. (Chap. 12, Sec. 1, p. 338)

vestigial (veh STIHJ ee ul) **structure:** structure, such as the human appendix, that doesn't seem to have a function and may once have functioned in the body of an ancestor. (Chap. 6, Sec. 2, p. 168)

villi (VIHL I): fingerlike projections covering the wall of the small intestine that increase the surface area for food absorption. (Chap. 18, Sec. 2, p. 534)

virus: extremely tiny piece of genetic material that infects and multiplies in host cells; surrounded by a protein coating. (Chap. 2, Sec. 3, p. 52) (Chap. 23, Sec. 2, p. 664)

vitamin: water-soluble or fat-soluble organic nutrient needed in small quantities for growth, for preventing some diseases, and for regulating body functions. (Chap. 18, Sec. 1, p. 522)

voluntary muscle: muscle, such as a leg or arm muscle, that can be consciously controlled. (Chap. 17, Sec. 2, p. 497)

W

water cycle: model describing how water moves from Earth's surface to the atmosphere and back to the surface again through evaporation, condensation, and precipitation. (Chap. 25, Sec. 2, p. 729)

water-vascular system: network of water-filled canals that allows echinoderms to move, capture food, give off wastes, and exchange carbon dioxide and oxygen. (Chap. 13, Sec. 4, p. 384)

wetland: a region that is wet most or all of the year. (Chap. 26, Sec. 3, p. 763)

X

xylem (ZI lum): vascular tissue that forms hollow vessels that transport substances, other than sugar, throughout a plant. (Chap. 9, Sec. 3, p. 257)

Z

zygote: new diploid cell formed when a sperm fertilizes an egg; will divide by mitosis and develop into a new organism. (Chap. 4, Sec. 2, p. 104)

Este glossario define cada término clave que aparece en negrillas en el texto. También muestra el capítulo, la sección y el número de página en donde se usa dicho término.

A

abiotic / abióticos: factores físicos inanimados del medio ambiente que incluyen el aire, el agua, la luz solar, el suelo, la temperatura y el clima. (Cap. 25, Sec. 1, pág. 720)

acid precipitation / precipitación ácida: precipitación con un pH menor de 5.6 (la cual ocurre cuando los contaminantes del aire, provenientes de la quema de combustibles fósiles, reaccionan con el agua de la atmósfera para formar ácidos fuertes) capaz de contaminar el agua, acabar con peces y plantas y perjudicar los suelos. (Cap. 27, Sec. 2, pág. 787)

active immunity / inmunidad activa: inmunidad duradera que resulta cuando el cuerpo produce sus propios anticuerpos como reacción a un antígeno específico. (Cap. 23, Sec. 1, pág. 661)

active transport / transporte activo: proceso que requiere energía en el cual las proteínas de transporte se enlazan con partículas y se mueven a través de la membrana celular. (Cap. 3, Sec. 2, pág. 77)

adaptation / adaptación: toda variación que le permite a un organismo adaptarse mejor a su ambiente. (Cap. 6, Sec. 1, pág. 158)

aerobe / aerobio: cualquier organismo que usa oxígeno para la respiración. (Cap. 7, Sec. 1, pág. 190)

aggression / agresión: comportamiento enérgico, como las peleas, que usa un animal para controlar o dominar a otro animal con el propósito de proteger sus crías, defender su territorio u obtener alimento. (Cap. 16, Sec. 2, pág. 468)

algae / algas: protistas que parecen plantas que producen oxígeno mediante la fotosíntesis. (Cap. 8, Sec. 1, pág. 213)

allele / alelo: formas alternas que un gene puede tener para un sólo rasgo; puede ser dominante o recesivo. (Cap. 5, Sec. 1, pág. 126)

allergen / alérgeno: sustancia que provoca una reacción alérgica. (Cap. 23, Sec. 3, pág. 673)

allergy / alergia: reacción hipersensible del sistema inmunológico frente a una sustancia extraña. (Cap. 23, Sec. 3, pág. 672)

alveoli / alvéolos: racimos minúsculos de paredes finas que se hallan en el extremo de cada bronquiolo y que están rodeados de capilares, donde se lleva a cabo el intercambio de dióxido de carbono y oxígeno. (Cap. 20, Sec. 1, pág. 577)

amino acid / aminoácidos: elemento constitutivo de una proteína. (Cap. 18, Sec. 1, pág. 519)

amniotic egg / huevo amniótico: huevo cubierto por una concha correosa que provee un ambiente completo para el desarrollo del embrión; para los reptiles es una adaptación importante para la vida en tierra. (Cap. 14, Sec. 4, pág. 417)

amniotic sac / saco amniótico: membrana protectora, delgada y llena de líquido, que se forma alrededor del embrión. (Cap. 22, Sec. 3, pág. 641)

anaerobe / anaerobio: cualquier organismo que puede vivir sin oxígeno. (Cap. 7, Sec. 1, pág. 190)

angiosperms / angiospermas: plantas vasculares con flores que produce un fruto que contiene una o más semillas; monocotiledóneas y dicotiledóneas. (Cap. 9, Sec. 3, pág. 259)

antibiotics / antibióticos: sustancias químicas producidas por algunas bacterias que se usan para limitar el crecimiento de otras bacterias. (Cap. 7, Sec. 2, pág. 195)

antibody / anticuerpo: proteína que se produce como respuesta a un antígeno específico; se puede adherir al antígeno y lo puede anular. (Cap. 23, Sec. 1, pág. 660)

antigen / antígeno: molécula compleja extraña al cuerpo. (Cap. 23, Sec. 1, pág. 660)

anus / ano: abertura al final del tracto digestivo por donde se expulsan los desechos del cuerpo. (Cap. 12, Sec. 3, pág. 351)

appendages / apéndices: estructuras adjuntas de los artrópodos, como piernas, alas o antenas. (Cap. 13, Sec. 3, pág. 374)

artery / arteria: vaso sanguíneo que saca sangre del corazón y que tiene gruesas paredes elásticas hechas de tejido conectivo y tejido de músculo liso. (Cap. 19, Sec. 1, pág. 550)

ascus / asco: estructura productora de esporas, en forma de saco, en los hongos ascomicetos. (Cap. 8, Sec. 2, pág. 226)

asexual reproduction / reproducción asexual: tipo de reproducción que comprende la fisión, gemación y regeneración, en el cual un progenitor produce un nuevo organismo que tiene DNA idéntico al organismo progenitor. (Cap. 4, Sec. 1, pág. 101)

asthma / asma: trastorno pulmonar en el cual los tubos bronquiales se contraen rápidamente y dificultan la respiración y causan estornudo o tos; puede ocurrir como una reacción alérgica. (Cap. 20, Sec. 1, pág. 582)

atmosphere / atmósfera: el aire que rodea la Tierra; está compuesta por gases, entre los cuales se incluye un 78 por ciento de nitrógeno, un 21 por ciento de oxígeno y 0.03 por ciento de dióxido de carbono. (Cap. 25, Sec. 1, pág. 721)

atriums / atrios: las dos cavidades superiores del corazón que se contraen al mismo tiempo durante un latido del corazón. (Cap. 19, Sec. 1, pág. 547)

auxin / auxina: hormona vegetal gracias a la cual las hojas y tallos de las plantas exhiben fototropismos positivos. (Cap. 11, Sec. 2, pág. 316)

axon / axón: estructura de la neurona que transmite mensajes de las células corporales. (Cap. 21, Sec. 1, pág. 601)

B

basidium / basidio: estructura reproductora en forma de bastón, en la cual los hongos producen esporas. (Cap. 8, Sec. 2, pág. 226)

behavior / comportamiento: la interacción de un organismo con otro organismo y su ambiente; puede ser innato o adquirido. (Cap. 16, Sec. 1, pág. 460)

bilateral symmetry / simetría bilateral: partes corporales distribuidas de manera semejante en ambos lados del cuerpo, de tal forma que cada mitad es un reflejo exacto de la otra mitad. (Cap. 12, Sec. 1, pág. 339)

binomial nomenclature / nomenclatura binaria: sistema para nombrar organismos basado en dos palabras, la primera palabra indica el género y la segunda palabra la especie. (Cap. 1, Sec. 4, pág. 20)

biogenesis / biogénesis: teoría que establece que todo ser vivo proviene de otros seres vivos. (Cap. 1, Sec. 3, pág. 19)

biological vector / vector biológico: organismo portador de enfermedad, como por ejemplo, una rata, un mosquito o una mosca, que propaga enfermedades contagiosas. (Cap. 23, Sec. 2, pág. 667)

biomes / biomas: áreas geográficas extensas con climas y ecosistemas similares; incluye la tundra, la taiga, el desierto, los bosques caducifolios de zonas templadas, los bosques pluviales de zonas templadas, los bosques pluviales tropicales y las praderas. (Cap. 26, Sec. 2, pág. 752)

biosphere / biosfera: parte de la Tierra que sostiene la vida; incluye la parte superior de la corteza terrestre, la atmósfera y toda el agua sobre la superficie de la Tierra. (Cap. 24, Sec. 1, pág. 692)

biotic / bióticos: factores del medio ambiente que son seres vivos o que una vez estuvieron vivos. (Cap. 25, Sec. 1, pág. 720)

bladder / vejiga: órgano elástico y muscular que retiene la orina hasta que ésta sale del cuerpo por la uretra. (Cap. 20, Sec. 2, pág. 586)

brain stem / bulbo raquídeo: conecta el encéfalo a la médula espinal y está compuesto del encéfalo medio, el puente de Varolio y la médula. (Cap. 21, Sec. 1, pág. 604)

bronchi / bronquios: dos conductos cortos que se bifurcan del extremo inferior de la tráquea y por los cuales se introduce el aire en los pulmones. (Cap. 20, Sec. 1, pág. 577)

budding / gemación: forma de reproducción sexual en que un organismo nuevo y genéticamente idéntico crece de un lado del organismo progenitor . (Cap. 8, Sec. 2, pág. 226)

C

cambium / cámbium: tejido vascular que produce células de xilema y floema a medida que crece la planta. (Cap. 9, Sec. 3, pág. 257)

capillary / capilar: vaso sanguíneo microscópico que conecta las arterias y las venas; tiene paredes de una célula de grosor, a través de las cuales se difunden los nutrientes y el oxígeno por todas las células corporales y se extraen los materiales de desecho y el dióxido de carbono. (Cap. 19, Sec. 1, pág. 551)

carbohydrate / carbohidrato: nutriente que por lo general es la fuente principal de energía para el cuerpo. (Cap. 18, Sec. 1, pág. 520)

carbon cycle / ciclo del carbono: modelo que describe cómo las células del carbono se movilizan entre el mundo vivo y el inanimado. (Cap. 25, Sec. 2, pág. 733)

cardiac muscle / músculo cardíaco: músculo involuntario y estriado que sólo se encuentra en el corazón. (Cap. 17, Sec. 2, pág. 499)

carnivore / carnívoro: animal que sólo se alimenta de otros animales o de los restos de otros animales. (Cap. 12, Sec. 1, pág. 335; Cap. 15, Sec. 2, pág. 441)

carrying capacity / capacidad de carga: el número mayor de individuos de una especie en particular que puede mantener un ecosistema de manera prolongada. (Cap. 24, Sec. 2, pág. 699)

cartilage / cartílago: tejido flexible y duro que une las vértebras y que compone todo o parte del endoesqueleto vertebrado. (Cap. 14, Sec. 1, pág. 399; Cap. 17, Sec. 1, pág. 492)

cell / célula: unidad básica de los seres vivos que puede realizar las funciones vitales; tiene una estructura ordenada y contiene material hereditario (Cap. 1, Sec. 2, pág. 10)

cell membrane / membrana celular: cubierta externa protectora de todas las células; formada por una capa doble de moléculas adiposas y controla la interacción entre la célula y el medio ambiente. (Cap. 2, Sec. 1, pág. 38)

cell theory / teoría celular: establece que todos los organismos están formados por una o más células, la célula es la unidad básica de la vida y todas las células provienen de otras células. (Cap. 2, Sec. 2, pág. 51)

Spanish Glossary

cellulose / celulosa: compuesto químico hecho de azúcares; forma fibras enredadas en las paredes celulares de muchas plantas y provee estructura y apoyo. (Cap. 9, Sec. 1, pág. 244)

cell wall / pared celular: estructura rígida que encierra, sostiene y protege las células vegetales, las células de las algas, de los hongos y de la mayoría de las bacterias. (Cap. 2, Sec. 1, pág. 39)

central nervous system / sistema nervioso central: división del sistema nervioso central, compuesta del encéfalo y la médula espinal. (Cap. 21, Sec. 1, pág. 603)

cerebellum / cerebelo: parte del encéfalo que controla los movimientos de los músculos voluntarios, mantienen el tono muscular y ayuda a mantener el equilibrio. (Cap. 21, Sec. 1, pág. 604)

cerebrum / cerebro: la parte más grande del encéfalo, donde se almacena la memoria, se controlan los movimientos y se interpretan los impulsos de los sentidos. (Cap. 21, Sec. 1, pág. 604)

chemical digestion / digestión química: ocurre cuando las enzimas y otras sustancias químicas rompen las moléculas grandes de alimento. (Cap. 18, Sec. 2, pág. 529)

chemosynthesis / quimiosíntesis: proceso en el cual los productores elaboran moléculas nutritivas ricas en energía a partir de sustancias químicas. (Cap. 25, Sec. 3, pág. 735)

chemotherapy / quimioterapia: uso de sustancias químicas para destruir células cancerosas. (Cap. 23, Sec. 3, pág. 676)

chlorophyll / clorofila: pigmento verde y absorbente de luz, fijado a los cloroplastos de las plantas y que es importante en el proceso de la fotosíntesis. (Cap. 11, Sec. 1, pág. 306)

chloroplast / cloroplasto: organelo de las células vegetales, de color verde y que contiene clorofila, que convierte la luz solar, el dióxido de carbono y el agua en azúcar. (Cap. 2, Sec. 1, pág. 42)

chordate / cordado: animal que posee un notocordio, un cordón nervioso, hendiduras branquiales y una cola en alguna etapa de su desarrollo. (Cap. 14, Sec. 1, pág. 398)

chromosome / cromosoma: estructura en el núcleo de una célula que contiene el material genético. (Cap. 4, Sec. 1, pág. 98)

chyme / quimo: producto líquido de la digestión. (Cap. 18, Sec. 2, pág. 533)

cilia / cilios: estructuras cortas filamentosas que se extienden de la membrana celular de un ciliado y las cuales le permiten moverse rápidamente. (Cap. 8, Sec. 1, pág. 217)

climate / clima: condiciones meteorológicas promedio de una región durante un período de tiempo, entre las cuales se incluyen el viento, la temperatura y la precipitación pluvial u otro tipo de precipitación como la nieve o la cellisca. (Cap. 25, Sec. 1, pág. 725)

climax community / comunidad clímax: etapa final estable de la sucesión ecológica, en que las plantas y los animales de una comunidad usan eficientemente los recursos y en la cual se mantiene el equilibrio mediante perturbaciones como los incendios. (Cap. 26, Sec. 1, pág. 751)

closed circulatory system /sistema circulatorio cerrado: sistema de circulación en que la sangre se mueve a través del cuerpo en vasos cerrados. (Cap. 13, Sec. 1, pág. 366)

cochlea / cóclea: estructura llena de fluido en el oído interno en donde las vibraciones sonoras se convierten en impulsos nerviosos que son enviados al encéfalo. (Cap. 21, Sec. 2, pág. 614)

commensalism / comensalismo: tipo de relación simbiótica en el cual un organismo se beneficia y el otro organismo no se ve afectado. (Cap. 24, Sec. 3, pág. 706)

community / comunidad: todas las poblaciones de diferentes especies que viven en un ecosistema. (Cap. 24, Sec. 1, pág. 694)

condensation / condensación: proceso que se efectúa cuando un gas se convierte en un líquido. (Cap. 25, Sec. 2, pág. 729)

conditioning / condicionamiento: ocurre cuando la respuesta a un estímulo se asocia con otro estímulo. (Cap. 16, Sec. 1, pág. 464)

consumer / consumidor: organismo que no puede fabricar moléculas ricas en energía, sino que obtiene su alimento al alimentarse de otros organismos. (Cap. 24, Sec. 3, pág. 705)

contour feathers / plumas de contorno: plumas livianas y fuertes que dan a las aves sus coloridos y formas y que se usan para el vuelo. (Cap. 15, Sec. 1, pág. 434)

control / control: el estándar que sirve para comparar los resultados obtenidos en un experimento. (Cap. 1, Sec. 1, pág. 9)

coral reef / arrecife de coral: ecosistema diverso formado de las conchas de carbonato de calcio secretadas por los corales. (Cap. 26, Sec. 3, pág. 765)

coronary circulation / circulación coronaria: flujo sanguíneo hacia los tejidos del corazón y fuera de éstos. (Cap. 19, Sec. 1, pág. 547)

courtship behavior / comportamiento de cortejo: comportamiento que permite que machos y hembras de una especie se reconozcan mutuamente y se preparen para el apareo. (Cap. 16, Sec. 2, pág. 469)

crop / buche: saco del sistema digestivo en el cual almacenan la tierra las lombrices de tierra. (Cap. 13, Sec. 2, pág. 370)

cuticle / cutícula: capa protectora y cerosa que cubre los tallos, hojas y flores de muchas plantas y que les ayuda a prevenir la pérdida de agua. (Cap. 9, Sec. 1, pág. 244)

cyclic behavior / comportamiento cíclico: comportamiento que ocurre en forma de patrones repetidos. (Cap. 16, Sec. 2, pág. 472)

cytoplasm / citoplasma: mezcla gelatinosa en continuo movimiento dentro de la membrana celular que contiene material hereditario y en la cual se lleva a cabo la mayoría de los procesos de una célula. (Cap. 2, Sec. 1, pág. 38)

D

day-neutral plant / planta de día neutro: planta que no necesita un fotoperíodo específico y que puede comenzar el proceso de floración a lo largo de un rango de períodos nocturnos. (Cap. 11, Sec. 2, pág. 318)

dendrite / dendrita: estructura de la neurona que recibe mensajes y los envía a las células corporales. (Cap. 21, Sec. 1, pág. 601)

dermis / dermis: capa de la piel debajo de la epidermis que contiene vasos sanguíneos, nervios, glándulas sudoríparas y sebáceas y otras estructuras. (Cap. 17, Sec. 3, pág. 503)

desert / desierto: el bioma más seco de la Tierra, con menos de 25 cm de lluvia anual; tiene dunas o suelo delgado con poca materia orgánica, y plantas y animales especialmente adaptados para sobrevivir condiciones extremas. (Cap. 26, Sec. 2, pág. 758)

diaphragm / diafragma: músculo situado debajo de los pulmones que se contrae y se relaja permitiendo así la entrada y salida de gases del cuerpo. (Cap. 20, Sec. 1, pág. 578)

dicot / dicotinedónea: angiosperma con dos cotiledones dentro de la semilla, partes florales en múltiples de cuatro u cinco y bultos vasculares en forma de anillos. (Cap. 9, Sec. 3, pág. 260)

diffusion / difusión: tipo de transporte pasivo celular en el que las moléculas se mueven desde áreas de mayor concentración a áreas de menor concentración. (Cap. 3, Sec. 2, pág. 75)

digestion / digestión: descomposición mecánica y química de los alimentos, de manera que las células lo puedan absorber y usar. (Cap. 18, Sec. 2, pág. 529)

diploid / diploide: célula cuyos cromosomas se dan en pares. (Cap. 4, Sec. 2, pág. 104)

DNA / DNA: ácido desoxirribonucleico; material genético de todos los organismos y compuesto de dos hebras retorcidas de moléculas de fosfato de azúcar y bases nitrogenadas. (Cap. 4, Sec. 3, pág. 110)

dominant / dominante: describe un rasgo que cubre o domina otra forma de dicho rasgo. (Cap. 5, Sec. 1, pág. 128)

down feathers / plumones: plumas esponjosas y suaves que proveen una capa de aislamiento cerca de la piel de las aves adultas y que cubren los cuerpos de las aves jóvenes. (Cap. 15, Sec. 1, pág. 434)

E

ecology / ecología: estudio de las interacciones que se llevan a cabo entre los organismos y su ambiente. (Cap. 24, Sec. 1, pág. 693)

ecosystem / ecosistema: todos los organismos vivos que habitan en un área y las cosas inanimadas en su ambiente. (Cap. 24, Sec. 1, pág. 693)

ectotherm / de sangre fría: animal vertebrado cuya temperatura interna cambia con los cambios en temperatura de su ambiente. (Cap. 14, Sec. 1, pág. 401)

egg / óvulo: célula haploide formada en los órganos reproductores femeninos. (Cap. 4, Sec. 2, pág. 104)

embryo / embrión: óvulo fecundado adherido a la pared uterina. (Cap. 22, Sec. 3, pág. 641)

embryology / embriología: estudio de los embriones y su desarrollo. (Cap. 6, Sec. 2, pág. 167)

emphysema / enfisema: enfermedad pulmonar en la cual se produce una dilatación de los alvéolos. (Cap. 20, Sec. 1, pág. 581)

endocytosis / endocitosis: proceso que permite que una célula deje pasar una sustancia al rodearla con la membrana celular. (Cap. 3, Sec. 2, pág. 78)

endoplasmic reticulum (ER) / retículo endoplásmico (RE): organelo citoplásmico que mueve materiales dentro de una célula y que está formado por una serie compleja de membranas plegadas; puede ser áspero (con ribosomas adheridos) o liso (sin ribosomas adheridos). (Cap. 2, Sec. 1, pág. 43)

endoskeleton / endoesqueleto: marco de apoyo para huesos y cartílago que provee un lugar interno para la adhesión de los músculos y protege los órganos internos de los vertebrados. (Cap. 14, Sec. 1, pág. 399)

endospore / endósporas: estructuras protectoras de paredes gruesas que producen los patógenos cuando las condiciones son desfavorables para la sobrevivencia. (Cap. 7, Sec. 2, pág. 199)

endotherm / de sangre caliente: animal vertebrado con una temperatura corporal interna constante. (Cap. 14, Sec. 1, pág. 401)

energy pyramid / pirámide de energía: modelo que muestra la cantidad de energía disponible en cada nivel alimenticio de un ecosistema. (Cap. 25, Sec. 3, pág. 737)

enzyme / enzima: tipo de proteína que regula casi todas las reacciones químicas de las células. (Cap. 3, Sec. 1, pág. 71; Cap. 18, Sec. 2, pág. 530)

epidermis / epidermis: capa exterior de la piel y la más delgada, la cual produce constantemente nuevas células para reemplazar las células viejas que se desprenden de su superficie. (Cap. 17, Sec. 3, pág. 502)

equilibrium / equilibrio: ocurre cuando las moléculas de una sustancia se esparcen uniformemente en otra sustancia. (Cap. 3, Sec. 2, pág. 75)

erosion / erosión: movimiento del suelo de un lugar a otro. (Cap. 27, Sec. 2, pág. 793)

estivation / estivación: inactividad en los meses calurosos y secos durante los cuales los anfibios se esconden dentro del suelo que está más fresco. (Cap. 14, Sec. 3, pág. 411)

estuary / estuario: área extremadamente fértil donde un río desemboca en un océano; contiene una mezcla de agua dulce y agua salada y sirve de vivero para muchas especies de peces. (Cap. 26, Sec. 3, pág. 766)

evaporation / evaporación: proceso que se lleva a cabo cuando un líquido se convierte en un gas. (Cap. 25, Sec. 2, pág. 728)

evolution / evolución: cambio, con el tiempo, en las características heredadas. (Cap. 6, Sec. 1, pág. 154)

exocytosis / exocitosis: proceso a través del cual las vesículas liberan sus contenidos fuera de la célula. (Cap. 3, Sec. 2, pág. 78)

exoskeleton / exoesqueleto: cubierta externa dura y gruesa que protege y da apoyo al cuerpo de los artrópodos, además de proveer un lugar para que se adhieran los músculos. (Cap. 13, Sec. 3, pág. 374)

F

fat / grasa: nutriente que almacena energía, acolchona los órganos y le facilita al cuerpo la absorción de las vitaminas. (Cap. 18, Sec. 1, pág. 521)

fermentation / fermentación: proceso en que las células carentes de oxígeno y algunos organismos unicelulares liberan pequeñas cantidades de energía de las moléculas de glucosa y producen desechos como el alcohol, el dióxido de carbono y el ácido láctico. (Cap. 3, Sec. 3, pág. 84)

fertilization / fecundación: en la reproducción sexual, la unión del espermatozoide y del óvulo. (Cap. 4, Sec. 2, pág. 104)

fetal stress / estrés fetal: puede presentarse durante el proceso de alumbramiento o después del nacimiento conforme el lactante se ajusta de un entorno acuoso, oscuro y de temperatura constante a su nuevo entorno. (Cap. 22, Sec. 3, pág. 644)

fetus / feto: bebé en desarrollo después de los primeros dos meses de embarazo hasta su nacimiento. (Cap. 22, Sec. 3, pág. 642)

fin / aleta: estructura en forma de abanico que usan los peces para cambiar de dirección, para el equilibrio y el movimiento. (Cap. 14, Sec. 2, pág. 403)

fission / fisión: la forma más sencilla de reproducción asexual en la cual se producen dos células nuevas con material genético idéntico al de la célula original. (Cap. 7, Sec. 1, pág. 190)

flagellum / flagelo: estructura larga y delgada en forma de látigo de algunos protistas que les facilita el movimiento a través de medios mojados o húmedos. (Cap. 7, Sec. 1, pág. 189; Cap. 8, Sec. 1, pág. 214)

food group / grupo de alimentos: grupo de alimentos que contienen el mismo tipo de nutrientes, como por ejemplo, el pan, el cereal, el arroz y los fideos. (Cap. 18, Sec. 1, pág. 526)

food web / red alimenticia: modelo que muestra las complejas relaciones alimenticias entre los organismos de una comunidad. (Cap. 25, Sec. 3, pág. 736)

fossil fuels / combustibles fósiles: recursos energéticos no renovables (carbón, petróleo y gas natural) que se formaron en la corteza terrestre durante un período de cientos de millones de años. (Cap. 27, Sec. 1, pág. 780)

free-living organism / organismo de vida libre: organismo que no depende de otro organismo para obtener alimento o un lugar para vivir. (Cap. 12, Sec. 3, pág. 348)

frond / fronda: hoja de helecho que crece desde el rizoma. (Cap. 10, Sec. 2, pág. 280)

G

gametophyte stage / etapa gametofita: etapa del ciclo de vida vegetal que comienza cuando las células de los órganos reproductores pasan por la meiosis y producen células haploides. (Cap. 10, Sec. 1, pág. 277)

gene / gene: sección de DNA en un cromosoma que contiene las instrucciones para la elaboración de proteínas específicas. (Cap. 4, Sec. 3, pág. 112)

genetic engineering / ingeniería genética: métodos biológicos y químicos que se usan para cambiar el arreglo del DNA de un gene con el propósito de mejorar la producción de cosechas, producir grandes volúmenes de medicamentos y cambiar el funcionamiento normal de células. (Cap. 5, Sec. 3, pág. 141)

genetics / genética: estudia la manera en que se heredan los rasgos a través de las acciones de los alelos. (Cap. 5, Sec. 1, pág. 126)

genotype / genotipo: la composición genética de un organismo. (Cap. 5, Sec. 1, pág. 130)

genus / género: grupo de especies similares. (Cap. 1, Sec. 4, pág. 24)

geothermal energy / energía geotérmica: energía calorífica en el interior de la corteza terrestre, disponible solamente cuando se localizan géiseres naturales o volcanes. (Cap. 27, Sec. 1, pág. 783)

germination / germinación: serie de eventos que dan como resultado el crecimiento de una planta a partir de una semilla. (Cap. 10, Sec. 3, pág. 292)

gestation period / período de gestación: período en que un embrión se desarrolla en el útero; el período de gestación varía según la especie. (Cap. 15, Sec. 2, pág. 445)

gills / branquias: órganos que intercambian el dióxido de carbono por oxígeno en el agua. (Cap. 13, Sec. 1, pág. 364)

gill slits / hendiduras branquiales: en los cordados en etapa de desarrollo, los pares de aberturas que se encuentran en el área entre la boca y el tubo digestivo. (Cap. 14, Sec. 1, pág. 399)

gizzard / molleja: estructura muscular del sistema digestivo en la cual la lombriz de tierra muele la tierra y la materia orgánica. (Cap. 13, Sec. 2, pág. 370)

Golgi bodies / cuerpos de Golgi: organelos que almacenan materiales celulares y los transportan dentro o fuera de la célula. (Cap. 2, Sec. 1, pág. 43)

gradualism / gradualismo: modelo que describe la evolución como un proceso lento mediante el cual una especie se transforma en otra especie, a través de una serie continua de mutaciones y variaciones que ocurren con el paso del tiempo. (Cap. 6, Sec. 1, pág. 160)

grasslands / praderas: regiones tropicales y de zonas templadas cuya precipitación anual varía de 25 a 75 cm; dominadas por comunidades clímax de pastos; ideales para el crecimiento de cosechas y el pastoreo del ganado vacuno y bovino. (Cap. 26, Sec. 2, pág. 759)

greenhouse effect / efecto invernadero: fenómeno de la atmósfera que atrapa el calor y que mantiene la Tierra con suficiente calor como para sostener la vida. (Cap. 27, Sec. 2, pág. 788)

guard cells / células guardianas: pares de células que rodean los estomas y controlan su apertura y cierre. (Cap. 9, Sec. 3, pág. 255)

gymnosperms / angiospermas: plantas vasculares que no florecen; generalmente tienen hojas en forma de agujas o de escamas y producen semillas que no están protegidas por el fruto; coníferas cicadáceas, ginkgoes y gnetofitas. (Cap. 9, Sec. 3, pág. 258)

H

habitat / hábitat: lugar en donde vive un organismo y que le provee los tipos de alimento, refugio, humedad y temperaturas necesarias para la sobrevivencia. (Cap. 24, Sec. 1, pág. 695)

haploid / haploide: célula que sólo tiene uno de cada tipo de cromosoma. (Cap. 4, Sec. 2, pág. 105)

hazardous wastes / residuos peligrosos: materiales de desecho, como los pesticidas y los restos de pintura, que son dañinos para la salud humana o venenosos para los organismos vivos. (Cap. 27, Sec. 2, pág. 794)

hemoglobin / hemoglobina: sustancia química en los glóbulos rojos que transporta oxígeno desde los pulmones hacia las células corporales y lleva parte del dióxido de carbono desde las células corporales, de regreso a los pulmones,. (Cap. 19, Sec. 2, pág. 557)

herbivore / herbívoro: animal que se alimenta solamente de plantas o partes de plantas. (Cap. 12, Sec. 1, pág. 335; Cap. 15, Sec. 2, pág. 441)

heredity / herencia: el traspaso de rasgos de los progenitores a la progenie. (Cap. 5, Sec. 1, pág. 126)

hermaphrodite / hermafrodita: animal que produce tanto espermatozoides como óvulos en el mismo cuerpo, pero cuyos espermatozoides no pueden fecundar sus propios óvulos. (Cap. 12, Sec. 2, pág. 342)

heterozygous / heterocigoto: describe al organismo que presenta dos alelos distintos para un rasgo. (Cap. 5, Sec. 1, pág. 130)

hibernation / hibernación: respuesta cíclica de inactividad y disminución del metabolismo, la cual ocurre durante períodos de temperaturas frías y abastecimientos limitados de alimentos. (Cap. 14, Sec. 3, pág. 411; Cap. 16, Sec. 2, pág. 473)

homeostasis / homeostasis: regulación de las condiciones internas de un organismo, las cuales lo mantienen vivo a pesar de los cambios en su ambiente. (Cap. 1, Sec. 2, pág. 15; Cap. 21, Sec. 1, pág. 601)

hominid / homínido: primate de aspecto humano que apareció entre hace 4 y 6 millones de años, se alimentaba de plantas y animales y caminaba derecho en dos piernas. (Cap. 6, Sec. 3, pág. 171)

homologous / homólogo: partes corporales semejantes en estructura y origen y que pueden ser semejantes en cuanto a su función. (Cap. 6, Sec. 2, pág. 168)

Homo sapiens / Homo sapiens: los primeros humanos que probablemente evolucionaron de los hombres de Cro-Magnon. (Cap. 6, Sec. 3, pág. 173)

homozygous / homocigoto: describe un organismo con dos alelos idénticos para el mismo rasgo. (Cap. 5, Sec. 1, pág. 131)

hormone / hormona: sustancia química que produce el sistema endocrino, se libera directamente en el torrente sanguíneo a través de glándulas sin conductos, actúa en tejidos asignados y puede acelerar o aminorar las actividades celulares. (Cap. 22, Sec. 1, pág. 628)

host cell / célula huésped: célula viva en la cual un virus se puede reproducir activamente o en la cual un virus puede ocultarse hasta que los estímulos ambientales lo activen. (Cap. 2, Sec. 3, pág. 52)

hybrid / híbrido: progenie que ha obtenido información genética distinta para un rasgo de cada progenitor. (Cap. 5, Sec. 1, pág. 128)

hydroelectric power / energía hidroeléctrica: electricidad producida cuando la fuerza hidráulica hace girar las aspas de una turbina generadora de electricidad. (Cap. 27, Sec. 1, pág. 781)

hyphae / hifa: masa de tubos multicelulares filamentosas que forman el cuerpo de un hongo. (Cap. 8, Sec. 2, pág. 224)

hypothesis / hipótesis: predicción que se puede poner a prueba. (Cap. 1, Sec. 1, pág. 8)

I

immune system / sistema inmunológico: grupo complejo de defensas que protege al cuerpo contra patógenos; este sistema incluye la piel y los sistemas respiratorio digestivo y circulatorio. (Cap. 23, Sec. 1, pág. 658)

imprinting / impronta: ocurre cuando un animal forma un vínculo social con otro organismo durante un período específico después del nacimiento o de salir del cascarón. (Cap. 16, Sec. 1, pág. 463)

incomplete dominance / dominancia incompleta: producción de un fenotipo intermedio al de los dos progenitores homocigotos. (Cap. 5, Sec. 2, pág. 134)

infectious disease / enfermedad contagiosa: enfermedad causada por un virus, una bacteria, un hongo o un protista y que se propaga de un organismo infectado o del medio ambiente a otro organismo. (Cap. 23, Sec. 2, pág. 667)

innate behavior / comportamiento innato: comportamiento con que nace un organismo y el cual no tiene que ser adquirido, como un reflejo o un instinto. (Cap. 16, Sec. 1, pág. 461)

inorganic compound / compuesto orgánico: compuesto cuyos constituyentes son otros elementos, en vez del carbono y cuyos átomos por lo general pueden arreglarse en sólo una estructura, como por ejemplo, el H_2O (Cap. 3, Sec. 1, pág. 71)

insight / discernimiento: forma de razonamiento que permite a los animales usar las experiencias previas para resolver nuevos problemas. (Cap. 16, Sec. 1, pág. 465)

instinct / instinto: patrón complejo de comportamiento innato, como por ejemplo, tejer una telaraña y el que puede demorar semanas en completarse. (Cap. 16, Sec. 1, pág. 462)

intertidal zone / zona intermareal: parte de la costa cubierta de agua durante la marea alta y que está expuesta al aire durante la marea baja. (Cap. 26, Sec. 3, pág. 766)

invertebrate / invertebrado: animal que carece de columna vertebral. (Cap. 12, Sec. 1, pág. 338)

involuntary muscle / músculo involuntario: músculo que no se puede controlar conscientemente, como el del corazón. (Cap. 17, Sec. 2, pág. 497)

Spanish Glossary

J

joint / articulación: cualquier lugar en donde se unen dos o más huesos; puede ser móvil o fija. (Cap. 17, Sec. 1, pág. 493)

K

kidney / riñón: órgano del sistema urinario en forma de frijol y que está formado por cerca de 1 millón de nefrones; filtra la sangre produciendo la orina. (Cap. 20, Sec. 2, pág. 584)

kingdom / reino: la primera y más grande categoría del sistema de clasificación de los organismos; se divide en grupos más pequeños: filo, clase, orden, familia, género y especie. (Cap. 1, Sec. 4, pág. 23)

L

larynx / laringe: vía respiratoria a la cual se encuentran adheridas las cuerdas vocales. (Cap. 20, Sec. 1, pág. 577)

law / ley: enunciado científico que describe cómo ocurren ciertos fenómenos en la naturaleza y que parece ser cierto en todo momento. (Cap. 1, Sec. 1, pág. 10)

lichen / liquen: organismo compuesto de un hongo y un alga verde o una cianobacteria. (Cap. 8, Sec. 2, pág. 228)

ligament / ligamento: banda resistente de tejido que mantiene unidos los huesos en las articulaciones. (Cap. 17, Sec. 1, pág. 493)

limiting factor / factor limitativo: cualquier cosa que puede limitar el tamaño de una población; incluye los rasgos vivos y los inanimados de un ecosistema, como los depredadores o la sequía. (Cap. 24, Sec. 2, pág. 698)

long-day plant / planta de día largo: planta que necesita, por lo general, noches cortas (menos de diez a 12 horas de oscuridad) para comenzar el proceso de floración. (Cap. 11, Sec. 2, pág. 318)

lymph / linfa: fluido tisular que se difunde en los capilares. (Cap. 19, Sec. 3, pág. 562)

lymphatic system / sistema linfático: transporta la linfa a través de una red de capilares y vasos linfáticos y la vacía en venas grandes cerca del corazón; ayuda a combatir infecciones y enfermedades. (Cap. 19, Sec. 3, pág. 562)

lymph node / ganglio linfático: órgano en forma de frijol ubicado por todo el cuerpo y el cual filtra los microorganismos y materias foráneas que han encontrado los linfocitos. (Cap. 19, Sec. 3, pág. 563)

lymphocyte / linfocito: tipo de glóbulo blanco que combate las infecciones. (Cap. 19, Sec. 3, pág. 562)

M

mammals / mamíferos: vertebrados de sangre caliente que tienen pelo, dientes especializados para comer ciertos alimentos y cuyas hembras poseen glándulas mamarias que producen leche para alimentar a sus crías. (Cap. 15, Sec. 2, pág. 440)

mammary glands / glándulas mamarias: glándulas productoras de leche en las hembras de los mamíferos y las cuales usan para alimentar a sus crías. (Cap. 15, Sec. 2, pág. 440)

mantle / manto: capa delgada de tejido que cubre los órganos corporales de los moluscos; secreta la concha o protege el cuerpo de los moluscos que no tienen conchas. (Cap. 13, Sec. 1, pág. 364)

marsupial / marsupial: mamífero que posee una bolsa externa para el desarrollo de su cría inmadura. (Cap. 15, Sec. 2, pág. 444)

mechanical digestion / digestión mecánica: descomposición de los alimentos al masticarlos en la boca y ser mezclados y revueltos en el estómago. (Cap. 18, Sec. 2, pág. 529)

medusa / medusa: forma libre de diversos grupos de cnidarios que tiene forma acampanada. (Cap. 12, Sec. 2, pág. 343)

meiosis / meiosis: proceso reproductor que produce cuatro células sexuales haploides a partir de una célula diploide y asegura que la progenie tenga el mismo número de cromosomas que el organismo progenitor. (Cap. 4, Sec. 2, pág. 105)

melanin / melanina: pigmento producido por la epidermis que protege la piel del daño causado por el Sol y que le provee a la piel y a los ojos su color. (Cap. 17, Sec. 3, pág. 503)

menstrual cycle / ciclo menstrual: ciclo de cambios mensual controlado por hormonas del sistema reproductor femenino. Incluye la maduración de un óvulo y la preparación del útero para un posible embarazo. (Cap. 22, Sec. 2, pág. 636)

menstruation / menstruación: descarga mensual de sangre y células tisulares que ocurre cuando el revestimiento uterino se desintegra y se desprende. (Cap. 22, Sec. 2, pág. 636)

metabolism / metabolismo: el total de todas las reacciones químicas en un organismo. (Cap. 3, Sec. 3, pág. 81)

metamorphosis / metamorfosis: proceso mediante el cual muchas especies de insectos cambian su forma corporal para convertirse en adultos; puede ser completa (huevo, larva, crisálida, adulto) o incompleta (huevo, ninfa, adulto). (Cap. 13, Sec. 3, pág. 376)

migration / migración: movimiento instintivo de ciertos animales de mudarse a lugares nuevos cuando cambian las estaciones, en busca de alimentos o para encontrar condiciones más propicias para el apareo. (Cap. 16, Sec. 2, pág. 474)

mineral / mineral: compuesto inorgánico que regula muchas reacciones químicas del cuerpo. (Cap. 18, Sec. 1, pág. 524)

mitochondrion / mitocondria: organelo celular que descompone lípidos y carbohidratos y libera energía. (Cap. 2, Sec. 1, pág. 42)

mitosis / mitosis: proceso celular en que el núcleo se divide para formar dos núcleos idénticos uno al otro e idénticos al núcleo original, en una serie de pasos (profase, metafase, anafase y telofase). (Cap. 4, Sec. 1, pág. 98)

mixture / mezcla: combinación de sustancias en que las sustancias individuales no cambian ni se combinan químicamente, sino que retienen sus propiedades individuales; pueden ser gases, líquidos o cualquier combinación de estos dos. (Cap. 3, Sec. 1, pág. 69)

molting / muda: desprendimiento y reemplazo del exoesqueleto de un artrópodo. (Cap. 13, Sec. 3, pág. 374)

monocot / monocotiledónea: angiosperma con un cotiledón dentro de la semilla; las partes de la flor están arregladas en múltiplos de tres y los tejidos vasculares se encuentran esparcidos a lo largo del tallo formando bultos. (Cap. 9, Sec. 3, pág. 260)

muscle / músculo: órgano que se puede relajar, contraer y que provee la fuerza para mover los huesos y las partes del cuerpo. (Cap. 17, Sec. 2, pág. 496)

mutation / mutuación: cualquier cambio permanente en un gene o cromosoma de una célula; puede ser beneficioso, perjudicial o puede tener un efecto mínimo en un organismo. (Cap. 4, Sec. 3, pág. 114)

mutualism / mutualismo: tipo de relación simbiótica en que ambos organismos se benefician. (Cap. 24, Sec. 3, pág. 706)

mycorrhizae / micorriza: red de hifas y raíces vegetales que ayudan a las plantas a absorber agua y minerales del suelo. (Cap. 8, Sec. 2, pág. 228)

N

natural resources / recursos naturales: partes del medio ambiente terrestre que suministran materiales útiles o necesarios para la supervivencia de los organismos vivos. (Cap. 27, Sec. 1, pág. 778)

natural selection / selección natural: término que significa que los organismos con rasgos mejor adaptados a su ambiente están más propensos a sobrevivir y reproducirse; incluye conceptos de variación, sobreproducción y competencia. (Cap. 6, Sec. 1, pág. 157)

nephron / nefrón: diminuta unidad filtradora del riñón. (Cap. 20, Sec. 2, pág. 585)

nerve cord / cordón nervioso: estructura tubular sobre el notocordio la cual se desarrolla en el encéfalo y la espina dorsal en la mayoría de los cordados. (Cap. 14, Sec. 1, pág. 399)

neuron / neurona: unidad básica funcional del sistema nervioso; compuesta del cuerpo celular, dendritas y axones. (Cap. 21, Sec. 1, pág. 601)

niche / nicho: en un ecosistema, se refiere a las maneras particulares en que un organismo sobrevive, obtiene alimentos y refugio y evita peligros. (Cap. 24, Sec. 3, pág. 707)

nitrogen cycle / ciclo del nitrógeno: modelo que describe cómo se mueve el nitrógeno de la atmósfera al suelo, pasando luego a los organismos vivos y, finalmente, de regreso a la atmósfera. (Cap. 25, Sec. 2, pág. 730)

nitrogen fixation / fijación del nitrógeno: proceso en el cual algunos tipos de bacterias que se hallan en el suelo convierten el gas de nitrógeno en una forma de nitrógeno que pueden usar las plantas. (Cap. 25, Sec. 2, pág. 730)

nitrogen-fixing bacteria / bacterias nitrificantes: bacteria que convierte el nitrógeno del aire en formas que pueden usar las plantas y los animales. (Cap. 7, Sec. 2, pág. 196)

noninfectious disease / enfermedad no contagiosa: enfermedad como, por ejemplo, el cáncer, la diabetes o el asma que no se propaga de una persona a otra. (Cap. 23, Sec. 3, pág. 672)

nonrenewable resources / recursos no renovables: recursos naturales, como por ejemplo, el petróleo crudo, los minerales y los metales, que se usan con mayor rapidez de lo que se pueden reemplazar por procesos naturales. (Cap. 27, Sec. 1, pág. 779)

nonvascular plant / plantas no vasculares: planta que absorbe el agua y otras sustancias directamente a través de sus paredes celulares y no a través de estructuras tubulares. (Cap. 9, Sec. 1, pág. 247)

notochord / notocordio: estructura firme pero flexible que se extiende a lo largo de la parte superior del cuerpo de un cordado. (Cap. 14, Sec. 1, pág. 398)

nuclear energy / energía nuclear: energía producida a partir de la separación de billones de núcleos de uranio mediante una reacción de fisión nuclear. (Cap. 27, Sec. 1, pág. 782)

nucleus / núcleo: organelo que controla todas las actividades de una célula y contiene material hereditario compuesto por proteínas y DNA. (Cap. 2, Sec. 1, pág. 40)

nutrients / nutrientes: sustancias en los alimentos que proveen energía y materiales para el crecimiento, desarrollo y reparación de las células; por ejemplo, proteínas, carbohidratos, grasas, vitaminas, minerales y agua . (Cap. 18, Sec. 1, pág. 518)

O

olfactory cell / célula olfativa: célula nerviosa nasal estimulada por moléculas en el aire, la cual envía impulsos al encéfalo, el cual interpreta los olores. (Cap. 21, Sec. 2, pág. 615)

omnivore / omnívoro: animal que se alimenta tanto de plantas como la carne de otros animales. (Cap. 12, Sec. 1, pág. 335; Cap. 15, Sec. 2, pág. 441)

open circulatory system / sistema circulatorio abierto: sistema circulatorio en que la sangre se mueve a través de vasos y entre los espacios alrededor de los órganos corporales. (Cap. 13, Sec. 1, pág. 364)

organ / órgano: estructura, como el corazón, compuesta por tipos diferentes de tejidos que funcionan en conjunto. (Cap. 2, Sec. 1, pág. 45)

organelle / organelo: estructura en el citoplasma de una célula eucariota que puede actuar como un lugar de almacenamiento, puede procesar energía, mover materiales o elaborar sustancias. (Cap. 2, Sec. 1, pág. 40)

organic compounds / compuestos orgánicos: compuestos que siempre contienen hidrógeno y carbono; los lípidos, las proteínas y los ácidos nucleicos son compuestos orgánicos que se encuentran en los seres vivos. (Cap. 3, Sec. 1, pág. 70)

organism / organismo: cualquier ser vivo; usa energía, está formado por células, se reproduce, responde a los estímulos, crece y se desarrolla. (Cap. 1, Sec. 2, pág. 14)

osmosis / ósmosis: tipo de transporte pasivo que se lleva a cabo cuando el agua se difunde a través de la membrana celular. (Cap. 3, Sec. 2, pág. 76)

ovary / ovario: órgano reproductor femenino que produce óvulos; se encuentra ubicado en la parte inferior del cuerpo. (Cap. 10, Sec. 3, pág. 287; Cap. 22, Sec. 2, pág. 635)

ovulation / ovulación: proceso mensual en que un ovario libera un óvulo que entra en el oviducto donde un espermatozoide puede fecundarlo. (Cap. 22, Sec. 2, pág. 635)

ovule / óvulo: en las gimnospermas, la parte reproductora femenina que produce huevos y tejidos almacenadores de alimento. (Cap. 10, Sec. 3, pág. 285)

ozone depletion / agotamiento del ozono: enrarecimiento de la capa de ozono de la Tierra debido a los clorofluorocarbonos que se escapan al aire y reaccionan químicamente con el ozono, separando sus moléculas. (Cap. 27, Sec. 2, pág. 789)

P

parasitism / parasitismo: tipo de relación simbiótica en que un organismo se beneficia y el otro organismo es perjudicado. (Cap. 24, Sec. 3, pág. 706)

passive immunity / inmunidad pasiva: inmunidad que resulta cuando el cuerpo recibe anticuerpos producidos en otro animal; no dura tanto tiempo como la inmunidad activa. (Cap. 23, Sec. 1, pág. 661)

passive transport / transporte pasivo: movimiento de sustancias a través de la membrana celular que no involucra el uso de energía celular; incluye la difusión, la ósmosis y la difusión facilitada. (Cap. 3, Sec. 2, pág. 74)

pasteurization / pasteurización: proceso que consiste en calentar un líquido a una temperatura que destruye la mayoría de las bacterias. (Cap. 23, Sec. 2, pág. 663)

pathogen / patógeno: organismo que causa enfermedad. (Cap. 7, Sec. 2, pág. 199)

periosteum / periósteo: membrana resistente y apretada que cubre la superficie de los huesos y que contiene vasos sanguíneos que transportan nutrientes al hueso. (Cap. 17, Sec. 1, pág. 491)

peripheral nervous system / sistema nervioso periférico: división del sistema nervioso; comprende todos los nervios fuera del sistema nervioso central, conecta el encéfalo y la médula espinal con otras partes del cuerpo. (Cap. 21, Sec. 1, pág. 603)

peristalsis / peristalsis: contracciones musculares que mueven el alimento a través del tracto digestivo. (Cap. 18, Sec. 2, pág. 532)

petroleum / petróleo crudo: recurso no renovable que se ha formado durante el transcurso de cientos de millones de años, principalmente de los restos de organismos marinos microscópicos enterrados en la corteza terrestre. (Cap. 27, Sec. 1, pág. 779)

pharynx / faringe: región en forma de conducto por donde pasan los alimentos, los líquidos y el aire. (Cap. 20, Sec. 1, pág. 576)

phenotype / fenotipo: apariencia física externa y comportamiento de un organismo. (Cap. 5, Sec. 1, pág. 130)

pheromone / feromona: poderosa sustancia química producida por un animal para influir sobre el comportamiento de otro animal de la misma especie. (Cap. 16, Sec. 2, pág. 469)

phloem / floema: tejido vascular que forma tubos que transportan azúcares disueltos por toda la planta. (Cap. 9, Sec. 3, pág. 257)

photoperiodism / fotoperiodismo: reacción de una planta a la duración de horas de luz y oscuridad cada día. (Cap. 11, Sec. 2, pág. 318)

photosynthesis / fotosíntesis: proceso mediante el cual las plantas y muchos otros productores utilizan la energía luminosa para producir glucosa y oxígeno a partir de dióxido de carbono y agua. (Cap. 3, Sec. 3, pág. 82; Cap. 11, Sec. 1, pág. 307)

phylogeny / filogenia: historia evolutiva de un organismo; sirve para que los científicos puedan clasificar los organismos en reinos. (Cap. 1, Sec. 4, pág. 23)

pioneer species / especie pionera: primeros organismos que crecen en áreas nuevas o que han sido perturbadas; desintegran las rocas y acumulan material en descomposición para que otras plantas puedan crecer en el lugar. (Cap. 9, Sec. 2, pág. 249; Cap. 26, Sec. 1, pág. 748)

pistil / pistilo: órgano reproductor femenino que se encuentra dentro de la flor de las angiospermas; consta de un estigma pegajoso (donde aterrizan los granos de polen) y de un ovario. (Cap. 10, Sec. 3, pág. 287)

placenta / placenta: órgano que parece un saco en el cual se desarrolla un embrión placentario y que absorbe oxígeno y alimento de la sangre de la madre. (Cap. 15, Sec. 2, pág. 445)

placental / placentario: mamífero cuyas crías se desarrollan dentro de una placenta en el útero de las hembras. (Cap. 15, Sec. 2, pág. 445)

plasma / plasma: parte líquida de la sangre, cuyo constituyente principal es el agua, en el cual se disuelven el oxígeno, los nutrientes y los minerales. (Cap. 19, Sec. 2, pág. 556)

platelet / plaqueta: fragmento celular de forma irregular que facilita la coagulación de la sangre y libera sustancias químicas que ayudan a formar la fibrina. (Cap. 19, Sec. 2, pág. 557)

pollen grain / grano de polen: estructura pequeña producida por los órganos reproductores masculinos de una planta de semilla; posee un revestimiento resistente al agua, se puede desarrollar a partir de una espora y contiene partes gametofitas que producen espermatozoides. (Cap. 10, Sec. 3, pág. 283)

pollination / polinización: traspaso de los granos de polen a la parte femenina de una planta de semilla efectuado por agentes como la gravedad, el agua, el viento y los animales. (Cap. 10, Sec. 3, pág. 283)

pollutant / contaminante: sustancia que contamina cualquier parte del medio ambiente. (Cap. 27, Sec. 2, pág. 786)

polygenic inheritance / herencia poligénica: ocurre cuando un grupo de pares de genes actúan en conjunto y producen un rasgo específico; por ejemplo el color de los ojos, cabello, piel o estatura de los humanos. (Cap. 5, Sec. 2, pág. 136)

polyp / pólipo: forma sésil de los cnidarios de forma tubular,. (Cap. 12, Sec. 2, pág. 343)

population / población: todos los organismos que pertenecen a la misma especie y que viven en una comunidad. (Cap. 24, Sec. 1, pág. 694)

postanal tail / cola: estructura muscular en el extremo del cuerpo de un cordado en desarrollo. (Cap. 14, Sec. 1, pág. 398)

preening / arreglarse las plumas con el pico: proceso en que un ave se frota aceite de una glándula sebácea en sus plumas para arreglárselas y hacerlas resistentes al agua. (Cap. 15, Sec. 1, pág. 434)

pregnancy / embarazo: período de desarrollo, generalmente cerca de 38 ó 39 semanas en los seres humanos, a partir de un óvulo fecundado hasta el nacimiento. (Cap. 22, Sec. 3, pág. 640)

primates / primates: grupo de mamíferos que incluye, entre otros, a los seres humanos, los monos y los simios, los cuales comparten características como pulgares oponibles, visión binocular y hombros flexibles. (Cap. 6, Sec. 3, pág. 170)

producer / productor: organismo que utiliza fuentes externas de energía como el Sol, para fabricar moléculas ricas en energía; por ejemplo, las plantas o algas verdes. (Cap. 24, Sec. 3, pág. 704)

protein / proteína: nutriente compuesto de aminoácidos que utiliza el cuerpo para el crecimiento y para el reemplazo y la reparación de las células corporales. (Cap. 18, Sec. 1, pág. 519)

prothallus / protalo: forma vegetal gametofita de un helecho, pequeña, verde y en forma de corazón, capaz de producir su propio alimento y absorber agua y nutrientes del suelo. (Cap. 10, Sec. 2, pág. 280)

protist / protista: organismo eucariota unicelular o multicelular que puede parecerse a las plantas, a los animales o a los hongos. (Cap. 8, Sec. 1, pág. 212)

protozoan / protozoario: protista unicelular que parece un animal y que puede vivir en el agua, en la tierra y en organismos vivos o muertos. (Cap. 8, Sec. 1, pág. 217)

pseudopods / seudópodos: extensión citoplásmica temporal que usan algunos protistas para la locomoción y para atrapar alimentos. (Cap. 8, Sec. 1, pág. 218)

pulmonary circulation / circulación pulmonar: flujo de sangre que va del corazón a los pulmones y regresa al corazón. (Cap. 19, Sec. 1, pág. 548)

punctuated equilibrium / equilibrio puntuado: modelo que describe la evolución rápida que ocurre cuando la mutación de unos cuantos genes da como resultado una especie que repentinamente se transforma en otra especie. (Cap. 6, Sec. 1, pág. 160)

Punnett square / cuadrado de Punnett: instrumento que se usa para predecir ciertos rasgos en la progenie, que muestra las distintas maneras en que los alelos se pueden combinar. (Cap. 5, Sec. 1, pág. 130)

R

radial symmetry / simetría radial: partes corporales distribuidas en círculo alrededor de un punto central. (Cap. 12, Sec. 1, pág. 339)

radioactive element / elemento radiactivo: elemento que emite una cantidad constante de radiación a medida que se transforma lentamente en un elemento no radiactivo. (Cap. 6, Sec. 2, pág. 165)

radula / rádula: en los gasterópodos, el órgano que parece una lengua con hileras de dientes y que usan para raspar y rasgar el alimento. (Cap. 13, Sec. 1, pág. 365)

recessive / recesivo: describe un rasgo que es cubierto o dominado por otra forma de ese rasgo y, por lo tanto, parece desaparecer. (Cap. 5, Sec. 1, pág. 129)

recycling / reciclaje: método de conservación que constituye una forma de reutilización y que requiere la transformación o reprocesamiento de un artículo o de un recurso natural. (Cap. 27, Sec. 3, pág. 797)

reflex / reflejo: comportamiento innato simple, como bostezar o parpadear, que es una respuesta automática y que no involucra el envío de un mensaje al encéfalo. (Cap. 16, Sec. 1, pág. 461; Cap. 21, Sec. 1, pág. 607)

renewable resources / recursos renovables: recursos naturales, como el agua, la luz solar y los cultivos, que la naturaleza recicla o reemplaza constantemente. (Cap. 27, Sec. 1, pág. 778)

respiration / respiración celular: serie de reacciones químicas utilizadas para liberar la energía almacenada en las moléculas de los alimentos. (Cap. 3, Sec. 3, pág. 83; Cap. 11, Sec. 1, pág. 309)

retina / retina: tejido sensible a la luz en la parte posterior del ojo; contiene bastones y conos. (Cap. 21, Sec. 2, pág. 611)

rhizoids / rizoides: estructuras parecidas a hilos que anclan las plantas no vasculares al suelo. (Cap. 9, Sec. 2, pág. 248)

rhizome / rizoma: tallo subterráneo de un helecho. (Cap. 10, Sec. 2, pág. 280)

ribosome / ribosoma: estructura pequeña en la cual las células producen sus propias proteínas. (Cap. 2, Sec. 1, pág. 42)

RNA / RNA: ácido ribonucleico que lleva consigo los códigos para la elaboración de proteínas del núcleo a los ribosomas. (Cap. 4, Sec. 3, pág. 112)

S

saprophyte / saprofito: organismo que se alimenta de los tejidos de otros organismos muertos o en proceso de descomposición. (Cap. 7, Sec. 2, pág. 196; Cap. 8, Sec. 2, pág. 224)

scales / escamas: placas duras y delgadas que cubren la piel de un pez y le protegen el cuerpo. (Cap. 14, Sec. 2, pág. 403)

scientific method / método científico: técnicas para solucionar problemas que sirven para investigar observaciones realizadas acerca de seres vivos o materia inerte; incluye los siguientes pasos: reconocer un problema, recoger información, formular y poner a prueba una hipótesis, analizar datos y sacar conclusiones. (Cap. 1, Sec. 1, pág. 7)

sedimentary rock / roca sedimentaria: tipo de roca, como la piedra caliza, que está más propensa a contener fósiles y que se forma cuando se cementan o compactan las capas de arena, lodo, arcilla o fango o cuando los minerales se depositan de una solución. (Cap. 6, Sec. 2, pág. 164)

semen / semen: mezcla de espermatozoides y un líquido que ayuda a los espermatozoides a moverse y que les sirve como una fuente de energía. (Cap. 22, Sec. 2, pág. 634)

sessile / sésil: se describe así un organismo que permanece adherido a un lugar durante toda su vida. (Cap. 12, Sec. 2, pág. 341)

setae / setas: estructuras que parecen cerdas en el exterior de cada segmento corporal y que facilita la locomoción de los gusanos. (Cap. 13, Sec. 2, pág. 369)

sex-linked gene / gene ligado al sexo: un alelo heredado en un cromosoma del sexo y que puede causar trastornos genéticos, como por ejemplo, el daltonismo o la hemofilia. (Cap. 5, Sec. 2, pág. 139)

sexual reproduction / reproducción sexual: tipo de reproducción en que dos células sexuales, por lo general un óvulo y un espermatozoide, se unen formando un cigoto, el cual se desarrolla en un nuevo organismo con su propia identidad. (Cap. 4, Sec. 2, pág. 104)

sexually transmitted disease (STD) / enfermedad transmitida sexualmente (ETS): enfermedad contagiosa, como la clamidia, el SIDA o el herpes genital, que se transmite de una persona a otra durante el contacto sexual. (Cap. 23, Sec. 2, pág. 668)

short-day plant / planta de día corto: planta que necesita, por lo general, noches largas (12 ó más horas de oscuridad) para comenzar el proceso de floración. (Cap. 11, Sec. 2, pág. 318)

skeletal muscle / músculo óseo: músculo estriado voluntario que mueve los huesos; funciona en pares y se adhiere a los huesos mediante tendones. (Cap. 17, Sec. 2, pág. 499)

skeletal system / sistema óseo: todos los huesos del cuerpo; forma un marco vivo interno que provee forma y apoyo, protege los órganos internos, mueve los huesos, forma las células sanguíneas y almacena compuestos de calcio y fósforo para uso posterior. (Cap. 17, Sec. 1, pág. 490)

smooth muscle / músculo liso: músculo involuntario no estriado que controla el movimiento de los órganos internos. (Cap. 17, Sec. 2, pág. 499)

social behavior / comportamiento social: interacciones entre los miembros de la misma especie; incluye el comportamiento de cortejo, el apareo, la obtención de alimentos, el cuidado de las crías y la protección mutua. (Cap. 16, Sec. 2, pág. 466)

society / sociedad: grupo de animales de la misma especie que viven y trabajan juntos de manera organizada en la que cada cual realiza una tarea específica. (Cap. 16, Sec. 2, pág. 467)

soil / suelo: mezcla de partículas minerales y rocosas, restos de organismos muertos, aire y agua que forma la capa superior de la corteza terrestre y que sostiene el crecimiento vegetal. (Cap. 25, Sec. 1, pág. 722)

sori / soros: estructuras de los helechos en los cuales se producen las esporas. (Cap. 10, Sec. 2, pág. 280)

species / especies: grupo de organismos que comparten características semejantes y que pueden procrear entre sí. (Cap. 6, Sec. 1, pág. 154)

sperm / espermatozoide: célula sexual haploide formada en los órganos reproductores masculinos. (Cap. 4, Sec. 2, pág. 104; Cap. 22, Sec. 2, pág. 634)

spiracles / espiráculos: aberturas en el abdomen y tórax de insectos, a través de la cual entra el aire y salen los gases de desperdicio. (Cap. 13, Sec. 3, pág. 375)

spontaneous generation / generación espontánea: teoría que dice que los seres vivos pueden originarse a partir de la materia inerte. (Cap. 1, Sec. 3, pág. 19)

sporangium / esporangio: cápsula de espora redonda de un hongo cigote. (Cap. 8, Sec. 2, pág. 227)

spore / espora: célula reproductora impermeable de los hongos; puede crecer en un nuevo organismo. (Cap. 8, Sec. 2, pág. 225)

spores / esporas: células haploides producidas en la etapa gametofita que se puede dividir por mitosis y formar estructuras vegetales o una planta nueva completa o que se puede desarrollar en células sexuales. (Cap. 10, Sec. 1, pág. 277)

sporophyte stage / etapa esporofita: etapa del ciclo de vida vegetal que comienza cuando un espermatozoide fecunda un huevo. (Cap. 10, Sec. 1, pág. 277)

stamen / estambre: órgano reproductor masculino que se encuentra dentro de la flor de las angiospermas; consta de una antera (donde se forman los granos de polen) y de un filamento. (Cap. 10, Sec. 3, pág. 287)

stinging cells: / células urticantes o nematocistos: cápsulas con estructuras embobinadas presentes en los tentáculos de los cnidarios que se pueden lanzar a manera de arpón para ayudar a capturar el alimento. (Cap. 12, Sec. 2, pág. 344)

stomata / estoma: pequeñas aperturas en la superficie de la mayoría de las hojas de las plantas que permiten la entrada y salida del dióxido de carbono, del agua y del oxígeno. (Cap. 9, Sec. 3, pág. 255; Cap. 11, Sec. 1, pág. 305)

succession / sucesión: cambios graduales naturales en los tipos de especies que moran en un área; puede ser primaria o secundaria. (Cap. 26, Sec. 1, pág. 748)

symbiosis / simbiosis: cualquier relación estrecha entre especies, incluye el mutualismo, el comensalismo y el parasitismo. (Cap. 24, Sec. 3, pág. 706)

synapse / sinapsis: pequeño espacio a través del cual se mueve un impulso desde un axón a las dendritas o al cuerpo celular de otra neurona. (Cap. 21, Sec. 1, pág. 603)

systemic circulation / circulación sistémica: la parte más grande del sistema circulatorio en que la sangre rica en oxígeno fluye a todos los órganos y tejidos corporales, excepto el corazón y los pulmones, y la sangre carente de oxígeno es devuelta al corazón. (Cap. 19, Sec. 1, pág. 549)

T

taiga / taiga: el bioma más grande del mundo, ubicado al sur de la tundra entre las latitudes de 50° N y 60° N; tiene inviernos fríos y largos, precipitación anual entre 35 cm y 100 cm, árboles coníferos siempreverdes y bosques densos. (Cap. 26, Sec. 2, pág. 754)

taste bud / papilas gustativas: principal receptor sensorial de la lengua; contiene vellos gustativos que envían impulsos al encéfalo, el cual interpreta los sabores. (Cap. 21, Sec. 2, pág. 616)

temperate deciduous forest / bosque caducifolio de zona templada: bioma que por lo general presenta cuatro estaciones bien marcadas, una precipitación anual entre 75 cm y 150 cm y comunidades clímax de árboles caducifolio. (Cap. 26, Sec. 2, pág. 755)

temperate rain forest / bosque pluvial de zona templada: bioma cuya precipitación anual varía de 200 cm a 400 cm, con temperaturas promedio entre 9°C y 12°C y bosques dominados por árboles con hojas en forma de agujas. (Cap. 26, Sec. 2, pág. 755)

tendon / tendón: banda gruesa de tejido que adhiere los huesos a los músculos. (Cap. 17, Sec. 2, pág. 499)

tentacles / tentáculos: estructuras móviles que poseen células urticantes y que rodean la boca de la mayoría de los cnidarios. (Cap. 12, Sec. 2, pág. 344)

testis / testículos: órgano masculino productor de espermatozoides y testosterona. (Cap. 22, Sec. 2, pág. 634)

theory / teoría: explicación de fenómenos o cosas basada en el conocimiento científico generado a partir de múltiples observaciones y pruebas. (Cap. 1, Sec. 1, pág. 10)

tissue / tejido: grupo de células semejantes que funcionan juntas para efectuar una tarea. (Cap. 2, Sec. 1, pág. 45)

toxin / toxina: sustancia venenosa que producen algunos patógenos. (Cap. 7, Sec. 2, pág. 199)

trachea / tráquea: conducto transportador de aire que une la laringe con los bronquios, está forrado de membranas mucosas y cilios y contiene anillos cartilaginosos resistentes. (Cap. 20, Sec. 1, pág. 577)

tropical rain forest / bosque pluvial tropical: el bioma más diverso biológicamente; tiene una temperatura promedio de 25°C y recibe entre 200 cm y 600 cm de precipitación anual. (Cap. 26, Sec. 2, pág. 756)

tropism / tropismo: reacción positiva o negativa a un estímulo externo como el tacto, la luz o la gravedad. (Cap. 11, Sec. 2, pág. 314)

tube feet / pedicelos: tubos hidráulicos de paredes huecas y delgadas que terminan en unas copas de succión y permiten la locomoción a los equinodermos. (Cap. 13, Sec. 4, pág. 384)

tundra / tundra: bioma sin árboles, frío y seco con menos de 25 cm de precipitación cada año, una temporada de crecimiento corta, permagel e inviernos que duran entre seis y nueve meses. (Cap. 26, Sec. 2, pág. 753)

U

umbilical cord / cordón umbilical: conecta el embrión a la placenta; mueve alimentos y oxígeno de la placenta al embrión y elimina los productos de desecho del embrión. (Cap. 15, Sec. 2, pág. 445)

ureter / uréter: conducto que transporta la orina desde los riñones hasta la vejiga. (Cap. 20, Sec. 2, pág. 586)

urethra / uretra: conducto que transporta la orina desde la vejiga y la expulsa del cuerpo. (Cap. 20, Sec. 2, pág. 586)

urinary system / sistema urinario: sistema de órganos excretores que elimina los residuos de la sangre, controla el volumen sanguíneo al eliminar el exceso de agua y mantiene el equilibrio en las concentraciones de sal y agua. (Cap. 20, Sec. 2, pág. 583)

urine / orina: líquido residual que contiene el exceso de agua, sales y otros residuos que el cuerpo no reabsorbe. (Cap. 20, Sec. 2, pág. 584)

uterus / útero: órgano hueco, muscular y con forma de pera donde un óvulo fecundado se desarrolla hasta convertirse en un bebé. (Cap. 22, Sec. 2, pág. 635)

V

vaccination / vacunación: acción y efecto de dar una vacuna a una persona o un animal, ya sea por vía oral o por inyección, con el fin de inmunizarlo contra una enfermedad. (Cap. 23, Sec. 1, pág. 661)

vaccine / vacuna: preparación que se elabora a partir de bacterias muertas o partículas dañadas de las paredes celulares de bacterias; se usa para prevenir algunas enfermedades. (Cap. 7, Sec. 2, pág. 201)

vagina / vagina: conducto muscular que conecta el extremo inferior del útero con la parte externa del cuerpo; el canal del nacimiento por el cual pasa el bebé cuando está naciendo. (Cap. 22, Sec. 2, pág. 635)

variable / variable: cada una de las condiciones que pueden cambiar durante un experimento. (Cap. 1, Sec. 1, pág. 9)

variation / variación: rasgo heredado que diferencia a un individuo de otros miembros de la misma especie y que resulta de una mutación de los genes del organismo. (Cap. 6, Sec. 1, pág. 158)

vascular plant / planta vascular: planta con estructuras en forma de tubo por donde se mueven los minerales, el agua y otras sustancias por toda la planta. (Cap. 9, Sec. 1, pág. 247)

vein / vena: vaso sanguíneo que regresa la sangre al corazón y que posee válvulas de una sola vía que impiden que la sangre sea devuelta al corazón. (Cap. 19, Sec. 1, pág. 550)

ventricles / ventrículos: las dos cavidades inferiores del corazón que se contraen al mismo tiempo durante un latido del corazón. (Cap. 19, Sec. 1, pág. 547)

vertebrae / vértebras: huesos del espinazo unidos por un cartílago flexible que protegen el cordón nervioso de los vertebrados. (Cap. 14, Sec. 1, pág. 399)

vertebrate / vertebrado: animal provisto de columna vertebral. (Cap. 12, sec. 1, pág. 338)

vestigial structure / estructura vestigial: estructura, como el apéndice humano, que no parece cumplir función alguna y que tal vez pudo haber funcionado en el cuerpo de un antepasado. (Cap. 6, Sec. 2, pág. 168)

villi / vellosidades intestinales: proyecciones largas y delgadas que cubren la pared del intestino delgado y las cuales aumentan el área para la absorción de los alimentos. (Cap. 18, Sec. 2, pág. 534)

virus / virus: pequeñísimo trozo de material genético que infecta y se multiplica en células huéspedes; rodeado por un revestimiento proteico. (Cap. 2, Sec. 3, pág. 52; Cap. 23, Sec. 2, pág. 664)

vitamin / vitamina: nutriente orgánico soluble en agua o en grasa y que es necesario para el crecimiento, para la prevención de enfermedades y para la regulación de las funciones corporales. (Cap. 18, Sec. 1, pág. 522)

voluntary muscle / músculo voluntario: músculo que puede controlarse conscientemente, como por ejemplo, un músculo de una pierna o un brazo. (Cap. 17, Sec. 2, pág. 497)

W

water cycle / ciclo del agua: modelo que describe cómo se mueve el agua de la superficie de la Tierra a la atmósfera para regresar nuevamente a la superficie a través de la evaporación, condensación y precipitación. (Cap. 25, Sec. 2, pág. 729)

water-vascular system / sistema vascular acuático: red de canales llenos de agua que permiten que los equinodermos se muevan, capturen alimentos, se deshagan de los desechos e intercambien dióxido de carbono y oxígeno. (Cap. 13, Sec. 4, pág. 384)

wetland / zonas pantanosas: áreas que se mantienen mojadas la mayor parte del año. (Cap. 26, Sec. 3, pág. 763)

X

xylem / xilema: tejido vascular que forma vasos huecos que transportan sustancias, excluyendo los azúcares, por toda la planta. (Cap. 9, Sec. 3, pág. 257)

Z

zygote / cigoto: nueva célula diploide que se forma cuando un espermatozoide fecunda un óvulo; se divide mediante mitosis y se desarrolla en un nuevo organismo. (Cap. 4, Sec. 2, pág. 104)

The index for *Glencoe Life Science* will help you locate major topics in the book quickly and easily. Each entry in the index is followed by the number of the pages on which the entry is discussed. A page number given in boldfaced type indicates the page on which that entry is defined. A page number given in italic type indicates a page on which the entry is used in an illustration or photograph. The abbreviation *act.* indicates a page on which the entry is used in an activity.

A

B

C

Index

D

Index

F

G

Index

H

Index

M

N

O

P

S

Index

T

U

V

Index

Art Credits

Glencoe would like to acknowledge the artists and agencies who participated in illustrating this program: Absolute Science Illustration; Andrew Evansen; Argosy; Articulate Graphics; Craig Attebery represented by Frank & Jeff Lavaty; CHK America; Gagliano Graphics; Pedro Julio Gonzalez represented by Melissa Turk & The Artist Network; Robert Hynes represented by Mendola Ltd.; Morgan Cain & Associates; JTH Illustration; Laurie O'Keefe; Matthew Pippin represented by Beranbaum Artist's Representative; Precision Graphics; Publisher's Art; Rolin Graphics, Inc.; Wendy Smith represented by Melissa Turk & The Artist Network; Kevin Torline represented by Berendsen and Associates, Inc.; WILDlife ART; Phil Wilson represented by Cliff Knecht Artist Representative; Zoo Botanica.

Photo Credits

Abbreviation key: AA=Animals Animals; AH=Aaron Haupt; AMP=Amanita Pictures; BC=Bruce Coleman, Inc.; CB=CORBIS; DM=Doug Martin; DRK=DRK Photo; ES=Earth Scenes; FP=Fundamental Photographs; GH=Grant Heilman Photography; IC=Icon Images; KS=KS Studios; LA=Liaison Agency; MB=Mark Burnett; MM=Matt Meadows; PE=PhotoEdit; PD=PhotoDisc; PQ=PictureQuest; PR=Photo Researchers; SB=Stock Boston; TSA=Tom Stack & Associates; TSM=The Stock Market; VU=Visuals Unlimited.

Cover Andy Rouse/DRK; **vii** John T. Fowler; **viii** Bob Daemmrich; **ix** Nigel Cattlin/Holt Studio International/PR; **x** Ray Elliott/Stone; **xi** Anthony Mercreca Photo/PR; **xii** Stuart Westmoreland/Mo Yung Productions; **xiii** Klaus Uhlenhut/AA; **xiv** Zefa Germany/TSM; **xv** Bob Krist/CB; **xvi** David Madison/Newsport Photography Inc.; **xviii** Raymond A. Mendez/AA; **xix** William Campbell/CB Sygma; **xx** Michael P. Gadomski/PR; **xxi** (t)Special Collections, National Agriculture Library, (b)Lappa/Marguart; **xxii** (t)Milton Rand/TSA, (b)Inga Spence/VU; **xxiii** MM; **xxv** Gopal Murti/PhotoTake NYC; **xxvi** KS; **1** Telegraph Colour Library/FPG; **2-3** Diane Scullion Littler; **3** (l)Jonathan Eisenback/PhotoTake NYC/PQ, (r)Janice M. Sheldon/Picture 20-20/PQ; **4** Mickey Gibson/AA; **4-5** A. Witte/C. Mahaney/Stone; **5** Joanne Huemoeller/AA; **6** Kjell B. Sandved/VU; **8 9** MB; **11** Tek Image/Science Photo Library/PR; **12 13** MB; **14** (t)Michael Abbey/Science Source/PR, (c)VU/Michael Delannoy, (b)AH; **15** MB; **16** (t, l to r)Dwight Kuhn, Dwight Kuhn, A. Glauberman/PR, MB, (b, l to r)Runk/Schoenberger from GH, Dwight Kuhn, Runk/Schoenberger from GH, Runk/Schoenberger from GH; **17** (t)Bill Beaty/AA, (bl)Tom & Therisa Stack/TSA, (br)Michael Fogden/ES; **18** AH; **19** Geoff Butler; **20** (tl)Dover Pictorial Archive, (tr cl cr)Janet Dell Russell Johnson, (b)Johnny Autrey; **22** (t)Arthur C. Smith III from GH, (bl)Hal Beral/VU, (br)Larry L. Miller/PR; **23** Doug Perrine/Innerspace Visions; **24** (l)Brandon D. Cole, (r)Gregory Ochocki/PR; **25** (l)R. Andrew Odum/Peter Arnold, (r)Zig Leszczynski/AA; **26** Alvin E. Staffan; **27** Geoff Butler; **28** (t)Jan Hinsch/Science Photo Library/PR, (b)MB; **29** MB; **30** (l)Eraldo Peres/AP, (r)Marc Von Roosmalen/AP; **31** Marc Von Roosmalen/AP; **32** (tl)Jeff Greenberg/Rainbow, (tr)Hans Pfletschinger/Peter Arnold, Inc. (bl)Peter B. Kaplan/PR, (bc)John T. Fowler, (br)Milton Rand/TSA; **33** (l)MB, (r)Will & Deni/PR; **36** Oliver Meckes/E.O.S./MPI-Tubingen/PR; **36-37** Tim Flach/Stone; **37** MM; **39** David M. Phillips/VU; **40** (t)Don Fawcett/PR, (b)M. Schliwa/PR; **42** (t)George B. Chapman/VU, (b)P. Motta & T. Naguro/Science Photo Library/PR; **43** (t)Don Fawcett/PR, (b)Biophoto Associates/PR; **47** (l)Biophoto Associates/PR, (r)MM; **48** (bkgd)David M. Phillips/VU, (t)Kathy Talaro/VU, (cl)courtesy Nikon Instruments Inc., (c)Michael Gabridge/VU, (cr)Mike Abbey/VU, (bl br)David M. Phillips/VU; **49** (tl)James W. Evarts, (tr)Bob Krist/CB, (cl)courtesy Olympus Corporation, (cr)Mike Abbey/VU, (bl)Karl Aufderheide/VU, (br)Lawrence Migdale/SB/PQ; **52** (l)Richard J. Green/PR, (c)Dr. J.F.J.M. van der Heuvel, (r)Gelderblom/Eye of Science/PR; **55** Pam Wilson/TX Dept. of Health; **56** (t)AMP, (b)MM; **57** AMP; **58** (t)Quest/Science Photo Library/PR, (b)courtesy California Univ.; **59** Nancy Kedersha/Immunogen/Science Photo Library/PR; **60** (t)Oliver Meckes/PR, (b)CDC/Science Photo Library/PR; **61** (l)Keith Porter/PR, (r)NIBSC/Science Photo Library/PR; **62** Biophoto Associates/Science Source/PR; **64** Bill Longcore/PR; **64-65** KS; **65** DM; **67** Bob Daemmrich; **69** (t)Runk/Schoenberger from GH, (b)Klaus Guldbrandsen/Science Photo Library/PR; **74** (l)John Fowler, (r)Richard Hamilton Smith/CB; **75** KS; **76** AH; **77** VU; **78** Biophoto Associates/Science Source/PR; **79** Stephen R. Wagner; **80** MM; **81** AH; **82** Craig Lovell/CB; **83** John Fowler; **84** David M. Phillips/VU; **85** (l)GH, (r)Bios (Klein/Hubert)/Peter Arnold, Inc.; **86** (t)Runk/Schoenberger from GH, (b)AH; **87** MM; **88** Lappa/Marguart; **89** The Just/Garcia/Hill Science Web Site; **90** (tl)Michael Pogany/Columbus Zoo, (tr)Bachman/PR, (b)Jim Strawser from GH; **91** CNRI/Science Photo Library/PR; **94** Biophoto Associates/PR; **94-95** Zig Leszcynski/AA; **95** MM; **96** (l)Dave B. Fleetham/TSA, (r)Cabisco/VU; **98** Cabisco/VU; **99** (t)Michael Abbey/VU, (others)John D. Cunningham/VU; **100** (l)MM, (r)Nigel Cattlin/PR; **101** (l)Barry L. Runk from GH, (r)Runk/Schoenberger from GH; **102** (l)Walker England/PR, (r)TSA; **103** Runk/Schoenberger from GH; **104** David M. Phillips/The Population Council/PR; **105** (t)Gerald & Buff Corsi/VU, (c)Fred Bruenner/Peter Arnold, Inc., (b)Susan McCartney/PR; **107** (l)John D. Cunningham/VU, (c)Jen & Des Bartlett/BC, (r)Breck P. Kent; **108** (tl)Artville, (tr)Tim Fehr, (c)Bob Daemmrich/ SB/PQ, (bl)Troy Mary Parlee/Index Stock/PQ, (br)Jeffery Myers/ Southern Stock/PQ; **114** Stewart Cohen/Stone; **116** (t)Tom McHugh/PR, (b)file photo; **117** Monica Dalmasso/Stone; **118** Philip Lee Harvey/Stone; **119** Lester V. Bergman/CB; **120** (t)John Mitchell/PR, (c)Camille Tokerud/PR, (b)David Scharf/Peter Arnold, Inc.; **121** (l)D. Yeske/VU, (r)GH; **124** David Phillips/Science Source/PR; **124-125** MB; **125** Geoff Butler; **126** Stewart Cohen/Stone; **129** (bkgd)Jane Grushow from GH, (l r)Special Collections, National Agriculture Library; **130** Barry L. Runk from GH; **132** Richard Hutchings/PR; **134** (t)Robert Maier/AA, (b)Gemma Giannini from GH; **135** Raymond Gehman/CORBIS; **136** Dan McCoy from Rainbow; **137** (l)Phil Roach/Ipol, Inc., (r)CNRI/Science Photo Library/PR; **138** Gopal Murti/PhotoTake NYC; **139** Tim Davis/PR; **140** (l)Alan & Sandy Carey/PR, (r)Renee Stockdale/AA; **143** Tom Meyers/PR; **144** (t)Runk/Schoenberger from GH, (b)MB; **145** Laura Sefferlin; **147** KS; **148** David R. Frazier Photolibrary; **152** Bios (Klein & Hubert)/Peter Arnold, Inc.; **152-153** Nigel Cattlin/Holt Studio International/PR; **153** AH; **155** Barbera Cushman/DRK; **156** (l)Tim Davis/PR, (c r)Tui De Roy/Minden Pictures; **158** (l)Gregory G. Dimijian, M.D./PR, (r)Patti Murray/AA; **159** (t)Darek Karp/AA, (b)Vonorla Photography; **160** (l)Joe McDonald/AA, (c)Tom McHugh/PR, (r)Tim Davis/PR; **161** James Richardson/VU; **162** Frans Lanting/Minden Pictures; **163** (l)Dominique Braud/ES, (c)Carr Clifton/Minden Pictures, (r)John Cancalosi/DRK; **164** (t)Larry Ulrich/DRK, (cl)Ken Lucas/VU, (cr)John Cancalosi/Peter Arnold, Inc., (bl)John Cancalosi/DRK, (br)Sinclair Stammers/Science Photo Library/PR; **165** John Kieffer/Peter Arnold, Inc.; **168** (l)Kees Van Den Berg/PR, (r)DM; **169** Peter Veit/DRK; **170** (l)Mark E. Gibson, (r)Gerard Lacz/AA; **171** (tl)Michael Dick/AA, (tr)Carolyn A. McKeone, (b)John Reader/Science Photo Library/PR; **172** (l)John Reader/ Science Photo Library/PR, (r)Archivo Iconografico, S.A./CB; **173** Francois Ducasse/Rapho/PR; **174** Kenneth W. Fink/PR; **174-175** AH; **176** (t)Lara Jo Regan/Saba, (b)Oliver Meckes/EOS/Gelderblom/PR; **178** (tl) Fritz Polking/VU, (tr)Dan Guravich/PR, (bl)Pascal Goetgheluck/Science Photo Library/PR, (br)Joe McDonald/VU; **179** (l)Koster-Survival/AA, (r)Stephen J. Krasemann/DRK; **180** Tom Tietz/Stone; **184-185** Richard Hamilton Smith/CB; **185** (l)courtesy Broan-NuTone, (r)CB; **186** M. Cobos/M. Yokoyama; **186-187** David Matherly/VU; **187** AH; **188** (l)Oliver Meckes/PR, (c r)CNRI/Science Photo Library/PR; **190** Dr. L. Caro/Science Photo Library/PR;

191 (tl)Dr. Dennis Kunkel/PhotoTake NYC, (tc)David M. Phillips/VU, (tr)R. Kessel/G. Shih/VU, (bl)Ann Siegleman/VU, (br)SCIMAT/PR; **192** (t)T.E. Adams/VU, (b)Manfred Kage/Peter Arnold, Inc.; **193** R. Kessel/G. Shih/VU; **194** T.E. Adams/VU; **195** (tl)M. Abbey Photo/PR, (tc)Oliver Meckes/Eye of Science/PR, (tr)S. Lowry/Univ. of Ulster/Stone, (bl)Richard J. Green/PR, (br)A.B. Dowsett/Science Photo Library/PR; **196** Ray Pfortner/Peter Arnold, Inc.; **197** (tl)Jeremy Burgess/SPL/PR, (tr)Ann M. Hirsch/UCLA, (c)Jeremy Burgess/SPL/PR, (bl)John D. Cunningham/VU, (br)Astrid & Hanns-Frieder Michler/SPL/PR; **198** (l)Paul Almasy/CB, (r)Joe Munroe/PR; **199** (t)Terry Wild Studio, (b)J.R. Adams/VU; **200** AMP; **201** John Durham/Science Photo Library/ PR; **202** (t)KS, (b)John Evans; **203** John Evans; **204** (tl)P. Canumette/VU, (tr)John Evans, (b)Ken Graham/BC; **204-205** Dr. Philippa Uwins, The Univ. of Queensland; **205** (t)Heide Schulx/ Max Planck Institute of Science, (b)West Chester Univ.; **206** (tl)VU/ David M. Phillips/VU, (tr)David Woodfall/DRK, (bl)George J. Wilder/VU, (br)Argus Fotoarchiv/Peter Arnold, Inc.; **207** (l)VU/ Edward Webber/VU, (r)Phillip Slattery/VU; **210** Volker Steger/ Peter Arnold, Inc.; **210-211** Art Wolfe; **211** (t)AMP, (b)Jana R. Jirak/VU; **213** (l)Jean Claude Revy/PhotoTake NYC, (r)Anne Hubbard/PR; **214** (tl)NHMPL/Stone, (tr)Microfield Scienctific Ltd./Science Photo Library/PR, (bl)David M. Phillips/PR, (br)M.I. Walker/ Science Source/PR; **215** (l)Pat & Tom Leeson/PR, (r)Jeffrey L. Rotman/Peter Arnold, Inc.; **216** Walter H. Hodge/Peter Arnold, Inc.; **217** Eric V. Grave/PR; **218** (t)Kerry B. Clark, (b)Astrid & Hanns-Frieder Michler/Science Photo Library/PR; **219** Lennart Nilsson/ Albert Bonniers Forlag AB; **220** (l)Ray Simons/PR, (c)MM/Peter Arnold, Inc., (r)Gregory G. Dimijian/PR; **221** (t)Dwight Kuhn, (b)AMP; **222** Richard Calentine/VU; **223** Biophoto Associates/Science Source/PR; **224** (l)Joe McDonald/BC, (r)James W. Richardson/VU; **225** Carolina Biological Supply/PhotoTake NYC; **226** (tl)file photo, (tr)Ken Wagner/VU, (b)Dennis Kunkel; **227** (l)Science VU/VU, (r)J.W. Richardson/VU; **228** (tl)Frank Orel/Stone, (tc)Charles Kingery/PhotoTake NYC, (tr)Bill Bachman/ PR, (b)Nancy Rotenberg/ES; **229** (tl)Stephen Sharnoff, (tr)Biophoto Associates/PR, (c)Stephen Sharnoff, (bl)L. West/PR, (br)Larry Lee Photography/CB; **230** (l)Nigel Cattlin/Holt Studios International/ PR, (r)Michael Fogden/ES; **231** Ray Elliott/Stone; **232** (t)Ken Wagner/VU, (b)AMP; **233** AMP; **234** (l)Walter Sanders/Time Pix, (r)Alvarode Leiva/LA; **235** Courtesy Beltsville Agricultural Research Center-West/USDA; **236** (t)Andrew J. Martinez/PR, (c)Dennis Kunkel, (b)Nigel Cattlin/Holt Studios/PR; **237** (l)Michael Delaney/ VU, (r)AMP; **238** Nigel Cattlin/Holt Studios/PR; **240** Harry N. Darrow/BC; **240-241** Tom Bean/DRK; **241** MB; **242** TSA; **243** Laat-Siluur; **244** (t)Kim Taylor/BC, (b)William E. Ferguson; **245** (tl)AMP, (tr)Ken Eward/PR, (bl)PR, (br)AMP; **246** (t, l to r)Douglas Peebles/CB, Edward S. Ross, Gerald & Buff Corsi/VU, Philip Dowell/ DK Images, Dan McCoy from Rainbow, (c)Martha McBride/Unicorn Stock Photos, (b, l to r)Gerald & Buff Corsi/VU, Mack Henley/VU, Steve Callaham/VU, David Sieren/VU, Kevin & Betty Collins/VU; **247** (t)Gail Jankus/PR, (b)Michael P. Fogden/BC; **248** (l)Larry West/BC, (c)Scott Camazine/PR, (r)Kathy Merrifield/ PR; **249** Michael P. Gadomski/PR; **251** (t)Farrell Grehan/PR, (bl)Steve Solum/BC, (bc)R. Van Nostrand, (br)Inga Spence/VU; **252** (t)Joy Spurr/BC, (b)W.H. Black/BC; **253** Farrell Grehan/PR; **254** AMP; **255** (l)Nigel Cattlin/PR (c)Doug Sokel/TSA, (r)Charles D. Winters/PR; **256** Bill Beatty/VU; **258** (t)Robert C. Hermes, (cl)Doug Sokell/TSA, (cr)Bill Beatty/VU, (b)David M. Schleser/PR; **259** (t)E. Valentin/PR, (cl)Joy Spurr/PR, (c)Eva Wallander, (cr) Dia Lein/PR, (bl)Wardene Weisser/BC, (br)Eva Wallander; **261** (l)Dwight Kuhn, (c)Joy Spurr/BC, (r)John D. Cunningham/VU; **262** (l)J. Lotter/TSA, (r)J.C. Carton/BC; **264** (t)Inga Spence/VU, (b)Jim Steinberg/PR; **265** David Sieren/VU; **266** Michael Rose/ Frank Lane Picture Agency/CB; **267** (l)Dr. Jeremy Burgess/Science Photo Library/PR, (r)Ron Levy/LA; **268** (t)Robert Hitchman/BC, (c)Stephen P. Parker/PR, (b)Milton Rand/TSA; **269** (l)Adam Jones/ PR, (r)William J. Weber; **272** Noble Proctor/PR; **272-273** Layne Kennedy/CB; **273** DM; **274** (l)Stephen Dalton/PR, (r)MM; **275** (l)Holt Studios/Nigel Cattlin/PR, (r)Inga Spence/VU; **276** (l)H. Reinhard/ Okapia/PR, (c)John W. Bova/PR, (r)John D. Cunningham/VU; **278** (l)Biology Media/PR, (c)Andrew Syred/Science Photo Library/PR, (r)Runk/Schoenberger from GH; **280 281** Kathy Merrifield 2000/PR; **282** MM; **283** (l)John Kaprielian/PR, (r)Scott Camazine/Sue Trainor/PR; **284** Dr. WM. H. Harlow/PR; **285** Christian Grzimek/OKAPIA/PR; **286** (l)M. J. Griffith/PR, (c)Stephen P. Parker/PR, (r)Dan Suzio/PR; **287** (t)Rob Simpson/VU, (c)Gustav Verderber/VU, (b)Alvin E. Staffan/PR; **288** (tl)C. Nuridsany & M. Perennou/Science Photo Library/PR, (tr)Merlin D. Tuttle/PR, (bl)Anthony Mercreca Photo/PR, (bc)Kjell B. Sandved/PR, (br)Holt Studios Ltd./PR; **289** William J. Weber/VU; **291** (tl)Kevin Shafer/CB, (tr)Dwight Kuhn, (c)Darryl Torckler/Stone, (bl)Dwight Kuhn, (bc)Tom & Pat Leeson, (br)Dwight Kuhn; **292 294** DM; **295** MM; **296** Michael Black/BC; **297** (t)courtesy NIGMS OCPL, (b)Kevin Laubacher/FPG; **298** (t)Zig Leszczynski/ES, (c)Tim Davis/PR, (b)MM/Peter Arnold, Inc.; **299** (l)Nils Reinhard/ OKAPIA/PR, (c)Adrienne T. Gibson/ES, (r)Oliver Meckes/PR; **300** Marcia Griffen/ES; **302** AMP; **302-303** Terry Thompson/ Panoramic Images; **303** MM; **305** Dr. Jeremy Burgess/Science Photo Library/PR; **306** (l)John Kieffer/Peter Arnold, Inc., (r)Runk/Schoenberger from GH; **307** M. Eichelberger/VU; **309** (t)Jacques Jangoux/Peter Arnold, Inc., (b)Jeff Lepore/PR; **310** Michael P. Gadomski/PR; **313** Howard Miller/PR; **314** (l)Scott Camazine/PR, (c r)MM; **317** (tl tr)Artville, (cl)Runk/Schoenberger from GH, (c cr)Prof. Malcolm B. Wilkins/Univ. of Glasgow, (bl)Eric Brennan, (br)John Sohlden/VU; **318** Jim Metzger; **320** (t)Ed Reschke/Peter Arnold, Inc., (b)MM; **321** MM; **322** Stone; **323** Kennedy Colombo; **324** (tl)Ed Reschke/ Peter Arnold, Inc., (tr)Runk/Schoenberger from GH, (bl)Holt Studios International/Nigel Cattlin/PR, (br)Laura Dwight/Peter Arnold, Inc.; **325** (l)Norm Thomas/PR, (r)S.R. Maglione/PR; **330-331** Stephen St. John/National Geographic Image Collection; **331** Glenn W. Elison; **332** Bruna Stude/Omni-Photo Communications; **332-333** A. Witte/C. Mahaney/Stone; **333** IC; **334** Zig Leszczynski/AA; **335** (l)Jeff Foott/DRK, (c)Leonard Lee Rue III/ DRK, (r)Hal Beral/VU; **336** (t)Ken Lucas/VU, (bl)Joe McDonald/ VU, (br)Zig Leszczynski/AA; **337** (tl)Tom J. Ulrich/VU, (tc)Peter & Beverly Pickford/DRK, (tr)Michael Fogden/DRK, (b)Stuart Westmoreland/Mo Yung Productions; **338** (l)Stephen J. Krasemann/ DRK, (r)Ford Kristo/DRK; **340** (l)Andrew J. Martinez/PR, (r)Glenn Oliver/VU; **343** (t)Norbert Wu/DRK, (bl)Fred Bavendam/Minden Pictures, (br)H. Hall/OSF/AA; **344** Gerry Ellis/ENP Images; **346** David B. Fleetham/VU; **347** Larry Stepanowicz/VU; **349** (tl)T.E. Adams/VU, (tr)Science VU/VU, (b)Oliver Meckes/Eye of Science/ PR; **350** Triarch/VU; **351** Oliver Meckes/Ottawa/PR; **352** (t)NIBSC/ Science Photo Library/PR, (cl)Sinclair Stammers/Science Photo Library/PR, (cr)Arthur M. Siegelman /VU, (b, l to r)Oliver Meckes/ PR, Andrew Syred/Science Photo Library/PR, Eric V. Grave/PR, Cabisco/VU; **353** R. Calentine/VU; **354** (t)T.E. Adams/VU, (b)Daemmrich Photography; **355** MM; **356 356-357** PD; **357** (l)Thayer Syme/FPG, (r)Shirley Vanderbilt/Index Stock; **358** (t)Kjell B. Sandved/VU, (bl br)R. Calentine/VU; **359** (l)Runk/ Schoenberger/GH, Inc., (r)James H. Robinson/AA; **361** Donald Specker/AA; **362** Meckes/Ottawa/Eye of Science/PR; **362-363** Frans Lanting/Minden Pictures; **363** John Evans; **364** Wayne Lynch/DRK; **365** (l)Jeff Rotman Photography, (r)James H. Robinson/AA; **366** (t)David S. Addison/VU, (b)Joyce & Frank Burek/AA; **367** Clay Wiseman/AA; **368** Bates Littlehales/AA; **369** Beverly Van Pragh/Victoria Museum; **370** Donald Specker/AA; **371** (t)Charles Fisher, Penn State Univ., (bl)Mary Beth Angelo/PR, (br)Kjell B Sandved/ VU; **372** St. Bartholomew's Hospital/Science Photo; **374** Tom McHugh/PR; **375** (t)Ted Clutter/PR, (b)Kjell B. Sandved/VU; **378** Lynn Stone; **379** (l)Bill Beatty, (r)Patti Murray/AA; **380** (tl)Bill Beatty/Wild & Natural, (tc)Robert F. Sisson, (tr)Lynn Stone, (cl) Brian Gordon Green, (c)Joseph H. Bailey/National Geographic Image Collection, (cr)Jeffrey L. Rotman/CB, (b)Timothy G. Laman/ National Geographic Image Collection; **381** (t)James P. Rowan/ DRK, (b)Leonard Lee Rue/PR; **382** Ken Lucas/VU; **383** TSA; **384** Scott Smith/AA; **385** Clay Wiseman/AA; **386** (tl)Andrew J. Martinez/PR, (tr)David Wrobel/VU, (b)Gerald & Buff Corsi/VU;

387 Ken Lucas/VU; **388 389** MM; **390** (t)David M. Dennis, (b)Harry Rogers/PR; **391** Mark Lennihan/AP/Wide World Photo; **392** (tl)Hal Beral/VU, (tr)Leroy Simon/VU, (bl)PR, (br)Joyce & Frank Burek/AA; **393** (l)Charles McRae/VU, (r)Mark Moffet/ Minden Pictures; **394** William Leonard/DRK; **396** Jean Hall/Holt Studios/PR; **396-397** Robert Lubeck/AA; **397** Laura Sifferlin; **398** Fred Bavendam/Minden Pictures; **399** Omni-Photo Communications; **400** (t to b)H. W. Robison/VU, Flip Nicklin/Minden Pictures, Flip Nicklin/Minden Pictures, John M. Burnley/PR, George Grall/National Geographic, M. P. Kahl/DRK, Grace Davies/Omni-Photo Communications; **401** T. A. Wiewandt/DRK; **402** IC; **403** (l)Meckes/Ottawa/PR, (cl)Rick Gillis/Univ. of Wisconsin-La Crosse, (cr r)Runk/Schoenberger from GH; **404** Ken Lucas/VU; **405** (tl)James Watt/AA, (tc)Norbert Wu/DRK, (tr)Fred Bavendam/Minden Pictures, (b)Richard T. Nowitz/PR; **406 408** Tom McHugh/PR; **409** (t)Tom McHugh/Steinhart Aquarium/PR, (bl)Bill Kamin/VU, (bc)Norbert Wu/DRK, (br)Michael Durham/Gerry Ellis/ENP Images; **410** Runk/Schoenberger from GH; **411** Fred Habegger/GH; **412** (t)David Northcott/DRK, (bl br)Runk/Schoenberger from GH; **413** (l)Runk/Schoenberger from GH, (r)George H. Harrison from GH; **414** (l)Mark Moffett/Minden Pictures, (r)Michael Fogden/DRK; **415** Lynn M. Stone; **416** Joe McDonald/VU; **418** (tl)Klaus Uhlenhut/AA, (tr)Rob & Ann Simpson/VU, (b)G. & C. Merker/VU; **419** (t)Mitsuaki Iwago/Minden Pictures, (b)Belinda Wright/DRK; **420** (tl)John Sibbick, (tr)Karen Carr, (c)Chris Butler/SPL/PR, (bl)Jerome Connolly, courtesy The Science Museum of Minnesota, (br)Chris Butler; **422** (t)Steve Maslowski/VU, (b)Michael Newman/PE; **423** KS; **424** (t)J. Carmichael/The Image Bank, (b)Carl Roessler/FPG; **425** (tl)Michael Fogden/AA, (tr)Tim Flach/Stone, (b)R. Rotolo/LA; **426** (tl)Marty Cordano/DRK, (tr)Tim Fitzharris/ Minden Pictures, (bl)Runk/Schoenberger from GH, (br)John Cancalosi/DRK; **427** (l)Des & Jen Bartlett/National Geographic, (r) David Northcott/DRK; **430** Des & Jen Bartlett/National Geographic; **430-431** Stephen J. Krasemann/DRK; **431** IC; **432** Michael Habicht/ AA; **434** (l)Crown Studios, (r)KS; **435** (l)Lynn Stone/AA, (r)Arthur R. Hill/VU; **437** (l)Zefa Germany/TSM, (r)Sid & Shirley Rucker/ DRK; **438** (clockwise from tr)Wayne Lankinen/DRK, Ron Spomer/VU, M. Philip Kahl/Gallo Images/CB, Rod Planck/PR, Steve Maslowski, Kennan Ward/CB; **440** Stephen J. Krasemann/DRK; **441** (t)Gerard Lacz/AA, (bl)Tom Brakefield/DRK, (br)John David Fleck/LA; **442** Bob Gurr/DRK; **443** Amos Nachoum/TSM; **444** (t)Jean-Paul Ferrero/AUSCAPE, (bl)Phyllis Greenberg/AA, (br)John Cancalosi/DRK; **445** (t)Carolina Biological Supply/PhotoTake NYC, (b)Doug Perine/DRK; **446** (t to b)Stephen J. Krasemann/DRK, David Northcott/DRK, Zig Leszczynski/AA, Ralph Reinhold/AA, Anup Shah/AA, Mickey Gibson/AA; **447** (t to b)Fred Felleman/Stone, Robert Maier/AA, Tom Bledsoe/DRK, Wayne Lynch/DRK, Joe McDonald/AA, Kim Heacox/DRK; **450** (t)Wayne Lankinen/DRK, (c)David Welling/AA, (b)Richard Day/AA; **451** MM; **452** (t)MB, (cl)Bob & Clara Calhoun/BC/PQ, (cr)Joe McDonald/AA, (b)Jeff Fott/DRK; **453** (t)Christie's Images, London/Bridgeman Art Library, (c)John Welzenbach/TSM, (b)MB; **454** (tl)Howie Garber/AA, (tr)Bob Gurr/DRK, (bl)Johnny Johnson/ DRK, (br)Hans & Judy Beste/AA; **455** (tl tr)Tom & Pat Leeson/ DRK, (b)Tom Brakefield/DRK; **458** Gary W. Carter/VU; **458-459** Robert Mackinlay/Peter Arnold, Inc.; **459** MB; **460** (l) Michel Denis-Huot/Jacana/PR, (r)Zig Leszczynski/AA; **461** (l)Jack Ballard/VU, (c)Anthony Mercieca/PR, (r)Joe McDonald/VU; **462** (t)Stephen J. Krasemann/Peter Arnold, Inc., (b)Leonard Lee Rue/PR; **463** (t)The Zoological Society of San Diego, (b)Margret Miller/Photo Reseachers; **466** Michael Fairchild; **467** (t)Bill Bachman/PR, (b)Fateh Singh Rathore/Peter Arnold, Inc.; **468** Jim Brandenburg/Minden Pictures; **469** Michael Dick/AA; **470** (l)Richard Thorn/VU, (c)Arthur Morris/VU, (r)Jacana/PR; **471** (tl)T. Frank/Harbor Branch Oceanographic Institution, (bl bc)Peter J. Herring, (others)Edith Widder/Harbor Branch Oceanographic Institution; **472** Stephen Dalton/AA; **473** Richard Packwood/AA; **474** Ken Lucas/VU; **476** (t)Dave B. Fleetham/TSA, (b)Gary Carter/VU; **477** The Zoological Society of San Diego; **478** Walter Smith/CB; **478-479** Bios (Klein/Hubert)/Peter Arnold, Inc.; **479** Courtesy The Seeing Eye; **480** (tl)Norbert Wu/Peter Arnold, Inc., (tr)Fritz Prenzel/AA, (b)Remy Amann-Bios/Peter Arnold, Inc.; **481** (l)Valerie Giles/PR, (r)J & B Photographers/AA; **482** Alan & Sandy Carey/PR; **486-487** Birgid Allig/Stone; **487** Don Mason/TSM; **488** PR; **488-489** Chris Butler/Science Photo Library/PR; **489** MM; **490** Michael St. Maur Sheil/CB; **491** John Serro/VU; **494** Geoff Butler; **495** PR; **496** MB; **497** AH; **498** (t)PD, (b)M. McCarron; **499** (l)Breck P. Kent, (c)Runk/Schoenberger from GH, (r)Carolina Biological Supply Co./PhotoTake NYC; **503** (t to b)Clyde H. Smith/Peter Arnold, Inc., Ed Bock/TSM, Erik Sampers/PR, Joe McDonald/VU, Dean Conger/CB, Art Stein/PR, Michael A. Keller/TSM, Peter Turnley/CB; **505** Jim Grace/PR; **506** PR; **507** MB; **510 511** Sara Davis/The Herald-Sun; **512** (t)Ken Lucas/VU, (c)Steve Prezant/ TSM, (b)Bob Krist/CB; **514** (tl)Breck P. Kent, (tr)Carolina Biological Supply Co./PhotoTake NYC, (b)Runk/Schoenberger from GH; **516** SIU/VU; **516-517** Meckes/Ottawa/PR; **518 519 520** KS; **521** (l)KS, (r)VU; **523** (nervous system)Sally J. Bensusen/Visual Science Studio, (cabbages, avocado) Artville, (skeleton, liver)DK Images, (doctor)Michael W. Thomas, (girls)Digital Vision/PQ, (cell membrane)Precision Graphics, (blood cells, blood clot)David M. Philips/VU, (others)Digital Stock; **524** Gary Kreyer from GH; **525** Larry Stepanowicz/VU; **526 527** KS; **529** (l)KS, (r)Tom McHugh/PR; **531** Geoff Butler; **533** (t)Custom Medical Stock Photo, (c b)Dr. K.F.R. Schiller/PR; **534** Biophoto Associates/Photo Reseachers; **536** (t)KS, (b)MM; **538** Eising/Stock Food; **539** Goldwater/Network/Saba; **540 541** KS; **544** Prof. S.H.E. Kaufmann & Dr. J.R. Golecki/Science Photo Library/PR; **544-545** Duncan Wherrett/ Stone; **545** MB; **546 549** AH; **551** MM; **552** (tl cr br)Stephen R. Wagner, (others)Martin M. Rotker; **553** (t)StudiOhio, (b)MM; **555** First Image; **557** National Cancer Institute/Science Photo Library/PR; **561** Meckes/Ottawa/PR; **562** AH; **564** (t)MM/Peter Arnold, Inc., (b)MM; **566** Time, Inc.; **567** (l)Science Photo Library/PR, (r)North Wind Picture Archive; **568** David Phillips/PR; **569** (tl)Manfred Kage/Peter Arnold, Inc., (tr)K.G. Murti/VU, (b)Don W. Fawcett/ VU; **572** Prof. P. Motta, Dept. of Anatomy, Univ. "La Sapienza", Rome/Science Library/Photo Researchers; **572-573** David Madison/Newsport Photography; **573** Geoff Butler; **574** Randy Lincks/ CB; **575** Dominic Oldershaw; **576** Bob Daemmrich; **579** Richard T. Nowitz; **581** (l c)SIU/PR, (r)Geoff Butler; **582** Renee Lynn/PR; **584** (l)Science Pictures Ltd./Science Photo Library/PR, (r)SIU/PR; **586** Paul Barton/TSM; **587** (l)Gunther/Explorer/PR, (c r)MB; **588** Richard Hutchings/PR; **589** Cabisco/VU; **590** (t)MM, (b)Larry Mulvehill/PR; **591** MM; **592** Lane Medical Library; **592-593** SPL/CB; **593** Custom Medical Stock Photo; **594** (t)Biophoto Associates/Science Source/PR, (b)Custom Medical Stock Photo; **595** (t)Gregg Ozzo/VU, (c)Ed Beck/TSM, (b)Tom & DeeAnn McCarthy; **598** Prof. P. Motta, Dept. of Anatomy, Univ. "La Sapienza", Rome/Science Photo Library/Photo Researchers; **598-599** John Terrance Turner/FPG; **599** MM; **600** KS; **601** A. & F. Michler; **607** KS; **608** Michael Newman/PE; **609** KS; **613** AH; **617** MB; **618** (t)Jeff Greenberg/PE, (b)AMP; **619** AMP; **620** Toni Morrison; **621** Nic Paget-Clarke; **622** (t)Bob Daemmrich/SB, (c)MM, (b)Christel Rosenfeld/Stone; **623** (l)David R. Frazier/PR, (r)Michael Brennan/ CB; **626** Profs. P.M. Motta & J. Van Blerkom/Science Photo Library/ PR; **626-627** Brownie Harris/TSM; **627** John Evans; **628** David Young-Wolff/PE; **630 631** Stephen R. Wagner; **637** Ariel Skelley/ TSM; **639** David M. Phillips/PR; **640** (l)Tim Davis/PR, (r)Chris Sorensen/TSM; **641** Science Pictures Ltd/Science Photo Library/PR; **642** Petit Format/Nestle/Science Source/PR; **644** (l)Jeffery W. Myers/SB, (r)Ruth Dixon; **645** (tl)MB, (tr)AH, (b)MB; **646** KS; **647** (l)NASA/Roger Ressmeyer/CB, (r)AFP/CB; **648** (t)Chris Carroll/CB, (b)Richard Hutchings; **649** MM; **650** (l)John Banagan/The Image Bank, (c)Ron Kimball Photography, (r)SuperStock; **651** (l)Martin B. Withers/Frank Lane Picture Agency/CB, (r)Joe McDonald/CB; **652** (t)DM, (c)David Woods/TSM, (b)David M. Phillips/PR; **653** (l)Bob Daemmrich, (r)Maria Taglienti/The Image Bank; **656** (l)Oliver Meckes/PR, (r)S. Lowry/Univ. Ulster/Stone; **657** KS; **658** Dr. P. Marazzi/Science Photo Library/PR; **659** (tl) Michael A. Keller/TSM, (tr)Runk/Schoenberger from GH, (b)NIBSC/ Science Photo Library/PR; **662** CC Studio/Science Photo Library/

PR; **665** (tl)VU, (tr)Jack Bostrack/VU, (cl)Cytographics Inc./VU, (cr)Cabisco/VU, (bl)Jack Bostrack/VU, (br)VU; **666** MM/Michelle Del Guercio/PR; **667** Nigel Cattlin, Holt Studios International/PR; **668** (t)Oliver Meckes/Eye of Science/PR, (b)VU; **669** Oliver Meckes/E.O.S/Gelderblom/PR; **670** MB; **672** (l)Caliendo/Custom Medical Stock Photo, (r)AMP; **673** (t)Andrew Syred/Science Photo Library/PR, (b)Custom Medical Stock Photo; **674** (t)Jan Stromme/BC, (c)J.Chiasson-Liats/LA, (b)Mug Shots/TSM; **678** (t)Tim Courlas, (b)MM; **679** MM; **680** Layne Kennedy/CB; **681** MB; **682** (t)Amethyst/Custom Medical Stock Photo, (c)Dr. P. Marazzi/Science Photo Library/PR, (b)USDA/Science Source/PR; **683** (tl)Gelderblom/Eye of Science/PR, (tr)Garry T. Cole/BPS/Stone, (bl)Oliver Meckes/Ottawa/PR, (br)David M. Philips/VU; **688-689** (t)Andrew A. Wagner, (b)Jodi Jacobson; **689** L. Fritz/H. Armstrong Roberts; **690** David Cavagnaro/DRK; **690-691** Johnny Johnson/DRK; **691** John D. Cunningham/VU; **692** Richard Kolar/AA; **692** (l)Adam Jones/PR, (c)Tom Van Sant/Geosphere Project, Santa Monica/Science Photo Library/PR, (r)G. Carleton Ray/PR; **693** (t)John W. Bova/PR, (b)David Young/TSA; **695** (l)Mitsuaki Iwago/Minden Pictures, (r)Zig Leszczynski/AA; **699** Joel Sartore from GH; **701** (t)Norm Thomas/PR, (b)Maresa Pryor/ES; **702** (c)Bud Neilson/Words & Pictures/PQ, (others)Wyman P. Meinzer; **704** (tl)Michael Abbey/PR, (tr)OSF/AA, (b)Michael P. Gadomski/PR; **705** (t, l to r)William J. Weber, Larry Kimball/VU, William J. Weber, George D. Lepp/PR, (b, l to r)Lynn M. Stone, Stephen J. Krasemann/Peter Arnold, Inc., AMP, William J. Weber; **706** (t)Milton Rand/TSA, (c)Marian Bacon/AA, (b)Sinclair Stammers/Science Photo Library/PR; **707** (t)Raymond A. Mendez/AA, (bl)Donald Specker/AA, (br)Joe McDonald/AA; **708** Ted Levin/AA; **709** Richard L. Carlton/PR; **710** (t)Jean Claude Revy/PhotoTake NYC, (b)OSF/AA; **711** Runk/Schoenberger from GH; **713** (l)courtesy US Census, (r)Eric Larravadieu/Stone; **714** (t)Tui De Roy/Minden Pictures, (c)Maslowski/PR, (b)Stephen J. Krasemann/DRK; **715** (l)C.K. Lorenz/PR, (r)Hans Pfletschinger/Peter Arnold, Inc.; **716** Scott Camazine/PR; **718** Jeff Greenberg/VU; **718-719** Steve Bly/International Stock; **720** Kenneth Murray/PR; **721** (t)Jerry L. Ferrara/PR, (b)Art Wolfe/PR; **722** (t)Telegraph Colour Library/FPG, (b)Hal Beral/VU; **723** (l)Fritz Polking/VU, (r)R. Arndt/VU; **724** Tom Uhlman/VU; **728** (l)Jim Grattan, (r)Bruce S. Cushing/VU; **731** (t)Rob & Ann Simpson/VU, (c b)Runk/Schoenberger from GH; **732** Stephen R. Wagner; **734** (l)WHOI/VU, (r)Wolfgang Baumeister/Science Photo Library/PR; **738** (t)MM, (b)Gerald and Buff Corsi/VU; **739** Jeff J. Daly/VU; **740** Gordon Wiltsie/Peter Arnold, Inc.; **742** (tl)Dwight Kuhn, (tr)Stephen J. Krasemann/DRK, (bl) Gregory K. Scott/PR, (br)Simaon Battensby/Stone; **743** (l)Soames Summerhay/PR, (r)Tom Uhlman/VU; **746** Les Christman/VU; **746-747** William Campbell/CB Sygma; **747** AH; **748** Jeff Greenberg/VU; **749** Larry Ulrich/DRK; **750** (bkgd)Craig Fujii/Seattle Times, (t)Jeff Henry, (c)Kevin R. Morris/CB, (b)Jeff Henry; **751** Rod Planck/PR; **753** (t)Steve McCutcheon/VU, (bl)Pat O'Hara/DRK, (br)Erwin & Peggy Bauer/TSA; **754** (tl)Peter Ziminski/VU, (tr)Leonard Rue III/VU, (bl)C.C. Lockwood/DRK, (br)Larry Ulrich/DRK; **755** (t)Fritz Polking/VU, (b)William Grenfell/VU; **756** Lynn M. Stone/DRK; **758** (l)Joe McDonald/DRK, (r)Steve Solum/BC; **759** Kevin Schafer; **761** W. Banaszewski/VU; **762** (l)Dwight Kuhn, (r)Mark E. Gibson/VU; **763** James R. Fisher/DRK; **764** WHOL, D. Foster/VU; **765** (l)C.C. Lockwood/BC, (r)Steve Wolper/DRK; **766** (t)Dwight Kuhn, (c)Glenn Oliver/VU, (b)Stephen J. Krasemann/DRK; **767** (l)John Kaprielian/PR, (r)Jerry Sarapochiello/BC; **768** (t)Dwight Kuhn, (b)John Gerlach/DRK; **769** Fritz Polking/BC; **770 771** Courtesy Albuquerque Public Schools; **772** (tl)Bob Gurr/DRK, (tr)M.C. Chamberlain/DRK, (b)David Pearson/VU; **773** (l)James P. Rowan/DRK, (r)John Shaw/TSA; **776** Rannels from GH; **776-777** GH; **777** AMP; **778** (l)Keith Lanpher/LA, (r)Richard Thatcher/David R. Frazier Photolibrary; **779** (l)Brian F. Peterson/TSM, (c)Ron Kimball Photography, (r)Solar Cookers International; **780** Larry Mayer/LA; **783** (t)Torleif Svenson/TSM, (c)Les Gibbon/Cordaiy Photo Library Ltd./CB, (b)Rob Williamson; **784** Sean Justice; **785** (t)Lowell Georgia/Science Source/PR, (cl)NASA, (c)CB, (cr)Sean Sprague/Impact Visuals/PQ, (bl)Lee Foster/BC, (br)Robert Perron; **786** Philippe Renault/LA; **787** (l)NYC Parks Photo Archive/FP, (r)Kristen Brochmann/FP; **790** AH; **791** (l)Jeremy Walker/Science Photo Library/PR, (c)John Colwell from GH, (r)Telegraph Colour Library/FPG; **793** (tl)Larry Mayer/LA, (tr)ChromoSohm/TSM, (c)David R. Frazier Photolibrary, (b)Inga Spence/VU; **794** (t)Andrew Holbrooke/TSM, (bl)AMP, (bc)IC, (br)AH; **796** Paul A. Souders/CB; **797** IC; **799** Larry Lefever from GH; **800** (t)Howard Buffett from GH, (b)Solar Cookers International; **801** John D. Cunningham/Visauls Unlimited; **802** Wilford Haven/LA; **802** Frank Cezus/FPG; **803** Nic Paget-Clarke; **804** (t)MB, (c)David R. Frazier Photolibrary, (b)George Diebold/TSM; **805** (l)Lebrum/LA, (r)Spencer Grant/PE; **806** (l)Steve McCutcheon/VU, (r)James N. Westwater; **810-811** PD; **812** (t)Carolyn A. McKeone/PR, (b)J. & P. Wegner/AA; **813** (tl)Yann Arthus-Bertrand/CB, (tr)Barbara Reed/AA, (bl)Chanan Photography, (br)J-L Klein & M-L Hubert/Okapia/Photo Resarchers; **814** (tl)Renee Stockdale/AA, (tr)Joan Baron/PR, (bl)Carolyn A. McKeone/PR, (br)Yann Arthus-Bertrand/CB; **815** (tl)Stephen Green/TSM, (tr)J & P Wagner/AA, (bl)Jane Howard/PR, (br)Ulrike Schanz/AA; **817** (tl)ES, (tr)Patti Murray/ES, (bl)Larry Ulrich/DRK, (br)Doug Sokell/TSA; **818** (tl)Bill Beatty/ES, (tr)Tom Bean/DRK, (bl)R. Ca-lentine/VU, (br)Gerald and Buff Corsi/VU; **819** (tl)C.C. Lockwood/DRK, (tr)Joseph G. Strauch Jr., (bl)John Frett, (br)Gerald and Buff Corsi/VU; **820** (t)PR, (b)David M. Dennis; **821** (tl)Roy Morsch/TSM, (tr)Donald Specker/AA, (bl)Roger K. Burnard, (br)Harry Rogers/PR; **822** (tl)Tom McHugh/PR, (tr)Donald Specker/AA, (cl)Harry Rogers/PR, (c)Carroll W. Perkins/AA, (cr)Patti Murray/AA, (b)Donald Specker/AA; **823** (tl)Harry Rogers/PR, (tr)Ken Brate/PR, (cl)James H. Robinson/PR, (cr)Linda Bailey/AA, (bl)Ed Reschke/Peter Arnold, Inc., (br)MM; **824** (t)Michael Newman/PE, (b)MAK 1 Photodesign; **825** (t)David Young-Wolff/PE, (b)W. Hill Jr./The Image Works; **826** (t)AH, (b)Marc Romanelli/The Image Bank; **827** (t)Rob Crandall/The Image Works, (bl)AH, (br)Michael Newman/PE; **828** Greg Probst/Stone; **829** (t)GH, (b)George Ranalli/PR; **830** (t)AH, (b)Tom Bean/Stone; **831** (t)Tom Bean/DRK, (b)Gary Braasch/Stone; **832** Timothy Fuller; **836** First Image; **839** Dominic Oldershaw; **840** StudiOhio; **841** First Image; **843** Richard Day/AA; **846** Paul Barton/TSM; **849** Charles Gupton/TSM; **859** MM; **860** (t)NIBSC/Science Photo Library/PR, (bl)Dr. Richard Kessel, (br)David John/VU; **861** (t)Runk/ Schoenberger from GH, (bl)Andrew Syred/Science Photo Library/ PR, (br)Rich Brommer; **862** (t)G.R. Roberts, (bl)Ralph Reinhold/ ES, (br)Scott Johnson/AA; **863** Martin Harvey/DRK.

Acknowledgements

From *Sula*, by Toni Morrison. Copyright © 1973 by Toni Morrison. Reprinted by permission of International Creative Management, Inc. The excerpt from "Sunkissed: An Indian Legend" is reprinted with permission from the publisher of *Tun-ta-ca-tun* (Houston: Arte Publico Press—University of Houston, 1986) "Beauty Plagiarized" by Amitabha Mukerjee. Reprinted by permission of the author. Excerpt from "Tulip" from *Turtle Blessing*, by Penny Harter, published by La Alameda Press, copyright (c) 1996 by Penny Harter. Reprinted by permission of the author.
Excerpt from "The Creatures on my Mind," by Ursula K. Le Guin, from *Harper's* (August 1990). Copyright (c) 1990 by Ursula K. Le Guin. Reprinted by permission of the author and the author's agent, Virginia Kidd.

PERIODIC TABLE OF THE ELEMENTS

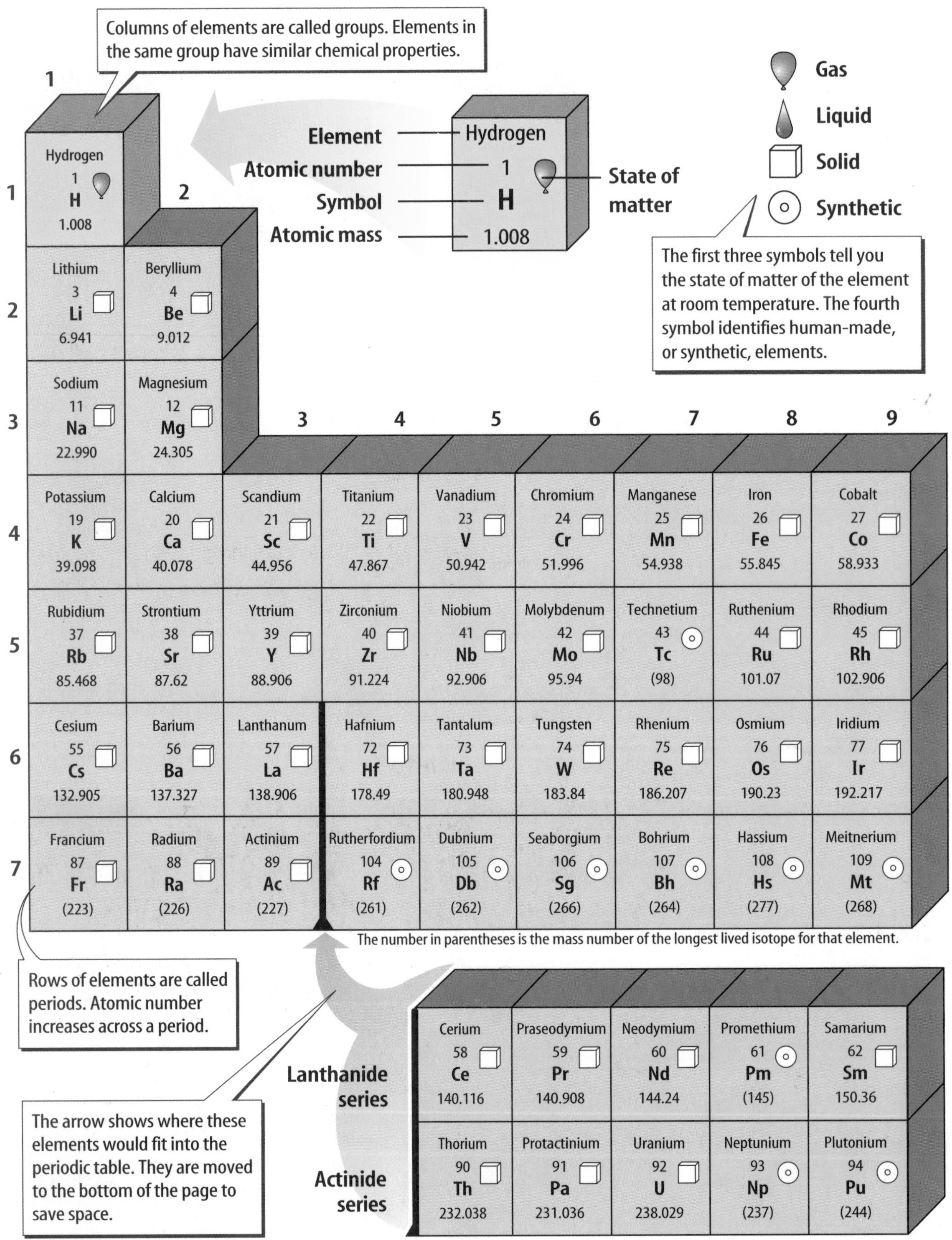

Period	1	2	3	4	5	6	7	8	9
1	Hydrogen 1 H 1.008								
2	Lithium 3 Li 6.941	Beryllium 4 Be 9.012							
3	Sodium 11 Na 22.990	Magnesium 12 Mg 24.305							
4	Potassium 19 K 39.098	Calcium 20 Ca 40.078	Scandium 21 Sc 44.956	Titanium 22 Ti 47.867	Vanadium 23 V 50.942	Chromium 24 Cr 51.996	Manganese 25 Mn 54.938	Iron 26 Fe 55.845	Cobalt 27 Co 58.933
5	Rubidium 37 Rb 85.468	Strontium 38 Sr 87.62	Yttrium 39 Y 88.906	Zirconium 40 Zr 91.224	Niobium 41 Nb 92.906	Molybdenum 42 Mo 95.94	Technetium 43 Tc (98)	Ruthenium 44 Ru 101.07	Rhodium 45 Rh 102.906
6	Cesium 55 Cs 132.905	Barium 56 Ba 137.327	Lanthanum 57 La 138.906	Hafnium 72 Hf 178.49	Tantalum 73 Ta 180.948	Tungsten 74 W 183.84	Rhenium 75 Re 186.207	Osmium 76 Os 190.23	Iridium 77 Ir 192.217
7	Francium 87 Fr (223)	Radium 88 Ra (226)	Actinium 89 Ac (227)	Rutherfordium 104 Rf (261)	Dubnium 105 Db (262)	Seaborgium 106 Sg (266)	Bohrium 107 Bh (264)	Hassium 108 Hs (277)	Meitnerium 109 Mt (268)

The number in parentheses is the mass number of the longest lived isotope for that element.

Lanthanide series	Cerium 58 Ce 140.116	Praseodymium 59 Pr 140.908	Neodymium 60 Nd 144.24	Promethium 61 Pm (145)	Samarium 62 Sm 150.36
Actinide series	Thorium 90 Th 232.038	Protactinium 91 Pa 231.036	Uranium 92 U 238.029	Neptunium 93 Np (237)	Plutonium 94 Pu (244)